A NEW DICTIONARY OF BIRDS

A NEW DICTIONARY OF BIRDS

Edited by
SIR A. LANDSBOROUGH THOMSON

McGRAW-HILL BOOK COMPANY
New York

Printed in Great Britain

Prefaces

By the President, British Ornithologists' Union

THE British Ornithologists' Union celebrated its Centenary in 1959 under the patronage of H.R.H. The Prince Philip, Duke of Edinburgh. In addition to the actual celebrations at Cambridge (the Union's birthplace) and in London, three special enterprises were undertaken. Two of these were ornithological expeditions, respectively to the Comoro Islands and to Ascension Island, the scientific results of which have appeared as a supplementary volume of the Union's journal *The Ibis*. The third enterprise was the preparation of the present work.

The task was undertaken as a service to ornithology and has produced a comprehensive book of reference, in a world context, for all who are interested in birds. Incidentally, its title is a tribute to the memory of Professor Alfred Newton, F.R.S., pre-eminent among the founders of the Union, whose *A Dictionary of Birds* (1896) is, and will remain, a classic of ornithological literature. The present work, however, is not based on its predecessor but is entirely new and differs in various respects of scope and plan.

Preparation of the work was entrusted to Sir Landsborough Thomson, a Past President of the Union and President of the XI International Ornithological Congress held at Basel in 1954. Few of those concerned with the initiation of the project can have had any real appreciation of the amount of work that its production on worthy lines would involve. Apart from any other considerations, ornithology today covers a far wider field than it did in Newton's time, and far more branches of knowledge are accepted as contributing to it. It would indeed have been impossible to attempt the present work, as Newton wrote his, with only a single scientific collaborator. Sir Landsborough recognised this from the outset. He sought the co-operation of authors, artists, and photographers in every part of the globe. Their numbers have grown to more than two hundred ; and it is a special pleasure to recall that practically without exception those who were approached for help have acceded generously and have given of their best. The contributors to the text are specialists in the ornithological or other subjects on which they write. Like the Editor, they have worked in a purely honorary capacity ; all royalties will accrue to the Union under its agreement with the publishers. In the circumstances the very proper decision has been taken that these proceeds will be set aside as the nucleus of an endowment for ornithological research and special publications.

Any work of this nature poses a major problem of organisation, beginning with the choice of heads and ending only with the last decision on typography and the final page proof ; and this is further complicated by the variety of the collaboration. The Editor has taken the whole of this huge task upon himself. Moreover, as a reference to the list of authors will show, he has actually written more main articles himself than any other author, with the addition of an enormous amount of in-filling and connective matter. It is a source of wonder, even to the Editor's friends who have had experience of his capacities, that he could have performed all this with no consistent help except that of his wife (to whom much credit is due), and should have done it while all the time taking part in many different aspects of scientific administration. In the result he has been responsible for a work that must be counted of great value, both presently and for years to come. For this broadly based centenary monument the British Ornithologists' Union has good reason to be grateful to all those who have contributed and to its architect.

R. E. Moreau

British Ornithologists' Union,
British Museum (Natural History),
London, S.W.7.   1964

By the President, American Ornithologists' Union

The American Ornithologists' Union extends its congratulations to the British Ornithologists' Union on the occasion of its recent Centenary and on the successful completion of the three great enterprises undertaken to mark its one hundredth birthday. The first two tasks, the ornithological expeditions to Ascension Island and to Comoro Islands, have been successfully completed and the wealth of new information they secured has been published in a special volume of *The Ibis*. Now we have the results of the third, A New Dictionary of Birds, prepared under the able editorship of Sir Landsborough Thomson.

The British Ornithologists' Union has allowed a number of us in the Americas the privilege and the pleasure of making contributions in fields of our special competence. We can take pride in feeling that we have had some part in the preparation of what is to be a landmark in the literature of ornithology.

Now that we have the finished product in hand, we can see that it is—and we never doubted that it would be—a worthy successor to Professor Alfred Newton's great volume, *A Dictionary of Birds*. The 'New Dictionary' takes its place as the backbone of an ornithological library, a comprehensive reference work that is indispensable. All ornithologists owe a debt of gratitude to the British Ornithologists' Union, and to the editor, for the production of this splendid volume that will be timeless.

Austin L. Rand

American Ornithologists' Union,
Chicago Natural History Museum,
Chicago, Illinois. 60605   1964

Contents

List of Major Articles on General Subjects

SCHEMATIC ARRANGEMENT

THE purpose of the following list is to present a brief survey, in logical instead of alphabetical order, of the subject field covered by this work. It will also serve to indicate the entries most suitable for deliberate reading, as distinct from quick reference on occasion. The major articles on bird groups are given separately in a classified list serving a similar purpose.

Some of the articles listed below are in fact quite short but have been included to round out the schematic treatment; and all contributed items are regarded as 'major'. The grouping is to some extent arbitrary—but see article ORNITHOLOGY—and some of the items could obviously have been placed under more than one of the headings used. Incidentally, the two lists together represent the basis on which the whole work was planned.

GENERAL

Comprehensive and Miscellaneous

ANIMAL KINGDOM
ZOOLOGY
AVES
ORNITHOLOGY
CONGRESSES, INTERNATIONAL
MUSEUM

BIRD-WATCHING
PHOTOGRAPHY
ILLUSTRATION, BIRD
BIBLIOGRAPHY
STATISTICAL SIGNIFICANCE

FORM AND FUNCTION

Facies and Integument

SIZE
WEIGHT
SHAPE AND POSTURE
TOPOGRAPHY
BILL
LEG
WING
TAIL
SKIN
INTEGUMENTARY STRUCTURES
OIL GLAND
NARIS
TONGUE

IRIS COLORATION
FEATHER
PLUMAGE
PLUMAGE VARIATION
PLUMAGE, ABNORMAL AND ABERRANT
MOULT
COLOUR
COLOUR SPECIFICATION
COLORATION, ADAPTIVE
MIMICRY
SEXUAL DIMORPHISM

9

FORM AND FUNCTION—*continued*

Skeleton, Musculature, and Locomotion

SKELETON
PALATE
PNEUMATISATION OF BONE
MUSCULATURE
LOCOMOTION
PERCHING

FLIGHT
FLIGHT, PRECOCIOUS
FLIGHTLESSNESS
SWIMMING AND DIVING
CARRYING

Nervous System and Senses

NERVOUS SYSTEM
SENSES
VISION
HEARING AND BALANCE
ECHO-LOCATION

SMELL
TASTE
TOUCH
TIME MEASUREMENT

General Physiology

VASCULAR SYSTEM
HEART
BLOOD
RESPIRATORY SYSTEM
SYRINX
HEAT REGULATION
TORPIDITY
ENERGY REQUIREMENTS

METABOLISM
NUTRITION
ALIMENTARY SYSTEM
MILK, PIGEON
EXCRETORY SYSTEM
EXCRETION, EXTRARENAL
ENDOCRINE SYSTEM
RHYTHM

Reproduction and Development

REPRODUCTIVE SYSTEM
EGG
EGGSHELL
EGGS, NATURAL HISTORY OF
DEVELOPMENT, EMBRYONIC

DEVELOPMENT, POSTEMBRYONIC
YOUNG BIRD
GROWTH
LONGEVITY

SYSTEMATICS AND EVOLUTION

Taxonomy and Nomenclature

SYSTEMATICS
TAXONOMY
CLASSIFICATION
ARRANGEMENT
TAXON
CLASS
ORDER
FAMILY
GENUS
SPECIES

SUBSPECIES
CLINE
NOMENCLATURE
TYPE-SPECIES
TYPE-SPECIMEN
NAME, ENGLISH
ASSEMBLY, NOUN OF
MEASUREMENT
PROTEINS AS TAXONOMIC CHARACTERS

Heredity and Evolution

GENETICS
EVOLUTION
NATURAL SELECTION
SPECIATION
RING SPECIES
INDIVIDUAL VARIATION

POLYMORPHISM
CONVERGENCE
HYBRID
HYBRIDISATION, ZONE OF SECONDARY

Ancestry of Birds

ORIGIN OF BIRDS
ARCHAEOPTERYX

FOSSIL BIRDS
RATITES, PHYLOGENY OF THE

DISTRIBUTION AND ECOLOGY

Distribution	DISTRIBUTION, GEOGRAPHICAL	NEARCTIC REGION
	PALAEARCTIC REGION	NEOTROPICAL REGION
	ETHIOPIAN REGION	OCEANIC BIRDS
	MALAGASY REGION	ANTARCTIC
	ORIENTAL REGION	RANGE EXPANSION
	AUSTRALASIAN REGION	MAPPING
Migration	MIGRATION	RADAR
	IRRUPTION	OBSERVATORY
	NAVIGATION	RINGING
	MOON-WATCHING	TRAPPING
Environmental Influences	CLIMATOLOGY	GEOLOGICAL FACTORS
	METEOROLOGY	VEGETATION
Ecology and Populations	ECOLOGY	POPULATION DYNAMICS
	BREEDING SEASON	LIFE, EXPECTATION OF
	PREDATION	PALATABILITY OF BIRDS AND
	NUMBERS	EGGS
	CENSUS	POLLINATORS AND
	COUNT	DISTRIBUTORS
Parasites and Diseases	ECTOPARASITE	DISEASE
	ENDOPARASITE	

ETHOLOGY (BEHAVIOUR)

Nature of Behaviour	LEARNING	REDIRECTION
	IMPRINTING	DISPLACEMENT ACTIVITY
	RECOGNITION	RITUALISATION
	SIGN STIMULUS	BEHAVIOUR, DEVELOPMENT OF
	RELEASER	COUNTING
	FIXED ACTION PATTERN	PLAY
	AMBIVALENCE	TAMENESS
Feeding and General Habits	NOCTURNAL HABITS	DROPPINGS
	FEEDING HABITS	DRINKING
	FOOD SELECTION	FEATHER MAINTENANCE
	PIRACY	ROOSTING
	GRIT	MAMMALS, ASSOCIATION WITH
	PELLET	CROCODILE-BIRD
Social and Sexual Manifestations	AGGRESSION	POLYGAMY
	DOMINANCE (2)	POLYANDRY
	DISPLAY	LEK DISPLAY
	DISTRACTION DISPLAY	COPULATION
	FLOCKING	SINGING
	TERRITORY	MIMICRY, VOCAL
	PAIR FORMATION	INSTRUMENTAL SOUNDS
	COURTSHIP FEEDING	SOUND RECORDING
Parental Activities	PARENTAL CARE	LAYING
	NEST	INCUBATION
	NEST SITE SELECTION	FEEDING OF YOUNG
	NEST BUILDING	PARASITISM
	NESTING ASSOCIATION	

BIRDS AND MAN

Impact and Utilisation	MAN, BIRDS AND	ORNAMENTATION, BIRDS IN
	EXTINCT BIRDS	HUMAN
	VANISHING BIRDS	IVORY, HORNBILL
	NATURALISED BIRDS	GUANO
	UTILISATION BY MAN	GUANO, CAVE
	GASTRONOMIC AND	GAME-BIRDS
	MEDICAL USES	WILDFOWL
	EDIBLE NESTS	DECOY
Conservation and Control	CONSERVATION	OIL POLLUTION
	PROTECTION	TOXIC CHEMICALS
	NESTBOX	CONTROL
	SCARING	QUELEA CONTROL
Aviculture and Domestication	AVICULTURE	DOMESTICATION
	CAGE BIRD	HOMING PIGEON
	FALCONRY	
Birds in Human Culture	FABULOUS BIRDS	MUSIC, BIRDS IN
	FOLKLORE	POETRY, BIRDS IN
	OMENS, BIRDS AS	SHAKESPEARE'S BIRDS
	HERALDIC BIRDS	BIBLE, BIRDS OF THE
	ART, BIRDS IN	

List of Major Articles on Bird Groups

TABLE OF CLASSIFICATION

THESE major articles are mostly entered under English names, as shown below, each such article covering a family or division of a family; in the few cases where that is necessary, the equivalent name in American usage is shown in parentheses. Entries under the scientific names of taxa are usually very short, and often mere cross-references, but where a longer article has been found necessary its title is shown separately below. See also Note on Classification Followed, immediately after this table; for the names of supra-ordinal taxa see article CLASS; for taxa without recent representatives see article FOSSIL BIRDS.

	Families	*Articles*
ORDER STRUTHIONIFORMES	**Struthionidae**	OSTRICH
ORDER RHEIFORMES	**Rheidae**	RHEA
ORDER CASUARIIFORMES	**Casuariidae**	CASSOWARY
	Dromaiidae	EMU
ORDER DINORNITHIFORMES	**Dinornithidae** (extinct) ⎱	MOA
	Anomalopterygidae (extinct) ⎰	
ORDER APTERYGIFORMES	**Apterygidae**	KIWI
ORDER AEPYORNITHIFORMES	**Aepyornithidae** (extinct)	ELEPHANT-BIRD
ORDER TINAMIFORMES	**Tinamidae**	TINAMOU
ORDER SPHENISCIFORMES	**Spheniscidae**	PENGUIN
ORDER GAVIIFORMES	**Gaviidae**	DIVER (Loon)
ORDER PODICIPEDIFORMES	**Podicipitidae**	GREBE
ORDER PROCELLARIIFORMES	**Diomedeidae**	ALBATROSS
	Procellariidae ⎱	PETREL
	Hydrobatidae ⎰	
	Pelecanoididae	DIVING PETREL

ORDER PELECANIFORMES		PELECANIFORMES
Suborder Phaethontes	**Phaethontidae**	TROPICBIRD
Suborder Pelecani		
Superfamily Pelecanoidea	**Pelecanidae**	PELICAN
Superfamily Suloidea	**Sulidae**	GANNET
	Phalacrocoracidae	CORMORANT
	Anhingidae	DARTER (Anhinga)
Suborder Fregatae	**Fregatidae**	FRIGATEBIRD
ORDER CICONIIFORMES		CICONIIFORMES
Suborder Ardeae	**Ardeidae**	HERON ; BITTERN
Suborder Balaenicipites	**Balaenicipitidae**	SHOEBILL
Suborder Ciconiae		
Superfamily Scopoidea	**Scopidae**	HAMMERHEAD
Superfamily Ciconioidea	**Ciconiidae**	STORK
Superfamily Threskiornithoidea	**Threskiornithidae**	IBIS ; SPOONBILL
Suborder Phoenicopteri	**Phoenicopteridae**	FLAMINGO
ORDER ANSERIFORMES		ANSERIFORMES
Suborder Anhimae	**Anhimidae**	SCREAMER
Suborder Anseres	**Anatidae**	DUCK
ORDER FALCONIFORMES		FALCONIFORMES
Suborder Cathartae	**Cathartidae**	VULTURE (2)
Suborder Falcones	**Accipitridae**	ACCIPITRIDAE ; HAWK ; VULTURE (1)
	Falconidae	FALCON
Suborder Sagittarii	**Sagittariidae**	SECRETARY-BIRD
ORDER GALLIFORMES		GALLIFORMES
Suborder Galli		
Superfamily Cracoidea	**Megapodiidae**	MEGAPODE
	Cracidae	CURASSOW
Superfamily Phasianoidea	**Tetraonidae**	GROUSE
	Phasianidae	PHEASANT
	Numididae	GUINEAFOWL
	Meleagrididae	TURKEY
Suborder Opisthocomi	**Opisthocomidae**	HOATZIN

ORDER GRUIFORMES
Suborder Mesoenatides
Suborder Turnices

Suborder Grues
  Superfamily Gruoidea

  Superfamily Ralloidea
Suborder Heliornithes
Suborder Rhynocheti
Suborder Europygae
Suborder Cariamae
Suborder Otides

ORDER CHARADRIIFORMES
Suborder Charadrii
  Superfamily Jacanoidea
  Superfamily Charadrioidea

  Superfamily Dromadoidea
  Superfamily Burhinoidea
  Superfamily Glareoloidea
  Superfamily Thinocoroidea
  Superfamily Chionidoidea
Suborder Lari

Suborder Alcae

ORDER COLUMBIFORMES
Suborder Pterocletes
Suborder Columbae

	GRUIFORMES
Mesitornithidae	MESITE
Turnicidae	BUTTONQUAIL
Pedionomidae	PLAINS-WANDERER
Gruidae	CRANE
Aramidae	LIMPKIN
Psophiidae	TRUMPETER
Rallidae	RAIL
Heliornithidae	FINFOOT (Sungrebe)
Rhynochetidae	KAGU
Europygidae	SUNBITTERN
Cariamidae	SERIEMA
Otididae	BUSTARD
	CHARADRIIFORMES
Jacanidae	JACANA
Rostratulidae	PAINTED SNIPE
Haematopodidae	OYSTERCATCHER
Charadriidae	PLOVER (1)
Scolopacidae	SANDPIPER
Recurvirostridae	AVOCET
Phalaropodidae	PHALAROPE
Dromadidae	CRAB-PLOVER
Burhinidae	THICKKNEE
Glareolidae	COURSER ; PRATINCOLE
Thinocoridae	SEED-SNIPE
Chionididae	SHEATHBILL
Stercorariidae	SKUA
Laridae	GULL ; TERN
Rynchopidae	SKIMMER
Alcidae	AUK
Pteroclididae	SANDGROUSE
Raphidae (extinct)	DODO
Columbidae	PIGEON

ORDER PSITTACIFORMES	**Psittacidae**	PARROT
ORDER CUCULIFORMES		
Suborder Musophagi	**Musophagidae**	TURACO
Suborder Cuculi	**Cuculidae**	CUCKOO
ORDER STRIGIFORMES	**Tytonidae** ⎫	
	Strigidae ⎬	OWL
ORDER CAPRIMULGIFORMES		
Suborder Steatornithes	**Steatornithidae**	OILBIRD
Suborder Caprimulgi	**Podargidae**	FROGMOUTH
	Nyctibiidae	POTOO
	Aegothelidae	OWLET-FROGMOUTH
	Caprimulgidae	NIGHTJAR
ORDER APODIFORMES		
Suborder Apodi	**Apodidae** ⎫	
	Hemiprocnidae ⎬	SWIFT
Suborder Trochili	**Trochilidae**	HUMMINGBIRD
ORDER COLIIFORMES	**Coliidae**	MOUSEBIRD
ORDER TROGONIFORMES	**Trogonidae**	TROGON
ORDER CORACIIFORMES		CORACIIFORMES
Suborder Alcedines		
Superfamily Alcedinoidea	**Alcedinidae**	KINGFISHER
Superfamily Todoidea	**Todidae**	TODY
Superfamily Momotoidea	**Momotidae**	MOTMOT
Suborder Meropes	**Meropidae**	BEE-EATER
Suborder Coracii	**Leptosomatidae**	CUCKOO-ROLLER
	Coraciidae	ROLLER ; GROUND ROLLER
	Upupidae	HOOPOE
	Phoeniculidae	WOOD-HOOPOE
Suborder Bucerotes	**Bucerotidae**	HORNBILL
ORDER PICIFORMES		PICIFORMES
Suborder Galbulae		
Superfamily Galbuloidea	**Galbulidae**	JACAMAR
	Bucconidae	PUFFBIRD
Superfamily Capitonoidea	**Capitonidae**	BARBET
	Indicatoridae	HONEYGUIDE

Superfamily Ramphastoidea	**Ramphastidae**	TOUCAN
Suborder Pici	**Picidae**	WOODPECKER
ORDER PASSERIFORMES		PASSERIFORMES
Suborder Eurylaimi	**Eurylaimidae**	BROADBILL
Suborder Tyranni		
Superfamily Furnarioidea	**Dendrocolaptidae**	WOODCREEPER
	Furnariidae	OVENBIRD (1)
	Formicariidae	ANTBIRD
	Conopophagidae	ANTPIPIT (Gnateater)
	Rhinocryptidae	TAPACULO
Superfamily Tyrannoidea	**Pittidae**	PITTA
	Philepittidae	ASITY
	Xenicidae	WREN (3)
	Tyrannidae	FLYCATCHER (2) ; SHARPBILL
	Pipridae	MANAKIN
	Cotingidae	COTINGA
	Phytotomidae	PLANTCUTTER
Suborder Menurae	**Menuridae**	LYREBIRD
	Atrichornithidae	SCRUB-BIRD
Suborder Oscines	**Alaudidae**	LARK
	Hirundinidae	SWALLOW
	Motacillidae	WAGTAIL
	Campephagidae	CUCKOO-SHRIKE
	Pycnonotidae	BULBUL
	Irenidae	LEAFBIRD
	Laniidae	SHRIKE
	Vangidae	VANGA
	Bombycillidae	WAXWING ; HYPOCOLIUS ; SILKY FLYCATCHER
	Dulidae	PALMCHAT
	Cinclidae	DIPPER
	Troglodytidae	WREN (1)
	Mimidae	MOCKINGBIRD
	Prunellidae	ACCENTOR

17

Suborder Oscines (*contd.*)	Muscicapidae	MUSCICAPIDAE ; THRUSH ; BABBLER ; RAIL-BABBLER ; PARROTBILL (1) ; GNATCATCHER ; WARBLER (1) ; WREN (2) ; FLYCATCHER (1) ; THICKHEAD
	Paridae	TIT
	Sittidae	NUTHATCH
	Certhiidae	TREECREEPER (1)
	Climacteridae	TREECREEPER (2)
	Dicaeidae	FLOWERPECKER
	Nectariniidae	SUNBIRD
	Zosteropidae	WHITE-EYE (1)
	Meliphagidae	HONEYEATER ; SUGARBIRD (1)
	Emberizidae	EMBERIZIDAE ; BUNTING ; CARDINAL-GROSBEAK ; TANAGER ; SWALLOW-TANAGER ; HONEYCREEPER (1)
	Parulidae	WARBLER (2)
	Drepanididae	HONEYCREEPER (2)
	Vireonidae	VIREO ; SHRIKE-VIREO ; PEPPER-SHRIKE
	Icteridae	ORIOLE (2)
	Fringillidae	FINCH ; DARWIN'S FINCHES (Galápagos Finches)
	Estrildidae	WEAVER-FINCH ; WHYDAH (1) (incertae sedis)
	Ploceidae	WEAVER ; SPARROW (1)
	Sturnidae	STARLING ; OXPECKER
	Oriolidae	ORIOLE (1)
	Dicruridae	DRONGO
	Callaeidae	WATTLEBIRD (2)
	Grallinidae	MAGPIE-LARK
	Artamidae	WOOD-SWALLOW
	Cracticidae	MAGPIE (2)
	Ptilinorhynchidae	BOWERBIRD
	Paradisaeidae	BIRD-OF-PARADISE
	Corvidae	CROW (1)

Note on Classification Followed

THE classification followed in this work, down to familial level, is shown in the foregoing table. It is that of the *Check-list of Birds of the World*, by the late J. L. Peters and his successors, which is itself essentially based on the system proposed by Wetmore. It seems likely that the *Check-list*, when completed, will be widely accepted as an international standard for general purposes of ornithology.

Below familial level—except where subfamilies are treated separately—the classification has been left largely to the individual contributors. In some cases these are taxonomists specialising in the groups concerned; in others, some more recent revision of the group has been preferred to an early volume of the *Check-list*; in others again, the *Check-list* itself has provided the basis. In the main, however, this work is not concerned with questions of generic taxonomy.

The sources of the table are:

(1) The volumes of the *Check-list* already published, covering all the non-passerine orders and some families of the Passeriformes.

(2) Mayr & Amadon (1951) for the suboscine families of the Passeriformes that are to be covered by Volume 8.

(3) Mayr & Greenway (1956) for the families of the Oscines, other than those covered by Volume 9 (which differs in recognising the Dulidae) and Volume 15. This third source was expressly intended to give the arrangement to be followed in the remaining volumes of the *Check-list*, and it has the further merit of having been agreed by a representative committee appointed by the XI International Ornithological Congress.

Certain minor differences between the foregoing table and the *Check-list* sources should be mentioned. The Apterygiformes are moved up one place to be next to the Dinornithiformes, seeing that the former are merged with the latter in Stresemann's system; and in the latter order another family, Anomalopterygidae, is separated from the Dinornithidae—see article MOA. The spelling 'Dromaiidae' is preferred to 'Dromiceiidae' for the reasons given in the article DROMAIIDAE. The names 'Podicipediformes' and 'Podicipitidae' replace 'Colymbiformes' and 'Colymbidae' in accordance with a decision of the International Commission on Zoological Nomenclature—see article COLYMBIDAE; and entry PODICIPITIDAE on the question of spelling. The family Cochleariidae has been omitted, being here treated at merged with the Ardeidae—see articles CICONIIFORMES and HERON. In accordance with a recent revision of the Falconiformes by Stresemann, a suborder Sagittarii is added, rendering superfamilies of the suborder Falcones superfluous—see article FALCONIFORMES. At least some of these changes seem likely to be incorporated in the new edition of Volume I of the *Check-list*, now in preparation. Further, as compared with Volume 2, ' Mesitornithidae ' replaces ' Mesoenatidae '—see entry MESITORNITHIDAE ; and ' Otididae ' replaces ' Otidae ' (error). Finally, as compared with Mayr & Greenway (1956), the new family Climacteridae has been added to the Passeriformes (E. Mayr, personal communication)—see article TREECREEPER (2) ; and the spelling ' Drepanididae ' is used as being more correctly derived than ' Drepaniidae '—see article DREPANIDIDAE.

Families recognised, or differently named, by Wetmore (1960) that are not included in the table receive entries in the body of this work. Differences at ordinal level between the Wetmore and Stresemann systems are also mentioned—see, especially, article ORDER. A few well known older or alternative names for higher taxa are also shown. Otherwise, the entries under scientific names refer only to the groups so named in the Table, or to sub-families and tribes mentioned by the authors of group articles (except nominate subfamilies and tribes, the names of which can be taken as subsumed by the familial names).

Wetmore, A. 1930. A systematic classification for the birds of the world. Proc. U.S. Natl. Mus. 76, Art. 24 : 1–8. (Revised versions 1934, 1940, 1951—and 1960, see below.)

Peters, J. L. 1931–51. Check-list of Birds of the World. Vols. 1–7. Cambridge, Mass.

Mayr, E. & Amadon, D. 1951. A classification of recent birds. Amer. Mus. Novit. no. 1496 : 1–42.

Mayr, E. & Greenway, J. C., Jr. 1956. Sequence of passerine families (Aves). Breviora 58 : 1–11.

Mayr, E. & Greenway, J. C., Jr. (eds.), 1960 et seq. Check-list of Birds of the World (a continuation of the work of the late James L. Peters). Cambridge, Mass. (Vol. 9, 1960 ; vol. 15, 1962 ; vol. 10, 1964.)

Wetmore, A. 1960. A classification for the birds of the world. Smiths. Misc. Coll. 139 (11) : 1–37.

List of Plates

IN COLOUR

BLACK-AND-WHITE (Photographs)
(*The countries named are those in which the photographs were taken*)

List of Contributors

AUTHORS

THESE are arranged alphabetically by surnames. For each author are given, in small capitals at the end, the titles of the articles for which he is responsible.

H. G. A. **Horace Gundry Alexander**, M.A. (Cambridge). Swanage, Dorset, England. Late Vice-President, British Ornithologists' Union. VANISHING BIRDS.

S. A. See under Sálim.

D. A. **Dean Amadon**, Ph.D. (Cornell), Sc.D. (Hobart). Chairman, Department of Ornithology, American Museum of Natural History, New York, U.S.A. ; late Vice-President, American Ornithologists' Union. STARLING.

R. J. A. **Richard John Andrew**, Ph.D. (Cambridge). Assistant Professor, Department of Biology, Yale University, New Haven, Conn., U.S.A. BEHAVIOUR, DEVELOPMENT OF ; FIXED ACTION PATTERN.

E. A. A. Rev. **Edward Allworthy Armstrong**, B.A. (Belfast), M.A. (Leeds), Hon. M.A. (Cambridge). Cambridge, England. Vice-President, British Ornithologists' Union. DISTRACTION DISPLAY ; FOLK-LORE ; LEK DISPLAY ; PARENTAL CARE ; POLYANDRY ; POLYGAMY ; WREN (I).

G. L. A. -W. **George Laidley Atkinson-Willes**. Central Organiser, National Wildfowl Counts, Wildfowl Trust, Slimbridge, Gloucestershire, England. COUNT.

D. A. B. **David Armitage Bannerman**, O.B.E., Sc.D. (Cambridge). Southwick, near Dumfries, Scotland. Late Special Scientific Assistant (Supernumerary Staff), British Museum (Natural History), London ; Hon. President, Scottish Ornithologists' Club ; Vice-President, Royal Society for the Protection of Birds ; late Vice-President, British Ornithologists' Union ; late Chairman, British Ornithologists' Club. GUINEAFOWL ; HORNBILL ; MOUSEBIRD ; OSTRICH ; SECRETARY-BIRD ; SUNBIRD ; WOOD-HOOPOE.

P. B. -S. **Ida Phyllis Barclay-Smith**, M.B.E. London, England. Secretary, International Council for Bird Preservation ; Secretary, Co-ordinating Advisory Committee on Oil Pollution of the Sea ; late Vice-President (formerly Hon. Secretary), British Ornithologists' Union ; Editor, *Avicultural Magazine*. OIL POLLUTION ; PROTECTION (main article).

J. B. **John Barlee,** M.Sc. (Trinity College, Dublin). Lecturer in Oceanography, Britannia Royal Naval College, Dartmouth, Devon, England. FLIGHT.

C. G. B. **Colin Gordon Beer**, M.Sc. (New Zealand), D.Phil. (Oxford). Associate Professor of Psychology, Rutgers University, New Jersey, U.S.A. INCUBATION ; SCARING.

A. d'A. B. **Angus d'Albini Bellairs**, M.A. (Cambridge), D.Sc. (London), M.R.C.S., L.R.C.P. (London). Reader in Anatomy, University of London, at St Mary's Hospital Medical School ; Hon. Herpetologist, Zoological Society of London. PALATE ; SKELETON.

J. B. (2) Professeur **Jacques Berlioz**, D.Pharm. (Paris). Muséum National d'Histoire Naturelle, Paris, France. Past President, Societé Ornithologique de France ; President, XII International Ornithological Congress, Helsinki 1958. HUMMINGBIRD (main article).

G. E. B. Professor **Geoffrey Emett Blackman**, M.A. (Oxford), F.R.S. Professor of Rural Economy, University of Oxford, England. VEGETATION.

E. R. B. **Emmet Reid Blake**, M.S. (Pittsburgh). Curator of Birds, Chicago Natural History Museum, Chicago, Ill., U.S.A. ORIOLE (2).

A. D. B. **Andrew David Blest**, B.Sc. (London), D.Phil. (Oxford). Lecturer, Department of Zoology, University College, London. RITUALISATION.

J. B. (3)　**James Bond**, B.A. (Cambridge).　Curator, Department of Ornithology, Academy of Natural Sciences of Philadelphia, Pennsylvania, U.S.A.　VIREO.

J. H. R. B.　**Jeffery Hugh Richard Boswall**.　Producer, Natural History Unit, British Broadcasting Corporation, Bristol, England.　SOUND RECORDING.

W. R. P. B.　**William Richmond Postle Bourne**, M.B., B.Chir. (Cambridge).　Watford, Hertfordshire, England.　Late Research Assistant, Edward Grey Institute of Field Ornithology, University of Oxford ; Editor of sea-bird reports, Royal Naval Bird Watching Society ; late Recorder (first), Cyprus Ornithological Society.　PETREL.

H. J. B.　**Hugh James Boyd**.　Senior Biologist, Wildfowl Trust, Slimbridge, Gloucestershire, England.　SWIMMING AND DIVING.

G. J. B.　**Gerrit Jeronimo Broekhuysen**, Ph.D. (Leiden).　Senior Lecturer in Zoology, University of Cape Town, South Africa ; late Chairman, South African Ornithological Society ; Editor, *The Ostrich*.　SUGARBIRD (I).

J. P. B. -L.　**John Philip Brooke-Little**, M.A. (Oxford), F.S.A.　Bluemantle Pursuivant of Arms, College of Arms, London.　Chairman, Heraldry Society ; Hon. Editor in Chief, *The Coat of Arms*.　HERALDIC BIRDS.

L. H. B.　**Leslie Hilton Brown**, B.Sc. (St Andrews).　Karen, Kenya.　Late Deputy Director of Agriculture, Kenya.　FALCON ; FLAMINGO ; HAWK ; VULTURE (I).

R. H. J. B.　**Ralph Henry Joseph Brown**, Ph.D. (Cambridge ; Trinity College, Dublin).　Assistant Director of Research, Department of Zoology, University of Cambridge, England.　ENERGY REQUIREMENTS.

E. J. M. B.　**Edward John Mawby Buxton**, M.A. (Oxford).　Malmesbury, Wiltshire, England.　OYSTER-CATCHER.

A. J. C.　**Arthur James Cain**, D.Phil. (Oxford).　Lecturer in Animal Taxonomy and Curator of the Zoological Collections, University of Oxford, England.　EVOLUTION ; GENETICS ; NATURAL SELECTION ; SPECIATION; WEAVER-FINCH.

B. C.　**Bruce Campbell**, Ph.D. (Edinburgh).　Woodstock, Oxfordshire, England.　Late Secretary, British Trust for Ornithology.　NESTBOX.

R. C. (2)　**Robert Carrick**, B.Sc. (Glasgow), Ph.D. (Edinburgh).　Senior Principal Research Officer, Division of Wildlife Research, Commonwealth Scientific and Industrial Research Organisation, Canberra, A.C.T., Australia.　PENGUIN (part).

R. C.　**Richard Carrington**.　London.　FABULOUS BIRDS.

C.　Viscount **Chaplin** (Anthony Freskyn Charles Hamby Chaplin).　Totnes, Devon, England.　Late Secretary, Zoological Society of London.　HUMMINGBIRD (part).

A. H. C.　**Alexander Hugh Chisholm**, O.B.E., Sydney, N.S.W., Australia.　General Secretary, Royal Australian Historical Society ; Past President, Royal Australasian Ornithologists' Union ; and late Hon. Editor, *The Emu*.　LYREBIRD ; SCRUB-BIRD.

T. C.　**Theresa Clay**, D.Sc. (Edinburgh).　Principal Scientific Officer, Department of Entomology, British Museum (Natural History), London ; late Vice-President, Royal Entomological Society.　ECTOPARASITE.

P. J. C.　**Peter John Conder**.　Secretary, Royal Society for the Protection of Birds, Sandy, Bedfordshire, England.　AVOCET.

R. K. C.　**Richard Kinahan Cornwallis**, M.A. (Oxford).　Market Rasen, Lincolnshire, England.　Vice-President, British Trust for Ornithology.　IRRUPTION.

H. B. C.　**Hugh Bamford Cott**, D.Sc. (Glasgow), Sc.D. (Cambridge).　Lecturer in Zoology and Strickland Curator, University of Cambridge, England.　COLORATION, ADAPTIVE ; PALATABILITY OF BIRDS AND EGGS.

S. C.　**Stanley Cramp**, B.A. (Manchester).　London, England.　Vice-President, British Trust for Ornithology ; Chairman, Joint B.T.O.—R.S.P.B. Committee on Toxic Chemicals ; Senior Editor, *British Birds*.　TOXIC CHEMICALS.

J. H. C.　**John Hurrell Crook**, B.Sc. (London), Ph.D. (Cambridge).　Lecturer in Animal Behaviour, Department of Psychology, University of Bristol, England.　DOMINANCE (2) ; FLOCKING.

J. M. C.　**John Michael Cullen**, D.Phil. (Oxford).　Senior Scientific Research Officer, Nature Conservancy Unit, Department of Zoology, University of Oxford, England ; Assistant Editor, *The Ibis*.　ROOSTING.

E. C.   **Everhard Curio**, Ph.D. (Berlin). Department of Zoology, University of Tübingen, Germany.
FLYCATCHER (1) (jointly) ; THICKHEAD.

G. de B.   Sir **Gavin de Beer**, D.Sc. (Oxford), Hon. Sc.D. (Cambridge), Hon. D. (Bordeaux ; Lausanne),
F.R.S., F.S.A. London, England. Late Director, British Museum (Natural History) ; formerly
Professor of Embryology, University of London ; Past President, Linnean Society of London ;
President, XV International Congress of Zoology, London 1958. ARCHAEOPTERYX ; RATITES,
PHYLOGENY OF THE.

H. G. D.   **Herbert Girton Deignan**, B.A. (Princeton). Lausanne, Switzerland. Late Curator of Birds,
United States National Museum, Washington, D.C., U.S.A. ; late Secretary, American
Ornithologists' Union. PARROTBILL (1).

J. D.   **Jean Theodore Delacour**, Lic.Sci. (Lille). Clères, Seine Maritime, France. Late Director, Los
Angeles County Museum, California, U.S.A. ; Research Associate, American Museum of Natural
History, New York ; Secretary-General, IX International Ornithological Congress, Rouen 1938.
BABBLER ; LEAFBIRD ; PHEASANT ; RAIL-BABBLER.

H. J. de S. D.   **Henry John de Suffren Disney**, M.A. (Cambridge). Curator of Birds, Australian Museum,
Sydney, N.S.W., Australia ; late Zoologist, Department of Agriculture, Tanganyika. QUELEA
CONTROL.

J. D. (2)   Professeur **Jean Dorst**, D.Sc. (Paris). Muséum National d'Histoire Naturelle, Paris ; President, Société Ornithologique de France ; President, Société Zoologique de France. BARBET ;
PARROT.

C. J. D.   **Christopher John Duncan**, Ph.D. (London). Department of Zoology, University of Liverpool,
England. SMELL ; TASTE ; TOUCH.

E. E. (2)   **Eugene Eisenmann**, S.B., LL.B. (Harvard). Research Associate, American Museum of Natural
History, New York, U.S.A. ; Past President, Linnaean Society of New York ; Past President,
Federation of New York State Bird Clubs ; late Editor, *The Auk*. PROTECTION (part) ; TROGON.

E. E.   **Erica Eisner** (Mrs G. M. Thomas), B.A. (Cambridge), B.Sc. (Oxford). Edinburgh, Scotland.
Formerly D.S.I.R. Research Fellow at University of Edinburgh. FEEDING OF YOUNG.

H. F. I. E.   Sir **Hugh Francis Ivo Elliott**, Bart., O.B.E., M.A. (Oxford). London, England. Late of
Tanganyika Administration ; Hon. Secretary, British Ornithologists' Union. FINFOOT.

E. A. R. E.   **Eric Arnold Roberts Ennion**, M.A. (Cambridge), M.R.C.S., L.R.C.P. (London). Marl-
borough, Wiltshire, England. Late Director, Monks' House Bird Observatory, Northumberland.
TRAPPING.

P. G. 'E.   Professor **Paul Gilbert 'Espinasse**, M.A. (Oxford). Professor of Zoology, University of Hull,
England. FEATHER.

R. A. F.   **Robert Alexander Falla**, C.M.G., D.Sc. (Auckland). Director, Dominion Museum, Wellington,
New Zealand ; Past President, Royal Society of New Zealand ; Past President, Royal Australasian
Ornithologists' Union. KIWI ; MOA.

I. J. F. -L.   **Ian James Ferguson-Lees**. Bedford, England. Executive Editor, *British Birds*. BITTERN ;
TREECREEPER (1).

J. F.   **James Maxwell McConnell Fisher**, M.A. (Oxford). Ashton, Northamptonshire, England.
Late Assistant Curator, Zoological Society of London ; late Hon. Secretary, British Trust for
Ornithology ; late Hon. Secretary and Hon. Treasurer, Association for the Study of Animal
Behaviour. EXTINCT BIRDS.

R. S. R. F.   **Richard Sidney Richmond Fitter**, B.Sc. Econ. (London). Chinnor, Oxfordshire, England.
Hon. Secretary, Fauna Preservation Society ; late Hon. Secretary, British Trust for Ornithology.
NATURALISED BIRDS.

C. A. F.   **Charles Alexander Fleming**, D.Sc. (New Zealand). Chief Palaeontologist, N.Z. Geological
Survey, Lower Hutt, New Zealand ; President, Royal Society of New Zealand ; Past President,
Ornithological Society of New Zealand. WATTLEBIRD (2)

E. T. B. F.   **Eric Thomas Brazil Francis**, B.Sc. (London), Ph.D. (Reading). Reader in Vertebrate Zoology,
University of Sheffield, England. EXCRETORY SYSTEM ; HEART ; VASCULAR SYSTEM.

H. F.   **Herbert Friedmann**, Ph.D. (Cornell). Director, Los Angeles County Museum, California.
U.S.A. ; late of United States National Museum, Washington, D.C. ; Past President, American
Ornithologists' Union. HONEYGUIDE.

H. J. F.   **Harold James Frith**, D.Sc.Agr. (Sydney). Chief, Division of Wildlife Research, Commonwealth
Scientific and Industrial Research Organisation, Canberra, A.C.T., Australia. MEGAPODE.

J. A. G.   **John Anthony Gibb**, D.Phil. (Oxford). Animal Ecology Division, Department of Scientific and

Industrial Research, Lower Hutt, New Zealand ; late of Edward Grey Institute of Field Ornithology, University of Oxford, England ; Vice-President, New Zealand Ecological Society.
NEST SITE SELECTION.

F. G. (2)   Professor **Frank Goldby**, M.D. (Cambridge), F.R.C.P. (London). Professor of Anatomy,
University of London, at St Mary's Hospital Medical School ; Past President, Anatomical Society
of Great Britain and Ireland. NERVOUS SYSTEM.

J. D. G.   **Jack William Davies Goodall**. Santiago, Chile. PLANTCUTTER ; SEED-SNIPE.

D. G.   **Derek Goodwin**. Senior Experimental Officer, British Museum (Natural History), London,
England. PIGEON.

A. P. G.   **Annie Purdie Gray**, M.A. (Glasgow). Scientific Information Officer, Commonwealth Bureau of
Animal Breeding and Genetics, Edinburgh, Scotland. HYBRID.

J. C. G., Jr.   **James Cowan Greenway**, Jr., A.B. (Yale). Research Associate and Trustee, American Museum
of Natural History, New York ; late Curator of Birds, Museum of Comparative Zoology, Harvard
College, Cambridge, Mass., U.S.A. GNATCATCHER ; HONEYCREEPER (2) ; HYPOCOLIUS ; PALM-
CHAT ; SILKY FLYCATCHER ; WAXWING.

A. W. G.   **Alan William Greenwood**, C.B.E., D.Sc. (Melbourne), Ph.D. (Edinburgh). Edinburgh,
Scotland. Late Director, Agricultural Research Council Poultry Research Centre, Edinburgh. EGG.

F. G.   **Finnur Gudmundsson**, Dr. rer. nat. (Hamburg). Director, Department of Zoology, Museum of
Natural History, Reykjavik, Iceland. DIVER.

M. F. H.   **Madeleine Fae Hall**, D.Phil. (Oxford). Staff, Zoological Society of London, England.
WHYDAH (1).

F. H.   **Frederick Nathan Hamerstrom**, Jr., A.B. (Harvard), M.Sc. (Iowa State), Ph.D. (Wisconsin).
Leader, Prairie Grouse Management Research Unit, Wisconsin Conservation Department,
Plainfield, Wisconsin, U.S.A. GROUSE (jointly).

F. H. (2)   Mrs **Frances Hamerstrom**, B.Sc. (Iowa State), M.Sc. (Wisconsin), Hon. D.Sc. (Carroll College),
Assistant Leader, Prairie Grouse Management Research Unit (as above). GROUSE (jointly).

J. G. H.   **Jeffrey Graham Harrison**, M.B., B.Chir. (Cambridge). Sevenoaks, Kent, England. Late
Secretary, British Ornithologists' Club, and formerly Editor of its *Bulletin*. LEG ; PNEUMATISATION
OF BONE ; TONGUE ; WING.

J. M. H.   **James Maurice Harrison**, D.S.C., M.R.C.S. (England), L.R.C.P. (London). Sevenoaks, Kent,
England. Late Vice-President, British Ornithologists' Union ; late Chairman, British Ornithologists' Club. MOULT ; PLUMAGE ; PLUMAGE, ABNORMAL AND ABERRANT ; PLUMAGE VARIATION.

T. H.   **Tom Harnett Harrisson**, D.S.O., O.B.E., Curator, Sarawak Museum, Kuching, Sarawak,
Malaysia. ECHO-LOCATION ; EDIBLE NESTS ; GUANO, CAVE ; IVORY, HORNBILL ; OMENS, BIRDS AS ;
ORNAMENTATION, BIRDS IN HUMAN.

P. H. T. H.   Rev. **Peter Harold Trahair Hartley**, M.A. (Oxford), B.Sc. (London). Badingham, Suffolk,
England. Late of Edward Grey Institute of Field Ornithology, University of Oxford ; Chairman
of Council, Royal Society for the Protection of Birds. FEEDING HABITS ; PREDATION.

F. H. (3)   Chief Justice **François Haverschmidt**, M.A. (Utrecht). Paramaribo, Surinam, S. America.
POTOO ; TRUMPETER.

W. C. O. H.   **William Charles Osman Hill**, M.D. (Birmingham). Associate Director, Yerkes Regional
Primate Centre, and Professor of Physical Anthropology, Emory University, Atlanta, Georgia,
U.S.A. ; late Prosector, Zoological Society of London ; late Vice-President, Anatomical Society
of Great Britain and Ireland ; late Editor, *Ceylon Journal of Science*. MUSCULATURE ; SYRINX.

R. A. H.   Professor **Robert Audley Hinde**, B.Sc. (London), D.Phil. (Oxford), Sc.D. (Cambridge). Royal
Society Research Professor, at University of Cambridge, England. COPULATION ; COURTSHIP
FEEDING ; DISPLAY ; NEST BUILDING ; PAIR FORMATION.

P. A. D. H.   **Philip Arthur Dominic Hollom**, Woking, Surrey, England. Editor (formerly senior), *British
Birds*. CENSUS.

R. C. H.   **Richard Constantine Homes**, B.Com. (London). Tadworth, Surrey, England. Past President,
British Trust for Ornithology ; Past President, London Natural History Society. BIRD-WATCHING.

F. S. H.   **Frank Stewart Howes**, C.B.E., M.A. (Oxford), F.R.C.M. Oxfordshire, England. Late Music
Critic, *The Times* ; Professor of the Royal College of Music, London. MUSIC, BIRDS IN.

H. G. H.   **Henry George Hurrell**, M.A. (Cambridge). South Brent, Devon, England. DIPPER.

J. C. D. H.   **John Charles Duncan Hutchinson**, M.A. (Cambridge). Ian Clunies Ross Research Laboratory,

Prospect, N.S.W., Australia ; late of A.R.C. Poultry Research Centre, Edinburgh, Scotland. HEAT REGULATION ; METABOLISM.

J. S. H.   Sir **Julian Sorell Huxley**, D.Sc. (Oxford), Dr.h.c. (Caracas ; San Carlos de Guatemala ; San Marcos de Lima ; Athens ; Columbia ; Birmingham), F.R.S. (Darwin Medallist, 1957). London, England. Late Director-General, U.N.E.S.C.O. ; late Secretary, Zoological Society of London ; late Professor of Zoology, King's College, London ; Past President, Institute of Animal Behaviour ; late Chairman, Association for the Study of Systematics. POLYMORPHISM.

A. I. I.   Professor **Alexandr Ivanovich Ivanov**, S.D. (Leningrad). Curator of Birds, Zoological Institute of the Academy of Sciences of the U.S.S.R., Leningrad, U.S.S.R. BULBUL.

A. R. J.   **Arthur Ramsden Jennings**, D.V.Sc. (Liverpool), M.A. (Cambridge), M.R.C.V.S. Lecturer in Animal Pathology, University of Cambridge, England. DISEASE.

G. C. A. J.   **George Christoffel Alexander Junge**, D.Sc. (Amsterdam). Senior Curator of Birds, Rijksmuseum van Natuurlijke Historie, Leiden, Netherlands. *Died 3 February 1962.* BUSTARD ; CRANE ; NIGHTJAR ; RAIL.

J. K.   **Janet Kear** (Mrs G. V. T. Matthews), B.Sc. (London), Ph.D. (Cambridge). Food Ethologist, Wildfowl Trust, Slimbridge, Gloucestershire, England. FOOD SELECTION.

A. K.   Professor **James Allen Keast**, M.Sc. (Sydney), Ph.D. (Harvard). Associate Professor of Biology, Queen's University, Kingston, Ontario, Canada ; late Curator of Birds, Reptiles, and Amphibians, Australian Museum, Sydney, N.S.W., Australia ; President, Royal Australasian Ornithologists' Union. CASSOWARY ; MAGPIE-LARK ; PLAINS-WANDERER.

J. J. K.   Associate Professor **Janusz Josef Klawe**, Dip.Com. (Grenoble), M.A. (Glasgow). Department of Geography, University of Alberta, Edmonton, Alberta, Canada ; late Lecturer in Geography, University of Edinburgh, Scotland. MAPPING.

M. K.   **Maxwell Knight**, O.B.E. Camberley, Surrey, England. PELLET.

D. L.   **David Lambert Lack**, Sc.D. (Cambridge), F.R.S. Director, Edward Grey Institute of Field Ornithology, University of Oxford, England ; late Vice-President, British Ornithologists' Union ; President, XIV International Ornithological Congress (1966). DARWIN'S FINCHES ; LIFE EXPECTATION OF ; POPULATION DYNAMICS ; RADAR ; SWIFT.

H. H. L.   **Hubert Horace Lamb**, M.A. (Cambridge). Research Division, Meteorological Office, Bracknell, Berkshire, England ; member, World Meteorological Organisation Working Group on Climatic Fluctuations. CLIMATOLOGY ; METEOROLOGY.

R. L.   **Raymond Paul Joseph Lévêque**, Lic.Sc. (Genève). Geneva, Switzerland. Late Director, Charles Darwin Research Station, Galápagos Islands. PENGUIN (part).

M. L.   **Monte Lloyd**, A.B. (California), Ph.D. (Chicago). Assistant Professor of Zoology, University of California, Los Angeles, California, U.S.A. ; formerly at Bureau of Animal Population, University of Oxford, England. STATISTICAL SIGNIFICANCE.

H. L.   **Hans Löhrl**, Ph.D. (München). Max-Planck-Institut für Verhaltensphysiologie, Vogelwarte Radolfzell, Schloss Möggingen, Radolfzell, Germany. NUTHATCH.

G. H. L.   Professor **George Hines Lowery**, Jr., B.S. (Louisiana State), Ph.D. (Kansas). Boyd Professor of Zoology and Director of the Museum of Natural Science, Louisiana State University, Baton Rouge, Louisiana, U.S.A. ; Past President, American Ornithologists' Union. MOON WATCHING (jointly).

R. H. M.   **Robert Helmer MacArthur**, M.S. (Brown), Ph.D. (Yale). Associate Professor of Zoology, University of Pennsylvania, Philadelphia, U.S.A. ECOLOGY.

J. D. M.   **James David Macdonald**, B.Sc. (Aberdeen). Deputy Keeper (in charge of Bird Section), Zoology Department, British Museum (Natural History), London, England. MUSEUM ; RESPIRATORY SYSTEM.

A. R. M.   **Arnold Robert McGill**. Sydney, N.S.W., Australia. Past President, Royal Australasian Ornithologists' Union ; Assistant Editor, *The Emu.* MAGPIE (2).

C. W. M.-P.   **Cyril Winthrop Mackworth-Praed**, O.B.E. London and Hampshire, England. Late Vice-President (formerly Hon. Secretary & Treasurer), British Ornithologists' Union ; late Chairman, British Ornithologists' Club. BROADBILL ; PITTA.

P. H. M. -B.   Sir **Philip Henry Manson-Bahr**, C.M.G., D.S.O., M.D. (London), F.R.C.P., Hon. M.D. (Malaya). Edenbridge, Kent, England. Consulting Physician, Hospital for Tropical Diseases, London ; late Chairman, British Ornithologists' Club ; late Vice-President, British Ornithologists' Union ; Past President, Royal Society of Tropical Medicine and Hygiene. INSTRUMENTAL SOUNDS.

S. M.   **Stephen Marchant**, B.A. (Cambridge).   Bureau of Mineral Resources, Canberra, A.C.T., Australia ; formerly engaged in geological work in Ecuador (1954–58), also in Egypt, Nigeria, and Iraq.   ANTBIRD ; FLYCATCHER (2) ; NEST ; NESTING ASSOCIATION ; OVENBIRD (1) ; WOODCREEPER ; VULTURE (2).

P. R. M.   **Peter Robert Marler**, Ph.D. (London ; Cambridge).   Associate Professor of Zoology, University of California, Berkeley, Cal., U.S.A.   AGGRESSION.

A. J. M.   Professor **Alan John Marshall**, B.Sc. (Sydney), D.Phil., D.Sc. (Oxford).   Professor of Zoology and Comparative Physiology, Monash University, Clayton, Victoria, Australia.   BOWERBIRD ; ENDOCRINE SYSTEM.

G. V. T. M.   **Geoffrey Venon Townsend Matthews**, Ph.D. (Cambridge).   Director of Research, Wildfowl Trust, Slimbridge, Gloucestershire, England.   HOMING PIGEON ; NAVIGATION ; TIME MEASUREMENT.

L. H. M.   **Leonard Harrison Matthews**, Sc.D. (Cambridge), F.R.S.   Scientific Director, Zoological Society of London, and Editor of its *Proceedings* and *Transactions* ; formerly member of scientific staff, ' Discovery ' Expedition.   ALBATROSS ; GASTRONOMIC AND MEDICAL USES ; REPRODUCTIVE SYSTEM ; TORPIDITY.

E. M.   Professor **Ernst Mayr**, Ph.D. (Berlin), Hon. D.Phil. (Uppsala).   Director, Museum of Comparative Zoology, and Alexander Agassiz Professor of Zoology, Harvard University, Cambridge, Mass., U.S.A. ; Past President, American Ornithologists' Union ; President, XIII International Ornithological Congress, Ithaca, N.Y., 1962.   NEARCTIC REGION ; NEOTROPICAL REGION.

R. M.   Colonel **Richard Meinertzhagen**, C.B.E., D.S.O.   London.   Late Vice-President, British Ornithologists' Union.   CRAB-PLOVER ; GRIT ; LARK ; PALAEARCTIC REGION (main article) ; PIRACY ; SANDGROUSE.

R. M. (2)   **Ronald Melville**, Ph.D. (London).   Senior Principal Scientific Officer, Royal Botanic Gardens, Kew, Surrey, England.   POLLINATORS AND DISTRIBUTORS.

A. H. M.   Professor **Alden Holmes Miller**, Ph.D. (U.C., Berkeley).   Director, Museum of Vertebrate Zoology, University of California, Berkeley, Cal., U.S.A. ; late Vice-Chancellor, University of California, Berkeley ; Past President, American Ornithologists' Union ; Vice-President, International Ornithological Congress.   MOCKINGBIRD.

R. E. M.   **Reginald Ernest Moreau**, Hon. M.A. (Oxford).   Research Officer, Edward Grey Institute of Field Ornithology, University of Oxford, England ; late Secretary and Librarian, East African Agricultural Research Institute, Amani, Tanganyika (1928–47) ; President, British Ornithologists' Union ; late Editor, *The Ibis*.   BREEDING SEASON ; COURSER ; ETHIOPIAN REGION ; MALAGASY REGION ; ORIOLE (1) ; OXPECKER ; SPARROW (1) (part) ; TURACO ; WEAVER ; WHITE-EYE (1).

G. M.   **Guy Reginald Mountfort**.   Woldingham, Surrey, England.   Late Hon. Secretary, British Ornithologists' Union.   BILL.

R. C. M.   **Robert Cushman Murphy**, Ph.B., Sc.D. (Brown), M.A. (Columbia), Dr.h.c. (San Marcos de Lima).   Lamont Curator Emeritus of Birds, American Museum of Natural History, New York, U.S.A. ; Past President, National Audubon Society, U.S.A. ; Past President, Biological Laboratory, Cold Spring Harbor, Long Island, N.Y.   DIVING PETREL ; GUANO.

R. K. M.   **Ronald Keir Murton**, Ph.D. (London).   Senior Scientific Officer (Ornithologist), Field Research Station of the Ministry of Agriculture, Fisheries, and Food, near Guildford, Surrey, England.   MILK, PIGEON.

R. J. N.   **Robert James Newman**, B.A. (Pennsylvania), Ph.D. (Louisiana State).   Curator, Museum of Zoology in the Museum of Natural Science, Louisiana State University, Baton Rouge, Louisiana, U.S.A.   MOON WATCHING (jointly).

E. M. N.   **Edward Max Nicholson**, C.B.   Director-General, The Nature Conservancy (Great Britain), London, England ; late Chairman, British Trust for Ornithology ; late Vice-President, British Ornithologists' Union ; President, Technical Meeting of the International Union for the Conservation of Nature and Natural Resources, Edinburgh 1956 ; late Senior Editor, *British Birds*.   CONSERVATION.

G. G. O.   **Gaston Georges Olivier**.   Elbeuf, Seine Maritime, France.   Past President, Société Ornithologique de France.   SHRIKE.

R. S. P.   **Ralph Simon Palmer**, Ph.D. (Cornell).   State Zoologist, New York State Museum and Science Service, Albany, N.Y., U.S.A. ; Editor, *Handbook of North American Birds* (1962 et seq.).   CARDINAL-GROSBEAK ; COLOUR SPECIFICATION ; LIMPKIN.

K. C. P.   **Kenneth Carroll Parkes**, Ph.D. (Cornell).   Curator of Birds, Carnegie Museum, Pittsburgh, Pennsylvania, U.S.A.   WARBLER (2).

C. M. P. **Christopher Miles Perrins**, B.Sc. (London), D.Phil. (Oxford). Scientific Officer, Edward Grey Institute of Field Ornithology, University of Oxford, England. WEIGHT.

C. R. S. P. Captain **Charles Robert Senhouse Pitman**, C.B.E., D.S.O., M.C. London. Late (for 26 years) Game Warden, Uganda Protectorate ; Vice-President, Fauna Preservation Society ; late Vice-President, British Ornithologists' Union ; late Chairman, British Ornithologists' Club. EGGS, NATURAL HISTORY OF ; JACANA ; PAINTED SNIPE ; PRATINCOLE ; SKIMMER ; THICKKNEE.

A. P. Professor **Adolf Portmann**, Ph.D. (Basel), Dr. h.c. (Aix-Marseille ; Freiburg i. Br.). Director, Zoological Institute, University of Basel, Switzerland ; Secretary-General, XI International Ornithological Congress, Basel 1954. DEVELOPMENT, EMBRYONIC (jointly) ; DEVELOPMENT, POSTEMBRYONIC (jointly).

R. J. P. Professor **Richard Julius Pumphrey**, Sc.D. (Cambridge), F.R.S. Derby Professor of Zoology, University of Liverpool, England. HEARING AND BALANCE.

A. L. R. **Austin Loomer Rand**, Ph.D. (Cornell), D.Sc. (Acadia). Chief Curator of Zoology, Chicago Natural History Museum, Chicago, Illinois, U.S.A. ; President, American Ornithologists' Union. ASITY ; BIRD-OF-PARADISE ; CUCKOO-ROLLER ; GROUND-ROLLER ; MESITE ; VANGA.

R. E. R. **Reginald Elson Rewell**, M.D. (London), M.R.C.P. Consultant Pathologist, United Liverpool Hospitals, and Lecturer in Clinical Pathology, University of Liverpool, England ; late Pathologist, Zoological Society of London. BLOOD.

L. E. R. **Lancelot Eric Richdale**, D.Sc. (Otago). Late of University of Otago, New Zealand, and at Edward Grey Institute of Field Ornithology, University of Oxford, England ; the Nuffield Foundation and Zoological Society of London. PENGUIN (part).

S. D. R. **Sidney Dillon Ripley**, M.A. (Yale), Ph.D. (Harvard). Secretary, Smithsonian Institution, Washington, D.C., U.S.A. ; late of Yale University. THRUSH.

B. B. R. **Brian Birley Roberts**, Ph.D. (Cambridge). Research Associate, Scott Polar Research Institute, Cambridge, England, and head of Polar Regions Section, Research Department, Foreign Office, London. Member—British Graham Land Expedition, 1934–7 ; Norwegian-British-Swedish Antarctic Expedition, 1949–50 ; United States Antarctic Expedition, 1960–61. ANTARCTIC.

S. A. **Sálim Ali**, Hon. D.Sc. (Aligarh). Bombay, India. Vice-President, Bombay Natural History Society ; late Editor, *Journal of the Bombay Natural History Society*. ORIENTAL REGION.

F. S. Professor **Finn Salomonsen**, Ph.D. (Copenhagen). Keeper of Bird Department, Zoological Museum, University of Copenhagen, Denmark ; President, Dansk Ornithologisk Forening ; late Editor, *Dansk Ornithologisk Forenings Tidsskrift*. FLOWERPECKER ; HONEYEATER.

A. W. S. Professor Emeritus **Arlie William Schorger**, Ph.B. (Wooster), M.A. (Ohio State), Ph.D. (Wisconsin), Hon. D.Sc. (Lawrence ; Wisconsin). University of Wisconsin, U.S.A. TURKEY.

A. G. O'C. S. Major-General **Anthony Gerald O'Carroll Scott**, C.B., C.B.E., D.L. Pavenham, Bedfordshire, England. President, British Falconers' Club. FALCONRY.

P. S. **Peter Markham Scott**, C.B.E., D.S.C., M.A. (Cambridge), Hon. LL.D. (Aberdeen ; Exeter). Hon. Director, Wildfowl Trust, Slimbridge, Gloucestershire, England ; first Vice-President and Chairman, World Wildlife Fund, and Chairman of its British National Appeal ; Chairman, Survival Service Commission, International Union for the Conservation of Nature. DECOY ; DUCK ; GAME-BIRDS ; WILDFOWL.

D. L. S. **Dominick Louis Serventy**, B.Sc. (Western Australia), Ph.D. (Cambridge). Principal Research Officer, Division of Wildlife Research, Commonwealth Scientific and Industrial Research Organisation, Nedlands, Western Australia ; Past President, Royal Australasian Ornithologists' Union ; Editor, *Western Australian Naturalist*. AUSTRALASIAN REGION ; EMU ; FROGMOUTH ; OWLET-FROGMOUTH ; TREECREEPER (2) ; WREN (2).

D. S. -S. **David Seth-Smith**. Guildford, Surrey, England. Late Curator of Birds, Zoological Society of London ; late Vice-President, British Ornithologists' Union ; late President, Avicultural Society. *Died* 30 *October* 1963. AVICULTURE.

A. S. Professor **Aharon Shulov**, D.Sc. (Jerusalem ; Naples). Head, Laboratory of Entomology and Venomous Animals, Hebrew University of Jerusalem, Israel ; Director, Jerusalem Biblical Zoological Garden. BIBLE, BIRDS OF THE.

C. G. S. Professor **Charles Gald Sibley**, Ph.D. (California). Professor of Zoology and Curator of Birds, Cornell University, Ithaca, N.Y., U.S.A. ; Secretary General, XIII International Ornithological Congress, Ithaca, N.Y., 1962. PROTEINS AS TAXONOMIC CHARACTERS.

H. S. **Helmut Sick**, Ph.D. (Berlin). Museu Nacional, Rio de Janeiro, Brazil. ANTPIPIT ; CURASSOW ; HOATZIN ; RHEA ; TAPACULO ; TINAMOU.

K. E. L. S. **Kenneth Edwin Laurence Simmons**. Reading, England ; lately of Ascension Island. FEATHER MAINTENANCE ; GREBE.

A. F. S. **Alexander Frank Skutch**, Ph.D. (Johns Hopkins). San Isidro del General, Costa Rica. Research Fellow, Department of Ornithology, American Museum of Natural History. JACAMAR ; MOTMOT ; PUFFBIRD ; SHRIKE-VIREO ; SUNBITTERN ; TANAGER ; TOUCAN.

W. J. L. S. **William Joseph Lambart Sladen**, M.B.E., M.D. (London), D.Phil. (Oxford). Associate Professor in Department of Pathobiology, Johns Hopkins University, Baltimore, Maryland, U.S.A.; late medical officer and biologist, Falkland Islands Dependencies Survey (now British Antarctic Survey). EXCRETION, EXTRARENAL ; PENGUIN (main article).

B. E. S. **Bertram Evelyn Smythies**, B.A. (Forestry) (Oxford). Conservator of Forests, Sarawak ; late Burma Forest Service. CUCKOO-SHRIKE ; WOOD-SWALLOW.

D. W. S. **David William Snow**, D.Phil. (Oxford). Director, Charles Darwin Research Station, Galápagos Islands ; late Resident Naturalist, New York Zoological Society's tropical field station, Trinidad. COTINGA ; HONEYCREEPER (I) ; MANAKIN ; OILBIRD ; PEPPER-SHRIKE ; SWALLOW-TANAGER ; TIT.

E. J. L. S. **Ernest Jackson Lawson Soulsby**, M.A. (Cambridge), Ph.D. (Edinburgh), M.R.C.V.S. Professor of Parasitology, School of Veterinary Medicine, University of Pennsylvania, Philadelphia, U.S.A. ; late Lecturer in Animal Pathology, University of Cambridge, England ; President, World Association for the Advancement of Parasitology. ENDOPARASITE.

H. N. S. **Henry Neville Southern**, M.A. (Oxford). Senior Research Officer, Bureau of Animal Population, University of Oxford, England ; late Editor, *Bird Study*. PARASITISM.

R. S. **Robert Spencer**, B.A. (Durham). Research Officer, Ringing and Migration Section, British Trust for Ornithology, Tring, Hertfordshire, England ; Secretary General, European Committee for Bird Ringing. RINGING.

J. S. **Joachim Steinbacher**, Ph.D. (Berlin). Curator, Natur-Museum und Forschungs-Institut ' Senckenberg ', Frankfurt-am-Main, Germany. WOODPECKER.

W. S. **Werner Hugo Stingelin**, Ph.D. (Basel). First Assistant, Zoological Institute, University of Basel, Switzerland. DEVELOPMENT, EMBRYONIC (jointly) ; DEVELOPMENT, POSTEMBRYONIC (jointly).

B. S. **Bernard Stonehouse**, B.Sc. (London), D.Phil. (Oxford). Senior Lecturer, Department of Zoology, University of Canterbury, New Zealand ; late Falkland Islands Dependencies Survey (now British Antarctic Survey), and Leader, British Ornithologists' Union Centenary Expedition to Ascension Island. FRIGATEBIRD ; PENGUIN (part) ; SHEATHBILL ; TROPICBIRD.

R. W. S. Professor **Robert Winthrop Storer**, A.B. (Princeton), Ph.D. (California). Professor of Zoology, and Curator of Birds in Museum of Zoology, University of Michigan, Ann Arbor, U.S.A. ; Vice-President, American Ornithologists' Union ; late Editor, *The Auk*. AUK.

E. S. Professor **Erwin Friedrich Theodor Stresemann**, Ph.D. (München). Berlin (West), Germany. Late Director, Zoologisches Museum Humboldt-Universität, Berlin ; President, Deutsche Ornithologen Gesellschaft ; President, VIII International Ornithological Congress, Oxford 1934 ; late Editor, *Journal für Ornithologie* ; Editor, *Zoologische Jahrbücher* (Syst.). FLYCATCHER (I) (jointly).

D. S. -S. **James Denis Summers-Smith**, B.Sc. (Glasgow), Ph.D. (Reading). Guisborough, Yorkshire, England. SPARROW (I) (main article).

E. S. (2) **Ernst Robert Sutter**, Ph.D. (Basel). Assistant Curator, Museum of Natural History, Basel, Switzerland ; Editor, *Ornithologische Beobachter*. BUTTONQUAIL.

W. E. S. Professor **William Elgin Swinton**, Ph.D. (Glasgow). Director, Royal Ontario Museum and Professor of Zoology, University of Toronto, Canada ; late of Palaeontological Department, British Museum (Natural History), London ; late Hon. General Secretary, British Association for the Advancement of Science ; late Vice-President, Linnean Society of London ; Past President, Museums Association. FOSSIL BIRDS ; ORIGIN OF BIRDS.

K. T. **Katharine Tansley**, D.Sc. (London). Lecturer, Institute of Ophthalmology, University of London. VISION.

A. L. T. Sir (**Arthur**) **Landsborough Thomson**, C.B., D.Sc. (Aberdeen), Hon. LL.D. (Aberdeen). Late Second Secretary, Medical Research Council, London, England ; a Trustee, British Museum (Natural History) ; Past President, Zoological Society of London ; Past President, British Ornithologists' Union ; late Chairman, British Trust for Ornithology ; President, XI International Ornithological Congress, Basel 1954. ACCENTOR ; AVES ; BEE-EATER ; CLASSIFICATION ; CORMORANT ; CROW (I) ; CUCKOO ; DARTER ; DISTRIBUTION, GEOGRAPHICAL ; FLIGHTLESSNESS ; GANNET ; GULL ; HAMMERHEAD ; HERON ; HOOPOE ; HYBRIDISATION, ZONE OF SECONDARY ; IBIS ; KINGFISHER ; LOCOMO-

TION ; MIGRATION ; NAME, ENGLISH ; NOMENCLATURE ; NUMBERS ; ORNITHOLOGY ; PASSERI-
FORMES ; PELICAN ; PLOVER (I) ; RANGE EXPANSION ; RHYTHM ; ROLLER ; SANDPIPER ; SENSES ;
SEXUAL DIMORPHISM ; SHOEBILL ; SIZE ; SPECIES ; SPOONBILL ; SWALLOW ; TAMENESS ; YOUNG
BIRD ; and unsigned editorial items throughout.

M. M. T.   Lady **Mary Moir Thomson**, M.A. (Aberdeen). London, England. (General assistance to Editor.)

W. H. T.   **William Homan Thorpe**, Sc.D. (Cambridge), F.R.S. Reader in Animal Behaviour, University of Cambridge, England ; Past President, British Ornithologists' Union ; Past President, Association for the Study of Animal Behaviour ; Joint Editor, *Behaviour*. COUNTING ; IMPRINTING ; LEARNING; MIMICRY, VOCAL ; SINGING.

N. T.   **Nikolaas Tinbergen**, Ph.D. (Leiden), M.A. (Oxford), F.R.S. Reader in Animal Behaviour, University of Oxford, England ; late Professor of Experimental Zoology, University of Leiden, Netherlands ; Past President, Association for the Study of Animal Behaviour ; Secretary General, XIV International Ornithological Congress (1966). AMBIVALENCE ; DISPLACEMENT ACTIVITY ; RECOGNITION ; REDIRECTION ; RELEASER ; SIGN STIMULUS ; TERRITORY.

A. C. T.   **Alexander Cockburn Townsend**, M.A. (Cambridge). Chief Librarian, British Museum (Natural History), London, England ; Hon. Secretary and Editor, Society for the Bibliography of Natural History. ILLUSTRATION, BIRD.

R. T.   **Richard Owen Tudor**. National Gallery, London, England. ART, BIRDS IN.

E. G. T.   **Evan Graham Turbott**, M.Sc. (New Zealand). Assistant Director, Canterbury Museum, Christchurch, New Zealand ; Past President, Ornithological Society of New Zealand. WREN (3).

C. T.   Professor **Cyril Tyler**, D.Sc. (Leeds), F.R.I.C. Professor of Physiological Chemistry, University of Reading, England. EGGSHELL.

C. V.   **Charles Vaurie**, D.D.S. (Pennsylvania). Associate Curator, Department of Ornithology, American Museum of Natural History, New York, U.S.A. ; Chairman, International Standing Committee for Ornithological Nomenclature. BUNTING ; DRONGO ; FINCH.

G. V.   **Henry Gwynne Vevers**, M.B.E., D.Phil. (Oxford). Curator of Aquarium, Zoological Society of London, England ; Zoological Secretary, Linnean Society of London. COLOUR.

O. V.   Professor **Otakar Voçadlo**, Ph.D. (Prague), M.A. (Cambridge). Professor of English Language and Literature, Caroline University, Prague, Czecho-Slovakia ; late Lecturer, School of Slavonic Studies, University of London ; Editor of first complete Czech annotated edition of Shakespeare's works (6 vols). SHAKESPEARE'S BIRDS.

K. H. V.   Professor **Karel Hendrik Voous**, Dr. (Amsterdam). Professor of Zoological Systematics and Zoogeography, Free (Protestant) University, Amsterdam, Netherlands ; and Hon. Research Associate, Zoological Museum, University of Amsterdam ; Hon. Editor, *Ardea* ; late Hon. Secretary, Netherlands Ornithological Union. OWL ; PALAEARCTIC REGION (part) ; WAGTAIL.

J. W.   **John Warham**. Durham City, England. Late independent research worker in Australia (1952–1960). PENGUIN (part).

U. W.   **Uli Weidmann**, Dr. Phil. (Zürich). Lecturer in Zoology, Birkbeck College, University of London, England. LAYING.

A. W.   **Alexander Wetmore**, Ph.D. (George Washington), D.Sc. (Wisconsin ; George Washington). Research Associate, Smithsonian Institution, Washington, D.C., U.S.A. ; late Secretary, Smithsonian Institution ; Past President, American Ornithologists' Union ; President, X International Ornithological Congress, Uppsala 1950. SCREAMER ; SERIAMA ; TODY.

I. A. W.   **Iolo Aneurin Williams**, M.A. (Cambridge). Editorial staff, *The Times*, London ; late Vice-President, Zoological Society of London. *Died 18 January* 1962. POETRY, BIRDS IN.

K. W.   **Kenneth Williamson**. Research Officer, Population Studies Section (formerly Migration Research Officer), British Trust for Ornithology, Tring, Hertfordshire, England ; late Director (1948–50), Fair Isle Bird Observatory, Scotland ; late Editor, *Bird Migration*. OBSERVATORY.

D.G.M.W.-G.   **David Grainger Marcus Wood-Gush**, B.Sc. (Rand), Ph.D. (Edinburgh). Agricultural Research Council Poultry Research Centre, Edinburgh, Scotland. DOMESTICATION.

A. N. W.   Professor **Alastair Norman Worden**, M.A. (Cambridge), B.Sc., (London), F.R.I.C., M.R.C.V.S. Director, Huntingdon Research Centre, Huntingdon, England ; late Milford Research Professor, University of Wales ; Editor, *Animal Behaviour*. ALIMENTARY SYSTEM ; NUTRITION.

V. C. W. -E.   Professor **Vero Copner Wynne-Edwards**, M.A. (Oxford). Regius Professor of Natural History, University of Aberdeen, Scotland ; Vice-President, British Ornithologists' Union ; Past President, Scottish Ornithologists' Club. OCEANIC BIRDS ; PHALAROPE ; SKUA.

J. J. Y. **John James Yealland**. Curator of Birds, Zoological Society of London, England ; Editor, *Bulletin of the British Ornithologists' Club*. CAGE BIRD.

G. K. Y. **George Kirkby Yeates**, B.A. (Oxford). Harrogate, Yorkshire, England. Late Photographic Editor, *British Birds* ; late Hon. Secretary, Zoological Photographic Club. PHOTOGRAPHY.

ARTISTS

Commander **Alfred Marcus Hughes**, O.B.E., R.N. (ret.).   Surrey, England. Plate 43, and text-figures in article EGGS, NATURAL HISTORY OF.

Chloë Elizabeth Talbot Kelly.   c/o British Museum (Natural History), London, England. Pls. 5, 6, 7, 8, 42, and most of the text-figures of birds.

David Morrison Reid-Henry.   Essex, England. Pls. 17, 32, 41.

Peter Markham Scott, C.B.E., D.S.C., LL.D.   Gloucestershire, England (see under Authors). Pl. 19, and text-figures in article DUCK.

Keith Shackleton.   London, England. Pl. 30 and a few text-figures.

Charles Frederick Tunnicliffe, R.A.   Anglesey, Wales. Pl 29.

Betty Temple Watts.   Canberra, Australia. Pl. 31.

Michael James Yule.   Lancashire, England. Pls. 18, 20, and various text-figures.

PHOTOGRAPHERS

G. Ronald Austing.   U.S.A. Plate 2a.

J. B. & S. Bottomley.   Lancashire, England. Pl. 39a.

G. J. Broekhuysen, Ph.D.,   South Africa (see under Authors). Pls. 22a, 35b, 37a.

Roy P. Cooper.   Melbourne, Australia. Pls. 26a and b, 33b.

Allan D. Cruickshank.   Florida, U.S.A. Pls. 11b, 12b, 48a.

C. C. Doncaster.   Hertfordshire, England. Pls. 4b, 12a, 24b, 34d.

M. D. England.   Surrey, England. Pl. 36a.

Crawford H. Greenewalt, Sc.D.,   Delaware, U.S.A. Pl. 44a.

Donald S. Hentzelman.   U.S.A. P. 46a.

Eric J. Hosking.   London, England. Pls. 3b, 21, 22b, 37b, 44b, 45a, 48b.

Russ Kinne.   Connecticut, U.S.A. Pls. 14b, 16b.

Christina Loke.   Singapore, Malaysia. Pls. 1, 4a, 13a, 33a, 46b.

Dato **Loke Wan Tho**.   Singapore, Malaysia. *Died 20 June 1964*. Pls. 23, 28c, 35a, 47a.

Svante Lundgren.   Upplandsboderne, Sweden. Pl. 9a.

Ilse Makatsch.   Bautzen, Germany. Pls. 11c, 34c.

John Markham.   London, England. Pls. 13b, 16d, 22c.

Jacques Masson.   France. Pl 10a.

R. K. Murton, Ph.D.,   Surrey, England (see under Authors). Pl. 28a.

Jean Prévost.   France. Pl. 38a and b.

Lt.-Col. **Niall Rankin**.   Isle of Mull, Scotland. Pl. 27a.

W. J. L. Sladen, M.B.E., M.D., D. Phil.,   Maryland, U.S.A. (see under Authors). Pl. 25.

Gordon Smith.   U.S.A. Pl. 11a.

M. F. Soper, D.Sc.,   New Zealand. Pls. 10b, 15, 39b.

Peter Steyn.   Southern Rhodesia. Pls. 9b, 34a.

P. O. Swanberg.   Skara, Sweden. Pls. 3c, 14c, 40b.

A. Landsborough Thomson.   London, England ; formerly Aberdeen, Scotland (see under Authors). Pl. 34b.

Dr **Zoltán Tildy**.   Buda-Pest, Hungary. Pls. 3a, 27b, 28b, 36b.

John Warham.   Durham, England ; formerly Australia (see under Authors). Pls. 13c, 14a, 16a, 16c, 45b, 47b.

Joe van Wormer.   U.S.A. Pls. 2b, 24a.

G. K. Yeates.   Yorkshire, England (see under Authors). Pl. 40a.

Editorial Introduction

I am but mad north-north-west ; when the wind is southerly
I know a hawk from a handsaw.

Shakespeare Hamlet.

THIS is a comprehensive work of reference on birds, and everything about them, on a world-wide basis. A large part of it consists of articles of encyclopaedia length, some dealing with general subjects and others with the various families of birds. These are interspersed with shorter entries defining special terms or the application of names. The arrangement is alphabetical, with abundant cross-references, so that the dictionary constitutes its own index.

As is reflected in its title, the present work had a prototype in *A Dictionary of Birds* (1896) by Professor Alfred Newton, F.R.S., assisted by Dr Hans Gadow, F.R.S. It is, however, in no sense a revision of that classic, but is an entirely new undertaking ; it is differently conceived in various respects, is less historical in its approach, and is the work of many hands.

Aim. The book is intended for readers of several different types—the general reader who wishes to extend his knowledge of birds or perhaps just to inform himself on particular points ; the ornithologist who requires information outside his individual field of expertise ; and the biologist who wishes to draw upon the specialised subject-matter of ornithology.

Largely for the non-professional ornithologist, it has been thought convenient to include certain ' background information ' from other branches of science concerned with environmental factors affecting bird-life, such as climate and vegetation ; and also from the main corpus of biological knowledge, dealing with such aspects as evolution and genetics. There is likewise an article on the application of statistical methods.

Another supplementary feature, of potential interest to all types of reader, is the group of articles on birds in human culture—for instance, as subjects of folk-lore, literature, and the arts.

Scope. The information presented is of two main kinds. First, there is information on general subjects relating to birds as a class—their structure, evolution, distribution, and classification ; their life histories and behaviour ; their adaptations to their environment ; and their relations with mankind. Second, there is information on different kinds of birds, for this purpose mainly treated by families. The major articles of both these types are cited in logical sequence in the two lists that amplify the general table of contents ; these lists give a more detailed indication of the scope of the work, and they should help the reader to choose the alphabetical headings under which he should look for any particular subject.

Arrangement. Although the arrangement is alphabetical, the principle has been followed of bringing related information together in major articles of the types already mentioned. It is, for example, both easier and more helpful to define a particular bone in the context of the skeleton as a whole, rather than in isolation under its own name. Many of the alphabetical entries are thus reduced to the status of cross-references to the relevant major articles. Other

33

minor entries simply define terms used in ornithological science ; many such terms are also more widely used, and no attempt has been made to provide a glossary of words that can be found in an ordinary dictionary and have no peculiar meanings in ornithological or related usage.

Language. The work is, furthermore, a dictionary in the English language. Scientific terms formed from classical languages do not appear as entry headings unless they are in such common use as to be practically anglicised, or unless they have no satisfactory equivalents in common speech. Synonyms in modern foreign languages are excluded on the same principle.

As regards the English names of birds, those chosen as entry headings are mainly the substantive names in standard use by British ornithologists ; the inclusion of dialect or archaic names is limited to those most widely occurring. On the other hand, accepted usage in North America, and elsewhere in the English-speaking world as far as practicable, has also been covered. For readers primarily speaking other languages, the work should be helpful to the understanding of publications in English that do not fully employ terms and names of international status.

As an exception, scientific names of groups above generic level have been used as entry headings, but mainly limited to those used in the classification here followed ; the families or subfamilies are, however, treated under their English names. The scientific names of genera are not used as entry headings, except where they are also the English substantive names ; but an alphabetical index of generic names mentioned in the text is given at the end of the volume, with cross-references to the English entries.

References. Citation of authorities for statements made has, in general, been considered to be superfluous ; even where an author is named, a precise reference may be omitted. References have thus been mainly limited to books, monographs, or important papers recommended as containing fuller accounts of particular subjects, and of course likely to open up still further vistas of reading. Publications cited are for the most part of recent date, purely historical references being exceptional ; the inquiring reader can work back from the newer to the older literature. Some relatively minor papers have been cited mainly because they are new—in some cases published since the respective articles to which they are appended were first written.

As this is a dictionary mainly of English terms and names, some bias in favour of references to works in that language has been deemed permissible. Such publications will, however, usually give references to the international literature that must be consulted by those wishing to go deeply into any question.

Illustrations. The text-figures illustrate the articles in which they are placed. The colour plates have been used to illustrate general aspects, e.g. sexual, seasonal, or age differences in plumage, for which black-and-white would have been inadequate. Miss C. E. Talbot Kelly, working in the British Museum (Natural History), has been responsible for five of the colour plates and for most of the text-figures of birds ; several other artists have contributed one or two plates, and in some cases a few drawings—D. M. Reid-Henry kindly undertook three plates as an urgent commission. There are also, among the text-figures, various diagrams supplied by the authors of articles.

The photographs in the half-tone plates have been chosen primarily to illustrate different activities of birds. They also show a selection of birds of many families and from various parts of the world—and incidentally the work of a good number of leading photographers of such subjects.

Collaboration. The wide subject coverage has been made possible by enlisting contributions from 172 ornithological and other specialists, drawn from every continent and from

22 countries.   Artists and photographers bring the total to well over 200, with 5 additional countries.   The articles on general subjects are mostly by authors in the United Kingdom ; the articles on bird groups are by authors widely spread throughout the world   To all the contributors, already listed, the Editor is most grateful for their collaboration.

For much helpful counsel, outside the scope of their own contributions, the Editor is indebted particularly to Dr A. J. Cain, E. Eisenmann, D. Goodwin, Dr David Lack, J. D. Macdonald, Dr L. Harrison Matthews, Dr Ernst Mayr, Colonel R. Meinertzhagen, Dr R. S. Palmer, Captain C. R. S. Pitman, Peter Scott, Dr D. L. Serventy, Dr W. H. Thorpe, Dr N. Tinbergen, Professor V. C. Wynne-Edwards, and J. J. Yealland ; and also, outside the list of authors, to Mrs B. P. Hall, C. J. O. Harrison, E. J. Hosking, C. Horton-Smith, Dr G. F. Mees, Dr R. G. Wolk, the library staff of the Zoological Society of London, and the staff in the Bird Room of the British Museum (Natural History).

Very special gratitude is due to R. E. Moreau, President of the British Ornithologists' Union and former Editor of *The Ibis*; in addition to writing several articles, he has responded generously to constant consultation by the Editor, and he has read almost the whole work in proof. In the day to day preparation, extending over seven years, the editor has had no more than occasional assistance except from his wife, without whom the task could not have been accomplished.

Finally, it is a pleasure to record the help given during the press stages by the staff of Thomas Nelson & Sons Limited, both in Edinburgh while the book was taking shape in print and in London when final arrangements for production were being made. The constructive advice of W. T. McLeod was invaluable during the earlier stage, and the meticulous questioning of textual details by Dr Katharine Davies was most helpful. The later stage went smoothly under the guidance of Christopher Busby and J. A. Beazley, with the constant attention of Mrs Julie Wood to matters of lay-out.

Amendment. In a work of this kind, absolute freedom from error is unattainable ; and the omission of entries that might have been useful is even more difficult to guard against. The Editor will welcome intimation of any necessary corrections or suggested additions; these will be noted for any list of corrigenda and addenda that may subsequently be considered advisable.

As regards the date of the work, it will be realised that it has been impossible to include all new information accruing during the years of preparation. No general dead-line has been drawn, however, short of the date of correcting first proofs.

A. Landsborough Thomson

London, 1964.

CITATION OF THIS WORK: SUGGESTED FORMS

Full general reference :
Thomson, A. Landsborough (Editor). 1964. *A New Dictionary of Birds.* London (Nelson) and New York (McGraw-Hill).

Abbreviated reference (with citation, if desired, of a particular editorial or anonymous article) :
Thomson, A. L. (ed.). 1964. *New Dict. Birds.* London & New York. (Article 'Migration').

Reference to a contributed article (e.g.) :
Moreau, R. E. 1964. Article 'Ethiopian Region' in Thomson, A. L. (ed.). *New Dict. Birds.* London & New York.

Dictionary A-Z

And other egles of a lower kinde,
Of which that clerkes well devysen conne.

Chaucer *Parlement of Foules*

A

ABDOMEN: the 'belly', being the part of the body containing the excretory, reproductive, and main digestive organs (see ALIMENTARY SYSTEM; EXCRETORY SYSTEM; REPRODUCTIVE SYSTEM); applied also to the ventral surface of the same region (see TOPOGRAPHY).

ABDUCTOR: see MUSCULATURE

ABMIGRATION: an anomalous migratory movement of a particular type (defined under MIGRATION).

ABNORMALITIES: see under BILL; MONSTROSITY; PLUMAGE, ABNORMAL AND ABERRANT; SKELETON

ABRASION: the effect of wear on the vane of a feather, involving some reduction of the tips of the barbs or their barbules; where these tips are coloured differently from the rest of the vane, their loss may substantially change the pattern and hue of the plumage generally (see PLUMAGE).

ABUNDANCE : see NUMBERS

ACANTHISITTIDAE: alternative name for the XENICIDAE; see also WREN (3).

ACCENTOR: former generic name used as substantive name of most species of Prunellidae (Passeriformes, suborder Oscines); in the plural, general term for the family. The only member to have a traditional English name is the Hedgesparrow (or Dunnock) *Prunella modularis*. The accentors are small birds with rufous or brownish grey upper parts, streaked or striped in most species; and with greyish under parts, usually marked with rufous in places. The general size and appearance are like those of a sparrow *Passer* sp., but the bill is more slender and pointed; the sexes are similar in plumage. Anatomically, they have the fringillid character of a true crop and a muscular gizzard (adapted to a diet of seeds at some seasons), but they are generally considered to have affinities with the thrushes (Turdinae).

They are mostly montane birds and very hardy, many remaining during the winter at high altitudes in the mountains of Eurasia; but some are migratory within the limits of the total range. They are unobtrusive and rather solitary, with short simple songs. They are ground-feeders, often creeping busily about with a mouse-like action, and in summer they are mainly insectivorous; in winter, however, they are able to subsist on seeds and berries. The nest is usually an open cup, placed on or near the ground—in a rock crevice or in a bush, according to the habitat of the species. The 3–5 eggs are bluish in some species, bright blue in others.

Alpine Accentor *Prunella collaris*.   *C.E.T.K.*

The family has the rare distinction of being to all intents exclusively Palaearctic, being widely distributed from the British Isles to Japan; isolated 'pockets' in south-western Arabia and in Formosa may be considered to be just outside the Region, but both are at considerable altitudes. There are a dozen species, all assigned to the genus *Prunella*. Two of them are birds chiefly of rocky alpine meadows, up to the snow-line; the majority mainly inhabit scrub vegetation at a somewhat lower level; and the remainder are found still lower, in coniferous forests or even deciduous woods.

The Alpine Accentor *P. collaris* is a species found

at the highest altitudes—in the mountains of north-west Africa and of southern and central Europe, eastwards through Asia to Japan. The Himalayan Accentor *P. himalayana* is found breeding as high as 17 000 feet above sea-level ; the Robin Accentor *P. rubeculoides* is also found at high altitudes in central Asia but shows a preference for dwarf rhododendron and other scrub, or willows and sedges on damp meadows. The Siberian Accentor *P. montanella* has a range apparently extending northwards beyond the taiga. The form found in the Yemen, breeding above 6000 feet, is *P. atrogularis fagani*, a race of the Black-throated Accentor, otherwise native to central Asia but found farther south as a winter visitor. The Maroon-backed Accentor *P. immaculata*, found from Nepal to western China, shows a preference for damp places deep in coniferous forests.

The Hedgesparrow *P. modularis* of Europe and adjacent parts of Asia is less of a montane species than its congeners. In the Caucasus it is found in scrub above the tree-line, but over much of western Europe it is found mainly in coniferous forest at no great altitude. In the British Isles it is a familiar bird of the hedgerows, which may be regarded as replacing the forest undergrowth of earlier times. The old vernacular name ' Dunnock ' is increasingly preferred by ornithologists to the more generally used misnomer. A.L.T.

Marien, D. 1951. Notes on the bird family Prunellidae in southern Eurasia. Amer. Mus. Novit. 1482 : 1–28.
Steinfatt, O. 1938. Das Brutleben des Heckenbraunelle, *Prunella m. modularis*. Orn. Mber. 46 : 65–76.
Vaurie, C. 1959. The Birds of the Palearctic Fauna vol. 1. London.

ACCIPITER: sometimes used in North America as a vernacular term for *Accipiter* spp., ' hawk ' having there a wider connotation than in Britain (see HAWK).

ACCIPITRES: alternative ordinal or subordinal name (see under FALCONIFORMES) ; the first order of Linnaeus.

ACCIPITRIDAE: see under FALCONIFORMES. The family includes the hawks, in a wide sense of the term, as distinct from the falcons (Falconidae). In the system here followed it comprises the sub-families Circinae, Polyboroidinae, Circaetinae, Accipitrinae, Milvinae, Perninae, Elaninae, Machaeramphinae, Pandioninae, Gypaetinae, and Aegypiinae—for the last two see VULTURE (1), for the remainder see HAWK. Some authors have separated the larger members of the Accipitrinae as the Buteoninae,

and have given other groups full familial rank (Aegypiidae, Pandionidae).

ACETABULUM: the hollow in the pelvic girdle, on each side, into which the head of the femur fits (see SKELETON).

ACQUIRED CHARACTERS: those arising during the life of the individual as the result of environmental or functional influences, as distinct from those expressing genetic constitution (see EVOLUTION; NATURAL SELECTION).

ACROMION: anterior projection of the scapula (see SKELETON).

ACROMYODI: see PASSERIFORMES; SYRINX

ACROPODIUM: the dorsal surface of the toes (see LEG).

ACROTARSAL: pertaining to the anterior surface of the tarsus.

ACTION PATTERN: see FIXED ACTION PATTERN

ACUTIPLANTAR: having the hinder aspect of the tarsus coming to an angle (applied to oscine Passeriformes) ; opposite of LATIPLANTAR (in general, see LEG).

ADAPTATION: the production of fitness for a particular function, the term being also applied to a character (structure, behaviour, etc.) specially providing such fitness (see EVOLUTION ; NATURAL SELECTION). ' Adaptive radiation ' denotes divergence in the characters of related forms that enables these to exploit different kinds of opportunity. ' Convergence ' denotes the adaptation of unrelated forms to similar functions, often giving rise to superficial resemblance (see CONVERGENCE). The term ' pre-adaptation ' is used in cases where, coincidentally, a character existed in advance of the opportunity to which it proved particularly suited.

ADDUCTOR: see MUSCULATURE

ADENOSINE TRIPHOSPHATE: the source of energy for, inter alia, muscular contraction (see METABOLISM).

ADJUTANT: also ' Adjutant-bird ' or ' Adjutant Stork ', substantive name of Asiatic species of *Leptoptilos* (see STORK).

ADRENAL GLAND: see ENDOCRINE SYSTEM

ADULT: theoretically, a bird that has reached its fullest development ; in practice, however, a term difficult to define precisely. Size is no criterion, as a bird is full-grown at a very early age (see also YOUNG BIRD). The implication is that the bird has attained, appropriately to season, definitive plumage (see MOULT) ; and also that it is capable of breeding (see MATURITY). For most purposes, plumage provides the only practicable criterion. Difficulties are that many species breed, some even more than once, before acquiring their best plumage; and that others may acquire adult nuptial dress without breeding in the first year of wearing it.

AEGITHALINAE: see TIT

AEGITHOGNATHOUS: see PALATE

AEGOTHELIDAE: see CAPRIMULGIFORMES; and OWLET-FROGMOUTH

AEGYPIINAE: see VULTURE (1)

AEPYORNITHES; AEPYORNITHIDAE: see below

AEPYORNITHIFORMES: an order, alternatively 'Aepyornithes', of extinct 'ratite' birds comprising only the family Aepyornithidae of Madagascar, of which representatives probably survived into historical times (see ELEPHANT-BIRD; also RATITES, PHYLOGENY OF THE).

AERATION: see RESPIRATORY SYSTEM

AEROPHANERIC: term applied to coloration important in aerial display (Armstrong).

AETHIINI: see AUK

AETIOLOGY: the science of causation, especially the causes of diseases (see DISEASE).

AFFERENT: carrying inwards, i.e. towards the centre ; applied especially to nerves, in respect of the direction in which they transmit impulses—contrasted with EFFERENT (see NERVOUS SYSTEM).

AFRICA: see ETHIOPIAN REGION (for Africa south of the Sahara) ; PALAEARCTIC REGION (for North Africa); MALAGASY REGION (for Madagascar). Note that the term 'Central Africa', more broadly used in earlier writings, has lately had a restricted political meaning.

AFTERSHAFT: or 'hyporachis', a counterpart feather growing from the same calamus as the feather proper and lying underneath the latter. Such a structure is found on all the body feathers of many kinds of birds, and on certain of the body feathers of other kinds, but not usually on the rectrices or remiges. In the Casuariiformes the aftershaft is almost a duplicate of the main feather. In many members of the Tinamiformes, Galliformes, Ciconiiformes, Falconiformes, and Psittaciformes the aftershaft is also comparable in size with the main feather, but it is less well developed and more

plumaceous. In most other groups it is relatively small and often vestigial. In a few, e.g. the pigeons (Columbidae), it is entirely absent. See FEATHER; PLUMAGE.

AGAMI: *Agamia agami* (see HERON).

AGE: see LIFE, EXPECTATION OF ; LONGEVITY ; POPULATION DYNAMICS ; also GROWTH ; MATURITY ; YOUNG BIRD

AGGRESSION: threatening behaviour, sometimes including attack. Overt aggression, in the form of pure physical assault, is indeed seldom seen among wild birds (apart from raptorial killing). Instead it is usually intermingled with or overlain by a variety of postures, movements, and vocalisations that serve as a threat, repelling or intimidating the opponent without actual combat. Aggression in this broader sense is widespread and serves an important function in the life of most birds by aiding them to repel predators and enabling them to compete more effectively with their fellows for such things as space, food, nesting and roosting sites, and mates.

In order to define its biological significance it is necessary to know the factors determining when and where aggression will appear. In a given bird this depends upon its physiological state, and upon what it sees and hears around it. Most prominent of the physiological factors involved here is the level of gonadal hormones in circulation. A rise in the level of testosterone in the blood produces a dramatic increase in the aggressiveness of many birds, often involving defence of a territory. The effects of oestrogen are less clear, involving both increase and decrease of aggressiveness in different species. This relationship with the sex hormones makes it necessary to separate the analyses of aggression in the breeding season, when their levels are high, and in winter, when the gonads have regressed (see ENDOCRINE SYSTEM ; REPRODUCTIVE SYSTEM).

In winter, internal factors other than the sex hormones may come into play, but we know little of their effects. Hunger may increase fighting in birds, as can be seen in Rooks *Corvus frugilegus* and Jackdaws *C. monedula* when snow restricts the availability of food. However, experiments with Yellowhammers *Emberiza citrinella* and Chaffinches *Fringilla coelebs*, in which a similar increase of fighting is seen when they are hungry, suggest that a reduction of fear is responsible, rather than an increase in aggressiveness. There are other birds, such as the Corn Bunting *Emberiza calandra*, that fight less when they are hungry. No doubt other factors such as thirst, and also the effects of previous learning, can play a role.

We know more about the external factors that evoke aggression. Again confining our attention to winter conditions, the simplest formulation for birds such as the Chaffinch involves the concept of individual distance (see under FLOCKING). While some birds tolerate companions at close quarters, or in contact with them, others will either attack or avoid another bird that comes too close. Violation of this critical distance is probably the main cause of fighting in winter flocks of such birds as Chaffinches, Yellowhammers, and Oregon Juncos *Junco oreganus*. The distance is not fixed, but varies within certain limits. One factor involved is the appearance of the approaching bird. A male Chaffinch will allow a female of his own species to come closer than a male before he shows signs of aggression. But if we colour the female's breast red in imitation of the male, she is no longer tolerated at close quarters. If a bird of another species approaches, the critical distance will be different again, and if the intruder happens to be a predator, we may expect a maximum intolerance of proximity.

The behaviour of the intruder may play a role, and also its individual characteristics. In an established flock of Chaffinches, a given bird will consistently allow some individuals to come closer than others before attacking them, and a stranger to the group will be much less tolerated. Conversely, the same individual may be more tolerated by some opponents than others. In Oregon Juncos different populations vary in their aggressiveness. In southern California the critical distance may be from 6 to 15 inches, while in Seattle it is twice as great. In these species the area maintained free of intruders is centred on an individual bird, but a further complication arises in White-fronted Geese *Anser albifrons*, where the area defended in winter flocks centres on the family group rather than on the individual. No doubt many other factors will be found to affect individual distance ; yet its role in causing aggression is basically a simple one. We can regard aggression as a means of enabling animals to obtain and keep those commodities needed for survival and reproduction. For survival in winter, the link with violation of individual distance is an effective way of assuring that aggression will be restricted to competitive situations where its value will be greatest. In the breeding season other considerations come in, because the nest is necessarily fixed in space ; it is in this circumstance that territorial behaviour typically appears (see TERRITORY).

In contrast with individual distance behaviour, the defended area constituting the territory is sta-tionary. Although some birds defend the territory in winter, this behaviour typically appears in spring. As the testosterone output of the gonads rises, the defended area becomes larger and begins to be attached to a certain place. Whether individual distance behaviour is usually superseded is uncertain, but in some species at least it persists during encounters between birds that are away from their territories. Meanwhile, a new set of factors enters to govern when and where territorial aggression will take place.

Of the internal factors, testosterone is probably dominant, although in females oestrogen is probably involved—and perhaps progesterone and prolactin as well. The external factors for aggression differ between male and female, each defending the territory primarily from conspecifics of the same sex. In males, song becomes significant as a stimulus for attack and may itself serve as a means of threat (see SINGING). Other species are relatively much less potent as stimuli for attack than birds of the same species, in contrast with winter fighting. However, there are occasions when they, too, evoke attack, especially when close to the nest. This is more common in hole-nesting birds, which often need to engage in interspecific competition in order to retain their nest sites.

Thus, as in winter, the external situations in which different birds show territorial aggression relate to the circumstances in which competition for essential commodities is most severe. In most cases, such as competition for mates or nesting sites, birds of the same species are the most serious contenders and it is towards them that territorial aggression is primarily directed. Where competition with other species becomes crucial, as is commonly the fact in winter and also in exceptional cases in the breeding season, the restrictions are widened, so that birds such as the Pied Flycatcher *Ficedula hypoleuca* will defend the nest hole not only from other flycatchers but also from tits (Paridae), Starlings *Sturnus vulgaris*, Redstarts *Phoenicurus phoenicurus*, woodpeckers (Picidae), and even from squirrels.

See also BEHAVIOUR, DEVELOPMENT OF ; DOMINANCE (2) ; and Plate 22a b (phot.).   P.M.

Andrew, R. J. 1957. Influence of hunger on aggressive behaviour in certain buntings of the genus *Emberiza*. Physiol. Zool. 30 : 177–185.

Boyd, H. 1953. On encounters between wild white-fronted geese in winter flocks. Behav. 5 : 85–129.

Collias, N. E. 1944. Aggressive behavior among vertebrate animals. Physiol. Zool. 17 : 83–123.

Hinde, R. A. 1959. Some factors influencing sexual and aggressive behavior in male chaffinches. Bird Study 6 : 112–122.

Marler, P. 1955–57. Studies of fighting in Chaffinches I–IV. Brit. J. Anim. Behav. 3 : 111–117, 137–146 ; 4 : 23–30 ; 5 : 29–37.

Sabine, W. S. 1959. The winter society of the oregon junco : intolerance, dominance, and the pecking order. Condor 61 : 110–135.

AGONISTIC: term applied to behaviour relating to combat (see AGGRESSION).

AILUROEDINAE: see BOWERBIRD

AIR-PASSAGES ; AIR-SACS: see RESPIRATORY SYSTEM

AKALAT: substantive name used in West Africa for *Malacocincla* ('*Illadopsis*') spp. (for subfamily see BABBLER), and in East Africa for chats of the genus *Sheppardia* (for subfamily see THRUSH).

AKEPA: *Loxops coccinea* (see HONEYCREEPER (2)).

AKIALOA: *Hemignathus procerus*, also called 'Sicklebill' (see HONEYCREEPER (2)).

AKIAPOLAAU; *Hemignathus wilsoni* (for family see HONEYCREEPER (2)).

ALA MEMBRANA: the wing membrane, on the posterior margin of the forewing and manus, from which the remiges grow (see WING).

ALAR: pertaining to the wing.

ALA SPURIA: the alula or 'bastard wing' (see WING).

ALAUDIDAE: a family of the Passeriformes, suborder Oscines (see LARK).

ALAUWAHIO: *Loxops maculata* (for family see HONEYCREEPER (2)).

ALBATROSS: substantive name of the species of Diomedeidae (Procellariiformes) ; in the plural, general term for the family. The albatrosses are placed in the same order as the families of smaller petrels and have the tubular nostrils characteristic of the order (see PETREL). They are pelagic birds of large size (28–53 inches long) and notable for their spectacular powers of flight. They are stoutly built, with large heads ; the plumage is mainly white or brown, usually with some darker brown or black on the wings and often on the back or tail ; the sexes are alike in most species. The bill is stout and strongly hooked, with a sheath made up of horny plates. The legs are rather short, the feet are webbed, and the hallux is absent or minute. The wings are long and very narrow ; and the tail is short or of moderate length. The cries are loud and harsh.

Albatrosses are mainly birds of the Southern Hemisphere, from below the tropic to the Antarctic, but a few species inhabit the North Pacific and there is also some vagrancy of southern species into northern seas. There are, in all, a dozen species in the genus *Diomedea* (split by some authors) and two in *Phoebetria*. Except at their breeding places, they are usually seen in flight over the ocean, and they can glide for long distances on motionless wings ; but they alight on the water—and can dive a little way below the surface—to obtain the marine animals on which they feed, of which squids form a large part.

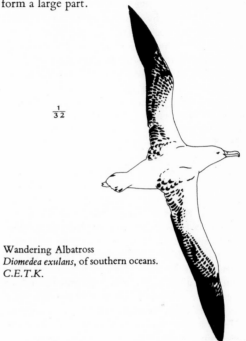

$\frac{1}{32}$

Wandering Albatross
Diomedea exulans, of southern oceans.
C.E.T.K.

Albatrosses mostly breed in large colonies on remote islands. There is evidence that, at least in some species, the birds remain permanently paired ; the sexes share the parental duties. Incubation lasts from two to three months. The nest is usually a mere hollow in the ground, or a heap of earth or vegetable matter. The single egg is whitish, generally speckled with red—especially at the blunt end. The chick is downy and nidicolous.

In all albatrosses there is a prenuptial display during which the tail is fanned, the wings are opened, the head is outstretched, and the tip of the bill is then buried in the plumage between the scapulars, to the accompaniment of gurgling and braying sounds, and in *Phoebetria* a shrill fluty scream. In the Royal Albatross *Diomedea epomophora* and Wandering Albatross *D. exulans* the display is more complicated because up to six or eight males (which are the first to arrive and take up territories at the breeding colonies) surround a single female and participate in a communal display. The display, which includes much rattling and vibrating of the bill and mutual touching of bill tips by male and female, culminates with the partners spreading the wings to their full extent. The initiative in the display is taken by the male, but the female also participates although on a slightly lower level of intensity.

The breeding season of the smaller albatrosses lasts about four to five months ; the young are eventually deserted by their parents but soon follow them to sea. The season is much longer in the Royal Albatross and Wandering Albatross, as the fledgling period lasts nearly a year, during the whole of which the parents feed the young at intervals. As a consequence these albatrosses breed only once in two years, and the new season's eggs are already laid before all the young of the previous season have left the colonies.

The downy nestlings, at least of some albatrosses, have the ability—commonly found in the Procellariiformes—of shooting out stomach oil as a form of defence. The proventriculus in petrels is comparatively large, and its mucosa is raised into longitudinal ridges so that its surface area is larger than in other birds. Lipoids other than triglycerides are concentrated in large quantities in the outer parts of the epithelial cells and probably represent the unsecreted stomach oil or its precursor ; only minute quantities of lipoids are present in the proventicular epithelial cells of other birds. The oil is usually coloured pink, and sets on cooling to a solid wax-like substance resembling spermaceti. It has been suggested that the primary function of the stomach oil, apart from defence, is to supplement the secretion of the preen gland ; it may be regurgitated in small quantities through the nostrils and seep down the grooves of the bill to be distributed over the plumage during preening. The shooting of the oil for defence may have evolved as an elaboration of the widespread habit among sea birds of vomiting the stomach contents to lighten the body for rapidity of escape when disturbed. It is also possible that the stomach oil may be concerned in the production of 'physiological' water, as the birds have no opportunity of drinking fresh water. See also OIL GLAND ; and EXCRETION, EXTRARENAL.

The most familiar species is the Wandering Albatross D. exulans, which is exceptional in showing sexual dimorphism in plumage. It is also the largest species, with a wing span of 11½ feet or more. It frequently follows ships, but the popular idea that the same individual does so for more than four to six consecutive days is probably erroneous ; great distances are nevertheless covered, and a ringed bird has been recorded some 6000 miles from its native locality. The species ranges over the oceans between 30° and 60° S. lat., breeding on such islands as Tristan da Cunha, South Georgia, and the Kerguelen and Auckland Islands.

The Blackbrowed Albatross D. melanophrys and the Greyheaded Albatross D. chrysostoma are species of somewhat similar distribution to the above ; the former has been recorded as a vagrant to the British Isles and even to the Arctic. The Royal Albatross D. epomophora is familiar in New Zealand seas. The breeding places of the North Pacific species of Diomedea are on such islands as Wake Island, the Marshall Islands, Laysan, and the Guadaloupe Islands. D. irrorata breeds in the Galápagos group, on the Equator.

The species of Phoebetria breed on islands in the southern oceans but do not form large colonies. They are distinguished from other albatrosses by the rather uniform dark colour, the long cuneate tail, and the incomplete white eye-ring.

See also ANTARCTIC ; FLIGHT ; OCEANIC BIRDS ; and Plate 27a (phot.).   L.H.M.

Bailey, A. M. & Sorensen, J. H. 1962. Subantarctic Campbell Island. Denver Mus. Nat. Hist. Proc. no 10. (Five albatross species nesting.)

Frings, H. and M. 1959. Observations on salt balance and behaviour of Laysan and Black-footed Albatrosses in captivity. Condor 61 : 305–314.

Frings, H. and M. 1961. Some biometric studies on the albatrosses of Midway Atoll. Condor 63 : 304–311.

Matthews, L. H. 1949. The origin of stomach oil in the petrels with comparative observations on the avian proventiculus. Ibis 91 : 373–392.

Rice, D. W. & Kenyon, K. W. 1962. Breeding distribution, history and populations of North Pacific albatrosses. Auk 79 : 365–386.

Richdale, L. E. 1952. Post-egg Period in Albatrosses. (Biological Monograph No. 4). Dunedin.

Yocom, C. 1947. Notes on behaviour and abundance of Black-footed Albatrosses in the Pacific waters off the continental North American shores. Auk 64 : 507–523.

(See also literature relating generally to the Procellariiformes cited under PETREL.)

ALBINISM: see PLUMAGE, ABNORMAL AND ABERRANT

ALBUMEN: see EGG ; PROTEINS AS TAXONOMIC CHARACTERS

ALCAE: see under CHARADRIIFORMES

ALCEDINES ; ALCEDINIDAE: see CORACIIFORMES ; and KINGFISHER

ALCEDINOIDEA: see under CORACIIFORMES

ALCIDAE: see under CHARADRIIFORMES ; and AUK

ALETHE: generic name used as substantive common name for species of chats (see CHAT ; THRUSH).

ALIMENTARY SYSTEM: consisting essentially, in all vertebrates, of a coiled tube, or gut, leading from mouth to anus, through which—along the axial cavity or lumen—food passes during the process of digestion ; a number of auxiliary organs are included in the system, notably the liver and the pancreas. See also INTESTINE.

Food is swallowed in a series of discrete masses, each mass being termed a bolus. The muscular walls of the gut form a constriction behind each bolus and a dilation in front of it. The progression of the band of constriction along the gut tube results in the movement of the bolus. The observed effect is that of waves of contraction passing along the gut, towards the cloaca, this characteristic pattern of muscular activity being termed 'peristalsis'.

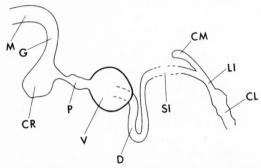

Schematic representation of the alimentary canal of a bird (lateral view from left) ; but the development of the parts, especially in the anterior section, differs greatly in relation to feeding habits. Thus, the crop may be rudimentary or absent, the proventriculus not strongly differentiated, and the gizzard much reduced.

M = mouth (buccal cavity) ; **G** = gullet (oesophagus); **CR** = crop (ingluvies) ; **P** = proventriculus ; **V** = ventriculus or gizzard ; **D** = duodenum ; **SI** = the loops of the small intestine here omitted ; **CM** = caecum (commonly two caeca) ; **LI** = large intestine (rectum) ; **CL** = cloaca.

The pancreas lies in the loop of the duodenum and its ducts discharge into the latter, as also does the bile duct (or ducts) from the liver. The salivary glands discharge into the mouth ; and other digestive secretions come from numerous small glands in the wall of the alimentary canal itself, notably in the proventriculus.

The buccal cavity leads also to the respiratory system through an aperture (glottis) behind the root of the tongue into the windpipe (trachea), the latter lying ventrally to the oesophagus. In addition to the rectum, the urinary and genital passages open into the cloaca.

A functional consideration of the alimentary system of vertebrates indicates that the following processes are involved.

    i. Trituration, or mechanical breakdown of food material.

    ii. Provision of lubricative fluid, assisting peristalsis.

    iii. Provision of enzymes for chemical breakdown of food.

    iv. Maintenance of the best operative conditions for these enzymes.

    v. Absorption of the nutrient products of enzymatic action.

    vi. Partial desiccation of waste material.

    vii. Elimination of chemically unchanged waste materials, the faeces, from the body.

    viii. Excretion of certain metabolic products that are not excreted by the urinary system (e.g. the bile pigments).

In addition, certain processes are available for the protection of the system against the ingestion of harmful or indigestible substances, including

    ix. Excessive mucus secretion into the lumen of the gut.

    x. Reversal of the peristaltic wave (antiperistalsis).

The following account describes the site and nature of these processes in birds, and indicates to some extent the ways in which the avian system may be modified towards the utilisation of specialised foods.

Mouth. The avian mouth carries a horny bill used for prehension of food (see BILL). This shows no trace of true teeth ; serrations on the bill occur in some groups (e.g. Anatidae) composed of a horny substance (keratin) quite unlike the calcified material of true teeth (linked in evolutionary thought with fish scales). Since little or no mechanical breakdown is performed in the mouth, the bill is capable of a wide gape and the pharynx region is widely distensible. The tongue is usually large and pointed, and commonly has an axial stiffening rod (hyoid) of bone (see TONGUE). The sense of taste appears to be located in sense organs lying not only in the tongue (never on special papillae) but also elsewhere in the buccal cavity (see TASTE). Salivary glands commonly occur in the floor and roof of the mouth, and also on the surface of the tongue. The mouth leads posteriorly to the gullet or anterior oesophagus.

Crop and Oesophagus. The crop is a thin-walled, distensible sac-like elaboration of the oesophagus. It has a single opening, connecting its cavity with the lumen of the oesophagus. The relative size of the crop is highly variable from species to species, depending largely on feeding habits ; it is found highly developed in grain-eating birds such as the Galliformes, is rudimentary in many groups and absent in some insect-eaters ; pigeons (Columbidae) have the crop divided into a pair of lateral sacs. The crop is enclosed by the skin antero-dorsally, by flight muscles extending backwards to the anterior margin of the sternum on either side, and by the oesophagus and the main column of the neck posteriorly. The primary function of the crop is that of food storage, especially during the breeding season, but in many species the food obtained by the adults undergoes some digestion before being offered to the young. Probably more common than originally supposed is the enrichment of this food for the young by the addition of a protein secretion from the cells lining the crop ; this secretion is familiar as crop-milk in pigeons, and has been described recently in the Budgerigar *Melopsittacus undulatus* although probably the secretion is proventricular in origin in the latter species (see MILK, PIGEON)

The crop contents are usually acid, due to a back flow from the proventriculus. The proventriculus amplifies the peristaltic waves initiated in the crop and passes the moist undigested food into the gizzard. Digestive juices are secreted by the glandular walls of the proventriculus ; they contain pepsinogen, precursor of the protein-digesting enzyme pepsin. Acid also secreted here converts the pepsinogen into pepsin. The pH of the proventriculus contents is found to be between 3 and 4·5 (i.e. acidity is quite high), and protein digestion can proceed. For 'stomach oil' see ALBATROSS.

Proventriculus and Gizzard. Proventriculus and gizzard together correspond to the mammalian stomach. The gizzard, or ventriculus, of grain-eating birds is an oval biconvex structure with dense muscular walls ; the corrugated, leathery lining is composed of material secreted by glands in the walls. Grit and small stones eaten by the birds collect in the gizzard, and trituration is effected by rhythmic contractions spreading through the immensely developed muscles (see GRIT) ; in the domestic fowl there are 3 or 4 contractions per minute. The muscles radiate from two tendons, one on each of the convex surfaces, and perform a circular grinding movement. A secretion here raises the acidity (pH 2 to 3·5) so that the rate of protein digestion is greatly increased. Other enzymes reported from the gizzard probably do not originate there, and their effectiveness under such conditions is probably very slight. The features of the gizzard are again broadly related to feeding habits. Grain-eating birds show extreme development, while fruit-eating and flesh-eating species show somewhat reduced gizzards, the muscles in particular being less massive. Observations on this relationship should, however, be warily treated. For a special adaptation see under FLOWERPECKER.

The exit from the gizzard into the duodenum is the pyloric orifice, guarded by the pyloric valve.

Valves of various types occur, and the valve is particularly prominent where large particles of grit, or pebbles, are habitually swallowed into the gizzard, as in the Ostrich *Struthio camelus*. The semi-liquid food leaving the gizzard is termed 'chyme'.

Small Intestine, Pancreas, and Liver. 'Duodenum', 'jejunum', and 'ileum' are terms borrowed from the nomenclature of the mammalian small intestine, and are applied with no great consistency to the avian system. Beyond the duodenum there are actually no clearly delineated areas in the avian intestine, so the duodenum and ileum are here considered to constitute the small intestine. The duodenum is always formed into a long loop, with the pancreas lying between the limbs of the loop. The secretions of the pancreas pass into the duodenum through a number (one to three) of ducts. Bile from the liver is also passed into the duodenum through one or more hepatic ducts. The pink, diffuse pancreas secretes enzymes for digestion of fats, carbohydrates, and proteins, together with a weakly alkaline fluid. The contents of the intestine are generally only slightly acid (pH about 6), and protein digestion is unlikely to occur here.

The liver is a relatively large bilobed organ, dark red in colour unless made paler by fat deposition. It lies in the ventral part of the body cavity, largely supported by the ribs. Where a gall-bladder is present, the hepatic duct is single. The bile secreted by the liver probably aids in the emulsification of fats prior to digestion, sometimes shows enzyme activity, and adds to the chyme the bile pigments which are eventually voided from the body. Avian bile is very slightly acid—unlike that of mammals, which is alkaline. For liver functions see also under METABOLISM.

In the ileum, digestion continues and absorption of the products takes place. Some enzymes are probably added by glands in the intestinal lining, the evidence suggesting that the enzyme in greatest concentration is pepsin or pepsin-like. The microscopic structure of the ileum shows many small finger-like processes extending into the lumen. These are called villi, and serve to increase the secretory and absorptive area of the intestinal lining. In the troughs between villi are found mucus glands. The outer layers of the intestinal wall are of muscle, the inner one having its component fibres lying parallel to the length of the intestine. Contraction of the inner layer provides constriction of the lumen, while contraction of the outer layer dilates the lumen. Both muscle layers are well supplied with nerves and blood-vessels. See also under MUSCULATURE.

Caeca and Large Intestine. Where the small

intestine runs into the large intestine two blind tubes, commonly several inches in length, branch off, one on each side. The lining of these tubes, or caeca, is similar to that of the small intestine, although the villi in the caeca are shorter. Frequently in parrots (Psittacidae) and in carnivorous birds with simpler digestive tracts, both caeca are lost. In the domestic fowl they are exceptionally well developed, and even more so in grouse *Lagopus* spp. One caecum may be lost where caecal reduction has occurred—as in grebes (Podicipitidae) and herons (Ardeidae).

Food passes the ileo-caecal valves and enters the two caeca, where it undergoes digestion by the agency both of enzymes and of bacteria. Some water is absorbed here. The large intestine, or rectum, is short and performs most of the absorption of water, and also rounds off the faeces into discrete boli. These boli pass finally into the three-chambered cloaca, from which they are deposited with the products of the urinary system. Absorption of more water from the faeces, as well as re-absorption of nearly all the urinary water, takes place in the cloaca, resulting in fairly viscous faeces capped with a characteristic white disc of uric acid from the urine (see DROPPINGS; EXCRETORY SYSTEM).

Certain orders of birds characteristically eliminate indigestible components of the food by regurgitation through the mouth (antiperistalsis). The pellets of the Strigiformes are a familiar example, containing fur and small bones, but pellets are also formed by a variety of fish-eaters, insect-eaters, and Corvidae (see PELLET); even some nectar-eating birds form an occasional pellet of hairs and solid vegetable matter.

See also DEVELOPMENT, EMBRYONIC; DEVELOPMENT, POSTEMBRYONIC.   A.N.W.

Worden, A. N. 1956. Functional Anatomy of Birds. London. (Chapter 6 describes the avian digestive system in non-technical language.)
Sturkie, P. D. 1954. Avian Physiology. Ithaca, N.Y. (Chapters 10 and 11 give a comprehensive technical account.)

ALLANTOIS: see DEVELOPMENT, EMBRYONIC

ALLELOMIMETIC: term sometimes applied to similar behaviour on the part of two or more individuals when some element of mutual stimulation is involved.

ALLELOMORPH: sometimes abbreviated to 'allele' (see GENETICS).

ALLEN'S RULE: that among the forms of a polytypic species, extensions of the body (in birds, chiefly bills) tend to be longer in the warmer parts of the total range and shorter in the cooler parts (see also BERGMANN'S RULE).

ALLOCHRONIC: existing at different levels of geological time (applied to two or more forms)—contrasted with SYNCHRONIC.

ALLOCRYPTIC: adventitious concealing coloration, as distinct from 'cryptic' coloration adapted to the purpose.

ALLOPATRIC: mutally exclusive geographically (applied to related taxonomic forms)—contrasted with SYMPATRIC; the context often implies that the respective areas are contiguous, but they do not overlap.

ALLOPREENING: term that has been introduced (with 'autopreening' as antonym) for preening of another bird, usually of the same species and commonly a mate—often mutual (see FEATHER MAINTENANCE).

ALLOSEMATIC: see under SEMATIC

ALLOTYPE: term sometimes applied to a paratype of the opposite sex from the holotype (see TYPE-SPECIMEN).

ALTERNATE PLUMAGE: see under MOULT

ALTITUDINAL DISTRIBUTION: distribution in accordance with height above sea-level in a particular area. See also MONTANE.

ALTRICIAL: helpless when hatched (see YOUNG BIRD).

AMADINI: see WEAVER-FINCH

AMAKIHI: *Loxops virens* (for family see HONEY-CREEPER (2)).

AMAZON: substantive name of *Amazona* spp. (see PARROT).

AMBIENS: a muscle of the leg (see MUSCULATURE). The presence or absence of this has been used as a taxonomic character. Garrod (1874) even proposed to divide birds into two subclasses, Homalogonatae ('typically-kneed', i.e. ambiens present) and Anomalogonatae (ambiens absent), but this classification produced too many inconsistencies in relation to other characters and was soon abandoned. The ambiens is a reptilian feature and, broadly speaking, is present in what we regard as the more primitive groups of birds and absent from the more highly developed, including the Apodiformes and the Passeriformes. It may be noted that the ambiens is present in the Falconiformes but not in the Strigiformes; and also that differences in this respect occur within certain groups, notably the Psittacidae and the Columbidae.

AMBIVALENCE: term applied to a movement that is the outcome of two incompatible behaviour tendencies, such as approach and avoidance, or flying and walking. Sometimes the movement is itself formally ambivalent, i.e. it is a 'mosaic' of behaviour components of each of the two tendencies. For instance, a Herring Gull *Larus argentatus* may stretch its neck and point its bill down as a preparation for pecking its opponent and raise its carpal joints as a preparation for delivering a wing-beat, and at the same time withdraw its neck, flatten its plumage, and stop advancing as a result of fear ; the combination of these elements gives rise to the 'upright posture'. In this case those elements of the two incompatible total patterns that can be performed together are shown. In other cases the really incompatible parts (e.g. approach and withdrawal themselves) are executed in quick alternation, as in the 'pendulum flights' of song-birds engaged in a territorial border clash. Ambivalent motivation can be inferred, apart from a formal analysis of the movement, from scoring the overt behaviour shown in rapid alternation with it ('time-score method') ; for instance, agonistic postures tend to alternate with overt attack and escape, but to a much lesser extent with, say, feeding, or nest building, or preening. A third method of analysis is based on a knowledge of the stimuli evoking overt behaviour ; if a movement is shown in situations known to provide stimuli for two incompatible behaviour patterns simultaneously, this movement is likely to be ambivalent with regard to its motivation. Often the three methods lead to corroborating results.

Many ambivalently motivated movements are not themselves formally ambivalent. Starlings *Sturnus vulgaris* engaged in a boundary fight often preen ; Eider Ducks *Somateria mollissima* staying with their ducklings while afraid of an approaching human observer show 'chin-lifting'. Often these movements contain some elements of the behaviours aroused, such as sleeking the plumage (a sign of fear), but the major part of the movement does not belong to the patterns aroused. In extreme cases of this kind it is usual to speak of a 'displacement activity' (see DISPLACEMENT ACTIVITY). In such cases, the time-score method and the analysis of the external situation often point to ambivalence of motivation.

The actual behaviour tendencies aroused may be of a very different nature. Tail-flicking in some birds may be due to the simultaneous arousal of 'hopping towards' and 'flying towards' an object (Andrew) ; many agonistic postures are the outcome of the specific arousal of attack and escape tendencies ; 'beak-hiding' in Kittiwakes *Larus* ('*Rissa*') *tridactylus* occurs when fear interacts with any tendency towards approach or staying (E. Cullen) ; chin-lifting in Eiders is also the result of a tendency to stay combined with fear.

Thus the term 'ambivalent' always refers to the underlying motivation ; in part of the examples it also refers to the form of the movement itself.

The postures resulting from ambivalent motivation have been shown in many cases to function as social signals, and comparative studies suggest that this is due to secondary evolutionary adaptation, roughly comparable to the secondary adaptation of the first walking leg of a lobster (the 'claw') to seizing and breaking food. Probably as a result of this, some such postures seem to have lost most or all of their original motivation and have become incorporated in a new functional system ; thus courtship seems to contain many postures that were originally threat postures (see DISPLAY ; RELEASER). However, even in such cases the methods discussed above may still reveal the original hostile motivation.   N.T.

Andrew, R. J. 1956. Some remarks on behaviour in conflict situations, with special reference to *Emberiza* spp. Brit. J. Anim. Behav. 4 : 41–45.
Tinbergen, N. 1951. The Study of Instinct. Oxford.

AMERICA: see NEARCTIC REGION ; NEOTROPICAL REGION. Note that the term 'Middle America' is now much used to designate the area comprising Mexico, Central America, and Panama (the last being by political history part of South America), and sometimes including the West Indies. This usage has the consequence that 'North America' is often used in ornithological literature as excluding Mexico.

AMERICAN USAGE: as regards vernacular names, see under NAME, ENGLISH.

AMETHYST: *Philodice mitchellii* (for family see HUMMINGBIRD)

AMINO-ACIDS: see METABOLISM

Plate 1 · Flight

Night Heron *Nycticorax nycticorax* (called Black-crowned Night Heron in North America) about to alight in shallow water, with wings braking and legs lowered (India). Note also the elongated plumes on the nape, worn by adults at all seasons.
Phot. Christina Loke, in Roshinara Gardens, Old Delhi.

(See articles FLIGHT ; HERON)

AMNION: see DEVELOPMENT, EMBRYONIC

AMNIOTA: term embracing reptiles, birds, and mammals (see ANIMAL KINGDOM).

AMNIOTIC CLOSURE: term for the protective sealing of the eyes and ears during the first few days of life in some birds, the function being analogous to that earlier performed for the embryo by the amnion (see DEVELOPMENT, POSTEMBRYONIC ; YOUNG BIRD).

AMPHIRHINAL: see NARIS

AMPULLA: term for a vesicle, among other things the dilated end of a semicircular canal in the labryinth of the ear (see HEARING AND BALANCE).

ANABOLISM: see METABOLISM

ANACROMYODIAN: see SYRINX

ANAGENESIS: see SPECIATION

ANALOGUE: a structure adaptively similar to another but of basically different nature—compare HOMOLOGUE.

ANATIDAE: see under ANSERIFORMES. The family comprises birds variously designated as 'ducks', 'geese', and 'swans'; but the application of these primary English names cuts across the taxonomic arrangement. For all, see under DUCK.

ANATOMY: bodily structure ; also the science of this. By derivation, the term relates to internal structure as revealed by dissection, as contrasted with external form—see MORPHOLOGY; but the two terms have come to be used almost synonymously. Special branches of anatomy, such as osteology, deal with particular systems of the body ; 'histology' refers to the microscopic structure of the tissues ; 'morbid anatomy' is diseased structure,

---

Plate 2 · Flight

a *Upper:* Red-tailed Hawk *Buteo jamaicensis* (a species of 'buzzard' in British usage) cóming in with tail braking and legs lowered—an albino adult (North America). Varying degrees of albinism are not uncommon in this species, and usual in the prairie race *B. j. kriderii.*
Phot. G. Ronald Austing, from National Audubon Society, U.S.A.

b *Lower:* Mallard *Anas platyrhynchos* (drake), apparently about to slow down or turn, with tail spread but legs still held back (North America).
Phot. Joe van Wormer, from National Audubon Society, U.S.A.

(See articles FLIGHT ; HAWK ; PLUMAGE, ABNORMAL AND ABERRANT ; DUCK)

---

or the branch of pathology dealing with this. The structure of birds is dealt with in this work under the names of the systems, organs, and tissues of the body, and under other special heads.

ANCONEAL: pertaining to the elbow ; sometime used with reference to the whole dorsal surface of the wing.

ANGULAR: a paired bone of the lower jaw (see SKELETON).

ANHIMAE ; ANHIMIDAE: see under ANSERIFORMES; and SCREAMER

ANHINGA: used (America) as vernacular name of *Anhinga anhinga* (see DARTER).

ANHINGIDAE: see under PELECANIFORMES ; and DARTER

ANI: substantive name of *Crotophaga* spp. (see CUCKOO).

ANIANIAU: *Loxops parva* (see HONEYCREEPER (2)).

ANIMAL KINGDOM: one of the two great categories of animate nature ; the subject matter of zoology (of which ornithology forms a part). The antithesis is, of course, with the Vegetable Kingdom ; for present purposes it is sufficient to say that at the higher levels the chief differences between animals and plants are self-evident, although at the lowest levels—particularly the unicellular—an entirely satisfactory definition is not easy. A brief survey of the Animal Kingdom is relevant here as providing the evolutionary context of the Class Aves ; and also some of the ecological context, in that animals of many other classes form part of the environment in which birds live. See also EVOLUTION ; VEGETATION ; ZOOLOGY.

Classification. Animals are often spoken of as being divided into vertebrates and invertebrates, and this indeed represents a convenient practical partition of the subject matter of zoology. From a strictly taxonomic point of view, however, it is not wholly logical, as there are transitional forms and the vertebrates are generally considered as constituting a taxon of at most the third rank. The main divisions are the Sub-kingdoms Protozoa and Metazoa—the unicellular and multicellular animals respectively. The Protozoa comprise a single phylum, while the Metazoa include numerous phyla that can, moreover, be grouped in various ways. A phylum may be divided into subphyla ; the next lower primary category is the class.

Sub-kingdom Metazoa. Beginning with the most lowly forms, the group of Mesozoa (Phylum Mesozoa) comprises some very simple parasitic organisms. The group of Parazoa (Phylum Porifera) comprises the sponges, which show some cellular differentiation but have no organised systems. All the remaining phyla are grouped as Eumetazoa ; they are characterised by having cells arranged in tissues, and these usually in organised systems ; a mouth and digestive tract are present (except in some degenerate parasites), and the body is not porous. The Phyla Coelenterata (jellyfishes, corals, etc.) and Ctenophora have a primary radial symmetry. Above this level a primary bilateral symmetry is the rule, although a secondary radial symmetry supervenes in some instances.

No more than mention need be made of the dozen phyla of worm-like animals, many of them parasitic, that were at one time mostly classed as ' Vermes ' but are not in fact a monophyletic group. In a taxonomic arrangement, the following sequence in ascending order of organic complexity would indeed be interrupted by quite different phyla ; Platyhelminthes (flatworms, including flukes and tapeworms) ; Nemertina ; Acanthocephala ; Aschelminthes (including rotifers and nematodes) ; Phoronida ; Ectoprocta (including bryozoa) ; Brachiopoda (lamp-shells) ; Sipunculida ; Annelida (segmented worms, including earthworms, marine polychaetes, and leeches) ; Chaetognatha (arrowworms) ; and Hemichordata (e.g. *Balanoglossus*). The annelids are highly organised animals, and the hemichordates come immediately below—or just among—the Chordata (see under).

Within the upper range of the foregoing, in terms of development of bodily organisation, come three distinctive phyla. First the Mollusca, many of them shelled (univalve or bivalve), including also the cephalopods (cuttlefishes, etc.). Second the Arthropoda (with jointed limbs), including crustaceans, insects, and arachnids. Third the Echinodermata, with a secondary (usually pentamerous) radial symmetry in the adult forms, e.g. sea-urchins and starfishes.

Phylum Chordata. Highest of all comes the phylum of chordate animals, characterised by having a dorsal nerve-cord and a skeletal notochord, the latter replaced in the development of the higher forms by a vertebral column. There are three subphyla (four, if the Hemichordata be included) ; Urochordata or Tunicata (ascidians and sea-squirts) ; Cephalochordata or Acrania (lancelets, e.g. *Amphioxus*) ; and the Vertebrata or Craniata. The last, in which a vertebral column and a skull are present, must be considered in a little more detail.

Subphylum Vertebrata. This consists of eight classes (the group earlier known as ' Pisces ' having been divided)—Agnatha (the jawless lampreys) ;

Placodermi (fossil only) ; Chondrichthyes (cartilaginous fishes) : Osteichthyes (bony fishes) ; Amphibia (newts, frogs, etc.) ; Reptilia ; Aves ; and Mammalia.

Various groupings of the higher classes can be made by adopting different criteria. Thus, ' Sauropsida ' is a term embracing Reptilia and Aves, these having important characters in common not shared by the ' Theropsida ' (Mammalia)—see ARCHAEOPTERYX ; ORIGIN OF BIRDS—or by the ' Ichthyopsida ' (Amphibia and fishes). Again, Reptilia, Aves, and Mammalia can be classed as ' Amniota ', having in common certain early developmental characters including the presence of a protective foetal membrane or amnion (the rest of the vertebrates being ' Anamnia ')—see DEVELOPMENT, EMBRYONIC. And the term ' Homotherma ' has been used for a ' grade ' (J. S. Huxley) in evolution—not a phylogenetic taxon—represented by the warm-blooded Aves and Mammalia.

Contrasting these last two, J. Arthur Thomson (*Outlines of Zoology*) said : ' Birds and Mammals have evolved along very different lines, Birds possessing the air and Mammals the earth, and it is difficult to say that either class is the higher. But apart from the fact, which prejudices us, that man himself is zoologically included among Mammals, this class is superior to Birds in two ways—in brain development, and in the relation between mother and offspring. In most Mammals there is a prolonged organic connection between the mother and the unborn young, which may have been, as Robert Chambers suggested, one of the conditions of progress. It is also characteristic of Mammals that the young are nourished after birth by their mother's milk, and it has been suggested that the usually prolonged infancy was one of the factors in the evolution of the humaner feelings.'

Birds. So, in the perspective of the Animal Kingdom as a whole, the taxonomic position of birds may be defined as ; Sub-kingdom Metazoa, Phylum Chordata, Subphylum Vertebrata, Class Aves (see AVES).

Parker, T. J. & Haswell, W. A. 1962. Text-book of Zoology. vol. 2, 7th edition (revised by Marshall, A. J.). London.
Young, J. Z. 1962. The Life of Vertebrates. 2nd ed. London.

ANISODACTYL: having three toes directed forwards and one (hallux) backwards (see LEG).

ANISOMYODIAN: see SYRINX

ANKLE: the intertarsal joint—sometimes popularly mistaken, in birds, for the knee (see LEG ; SKELETON).

ANKYLOSIS: a stiffening or fixed union of a joint, a natural feature of development in some joints, but also occurring as a pathological condition of joints that are normally movable (see SKELETON).

ANOMALOGONATAE: see AMBIENS

ANOMALOPTERYGIDAE: see under DINOR-NITHIFORMES; and MOA

ANOSMATIC: without olfactory sense (see SMELL).

ANSERANATINAE: see DUCK

ANSERES: the third order of Linnaeus; and see below.

ANSERIFORMES: order, alternatively 'Anseres', comprising the small Neotropical suborder Anhimae with its sole family Anhimidae (see SCREAMER), and the large cosmopolitan suborder Anseres with its sole family Anatidae (see DUCK). Although these groups show affinities in their anatomy, they are very different in external appearance and mode of life. Among the most obvious characters common to both are the unspotted eggs and the nidifugous young clad in thick down. In the Anseres (in the subordinal sense) the front three toes are connected by a web and the small hind-toe is placed high; in the Anhimae there is only a slight web, and the hind toe is long and on the same level as the others. In the Anseres the bill and tongue have special characteristics. In Stresemann's system the two are treated as separate orders.

A family based on the fossil type-genus *Paranyroca* is also placed in this order (suborder Anseres).

ANSERINAE: see DUCK

ANTARCTIC: now generally defined as the area southward of the Antarctic Convergence, the circumpolar line along which cold, northward-going Antarctic surface water sinks beneath warmer sub-antarctic water. In many places, although not everywhere, this line is easily and precisely distinguished by the sudden change in surface temperature. It forms an important physical and faunistic boundary between the Antarctic and sub-antarctic zones, and probably forms the extreme northerly limit of pack ice. Each zone has its characteristic birds, and even if no other evidence of crossing a convergence were available the change in the kinds of birds noticed would give a general indication. The Convergence roughly follows the 50th parallel of latitude throughout most of the Atlantic and Indian Ocean sectors, but in the Pacific sector it is located between 55° and 62° S. lat.

The Antarctic thus comprises the continent of Antarctica together with its off-lying islands, sea ice, and ocean. Judged from this viewpoint, the following island groups are Antarctic; South Shetland Islands, South Sandwich Islands, South Orkney Islands, South Georgia, Bouvetøya, Heard Island, Balleny Islands, Scott Island, and Peter I Øy. Îles Kerguelen lie just on the convergence. Prince Edward Islands and Îles Crozet lie northwards of the convergence but so close to it that the cold Antarctic surface water has not had time to sink far below the surface and upwells against the obstructions formed by them. All these islands, therefore, have Antarctic characteristics. The Falkland Islands, Tristan da Cunha, Gough Island, Île Saint-Paul, Île Amsterdam, and Macquarie Island are sub-antarctic.

Relations between land and sea are by no means simple in their effect upon bird-life. A classic example is the upwelling of cold water along the Humboldt Current on the west coast of South America; this is correlated with a marked northward extension of several Antarctic species. Upwelling also produces significant biological effects at the oceanic islands lying north of the convergence.

Avifauna. The sub-antarctic islands are situated in vast expanses of ocean. Each of them supports a high concentration of birds during the breeding season. Penguins (Spheniscidae) occupy the coastal slopes, the smaller albatrosses (Diomedeidae) and the shags *Phalacrocorax* spp. crowd the cliff ledges, the larger albatrosses are scattered over the higher and flatter ground, and smaller petrels (Hydrobatidae and Procellariidae) honeycomb the surface soil with their burrows. Every available niche seems to be filled.

In the whole region described above as possessing true Antarctic characteristics, only about eighty species of bird have been recorded, and less than half of these are known to breed in the area. The environmental contrast between the oceanic sub-antarctic islands and Antarctica is profound, yet the northward extension of the continent in the Graham Land peninsula and the loop of islands known as the Scotia Arc provide relatively favourable conditions. About ten more northern species have obtained a local foothold in this region, and strays from continental South America are not uncommon. In the Graham Land peninsula there is a notable difference in the southern limit of breeding species between the west and east coasts. There is an obvious correlation here with climatic and other environmental factors, especially the huge Larsen Ice Shelf on the east coast, with no coastal rock outcrops to provide nesting sites.

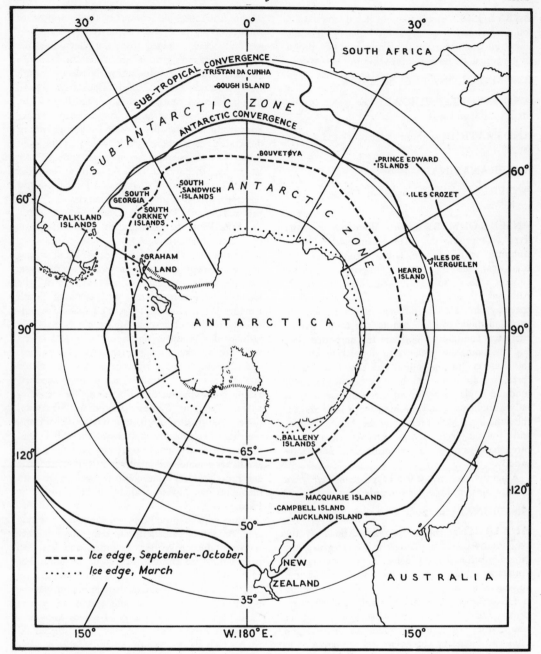

The Antarctic and Sub-tropical Convergences, and apparent mean position of the ice edge in summer and winter.

The area of Antarctica is about 5 300 000 square miles. Almost the entire coastline of about 14 000 miles has now been roughly mapped, but knowledge of the interior is much more sketchy. Antarctica has a greater average elevation than any other continent, probably about 6500 feet. It is covered by an immense ice sheet of great thickness, rising to 13 400 feet in the centre, reaching almost everywhere to the coast, and in many places spreading out over the sea as ice shelves. Extensive mountain ranges, with peaks rising through the ice sheet to over 13 000 feet, are situated in various parts of the continent. Except in Graham Land and Victoria Land, very little rock is visible along most of the coastline. The continental ice or ice shelves terminate abruptly in vertical ice cliffs which are generally 50–100 feet high. The exposed rock areas that do exist range from isolated nunataks or islets to extensive ice-free hills or mountains. There are, however, many stretches of coast, 100 miles or more in length, where exposed rock is completely absent.

Inland in Antarctica, conditions support no living organisms on which birds can subsist. There is no shallow inter-tidal zone such as could provide for waders (Charadrii), and all resident birds are either ocean-feeders or dependent during the short summer on other coastal species. For example, the sheathbills (Chionididae), feed on seal placentae, droppings, and the refuse found in penguin and shag colonies. Dominican Gulls *Larus dominicanus* are also almost omnivorous and manage to survive in the more northerly areas on a similar diet, supplemented by what they can pick up in the narrow inter-tidal zone.

The whole region is subject to very cold and tempestuous weather. The world's record low temperature of –91·2° C (–132·2° F) has been measured at an inland station. Blizzards are common at all seasons in Antarctica and in the belt of pack ice. Farther north, between approximately 60° and 65° S. lat., strong westerly winds prevail in what is known as the West Wind Drift (see CLIMATOLOGY).

The distribution and seasonal variation of pack ice also have biological significance. The ice edge retreats from its northernmost limit in September-October to its southernmost position in February-March. There is great variation from year to year, but the seasonal fluctuations are most frequently spread over less than five degrees of latitude.

For these reasons, breeding birds are restricted to the rocky coasts and off-lying islands. Only one species is certainly known to nest in the inland mountains of Antarctica, the Snow Petrel *Pagodroma nivea*, but even these have not yet been found breeding more than about 150 miles inland. Otherwise, the only birds often seen far inland are Skuas *Catharacta skua* subsp.—as much as 600 miles from the sea on the polar plateau. There are also a few rather unexpected records of Adélie Penguins *Pygoscelis adeliae* far inland on the ice sheet. Antarctic birds are essentially marine, poor in number of species but enormously rich in number of individuals. Some of the largest bird colonies in the world are to be found on the sub-antarctic islands. The only real land bird is a pipit *Anthus antarcticus*, which is found at South Georgia. There were formerly a rail *Hypotaenidia macquariensis* and a ground parakeet *Cyanorhamphus erythrotis* at Macquarie Island, but these were exterminated about 1890 by sealers and the cats and rats which these

introduced. There is a pintail, *Anas georgica*, peculiar to South Georgia ; and another pintail, *A. eatoni*, with two subspecies restricted to Îles Kerguelen and Îles Crozet respectively. The Grey Duck *A. superciliosa* breeds at Macquarie Island. Two other land birds have been introduced into Macquarie Island : the New Zealand Woodhen *Gallirallus australis*, brought by sealers about 1886, and the Starling *Sturnus vulgaris*, apparently self-introduced (at this final stage of spread) about 1930.

Apart from these, and occasional strays from lower latitudes, Antarctic birds are exclusively marine. They belong to only five groups ; penguins (Spheniscidae) ; petrels (Procellariiformes) ; skuas, gulls, and terns (Charadriiformes, suborder Lari) ; shags (Phalacrocoracidae) ; and sheathbills (Chionididae). Despite their abundance, only a few of these have yet been intensively studied, and the validity of their subspecific definition is in many cases questionable.

Any voyager southwards will meet with much the same sequence of sub-antarctic species of birds. The number and diversity of petrels to be seen in the open ocean is astonishing—a continuing source of interest. Roughly two-thirds of the hundred or so species of petrels and albatrosses breed only in the Southern Hemisphere, and they are chiefly concentrated on the islands of the Southern Ocean. With the exception of the diving-petrels (Pelecanoididae), all are capable of long-sustained flight and are completely independent of land except for nesting. They are admirably adapted for soaring flight in the West Wind Drift, where calms are relatively rare. Even where there is no special cause for concentration, such as breeding sites or food, it is often possible to see several hundred birds within the field of vision round a ship. Because of their size and strong effortless flight, three species attract special attention ; the Wandering Albatross *Diomedea exulans*, with its 12-foot wing span, the Black-browed Albatross *D. melanophris*, perhaps the commonest, and the Giant Petrel *Macronectes giganteus*. Most of the species are circumpolar in distribution and the majority show a uniformity that makes it difficult to detect distinct subspecies.

The evidence suggests that while the breeding adults of many species are restricted to a particular area during the nesting season, the remainder, and especially immature birds, may and do encircle the globe in high latitudes. There is a tendency in the zone of the West Wind Drift for birds to drift eastwards across a belt of surface water that remains a uniform food environment. There is probably little interchange of breeding populations between the different islands, but this remains to be established by ringing. The Giant Petrel has so far been the most extensively ringed species ; during the past 15 years more than 10 000 have been marked. The recoveries indicate that young Giant Petrels disperse from their breeding places and, influenced by westerly winds, make circumpolar journeys during their first autumn and winter. They move into the lower latitudes of Australia, South America, and South Africa, and some approach the Equator. Adults return annually to the same colony. The larger albatrosses have produced fewer migration records, but their constancy of return to the same nest site, and often to the same mate, has already been established by ringing (see also OCEANIC BIRDS).

In addition to the regular resident species of petrel, which remain near their breeding grounds or circulate round the zone to which they are adapted, there are several summer breeders which spend their non-breeding periods in the Northern Hemisphere. Notable examples are Wilson's Petrel *Oceanites oceanicus*, possibly the most abundant of all Antarctic birds, and the Sooty Shearwater *Puffinus griseus*.

The number of species to be seen in the belt of pack ice is very much smaller than in the open ocean. Emperor Penguins *Aptenodytes forsteri* and Adélie Penguins *Pygoscelis adeliae* migrate northwards from Antarctica as far as the ice edge. Both are circumpolar and common. But the most characteristic birds of the pack ice are Snow Petrels *Pagodroma nivea* and Antarctic Petrels *Thalassoica antarctica*.

The avifauna of great stretches of the coastline of Antarctica is still quite unknown. Only fourteen species have been recorded as breeding on the continent. The number is so small that they are worth listing ; Emperor Penguin, Adélie Penguin, Gentoo Penguin *Pygoscelis papua*, Ringed Penguin *P. antarctica*, Silver-grey Fulmar *Priocella antarctica*, Cape Pigeon *Daption capensis*, Antarctic Whalebird *Pachyptila desolata*, Snow Petrel, Antarctic Petrel, Wilson's Petrel, Blue-eyed Shag *Phalacrocorax atriceps*, Dominican Gull, Antarctic Tern *Sterna vittata*, and Skua. It is likely that this list will be extended by further exploration.

Penguins. Penguins are the most truly Antarctic of all birds. Eight species breed in the area and six of these are restricted almost completely to it. They provide a supreme example of adaptation to a severe environment. The most interesting is the Emperor Penguin, which inhabits the pack ice and lays its single egg on the fast ice close inshore in the middle of winter darkness, when the temperature is around –70° F. This species is subjected to the most extreme cold with which any breeding bird is known to contend. It also illustrates our present lack of knowledge of Antarctic birds. Prior to the special effort devoted to Antarctic exploration associated with the International Geophysical Year (1957–58), six colonies of Emperors were known. Since the beginning of the I.G.Y., eight additional colonies have been discovered. The Adélie Penguin may also be cited as an illustration of the rigorous climatic conditions under which birds can flourish. The breeding season starts when they return to the colonies in September and October. They may have to travel 200 miles or more from their winter quarters in the pack ice, the last stage being over many miles (up to 60) of rough sea-ice which has not broken away from the land. Adélies return to their old nest sites from year to year, yet at the beginning of the season these sites are often covered by a foot or more of snow. See also PENGUIN.

Shags. Problems of Antarctic bird distribution not already mentioned may be illustrated by brief reviews of the shags (or cormorants) and terns occurring in the region. The Antarctic and subantarctic shags form a circumpolar group of which the taxonomic status is still open to doubt. There are probably three species : *Phalacrocorax albiventer* (with possibly three subspecies), *P. atriceps* (with possibly four subspecies), and *P. verrucosus*. The shags of the first two groups seem to be derived from ancestors in the Fuegian region which spread eastward along the West Wind Drift. The races of *P. albiventer* range from Tierra del Fuego and the Falkland Islands through the largely sub-antarctic zone over Îles Crozet and Prince Edward Islands to Macquarie Island ; while *P. atriceps*, although found far to the north on the coasts of South America, has a more southern distribution than *P. albiventer*, reaching from the South Shetland Islands and Graham Land through the South Orkneys and South Sandwich Islands to Heard Island. The shags of Kerguelen have been described as a distinct species, *P. verrucosus*, with probable affinities to more northern groups. See also CORMORANT.

Terns. There are three species of tern ; the Arctic Tern *Sterna paradisaea*, which is a non-breeding seasonal migrant from the Northern Hemisphere to the Southern Ocean ; a second strongly marked species, *S. virgata*, is endemic at a number of islands lying near the Antarctic Convergence ; the third, *S. vittata*, known as the Antarctic Tern, is widely distributed as a breeding species throughout the whole sub-antarctic and Antarctic marine zones and differentiates into at least six local subspecies. Where the last two species overlap (i.e. at Kerguelen) a significant ecological difference has been noted which points to the kind of field observation required to evaluate their range relationships. *S.*

virgata lays two eggs in October-November, to be replaced in the same nesting areas in January-February by *S. vittata*, which lays only one egg. The former is an exclusively marine feeder, while the latter subsists on spiders, insects, and the like, from the inland marshes. Interspecific competition is thus avoided. Arctic Terns in heavy moult are abundant in the pack ice during December-January, and were, until recently, confused with the other species. It is of special interest that a uniform subantarctic environment encompassing more than ninety degrees of longitude at 40° S. lat. should be inhabited by a single subspecies, *S. vittata tristanensis*, which is distinct from the form confined to a few islands in latitudes ten degrees farther south. This distribution is in harmony with that of the albatrosses, shags, and other species, including plants. See also TERN.   B.B.R.

Roberts, B. B. 1941. A bibliography of Antarctic ornithology. Brit. Graham Land Exped. 1934-37. Sci. Rep. 1 : 337-367.

ANTBIRD: substantive name of some species of Formicariidae (Passeriformes, suborder Tyranni) ; in the plural, now preferred to 'ant-thrushes' as a general term for the family. As the group is purely Neotropical, English names for most of the 223 species, placed in 53 genera, are either lacking or of recent invention. While 'antbird' serves as the substantive name in such genera as *Cercomacra*, *Melanopareia*, *Hylophylax*, and *Xenornis*, for the remainder the name is usually compounded from the prefix 'ant' and the name of some other bird.

Hoffman's Black-faced Antbird *Formicarius analis hoffmanni*, of Costa Rica and Panama. *C.E.T.K.*

Thus we have 'ant-thrush' (*Formicarius, Chamaeza, Phaenostictus*, etc.), 'antshrike' (*Taraba, Thamnophilus, Sakesphorus*), 'antwren' (*Myrmotherula, Terenura, Microrhopias*, etc.), 'antvireo' (*Dysithamnus*), 'antpitta' (*Pittasoma, Thamnocharis, Grallaria*, etc.) ; or more general terms are used, e.g. 'antcatcher' (*Rhopornis, Sclateria*), 'antcreeper' (*Myrmoborus*), 'bush-bird' (*Thamnistes*), 'bush-shrike' (*Cymbilaimus, Batara*), 'bare-eye' (*Phlegopsis*), or 'fire-eye' (*Pyriglena*).

In general it may be said that these names are thoroughly misleading. Although some species are addicted to following columns of marching ants, e.g. the Spotted Antbird *Hylophylax naevioides*, others such as the Black Antwren *Myrmotherula axillaris* feed well above the ground and show no predilection for ants. The resemblance of different genera to other birds is mostly superficial or non-existent. In plumage, only the Short-tailed Antthrush *Chamaeza brevicauda* looks like a thrush (Turdinae), and species of *Taraba* and *Thamnophilus* may resemble some of the black-and-white shrikes (Laniidae) ; the antvireos behave like vireos (Vireonidae), but do not look much like them although they are one of the very few genera in the family with some yellowish tint in the plumage ; the antwrens show no resemblance to Troglodytidae except in size ; but the antpittas are more appropriately named, at least as regards shape, size, and terrestrial habits, although they are much more soberly coloured than the Pittidae.

Characters. All are fairly small birds, the largest (in genera such as *Formicarius, Chamaeza, Taraba, Pittasoma, Grallaria*, and *Thamnocharis*) being about 9-12 inches in total length. The plumage is always dull, although not necessarily unhandsome, in shades of black, grey, brown, rufous, chestnut, olivaceous, and white. Sexual dimorphism is characteristic, whereby the black or darker parts of the plumage in the male are partly or entirely replaced by brown, rufous, or chestnut in the female. This character is less marked or absent among the ant-thrushes and antpittas, as well as in a few other genera such as *Melanopareia* ; this last is unusual in being rather brightly coloured above in black and rufous, and creamy white below with a large black throat-band merging below into a chestnut edging. The crown feathers are often stiff and more or less in the form of a short crest, particularly among the antshrikes, while the White-faced Antcatcher *Pithys albifrons* of northern South America has the feathers of the fore part of the head long, silky, and white to form both a crest and a beard. The feathers of the back, rump, and flanks are often long, loose, and silky, as in the antshrikes *Sakesphorus* spp. ; and throughout the family the wing is short and rounded. The bill is normally stout and strong, or very strong ; and the upper mandible is hooked, with a notch just behind the hook. The feet and legs are strong and well developed, especially in the terrestrial antpittas. The voice is generally harsh and unmusical; species of *Sakesphorus* have monotonous song-calls of low, evenly spaced notes, and characteristic ' churring ' alarm calls, but others have harsh staccato calls and whistles.

Ecology. The family is composed of birds that essentially live in thickets and forest undergrowth, or at least in areas with good cover. A few, such as the antwrens and antvireos, lead a more arboreal existence, hunting through trees above the ground ; and the antpittas in general are terrestrial, stalking about the forest floor with their short tails held erect. As would be expected with such birds, the flight is not normally strong or sustained, being usually for only short distances with rapidly beating wings, and some species are unwilling to leave cover and cross open spaces.

The members of the family are undoubtedly insectivorous, although some species are said to take young birds ; but by no means all species habitually or even often prey upon ants or collect their food in association with marching ant columns.

Breeding. Breeding habits have been described for only a few species, and what is known may not be typical. The nest seems usually to be a more or less skilfully woven open cup, slung by the rim from thin bifurcating twigs and branches, and often as deep as it is wide (e.g. the Black-crested Antshrike *Sakesphorus canadensis* and the White-naped Antshrike *S. bernardi*), but some species support their nests in forks, e.g. Swainson's Antcatcher *Myrmeciza longipes*. The Rufous-necked Ant-thrush *Formicarius analis* of Trinidad, Central America, and northern South America nests in holes in tree stumps ; *Grallaria guatemalensis*, the antpitta of similar distribution, is suspected of nesting in cavities in epiphytes well above the ground ; other species are said to nest on the ground.

The clutch size may be normally two, as is usually claimed, but the White-naped Antshrike of Ecuador at least often lays three eggs and this may be more common than has been suspected. The usual egg type is of a white or creamy white ground with blotches, spots, or scrawls of brown, purple, lavender or reddish, often concentrated as a zone at the larger end as with the Barred Antshrike *Thamnophilus doliatus*, species of *Sakesphorus*, and the Black Antwren ; but some species, such as the Rufous-necked Ant-thrush, have immaculate white eggs. The eggs are laid at an interval of about 48

hours in the Black-crested Antshrike, and this may or may not be typical. Incubation and nestling periods have been determined for a mere handful of species in Central America, Surinam, and Ecuador, the incubation being between 14 and 17 days in different species and the nestling period 9–13 days. In those species which have been adequately observed, such as the Black-crested Antshrike and the Slaty Antshrike *Thamnophilus punctatus*, the sexes share incubation and feeding of the young, and the female broods at night.

Distribution. The family is confined to Central and South America, essentially in areas of lowland and mountain forest. Its northern limit is in the southern part of Mexico as far as such conditions exist. It is represented in Trinidad and Tobago, but not in the Antilles. Southwards it reaches the plains of La Plata in the Argentine, and also Bolivia and Peru ; but it is entirely absent from Chile and the treeless areas south of La Plata, its limit being farther south on the east than on the west of the Andes. Thus, the family is essentially Neotropical, and like so many groups of similar distribution it is very poorly known. No comprehensive account of it has ever been written ; and in spite of their number all that is known about the great majority of species is their appearance. No species is migratory, so far as known.   S.M.

Haverschmidt, F. 1953. Notes on the life history of the Black-crested Ant Shrike in Surinam. Wilson Bull. 65 : 242–251.
Marchant, S. 1960. The breeding of some S.W. Ecuadorian birds. Ibis 102 : 349–382, 584–589.
Skutch, A. F. 1945. On the habits and nest of the Antthrush *Formicarius analis*. Wilson Bull. 57 : 122–128.
Skutch, A. F. 1946. Life histories of two Panamanian antbirds. Condor 48 : 16–28.

ANTCATCHER : substantive name of *Rhopornis ardesieca*, *Sclateria naevia*, *Pithys* spp., *Myrmeciza* spp., et al. (see ANTBIRD).

ANT-CHAT : substantive name of *Myrmecocichla* spp. (see THRUSH).

ANTCREEPER : substantive name of some species of Formicariidae, e.g. *Myrmoborus* spp. (see ANTBIRD).

ANTEPISEMATIC : see under EPISEMATIC

ANTHROPOMORPHISM : denotes, in the biological context, the fallacy of describing or interpreting the actions of animals, other than Man, in terms of human actions and mental processes.

ANTIBODIES : see BLOOD; PROTEINS AS TAXONOMIC CHARACTERS

ANTICOELOUS: see INTESTINE

ANTICRYPTIC: see under CRYPTIC

ANTIGEN: see SEROLOGICAL CHARACTERS; and PROTEINS AS TAXONOMIC CHARACTERS

ANTING: see under FEATHER MAINTENANCE

ANTIPHONAL SONG: 'duetting' (see SINGING).

ANTPECKER: alternative substantive name of the Flowerpecker Finch *Parmoptila woodhousei* (see WEAVER-FINCH).

ANTPIPIT: substantive name, alternatively 'gnat-eater', of species of Conopophagidae (Passeriformes, suborder Tyranni); in the plural, either name serves as a general term for the family. This Neotropical group of only eleven species is considered to be related to the Formicariidae, Rhinocryptidae, and Furnariidae, on account of certain anatomical characteristics, especially of the syrinx. They are insectivorous ground-dwelling birds of the tropical forests of South America. There are two genera, dissimilar in appearance.

Chestnut-belted Gnateater *Conopophaga aurita*, of tropical South America. *C.E.T.K.*

The nine species of *Conopophaga* are ball-like, 'neckless' little birds with long, thin legs and long toes, rounded wings, short and soft tail, and body heavily covered with long feathers. Their shape, and sometimes colour, is reminiscent of the Robin *Erithacus rubecula* of Europe, but they are bigger and heavier. Behind the eye there is a slightly protruding tuft of rather elongated silky feathers, usually of a strikingly white colour contrasting sharply with the rest of the plumage (post-ocular stripe). The sexes are usually quite differently coloured. The birds live in pairs in shrubs and the low branches of trees, and they feed on small—occasionally larger—insects. The name '*cuspidor*' (spitter), used in south-eastern Brazil, refers to the short, rasping alarm note.

The Silvery-tufted Gnateater *Conopophaga lineata*, distributed from Brazil to Paraguay and northern Argentina, is about 5½ inches long (weight ca. 21 grams), generally earth-brown in colour with rusty foreneck and nearly white belly; the post-ocular stripe is white in the male, grey in the female. During the breeding season, towards the end of the calendar year, the male emits a simple whistling melody ending in a few lower and more accented notes; he can also produce a harsh sound with his wings. The nest is firmly based close to the ground; it is bowl-shaped, open at the top, carefully constructed of large dry leaves, and lined with fibres. The 2 eggs are yellowish with light brown, partly smudged spots, especially towards the round end. In the Black-cheeked Gnateater *C. melanops* of Brazil the male has a cinnamon crown, sides of the head black, under parts ash-grey and white; the female resembles that of *C. lineata*. The vocalisation consists of the above-mentioned alarm note and a full melodious song that ascends in a long drawn-out scale. The nest and eggs are similar to those of *C. lineata*; the sexes seem to share incubation, and if disturbed at the nest the parent leaves, feigning injury.

In the two species of *Corythopis* the body is of more elongated shape, the tail is relatively long, and the legs are long; the body proportions and plumage coloration resemble those of pipits *Anthus* spp., but the size is less. The sexes look alike. Delalande's Gnateater *Corythopis delalandei*, distributed from Brazil to Paraguay and northern Argentina, is 4¾ inches long (weight ca. 14 grams) and has the upper parts olive and the under parts white with black spots on the chest. It lives in tall forests with undergrowth, where it *walks* about on the ground. It eats insects, caterpillars, and spiders. It is a cautious bird, emitting a clicking sound when disturbed; the song is a short uncertain whistle. The nest is on the ground.   H.S.

Beebe, W. 1925. Studies of a tropical jungle. Zoologica (New York) 4, no. 1.
Ihering, H. von. 1900. Catálogo critico-comparativo dos ninhos e ovos das aves do Brasil. Rev. Mus. Paul. 4: 191–300.
Snethlage, E. and Schreiner, K. 1929. Beiträge zur brasilianische Oologie. Verh. VI Internat. Orn. Kongr., Kopenhagen 1926: 576–640.

ANTPITTA: substantive name of *Thamnocharis dignissima* and species of *Pittasoma*, *Grallaria*, and *Grallaricula* (see ANTBIRD).

ANTRORSE: directed forwards ; applied, e.g., to rictal bristles that do not conform with the usual backward direction of plumage elements.

ANTSHRIKE: substantive name of *Taraba major*, *Thamnophilus* spp., *Sakesphorus* spp., and *Cymbilaimus lineatus* (see ANTBIRD).

ANT-TANAGER: substantive name of *Habia* spp. (see TANAGER).

ANT-THRUSH: substantive name of *Formicarius* spp., *Chamaeza* spp., *Myrmornis torquata*, and *Phaenostictus mcleannani* (see ANTBIRD) ; and of *Neocossyphus* spp. (for subfamily see THRUSH) ; sometimes used also for species of Pittidae (see PITTA).

ANTVIREO: substantive name of *Dysithamnus* spp. and allies (see ANTBIRD).

ANTWREN: substantive name of *Myrmotherula* spp., *Terenura* spp., *Microrhopias quixensis*, et al. (see ANTBIRD).

ANVIL-HEAD: name sometimes used for *Scopus umbretta* (see HAMMERHEAD).

AORTIC ARCH: see DEVELOPMENT, EMBRYONIC ; VASCULAR SYSTEM

APALIS: generic name used as substantive name of *Apalis* spp. of Africa (for subfamily see WARBLER (1)).

APAPANE: *Himatione sanguinea* (see HONEY-CREEPER (2)).

APODI; APODIDAE: see below

APODIFORMES: an order comprising the sub-order Apodi with the families Apodidae and Hemiprocnidae (see SWIFT), and Trochili with the sole family Trochilidae (see HUMMINGBIRD). An alternative name for the order is ' Machrochires ' (also formerly ' Cypseli ' and ' Micropodiformes '). In Stresemann's system the two suborders are given separate ordinal rank, the name of the former spelt ' Apodes '.

A family based on the fossil type-genus *Aegialornis* is provisionally placed in this order (suborder Apodi).

APONEUROSIS: a flattened tendon for the insertion of a muscle (see MUSCULATURE).

APOSEMATIC: having a protective role—applied particularly to coloration. ' Proaposematic ' means that the protection is in the form of a warning (e.g. of unpalatability) ; ' pseudaposematic ' means that the warning is a bluff (protective mimicry) ; ' synaposematic ' means that the warning signal is shared in common with other species.

Compare EPISEMATIC ; and, in general see COLORATION, ADAPTIVE ; MIMICRY.

APOSTLEBIRD: *Struthidea cinerea* (see under MAGPIE-LARK).

APPENDICULAR SKELETON: the part of the skeleton consisting of the pectoral and pelvic girdles and the limbs ; contrasted with the AXIAL SKELETON (see SKELETON).

APPETITIVE BEHAVIOUR: ' the variable introductory phase of an instinctive behaviour pattern or sequence ' (Thorpe 1951)—compare CONSUMMATORY ACT.

APPLIED ORNITHOLOGY: the application of ornithological knowledge to human activities concerned with birds (see especially AVICULTURE ; CONSERVATION ; DOMESTICATION ; FALCONRY ; GAME-BIRDS ; GUANO ; PROTECTION ; also MAN, BIRDS AND, and UTILISATION BY MAN, with cross-references thereunder).

APTERIUM: an area of skin from which no feathers grow (except down), between the pterylae —compare PTERYLA (and see PLUMAGE).

APTERYGES; APTERYGIDAE: see below

APTERYGIFORMES: an order, alternatively ' Apteryges ', comprising only the family Apteryg-idae (see KIWI) ; in Stresemann's system the Apteryges include also the Dinornithidae (see MOA ; also RATITES, PHYLOGENY OF THE).

APTOSOCHROMATOSIS: change of colour (hypothetical) in a fully developed feather (see under MOULT).

AQUATIC HABIT: for adaptations to this see SWIMMING AND DIVING ; VISION.

AQUINTOCUBITALISM: or ' diastataxis ' (see PLUMAGE ; WING).

ARAÇARI: substantive name of *Pteroglossus* and *Andigena* spp. (see TOUCAN).

ARAMIDAE: see under GRUIFORMES ; and LIMPKIN

ARCHAEOPTERYX: *Archaeopteryx lithographica* von Meyer—a species of fossil bird found in lithographic limestone of the Upper Jurassic, Middle Kimmeridgian zone of *Neochetoceras steraspis*, of Bavaria. It is known from three specimens of skeletal remains and impressions of feathers.

1. The London specimen found in 1861 in the Ottmann quarry near Solnhofen in the Langenalt-heimer Haardt, near Pappenheim, Bavaria, now preserved in the British Museum (Natural History) ; the remains are contained on a slab and its corre-

sponding counter-slab (Owen 1863 ; de Beer 1954).

2. The Berlin specimen found in 1877 in the Dürr quarry at Wegscheidt on the Blumenberg near Eichstätt (14 km. from Solnhofen), now preserved in the Geological-Palaeontological Museum of the Humboldt University in Berlin (Dames 1884, 1897).

3. The Erlangen specimen found in 1956 in the Opitsch quarry near Solnhofen in the Langenaltheimer Haardt, at a point 250 metres distant from that where the London specimen was found and in a bed 6 metres above the bed corresponding to the horizon of the London specimen ; it is preserved in the Geological Institute of the University of Erlangen and its remains are contained on a slab and counter-slab (Heller 1959).

In addition to these more or less complete skeletons of *Archaeopteryx*, two other fossils must be mentioned. One is a single feather (flight feather or covert) found in 1860 in the communal quarry at Solnhofen and regarded by von Meyer as belonging to an animal conspecific with *Archaeopteryx lithographica*. The limestone slab containing the mineralised feather is preserved in the Munich Museum ; the counter-slab containing the impression of the feather is preserved in the Berlin Museum. The other fossil is a single downy contour feather found shortly before 1954 in the Upper Jurassic Kimmeridgian lithographic limestone quarry at Rubies, Santa Maria de Meya, Sierra de Montsech, near Lerida, Spain ; while several of the associated fossils from Santa Maria de Meya are conspecific with these found in Solnhofen, it is not possible to assert that the feather belongs to *Archaeopteryx lithographica*.

The dimensions of the London and Erlangen specimens are almost identical and give the bird the size of a Magpie *Pica pica*. The Berlin specimen is slightly smaller, and it has been called *Archaeopteryx* 'siemensi' and '*Archaeornis siemensi*' on grounds that have not stood up to scrutiny. Its conspecificity with the London and Erlangen specimens, under the name *Archaeopteryx lithographica* von Meyer 1861, can be accepted, and the smaller size and trifling differences shown by the Berlin specimen can be attributed to immaturity or difference of sex, or both.

The following description is based on all three specimens, with indication of the specimen in which the structures in question are best preserved.

Skeletal Structure (compare SKELETON). The skull (Berlin) is of a typical diapsid type in which the superior and inferior temporal fossae are confluent as a result of the loss of the superior temporal bar. The orbit is large and the eye is protected by a ring of sclerotic plates. A pre-orbital fossa is present, as is a fenestra in the mandible.

The premaxilla bears six teeth, the maxilla seven, and the dentary three. The teeth are restricted to the anterior half of the jaw. In structure (London) the teeth are peg-like with expanded bases fitting into sockets in the bone. Alternate sockets are empty, showing that the reptilian mode of tooth-replacement applied.

The palate (Berlin), in so far as it can be made out, was of schizognathous (neognathous) type (see PALATE), and it is probable that the skull was kinetic, with possibility of limited internal movement, allowing the upper jaw to be raised and the gape widened.

The brain-case (London) reveals the structure of the brain in the form of the endocranial cast. The cerebral hemispheres are parallel elongated cylinders with smooth surfaces. The midbrain with paired optic lobes separates the cerebral hemispheres from the hindbrain and cerebellum, which latter is small and in no way covers the midbrain. The brain is therefore similar in structure to that of reptiles and completely different from that of all other known birds, including the Cretaceous flying birds (see NERVOUS SYSTEM).

The vertebral column is made up of approximately 10 cervical, 12 thoracic and lumbar, 6 sacral, and 20 caudal vertebrae. The elongated caudal vertebrae support a tail as long as the remainder of the body, as in reptiles but in no other known birds. The centra of the vertebrae are hour-glass shaped and have simple disc-like concave facets with which they articulate with their neighbours, and therefore conform to the amphicoelous reptilian type. The six sacral vertebrae have stout transverse processes attached to the ilia of the pelvic girdle, and the five hindermost sacral vertebrae are fused together.

Cervical ribs are borne by cervical vertebrae 2 to 7 inclusive. Thoracic ribs articulate with thoracic vertebrae 1 to 11 inclusive. The ribs are unjointed, cylindrical, slightly curved rods, differentiated proximally into capitular and tubercular heads, ending distally in simple points without any contact with the sternum. The ribs have no uncinate processes. About one dozen pairs of abdominal ribs or gastralia are present.

The pectoral girdle (London) consists of elongated curved scapulae fused with stout coracoids, each bone contributing to the concavity of the glenoid fossa. The scapula and coracoid form a wide angle between them and lie in prolongation of one another along the arc of a circle. The sternum (London) has been recognised in a flat plate of incompletely ossified bone devoid of any trace of a keel. The clavicles are fused distally in the midline to form a flat boomerang-shaped furcula.

The humerus bears a low crista pectoralis on which the pectoral muscle was inserted, a shallow trough on its ventral surface lodging the biceps muscle. The ulna is slightly longer than the radius.

The carpus (Berlin) reveals the presence of two proximal carpals (radiale and ulnare) and three distal carpals (carpal 1 and 2 fused together, and carpal 3). The extent to which these carpal bones are fused together is uncertain. It is possible that the third distal carpal is fused with the base of the third metacarpal.

There are three entirely separate and unfused digits, of which the second is the longest (Berlin and Erlangen). Metacarpal 1 is short and bears two phalanges. Metacarpal 2 is the longest and bears three phalanges. Metacarpal 3 is slightly shorter than 2 and bears four phalanges, of which the proximal two are together almost equivalent in length to the proximal phalanx of the second digit. In each of the three digits the distal phalanx is differentiated into a long, curved, laterally compressed claw with needle-sharp point.

Except for the possible fusion of the 3rd distal carpal to the proximal end of the 3rd metacarpal, there is no trace of the fusion of the bones of the wrist and hand into a carpometacarpus.

In the pelvic girdle (London, Berlin), the ilium is elongated in the axis of the vertebral column and loosely attached on the median side to the transverse processes of six sacral vertebrae. The acetabulum is perforated and takes the form of a tube, the bony wall of which is formed mostly by the ilium and partly by the ischium and the pubis. The ischium is a short bone projecting postero-ventrally from the acetabulum and ending distally in two sharp processes which bend towards the middle line and may have been connected with their fellows of the other side by cartilage or ligament. The pubis is very long, slender, and straight, and is directed backwards as in other birds. Distally each pubis fuses with its fellow of the opposite side and forms a pubic symphysis. The bones of the pelvic girdle are all separate from one another on each side.

The femur has a bent shaft, but the tibia (which is longer) is straight with a slight cnemial crest and two large articular condyles at its proximal end. Distally the tibia appears to be fused with the proximal pre-axial tarsal element, the tibiale, to form a tibiotarsus. The fibula is a very slender bone by the side of the tibia and extends distally as far as the distal end of the tibia. The post-axial proximal tarsal element, the fibulare, appears to be fused with the fibula.

The foot has four digits. The metatarsals of digits 2, 3, and 4 (Erlangen) are elongated and lie parallel with one another in the plantar plane. Their proximal ends are fused with one another and with the distal tarsals, forming a tarsometatarsus as in other birds, but it is possible that this fusion may not be present in incompletely ossified individuals such as the Berlin specimen.

The metatarsal of digit 1 is imperfectly known, but its distal end lies close to the distal end of metatarsal 2. Digit 1 has two phalanges, digit 2 three, digit 3 four, and digit 4 four. In each case the terminal phalanx is differentiated into a claw, and the London specimen shows plainly that digit 1 is opposed to the remaining digits of the foot. This means that the hallux or first toe is opposable as in other birds.

Pneumaticity of the bones has not been demonstrated in *Archaeopteryx*. The long bones have spacious internal cavities and thin walls, but pneumatic pores through which diverticula of the air-sacs might have penetrated into the bone-cavities have not been found.

Plumage. The plumage of *Archaeopteryx* is its most important feature, for the structure of the feathers—as revealed in the mineralised isolated Munich specimen and the impressions made in the matrix by the feathers of the other specimens—shows that *Archaeopteryx* had feathers indistinguishable from those of modern flying birds (see FEATHER). The flight feathers (remiges) consist, in each case, of a quill continued into a rachis bearing on each side a vane composed of barbs, with barbules kept in place by hamuli. In the tail feathers (rectrices) the two vanes of each feather are equal in width. In the wing feathers the distal vane is narrower than the proximal vane as in modern birds. Dark brown pigment is present in the vane of the Munich feather, which must have been coloured as in a thrush *Turdus* sp.

Coverts were also present, shorter than the flight feathers, and also contour feathers (Berlin) all over the body, including 'breeches' on the tibiotarsus.

The remiges were attached to the skeleton of the forelimb as in modern flying birds (London). Ten secondary remiges were attached to the ulna and six primaries to the second metacarpal, with the same system of vane-overlap and method of folding the wings as in modern flying birds. In addition, smaller feathers were borne on the two proximal phalanges of digit 2, leaving only the terminal claw phalanx unfeathered. Flight feathers were moulted symmetrically on the two wings.

On the strength of the Berlin specimen, Steiner

has claimed that *Archaeopteryx* was aquintocubital (see PLUMAGE). This has not been confirmed in the London specimen, because the feather in the position of the 5th secondary remex is broken off and it is impossible to say whether it was a remex or a covert; but the conditions are not incompatible with the possibility that the London specimen was aquinto-cubital, because the contour of the impressions of the secondary remiges shows an irregularity between the 4th and the 6th.

Mode of Life. A number of structural features give clear indications of the bird's mode of life. The opposable hallux, enabling the foot to grasp twigs and branches of trees, and the strengthening of the feet by the formation of the tarsometatarsus, show that *Archaeopteryx* was adapted to live in trees ; and the claws on its wings show how it climbed up their trunks.

The following features supply definitive proof that *Archaeopteryx* was incapable of active flight against gravity :

1. The absence of a carina on the sternum, the feeble development of the pectoral crest on the humerus, and the shortness of the coracoid show that the pectoral muscles were poorly developed.

2. The condition of separate bones in the hand (no carpometacarpus) and the consequent looseness of the feathers inserted on it show that *Archaeopteryx* could not exert effective downward pressure on the air, but was able only to glide.

3. The long tail containing many free vertebrae (no pygostyle) shows that no aerial manoeuvring was possible, but only gliding.

4. The small size of the cerebellum shows that the sensory-motor coordination necessary for active flight was impossible. The movements of *Archaeopteryx* in the air were therefore restricted to gliding, for which its structure is well adapted. It climbed up the trees with its claws and glided from higher to lower branches and to the ground.

The small number of teeth in *Archaeopteryx*, their small size, and their restriction to the front half of the gape of the mouth suggests that they were adapted to snapping for insects, and it was probably in search of this source of food that *Archaeopteryx* evolved its arboreal manner of life.

These conclusions help to explain the curious assortment of fossils with which *Archaeopteryx* is associated in the Solnhofen limestone. It includes land plants, insects, pterodactyls, crinoids, crustacea, king-crabs, ammonites, and fishes. These marine, terrestrial, and aerial organisms find themselves embedded together, as F. E. Zeuner has suggested, in shallow seas or lagoons fringed by coastal dunes and forests exposed to violent offshore winds with large rise and fall of tide. The receding sea would leave the marine animals stranded on mud flats, the wind would bring in the terrestrial and aerial forms, and the wind-borne dust would embed them in fine silt.

The Evolution of Birds. The ancestors of birds were a group of reptiles known as the Pseudosuchia, found in the Lower Trias of Europe and South Africa, of which *Euparkeria capensis* is an example (see ORIGIN OF BIRDS). Simpson has pointed out that, in the evolution from reptiles into modern birds, there were four basic functional changes in the skull.

1. The development of a bill with elongation of the premaxilla and eventual loss of teeth.

2. Increase in size of the eye and orbit.

3. Increase in size of the brain and brain-case.

4. Development of the streptostylic condition of the jaw with a movable quadrate.

In every one of these conditions *Archaeopteryx* is intermediate between a reptile such as *Euparkeria* and modern flying birds.

The structure of *Archaeopteryx*, the features that it possesses, the features that it does not possess, and the time of its appearance in the geological record, all lead to the conclusion that *Archaeopteryx* was on the direct line of evolution from the reptilian ancestors to modern flying birds.

Comparison of *Archaeopteryx* with its reptilian ancestors on the one hand, and with its modern avian descendants on the other, reveals the fact that in many of its features *Archaeopteryx* is either typically reptilian or typically avian, so that *Archaeopteryx* presents a mosaic of reptilian and avian pieces. The reptilian features are :

1. The long tail with twenty free vertebrae.

2. The amphicoelous articulation between the vertebral centra.

3. The short sacrum involving only six vertebrae.

4. The free metacarpal bones in the hand.

5. The claws on each of the fingers of the hand.

6. The thecodont teeth with alternate socket replacement.

7. Simple unjointed ribs.

8. Gastralia.

9. The simple brain with elongated smooth cerebral hemispheres and small cerebellum.

The avian features are :

1. The feathers, identical with those of modern birds.

2. The arrangement of feathers on the forearm and their differentiation into primaries borne on the hand and secondaries on the ulna.

3. The fusion of the clavicles into a furcula.

4. The pubes directed backwards.

5. The fusion of the distal tarsals and metatarsals into a tarsometatarsus.

6. The opposable hallux in the foot.

Archaeopteryx therefore provides an example of the process known as mosaic evolution, showing that, in the transition from one vertebrate class to another, the various parts of the body are not themselves intermediate in type, but are typical either of the class from which evolution had proceeded or of the class towards which evolution was proceeding. The parts underwent complete transformation one after the other.

The Evolution of Flight. On the question of the origin of feathers themselves *Archaeopteryx* can give only indirect indications. It is probable that feathers started as frayed scales which necessarily resulted in the production of a heat-insulating layer surrounding the body. This must have conferred advantage from the start on organisms evolving towards a homoeothermous type of physiology, which the ancestors of *Archaeopteryx* undoubtedly were. The earliest feathers were therefore probably down feathers, and the subsequent evolution of ' flight' feathers must have been associated with the development of the habit of gliding. Since *Archaeopteryx* already possessed fully differentiated downy body feathers and flight feathers, it supplies no evidence on which were evolved first, but its condition shows nothing incompatible with the view outlined above (Fürbringer ; Tucker).

On the other hand, the conditions in *Archaeopteryx* supply valuable evidence on the origin of flight in birds (see FLIGHT). The wing, the flight feathers, and their arrangement, were not evolved in the first place for active flight against gravity at all, but for leaping and gliding by making use of gravity. In evolution up to *Archaeopteryx*, with every variation in the direction of larger and longer feathers increasing the area of the bearing surface of the wing, more effective, longer leaps and glides at shallower angles became possible, and conferred advantage from the start and throughout the improvement of performance.

In subsequent evolution after *Archaeopteryx*, the wing adapted for gliding was later re-adapted to flying by the development of the carpometacarpus, carina, pectoral crest, and pectoral muscles. At the same time the tail was shortened, its terminal vertebrae were reduced to a pygostyle, and the tail feathers spread out into a fan serving as an aerial brake. The cerebellum increased in size and complexity, making possible the coordination of movement covering the static and dynamic requirements of an animal moving rapidly and suddenly in all three dimensions of space.

It may therefore be said that *Archaeopteryx* confirms the correctness of the so-called arboreal ' proavis' theory of the origin of flight.

G. de B.

de Beer, G. 1954. *Archaeopteryx lithographica*. London : British Museum (Natural History). (Gives the literature up to 1954, since when the following works refer.)
Condal, L. F. 1956. Notice préliminaire concernant la présence d'une plume d'oiseau dans le Jurassique Supérieur du Montsech (Province de Lérida, Espagne). Acta XI Congr. Internat. Orn., Basel 1954 : 268–269.
de Beer, G. 1954. Archaeopteryx and Evolution. Advancement of Science 42 : 160–170.
de Beer, G. 1956. The evolution of the ratites. Bull. Brit. Mus. (Nat. Hist.), Zool. 4 : 57–70.
Heller, F. 1959. Ein dritter *Archaeopteryx*-Fund aus den Solnhofer Plattenkalken von Langenaltheim/Mfr. Erlanger geol. Abh. 31 : 1–25.
Steiner, H. 1956. Die taxonomische und phylogenetische Bedeutung der Diastataxie des Vogelflügels. J. Orn. 97 : 1–20.
Verheyen, R. 1958. Note sur l'absence de la cinquième remige secondaire (diastataxie) dans certains groupes d'oiseaux récents et fossiles. Gerfaut 1958 : 157–166.

ARCHAEORNITHES: a subclass (see under CLASS ; also ARCHAEOPTERYX ; FOSSIL BIRDS).

ARCTIC: unlike the Antarctic, does not represent a separate zoogeographical area but rather the northern extremities of the Palaearctic and Nearctic Regions (together Holarctic). See DISTRIBUTION, GEOGRAPHICAL ; NEARCTIC REGION ; OCEANIC BIRDS ; PALAEARCTIC REGION.

ARCTOGAEA: a grouping by T. H. Huxley (1868) of the classical zoogeographical regions that excludes only the Neotropical and Australasian Regions, which he called ' Neogaea' and ' Notogaea' respectively ; Arctogaea has more recently been termed ' Megagea' (see DISTRIBUTION, GEOGRAPHICAL).

ARDEAE; ARDEIDAE: see under CICONIIFORMES. For the purposes of this work, *Cochlearius* is included in the Ardeidae, although by some regarded as constituting a separate monotypic family. There are two subfamilies, Ardeinae (see HERON), and Botaurinae (see BITTERN).

ARENA DISPLAY: see LEK DISPLAY

ARGUS: substantive name, alternatively ' argus pheasant', of the Great Argus *Argusianus argus* and the Crested Argus *Rheinartia ocellata* (see PHEASANT).

ARRANGEMENT: in taxonomy, the process (and its result) of placing the items of a category, i.e. the taxa of next lower rank, in some sequence or pattern. In any work in which birds have to be systematically listed, there arises not only the matter of assigning them to their appropriate taxa but also the question of arranging the items within a taxon—it may be species within a genus (or subgenus, if any), or genera within a family (or subfamily or tribe), or the like. Subspecies are commonly arranged, within the species, on some geographical basis ; this is reasonable, as subspecies are in fact geographical forms and by definition allopatric. At other levels there is a convention that the items are arranged in a 'natural' sequence, which is supposed to keep together those that are most closely related ; and the more 'primitive' (according to belief) are placed first. The objection to this, strongly voiced by some taxonomists, is that the information necessary for confidently making such an arrangement seldom exists ; and that, if it did, the facts could often not be adequately expressed in any linear sequence. On this view, the so-called 'natural' arrangement is apt to be pretentious and misleading ; and as reasons are seldom stated, the basis cannot be critically examined and the practice is thus devoid of scientific value. The alternative course—frankly admitting ignorance —is to arrange the items within each taxon alphabetically ; this is already followed by taxonomists dealing with certain other classes of animals and has obvious convenience for the reader where the number of items is considerable. Those who advocate this procedure suggest that it remains possible to indicate any views about particularly close relationship by some use of explained symbols.

ARROWSNAKE: see BIBLE, BIRDS OF THE

ARTAMIDAE: a family of the Passeriformes, suborder Oscines (see WOOD-SWALLOW).

ART, BIRDS IN: bird subjects that have from the very earliest times featured in man's artistic efforts. Amongst the pictures which have survived through the ages not the least interesting are those painted by the ancient Egyptians ; birds were thought to be 'winged souls' and some species were assigned to particular gods, a hawk being the emblem of Horus, and Thoth (god of learning) being represented by the Sacred Ibis, to quote two examples. The discovery at Hermopolis of a great number of mummified Ibises, with their likenesses painted on their wrappings, seems to denote that this species was the object of a cult. The belief that a soul should not go unattended to the next life is accountable for the interesting pictures found on the walls and sarcophagi of excavated tombs. Originally food, chattels, and slaves were buried with the deceased, but later this practice gave way to pictorial records of the dead man's life and everything connected therewith. Some fascinating examples of these early Egyptian bird paintings are to be seen in the British Museum ; ducks swimming in a pond, geese feeding, and—of greater interest still—a study of fowlers surrounded by a variety of birds in flight. Birds were also popular with the artists of ancient Greece, who introduced them into their still-life paintings of fruit and flowers in much the same way as did the Dutch painters many centuries later. Examples of bird studies by Greek artists were brought to light in the excavations of Pompeii and Herculaneum.

Passing from ancient times to the Middle Ages, those who have looked closely at illuminated manuscripts will have noticed how often brilliant tiny bird forms were used in decorating the elaborate borders of psalters and breviaries. At first these were inclined to be somewhat linear and frequently fabulous representations ; but in the thirteenth century nature came to be studied more closely, with the result that the pictures gained realism and animation. In the middle of the century the Emperor Frederick II wrote his treatise on falconry, *De Arte Venandi cum Avibus* (now in the Vatican), with very carefully executed marginal illustrations of hawking scenes and bird life. Another example of this type of illustration is in the British Museum (Add. MSS. 27695, 28 841) ; it consists of fragments of a Latin 'Treatise of the Vices' written by one of the Cocharelli family of Genoa towards the end of the fourteenth century, and the characteristics of the birds which appear in this manuscript, their postures, movements, and flight denote a remarkably keen study of avian life. Another document of great interest is the sketchbook of a fourteenth-century monk in the Pepys Library at Magdalene College, Cambridge ; this contains several pages devoted to coloured studies of birds, the majority of which are identifiable.

With the Renaissance came a break with tradition, and art ceased to be controlled by the Church. Painters expressed themselves more freely and with greater imagination, and all forms of nature received their closer attention. Giotto was one of the first to adopt naturalism in art, and at Assisi is still preserved amongst his frescoes the touching scene of a group of small birds listening attentively to St Francis preaching, whilst a late-comer flutters down to join the congregation. From the fourteenth century onwards, birds appeared frequently in the works of the great masters, sometimes in a symbolic role or in some mythological composition, sometimes as pets in portrait studies or as colourful details in landscapes. Since many birds appear in pictures in the National Gallery in London, it is proposed to refer to a few of these pictures with an explanation of their particular significance in each instance.

Those well acquainted with religious paintings may have noticed how often the Goldfinch is depicted. On account of his preference for thorns and thistles he was adopted by the Church to symbolise the Passion of Christ, and in the National Gallery he is several times represented. Baroccio in his 'Holy Family' (No. 29) places the bird in the hand of St John, who holds it high out of reach of an interested cat; whilst in Benozzo's altarpiece (No. 283) a Goldfinch has settled at the Madonna's feet in company with a Great Tit, the latter having no particular significance so far as is known. In Cima's 'Madonna and Child' (No. 634) a Goldfinch flutters in the hand of the Christ Child. Crivelli made two very different studies of this bird (Nos. 668, 788); in both pictures the usually gay little creature sits dejectedly on a leafless branch with his back turned on the spectator. A whole 'charm' of Goldfinches captured by the brush of Rubens is to be seen fluttering in a thicket in his famous landscape 'Chateau de Steen' (No. 66).

The Peacock graces many a Nativity and Annunciation, and in his wonderful painting of the latter scene (No. 739) Crivelli has shown to the full the grace and dignity of this bird, the symbol of Immortality owing to the legend that its flesh does not decay. Botticelli introduces it into his 'Adoration of the Magi' (No. 1033). The Peacock is perhaps best known as representing Pride and Vanity; and in classical mythology it is assigned to the goddess Juno, whom it accompanies in Rubens's 'Judgment of Paris' (No. 194) and is shown having an altercation with Paris's dog. In the same picture figures Minerva's owl, here symbolising the wisdom of its mistress, although in the Christian Church it was sometimes adopted as a Satanic symbol due to its preference for darkness and horror of the light. As a symbol of wisdom, an owl is sometimes shown with St Jerome, as in the picture by Tura (No. 773).

That such a pleasant creature and charming songster as the Blackbird should be connected with the Prince of Darkness seems hard indeed, but in the eyes of the early Church apparently the bird's very charms were sufficient to merit such an association. The dove, besides representing the Holy Ghost, also stood for Purity and Peace and is often shown with the Blessed Virgin, especially in scenes of the Purification, it being customary on such an occasion to make an offering of a pair of Turtle Doves in the Temple. A Turtle Dove can

be seen in Crivelli's 'Annunciation' to which reference has already been made. In mythology the dove is attributed to Venus. The Partridge, chosen to signify Truth, was also curiously enough sometimes symbolic of the Devil. Two of Catena's pictures include it (Nos. 234, 694), and in Antonello's 'St Jerome' (No. 1418) a Partridge and a Peacock are in the foreground with their backs turned to each other, which possibly indicates that here they represent Truth and Vanity respectively. In Crivelli's 'Madonna and Child' (No. 724), perched high on the ornate throne is a Swallow, placed there as the symbol of the Incarnation. Scenes of the Annunciation also show this bird, which was connected too with the Resurrection owing to a belief that in winter it hibernated in the mud to emerge again at springtime to herald the reblossoming of nature.

The domestic cock, associated with St Peter, denotes watchfulness and vigilance because of its early rising. It was also the emblem of St Vitus of Bohemia, under whose patronage come actors, dancers, and those who find difficulty in rising in the morning. Another bird denoting vigilance is the Crane. According to a legend the King of the Cranes was guarded each night by sentries standing on one foot with a stone in the other; if sleep overcame them the stone was supposed to drop on the other foot and awaken them.

The Eagle symbolised the Resurrection and also became the emblem of St John the Evangelist. In Mantegna's 'Agony in the Garden' (No. 1417) a Golden Eagle, which has been referred to as the 'Bird of Fate', occupies a prominent place in the picture. It is also to be seen in greater detail in the painting ascribed to Damiano Mazza (No. 32) showing the bird carrying off Ganymede to Olympus. A very much finer eagle painting is contained in the picture by Rubens of 'Prometheus Bound'. In this, as in others where birds or other animals were concerned, Rubens collaborated with Frans

---

Plate 3 · Flight

a *Upper* : Spoonbills *Platalea leucorodia* flying in a group, with necks extended, bills forward, and long legs trailing (Hungary). *Phot. Zoltán Tildy.*

b *Lower left* : Nightjar *Caprimulgus europaeus* (male) hovering during nocturnal flight (England). *Phot. Eric Hosking, by flashlight.*

c *Lower right* : Arctic Tern *Sterna paradisaea* sailing overhead, with tail widespread and bill at a downward angle (Sweden). *Phot. P. O. Swanberg.*

(See articles FLIGHT ; SPOONBILL ; NIGHTJAR ; TERN)

Snyders. The painting is now in Philadelphia, but Snyders's remarkable sketch for it can be seen in the British Museum. The story of Jupiter's attentions to Leda, in the guise of a Swan, captured the imagination of more than one painter. The National Gallery picture after Michelangelo (No. 1868) shows the most intimate phase of the liaison between the god and his mortal mistress, whilst Leonardo da Vinci in his treatment of the subject (Galleria Borghese, Rome, and other versions elsewhere) depicts the couple standing happily side by side whilst their offspring hatch out of egg-shells in the background.

So far, reference has been made to the birds which appear in the paintings of the Italian school and chiefly those of a religious nature ; but mention must be made of the Dutch painters of the seventeenth century, not a few of whom specialised in the painting of birds. Whilst their still-life pictures very often contained a profusion of dead game-birds of every kind, the studies of live birds are very much more interesting ; there are some very fine examples in the Wallace Collection (London). One painting there, by d'Hondecoeter, shows a domestic rooster and a Peacock stepping out side by side through a farm-yard with all the dash and swagger of Regency dandies. A coloured drawing by the same artist, in the British Museum, portrays the same two species engaged in a fight, with smaller fowls fluttering round them.

The Wallace Collection also has paintings of Peacocks, and of macaws and other birds of the parrot family, by Jan Weenix, a cousin of d'Hondecoeter ; and there are studies of hawks by Joannes van Noord, and of Pheasants and other game-birds by Desportes. The French painter Oudry is well represented in this collection by some very fine action pictures such as ' A Fox in a Farmyard ', ' Hawk attacking Partridges ', ' Hawk attacking Wild Duck ', and ' Wild Duck aroused '. Another seventeenth-century bird painter of note was Jakob Bogdany, of Hungarian origin, who was employed by William III to decorate the royal

palaces. He specialised in exotic fowls, which are to be seen in the large collection of his works at Kew Palace.

Finally must be recorded the name of an English painter of the same period as those already recently mentioned. He is Francis Barlow, a native of Lincolnshire, who specialised in sporting pictures and painted birds with great spirit and accuracy. The owners of large country houses were so taken with his work that they employed him to decorate their ceilings. His pictures are mostly in private collections, but his ' Owl being Mocked by Small Birds ' may be seen at Ham House (London). At the British Museum, besides a drawing of an eagle carrying off a duckling, there is a large collection of his illustrations for Aesop's Fables (published 1666), quite a number of which are bird pictures. There are also water-colours by Barlow at the Victoria and Albert Museum, and the Marquess of Bath's collection at Longleat contains striking portraits of a Cassowary and an Ostrich.

Although birds are to be discovered in numerous paintings, where they form but small details in a large composition, they are apt to be overlooked by the spectator. It is hoped that the foregoing notes may show that, although not as interesting as bird-watching in the field, bird-spotting on canvas can be a very agreeable pastime.

See also ILLUSTRATION, BIRD.   R.T.

ARTENKREIS : see under SUPERSPECIES ; and RASSENKREIS

ARTERY : see HEART ; VASCULAR SYSTEM

ARTICULAR : when used as a noun, a paired bone of the lower jaw (see SKELETON).

ARTICULATION : jointing (see SKELETON).

ASITY : native name now used as English substantive name of the two species of *Philepitta* in the Philepittidae (Passeriformes, suborder Tyranni) ; in the plural (' asitys '), serves as a general term for the family. The group otherwise consists of two species of *Neodrepanis*, called ' false sunbirds ' ; and as a whole it is restricted to the forests of the island of Madagascar. This family belongs to the assemblage of primitive perching birds, related by the simple musculature of the syrinx to the tyrant-flycatcher group (Tyrannidae, etc.) so plentiful in the New World, but in the Old World represented only by the pittas (Pittidae), the New Zealand wrens (Xenicidae), and the present family. This, and the great difference between the two genera in the family, indicate that it is a relic of considerable antiquity in Madagascar.

Plate 4 · Flight—Carrying Food

a *Upper :* Hoopoe *Upupa epops* bringing a mole-cricket (*Gryllotalpa*) to nesting hole in tree (France). The wings are in the middle of the up-stroke, with primary feathers separated.

Phot. C. C. Doncaster.

b *Lower :* Green Barbet *Megalaima zeylanica* bringing berries to young in nest-tunnel in tree (India).

Phot. Christina Loke.

(See articles FLIGHT ; CARRYING ; HOOPOE ; BARBET)

Asitys are about 6 inches long, with a stout body, bill not as long as the head and broad at the base, wings and perching feet of moderate length, and tail short. The Velvet Asity *P. castanea* lives in the humid forests of eastern Madagascar. The female and young male are olive green above and greenish white scaled with olive below. The male when freshly moulted is black with most of the feathers heavily fringed with yellow ; these yellow fringes wear off and the bird is then velvety black and develops a large greenish wattle above the eye.

½

Velvet Asity *Philepitta castanea.* *C.E.T.K.*

The Velvet Asity is usually a solitary bird of the undergrowth and low trees in the forest where it perches, a plump, quiet, and sluggish bird. It allows a close approach and when alarmed flies but a short distance. Although ordinarily no note is heard from it, a whistled, thrush-like song has been reported. Small fruit plucked from forest shrubs is its ordinary food. A nest recorded was a pear-shaped pensile structure, the top of the nest woven about the supporting branches, with a projecting roof over the side entrance near the top. The three eggs were elongated ovate and pure white.

The second species, Schlegel's Asity *P. schlegeli*, lives in the forests of western Madagascar. It is yellower in colour, the male has only the top of the head black, and the wattle surrounds the eye.

The False Sunbird *Neodrepanis coruscans* is about 4 inches long, with a short tail and a long, deeply curved bill. It is iridescent blue above, dull yellow below, and with a large wattle around the eye ; the female lacks the wattle and is dark green above and yellowish below. For many years it was considered to be a true sunbird (Nectariniidae). Little is known about its habits beyond the fact that it is a quiet, slow-moving, solitary bird of the dark undergrowth in Madagascar's humid forests. There it usually searches for insects on the bark of twigs

and branches, but has occasionally been seen to visit certain flowers with long corollas where it fed like a sunbird. A second species, *N. hypoxantha*, with a finer bill and brighter colour, is known from only a few specimens from eastern Madagascar.

A.L.R.

Rand, A. L. 1936. The distribution and habits of Madagascar birds. Bull. Amer. Mus. Nat. Hist. 72 : 143–499. (Habits, pp. 425–427, 472–473.)
Amadon, D. 1951. Le Pseudo-souimanga de Madagascar. Oiseau 21 : 59–63. (Taxonomy.)

ASPERGILLOSIS : see DISEASE

ASSEMBLY, NOUN OF : a collective noun for a number of birds (or other animals) of one kind together ; some of these words are of general application, while others have restricted meanings. The usual term for an assemblage of birds is ' flock ' ; sometimes ' flight ' if they are on the wing ; sometimes ' party ' if the number is quite small. Other ordinary English words can of course be used for descriptive purposes in appropriate circumstances, e.g. ' assemblage ', ' congregation ', ' multitude ', ' horde ', ' host ', and (on the water) ' raft '. The word ' brood ' is used for the chicks or nestlings hatched from a ' clutch ' or ' set ' of eggs laid by one hen bird for simultaneous incubation. Birds breeding gregariously are referred to as a ' colony '. ' Pair ' means a male and a female, presumably united. ' Brace ' means two birds, usually dead—a measure used in counting the sportsman's ' bag '.

Then there are the special nouns of assembly which it is correct, or supposedly correct, to apply to particular kinds of birds in preference to the more general term, and only to such kinds. Some of these are genuine items from the vocabulary of medieval venery, whether now obsolete or still to some extent current (mainly among sportsmen). Others are mere inventions of later pedantry. Others again are erroneous, having found their way into the category by misconception. No attempt at an exhaustive list need be made here.

The word ' covey ' is used for a family party or similarly sized flock of partridge or grouse, and is perhaps the only one of these special words that has any wide currency in English as spoken in Great Britain at the present day. There are some people, however, who would always be careful to speak of a ' gaggle ' or (if flying) ' skein ' of geese, a ' pack ' (bigger than a covey) of grouse, a ' wisp ' of snipe, or a ' spring ' of teal. On the other hand, one would be only half serious in speaking of a ' murder ' of crows, a ' charm ' of goldfinches, a ' watch ' of nightingales, a ' nye ' (various spellings) of phea-

sants, a 'clattering' of choughs, a 'covert' of
coots, a 'siege' of herons or bitterns, a 'fall' of
woodcock', a 'herd' of cranes, curlew, or swans,
a 'trip' of dotterel, a 'bevy' of quail, a 'chattering'
or 'murmuration' of starlings, or a 'dissimulation'
of small birds.

There are a few specific terms for colonies,
according to the kind of bird concerned. 'Rookery'
and 'heronry' are of the best usage, and the former
has been adopted also for penguins (Spheniscidae)
by ornithologists in the Antarctic. Others are
easily invented, where euphony permits, and some
have wide currency—'gullery', 'ternery', 'swannery'; but 'loomery' (guillemots) is a more
sophisticated usage. These inventions are not free
from affectation, however, and the general term
'colony' is usually to be preferred.

Hare, C. E., 1939. The Language of Sport. London.

ASSOCIATION, INTERSPECIFIC: either
between different species of birds or between birds
and other than avian species—see under CROCODILE-
BIRD ; FEEDING HABITS ; FLOCKING ; HONEYGUIDE ;
MAMMALS, ASSOCIATION WITH ; MAN, BIRDS AND ;
NESTING ASSOCIATION ; OXPECKER ; PARASITISM ;
TAMENESS.

ASYMMETRY: a condition not usually present
in any marked degree in the external characters of
birds, apart from individual abnormalities. A
striking exception is that of the Wrybill Plover
Anarhynchus frontalis, in which the bill is deflected
to the right (see BILL ; PLOVER). Not ordinarily
visible is the often great disparity between the ear
openings on the two sides in owls (Strigiformes)
(see HEARING AND BALANCE ; OWL). As in mammals,
there is some asymmetry in the internal organs ;
thus, only the right aortic arch develops (in mammals
it is the left)—see VASCULAR SYSTEM ; and only the
left ovary of birds is functional as a rule (see
REPRODUCTIVE SYSTEM). See also FOOTEDNESS.

ATAVISM: see PLUMAGE VARIATION

ATLAS: the first vertebra, articulating with the
skull (see SKELETON).

ATMOSPHERE : see CLIMATOLOGY; METEOROL-
OGY

ATRESIC: having no opening.

ATRICHORNITHIDAE: see under PASSERI-
FORMES ; and SCRUB-BIRD

ATRIUM: a chamber, especially one or other of
the anterior chambers of the heart ('atria', formerly
more often called 'auricles'—see HEART).

ATTACK: see AGGRESSION

ATTILA: generic name used as substantive name
of *Attila* spp. (see COTINGA).

AUDITORY MEATUS: see HEARING AND
BALANCE

AUGURY: see OMENS, BIRDS AS ; ORNITHOMANCY

AUK: substantive name of three species of Alcidae
(Charadriiformes, suborder Alcae) ; in the plural,
general term for the family and suborder (in a more
restricted sense, the 'true auks' are *Pinguinus* and
Alca). Other substantive names used for species or
groups of species are 'auklet', 'dovekie', 'guillemot', 'murre', 'murrelet', 'puffin', and 'tystie';
of these, 'murre'—although an old local name in
Britain—is now American usage, where British
ornithologists say 'guillemot'. The Alcidae are a
family of wing-propelled diving birds inhabiting
the colder parts of the northern oceans, reaching
fresh water in the Baltic and warm water in the
Gulf of California (see also OCEANIC BIRDS). The
family is an ancient and diverse group including
about 22 species (some with subspecific forms)
placed in 10–14 genera and 7 tribes.

Razorbill (or Razorbilled Auk) *Alca torda*. C.E.T.K.

Auks are rather 'chunky' birds of from small to
large size (6–30 inches long). The bill varies in
form from nearly cylindrical and pointed to rather
broad and leading to a distensible throat pouch
(dovekie) ; and to laterally compressed, very high,
and ornamented with brightly coloured horny
plates which are shed after the breeding season
(puffins, some auklets). In the Crested Auklet
Aethia cristatella the plates give out an odour like
that of tangerine oranges. The legs are short ; the
first toe is lacking or vestigial, the other three are
fully webbed. The wings are short and more or
less pointed ; the tail is short. In all but a few
species (*Pinguinus, Aethia pusilla, A. pygmaea*), the
flight feathers are moulted simultaneously, and so
there is a period of temporary flightlessness.

Black, grey, and white predominate in the plumage ; cryptic coloration is found in the breeding dress of the Marbled Murrelet *Brachyramphus marmoratus* and Kittlitz's Murrelet *B. brevirostris*. Bright colours, if present, are found on bill, feet, and lining of mouth. White patches on the face or elongated plumes on the head, sometimes both, are found in several species. Most have distinct winter and nuptial plumages, the latter often attained by a moult of the head and neck feathers.

Auks are predominantly pelagic, remaining at sea except during the breeding season. Considerable movements of some species during the winter have been shown by ringing, e.g. of Razorbills *Alca torda* from Britain to the central Mediterranean and of Puffins *Fratercula arctica* from Britain to Newfoundland. The diet consists almost entirely of fish and marine invertebrates, especially crustaceans. The prey is usually obtained by under-water pursuit ; a few forms are bottom-feeders. The birds submerge with a kick of the feet while partially spreading the wings, the wing-tips and tail being the last parts to go under. While the bird is under water the wings are used for propulsion, whereas the feet are used in steering (see SWIMMING AND DIVING). In the air, auks fly rapidly and directly with fast wingbeats (see FLIGHT) ; the neck is retracted, and the feet may be covered by the plumage of the underparts, especially during long flights. On the ground, the posture may be upright (true auks, murres), duck-like (tysties), or intermediate (puffins), the position and proportions of the legs differing from group to group. The birds are usually silent except in the nesting season, when vocalisations may be conspicuous and vary widely from sibilant noises (tysties) to growling sounds (true auks, murres).

Most auks nest colonially. Eggs may be laid on cliff ledges, in crevices, among rocks, under plants and other objects, in burrows, or on bare ground above the timber-line. Little or no nesting material is used. Some (true auks, murres) rest the egg across the tarsi while incubating. Eggs range from strongly pyriform and highly variable in colour and marking (true auks, murres) to ovoid and immaculate. The usual clutch is one or two. The young are downy on hatching and remain in the nest from less than two days (some murrelets) to seven weeks (puffins). Both parents take part in incubation and in care of the young.

The family is most numerous in the North Pacific, where 16 species occur, 12 of them being endemic. Seven species, including the extinct Great Auk, are or were found in the North Atlantic. The Common Murre (or Guillemot) *Uria aalge*, the Thick-billed Murre (or Brünnich's Guillemot) *U.*

lomvia, and the Black Guillemot (or Tystie) *Cepphus grylle* are panboreal, although the last—unlike the two murres—does not nest south of Bering Strait, being replaced in the North Pacific by the related Pigeon Guillemot *C. columba*. The Common Puffin *Fratercula arctica* of the North Atlantic is replaced by the closely related Horned Puffin *F. corniculata* in the North Pacific. The remaining genera are confined either to the Atlantic or to the Pacific.

The first tribe (Alcini) contains the extinct Great Auk *Pinguinus impennis*, the Razor-billed Auk (or Razorbill) *Alca torda*, and the murres or guillemots of the genus *Uria*. All are dark above and white below. The throat is white in winter and black or brown in summer. The true auks are confined to the Atlantic. Although the two murres are sympatric over much of their ranges, the thick-billed species nests farther north (to Spitsbergen and Franz Josef Land) and the common species farther south (to northern Portugal and southern California). A ' ringed ' or ' bridled ' mutant of *Uria aalge* is found in the Atlantic ; these birds, having a white eye-ring and a white line along the postorbital crease, occur with increasing frequency from SSE. to NNW., with a reversal of the trend in Iceland (see POLYMORPHISM). The young take to the water at an age of two to three weeks, at which time they are from a third to half grown and have wing coverts (but not remiges) large enough for the wing to be used effectively for propulsion under water.

The Great Auk (or Garefowl) has been extinct for over 100 years (see EXTINCT BIRDS). It was the largest of the family and was flightless. The large keel on the sternum provided attachment for powerful pectoral muscles, and the short but strong wings were well adapted for use under water. Unlike most other auks, it did not moult all the flight feathers simultaneously but shed them in sequence like most other birds. Its subarctic breeding range included off-shore islands from Great Britain (St Kilda) to Iceland, southern Greenland, and the Gulf of St Lawrence. In winter, it wandered south to southern Spain and Florida. Well known to early sailors, who killed many for food, it was the original ' penguin ', this vernacular name being later applied to the similarly adapted Spheniscidae of the Southern Hemisphere. The smaller Lucas auks *Mancalla californiensis* and *M. diegense* (of the extinct family Mancallidae), well known Californian fossils of the Pliocene age, had even more flipper-like wings than those of the Great Auk.

The second tribe (Plautini) contains only the

Dovekie (or Little Auk) *Plautus alle* of the North Atlantic and the adjacent parts of the Arctic Ocean. Coloured like the Alcini, the Dovekie nests in crevices among rocks and lays a single, pale blue egg which is usually unmarked. Ecologically it corresponds to the small auklets of the North Pacific.

The Tystie (or Black Guillemot) *Cepphus grylle* and its congeners constitute the tribe Cepphini. They have a complete body moult in the winter or spring, producing a black nuptial plumage with white wing or cheek patches. The feet and mouth linings are bright red. In winter the under parts and varying amounts of the upper parts are white. These birds depend to a larger extent on benthic animals for food and tend to be less gregarious during the breeding season than most other auks. The nest sites in which the two spotted eggs are laid run nearly the gamut of types used by the whole family. The young remain in the nest until fully fledged (about 39 days).

In the related tribe Brachyramphini, comprising the Marbled Murrelet *Brachyramphus marmoratus* and Kittlitz's Murrelet *B. brevirostris* of the North Pacific, there is also an extensive prenuptial moult from the dark grey and white winter plumage, in the former into a plumage barred with rufous and brown, and in the latter into a mottled blue-grey and buff one. The nesting habits of the Marbled Murrelet, of which the breeding distribution coincides with the coastal coniferous forest belt, are unknown; Kittlitz's Murrelet is a solitary nester, depositing its eggs on bare ground among lichen-covered stones above the timber-line in Alaska and on adjacent islands.

The other murrelets (tribe Synthliboramphini) either have no distinct nuptial plumage (Craveri's Murrelet *Endomychura craveri* and Xantus's Murrelet *E. hypoleucus*), or the seasonal differences are limited to the plumage of the head (the Ancient Murrelet *Synthliboramphus antiquus* and the Japanese Murrelet *S. wumizusume*). Unlike the Brachyramphini, these birds have long, narrow tarsi, and the young, hatched with feet of nearly the adult size, take to the water when less than two days old.

The abundant small auklets *Aethia* spp. and *Ptychoramphus aleuticus* of the North Pacific (tribe Aethiini) and the related puffins *Fratercula* spp., *Cerorhinca monocerata*, and *Lunda cirrhata* (tribe Fraterculini) nest in crevices or burrows; the puffins dig their own nesting holes, the claw of the second toe being modified for this purpose. The normal clutch is a single, immaculate or obscurely marked egg. The young remain in the nest until fledged—up to 50 days in the case of the Common (or Atlantic)

Puffin *Fratercula arctica*. During the breeding season adults of most species have elongated plumes on the head and brightly coloured plates on the bill. The Common Puffin and the Horned Puffin *F. corniculata*, in addition to plates on the bill, have horn-like or plate-like structures above and below the eye and fleshy rosettes at the gape. Puffins, like most other auks, are an important source of food for northern peoples; and the eggs of many species of auks are collected in great numbers for food, particularly in Novaya Zemlya, where murres have been 'managed' for this purpose.

See Plate 29 (colour; Puffin)   R.W.S.

Kozlova, E. V. 1957. Fauna of the U.S.S.R.—Birds: Alcae. Moscow. (Eng. trans. Israel Program. Sci. Trans. no. 227.)

Kraskovski, S. K. 1937. The biological basis for the economic exploitation of bird-cliffs. Affaif [studies] on the biology of the guillemot (*Uria lomvia* L.). Trans. Arctic Inst. U.S.S.R. 77 Biol.: 33–91. (English summary.)

Lockley, R. M. 1953. Puffins. London and New York.

Paludan, K. 1947. Alken. Copenhagen.

Richardson, F. 1961. Breeding biology of the Rhinoceros Auklet on Washington Island, Washington. Condor 63: 456–473.

Salomonsen, F. 1944. The Atlantic Alcidae. Medd. Göteborgs Mus., Zool. Avdel. 108: 1–138.

Southern, H. N. and Reeve, E. C. R. 1942. Quantitative studies in the geographical variation of birds. The Common Guillemot (*Uria aalge* Pont.). Proc. Zool. Soc. Lond. 111A: 255–276.

Storer, R. W. 1945. Structural modifications in the hind limb in the Alcidae. Ibis 87: 433–456.

Storer, R. W. 1945. The systematic position of the murrelet genus *Endomychura*. Condor 47: 154–160.

Storer, R. W. 1952. A comparison of variation, behaviour and evolution in the sea bird genera *Uria* and *Cepphus*. Univ. Calif. Publ. Zool. 52: 121–222.

Storer, R. W. 1960. Evolution in the diving birds. Proc. XII Internat. Congr., Helsinki 1958: 694–707.

Thomson, A. L. 1953. The migrations of British auks (Alcidae) as shown by the results of marking. Brit. Birds 46: 3–16.

Tschanz, B. 1959. Zur Brutbiologie der Trottellumme (*Uria aalge* Pont.). Behaviour 14: 1–100.

Tuck, L. M. 1960. The Murres, their distribution, populations and biology—a study of the genus *Uria*. (Canadian Wildlife Series no. 1.) Ottawa.

AUKLET: substantive name of *Aethia* spp. and *Ptychoramphus aleuticus* (see AUK).

AURICLE: in general, an ear-shaped lobe; formerly the common term (in the plural) for what are now more usually called the 'atria' of the heart (see ATRIUM: HEART).

AURICULARS: the ear coverts (see PLUMAGE; TOPOGRAPHY).

AUSTRAL: term applied in North America to a climatic life-zone, or series of zones, lying south of the 'boreal' (see BOREAL; LIFE-ZONE).

AUSTRALASIAN REGION: comprising the Australian and New Zealand Regions of some zoogeographers, but in respect of avifauna more appropriately treated as a unit with subdivisions (see DISTRIBUTION, GEOGRAPHICAL). The heart of the Australasian Region is the island continent of Australia, with an area of about 2 975 000 square miles. New Guinea (the south-eastern part of which is called Papua) covers an area of 345 000 square miles, and New Zealand and its Dependencies 104 000 square miles. The total land area of the Region, including the smaller island groups, is about 3 461 000 square miles.

Australia extends between 11° and 43° S. lat., and nearly 40 per cent of its total area is within the tropics. It is a land of low, subdued relief with large expanses of plain, and with a notable absence of mountains of alpine type, conditions that impart a certain uniformity of landscape and vegetation. The climate is predominantly warm and dry, the continent having an arid centre with concentric zones of more favoured country, culminating in restricted humid areas in interrupted coastal strips, particularly in the east, south-east, and south-west. Both New Guinea and New Zealand, with their high mountain cordilleras and lush vegetation—the one tropical, the other temperate—present marked physiographic and vegetational contrasts to their larger neighbour.

Relative to area, within the Region, Australia has the lowest number of bird species. Mayr & Serventy list some 650 species for Australia and about the same number for New Guinea. New Zealand has 215 species. Keast gives 568 *breeding* species for Australia and about the same for New Guinea—allowing for overlap, 906 for both together.

Origin of the Avifauna. Geologically, Australia has been separated from the Asiatic landmass since the early Tertiary, and perhaps since much earlier. Land connections existed between New Guinea and Australia in the early Tertiary and again at the end of the Tertiary. The past relations of New Zealand are shrouded in uncertainty, but land connection with the Australian continental shelf, if it ever occurred, was improbable after the Mesozoic. The Polynesian archipelagos have always been isolated oceanic islands, but there is evidence that during the Tertiary they were both more extensive and more numerous than at present (Mayr 1953a).

Thus, not only Australia itself but the island groups near it have been cut off from the great landmasses of the world, and mostly from each other, since before birds of modern type evolved. Nevertheless, the avifaunas of Australia, New Guinea, and most of the southern Polynesian islands not only show common relationships but point to an ultimate derivation from that of Asia (Mayr 1944c). It was from here, the Eastern Palaeotropical or Oriental Region, that the ancestors of the Australasian avifauna originated.

'The existing avifauna of Australia and New Guinea, all apparently derived originally by island hopping across a sea barrier, has attained various levels of endemism. The older arrivals have undergone secondary differentiation, and there is an accumulation of a large number of peculiar families, second only in number to those of the Neotropical Region. The later immigrants show progressively closer relationship with Palaeotropical and Palaearctic forms, and most of the widespread families are represented. The process of colonisation is still going on' (Serventy 1960). Contrary to the implications of theories of continental drift, the Australian avifauna shows no affinity with that of the Neotropical Region; nor with that of the Ethiopian, except by way of the Oriental. The birds of the Hawaiian Islands have relations essentially with the Nearctic Region, although other elements of the fauna and flora show an Australasian affinity (Mayr 1943), including two bird groups that represent a honeyeater (Meliphagidae) and a flycatcher (Muscicapinae) invasion respectively.

The division between the Australasian and Oriental Regions was named Wallace's Line by T. H. Huxley (see under ORIENTAL REGION), but the faunal situation here is better expressed by considering the boundary as a transitional area rather than an arbitrary line. Movement across it has mostly been a one-way traffic—from the larger landmass of the Orient to the smaller Australasian land units, and very little in the reverse direction. The explanation seems to be that species developed on larger landmasses have an evolutionary premium, as it were, over those evolved in smaller areas (Storr). Modern studies on the colonisation of this area, and on the routes by which the ancestors of existing Australasian birds have crossed over from Asia, have been published by Stresemann (1939) and by Mayr (1944 a, b, c).

Although most of the Old World bird groups sent representatives to Australasia, on one or other of the many colonising waves that went on throughout the Tertiary and are still in progress, there are some noteworthy absentees which either never succeeded in making the passage or later became extinct in the Region. Among these are the flamingos (Phoenicopteridae), Old World vultures (Aegypiinae), pheasants (Phasianidae) other than quail (*Coturnix*, *Synoicus*), skimmers (Rynchopidae), sandgrouse (Pteroclididae), trogons (Trogonidae), barbets (Capitonidae), woodpeckers (Picidae), broad-bills (Eurylaimidae), true finches (Fringillidae), and buntings (Emberizidae). Flamingos occurred in the Tertiary, a fossil tarsometatarsus from a probable Oligocene deposit having been recently discovered (Stirton et al. 1961). In other cases there is only a slight penetration of Old World forms into or across the transition area ; thus, the bulbuls (Pycnonotidae) have entered the Moluccas. One of the hornbills (Bucerotidae) has penetrated widely into the region, through New Guinea, reaching the Solomon Islands in the south-west Pacific, but skirting continental Australia. Similarly, one of the shrikes (Laniidae) has entered New Guinea but has failed to colonise Australia. A third curious example is the widespread thrush genus *Turdus*, which has by-passed Australia completely but established itself in New Guinea, on some Pacific islands, and on Lord Howe Island, between Australia and New Zealand.

Migrants. With the striking exception of the Palaearctic-breeding waders (Charadriidae and Scolopacidae), of which a swarm of species 'winter' in Australasia, there is a dearth of Old World migrants into the region. Two swifts (Apodidae) are regular migrants to southern Australia and a cuckoo (*Cuculus saturatus*) to northern Australia ; but the migratory passerines almost entirely fail to reach Australia. The eastern race of the Swallow *Hirundo rustica gutturalis* includes the extreme north-west of Australia as part of its wintering area, and there are two records of the Yellow Wagtail *Motacilla flava* and one of the Reed Warbler *Acrocephalus orientalis*. By contrast with the huge numbers of Palaearctic migrant passerines that pour into southern Africa during the northern winter, their absence from Australia is very striking.

Endemism. Within the Australasian Region there has been much secondary differentiation, so that endemic families, subfamilies, and genera have evolved, according to the antiquity of the original colonisation. Mayr (1944c) has attempted a chronological analysis of some of them. Of many of the old endemic groups there is left little evidence as to what are their closest modern allies elsewhere. These are, for example, the emus (Dromaiidae), cassowaries (Casuariidae), megapodes (Megapodidae), many of the parrot-cockatoo groups (Psittacidae), frogmouths (Podargidae), lyrebirds (Menuridae), scrub-birds (Atrichornithidae), magpie-larks (Grallinidae), wood-swallows (Artamidae), honeyeaters (Meliphagidae), bower-birds (Ptilonorhynchidae), and Australian 'magpies' (Cracticidae). Later arrivals have produced characteristic families, of which the Old World connections are not difficult to recognise, these including various flycatchers (Pachycephalinae ; *Petroica*) allied to the Musicicapinae, the many Australian warblers (Malurinae) allied to the Sylviinae, and the Australian treecreepers (Climacteridae).

Still more recent colonisers, which Mayr tentatively dates from the Pliocene, include a quail (*Synoicus*), various kingfishers ('*Syma*', *Dacelo*), and flycatchers (*Rhipidura*, *Myiagra*, *Microeca*). Late Pliocene or Pleistocene invaders have produced endemic species of such Old World genera as *Coturnix*, *Rallus*, *Podiceps*, *Grus*, *Accipiter*, *Halcyon*, *Zosterops*, *Corvus*, and many more. A reed warbler *Acrocephalus stentoreus* and a pipit *Anthus novaeseelandiae*, among others, are only subspecifically separable. Colonisation still continues, and the latest, the Cattle Egret *Ardeola ibis*, has arrived only during the last decade or two.

Subregions. In Australia itself the existing fauna can be grouped into three major assemblages (Serventy & Whittell) : a northern tropical (the Torresian Fauna), a south-eastern and south-western temperate (the Bassian Fauna), and over most of the arid and semi-arid interior a widespread Eyrean Fauna. In the south-west of Australia there is an intermingling of Bassian and Eyrean elements.

The New Guinea Subregion has been summarised by Mayr (1953), who draws attention to the fact that, although the fauna as a whole is strongly Australo-Papuan in character, there is a high degree of striking endemism. Groups such as the cassowaries (Casuariidae) and birds-of-paradise (Paradisaeidae) are almost endemic, and there are many peculiar genera such as the crowned pigeons *Goura* spp.

The fauna of the other large island in the region —New Zealand—has been analysed by Falla (1953), who has shown that the bulk of the land birds of that area have originated, as far as can be ascertained, from Australia by a series of trans-ocean invasions through the Tertiary and continuing into our own times. Several peculiar New Zealand forms are now known to have affinities with archaic Australian types. Thus the owl-parrots (Strigopinae) have been shown by several authors to have an alliance with the Australian *Geopsittacus*, a stock now dying out. The New Zealand wattle-birds (Callaeidae), including the peculiar Saddleback *Philesturnus carunculatus*, the Huia *Heteralocha acutirostris*, and the kokakos *Callaeas* spp., are believed to be derivatives of a form from which the present-day Australian Apostlebird *Struthidea cinerea* and other Grallinidae are perhaps descended. These comparatively frequent invasions of Australian stocks into New

Zealand, no doubt explain why there has not been an adaptive radiation from a few ancestral types such as has taken place in a spectacular manner on the isolated Galápagos and Hawaiian archipelagos. The repeated invasions from Australia, tending to fill available ecological niches with aggressive new arrivals, would be inimical to the radiation and expansion of an autochthonous fauna. Fleming has pointed out that the family Callaeidae would be the nearest approach to such an adaptive radiation in New Zealand.

Falla has drawn attention to the very interesting fact that in Pleistocene and early Recent times a vigorous waterfowl and open-country fauna allied to Australian types flourished in New Zealand and then died out, possibly because of the onset of an arid cycle. These included a swan allied to the Australian Black Swan *Cygnus atratus*, a large eagle *Harpagornis moorei*, a coot *Palaeolimnas*, a corvid, and representatives of two Australian monotypic ducks (*Biziura* and *Malacorhynchos*).

The extinct moas (Dinornithidae) and the probably related kiwis (Apterygidae) have occurred nowhere else than in New Zealand, so far as known, and the alleged fossils of both recorded from Australia are now disputed. Mayr & Amadon (1951) accept the view that they are allied to the emus. Fleming has suggested that the moas and their kin, alone among birds, ' appear to be remnants of the ancient fauna which walked into New Zealand ', although there is no definite evidence of a land connection.

Mayr (1940) has shown how the birds of the various Polynesian islands have been derived by island-hopping from the landmasses to the west, the islands demonstrating clearly the phenomenon of numerical reduction of species with increased distance from continents. New Guinea has supplied most of the colonists that radiated in the Fijian and Samoan groups, and these islands in turn sent colonists onwards. The New Caledonian fauna seems to have been derived from both New Guinea and Australian sources.

Double Invasions. This stocking of the various parts of the Australasian Region by progressive invasions, originally from the Old World and then into its various components from west to east, has provided many nice examples of the phenomenon of double or even multiple invasions. Only a few examples need be mentioned. Australia is the only area where two species of the genus *Elanus* occur, the older invader having differentiated into the rather striking Letter-winged Kite *E. scriptus*, which has a breeding range (in the arid interior) distinct from that of the later invader, the Black-shouldered

Kite *E. notatus*. The Chestnut-breasted Teal *Anas castanea* represents an earlier invasion of the grey teal group to which *Anas gibberifrons* belongs, and it is now restricted to the more southern parts of Australia. It colonised New Zealand, where it developed into the Brown Teal *A. castanea chlorotis* ; from there it entered the Auckland and Campbell Islands, differentiating into the local flightless races, *A. c. aucklandica* and *A. c. nesiotis*. As a result of the second invasion, the Grey Teal *A. gibberifrons* has generally colonised Australia and is becoming established in New Zealand. There are several instances of double invasions from New Guinea into the Cape York region of Australia, particularly in the honeyeaters (Meliphagidae) ; and a series of them into Tasmania (in the genera *Sericornis, Acanthiza, Pardalotus,* and *Strepera*). Even in Australia itself the intermittent opening and closing of the coastal corridor between the humid areas of south-eastern and south-western Australia has provided opportunities for double invasions into southern Western Australia (in *Malurus* and *Eopsaltria*).

See Plate 31 (colour ; characteristic species).

D.L.S.

Zoogeographical references

Falla, R. A. 1953. The Australian element in the avifauna of New Zealand. Emu 53 : 36–46.

Falla, R. A. 1955. New Zealand bird life past and present. Cawthron Inst. Lecture Ser. 29 : 3–14.

Fleming, C. A. 1957. Trans-Tasman relationships in natural history. *In* Science in New Zealand. Wellington.

Keast, A. 1961. Bird speciation on the Australian continent. Bull. Mus. Comp. Zool. Harvard no. 123 : 307–495.

Mayr, E. 1940. The origin and history of the bird fauna of Polynesia. Proc. 6th Pacific Sci. Congr. 4 : 197–216.

Mayr, E. 1943. The zoogeographical position of the Hawaiian Islands. Condor 45 : 45–48.

Mayr, E. 1944a. Timor and the colonization of Australia by birds. Emu 44 : 113–130.

Mayr, E. 1944b. Wallace's Line in the light of recent zoogeographical studies. Quart. Rev. Biol. 19 : 1–14.

Mayr, E. 1944c. The birds of Timor and Sumba. Bull. Amer. Mus. Nat. Hist. 83 : 123–194.

Mayr, E. 1953. Report of the standing committee on distribution of terrestrial faunas in the inner Pacific. Proc. 7th Pacific Sci. Congr. 4 : 5–11.

Mayr, E. 1953. Fragments of a Papuan ornithogeography. Proc. 7th Pacific Sci. Congr. 4 : 11–19.

Mayr, E. & Amadon, D. 1951. A classification of recent birds. Amer. Mus. Novit. no. 1496 : 1–42.

Mayr, E. & Serventy, D. L. 1944. The number of Australian bird species. Emu 44 : 33–40.

Serventy, D. L. 1960. Geographical distribution of living birds. *In* Marshall, A. J. (ed.). The Biology and Comparative Physiology of Birds vol. 1. New York and London.

Serventy, D. L. & Whittell, H. M. 1962. Handbook of the Birds of Western Australia. 3rd. ed. Perth, W. A.

Stirton, R. A., Tedford, R. H. & Miller, A. H. 1961. Cenozoic stratigraphy and vertebrate palaeontology of the Tirari Desert, South Australia. Rec. South Austral. Mus. 14 : 1–61.

Storr, G. M. 1958. Are marsupials ' second-class ' mammals ? W. A. Naturalist 6 : 179–183.

Stresemann, E. 1939. Die Vögel von Celebes. J. Orn. 87 : 299–425.

Avifaunistic references

Iredale, T. 1956. Birds of New Guinea. 2 vols. Melbourne.

Oliver, W. R. B. 1955. New Zealand Birds. 2nd ed. Wellington.

Mathews, G. M. 1910–27. The Birds of Australia. 12 vols. London.

Mathews, G. M. 1928. The Birds of Norfolk and Lord Howe Islands and the Australasian South Polar Quadrant. London.

Mathews, G. M. 1936. A Supplement to the Birds of Norfolk and Lord Howe Islands to which is added those Birds of New Zealand not figured by Buller. London.

Mayr, E. 1945. Birds of the Southwest Pacific. New York.

North, A. J. 1901–14. Nests and Eggs of Birds found Breeding in Australia and Tasmania. 2 vols. Sydney.

Campbell, A. J. 1901. Nests and Eggs of Australian Birds. Sheffield and Melbourne.

Leach, J. A. 1958. An Australian Bird Book. 9th ed. Melbourne.

Cayley, N. W. 1958. What Bird is That ? 2nd ed. Sydney.

AUSTRINGER: see FALCONRY ; SHAKESPEARE'S BIRDS

AUTECOLOGY: term for the ecology of individuals—contrasted with SYNECOLOGY (see also ECOLOGY).

AUTOCHTHONOUS: applied to species, etc., meaning aboriginally INDIGENOUS.

AUTOLYCISM: term applied by Meinertzhagen to the use that birds make of other species of animals, including other avian species and man, in ways that are not strictly parasitic, commensal, or symbiotic ; in particular the use of man-made buildings as nesting sites and of human activities (agriculture, fisheries) as feeding opportunities, but also a variety of associations between different bird species and between birds and animals of other classes (see CROCODILE-BIRD ; FEEDING HABITS ; HONEYGUIDE ; MAMMALS, ASSOCIATION WITH ; MAN, BIRDS AND ; NESTING ASSOCIATION).

AUTOMOLUS: generic name used as substantive name, alternatively ' foliage-gleaner ', of *Automolus* spp. (see OVENBIRD (1)).

AVADAVAT: substantive name of two Asian *Estrilda* spp. (see WEAVER-FINCH).

AVAILABILITY: of scientific names, see NOMENCLATURE.

AVERAGE: see MEAN, ARITHMETIC ; STATISTICAL SIGNIFICANCE

AVES: plural of the Latin ' avis ' and used as the scientific name of the Class of animals known as birds (see ANIMAL KINGDOM). The common name is, in this instance, as precise as the scientific one (see BIRD). A primary definition may indeed be taken as self-evident ; the category is perfectly distinct in the mind of anyone who has grasped the elementary fact that bats are, and pterosaurs were, animals of quite different sorts. This is because birds possess obvious characteristics that distinguish them easily from all other animals. Moreover, the main characteristics are present in all birds, producing a high degree of resemblance between one kind and another.

The distinctiveness and relative uniformity in the Class are due to its high degree of specialisation. This has separated birds sharply from all other kinds of animal ; and it has at the same time imposed strict limits, within the Class, on the possible extent of divergence from the general type. The specialisation is for flight, and it follows lines of adaptation different from those of other flying animals (see FLIGHT ; WINGS, COMPARATIVE ANATOMY OF). Apart from the flightlessness of nearly all very young birds, it is true that a few species lack the power completely ; but this can be regarded as a secondary loss, incurred after the main line of evolution had been determined, seeing that the associated adaptations are to a great extent retained. Thus, just as flight is the outstanding characteristic of birds in general, so the immediately obvious thing about the exceptions is that they do not fly (see FLIGHTLESSNESS ; RATITES, PHYLOGENY OF THE).

The first essential character in the specialisation of birds for flight is the modification of the forelimbs as wings (see WING). That the wings are in some birds used, also or instead, as swimming organs, and in others have become rudimentary, is merely incidental. The possession of wings, except in some instances where the function has been lost, is associated with a great development of breast muscles and with a keel on the sternum for their attachment (see MUSCULATURE ; SKELETON). It is associated also with a fused rigidity of parts of the skeleton providing a fulcrum, with remarkable lightness in weight, and with a general ' streamlining ' of the body (see PNEUMATISATION OF BONE ; RESPIRATORY SYSTEM ; SHAPE AND POSTURE).

Likewise associated with flight, although also (and perhaps originally) serving other purposes, is the plumage (see FEATHER ; PLUMAGE). This character is unique, as feathers are not found in any other kind of animal and are present in all birds except the very young of some forms (see YOUNG BIRD). Feathers are thus conclusively diagnostic of the Class ; they are present in the earliest known fossil (see ARCHAEOPTERYX).

The modification of the forelimbs for a special purpose has the consequence that birds are necessarily bipedal in their terrestrial stance and locomotion (see SHAPE AND POSTURE ; LOCOMOTION). It likewise throws upon the head, armed with its bill (or beak) and sometimes on an elongated as well as flexible neck, most of the ' manual ' functions performed by the forelimb in many other animals (see BILL) ; only in relatively few birds are the hindlimbs so used to any considerable extent (see FEEDING HABITS ; LEG).

Birds share with mammals alone (at least at the present day) the character of being ' warm-blooded ', which together with an intense metabolism enables the possessor to lead a highly active life in a widely variable environment (see HEAT REGULATION ; METABOLISM). Also correlated with the mode of life of a flying animal are the facts that a bird lays only one egg at a time, thus causing the minimum of change of weight in the gravid female (see LAYING), and that development of the young is usually very rapid, thus reducing the period of vulnerability during which the advantages of being able to fly have not yet been attained (see DEVELOPMENT, EMBRYONIC ; DEVELOPMENT, POSTEMBRYONIC).

The Aves share with some other classes such characters as being chordate, vertebrate, tetrapod (four-limbed), amniote, and (as already mentioned) oviparous (see ANIMAL KINGDOM). In various other respects of form and function, not too greatly involved in the specialisation, they show some general conformity with other vertebrate animals, although the same ends may be achieved in different ways. In complexity of structure and in development of mental functions, the Aves may be said to stand parallel, if not quite level, with the Mammalia at the highest points of evolution. For their descent see ARCHAEOPTERYX ; FOSSIL BIRDS ; ORIGIN OF BIRDS.

Despite the relatively high degree of structural uniformity among birds, as contrasted with other classes, they show great ecological diversity. Birds have indeed exploited every mode of life that is open to them. They are found in every part of the world except the polar wastes (see DISTRIBUTION, GEOGRAPHICAL), and they live in extremes of climate, although sometimes only seasonally (see MIGRATION). They inhabit environments ranging from the oceanic to the montane, from open plains to tropical forest, and from deserts to habitations of mankind (see ECOLOGY). They subsist on a wide variety of vegetable and animal foods, obtained in diverse ways (see FEEDING HABITS). They breed in all sorts of situation, from burrows in the earth to the highest treetops (see NEST). They fly and run, swim and dive (see FLIGHT ; LOCOMOTION ; SWIMMING AND DIVING). They may skulk in hiding, may keep largely to the water, may run boldly in the open, or may soar conspicuously in the sky. They may be solitary or gregarious (see FLOCKING), and they may be silent or noisy, uttering harsh cries, resonant notes, or musical song (see SINGING; also INSTRUMENTAL SOUNDS). Their behaviour has many facets, sometimes including elaborate displays (see DISPLAY). Sometimes, quite small differences in adaptation enable closely related species—or unrelated species of similar mode of life—to inhabit the same area without extreme competition.

With all these variations on the main theme, it is not surprising that categories and kinds of birds have multiplied exceedingly. Apart from birds of the past, known only from the geological record or more recently lost, there are about 8600 species of birds living in the world today. On the classification followed in this work, these are divisible among 27 orders, comprising 154 families (see CLASSIFICATION ; and List of Major Articles on Bird Groups at the beginning of the volume).

See also ORNITHOLOGY.   A.L.T.

(The following is a chronological list of some general works published in the present century, or in the last dozen years of its predecessor ; some of them contain abundant references to earlier sources.)

Fürbringer, M. 1888. Untersuchungen zur Morphologie und Systematik der Vögel, zugleich ein Beitrag zur Anatomie der Stütz- und Bewegungsorgane. 2 vols. Amsterdam.
Gadow, H. F. 1891. Vögel. In Bronn (ed.). Klassen und Ordnungen des Thier-Reichs vol. 6. Leipzig.
Newton, A. (assisted by H. Gadow). 1896. A Dictionary of Birds. London.
Beddard, F. E. 1898. The Structure and Classification of Birds. London.
Pycraft, W. P. 1910. A History of Birds. London.
Thomson, J. A. 1923. The Biology of Birds. London.
Stresemann, E. 1927–34. Aves. In Kükenthal, W. & Krumbach, T. (eds.). Handbuch der Zoologie vol. 7 : pt.2. Berlin.
Groebbels, F. 1932–37. Der Vogel. 2 vols. Berlin.
Grassé, P.-P. et al. 1950. Oiseaux. In Grassé, P.-P. (ed.). Traité de Zoologie vol. 15. Paris.
Wolfson, A. (ed.). 1955. Recent Studies in Avian Biology. Urbana, Ill.
Wing, L. W. 1956. Natural History of Birds : a Guide to Ornithology. New York.
Gilliard, E. T. 1958. Living Birds of the World. London.
Van Tyne, J. & Berger, A. J. 1959. Fundamentals of Ornithology. New York.
Marshall, A. J. (ed.). 1960–61. Biology and Comparative Physiology of Birds. 2 vols. New York and London.
Austin, O. L. 1961. Birds of the World. New York. (London ed. 1962.)

AVIAN: pertaining to birds. The alternative form 'avine', although said to be classically preferable, is little used.

AVIARY: see AVICULTURE

AVICULTURE: term applied to the practice of keeping birds of wild species in aviaries or enclosures, with the object of studying their habits and, if possible, inducing them to breed successfully under conditions as nearly as practicable approaching those found in nature ; an educational purpose is also served when the birds are exhibited to the public in zoological gardens (see also CAGE BIRD). Birds large and small from many parts of the world have been and are being kept, and in many cases bred with complete success ; guarded as they are from the attacks of their natural predators, they attain their full span of life, in some cases far exceeding that normally reached in the wild state (see LONGEVITY).

Under avicultural conditions much has been learnt of the very remarkable and diverse methods adopted by birds of brilliant plumage in the display of their ornamentations during courtship. This applies especially to such as the birds-of-paradise (Paradisaeidae), of which the small and lovely King Bird-of-paradise *Cicinnurus regius* has recently been bred by an aviculturist in Stockholm (see BIRD-OF-PARADISE). The pheasants (Phasianidae) are another brilliant group with very spectacular displays, rarely to be seen in the wild state but readily observable in enclosures (see PHEASANT). Especially noteworthy is the display of the great Argus Pheasant *Argusianus argus*, of the jungles of the Malay Peninsula and the East Indies, which during display hides his head behind his enormous and highly decorated wings.

The strange habits of the tinamous (Tinamidae) of the Neotropical Region, and of the hemipodes or bustard-quails (Turnicidae) which are to be found from Africa and southern Europe east to Australia, have been observed in captivity and consist in the female assuming some of the usual habits of a male in that she courts him by a loud voice and display and leaves to him the incubation of the eggs and rearing of the chicks (see BUTTONQUAIL ; TINAMOU). Analytical studies of behaviour may be made when birds are kept under experimental conditions, e.g. in rearing young birds in isolation from parental or social influences (see SINGING).

By means of aviculture, species which have become nearly extinct have been given a new lease of existence. A case in point is that of the Hawaiian Goose *Branta sandvicensis*, which for years had been rapidly declining in the number left in the wild state. It was decided to take some few into captivity, with the result that a couple of these very handsome birds were sent to the care of the Wildfowl Trust in England with a view to their breeding ; they proved to be both females, each producing a clutch of infertile eggs, but a gander was procured and in the following year young were hatched. From then on these birds have increased in a most encouraging way, and some have been placed in charge of other breeders with very satisfactory results. In 1963, thirteen years after the first breeding at Slimbridge, there were some 210 living descendants, including 30 returned to the wild in Hawaii in 1962 to re-establish the exterminated population on the island of Maui.

The very rare Hawaiian Duck (or Koloa) *Anas platyrhynchos wyvilliana* is another of those forms nearing extinction which the Wildfowl Trust is doing its best to save, with results that appear hopeful. Pheasants, such as the Swinhoe Pheasant *Hierophasis swinhoii* and the Mikado Pheasant *Syrmaticus mikado* from Formosa, and some that have for long been common in captivity, such as the Golden Pheasant *Chrysolophus pictus* and Chinese Silver Pheasant *Gennaeus nycthemerus nycthemerus*, now seem to be existing chiefly as aviary birds.

Steps are being taken in the United States to save such species as the Whooping Crane *Grus americana* and Trumpeter Swan *Cygnus cygnus buccinator*, two of their finest birds, by placing a few of them in enclosures with conditions suitable for their breeding ; it is hoped that by this means, if by no other, they may be saved (see also VANISHING BIRDS).

In Australia some of the beautiful grass parakeets (in the subfamily Psittacinae) have become very scarce owing to the cultivation of land which formerly grew an abundance of wild grasses, the seeds of which formed their principal food (see PARROT). To mention one species only, Bourke's Grass Parakeet *Neophema bourkii* of the Australian interior, which at one time was believed to be practically extinct, is now being bred extensively by aviculturists in Europe and America, especially in the favourable climate of California (where one aviculturist has said that there are now enough to ensure the perpetuation of the species).

As proof of what aviculture can do for the increase of a species one has only to consider the case of the Budgerigar *Melopsittacus undulatus*, although it is not suggested that this is in any danger of extinction in the wild state. It was brought to England by the ornithologist John Gould in 1840 and from the first took very kindly to captivity, thriving so well that in little over a century it has become the most popular of cagebirds and thoroughly domesticated.

While the term 'aviculture' is not generally applied to birds that have long since become domesticated, such as the Canary *Serinus canarius canarius* or tame pigeon (Rock Dove) *Columba livia*, it was through such methods that their present abundance and tameness were attained. There is little doubt that other species which have become extinct, such as the Passenger Pigeon *Ectopistes migratoria* and Carolina Parakeet *Conuropsis carolinensis* of North America—and even the Dodo *Raphus cucullatus* of Mauritius and the Solitaire *Pezophaps solitaria* of Rodriguez—could have been saved if carefully tended in suitable accommodation under the processes of aviculture (see EXTINCT BIRDS).

†D.S.-S.

Avicultural Magazine 1894 et seq. (Bimonthly journal of the Avicultural Society.)
Boosey, E. 1956. Foreign Bird Keeping. London.
Johnson, A. A. & Payn, W. H. 1957. Ornamental Waterfowl : a guide to their care and breeding. London.

AVIFAUNA : the bird-life of an area.

AVOCET : substantive name of species in one genus of Recurvirostridae (Charadriiformes, suborder Charadrii) ; used without qualification for *Recurvirostra avosetta* ; in the form 'avocets and stilts', general term for the family. This almost cosmopolitan group comprises four avocets *Recurvirostra* spp. and three species in monotypic genera —the Stilt *Himantopus himantopus* (the several races having different adjectival English names), the Banded (or Redbreasted) Stilt *Cladorhynchus leucocephala* and the Ibisbill *Ibidorhyncha struthersii*.

Avocets and stilts are long-legged, long-billed wading birds of moderate size (11½–19 inches in length, including bill). Avocets have strongly recurved, slender, awl-like bills ; stilts have slender bills which are almost straight (slightly up-tilted) ; while the Ibisbill has a strongly decurved bill, and also much shorter legs than the other members of the family. The legs of stilts are longer in proportion to the remainder of the body than in any other birds except flamingos (Phoenicopteridae). In general, the feet have slight or larger webs (small lobes in the Ibisbill) and the hind toe is rudimentary or absent. The head is small and the neck rather long ; the wings are long and pointed ; the tail is short and square.

In colour, most species show a pattern of black and white, but some have patches of tan to chestnut on some part of the head, neck, or breast ; the Ibisbill is peculiar in having the upper parts grey (with a black facial mask and black breast-band). The bill is dark in most, but red in the Ibisbill ; the legs of avocets are of a slaty colour, those of the

Stilt some tone of red (according to race, age, and season) ; and in the Stilt the bright red iris is noticeable under good conditions. Throughout the family, the sexes are either alike or little different. Immature birds tend to have some brown in the plumage. The usual calls are clear yelping notes.

Avocet *Recurvirostra avosetta*, the Palaearctic and African species. *C.E.T.K.*

Behaviour. Avocets and stilts frequent shallow lakes, marshes, and pools. Stilts, although found at the edges of large brackish or salty lakes, appear more commonly than avocets in freshwater areas and flooded marshlands, especially open and more or less weedy shallows with floating weeds and tussocks of rush, sometimes with fairly deep mud ; occasionally they are found by streams and rivers. They walk gracefully with long strides which quicken almost to a run. In water they wade to above the intertarsal joint, even belly-deep in soft mud, and pick up insects from the surface and from floating vegetation. In deepish water or mud they lift their legs very high. To pick up food from the ground they have to flex their legs quite appreciably. The Banded Stilt has habits similar to those of *Himantopus* and is a bird of salt marshes.

The Avocet of the Palaearctic breeds in much more saline areas near the coast, river deltas, muddy flats and lagoons, and salt marshes, although in some parts of the breeding areas in the Netherlands the salinity of the water is quite low ; in the feeding zones where there is little vegetation they catch their food by a side-to-side sweep of the bill through the surface slime exposed by the receding tide or two or three inches below the surface. In deep water they put their heads beneath the surface and 'up-end'. Avocets will peck at insects on the surface of the water. Both adults and young (a few hours old) can swim quite freely. In flight the neck is slightly extended and the long legs trail behind the tail. They are frequently seen in flocks.

The other avocets have similar habits, but the Chilean species lives at high altitudes.

The Ibisbill differs from other members of the family not only in its down-curved bill but in its habitat, which consists of shingly islands in rivers on the high plateaux of central Asia. It searches for its food, sometimes wading up to its breast, by probing under the rounded stones, for which purpose its decurved bill is admirably suited.

The Black-winged Stilt usually nests in colonies near or in shallow lagoons or on flooded areas near rivers. Some nests are substantial, built up of stalks and mud from the bottom of the water, but when built on tussocks the nests may be slight. The clutch usually consists of four ovate eggs, but sometimes three or five may be laid. The ground colour is clay with black spots and irregular blotches and a few ashy shell marks. The eggs are laid from April to June, and both parents incubate for a period of 25–26 days. The downy young leave the nest soon after hatching. A single brood is reared in a season.

Avocets usually nest in colonies ; the following details refer more particularly to *R. avosetta*. The nests are sometimes as little as two feet apart on muddy or sandy flats and islands, with or without scrub patches under which the young hide when alarmed. In sandy areas no nest material is used, but on muddy islands dead vegetation is placed in the scrape and the nest is built almost in process of the display. It increases in bulk throughout the incubation period, particularly when high water threatens the site.

The Avocet has many forms of display. Coition is preceded by a rather elaborate ceremonial. The female crouches with her neck outstretched and lowered so that her chin and bill are only just above water level. The male preens constantly, walking from one side to the other of the female, gradually getting closer until he brushes up against her tail as he passes. Eventually he jumps on the female's back. After coition the male jumps off and leaves one wing stretched over the female's back as both birds run forward with bills crossed. After a few paces their paths diverge.

There are other displays, in one of which up to a dozen birds may perform. This is in some ways similar to the ' piping ' display of the Oystercatcher

Haematopus ostralegus in that the bills are pointing, although not vertically, to the ground and the birds are grouped. This display often leads to wing-fighting in which the birds stand side by side and edge towards one another and then strike each other with the wing, often rising in the air to administer a blow. Bills are very rarely used to stab but only to grasp ; trespassing young chicks are shaken to death.

Normally four, but sometimes any number between two and eight, eggs are laid from the latter half of April but mostly in the second week of May. Although Avocets are single-brooded, replacement clutches are laid after the loss of eggs or young. The egg is ovate in shape and the ground colour is clay-buff, spotted irregularly, but not as a rule heavily, with black and a few shell marks. Both parents have incubation patches and share in brooding. The incubation period is about 22–24 days. The young fend for themselves from hatching, at first tended by their parents and becoming finally independent of these when about ten weeks old. O. Heinroth estimates that fledging is completed in six weeks.

Distribution. The Avocet *R. avosetta* is a Palaearctic and Ethiopian species which breeds on the coasts of the North Sea and Baltic. It also breeds around the Mediterranean and from the Caspian Sea eastwards to northern China and as far south as Iraq and Baluchistan. Northern birds winter in Africa and southern Asia. The Avocet had ceased to breed in the British Isles for nearly a century (last nests 1837 and 1842) until two pairs bred in Ireland in 1938. Then in 1947 four pairs bred at Minsmere and four pairs on Havergate Island, both localities in Suffolk. The latter site was bought by the Royal Society for the Protection of Birds, and the colony increased to about 90 pairs in 1957. Outside this colony at Havergate, single pairs have attempted to breed on Buss Creek, Suffolk, in 1954, and a pair successfully reared young in Kent in 1958 and another at Minsmere again in 1963. Some Avocets winter in the west of England and sometimes in South Wales.

The American Avocet *R. americana* is a slightly larger bird with a suffusion of cinnamon colour on head and neck in the breeding season ; it breeds as far north as southern Canada and reaches Central America in winter. The Chilean Avocet *R. andina*, darker above than its congeners, frequents saline lagoons in the Andes. The Red-necked Avocet *R. novaehollandiae*, in which the head and neck are reddish brown, belongs to Australia and has occurred occasionally in New Zealand.

The Stilt *Himantopus himantopus* is an almost

cosmopolitan species of which five geographical races (by some authors granted specific rank) are recognised. The Black-winged Stilt *H. h. himantopus*, with white head and neck, breeds in the southern Palaearctic, from the Mediterranean area east to China, and also throughout much of southern Asia, Africa, and Madagascar ; it has bred irregularly in the Netherlands and Belgium and is an occasional visitor to the British Isles (two pairs breeding in Nottinghamshire in 1945). The Black-necked Stilt *H. h. mexicanus*, in which the crown and hind neck are dark (continuously with the back), breeds from southern North America to northern South America, including the West Indies and the Galápagos Islands. The White-headed (or Pied) Stilt *H. h. leucocephalus* is the representative form in Australasia ; melanistic as well as black and white birds are found in New Zealand. Other races are found in the middle latitudes of South America and in Hawaii. The so-called Black Stilt *H. ' novaezeelandiae '* of New Zealand probably consists of melanistic mutants, and intermediates occur.

The quite distinct Banded (or Red-breasted) Stilt *Cladorhynchus leucocephala*, with a chest-band of bright chestnut and yellowish legs, is confined to Australia. There it breeds beside salt lakes in the interior, feeding on the shrimps which multiply when these temporary waters form. The colonies are often very large but tend to shift their locations,

and for long no site was known. The eggs have been described as chalky and the downy young as pure white.

The Ibisbill *Ibidorhyncha struthersii* is found on the high plateaux of central Asia, from Turkestan to Kashmir and northern Burma. In winter it comes down almost to plains level in the Himalayan foothills.

See Plate 27b (phot. ; Avocets). J.P.C.

McGilp, J. N. & Morgan, A. M. 1931. The nesting of the Banded Stilt (*Cladorhynchus leucocephalus*). S. Australian Orn. 11 : 37–52.

Makkink, G. F. 1936. An attempt at an ethogram of the European Avocet (*Recurvirostra avosetta* L.). Ardea 25 : 1–62.

Jones, J. 1945. The Banded Stilt. Emu 45 : 1–36, 110–118.

AXIAL SKELETON: the part of the skeleton consisting of the skull, vertebral column, ribs, and sternum ; contrasted with the APPENDICULAR SKELETON (see also SKELETON).

AXILLARIES: (plural) the feathers in the axilla (' armpit ')—see TOPOGRAPHY.

AXIS: the second vertebra, immediately posterior to the atlas (see SKELETON).

AYTHYINI: see DUCK

AZURECROWN: substantive name of some *Amazilia* spp. (for family see HUMMINGBIRD).

B

BABBLER: substantive name of many species of the subfamily Timaliinae of the Muscicapidae (Passeriformes, suborder Oscines) ; in the plural, general term for the subfamily. (The name has also been applied to some Rhinocryptidae—see TAPACULO.) In fact, the Old World insect-eaters assembled under the general name of 'babblers' belong to different groups that are a little more closely related to one another than they are to others. They have sometimes, particularly in the past, been considered as making up a family, Timaliidae ; but they are better considered as a subfamily of the large family of the Old World insect-eaters, Muscicapidae, which includes also the thrushes (Turdinae), the flycatchers (Muscicapinae), the warblers (Sylviinae), and others. It is to the warblers that they are the nearest ; some forms are intermediate and therefore difficult to attribute to one or the other subfamily (*Oxylabes*, *Megalurulus*, *Ortygocichla*). (For taxonomy see Delacour 1946.)

General Characteristics. Babblers have characteristically short, rounded wings and are poor flyers. They are thick in shape ; the tail, often fairly long, hangs loosely, and the folded wings

Blackcap Babbler *Turdoides reinwardii*, of West Africa. *C.E.T.K.*

are not held close to the body. The birds move restlessly through branches and on the ground, jumping about and digging among dead leaves. The bill and legs are strong. The birds live usually in the undergrowth, sometimes on the ground, among thick underbrush, fallen branches, ascending vines, and evergreen trees ; there they may be observed searching for berries and insects with brusque movements and much fluttering of wings and tail, the while emitting noisy calls. They possess, as a rule, a loud and varied voice, to which they owe their name, as they use it constantly ; some even sing very well, having full, ringing notes. They generally keep to thick woods, forests, bushes, and tall grass, most species seldom entering gardens and orchards. Except during the breeding season, they go in small flocks, often mixing with other birds and forming those composite hunting parties so characteristic of tropical jungles.

Unlike their relatives the thrushes and the flycatchers, young babblers in their first plumage are never spotted ; neither are they yellowish like young warblers. Many of the species are brightly garbed and elegantly marked, showing in certain cases beautiful shades of crimson, yellow, or green, but seldom any metallic colours. There are also many more or less plain brown birds among them. See also FEATHER MAINTENANCE.

The majority of the babblers make large cup-shaped nests, but a number build domed structures ; most of the nests are placed on trees and bushes, some on the ground and in clumps of grass. The eggs vary much in colour, some being plain white or blue, while others are spotted and blotched.

Distribution. Babblers belong to the Old World, their ecological niche being occupied in the Americas by the antbirds (Formicariidae), structurally very different but having generally similar habits and aspect, a curious case of convergence. The babblers are found abundantly throughout the Oriental Region, including China and the Philippines, and they extend to the Celebes, New Guinea, Australia,

Africa, and Madagascar ; and if *Chamaea* be included, that gives the group a representative in the New World.

At least six tribes can be recognised ; the jungle babblers (Pellorneini), the scimitar babblers and wren-babblers (Pomatorhinini), the tit-babblers (Timaliini), the Wren-tit and allies (Chamaeini—if not part of the Panurini, see below), the song babblers (Turdoidini), and the rockfowl (Picathartini). Some authors would add the rail-babblers although the present writer prefers to regard these as a separate subfamily (Cinclosomatinae) of the Musci-capidae, and they are here given an article of their own (see RAIL-BABBLER). On the other hand, the writer would include the reedlings (Panurini), and with them the parrotbills and the Wren-tit *Chamaea fasciata*, but in the classification followed in this work the reedlings and parrotbills are assigned to the subfamily Paradoxornithinae (see PARROTBILL).

Jungle Babblers. The tribe Pellorneini is com-posed of babblers that live near the ground in the forest undergrowth, always under cover. They build ball-like nests and their eggs are spotted. They feed mostly on insects and usually remain silent. Both sexes are alike and never show bright colours ; they are mostly plain brown, almost white below, or slightly marked with chestnut, grey, and black. The bill is rather slender, but often hooked at the tip. They resemble in appearance small robins *Erithacus* spp. and warblers (Sylviinae). They are found in both the Oriental and the Ethiopian Regions, and are particularly numerous in Malaysia, reaching the Celebes and the Philippines. Because of their sombre plumage and skulking habits, they are not easy to observe or to identify. There are five distinct genera ; *Pellorneum*, uniform brown above, nearly white and sometimes spotted under-neath, with a slender bill, long legs, and a short tail ; *Trichastoma*, similar, but coarser and with a thicker bill ; *Ptyrticus* (monotypic—the Thrush-babbler *P. turdinus*, an African species), spotted on the breast ; *Malacopteron*, with longer tail and wings, shorter legs, and a hooked bill, and living mostly on the branches of low trees and bushes ; and *Leonardina*, a plain brown, thrush-like bird of the Philippines, where it is very rare.

Scimitar Babblers and Wren-babblers. Al-though the babblers included in the tribe Pomator-hinini form two quite different-looking groups, if the extremes are considered, they are linked by intermediates in a way that shows their true close relationship. They are generally ground-dwelling birds that live under low bushes or piles of dead wood and in long grass, less often on low trees and creepers. They are insectivorous and feed mostly on

the ground, turning up dead leaves with their bills, in search of insects and worms. A few sing very well. They build covered, ball-like nests on or close to the ground ; the eggs are pure white, seldom slightly spotted. Their plumage is brown, more or less strongly marked and streaked with white, black, grey, chestnut, or some shade of red ; the sexes are alike. They live in pairs or family groups. Like the jungle babblers, they are shy and hard to detect among the vegetation, or among the rocks to which they are partial. They are found in the Oriental Region, including the Philippines, and in New Guinea and Australia. There are 11 genera and 28 species, some with many subspecies.

The scimitar babblers have long, curved bills and moderately long tails, while the wren-babblers have short tails and almost straight, fairly short bills ; but two genera link them perfectly. The Australian and New Guinean scimitar babblers *Pomatostomus* spp. appear a little less specialised and have a thicker bill than those of the Oriental Region (*Pomatorhinus*), and they differ furthermore in their living and nesting habits ; the Himalayan and Yunnanese *Xiphirynchus* has the longest, thinnest, and most curved bill of all. Nearly all have well-marked and varied plumage and frequent the ground, but also bushes, creepers, and long grass.

Danjou's Babbler *Jabouilleia danjoui* has a relatively short bill and tail ; it lives in the hills of Indochina, where it is very rare. The Long-billed Wren-babbler *Rimator malacoptilus* of the Himalaya and neighbouring mountains has the long, curved bill of the scimitar babblers, but the very short tail and streaked, long feathers of the wren-babblers, thus linking the two groups. The wren-babblers proper consist of the genera *Ptilocichla*, from Borneo, Palawan, and the Philippines, with long lanceolated feathers (3 species) ; the monotypic *Kenopia* from Malaysia, a short-billed, streaked bird ; *Napothera*, from India, Indochina, and Malaysia, with long legs and brown plumage mottled and streaked with buff and black, the five species differing much in size ; *Microura* (2 species), with a weak bill and almost tailless, and *Spelaeornis*, both very small wren-like birds from the Himalaya, the mountains to the east, and Malaysia ; and *Sphenocichla*, a curious, larger bird from the Himalaya, with a sharp conical bill and a longer tail.

Tit-babblers. The tribe Timaliini is composed of 6 genera and 35 species of small birds with rather short, pointed bills, and with tails of moderate length. The plumage is soft and fluffy, with the feathers of the back long and sometimes disinte-grated ; brown, chestnut, grey, yellow, white, and black are the dominant colours, often forming pretty patterns ; the sexes are similar. They live on trees, or more often in bushes, bamboos, tall grass, and reeds, and seldom come to the ground ; the eggs are slightly spotted. They inhabit the Oriental Region and Madagascar.

The Madagascar jerys *Neomixis* spp. consist of 4 species of very small birds, yellowish olive, with thin, pointed bills much like that of *Stachyris* ; they are very similar to the smaller species of that genus. The tree babblers form the large genus *Stachyris* (24 species) ; they vary much in colour and size and inhabit the Oriental Region, being particularly numerous in Malaysia and the Philippines.

The two Indian monotypic genera *Dumetia* (Rufous-bellied Babbler *D. hyperythra*) and *Rhopocichla* (Black-headed Babbler *R. atriceps*) are mostly brown and have open nostrils, like the true titbabblers *Macronus* (including ' *Mixornis* '), the four species of which have the bill a little depressed near the base and very long feathers on the back. One species (*M. gularis*) has many local subspecies throughout most of the range of the tribe ; another one is peculiar to the Philippines (*M. striaticeps*). The Redcapped Babbler *Timalia pileata* (various races) lives in the high cane grass, from India to southern China and Indochina, reappearing in Java. It has a longer and broader tail and a higher bill ; it forms a link with the next tribe, being nearly related to *Chrysomma*.

Wren-tit and Allies. This tribe becomes ' Chamaeini ' by the removal to another subfamily, in the classification adopted for this work as a whole, of the other elements that in the present writer's view constitute the Panurini. The Wrentit *Chamaea fasciata*, in a monotypic genus, is a bird of much disputed affinities and has sometimes been placed in a family of its own, but the consensus of current opinion puts it among the babblers. This has the effect of extending the range of that group to the New World, the Wren-tit being an inhabitant of the Pacific coast of North America from Oregon to Baja California. It is a mainly brown bird, with a fluffy plumage and a long tail that brings the total length to about $6\frac{1}{2}$ inches ; it frequents low scrub and has harsh call-notes and a loud song. It very closely resembles, in shape and colour, the Rufous-crowned Babbler *Chrysomma* (' *Moupinia* ') *poecilotis* of western China, itself very similar to Jerdon's Babbler *C. altirostre* of India ; the widespread Oriental Golden-eyed Babbler *C. sinense* has a rather high bill and white under parts. These *Chrysomma* spp. may be the nearest relatives of *Chamaea*.

The Song Babblers. The tribe Turdoidini is the largest, with 17 genera and 140 species distributed throughout Africa and southern Asia ; it includes all the more brightly coloured forms, as well as the best songsters of the family, the voice being loud, full, and melodious in the majority of them. All hues are represented among the members of the tribe, and the pattern is often striking. The sexes are alike in most species, but more or less different in a few. The bill, legs, and feet are strong ; the wing is rounded and held loosely, and it is often adorned with beautiful colours ; the tail is broad, moderate to very long, usually held hanging between the wings. Many are adapted to an arboreal life, although they often feed on the ground. They are noisy, and their calls and songs are abrupt, like their actions. They have a peculiar way of jumping around, of moving brusquely and of making jerky, short flights from limb to ground and back. They go about in flocks, often associated with other birds, and they always keep to the cover of brush, creepers, and trees, usually in woods and forests ; only a few come to savannas and gardens, then keeping to thickets and hedges. They feed on berries and insects. Their nests are cup-shaped, with rare exceptions, and placed on low trees, in bushes and creepers ; only a few build on the ground or in holes, making covered nests of moss and grass. Their eggs are either a uniform blue, or white and lightly spotted. They are the most specialised birds of the subfamily, and they live mostly in tropical and eastern Asia, Malaysia, and Africa, one species extending to North Africa, Asia Minor, and Arabia.

The most primitive genus is *Turdoides*. These birds are uniform brown or streaked, fairly large, with a long, sometimes pointed, tail, and the bill slightly curved. They inhabit the scrub of rather dry countries. There are 26 species, the ' Seven Sisters ' (or Jungle Babbler) *T. somervillei* of India and the fulvous babblers of North Africa being the best known of them. The two species of *Babax* are similar in their curved bill and streaked plumage, but their pattern is more elaborate. See Plate 46b (phot.).

Babax constitutes a link with the laughing thrushes (or ' jay-thrushes ') *Garrulax* spp., a large genus of some 50 species, with thicker, straighter bills and more elaborate plumage. All the laughing thrushes are of fairly large size, and some are crested. They live in moister country, and most of them are found only in forests. Many are brown with black, chestnut, grey, and white markings, but some are beautifully adorned with yellow, crimson, or olive green on the wings and tail. They have a loud, full voice, and a few sing very well, particularly the Hwamei *G. canorus* and the White-cheeked Jay-thrush *G. chinensis*, which are highly regarded as cage birds in China.

The three species of laughing thrushes in the genus *Liocichla*, found in the Himalaya, northern Indochina, western China, and Formosa, are smaller and lighter in build and are brightly coloured in red, yellow, or green, particularly on the face and wings. The two species of *Leiothrix* are closely related but smaller. One is very well known in captivity as the Pekin Robin *L. lutea*, olive green with red and yellow markings on the wings ; it lives in the Himalayas and southern China. The Silver-eared Mesia *L. argentauris* is more southern in range and has a black head ; the sexes differ slightly. The pretty, very small, fire-tailed *Myzornis pyrrhoura*, green and black, belongs to the Himalaya. One species of *Cutia* and five of *Pteruthius*, with a rather short tail and a varied plumage of black, white, grey, yellow, chestnut, and slaty blue, are found in the hill forests of India, Indochina, and Malaysia ; the *Pteruthius* spp. have short, thick, hooked bills. The sexes are different.

The White-headed Babbler (*Gampsorhynchus*) resembles a small laughing thrush, but has a strongly hooked bill ; it is light brown, with a white head. It is mostly arboreal, as are the small sivas *Minla* spp. The latter have a weak bill and a fairly long tail, and their colours are bright and varied, one of the four species having blue on the wings and tail, another yellow and pink. The sexes are alike or slightly different. The crested babblers *Yuhina* spp. are closely related, some very small, with a shorter tail ; the head has a full crest, and their main colours are brown and grey with pretty black, white, or chestnut markings. The last three genera inhabit the forests of the Oriental Region. The nun babblers *Alcippe* spp. are small, or very small, and have a shorter bill, 14 species being found in the Oriental Region and 3 in Africa ; many show discreet tones of brown and grey, while others are brilliantly marked with chestnut, yellow, white, and black.

The African genera *Lioptilus* (5 species) and *Phyllanthus* (monotypic—the Capuchin Babbler *P. atripennis*) are larger, particularly the latter, with a showy pattern but without brilliant colours. They are close relatives of the Oriental sibias *Heterophasia* (7 spp.) and *Crocias* (2 spp.), and are of moderate size ; the tail can be very long (in one species), and the bill is slightly curved. They are very elegantly dressed in grey, black, white, and chestnut. Their habits are arboreal, and they feed on the nectar and pollen of flowers as well as on berries and insects.

Rockfowl. The West African Picathartini are probably large and specialised babblers, not very distant from the laughing thrushes ; they have also been called ' bald crows ' and by other names. The two species differ particularly in the coloration of the skin of the bare head. They have a large and coarse bill and legs and loose, rounded wings and tail. They are babbler-like in their actions and general behaviour. The Grey-necked Rockfowl *Picathartes gymnocephalus* (with bright yellow on the bald head) is known from Sierra Leone, Ghana, and Togo, and the White-necked Rockfowl *P. oreas* (with pink head) from Cameroons. A nesting group of the latter was found among immense rocks in the depths of hill forest ; the nests were cups of mud applied to vertical faces (under overhangs) or in fissures in the rock. The birds feed on insects and amphibians obtained on the ground, particularly near forest streams, where they proceed by very long hops.

See Plates 30 (colour) and 43 (egg). J.D.

Delacour, J. 1946. Les timaliinés. Oiseau 16 : 14–31.
Delacour, J. & Amadon, D. 1951. The systematic position of *Picathartes*. Ibis 93 : 60–62.
Erickson, M. M. 1938. Territory, annual cycle, and numbers in a population of wren-tits (*Chamaea fasciata*). Univ. Calif. Publ. Zool. 42 : 247–333.

BABBLER, RAIL : see RAIL–BABBLER

BACK : see TOPOGRAPHY

BALAENICIPITES ; BALAENICIPITIDAE : see under CICONIIFORMES ; and SHOEBILL

BALANCE : see HEARING AND BALANCE

BALDPATE : a name for the American Wigeon *Anas americana* (see DUCK).

BALEARICINAE : see CRANE

BANANAQUIT : *Coereba flaveola* ; may also be used for related species (see HONEYCREEPER (1)).

BANDING : see RINGING

BANTAM : a miniature breed of domestic fowl.

BARB : alternatively ' ramus ', a lateral branch of the rachis of a feather, i.e. a constituent unit of the vane (see FEATHER).

BARBET : substantive name of the species of Capitonidae (Piciformes, suborder Galbulae) ; in the plural, general term for the family. The name comes from the tufts of feathers around the nostrils, and from the rictal and chin bristles that are well developed in most species. The barbets are strongly built, small birds ($3\frac{1}{2}$ to 12 inches in length), with large heads and stocky bodies. The bill is stout, heavy, and conical, with a sharp tip. The wings are rather short and rounded. The flight is weak, although swift for short distances. The tarsi are short and the zygodactyl feet show four well developed toes with broad soles. The rather sparse, coarse plumage is often brightly coloured, in some species even gorgeously multicoloured. The head and foreparts of many Asian barbets are adorned by the vivid juxtaposition of red, yellow, blue, and white areas. The sexes are alike in most species.

Spot-crowned Barbet *Capito maculicoronatus*, of Central America. *C.E.T.K.*

Most of the barbets live singly or in pairs, Strictly arboreal, they are primarily forest birds, spreading into cultivated areas that are still well timbered. They frequent the tops of trees, where occasionally they may be very active but more often spend the time perched motionless on branches. Some of them are able to climb up tree trunks like woodpeckers (Picidae). Primarily vegetarian, they feed chiefly on fruits, berries, and seeds ; but in some cases they relish a mixed diet of vegetable food and insects, and a few species indeed are mainly insectivorous and hunt their prey on tree trunks and branches or among the leaves.

Most barbets utter a succession of monotonously repeated, single notes, often harsh and shrill ; there are also clear cheery whistling calls. One of the Asian species, *Megalaima haemacephala*, has been given the common name of Coppersmith on account of its metallic note. In some barbets ' duetting ' has been noted.

Barbets nest in holes, usually excavated by themselves in decaying trees but sometimes in sandbanks. The female lays 2–5 rounded eggs, pure glossy white, which are incubated by both parents. The young remain in the nest for some time. A few species nest in small colonies. African barbets are among the most frequent foster-parent victims of the parasitic honeyguides (Indicatoridae).

Barbets are among the truly typical birds of the tropical forests of most of the world, where they are sedentary. They are not found in the

Antilles or Madagascar, nor in Australasia eastwards from Borneo and Bali. America, Africa, and Asia all have their own various species of barbets peculiar to each continent. They have reached their highest diversity of speciation in Africa and Asia, with several well-defined genera ; there are fewer species in the American tropics, constituting only two genera.

As a whole, the family comprises 13 genera and 76 species. Barbets are somewhat intermediate between typical Piciformes (e.g. Picidae) and certain Coraciiformes (Alcedinidae, Coraciidae, etc.), as confirmed by several anatomical and biological characteristics. Some authors include them in one family with the honeyguides (Indicatoridae) and the puffbirds (Bucconidae). They certainly constitute an ancient group, probably originating in the Old World.

The American species are the most brilliant of all the barbets ; their bristles are generally less developed than those of the Old World species ; some species show a strong sexual dimorphism. These Neotropical birds typically live in dense forests. The biology of the Prong-billed Barbet *Semnornis frantzii* has been thoroughly studied by Skutch. It is largely vegetarian, eating fruits, berries, and even the petals of flowers. During the non-breeding season, it gathers in small, noisy flocks, foraging about through the forest and spending the nights in ' dormitories ', such as woodpecker holes, that sometimes contain as many as sixteen individuals. According to Skutch, Salvin's Barbet *Eubucco bourcieri salvini* is very different in its habits, being solitary, silent, and insectivorous ; it seeks its food among the trees, giving special attention to curled-up dead leaves where insects are plentiful.

Except for a few of the more specialised types, all Asian barbets belong to the genus *Megalaima*. Some of them are brightly coloured, such as the Gaudy Barbet *M. mystacophanes* of Malaya and the Blue-throated Barbet *M. asiatica*, a common bird in India. Others are duller, such as the Green (or Brownheaded) Barbet *M. zeylanica*, which is plain green and brown. The Fire-tufted Barbet *Psilopogon pyrolophus* of Malaya and Sumatra has branching loral bristles that are red instead of the usual black. See Plate 4b (phot.).

The barbets are more abundant in Africa than in any other part of the world. Some of them are well adapted to live in savanna country, especially in the acacia-park areas and even in the semi-arid belt, where they nest in dead trees or in the candelabra *Euphorbia* ; notable examples are the Bearded Barbet *Lybius dubius* of West Africa and the Pied Barbet *L. leucocephalus* of central and eastern Africa.

These birds are characterised by a strong bill, the upper mandible of which is indented by grooves and 'teeth' along the cutting edge. Their plumage is mainly black and white, with scarlet areas on throat or belly. On the other hand, some tinker-birds *Pogoniulus* spp.—the smallest of all barbets (averaging the size of a Goldcrest *Regulus regulus*)—are forest birds. This is true also of *Gymnobucco* spp., easily recognised by their dull plumage of pure dark brown. In some of them, such as the Naked-faced Barbet *G. calvus*, the entire crown and face are naked. All of these are noisy birds, often fighting one another and moving about in flocks ; they live in small colonies of 4–12 pairs, and nest in holes in dead trees.

The Yellow-breasted Barbet *Trachyphonus margaritatus*, characterised by its peculiar colour pattern and spotted upper parts, is a bird of the arid belt of northern tropical Africa, distributed from the Aïr and the extreme north of Nigeria eastwards to the Red Sea coast. It nests in burrows excavated in the soft earth of steep banks, mainly along the borders of the wadis. It has 3 congeners.

J.D. (2)

Marshall, C. H. T. & G. F. L. 1871. A Monograph of the Capitonidae. London.
Ripley, S. D. 1945. The barbets. Auk 62 : 542–563.
Skutch, A. F. 1944. The life-history of the Prong-billed Barbet. Auk 61 : 61–88.

BARBICEL: a process on a barbule (radius) of a barb (ramus) of a feather ; the hooked barbicels on the distal side of a barbule engage with the spoon-shaped proximal barbicels of the next barbule, thus maintaining the coherence of the vane (see FEATHER).

BARBTAIL: *Premnoplex brunnescens* (see OVENBIRD (1)).

BARBTHROAT: substantive name (sometimes 'hermit') of *Threnetes* spp. (for family see HUMMINGBIRD).

BARBULE: alternatively 'radius', a lateral branch of a barb (ramus)—see FEATHER.

BARE-EYE: substantive name of *Phlegopsis* spp. (see ANTBIRD).

BARRANCOLINO: *Teledromas fuscus* (see TAPACULO).

BARRIER : see DISTRIBUTION, GEOGRAPHICAL ; HYBRIDISATION, ZONE OF SECONDARY ; REPRODUCTIVE ISOLATION ; SPECIATION

BARWING: substantive name of *Actinodura* spp. (for subfamily see BABBLER).

BASIC PLUMAGE: see under MOULT

BASIOCCIPITAL: a paired bone of the skull (see SKELETON).

BASISPHENOID: a paired bone of the skull (see SKELETON).

BASSIAN: see AUSTRALASIAN REGION

BASTARD WING: the alula (see WING).

BATELEUR: *Terathopius ecaudatus*, an aberrant African harrier-eagle (see HAWK).

BATESIAN MIMICRY: see MIMICRY ; COLORATION, ADAPTIVE

BAT-HAWK: *Machaerhamphus alcinus* (see HAWK).

BATHING: see FEATHER MAINTENANCE

BATING: term used in FALCONRY.

BAYA: name sometimes used alone for the Baya Weaver *Ploceus philippinus* of India and elsewhere (see WEAVER).

BAZA: substantive name of Asiatic *Aviceda* spp. (see HAWK).

BEAK: synonymous with BILL.

BEAUFORT SCALE: see METEOROLOGY

BECARD: substantive name of species of *Pachyramphus* and *Platypsaris* (see COTINGA).

BECCAFICO: a familiar Italian name ('fig-eater') applied almost indiscriminately to small passerine birds frequenting gardens in autumn and often caught for the table—perhaps particularly Garden Warbler *Sylvia borin* (see WARBLER (1)).

BEE-EATER: substantive name of all species of Meropidae (Coraciiformes, suborder Meropes) ; in the plural, general term for the family. It is an entirely Old World group, and predominantly Afro-Asian and tropical. Despite some diversity in size (6–14 inches in length) and much in colour, it is a homogeneous family showing adaptation to a common mode of life. The birds are insectivorous, bees and wasps being largely taken ; the prey is caught in the air, either in the course of continuous hawking or during short flights from a perch—but *Merops apiaster* has been recorded as plunging into water for food. Except in their nesting habits they are arboreal, but telegraph wires now provide a favourite substitute for branches in many instances, and some of the smaller species frequent quite low bushes ; some species inhabiting open country will perch on the backs of moving animals, including bustards (Otididae).

The bill of the adult is characteristic—rather long,

slender, laterally compressed and decurved to a sharp point. The small feet are syndactyl. The wings are long and pointed, adapted to a buoyant, wheeling flight. The tail is long, sometimes with the central pair of rectrices slightly or greatly elongated beyond the others, sometimes square or nearly so at the end, and in one species strongly forked.

The plumage has usually an all-over pattern of bright colours, and in the few exceptions there are at least bright patches ; the sexes are alike or closely similar. Green is often the predominant colour, but yellow, blue, and red of various shades are also frequent components of the pattern ; white patches occur, and a bold black stripe running back from the base of the bill through the eye is a usual feature.

Most species are gregarious, and some perform mass evolutions in the air. Trilling calls are often uttered in flight ; other notes have been described as chirps, whistles, and croaks. Most species are likewise colonial in their breeding habits. The nest is a burrow, usually several feet in length and often with a bend in it ; the terminal chamber is unlined. This burrow is excavated more or less horizontally in a bank, often of a river, or sometimes in level ground. The eggs number 2–5 or more and are pure white. The young are naked at hatching and remain in the nest until fledged in a plumage not unlike that of the adult. Both parents take part in excavating the nest, incubating the eggs, and caring for the young.

Altogether, bee-eaters are most attractive birds, not only for their bright colours and graceful flight, but also because they are easy to approach and show little fear of man. Their numbers, too, are often spectacular—hundreds and even thousands of birds in some cases—whether at their nesting colonies, or wheeling, fluttering, and gliding over some tropical river, or in attendance at a grass-fire.

The family is restricted to the tropical and milder temperate parts of the Old World ; it is not represented in New Zealand. The birds breeding in temperate areas are migratory, wintering in the tropics ; and some of the purely tropical species also perform migrations. The 24 species, some with several subspecific forms, are assigned to 7 genera, 3 of which are monotypic. One genus and 2 of its species are widespread within the range of the family ; 4 genera and 15 species are purely African ; 2 genera and 6 species are purely Asian ; one species is native to Australia. Some are birds of relatively open country and others of forest ; the vicinity of water is favoured by many.

The largest and most widely distributed genus is *Merops*, with 9 species and a range from southern Europe to Australia. The European Bee-eater *M. apiaster* breeds from the Iberian Peninsula and North Africa eastwards to western Siberia and Kashmir, and migrates to tropical and southern Africa and to north-western India ; it has bred, exceptionally, in the British Isles and elsewhere north of its usual range ; and there is a breeding population in South Africa, migrating north therefrom, which may possibly have become detached from the Northern Hemisphere migrants. The plumage is largely green-blue, with much chestnut on the upper parts and with a bright yellow throat.

The Blue-cheeked Bee-eater *M. superciliosus*, with several races (of which *M. s. persicus* was probably the one to occur in the Scilly Isles in 1952), is distributed from North Africa and Palestine to New Guinea ; in the western part of this range the birds migrate to southern Africa, but there is also a population (the nominate race, as it happens) which breeds locally in eastern Africa and commonly in Madagascar, whence some of the birds apparently migrate to Africa northwestwards. The Carmine (or Nubian) Bee-eater *M. nubicus* has a striking plumage mostly of carmine except for a glossy green head ; the central tail feathers are much elongated. It breeds in the open country just south of the Sahara and migrates almost to the equatorial forest ; its flocks provide a spectacle of great beauty on the larger rivers of West Africa. The Rainbow Bee-eater (or Rainbow-bird) *M. ornatus* is the Australian representative of the family, migrating north in the non-breeding season to the Celebes and New Guinea.

In the genus *Melittophagus* the tail is square or slightly forked ; there are 8 species, all purely African. They are among the smaller bee-eaters and include the Little (or Least) Bee-eater *M. pusillus*, of which races are found from Senegal and Eritrea to Natal. It is a very approachable although restless little bird, some 6 inches long, frequenting bushes on open ground ; from behind, its mainly green plumage makes it difficult to see, but from in front the brilliant yellow throat, bounded below by black and then chestnut, is conspicuous. The Black Bee-eater *M. gularis*, distributed from Sierra Leone east to Uganda and south to Angola, has a scarlet throat and cobalt blue on the rump and in streaks on the breast.

The genus *Aerops*, with 2 species, is also mainly African, but the White-throated (or Black-crowned) Bee-eater *A. albicollis* is found also in south-western Arabia. The Swallow-tailed Bee-eater *Dicrocercus hirundineus* and the Black-headed Bee-eater *Bombylonax breweri*, sole members of their respective genera, are likewise African.

The two species of *Nyctyornis* belong to southern and south-eastern Asia, and *Meropogon forsteni* is confined to the Celebes. In both these genera there are elongated feathers, forming a sort of bib, on the chin and throat.

See Plate 17 (colour)   A.L.T.

Dresser, H. E. 1884. A Monograph of the Meropidae. London. (Colour plates.)

Marien, D. 1950. Notes on some Asiatic Meropidae. J. Bombay Nat. Hist. Soc. 49 : 151–164.

Peters, J. L. 1945. Check-list of Birds of the World vol. 5. Cambridge, Mass.

BEGGING DISPLAY: see FEEDING OF YOUNG ; also BEHAVIOUR, DEVELOPMENT OF

BEHAVIOUR: see the entries named in the List of Major Articles on General Subjects at the beginning of the volume, under the heading ' Ethology (Behaviour) '. These two terms are nearly synonymous, but perhaps ' ethology ' tends to suggest a descriptive approach (observation of habits) and ' behaviour ' an analytical—often experimental—one (e.g. in terms of stimuli and responses). Several of the short entries defining behavioural terms are quoted from the under-mentioned report of a round-table conference (Thorpe).

Hinde, R. A. 1961. Behaviour. *In* Marshall, A. J. (ed.). Biology and Comparative Physiology of Birds. vol. 2. New York and London.

Thorpe, W. H. 1951. The definition of some terms used in animal behaviour studies. Bull. Anim. Behav. no. 9 : 34–40.

BEHAVIOUR, DEVELOPMENT OF: a study so far largely concerned, in respect of birds, with the age at which particular instinctive acts appear and with their later changes in form. Many factors influence the development (or ontogeny) of behaviour. Some behaviour patterns may be impossible at first, simply because certain sense organs and muscles are not yet functioning. Thus, a newly hatched passerine may be deaf and blind, with only the muscles extending the neck and legs adequately developed. Hormone levels in the blood may be abnormal ; androgen secretion is usually very low in the young male, for instance, and on this score alone sexual or aggressive behaviour is likely to be absent.

Nevertheless, changes in the central nervous system certainly underlie many of the changes in behaviour. It is usual to distinguish between behavourial changes due to maturation, i.e. developmental changes in a behaviour pattern which do not depend on its being performed, and those due to learning, but critical experiments are difficult to devise (see LEARNING). Changes that seem obviously due to learning by practice may in fact be caused by maturation ; Grohmann prevented young pigeons from using their wings whilst they were reared and found that they flew as well as controls when finally released. On the other hand, recent work suggests that learning during early manipulation of nest material may affect nest building. In some instances there is an innate disposition to learn a particular type of behaviour, e.g. a particular song (see IMPRINTING), and learning may be so rapid as to simulate maturation.

Behaviour possessed by a bird's ancestors but lost in the course of evolution may reappear during ontogeny (see below, D) ; other behaviour patterns evolved in relation to the peculiar needs of young birds appear precociously, and then disappear during development.

(A) The Appearance of Adult Instinctive Behaviour. Fixed action patterns that in the adult are associated with other ' FAPs ' to express a particular drive are often given independently at their first appearance and are not preceded by appropriate appetitive behaviour (see FIXED ACTION PATTERN). In some instances no organised appetitive behaviour connected with the appropriate drive exists as yet (e.g. ' stick quivering ' in the nest building of the Cormorant *Phalacrocorax carbo* at its first appearance); in others the behaviour sequence of which the FAP will form part exists, but independently. Thus nestling buntings (Emberizidae) beg when hungry, and use the adult feeding movement of pecking only in curiosity. The spontaneous occurrence of stereotyped behaviour patterns is not confined to early stages of development ; it occurs also in play (e.g. hunting play in the Bald Eagle *Haliaetus leucocephalus* and other raptors). It is interesting, too, that play tends to occur in the juvenile rather than in the mature adult.

The course of development of pecking has been traced in the chick from the first appearance of its reflex components. On the fourth day of embryonic life the head nods in response to tactile stimulation, and the bill may open and close. By the twelfth day bill-opening always follows a nod, and swallowing may occur. Thus, even at this lowest level, components tend to appear first independently of each other. (See also DEVELOPMENT, EMBRYONIC.)

Several types of change may occur in a FAP after its first identifiable appearance. An initially distorted and perhaps low intensity behaviour pattern may slowly assume the adult form. Sometimes the causes for this are not clear ; sometimes a change occurs in the underlying motivation or in the stimuli to which the FAP is orientated (see below,

C2). Certain adult call-notes develop as speciali-sations of a more complex call-note given in youth. There is some evidence that a motor pattern and the mechanism responsible for its release may mature independently (see below, A3 and C2).

In the following sections, which are concerned with the development of the main systems of instinctive behaviour, an attempt has been made to draw examples from both nidicolous and nidifugous birds, since their degree of maturity at hatching is so different. Dates usually apply to hand-reared birds, and 8–12 days may be taken as the age of leaving the nest in the passerines considered. (See YOUNG BIRD.)

1. *Locomotion.* Passerines are usually capable only of feeble ill-co-ordinated leg movements at hatching, but climbing becomes possible at ca. 7 days. Some birds (e.g. Skylark *Alauda arvensis*, Raven *Corvus corax*) which tend to walk when adults, hop just after leaving the nest, and recapitulation of an ancestral condition seems likely. Most nidifugous birds can walk at hatching.

Nearly all birds are at first incapable of flight. Later they spend periods in spontaneous wing-flapping ; at this period at least, flight appears to have its own independent motivation. In passerines (e.g. Song Sparrow *Melospiza melodia*) such wing-flapping (ca. 7 days) is soon followed by short flights (ca. 10 days), which often end by the bird alighting on a fellow instead of on a perch. Herring Gulls *Larus argentatus* first flap when their wings are almost without quills (10 days). Ritualised intention movements of flight, such as tail-flicks, appear at the same time as flight in passerines (ca. 10 days).

2. *Care of body surface.* Preening, yawning, and stretching are usually incomplete or ill-co-ordinated when they first appear (ca. 5 days, Song Sparrow, Blackbird *Turdus merula*). Naked areas may be, as it were, preened with slow bill movements which never touch the body surface. At first only back and shoulders are attended to ; later other parts are reached, the tail and rump being last (ca. 12 days). In the same period, scratching (5–7 days) and shaking the feathers (ca. 10 days) appear. Bathing is usually the last to be observed (13–20 days, various passerines ; ca. 4 days, Blackheaded Gull *Larus ridibundus*). Components may be given independently (e.g. horizontal wing movements, Song Sparrow). Bathing is usually first released by the young bird getting its bill wet after pecking at water in curiosity ; bill washing may be released by a shiny surface alone (Arctic Skua *Stercorarius parasiticus*). The first complete bathing thus released may be carried out on a dry surface.

3. *Fear behaviour.* In passerines the first fear response to be given (6–7 days) is cowering, which differs from the posture of an adult 'frozen' in a crouch, ready to take off, in that the head may rest on the ground and the wings be slightly raised. Like an adult fear reaction it is given to any strange, and in particular to any sudden, stimulus. The alarm cry of the adult may be very effective ; nestling Blackbirds duck on hearing it and cease begging. In many nidifugous birds it produces crouching and freezing, sometimes preceded by a short run, even just after hatching ; Herring Gull chicks will cease begging calls in the egg on hearing an alarm call.

In the Yellowhammer *Emberiza citrinella*, high calls like those given by an adult in pain appear soon after (9 days), together with actual fleeing (see below, C). The intensity of fear responses continues to increase until ca. 20 days, when gaping and other temperature regulatory responses begin to follow them as in the adult. Development in the perception of stimuli releasing fear responses continues even longer. In the Chaffinch *Fringilla coelebs* at ca. 21 days more intense fear responses are given to a rectangular object than to an owl model, but at about 30 days the reverse is true.

4. *Aggression.* Aggressive responses tend to appear somewhat later than fear responses, although certain nidicolous species, e.g. the domesticated Blond Ringdove (or Collared Dove) *Streptopelia 'risoria'*, hawks (Accipitridae), and owls (Strigiformes), gape or snap at an approaching hand, and young Great Spotted Woodpeckers *Dendrocopos major* and Lesser Spotted Woodpeckers *D. minor* may peck each other severely whilst still in the nest.

In the Yellowhammer and Song Sparrow the threat note is first heard at 17–25 days, and full threat postures are given at 20–35 days (see below, D). At first they are not associated with attacks, and are usually of low intensity. In the nidifugous birds threat appears earlier (ca. 4 days in Arctic Skua). Androgen secretion is probably important in the development of aggressive behaviour. Male cockerels usually begin sparring at ca. 22 days, but androgen injections will induce aggressive behaviour in chicks a few days old.

5. *Sexual behaviour and courtship.* It is impossible at present to determine whether changes in the complex motivation of courtship displays are involved in their changes of form during development. A motivational change certainly appears to explain the fact that courtship displays of the male Chaffinch given very early in the season resemble the threat display, and only later take on their normal form.

The 'head-back' display of Cormorant courtship

at first (ca. 6 weeks) consists of gaping upwards, with a series of calls. Later the head is thrown right back, and the calls become more rapid, until the adult condition is attained ; at about the same time (2–3 months) the first copulation attempts occur. The first appearances of the display are apparently spontaneous, but later it is used in greeting. The similar 'clappering' display of the White Stork *Ciconia ciconia* appears at only a few days of age. In the Blackbird the 'fluffed' display of male courtship may be shown at 40 days, the first male copulation attempts at 40 days, and the first female soliciting postures and calls at 34 days. The White-throat *Sylvia communis* shows male courtship at 20–30 days and copulation attempts at ca. 80 days.

The male's first attempts at copulation may involve mounting alone (Cormorant), or also pressing the cloaca against the object mounted. Hand-reared passerines often attempt to copulate with the human hand (cf. IMPRINTING).

The level of sex hormone secretion is important in the development of sexual behaviour and court-ship. Cockerels normally first show treading at 80 days, but testosterone injections will induce it at 15 days and crowing at 4 days. In the Herring Gull, androgen injections will produce courtship display well before the end of the first year instead of after three years, and may induce the change of voice quality to that of the adult at between 45 and 62 days.

6. *Nest building and parental behaviour.* In the Cormorant the nest-building movement of 'quiver-ing' a twig appears at 2 weeks, but the twig is not fastened in place. At 4–5 weeks it is continued until the twig is caught in place in the nest. Whitethroats begin to carry leaves or grass at 6–7 weeks.

Parental behaviour may appear early, probably because the behaviour of sibs is such an effective releaser for it. Feeding a sib has been reported at 12 days in a hybrid dove, and at 40–50 days in a number of passerines.

7. *Call notes.* Several examples exist of the development of two or more adult call notes from constituents of a complex call given in youth. In its first autumn the Chaffinch gives an alarm call 'tew' which is absent in the adult, but widespread amongst other finches. One of its component notes gradually changes into the adult social call, whilst occasional intermediates suggest a connection between other components and the two adult alarm calls. Recapitulation of an evolutionary change seems likely here, but dubious in the two following examples (cf. below, D) : in the Blackbird a single begging call gradually differentiates into a contact call and an alarm call, and in the Cormorant a call

given by fighting nestlings gives rise to two alarm calls.

Not only may the form of a call change during development but also the situation eliciting it. This is especially common in the case of begging calls, e.g. that of the Chaffinch may later be used briefly as a contact call.

(B) The Role of Learning. Many of the changes in instinctive behaviour during development probably depend on early learning, but definite examples of this are as yet few, except for the learning of releasing stimuli. Thus Jackdaws *Corvus monedula* learn to give fear responses to objects such as cause experienced birds to give alarm notes, and chicks learn at which objects to peck when feeding. In some cases a fixed action pattern may be learnt ; thus, the general form of Chaffinch song is innate but its details are learnt (see LEARNING ; SINGING).

(C) Behaviour Peculiar to the Young Bird. Behaviour patterns evolved in relation to the needs of life in a nest and to dependence on parents for food appear precociously in the nestling, only to disappear in the course of development. In some circumstances they may reappear in the adult.

1. *Hatching.* The eggshell is broken by a series of blows from the bill with its egg-tooth. Blows often alternate with periods of rest, and hatching itself may take anything from a few minutes, e.g. in woodpeckers (Picidae) and grebes (Podicipitidae), to several days (Sooty Shearwater *Procellaria griseus*). The hatching Herring Gull appears always to peck at the upper half of the egg.

2. *Begging behaviour and adult feeding.* In many birds the change from the feeding behaviour of the young to that of the adult is gradual. Ducks (Anatidae), waders (Charadrii), and most game-birds (Galliformes) begin to feed themselves im-mediately ; young birds-of-prey from the first tear at the food brought by their parents. In others, the young bird begs for its food but uses the adult movement of pecking in feeding. Thus in the Herring Gull the first begging (excluding notes heard in the egg) occurs a few hours after hatching and consists of repeated pecks at the parent's bill-tip, but even at this age pecks may be directed at regurgitated food on the ground. However, where the parent puts food into the chick's gape, e.g. in crows (Corvidae), swallows (Hirundinidae), and finches (Fringillidae), the behaviour used by the young in feeding is so different from that used by the adult that the second does not develop out of the first.

In such birds (e.g. Song Sparrow, Reed Bunting *Emberiza schoeniclus*, Blackbird), begging may be divided into three development stages. On the first and second days the bird gapes vertically, often with a special call, in response to very varied auditory and tactile stimuli, or sometimes apparently spontaneously. By the 5th or 6th day the bird is beginning to gape in response to visual stimuli. For about a day it may still direct the gape vertically, but gradually it begins to turn the gape towards the visual stimulus. Wing vibration and characteristic head movements (if present) appear at this stage. The effect of hunger on gaping has been carefully analysed for Greenfinches *Carduelis chloris* of this age; an increase of hunger causes gaping to be given to a wider range of stimuli, but has no effect on the ease with which it is exhausted (see FIXED ACTION PATTERN).

In the third stage other motivations than hunger begin to influence begging. Fear responses appear (ca. 15 days, Reed Bunting). Thus the bird will often back away whilst begging, give high fear calls in place of begging calls, and raise the crest. Sometimes apparently aggressive responses are shown, such as threat calls.

Throughout the same period adult feeding responses are developing quite independently. The first pecks (ca. 9 days) are directed at almost any distinctive object, apparently in curiosity. When hungry the birds always beg; they even beg at food that has fallen to the floor, instead of pecking at it. Later the bird gets some food by pecking but begs whenever the parent appears. The parents' unwillingness to continue feeding probably helps to terminate begging.

Adult feeding behaviour usually shows progressive improvement, in which learning may well be important. A young Montagu's Harrier *Circus pygargus* is first fed when perched; later food is offered in the air, and finally it is dropped to be intercepted. Young Great Tits *Parus major* are at first clumsy and peck at objects out of reach, but a week after leaving the nest they show adult skill in handling insect prey.

Young Arctic Skuas give the movements of ' fishing from the water surface ', characteristic of gulls (Larinae) in response to floating objects, although the adult does not show such behaviour; recapitulation may be involved.

3. *Defaecation* is specialised in young nidicolous birds. Typically (e.g. in finches) the nestling turns round when it has been fed, raises its cloaca and extrudes a dropping enclosed in a mucilaginous envelope. Adult defaecatory behaviour appears on leaving the nest; at the same time (or just before, as in the Snow Bunting *Plectrophenax nivalis*) the envelopes cease to be produced.

4. *Restriction of locomotion and leaving the nest.* A young nidicolous bird is usually capable of sustained locomotion some days before leaving the nest. Nevertheless it moves only within the nest, or at most makes short excursions a day or so before leaving. Even in the absence of a nest, young *Caprimulgus* spp. keep so closely to one spot that it is soon marked by a ring of excreta, within which they live. Leaving the nest depends partly on the loss or reduction in the tendency to maintain physical contact with other nestlings. Grohmann suggests that it may also depend on the loss of a specific inhibition of locomotion. Ailing nestlings may leave the nest prematurely (e.g. Song Sparrow); possibly they lack this inhibition.

In many passerines (e.g. Chaffinch, buntings) the nestlings scatter, and each finds a separate perching place where it continues to spend most of its time motionless. In others (e.g. tits *Parus* spp.) the members of the brood remain together and show no restriction of locomotion.

The earliest date at which nestlings will leave the nest is probably determined by the maturation of fear responses. In many passerines, if the nest is disturbed towards the end of the nestling period (e.g. from 9 days, Blackbird), the young crouch, and then suddenly leave, scattering in all directions. It is difficult to get them to remain in the nest afterwards, which suggests that there has been some very sudden behavioural change.

5. *Reappearance of begging behaviour in the adult.* Many female passerines use a display very like that of begging during courtship feeding (e.g. crows, tits, many finches). This may be compared with the observation that a senile Whitethroat began to beg to its hand-rearer and give fledgling contact notes; regression continued until just before death, when it was directing its gape vertically upwards and giving nestling begging calls. Infantile behaviour patterns are thus latent in the adult.

(D) Recapitulation during Development of Behaviour. The reappearance of ancestral call notes in early development (see above, A7) is good evidence that behaviour, like structure, may show recapitulation in development (cf. also above, hopping A1 and fishing C2). Such an effect is not, however, likely to be constant or easily predictable. It must presumably depend on recapitulation in neural development, and this is studied at second hand when one is studying behaviour. A behaviour pattern may have matured long before it is released by appropriate stimuli. A second complication is that behaviour patterns that have become part of complex displays may appear first in such displays, instead of independently, thus reversing the order of evolution. In passerines, flapping wing movements may appear first in begging and even turn into true flight in very intense fledgling begging.

A final and purely methodological difficulty is that distinctive movements are relatively few and may serve several motivations (e.g. gaping in yawning, temperature regulation, begging, and aggression). Sequences of development in which one pattern appears to develop gradually into another may be due rather to the patterns sharing a number of such components than to actual recapitulation. In the Reed Bunting, begging and the head-forward threat posture share gaping, neck extension, and directing the bill towards a visual stimulus. Begging gradually becomes almost identical with the threat posture as motivational changes occur, giving every appearance of a development of the second from the first.

R.J.A.

Kortlandt, A. 1940. Ein Übersicht der angeborenen Verhaltungsweisen des Mittel-Europäischen Kormorans (*Phalacrocorax carbo sinensis*), ihre Funktion, ontogenetische Entwicklung und phylogenetische Herkunft. Arch. Neerl. Zool. 4 : 401–442.
Nice, M. M. 1943. Studies in the life history of the Song Sparrow II. Trans. Linn. Soc. N.Y. 6 : 1–328.
Nice, M. M. 1962. Development of behaviour in precocial birds. Trans. Linn. Soc. N.Y. 8 : 1–211.
Heinroth, O. & Heinroth, M. 1924–33. Die Vögel Mitteleuropas. Berlin.
Tinbergen, N. 1951. The Study of Instinct. Oxford.

BELLBIRD: substantive name of *Procnias* spp. (see COTINGA) ; also of the Crested Bellbird *Oreoica guttaralis* (see THICKHEAD) ; and name of *Anthornis melanura* (see HONEYEATER).

BELL-MAGPIE: see MAGPIE (2)

BELL-MINER: *Manorina melanophrys* (see HONEYEATER).

BELL-SHRIKE: sometimes used as substantive name of certain *Laniarius* spp. (see SHRIKE).

BELLY: the ABDOMEN ; or the ventral surface area roughly corresponding thereto (see TOPOGRAPHY).

BELT: a broad band, in some plumage patterns, across the breast or belly (see TOPOGRAPHY).

BENGALESE: see CAGE BIRD

BENTBILL: substantive name of *Oncostoma* spp. (see FLYCATCHER (2)).

BERGMANN'S RULE: that, among the forms of a polytypic species, body-size tends to be larger in cooler parts of the total range and smaller in the warmer parts (see also ALLEN'S RULE ; WING).

BERI-BERI: see DISEASE ; NUTRITION

BERRYEATER: substantive name of *Ampelion* spp. (for family see COTINGA).

BEWIT: term used in FALCONRY.

BIBLE, BIRDS OF THE: less than forty species are mentioned in the Bible, out of over 400 resident in or migrating through Israel. Half of the names are included in the lists of the unclean birds mentioned in Leviticus 11 and in Deuteronomy 14 ; the two lists are very similar, with several variations in the order and only one name mentioned in one list and not in the other. The other names, some of which are difficult to identify, are scattered through the books and include names of birds (and other creatures) characteristic of deserts and other lonely places. Doves and young pigeons are connected with the ritual sacrifice in the Temple, and they are most frequently mentioned in the Bible. Passages striking in their beauty refer to such migrating birds as the Turtle Dove and White Stork (Song of Songs, 2, 12 ; Jer. 8, 7)—see also under QUAIL.

The identification of the names of birds and other animals met with difficulties as early as the time of the translation of the Bible into Greek, in the third century B.C. It is quite possible that in different parts of the Land of Israel different tribes, or even smaller population units, used different names for the same creatures ; and when these names were included in the books of Law and the books of the Prophets they could obviously give rise to controversy. The discussion in the Talmud, centring on the difficulty of identifying birds subject to ritual prohibitions, shows that there were localities where certain birds were eaten which were considered to be unclean elsewhere (E. Billig, personal communication).

The divergence in the identification of the names mentioned in the Bible grew immensely when translators and expositors came to be persons who lived outside of the Land of Israel and imagined that the animals of their own countries were identical with those mentioned in the Bible. The ever-growing number of languages into which the Bible is being translated reflects the difficulties regarding such identifications for people of countries with different flora and fauna from that of the Land of Israel. Even in revised English translations (e.g. King James's Bible) the same Hebrew names are sometimes translated in various ways, as can be seen from the appended table ; this is also true of a more recent translation such as that of the Jewish Publication Society of America. There is no unanimity even among Israeli scientists regarding the meaning of some of the Biblical names and their uses in modern Hebrew. However, the differences over the names of birds are few in comparison with those over the names of mammals.

The Table presents English translations of the names of the birds mentioned in the Hebrew Bible, along with their scientific identification as generally accepted in Israel today. The English names are those used in King James's Bible, with those in the J.P.S.A. Bible (where different) for comparison. The list of quotations is not complete, but it includes the most typical and commonly cited passages.

Table showing English names used in translating from the Hebrew as compared with the modern identifications made by Israeli zoologists.

The first column gives the names used in King James's Bible—the Authorised Version (Old Testament) ; where a name is widely at variance with the modern identification it is placed within quotation marks. More than one entry for the same name indicates that different Hebrew words are represented. Where the name used in the recent translation issued by the Jewish Publication Society of America is different, it follows within brackets. The second column gives selected references to the use of the name in King James's Bible ; ' L ' =Leviticus, chapter 11, 'D '=Deuteronomy, chapter 14.

	BIBLICAL REFERENCE	ZOOLOGICAL IDENTIFICATION
' arrowsnake ' (great owl)	Isa. 34, 15	Long-eared Owl *Asio otus*
' bittern '	Isa. 14, 23 ; 34, 11 ; Zeph. 2, 14	Long-eared Owl (Aharoni) *Asio otus*
birds	Gen. 7, 14 ; Ps. 104, 17	general
birds, ravenous	Ezek. 39, 4	eagles *Aquila* sp.
bird, speckled (speckled bird-of-prey)	Jer. 12, 9	eagle *Aquila* sp.
' cormorant '	L ; D	Fish Owl *Ketupa zeylonensis*
' cormorant ' (pelican)	Isa. 34, 11 ; Zeph. 2, 14	pelican *Pelecanus* sp.
' crane ' (swallow)	Isa. 38, 14 ; Jer. 8, 7	Swift *Apus apus pekinensis*
' cuckow ' (sea-mew)	L	gull *Larus* sp.
' doleful creatures ' (ferrets—*sic*)	Isa. 13, 21	Eagle Owl *Bubo bubo aharonii*
dove	Gen. 8, 8 ; Isa. 38, 14 ; 59, 11 ; 60, 8 ; Hos. 7, 11 ; 11, 11 ; Ps. 55, 6 ; Song of Songs 2, 14 ; 5, 2 ; 5, 12 ; 6, 9 ; Nah. 2, 7 ; Ezek, 7, 16 ; Jer. 48, 28	pigeon *Columba* sp.
dove, turtle	Gen. 15, 9 ; Lev. 1, 14 ; 14, 30	Turtle Dove *Streptopelia turtur*
' eagle '	Exod. 19, 4 ; Deut. 32, 11 ; Isa. 40, 31 ; Jer. 4, 13 ; Ezek. 17, 3 ; Ps. 103, 5 ; Pr. 30, 17 ; Lament. 4, 19	Griffon Vulture *Gyps fulvus*
' eagle ' (vulture)	Hab. 1, 8 ; Job 39, 27	Griffon Vulture *Gyps fulvus*
' eagle ' (great vulture)	D	Griffon Vulture *Gyps fulvus*
' eagle, gier ' (carrion vulture)	L ; D	Egyptian Vulture *Neophron percnopterus*
fowl	Gen. 7, 14	general
fowl	Ps. 8, 8	general
fowl ; fowls of the mountains (birds-of-prey ; ravenous birds of the mountains)	Gen. 15, 11 ; Isa. 18, 6	eagles *Aquila* sp.
fowl, fatted	Kings I, 4, 23	swan *Cygnus* sp.
glede	D	kite (Aharoni) *Milvus* sp. or buzzard (Margolin) *Buteo* sp.
hawk	L ; D ; Job 39, 26	hawk *Accipiter* sp.
' hawk, night '	L ; D	falcon *Falco* sp.
heron	L ; D	herons *Ardeidae* spp.
kite	L	Black Kite *Milvus migrans*
' kite ' (falcon)	L ; D	buzzard, or kite (Aharoni) *Buteo* sp. or *Milvus* sp.
' lapwing ' (hoopoe)	L ; D	Hoopoe *Upupa epops*
' ospray '	L ; D	Cinereous Vulture *Aegypius monachus*
ossifrage (bearded vulture)	L ; D	Lämmergeier *Gypaetus barbatus*
ostrich	Lament. 4, 3	Ostrich *Struthio camelus*
' ostrich ' (stork)	Job 39, 13	White Stork *Ciconia ciconia*

' owl ' (ostrich)	L ; Isa. 13, 21	Ostrich Struthio camelus
owl, great ; owl	L ; Isa. 34, 11	Short-eared Owl Asio flammeus
owl, little ; owl of the desert (owl of the waste places)	L ; D ; Ps. 102, 6	Little Owl Athene noctua
owl, screech (night monster)	Isa. 34, 14	Tawny Owl Strix aluco
partridge	Sam. I, 26, 20 ; Jer. 17, 11	partridge (See-see) Ammoperdix heyi
' peacock '	Kings I, 10, 22	parrot Psittacidae sp.
' peacock ' (ostrich)	Job 39, 13	Ostrich Struthio camelus
pelican	L ; D ; Ps. 102, 6	pelican Pelecanus sp.
pigeon, young	Gen. 15, 9	pigeon Columba sp. (juv.)
pigeon, young	Lev. 14, 30	pigeon Columba sp. (juv.)
quail	Exod. 16, 13 ; Num. 11, 31 ; Ps. 105, 40	Quail Coturnix coturnix
raven	L ; Kings I, 17, 6 ; Song of Songs 5, 11	raven or crow Corvus sp.
' raven ' of the valley	Pr. 30, 17	Magpie Pica pica bactriana
singing of birds	Song of Songs 2, 12	Nightingale Luscinia luscinia
sparrow	Ps. 102, 7	House Sparrow Passer domesticus bibl
stork	L ; D ; Jer. 8, 7 ; Zach. 5, 9 ; Ps. 104, 17	White Stork Ciconia ciconia
swallow (crane)	Isa. 38, 14 ; Jer. 8, 7	swallow (Aharoni) or crane (Margoli Hirundinidae sp. or Gruidae sp.
' swan ' (horned owl)	L ; D	Barn Owl Tyto alba
turtle (turtle dove)	Num. 6, 10 ; Song of Songs 2, 12 ; Jer. 8, 7	Turtle Dove Streptopelia turtur
' vulture ' (kite)	D ; Isa. 34, 15	Black Kite Milvus migrans
' vulture ' (falcon)	Job 28, 7	buzzard Buteo sp.

Two Hebrew names, *zipor* and *of*, are used for birds in general. It was admitted by some scholars, and generally accepted in Israel, that the first denominates small birds and the second the large ones. It is doubtful, however, whether such a distinction was carefully followed in the Bible. Another reservation concerns the frequent combination of two Hebrew names for Turtle Dove (*tor*) and young pigeon (*yona*—also *gozal*). There are also names which might have been used for birds but are of doubtful meaning, e.g. *sechvi* (rooster or soul), *thinshemeth* (chameleon or owl), *kipod* (owl in translation but hedgehog in colloquial Hebrew), and *atalef* (now considered to refer to a bat). The name *hogla* is commonly used now in Israel for the Stone Partridge ; in the Bible it is used as a place-name (Beth Hogla).

Canon Tristram was the first man to try to base the identification of the flora and the fauna of the Bible upon their study in the Land of Israel. During several journeys, spread over some twenty years, he studied the habits of the beasts and birds as well as the local names still in use by the population. His excellent work was of value to the J.P.S.A., which undertook a new translation of the Bible on behalf of Jewish authorities in the years 1892–1915. The next step was made by Aharoni, the first zoologist to live and work permanently in Palestine. When writing a first zoological school text in Hebrew, he introduced into the everyday usage of the Hebrew-speaking school-children names which later became commonly accepted. Margolin increased the general knowledge of the flora and fauna of the Bible in Israel by teaching schoolmasters in his institution and through his books. Although Bodenheimer doubted the possibilities of exact identification of the animals of the Bible, the use of names introduced into everyday life became so widespread that now it is in practice less important whether the names used by Israelis today are or are not the same as those used by their forefathers. The living Hebrew now spoken in Israel has brought the names of birds and other animals mentioned in the Bible into common use ; in this way names again attach to observable realities instead of being disputable scholastic terms.   A.S.

Tristram, H. B. 1911. The Natural History of the Bible. London.
Aharoni, J. 1941–42. [Key to Palestine Birds—in Hebrew.] Jerusalem.
Margolin, J. 1947. [Zoology—in Hebrew.] Tel-Aviv.
Bodenheimer, F. S. 1956. Animal Life in Biblical Lands. Jerusalem.

BIBLIOGRAPHY : to this, the most useful guide for the ornithologist is the section ' Aves ' of the *Zoological Record*, published annually by the Zoological Society of London (see ZOOLOGICAL RECORD). Giving short summaries as well as titles, but with a less complete coverage of ornithology, are the volumes of *Biological Abstracts* published since 1927 under the auspices of the Union of American Biological Societies. Many ornithological periodicals publish reviews, abstracts, or lists of titles of current literature (see under ORNITHOLOGY). Scientific books and papers on birds, including occasional review articles on particular topics, commonly give abundant references to earlier publications. Certain purely bibliographical works on birds have been published. The catalogues of major zoological libraries are also useful.

Irwin, R. 1951. British Bird Books : an index to British Ornithology A.D. 1481 to A.D. 1948. London.
Mullens, W. H., Swann, H. K. & Jourdain, F. C. R. 1919–20. A Geographical Bibliography of British Ornithology from the earliest times to the end of 1918. London. (Earlier work by the first two authors, 1917.)
Ronsil, R. 1948. Bibliographie ornithologique française vol. I. Paris.
Stone, W. 1933. American ornithological literature, 1883–1933. In A.O.U., Fifty Years Progress in American Ornithology, 1883–1933. Lancaster, Pa.
Strong, R. M. 1939–59. A Bibliography of Birds. Chicago. (Parts 1 & 2, Authors, 1939 ; Part 3, Subject index, 1946 ; Part 4, Finding index, 1959.)

BICEPS : see MUSCULATURE. The presence or absence of a ' biceps slip ', a division of the humeral head of this flexor of the forearm, has been used as a taxonomic character.

BILE : the secretion of the liver into the small intestine (see ALIMENTARY SYSTEM ; LIVER).

BILL : alternatively ' beak ' and technically ' rostrum ', the projecting jaws of a bird, with their horny sheaths. The whole consists of the upper mandible (or maxilla) and the lower mandible ; the former is based on the facial bones, especially the premaxillae, and the latter on the composite jaw-bones (see SKELETON). The horny coverings of both are formed by the outer layers of the Malpighian cells of the epidermis (see SKIN). The whole horny structure is known as the rhamphotheca, the upper and lower portions being sometimes separately designated rhinotheca and gnathotheca.

Upper Mandible. For descriptive purposes this may be divided into the culmen, or dorsal ridge from the tip (dertrum) of the bill to the forehead, and the upper mandibular tomia, or lateral cutting edges. In most birds the external covering is fused into a single hard sheath ; in parrots (Psittacidae), however, there is limited vertical movement on a ' hinge ' between the premaxillae and the skull. In a few families, such as the albatrosses (Diomedeidae), division of the mandible into distinct horny sections is apparent. Most limicoline birds (Charadrii) have relatively soft ' leathery ' coverings to their bills ; in geese (Anser spp. etc.), while much of the sheath is soft, the tip forms a hard ' nail ' well adapted to cropping vegetation. The proximal portion of the mandible may be soft and thickened, forming a sensitive cere, as in diurnal birds-of-prey (Falconiformes), in which it is naked, and in parrots, in which it is usually feathered ; or it may have a soft, swollen operculum above the nostrils, as in pigeons (Columbidae).

The nostrils or external nares with circular, oval, or linear openings, are usually separated by a cartilaginous or ossified medial septum, as in e.g. the owls (Strigiformes), but in certain families such as the gulls (Laridae) and cranes (Gruidae) this feature is absent (see NARIS). In the fulmars and shearwaters (Procellariidae) the nostrils are in paired tubes separated by a septum on top of the culmen, but in the storm petrels (Hydrobatidae) they are in a single tube. Darters (Anhingidae) and cormorants (Phalacrocoracidae) have only rudimentary nostrils that close after the young leave the nest ; gannets (Sulidae), which plunge into the sea after fish from a considerable height, have no external nostrils but wide inner apertures communicating with the mouth and, like adult cormorants, they breathe through the mouth. The nostrils of most small passerine birds open into a slight superficial depression, the nasal fossa. The position of the nostrils relative to the base of the bill shows considerable differences ; but only in the kiwis (Apterygidae), nocturnal species with a highly developed olfactory system, are the nostrils located at the tip of the bill. (see SMELL).

Lower Mandible. The chief characters of the lower mandible are the lower mandibular tomia, or cutting edges, the mandibular ramus, extending posteriorly on either side of the jaw, and the gonys, or ventral ridge formed by the junction distally of the two halves of the jaw, as clearly seen in gulls for example. The full-length apposition of the closed mandibles is known as the commissure. The gape or rictus is the mouth opening, formed in the angle between the two mandibles when the lower jaw is dropped.

Regeneration and Moult. Regeneration of the rhamphotheca of both mandibles and even of the bones of the bill damaged in combat has been recorded in storks (Ciconiidae) and in the domestic fowl. As a result of damage and imperfect regeneration, or possibly genetic defect, various deformities occur. The effects of normal wear, occurring particularly at the tip of the bill in many species, are compensated by additional growth. The external surfaces of the bills of parrots and some other species are renewed by a process of irregular ' peeling '. In puffins Fratercula spp. the much

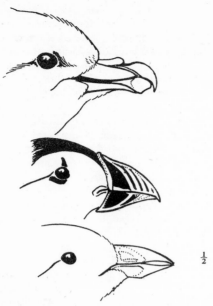

FIG 1 (a) Fulmar *Fulmarus glacialis*, compound bill and tubular nostrils;

(b) Puffin *Fratercula arctica* in breeding season, bill with outer sheath (for coloration see Plate 29);

(c) Puffin in winter, showing bill after sheath has been moulted. *C.E.T.K.*

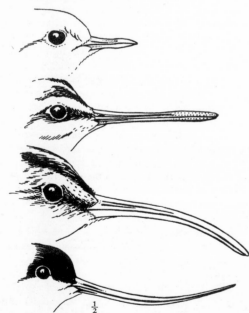

FIG 2 (a) Golden Plover *Pluvialis apricarius*, bill of moderate length;

(b) Snipe *Gallinago gallinago*, long straight bill;

(c) Whimbrel *Numenius phaeopus*, long decurved bill;

(d) Avocet *Recurvirostra avosetta*, long recurved bill.

C.E.T.K.

enlarged and laterally flattened and decorated outer sheaths are shed after the breeding season, leaving smaller, unembellished bills of a different shape during winter. Laterally compressed bills occur in other genera of the Alcidae and many are brightly coloured in summer.

Appendages. Seasonal ornamentations or appendages to the bills of male birds occur in many species. Some pelicans (Pelecanidae), for example, grow several erect horny plates, which are cast after breeding; these birds also show maximum development of the membranous gular sac, which extends the whole length of the lower mandible and embraces the chin, gular region, and jugulum. In many birds, such as coots *Fulica* spp., turacos *Musophaga* spp., a megapode *Megacephalon maleo*, and scoters *Melanitta* spp., the base of the culmen and the forehead are swollen to form ornamental plates, knobs, or humps. These embellishments are seen in extreme form in the hornbills (Bucerotidae). The swellings are in most instances of light and spongy tissue, but in the Helmeted Hornbill *Rhinoplax vigil* the bones of the enlarged forehead have a dense epidermal covering with the consistency of ivory (see IVORY, HORNBILL).

Sexual Dimorphism. Notable dimorphism in structure is uncommon, but it is well illustrated in the bill of the Huia *Heteralocha acutirostris*, the male's being relatively short, stout, and almost straight, and the female's slender, decurved, and nearly twice as long. Dimorphic bills can also be seen in certain hornbills, in some of which the disparities in size and shape are considerable (e.g. the Rufous-necked Hornbill *Aceros nipalensis*). Differences between the colours of the bills of males, females, and young occur in many species; there are also seasonal changes in colour (see also SEXUAL DIMORPHISM).

Early Development. The bills of embryo birds develop a calcareous, scale-like 'egg-tooth' on the tip of the upper mandible with which the eggshell is later perforated; this feature is shed within a few days of hatching. In some species, e.g. American Woodcock *Philohela minor*, there is another egg-tooth on the lower mandible. Nestling honeyguides (Indicatoridae) possess a pair of sharp mandibular and maxillary hooks which are shed about the time the eyes open; with these interlocking 'teeth —a unique adaptation—the young parasite kills the nestlings of its host species. The linings of the mouths of altricial nestlings are usually vividly coloured, and both the palate and tongue are often embellished with coloured spots (see TONGUE). The rictal regions are first much swollen; this swelling and the soft operculum found above the nostrils of nestlings of certain species disappear as the bill hardens and assumes adult proportions. Species with highly adapted bills, such as curlews *Numenius* spp. and flamingos (Phoenicopteridae), have bills of generalised form in the early nestling stage.

Functions. The bill serves many of the purposes of a ' hand ', the specialised forelimbs of birds being little available for these. Notably it is used in nest building, which in some instances demands a high degree of dexterity, and in preening the feathers (see NEST BUILDING ; FEATHER MAINTENANCE). It is also a weapon ; and, as already noted, it may bear ornamental or other colouring, excrescences, or appendages. Above all it is used in feeding, being in effect an extension of the jaws, and it is to this function that its structure shows the greatest variety of special adaptations (see FEEDING HABITS).

Adaptation to Feeding Habits. The external characters of the bills of different species vary greatly in accordance with feeding behaviour. Some reveal high degrees of adaptation, in both shape and proportionate size. The following are typical examples, the characters described being not necessarily exclusive to the groups or species mentioned.

The long, dagger-shaped bills of most herons and bitterns (Ardeidae) are well adapted to seizing quick-moving prey in shallow water or among reeds. A more perfected development for grasping fish is seen in the bills of mergansers *Mergus* spp., which have saw-like tomia ; the bills of toucans (Ramphastidae) have similar toothed serrations for securing food. The elongated, slender bills of most wading birds of the Charadriiformes are adapted to probing in mud or sand, typical straight and pliable examples being seen in the Snipe *Gallinago gallinago* and Woodcock *Scolopax rusticola* ; deeply decurved examples occur in the curlews *Numenius* spp. The avocets (Recurvirostridae) feed largely on the surface of shallow water and have slender, much recurved bills. In the Wrybill Plover *Anarhynchus frontalis* the whole of the distal half of the bill is curved to the right. A highly specialised mode of feeding is illustrated by the Spoonbill *Platalea leucorodia*, which has the tip of the bill flattened and enlarged in spatulate form, and in the Shoveller *Spatula clypeata*, which has a wide, spoon-shaped bill. The boat-shaped bills of the Shoebill *Balaeniceps rex* and the Boatbill *Cochlearius cochlearius* are other examples. An even more extreme adaptation occurs in the skimmers (Rynchopidae), in which both the lower mandible and its supporting jaw-bones are much elongated, to serve as a projecting scoop (although laterally compressed) in skimming food from the surface of the water in flight. The bills

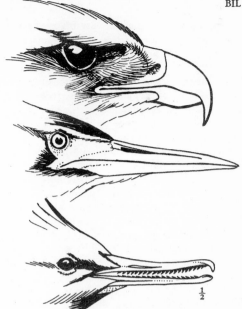

FIG 3 (a) Golden Eagle *Aqulia chrysaetos*, raptorial bill ;
    (b) Bittern *Botaurus stellaris*, spear-like bill ;
    (c) Red-breasted Merganser *Mergus serrator*, saw bill.
    C.E.T.K.

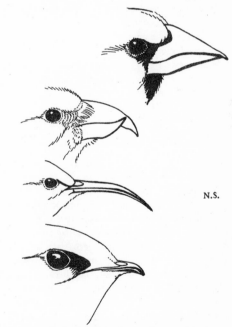

FIG 4 (a) Hawfinch *Coccothraustes coccothraustes*, large conical bill ;
    (b) Crossbill *Loxia curvirostra*, bill with tips of upper and lower mandibles crossing ;
    (c) Scarlet-breasted Sunbird *Chalcomitra senegalensis*, bill adapted to nectar-feeding ;
    (d) Alpine Swift *Apus melba*, weak bill in a bird that catches insects with open gape. *C.E.T.K.*

of flamingos are angled downwards in the middle and equipped with a series of elaborate plates or lamellae, which sieve food from muddy water, the bill being held in an inverted position (see FLAMINGO). Lamellae are present also in the bills of swans, geese, and ducks (Anatidae) and in prions *Pachyptila* spp. The maximum development of lamellae is seen in the brush-like mass inside the bill of the Openbill Stork *Anastomus oscitans*; this species shows a further peculiarity in that it has a gap halfway along the closed mandibles.

The finches and grosbeaks (Fringillidae), the buntings (Emberizidae), the weavers and sparrows (Ploceidae), and others have stout bills, conical in section, and well adapted to cracking seeds. The commissures in this group of birds are characteristically angulated. A notably wide range of variation in the bill is found in the Reed Bunting *Emberiza schoeniclus* (see BUNTING). A species showing remarkable specialisation is the Hawfinch *Coccothraustes coccothraustes*, which has a very highly developed musculature of the jaws and skull, and ridged bosses or 'anvils' on the palate and inside the lower mandible, enabling it to crack the stones of cherries and even of olives. Somewhat similar, but transverse, rasp-like ridges are found inside the bills of certain parrots; with these the hardest fruit-stones are reduced to fine particles. Another striking adaptation is illustrated by the bills of adult crossbills *Loxia* spp., the mandibles being sharply pointed and widely crossed over (to right or left in about equal numbers) to aid the rapid extraction of seeds from fir-cones.

Birds-of-prey, both diurnal and nocturnal (Falconiformes and Strigiformes), have powerfully hooked and sharply pointed bills, well adapted to killing and tearing up their food. The small, chiefly insectivorous members of the Falconidae have bills of delicate proportions, but in the larger eagles such as *Haliaetus* the proportions are massive. The bills of shrikes (Laniidae) are sharply hooked at the tip and the upper mandibular tomium has a distinct 'tooth'; several 'teeth' are apparent in the upper mandibles of trogons (Trogonidae).

Small insectivorous birds, typified by the Old World and New World warblers (Sylviinae and Parulidae) have small and usually slender bills. Treecreepers (Certhiidae), which seek small insects in the bark of trees, also have slender but longer and decurved bills. The long and finely curved bills of some hummingbirds (Trochilidae) show perfect adaptation to picking minute insects from the throats of flowers. The bills of this family are in addition well adapted to feeding on nectar, as in varying degree are those of the sunbirds (Nectar-iniidae), the honeyeaters (Meliphagidae) the Hawaiian honeycreepers (Drepanididae), and the flowerpeckers (Dicaeidae). Some insectivorous families such as the nightjars (Caprimulgidae), which are crepuscular feeders, and some birds of smaller size such as the flycatchers of the Muscicapinae and Tyrannidae, have forward-pointing rictal bristles; like the swifts (Apodidae) and swallows (Hirundinidae), they have very broad gapes which facilitate the capture of flying insects. An adaptation to a highly specialised method of feeding is found in the Buphaginae (see OXPECKER).

Woodpeckers (Picidae) are equipped with sturdy chisel-tipped bills for the excavation of nest-holes in tree-trunks and for reaching wood-boring insects.

G.M.

Pomeroy, D. E. 1962. Birds with abnormal bills. Brit. Birds 55 : 49–72. (Deformities.)

BILLING: caressing with the bill.

BILL SOUNDS: see INSTRUMENTAL SOUNDS

BIMACULATION: the occurrence of two spots, e.g. in the facial plumage of certain ducks (Anatidae) —see PLUMAGE VARIATION.

BIMODAL: see under MEAN, ARITHMETIC ; STATISTICAL SIGNIFICANCE

BINOMINAL SYSTEM: see NOMENCLATURE

BIOCENOSIS: ecological term (plural 'biocenoses') for an association of living things inhabiting a uniform division of the 'biosphere'; in other words, the ecological community found in a particular 'biotope' (see under BIOSPHERE).

BIOCHORE: see under BIOSPHERE

BIOCYCLE: see under BIOSPHERE

BIOLOGY: the science of life—the study of animate nature. The antithesis is with the physical sciences, apart from the applications of these to the study of living matter. The term 'biological' does not exclude the study of dead specimens as one of the approaches to the problems of the living organism, although sometimes loosely used as if it did.

BIOMASS: quantitative term used in ecology— the total weight of organisms per unit area of land, or the total weight of organisms of a specified kind (e.g. birds).

BIOME: term for a major biotic community, i.e. one existing in a wide area defined by certain general environmental features (and possibly including both land and fresh water)—contrast LIFE

ZONE. An equivalent term in respect of animal life only is ' zoome ' (and in respect of plants only, ' phytome ').

BIOMETRICS: alternatively ' biometry ' and ' biostatistics ', the science of the analysis of quantitative biological data (see STATISTICAL SIGNIFICANCE).

BIONOMICS: term equivalent to ECOLOGY.

BIOSPECIES: see under SPECIES

BIOSPHERE: ecological term for the sum total of the environments capable of supporting life, i.e. the ' habitable globe ' as regards animals and plants. The biosphere is divisible into three ' biocycles '— ocean, fresh water, and land. These in turn are divisible into ' biochores ' ; thus the main biochores in the terrestrial biocycle are forest, dry open land, moist open land, high montane and polar areas. Biochores are in turn made up of ' biotopes ', which are particular areas substantially uniform in their environmental conditions and living inhabitants (see ECOLOGY).

BIOTA: term coined to comprehend both the fauna and the flora of an area (see FAUNA).

BIOTOPE: see under BIOSPHERE

BIOTYPE: a population of the same genotype (in the proper sense of the latter term)—see GENOTYPE.

BIPEDAL: two-footed, in the sense that the fore-limbs are not used for walking ; but compare the special meaning of TETRAPOD, also applied to birds.

BIRD: term applied, in different contexts, either to an individual animal or to a species (or subspecific form) belonging to the class Aves ; occasionally to an imaginary generalised type ; also used adjectivally (e.g. bird song), or as part of the name of a species or group (e.g. tropicbird, bird-of-paradise)—see AVES.

BIRD-OF-PARADISE: substantive name of most species of Paradisaeidae (Passeriformes, sub-order Oscines) ; in the plural, general term for the family. The centre of abundance of the family is New Guinea and its islands, with a few species in nearby areas in northern Australia and in the Molucca Islands. There are some 40 species, although whether the allocation of a few less specialised forms should be to this family or to the closely related bowerbirds (Ptilonorhynchidae) is in doubt. Otherwise, birds-of-paradise seem to be relatives of the crows and jays (Corvidae), which they resemble in size and in being robust, active birds with stout bills, strong perching feet, and loud, often harsh, voices. They are tree birds, of the forests ; and many live only in the mountains,

some at considerable altitudes. Some commonly visit fruit trees to feed, but they also search for insects, small tree frogs, and lizards among the branches and leaves. They are not gregarious, and, except at fruit trees and (in a few species) at their communal displays, the birds are usually found singly or (some species) in pairs.

A few species are all black, without special decoration except for gloss in the plumage or wattles, and without sexual dimorphism. At the other extreme are many species with plain females and males that are either mostly black and decorated with many bizarre plumes, or brightly coloured and possessing elaborate decorative plumes.

The type of breeding behaviour is correlated with the degree of sexual dimorphism. The species with little or no sexual dimorphism form monogamous pairs, as in typical song-birds, and the male assists the female in nest duties. In the species with great sexual dimorphism no pairs are formed ; the males display and the females come to these display areas, mate, and then nest and raise their young independently of the males.

Some species clear display grounds on or near the forest floor and display singly ; others display on branches high in the trees, and some of these gather and display in communal groups. The displays of the males utilise the strange ornamentation— whether it be head or tail plumes, back capes or breast shields, or flank plumes—by erecting and spreading these feathers and then engaging in ritualised performances that are aptly called dances, and in striking strange poses. Some even display by holding themselves in a horizontal position, or even upside down beneath a branch.

The nest (known for only some species) is usually a rather bulky basin-shaped affair of twigs on a branch, but in one species, the King Bird-of-paradise *Cicinnurus regius*, it is in a hole in a tree. The clutch consists of one or two eggs, on which a pale background colour is marked with irregular, longitudinal lines.

Correlated with the polygamous, fleeting mating of the ornamented species and their lack of any pair-bond, is the relatively large number of known hybrids. Thirteen intergeneric hybrids have been named as species, and many of these had generic rank proposed for them. In the plume birds of the genus *Paradisaea*, four intra-generic hybrids were named, three of them as species.

The discovery of so many natural hybrids since 1873, from such an inaccessible area as New Guinea, was due to the birds being very popular and abundant in the millinery plume-trade in Europe ; this began in 1522, when the Spaniards secured plumes in the Moluccas that had reached there by native trade routes from New Guinea. Although the export trade in plumes has largely ceased, the natives still use a few plumes as ornaments, especially in certain dances (see ORNAMENTATION, BIRDS IN HUMAN).

The best-known species are the large plume birds of the genus *Paradisaea*, such as the Greater Bird-of-paradise *P. apoda* of the Aru Islands and New Guinea (introduced into Little Tobago in the West Indies in 1909). Elongated flank plumes, usually white, yellow, or red, long central tail 'wires', and communal dances characterise most of this group. However, the Blue Bird-of-paradise *P. rudolphi* has blue plumes and hangs below its perch in its display. The King Bird-of-paradise (above) is the smallest species and is red above, with wire-like elongated curled central tail feathers tipped with 'flags', white below with green flank tufts ; it displays in trees.

The small Magnificent Bird-of-paradise *Diphyllodes magnificus* has a red back, a glossy golden ruff, an iridescent green breast shield, and two long, thin, curled tail feathers. It clears an area for its display on the ground in mountain forests. The small King of Saxony Bird-of-paradise *Pteridophora alberti* is notable for its head plumes, which may be 18 inches long, more than twice the length of the bird. One plume rises from each side of its head, and these plumes are wire-like, each with a close-set series of little, celluloid-like 'flags' along one side. This species displays alone, high in trees.

The Twelve-wire Bird-of-paradise *Seleucidis melanoleuca* is a large species, mostly black, but with yellow flank tufts and with the tips of six feathers on each side recurved as wire-like extensions reaching forward about as far as the breast. The Superb Bird-of-paradise *Lophorina superba* is a medium-sized black species with a velvety elongated cape and a metallic breast shield with the corners greatly elongated. The six-wired birds-of-paradise *Parotia* spp. are also mostly black and have three long wire-like plumes on each side of the crown, reaching to the lower back and ending in small 'flags'.

The long-tailed birds-of-paradise *Astrapia* spp. are high-mountain birds, mostly black but with very long tails several times the length of the body. In most, the feathers are broad and black ; but in one, *A. mayeri*, they are narrow, excessively long, and white. The sickle-billed birds of paradise *Epimachus* spp. are also high-mountain species, mostly black and brown in colour, with small flank tufts and much elongated slender tails. The short-tailed, medium-sized d'Albertis's Sicklebill *Drepanornis albertisi* is rather modestly brown, with short tufts on neck and flanks.

The above species, all of New Guinea or nearby islands, show the main types of ornamentation in the male in this family. Also in this family are the rifle-birds, *Craspedophora* and *Ptiloris*, rather large, mostly black with iridescent throat patches and with or without small flank plumes ; they live in New Guinea and Australia. Chiefly in New Guinea are several all-black species in which the sexes are alike, and in at least some of which monogamous pairing occurs. They include the large McGregor's Bird-of-paradise *Macgregoria pulchra*, with a large yellow eye-wattle ; the smaller Wattled Bird-of-paradise *Paradigalla carunculata*, with yellow wattles in front of the eye ; and the manucodes, *Manucodia* and *Phonygammus*, with ornamentation restricted to gloss and to having some feathers lanceolate or with a curious crinkled texture.

As outliers, beyond the New Guinea and northern Australia area, we have the large Paradise-crow *Lycocorax pyrrhopterus* of the Moluccas, with a silky black plumage and brown wings, and the smaller Wallace's Standard-wing *Semioptera wallacei*, with elongated plumes on the bends of its wings and a green breast-shield with greatly lengthened outer corners.

Mayr (1962) divides the family into the Cnemophilinae (*Loria, Loboparadisea, Cnemophila*—and Bock adds *Macgregoria*) and Paradisaeinae, the former being regarded as the more primitive.

See Plates 6, 31 (colour) and 43 (egg). A.L.R.

Bock, W. J. 1963. Relationships between the birds of paradise and the bower birds. Condor 65 : 91–125.
Iredale, T. 1950. Birds of Paradise and Bower Birds. Melbourne.
Mayr, E. 1941. List of New Guinea Birds. New York. (List of species and hybrids, pp. 167–183.)
Mayr, E. 1962. Family Paradisaeidae. *In* Mayr, E. & Greenway, J. C., Jr. (eds.). Check-list of Birds of the World vol. 15. Cambridge, Mass.
Rand, A. L. 1938. On the breeding habits of some birds of paradise in the wild. Amer. Mus. Novit. no. 993 : 1–8.
Ripley, S. D. 1950. Strange courtship of birds of paradise. Natl. Geog. Mag. 97 : 247–278. (Displays, coloured plates.)

BIRD-OF-PREY: in the most general sense, a species that hunts and kills other animals (particularly the higher vertebrates) for food ; in a more specialised sense (and regardless of habits), a member of the Falconiformes ; in the plural, general term for that order (see FALCON ; HAWK ; SECRETARY-BIRD ; VULTURE (1) ; VULTURE (2)) ; sometimes extended to cover the Strigiformes, the qualifications 'diurnal' and 'nocturnal' then being used to distinguish the two groups (see OWL). The term 'raptor' is sometimes used in similar senses.

BIRD'S NEST SOUP: see EDIBLE NESTS

BIRD-WATCHING: a term popularly applied to all field observation of birds, but by ornithologists sometimes restricted to looking at birds for one's own personal enjoyment rather than with any scientific motive. The distinction, however, is not so clear as it used to be early in the century ; then the serious ornithologist was usually a museum worker, whose excursions into the field were primarily to collect specimens for further work in the museum, and the few people who watched birds seldom had any scientific interest. The term bird-watcher in its literal sense could apply perfectly to men such as Gilbert White, Edmond Selous, or Viscount Grey of Fallodon, all of whom amassed in their own ways a store of valuable information on bird behaviour ; but they and a few like them were distinguished exceptions to the rule that a bird shot constituted the only scientific record. The conception of field ornithology was evolving fast before the First World War, but it then suffered a long setback from which the first real signs of recovery in the United Kingdom were in the mid-twenties at Oxford. There a new generation of field ornithologists was being trained by W. B. Alexander and B. W. Tucker, while the local ornithological society was setting a pattern of the greatest significance and was to become the proto-type of local societies all over the country. It was within this framework that the enormous increase in serious bird-watching in Britain took root in the ensuing years.

The census of heronries organised by E. M. Nicholson, through the journal *British Birds*, showed how the efforts of the growing number of amateur bird-watchers could be harnessed on a national scale (see also CENSUS). Its success must have encouraged H. F. Witherby (the editor-in-chief) and Nicholson (the organiser) in the leading roles that they were to play in the foundation in 1932 of the British Trust for Ornithology, which was to provide a permanent machinery for future co-operative inquiries.

It was about this time that young people in the towns were turning more and more to the country-side for their recreation, and the growing interest in bird-watching that gathered momentum in the thirties undoubtedly owed much to the popularity of the hiking movement. As this itself may well have been indirectly an escape reaction from the uncertainties of the time, it is not surprising that during the Second World War bird-watching attracted many newcomers among servicemen banished to remote parts of the world, often with time on their hands. While the ordinary country-man is often mildly interested in birds, and quite knowledgeable within limits, the modern bird-watcher is much more often an urban dweller ; and one of the most interesting features of this development is that it knows no social boundaries.

Many bird-watchers never progress, or want to progress, beyond proficiency in the field identification of birds, and there is indeed a thrill in tracking a bird that is elusive and in learning to do so by ear as well as by sight. The appeal of watching birds may derive, however, from a variety of reasons. It may be purely aesthetic, it may satisfy the collector's instinct in amassing a long list (' tally ') of species identified, nests found, or birds ringed ; or it may be merely a pursuit that adds interest to walking for recreation or exercise. On the other hand, it may come from a desire to find out for oneself something about the lives of birds, or of course from a combination of all these reasons. Whatever the inducement for others, the serious student often reacts against interference of the ' rubber-necking ' variety, and it is sometimes said that the ' bird-watcher ' is the bird's worst enemy, or in other words that there is danger to the bird in too close an interest in breeding behaviour. In particular cases this may well be so ; but the interest of as large a section of the public as possible is required to educate the rest and to foster conservation. This interest is growing rapidly, not only in the more temperate countries of the Northern Hemisphere but also in some of the more southerly countries where popular interest in birds has hitherto been confined to *la chasse*. Unfortunately, very few of those who look in their thousands at popular nature programmes on television ever go so far as to give active support to a society devoted to bird study or protection.

Fifty years and more ago serious bird-watching in the field was an individual pursuit, concerned primarily with behaviour and then mostly in the breeding season. In the last thirty years or so there has been a widening of interests, ranging from individual studies of the life-cycle of a single species to population studies with a network of observers on a local, national, or international scale, as in the case of the Gannet *Sula bassana*. Many bird-watchers dislike joining in organised inquiries, while others derive satisfaction from playing a part, however small, in large-scale investigations. The day is far off when there will not be ample scope for both individual and corporate research.

Much amateur effort has gone into ringing (or ' banding ' in America), the results of which have confirmed some early conceptions of migration but are continually bringing to light new, and often unsuspected, facets of bird movement (see RINGING). The enthusiasm devoted to ringing has also provided invaluable data for studies in population dynamics, for example in calculations of the expectation of life and mortality rates (see LIFE, EXPECTATION OF ; POPULATION DYNAMICS). The use of nest record cards, even although they are often too incomplete for many of the potential forms of analysis, has been another largely amateur contribution to the study of population problems and the breeding cycle. The dual interest of bird-watchers in migration and in ringing, almost as a sport in its own right, has led to the establishment of many coastal observatories and to the development of migration research centres in several countries (see OBSERVATORY, BIRD).

While bird-watching may be thought of mainly as an amateur pursuit, it is one of the intrinsic features of ornithology as a natural science that the modern professional is usually as much a field observer as a museum worker, and much professional work in recent years has been the product of intensive watching in the field. A rigid division between professional and amateur is largely a thing of the past, and while there are some problems requiring time that only the former can give there are others that need more extensive observation in which co-operative effort is essential. Bird-watching embraces many levels of interest and skill, and it is from the encouragement of the more advanced exponents that the rest can derive most benefit.

See also PHOTOGRAPHY.   R.C.H.

BISHOP : substantive name of some *Euplectes* spp. (see WEAVER).

BITTERN : substantive name of the species of the Botaurinae, a subfamily of the Ardeidae (Ciconii-formes, suborder Ardeae) ; in Britain commonly used without qualification for the sole native species ; in the plural, general term for the subfamily. The other subfamily is the Ardeinae, which includes the so-called ' tiger bitterns ' or tiger herons (see HERON). The bitterns are closely related to the herons and, indeed, some authorities do not separate the two sub-families. However, bitterns generally have shorter necks, shorter legs, and stouter bodies ; they are more secretive and solitary, not really colonial like most herons, and accordingly are more cryptically coloured, largely lack the exaggerated head, breast, and scapular plumes, and have developed distinctive spring calls for use by the male as well as circling advertisement flights ; they are more crepuscular, and the spring ' song ' is uttered both by day and

by night ; they breed on the ground or in marshes, not usually in trees or bushes, and they feed essentially in reeds, high sedge, and similar places ; when alarmed they adopt a remarkable concealment posture rather than take flight ; the inner toe is longer than the outer, not the other way round as in herons ; they have only two pairs of powder-down patches (breast and rump), as against three or four in the herons ; and they have 8 or (more usually) 10 tail feathers, as against 12. Their bills are strong and pointed, and both mandibles are finely serrated near the tip ; the toes are long and slender, and the middle claw is pectinated.

Following the classification of Bock, there are 2 genera, together containing 12 species. *Botaurus* spp. are large and heavy, with soft plumage beautifully variegated with browns, buffs, blacks, and yellows in a cryptic pattern of streaks and bars ; the sexes are similar ; they usually walk deliberately, with feet lifted slowly, and they rarely perch off the ground (although they do climb awkwardly in reeds) ; the males have far-carrying, singly uttered ' booming ' or ' thunder-pumping ' calls in spring. *Ixobrychus* spp. are much smaller, with dove-sized bodies and a more contrasting plumage pattern made up of large patches of dark and pale colours, including black and almost white ; the sexes are markedly dissimilar in a majority of the species (wherein they differ also from all the herons) ; they run rapidly on the ground and climb nimbly in reeds and trees ; the spring calls of the males are guttural cooing or croaking sounds uttered in long series. Perhaps the difference in size and agility is best emphasised by the fact that most *Ixobrychus* spp. do not weigh more than 5–6 ounces (one species as little as 2–3), while *Botaurus* spp., with twice the length and three times the wing-span, weigh 1–3 pounds.

Although bitterns do not have the elaborate plumes of many herons, the feathers of the crown and lower neck are modified to a greater or lesser extent, and pale scapular tufts are used in the displays of at least one species of *Botaurus*. Both large and small bitterns take a wide variety of aquatic prey including fish, crustaceans, small mammals and reptiles, amphibians, and insects, but some species or populations are almost exclusively fish-eaters while others are largely insectivorous. All nest in freshwater reed, sedge, and other aquatic vegetation, in marshes, lakes, or large rivers. *Botaurus* spp. build up a platform of reeds and sedge 4–5 inches above water level, while *Ixobrychus* spp. make more of a nest 1–2 feet (even up to 10–20 feet) above shallow water in dense vegetation or even in trees. The eggs are commonly 4–6 in number, but up to 10 have been recorded in *Ixobrychus*. They are white to bluish or greenish (*Ixobrychus*) or buffish-brown to olive-brown (*Botaurus*), smooth but with little or no gloss and generally without markings (although there may sometimes be a few fine brown speckles near the large end). In *Botaurus* incubation and care of the young is by the female alone, in *Ixobrychus* by both sexes.

The subfamily has a wide distribution: 2 species breed in Europe, 6 in Asia, 3 in Africa, 3 in Australasia, 2 in North America, and 3 in South America. There is thus a fairly even scatter through the various zoogeographical regions, but *Botaurus* in particular is mainly found in temperate zones, and all the bitterns are largely confined between 60°N and 40°S lat. Most, especially *Ixobrychus* spp., are at least partial migrants—and summer visitors to the colder parts of their range. The 4 species of *Botaurus* —the Eurasian Bittern *B. stellaris* (also found in South Africa), the Australian Bittern *B. poiciloptilus*, the American Bittern *B. lentiginosus*, and the South American (or Pinnated) Bittern *B. pinnatus*—are allopatric and together form a superspecies, some of them possibly even conspecific. Another super-species is formed by the tiny Least Bittern *I. exilis* of America, the Little Bittern *I. minutus* of Eurasia, Africa, and Australia, and the Chinese Little (or Yellow) Bittern *I. sinensis*. Other members of this genus include the Variegated (or Streaked) Little Bittern *I. involucris* of South America, the African Dwarf Bittern *I. sturmii*, and Schrenk's Little Bittern *I. eurhythmus* and the Cinnamon Little Bittern *I. cinnamomeus*, both of southeast Asia. One other is less clearly related and was formerly placed in a separate genus ; this is the Black (or Mangrove) Bittern *Ixobrychus* (' *Dupetor* ') *flavicollis*, found from southeast Asia to Australia. It is larger than other *Ixobrychus* spp., but very similar in behaviour, plumage type, and sexual dimorphism. This species has the feathers of the crown and lower neck more nearly developed as plumes than any of the other bitterns ; it has black, reddish, and partly white colour phases in the same population (*I. exilis* also has a melanistic phase).

Several habits are almost or entirely peculiar to the group. Most striking is the concealment posture, shared only with the tiger herons. In this the bird becomes completely rigid with the bill and neck pointed stiffly skywards and the feathers tightly compressed so that the whole body appears elongated ; the bird keeps its underside towards the source of danger, watching with unwinking yellow eyes swivelled downwards, and revolves slowly (or whirls with great rapidity) if the observer or other threat moves round. The striped underside (or plain dull buff under parts in some *Ixobrychus*) fit in remarkably with a background of dead reeds, and the bird in this posture is almost invisible. In a light breeze, at least some species will sway with the reeds. *Ixobrychus* may even let itself be picked up; W. H. Hudson described how *I. involucris* in South America allowed him to push its head down until this touched its back, and when he removed his hand the head and neck flew up to the original position like a steel spring. This protective posture is adopted even by downy young only a few days old. (See Plate 23.)

The bitterns share with the herons the use of powder-down patches and a pectinated middle claw to clean their plumage. Percy showed that the head is rubbed in these patches until covered with the powder, which is then allowed to soak up fish slime and oil (probably also excess preen oil) before being combed off by vigorous movements of the toothed claw.

The booming of large bitterns is probably one of the most far-carrying of all bird sounds. It is audible to the human ear at distances of from 1 to as much as 3 miles, depending on the conditions. The male's oesophagus is specially modified in the breeding season so that it can be inflated and act as a resonating chamber in the production of this extraordinary sound. The bird utters a series of clicks or coughs, breathes in deeply with its head thrust forward and whole body vibrating, and then raises its head and neck to produce the deep resonant boom in a great exhalation ; this performance is commonly repeated several times. A comparable noise is produced by the tiger herons.

(See Plates 23 (phot.) and 43 (egg). J.F.-L.

Bock, W. J. 1956. A generic review of the family Ardeidae (Aves). Amer. Mus. Novit. no. 1779: 1–49.
Percy, W. 1951. Three Studies in Bird Character: Bitterns, Herons and Water-Rails. London.

BITTERN, SUN-: see SUNBITTERN

BLACKBIRD (1): in Britain, *Turdus merula* ; also used as substantive name of some congeners elsewhere (see THRUSH).

BLACKBIRD (2): in North America, substantive name of certain Icteridae, especially *Agelaius* spp. (see ORIOLE (2)).

BLACKCAP: *Sylvia atricapilla* (see WARBLER (1)).

BLACKCOCK: special name for the male of the Black Grouse *Lyrurus tetrix*, the female being called ' greyhen ' (see GROUSE).

BLACKEYE: substantive name of *Chlorocharis emiliae* (see WHITE-EYE).

BLACKSTART: *Cercomela melanura*, of south-western Asia and north-eastern Africa (for sub-family see THRUSH).

BLADDER, URINARY: an organ not present in birds (see EXCRETORY SYSTEM).

BLASTODERM; BLASTODISC: see DEVELOPMENT, EMBRYONIC ; EGG ; REPRODUCTIVE SYSTEM

BLOOD: the fluid that, in all vertebrates, carries oxygen from the lungs to the tissues and returns carbon dioxide (see VASCULAR SYSTEM) ; carries soluble products of digestion to storage or modifying organs such as the liver and to the tissues (see ALIMENTARY SYSTEM) ; and carries waste substances in solution to the kidneys (see EXCRETORY SYSTEM). Antibodies produced against invading organisms are distributed ; so also are hormones from the endocrine glands (such as the pituitary or thyroid) to their sites of activity, which may be further endocrine glands, the specific organs to be affected, or the tissues in general (see ENDOCRINE SYSTEM). Above all, blood is the vehicle by which the 'internal environment' of the tissues is kept constant.

Blood consists of two main parts, one cellular and the other fluid. The white cells or leucocytes help to combat infections, while the erythrocytes or red cells (corpuscles) have as their main function the carriage of oxygen and carbon dioxide. The erythrocytes are, of course, too small to be visible individually and so form the red coloration. The cells are suspended in the fluid element, the plasma.

Plasma. This itself consists of two parts, water and proteins (substances of very large molecules containing nitrogen). Food and waste products are dissolved in the water, while the proteins behave usually as a colloidal suspension. Antibodies are likewise proteins and in adult animals are an appreciable fraction of those in the blood. The blood proteins may be divided into classes because their molecular sizes tend to fall into definite groups, although with no absolute divisions between them. These can be separated by techniques such as electrophoresis or chromatography, in which the molecules of different sizes move at different speeds under the influence, respectively, of an electric current or of an advancing capillary front.

Erythrocytes. In all vertebrates the erythrocytes start their development as nucleated cells, but those of mammals lose their nuclei before being pushed out into the blood stream (except in conditions of disease). In birds—as also in reptiles, amphibia, and fishes—the erythrocytes retain the nuclei ; they are also oval, although flattened. (In mammals the erythrocytes are round—except in the Camel,

Llama, and Vicuna, where they are again oval.) In birds they are large ; thus in man there are about 5 million per c.mm., but in birds about 2 million. The smaller ones are more efficient. In a remarkable series of papers in the *Proceedings of the Zoological Society of London* round about 1850, George Gulliver recorded the measurements of the red cells of many animals, including birds. He pointed out that there was a fairly consistent average for a species but wide variations between different species. However, there was no relation between these measurements and the accepted systematic classification, e.g. in the owls (Strigiformes), of which he examined several species which would still be considered as closely related. The average life of a red cell is only a few weeks, after which it is removed from the circulation by the so-called 'reticulo-endothelial system' and replaced by new cells formed in the sinusoids of the bone-marrow by a process of development strictly comparable to what is found in mammals.

Haemoglobin. It is this red pigment of the cells that is fundamentally responsible for the complex series of changes by which oxygen is absorbed or liberated by the red cells as required. Chemically it is similar in all vertebrates, a protein containing iron, and recent work by the techniques mentioned above has shown in many groups of animals that it can be divided into several slightly different substances. In birds, electrophoretic methods have as yet failed to subdivide the haemoglobin in some of the birds that have been examined, e.g. some pigeons (Columbidae) and penguins (Spheniscidae). Chromatography, however, has revealed five types, some of which appear to be similar to those of man, e.g. human Haemoglobin E, which is an inherited abnormality responsible both for the rare disease called thalassaemia and for a marked degree of resistance to infestation with malaria parasites. In birds the arrangement of the five types of haemoglobin in the species examined bears some relationship to broad systematic factors. Thus, one factor found in the older groups such as Pelecaniformes, Falconiformes, or Ciconiiformes is absent in those believed to be of intermediate antiquity, such as Cuculiformes, and yet reappears in Passeriformes.

Leucocytes. As with so much detailed work on birds, most observations have been made on such domesticated species as fowls and pigeons. Their blood contains about 5000 leucocytes per c.mm., but variations have been observed with season and with laying times. In contrast to mammals, except very young ones, the blood contains a greater proportion of lymphocytes than the granulocytes which ingest invading bacteria. The granulocytes also differ in having nuclei split into many small lobes, but otherwise the cells and their mode of development differ little from those of mammals.

Blood Groups. The importance of these in human blood transfusion is well known. They depend on specific antigens present in the plasma, red cells, and other tissues, and forming several series independent of each other and controlled by a number of genes inherited according to the established laws of genetics (see GENETICS). They form, indeed, one of the best worked-out series of inherited factors, have been correlated with liability to certain diseases, and provide very important evidence with regard to the relationship between races of mankind. In domestic fowls no less than twelve distinct series have been described using saline agglutination of cells with iso-immune sera ; complement fixation techniques have not proved as satisfactory. There are some cross reactions, so some antigenic material must be common to several series, but genetically they segregate independently. The ' B ' system at least seems to be related to the production of antibodies to tissue grafts from other individuals, while some heterozygotes of this system appear to confer an increased survival to the lines bearing them. In the Golden Leghorn fowl an antigen for human serum has been found in the erythrocytes. The male bird may carry the double gene on his ZZ chromosome while the female can have only one on her ZW chromosome, which has analogies with some aspects of the well-known Rhesus blood group system of man, although the arrangement of the sex chromosomes as between males and females is reversed in mammals and birds. In ducks one blood group is sex-linked, a condition only recently found in one human blood group (see GENETICS). Serological differences between species have been investigated in the genus *Streptopelia* (Columbidae) ; the differences between *S. ' risoria '*, *S. chinensis*, and *S. senegalensis* have been resolved serologically into a number of specific antigens, some of which are held in common between two species.

Systematic Serology. Birds certainly produce antibodies to many antigens introduced from outside, e.g. bacteria and the blood of other animals ; those of the former class are presumably of use to the bird as to other animals, but the latter are of course an entirely artificial phenomenon. In mammals, the specific antibodies to the blood of different species produced in one experimental animal, e.g. the Rabbit, have been shewn to be related for systematically related species ; but such work on birds has so far led to equivocal results.

For tests utilising blood serum, haemoglobin crystal patterns, and erythrocyte haemolysis see PROTEINS AS TAXONOMIC CHARACTERS.   R.E.R.

Conference 1962. Blood groups in infrahuman species. Ann. N.Y.Acad. Sci. 97 : 1–328. (Papers by many authors.)

Lucas, A. M. & Jamroz, C. 1961. Atlas of Avian Haematology. U.S. Dept. Agric., Agric. Mon. 25. Washington, D.C.

BLOOD VESSELS : see HEART; VASCULAR SYSTEM

BLOSSOMCROWN : *Anthocephala floriceps* (for family see HUMMINGBIRD).

BLUEBILL (1): substantive name of *Spermophaga* spp. (see WEAVER-FINCH).

BLUEBILL (2): a name in North America for the Scaup *Aythya marila*, and in Australia for the Australian Stifftail *Oxyura australis* (see DUCK).

BLUEBIRD : substantive name of *Sialia* spp., of North and Middle America (see THRUSH).

BLUEBIRD, FAIRY : see FAIRY-BLUEBIRD ; and under LEAFBIRD

BLUECREST : *Orthorhyncus cristatus* (for family see HUMMINGBIRD).

BLUETAIL : *Tarsiger cyanurus*, of the eastern Palaearctic (one of the bush-robins)—for subfamily see THRUSH.

BLUETHROAT : *Luscinia svecica*, of the northern Palaearctic (for subfamily see THRUSH).

BOATBILL : otherwise the Boat-billed Heron *Cochlearius cochlearius*, of the Neotropical Region (see HERON).

BOATSWAIN-BIRD : see BO'SUN-BIRD

BOBOLINK : *Dolichonyx oryzivorus*, native to North America (see ORIOLE (2)).

BOBWHITE : *Colinus virginianus*, one of the American quails (Odontophorinae)—see under PHEASANT.

BODY : see SHAPE AND POSTURE ; TOPOGRAPHY ; and for care of body surface see FEATHER MAINTENANCE.

BOG-BIRD : name sometimes applied to *Balaeniceps rex* (see SHOEBILL).

BOKMAKIERE : well-known Afrikaans name (from the duetting call) for *Telephorus zeylonus* (see SHRIKE).

BOMBYCILLIDAE : a family (Passeriformes, suborder Oscines), formerly called ' Ampelidae ', that in the classification here followed includes the Bombycillinae (see WAXWING) ; Ptilogonatinae (see SILKYFLYCATCHER) ; and Hypocoliinae (see HYPO-COLIUS) ; while the Dulidae are sometimes also included, reduced to subfamilial rank (see PALMCHAT). No final agreement has been reached among ornithologists as to the groups to be included, some authorities considering all four to be equally of family rank, while others compromise in various ways ; but all believe these taxa to be closely related.

Greenway, J. C., Jr. 1960. Family Bombycillidae. *In* Mayr, E. & Greenway, J. C., Jr. (eds.). Check-list of Birds of the World vol. 9. Cambridge, Mass.

BONE : see SKELETON ; PALATE ; PNEUMATISATION OF BONE ; also, with regard to bone formation, under ENDOCRINE SYSTEM.

BONXIE : local name, in Shetland (sole British breeding locality), for the Great Skua *Catharcta skua* (see SKUA).

BOOBY : substantive name of certain *Suia* spp. (to which ' gannet ' is sometimes alternatively applied, in addition to being invariably used for other species)—see GANNET.

BOOMING GROUND : special term in North America for the social display ground of the Greater Prairie Chicken *Tympanuchus cupido* (see GROUSE ; LEK).

BOOTED : otherwise ' holothecal ' or ' ocreate ', term applied to the horny covering of the tarsus when it, or most of it, is in an undivided piece (see LEG ; compare LAMINIPLANTAR ; SCUTELLATE). In poultry literature ' booted ' means having a feathered tarsus ; in general this is not an ornithological usage, ' rough-legged ' being preferred, but the adjective has that sense in the name of the Booted Eagle *Hieraaetus pennatus*.

BOREAL : term applied in North America to a climatic life zone immediately south of the Arctic and subdivided into ' Hudsonian ' and ' Canadian ' (see LIFE ZONE).

BO'SUNBIRD : sailors' name for *Phaethon* spp. (see TROPICBIRD). It is said to ' carry a marlin-spike in the tail '.

BOTANICAL FACTORS : see VEGETATION ; also POLLINATORS AND DISTRIBUTORS

BOTAURINAE : see BITTERN

BOUBOU : substantive name of some *Laniarius* spp. (see SHRIKE) ; to be distinguished from BRUBRU.

BOWERBIRD : name applied to the species

of Ptilonorhynchidae (Passeriformes, sub-order Oscines) not included in the second subfamily, Ailuroedinae (catbirds). Members of the last named group do not build bowers and are dealt with separately below. The family as a whole is widespread in Australia and New Guinea and is restricted thereto. Its nearest affinities are probably to the Paradisaeidae.

Bowerbirds range from thrush-size almost to crow-size (9–$14\frac{1}{2}$ inches long) and the males are usually beautiful. Most have coloured ornamental plumes of various kinds. In some almost all feathers produce brilliance by means of ' interference ' effects. In others there is a brief nuchal crest, in another a ruff draping much of the back. The sexes are rarely alike. Wings and tail tend to be short, the legs short and strong ; the bill is short and strong, sometimes decurved, and slightly hooked.

They are forest birds and spend little of their time on the ground except at their displaying places. They can fly strongly. They are essentially fruit eaters, but they also eat quantities of insects and molluscs. The call notes are generally loud and penetrating, and there is often a superlative power of mimicry. The open nest of twigs is placed in a tree. The 1–3 eggs are pale with characteristic hieroglyphic markings, or white. In the very few species at all well-known the female alone incubates and cares for the young ; the latter are downy and nidicolous.

The most interesting characteristic is of course the habit that gives the birds their common name. Only the bowerbirds proper (Ptilonorhynchinae) make bowers. The bower is built on the ground and has no direct connection with the nest, which is always in a tree and may be some hundreds of yards away. At each bower is a display ground which the owner strews with coloured or, in some species, pallid and reflecting articles. Contrary to general belief, decorations are selected with great discrimination. Members of the genera *Ptilono-rhynchus*, *Chlamydera*, and *Sericulus* paint their bowers with fruit-pulp, or charcoal, or comminuted dry grass mixed with saliva.

Bowerbirds. Experimental work has shown that gonadectomy inhibits display and bower building, and injections of testosterone re-establish it. Postnuptial (out-of-season) display occurs after the rehabilitation of the testis interstitium, and is of the same nature as the autumnal display of other birds.

True bowerbirds appear to fall into three distinct groups. These are : (1) the platform builders *Archboldia* ; (2) the maypole builders (*Priono-dura*, *Amblyornis*) ; and (3) the avenue builders (*Ptilonorhynchus*, *Chlamydera*, *Sericulus*). Few details are available concerning the display of the first two groups, all of which except the Golden Bowerbird *Prionodura newtoniana* are confined to the rain-forests of New Guinea. The fundamental maypole structures are a central growing sapling with a cone of fabric packed around its base. The Golden Bowerbird, which measures only 9½ inches long, may nevertheless extend this cone to a height of about 9 feet. Another species, the Brown Bowerbird *Ambylornis inornata*, surmounts a dwarf cone with a conical waterproof hut. A third, *A. subalaris*, builds above the cone a hemispherical hut fronted by a stockade ; and a fourth, *A. macgregoriae*, surmounts the basal cone with a cylinder of moss and fibre that extends up the central sapling. Fruits, flowers, beetles' wing-cases, and other coloured objects are used to decorate various parts of the structures or their surroundings.

The avenue builders are widespread in both Australia and New Guinea. The male of each species lays down a foundation platform of twigs, and in this he wedges twin parallel walls of twigs that sometimes arch overhead. At one end, or sometimes both ends, of the bower the males arrange their display things. One species replaces the terminal display grounds with two additional walls, built at right angles to the original ones ; it thus achieves three avenues, and in all of these it places decorations.

Among avenue builders the male builds a bower early in the season. To this he attracts a female and there displays at the focal point of his territory. The male rapidly achieves spermatogenesis, but the female lags behind. The male displays (' dances ') for several months, while the female remains passively in waiting. During this lengthy period of androgen liberation there occurs the remarkable display of bower painting, vocal mimicry of other birds, and the insatiable collection of coloured or otherwise distinctive display things. In the Satin Bowerbird *Ptilonorhynchus violaceus*, and possibly in several other species, the collected display objects are coloured similarly to rival males. With these objects in his bill the male displays energetically, and often violently, but does not approach the female. The display before the watching female continues unabated until the forest becomes seasonally full of the insect food on which the young will be fed. Only then does the female adopt the crouching soliciting position that temporarily transfers the male's physical attention from his display objects. The female now leaves the bower and alone builds the nest and rears the young. The male may continue his behaviour for several more weeks.

There appears to be no general correlation between the *brilliance* of the plumage and that of the assembled display objects. Certainly the most sombre-hued of all bowerbirds, the Brown Bowerbird, accumulates an extremely colourful display outside its hut. But the Satin Bowerbird, with plumage and eyes that flash brilliantly in the sunlight, assembles an equally arresting display in front of its avenue.

Bower building by both avenue and maypole types probably originated as a form of displacement activity. The males as well as the females of most passerine birds possess an inherent urge to build nests. Today only female bowerbirds seem to build nests ; these are built of twigs. The males, on the other hand, have taken to building twig bowers in the display ground ; and here they spend much of their time during the sexual season. The display ground is the focal point of their activity, and—together with the female—of their interest. Nest building among females is essentially controlled by the seasonal liberation of hormones, and the same appears to be true of male bower building. In short, nest building is of a bisexual nature, and this has made possible bower construction as a displaced building drive, the new product of which has become valuable, ritualised, and permanent in the course of the evolution of each species.

Bower painting is probably a displaced form of the courtship feeding that is widespread among passerine and other birds. Instead of projecting his attention on the watching female, the male does so on his bower, which—along with its decorations—is his chief physical preoccupation (apart from feeding and threat) during the weeks or sometimes months of spermatogenesis.

See Plates 26b (phot.) and 31 (colour).

Catbirds. Of the three catbirds, the Green Catbird *Ailuroedus crassirostris* and the White-throated Catbird *A. buccoides*, two greenish species, indulge in arboreal displays in much the same manner as other passerine birds ; the third, the brown Stagemaker (or Toothbilled Catbird) *Scenopoeetes dentirostris* of tropical Queensland, has taken partly to the rain-forest floor. Here it clears a space on the ground and covers this with fresh leaves, which it cuts each morning by means of its ' toothed ' bill. The leaves are placed with paler under-surfaces uppermost, thus creating the more striking effect against the dark earth. From a singing-stick above the decorated stage the bird calls loudly and continuously and so advertises its presence and its decorated stage to every potential mate or rival within many hundreds of yards. The precise function of the stage is unknown, but the scanty available data suggest that it, and the vocal display from above, are means towards cementing the pair-bond and effecting the synchronisation of the joint sexual processes of the pair. Finally it may be the mating place, when the monsoon begins and brings with it the seasonal harvest of insect food on which the young will be fed. A.J.M.

Bock, W. J. 1963. Relations between the birds of paradise and the bower birds. Condor 65 : 91–125.
Gilliard, E. T. 1959. The courtship behaviour of Sandford's Bowerbird (*Archboldia sanfordi*). Amer. Mus. Novit. no. 1935 : 1–18.
Gilliard, E. T. 1959. A comparative analysis of courtship movements in closely allied bowerbirds of the genus *Chlamydera*. Amer. Mus. Novit. no. 1936 : 1–8.
Iredale, T. 1950. Birds of Paradise and Bower Birds. Melbourne.
Marshall, A. J. 1954. Bower-birds. Their Display and Breeding Cycles : a preliminary statement. Oxford.
Mayr, E. 1962. Family Ptilinorhynchidae. *In* Mayr, E. & Greenway, J. C., Jr. (eds.). Check-list of Birds of the World vol. 15. Cambridge, Mass.

BRACE: collective noun for two birds (etc.) of the same species, irrespective of sex ; mainly used in the plural (unchanged) for the enumeration of dead game (e.g. $3\frac{1}{2}$ brace=7 birds of a kind)—cf. PAIR.

BRACHYPTERACIINAE: see CORACIIFORMES ; and GROUND-ROLLER

BRACHYRAMPHINI: see AUK

BRAILING: rendering a captive bird incapable of flight by binding the manus to the forearm so that the wing so treated cannot be unfolded (compare CLIPPING ; PINIONING).

BRAIN: see NERVOUS SYSTEM

BRAIN-FEVER BIRD: name applied to the Hawk Cuckoo *Cuculus varius* of India, both representing the sound made (' brain fever, brain fever ') and suggesting the wearisome effect of its loud and constant reiteration ; sometimes misapplied to other species, for the second of these reasons (see CUCKOO).

BRAMBLING: *Fringilla montifringilla*, native to the northern Palaearctic (see FINCH).

BRANT: North American name for the Brent Goose *Branta bernicla* (see under DUCK).

BRASSYTAIL: *Metallura aeneocauda* (for family see HUMMINGBIRD).

BREAST: see TOPOGRAPHY

BREATHING: see RESPIRATORY SYSTEM

BREEDING BIOLOGY: see the entries named in the List of Major Articles on General Subjects at the beginning of the volume, especially under the subheadings ' Reproduction ', ' Ecology and Populations ', ' Social and Sexual Behaviour ', ' Parental Activities ' ; also articles on separate groups.

Davis, D. E. 1955. Breeding biology of birds. *In* Wolfson, A. (ed.), Recent Studies in Avian Biology. Urbana, Ill. (A general review.)
And references under more specialised entries.

BREEDING SEASON: the period of the year during which, in a particular area, birds of a given species mate, build their nests, lay their eggs, and rear their young—more particularly, the period of laying. Most species of birds lay eggs during only a few weeks or months of the year in any given locality, and this period is strictly determined by natural selection, operating through two sets of factors. The ' ultimate factors ' are those of food, cover, and breeding site, which in nearly all environments are vastly more favourable for the reproduction of any given species of bird during one part of the year than during the remainder. Birds that lay at the ' wrong ' time of the year leave few or no young to perpetuate their strain. The other set of factors, the ' proximate ', provide for the timing mechanism of the individual, ensuring that it is ready to breed as soon as reproduction is likely to be successful. These proximate factors are themselves of two types : one is concerned with physiological changes (see ENDOCRINE SYSTEM; REPRODUCTIVE SYSTEM), and the other with changes in the bird's environment by which the physiological changes are stimulated or retarded (see CLIMATOLOGY; VEGETATION).

In the environment of western Europe, certain ultimate factors combine to ensure that nearly all species breed in spring and early summer : the temperatures are rising, which favours survival of eggs and nestlings ; vegetation is growing, which increases cover and hence nesting sites for many species ; days are lengthening, which provides a longer working day when young have to be fed ; finally, and most generally applicable of all, food for the young—which require first-class (mainly animal) protein—is sufficiently abundant to be collected by the parents with the rapidity that is essential. There is much circumstantial evidence that the food factor is as a rule the predominant one, as indicated by the following examples. In Europe the breeding season of the Robin *Erithacus rubecula*, which feeds its young chiefly on leaf-eating caterpillars, reaches its height some weeks before that of the Spotted Flycatcher *Muscicapa striata* and the hirundines, which need the winged insects that become abundant after the larvae. The Sparrowhawk *Accipiter nisus* lays in May, so that it can feed its young when the woodland song-birds on which it mainly preys are most numerous ; the Hobby *Falco subbuteo* lays a month later and thus can use for its young the late-summer abundance of hirundines and dragonflies. The Crossbill *Loxia curvirostra*, the only European passerine to lay in winter, by so doing can feed its young on conifer seed before it is shed in April. In the mountains of Central America a parallel is provided by the honey-eating species, mainly hummingbirds (Trochilidae), nesting in the coldest season of the year, which is avoided by nearly all the passerines but is richest in the necessary flowers. The factor of food for the nestlings is not, however, always obviously the dominant one ; for example, unlike all the other swallows of southern Africa, *Hirundo griseopyga* nests in the dry season, the period when its nest-holes, situated in flat ground, will not be swamped. And, unlike all the other penguins (Spheniscidae), the Emperor Penguin *Aptenodytes forsteri* breeds in the worst winter in the world, that of the Antarctic, for only by so doing can its slow-growing chick be launched by the time that the sea-ice disperses late in the following spring. Meanwhile, in even the most familiar of avifaunas there are many instances of closely related species that differ in breeding season for reasons still unknown ; e.g. the Raven *Corvus corax* lays weeks before the Carrion Crow *C. corone*, and the Yellowhammer *Emberiza citrinella* before the Corn Bunting *E. calandra*.

Circumstantial evidence shows that ultimate factors determine the end of the breeding season no less than the start. The Great Tit *Parus major* and Blue Tit *P. caeruleus* each year (by means still unknown) synchronise their first broods with the brief period when caterpillars are exceptionally abundant, which lasts only long enough for one brood. When, occasionally, tits lay a second brood, the chicks have to be fed on oddments and the success is low. Again, the Starling *Sturnus vulgaris* depends on 'leather-jackets' (tipulid larvae) for feeding its young. It has been ascertained that in a locality in Aberdeenshire where the leather-jacket season is exceptionally short the Starlings have only one brood, but no more than sixteen miles down the valley, where the larvae are available for longer, the local Starlings regularly raise two broods. In Britain the resident doves *Columba* spp. breed over a longer period of the year than other birds ; this is no doubt connected with the fact that they feed their young on a crop secretion and so are independent of the seasonal abundance of any particular type of food.

It appears that in the North Temperate Zone the birds, with the solitary exception of Eleanora's Falcon *Falco eleanorae* in the Mediterranean, begin to breed in the first half of the year. This applies to the northern sea birds as well as to the land birds, but for reasons unknown the South Temperate sea birds show some exceptions. Certain gulls (Larinae) in the south-west of South Africa and in Australia have a mid-winter breeding season as well as one in late spring. It may be mentioned here also that a few birds, all of very large size, have young that develop too slowly for the parents to breed each year. Condors (of the family Cathartidae) and some of the albatrosses (Diomedeidae) are thus constrained to breed only every other year. The King Penguin *Aptenodytes patagonica*, with a chick that is dependent for eleven months, is ready to lay only at intervals of some sixteen months ; as its breeding cannot succeed unless it gets its chicks launched before the winter, it breeds only twice in every three years—probably a unique cycle (see PENGUIN).

In the tropics as a whole the breeding seasons of the birds are exceedingly complicated. Their ecological relations do not differ in kind from those in the more familiar temperate regions, but the phenomena are in some ways more spectacular and their local variations are more striking. For example, even in so small an area as Eritrea, in most of the country the main breeding season is during the summer rains ; but in the coastal strip, where the scanty rain of the year falls in the winter, the birds breed then. In Central America it has been noted how birds of the same species tend to breed some weeks apart on opposite sides of a mountain range. In Australia and South West Africa, during droughts, a local thunderstorm may provide an oasis of breeding.

Large areas of the tropics show environments for which there is no parallel elsewhere—areas of sea in which there seems to be little seasonal change except in wind, and areas of evergreen forest where there is no change in aspect and little in temperature. Even there seasonal breeding is the rule. The marine breeding seasons in the tropics vary greatly ; for the same species they can differ on neighbouring islands (as, for example, between Cocos-Keeling and Christmas) or, as in the Sooty or 'Wideawake' Tern *Sterna fuscata*, show utterly different régimes ; on Ascension Island this bird shows a unique periodicity of (on average) 9·6 months, but in its other Atlantic stations it breeds annually. Of the marine biology to which these differences are presumably related, nothing is known.

In the evergreen forests of the tropics well-defined breeding seasons have been found in most areas that have been studied. This has been shown in parts of India, Malaysia, and America, while in the mountain forests of eastern Africa the breeding seasons are as sharply limited as at higher latitudes ; at present it is impossible to suggest any reason for this limitation. So far, it is mainly in parts of the Congo forest that the specific breeding seasons have been shown to be ill-defined.

For the drier parts of the tropics the most extensive data come from Africa. Close to the Equator, where there are two rainy seasons, there are two breeding seasons for many species of birds, and it seems probable that to some extent the same individuals participate in both. Where there is only one rainy season it can plainly be seen how the breeding seasons of the different ecological groups of the birds tend to differ. Thus, most of the insectivorous species begin to breed as soon as the new foliage provides the basis for a flush of insect life (which may well be before the end of the dry season), while the species dependent on long grass for nesting or for food (or for both) lay much later. In the savannas the ground-nesting birds have to avoid the hazard of the great grass-fires ; some achieve this by laying at the very beginning of the dry season, others by laying late, when the fires have passed. Many birds of the rivers nest early in the dry season ; then the water is low, sandbanks are exposed as nesting sites, and holes in banks are not likely to be swamped by rising waters—while for the fish-eaters food may be easier to catch. For the raptorial birds in Africa the breeding seasons are particularly complicated ; the bigger, although not the smaller, species tend to breed in the dry season, when at least in some cases vertebrate prey is probably more numerous and accessible.

The proximate factors in birds' breeding—those which, in conjunction with the individual's physiological condition, stimulate the bird to breed—are also complex. To ensure that the bird shall be in a state to breed at the most favourable time of year any internal rhythm needs to be controlled by external factors, and these certainly differ with latitude and environment. In higher latitudes the most dependable factor is day-length, and this has been shown experimentally to have an effect on the gonads. But even if changes in day-length were enough—and it is not clear that alone they are fully effective—they become progressively less at lower latitudes and at the Equator practically cease to exist. In the temperate zones the spring increase in warmth is also undoubtedly a proximate factor, for it is common knowledge that resident species tend to breed earlier in mild, ' early ' springs than in cold, ' late ' springs. It might be suggested that this effect depended at least in part on the state of

the vegetation, but it has been demonstrated how in the Swift *Apus apus* actual egg-laying is related to the weather five days before.

In the tropics, where day-length changes little and increase in temperature is as likely to be inimical as not, other proximate factors must be sought. Here it seems that rainfall and changes in vegetation, possibly acting through visual perception, are dominant influences. Some species seem to be affected by the mere falling of rain ; and, if a rainy season that has started fails to follow its normal course, breeding stops. In the driest areas, such as South West Africa and parts of Australia, where years can go by without rain, breeding follows quickly whenever it falls. Ducks (Anatidae) breed along the course of a river running towards the dry heart of Australia whenever rain in the upper part of the basin produces a flood, whether at intervals of more than twelve months or of less ; but the rare local rains do not stimulate them. Indeed, even in areas with a regular climate (of monsoon type) the provision of nesting sites at an abnormal time of year can stimulate abnormal breeding, as recorded for *Cisticola* spp. on a chance inundation in Nyasaland. A still more delicate control has been noted in Mexico, where hummingbirds (Trochilidae) that were able to find suitable, pliable nesting material in narrow humid gullies started to breed earlier than those of the same species in the surrounding drier country. R.E.M.

Marshall, A. J. 1961. Breeding seasons and migration. *In* Marshall, A. J. (ed.). Biology and Comparative Physiology of Birds vol. 2. New York and London.
Miller, A. H. 1955. Breeding cycles in a constant equatorial environment in Colombia, South America. Acta XI Congr. Intern. Orn., Basel 1954 : 495–503.
Serventy, D. L. & Marshall, A. J. 1957. Breeding periodicity in Western Australian birds. Emu 57 : 99–126.
Stonehouse, B. 1960. The King Penguin *Aptenodytes patagonica* of South Georgia. I. Breeding behaviour and development. Falkland Is. Depend. Surv. Sci. Rep. 23 : 1–81.
Symposium 1950. Series of articles on breeding seasons of birds by various authors. Ibis 92 : 173–316, 419–434.

BRIDLING : a facial plumage marking that resembles a bridle, e.g. in the Bridled Tern *Sterna anaethetus*, in a ' morph' of the Guillemot (or Murre) *Uria aalge* (see POLYMORPHISM), and in some ducks (Anatidae—see PLUMAGE VARIATION). ' Bridling ' is also a behaviour term, applied by Cullen & Ashmole (1963) to a form of display in the Black Noddy *Anous tenuirostris*.

BRILLIANT : substantive name of *Heliodoxa* spp. (for family see HUMMINGBIRD).

BRISTLE: a modified feather, consisting of a shaft with usually little or no vane and resembling a stiff hair (see FEATHER ; PLUMAGE).

BRISTLE-BILL: used as a substantive name of *Bleda* spp., of tropical Africa (see BULBUL).

BRISTLE-BIRD: substantive name of *Dasyornis* spp., of Australia (see WREN (2)).

BRISTLEHEAD: substantive name of the Bornean Bristlehead *Pityriasis gymnocephala*, an aberrant form provisionally placed in a subfamily of its own among the Laniidae (see SHRIKE).

BROADBILL: substantive name of the species of Eurylaimidae (constituting the suborder Eurylaimi of the suboscine Passeriformes) ; in the plural, general term for the family. (Also a name in North America for the Scaup *Aythya marila*—see DUCK.) This is a group of mainly brightly coloured birds of striking plumage, inhabiting the Old World tropics from Africa to the Philippines. They are allied to the Pittidae but have very different habits (see PITTA). Anatomically they differ from the pittas in the method of attachment of the intrinsic muscles of the syrinx and in their short tarsi, and from them and from all the Passeriformes of their area in the structure of the plantar tendons. Their notable external features are the short rounded wings, rounded tail (graduated if long), strong feet, and flat, wide, slightly hooked bill. The gape is wide, the head broad, the eyes large ; the body is stout. They are 5–11 inches long. In the plumage, bright greens and blues are common, but pink, crimson, and black also occur ; the sexes are usually, but not always, distinct.

Fourteen species are known, and these are usually placed in eight genera (five of them monotypic), mostly distinguished by the shape of the bill. In the three green broadbills *Calyptomena* spp. (two confined to Borneo) the bill is relatively small and is covered at the base by a tuft of feathers ; this genus is placed in a separate subfamily (Calyptomeninae). The Wattled Broadbill *Eurylaimus steerii* of the Philippines, in the typical subfamily (Eurylaiminae), has blue wattles round the greenish-blue eyes.

Broadbill species are most numerous in Malacca, Sumatra, and Borneo, extending to India and the Philippines. One of the most remarkable discoveries of the last half-century is that of a closely allied genus, *Pseudocalyptomena*, in a mountainous area of the eastern Congo. The species of the common African genus *Smithornis*, previously classed with the Muscicapinae, are now known to be aberrant broadbills.

Broadbills are in the main birds of forest, especially of secondary jungle, but they occur also in mountain forest and in riparian scrub and mangrove swamps, some species often visiting gardens and cultivated areas. They are usually seen in parties ; and they are fairly noisy, especially in the morning, but on the whole are rather lethargic birds not easily scared away and tending to stand still rather than fly when alarmed.

Green Broadbill *Calyptomena viridis*, of Borneo. *C.E.T.K.*

The general breeding habits are similar throughout the group. The nest is a pear-shaped object of remarkable construction, usually with a long neck and with an untidy tail of material below—in some species the whole structure may be five or six feet long. It is made of any available material—twigs, leaves, grass, or tendrils, often decorated outside with lichen or moss—and there is usually a porch over the entrance in the side. It is slung from boughs, bamboos, creepers, or tall plants, and in the majority of cases is suspended over water. The eggs are normally 2–4 (up to 5 or 6 in the Longtailed Broadbill *Psarisomus dalhousiae* of Asia). They are white, cream, or pinkish in ground colour, with a variable amount of purplish or reddish spotting and speckling, sometimes sparse, sometimes almost hiding the ground colour. In the genera *Calyptomena* and *Smithornis* the eggs are unmarked, being cream in one case and white in the other.

Most genera are insectivorous, so far as is known, and the larger species also add small lizards and frogs to their diet. They feed mainly by searching along the boughs of trees, but they are also extremely good at taking insects on the wing. As an exception, *Calyptomena* spp. are mainly, if not entirely, frugivorous.

The calls are more varied than most of the habits

of the family and some are strikingly distinct. *Eurylaimus* spp. and the Black-and-red Broadbill *Cymbirhynchus macrorhynchos* commonly utter a short series of single notes ending with a metallic churring noise. An exception to this is the Wattled Broadbill *E. steerii* of the Philippines, which has soft musical notes and a clear whistle ; it also makes a loud whirring noise with its wings in short flights and indulges in much loud bill-snapping. The Frilled Tody Broadbill *Serilophus lunatus* is somewhat similar, uttering soft musical whistles and a low churring ; the Longtailed Broadbill has a shrill whistle, a soft churring note, and harsh alarm calls ; the Dusky Broadbill *Corydon sumatranus* has mellow musical notes and a clear whistle, while the only call recorded for *Calyptomena* spp. is a soft whistle. As regards the two African genera, Grauer's Broadbill *Pseudocalyptomena graueri* is extremely rare and little known, and so far no sound, vocal or mechanical, has been heard ; it has no congeners. The African Broadbill *Smithornis capensis*, on the other hand, is remarkable in making a sudden loud, jarring, vibrating, trilled croak, quite unavian in character, and doing so during very short circular flights with vibrating wings ; whether this noise is vocal or mechanical is not known, and the only note definitely identified as vocal is a rather weak little squeaking call. The Redsided Broadbill *S. rufolateralis* has a similar note, likened to a Klaxon horn.

C.W.M.-P.

Peters, J. L. 1951. Check-list of Birds of the World vol. 7. Cambridge, Mass.

BRONCHUS: see RESPIRATORY SYSTEM; and under SYRINX

BRONZEWING: sometimes used alone as substantive name of various Australian 'bronzewing pigeons', in several genera (see PIGEON).

BROOD: collectively, the young hatched from a single clutch of eggs.

BROODING: sitting on the young, usually in the nest and mainly to keep them warm (although the young may also be covered by the parent as a protection against hot sun or predators) (see PARENTAL CARE) ; sometimes also used of sitting on eggs (see INCUBATION).

BROOD-PATCH: see INCUBATION ; also ENDO-CRINE SYSTEM

BROWNBUL: used as a substantive name for some African species of Pycnonotidae (see BULBUL).

BRUBRU: *Nilaus afer* (see SHRIKE)—to be distinguished from BOUBOU.

BRUSH-BIRD: earlier substantive name of *Atrichornis* spp. (see SCRUB-BIRD).

BRUSH-FINCH: substantive name of *Atlapetes* spp., of the Neotropical Region (see BUNTING).

BRUSH-TURKEY: name used in Australia for *Alectura lathami* ; in the plural, serves as a general term for this and allied genera (see MEGAPODE).

BUBALORNITHINAE: see WEAVER

BUCCAL: pertaining to the mouth (buccal cavity) —see TONGUE.

BUCCONIDAE: see under PICIFORMES ; and PUFFBIRD

BUCEROTES; BUCEROTIDAE: see CORACII-FORMES ; and HORNBILL

BUCORACINAE: see HORNBILL

BUDGERIGAR: *Melopsittacus undulatus* ; also 'betcherrygah' and other transliterations of the aboriginal name (see PARROT ; also CAGE BIRD ; GENETICS).

BUFFLEHEAD: *Buceph alaalbeola* (see DUCK).

BULBUL: substantive name of most species of Pycnonotidae (Passeriformes, suborder Oscines) ; in the plural, general term for the family. The substantive name 'greenbul' is applied to some species in several genera, and others sometimes used are 'brownbul', 'leaflove', and 'bristle-bill' (*Bleda*). The bulbuls are an Old World and largely tropical group of birds of moderate size varying from that of a Sparrow *Passer domesticus* to about that of a Blackbird *Turdus merula*. Bulbuls have rather short concave wings and comparatively long square, rounded, or slightly graduated tails. Their bills are never large, but slender (except in *Spizixos* spp.), notched, and with rictal bristles usually well developed ; the nostrils are long or oval, more or less operculated. The tarsi and toes are always rather weak, usually small, and often very short. The body feathers are long, soft, and fluffy, particularly on the lower back. There are always some hair-like feathers on the nape, often long and conspicuous, sometimes weak and difficult to detect. In some species there is a distinct crest.

Bulbuls are not brightly coloured birds. Most of them are olive-green, yellow, or brown ; only one species is black. Many species have crimson, yellow, white, or rufous under tail coverts, and some have bright yellow or scarlet spots or streaks on the head and conspicuous ear coverts. The upper parts are usually uniform in colour, but in a number of species a rust-red or reddish brown tail contrasts with the upper parts. In all bulbuls, males and females are alike in plumage, and usually also in size. Immature birds are unspotted and very similar to adults in appearance.

With a few exceptions, e.g. *Hypsipetes* ('*Microscelis*') spp., bulbuls, like many forest birds, have feeble flight. Most species are sedentary, but some migrate in winter from north to south, or desert the highest level and descend to the plains.

Red-vented Bulbul *Pycnonotus* ('*Molpastes*') *cafer*. C.E.T.K.

Many bulbuls live in dense forests or on their edges, others inhabit sparsely wooded or bushy localities, and quite a number frequent cultivation and gardens near human dwellings. Some species live high in mountains, at altitudes of 5000–10 000 feet above sea level. Many species of bulbuls are very secretive and tend to keep to impassable thickets, but some are very familiar and unafraid of man, being very common in gardens, orchards, or parks. Except when breeding, bulbuls are gregarious and are very noisy birds ; some species are good songsters. Fruit and berries form the food of most species ; some feed on buds and the nectar of flowers ; several species are insectivorous, but they collect insects on trees and bushes and do not catch them on the wing.

The nests are usually substantial and cup-shaped, made of twigs, stems, dead bamboo leaves, seldom of mosses, and lined inside with grasses or fine roots. Frequently they are built in bushes or low trees 3–10 feet from the ground. Only some *Hypsipetes* spp. place their nests at a height in forest trees, 25–50 feet from the ground. The eggs are commonly 2 or 3 in number ; very few species have clutches of 4 or 5. The pink to white eggs are heavily marked. Both sexes incubate and also tend the young.

Bulbuls are widely distributed in Africa (except in desert regions), in Madagascar and the Mascarene Islands, in southern parts of Asia (Syria, Afghanistan, central China, Hokkaido, and south Sakhalin form the northern limit), the Malay Archipelago, the Philippines, and the Moluccas. The family includes 15 genera (according to Rand & Deignan) and about 120 species. Of these, 10 genera are confined to Africa and Madagascar (or to one or other), and 2 to southern Asia ; *Pycnonotus* and *Criniger* are widely distributed in both Africa and Asia, while *Hypsipetes* extends from Madagascar and the Mascarene Islands to eastern Asia.

The typical genus includes nearly 50 species. The African Bulbul *Pycnonotus barbatus* is widely distributed in Africa, with numerous races. There are other African and Asian species generally similar in size and plumage (dusky coloured with bright under tail coverts), such as the White-cheeked Bulbul, *P. leucogenys* and the White-eared Bulbul *P. leucotis*, the Chinese Bulbul *P. sinensis*, the Red-whiskered Bulbul *P. jocosa*, and the Red-vented Bulbul *P. cafer*. Most of them are birds of open country, villages, and town gardens, but not of dense forests. The insectivorous Striated Bulbul *P. striatus*, olive but striped above with white, is common in mountain forests of south-eastern Asia. Two species of olive-green Finch-billed Bulbuls *Spizixos canifrons* and *S. semitorques*, with short and thick bills, live in the same area and habitat.

Five *Chlorocichla* spp. inhabit the scrub of tropical Africa. Numerous *Phyllastrephus* spp., with males larger than females, are distributed in the forests of tropical Africa and Madagascar. Very similar to each other (often fully crested, and olive, yellow, or brown) are *Criniger* spp. distributed from Africa (4) to south-eastern Asia (5). The range of the Black Bulbul *Hypsipetes* ('*Microscelis*') *madagascariensis*, with numerous black, black-and-white, and grey local forms, extends from Madagascar to eastern Asia. Its relative, the Brown-eared Bulbul *H. amaurotis*, inhabits islands and coasts of eastern Asia from the Philippines to Sakhalin. These and other species of the genus have elongated and pointed feathers on the crown. They often eat buds and nectar on flowering trees. A.I.I.

Delacour, J. 1943. A revision of the genera and species of the family Pycnonotidae (Bulbuls). Zoologica (New York) 28 : 17–28.

Rand, A. L. & Deignan, H. G. 1960. Family Pycnonotidae. *In* Mayr, E. & Greenway, J. C., Jr. (eds.). Check-list of Birds of the World vol. 9, Cambridge, Mass.

And regional works, African and Asian.

BULLFINCH: substantive name of *Pyrrhula* spp.; used without qualification, in Britain, for *P. pyrrhula*; applied in the West Indies to species of *Loxigilla* and *Melopyrrha* (see FINCH ; also CAGE BIRD). See Plate 6 (colour).

BUNTING: substantive name of Old World species of Emberizinae, a subfamily included either in the Emberizidae, if that be kept as a separate family, or in the Fringillidae (Passeriformes, suborder Oscines) ; in the plural, general term for the subfamily. In North America, most of these birds have the substantive names ' sparrow ' or ' finch ', the name ' bunting ' being mainly used for brightly coloured species of the subfamily Pyrrhuloxiinae (' Richmondeninae ')—see CARDINAL-GROSBEAK.

Habitat. The buntings (Emberizinae) are predominantly terrestrial, or dwell in bushes and thickets, as the food of the adult consists chiefly of seeds secured for the greater part by foraging on the ground, but their habitat preferences vary greatly. Many species inhabit grasslands or weedy and bushy areas in open or fairly open regions ; some, especially tropical species, frequent open woodlands or the edges of forest, but usually avoiding the denser and higher growth. With these few restrictions, buntings can be found anywhere and in all sorts of climates, from the hottest or most arid to the coldest and most humid, from the seashore to the very high and barren plateaux of the Andes, and from virtually one end of the earth to the other. Some American species inhabit Tierra del Fuego or the high Arctic ; the Snow Bunting *Plectrophenax nivalis* breeds at the tip of northern Greenland, farther north than any other land bird.

Behaviour. Some aspects of their behaviour also show enormous variation, for instance song and reactions towards man. The song can be loud, rich, and full, and most musical, or so feeble as to be scarcely audible to man, being very highly pitched and similar to the buzz of an insect. The Snow Bunting and the House Bunting *Emberiza striolata* are so confiding that they nest by preference in occupied dwellings when available, whereas other buntings are amongst the most wary and furtive of all birds.

Physical Characteristics. In contrast to these variations, the physical characteristics of the buntings and New World sparrows are rather homogeneous. They are small birds with legs of medium length and big feet equipped for scratching. The tail is fairly long in many species, sometimes graduated or slightly forked. The size averages about 6 inches or a little less, but some species are slightly smaller and some attain 7-8 inches in length ; the larger ones are the American towhees *Pipilo* spp. and some *Emberiza* spp. of Eurasia. The bill is short, or relatively so, conical and attenuated, and some typical *Emberiza* spp. are provided with a hump in the roof of the mouth for crushing seeds. In the Reed Bunting *E. schoeniclus* the shape of the bill varies geographically to a remarkable extent, from very small, slight, and very attenuated, to globular and massive, parrot-like in shape, these variations being correlated to the type of reed beds that the bird inhabits. The wing, which has nine obvious primaries (although a vestigial and hidden outer primary may be present), is long and pointed in most migratory species, rounded and short in most sedentary species. Some buntings and New World

---

ca. ⅙ nat. size

Plate 5 · Permanent Sexual Dimorphism by C. E. TALBOT KELLY

The species shown are characterised by a strongly marked sexual dimorphism in the plumage of adults at all times, with little or no seasonal change ; smaller examples are shown in Plate 6 See article SEXUAL DIMORPHISM.

Koel *Eudynamys scolopacea* (southern Asia and Australasia)
1 Female, **2** Male

Eclectus Parrot *Lorius roratus* (Australo-Papuan area)
3 Female, **4** Male

Redfooted Falcon *Falco vespertinus* (Siberia and eastern Europe)
5 Female, **6** Male

Mandarin Duck *Aix galericulata* (eastern Asia)
7 Female, **8** Male

Lady Amherst Pheasant *Chrysolophus amherstiae* (eastern central Asia)
9 Female, **10** Male

Black Grouse *Lyrurus tetrix* (Palaearctic Region)
11 Female, **12** Male

C. E. Talbot Kelly.

C.E.Talbot Kelly.

sparrows are attractively coloured and patterned, but the plumage is never brilliant. It is brownish, greyish, or olivaceous as a rule, streaked or disruptive in pattern, with various combinations of black, white, yellow, green, or reddish. Some species have a short crest, but *Melophus lathami* has a long pointed one.

Breeding. The nest of the typical buntings and New World sparrows is cup-shaped, or is domed in many tropical members of the group ; it is usually built by the hen only, although the male may be in attendance. Grasses and fine roots and sometimes moss and lichens are the chief building material, and a few hairs are added to the lining where they can be found, and also feathers in some instances. It may be built in a bush or tree, but usually not very high above the ground ; or it may be built on the ground. The choice of the site seems to be less important than secure support and concealment. The Reed Bunting may build among reeds in shallow water, and some species nest in holes in trees or on the ground or in crevices among boulders. The eggs may be immaculate or marked with blotches and straggling lines ; 2-6 are laid, rarely more, and may be incubated by the female alone or by both sexes. In two typical emberizines from the New and Old Worlds, the Song Sparrow *Melospiza melodia* of America and the Corn Bunting *Emberiza calandra* of Eurasia, the breeding habits are similar. Both birds lay 3–5 eggs that are incubated by the hen alone for 12-13 days. The eggs of the Song Sparrow vary from bluish to greyish-green and are spotted with brown ; those of the Corn Bunting vary from

almost white to pale brown and are spotted with very dark brown. The young of the buntings and New World sparrows are cared for by both parents, or by the hen alone in a few species.

Taxonomy. The writer of this article is among those who prefer to place the buntings and New World sparrows in a family apart from the cardueline finches ; the latter are clearly of Old World origin, and some authors (such as Sushkin and Tordoff) have suggested that they are related to the weavers (Ploceidae). The Emberizidae, on the other hand, are a New World group that has spread to the Old and has become differentiated there in only two genera, the monotypic *Melophus* and *Emberiza*, which latter has undergone much adaptive radiation and has 37 species. The other two genera found in the Old World are the monotypic *Plectrophenax* (the Snow Bunting) and *Calcarius* (the Lapland Bunting and longspurs) ; these two genera are circumpolar and, properly speaking, are therefore not typical elements of either the New or Old World avifauna. In America, authorities differ, and a number of genera that were placed by Hellmayr (1938) in his subfamily Carduelinae were transferred subsequently by other authors to the ' subfamily' Emberizinae. Many authors consider that these two ' subfamilies' form but a part of a large and all-embracing family, the Fringillidae, in which are included also the subfamilies Geospizinae (the Galápagos, or Darwin's, finches), the Fringillinae (the chaffinches and Brambling), and the Richmon-deninae or Pyrrhuloxiinae (the cardinals and allies). The boundaries between the latter and the emberi-

---

Plate 6 · Permanent Sexual Dimorphism by C. E. TALBOT KELLY

The species shown are characterised by a strongly marked sexual dimorphism in the plumage of adults at all times, with little or no seasonal change ; larger examples are shown in Plate 5. See article SEXUAL DIMORPHISM.

Leaden Flycatcher *Myiagra rubecula* (Australia and New Guinea)
1 Female, **2** Male

Painted Bunting *Passerina ciris* (North America)
3 Female, **4** Male

Scarlet Honeyeater *Myzomela sanguinolenta* (Australia)
5 Female, **6** Male

Bullfinch *Pyrrhula pyrrhula europoea* (Europe)
7 Female, **8** Male

King Bird-of-paradise *Cicinnurus regius rex* (New Guinea)
9 Female, **10** Male

Flame Dove *Ptilinopus victor* (Fiji Islands)
11 Male, **12** Female

Blue-headed Pitta *Pitta baudi* (Borneo)
13 Female, **14** Male

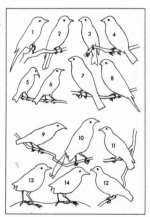

Upper part ca. ¾ nat. size ;
lower part ca. ½ nat. size

zines, and even the tanagers, are very difficult to draw in the New World.

Old World Forms. The buntings of the Old World, at any rate, differ clearly from the finches and do not present a taxonomic problem. They number 40 species : the circumpolar Snow Bunting and Lapland Bunting, the typical buntings *Emberiza* spp., and the Crested Bunting *Melophus lathami*. *Emberiza* is best represented in the Palaearctic Region, with 29 species restricted to that region ; an additional one, the House Bunting *E. striolata*, is shared by the Palaearctic and Ethiopian Regions ; and seven are Ethiopian. The most familiar is probably the Yellowhammer *E. citrinella*, which inhabits western Eurasia to Iran and central Siberia. The Crested Bunting inhabits northern India and the Indo-Chinese countries and is the only member of the family in tropical and subtropical Asia. It is interesting also because the male differs from all other buntings by having a long pointed crest and has an unusual plumage for a bunting, being glossy blue-black, unstreaked and unspotted, with chestnut wings and tail ; the female is streaked, however, has no crest, and resembles many other buntings.

New World Forms. The systematic position of some New World groups is so uncertain that it is very difficult to compare the Emberizinae of the Old World with those of the New, but the species are far more numerous and more diverse in the Western Hemisphere. If we accept Hellmayr's list of his Emberizinae, which represents the most restricted concept, we find that it consists of 52 genera with a total of 157 species ; an additional one, the Rustic Bunting *E. rustica*, wanders occasionally to the Aleutians but is not American. The great diversity of the New World birds cannot be denied ; but, nevertheless it is over-emphasised by the recognition of too many genera, as 26 of the 52 acknowledged by Hellmayr are monotypic and another 12 consist of two species only. The genus *Atlapetes* (brush-finches) is the largest, numbering 27 species according to Hellmayr ; these are distributed from Mexico south to the Guianas and Brazil in the east, and to Peru, Bolivia, and northwestern Argentina in the west. They are relatively large and stout birds, predominantly olivaceous in coloration, and, as their name indicates, inhabit brushy areas.

Two other well-known genera are the towhees *Pipilo* spp., the largest and most colourful emberizines of the New World, and the juncos *Junco* spp. Examples widespread in North America are the Rufous-sided Towhee *P. erythrophthalmus* (many subspecies) and the Slate-coloured Junco *J. hyemalis*. These two genera are essentially North American. In that region there are many streaked species living

in marsh, grassland, and shrubs, called 'sparrows' and placed in a number of genera. The best known of these, and probably of all the Emberizinae, is undoubtedly the Song Sparrow *Melospiza melodia*, which has been brilliantly studied by Mrs Nice ; these studies are of wide application in the study of the life histories and behaviour of all passerine birds. Two other American buntings specially worthy of mention are the White-crowned Sparrow *Zonotrichia leucophrys*, which has served for many physiological studies of basic importance, and the charming Rufous-collared Sparrow *Z. capensis*, which covers a huge geographical range from Mexico southward. Other well-known North American species include the Savannah Sparrow *Passerculus sandwichensis*, the Sharp-tailed Sparrow *Ammospiza caudacuta*, the Vesper Sparrow *Pooecetes gramineus*, the Tree Sparrow *Spizella arborea*, and the Fox Sparrow *Passerella iliaca* (many subspecies).

See Plates 6 and 29 (colour). C.V.

Davis, J. 1952. Distribution and variation of the Brown Towhees. Univ. Calif. Publ. Zool. 52 : 1–120.

Nice, M. M. 1937, 1943. Studies in the life history of the Song Sparrow. Trans. Linn. Soc. N.Y., nos. 4 and 6.

BUPHAGINAE: see OXPECKER ; and under STARLING

BURGOMASTER : sailors' name for the Glaucous Gull *Larus hyperboreus* (see GULL).

BURHINIDAE : see under CHARADRIIFORMES ; and THICKKNEE

BURHINOIDEA : see under CHARADRIIFORMES

BURROWING : see NEST

BUSH-BIRD : substantive name of *Thamnistes* spp. (see ANTBIRD).

BUSH-CREEPER : substantive name, in Africa, of *Macrosphenus* spp. (for subfamily see BABBLER).

BUSH-HEN : name used in Australia for *Amaurornis ruficrissus* (see RAIL).

BUSH-SHRIKE : substantive name of some species of Malaconotinae ; in the plural, general term for the subfamily (see SHRIKE).

BUSH-SKULKER : *Argya fulva* of Africa (for subfamily see BABBLER).

BUSH-TANAGER : substantive name of *Chlorospingus* spp. (see TANAGER).

BUSHTIT : substantive name of *Psaltriparus* spp., of the New World (see TIT).

BUSTARD : the most usual substantive name of species of Otididae (Gruiformes, suborder Otides) ;

in the plural, general term for the family. This is a well-defined Old World family of medium-sized to large birds ($14\frac{1}{2}$–52 inches in length), terrestrial in habits and well adapted for their life in deserts and grassy or bushy plains. The fairly strong legs, with the tibia largely bare and three short and stout front toes with broad soles, are suited to swift running ; the hallux is absent. The head is flattened, as is the bill. The neck is long and rather thick. The wings are moderate in length, and broad ; the flight is in general laboured, but powerful and rapid. Bustards sometimes hide by crouching in case of danger. The tail is moderately long and rounded in outline. The upper plumage varies from grey or brown to buff, with darker, often black, vermiculations and white patches ; the under parts may be pale buff or almost white, or may be black or bluish. Ornamental plumes are generally present, occurring on head, nape, cheeks, throat, or foreneck, and are used in the remarkable terrestrial displays. Courtship flight is also known. In the males of some species the gullet is widened or there is a gular pouch acting as a sounding board for their peculiar calls during posturing. The sexes are mostly unlike in plumage and differ in size, the males being larger.

In some species the male remains near the female during brooding ; others are promiscuous, eggs and young being tended by the females alone. The number of eggs varies, according to species, 1–5, and they are brownish to greenish with dark spots and blotches. The eggs are mostly deposited in a trampled or scratched hole on the bare ground. The downy young are sandy-coloured with dark spots and leave the nest soon after hatching. In many species seasonal migrations take place, but more data are necessary before these movements can be properly understood.

The birds are omnivorous, animal as well as vegetable matter being taken. In some species family parties or small flocks are formed outside the breeding season ; others are not gregarious. In the sleeping attitude the head is sunk between the shoulders.

The Otididae are restricted to the Old World and the family consists of 22 species, usually arranged in 10 genera. Of these a few are Eurasian, one Australian, and all the others purely African in distribution. The Great Bustard *Otis tarda* is a Palaearctic species with a discontinuous distribution; the main centre is in western and central Asia. In western Europe it is found in some scattered areas, remnants of a former wider distribution ; it ceased to breed in Britain about 1832.

The Little Bustard *O. tetrax* has a similar distribu-tion to that of the Great Bustard, and still breeds sparingly in south-western Europe. The male is distinguished by the black-and-white neck collars. The Houbara Bustard *Chlamydotis undulata* is partly African and partly Asian in distribution, occurring from the Canary Islands through northern Africa to south-western Asia ; it is notable for the elongated white crown feathers and the long black-and-white feathers along the sides of the neck. The eastern population is known as Macqueen's Bustard.

Kori Bustard *Ardeotis kori*. C.E.T.K.

The four species of the genus *Neotis* are rather large birds and all inhabit Africa. Denham's Bustard *N. denhami* is largely distributed over Africa south of the Sahara ; it has the crown black with a white streak over the centre, a pale rufous neck, and black wings boldly marked with white. The Nubian Bustard *N. nuba* occurs in the central and eastern part of north tropical Africa ; it is a steppe bird, tawny rufous on the upper parts, with a black line over the eyes, a black chin, and greyish neck. Heuglin's Bustard *N. heuglinii* has a black face and a rufous breast band ; it occurs in eastern Abyssinia and Somalia. The South African congener is Ludwig's Bustard *N. ludwigii*, not unlike Denham's Bustard but lacking the black crown and having the foreneck darker.

The largest representatives of the family are found in the genus *Ardeotis*, distributed over Africa, India, and Australia. The Arabian Bustard *A. arabs* inhabits the northern part of Africa and southern Arabia, the Kori (or Giant) Bustard *A. kori* East and South Africa. The first is sandy buff above, the latter dark brown with sandy vermiculations. Both have the neck feathers long and incoherent, with narrow transverse bands. The Great Indian Bustard *A. nigriceps* has a black crown and white neck without transverse bars and is found in north-western India. The Australian Bustard *A. australis* is not unlike *A. nigriceps* but is slightly darker and has dusky freckles on the neck. All have striking displays, and the males exceed the females a good deal in size. Too much shooting has reduced numbers in settled areas.

The Crested Bustard *Lophotis ruficrista*, with black under parts and a tuft of pink feathers on the nape, is an African species preferring bushy country. The Black Korhaan *Afrotis atra*, with black under parts, neck, and sides of face and white ear coverts, is a species of southern Africa.

The genus *Eupodotis* contains five African species, of which the rather similar Karroo Korhaan *E. vigorsii* and Rüppell's Korhaan *E. rueppellii* occur in South Africa, living in barren and stony districts ; these are small bustards, *E. vigorsii* brownish with a black throat, *E. rueppellii* paler with a black throat-line bordered by blue-grey. The Blue Korhaan *E. caerulescens* occurs in the same habitat, but is slightly larger and has the neck and under parts entirely bluish. The Senegal Bustard *E. senegalensis* has a wider distribution, from South Africa north to Senegal and western Ethiopia. The small Little Brown Bustard *E. humilis* is restricted to Somaliland.

Widely spread over tropical parts of Africa is the Black-bellied Bustard *Lissotis melanogaster*, occurring in different kinds of grassland or light bush. It has a long and thin neck, black under parts and much white on shoulders and wing. The nearly related Hartlaub's Bustard *L. hartlaubii* is restricted to eastern Africa and has the lower back and rump black.

The beautiful Bengal Florican *Houbaropsis bengalensis* occurs in northern India ; the head, neck, and under parts are velvety black in the adult male, contrasting with the largely white wings, while the females and young males are of a tawny buff colour speckled with very dark buff. The smallest bustard is the Lesser Florican *Sypheotides indica*, a species also inhabiting India ; it has the head and neck black, with long black ear-plumes and a white throat. Both species are much harassed by shooting, as they are good table birds. †G.C.A.J.

Gewalt, W. 1959. Die Grosstrappe. Berlin. (Monograph on the Great Bustard.).

BUSTARD-QUAIL: synonymous with BUTTON-QUAIL

BUTCHER-BIRD: popular name in Britain and North America for *Lanius* spp. (see SHRIKE) ; in Australia for some species of Cracticidae (see MAGPIE (2)). In both cases the name relates to the habit of forming a 'larder' of the prey.

BUTEO: sometimes used in North America as a vernacular term for *Buteo* spp., there included under the general term 'hawk' although in Britain called 'buzzards' (see HAWK).

BUTEONINAE: subfamily used by some authors for, in the system followed in this work, the larger members (buzzards and eagles) of the subfamily Accipitrinae of the Accipitridae (see HAWK).

BUTT: an earthwork—usually one of a series in line—erected for the concealment of persons waiting to shoot driven birds, notably Red Grouse *Lagopus scoticus*.

BUTTERBALL: a name applied in North America both to the Bufflehead *Bucephala albeola* and to the Ruddy Duck *Oxyura jamaicensis* (see DUCK).

BUTTONQUAIL: substantive name, alternatively 'hemipode', of species of Turnicidae (Gruiformes, suborder Turnices) ; often used without qualification for the sole European species ; in the plural (alternatively 'hemipodes'), general term for the family. The latter and the Australian monotypic family Pedionomidae (see PLAINS-WANDERER) together form the suborder. This small Old World group of only some 15 species is also considered to be allied to the sandgrouse (Pteroclididae) and the pigeons (Columbidae). The buttonquails or hemipodes are terrestrial grassland birds inhabiting mainly the tropics and subtropics and remarkably resembling true quails *Coturnix* spp. (Phasianidae) in general appearance, plumage pattern, habitat preference, and mode of life. They are $4-7\frac{1}{2}$ inches in length. The family is characterised by having only three toes on the foot, a hind toe being absent. In flight the wings appear much rounded and the short tail is barely visible. The bill is like that of a quail but generally rather small and slender. A crop is missing.

They live very secretively in arid or marshy grass and brush country, savannas, and more open woodland ; they are hard to flush, and if startled from cover fly merely a short stretch over the tops of the grass. The food consists of grass-seeds, grain, shoots, and small insects, for which they scratch in the ground. Water is taken with a 'bibbling' action of the mandibles and without raising the head at each mouthful as do most birds. They are fond of dusting. Buttonquails are usually seen singly, in pairs or in small family parties, but some species tend to keep together in coveys of 15–30 birds. According to local climatic conditions, they are sedentary, nomadic, or migratory.

½

Striped Buttonquail (or Andalusian Hemipode)
Turnix sylvatica. C.E.T.K.

The female is larger and more brightly coloured than the male, is extremely pugnacious against rivals of the same sex, and takes the leading part in courtship. In the breeding season she utters a loud drumming or booming call, only the hen being provided with a specialised vocal organ—an inflatable bulb of the oesophagus and an enlargement of the trachea. The nest is placed on the ground in a shallow depression scratched among grass, in a tussock, or beneath the shelter of a low bush or herbage. It is built of dry grasses and dead leaves, and varies from a more or less well-made cup to a substantial domed structure with a lateral entrance, sometimes with a short covered runway leading to it. Both sexes bring material, which they jerk in plover-like manner over their shoulders towards the nesting place, and work in turn from inside. The eggs are commonly 4 in number (in *Ortyxelos* only 2), short ovate to pyriform, rather glossy, pale greyish to buffish in ground colour and profusely freckled, dotted, and blotched with chestnut, dark brown, slaty-grey, or other shades. The male performs the duties of incubation and later of rearing the young, although the female may occasionally assist during a few days after laying. The behaviour of birds breeding in captivity and circumstantial evidence from field observations strongly suggest that the hen lays several sets of eggs to be attended by different males.

Besides these and other peculiarities in the breeding behaviour, the buttonquails show a rather special kind of nidifugous development. Their incubation period of only 12–13 days is by far the shortest among birds with young hatching in a similarly advanced state, and even ranks near the lower limit known in the nidicolous group. The downy chicks leave the nest soon after hatching, are very agile and follow the male parent, by which they are brooded and fed, the food being presented in the tip of the bill. They begin to flutter when about one week old, and after another week they can fly and look after themselves, although the family keeps together for one or two more weeks, and finally at the age of 6–7 weeks they attain the size and weight of adults. During this short growing period, characterised by a steady gain in weight, two moults are accomplished. At the end of the second week most of the natal down is replaced by juvenile features, and at the same time, when the bird is scarcely half-grown, a complete moult of the juvenile plumage begins. This is completed at the age of about 10 weeks, and results either in the adult postnuptial plumage or directly in the nuptial one. In the rapid succession of plumages and in many other feathers the buttonquails present a remarkable convergence towards the gallinaceous type of development, which implies a very early ability to fly. They differ, however, in that the adaptation of the growing wing to continuous use is attained in a less specialised manner; all the juvenile quills grow out nearly together, the only important modification being that the inner primaries are considerably reduced in size, particularly the innermost one, which remains almost vestigial. This primary is the first to be shed, the process taking place before the outer juvenile quills are fully grown. Sexual maturity too is reached at an early age, at least in birds reared in confinement; these may begin to lay in the fourth to fifth or even third month of life.

The typical genus of the family includes 13 species, 6 of which inhabit the Australasian Region. The other *Turnix* species are found in Africa, Madagascar, and the warmer countries of Asia, only one extending to Europe (in its extreme south-western part). This widely distributed (mainly Indo-African) Buttonquail (also called Striped or Little Buttonquail or Andalusian Hemipode) *Turnix sylvatica*, is a bird with greyish-rufous, variably blotched and streaked upper parts, and pale below except for the rufous breast flanked with dark spots; its Philippine race is the smallest representative of the genus. In this species the sexual dimorphism in coloration is much less conspicuous than in the Barred (or Common) Bustardquail *T. suscitator* of India and eastern Asia, in which the female acquires a black throat and chest in nuptial plumage. Many females are trapped by the use of female decoy birds and then kept to be pitted against each other.

Several species have similar black markings below, such as the Madagascar Buttonquail *T. nigricollis* and the Blackbreasted Buttonquail *T. melanogaster*, a very rare bird of the rain-forest scrubs of Queensland.

One of the finest and largest species is the brightly coloured Ocellated (or Spotted) Buttonquail *T. ocellata* of Luzon (Philippines). In the Yellowlegged (or Indian) Buttonquail *T. tanki* the hen is distinguished by a broad orange-rufous nuchal collar ; it has a breeding distribution from India to Manchuria and is migratory in the northern part of its range. The similar Spotted (or Redbacked) Buttonquail *T. maculosa*, ranging from Australia, New Guinea, and Melanesia to the Lesser Sunda Islands and Mindanao, seems to be its eastern counterpart. Some of the smaller Australian species are remarkable for their stout bill, such as the Redchested Buttonquail *T. pyrrhothorax*, which (like *T. maculosa*) has spread northwards, leaving two small island populations on Sumba and Luzon.

The second, and quite different, genus is monotypic. The little Lark-quail (often misnamed Quail-plover) *Ortyxelos meiffrenii* inhabits very dry sandy scrub country in the tropical grassland belt from Senegal to East Africa. It has sandy-rufous upper parts, rather long black-and-white wings, a strong jerky flight ; it resembles a tiny courser *Cursorius* sp. on the ground and a bushlark *Mirafra* sp. on the wing.   E.S.

Hoesch, W. 1959. Zur Brutbiologie des südafrikanischen Laufhühnchens *Turnix sylvatica lepurana*. J. Orn. 100 : 341–349.

Hoesch, W. 1960. Zum Brutverhalten des Laufhühnchens *Turnix sylvatica lepurana*. J. Orn. 101 : 265–275.

Niethammer, G. 1961. Sonderbildungen an Oesophagus und Trachea beim Weibchen von *Turnix sylvatica lepurana*. J. Orn. 102 : 75–79.

Seth-Smith, D. 1903. On the breeding in captivity of *Turnix tanki*, with some notes on the habits of the species. Avicult. Mag. (2) 1 : 317–324.

Seth-Smith, D. 1905. On the breeding of *Turnix varia*. Avicult. Mag. (2) 3 : 295–301.

Sutter, E. 1955. Über die Mauser einiger Laufhühnchen und die Rassen von *Turnix maculosa* und *sylvatica* im indo-australischen Gebiet. Verh. Naturf. Ges. Basel 66 : 85–139.

Sutter, E. & Cornaz, N. 1963. Ueber die Gewichtsentwicklung und das Schwingenwachstum junger Spitzschwanz-Laufhühnchen, *Turnix sylvatica*. Orn. Beob. 60 : 213–223

BUZZARD : substantive name of *Buteo* spp. (Accipitrinae) ; also used, in combination, for the honey-buzzards *Pernis* spp. (Perninae)—for both these subfamilies of the Accipitridae see HAWK. In America, where true buzzards are named ' hawks ' (which they of course are), ' buzzard ' is a popular misnomer for members of the Cathartidae (see VULTURE (2)), and is sometimes also applied to the Caracara *Caracara cheriway* (see under FALCON).

C

CACHALOTE: substantive name of *Pseudoseisura* spp. (see OVENBIRD (1)).

CACIQUE: substantive name of species in four tropical genera (*Cacicus*, etc.) of the Icteridae (see ORIOLE (2)).

CADGE: term used in FALCONRY

CAECUM: a blind tube branching from the junction of the small intestine and large intestine, usually paired ('caeca') but in some taxonomic groups single or absent (see ALIMENTARY SYSTEM).

CAGE BIRD: a somewhat vague term applied generally to a variety of the smaller birds (mostly psittacine and passerine) commonly kept in captivity, particularly captivity on a domestic scale rather than in sizeable aviaries (see AVICULTURE).

A former favourite was the Barbary dove, of which Eleazar Albin wrote in 1740 : 'They are tame pretty Birds, and kept in Cages by the Curious, in which they will breed and bring up their young.' There is some doubt regarding the origin of this dove, but it appears to have descended either from the nominate race of the Collared Dove *Streptopelia decaocto* or from the race *S. d. roseogrisea*. A variety of the Barbary dove generally known as the 'White Java dove' is frequently kept and bred, although—like so many of the so-called cage birds—more often in aviaries than in cages. The Diamond Dove *Geopelia cuneata* of Australia is another favourite that has produced a pale mutation in captivity.

The Budgerigar *Melopsittacus undulatus*, first brought alive from its native Australia by Gould in 1840, is now an extremely popular household pet, no doubt on account of its gay colouring, its vivacity, and its ability to mimic (albeit rather indistinctly) the human voice. In addition to being kept in cages, this small parrakeet is kept in aviaries from which the birds can fly out, returning for food, nesting activities, or roosting. Such free-flying birds are known as 'homing' Budgerigars, although there is no evidence that they are able to find their way from any appreciable distance. A great variety of colour forms has been evolved by selective breeding from mutations.

There are a few instances of cockatoos (Kakatoeinae) reputed to have lived for over a hundred years in captivity ; and certain of the Psittacinae, notably the Grey Parrot *Psittacus erithacus* of Africa and some of the Amazon Parrots *Amazona* spp., have long been favoured as household pets on account of their ability to mimic a wide range of sounds. Among passerine birds, the Hill Mynah *Gracula religiosa* is sometimes kept for the same reason.

The Canary *Serinus canaria* of the Canary Islands, Madeira, and the Azores, was first imported into Europe during the sixteenth century and now exists in a diversity of form, colour, and plumage pattern. The 'Roller' canary, trained when young by hearing older males, is famed for the beauty and variety of its song. Hybrids between the Canary and other finches, chiefly the Goldfinch *Carduelis carduelis* and the Greenfinch *C. chloris*, are bred ; the progeny are known among bird fanciers as 'mules'. The 'Bengalese', a cage bird of eastern Asian origin, has long been domesticated and a range of colour forms has been produced ; there was at one time some doubt as to its ancestry, but it is now generally agreed that this lies with one of the mannikins, *Lonchura striata*. The Zebra Finch *Poephila* ('*Taeniopygia*') *castanotis* of Australia might also be described as domesticated, as it exists as a captive bird in a variety of selectively bred colour forms. These three species may be said to be true cage birds, in that they have been kept and bred in cages for a number of generations. It may be noted that the Canary is one of the true finches (Fringillidae) but that the other two are weaver-finches (Estrildidae), a group to which several other cage birds belong, including the Java Sparrow *Padda oryzivora*.

The Skylark *Alauda arvensis*, Wood Lark *Lullula arborea*, and other British native passerines such as the Blackbird *Turdus merula*, Song Thrush *T. philomelos*, Goldfinch, and Linnet *Acanthis cannabina*, were formerly commonly kept as song-birds, and the Jay *Garrulus glandarius* and Magpie *Pica pica* for their prowess as mimics. The Bullfinch *Pyrrhula pyrrhula* was taught to pipe simple tunes, the instruction—as in the case of the first 'Roller' canaries—being done principally in parts of Germany.

Exhibitions of 'cage birds' are held, chiefly during the winter months, the birds being shown in small cages specially constructed for such occasions. It is here that the imprecise nature of the term is evident, for such birds as the smaller species of Phasianidae and Rallidae, the turacos (Musophagidae), hummingbirds (Trochilidae), toucans (Ramphastidae), and woodpeckers (Picidae), most of which are usually kept in large 'flights' or aviaries, are also exhibited.

A utilitarian use of cage birds is the keeping of Canaries in mines for the early detection of toxic gas, to which the birds are particularly sensitive.

J.J.Y.

Boosey, E. 1956. Foreign Bird Keeping. London.

CAHOW: local name for the Blackcapped Petrel *Pterodroma cahow* breeding in small numbers on Bermuda, where it was rediscovered in recent years after having been thought to have become extinct (see PETREL).

Murphy, R. C. & Mowbray, L. S. 1951. New light on the Cahow, *Pterodroma cahow*. Auk 68 : 266–280.

CAIQUE: substantive name of species in the Neotropical genus *Pionites* (for family see PARROT).

CAIRININI: see DUCK

CALAMUS: the hollow proximal portion of the shaft of a feather, below the vane (see FEATHER).

CALCIUM METABOLISM: see METABOLISM ; NUTRITION

CALFBIRD: one name for *Perissocephalus tricolor* (also 'Capuchinbird')—for family see COTINGA.

CALIDRITINAE: see SANDPIPER

CALLAEIDAE: a family of the Passeriformes, suborder Oscines (see WATTLEBIRD (2)). The editors of the *Check-list of Birds of the World*, vol. 15, have deliberately retained this traditional spelling, although a purist would prefer 'Callaeatidae', or possibly 'Callaeadidae'.

CALL-NOTE: see SINGING

CALYPTOMENINAE: see BROADBILL

CAMPEPHAGIDAE: a family of the Passeriformes, suborder Oscines (see CUCKOO-SHRIKE).

CAMPO: term used in South America for a habitat consisting of grassy plains with scattered bushes and low trees.

CANARY: *Serinus canaria* (see FINCH ; and CAGE BIRD ; SINGING).

CANCELLATE: marked with cross lines, as on the webs between the toes of some water birds (see LEG).

CANCER: see DISEASE

CANOPY FEEDING: see under HERON

CANVASBACK: *Aythya valisineria*, a North American species of pochard (see DUCK).

CAP: an area of distinctive colour, in some plumage patterns, covering part of the top of the head, and sometimes down to the nape (see TOPOGRAPHY).

CAPERCAILLIE: name (of Gaelic origin, and sometimes spelt 'capercailzie') of *Tetrao urogallus*, and can be applied also to *T. parvirostris* (see GROUSE).

CAPITONIDAE: see under PICIFORMES ; and BARBET

CAPITONOIDEA: see under PICIFORMES

CAPON: a castrated domestic fowl.

CAPRIMULGI; CAPRIMULGIDAE: see below

CAPRIMULGIFORMES: an order, alternatively 'Caprimulgi', comprising the following suborders and families, the latter dealt with separately as shown :

Steatornithes : Steatornithidae see OILBIRD
Caprimulgi : Podargidae   see FROGMOUTH
              Nyctibiidae   see POTOO
              Aegothelidae   see OWLET-
                                  FROGMOUTH
              Caprimulgidae see NIGHTJAR

The nightjars are known in America as 'nighthawks' and 'goatsuckers'. The owlet-frogmouths are sometimes called 'owlet-nightjars', and the potoos 'tree-nightjars'.

CAPUCHINBIRD: one name for *Perissocephalus tricolor* (also 'Calfbird')—for family see COTINGA.

CARACARA: substantive name of some species of Daptriinae ; used without qualification, in the U.S.A., for *Caracara cheriway* ; in the plural, general term for the subfamily (see FALCON).

CARBOHYDRATE METABOLISM: see
METABOLISM ; NUTRITION

CARDINAL : substantive name best restricted to
Pyrrhuloxia ('*Richmondena*') *cardinalis* and *P. phoenicea* ; used without qualification, in the U.S.A.,
for the former species (also known locally as
'Cardinal Redbird', etc.)—see below. The name
is misapplied to some other reddish birds, e.g.
certain South American tanagers (Thraupinae) ;
and it is used in the Old World for *Foudia madagas-
carensis* (for family see WEAVER).

CARDINAL-GROSBEAK : in the plural, general
term for the subfamily Pyrrhuloxiinae (see EM-
BERIZIDAE). The subfamily has formerly been
known as 'Richmondeninae' (based on a genus
now merged) and 'Cardinalinae' (based on a
generic name found to be preoccupied). There is
some doubt about the position of certain genera,
but a tentative list of those that should be included
is : *Caryothraustes, Cyanocompsa, Guiraca, Passerina,
Periporyphus, Pheucticus* (including '*Hedymeles*'),
Pitylus, Pyrrhuloxia (including '*Richmondena*'),
Rhodothraupis, Saltator, and *Spiza*. In English terminology, the commonest substantive name is
'grosbeak', but others are 'cardinal' (see above),
'pyrrhuloxia', 'bunting', 'saltator', and 'dickcissel'.

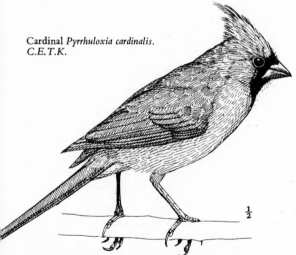

Cardinal *Pyrrhuloxia cardinalis*.
C.E.T.K.

½

The cardinal-grosbeaks are almost all 'buntings'
of from medium to large size (see BUNTING) ; and
the males are usually brightly coloured. This
group of a dozen genera is confined to the New
World and is predominantly tropical in distribution
—but with five genera represented among birds
breeding north of the Mexican border. Some of
the North American species are highly migratory.

Nest sites vary from on the ground to high in a tree.

The best-known species is the Cardinal *Pyrrhuloxia
cardinalis*, which occurs naturally from parts of
temperate North America south into Central
America and on certain adjacent islands ; it has
been introduced successfully into the Bermudas and
south-western California—also into Hawaii, where
it breeds all the year round and has become a pest
to fruit growers. It is about 7½–9 inches long,
varying somewhat geographically, and weighs
35–50 grams. The bill is large and stout, nearly
conical ; the head is conspicuously crested in both
sexes ; the wings are very short and rounded, the
tail relatively longer. Adults have a black 'bib'
about the base of the bill and extending to the
upper throat. In the male the remainder of the
feathering and also the bill are some variant of
scarlet-orange to deep scarlet. The female has more
muted coloration, the reds being mixed with browns
and buffs. The juvenile plumage closely resembles
that of the adult female but lacks the 'bib'.
Numerous subspecies have been named, mainly on
the basis of geographical variation in colour. The
habitat varies from moist to very arid, usually with
a mixture of clearings and young trees, or bushes
or vines ; mixed growth at woodland edges is
favoured. The Cardinal is also a common bird in
suburban gardens, coming readily to bird-baths and
feeding stations. It is usually sedentary, but some
ringed individuals have travelled considerable
distances.

The male Cardinal utters a series of loud, clear
whistling notes, very reminiscent of a person calling
a dog. The nest, typically, is placed 4–5 feet from
the ground, in a shady situation such as within a
young evergreen, a hedge, or a tangle of vines. It
varies from flimsy to compact, and is quite large for
the size of the bird. There are usually three eggs,
very pale blue finely spotted with browns and
lavender. Only the female incubates (12–13 days)
and broods ; the male feeds her, usually away from
the nest. The young leave the nest in 9–10 days,
and for some time thereafter the male tends and
feeds them while the female may begin building a
new nest. The pair-bond is maintained for successive broods through the season and, in some known
instances, has persisted for as long as three years.
In the latitude of Tennessee, four broods are commonly reared during the period April-August ;
and the species evidently breeds throughout the year
at some more southerly localities.

Other North American members of the subfamily
include the Blue Grosbeak *Guiraca caerulea* (the male
dark blue all over, except for tan wing-bars), the
Indigo Bunting *Passerina cyanea* (the male all blue),

the Rose-breasted Grosbeak *Pheucticus ludovicianus* (the male mainly black and white, apart from the breast patch), and the Dickcissel *Spiza americana* (the male a brownish bird with yellow breast and black 'bib'). The Painted Bunting *Passerina ciris* has been described as 'the most gaudily coloured American bird'; the male has red under parts and rump, green on the back, and blue on the head and wings; the female is green above and yellowish-green below. The remaining genera are represented only in the Neotropical Region, but—except for *Periporyphus*—as far north as Middle America. The Streaked Saltator *Saltator albicollis* is found on some of the Lesser Antilles as well as on the mainland.

For other uses of the name 'grosbeak' see GROSBEAK; and FINCH.   R.S.P.

Laskey, A. R. 1944. A study of the Cardinal in Tennessee. Wilson Bull. 56 : 27–44.

CARDIOVASCULAR SYSTEM: see BLOOD; HEART; VASCULAR SYSTEM

CARDUELINAE: see FRINGILLIDAE; and FINCH

CARIAMAE; CARIAMIDAE: see under GRUIFORMES; and SERIEMA

CARIB: substantive name of *Eulampis jugularis* and *Sericotes holosericeus* (for family see HUMMINGBIRD).

CARINA: see below

CARINATE: having a keel (carina) on the sternum, the converse of RATITE (see also SKELETON).

CAROTENOID PIGMENTS: see COLOUR

CAROTID ARTERIES: the main vessels passing up the neck to the head; the various different arrangements have been used as taxonomic characters (see VASCULAR SYSTEM).

CARPAL: name of small bones of the 'wrist', the carpal joint being the articulation of the manus with the radius and ulna and forming the forward pointing prominence of the folded wing (see SKELETON; WING).

CARPOMETACARPUS: the main bony structure of the 'hand' in birds, formed by the fusion of carpal and metacarpal elements (see SKELETON; WING).

CARRYING: transportation of various objects by birds. These are principally : (*a*) items of food for the bird's own consumption at another spot or to give to its mate (during courtship or on the nest) or young (see COURTSHIP FEEDING; FEEDING HABITS; FEEDING OF YOUNG); (*b*) nesting materials (see

NEST BUILDING); (*c*) nest refuse, including the shells of hatched eggs and the faeces of the nestlings (see PARENTAL CARE). There are also a few known instances in which birds transport their eggs or young.

Most birds carry objects grasped in the bill. Food is often carried inside the mouth, or farther down the alimentary canal and regurgitated. Only some raptorial birds carry prey or other objects in their talons (and not to the exclusion of use of the bill for lighter weights). Love-birds *Agapornis* spp. carry nest material among the feathers on the rump. The larger penguins *Aptenodytes* spp. waddle about with the single egg or small chick resting on the tarsi, the position in which it is incubated or brooded. The Black Vulture *Cathartes aura* sometimes moves its eggs about the laying area. Some aquatic birds habitually carry their young on their backs when swimming, e.g. swans *Cygnus* spp. and grebes (Podicipitidae). A few birds with nidifugous young occasionally transport their young in flight; for example, the Woodcock *Scolopax rusticola* does so, holding the small chick between its legs; other species in which the same behaviour has been recorded include the American Woodcock *Philohela minor*, the Common Sandpiper *Actitis hypoleucos*, and the White-browed Coucal *Centropus superciliosis* of Africa. (See Plates 4 and 9 (phot.).)

There is also the incidental transportation of, notably, plant pollen and seeds (see POLLINATORS AND DISTRIBUTORS); and the role of vector of parasites and infective organisms (see ECTOPARASITE; ENDOPARASITE; DISEASE; VECTOR).

CARTILAGE: see SKELETON

CARUNCLE: see INTEGUMENTARY STRUCTURES

CASQUE: an enlargement on the upper surface of the bill, in front of the head, as in most species of hornbills (Bucerotidae)—or on top of the head, as in cassowaries (Casuariidae). Compare HELMET; SHIELD, FRONTAL; and see BILL; IVORY, HORNBILL.

CASSOWARY: substantive name of the three species of the Casuariidae (Casuariiformes); in the plural, general term for the family. Cassowaries are large, heavy-bodied 'ratites' with a restricted range in the Australo-Papuan area (New Guinea, Aru Islands, Ceram, New Britain, Jobi, and the eastern seaboard of north-eastern Australia from Cape York south to about Cardwell). They are typically rain-forest dwellers. The close relatives of the cassowaries are the emus (Dromaiidae) of Australia, the two families together composing the order Casuariiformes (see EMU; RATITES, PHYLOGENY OF THE). Part of the tibiotarsus (distal end) of a cassowary closely related to, or even conspecific with, *Casuarius bennetti* is known from the Pleistocene of New South Wales (Miller 1962).

Cassowaries have coarse, bristle-like, drooping plumage, black in colour in the adult. The featherless head and neck are surmounted by a pronounced bony helmet, or 'casque', that rises from the top of the skull. This is believed to function in warding off thorny vines and undergrowth, a suggestion supported by the fact that the wing quills, which show no trace of vaning, are reduced to bare but prominent black spines, curving around the wedge-shaped body and diverting impediments so that when the bird is running in its characteristic position, with the head held forward, it can make relatively rapid progress through the jungle. A conspicuous feature is the presence of wattles of coloured flesh hanging from the bare, or partly bare, neck ; but these are lacking in the smallest species, the drab Bennett's Cassowary *Casuarius bennetti*. The bill is short, strong, and laterally compressed. In the very reduced wings the remiges are, as noted, reduced to bare shafts ; the tail lacks characteristic rectrices. The legs are stout and powerful, the innermost of the three toes (numbers 2, 3, and 4 in the fundamental digital series) being armed with a long, sharp claw —a deadly weapon in combat, when the bird leaps feet first at its adversary. There have been various human fatalities among New Guinea natives as the result of an encounter with a cornered cassowary, and one case of a European boy similarly killed in Queensland. The body length of the One-wattled Cassowary *C. unappendiculatus* of New Guinea is given as 52–65 inches, whilst, if anything, the larger specimens would exceed the 70–120 pounds recorded weight of a healthy adult Emu *Dromaius novaehollandiae*. The Australian form stands $4\frac{1}{2}$–5 feet high. Females are larger than males. See Plate 31.

A study of the biology and breeding habits of the Australian Cassowary *Casuarius casuarius johnsonii* was made during 1911–12 by E. D. Frizelle on behalf of H. L. White. The birds were found to occur largely singly or in pairs, but on occasion as many as six were seen together. Territories were found to be occupied during the laying season, apparently varying in extent from half a square mile to two square miles (Rockingham Bay district of Queensland). During this time the birds were quite aggressive. Cassowaries were found to rest, from about noon to 4.0 p.m., in regular sunny spots, and to have regular runs or tracks through the undergrowth. From time to time they were seen crossing creeks at regular points ; they swim readily. Eggs were found in the nest from the middle of June until about the end of August, with a record for as late as the middle of September. July and August were found to be the main months for laying. The broods of 3–4 young birds, brown and initially striped, were first seen in September and remained in company with the adult until January.

The egg sizes of the Australian Cassowary, perhaps the largest form, are given by White ; the averages of five separate clutches varied from $4\cdot87 \times 3\cdot67$ to $5\cdot58 \times 3\cdot78$ inches. The eggs vary in colour from pale to dark green, being said to be darker in fresh than in incubated specimens. The shell texture may be smooth or rough, depending on the individual bird. As in the other 'ratites', incubation of the eggs (which are laid in a clearing on the forest floor) is the province of the male, as is the care of the young.

The food of the Australian Cassowary varies somewhat seasonally but includes the seeds of various palms (often knocked down by fruit pigeons), quandongs, 'wild plums', figs, and other wild fruits and berries (White). Observations in New Guinea have shown that insects and plant tissues are also consumed.

For a long time it was believed that there were six species of cassowaries, but two of these were based on captive birds of unknown origin and a third has since appeared to be merely a geographical representative of one of the others. Accordingly, Mayr reduced the number to three species ; *C. casuarius*, *C. unappendiculatus*, and the dwarf *C. bennetti*. Of these, the first includes all the two-wattled forms and is the species represented in Australia ; the third is the only one represented in New Britain.

All in all, the call-notes—deep booming or croaking sounds—are more often heard than the birds are seen. Their wary habits and the thickness of the jungle provide abundant protection for such otherwise conspicuous birds.

Young cassowaries are frequently kept by the natives of New Guinea, being reared in enclosures until large enough to be eaten.   A.K.

Mayr, E. 1940. Birds collected during the Whitney South Sea Expedition XLI. Notes on New Guinea birds VI. Amer. Mus. Novit. no. 1056 : 1–12.
Miller, A. H. The historical significance of the fossil *Casuarius lydekki*. Rec. Austr. Mus. 25 : 235–237.

CAST ; CASTING : same as PELLET.

CASTLE-BUILDER : name sometimes applied to species of spinetails (Synallaxinae)—see OVENBIRD (1).

CASUARII ; CASUARIIDAE : see below

CASUARIIFORMES : an order, alternatively

'Casuarii', of 'ratite' birds comprising the families Casuariidae and Dromaiidae (see CASSOWARY; and EMU ; also RATITES, PHYLOGENY OF THE). These are very large running birds, of which the cassowaries are found in Australia and New Guinea and the sole surviving species of emu only in Australia. A family based on the fossil type-genus *Dromornis* is also placed in this order.

CATACROMYODIAN: see SYRINX

CATAMBLYRHYNCHIDAE: a family (Passeriformes, suborder Oscines) recognised by some authors ; but in the system here followed the sole member is included in the Thraupinae (Emberizidae) —see FINCH, PLUSHCAPPED.

CATBIRD (1): substantive name, in North America, of *Dumetella carolinensis* and *Melanoptila glabrirostris* (see MOCKINGBIRD).

CATBIRD (2): substantive name, in Australia, of *Ailuroedus* spp. and *Scenopoeetes dentirostris* (see BOWERBIRD).

CATBIRD (3): substantive name of the Abyssinian Catbird *Parophasma galinieri*, variously regarded as a flycatcher or a babbler (for family see MUSCICAPIDAE).

CATERPILLAR-BIRD ; CATERPILLAR-SHRIKE: names sometimes applied to species of Campephagidae or, in the plural, used generally for the family (see CUCKOO-SHRIKE).

CATHARTAE; CATHARTIDAE: see under FALCONIFORMES; and VULTURE (2)

CAUDAL: pertaining to the tail, or the region of the tail ; or (relatively) nearer the tail.

CELL: in its special sense, a unit mass of living matter. Except in the simplest (unicellular) forms of animal life, a very large number of cells make up an organism, constituting its various tissues (see TISSUE). A cell usually has a nucleus, in which are found the chromosomes carrying the genes for the different heritable characters (see GENETICS). Cells multiply by a process of division (mitosis) in which every chromosome is split into two, one half going with each daughter nucleus. The final division leading to the formation of a germ-cell or gamete (whether spermatozoon or ovum) is a reduction-division (meiosis), in which the number of chromosomes is halved in each resulting 'pronucleus' (yielding the 'haploid' instead of the usual 'diploid' number). See also BLOOD.

CENSUS: term best restricted to estimates of breeding populations, counts made in other cir-cumstances having usually a more transient validity (see COUNT). In practice the breeding census must often be broadened to become a census during the breeding season of adult or apparently adult birds, owing to (a) the difficulty in many cases of establishing readily whether or not a particular individual is actually breeding, and (b) the impossibility in the field of telling by plumage alone whether some species (Arctic Skua *Stercorarius parasiticus*) are sexually mature.

In Britain the first census of more than a local nature was the 1928 census of the Heron *Ardea cinerea* organised by E. M. Nicholson. This has been followed by wide-scale breeding-season surveys of other large and conspicuous birds such as Great Crested Grebe *Podiceps cristatus*, Blackheaded Gull *Larus ridibundus*, Gannet *Sula bassana*, Fulmar *Fulmarus glacialis*, Rook *Corvus frugilegus*, Mute Swan *Cygnus olor* ; the numbers of breeding pairs of some of the scarcer birds-of-prey (Falconiformes) have also been closely assessed. In Germany the population of the White Stork *Ciconia ciconia* has for long received special attention.

A knowledge of the numbers of a species is helpful to a better understanding of many aspects of its biology and may also provide material for more general studies (see NUMBERS; POPULATION DYNAMICS). In addition, such knowledge has a practical utility in any attempt at assessment of the ecological status of species and at deciding whether it requires either protection or control ; and in studies, for example, of the effects of weather or the importance of food or of nesting sites it is necessary to know the changes in numbers from year to year. For such a purpose a census on a national scale is too cumbersome, indeed quite impossible for most species, and a detailed annually repeated investigation of a sample population or relatively small area is undertaken. Tits *Parus* spp. have proved a popular subject for such researches, particularly in the Netherlands and Britain. Other hole-nesting species have been studied in Germany and elsewhere, as well as colonies of gulls and terns (Laridae). In the U.S.A. special attention has been paid to game-birds (Galliformes).

Of the various methods of conducting a census, the better known include :

1. Counting nests individually (suitable for species nesting conspicuously in moderate or small colonies, such as Heron or Rook).

2. Counting conspicuous birds individually (e.g. Great Crested Grebe).

3. Counting birds on nests (with or without help of photography) within a certain restricted area and applying the density thus ascertained to the whole breeding area—a sampling method that may be

helpful in the case of very large colonies of cliff-nesting birds.

4. By means of transect counts in one type of habitat to calculate the density of the species in that particular habitat. The most painstaking and ambitious application of the transect count is the work of E. Merikallio in estimating the total number of each species of bird in Finland ; in this case the data were derived from repeated transects scattered throughout the country, and the figures compiled from observations made along a main belt extending 25 metres on each side of the survey line, supplemented by an ' auditory belt ' nearly seven times as wide.

A single observer working alone can do valuable census work, particularly if the counts are repeated on similar lines for several years. However, the scope of a lone worker is obviously restricted, and the development of the census to cover wider fields was a pioneer activity of ornithological team work. The team should be mobilised and organised in advance so that coverage may be as complete as possible.

In order that results may be reasonably uniform in a wide-scale census, a questionnaire should be prepared stating clearly the object of the census, the unit to be counted (e.g. ' occupied nests ' or ' adults present in the breeding season '), and defining any points of ambiguity (e.g. what is meant by breeding season). Generally speaking, the simpler the questionnaire and the fewer its questions, the better will be the response and the coverage that it obtains.

Seldom can a census be absolutely accurate, and it is necessary to attempt an assessment of its validity. Pitfalls include misidentification, false assumptions (e.g. that all nests in a rookery, heronry, or martin colony are occupied), and inconspicuousness. This last varies widely between one species and another, and may vary within the same species with the time of day, weather conditions, type of cover, and so on. It is therefore most desirable to go over the census area several times, but even so in certain circumstances some weighting of the counts may be necessary to compensate for unobtrusiveness. A further point is that singing males must not be equated with breeding pairs ; in fact the male that has failed to find a mate will often be the most ardent singer.

Various statistical considerations are involved in different methods of counting and in procedures for comparing the results in one year with those in another (see STATISTICAL SIGNIFICANCE).

P.A.D.H.

Merikallio, E. 1958. Finnish Birds. Their Distribution and Numbers. Helsinki.

CENTROPODINAE: see CUCKOO

CEPPHINI: see AUK

CERE: the fleshy covering of the proximal portion of the upper mandible in some orders of birds (see BILL).

CEREBELLUM: part of the hindbrain (see NERVOUS SYSTEM).

CEREBRAL HEMISPHERES: parts of the forebrain (see NERVOUS SYSTEM).

CEREOPSIS: generic name sometimes used as English name of *C. novaehollandiae*, otherwise the Cape Barren Goose (see under DUCK).

CEROPHAGY: eating wax (see HONEYGUIDE).

CERTHIIDAE: a family of the Passeriformes, suborder Oscines (see TREECREEPER (1)).

CERVICAL: pertaining to the neck.

CERYLINAE: see KINGFISHER

CHACHALACA: substantive name of some species of Cracidae (see CURASSOW).

CHAETURINAE: see SWIFT

CHAFFINCH: substantive name of two species of *Fringilla* ; used without qualification for *F. coelebs* (see FINCH).

CHAJA: name commonly used in parts of South America for the Crested Screamer *Chauna torquata* (see SCREAMER).

CHALAZA: see EGG

CHAMAEINI: see BABBLER

CHAPARRAL: an environment, consisting of dense shrubs and stunted trees, characteristic of parts of North America.

CHAPARRAL-COCK: name applied to the Greater Roadrunner *Geococcyx californianus* (see CUCKOO).

CHARADRII; CHARADRIIDAE: see below

CHARADRIIFORMES: an order comprising the following suborders and families, the latter dealt with separately as shown :

Charardii :
    Superfamily Jacanoidea
        Jacanidae   see JACANA
    Superfamily Charadrioidea
        Rostratulidae   see PAINTED SNIPE
        Haematopodidae   see OYSTERCATCHER
        Charadriidae   see PLOVER (1)
        Scolopacidae   see SANDPIPER
        Recurvirostridae   see AVOCET
        Phalaropodidae   see PHALAROPE

Superfamily Dromadoidea
Dromadidae   see CRAB-PLOVER
Superfamily Burhinoidea
Burhinidae   see THICKKNEE
Superfamily Glareoloidea
Glareolidae   see PRATINCOLE;
                    COURSER
Superfamily Thinocoroidea
Thinocoridae   see SEED-SNIPE
Superfamily Chionidoidea
Chionididae   see SHEATHBILL
Lari :
Stercorariidae   see SKUA
Laridae   see GULL; TERN
Rynchopidae   see SKIMMER
Alcae :
Alcidae   see AUK

Some authors treat certain of the above families as (at most) subfamilies, and the merging of these involves using such familial names as Charadriidae and Laridae in a wider sense. Stresemann places the Jacanidae, Thinocoridae, and Alcidae in three separate orders ; his order Laro-Limicolae is thus the equivalent of the Charadriiformes without these.

The Charadrii are equivalent to the former order Limicolae—the ' waders ' of British and ' shore-birds ' of American usage. They are birds of from small to moderate size, ground-living and usually ground-nesting ; they mostly frequent the vicinity of water, either inland or on the sea coast. Most of them prefer open situations, relying for safety on cryptic coloration, wariness, and mobility ; some live in marshes, and a few in woodland. They can run swiftly for short distances and fly strongly ; the phalaropes habitually swim. Their bills show a variety of specialised forms adapted to probing in soft ground and so on. A long bill is often correlated with long legs. In some the front toes are more or less webbed ; the hind toe is small or absent except in the specialised 'lily-trotting' foot of jacanas. Most of them are markedly gregarious except when breeding ; and many perform long migrations. The great majority of the species are comprised in two large cosmopolitan families, Charadriidae (plovers) and Scolopacidae (sandpipers, snipe, etc.). Some of the smaller families are also worldwide in distribution, while others are more restricted—sometimes to the tropics or some part thereof, the phalaropes to the far north (except as migrants), and the sheathbills to the far south.

The Lari comprise the gulls and allied groups, birds of from fairly small to rather large size, web-footed and often with predominantly white plumage. They frequent sea coasts, inland waters, and marshes.

They are highly gregarious and breed colonially, using a variety of nesting sites. The skuas are parasitic in their feeding habits. The suborder is cosmopolitan in distribution and some species are notable migrants. The Alcae are highly specialised for swimming under water ; they are exclusively marine and restricted to the Northern Hemisphere.

Families based on the fossil type-genera *Rhegminornis* and *Presbyornis* are also placed in this order (suborder Charadrii).

CHARADRIOIDEA: see above

CHARM: see ASSEMBLY, NOUN OF

CHAT (1): substantive name, in whole or part, of some species of Turdinae (see THRUSH) ; in the plural, general term for a subgroup (' chat-thrushes ') of this subfamily, and more particularly for some of the genera, e.g. stonechats and whinchats *Saxicola* spp., wheatears *Oenanthe* spp., redstarts *Phoenicurus* spp., robin-chats *Cossypha* spp., cliff-chats *Thamnolea* spp., sooty chats or ant-chats *Myrmecocichla* spp. The name refers to the harsh ' chacking ' notes of many of these birds.

CHAT (2): substantive name, in America, of certain species of Parulidae, e.g. *Icteria virens* and *Granatellus* spp., likewise ' Ground-chat ' for *Chamaethlypis poliocephala* (see WARBLER (2)).

CHAT (3): substantive name, in Australia, of *Ephthianura* spp. (see under WREN (2)).

CHAT, PALM: see PALMCHAT

CHEEK: see TOPOGRAPHY

CHEER: *Catreus wallichi* (see PHEASANT).

CHEMICAL POISONS: see TOXIC CHEMICALS

CHEST: the THORAX ; if used to designate a surface area, practically synonymous with breast (see TOPOGRAPHY).

CHEWINK: alternative name for the Rufous-sided Towhee *Pipilo erythrophthalmus* (see BUNTING).

CHICK: see under YOUNG BIRD

CHICKADEE: substantive name, in North America, of some *Parus* spp. (see TIT).

CHIN: see TOPOGRAPHY

CHIONIDIDAE: see under CHARADRIIFORMES ; and SHEATHBILL

CHIONIDOIDEA: see under CHARADRIIFORMES

CHI-SQUARE TEST: see STATISTICAL SIGNIFICANCE

CHLOROPHONIA: generic name used as substantive name of *Chlorophonia* spp. (see TANAGER).

CHLOROPSEIDAE: name used by Wetmore for a family equivalent to the Irenidae (in the system followed here) less *Irena* (see LEAFBIRD).

CHOANA: a funnel-shaped passage; especially one of the interior nares (see NARIS; SMELL).

CHORDATES: see ANIMAL KINGDOM

CHORDEILINAE: see NIGHTJAR

CHOUGH (1): substantive name of *Pyrrhocorax* spp., used without qualification, in Britain (but sometimes 'Cornish Chough'), for *P. pyrrhocorax* (see CROW).

CHOUGH (2): substantive name, in Australia, of *Corcorax melanorhamphos* (see under MAGPIE-LARK).

CHROMATOGRAPHY: see PROTEINS AS TAXONOMIC CHARACTERS

CHROMOSOME: see CELL; GENETICS

CHRONOCLINE: term introduced by G. G. Simpson for the gradation of a form in time, going back towards an ancestral type.

CHRONOMETER, BIOLOGICAL: see TIME MEASUREMENT

CHUCK-WILL'S-WIDOW: *Caprimulgus carolinensis* (see NIGHTJAR).

CHUKAR: *Alectoris graeca* (see under PHEASANT).

CHYME: the semi-fluid partly digested food leaving the gizzard for the duodenum (see ALIMENTARY SYSTEM).

CICADA-BIRD: Australian name of *Coracina* ('*Edoliisoma*') *tenuirostra* (see CUCKOO-SHRIKE).

CICONIAE ; CICONIIDAE: see below

CICONIIFORMES: an order, alternatively 'Gressores' and formerly also 'Herodiones', comprising the following suborders and families, the latter dealt with separately as shown :

Ardeae :
    Ardeidae   see HERON ; BITTERN
Balaenicipites :
    Balaenicipitidae   see SHOEBILL
Ciconiae :
    Superfamily Scopoidea
      Scopidae   see HAMMERHEAD
    Superfamily Ciconioidea
      Ciconiidae   see STORK
    Superfamily Threskiornithoidea
      Threskiornithidae see IBIS ; SPOONBILL
Phoenicopteri :
    Phoenicopteridae   see FLAMINGO

The monotypical family Cochleariidae is here merged in the Ardeidae, but the point is controversial ; the affinities of *Balaeniceps*, here retained in a monotypical family, are in some doubt. Some authors, including Stresemann, treat the Phoenicopteri as a separate order.

The Ciconiiformes are mainly large birds, characteristically with long legs and long bills, adapted for wading in shallow water or marshes and mostly living on fish or other animal prey. The flamingos have distinctive feeding habits, with a specialised bill adapted thereto.

Families based on the fossil type-genera *Scaniornis*, *Palaelodus*, and *Agnopterus* are also placed in this order (Suborder Phoenicopteri).

CINCLIDAE: a family of the Passeriformes, suborder Oscines (see DIPPER).

CINCLOSOMATINAE: see MUSCICAPIDAE ; and RAIL-BABBLER

CIRCADIAN: term applied to a biological rhythm of about a day, i.e. circa 24 hours (see RHYTHM ; TIME MEASUREMENT).

CIRCAETINAE: see HAWK

CIRCINAE: see HAWK

CIRCULATION: see HEART ; VASCULAR SYSTEM

CLADISTIC: in an evolutionary sense, tending to branch.

CLADOGENESIS: see SPECIATION

CLADORNITHES: see under PELECANIFORMES

CLAMATORES: see under PASSERIFORMES

CLASS: a primary taxonomic category ; all birds, including those known only from fossils, constitute a single 'class' of animals, the Class Aves (see ANIMAL KINGDOM ; AVES ; TAXON). A class is divided into 'orders', but these may be grouped in intermediate categories such as subclasses and superorders.

Subclasses. The division of the Class Aves into subclasses has no practical application to the taxonomy of geologically recent birds, all the orders of which fall in the subclass Neornithes ; the most ancient of the fossil birds, the Archaeornithiformes of the Jurassic, are placed by Wetmore in his only other subclass, the Archaeornithes.

Superorders. Wetmore (1960) divides the Neornithes into the superorders Odontognathae, Ichthyornithes, Impennes, and Neognathae. Of these, the first and second include only fossil birds ; the third includes only the Sphenisciformes (penguins) ; and all other recent (and some fossil) birds are assigned to the Neognathae. So far as birds of today are concerned, therefore, use of the super-ordinal category involves nothing beyond the question whether the penguins differ more, funda-mentally, from all other recent orders than these differ from each other—a point on which many disagree with Wetmore. Formerly, he had placed the 'ratite' orders and the Tinamiformes in a superorder Palaeognathae of an earlier system, but this he now rejects (see also RATITES, PHYLOGENY OF THE).

CLASSIFICATION: the grouping of forms in categories, and of these in still wider categories, and so on. Classification is the subject matter of tax-onomy, itself such a large part of systematics as to be almost synonymous therewith, and nomenclature is its tool (see NOMENCLATURE ; SYSTEMATICS ; TAXON ; TAXONOMY).

Artificial and Natural Systems. An artificial system of classification is one based on considerations of convenience, perhaps on the differences shown in one particular character arbitrarily chosen as the criterion ; a natural system purports to reflect a general reality inherent in the subject material. In some degree, however, all systems of zoological classification are artificial in that they contain a large subjective element. On the other hand, most authors who have attempted to classify birds have based their systems on some theory of the natural pattern ; we dismiss these systems as unnatural only because we regard the particular theories as unten-able.

Aristotle, and his followers after the Renaissance, gave function priority over form and classified birds according to such characters as habitat, locomotion, or food—even on whether they bathed in dust or in water, or on whether or not they sang. It was Willughby and Ray in 1676 who first took morpho-logical characters as the basis of a system ; but they, and their followers for more than a century, used such diagnostic criteria as form of bill and feet and the size of the body—characters which we now regard as obviously adaptive rather than funda-mental, and therefore of secondary value for the purpose. This purpose, since the influence of Darwin's thought took full effect, has been to classify birds in accordance with what we judge to be their kinship with each other in evolutionary descent from a common ancestral form—their 'phylogenetic relationship'. Modern morpho-logical taxonomy stems largely from Fürbringer (1888).

Horizontal and Vertical Systems. A horizontal system of classification is one that includes only birds existing at the present level of geological time. A system thoroughly phylogenetic in its scope must, however, take into account also those fossil forms that produce a vertical arrangement in which, so to speak, time is a dimension. Such an arrangement can be depicted as a branching tree.

Symmetry and Asymmetry. In the last pre-evolutionary phase of thought, notably during the first half of the nineteenth century, ideas of classifi-cation were governed by metaphysical notions regarding the pattern of creation ; facts were thus pressed into a preconceived mould, often of a geometrical or numerical kind—everything must be arranged in concentric circles, or by sixes, or fives, or fours. The position as we see it today is very different, and our various attempts at a phylogenetic tree are far from being symmetrical ; we indeed come to see more and more that our orderly arrange-

---

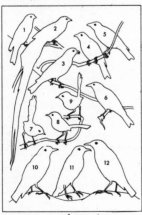

ca. ½ nat. size

Plate 7 · Seasonal Sexual Dimorphism by C. E. TALBOT KELLY

The species shown are characterised by a strongly marked sexual dimorphism in breeding plumage, with a strongly marked seasonal change in the male. The result of the latter is that the sexes are more alike, and sometimes closely alike, in the off-season (whether or not there is some minor seasonal change in the female). See article SEXUAL DIMORPHISM.

Paradise Whydah *Vidua paradisea* (Africa)
1 Female, **2** Breeding male
(*off-season male similar to female*)

Scarlet Tanager *Piranga olivacea* (North America)
3 Female, **4** Off-season male, **5** Intermediate male, **6** Breeding male

Splendid Fairy Wren *Malurus splendens* (Western Australia)
7 Female, **8** Off-season male, **9** Breeding male

Rock Thrush *Monticola saxatilis* (Eurasia)
10 Female, **11** Off-season male, **12** Breeding male

C.E.Talbot Kelly.

C. E. Talbot Kelly.

ment is imposed on a reality following a pattern very variable in its parts. We therefore have to reconcile ourselves to the inevitability that our categories of the same nominal rank are not of the same value in their distinctiveness, are not divisible in like manner, and are not equal in the number of forms that they comprehend. The evolutionary process has been sometimes rapid and sometimes slow, sometimes prolific and sometimes meagre in its results.

Taxonomic Categories. Present-day classification is based on the belief that the category that has objective reality is the species, which is regarded as a natural entity ; it is the lowest category characterised by inherent reproductive isolation (see SPECIATION ; SPECIES). All other categories, lower or higher, are subjective. Subspecific categories represent our ideas of the relationship between populations within the species. Subspecies often show gradations, and their reproductive isolation is incidental to their distribution and liable to break down. Supraspecific categories represent our ideas of the phylogenetic grouping of species. It may be remarked, however, that Linnaeus regarded the genus—his particular invention, and a wider category than most of the genera of today—as having objective reality ; and in palaeontology the available material is so small that the genus tends to be regarded as a more useful category than the species.

Linnaeus was the father of the present terminology of taxonomic categories. He recognised *classis*, *ordo*, *genus*, *species*, and *varietas* ; his conception of the last was quite different from the subspecific category of today. All modern systems interpolate family between order and genus. Many go much further, so that it is possible to have a hierarchy of

categories comprising class, subclass, cohort, super-order, order, suborder, superfamily, family, sub-family, tribe, genus, subgenus, superspecies, species, subspecies (see TAXON ; also CLASS ; FAMILY ; GENUS ; ORDER ; SPECIES ; SUBSPECIES ; SUPERSPECIES).

The definition of any particular higher category, from a genus upwards, depends on a degree of resemblance (of a nature suggesting phylogenetic affinity) between its members—the lower the category, the greater the resemblance—and on the existence of a distinct gap between it and other categories of the same rank. The latter criterion makes it possible to have a monotypic category, containing only one unit of the next rank below ; and it even happens that an order may contain a single family, a single genus, and a single species.

It is obvious that judgment of requisite degrees of resemblance and requisite sizes of gap must be largely subjective, and therefore variable between one author and another. Ornithologists, dealing with a class showing a smaller range of diversity than some others, have tended to base orders and families on relatively small differences. They may, however, vary greatly among themselves in their choice of criteria ; thus, Wetmore has divided recent birds into twenty-seven orders, while Stresemann allocates them to fifty on an otherwise similar system (see ORDER).

Current Systems. One must not seek to stereotype systematic thought and thus to deter progress ; but, with such diverse views on the part of specialists, it is for most purposes of ornithology desirable to standardise—at least for a time—one particular system. That followed in the present work down to familial level, and set out at the beginning of the volume, is the now widely adopted

---

ca. ¼ nat. size

Plate 8 · Seasonal Change (Sexes Alike) by C. E. TALBOT KELLY

The species shown are characterised by a strongly marked seasonal change in both sexes, with little or no sexual dimorphism. In the case of the Ptarmigan, the females have yellowish brown rather than grey in summer and autumn, lack the black lores in winter, and have a smaller red wattle over the eye at all seasons. See article PLUMAGE.

Black Coucal *Centropus toulou* (tropical Africa)
1 Non-breeding plumage, **2** Breeding plumage

Ptarmigan (Rock Ptarmigan) *Lagopus mutus* (Holarctic distribution, in high latitudes or at high altitudes) **3** Male in winter, **4** Male in summer, **5** Male in autumn

Blackheaded Gull *Larus ridibundus* (Palaearctic Region)
6 Winter plumage, **7** Breeding plumage

Grey (or Black-bellied) Plover *Pluvialis squatarola* (Holarctic distribution, breeding in high latitudes) **8** Winter plumage, **9** Breeding plumage

Slavonian (or Horned) Grebe *Podiceps auritus* (Holarctic distribution)
10 Winter plumage, **11** Breeding plumage

system of Peters, based on Wetmore (see List of Major Articles on Bird Groups, and Note on Classification Followed (with references)).

A.L.T.

Fürbringer, M. 1888. Untersuchungen zur Morphologie und Systematik der Vögel, zugleich ein Beitrag zur Anatomie der Stutz- und Bewegungsorgane. Bijdr. Dierk. K. Zool. Genootschaps. Afl. XV. 2 vols. Amsterdam.
Stresemann, E. 1950. The development of theories which have affected the taxonomy of birds. Ibis 92 : 123–131.

CLAVICLE: a paired bone ('collar bone') of the pectoral girdle, the two clavicles in birds being fused to form the furcula ('wishbone' or 'merrythought')—see SKELETON.

CLAW: for those on the toes, see LEG ; also MOULT ; for those sometimes borne on the manus, see WING.

CLEIDOIC: term descriptive of the totally enclosed condition of eggs of the type produced by birds. Such an egg represents a virtually sealed physiological system (except for some gaseous exchange) during the period of incubation, a condition that makes certain adaptations necessary, e.g. as regards excretion. See DEVELOPMENT, EMBRYONIC ; EGG ; EXCRETORY SYSTEM ; NUTRITION.

CLIMACTERIDAE: a family of the Passeriformes, suborder Oscines (see TREECREEPER (2)).

CLIMATOLOGY: the study of climate, the total experience of the weather over a long period of time (measured in years, although properly analysed in such a way as to bring out seasonal characteristics) ; distinguished from meteorology, which is concerned with instantaneous weather or at most with the weather over short periods (measured in days)—see METEOROLOGY. For the present purpose, climate is regarded as an important element in the environment of bird-life in various parts of the world at different seasons and through the ages.

General Atmospheric Circulation. The unequal heating of the Earth's surface by the sun drives the atmospheric circulation, which may be regarded as a convection system on the grandest scale. The main streams of the atmospheric circulation, carrying most of the momentum, are general westerly currents ('the upper westerlies'), found in most latitudes over both hemispheres from within the tropics to the poles, and extending from a base level that is generally either at the surface or within the bottom mile or so (1 to 2 km.) of the atmosphere up to heights of well over 10 miles (over 15 km.). The form of this wind current has been likened to a broad meandering river, which branches and swirls,

swinging sometimes far north and south, on its way around the world. There is a general level of maximum winds at a height of 6 to 8 miles (approx. 10 to 12 km.) ; speeds of 100–200 knots or more are fairly commonly reached in the fastest moving parts of the airstream, known as 'jet-streams', 1000 miles (1000 to 2000 km.) or more in length and generally 100–200 miles (say 100–300 km.) in width.

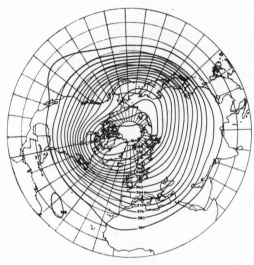

FIG 1. Mean height in dekametres of the 500 mb. surface : Northern Hemisphere, average for the months January, April, July, and October (Period 1949–53).
Reproduced from the 'Meteorological Magazine' by permission of the Controller of H.M. Stationery Office.

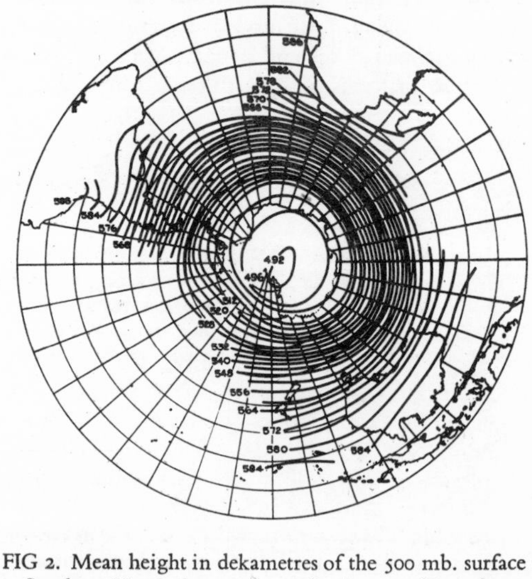

FIG 2. Mean height in dekametres of the 500 mb. surface : Southern Hemisphere, average for the year (Period 1952–54 approx.).
Reproduced from the 'Meteorological Magazine' by permission of the Controller of H.M. Stationery Office.

Poleward swings of the upper westerlies around broad 'upper ridges' occur over regions with climates warm for their latitude (e.g. the warm waters of the North Atlantic Drift), and over more transient advances of tropical air in the lower atmosphere ; conversely, broad 'upper troughs' are found over regions of cold surface and outbreaks of polar air. The 'warm ridges' and 'cold troughs' in the upper westerlies have larger latitudinal amplitude in the Northern Hemisphere than in the Southern, and in winter than in summer.

Figures 1 and 2 show the general circulation at a height of 3 to 4 miles over the Northern and Southern Hemispheres by means of the average topography (heights in dekametres) of the 500-millibar constant pressure surface. About half the atmosphere lies below this level and air density is about half what it is at sea level. Winds blow nearly along the contours of the pressure surface, wind speed increasing with the gradient. Notice that the Southern Hemisphere circulation is stronger than the Northern. Semi-permanent cold troughs are found over north-east Canada and over or near north-east Asia, whilst warm ridges lie over or near the Rocky Mountains and the eastern North Atlantic.

Disequilibrium, associated with accelerations and retardations in the upper west winds, gives rise to regions of high and low surface pressure—the familiar 'anticyclones' and 'depressions' respectively of the surface weather map. The most regular of these systems appear on Figures 3 and 4, which show the average pressure at mean sea level over the world in January and July. Notice particularly :

(i) *The subtropical anticyclones*—belts of high average pressure along the warm fringe of the upper westerlies, in subtropical latitudes ; there are several separate anticyclone cells, most pronounced over the oceans.

(ii) *The subpolar zone of low pressure*—belts of low average pressure along the cold fringe of the upper westerlies, near the polar circles ; the principal centres of low pressure are also over the oceans, particularly near Iceland, the Aleutians, in the southern Indian Ocean, and near some of the great bights in the coast of Antarctica.

Prevailing Winds. The main regions of high and low pressure determine the winds prevailing in the lower atmosphere (cf. Figs. 5 and 6). The surface wind normally has a component of motion across the isobars, but winds at 1500 to 3000 feet (say 500 to 800 metres) above the surface blow very nearly along the isobars of sea-level pressure. The circulation is clockwise around anticyclones and counter-clockwise around depressions in the Northern Hemisphere (Buys-Ballot's law), and contrariwise in the Southern Hemisphere.

We distinguish the following principal wind regimes.

1. *The Polar Easterlies.* Over the central regions of the Greenland and Antarctic ice-caps and of the Arctic pack-ice, mainly light and variable surface winds prevail. But nearer the fringe of the ice-covered region more and more generally outblowing winds, north-easterly in the Arctic and south-easterly in the Antarctic, are found. The cold, dense air drains off the ice-caps in a system of 'katabatic winds' of great persistence, following the natural drainage channels and converging in coastal valleys and fjords to blow at times with hurricane force.

2. *The Subpolar Low Pressure Belt.* Low average pressure results from the succession of (mainly eastward) travelling 'polar front' depressions. (The 'front' is the moving boundary where airstreams of polar and tropical origin converge.) This is a zone of winds of very variable directions, but frequently of gale force. Gales are commonest over the oceans, except for certain localities in Antarctica and Greenland ; the strongest gales, however, occur in the cold polar air along mountainous sections of the coasts in high latitudes and amongst the mountains, where they are liable to blow for several days without abating.

3. *The Prevailing Westerlies of Middle Latitudes (The Brave West Winds).* Warm airmasses emerge from the northern and southern subtropical anticyclones and blow towards higher latitudes as prevailing SW. and NW. winds respectively. Before reaching the subpolar zone of minimum pressure they encounter the polar front and rise over the denser polar air, which also generally blows from westerly points once it has penetrated into latitudes less than 60°. Uplift of the warmer air produces extensive belts of cloud and rain. The wind direction varies a good deal, mainly between SW. and NW., and the strength is very variable ; gales are frequent over the oceans.

4. *The Horse Latitudes.* A zone of generally light, variable winds circulating outwards from the anticyclones in the subtropical belt. The air is partly supplied by subsidence from higher levels. This is the arid zone, in which most of the great deserts occur.

5. *The Trade Winds.* These are driven towards lower latitudes from the northern and southern subtropical anticyclones as NE. and SE. winds respectively ; amongst the most persistent windstreams on Earth but generally of moderate strength.

Sunny weather and broken cloud are characteristic. When the subtropical high pressure belt is disrupted or displaced, however, the Trade Winds may be missing in the sector concerned, sometimes for weeks. Especially in late summer, very violent tropical revolving storms, or 'cyclones' (also known as 'hurricanes' and 'typhoons'), are liable to form in the Trade Wind zone and may grow to affect an area 200 to 400 miles (300 to 600 km.) wide across their path. Heavy rains and violent cloud development occur in the occasional tropical cyclones, but it is rare for one place to experience more than one or two of these in the same year, and many places, especially inland, are virtually immune ; the South Atlantic Ocean, also, gets no tropical cyclones.

6. *The Doldrums.* The Trade Winds from either hemisphere meet in a belt of relatively low pressure and generally light winds from variable directions. This is the zone of equatorial rains and thunderstorms ; convergence of the windstreams gives rise to vertical currents of great violence (of the order of 1000 to 2000 feet a minute in some cases) and cumulonimbus clouds tower up to extreme heights of 50 000–60 000 feet (15–17 km.). The principal convergence does not coincide with the geographical Equator ; moreover, it undergoes seasonal shifts.

Seasonal Changes. The general zonal arrangement of the atmospheric circulation at the surface and aloft moves generally north and south with the zenith sun at noon, but the progression is not smooth and is liable to setbacks ; moreover, the over-all seasonal displacement of the circulation does not amount to more than about ten degrees of latitude (cf. Figs. 3 and 4, 5 and 6).

The seasonal change is greatest over Asia. This may be attributed ultimately to the different thermal properties of land and water surfaces, resulting in the most extreme seasonal range of temperature over the world's greatest landmass. The shift of latitude of the upper westerlies from winter to summer is greater here than anywhere else. In June to August, when the westerlies are farthest north, an important current of upper east winds is developed all along the southern flank of Asia (about 25° N. lat.) and south of the Sahara. The surface monsoonal low pressure system partly underlies this upper current. 'Monsoon' is originally an Arabic word meaning 'season', but is applied in meteorology chiefly to wind and pressure regimes that reverse with the seasons. Average surface pressure is high over most of Asia in winter and low in summer. The equatorial rainbelt gets drawn as far as 25–35° N. lat. in this sector into the summer

monsoon low pressure region. South of this, India experiences generally SW. surface winds in summer, whereas NE. winds prevail in winter bringing much drier cool air from Tibet and China.

Surface Effects and Local Influences. Climate also registers the effects of different types of surface upon the atmosphere and vice versa.

Ocean currents are for the most part wind-driven. The main horizontal currents of the ocean surface show a remarkable parallelism with the prevailing surface winds. Moreover, shifts of the atmospheric circulation, associated with good or bad years and with climatic changes, are believed to involve corresponding shifts of the ocean currents and their boundaries, thereby changing the temperature distribution and shifting the frontiers of the communities of marine life.

Oceans exert less friction upon the air than land. Hence windiness is a characteristic of the oceans and of maritime climates. The surface temperature of great water bodies responds slowly to heating and cooling. Seasonal changes are damped and delayed (see also METEOROLOGY). The much more rapid heating and cooling of dry land gives rise to systems of land and sea breezes at coasts, blowing onshore by day and offshore at night.

Snow and ice cool extremely rapidly under clear skies at night and their temperature can never rise above 0° C by day. Invading warm air is chilled and produces extensive low cloud and fog.

Mountains in the path of the wind create turbulence, which in suitable conditions extends up to many times the height of the mountains over which the air is passing. Extensive cloudmasses and rainfall develop where air is lifted over the windward side of a range ; the latent heat of condensation passes into the air, and lee-side places may therefore experience warm, dry air and much clearer skies. In winter, however, if the low ground beyond the mountain range is covered by snow and extensive cold air, the density of warm air coming over the range may be such that it cannot sink to the low ground or displace the cold air stagnating there. In some cases mountain ranges act as complete barriers to surface airstreams. Hence mountain ranges greatly sharpen the climatic frontiers between warm and cold, oceanic and continental regions.

Normally temperature falls with increasing height at varying rates up to 1° C/100 m. (5·4° F/1000 ft.). Hence mountain climates are generally cooler than those of the surrounding lowlands, except in special weather conditions such as still air and strong sunshine heating the rock or upland vegetation. On cold clear nights mountainous country develops a system of downslope cold breezes near the surface

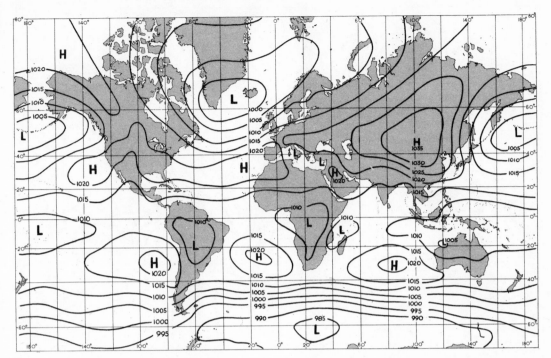

FIG 3. Average atmospheric pressure at mean sea level (in millibars) : January (the period 1900–50 approx.).

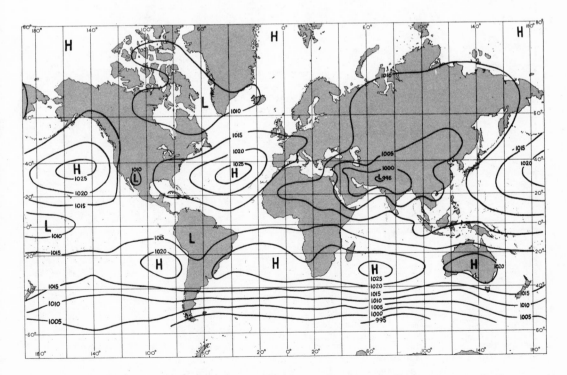

FIG 4. Average atmospheric pressure at mean sea level (in millibars) : July (the period 1900–50 approx.).

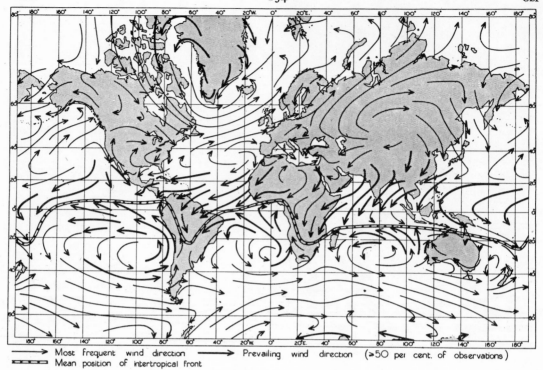

Most frequent wind direction ⟶ Prevailing wind direction (≥50 per cent. of observations)
Mean position of intertropical front

FIG 5. Prevailing surface winds: January. (Period: 1900–50 approx.).

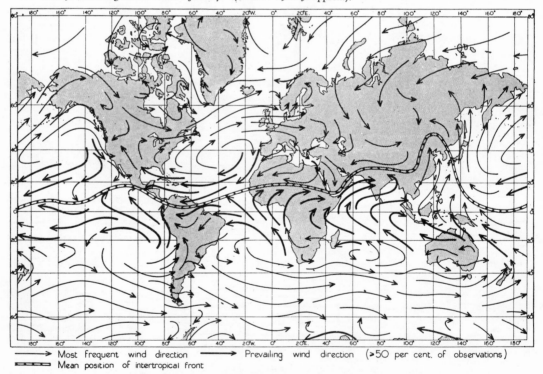

Most frequent wind direction ⟶ Prevailing wind direction (≥50 per cent. of observations)
Mean position of intertropical front

FIG 6. Prevailing surface winds: July. (Period 1900–50 approx.).

Figs 5 and 6 reproduced from the 'Handbook of Aviation Meteorology' by permission of the Controller of H.M. Stationery Office.

(see 'katabatic winds' above, in connection with the polar ice-caps) ; lowest temperatures are then observed in the valley bottoms ('inversion of temperature'). Conversely, under conditions of strong heating, gentle upslope 'anabatic breezes' are developed, and convergence over the ridges supplies a vertical current in which cumulus cloud may form.

Study of the course of the 'isotherms' (lines of equal temperature) on any climatic map reveals that, in addition to the obvious general effect of latitude, modifications introduced by prevailing winds and ocean currents are important. The extreme case is found off northern Norway near the north-eastern extremity of the main Atlantic depression track, where the winter climate, although stormy, is excessively warm for the latitude.

Moisture is also transported by airstreams from the ocean, but rainfall amounts decrease sharply beyond the first mountain ranges.

Important Types of Climate. Numerous attempts at climatic classification may be found in text-books, in some atlases, and in wall maps used in schools. The most satisfactory are 'genetic' classifications, in which climatic zones and regions are clearly related to the main features of the general circulation of the atmosphere which produce them. Such classifications avoid false constructions that are liable to arise when like effects chance to come from unlike causes ; it is also relatively easy to allow for appropriate shifts and modification of climatic boundaries which should accompany changes in the large-scale circulation of the atmosphere (climatic changes) from decade to decade or from one geological epoch to another. The best 'genetic' classifications, based upon modern understanding of the role of the upper westerlies (see above), are not yet widely available in map form (see, however, Flohn 1950, 1957).

For the present purpose the following chief climatic types may usefully be distinguished. In most of the zones defined, oceanic and continental, windward and leeward, lowland and mountain types may be separated. Climates on high mountains and plateaux are cool or cold for their latitude, but enjoy the same seasonal variations (or lack of them) as characterise the latitude zone in question.

1. *Equatorial Rain Zone.* Always warm and moist. Heavily clouded. Rains characteristically heavy. Seasonal variations generally slight. Winds variable, often westerly (at least in the rainiest sectors), mostly light except in occasional rain squalls. Zone of hard-wood forests (jungle) and swamps (e.g. Amazon, Congo, East Indies). Example : Singapore (1° N. 104° E., 33ft. a.s.l.) has normal maximum day temperature 30–31° C (86–88° F), minimum 23–24° C (73–75° F) in every month of the year ; rainfall averages 7–10 inches in each month, falling on 11–19 days of the month.

2. *Regions of Monsoon Rains.* Dry NE. or SE. Trade Wind regime (in winter) alternates seasonally with equatorial rains (in summer) as the intertropical convergence (between the circulations over the Northern and Southern Hemispheres) moves north and south. Commonly, several months in the transition seasons have sporadic showery precipitation ('little rains'). Vegetation ranges from savanna (park-land) to jungle. Extreme example : Cherrapunji, Assam (25° N. 92° E., 4309 ft. a.s.l.) has on average less than an inch of rain in the driest months, December and January, falling on about one day in each month ; normal rainfall amounts increase to 2 to 7 inches a month in February, March, and November, whereas 50 to 100 inches or more fall in each of the principal monsoon months May–August, falling on 22 to 27 days a month ; normal maximum day temperatures range from 23° C (73° F) in the warmest to 15° C (60° F) approx. in the coldest months. Bombay, Calcutta, northern Australia, the Guianas, and parts of Brazil supply examples of similar climate, with appropriately higher temperatures near sea level and with less rainfall in the less mountainous terrains. The highest temperatures commonly occur in the transition months, especially just before and just after the principal rains.

Monsoon climates also occur in Africa north and south of the Equator with the seasonal northward and southward march of the equatorial rainbelt. For example, Nigeria in the north and Rhodesia in the south get seasonal rains respectively in the Northern and Southern Hemisphere summers. Towards the desert fringe places such as Lake Chad and Khartoum experience regular rains only for a few weeks about the time of the extreme northward advance of the rainbelt associated with the intertropical convergence between the wind circulations of the Northern and Southern Hemispheres. But at such places the rainfall is somewhat sporadic and thundery ; still more so is any rainfall nearer the desert or outside the peak rain season at these same places.

3. *The Trade Wind Zone.* Best developed over the oceans. Persistent moderate breezes, pleasantly cool over the sea, rather hot over land. Small cumulus cloud and sunshine are characteristic, except during the occasional interruptions of the regime (see above). Merges with the arid zone over land, vegetation ranging from steppe to desert types although richer and more varied on islands.

Examples : Cape Verde Islands and Saint Helena, rainfall ranging from 5 inches a year or less at low-lying places on the lee side to 30 inches at higher levels with more exposure to moisture carried by the wind. Port Étienne (21° N. 17° W., 13 ft. a.s.l.) on the west coast of Africa gets on average less than 2 inches of rain a year.

4. *The Arid Zone.* The regions principally dominated by subtropical high pressure and light winds, extended over the continents where the breezes have long land tracks from the high pressure regions. Clear skies characteristic. Very rarely a heavy thundershower falls and produces temporary flooding and torrents in the usually dry water-courses. Considerable seasonal and diurnal ranges of temperature, especially over land. Example : Ghadames, Fezzan (30° N. 10° E., 1184 ft. a.s.l.) has on average 1 inch of rain a year ; maximum day temperatures normally exceed 40° C (104° F) in June, July, and August, when the night minima are on average about 22° C (72° F) ; maximum temperatures in January are sometimes below 15° C (59° F), and some night frosts usually occur in each winter month.

5. *The Subtropical Winter-Rain Zone.* Places about 35–45° N. and 30–40° S. come under the influence of the subtropical anticyclones in summer and the belt of prevailing westerlies in winter. The summers are predominantly fine and calm, the winters wet and windy. Characteristic vegetation—hard-leafed species able to retain moisture during the dry, hot summers. Example : Malta (36° N. 15° E.) normally has no rain between late May and early September, but gets 3 to 4 inches in each winter month, falling on 8 to 13 days of the month ; average maximum day temperatures in the warmest month are close to 30° C (84–86° F) and in January-February about 15° C (59° F) ; average night minimum temperatures are about 23° C (73° F) and 11° C (51–52° F) respectively. Continental places in this zone (e.g. California and South Australia) get wider ranges of temperature, including some night frosts.

6. *The Temperate Zone.* The zone of prevailing westerlies, affected by (mainly eastward) travelling depressions and anticyclones and frequent changes of weather. Most precipitation occurs in travelling 'frontal' belts (warm front, cold front, and occlusion rains). Necessarily subdivided into oceanic, transitional (western parts of continents), and continental regions. The continental regions have mainly summer precipitation, elsewhere precipitation is rather evenly divided between the seasons. These regions are quoted above in descending order of windiness, cloud cover, and rainfall, and in ascending order of the temperature ranges from day to night and summer to winter. The continental type is missing in the Southern Hemisphere. Vegetation ranges from grassy or heathery moors in the most wind-swept oceanic regions to deciduous forest in the transition region, and pine and birch forest in the regions with coldest winters. Examples are given in the Table below.

7. *The Subpolar Zone.* Cyclonic activity and strong winds (from various directions) characteristic, especially over the oceans, coasts, and bare lowlands. Frequent rather than heavy precipitation (mainly as snow during 8 months of the year). Skies mainly overcast, although clear skies become frequent near the continents with winds off the land. Tundra vegetation, which is snow-covered much of the year except close to open sea. Examples : parts of coastal Greenland, northern Iceland, Jan Mayen and other northern isles, parts of Arctic Siberia and Arctic Canada, islands south of 50° S. ; maximum temperatures in the warmest months normally reach about 10° C (50° F), very occasionally a good deal higher ; frost may occur in any month and lasts for long periods in winter, although winter thaws occur from time to time.

8. *The Polar Caps.* The climate of the central Arctic pack-ice is characterised by overcast and foggy summers, when there are leads of open water, some precipitation falls as rain, and pools of water lie on the ice-floes from which the winter snow-cover has melted. Temperatures in the central Arctic reach a summer maximum of 0 to +3° C (32–37° F) and fall to about −40° C (−40° F)

		Valentia, Ireland 52° N. 10° W. 30 ft. a.s.l.	Berlin, Germany 53° N. 13° E. 187 ft. a.s.l.	Irkutsk, Siberia 52° N. 104° E. 1532 ft. a.s.l.
January	Mean daily max. temp.	+9° C (49° F)	+2° C (35° F)	−16° C (+3° F)
	Mean daily min. temp.	+6° C (42° F)	−3° C (27° F)	−26° C (−15° F)
	Days with rain or snow	25	10	3
July	Mean daily max. temp.	+18° C (64° F)	+24° C (74° F)	+21° C (70° F)
	Mean daily min. temp.	+13° C (55° F)	+13° C (55° F)	+10° C (50° F)
	Days with rain	21	10	9

occasionally in winter, when the weather is often clear. By contrast the climates of the Greenland and Antarctic ice-caps are dominated by clear skies and subfreezing temperatures all the year round. The lowest temperatures may occur at any time during the main six months of winter and reach —60 to —80° C. (Extreme winter temperatures in north-east Siberia reach similar values.) The occasional precipitation is normally rather light snow, falling at any time of the year when a front with its cloudsheet intrudes and sometimes passes right across the ice-cap. The latter phenomenon becomes rarer over the wider parts of the ice-cap ; it is common and gives frequent snowfall over southern Greenland, but is believed to be very unusual over the broadest part of Antarctica. Winds over about 15 knots raise loose snow from the surface, where blowing snow (' blizzards ') frequently makes conditions severe and visibility zero, although the air remains clear higher up. See also ANTARCTIC.

Long-term Anomalies and Climatic Changes.
Spells of abnormal weather in any part of the world, lasting a few days, weeks, or months, and sometimes giving a distinctive stamp to an individual season, are associated with anomalies in the position and intensity of the principal currents of the atmospheric circulation. Shifts of latitude, unusual longitudinal position of the ridges and troughs (' waves ') in the upper westerlies, corresponding anomalies in the main regions of high and low surface pressure, and some eccentricity of the whole circulation with respect to the pole may all be involved. Such changes of climate as are perceptible even from decade to decade are associated with similar shifts in the average circulation.

Anomalies in the prevailing winds have important effects upon temperature and rainfall. In individual winters when winds from continental Europe replace the more usual westerlies, average temperatures in southern England may be as low as those of a normal winter in Poland or southern Sweden. The favourable climate of the 1930s meant that winters in the Gulf of Finland were no colder than the nineteenth-century average for Denmark. Flowering dates and the length of the growing season were correspondingly affected. Similar changes in the past 60 or 70 years led to changes of 30 to 50 per cent in the annual rainfall of some places in the tropics and in the hearts of the continents, particularly near the fringes of the desert zone ; changes of 15 to 30 per cent occurred in parts of the temperate zone and of 50 per cent or even more in the Arctic, especially around the Norwegian-Greenland Sea. It is thus clearly im-

portant, when examining any climatic tables or maps, to know to what epoch or period of years they refer.

Great changes of climate have occurred since the retreat of the Quaternary Ice Sheets in Europe and America ten thousand years ago. Between 5000 and 3000 B.C. (Post-glacial Climatic Optimum) the climate of northern Europe was much warmer than now, although the climate of the desert zone was less extreme and migration routes across the Sahara for animals and men were in use. Climatic deterioration followed at first gradually, then more abruptly about 500 B.C. Between about A.D. 400 and 1000 or 1200 the climate of northern Europe and the Atlantic was again rather warmer than now ; the deserts of Asia became more arid than formerly. Next followed some centuries of climatic instability with great and erratic changes leading up to the so-called Little Ice Age between about A.D. 1550 and 1850 or later, when the Alpine and northern glaciers reached their most advanced stages in historical times. The present century has seen a considerable amelioration ; but in the 1940s and 1950s the warming trend has ceased in some parts of the Northern Hemisphere, especially in the European sector.   H.H.L.

Brooks, C. E. P. 1949. Climate through the Ages. 2nd ed. London.
Flohn, H. 1950. Neue Anschauungen über die allgemeine Zirkulation der Atmosphäre und ihre klimatische Bedeutung. Erdkunde 4 : 141–162.
Flohn, H. 1957. Zur Frage der Einteilung der Klimazonen. Erdkunde 11 : 161–175.
Lamb, H. H. 1963. On the nature of certain climatic epochs which differed from the modern (1930–39) normal. Proc. W.M.O./U.N.E.S.C.O. Rome (1961) Symposium on climatic changes (Arid Zone XX) : 125–150. Paris.
Meteorological Office 1939. Meteorological Glossary. 3rd ed. London (H.M.S.O.—M.O. 225).
Meteorological Office 1958. Tables of temperature, relative humidity and precipitation for the world. London (H M.S.O.—M.O. 617, available in six parts).
Meteorological Office 1959. Handbook of Aviation Meteorology. London (H.M.S.O.—M.O. 630).
Nairn, A. E. M. (ed.). 1961. Descriptive Palaeclimatology. New York.
Tannehill, I. R. 1952. Weather around the World. 2nd ed. Princeton.
The climatic maps in any good atlas may also be found convenient.

CLIMAX COMMUNITY: a biotic community representing the maximum ecological development possible in the particular environment (compare SERAL COMMUNITY).

CLIMBING: see LOCOMOTION

CLIMOGRAPH: an ecological method of combining experimental data and field observations in the form of a contoured diagram expressing the effects of temperature and humidity, acting together, in the range of a species under study (see ECOLOGY).

CLINE: term introduced by J. S. Huxley (1939) for a population aggregate (within a species) showing gradation in its characters from one end of its range to the other. A cline has itself no status in nomenclature. It may include forms to which subspecific names have been attached, although where the gradation is continuous (as happens in the absence of barriers) the validity of such subspecies becomes questionable (see SUBSPECIES; and DEME). Nevertheless, the forms at the extremities of a cline may show striking differences when directly compared with each other, and this may be true also of intermediate forms taken from points sufficiently far apart in the clinal range ; in such cases the use of subspecific names may have a practical convenience in providing taxonomic points of reference. Notations have been suggested for the designation of clines in terms of their geographically extreme forms, but this procedure seems to import a concept too rigid for the reality. The fact is that different characters may show clinal variation independently of each other, and sometimes in different directions, e.g., some from east to west and others from north to south. A cline is therefore a phenomenon of the variation of a population aggregate rather than the aggregate itself ; and the adjective ' clinal ' is perhaps more useful than the noun. See also RATIO-CLINE.

CLIPPING: rendering a captive bird temporarily incapable of flight by cutting the primary feathers of one wing ; these feathers are replaced at the next moult (compare PINIONING).

CLOACA: the combined terminal opening of three physiological systems (see ALIMENTARY SYSTEM ; EXCRETORY SYSTEM ; REPRODUCTIVE SYSTEM). This single opening in birds (and reptiles) contrasts with mammals, wherein the alimentary system has a separate terminal opening to the exterior.

CLOCK, BIOLOGICAL: see TIME MEASUREMENT

CLOUD: see METEOROLOGY ; MIGRATION ; NAVIGATION

CLOUD-SCRAPER: substantive name of some *Cisticola* spp. (see WARBLER (1)).

CLUTCH: a set of eggs, i.e. the complete number laid by one female that are brooded simultaneously (written c/1, c/2, c/3, etc.). For size of clutch, characteristic for particular species but often variable

within limits, see EGGS, NATURAL HISTORY OF ; LAYING ; also ECOLOGY ; FEEDING OF YOUNG ; POPULATION DYNAMICS. For exceptions see PARASITISM.

CNEMOPHILINAE: see BIRD-OF-PARADISE

COB: special term for a male SWAN.

COCHLEA: part of the ear (see HEARING AND BALANCE).

COCHLEARIIDAE: a monotypic family of the Ciconiiformes (suborder Ardeae) recognised by some authors (e.g. Wetmore, Peters) for the Boat-billed Heron *Cochlearius cochlearius*, which in this work (following Mayr & Amadon and Bock) is treated as a member of the Ardeidae (see HERON).

COCK: a male bird ; applied without qualification to the male of the domestic fowl—compare HEN. Special terms apply to the males of some species, e.g. DRAKE, GANDER, COB, TIERCEL, BLACKCOCK. The names of certain species have also a special use as terms for the male, e.g. RUFF, and formerly MALLARD.

COCKATIEL: *Nymphicus hollandicus* of Australia (for family see PARROT).

COCKATOO: substantive name of species of Kakatoeinae ; in the plural, general term for the subfamily (see PARROT).

COCK-FIGHTING: also called ' cocking ', the sport of pitting male domestic fowls against each other in combat ; the ' game-cocks ' used are specially bred and trained for the purpose (see DOMESTICATION). Betting on the results is a major element. The word ' cockpit ' originally signified an enclosure where the ' mains ' were held. The sport originated in ancient times in Asia, where the natural spurs on the tarsi were often made more deadly by fitting them with iron spikes. It spread to Greece in classical times, later to Rome, and thence to other parts of Europe, and eventually to the New World. It has been prohibited by law in Great Britain since 1849, and it is now generally banned in many countries, including Canada and the United States. In eastern Asia, female Barred Bustardquail *Turnix suscitator* are caught and kept for fighting, as also are male Quail *Coturnix coturnix* ; and the Russians have a fighting breed of domestic goose.

COCK-OF-THE-ROCK: substantive name of *Rupicola* spp. (see under COTINGA).

COEREBINAE: see EMBERIZIDAE ; and HONEY-CREEPER (1)

COHORT: a taxonomic category sometimes

interpolated between subclass and superorder (see CLASSIFICATION).

COITION: see COPULATION

COL: see METEOROLOGY

COLETO: name, in the Philippine Islands, for *Sarcops calvus* (see STARLING).

COLIIDAE: see below

COLIIFORMES: order comprising only the Coliidae (see MOUSEBIRD).

COLLAR: a band or patch of distinctive colour, in some plumage patterns, at least partly encircling the neck (see TOPOGRAPHY).

COLONY: a number of birds breeding gregariously, the term vaguely including the location and the nests. For special terms see ASSEMBLY, NOUN OF.

COLORATION, ADAPTIVE: embraces those visual phenomena that subserve survival or reproductive functions in the various relationships between predators and prey, between members of the same or the opposite sex or of a social group, or between parent and offspring. The term may thus be used to include not only modifications of colour, but all aspects of form, adornment, pattern, posture, activity, and background that together determine an animal's appearance in nature and are of value in the struggle for existence. Animal coloration must always be considered in relation to the behaviour associated with it, and to the effect of this upon a potential observer. (For the physical basis of coloration see COLOUR.)

Coloration characteristics fall broadly into two groups ; those promoting concealment (cryptic) and those enhancing conspicuousness (phaneric). The former, making for effacement, hinder detection ; the latter, acting as advertisements, facilitate identification. The optical-psychological principles upon which recognition of a bird (or of any other solid object) depends include : differences of hue and tone between object and background ; differential effects of light and shade, or of relief, that convey the appearance of solidity ; shape, or surface-continuity framed by a characteristic contour ; cast shadow ; and movement. The effectiveness of cryptic and phaneric coloration is due to the suppression or exaggeration, respectively, of these visual characters.

Cryptic Coloration. The biological role of cryptic coloration is limited to predator-prey relationships, either affording protection against enemies (procryptic) or facilitating capture of food (anticryptic). Among birds procryptic coloration is common, and anticryptic rare. Again, cryptic coloration may afford either general concealment or special disguise ; instances of the latter are rare in birds. The two categories intergrade in a type of coloration known as 'background picturing'.

General Resemblance. Every major habitat provides examples of birds that wear cryptic plumage— white in snowlands, e.g. Snowy Owl *Nyctea scandiaca*, Ptarmigan *Lagopus mutus* in winter dress ; ochre, buff, or sandy-grey in deserts, e.g. sandgrouse (Pteroclididae), thickknees (Burhinidae), wheatears *Oenanthe* spp., larks (Alaudidae) ; green in the rain-forest canopy or dense foliage, e.g. toucanets (Ramphastidae), some parakeets and conures (Psittacidae), fruit pigeons (Treroninae) ; variegated browns among grass and reeds, e.g. many waders (Charadrii), crakes (Rallidae), bitterns (Botaurinae), buntings (Emberizidae), grass warblers *Cisticola* spp. (Sylviinae). Of special interest in this connection are species and races of desert larks (*Ammomanes, Mirafra, Spizocorys*) with plumage closely matching the particular ground on which they occur—whether black lava, red or brown earth, or white sand. Such birds have clearly defined habitat preferences, and are reluctant to leave their own terrain for adjoining ground of a different hue (see LARK).

Obliterative Shading. Graded coloration, ranging from darkest on the back to lightest on the under parts, neutralises relief and thus renders the solid body as an apparently flat surface. Obliterative shading forms a basis for the coloration of nearly all cryptic birds, whether or not they carry a superimposed pattern ; it reaches its highest perfection in various terrestrial birds of open country, such as bustards (Otididae), thickknees, buttonquails (Turnicidae), francolins *Francolinus* spp., and sandgrouse.

Disruption. In its concealing role, pattern prevents or delays recognition by attracting an observer's attention to itself and away from the form that bears it. Such a distractive effect depends upon the colours being characteristic also of the background (Woodcock *Scolopax rusticola*, Partridge *Perdix perdix*) and embodying strongly contrasted tonal elements that transgress anatomical form and contour and so visually break up surface continuity (Turnstone *Arenaria interpres*, Killdeer *Charadrius vociferus*, Cream-coloured Courser *Cursorius cursor*). Many birds carry dark head-markings so disposed as to coincide with and include the otherwise conspicuous eye. Such coincident elements may take the form of horizontal stripes, e.g. Bobwhite *Colinus virginianus*, Quail *Coturnix coturnix*, Snipe *Gallinago gallinago*, Whimbrel *Numenius phaeopus*, Dotterel *Eudromias morinellus* ; or of vertical bars, e.g. Woodcock ; or of a combination of both, e.g. Ringed Plover *Charadrius hiaticula*.

Immobility, and Shadow Concealment. Effective

concealment is possible only when it is accompanied by cryptic quiescence. Immobility and the squatting posture, as a reaction to danger, are most highly developed in various cryptic ground-nesting birds of several groups—some female ducks (Anatidae) and game-birds (Galliforme), snipe, woodcock, plovers (Charadriidae), coursers *Cursorius* spp., bustards, nightjars (Caprimulgidae), larks; also in highly cryptic nidifugous young, such as Ruffed Grouse *Bonasa umbellus*, Stone-curlew *Burhinus oedicnemus*, Lapwing *Vanellus vanellus*, Ringed Plover, Oystercatcher *Haematopus ostralegus*, and Little Tern *Sterna albifrons*. The crouching posture also serves to obscure or reduce the tell-tale shadow cast by the body.

Background Picturing. Disruptive patterns afford concealment in relation to a generalised background. The coloration of species that rest or nest in a specialised habitat may be correlated more closely with the environment; in such species the disruptive design is scenic, and tends to reproduce the background configuration against which it is likely to be displayed —whether of heath, grass, or reed. Such colour schemes are always rendered more effective by appropriate cryptic postures, for example, prone in Owl Parrot *Strigops habroptilus*, Ptarmigan, and Golden Plover *Pluvialis apricarius*, vertical and frontal in Bittern *Botaurus stellaris* and Little Bittern *Ixobrychus minutus* (see Plate 23 (phot.)).

Special Resemblance. In a few highly specialised cases, cryptic coloration exerts its effect by disguise rather than concealment—colouring, form, and posture combining to produce a more or less exact resemblance to some familiar object of the habitat. Various Caprimulgiformes afford the best examples among birds. In their usual prone position on the ground, many nightjars resemble fallen bits of wood; frogmouths (Podargidae), which nest on a horizontal tree-fork, adopt an oblique posture and so simulate a broken branch; while the Grey Potoo *Nyctibius griseus*, which lays its single egg on top of a broken tree-stump, incubates in a stiffly erect posture. All these birds close the eyes when in the presence of an intruder, and remain motionless. Nestlings of the Black-backed Pied Shrike *Hemipus picatus* face one another with their bills pointing upwards and nearly meeting, their coloration and attitude causing the lichen-garnished nest with its contents to resemble a snag on the branch.

Phaneric Coloration. Conspicuousness, the basis of all phaneric characters, depends upon the exaggeration of those visual attributes—colour, relief, form, and movement—that tend to be suppressed in cryptic species. Brilliant hues and textures alien to the environment are widely developed, notable examples being seen among gallinules *Porphyrio* spp., macaws (Psittacidae), turacos (Musophagidae), toucans (Ramphastidae), kingfishers (Alcedinidae), woodhoopoes (Phoeniculidae), glossy starlings *Lamprotornis* spp., tanagers (Thraupinae), and the males of many ducks and game-birds. Countershading is replaced by self-coloration, which reaches the height of conspicuousness in uniformly white or black birds, e.g. swans *Cygnus* spp., pelicans (Pelecanidae), egrets *Egretta* spp., spoonbills (Plataleinae), cockatoos (Kakatoeinae), and crows *Corvus* spp. Colours and patterns are generally displayed constructively (crest, breast, ruff, tail, and so on); and the contour is often conspicuously framed with a marginal pattern (tail of Ruffed Grouse, throat of King Bird-of-paradise *Cicinnurus regius*). Frequently, the eye is made prominent in its setting of feathers, e.g. owls, white-eyes *Zosterops* spp., or ornamental skin, e.g. many vultures (Aegypiinae), storks (Ciconiidae), cranes (Gruidae), game-birds, hornbills (Bucerotidae), and toucans. Eye-spots are displayed (Argus Pheasant *Argusianus argus* and peacock pheasants *Polyplectron* spp.) and reach their most extravagant appearance in the huge paired ocelli, each formed by a purple-red gular sac framed in a broad circle of white feathers, in Richardson's Grouse *Dendragapus obscurus richardsoni*. Adornments (plumes, fans, ruffs, wattles, inflatable air-sacs, and the like), and above all specialised activity (including orientated postures, antics, dances, and utterance of sounds both vocal and instrumental) contribute further to the impact made upon the observer.

Phaneric (unlike cryptic) coloration subserves a wide range of biological functions, both interspecific and intraspecific—in relations between enemies and prey (warning, adventitious warning, bluff, Batesian mimicry, and deflection); between rival males (threat and distance recognition); between opposite sexes (sex recognition and epigamic display); between members of the same or different species (social, and specifically distinct signals); and between parent and offspring (feeding releasers and indicators).

Warning Coloration and Adventitious Warning. Warning characters (proaposematic) are associated with deterrent or noxious attributes that render a species relatively unacceptable to predators (see PALATABILITY OF BIRDS AND EGGS). In another category (allosematic) are certain relatively defenceless birds that habitually nest close in association with aggressive aposematic aculeate hymenoptera such as *Polybia, Polistes, Apis, Azteca, Oecophylla*. The insects tolerate the presence of the birds (which build pensile or covered nests) but not other intruders; thus the birds secure themselves from attack by most enemies. Such nesting associations are known among tropical birds of widely different groups—Caciques (*Cassicus*) in South America ; mannikins (*Lonchura*), weaver-finches (*Uraeginthus*), and striped swallows (*Hirundo*) in Africa ; bayas (*Ploceus*) in Malaya ; and bush-warblers (*Gerygone*) and weaver-finches (*Steganopleura*) in Australia (see also NESTING ASSOCIATION).

False Warning Coloration. Bluffing characters (pseudaposematic) include so-called ' terrifying actions '—fluffing of feathers, spreading wings, demonstrating with claws or bill—as in the intimidating displays of young owls (Strigiformes) and hawks (Falconiformes), and Basetian mimicry. Instances of the latter are rare among birds e.g. *Oriolus* ('*Mimeta*') and *Philemon* in Indonesia (see MIMICRY). In an aggressive (pseudepisematic) rather than a protective role are the wonderfully detailed mimetic resemblances that the eggs of various cuckoos (Cuculidae) bear to those of the foster-parents (see PARASITISM).

Deflection Displays. These serve to deflect the attention of enemies away from the more to the less biologically valuable or vulnerable members (incubating parent, or nestlings) of a social group. Inter-individual deflection (parasematic) operates both in the relations between the sexes and in those between parents and offspring. In the former category is the conspicuous appearance of various male ducks (Anatidae) and pheasants (Phasianidae), and the delayed moult of certain male ptarmigan *Lagopus* spp., which diverts attention from the incubating female ; in the latter, the so-called ' injury-feigning ' behaviour of the brooding parent, whose movements and posturing (falling, lying on one side, leg-trailing, wing-dragging, wing-flapping, or quivering) advertise its whereabouts at a distance from the nest. Such displays are known to occur in many avian orders— Gaviiformes, Anseriformes, Galliformes, Gruiformes, Charadriiformes, Columbiformes, Strigiformes, Caprimulgiformes, Passeriformes (see DISPLAY) ; they do not appear to have been recorded in any other class of animals.

Social Signalling Characters. Social recognition, or guide-marks (proepisematic), such as those displayed in flight on the wings, tail, and rump of many waders (Charadrii), serve to ensure contact between members of a flock, or to release and direct following behaviour. The patterns have few components and are striking and distinctive. In cryptic nidifugous young (Lapwing, Ringed Plover, Egyptian Plover *Pluvianus aegyptius*) a white nuchal band, when displayed, assists the parent to locate and reassemble the brood. The predominantly white plumage of many sea birds—gannets (Sulidae), albatrosses (Diomedeidae), gulls (Larinae), and some terns (Sterninae)

—is socially advantageous as a signal of the whereabouts of a locally and sporadically plentiful foodsupply (fish shoals, etc.). In a different catagory are the specifically distinctive characters that serve to prevent confusion with members of closely related species. Notable examples are the almost heraldic colour-schemes of toucans (Ramphastidae), the speculum in ducks (Anatidae), and the head and neck characters of penguins (Spheniscidae) and auks (Alcidae).

Threat and Distance Recognition. Threat characters are directed against rivals of the same sex, usually (antepisematic) and associated with combat, actual or potential. Under this head are included closerange aggressive threat, in which the characters displayed indicate a readiness to fight (Blackcock *Lyrurus tetrix*, Junglefowl *Gallus gallus*, and Ruff *Philomachus pugnax*) ; and recognitional threat, which advertises the presence of a potential competitor at a distance. Characters (both visual and auditory) used in the latter context are generally significant in relation to territorial defence (monogamous, and some polygamous, territorial species) ; by deterring a rival from intrusion, they obviate the need for combat.

Courtship and Display. Characters that promote the meeting and mating of the sexes and subsequent phases of the reproductive cycle (epigamic) are discussed elsewhere (see DISPLAY).

Feeding Indicators and Releasers. Adornments with a releasing and directing function connected with the feeding of nidicolous young are found in several orders. Nestlings that are directly fed by parent or fosterer (e.g. Passeriformes, Cuculidae) commonly have the gaping display enhanced by wide bill flanges and a brilliant mouth-lining (see TONGUE). Red, orange, and yellow (the colours displayed by ornithophilous flowers) are frequent in these quasifloral displays, which may, as in the Bearded Reedling *Panurus biarmicus* (white projections set on a background of red and black and surrounded by the yellow gape), be detailed and elaborate. The mouths of various nestlings reared in dimly lit surroundings are bordered with white (Jackdaw *Corvus monedula*, glossy starlings *Lamprotornis* spp.). In some species of which the young are nidifugous, or thrust their heads into the parent's mouth to obtain food, the parent carries the relevant ornaments. Thus the red spot on the gonys of the adult Herring Gull *Larus argentatus* releases and directs the pecking response ; while in the Gannet *Sula bassana* and Cormorant *Phalacrocorax carbo* the mouth-lining of the adult displays conspicuous colour—black in the former, yellow in the latter (see RELEASER).

H.B.C.

Armstrong, E. A. 1947. Bird Display and Behaviour. 2nd ed. London.

Cott, H. B. 1957. Adaptive Coloration in Animals. 2nd ed. London.

COLOUR: in birds especially that of the feathers (see FEATHER; PLUMAGE). The colours are due to the reflection of some but not all the components of the incident white light. When all the components of white light are reflected the bird will appear white. There are two ways in which colours can be removed from incident white light—(a) by the physical nature of the reflecting surface, to give structural colours; and (b) by certain chemical attributes, to give pigmentary colours. Some colours are due to a combination of these two methods. The removal of some parts of the spectrum by these methods results in the reflection of the remaining parts.

Structural Colours. Those of birds are due either to interference, giving iridescent colours that change with the angle of view, as in soap bubbles, or to the scattering of light, giving non-iridescent structural colours. The structure responsible for iridescence is present in barbules that are flattened for part of their length and twisted at right angles so that one of the flat sides comes to face the observer. This torsion of the barbules is accompanied by loss of the hooklets and flanges; this reduces the mechanical strength of the vane, and so fully iridescent colours are not found in flight feathers. It was formerly thought that all iridescent colours were due to interference in the thin outer layer of the barbule keratin, and that the melanin pigment (see below) within the barbule served only as a background to prevent the reflection of other light. It has now been found that in some feathers, including those of hummingbirds (Trochilidae), the melanin granules are themselves responsible for the interference. These granules have a high refractive index, show iridescent metallic colours, and are arranged in a single layer beneath the surface of the barbule. In pigeons (Columbidae) the melanin granules impinge on the outer surface of the barbule to give iridescent colours, but in white pigeons, lacking melanin, it is probable that the weak iridescent colours are produced by interference between the layers of keratin in the barbules.

Non-iridescent structural colours do not alter with the angle of vision. They are produced by the scattering of the shorter waves in white light by very small particles, as occurs in a blue sky; this is sometimes known as Tyndall scattering. If the diameter of the particles is less than the wave-length of red light (i.e. less than ca. 0·6 μ), more of the short-wave components of white light will be reflected and the structure will appear blue. In non-iridescent blue feathers the scattering particles are actually minute air-filled cavities within the keratin of the barb; if these cavities are filled with a suitable liquid the blue colour disappears, but returns when the liquid evaporates. Such feathers appear blue only in reflected light; when seen in transmitted white light they are dull brown owing to the background of melanin granules in the barbs.

Whiteness in feathers is due, as in snow and milk, to the refraction and reflection of incident light from innumerable surfaces between two substances of different refractive index. In feather vanes the two substances are air on the one hand and the surface of the barbs and barbules on the other. In the proximal part of the quills the whiteness is due to reflection from solid keratin.

Pigmentary Colours. These are widespread in birds, in the bill and 'soft parts' as well as in the feathers. The commonest pigment of birds is melanin, the exact chemical composition of which is unknown. Melanin usually occurs as granules, is insoluble in most solvents (but can be dissolved in alkalis), and has no characteristic absorption bands. In spite of its name, melanin is not always black, and may be brown, red-brown, or even yellow. When black or dark brown it is usually known as eumelanin, when light brown or yellow as phaeomelanin. Black eumelanin occurs in crows *Corvus* spp., Blackbird *Turdus merula*, some gallinaceous birds, and many others; brown and red-brown phaeomelanin is responsible for the duller colours of many birds showing protective coloration, and yellow phaeomelanin gives, for instance, the yellow colour of the down in domestic chicks. Melanin formation in birds may be influenced by sex, age, and season (see PLUMAGE; PLUMAGE, ABNORMAL AND ABERRANT).

Carotenoids are organic compounds consisting of carbon and hydrogen (carotenes) or carbon, hydrogen, and oxygen (xanthophylls). They are soluble in organic solvents and are characterised by their behaviour in solution and on a chromatographic column, and also by their absorption spectra. They are responsible for the colour of many red and orange feathers and of some yellow ones. Egg yolk is coloured by two carotenoids, lutein and zeaxanthin, and the red of the wattles of the Pheasant *Phasianus colchicus* is due to astaxanthin. The growing feathers of Canaries *Serinus canaria* can be made red by feeding with paprika, which contains capsanthin. Oriental fruit pigeons *Ptilinopus* spp. have a dark red carotenoid, rhodoxanthin, in their feathers.

Like other animals, birds are unable to synthesise

carotenoids, and they obtain them either directly or indirectly from plants. The bright red yolk of the eggs of the Gentoo Penguin *Pygoscelis papua* is due to astaxanthin present in the crustaceans that the birds eat, and the pink of flamingos (Phoenicopteridae) is due to a similar pigment derived from blue-green algae and aquatic invertebrates. The deposition of carotenoid in bird tissues is often selective ; thus feathers have only xanthophylls, whereas bill and skin may have both carotenes and xanthophylls.

Haemoglobin, the red tetrapyrrole respiratory pigment of vertebrates and of some invertebrates, is not normally seen as an external colour in birds. It is, however, responsible for the colouring of the wattles of the Turkey *Meleagris gallopavo* and of the bare head and neck of some vultures (Aegypiinae). There are also other tetrapyrrole pigments that colour birds. Protoporphyrin occurs in the eggshells of many birds ; a fragment of domestic hen eggshell shows absorption bands when seen in transmitted light, and also the typical red fluorescence of prophyrins in ultraviolet light. This fluorescence has been seen in the eggs of representatives of thirteen orders. Porphyrin also occurs in the feathers of owls (Strigiformes) and bustards (Otididae), whence it has been crystallised and shown to be coproporphyrin III. In some birds the pink colour of the down is due to porphyrin.

The bright red wing-feathers of turacos (Musophagidae) are coloured by turacin, a copper porphyrin pigment. This pigment is easily extracted from the feathers by dilute ammonia to give a purple-red solution. Being a metalloporphyrin (unlike protoporphyrin and coproporphyrin), this solution does not fluoresce while the copper atom is attached to the porphyrin, but when acid is added the copper breaks off and fluorescence appears. The green feathers of some turacos contain turacoverdin, the relationship of which to turacin is not completely understood. See also TURACO.

Two types of pigment, of unknown composition, occur in certain parrots (Psittacidae). In one type the pigment is pale yellow in visible light and fluorescent yellow-gold, sulphur-yellow, or green in ultraviolet light. The fluorescence disappears in alkali, but is not affected by acid. The crest of some cockatoos *Kakatoe* spp. is coloured by one of these pigments. They occur particularly in Australian parrots, although not in lories (Loriinae) or the Eclectus Parrot *Lorius roratus*, but are rare in New World parrots.

The second type consists of non-fluorescent red or yellow pigments, found in the Budgerigar *Melopsittacus undulatus*, *Amazona leucocephala*, and some other parrots. They are quite distinct from carotenoids in chemical behaviour, and also in the way they are deposited in the keratin of the feather.

Combined Effects. Some colours may be due to the combined action of two or more pigments, or of pigment and structure. Thus in many green feathers the outer layers of the barbs contain a yellow pigment that filters some of the short-wave rays out of the incident white light. Below this filter lie box cells containing minute air spaces that scatter the remainder of the short waves ; as a result the feather appears green. If the filter pigment is dissolved out the feather becomes blue, as in ordinary Tyndall scattering. It is probable that when the filter is carotenoid it can be bleached out under natural conditions ; this occurs in the tropical magpie, *Cissa*, which is green in the subdued light of the forest, but blue when living in open sunny country.

Olive-green is not caused by a yellow filter overlying a scattering layer backed by melanin, but by the juxtaposition of tiny spots of black and yellow pigment, which gives the sensation of olive-green. Thus in the Greenfinch *Carduelis chloris* and in some tits (Paridae) there is melanin in the barbule tips and yellow carotenoid in the barbs and the bases of the barbules. In the green bill of a Mallard *Anas platyrhynchos* oily yellow carotenoid droplets are interspersed with melanin granules in the melanocytes.

Purple is produced by a mixture of red and blue-violet and occurs in some feathers as a mixture of Tyndall scattering and red pigment, e.g. in the Blossom-headed Parakeet *Psittacula cyanocephala*, in which the barbs have structure producing scattered blue, and the barbules contain red pigment.

Colours in birds may be modified by the presence of a structural attribute which alters the surface texture. If short feathers grow out perpendicularly from the body they produce the appearance of velvet, e.g. the breast pad of the Greater Bird-of-paradise *Paradisaea apoda* or the nape feathers of the Teal *Anas crecca*. Twisting of the barbs so that their flat shiny surfaces are exposed gives an effect of lacquer, e.g. in some pittas *Pitta* spp. Powder particles on the feather surface will reflect light at numerous surfaces, so that less light is able to penetrate and to be absorbed or reflected ; this occurs in some pigeons (Columbidae) and cranes (Gruidae) and produces dull, greyish colours.

Cosmetic Coloration. There is evidence that some birds adorn their plumage with coloured secretion from the preen gland (see OIL GLAND). The Great Indian Hornbill *Buceros bicornis* rubs its bill on the outlet of this gland and transfers the yellow secretion thus acquired to some of the white feathers on the wings. The pigment, now known to be carotenoid (Vevers in press), bleaches and oxidises in air and light, and it is renewed at frequent intervals. Such cosmetic coloration may also account for the pink suffusions seen on the breast of the Blackheaded Gull *Larus ridibundus* and the White (or Rosy) Pelican *Pelecanus onocrotalus* during spring (Stegmann 1956). These colours are known to disappear quickly in most museum skins. (The fading of museum skins in general is not understood, although some internally deposited carotenoids—see *Cissa* above—are known to fade in light.) It is possible that cosmetic coloration may occur in other birds related to the gulls (Larinae) and waders (Charadrii).   G.V.

Fox, H. M. & Vevers, G. 1960. The Nature of Animal Colours. London.
Stegmann, B. 1956. Ueber die Herkunft des flüchtigen rosenroten Federpigments. J. Orn. 97 : 204-205.

COLOUR SPECIFICATION: involves the integration of (1) language or symbols, (2) either colours of which the names are widely understood or else colour samples in an atlas or chart, and (3) the variables in biological materials being described. The result should be comprehensible to persons other than the describer! Specification can be done at different levels. One is by use of generally understood colour terms, in combination with modifiers as needed, as is done in most non-technical works on ornithology. Another consists in comparing biological materials with colour samples on a chart or in an atlas, these being designated by words or symbols. The latter can be more precise, but the reader of descriptions prepared in this manner must have access to an equivalent copy of the chart or atlas in order fully to comprehend the descriptions.

In practice in taxonomy, and in view of the range of variation in most biological materials, one compares specimens or series of them—not colour descriptions of each ; describing is an aftermath of comparing. The specimens then become the points of reference, not named colours in an atlas (although the describing may be in terms from an atlas—see TYPE SPECIMEN). To utilise the results of such comparisons to the full one must again refer to the same or equivalent specimens.

In written descriptions that are intended to be meaningful to the majority of readers, it is desirable to use as few colour terms as possible. For most persons, such a list probably does not exceed fifty terms. An analysis of all terms used in all descriptions in several standard works (including the *Handbook of British Birds*) reveals that a larger list is unnecessary.

The following includes the *colours* that are in widespread accepted use, the *names* being those in general use except that certain 'pure' or 'spectral' colours are more accurately designated ; after a 'spectral' colour is listed, any of its 'impure' derivatives that are included here follow in parentheses : ruby (rose, dusky brown, pink), scarlet (blackish brown), scarlet-orange (chestnut, brownish red, fuscous, rufous, flesh, sepia, tawny, cinnamon), orange (brownish olive, buffish brown, smoke-grey), orange-yellow (olive, buffish yellow, cream, straw-yellow), yellow, yellow-lime, lime, lime-green, green, emerald, turquoise, turquoise-cobalt, cobalt (pearl-grey), cobalt-ultramarine, ultramarine, ultramarine-violet, violet (sooty black), violet-magenta, magenta.

Such colour terms can be modified, as required and where logical, by terms of 'lightness'—pale, light, medium, dark, deep. Or they can be modified by combination with neutrals ; pale greyish, light greyish, etc. Note that *black* and *white* are absolutes ; attempts to modify them, such as 'greyish white' or 'brownish black' are incorrect. Metallic colour names widely used in ornithology are : bronzy, coppery, golden, leaden, silvery. They combine colour and texture. The following terms or phrases, which refer to texture alone or are used in combination with colours, are also widely used in ornithology : burnished, dull, glossy, hoary (or frosted), iridescent, having a sheen, silky, velvety, waxy.

If one departs from generally understood terms and uses a chart or atlas, the standard used should always be clearly indicated. Many coloured descriptions have been based on Ridgway's *Color Standards and Color Nomenclature* (Washington, D.C. 1912), now a rare book. A more workable standard, but using symbols instead of words, is the Villalobos-Dominguez & Villalobos *Atlas de los Colores* (Buenos Aires. 1947) ; it includes a concordance of symbols and Ridgway names.   R.S.P.

Palmer, R. S. 1962. Handbook of North American Birds vol. 1. New Haven, Conn., & London. (See Introduction, at pp. 4 and 8, with colour chart.)

COLOUR VISION: see VISION

COLUMBAE; COLUMBIDAE: see below

COLUMBIFORMES: an order, alternatively 'Columbae', comprising the suborders Pterocletes (family Pteroclididae—see SANDGROUSE) and Columbae (families Columbidae—see PIGEON, and the extinct Raphidae—see DODO). In Stresemann's system these suborders are given separate ordinal rank.

COLUMELLA AURIS: the ear ossicle, alternatively 'stapes' (see SKELETON ; also HEARING AND BALANCE).

COLY: alternative name for MOUSEBIRD.

COLYMBIDAE: together with 'Colymbiformes' (alternatively 'Colymbi'), discarded familial and ordinal names formed from the generic name *Colymbus* Linnaeus 1758. All of these became ambiguous—and the source of much confusion—owing to a doubt about the designation of the type-species, which had led ornithologists in the Old World to apply the names to the divers (otherwise *Gavia* Foster 1788, Gaviidae) and those in the New World to the typical grebes (otherwise *Podiceps* Latham 1787, Podicipitidae). As it had been found impossible to reach agreement on the correct use of the names, there was a widespread feeling among ornithologists that they should be entirely suppressed, in favour of the names next in priority in the respective groups (and already partially current). A decision to this effect was given by the International Commission on Zoological Nomenclature in 1956. Incidentally, the first spelling (by page priority) given by Linnaeus was *Columbus*, which could not be used to form familial and ordinal names distinguishable from those formed from *Columba* Linneaus 1785 for the pigeons (Columbidae, Columbiformes)—so that some sacrifice of strict priority had already been made. See GAVIIDAE ; PODICIPITIDAE ; NOMENCLATURE.

Salomonsen, F. 1951. A nomenclatorial controversy : the genus *Colymbus* Linnaeus 1758. Proc. X Internat. Orn. Congr., Uppsala 1950 : 149–154.
Hemming, F. 1956. Opinion 401. Opinions and Declarations rendered by the International Commission on Zoological Nomenclature 13 : 1–64.

COMB: see INTEGUMENTARY STRUCTURES ; for its growth, see also ENDOCRINE SYSTEM.

COMBASSOU: substantive name, alternatively 'indigo-bird' or 'indigo-finch', of *Hypochera* spp. (see WHYDAH (1)).

COMBAT: see under AGGRESSION ; DOMINANCE (2) ; TERRITORY

COMET: substantive name of *Polyonymus caroli*, *Sappho sparganura*, and *Zodalia glyceria* (see HUMMINGBIRD).

COMFORT MOVEMENTS: see under FEATHER MAINTENANCE

COMMENSALISM: see under PARASITE ; also FEEDING HABITS

COMMISSURE: the line of apposition of the closed mandibles, as viewed laterally (see BILL).

COMPLEX: in taxonomy, a neutral term used when the precise status and interrelationships of a group of forms is in doubt.

COMPROMISE BEHAVIOUR: see AMBIVALENCE

CONCHA: part of the ear (see HEARING AND BALANCE ; OWL).

CONDITIONING: see LEARNING

CONDOR: substantive name of the two species of Cathartidae that are placed in *Vultur* and *Gymnogyps* respectively (see VULTURE (2)).

CONDYLE: an articulating process on a bone (see SKELETON).

CONEBILL: substantive name of *Ateleodacnis* spp. (for family see WARBLER (2)) ; and of *Conirostrum* spp. (for subfamily see HONEYCREEPER (1)).

CONFIDENCE LIMITS: see STATISTICAL SIGNIFICANCE

CONGENERIC: of two or more species, meaning that they are, or should be, placed in the same GENUS.

CONGRESSES, INTERNATIONAL: gatherings for scientific discussion and for establishing personal contacts—also, on occasion, for reaching agreement on courses of action. International Ornithological Congresses are now held at intervals of four years. Continuity is provided by an International Ornithological Committee of one hundred members, meeting during the course of each Congress ; this body fills vacancies in its own number, decides general questions concerning the regulation of Congresses, chooses the country in which the next is to be held, and elects a President for the succeeding Congress. There is also a small Permanent Executive Committee that makes recommendations to the International Ornithological Committee and deals with any matters arising during the interval between Congresses ; the constitution of this body is governed by the rule adopted in 1954—Acta XI Congressus Internationalis Ornithologici : 42, Decision 3 (publ. Basel, 1955).

The following International Ornithological Congresses have been held, under the Presidents named.

I   1884   Vienna
              Dr Gustav Radde (*Austria*)

II 1891   Budapest
              Prof. V. Fatio (*Hungary*)

III	1900	Paris
		Dr Émile Oustalet (*France*)
IV	1905	London
		Dr R. Bowdler Sharp (*Great Britain*)
V	1910	Berlin
		Prof. Anton Reichenow (*Germany*)
VI	1926	Copenhagen
		Dr Ernst Hartert (*Germany and Great Britain*)
VII	1930	Amsterdam
		Prof. Einar Lönnberg (*Sweden*)
VIII	1934	Oxford
		Prof. Erwin Stresemann (*Germany*)
IX	1938	Rouen
		Prof. Alessandro Ghighi (*Italy*)
X	1950	Uppsala
		Dr Alexander Wetmore (*U.S.A.*)
XI	1954	Basel
		Sir A. Landsborough Thomson (*Great Britain*)
XII	1958	Helsinki
		Prof. Jacques Berlioz (*France*)
XIII	1962	Ithaca, N.Y.
		Dr Ernst Mayr (*U.S.A.*)

Congresses that were to have been held at Sarajevo in 1915 and in the U.S.A. in 1942 could not take place. The Fourteenth Congress is due to be held in Great Britain in 1966 under the presidency of Dr David Lack (Great Britain).

Each Congress is followed by the publication of a special volume of *Verhandlungen*, *Proceedings*, *Comptes Rendues* or *Acta*, edited by its General Secretary. The proceedings of the Third and Fourth Congresses constituted volumes of the former international journal *Ornis*. The Presidential Address at the VIIIth Congress gave the history of the earlier meetings.

Apart from the regular series as above, there have been occasional special meetings with a strong international flavour—for instance, the British Ornithological Conference at Edinburgh in 1947, and the Pan-African Ornithological Congress at Livingstone, Northern Rhodesia, in 1957.

The International Congresses of Zoology, held at intervals of five years, are also of interest to ornithologists in a more general way. They have a particular importance in that they constitute the final authority on questions of zoological nomenclature and appoint the standing International Commission on that subject (see NOMENCLATURE).

CONNECTIVE TISSUE: a general term for a variety of fibrous and other tissues of the body, including ligaments and tendons (see also under MUSCULATURE).

CONOPOPHAGIDAE: see under PASSERIFORMES; and ANTPIPIT

CONSERVATION: measures seeking to minimise or prevent reductions in bird numbers, extinction of species or races, loss of variety in the species composition of the avifauna in any given area, and, more generally, any unnecessary or sweeping change away from natural conditions for bird-life; the methods discussed here are aided by legal protection (see PROTECTION; also OIL POLLUTION; TOXIC CHEMICALS).

While the scientific basis of natural regulation of animal numbers is still imperfectly understood, policy and practice must—pending further research —proceed on the best available assumption. The traditional assumption, which dies hard, is that the welfare of birds can best be promoted by stopping deliberate human persecution except of predators, which, being themselves engaged in 'persecution' of other birds, should be ruthlessly repressed or even extirpated. The modern assumption is that successful conservation requires above all the maintenance of an adequate ecological base, and that birds will flourish if satisfactory habitats are kept in existence for them—including cover, food, water, and the necessary conditions to satisfy behavioural needs (such as open space or singing stands) and to give freedom from an unacceptable level of disturbance. The scientific basis of modern conservation is therefore sought in studies of the factors that influence the choice and successful exploitation of habitat by different species of birds, and in research on the factors present in soil, climate, hydrology, vegetation, and fauna which together determine the maintenance of any given distribution of habitats (see CLIMATOLOGY; ECOLOGY; VEGETATION). In other words, the modern approach is 'Look after the habitat and the birds will look after themselves'. There are some obvious exceptions to this, but they are readily ascertainable, and most are indeed widely familiar.

Research into bird ethology, ecology, population dynamics, and distribution therefore coincides very largely with the basic research needs for conservation in the ornithological sphere. Research on general habitat factors is equally needed for many other purposes, including land use and land management. Stress was for a time laid on 'economic ornithology', but this approach no longer appears very fruitful, since few if any birds can be shown to be simply and exclusively 'beneficial' or 'injurious'. If birds do play a vital part in the maintenance of conditions required for such human activities as agriculture or forestry (see PREDATION), it can almost certainly be only through such multifarious and indirect processes that any attempt to separate them from their whole ecological context is not scientifically sound.

The principal specialised studies involved in bird conservation are concerned with applied problems. These include the artificial creation of suitable sheets of water ; the best siting, density, and design of nestboxes for hole-nesting species ; the artificial provision of food, e.g. in frosty weather ; and different treatments of woodland clearings and fringes, or hedgerows and rough herbage in fields, to provide suitable habitat for game-birds and other species that it is desired to encourage.

Scientific conservation calls for extensive controlled experiments of these types, and they are being increasingly carried out—especially in North America and a number of European countries including Great Britain. For example, Bruns in Germany, Campbell in England, and McCabe in Wisconsin, U.S.A., have conducted experiments into the possibilities of increasing bird populations by producing extremely high concentrations of nestboxes (see NESTBOX). In Scandinavia substantial increases of breeding range of the Goldeneye *Bucephala clangula* have been achieved by provision of suitably designed nestboxes. In America, Wood Duck *Aix sponsa* have been locally much increased by provision of raccoon-proof nestboxes, usually fixed to standards rising out of water. The attraction of ducks to artificial decoy ponds has a long history in Europe (see DECOY), and recently pools to encourage wildfowl have been constructed in large numbers in North America. Some British Nature Reserves such as Wicken Fen near Cambridge and Morton Lochs, Fife, have pools made for this purpose, and wild ducks and swans (Anatidae) have been attracted by the pond made for the worldwide collection of the Wildfowl Trust at Slimbridge, Gloucestershire. Many artificial waters made for other purposes, such as reservoirs, have similar effects. In some cases, as in the Pen Ponds, Richmond Park, Surrey, and at Patuxent Research Station, Maryland, U.S.A., artificial islets have been successful in attracting and giving cover for nesting wildfowl. Floating rafts have also been used, and this method is being adopted on a large scale to extend the breeding area of the commercially exploited guano cormorants (Phalacrocoracidae) on islands off Peru (see GUANO).

Study of foods most suitable for different species of ducks, by the U.S. Food and Wildlife Service and other bodies, has led to extensive experiments in artificially sowing seed of plants such as wild rice (sometimes from the air) and artificially repressing—by mechanical or chemical means—competing aquatic vegetation of no food value. At Patuxent and elsewhere, artificial pools have

been regularly drained in late summer and reflooded in autumn to enable rich plant growth at the bottom to add to the available food supply. In the Netherlands, England, and elsewhere, wild swans *Cygnus* spp. and others have been artificially fed during severe cold, where necessary by helicopter.

Artificial planting of tree cover for game-birds (especially Pheasants *Phasianus colchicus*), provision of rough verges to fields for the use of breeding Partridges *Perdix perdix*, and systematic burning of heather with the aim of keeping moors suitable for Red Grouse *Lagopus scoticus*, are among many conservation practices long familiar to sportsmen in Britain. Under the guidance of the Committee on Bird Sanctuaries in Royal Parks, berry-bearing trees and shrubs, such as *Sorbus* spp., have been planted at many places in the Greater London parks to attract birds, and dead or hollow trees have been preserved for this purpose. In America, plants such as *Lespediza* have been widely planted to encourage quail (Odontophorinae) and other species, and hedgerows have been brought into existence on a large scale for wildlife conservation.

A considerable body of empirical knowledge therefore exists regarding possible techniques for use in the conservation of bird life. This knowledge has, however, not yet been comprehensively assessed or related scientifically to fundamental studies in ethology, ecology, and population dynamics. Studies with this object are in progress in Britain for a number of species such as the Red Grouse by Jenkins and Watson at Aberdeen University ; the Wood Pigeon *Columba palumbus* by officers of the Ministry of Agriculture, Fisheries, and Food ; the Partridge by A. D. Middleton and others at Fordingbridge, Hampshire ; and various species of Anatidae by the Wildfowl Trust. Campbell's study of the Pied Flycatcher *Ficedula hypoleuca* in the Forest of Dean, Gloucestershire, should also be mentioned ; as a by-product of this, the species was successfully attracted to build up a nestbox colony in Yarner Wood Nature Reserve, Devon, south of its previous breeding range in England. These and other studies elsewhere promise to allow hit-or-miss empirical methods to be replaced by a more scientific approach to conservation. Such an approach involves being able to answer, for example, the following questions.

(a) Is conservation necessary, e.g. are numbers declining or is the species or bird population actually threatened in some way ; or, conversely, is it possible and desirable to increase its numbers or range ?

(b) If so, what are the precise ethological factors involved in the birds' capacity to flourish in their environment, and the precise ecological factors involved in modifying the environment as may be required?

(c) If the problem is capable of satisfactory solution theoretically, what techniques and measures are available to achieve a solution in practice?

For example, ethological studies may show that a particular species is polygamous and practises communal displays (see LEK DISPLAY) ; its survival may therefore be dependent on a habitat being sufficiently rich to maintain a high local density, i.e. the fairly high threshold density necessary for survival. A wide-ranging species, for instance a predator, may need a larger hunting area than is available, as where land reclamation has reduced the extent of suitable habitat. On the other hand, a habitat may be fully suitable except for a short period each year when snow, ice, drought, or some other extreme conditions render it unsuitable unless conservation can provide a temporary palliative over that period. Relations with other species (e.g. seizure of nest sites of hole-nesting birds by more aggressive species) may call for some limited intervention, especially where the species causing the trouble have been led to colonise or increase by human interference of some sort. Control measures may also be necessary in the few cases where undue multiplication leads to serious damage to human interests (see CONTROL ; QUELEA CONTROL).

Difficult and controversial issues arise in connection with proposals for introduction not only of exotic species, but of species perhaps native to similar habitats not far away, and even in some cases formerly indigenous at the place in question (see NATURALISED BIRDS). So much harm has been done by thoughtless introductions, and the indirect consequences of such interference are so unpredictable, that most authorities at present take an ultra-cautious attitude towards any such projects. In principle there may be no logical objection to introduction in a world where so much other human interference is unavoidable, but its practice in the present state of ignorance about possible repercussions can rarely be justified. Artificial attraction of birds and artificial increase of their numbers may also have dangers, but these tend to be more easily controlled if need arises.

Apart from legal protection, probably the most important type of conservation effort is the provision of nature reserves, refuges, sanctuaries, and similar protected areas. Except in the case of rare and localised birds, these cannot help more than a small part of the population of a given species. Nevertheless, apart from their direct value they are important for adding to our knowledge and experience in conservation and as centres for the education of public opinion. In the case of vulnerable migratory species, such as ducks, geese, and swans, refuges need to be planned on a national or international basis to give protection not only in summer and winter quarters but at intermediate staging points. In North America, this has for some years been successfully organised between the United States and Canada, under the 1916 Migratory Birds Treaty, and some progress is informally being made towards similar arrangements for north-western Europe.

Other types of reserve are specially designed for the protection of a particular rare species or group of species, e.g. a colony of breeding sea birds. Others may be chosen as good surviving samples of a particular natural or semi-natural habitat, such as primitive fenland, bog, or pine forest, in which the characteristic birds survive with their animal and plant allies. Such nature reserves not only permit the study of conservation problems, and the application of suitable remedial measures where necessary, but can also, if strictly supervised, give birds the freedom from disturbance (even by birdwatchers) that is often vital and is increasingly difficult to ensure in modern conditions.

A special and growing problem of conservation is the early recognition and prompt and effective treatment of situations where a species or subspecies is threatened with actual extinction, often as a result of economic development or some hasty and ill-advised human interference with nature. A number of such species are listed by the International Council for Bird Preservation (I.C.B.P. or C.I.P.O.) and by the International Union for the Conservation of Nature (I.U.C.N.), whose Survival Service attempts to watch over and help them. The resources available are, however, still far too small to hold out assurance of success, and this is among the weakest points in the present state of world conservation.

E.M.N.

CONSPECIFIC: of two or more subspecies or other forms, meaning that they belong to the same species (or should be so regarded, although considered by others to be specifically distinct) —see SPECIES.

CONSUMMATORY ACT: 'an act which constitutes the termination of a given instinctive behaviour pattern or sequence' (Thorpe 1951), bringing about a sudden drop in motivation —compare APPETITIVE BEHAVIOUR ; SPECIFIC ACTION POTENTIAL.

CONTINGENCY TABLE: see STATISTICAL SIGNIFICANCE

CONTOUR FEATHER: any feather that forms part of the visible external surface of the body (not excluding remiges and rectrices)—see PLUMAGE.

CONTROL: deliberate action by man to limit or reduce the numbers of a wild species, where potential increase of existing abundance is thought to be detrimental to human interests ; a negative aspect, so to speak, of CONSERVATION. The occasion for control may arise from the development of human activities of a vulnerable kind. Or it may arise from increase in bird numbers indirectly caused by man—removal of natural checks, as by the destruction of predators ; incidental provision of a more favourable environment (habitat, food supply, nesting sites) for certain species ; artificial introduction of species into new areas.

Control measures in particular interests are sometimes instituted privately or locally. Thus, landowners concerned to preserve game may reduce or even exterminate species of birds-of-prey ; and fishermen (for pleasure or profit), both freshwater and marine, have sometimes outlawed their avian competitors. Farmers and fruit-growers may destroy birds in defence of their crops (see also SCARING). Urban authorities may seek to safeguard amenities against such birds as the House Sparrow *Passer domesticus* and the Starling *Sturnus vulgaris* ; and those in charge of airports have a problem in keeping their runways clear of gulls (Larinae) and other birds. Those responsible for the conservation of, say, a mixed sea-bird colony may try to achieve a desirable balance by controlling robber species such as the Herring Gull *Larus argentatus*.

Unfortunately, many such measures have been based on ignorance. The destruction of birds-of-prey has too often been indiscriminate, paying little regard to the feeding habits of particular species— and none to the law ; action against fish-eating birds, although on a much smaller scale, has been even more misguided. On the other hand, there are instances in which a bird species becomes an agricultural pest of such importance as to require officially organised countermeasures over a wide area—the Wood Pigeon *Columba palumbus* is a British example, while the House Sparrow and the Starling have become a nuisance also in countries into which they have been introduced (see NATURALISED BIRDS). For one of the most deliberate, large-scale attempts at control, see QUELEA CONTROL ; also EMU.

CONURE: substantive name of species in several Neotropical genera, e.g. *Aratinga*, of Psittacidae (for family see PARROT).

CONVERGENCE: evolution on lines tending to produce similarity between unrelated or only distantly related forms as a result of adaptation to a like mode of life—the antithesis of radiation in its evolutionary sense (see ADAPTATION ; EVOLUTION ; RADIATION (1)). Examples of modes of life leading to convergent adaptations are running (in place of flight), aquatic habitat, aerial pursuit of insect prey, and raptorial feeding habits ; but there are many others.

Convergence is all the more important as a phenomenon of avian evolution because it is superimposed on a high degree of uniformity in basic structure within the class. For that reason it is confusing to taxonomists, who have difficulty in distinguishing between characters that are primary, and therefore of phylogenetic significance, and characters that are secondary in that they are the result of special adaptations (as contrasted with the general adaptations common to all birds).

Convergence can be extremely subtle in its manifestations, producing similarity not merely in a few characters but in a whole series of characters, even of minute detail, that are advantageous for the particular mode of life. The resemblance may indeed have so many facets as to arouse scepticism concerning the absence of a close relationship. This is a frame of mind induced by the misleading process of enumerating points of similarity as if they were quite independent instead of being items in a 'constellation of characters' contributing to a single adaptation.

At the same time it has to be realised that phylogenetic relationship and convergent adaptation need not be mutually exclusive. Convergence may occur between forms that had diverged not very far back in the evolutionary process.

CONVERSION TABLES: for factors for converting between the British and the metric systems see Tables at the end of the volume.

CO-ORDINATE: term used in taxonomy to mean 'of equal nomenclatural status' (see GROUP (1) ; NOMENCLATURE).

COOT: substantive name of *Fulica* spp. ; used without qualification in Britain for *F. atra* ; has also been misapplied to gallinules *Porphyrio* spp. (see RAIL).

COPPERSMITH: *Megalaima haemacephala* (see BARBET).

COPPERTAIL: substantive name of some *Metallura* spp. (for family see HUMMINGBIRD).

COPRODAEUM: name sometimes applied to the part of the cloaca into which the rectum opens (see ALIMENTARY SYSTEM).

COPULATION: the sexual act, leading to fertilisation of the ova of the female by spermatozoa from the male (see REPRODUCTIVE SYSTEM) ; also termed 'coition'. This usually occurs with maximum frequency a day or two before the first egg is laid, although the precise interval varies with species, clutch size, and other factors.

Although the Anatidae have penes, the males of most species of birds have no specialised intromittent organs. Furthermore, copulation involves bodily contact with another individual, which is avoided at other times. For these reasons many, and perhaps most, copulation attempts are unsuccessful, the principal cause of failure being a sudden change-over to aggressive or fleeing behaviour in one of the partners (see PAIR FORMATION ; and DISPLAY).

Normally, of course, the male mounts the female, but reversed mounting occurs as a usual sequel to copulation in many species. Homosexual mounting has been observed in a number of cases. Such phenomena are, as might be expected, more frequent in species in which the sexes are alike in colour ; but it is probable that in most species each sex can show the sexual behaviour characteristic of the other if appropriate conditions arise.

In a successful copulation the tail of each bird is displaced laterally, and the feathers round the cloacae are turned back so that the engorged lips of the two cloacae can come into juxtaposition. Copulation usually occurs on the ground or on a perch, but some species may copulate on the water (e.g. Anatidae) and a few even on the wing (Apodidae). See also BEHAVIOUR, DEVELOPMENT OF.

R.A.H.

COQUETTE: substantive name of *Lophornis* spp. (see HUMMINGBIRD).

CORACIAE; CORACII; CORACIIDAE: see below

CORACIIFORMES: an order comprising the following suborders and families, the latter dealt with separately as shown.

Alcedines :
    Superfamily Alcedinoidea
      Alcedinidae   see KINGFISHER
    Superfamily Todoidea
      Todidae   see TODY
    Superfamily Momotoidea
      Momotidae   see MOTMOT

Meropes :
    Meropidae   see BEE-EATER
Coracii :
    Leptosomatidae see CUCKOO-ROLLER
    Coraciidae   see ROLLER ; GROUND-ROLLER
    Upupidae   see HOOPOE
    Phoeniculidae see WOOD-HOOPOE
Bucerotes :
    Bucerotidae   see HORNBILL

The above is the classification used by Peters, and it differs from Wetmore's only in that the latter treats the subfamily Brachypteraciinae (ground-rollers) of the Coraciidae as a separate family. In Stresemann's system the assemblage is divided into no less than six orders, as follows : Halcyones (Alcedinidae), Todi (Todidae), Momoti (Momotidae), Meropes (Meropidae), Coraciae (Leptosomatidae, Coraciidae, Brachypteraciidae), and Upupae (Upupidae, Phoeniculidae, Bucerotidae). As the Wetmore-Peters classification divides the Alcedines into three superfamilies with one family apiece, the chief difference in grouping lies in whether the hoopoes are bracketed with the rollers or with the hornbills. As regards the differences in the ranks accorded to the taxa, the position is that the assemblage includes 9–10 mostly distinctive families falling into 6–7 well defined groups ; and that although these have been generally accepted as related, on the basis of resemblances in anatomy and pterylosis between each group and some of the others, the assemblage as a whole is not easy to characterise as an order. Among structural points, there is a tendency for the three forward toes to be connected together ; syndactyly is most marked in the Alcedinidae and Meropidae.

Very many members of the order are birds of brilliant plumage. Other striking features often present include long tails, crests, and large bills. Most of the species are partly arboreal, but many find their food (largely animal) on the ground— some in the air (bee-eaters) or in the water (some kingfishers). They usually nest in holes, some excavating burrows for themselves (kingfishers, todies, motmots, bee-eaters) ; the nesting habits of the hornbills are especially remarkable. The eggs are white or slightly tinted. The young at hatching are blind, helpless, and (except in hoopoes) naked.

The order as a whole is cosmopolitan, but of the families this is true only in respect of the Alcedinidae ; of the rest, two families are Neotropical and the others confined to the Old World. In some cases the distribution is very restricted, e.g. to the West Indies (Todidae) or to Madagascar and the Comoros (Leptosomatidae).

CORACOID: a paired bone (not present in mammals) of the pectoral girdle (see SKELETON).

CORCORACINAE: see under MAGPIE-LARK

CORDON-BLEU: substantive name of some waxbills *Estrilda* spp. (see WEAVER-FINCH).

CORELLA: substantive name, in Australia, of *Kakatoe* spp. (see PARROT).

CORMORANT: substantive name of nearly all species of Phalacrocoracidae (Pelecaniformes, suborder Pelecani) ; used without qualification in the British Isles for one of the species found there ; in the plural, general term for the family. The other substantive name used is 'shag', which has a specific application in the British Isles but is otherwise merely an alternative. This is a family of aquatic birds represented on the coasts of nearly all the world and on many inland waters as well. It includes about 30 species (some with subspecific forms), and these are placed in 2–3 genera.

Pigmy Cormorant *Phalacrocorax pygmaeus.*   *C.E.T.K.*

Cormorants are birds of from medium to large size (19–40 inches long), with long necks and bodies. The bill is of moderate length, rather slender, cylindrical, and strongly hooked. The short legs are set far back, and the large feet are totipalmate. The wings are relatively short ; the tail is rather long, sometimes markedly long, and very stiff.

The plumage is predominantly dark, in fact often black with a greenish or bluish metallic sheen. Some species have white on the throat or under parts ; a few are mainly grey. There is sometimes bright colour (blue, green, yellow, orange, red) in the iris, on the bill, and on the bare skin of the face ; in a few cases the legs are brightly coloured (yellow, red). Crests and ornamental patches of white are common in breeding plumage. The sexes are alike. Immature birds tend to be browner and duller, with paler under parts in species where these are dark in the adult.

Cormorants frequent coasts and large rivers and lakes ; some species are purely maritime and others largely restricted to inland waters, while others again are found in both habitats. They swim low in the water, but do not spend much time there except for the purpose of feeding. The food consists largely of fish, although crustaceans and (in fresh water) amphibians are also taken. Fish are caught by underwater pursuit, the birds diving from the surface. Sometimes the bird submerges gently, but more often it takes a forward leap almost clear of the water. It swims underwater without aid from the wings except in braking (see SWIMMING AND DIVING). It may reach a considerable depth, but it commonly brings its catch to the surface before swallowing it, although small fish are apparently sometimes swallowed underwater. (Cormorants of two species, *Phalacrocorax carbo* and the Japanese Cormorant *P. capillatus,* have for long been tamed in the Orient for the assistance of fishermen ; leather collars prevent them from swallowing (see DOMESTICATION).) Some species first detect the presence of fish from the air. The birds, although rising from the water laboriously, fly strongly with steady wing-beats and occasional short glides ; the neck is extended during flight. They usually fly not far above the surface of the water, but when crossing land they tend to go higher ; they have even been known to soar. On the ground, or on trees, the posture is upright, with the neck curved and often with the wings held extended to dry, but the birds move about very little. They are in the main silent, but make various guttural sounds at the nest ; the Bank Cormorant *P. neglectus* of South Africa is described as uttering a 'loud melancholy cry' when disturbed.

Most cormorants breed colonially. The nests may be on rocky islets, on cliff ledges, or in trees ; some species use different sites according to locality.

The nest may be a rather bulky structure of seaweed, vegetation, or sticks, depending on the site. The pale blue or green eggs have a chalky outer layer ; they are unmarked except in the Socotra Cormorant *P. nigrogularis*. The usual clutch is 2–4 or more. The nidicolous young are naked on hatching but acquire a down plumage. Both parents take part in incubation and in care of the young.

Coastally, cormorants are found very widely— from Greenland to the sub-antarctic islands—except in the central area of the Pacific Ocean. Suitable inland waters in all continents are also frequented, the largest area of land without representation of the family being in northern Asia. Birds breeding in high latitudes are migratory ; and even in the tropics some species are common in areas in which they are not known to breed. The grey species are found only in the Southern Hemisphere, and a group of small species with long tails is restricted to the Old World. One species of cormorant, *P. perspicillatus* of Bering Island, became extinct over a century ago (see EXTINCT BIRDS).

The largest and most widely distributed species, with many races, is the Cormorant *Phalacrocorax carbo* familiar in the British Isles, also called the Common Cormorant in a wider context, and Great Cormorant in North America and Black Cormorant in Australasia. Its breeding range extends from eastern Canada and Greenland, through Europe, Africa, and much of Asia, to Australia and New Zealand. The adult is predominantly black, with some bronze and dark grey and a small patch of white on the throat (whole foreneck and breast white in the African race *P. c. lucidus*). In breeding plumage there is a short crest, a hoary sprinkling of white on the neck, and a white patch on each flank. Immature birds are browner, and with more or less pale under parts. Its habitat and choice of nesting sites are variable ; thus, in Great Britain it is a coastal bird, nesting on rocks, whereas in parts of Ireland it lives on lakes and nests colonially in trees.

The other species found in the British Isles—also elsewhere in Europe and in north-western Africa— is the Shag *P. aristotelis*, sometimes called the Green Cormorant. It is a smaller bird with a definite green tinge and, in the breeding season, a crest that curves forwards. The most widespread species in North America is the Double-crested Cormorant *P. auritus*, but Brandt's Cormorant *P. penicillatus* is the commonest on the Pacific coast of the United States. The Olivaceous Cormorant *P. olivaceus* ranges from Mexico to Tierra del Fuego. The Red-faced Cormorant *P. urile* breeds in the Bering Sea area but reaches Formosa in winter. The Cape Cormorant *P. capensis* is a valuable source of guano in South Africa (see GUANO). The Little Black Cormorant *P. sulcirostris* ranges from Borneo to New Zealand.

All the species so far mentioned by name in this article are predominantly dark birds, and of at least medium size ; there are others of which the same is true. There is a smaller number of species, also sizable, in which the plumage is mainly white below. These include the Guanay Cormorant *P. bougainvillii*, which is of great economic importance on the coast of Peru (see GUANO) ; the Pied (or Yellow-faced) Cormorant *P. varius* of Australia (where it is found on swamps and rivers as well as on the coast) and New Zealand ; the Rough-faced Shag *P. carunculatus* of New Zealand and the island groups in that area (several insular races, showing differences mainly in the colour of the face and in the development of caruncles) ; and the Blue-eyed Shag *P. atriceps* of southern South America and islands of the Antarctic seas. There are also a few species in which the plumage is mainly dark grey ; they include the Spotted Shag *P. punctatus* of the New Zealand coasts, with dark blue face and yellow feet, and the Red-legged Cormorant *P. gaimardi* of southern South America, with bright yellow bill, orange face, and coral-red feet.

Sometimes placed in a separate genus, *Halietor*, are four species distinguishable by their small size and relatively longer tails. They are mainly inhabitants of rivers and lakes in tropical or sub-tropical countries. The Pigmy Cormorant *P. pygmaeus* ranges from Hungary and Algeria to Afghanistan ; the Long-tailed Shag (or Reed Duiker) *P. africanus* is found on the great rivers and lakes of Africa and in Madagascar ; the Little Cormorant *P. niger* is found from India to Borneo, and the Little Pied Cormorant *P. melanoleucos* in New Guinea, Australia, and New Zealand.

Finally, there is the Flightless Cormorant *Nannopterum harrisi* of the Galápagos Islands. It is one of the largest species and with mainly dark plumage ; the iris is bright blue. The wings are very much reduced in size and quite useless for flight, but they are nevertheless held extended to dry as in flying species ; the sternum has no keel. It is a clumsy and vulnerable bird on land at its nesting sites near the shore but, like its relatives, is master of its element in the sea.

See also ANTARCTIC. A.L.T.

CORNCRAKE : *Crex crex*, sometimes called 'Landrail' (see RAIL).

CORNEA : part of the eye (see VISION).

CORNEOUS: horny.

CORONARY VESSELS: see HEART

CORONET: substantive name of *Boissonneaua* spp. (for family see HUMMINGBIRD).

CORPUSCLE, RED: see BLOOD

CORPUS LUTEUM: (plural 'corpora lutea') —see REPRODUCTIVE SYSTEM.

CORPUS STRIATUM: part of the forebrain (see NERVOUS SYSTEM).

CORRELATION: statistical (not necessarily causal) association between two (or more) phenomena, one tending to vary directly or inversely as does the other. The degree of correlation may be expressed as a coefficient of which the values range from $+1$ (complete direct association) to -1 (complete inverse association), lower values than unity representing weaker associations and zero representing none at all. See further under STATISTICAL SIGNIFICANCE.

CORTEX: for that of the cerebral hemispheres (part of the forebrain) see NERVOUS SYSTEM ; for that of the adrenal glands see ENDOCRINE SYSTEM.

CORVIDAE: a family of the Passeriformes, suborder Oscines (see CROW (1)).

COSMETIC COLORATION: see COLOUR

COSMOPOLITAN: distributional term applied to species or higher taxa found in all the main zoogeographical regions—or at least in most of them, and certainly in both Old and New Worlds and in both Northern and Southern Hemispheres (see DISTRIBUTION, GEOGRAPHICAL).

COSTAL: pertaining to the ribs (see SKELETON).

COT ; COTE : a shelter for domesticated birds (or other animals), especially doves, i.e. 'dovecots'.

Hornell, J. 1947. Egyptian and medieval pigeon houses. Antiquity 21 : 182–185.

COTINGA: substantive name of some species of Cotingidae (Passeriformes, suborder Tyranni) ; in the plural, general term for the family. This Neotropical group contains about 90 species and is allied to the manakins (Pipridae) and the tyrant-flycatchers (Tyrannidae) ; it is uncertain to which of the three families some intermediate genera should be assigned.

Cotingas range from the size of a finch (Fringillidae sp.) up to the size of a crow (Corvidae sp.) and are very diverse in external appearance, although typically they are alike in possessing rather broad bills hooked slightly at the tip, rounded wings, and short sturdy legs. Many species are of undistinguished appearance with little difference between the sexes ; in others the males have plumage of brilliant or unusual colours, curiously modified feathers on the wing and the head region, peculiar fleshy wattles, or patches of brightly coloured naked skin ; in most of these species the females are inconspicuously coloured.

Outstanding among them are the cocks-of-the-rock *Rupicola* spp. (2), in which the male is orange or red with a helmet-like crest concealing the bill, and has modified secondary feathers ; the Umbrella-bird *Cephalopterus ornatus* with a black umbrella-like crest and a feathered wattle, as long as the bird itself, hanging from the throat ; the White Bellbird *Procnias alba* with an upstanding fleshy process, studded with small star-like feathers, growing from the base of the upper mandible ; the Three-wattled Bellbird *P. tricarunculata* with three tapering fleshy processes arising from the base of the bill, one on top and one at each side ; and the Mossy-throated Bellbird *P. averano* with a mass of pendent black fleshy wattles hanging like a beard from the throat. In several species one of the outer primaries is short and peculiarly modified, being notched, attenuated, or twisted ; in none has the function of this modification been explained.

Bearded (or Mossy-throated) Bellbird *Procnias averano*. C.E.T.K.

The family is nearly confined to the tropical areas of Central and South America. One species just reaches the extreme south of the United States (the Rose-throated Becard *Platypsaris aglaiae*), and one species occurs in Jamaica (the Jamaican Becard *P. niger*).

No other New World family rivals the cotingas

in strangeness of appearance, but because they are mainly forest birds, living in the tree-tops, little is known about most of the species beyond their appearance and their more outstanding calls. Their voices are as diverse as their plumages ; some have musical whistles while others utter resounding hammer-like notes, bell-like tollings, grunts, croaks, or calf-like lowings. The breeding of most of the species is unknown ; those in which it is known build various kinds of nests. The becards *Pachy-rhamphus* spp. and *Platypsaris* spp. construct very bulky covered nests with a side entrance ; the Mossy-throated Bellbird and Pompadour Cotinga *Xipholena punicea* build flimsy platforms of interlaced twigs ; the Cock-of-the-rock fixes a nest of mud and vegetable fibres to a rock-face ; while the tityras *Tityra* spp. and Polymorphic (or Bright-rumped) Attila *Attila spadiceus* nest in holes in trees. The usual clutch of the hole-nesting species seems to be 2, 3, or 4 eggs, that of the Cock-of-the-rock 2 eggs, and that of the platform-nesting species 1 or 2 eggs. The eggs that are known are olive, pale brown, or grey in ground-colour, with darker brown spots. In the tityras and becards both sexes attend the nest and feed the young, although only the female incubates. In the species with extreme sexual dimorphism it is probable that the males take no part in the nesting. The Cock-of-the-rock *Rupicola rupicola* is semi-social in its breeding ; several nests may be built within a few yards of each other on the same rock-face.

The bizarre ornaments of the male cotingas, and their unusual calls, are probably in every case used in courtship, but few species have been studied. The Umbrella-bird, in display, spreads its crest to cover the whole top of the head and produces a rumbling sound from the modified trachea and syrinx. The Cock-of-the-rock is the only cotinga known to perform social or lek displays (see LEK DISPLAY). Several males gather at a display ground, where each displays on a small cleared area or ' court ' similar to the courts used by the manakins of the genus *Manacus* (see MANAKIN). In contrast to the very active displays of manakins, the much larger Cock-of-the-rock adopts absolutely static postures on the court and may hold these for minutes on end. The part played by the females at the display grounds has not yet been studied.

D.W.S.

Gilliard, E. T. 1962. On the breeding behaviour of the Cock-of-the-rock (Aves, *Rupicola rupicola*). Bull. Amer. Mus. Nat. Hist. 124 : 31–68.
Sick, H. 1954. Zur Biologie des amazonischen Schirm-vogels, *Cephalopterus ornatus*. J. Orn. 95 : 233–244.
Skutch, A. F. 1946. Life history of the Costa Rican Tityra. Auk 63 : 327–362.
Skutch, A. F. 1954. Life history of the White-winged Becard. Auk 71 : 113–129.
Snow, B. K. 1961. Notes on the behaviour of three Cotingidae. Auk 78 : 150–161.

COTINGIDAE: see under PASSERIFORMES ; and COTINGA

COTYPE: see TYPE-SPECIMEN

COUA: substantive name of *Coua* spp. ; in the plural, general term for the subfamily Couainae (see CUCKOO). See Plate 8 (colour).

COUAINAE: see CUCKOO

COUCAL: substantive name of *Centropus* spp. ; in the plural, general term for the subfamily Centropodinae (see CUCKOO).

COUNT: a method of studying populations by counting or estimating the numbers of individuals of certain species present at a specified place on a definite date ; more particularly, the study of fluctuations in numbers by repeated synchronised counts at regular places taken as providing a sample representative of a large area. Whereas the term ' census ' usually refers to a breeding population (see CENSUS), ' count ' is more often used in respect of non-breeding birds, notably wintering flocks of gregarious species ; owing to migratory movements, moreover, a series of counts may bring elements of different populations into the picture in the course of a season. Although the method has been applied to game-birds (Galli-formes) also, it is especially suitable for the study of wildfowl (Anatidae), and it is for them that it has been notably developed in pioneer work in Great Britain. The remainder of this article accordingly deals solely with the complex system of winter counts whereby trends in the European population of migratory wildfowl are kept under annual review.

This investigation, which began in 1948, now extends over most of northwestern Europe, and has become one of the most intensive and sustained efforts in the history of ornithology. In Britain alone more than 50 000 records have been received in the course of 14 years from a total of some 2000 places ; with an average of 4 or 5 species to each return, the data already available amount to upwards of a quarter of a million entries. Although con-cerned with all the Anatidae, the emphasis of the inquiry is centred around the common species and more especially on the ducks.

In the design of the investigation many factors are taken into account. First, it deals not with a single species, but with a dozen or more, all highly migratory and all with their own variation in behaviour and distribution. It is also possible that several populations may pass through the same district in the course of each winter. The counts are therefore made at monthly intervals between September and March, the dates being synchronised throughout to avoid any duplication in the records. Owing to the wide distribution of the species a complete census is clearly impracticable, and the study perforce depends on regular observations from the more important resorts. This sample, although covering only a small part of the total wildfowl habitat, includes a substantial proportion of the total population. In Britain, where some 600 volunteers are counting regularly, it is estimated that 10–20 per cent of the Mallard *Anas platyrhynchos*, Teal *A. crecca*, and Wigeon *A. penelope* in the country, and an even larger proportion of the Pochard *Aythya ferina* and Tufted Ducks *A. fuligula*, are included in the records. Elsewhere in Europe the inquiry is less intense, and the sample is smaller.

The analysis of the British data is based essentially upon a direct comparison of the number of birds occurring on the same sample of waters in different years. In the first instance these comparisons are made for each month, and a report is distributed within a week or two of each new count being made. At the end of the season the monthly results are combined to provide a set of annual indices, which reflect the relative abundance of the various species over the winter as a whole. These single figures are designed to emphasise the months in which the birds are most numerous, and attach little importance to occasional variations in the arrival and departure dates of the migratory flocks. Results show that the British population of Mallard, Pochard, and Tufted Ducks has increased during the period 1948–62, and that the numbers of Teal and Wigeon have fluctuated about a constant level.

Amongst the possible sources of error is the ability of observers to render an accurate return. In Britain this presents no great difficulty, the population on most waters being such that a count and recount of individual birds is often possible. It is only when the flocks are unusually large or restless that recourse has sometimes to be made to estimates. To test the accuracy of the latter, observers were asked to assess the number of birds on 12 photographs, shown for a limited length of time. Individual answers differed considerably, but when the various under-estimates and over-estimates were set against each other the net discrepancy amounted to only 10 per cent. Tests were also devised to discover whether a programme of monthly counts can be relied upon to reflect the true pattern of a population, despite the influences of local movement and other factors on its stability. For this, use was made of a three-year run of almost daily counts available from one particular water. These showed that a count made on a set date was often unrepresentative of the mean population in the month, but that over a long period the variations cancelled out, giving a good indication of the average numbers present. Even more encouraging was the effect of combining the data from this one water with those from another some long distance away. When this was done the individual fluctuations again offset each other, and the combined population proved much more stable than either of its components. Thus the larger the number of observers and the longer the series of records, the more accurate the results are likely to be.

In addition to their use in the study of population trends, the counts provide a vast amount of information on the distribution and movements of the winter population, data that have proved invaluable in the selection of a national network of wildfowl refuges. In this, and in many other fields of wildfowl research, they provide the basis upon which the whole programme of conservation is founded.

G.L.A.-W.

Atkinson-Willes, G. L. (ed.). 1963. Wild Fowl in Great Britain. Mono. Nature Conservancy no. 3. London.

Eltringham, S. K. & Atkinson-Willes, G. L. 1961. Recent population changes in British ducks. Wildfowl Trust 12th Annual Report : 40–57.

Matthews, G. V. T. 1960. An examination of basic data from wildfowl counts. Proc. XII Internat. Orn. Congr., Helsinki 1958 : 483–491.

COUNTERSINGING: singing in rivalry with another male within hearing ; or 'duetting' between male and female of a pair (see SINGING).

COUNTING: term loosely applied to manifestations of a number sense. Experiments on this number sense or 'counting' ability of birds and other animals have been carried out for over fifty years, but it was not until comparatively recently that the difficulties of the task came to be fully realised. Consequently much of the earlier work, and some indeed of the later work, is now seen to be unreliable as evidence for any kind of counting ability. The fact that a bird discontinues ovulation and commences incubation when a certain number of eggs are in the nest (not when a certain number of eggs have been laid) is certainly not evidence for counting ability : the bird may merely be reacting to certain visually observed proportions of egg to nest, or it might be responding to the growing amount of stimulation received through the brood patches.

During the course of some of the early work on counting by mammals, results were obtained that suggested not merely counting, but mathematical ability of a high order. It was eventually shown, however, that the animals could give these results only when they could see the trainer and when the trainer himself knew the answer. In some cases there seems to be no doubt that the trainers actually believed that their pets were displaying intelligence of the highest order. Yet in the end it became abundantly clear that when the horse or the dog was giving its answer, by stopping its stamping or barking when the correct number had been reached, it was not giving evidence of a counting ability at all but had merely been extremely sensitive to minute, probably involuntary, signs and signals which the owner made. These 'clever' animals could never actually solve any problems by themselves ; they merely obeyed their masters' signs, which—given at the proper moment—stopped the stamping or barking by which they were spelling out their answers. The classic example of this was the horse ' Clever Hans ' ; and, ever since, mistakes of this kind in animal psychology have been called ' Clever Hans errors '. Precautions at least as rigid, to exclude such errors, are required when dealing with birds, because the bird's ability to perceive visual patterns and movement is probably greater than that of horses or dogs, and they are certainly no less intelligent in circumstances of this kind. It is certain that many of the earlier experiments on counting by birds are open to just the same objections as were the experiments with ' Clever Hans '.

One of the first types of study was that in which domestic fowls were trained to take grains of corn from rows in which every second grain was glued to a cardboard base. When such rows were presented to the birds they soon learned to eat the loose ones without touching the fixed ones. In addition, one hen learned to select every third grain without touching the others, although no bird was successful in selecting every fourth grain. There is now no doubt that the birds, at least in many of these experiments, had learned to distinguish in some way between loose and fixed grains ; and when the experiments were repeated under more rigorous conditions, with all secondary cues excluded, many of the results could not be confirmed. Nevertheless, even where all secondary cues were excluded, strict alternation in rows of grains, all of which were loose, could be obtained ; but it took a far longer time for the bird to reach a satisfactory level of performance—five to six hundred experiments and seventeen to twenty training days—and even this was some way from perfection. However, such experiments did succeed in demonstrating a true alternation habit, i.e. an ability to take every second grain only ; and this habit could be maintained even if the distance between the grains was increased or decreased, provided that this was done gradually. Another objection that can be raised to some of the early experiments in which the bird had to ' count ' numbers of objects presented successively is that the results may be due to a training rhythm. It is well known that both pigeons and fowls can be trained to a rhythm and can be induced to perform the same actions several times in succession, independently of any temporal rhythm.

The study of the counting abilities of birds was put on an entirely new footing by the elaborate experiments of Köhler and his school, in which extraordinary precautions were taken to avoid errors of the ' Clever Hans' type. In these experiments, and during training for them, the observer and the animals were always separated by a partition so that the experimenter was never seen by the bird although, while at work, he was able to watch it through the view-finder of a cine-camera fitted into the wall. When a deterrent was required in conditioning there was only one degree of punishment and this was always the same—namely a light touch on the back by means of a mechanically operated stick—so that it was impossible for the experimenter inadvertently to give signs by means of the punishing apparatus. In many of the experiments the bird was left entirely to itself and the result recorded automatically by a cine-camera, so that all possibility of an investigator inadvertently giving cues was ruled out. By such methods Köhler and his associates demonstrated that birds have what he calls an ' unnamed number ' concept. The experiments were of two main types, simultaneous presentation and successive presentation. Köhler suggests that man would never have started counting, that is to name numbers, without the possession of two pre-linguistic abilities, viz. that of being able to compare groups of units presented simultaneously side by side, and the ability to remember or to estimate numbers of incidents following each other and thus to keep in mind numbers presented successively in time, independently of rhythm or any other cue. The first problem was presented to birds in a number of different ways, starting with only two groups of edible units (e.g. grains of corn, fruit, pieces of biscuit), the two groups differing by one unit only. In this way a Raven *Corvus corax* and a Grey Parrot *Psittacus erithacus* were taught to open that box which had the same number of spots on the lid as there were on the key card presented to them. These birds thus eventually learned to distinguish between five groups indicated by 2, 3, 4, 5, and 6 black spots on the lids of small boxes, the key being one of these numbers (i.e. a group of one of these numbers of objects) lying on the ground in front of the boxes. The Raven learned to raise only that one of the five lids which had the same number of spots as the key pattern had objects. As a control, every other factor was changed in a random manner from experiment to experiment. There were, for instance, 15 positions of the 5 boxes and many different position of the key pattern. Again, the number of units in the key pattern changed with each experiment and there were 5 places for the number of spots on a lid to correspond to that of the key. In the final series of experiments in this investigation, for each trial the experimenter broke afresh a flat plasticene cake into pieces of highly irregular outline, the area of a piece varying from 1 to 50 units, care being taken always to make the arrangement and general appearance of the positive number, which constituted the key pattern, as unlike as possible to the number on the correct lid. Nevertheless, when all such extraneous clues were eliminated, the bird succeeded in choosing the positive lid according to the only item that was not changing through all the experiments, i.e. the number characteristic of the particular key pattern presented (Fig. 1).

FIG 1. A problem successfully solved by the Raven 'Jacob'. The arrows point in each case from the 'key' pattern of plasticene pieces to the only box in each group of five which the bird opened (see text). *From O. Koehler 1949.*

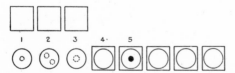

FIG 2. The Jackdaw has removed the cards covering each of the first three boxes and has taken the four baits which they contained. The remaining boxes are closed; no. 4 is empty and no. 5 contains the last 'allowed' bait (see text). *From O. Koehler 1949.*

In presenting the numbers successively many different methods were employed. At first birds were trained to eat only 'x' grains out of many offered in a heap in circumstances such that the configuration of the heap gave no cue. Another task was to take only 'x' number of peas which were discharged from a chute into a cup one after another at randomly varied intervals ranging from 1 to 60 seconds. In this experiment the pigeon never sees more than one pea in the cup. It always has the same view and there is no visible cue for distinguishing the last 'allowed' pea from the first 'forbidden' one.

Another experiment involved opening the lids of boxes standing in a long row until 'x' baits had been secured. Since the baits were arranged in the boxes in 20 or more different distributions from one experiment to the next, the number of lids actually to be opened in order to get the required number was constantly changing. For instance, if the bird is to be trained to take 5 baits it may have to open any number of boxes between 1 and 7. The bird thus learns to open lids for up to 'x' baits, so that the number of lids it has to open to get 5 (when 'x'=5) changes with each experiment. One Jackdaw *Corvus monedula* could learn four problems of this kind at the same time. It learned to open black lids until it had secured 2 baits and green lids until it had secured 3, red lids up to 4, and white lids up to 5. Similar results were obtained from Budgerigars *Melopsittacus undulatus* with a bell indicating 2 and a buzzer indicating 3. In these experiments—since, as far as can be seen, all external cues were successfully excluded—we can assume that only an inner token can be responsible for a bird ceasing action when the required number was reached. It is as if the bird is doing some inward marking of the units he is acting upon. This supposition is strengthened by the fact that sometimes these supposed inward markings show themselves in external behaviour in the form of intention movements. Thus a Jackdaw, given the task of raising lids until it had secured 5 baits, which in this case were distributed in the first five boxes in the order 1, 2, 1, 0, 1, went home to its cage after having opened 3 lids only and consequently having 4 baits (Fig. 2). The experimenter was in the act of recording 'One too few. Incorrect solution'; when the Jackdaw returned. It then went through a remarkable performance : it bowed its head once before the first box it had emptied, made two bows before the second box, one before the third. It then went farther along the line, removed the fourth lid (the box with no bait) and then the fifth and took out of this the last, fifth, bait. Having done this it left the rest of the line of boxes untouched and went back to its cage as if regarding the experiment as over. It appears from this 'intention' bowing, repeated the same number of times before each opened box as on the first occasion when it found the baits in them, that the bird remembered its previous actions. It seems as if it became aware that the task was unfinished and so returned and commenced again 'picking up' in vacuo, with intention movements, baits that previously it had actually picked up. When, however, it came to the last two boxes, which by mistake it had omitted to open on its first trip, it performed the full movements and thus completed the task.

The simplest explanation Köhler has to offer for this intention marking is that it may consist in equal marks—as if we were to think of or give one nod of the head for one, two for two, and so on. This is called thinking unnamed numbers, and for the great majority of experimental results at present available it is not necessary to suppose that the bird does the marking by unequal or qualitatively different marks in a fixed order, as we do when we think of the words for 1, 2, 3, 4, 5 or, alternatively, a phrase of five different syllables. More recently, Lögler has shown that a bird trained to open a box with, say, three spots on a lid as a result of seeing three flashes of light, will then go, without further learning, to the same box when it hears three sounds of varying pitch or three random alternations of sound and light. There is good evidence for the ability of birds to transfer the idea of number from one quality to another and also to combine successive and simultaneous recognition of number. This is a big advance on anything previously established, but it still remains a special solution only, i.e. the bird having been trained, say, to open box No. 3 when it sees three spots, box No. 4 when it sees four spots, and box No. 6 when it sees six spots, will not necessarily go and open box No. 5 when it hears 5 blasts of a whistle—provided, of course, that it has not been taught the number 5 before. In other words, there is as yet no evidence that animals have a power of expanding their general concept of number to other numbers of a series, i.e. that they can do arithmetic and have the general power of abstract dealing in numbers.

One of the most significant conclusions coming from this line of work concerns the comparison with human counting abilities. If a human being is shown a number of objects or a group of figures by means of a lantern slide projected on a screen for a brief and exactly determined period of time (tachistoscope)—sufficiently long for them to be seen but too short for counting to take place—it is found that the limit of achievement is of the same order as that shown by birds. Thus, most people would be able to distinguish 4 from 3, 5 from 4, and many 5 from 6 and 6 from 7. Only a very few persons are able to distinguish 7 from 8, provided full precautions are taken that the configuration of the pattern is not such as to give them a cue ; and, so far as is known, no one has the ability to distinguish larger groups in such circumstances. This limitation in the ability to distinguish number, when the circumstances are such that counting in the full sense of the word cannot be done, has now been shown to apply to six or seven different species, including man. For ourselves, the two abilities, namely to grasp numbers simultaneously (differentiating between groups seen side by side) or successively, have in common only the absolute idea of unnamed numbers. The hypothesis suggests itself, therefore, that these two basic pre-linguistic features which may together be described as unnamed thinking may be common to birds, to some mammals, and to man. Köhler points out that very many ideas come to us in wordless form, as they must do to other animals—the essential difference is that we can recount ideas afterwards in words whereas animals, so far as we know, cannot. Man has the ability, which other animals lack, of using abstract symbols. Thus the words 'one', 'two', 'three', 'four', and so on 'stand for' numbers even although the symbols themselves have no numerical qualities ; that is to say, the word 'three' has nothing triplicate about it, nor has the word 'four' any quadruple qualities. The ability to use abstract symbols in this way, and the ability to provide an absolutely general solution to the problem of numerical entities, constitute, as at present seen, the essential difference between the 'pre-linguistic' number sense of birds and other animals and the true counting of man.

W.H.T.

Köhler, O. 1950. The ability of birds to 'count'. Bull. Anim. Behav. no. 9 : 41–45.
Köhler, O. 1956. Thinking without words. Proc. XIV Internat. Congr. Zool., Copenhagen 1953 : 75–88.
Lögler, P. 1959. Versuche zur Frage des 'Zahl'-Vermögens an einem Graupapagei und Vergleichsversuche an Menschen. Z. Tierpsychol. 16 : 179–217. (English summary.)
Thorpe, W. H. 1963. Learning and Instinct in Animals. 2nd ed. London.

COUROL : alternative name for *Leptosomus discolor* (see CUCKOO-ROLLER).

COURSER : substantive name of most species of Cursoriinae ; in the plural, general term for this subfamily of the Old World family Glareolidae (Charadriiformes, suborder Charadrii) ; for the other subfamily; the Glareolinae, see PRATINCOLE. The coursers constitute a small group consisting of one Australian species, the so-called Australian Dotterel *Peltohyas australis* ; 2 Indian species, the Indian Courser *Cursorius coromandelicus* and *Rhinoptilus bitorquatus* (probably now extinct) ; and 6–7 African species, namely, 2–3 *Cursorius* spp., 3 *Rhinoptilus* spp., and the so-called Egyptian Plover *Pluvianus aegyptius*.

All are plover-like birds, as suggested by the common names quoted, the biggest no bigger in body than a Redshank *Tringa totanus*, with more or less elongated legs, pointed bills, and no hind toe. The sexes are alike. Except for the Egyptian Plover, all the species are predominantly sandy-coloured or brown, have a pectinated middle toe, and live on semi-desert or other almost bare ground or very short grass. Their cries are on the whole rather plover-like. One species, the Bronze-winged Courser *R. chalcopterus*, is largely nocturnal. Without making any nest, they lay eggs that are more or less buff and are heavily blotched or lined—2 or 3 in all species except the Double-banded Courser *R. africanus*, which lays only one.

Temminck's Courser *Cursorius temminckii*.   *C.E.T.K.*

The most familiar species, the Cream-coloured Courser *C. cursor*, extends from the Cape Verde Islands to Persia and northern Kenya (and in the form *C. rufus*, which may be conspecific, perhaps reappears in South West Africa). It is a familiar bird of naked country bordering the Sahara, both north and south, and while lacking well defined migrations has occurred as a vagrant over much of Europe ; when approached in its native deserts it runs a short distance with shoulders hunched and long white legs twinkling, then stops and rears up for a good look. Temminck's Courser *C. temminckii* is a much smaller bird, found in the drier parts of Africa south of the Sahara ; it is capped by a chestnut crown surrounded by white and then black. The Double-banded Courser *R. africanus* has been recorded as laying its single egg on bare ground at the height of the dry season in the lowlands of northern Tanganyika ; throughout the hours of daylight the parent birds alternately stood over—not brooded—the egg, and subsequently the chick, to protect it from the blazing sun.

The Egyptian Plover *Pluvianus aegyptius* differs considerably from the other members of the subfamily. It has the upper parts mainly pure grey and the under parts tawny buff, but there is a striking pattern of very dark green—looking almost black—on the crown and in the form of broad eye-stripes which unite on the back and continue as a median line and also connect with a pectoral band of the same colour ; there is also a black bar on the wing that is conspicuous in flight. The legs are blue and the middle toe is not pectinated. It differs also in habits, having a close attachment to the margins and sandbanks of rivers. Controversy has attended it, some authors reproducing freely the story of Herodotus that it habitually cleans up the interior of the crocodile's mouth (see CROCODILE-BIRD). Its nesting habits are peculiar, for as a rule its eggs are more or less buried in sand. It has, moveover, been reported on good authority that the parent sometimes moistens the sand by regurgitating water over it, and also that the chicks, flattening themselves on the sand when danger approaches, are temporarily and most efficiently buried by the parent (Butler).

See Plate 43 (egg).   R.E.M.

Butler, A. L. 1931. The chicks of the Egyptian Plover. Ibis (13) 1 : 345–347.

COURT: alternatively 'arena' (and various special terms)—see LEK DISPLAY.

COURTSHIP: term used, in the study of bird behaviour, to cover a wide range of activities of which the function seems to lie in attracting a mate, maintaining the pair bond, and in facilitating copulation and parental activities (see PAIR FORMATION ; also COPULATION ; COURTSHIP FEEDING ; DISPLAY ; INCUBATION ; INSTRUMENTAL SOUNDS ; LEK DISPLAY ; PARENTAL CARE ; SINGING ; TERRITORY).

COURTSHIP FEEDING: the feeding of one member of an adult pair by the other. In sexually dimorphic species it is normally the male that feeds the female, but where the behaviour and plumage of the sexes is similar, the reverse sometimes occurs ; further, in species where the female takes the active role in courtship, she may regularly feed the male.

Courtship feeding is usually most frequent before or during the period of copulation and egg-laying, but often it continues during incubation. During incubation the actual food exchanged may be important as such, but usually it is of little consequence—many cases of a female begging from a male although already carrying food herself have been recorded. Indeed, in many species courtship feeding is much more common before than during incubation ; and in many others elaborate ceremonials of billing, scissoring, and the like, in which no food is passed, occur as well as, or instead of, courtship feeding itself.

The movements used by each species in courtship feeding are usually closely similar to those of juvenile begging and feeding the young. Thus in cardueline finches the male regurgitates the food, whereas in tits (Paridae) it is passed directly from his bill. Often the posture adopted by the female resembles not only the begging of the young, but also the female copulatory posture and the submissive posture. The movements may, however, become further ritualised, and elaborate ceremonials, such as the fish-flight in terns (Sterninae), may be incorporated (see RITUALISATION). Billing and scissoring movements may be a further development of courtship feeding, or they may be independently derived from movements used in feeding the young or in aggression.

Courtship feeding does not, in general, occur in birds that do not form pairs, and presumably it has a survival value relating to the pair bond. Its precise function varies between species. In some it is closely related to copulation, the male feeding the female while copulating, or just before or afterwards. In others it occurs at the same stage in the cycle as copulation, but not in immediate temporal relation with it (see also COPULATION). Here it may have a function in reducing aggression between the partners, perhaps promoting habituation to the proximity of the mate and thus facilitating sexual and, later, parental behaviour (see PAIR FORMATION) ; in general it is commoner in sexually monomorphic species (i.e. where both sexes carry the releasers for aggressive behaviour). However, even when the peaks of courtship feeding and copulation occur at the same stage in the reproductive cycle, courtship feeding usually starts well before and lasts after copulation. In other species there seems to be no

relation with copulation except that both occur in the breeding season ; in such cases little can be said about the functions of courtship feeding except that it presumably plays a general role in promoting and maintaining the pair bond.

See Plate 28b (phot.).   R.A.H.

Lack, D. 1940. Courtship feeding in birds. Auk 57 : 169–178.

COVERT: also ' tectrix', term for any of the contour feathers that overlie, dorsally or ventrally, the bases of the remiges and rectrices ; applied also to the auriculars (ear coverts), concealing the external auditory meatus. There are upper and under tail coverts, and upper and under wing coverts. In the wing, the upper coverts in particular form several distinct rows, designated (from distal to proximal) as primary, greater, median, and lesser coverts (see WING).

COVEY: see ASSEMBLY, NOUN OF

COWBIRD: substantive name of species in several genera (*Molothrus*, etc.) of Icteridae (see ORIOLE (2)). See Plate 46a (phot.).

CRAB-PLOVER: *Dromas ardeola*, sole member of the Dromadidae (Charadriiformes, suborder Charadrii). It is a very distinctive bird, about 15 inches long, with the plumage white in both sexes except that the primaries and mantle are black. The black bill is moderately long, straight, laterally compressed, and remarkably stout. The legs are long, the wings long and pointed ; the tail is short.

Crab-plover *Dromas ardeola*, sole species.   C.E.T.K.

The Crab-plover is a coastal species, frequenting open shores and reefs ; it feeds on crustaceans, notably crabs, and on molluscs. The birds are noisy, with raucous cries, and far from shy ; they are gregarious and sometimes found in enormous flocks; they have been seen perched on the backs of hippopotamus basking in sea-water.

Nesting is in colonies, the single egg being laid at the end of a tunnel excavated in the sand; this is often on level ground, dipping at first and then rising to an unlined terminal chamber, and may be 4–5 feet long or more. The egg is white (unique for the Charadrii) and very large in proportion to the bird. The downy chick is nidicolous.

The species is found on the northern and western coasts of the Indian Ocean, from the Persian Gulf to the Andaman Islands on the one hand and to the Gulf of Aden (scarce in the southern Red Sea) and south to Natal and Madagascar on the other. In the southern parts of this range it is only a non-breeding visitor. R.M.

CRACIDAE: see under GALLIFORMES; the family comprises the curassows, guans, and chachalacas (see under CURASSOW).

CRACOIDEA: see under GALLIFORMES

CRACTICIDAE: a family of the Passeriformes, suborder Oscines (see MAGPIE (2)).

CRAKE: primary or alternative substantive name of many species of Rallidae (see RAIL).

CRANE: substantive name of the species of Gruidae (Gruiformes, suborder Grues); in the plural, general term for the family. Cranes are large, long-necked and long-legged birds of powerful flight. The largest species stand 5 feet high and have a wing-span of $7\frac{1}{2}$ feet. The straight bill varies in size and shows lateral grooves on each side of the lower mandible. The nostrils are about half way down the upper mandible in nasal grooves. The tail is short. The tibiae are partly bare; the toes are strong and connected at the base by a membrane; the hind toe is elevated. The characteristic call is loud and trumpet-like, in some species more whistling, in others a rather plaintive sound (*Balearica*). The sonorous voice is connected with the remarkable shape of the trachea. In most species the windpipe is convoluted in the males (not always in the females), entering behind the clavicles into a hollow space in the keel of the sternum. In *Balearica*, however, the windpipe is nearly straight.

The plumage varies from white to slate-grey with black primaries; in some species the head is partly bare, with a reddish tinge. The sexes are alike in plumage or nearly so, the males being slightly larger. Young birds have the feathers brownish tipped. The flight feathers are moulted simultaneously, except in *Anthropoides* and *Balearica*. The innermost secondaries are incoherent and much elongated, forming a drooping cover over the hind part of the body. Cranes are terrestrial in habit, prefer plains or marshy ground, and like wild and remote country for breeding; the decrease of such areas has for many species involved a decline in numbers. The food consists of vegetable matter and small animals such as insects, mice, and small birds.

Demoiselle Crane
Anthropoides virgo. C.E.T.K.

$\frac{1}{9}$

Cranes probably pair for life. A well-known ceremonial behaviour is the dance, which is performed by some species at all seasons of the year; the birds walk with quick steps and outstretched wings, bowing their heads, jumping in the air and suddenly stopping in an erect attitude. Some species build a nest, others deposit their eggs in a hollow in bare ground. The number of eggs is normally 2, occasionally 1 or 3. The colour varies from light blue, very pale green, olive brown to buffish, plain or more generally speckled with reddish or purplish spots and blotches. The downy young are cared for by both sexes and run soon after hatching. All northern species are migratory. Although not gregarious during the breeding season, some species gather in large flocks after it, covering great distances in company during migration; they then fly with outstretched necks in 'V' formation or in line, making themselves conspicuous by their resonant calls.

There are 14–15 species, arranged in 5 genera and

sometimes in 2 subfamilies, Gruinae and Baleari-cinae, the latter with only one genus. Cranes are distributed over all the continents, except South America, but are absent from Madagascar, the Indo-Malayan area, New Zealand, and Polynesia. The typical genus consists of 10 species, of which 2 are very near extinction, and has its headquarters in eastern Asia. The Common Crane *Grus grus* is slate-grey with a red patch on the hind crown and white on the sides of the head and neck ; it breeds from north-eastern Europe to eastern Asia and winters in parts of northern Africa and southern Asia—not crossing the western Sahara, but reaching the tropics in the Sudan.

The related Black-necked Crane *G. nigricollis* is an inhabitant of high central Asia. In North America and eastern Siberia the Sandhill Crane *G. canadensis* is found ; it is slightly smaller than the Common Crane, and distinguished by a slate-grey neck and a bare red patch from the base of the bill to the middle of the crown. Formerly abundant, the Sandhill Crane is now greatly reduced in numbers ; the northern populations migrate to the southern United States and Mexico, while in Florida a resident population is found. The Hooded Crane *G. monacha*, with the neck and head white except for a black and red bare patch, is a species belonging to eastern Asia ; formerly it was a common winter visitor to Japan, but now only a few hundred birds are known to winter there. Another species that has become alarmingly scarce is the Manchurian Crane *G. japonensis*, a large white bird with black wings, a dark grey face, and a broad streak of the same colour running down-wards at either side of the neck ; the breeding grounds are found in eastern Siberia and in Japan. The American Whooping Crane *G. americana*, white with black wings and with red bare skin around the bill, is at the brink of extermination ; the population has shrunk to such an extent that it is doubtful whether the energetic efforts that are being made to save the species will prove successful (see VANISHING BIRDS ; and Plate 11b (phot.)).

The Siberian White Crane *G. leucogeranus* is known to breed in restricted areas in Siberia ; the western populations migrate to India, and the shores of the Caspian Sea, and the eastern populations winter in China. The White-necked Crane *G. vipio* has its breeding quarters in southern Siberia and is found during the winter in Korea and parts of Japan and China ; it is a slate-grey bird with white head, hindneck, and secondaries. The blue-grey Sarus Crane *G. antigone* is distributed in northern India, and another race is found in Siam and adjoining countries ; the head and upper

neck are bare and red. The grey Australian Crane (or Native Companion) *G. rubicunda* lives in Australia and New Guinea ; the head is bare and green, with the sides of the face and back of the head red. The beautiful Demoiselle Crane *Anthropoides virgo* occurs from the Dobruja in eastern Europe through the greater part of Central Asia and winters in north-eastern Africa, India, and China ; it is a smaller species, with the head and neck black, long black lanceolate feathers falling over the breast, and long white plumes behind the ear coverts. The Blue (or Stanley) Crane *Tetrapteryx paradisea* is restricted to South Africa and is still common there, preferring the open plateaux ; it is pearl-grey with long almost black innermost secondaries extending far beyond the tail. Another species occurring in eastern and southern Africa is the Wattled Crane *Bugeranus carunculatus*, a large bird, dark slate with a white neck and two lappets hanging from the head ; it is not common and frequents marshy places.

The Crowned Crane (or Crown-bird) *Balearica pavonina* is widely distributed in Africa from Abyssinia, the Sudan, and Senegal southwards and is notably abundant in Uganda, of which country it is the national emblem ; there are several races, of which *B. p. regulorum* of South Africa (with grey instead of black neck) is treated by some authors as a separate species. The forecrown is covered by velvety black plumes, and there is a distinctive tuft of stiff straw-coloured feathers on the nape ; the bare cheeks and throat are pink and white, and the eye is pearl-coloured ; the general plumage is dark, with the bill and legs black. The South African form, once common, is becoming scarcer owing to human persecution and the drainage of swampy ground. See Plate 30 (colour).   †G.C.A.J.

CRANIAL : pertaining to the skull.

CRANIATA : alternative name of the Subphylum Vertebrata (see ANIMAL KINGDOM).

CRÈCHE : an assemblage pooling the still dependent young of several pairs of a species, e.g. Eider *Somateria mollissima*, Emperor Penguin *Aptenodytes forsteri*, Greater Flamingo *Phoenicopterus ruber*. The term seems particularly apt in those cases where only a few adult birds are usually present, although these may not have any special role as guardians.

See Plate 38b (phot.).

CREEPER : an element in substantive names used (some also as general terms) in several families of the Passeriformes ; although used alone by American ornithologists for *Certhia*, it is more often written as part of a compound word—for Certhiidae see TREECREEPER (1) ; for Climacteridae see TREECREEPER (2) ; for Sittidae (Wallcreeper, etc.) see under NUTHATCH ; for Coerebinae see HONEYCREEPER (1) ; for Drepanididae see HONEYCREEPER (2) ; for Timaliinae (bushcreeper) see BABBLER ; for Dendrocolaptidae see WOODCREEPER ; for Formicariidae (antcreeper) see ANTBIRD ; for Furnariidae (earthcreeper, streamcreeper) see OVENBIRD (1). The word is, however, used by itself in the Australasian Region as the substantive name of *Finschia* spp. (for subfamily see FLYCATCHER (1)).

CREPUSCULAR HABITS: see under NOCTURNAL HABITS

CRIMSON-WING: substantive name of *Cryptospiza* spp. (see WEAVER-FINCH).

CRISSUM: the area round the vent, with the under tail coverts (see TAIL ; TOPOGRAPHY).

CROCODILE-BIRD: name designating an African bird (or birds) said by Herodotus and Pliny to pick food (leeches, débris) from the gums of basking crocodiles, even entering the open mouth ; usually identified with either the so-called Egyptian Plover *Pluvianus aegyptius* (see under COURSER), or the Spur-winged Plover *Vanellus* ('*Hoplopterus*') *spinosus* (see PLOVER), and perhaps applicable to both these species and to some others. The subject is controversial, because many observers who have had ample opportunities have never seen the birds feed from, still less enter, the crocodile's mouth and are accordingly sceptical. The number of positive modern records of any reliability is indeed so small that one may doubt whether this particular action of entering the mouth is frequent. It is not in dispute, however, that both the species named above commonly associate with basking crocodiles and feed close to them or on their ectoparasites (tsetse flies, etc.). This latter habit is also shown by the Common Sandpiper *Actitis hypoleucos* while in Africa during the northern winter—and has likewise been recorded from Borneo (see SANDPIPER). Many other species fearlessly keep company with basking crocodiles, even sleeping beside them or standing on them. The Water Dikkop *Burhinus vermiculatus* goes further in apparently having a nesting association with the crocodile, laying its eggs at the same time (when the river is low) and often incubating them within a few feet of the brooding reptile (see THICKKNEE).

As in other circumstances the crocodile regularly preys on waterfowl, this mutual tolerance is remarkable ; one recalls the different reactions of antelopes and the like to lions when the latter are respectively hunting and resting. It seems likely that the birds are of more value to the crocodile as sentinels, giving early warning of the approach of danger, than in removing parasites. To some of the birds the crocodile's parasites are food, and to the nesting Water Dikkop its proximity may provide some protection against egg-eating predators. With other species of birds the relationship seems to be casual. The evidence has recently been summarised by Cott.

Cott, H. B. 1961. Scientific results of an inquiry into the ecology and economic status of the Nile Crocodile (*Crocodilus niloticus*) in Uganda and Northern Rhodesia. Trans. Zool. Soc. Lond. 29 : 211–350.
Meinertzhagen, R. 1959. Pirates and Predators. Edinburgh and London.

CROMBEC: substantive name of *Sylvietta* spp. (Africa)—for subfamily see WARBLER (1).

CRONISM : see KRONISMUS

CROP: also called 'ingluvies' (see ALIMENTARY SYSTEM ; MILK, PIGEON).

CROSS: see HYBRID

CROSSBILL: substantive name of *Loxia* spp. (see FINCH). See Plate 29 (colour).

CROTOPHAGINAE: see CUCKOO

CROW (1): substantive name of many species of Corvidae (Passeriformes, suborder Oscines) ; in the plural, general term for the family, although also, in a more restricted sense, for the typical crows *Corvus* spp. Outside the typical genus, the most frequent substantive names are 'jay', and 'magpie' (varied to 'tree-pie' in one genus), while 'nutcracker', 'chough', and 'piapiac' are special names for one or two species in each case. Within *Corvus*, 'raven' is applied to various large species, while 'rook' and 'jackdaw' are special names. As noted elsewhere, the names 'crow' and 'jay' occur as misnomers for unrelated birds, while 'magpie' and 'chough' have other meanings in Australian ornithological usage.

General Characters. The crows, as a family, may represent the furthest stage so far reached in avian evolution ; much in their behaviour suggests a highly developed mentality, and some species have a complex social organisation. This is not to say that they show extreme specialisation ; on the contrary, they are characterised by great adaptability. They are certainly successful, as judged by the large number of species and the almost world-wide distribution.

They are large birds, by the standards of the Passeriformes, and they include the largest members of that order. The bill is stout, fairly long, and often with a small terminal hook. The nostrils are usually round, without an operculum, and shielded by bristles directed forwards. The legs and feet are robust, the tarsi strongly scutellated in front and booted behind. The birds are strong on the wing, and the tail is stiff.

While the typical crows are either wholly black, including bill and legs, or black with some white, grey, or brown, the jays and magpies often have bright colours, especially blues and greens ; further, many of the jays and magpies have very long tails, and some of the jays are crested. The sexes are alike in plumage, or nearly so, and there is no marked seasonal change.

General Behaviour. The birds are strong fliers, bold and aggressive, commonly gregarious. They frequent trees, bushes, cliffs, and buildings, but much feeding may be done on the ground. Many of the species are practically omnivorous, taking both animal and vegetable food. They have definitely predatory tendencies, and some are relentless robbers of the eggs and young of other birds ; carrion is not always despised, and some find their food among the jetsam of the seashore. Insects are taken, especially by the smaller species, and vegetable diet includes such items as acorns and the seeds of pine-cones, and sometimes soft fruits. The birds are among those that hold food with the foot while tearing it with the bill. Species of jays, magpies, and nutcrackers living in high latitudes or altitudes have the habit of hiding excess food for use in time of scarcity (see FEEDING HABITS).

The calls are loud, and for the most part harsh and discordant. Nevertheless, some species have a not unmelodious subsong, or 'whisper-song', uttered by both sexes and audible only at very short range (see SINGING). Some show considerable powers of mimicry, at least in captivity (see MIMICRY, VOCAL).

Reproduction. Breeding is often colonial, but not necessarily so even in species that are markedly gregarious at other times. In at least some species pairing is for life. Courtship feeding is common, and the male continues to feed the female while she is sitting on the nest. Both sexes take part in building the nest. Only the female incubates the eggs or broods the young, but the male helps to feed the latter and sometimes performs most of that task ; food is brought in the throat. Help in feeding the young, and even in nest-building or in feeding the sitting female, is often given by non-breeding 'helpers', presumably immature.

The nest tends to be a bulky structure of coarse twigs, variously lined ; it is usually open, but in some species roofed over. It is placed in a tree or bush, or on a cliff or building. The eggs are 2–4 in some tropical jays, but in other species may number up to 9 or more. The colour ranges from buff or cream to green or greenish-blue, and there is usually heavy blotching or spotting with brown or other colours. Incubation periods are recorded as 16–21 days. The young are hatched blind, helpless, and either naked or with sparse down. They may be fledged in 20 days, but in some of the larger species 5–6 weeks may be spent in the nest.

Social Organisation. Species of Corvidae that breed colonially, as well as being gregarious at other times, often show a highly developed social organisation. This is familiar, in Europe, in the case of the Rook *Corvus frugilegus*, frequently breeding near human habitations (' the black republic in his elms '), and anthropomorphic misinterpretations find some popular credence. In the Jackdaw *C. monedula* it was the subject of a classical study by Lorenz ; two points may be briefly mentioned. Whereas crows of non-social species will tolerate only their mates in the nesting territory, Jackdaws do not resent the presence of ' the well-known co-citizens of the colony ' ; on the other hand, the reaction to the intrusion of strange members of the species is vigorously hostile and unanimously concerted. (This contrasts with the state of affairs more commonly found in colonial birds, where exiguous individual territories are defended by the pair against the nearest neighbours as well as against any outsiders (see TERRITORY).) Secondly, although a ' peck order ' definitely exists within a Jackdaw community, the latter will rally as a whole to stop the fight if a hard-pressed subordinate bird retreats to its nest and utters a peculiar cry. (In a more intensely territorial species, the weaker bird would gain an advantage from the mere fact of being back on its own ground—see also DOMINANCE (2).) There are various other ways in which help appears to be given to a member of a corvid community by its fellows, and this quite apart from any pair bond or parental link.

Distribution. The family is almost cosmopolitan, but is most abundantly represented in temperate parts of the Northern Hemisphere. It is, however, unrepresented in· New Zealand and in most of the archipelagos of the Pacific Ocean ; in South America the only representatives are jays.

The typical crows have a distribution virtually as wide as that of the family, apart from their absence from South America ; they are the only representatives of the family in Africa south of the Equator, in the Malagasy Region, and in Australasia and Oceania. Of the genera of jays, 8 (on the classification followed here) belong purely to the New World, 1 is Holarctic, 1 Palaearctic, and 1 (primitive and monotypic) Oriental. Of the genera of magpies, 6 (including 1 primitive and monotypic, another monotypic) are Oriental, 1 (monotypic) is Palaearctic, and 1 Holarctic. The ground-jays and the choughs are Palaearctic (with an outlying colony of choughs in Ethiopia), the nutcrackers Holarctic. Two aberrant monotypic genera, not closely related to each other, are found in northern tropical Africa.

Most members of the family are sedentary, but some may show weather movements, while a few perform regular migrations within the North Temperate Zone (see MIGRATION).

Taxonomy. The Corvidae probably have their nearest relatives in the birds-of-paradise (Paradiseaidae) and other Australasian families of crow-like birds, and possibly also the Old World orioles (Oriolidae) and the drongos (Dicruridae). Within the family, the taxonomy and nomenclature followed here is that of Blake & Vaurie (1962). On that basis there are 26 genera and 103 species, in some cases with numerous subspecific forms. Some authors have attempted a grouping in 2 subfamilies, the jays and magpies (Garrulinae) on the one hand and the true crows (Corvinae) on the other ; but no such division can be sharply drawn. In the systematic survey below, the common names used as subheadings are intended merely for convenience of presentation ; they carry no taxonomic implications, although the arrangement in fact (with one trivial exception) does no violence to the sequence of genera used by the authority followed.

Primitive Forms. Two monotypic genera are placed, respectively, first and second in the arrangement here followed, being regarded as primitive forms. The Shrike-jay (or Crested Jay) *Platylophus galericulatus* is a bold, noisy bird of the forests of Malaysia and Indonesia—small for this family (10 in.), with brownish plumage except for a white crescent on each side of the neck, and with a stiff crest projecting backwards from the occiput. The White-winged (or Black-crested) Magpie *Platysmurus leucopterus*, found in the same area, is a larger species (14 inches), with black plumage except for a white streak revealed when the wing is spread, and with a small ragged crest on the crown.

American Jays. Nearly 30 species of jays, with many geographical races, are assigned to genera peculiar to the New World—8 such genera, including 3 monotypic, in the classification here followed. The Piñon Jay *Gymnorhinus cyanocephala*, sole member of its genus, has a breeding distribution restricted to montane areas in the western United States. It is a stumpy bird with mainly blue-grey plumage, and is gregarious in its habits.

The Blue Jay *Cyanocitta cristata* is a familiar North American bird, distributed from southern Canada to the Gulf of Mexico. Its upper parts are bright blue, with white patches on wings, and tail and it has a pointed crest. Its sole congener, Steller's Jay *C. stelleri*, ranges from Alaska to Nicaragua, mainly on the western side of the continent. The Scrub (or Florida) Jay *Aphelocoma coerulescens*, ranging from the northwestern United States to Florida and Mexico, is predominantly deep blue and brownish above, with no white on the tail and no crest. It has two congeners, in Middle America.

The species of *Cyanolyca* (7), *Cissilopha* (3), and *Cyanocorax* (10) are all inhabitants of tropical America. The last mentioned includes the Green Jay *C. yncas*, found from Texas to Peru ; it is a small, long-tailed species, mainly green above, with a blue crest and bright yellow lateral rectrices and under parts.

The remaining two genera are both found in Middle America ; and they are both monotypic, although the Brown Jay *Psilorhinus morio* has a morph (with a white-tipped tail) that has in the past been named as a separate species ('*mexicanus*'). This species is large for a jay (17 inches), but has no bright coloration and no crest. It has a remarkable 'furcular sac' which is a diverticulum of the clavicular air sac ; its sudden inflation (or perhaps deflation) produces a snapping sound or 'hiccup' (Sutton & Gilbert 1942). The White-throated Magpie-jay *Calocitta formosa* is also a large species, with considerable resemblance to members of the genus *Cyanocorax*. The tail is very long and graduated ; some of the feathers on the crown are elongated to form a conspicuous crest. The life histories of both these birds have been closely studied by Skutch.

Typical Jays. The Jay *Garrulus glandarius* is the original bearer of the common name. It is a medium-sized crow with pinkish-brown body plumage, white rump and wing-patch, black tail, beautiful blue and black barred wing coverts, and a black-and-white erectile crest. It is essentially a woodland bird, feeding on acorns during much of the year but also taking the eggs and young of other birds in the breeding season ; in winter and spring the adults subsist largely on acorns previously hidden. It is a heavy flier, and its progression on the ground is by long hops. Its many races are widely distributed in the Palaearctic Region, except the most northern parts and central Asia. It has two congeners, generally similar birds, the Lanceolated Jay *G. lanceolatus* in the Himalaya and the Purple Jay *G. lidthi* in the Ryukyu Islands.

The other genus is Holarctic, but there seems to be little doubt that it is of Old World origin. The Siberian Jay *Perisoreus* ('*Cractes*') *infaustus* is slightly smaller than *Garrulus glandarius* and of much less colourful plumage—mainly brown and grey, but bright rufous on the wing, rump, and sides of tail. It is a Palaearctic species with a more northern range than *Garrulus*. It is replaced in Szechwan by *P. internigrans*. In northern America there is the similar Grey (or Canada) Jay *P. canadensis*, with a white forehead and black nape and lacking the reddish feathers.

See Plates 40b (phot.) and 42 (colour).

Magpies. The name 'magpie' has come to be applied to a number of species that are not pied at all but have some general resemblance to *Pica*, usually including the long tail. Species of two genera of brightly coloured magpies inhabit southeastern Asia from India to China and to the Great Sunda Islands ; examples must suffice. The Yellow-billed Blue Magpie *Urocissa flavirostris* has the characters indicated by its name, and also an exceedingly long tail— some 18 inches on a body scarcely half that length ; it is an inhabitant of the wooded slopes of the Himalaya. It has four congeners. The Green Magpie *Cissa* (not '*Kitta*') *chinensis*, widespread in southeastern Asia, is mainly light green, with white-spotted brown primaries and with the bill, feet (including claws), and irides red ; it has whistling calls and feeds largely on bees and other insects. Its sole congener is the similarly coloured Short-tailed Green Magpie *C. thalassina*. (See Plate 17 (colour).)

In a monotypic genus, the Azure-winged Magpie *Cyanopica cyanus* is decidedly smaller than *Pica* spp. but has the same general shape, with the long, graduated tail. The plumage is largely brownish-grey, with a deep black cap descending to the nape and with light blue wings and tail. The species is remarkable for its discontinuous distribution ; it is found only at the extremes of the Palaearctic Region, in the Iberian Peninsula in the west and in northern China, Mongolia, and Japan in the east. The Iberian population is subspecifically distinct from the group of races in the Far East, but the history of the distribution of the species as a whole is not known.

Species of 3 genera of 'tree-pies' and racquet-tailed magpies inhabit southeastern Asia, from India to southern China and as far as Bali—*Dendrocitta* (4 spp.), *Crypsirina* (2 spp.), and *Temnurus* (monotypic). They have plumage of less bright colours than the other group from this area, mentioned above, and indeed *C. temia* and *T. temnurus* have black plumage. There is a tendency for the rectrices to increase in width distally, and in *Crypsirina* the two central feathers end in definite 'racquets'. The birds are primarily arboreal. The Malaysian Treepie *D. occipitalis*, of the mountains of Borneo and Sumatra, has pale brownish plumage, with white on the back of the head, black

on the wings, and a long, mainly grey, tail ; it feeds largely on berries, but also on seeds and insects.

The typical Magpie *Pica pica* is 18 inches in length, counting the long graduated tail, and has a conspicuous pied plumage ; the scapulars and under parts are white, the rest black with green, blue, and purple glosses. It has strong predatory tendencies, but takes much of its food—animal and vegetable— on the ground. It builds a large domed nest of sticks, with a lining of hardened mud, in dense bushes or tall trees. It is widely distributed in the Palaearctic Region, except in the treeless north, and in the western half of North America. In the latter it is known as the Black-billed Magpie to distinguish it from the Yellow-billed Magpie *P. nuttalli* of California, otherwise similar and sometimes considered to be conspecific.

Aberrant Forms. There are two monotypic genera with affinities so obscure that their inclusion in the family at all has sometimes been doubted. They are quite unlike each other and are taken together here merely for convenience (in the arrangement otherwise followed, *Ptilostomus* is placed immediately after *Pyrrhocorax*). It was only in 1938 that *Zavattariornis stresemanni*, sometimes called Stresemann's Bush-crow, was first described (Moltoni). It is confined to southern Ethiopia, where it inhabits the thorn bush and builds large domed nests. It is a relatively small crow (about 12 inches), mostly grey above, with blue-black wings and tail, and white below ; a patch of bare skin round the eye is said to be blue in life.

The Piapiac *Ptilostomus afer* is a familiar bird in West Africa and eastwards to Uganda. It is smaller in body than a magpie *Pica* sp., and similarly has a long graduated tail ; the legs and feet are notably strong. The plumage is glossy black, tinged with brown on wings and tail ; the bill is reddish except at the tip while the bird is immature, but is wholly black in the adult. The birds are usually to be seen in small flocks, on the ground (feeding largely on insects) or in palm trees. They show slight fear of man and are common about villages, often associating with sheep and goats, at times perching on their backs (as on those of large wild mammals, including elephants, in the limited parts of the range where such are common).

Ground Jays. The group of ground or running jays comprises 4 *Podoces* spp. and *Pseudopodoces humilis*. They live on the semi-arid plateaus of central Asia and are highly specialised members of the family. As the name implies, they are largely terrestrial and tend to run rather than take to the air. They are relatively small birds, sandy-coloured except that the rather short wings and tail are dark ; the legs are long in proportion. *Pseudopodoces* is the smallest of the group and looks more like one of the larks (Alaudidae) than a crow. It also departs from the family norm by nesting in crevices in walls or in rodent holes, and in having white eggs. The species of *Podoces* usually build nests in bushes, and they have spotted eggs.

Nutcrackers. The Nutcracker *Nucifraga caryocatactes*, with thick-billed and slender-billed races, is an inhabitant of coniferous forests in high latitudes and altitudes of the Palaearctic Region. It is a small crow with chocolate-brown plumage boldly speckled with white. It feeds largely on the seeds of *Pinus cembra*, but also on nuts, berries, and insects. The habit of storing food is particularly well developed. Clark's Nutcracker *N. columbianus* inhabits corresponding country in western North America and has similar habits ; it differs in appearance in having the plumage largely grey, with black-and-white wings and tail. (See Plate 14c (phot.).)

Choughs. The two species of *Pyrrhocorax* are birds of medium size for this family, with glossy black plumage and slender decurved bills ; the bill and the legs are brightly coloured in the adult. They are gregarious birds of strong and often acrobatic flight, dwelling on cliffs, and uttering whistling cries. The Chough *P. pyrrhocorax* (red bill and legs) still exists precariously on the western coasts of the British Isles ; it is almost absent from the Alps, but otherwise has a distribution roughly similar to that of the Alpine Chough *P. graculus* (shorter yellow bill, red legs). Both species inhabit the mountain areas from the Iberian Peninsula and the Atlas eastwards to central Asia and China, but the Alpine Chough is found at higher altitudes and does not use maritime cliffs. Alpine Choughs readily become tame in the vicinity of mountain huts where they obtain food ; one of the Mount Everest expeditions recorded them as in attendance at a camp about 27 000 feet above sea level.

Typical Crows. It is generally agreed that these are the most advanced members of the family ; they have in fact been described as ' in many ways the most adaptable and highly evolved of all birds ' (Mayr & Amadon 1951). Evidence of their success is that, as already mentioned, they are as widely distributed throughout the world as the family, except that they are absent from South America.

They are nearly all large birds, none really small, and some are very large for passerines. The plumage is often entirely black, and with black bill and legs as well, but the feathers may show a metallic gloss, from purple to blue in tint. Some species have parts of the plumage brownish or grey, even white, but bright pigments are absent. They tend to be omnivorous and in part predacious. When feeding on the ground they walk, but they roost and nest on trees and cliffs, often in very inaccessible places. They are strong fliers, often indulging in aerobatics. They are cunning and wary, and often highly gregarious. Their calls are loud and commonly harsh.

Meinertzhagen (1926) placed all the typical crows in the genus *Corvus*, and this course has been followed by Amadon and by Blake & Vaurie, among others ; such names as ' *Coloeus* ', ' *Corvultur* ', and ' *Rhinocorax* ' may therefore be relegated to the synonymy. Affinities within the genus are difficult to determine, and for the purpose of the present summary a geographical arrangement (ignoring slight overlaps of the boundaries of Regions) is convenient.

Palaearctic. The Rook *Corvus frugilegus* is a rather distinctive representative, with the white bare skin of the face (in the adult), the relatively bland ' caw ', and the highly social behaviour, including colonial nesting ; the tall trees in which its ' rookeries ' are built are often near human habitations. Similar in size is the Carrion (and Hooded) Crow *C. corone*, of harsher voice, more predacious habits, and less gregarious behaviour in the breeding season. It is at present usual to regard the all-black Carrion Crow and the partly brownish-grey Hooded Crow as conspecific—*C.c. corone* and 1 other race ; *C.c. cornix* and 3 other races—because they replace each other geographically and interbreed freely where their ranges meet ; but the intermediates are presumably selected against, seeing that the main populations apparently remain pure (see HYBRIDISATION, ZONE OF SECONDARY ; SPECIATION ; SPECIES). The Hooded Crow is a notable migrant, in huge daytime flocks, in northern Europe.

Smaller, and indeed small for the family, is the Jackdaw *C. monedula*, with grey nape and a preference for cliffs and buildings ; larger, and indeed the largest passerine species (25 inches long), is the Raven *C. corax*, a fierce, crafty bird now largely restricted to remote mountain areas but with a wide Holarctic range (extending also to Central America).

In the more easterly parts of the Palaearctic Region the Jackdaw is replaced by *C. dauuricus*, sometimes called the Daurian Jackdaw, and there are two other members of the genus—the Jungle Crow *C. macrorhynchos* (also widespread in the Oriental Region) and the Collared Crow *C. torquatus*.

Nearctic (and Neotropical). In North America, in addition to the Raven *C. corax*, there is the widespread Common Crow *C. brachyrhynchos*, not unlike the Carrion Crow. Of more restricted distribution are the White-necked Raven *C. cryptoleucus*, the Northwestern Crow *C. caurinus*, and the Fish Crow

C. ossifragus ; the last is a shore-feeder of the Atlantic and Gulf coasts and some of the major river systems. Except that *C. corax* ranges as far south as Nicaragua, the only Neotropical members of the genus are four insular species, said to be largely frugivorous, in the Greater Antilles. (See Plate 12b (phot.).)

Ethiopian (and Malagasy). The Pied Crow *C. albus* is a familiar bird throughout most of tropical and southern Africa, except in rain-forest and desert areas; and it is the only member of the family found in Madagascar. It is a large species, in which the glossy black plumage is relieved by white across the base of the hindneck and on the chest and upper belly. Also widespread, in eastern and southern Africa, is the Black Crow (or Cape Rook) *C. capensis*, which builds a large cylindrical nest primarily consisting of a basket-work of dead twigs ; this is open at top and bottom, and the latter is filled in by lining material resting on the branch supporting the structure (Skead).

The Brown-necked Raven *C. ruficollis*, of northern and northeastern Africa (also southeastern Asia), is sometimes treated as conspecific with *C. corax*. There are also the African White-necked Raven *C. albicollis* in the east and south, the Thick-billed Raven *C. crassirostris* in the northeast, and the Fantailed Raven *C. rhipidurus* in northeastern Africa and also in the Near East.

Oriental. The common crows of southern Asia are the widely distributed (also eastern Palaearctic) Jungle Crow *C. macrorhynchos*, the House Crow *C. splendens* of India and adjacent countries, and the Slender-billed Crow *C. enca* distributed from Malaya to the Philippines. Two other species are found in the Celebes and on the island of Flores, respectively.

Australasian (and Oceanic). Australia has the Australian Raven *C. coronoides*, the Australian Crow *C. orru*, and the Little Crow *C. bennetti*. Two other species are found in the New Guinea area. Four species are peculiar, respectively, to the Moluccas, to the Solomon Islands, to New Caledonia and the Loyalty Islands, and to the Mariana Islands. Most isolated of all is the Hawaiian Crow *C. tropicus*, inhabiting one of the islands of Hawaii. There are no representatives in New Zealand or in any of the archipelagos of the Pacific Ocean not mentioned above. A.L.T.

Amadon, D. 1944. The genera of the Corvidae and their relationships. Amer. Mus. Novit. no. 1251 : 1–21.
Amadon, D. 1944. A preliminary life history study of the Florida Jay *Cyanocitta c. coerulescens*. Amer. Mus. Novit. no. 1252 : 1–22.
Bent, A. C. 1946. Life histories of the North American jays, crows, and titmice. Bull. U.S. Natl. Mus. 191 : 1–495.
Blake, E. R. & Vaurie, C. 1962. Family Corvidae. *In* Mayr, E. & Greenway, J. C., Jr. (eds.). Check-list of Birds of the World vol. 15. Cambridge, Mass.
Goodwin, D. 1952. A comparative study of the voice and some aspects of the behaviour in two old-world jays. Behav. 4 : 293–316.
Hardy, J. W. 1961. Studies in behaviour and phylogeny of certain new-world jays (Garrulinae). Univ. Kansas Sci. Bull. 42 (2) : 13–149.
Kramer, G. 1941. Beobachtungen über das Verhalten der Aaskrähe (*Corvus corone*) zu Freund und Feind. J. Orn. Festschr. O. Heinroth : 105–131.
Linsdale, J. M. 1937. The natural history of magpies. Pacific Coast Avifauna no. 25. Berkeley, Cal.
Lorenz, K. 1935. Der Kumpan in der Umwelt des Vogels. J. Orn. 83 : 10–213, 289–413 ; and The companion in the bird's world. Auk 1937 : 245–272. (Jackdaws.)
Skead, C. J. 1952. A study of the Black Crow *Corvus capensis*. Ibis 94 : 434–451.
Skutch, A. F. 1960. Life histories of Central American birds II. (Pacific Coast Avifauna no. 34.) Los Angeles.
Strauss, E. 1939. Vergleichende Beobachtungen über Verhaltensweisen von Rabenvögeln. Z. Tierpsychol. 2 : 145–172.
Yeates, G. K. 1934. The Life of the Rook. London.
And regional works.

CROW (2): name misapplied to a variety of birds that are not members of the Corvidae. Thus, ' Bald Crow ' is sometimes used for the two species of *Picathartes* (see under BABBLER) ; ' John Crow ' (also ' Carrion Crow ') is a popular misnomer in America for species of Cathartidae (see VULTURE (2)), and ' Rain Crow ' for the Great Lizard Cuckoo *Saurothera merlini* in the West Indies (see CUCKOO) ; ' Piping Crow ' is an alternative substantive name in Australia for *Strepera* spp. (Cracticidae—see MAGPIE (2)), and ' Wattled Crow ' in New Zealand for *Callaeus* spp. (Callaeidae—see WATTLEBIRD (2)). See also FRUITCROW (Cotingidae) ; KING-CROW (Dicruridae) ; PARADISE CROW (Paradisaeidae ; and two items below.

CROWN: see TOPOGRAPHY

CROWN-BIRD: alternative name of the Crowned Crane *Balearica pavonina* (see CRANE).

CROW-PHEASANT: name, also ' Griffin's Pheasant ', applied in India to a species of coucal, *Centropus sinensis* (see CUCKOO).

CROW-SHRIKE: name sometimes applied to *Strepera* spp. (see MAGPIE (2)).

CRURAL: pertaining to the leg, especially the tibiotarsus (see LEG).

CRYPTIC: term applied to coloration or other characters that, by providing concealment or disguise, afford protection against enemies (procryptic) or facilitate capture of prey (anticryptic) ; —see COLORATION, ADAPTIVE ; NATURAL SELECTION. The opposite is PHANERIC.

CRYPTIC SPECIES: alternative term for SIBLING SPECIES.

CRYPTOPTILE: term applied to the hypothetical early representatives of feathers in the remotest ancestry of birds ; sometimes also to the first filaments appearing from the feather papillae in a young bird (see PLUMAGE).

CRYPTURI: see TINAMIFORMES

CUBITAL: obsolescent alternative for 'secondary' in the terminology of wing feathers (see PLUMAGE ; WING).

CUCKOO: substantive name of many members of the Cuculidae (Cuculiformes) ; used without qualification in Britain, with equivalents in other European languages, for *Cuculus canorus* ; in the plural, general term for the family. The name derives from the familiar call of the European species mentioned ; it is also associated in thought with the parasitic breeding habits of this and all other members of the typical subfamily (and a few members of another), but as such habits are not peculiar to cuckoos they are discussed elsewhere (see PARASITISM). It is debatable whether the Cuculidae should be regarded as the sole family in its order, or should be grouped therein with the Musophagidae as in the classification followed in this work (see TURACO). In any event, the family itself is a large and diversified one with a world-wide distribution—about 127 species, grouped in 38 genera constituting 6 subfamilies.

Taking the family as a whole, the cuckoos range in size from that of a House Sparrow *Passer domesticus* to that of a Raven *Corvus corax* ($6\frac{1}{4}$ to $27\frac{1}{2}$ inches long). The shape of the body tends to be somewhat elongated, with a neck of moderate length. The tail may be very long and is at least of medium length ; it is often graduated, and in one species sometimes forked. The wings are from medium to long. The legs, except in ground-living species, are short ; the feet are zygodactyl, with the outer toe reversible. The bill is of moderate length, stout, and slightly decurved—sometimes very heavy. There is often a coloured ring of bare skin round the eye, and conspicuous eyelashes are sometimes present ; a few species are crested. The plumage is rather loose, sometimes wiry. Browns and greys are common colours, but black and various bright hues occur in some species ; the colour may be uniform, or there may be much barring and streaking (especially on the under parts), or the pattern may be strikingly contrasted. Some of the parasitic species show remarkable mimicry of the appearance of birds in unrelated groups, either predatory species alarming

to the potential hosts or the host species itself (see MIMICRY). Usually, but not always, the sexes look alike.

Cuckoos, in the wide sense, are mainly arboreal birds, but a few are terrestrial ; of the latter some scarcely fly, although the flight of many cuckoos is notably strong and some that breed in high latitudes perform long migrations. They are largely insectivorous, but molluscs, small vertebrates, and fruits are also eaten. As a rule, the calls are monotonous repetitions of loud notes ; as in the Cuckoo *Cuculus canorus*, the best-known call may be of the nature of a song, uttered by the male only. Except in one genus, the birds are mainly solitary.

Great Spotted Cuckoo
Clamator glandarius. C.E.T.K.

In the non-parasitic species, both parents incubate the eggs and care for the young. The nest is made of twigs or herbage and is often just a very shallow cup ; but the birds in one genus build domed nests, and in another there is communal nesting. The eggs are of various colours, some plain and others spotted, and the clutch is 2–6. In some parasitic cuckoos, great variation in egg colour is found within the species, and this has a mimetic aspect (see PARASITISM). Whether a species be parasitic or not, the young are nidicolous, and more or less naked at hatching.

In addition to cuckoos named as such, the family includes anis, guiras, roadrunners, ground-cuckoos, couas, coucals, and a few with special names such as 'koel' and 'yellowbill'. The assemblage shows considerable diversity in appearance and manner of life, and it is best discussed further under the headings of the six subfamilies that are recognised. Of these, be it first noted, three are purely Old World, one of them restricted to Madagascar ; one is purely New World and another largely so ; the remaining subfamily is widespread in both hemispheres but nevertheless absent from Europe and from Australia.

Parasitic Cuckoos. The subfamily Cuculinae comprises some 47 species assigned to 16 genera, all of them having the parasitic breeding habits described in another article, although with variations in detail (see PARASITISM). It is restricted to the Old World, but it is therein widely represented, from northern Europe to Polynesia and New Zealand. The genus *Cuculus* alone, with 12 species, is distributed as far as Australia. The Cuckoo *C. canorus* breeds almost throughout the Palaearctic Region, migrating to Africa and southern Asia ; another race breeds in most parts of Africa that are neither desert nor rain-forest. Its congeners include the Black Cuckoo *C. clamosus* of tropical Africa, and the Hawk Cuckoo *C. varius* known in India as the 'Brain-fever Bird' and closely resembling the Shikra *Accipiter badius* in plumage. The Great Spotted Cuckoo *Clamator glandarius*, with a footing in southern Europe, represents a genus of 5 species found in Africa and southern Asia. *Cercococcyx* and *Chrysococcyx*, with 3 and 4 species, are African genera of which the latter is notable for the bright glosses of its members ; the Emerald Cuckoo *Chrysococcyx cupreus* has plumage of brilliant golden-green with bright yellow on the body, and the white-bellied Didric Cuckoo *C. caprius* shows a good deal of coppery red on the upper parts. *Cacomantis* is an Oriental and Australasian genus of 5 species, extending to Polynesia. *Chalcites*, with 8 species, is also Oriental and Australasian ; and the nominate race of the Shining Cuckoo *C. lucidus* breeds in New Zealand and migrates thence as far as the Solomon and Bismarck Islands—perhaps the most remarkable trans-oceanic migration by a land bird.

The remaining genera are monotypic, and half of them are restricted to the Australasian Region ; three may be mentioned. The Long-tailed Cuckoo *Urodynamis taitensis* breeds only in New Zealand and winters chiefly in the Society Islands, Samoa, Tonga, and Fiji. The Koel *Eudynamys scolopacea*, with many races, is widely distributed from India and China to New Guinea and parts of Australia. It is a familiar bird in India, frequenting trees in gardens and named from its repetitive disyllabic call. It is parasitic on the House Crow *Corvus splendens*, and several eggs may be laid in a single nest. The male is all black with a metallic gloss and the female brown with pale spots ; it is noteworthy that the fledglings of both sexes are black, like those of the foster species, and the eggs also resemble those of the host but are rather smaller. Another instance of mimetic adult plumage is found

in the Drongo Cuckoo *Surniculus lugubris* of Asia, which parasitises *Dicrurus* spp. in different areas and resembles a drongo not only in its black plumage but in sometimes having—uniquely in the Cuculidae —a forked tail.

See Plate 5 (colour).

Non-parasitic Cuckoos. The subfamily Phaenicophaeinae is represented in the New World by the genera *Coccyzus*, *Piaya*, and *Saurothera*. Most of the species are tropical, but some in the first genus extend farther north. The Black-billed Cuckoo *Coccyzus erythrophthalmus* and the Yellow-billed Cuckoo *C. americanus* in fact reach southern Canada as breeding birds, and both these migratory species have occurred in Europe as stragglers. They build loose and shallow nests of twigs in trees at no great height, and they lay 2–6 or more plain blue eggs. The lizard cuckoos *Saurothera* spp. are confined to the West Indies.

Africa has only the Yellowbill *Ceuthmochares aereus*, of widespread distribution there (several races) ; it is a bird that creeps about in thick bush but betrays its presence by frequent, although not loud, calling. Tropical Asia has eight genera, of which all but *Rhopodytes*, in which the species have the substantive name 'malkoha', are monotypic ; of that genus, the Small Green-billed Malkoha *R. viridrostris* is a well-known Indian bird. The Sirkeer *Taccocua leschenaultii* is also found in India, and *Phaenicophaeus pyrrocephalus* in the extreme south of India and in Ceylon. The remaining genera belong to the area between Malaya and the Philippines.

Anis and Guiras. The subfamily Crotophaginae is a small one, comprising two genera—one with three species and the other monotypic ; these are confined to the New World and mainly to its tropical portions. The anis are medium-sized non-parasitic cuckoos with almost black plumage, long and nearly square-ended tails, and extremely heavy hooked bills ; the wings are short and the flight is weak. They are remarkable, in this family, for their gregarious habits ; these go so far as the building of communal nests. Such a nest is a bulky structure of sticks in which several females lay their eggs ; these are blue under a white chalky deposit. The nests are placed in trees, but the birds find much of their insect food on the ground and often accompany grazing cattle. The Smooth-billed Ani *Crotophaga ani* is found from Panama to the Argentine and on many of the larger islands of the West Indies ; it has two congeners. The remaining member of the group is the Guira *Guira guira*, restricted to eastern tropical South America.

Roadrunners and Ground-cuckoos. The

subfamily Neomorphinae is strangely distributed in having five genera in the New World and one in south-eastern Asia ; this last, *Carpococcyx*, has a species with races in Borneo and Sumatra and another species in Siam and Indo-China. The subfamily is also remarkable in having three species with parasitic breeding habits like those of the Cuculinae ; these are the Striped Cuckoo *Tapera naevia* in a monotypic genus, the Pheasant-cuckoo *Dromococcyx phasianellus*, and its sole congener the Pavonine Cuckoo *D. pavoninus*. These last two genera of ground-cuckoos, together with *Morococcyx erythropygus* in another monotypic genus and *Neomorphus* (5 spp.), are restricted to the Neotropical Region.

In the southern United States, particularly on the western side, one finds the Greater Roadrunner *Geococcyx californianus*, also known as ' Chaparral Cock '. It is a handsome black and amber bird, 20–24 inches long and of slender build, with a small shaggy crest and a long graduated tail which is often cocked up. It can fly, with its short rounded wings, but is in fact mainly terrestrial in habit ; the legs are long and strong, and there is some general resemblance to a gallinaceous bird. It can run very fast and preys on various ground animals, being able to cope even with a rattlesnake. It shows inquisitiveness in the neighbourhood of camps. The call is described as a descending series of half-a-dozen dove-like notes ; a clacking noise is also made with the mandibles. The sole congener, the Lesser Roadrunner *G. velox*, ranges from Mexico to Central America.

Couas. The subfamily Couinae is restricted to the Malagasy Region and comprises 10 species (one perhaps now extinct) in a single genus. They are relatively little known, but they are non-parasitic in their breeding habits and to some extent gregarious. The Crested Coua *Coua cristata* is a handsome and noisy bird of the forest. Other species are largely terrestrial and found in more open country. In particular, the Running Coua *C. cursor* inhabits the arid brush and calcareous plateau. Rand describes it as usually seen walking about, but running rapidly when alarmed and sometimes interrupting its stride with hops ; it often perches on bushes or low trees and can fly fairly well in a heavy laboured fashion.

Coucals. The subfamily Centropodinae consists of a single genus with about 27 species (many subspecies) distributed from Africa and Madagascar through southern Asia to Australia and the Solomon Islands. They are of medium or large size by the standards of the family, with long graduated tails, short wings, and heavy hooked bills. Coucals are clumsy birds, and some of their movements have a clownish effect. They are poor fliers and spend much of their time on the ground, particularly among herbage. The food consists mainly of insects, especially those of larger size, but some species take small reptiles and rodents—even young birds. The nest is a globular structure of grass with an entrance in the side and is placed near the ground, or at no great height above it, among vegetation. Sometimes there is a short entrance tunnel lined with green leaves, the latter being replaced from time to time. The 3–5 roundish eggs are almost white ; at least in some species, incubation begins with the laying of the first egg, so that hatching is staggered at daily intervals.

The Senegal Coucal *Centropus senegalensis* is a familiar bird of the savanna country of tropical West Africa, all the more because it shows no great shyness of man ; the bubbling series of notes on a descending scale, often heard by night as well as by day, also calls attention to it. It is mainly warm brown above and nearly white below ; but the head and hindneck are almost black, with a greenish gloss. The red eye is noticeable at short range ; the bill is black and the legs are slaty-blue. Another and similar African species, the White-browed (or Hackle-necked) Coucal *C. superciliosus*, has been recorded as flying with one of its young between its thighs, transporting it from an area of danger such as a bush fire (see CARRYING). Other species have darker plumage ; thus *C. sinensis*, commonly known in India as the Crow-pheasant, is a large black bird with chestnut wings. (See Plate 8 (colour).)   A.L.T.

Davis, D. E. 1940. Social nesting habits of the Smooth-billed Ani. Auk 57 : 179–218.

Friedmann, H. 1948. The Parasitic Cuckoos of Africa. Wash. Acad Sci. Monogr. no. 1.

Herrick, F. H. 1910. Life and behaviour of the Cuckoo. J. Exper. Zool. 9 : 169–233. (Comparison between *Cuculus canorus* and *Coccyzus* spp.)

Peters, J. L. 1940. Check-list of Birds of the World vol. 4. Cambridge. Mass.

Rand, A. L. 1936. The habits and distribution of Madagascar birds. Bull. Amer. Mus. Nat. Hist. 72 : 143–499.

Stresemann, E. & V. 1961. Die Handschwingen-Mauser der Kuckucke (Cuculidae). J. Orn. 102 : 317–352.

See also references under PARASITISM.

CUCKOO-FALCON: *Aviceda cuculoides* of tropical Africa and allies, ' falcon ' being a misnomer (see HAWK).

CUCKOO-ROLLER: *Leptosomus discolor*, sole member of the Leptosomatidae (Coraciiformes, suborder Coracii). This monotypic family is restricted to Madagascar and the nearby Comoro

Islands ; the bird is called 'Courol' in some works, and less frequently 'Kirombo'. It is about 17 inches long, with a rather stout bill (broad at the base), rather long ample wings, a moderately long tail, and very short legs. The outer toe is capable of being turned backwards, somewhat recalling that of a cuckoo (Cuculidae sp.). There is a pair of powder-down patches, one patch on each side of the rump ; it is probable that the greyish bloom so characteristic of the plumage is due to this powder-down. The feathers of the lores sweep forward and upward to conceal the base of the bill ; there is also a short crest in both sexes, adding to the apparent size of the large head. The relationships of the Cuckoo-roller are with the Madagascar ground-rollers (Brachypteraciinae) and with the true rollers (Coraciinae), of the family Coraciidae (see GROUND-ROLLER ; ROLLER).

$\frac{1}{4}$

Cuckoo-roller *Leptosomus discolor*, sole species. *C.E.T.K.*

The sexes are quite different in colour. The male has the upper parts, except the hindneck, slaty grey with iridescent green or copper, depending on the incidence of light ; the under parts and the hindneck are ashy grey. The female has the hindneck barred black and rufous and the under parts pale rufous, boldly spotted with black. The young male is like the female.

Forests and brushlands are the home of this conspicuous, noisy bird, where it lives in the tree-tops, slow wing-beats carrying it in bounding graceful flight over the trees. Often the Cuckoo-roller goes in small parties, circling about and frequently giving a loud, whistled 'wheee' repeated at intervals, or a 'wha-ha-ha . . .'. When it gives its call from the top of some stub or branch, the bird leans forward and its throat swells out, the size being accentuated by the long loose throat feathers.

The food, consisting of chameleons and of locusts, caterpillars, and other large insects, is found in the tree-tops. Hairy caterpillars are evidently favoured, for the bird's stomach is often lined with hairs from these insects. Large caterpillars and probably other prey are held in the bill and beaten against the perch to subdue them before they are swallowed.

Little is known about the nesting of this species. The breeding season appears to coincide with the rainy season. The bird performs aerial evolutions above the forest, flying upward on quickly beating wings and plunging downward on set wings, presumably a part of courtship. The eggs are white and are laid in a hole in a tree-trunk. Native reports also credit this bird with nesting in a hole in a bank.   A.L.R.

Dresser, H. E. 1893. Monograph of the Coraciidae. Farnborough. (See pp. 101–108, Pls. 26, 27.)
Rand, A. L. 1936. The distribution and habits of Madagascar birds. Bull. Amer. Mus. Nat. Hist. 72 : 143–499. (See 417–418 ; habits.)

CUCKOO-SHRIKE: substantive name of some species of Campephagidae (Passeriformes, suborder Oscines) ; in the plural, general term for the family. Various other substantive names are applied—usually or alternatively, and without much consistency—to different species, some being compounds including the word 'shrike' ; and in one section of the family the name 'minivet' is used. 'Caterpillar-birds' is sometimes used as a general term for the family. Its members have nothing to do, in terms of near relationship, with either cuckoos (Cuculidae) or shrikes (Laniidae).

The family has a palaeotropical distribution, and it comprises two distinct groups—the rather drab and dull cuckoo-shrikes proper, and the colourful and lively minivets. Of the cuckoo-shrikes proper, some are known as 'greybirds', 'trillers', 'caterpillar-shrikes', 'flycatcher-shrikes', 'wood-shrikes' (also used for Prionopidae), 'Cicada-bird', and 'Pied Shrike'. The name 'cuckoo' perhaps derives from the grey coloration, sometimes conspicuously barred, and the name 'shrike' from the strong notched bill. They are curious birds, varying in size from that of sparrows *Passer* spp. to that of pigeons *Columba* spp., and the prevailing colours are light and dark grey, more rarely black and white. The wings are rather long and pointed, and the tail is moderately long and round ; rictal bristles are well developed and in many species partially conceal the nostrils. The sexes differ in depth of colouring, the female being a pale and washed-out version of the male. The young often have a white nestling plumage, exchanged for a plumage resembling that of the female at the post-juvenile moult.

All the cuckoo-shrikes are arboreal ; only the aberrant Ground Cuckoo-shrike *Pteropodocys maxima* of Australia spends much time on the ground, although the Pied Triller *Lalage nigra* of Malaysia often drops down to the ground for a few moments when feeding. A few species are restricted to the true forest, but the rest are more typical of the forest edge, secondary growth, gardens, and coastal vegetation. The call-notes are loud, either whistles or rather disagreeable squawks.

$\frac{1}{2}$

Black Cuckoo-shrike *Campephaga phoenicea.* C.E.T.K.

The minivets *Pericrocotus* spp. are a distinctive group, the size of wagtails *Motacilla* spp. and with the tail moderately long and graduated. In most species the male is a striking red and black, whereas the female is yellow or orange and black or grey. They are essentially birds of the tree-tops and are usually seen in flocks of a dozen or more individuals, which communicate with soft and musical call-notes as they flit from tree to tree in ' follow-my-leader ' fashion, searching the foliage for insects. Bright tones harmonise well with the Burmese scene, and the splashes of scarlet and yellow afforded by a flock of these birds fluttering about in the tree-tops, or flying across a clearing, are a perpetual source of delight in the teak forests, where they are among the most characteristic birds. A feature of the montane forests, from the Himalaya to Borneo, is the mixed hunting parties of birds that pass through the trees from time to time. Such parties usually include babblers (Timaliinae), warblers (Sylviinae), flycatchers (Muscicapinae), and others, with one or two species of cuckoo-shrike or minivet.

The courtship display of some of the larger cuckoo-shrikes is peculiar. The male lifts each wing alternately, without opening the feathers, perhaps half-a-dozen times, calling vigorously while doing so. The performance is repeated at intervals, and is a most distinctive field character. Both sexes build the nest, but in many species only the female incubates. The nest is usually placed high up in the fork of a tree, and is difficult to see from below ; it is a shallow little cup of fine twigs, roots, and grasses, or moss and lichen, usually lined. The minivets build a shallow but massive little cup of fine twigs, roots, and so on, often matted with cobwebs and studded with lichens so that it resembles the twig on which it is placed. The clutch consists of 2–5 eggs, usually pale green when fresh but apt to fade quickly if exposed to light, marked with brown, grey, or purple ; the eggs of some minivets are white or greyish in ground colour.

The cuckoo-shrikes are an Old World and mainly tropical family, ranging from Africa across southern Asia and Malaysia to Australia and the western Pacific. The minivets are absent from Africa and Australia, but extend up into the far eastern Palaearctic Region (eastern Siberia, China, Japan, the Ryukyus), whence one species, *Pericrocotus divaricatus*, migrates in winter to the Oriental Region ; this is the only long-range migrant in the family, although some species move about seasonally, especially in Australia.

The most recent estimate is that the family includes 70 species, which may be allocated to 9 genera. Three genera, *Pteropodocys*, *Campochaera*, and *Chlamydochaera*, are monotypic ; the remaining 6 are *Tephrodornis*, *Hemipus*, *Campephaga* (including ' *Lobotos* '), *Lalage*, *Coracina* (including ' *Edolisoma* '), and *Pericrocotus*.

A notable peculiarity is that, in most species, the feathers of the back and rump are thickly matted, partially erectile, and equipped with rigid pointed shafts ; these spine-like feathers are easily shed, and according to Gilliard it is possible that they act as a mechanism of defence, as in the trogons (Trogonidae) and pigeons (Columbidae). The White-winged Triller *Lalage sueurii* of Australia is noteworthy as being the only member of the family known to have two moults yearly ; the normal postnuptial moult in the autumn produces an eclipse plumage, which in the male (but not in the female) differs strikingly from the breeding plumage.

Several species of cuckoo-shrikes of the genus *Campephaga* are inhabitants of Africa. For example, the Black Cuckoo-shrike *C. phoenicea* (with which red and yellow ' shouldered ' forms are now regarded as conspecific) ranges from Senegal and the Sudan to Cape Province. It is 8 inches in length ; the male is mainly black, strongly glossed with steel-blue, and in one phase has scarlet lesser wing coverts (the feathers having yellow bases and in some specimens being yellow throughout) ; the female is dull brown with some darker barring. The call is a soft double whistle. The bird feeds on insects, caterpillars being widely consumed. The Wattled Cuckoo-shrike *Campephaga* ('*Lobotos*') *lobata* is a bird of about the same size with a limited range in West Africa ; it must indeed be accounted a rare and little-known bird. It has the aberrant character, in the male, of a yellow wattle near the gape under each dark red eye ; this sex is largely green on the upper parts and chestnut on the rump and under parts, with a black and yellow tail.

Indian examples are the Pigmy Triller (or ' Pied Shrike ') *Hemipus picatus*, which catches flying insects after the manner of flycatchers (Muscicapinae), and the Short-billed Minivet *Pericrocotus brevirostris,* a gregarious and strictly arboreal bird with the general habits already described for the genus. Of the latter, Whistler remarked that it is by no means shy and that the black and scarlet of the males and the yellow of the females is so conspicuous and so attractive in the sunlight as to make the species one of the best known birds of the Himalaya and northern India generally.

The Black-breasted Triller *Chlamydochaera jefferyi* is a montane species with a restricted distribution in Borneo from Mt. Kinabalu to Mt. Dulit. First discovered by John Whitehead during his exploration of Mt. Kinabalu, and seen or collected by several other naturalists since, it is still a little-known species ; it has a striking black and buff pattern about the head, and it eats nothing but fruit.

Deignan has observed the Ground Cuckoo-shrike *Pteropodocys maxima* in central Australia and describes (personal communication) its peculiar habits ; it frequents treeless plains, perches on fence posts, flies after insects like a swallow *Hirundo* sp., and runs strongly on the ground unlike any other member of the family.

Short accounts of one or more members of the family are to be found in the handbooks covering the areas from Africa to the western Pacific, but there is no monograph dealing with the family as a whole. B.E.S.

Delacour, J. 1951. The lesser greybirds (*Coracina*) of Asia and Malaysia. Amer. Mus. Novit. no. 1497 : 1–15.
Peters, J. L., Mayr, E. & Deignan, H. G. 1960. Family Campephagidae. *In* Mayr, E. & Greenway, J. C., Jr.

(eds.). Check-list of Birds of the World vol. 9. Cambridge, Mass.

CUCKOO'S LEADER ; CUCKOO'S MATE : popular name, in Britain, for the Wryneck *Jynx torquilla* (see under WOODPECKER). It refers to the approximately simultaneous appearance in spring of this now uncommon summer visitor and the Cuckoo *Cuculus canorus.*

CUCULI ; CUCULIDAE : see below

CUCULIFORMES : an order, alternatively ' Cuculi ', comprising the suborders Musophagi (family Musophagidae—see TURACO) and Cuculi (family Cuculidae—see CUCKOO), in Stresemann's system treated as separate orders.

CULINARY USES : see GASTRONOMICAL AND MEDICAL USES

CULMEN : the dorsal ridge of the upper mandible, from forehead to tip (see BILL).

CURASSOW : substantive name of some species of Cracidae (Galliformes, suborder Galli) ; in the plural, serving as a general term for the family, other members of which are called, mainly, ' guans ' and ' chachalacas '. The family is restricted to the warmer zones of the New World, and in South America the birds largely take the place of the Phasianidae, which they resemble in many details. The Cracidae are lean birds with long and heavy tails. In size they vary from half that of a pheasant *Phasianus* sp. to nearly that of a turkey *Meleagris* sp. The true curassows (*Crax, Mitu, Pauxi*) are very conspicuously crested with curved feathers. The birds usually stay in trees, either in the forest or at its edge. They run with great agility along the branches, jumping up and up until they reach the tree-top, from where they take off, half gliding, half fluttering. The wings are short and round, and markedly concave. The bill is heavy and bent, frequently with a shiny coloured cere. Certain species have a solid crest, knob, or similar ornament at the base of the upper mandible (*Mitu, Crax, Pauxi*). The legs are long and strong, the toes are heavy and fairly long and have bent claws. The birds do not scratch for food as much as other gallinaceous birds, although they often come down to the ground to feed on fallen fruit and flowers. They like to feed on buds and tender leaves and occasionally small animals such as insects or frogs. They store food in the crop or in the greatly expandable oesophagus ; they have a muscular stomach. Certain species (*Penelope*) eat fruit; the stones pass whole through the alimentary tract or are spat out. The birds use grit.

The voice is amplified by means of an extended trachea, usually looped, the curve sometimes reaching to the abdomen (e.g. *Ortalis*, *Penelope*). A system of air-chambers in the neck also appears to serve as voice amplifiers (*Crax*). The voice is loud, raucous (*Penelope*), crying (*Ortalis*), or whistling (*Pipile*), sometimes of a strange muffled quality (*Crax*).

During courtship the male comes down to the ground, walking about in front of the female, strutting with head erect and making a low call (*Ortalis*). During the nesting season some species produce a loud noise with the wings (e.g. *Pipile*). The Cracidae build their nests of dry twigs and leaves loosely joined together ; it is quite small in relation to the size of the birds ; the nest cup is at times relined with fresh material. The nest is at a height of a few yards in trees, sometimes in branches overhanging water or even quite near the ground. A few species nest on the ground (e.g. *Penelopina nigra* of Mexico). Sometimes the nest of another bird is used as a base for building.

Black Curassow *Crax nigra*, of northern South America. *C.E.T.K.*

$\frac{1}{15}$

The clutch consists of 2–3, rarely 4, eggs. These are strikingly large, white, with shell rough (*Crax*, *Ortalis*) or smooth (*Penelope*). Incubation lasts 22 (*Ortalis*), 29 (*Crax*), or 34 (*Pauxi*) days. The young are hatched with well developed primaries and secondaries. They are led out of the nest by the hen on their first day and hide in the branches. They are able to fly after three or four days, and they soon do not hesitate to take off from the end of a branch to fly to a neighbouring tree, following the hen or both parents. The latter present food in their bills to the young, and this is mostly of animal origin. The colouring of the young is light brown and black ; at times a striped pattern appears. Some species do not breed until two years old.

Parents and offspring keep together for some months ; later they join with others to form flocks of 10–20 or even more, and remain in these until the next breeding season. The adult cocks claim territories, in which they call persistently. In *Crax*, *Pipile*, and *Penelope* the same individuals appear to pair in succeeding years, thus forming a continuous monogamous relationship. Chachalacas are at least partly polygamous and form nesting colonies (e.g. *Ortalis ruficauda*). Males co-operate at times in nest building (*Ortalis*). Parental care varies with species, but little is known about it ; in some curassows (*Crax*) the male takes part in feeding the young. The question of sex ratio has also not been sufficiently clarified ; a ratio of 1 : 1 has been noted in several species of *Penelope* and *Ortalis*, but females predominate in some *Crax* spp. All species are sought after as gamebirds. Reproduction of curassows in captivity is rarely successful, although young which have been hatched under a domestic hen become quite tame.

The range of the family extends from the southern United States to northern Argentine. There are 11 genera and 43 species. The latter include 12 species of true curassows. The Great Curassow *Crax rubra*, weighing approximately $10\frac{1}{2}$ lb. (4800 grams), ranges from Mexico to Ecuador ; the adult male is black with a greenish or bluish sheen above, white on belly and sides, and has stiff, narrow crest-feathers strongly recurved at the tips, and the base of the bill ornamented with a large yellow knob which increases in size during the courtship period ; the female is brown. In the Helmeted Curassow *Pauxi pauxi* the sexes are alike —both black and white, and both having a large helmet-shaped horny ridge on the base of the bill, the bluish-grey colour of this ridge contrasts strikingly with the red of the bill itself ; it is 40 inches long, weighs about 8 lb. (3600 grams), and inhabits the mountain forests of Venezuela. The Razorbilled Curassow *Mitu mitu*, which is called ' mutum ' by the Brazilians, is black with a bluish sheen in both sexes, with brown on the belly, and with a high narrow frontal comb of the same red colour as the bill ; it weighs about $7\frac{3}{4}$ lb. (3500 grams) and inhabits the Amazon region and northern Brazil.

There are 12 species of guans, some of them with the names ' jacu ' and ' camata '. In the Purple Guan *Penelope purpurascens* the sexes are alike in appearance, greenish olive to brown, the base of the throat and the breast with white spots ; there is bare skin round the eyes and on the upper part of the neck, the naked throat being yellowish red and strikingly visible while the bird is calling ; the weight is about $4\frac{1}{4}$ lb. (1900 grams), and the species ranges from Mexico to Ecuador. There are three species of Piping Guan *Pipile* spp. ; in *P. cumanensis* the sexes are alike, black with white spots on breast and wings and a white cap on the head ; the face is bare and white, the naked throat is shiny blue and red with a long wattle ; the weight is about 2½ lb. (1200 grams), and the range is Guiana, Brazil, Peru, and Bolivia.

There are 11 species of chachalaca, some called ' arecuă '. In the Plain Chachalaca *Ortalis vetula* the sexes are alike, with the upper parts dark olive-brown, the lower parts lighter, and the tail greenish black ; the bird is 20 inches long and weighs about 1¼ lb. (550 grams). It ranges from Texas and Mexico to Nicaragua. The name ' chachalaca ' is derived from the call.   H.S.

Bent, A. C. 1932. Life History of North American Gallinaceous Birds. U.S. Natl. Mus. Bull. 162 : 345–352.
Schäfer, E. 1953. Estudo bio-ecológico comparativo sobre algunos Cracidae del Norte y Centro de Venezuela. Biol. Soc. Venez. Cienc. Nat. 15 : 30–63.
Wagner, H. O. 1952. Die Hokkohühner der Sierra Madre de Chiapas, Mexico. Veröff. Unterseemus Bremen 2 A : 105–128.

CURLEW: substantive name of *Numenius* spp. ; used without qualification, in Britain, for *N. arquata* (see under SANDPIPER).

CURLEW, BEACH: name used in Australia for *Orthorhamphus magnirostris* (see THICKKNEE).

CURLEW, STONE: see STONE-CURLEW; THICK-KNEE

CURRAWONG: substantive name of *Strepera* spp. (see under MAGPIE (2)).

CURSORIAL: adapted to running (see LOCO-MOTION ; RATITE).

CURSORIINAE: see COURSER

CUSHAT: popular name (with several variants) in Britain for the Wood Pigeon *Columba palumbus* (see PIGEON).

CUTICLE, EGGSHELL: see EGG ; EGGSHELL

CUT-THROAT: *Amadina fasciata* (see WEAVER-FINCH).

CYCLARHINAE: see under VIREONIDAE ; and PEPPER-SHRIKE

CYCLOCOELOUS: see INTESTINE

CYGNET: special term for a young SWAN.

CYPSELI: see APODIFORMES

Plate 9 · Flight—Carrying Prey

a   *Upper :* Osprey *Pandion haliaetus* carrying a fish in its talons (in this instance, those of one foot) and about to land on its tree-top nest (Sweden).
Phot. Svante Lundgren.

b   *Lower :* Black-throated Snake Eagle *Circaetus pectoralis* bringing a small cobra *Naja nigricollis* for its eaglet (out of sight) in a tree-top nest (Southern Rhodesia). The snake is about 2½ feet long and more than half of it is in the bird's crop. The flight pattern and method of carrying are characteristic ; note also the feet, relatively small for a raptor.
Phot. Peter Steyn.

D

DABCHICK: alternative name for certain of the smaller Podicipitidae (see GREBE).

DACELONINAE: see KINGFISHER

DACNIS: generic name used as substantive name of *Dacnis* spp. (see HONEYCREEPER (1)).

DAMAGE BY BIRDS: see under CONTROL

DAMBO: an environment, consisting of grassy land that seasonally becomes marsh, characteristic of parts of tropical Africa.

DANCING GROUND: special term in North America for the social display ground of the Sharp-tailed Grouse *Pedioecetes phasianellus* (see GROUSE; LEK).

DAPTRIINAE: see FALCON

Plate 10 · Flightlessness

a *Upper* : Adélie Penguin *Pygoscelis adeliae*—adult with well-grown chick in down (Antarctica). This penguin species of medium size is widely distributed in the Antarctic, at some places breeding in vast numbers. Like all other Spheniscidae, it has the wings modified as flippers for swimming. For other penguin photographs see Plates 25 and 37. *Phot. Jacques Masson, Expéditions polaires françaises.*

b *Lower* : Kiwi *Apteryx australis*, at night (New Zealand). This and the two other species of kiwi, likewise confined to New Zealand, are practically wingless and tail-less, with hair-like plumage, a long probing bill with nostrils near the tip, and strong feet for scratching in the ground. They constitute one of the orders of ' ratite ' birds, all of which are flightless ; whereas the others compensate by being large and swift-running, the kiwis are only fowl-sized and rely on skulking and nocturnal habits for security.

Phot. M. F. Soper, by flashlight.

(See articles FLIGHTLESSNESS ; PENGUIN ; KIWI ; RATITE)

DARTER: substantive name, alternatively ' snake-bird ' or (in the New World) ' anhinga '; of the species of Anhingidae (Pelecaniformes, suborder Pelecani) ; in the plural, general term for the family. The latter consists of half-a-dozen forms, geographically replacing each other, which taxonomists variously group in from one to four species. There is in any event only a single genus ; some authorities place it in the Phalacrocoracidae (see CORMORANT), instead of recognising a separate family. Anatomical differences include the peculiar articulation of the cervical vertebrae in the darters, and the presence of a single carotid artery instead of the two found in cormorants. The stomach is described as being unusual in possessing a peculiar pyloric lobe lined with a mat of hair-like processes.

Darters do in fact resemble attenuated cormorants ; and their habits are generally similar to those of cormorants, with which they sometimes associate, although they are purely birds of inland (including tidal) waters and confined to tropical and subtropical areas. They are about 35 inches in length, but bill, neck, and tail account for much of this. The bill is rather long, thin, and pointed (not hooked). The head is very small and the neck extremely long and slender. The neck is ' marked by a peculiar conformation of the cervical vertebrae through which the beak becomes a triggered spear in feeding ; the bridge of Dönitz on the ninth vertebra is an important part of this arrangement ' (Wetmore). The body is very much elongated the wings are long and pointed ; the stiff tail is markedly long. The legs are short, with totipalmate feet, and set far back. The plumage is largely black or dark brown, with white spots and streaks on the upper parts and some pale areas below. There is some difference in the plumage of the sexes, and the male acquires pale plumes on the sides of the head and neck in the breeding season.

The birds inhabit the wooded shores of rivers and lakes, perching with upright stance on trees or on half-sunken logs, and often holding their wings open to dry. They feed in the water, catching fish and other animal prey by under-water pursuit. The fish is apparently sometimes speared, perhaps to kill it, but is commonly brought to the surface between the mandibles ; it is then tossed in the air, caught in the mouth, and swallowed head foremost. On the surface the birds often swim in a deeply submerged position, with only head and neck showing (see SWIMMING AND DIVING). The snaky to-and-fro movements of the kinked neck are highly characteristic. Although the birds take off from the water with difficulty, and also alight clumsily, they are excellent fliers—flapping flight, gliding, and soaring ; the neck is held extended and the tail feathers spread. They are rather silent, but harsh croaks and whistling notes are used at the nest.

Head and neck of Indian Darter *Anhinga melanogaster*, of southern Asia. *C.E.T.K.*

Darters breed in colonies, building bulky nests of sticks in trees or bushes near the water—sometimes overhanging it. The 3–6 eggs are pale bluish or greenish with an outer chalky layer. The nidicolous young are naked on hatching, but later acquire down on the body. Both parents incubate the eggs and tend the young.

The family is represented in all the main continents except Europe, in their tropical and subtropical parts, and also in Madagascar ; it is absent from Polynesia and New Zealand. From some areas the birds migrate, gregariously. Purely for convenience, four species are treated as having that status in the following statement.

The Anhinga *Anhinga anhinga* (the name is Brazilian in origin) of the New World, commonly called 'Snake-bird' or by the popular misnomer 'Water Turkey', has races distributed from the southern United States to the northern Argentine. The African Darter *A. rufa* is found throughout

Africa south of the Sahara, with races in Madagascar and the Middle East. The Indian Darter *A. melanogaster* inhabits southern Asia, from India to the Celebes ; and the Australian Darter *A. novaehollandiae* inhabits New Guinea and Australia (and has occurred accidentally in New Zealand).

A.L.T.

DARWINISM: see EVOLUTION

DARWIN'S FINCHES: general term (' Galápagos finches ' in American usage) for the Geospizinae, usually classified as a subfamily of the Fringillidae (Passeriformes, suborder Oscines). The group is confined to the Galápagos Islands, except for one species on Cocos Island 600 miles to the north-east. Their nearest relatives on the American mainland are not known, but are presumed to have been finches (Fringillidae). There have been differences of opinion concerning the precise number of genera and species, but on a conservative view 13 species, placed in 3 genera, are found in the Galápagos, with one other monotypic genus on Cocos. Some of the species vary subspecifically.

These birds are of historical interest because, as is clear from an addition made in the second edition of Darwin's *Voyage of the 'Beagle'*, they provided one of the chief stimuli for their discoverer's theory of evolution. Their special interest today is in providing the best example, in birds, of an adaptive radiation into different ecological niches that is sufficiently recent, geologically speaking, for intermediate and transitional steps to have survived. The chief morphological variation is in the bill, which is (i) of fringilline type in the seed-eating species of *Geospiza*, in which it ranges from small to enormous ; (ii) long, pointed, and somewhat decurved in *G. scandens*, which feeds primarily on cactus ; (iii) rather parrot-like in *Camarhynchus crassirostris* ; (iv) somewhat similar but smaller in the insectivorous, rather tit-like *C. parvulus* and related forms ; (v) like that of a nuthatch in *C. pallidus* ; and (vi) warbler-like in *Certhidea olivacea*. *Camarhynchus pallidus* not only excavates in wood like a nuthatch *Sitta* sp., but has the unique habit of picking up a cactus spine, or breaking off a small twig, and probing it into crevices, or into the trenches which it has dug, to drive insects out. *Certhidea olivacea* is warbler-like in general appearance and habits, but various characters show that it is one of the Geospizinae. *Pinaroloxias inornata* of Cocos is intermediate in bill and plumage between *Certhidea* and *Geospiza*. Up to 10 species of Darwin's finches occur together on the central islands of the Galápagos group, in some cases certainly, and in the rest presumably, in different ecological niches. On the small outlying islands there are fewer species, and some of these have bills intermediate between those of species found in the central islands, presumably because they combine the ecological niches of these other forms absent from the outlying islands.

The whole group provides fascinating material for studies of the origin of species and of ecological isolation. The only at all comparable group is the Family Drepanididae of the Hawaiian islands, which have evolved much further than the Geospizinae, providing greater diversity and more extreme types but fewer surviving transitional forms (see HONEYCREEPER (2)). The primary factors in the evolution of both groups are considered to be (i) the existence of a group of islands, allowing the geographical isolation of subspecies, and also the chance for such forms to meet again later on the same island ; and (ii) the extreme isolation of the archipelagos from other land masses, with the result that hardly any other land birds have reached them, thus allowing great ecological divergence free from competition with mainland types. Forms differentiated on separate islands can persist alongside each other as separate species when they meet again later, provided that they have become sufficiently distinct both genetically and ecologically in their period of isolation. After this, natural selection will favour increasing ecological divergence, and so an adaptive radiation can gradually be built up.   D.L.

Bowman, R. I. 1961. Morphological variation in the Galápagos finches, Univ. Calif. Publ. Zool. 58 : 1–302.

Lack, D. 1945. The Galápagos finches (Geospizinae) : a study in variation. Occas. Papers Calif. Acad. Sci. 21 : 1–158.

Lack, D. 1947. Darwin's Finches. Cambridge.

DAW: popular abbreviation of JACKDAW.

DAYAL-BIRD: alternative name (variously spelt), in India, of the Magpie Robin *Copsychus saularis*.

DEATH-RATE: see LIFE, EXPECTATION OF ; LONGEVITY ; POPULATION DYNAMICS

DECOMPOSED: apart from its ordinary meaning, a rather ambiguous term sometimes applied to feathers, e.g. ornamental plumes, of which the vanes are incoherent because the barbules on adjacent barbs do not engage.

DECOY: derived from Dutch words 'eende' meaning ducks and 'kooi' meaning cage or trap, a duck decoy being a device constructed on the edge of a lake, or round a pond specially dug for the purpose, in which wild ducks *Anas* spp. etc. are

caught. Typically the device is set in a woodland and consists of a pond of one to three acres, from which radiate four to eight 'pipes'—curved tapering ditches, each covered by a tapering tunnel of netting stretched over semicircular hoops. The pipes may be 50–70 yards long, 15–25 feet wide at the mouth and the hoops at the mouth 6–15 feet above the water. The success of the system depends on the mobbing behaviour of ducks when confronted with a predator. By using a trained dog which the ducks will follow, the decoyman entices them into the pipe. Along the outside of the curve is a range of 6-foot-high screens in an overlapping pattern ; these work on the principle of a sunblind, hiding the decoyman from the birds on the pond but allowing him to be seen by those in the pipe. In between these high screens, and making in plan a zig-zag pattern, are screens about 1½ feet high known as 'dog-leaps'.

On many quite small decoy ponds a thousand, sometimes several thousand, ducks may be resting during the day. Selecting the best pipe for the wind direction, the decoyman peeps through a tiny slit in one of the screens near the mouth of the pipe. If the ducks are suitably placed he signals to the dog, which then jumps over the dog-leap, runs round the screen *away* from the ducks and returns to its master over the next dog-leap. Immediately, the ducks start to swim towards the pipe, apparently drawn partly by bravado and partly by curiosity. The process is repeated round the next screen, and the next ; watching through each successive 'peep hole' the decoyman gradually works the dog up the pipe, the ducks following often only a few yards behind. When as many as possible have been drawn in (it may be only one or two, or it may be 70) the decoyman or a colleague runs silently by a screened path to the mouth of the pipe and appears suddenly to the ducks in the pipe. He is in the outermost gap in the screens, known as the 'show place'. The retreat of the ducks to the open pond appears to be cut off and they try to escape by flying farther up the ever narrowing pipe. The decoyman follows, constantly in their sight through the gaps in the screens, until he drives the birds into the detachable 'tunnel net' at the end. Meanwhile the remaining birds on the pond have seen nothing but the dog and are therefore undisturbed. Such catches may be made several times in a day.

The device was perfected in Holland in the late sixteenth century. More than 200 decoys were built in England, although only a handful now remain and are mostly used for ringing. Some of those in Holland still send thousands of ducks to market each year ; in 1956 it was estimated that some 300 000 ducks were caught in the 100 remaining Dutch decoys. The first and only decoy in the New World was built at the Delta Waterfowl Research Station in Manitoba, Canada, in 1949.

There are many variants on the method described above. Cats and ferrets have been successfully used instead of dogs, and also stuffed foxes and stuffed stoats. In certain decoys tame ducks are trained to come for food, offered either in conjunction with the appearance of the dog or by itself to the accompaniment of a soft whistle. These decoy ducks lead their wild fellows but do not react to the appearance of the decoyman and so are not caught. Tame ducks used in a similar way to entice their fellows to destruction in wildfowling (or ' duck hunting ' as it is called in North America) are frequently described as ' decoy ducks ' or ' decoys ', and the word also includes dummy birds used to attract wild ones within gunshot. From this usage the word ' decoy ' has been further extended to human deceptions.   P.S.

DEFAECATION :   see ALIMENTARY SYSTEM ; BEHAVIOUR, DEVELOPMENT OF ; DROPPINGS ; PARENTAL CARE

DEFINITION : in taxonomy, see under DESCRIPTION.

DELTOID : see MUSCULATURE

DEME : term (used more by botanists than by zoologists) for a local population that can in some way be considered separately from other populations of the same species. The deme has no status in nomenclature, and the term may thus be useful in the discussion of what is often an essentially fluid situation, wherein adherence to rigid concepts of taxonomy would obscure the reality (see SUBSPECIES ; SYSTEMATICS).

DENDROCOLAPTIDAE : see under PASSERIFORMES ; and WOODCREEPER

DENDROCYGNINI : see DUCK

DENSITY : see AGGRESSION ; ECOLOGY ; FLOCKING ; POPULATION DYNAMICS ; TERRITORY

DENSITY-DEPENDENCE : see POPULATION DYNAMICS

DENTARY : a paired bone of the lower jaw (see SKELETON).

DERMIS : the inner layer of the SKIN.

DERTRUM : term sometimes applied to the tip or hook (if any) of the upper mandible (see BILL).

DESCRIPTION : term used in taxonomy for a statement of the observed taxonomic characters of a specimen or a taxon. A ' definition ' or ' diagnosis ' is a statement only of the distinguishing characters of a taxon.

DESIGNATION : term used in taxonomy for the express act of an author in fixing the type-specimen or type-species of a taxon, or in stating a type-locality (see NOMENCLATURE ; TYPE-LOCALITY ; TYPE-SPECIES ; TYPE-SPECIMEN).

DESMOGNATHOUS : see PALATE

DETERMINATE LAYERS : see LAYING

DEVELOPMENT, EMBRYONIC : from fertilisation of the egg-cell (ovum) to the emergence of the young bird from the shell (see EGG ; HATCHING ; REPRODUCTIVE SYSTEM). The primitive mode of development in vertebrates transforms the whole egg-cell into an embryo ; the eggs of lampreys or amphibians typify this ' holoblastic ' mode. The germs of birds, like those of reptiles, belong to a completely different type. Of the huge egg-cell (represented by the whole of the yellow yolk), only a small fraction takes part in the formation of the embryo. Much of this small formative area has the function of providing transitory structures of vital importance ; these are the amnion, yolk-sac, and allantois, enabling the embryo to exist under the peculiar conditions of a complicated egg-system. This kind of development, in contrast to the holoblastic, is called ' meroblastic ', only part of the formative germ-plasm being used in building up the embryo.

Fertilisation. Already in the follicular state (in the ovary), the nucleus of the egg-cell (generally known as ' germinal vesicle ') takes its position at the periphery, where it forms a blastodisc with the cytoplasm of the polar ring and the outer zone of the periblast (Fig. 1).

In the upper part of the oviduct, the spermatozoids penetrate into the egg-cells. The insemination must be considered as a physiological polyspermy, several spermatozoids normally entering the blastodisc (3–5 in the domestic fowl, 12–25 in the pigeon) ; only one of them unites with the female pronucleus.

After union of the pronuclei, the nucleus commences the divisions of the new development and segmentation begins. 25 hours after fertisation an ' area opaca ' is formed consisting of a cellular inner zone and an outer ring of syncytial periblast ; the two are clearly different from the inner ' area pellucida ' representing the original segmented blastoderm. Some of the nuclei of the periblast are found under the outer zone of the area pellucida

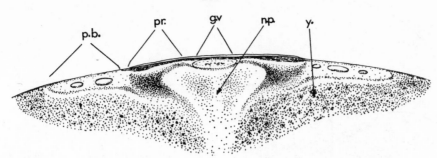

FIG 1. Structure of the unfertilised blastodisc; two concentric cytoplasmatic zones surround the central germinal vesicle.   *From Romanoff.*

pb the outer periblast, which contains lacunae in its cytoplasm **pr** the inner polar ring, with a more dense cytoplasm **gv** the germinal vesicle (egg nucleus), in which can be seen the chromosomes **np** nucleus of Pander (white yolk) **y** yellow yolk

and contribute, probably together with the plasm of the periblast, to the transformation of the vitellus and thus produce a subgerminal cavity filled with liquid yolk. When the egg is laid, the segmentation area or blastoderm has a diameter of 3·5-4·5 mm. in the domestic fowl.

Incubation may begin with the laying of the first egg (Gaviidae, Larinae, Ciconiiformes, Strigiformes, Falconiformes), or only after the last egg of a clutch is deposited (see INCUBATION). The development of the germ may be interrupted for days, in many cases even for weeks as in the domestic fowl.

Gastrulation. The next step produces a two-layered germ; this process corresponds to the formation of a primitive embryonic gut or archenteron and is generally termed gastrulation. In birds there is never a real archenteron with a primitive mouth or blastopore as in holoblastic germs; the events of this gastrulation in birds are but remotely derived from the primitive type of Vertebrates. At least with the start of the incubation period, often before, the separation of two layers, epiblast and endoblast, is under way. Since the classic work of Duval, theoretical discussion of gastrulation in birds has never ceased. We can give only a rapid survey of three main lines of this discussion.

According to Duval (1884) and Patterson (1909) the caudal border of the blastoderm folds in and spreads out under the surface, thus producing an endoblast underneath the epiblast. On the other hand, Graeper (1929) and Mehrbach (1935) suppose that, at several points of the laminar segmentation-disc, cells emigrate under the surface and finally constitute a continuous endoblast. On a third view (Peter 1938, Spratt 1946, Rudnick 1944-48, Pasteels 1945), the endoblast is thought to derive

from the multistratified blastoderm. At present, this most recent interpretation is widely accepted in principle.

Recently, however, the old problem has been studied once more by Lutz and his school (1955, 1956). His observation in vitro, aided by the method of chinese ink particles, shows morphogenetic movement quite similar to those described by Duval and Patterson—invagination of the caudal border of the blastoderm, and in a less striking way of the lateral and anterior borders. These movements carry the material of the endoblast under the surface layer.

The experimental work of Lutz (1956) suggests that the polar differentiation of the blastoderm is not stabilised before gastrulation; as a result of cutting the posterior (and most important) invagination border, the anterior border acquires a leading position, and an inverse embryo is produced. In the normal development the advancement of the posterior border seems to determine the longitudinal axis and the poles of the future germ.

Formation of the Mesoblast. At the next step—the stage of the 'primitive streak'—a third germ layer, the mesoblast, is formed. Experimental study enables us to trace the approximate areas of the future mesoblast back into the 'pre-streak stage' (Figs. 2 and 3).

The primitive streak grows in the direction of the cephalic end until the eighteenth or nineteenth hour of incubation. Partly by interior growth of the tissue, partly by addition of new material at the two ends, this region attains a clear differentiation; a massive Hensen's node marks the fore end, a primitive pit follows and the caudal part forms a primitive groove (Fig. 4). The whole primitive streak is a zone of high morphogenetic activity; mesoblastic tissue is pushed forward between epiblast and endoblast. By general agreement the primitive streak is regarded as homologous with the blastopore of the more primitive holoblastic vertebrate germs—a blastopore with closed lips and never leading to anything like a hollow archenteron.

The most lateral parts of the definitive mesoblast

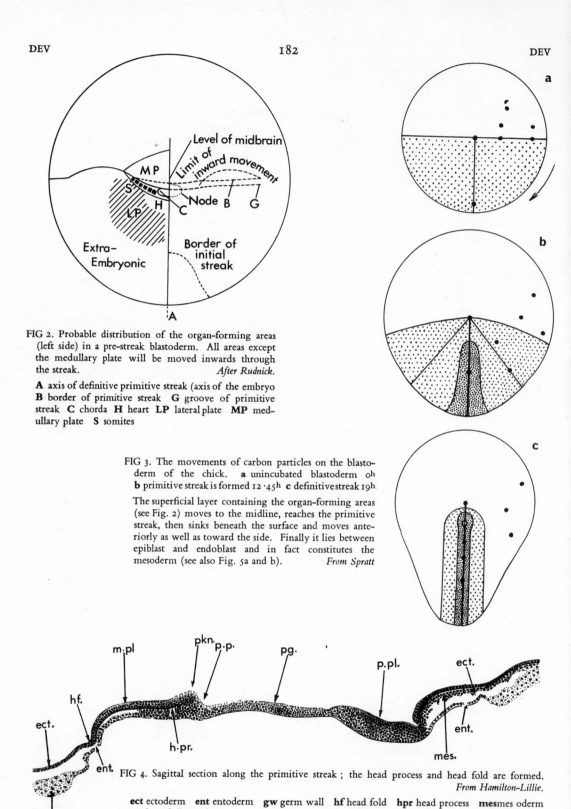

FIG 2. Probable distribution of the organ-forming areas (left side) in a pre-streak blastoderm. All areas except the medullary plate will be moved inwards through the streak.   *After Rudnick.*

A axis of definitive primitive streak (axis of the embryo **B** border of primitive streak **G** groove of primitive streak **C** chorda **H** heart **LP** lateral plate **MP** medullary plate **S** somites

FIG 3. The movements of carbon particles on the blastoderm of the chick. **a** unincubated blastoderm 0h **b** primitive streak is formed 12·45h **c** definitive streak 19h.

The superficial layer containing the organ-forming areas (see Fig. 2) moves to the midline, reaches the primitive streak, then sinks beneath the surface and moves anteriorly as well as toward the side. Finally it lies between epiblast and endoblast and in fact constitutes the mesoderm (see also Fig. 5a and b).   *From Spratt*

FIG 4. Sagittal section along the primitive streak ; the head process and head fold are formed.
From Hamilton-Lillie.

ect ectoderm **ent** entoderm **gw** germ wall **hf** head fold **hpr** head process **mes** mes oderm **mpl** medullary plate **pg** primitive groove **pkn** primitive knot **ppl** primitive plate **pp** primitive pit are the first to be invaginated ; the more central areas of the segmented part of the mesoblast and the unsegmented material of the chorda are formed towards the end of this process. Once these movements are accomplished, the epiblastic material of the future medullary plate has reached the primitive streak at the lateral border of the anterior part, and in front of Hensen's node (Fig. 5).

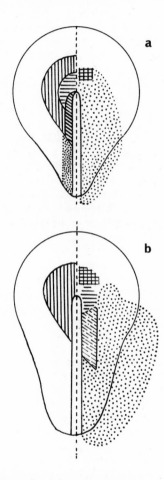

FIG 5. Morphogenetic movements during gastrulation. The presumptive areas are marked.

a definitive streak, chorda and somites are still in a superficial position (left side), while the lateral plate mesoderm and the cephalic mesoblast are invaginated (right side)

b in a later stage, the medullary plate material has reached the midline (left side), the mesoderm of the somites and the chorda-mesoblast are invaginated (right side).   *After Pasteels.*

vertical lines:neural tissue horizontal lines:chorda dots: lateral plate oblique lines:somites crossed lines:cephalic mesoblast

Regression of the Primitive Streak. After about 20 hours of incubation the formative material has reached its definitive positions. As soon as a mesoblastic head process is developed in front of Hensen's node, this node is displaced in the caudal direction and the whole primitive streak shortens and vanishes in the following 24 hours. The node itself marks the caudal end of the zone of differentiation and disappears in the formation of the tail bud. The typical organs of a vertebrate embryo begin to appear.

During this period the most lateral parts of the mesoblast grow out under the area pellucida and reach the area opaca, thus adding a third layer to this two-layered region. Continuing the future coelomic cavity of the body, the mesoblast forms an extra-embryonic coelome ; the splanchnopleure of the coelome, covering the future vitelline endoblast, contains blood islands and the material of the extra-embryonic blood vessels.

At the limit of this area vasculosa the tissues still remain two-layered. The area vitellina may be divided into a broader area vitellina interna and the area vitellina externa, the latter forming the zone of proliferation where ectoderm and endoderm are continuously separating during the advancement of the border of the blastodisc (Fig. 6).

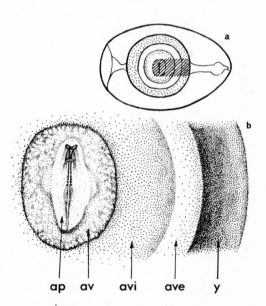

ap   av   avi   ave   y

FIG 6. **a** and **b**. Five different concentric blastoderm zones surround the embryo (the lower figure is an enlargement of the part shaded in the upper) :

ap, the area pellucida **av**, the three-layered blood islands containing area vasculosa **avi, ave**, the two-layered area vitellina interna and area vitellina externa **y** yellow yolk

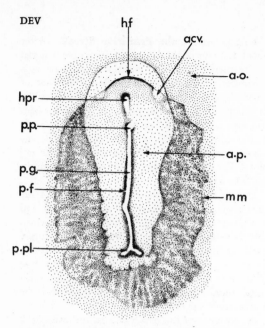

FIG 7. Dorsal view of a *Gallus* blastoderm immediately after beginning of the regression of the primitive streak. The head process is formed ; the head fold and the amnio-cardiac vescicles are in process of formation.
After Hamilton-Lillie.

acv amnio-cardiac vesicles **ao** area opaca **ap** area pellucida **hf** head fold **hpr** head process **mm** margin of mesoderm **pf** primitive fold **pg** primitive groove **pp** primitive pit **ppl** primitive plate

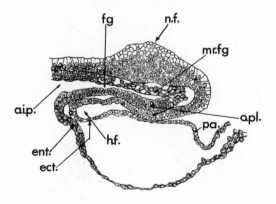

FIG 8. Sagittal section of the head of a 4 somite embryo (*Gallus*). The head is clearly elevated and separated by the deep head fold from the proamnion. Neural fold and fore-gut are formed. *After Hamilton-Lillie.*

aip anterior intestinal portal **ect** ectoderm **ent** entoderm **fg** fore-gut **hf** head fold **mrfg** mesenchymatic roof of fore-gut **nf** neural fold **opl** oral plate **pa** pro-amnion

Formation of the Embryo and Organogenetic Processes. In the few hours immediately following the beginning of the regression of the primitive streak, the principal organs of the germ are built up. This starts with the formation of the ' head process ', a rod-like cell-mass in front of the primitive node. This mass later produces the notochord or chorda dorsalis. The anterior end of this notochord—the prechordal plate—gives rise to the major part of the mesenchymatic tissue of the head.

As soon as the head process has appeared, the elevation of the embryo above the surface of the blastoderm begins by the invagination of the ventral head fold ; the region of the medullary plate grows out and the underlying endoderm, intimately related to the prechordal plate, follows the movement (Figs. 7 and 8). Thus the outgrowth of the head contains the fore-gut. In a germ of 26–29 hours the tubular fore-gut is continuous with the primitive flat layer of the endoderm. By concrescence the tubular part elongates in the caudal direction. In the ventral part of the head, ectoderm and endoderm are in contact on a small surface—the oral plate, where later on the mouth is formed (Fig. 8). During the same time the dorsal part of the neural folds are uplifted and, by their closure along the dorsal midline, produce the neural tube ; the primitive nervous system is thus formed.

Meanwhile, the development of the mesoblastic parts has begun. We have noted that the material of this mesoblast has been shifted into position between ectoderm and endoderm through the region of the primitive streak ; up to 25–30 hours the mesoblastic tissue is still in continuity with this zone. In front of this region the mesoblast is already differentiated into three parts—the axial notochord and two lateral cell-masses. Figure 9 shows the structure of these lateral masses ; the paraxial mesoderm near the notochord gives rise to the somites (segments) ; the lateral plates prepare the formation of the coelomic cavities ; and between somites and lateral plates are the intermediate cells, giving origin to the primitive kidneys.

The growth of the lateral mesoblast proceeds not only in a lateral direction, but also surrounds the head and leaves only a small frontal zone free of mesoblast, the proamnion, consisting only of ectoderm and endoderm (Fig. 10). In the head region, the lateral plates form a pair of coelomic vesicles, the amnio-cardiacal vesicles. Their medial parts produce the heart of the embryo (Figs. 7, 10, 12).

By tranverse splitting in the paraxial mesoblast, a series of paired somites is formed—7 already after about 30 hours of incubation. The formation of

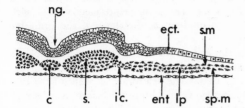

FIG 9. Transverse section in the somite forming area of
22h *Gallus* embryo. The notochord is clearly separated from the somite mesoderm. In the lateral plate the
somatic and splanchnic mesoderm layer are in process
of formation. The space between them is the first sign
of the future coelom cavity.   *After Duval.*

c chorda   **ect** ectoderm   **ent** entoderm   **ic** intermediate cells   **lp** lateral plate   **ng** neural groove
s somite   **sm** somatic mesoderm   **spm** splanchnic
mesoderm

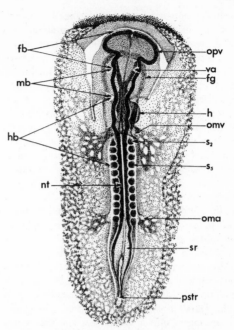

FIG 11. A twelve somite *Gallus* embryo, dorsal aspect
(the first incomplete somite is not shown).

fb fore-brain   **fg** fore-gut   **h** heart   **hb** hind-brain
mb mid-brain   **nt** neural tube   **oma** omphalo mesenteric artery   **omv** omphalo mesenteric vein   **opv** optic
vesicle   **pstr** primitive streak   **s** somite   **sr** sinus rhomboidalis   **va** ventral aorta

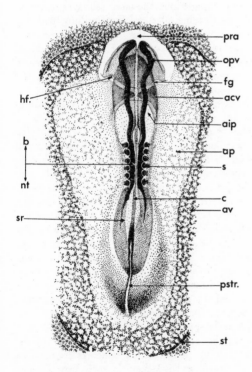

FIG 10. A seven somite *Gallus* embryo, dorsal aspect (the
first incomplete somite is not shown).

acv amnio-cardiac vesicles   **aip** anterior intestinal portal
ap area pellucida   **av** area vasculosa   **b** brain   **c** chorda
fg fore-gut   **hf** head fold   **nt** neural tube   **opv** optic
vesicle   **pra** pro-amnion   **pstr** primitive streak
s somite   **sr** sinus rhomboidalis   **st** sinus terminalis

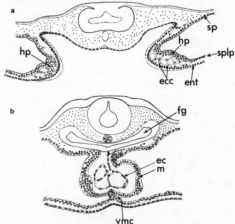

FIG 12. Two stages in the formation of the heart (cross
sections).

a a six somite *Gallus* embryo with bilateral heart
primordia.   **b** an eight somite *Gallus* embryo.   The
endocardium is in process of formation of the unpaired
tube.   *After Mollier.*

ec endocardium   **ecc** endocardial cells   **ent** entoderm
fg fore-gut   **hp** heart primordia   **m** myocardium
sp somatopleura   **splp** splanchnopleura   **vmc** ventral
mesocardium

the neural tube is accomplished during this period. It starts in the region of the future midbrain and proceeds in anterior and posterior directions. Near the primitive groove the folds are still separated and form a zone of undifferentiated medullary plate which has been called the 'rhomboidal sinus'. A vesicular enlargement of the forebrain (the origin of the optic vesicles) is just indicated in this stage.

In an embryo of 12 somites the fundamental structure of the vertebrate organisation is elaborated. The brain is on its way from a stage of 3 vesicles (prosencephalon, mesencephalon, and rhombencephalon) to the definitive structure of 5 parts (Fig. 11). Between the cubes of the somites and the lateral plates the segmented material of the 'nephrotomes' is ready to form the transitory kidney (mesonephros). In the anterior part of the trunk they build the cephalic kidney or pronephros—a rapidly vanishing structure. Under the fore-gut, the tubular heart is visible, somewhat curved to the right, caudally continuous with the two omphalomesenteric veins and the extra-embryonic vascular area. Rostrally the heart tapers into a ventral aorta. This vessel divides into two branches, or mandibular arteries, each leading to a dorsal aortic root. Caudally these two vessels are in relation with the extra-embryonic blood system (Fig. 11).

Some of the processes leading to this stage of 12 somites need a more detailed account.

(a) The extra-embryonic blood system. The 'blood islands', forerunners of the vessels and the source of the first blood-cells, form very early (before the head process appears) a caudal horseshoe-shaped part of the area opaca—the future area vasculosa. The islands expand in an anterior direction and appear in the area pellucida. Each of them consists of a cell mass of 'haemangioblasts'. Later on the area vasculosa acquires a distinct outer limit by the ring of the vena terminalis. The blood islands are situated as a thickened part of the splanchnopleure between the extra-embryonic coelom and the endoderm. The somatopleure is free of blood and vessels (Fig. 14). During the stage of 5 to 7 somites the haemangioblasts unite in strands of cells and form a plexus by centripetal advance. The cells partly form the endothelial wall of the future vessels and partly develop into the first red blood-cells or erythroblasts. The network thus formed enters into contact with the central vessels leading to the heart.

(b) Formation of the heart. Simultaneously with the embryonic and extra-embryonic vessels, the formation of the heart begins and unites these two parts of the circulation. The cardiogenic material is of a very early determination; experimental research shows potentialities of heart formation in tissues of the blastoderm before incubation as well as in a blastoderm at the stage of the primitive streak.

At the end of this latter phase cardiogenic cells are situated at each side of Hensen's node and the head process. The ventromedian walls of the two amniocardiac vesicles begin to thicken in the 3 to 5 somites stage (varying in different species); the thickened part differentiates into two tissues—a thin endocardium and a more massive myocardium. The endocardium arises by vacuolisation of the solid inner layer of the mesocardium and comes into contact caudally with the vessels of the area pellucida, and at the anterior pole with the ventral cephalic aorta. The whole heart is clearly part of the total vascular system differentiated as a specialised motor structure.

The two heart-vesicles join, ventrally to the elongating pharyngeal part of the fore-gut, in the 7–8 somites stage. Endocardium and myocardium fuse into a single tube, the outer cell layer (epimyocardium) forming a ventral mesocardium with the splanchnopleure. On the dorsal side the two myocardia join somewhat later and form a dorsal mesocardium, the caudal part of which persists. This step is accomplished only after the dissolution of the ventral mesocardium. The outer wall of the amniocardiac vesicles produces the pericardium (Fig. 12).

The heart is limited in its early growth; the mesocardium fixes it, while the yolk is a ventral obstacle. The growing heart-tube turns first to the right and becomes U-shaped. The final result of this growth is a complete loop, part of the dorsal mesocardium being destroyed during the process. The space between myocardium and endocardium is filled for a time with a jelly transmitting the pressure of the early muscular contraction to the endocardium. As early as the 7 somites stage, pumping movements of the heart can be observed, but the normal contractions start with 9 somites (fowl), or 13–14 somites (duck), after the union of the paired heart-primordia.

The development of the embryonic blood-vessels follows the lines of the extra-embryonic part— except for blood formation, which is confined to special organs and is lacking in these vessels. The dorsal aorta develops from ventral cells of the somites and from material of the inner part of the lateral plate. In front of the first pair of somites the unsegmented mesoblast furnishes the material of the paired aorta. The lumen of the aorta is formed by fusion of separate lumina of the mesoblastic tissue. The aorta enters into contact with the cephalic aorta of the ventral side by a first pair of aortic arches—in front of the first gill-slit ; in the caudal end the main vessels open into the extra-embryonic system of capillaries.

Later on a system of 6 aortic arches is developed ; the first disappears during the third or fourth day, the second during the fourth to fifth day, the fifth on the sixth day. The three persistent arches are particularly important :

arch III, forming the carotid system
arch IV, the definitive dorsal aorta
arch VI, the pulmonary arteries

At the caudal end of this region of aortic arches, the two aortic roots form an unpaired dorsal aorta. This main vessel divides again, each branch giving off a big omphalomesenteric artery to the yolk-sac and continuing as a smaller caudal artery on each side (Fig. 11).

The venous system is slower in its development. While the arteries have reached the stage just described (12 somites), the only venous part is the connection between the capillaries of the yolk-sac and the heart—a pair of omphalomesenteric veins in more advanced embryos. The two veins unite as a common trunk leading to the venous sinus of the heart. This ductus venosus becomes elongated with the growth of the foregut ; in later phases it comes into close relation with the liver.

(c) *The neuromeres.* Mention has already been made of the serial vessels of the developing brain. During their formation another series of metameric structures appears at the fore end of the neural tube. These ' neuromeres ' (described as early as 1828 by von Baer and 1825 by Remak) are the subject of various interpretations. As they are evidently more primitive than the vesicles they play a great role in any theory concerning the head segmentation of the early Vertebrates. Controversial interpretations have sometimes gone as far as to deny the reality of the neuromeres. For a detailed account of the problem of the segmental structure of the head see de Beer (1937).

The recent work of Källén (1955) shows the presence of these segmental structures of the brain in all groups of Vertebrates ; they are not limited to the rhombencephalon, as early observers thought, but occur in the anterior vesicles as well.

Formation of the Amnion, External Form and Rotation of the Embryo. In a 12 somites embryo only the anterior part of the head is elevated by the ventral head-fold above the surface of the germinal disc ; the rest of the embryo lies in the level of the yolk surface. The embryo is not yet twisted and no trace of the amnion is visible. As soon as the regression of the primitive streak is

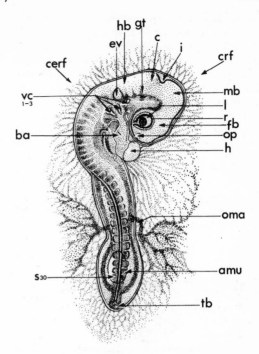

FIG 13. Dorsal view of a 31 somite *Gallus* embryo.
After Hamilton-Lillie.

amu amniotic umbilicus **ba** bulbus arteriosus **c** cerebellum **cerf** cervical flexure **crf** cranial flexure **ev** ear vesicle **fb** fore-brain **gt** ganglion of trigeminus **h** heart **hb** hind-brain **i** isthmus **l** lens **mb** midbrain **oma** omphalo-mesenteric artery **op** olfactory pit **r** retina **s** somite **tb** tail bud **vc** visceral cleft

accomplished, all general features of the embryo are present (Fig. 13). When the tail bud is formed the following notable events have taken place :

1. Elevation of the whole embryo above the surface of the yolk-sac.
2. Formation of the amnion.
3. Rotation of parts of the embryo in relation to the original plane of symmetry.
4. Flexures of the neural tube in the cervical and the midbrain region.

The embryo is separated from the yolk-sac by lateral folds continuing the first anterior head fold. The process involves the ectoderm and the adjacent somatopleure. In the 12 somites embryo this folding is complete and the tail region begins to separate from the yolk-sac. The splanchnopleure takes part in the embryo-forming process by ventral fusion isolating the intestine (which has been wide open towards the yolk).

As this process goes on, ectoderm and somatopleure begin to fold up the protective membrane called the amnion. The starting point is an ectodermal thickening (the ectamnion) at the anterior margin of the pro-amniotic region. In the 14–15 somites stage the amniotic head fold (involving the somatopleure) is formed. The head turns out of the original symmetric plane into a lateral position and sinks deeper into the yolk. The amnion grows out in the caudal direction, where in the majority of birds it meets with a caudal fold ; *Diomedea*, *Fulica*, and *Puffinus* are known as exceptions, in which the cephalic amnion alone forms the whole protective sheet. As a result four layers are established : the outer ectoderm and the mesoblast form the serosa or chorion, the mesoblast and the inner ectoderm constitute the amnion. The two structures meet in the sero-amniotic suture formed by the fusion of the ectoderm (see Fig. 14).

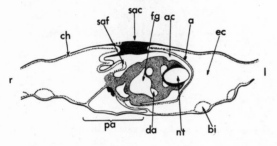

FIG 14. Semidiagrammatic representation of a cross section through the cephalic portion of a 48 hour *Gallus* embryo.   *After Hirota.*

a amnion   **ac** amniotic cavity   **bi** blood islands
ch chorion   **da** dorsal aorta   **ec** extra-embryonic
coelom cavity   **fg** fore-gut   **l** left   **nt** neural tube
pa proamnion   **r** right   **sac** sero-amniotic connection
(ectamnion)   **saf** secondary amniotic fold

The closure of the ventral body wall leads to the formation of a narrow umbilical cord connecting the embryo with the extra-embryonic structures. This umbilical cord is continuous with the ectoderm of the amnion and contains : (1) the yolk stalk, a connection of the yolk-sac with the intestine, (2) the stalk of the allantois, and (3) the extra-embryonic blood-vessels.

Figure 14 shows a transverse section of an embryo of 48 hours ; the sero-amniotic suture is shown in black. Originally arising over the dorsal midline of the germ, it has now shifted to the right ; the right amniotic wall is folded, while the left side of the amnion is extended. This difference is the result of the rotation of the embryo. The lateral position allows another movement ; the prosencephalon, representing at first the anterior pole of the germ, turns caudally by a first or cranial flexure in the region of the midbrain. A second or cervical flexure finally bends the prosencephalon through

about 180° ; the 'anterior' pole thus comes in contact with the heart and the cephalic aorta or arterial bulb (see Fig. 13).

During the time from 31–96 somites the embryo turns completely to the left side ; back and tail are curved ventrally and the whole body now assumes the typical shape of an embryo of the Amniota, the bent head approaching the tail.

Development of External Features and Transitory Structures. (*a*) *External form.* At first the nervous system, somites, and heart determine the general aspect of the germ. Subsequently the limbs, the ventral bulk of the trunk, and the great head with eyes and bill are the dominating features of the embryo (Figs. 15, 16, 17). The tail, conspicuous in the beginning, is soon eclipsed by the developing wings and legs.

The heart is clearly part of the head at the start ; it is now displaced to the thorax and the neck is formed. The cranial flexure of the brain vanishes as the neck quickly acquires considerable length. The three visceral clefts of the fore-gut present at the beginning of the third day are transformed at the seventh day and externally closed—except for the first one, of which the superior part forms the auditory meatus while the mandibular arch develops into the maxillary and mandibular process.

The early development, until the ninth day, shows an astonishing agreement in the various groups of birds, even in forms with very different incubation periods. Of course, a detailed study shows significant and interesting variation ; but for a general account the domestic fowl serves as a standard type. About the tenth day, the general features common to all birds are established, and the further development produces the special group characters, particularly the extreme differences between the well developed and largely independent nidifugous young and the undeveloped altricial or nidicolous type of progeny (see YOUNG BIRD).

(*b*) *Development of the transitory organs.* The extra-embryonic structures are transitory organs of great functional importance. The amnion furnishes mechanical protection as well as a first fluid surrounding for the germ ; the yolk-sac acts as an alimentary structure ; and the allantois serves embryonic respiration as well as accumulating excretory substances. These three organs are marked characters of what has been termed the 'closed-box' or 'cleidoic' egg-system (Needham 1932).

After a few days of incubation the embryo is clearly separated from the yolk and surrounded by the amnion. A narrow tube (the yolk stalk) connects the foetal intestine with the endoderm of the yolk-sac ; but no yolk material passes

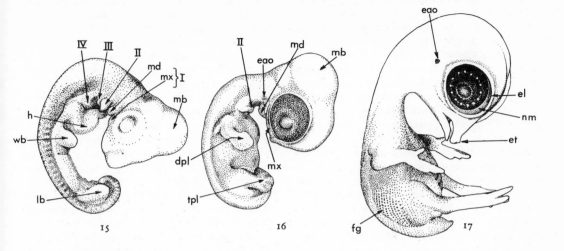

FIGS 15–17. Development of external form. FIG 15 : A 4½ day *Gallus* embryo : the limbs are still in bud stage ; visceral clefts and arches are clearly visible. ×8. FIG 16 : 6 days, digital and toe plates are formed. Visceral arch II has overgrown the arches III and IV. ×4·2. FIG 17 : 9 days, digits and toes are in process of forming. The beak is conspicuous ; on the tip of the maxilla the egg tooth is visible. The general form of a bird is established. ×4.

I–IV visceral arches   **dpl** digital plate   **eao** external auditory opening   **el** eye lid   **et** egg tooth   **fg** feather germs   **h** heart   **lb** limb bud   **mb** mid-brain   **md** mandible   **mx** maxilla   **nm** nicticating membrane   **tpl** toe plate   **wb** wing bud

through it into the digestive tract (except at hatching). The whole alimentation is performed by the yolk-epithelium and the blood system of the yolk-sac. Endodermal folds penetrate into the yolk and enlarge the inner absorbing surface.

After the fourth day the amnion undergoes important changes ; smooth muscle fibres develop in its mesoblastic layer and spontaneous rhythmical contractions move the fluid contents of the amniotic cavity. They reach a maximum on the eighth day and cease at about 13 days (Fig. 18).

The nourishing and protecting transitory structures are already far developed when the third organ, the allantois, begins to grow out. The allantois starts as a ventral evagination of the hindgut, formed by a thin endoderm wall and a thicker layer of mesoderm which very soon produces a rich supply of blood-vessels. As early as the fourth day uric acid is transported from the mesonephros and stored in this developing external urinary sac. Later on this function is taken over by the definitive kidney. The rapidly growing allantois spreads out into the extra-embryonic coelom along the right side of the embryo. As soon as it reaches the chorion, the allantois comes into close contact with it, thus forming the chorio-allantoid membrane tightly

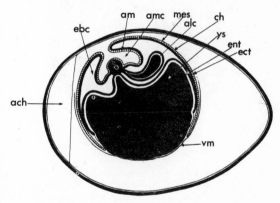

FIG 18. Semi-diagrammatic representation of a transverse section through a *Gallus* embryo. The amnion is not yet closed—the allantois is growing out into the extra-embryonic cavity.   *After Duval.*

ectoderm : cellular   entoderm : white   mesoderm : black   allantois cavity and yolk : black   extra-embryonic cavity and albumen : stippled

ach air chamber   **alc** allantois cavity   **am** amnion   **amc** amnion cavity   **ch** chorion   **ebc** extra-embryonic coelom cavity   **ect** ectoderm   **ent** entoderm   **mes** mesoderm   **vm** vitelline membrane   **ys** yolk sac

fitted to the egg-shell and serving as the respiratory surface of the germ (Fig. 19).

On the ninth day the allantois fills the whole available extra-embryonic space as a flat sac filled with urinary substance, the outer wall being everywhere in contact with the chorion. The yellow yolk diminishes gradually, the 'white yolk' or albumen shrinks by loss of water and retreats in the region of the yolk-sac umbilicus at the distal pole of the yolk-sac (generally at the pointed end of the egg).

About the ninth day the allantois reaches this white yolk and gradually surrounds its whole mass. On its way it overlaps the sero-amniotic connection. Finally, the folds of the advancing allantois enclose the white yolk and form the 'albumen-sac'—a process accomplished at the twelfth day in the domestic fowl. At 16 days practically the whole albumen has been resorbed.

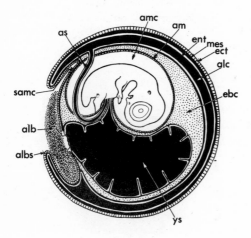

FIG 19. Semi-diagrammatic representation of a sagittal section through a chick embryo of 9 days of incubation. The amnion is now closed and in contact with the chorion in the sero-amniotic connection. The allantois is expanded around the amnion and the yolk-sac and its outer wall are fused with the chorion. The albumen sac is in process of forming.

After Hamilton-Lillie.

ectoderm : cellular entoderm : white mesoderm : black allantois cavity and yolk : black extra-embryonic cavity and albumen : stippled

am amnion **amc** amnion cavity **alc** allantois cavity
alb albumen **albs** albumen sac **as** allantois stalk
ect ectoderm **ent** entoderm **ebc** extra-embryonic
coelom cavity **mes** mesoderm **samc** sero-amniotic
connection **ys** yolk sac

Hatching. Hatching is prepared for by several synchronised processes. It often takes some hours, but may be reduced to about half an hour in small birds. The young bird has to change from breathing in the amniotic liquid to respiration in air, and it must break the hard egg-shell by its own means. The time of hatching is fixed for each species by an innately determined series of events.

Some days before it breaks the shell the embryo starts swallowing the amniotic liquid. The tissues of the young bird, particularly the muscles, thus acquire a very high water content at birth, but this diminishes rapidly. The contents of the albumen-sac go the same way. The yolk-sac is driven into the body cavity by movements of the abdominal musculature. The new-born bird always has an internal yolk-sac, of which the mass varies from 25 per cent of the bird-weight in the Ostrich *Struthio camelus* to about 5 per cent in small passerines. The yolk mass vanishes rapidly during the first 6 days after hatching.

During incubation a constant loss of water by evaporation produces an air chamber between the two shell-membranes (at the blunt pole of the egg). An aerated space is thus formed, into which the bill of the embryo penetrates. This moment marks the beginning of air respiration and is often announced by the chirping of the baby bird—two or even three days before hatching. The blood supply of the allantois is still functioning and provides the necessary oxygen, the air-chamber being rich in carbon-dioxide and insufficient for the respiratory needs of the young bird.

Very soon a partial respiration by the lungs is started, the egg-shell is opened, and the rapid drying up of the allantois begins. The vessels of the allantois are functional until the last moment before the navel is closed. At the moment of hatching the adult type of breathing is firmly established.

Immediately before the bill enters the air-chamber, the embryo changes from a transverse position into a longitudinal one, thus directing its bill towards the air space. This movement permits the use of a special tool for hatching—the 'egg-tooth' on the tip of the upper mandible. The formation of this instrument, present in the great majority of birds, begins about the sixth day (fowl, duck). It is a horny structure without any mineral substance. In some birds a corresponding thickening is produced also at the tip of the lower mandible.

The egg-tooth produces the first openings ; stretching of the head and movements of the legs help to the bursting of the shell. Sooner or later after hatching the shell-breaking tool is lost—in some groups, such as penguins (Spheniscidae), not for some weeks.

No egg-tooth is formed in the Ostrich and in Megapodiidae, but it is not yet known whether this condition is primitive or secondary ; the young at hatching are very far developed in these birds and are strong enough to break the egg-shell by movements alone. The shell is always weaker after incubation through loss of mineral substances dissolved out of the shell, transported by the blood, and used to prepare the first ossification of the skeleton.   A.P. & W.S.

Bellairs, R. 1960. Development of birds. *In* Marshall, A. J. (ed.). Biology and Comparative Physiology of Birds vol. 1. New York and London.
de Beer, G. R. 1937. The Development of the Vertebrate Skull. London and New York.
Duval, M. 1889. Atlas d'embryologie. Paris.
Hamilton, H. L. 1952. Lillie's Development of the Chick 3rd ed. (revised Hamilton). New York.
Keibel, F. & Abraham, K. 1900. Normentafeln zur Entwicklungsgeschichte der Wirbeltiere. II Normentafel zur Entwicklungsgeschichte des Huhnes (*Gallus domesticus*). Jena.
Lutz, H. 1955. Contribution expérimentale à l'étude de la formation de l'endoblaste chez les oiseaux. J. Embryol. exper. Morphol. 3 : 59–76.
Needham, J. 1931. Chemical Embryology. New York.
Pasteels, J. 1950. *In* Grassé, P-P. (ed.). Traité de Zoologie 15, Oiseaux.
Patten, B. M. 1951. Early Embryology of the Chick. Revised ed. Philadelphia.
Romanoff, A. L. 1960. The Avian Embryo : Structural and Functional Development. New York.
Waddington, C. H. 1952. The Epigenetics of Birds. Cambridge.

DEVELOPMENT OF BEHAVIOUR: see BEHAVIOUR, DEVELOPMENT OF

DEVELOPMENT, POSTEMBRYONIC: from the time of hatching onwards. As birds must have evolved from unknown reptilian ancestors in the early Mesozoic period (see ORIGIN OF BIRDS), the typical ontogenetic development of Reptilia has to be considered as basic for the Aves. Slight association between parents and offspring, a high degree of independence of the newly hatched young, a long incubation period, and a large clutch-size are typical features of this primitive mode of development. Complicated nest building, intense care for eggs and offspring, and a very dependent state of the young at the time of hatching are secondary characters. We may therefore regard the two extreme types of the hatching bird, the nidifugous (precocious) and the nidicolous (altricial) as the initial and terminal stages of a process (see YOUNG BIRD) ; several independent lines of evolution lead from the ancestral nidifugous types to very different secondary stages of nidicolous young in the various groups.

Transitory Closure of the Sense Organs. At hatching, in the extreme forms of nidicolous birds, the eyes and the ears need a liquid environment for their growing tissues. This condition is assured by an early closing of the eye-lids and of the outer walls of the auditory meatus. In striking contrast to nidicolous mammals (rats, mice, rabbits), the closure is not a complete one in birds but consists in a simple contact of the outer layers of the epidermis. Some days after hatching this contact ceases. As the transitory confinements of these sense organs have the same function as that of the amnion during embryonic life, they are termed 'amniotic closures'. The nasal openings undergo an apparently similar transformation ; but examination shows quite a different process, occurring in nidifugous as well as in nidicolous young and being without any protective significance.

Skin and Feathers of Nidicolous Birds. Primitively, the feathers develop directly from the papillar stage to the first definitive feather (see FEATHER) ; megapodes (Megapodiidae) exemplify this. In most nidifugous young, however, the first generation of feathers is transformed into down structures of various types, assuring a protection for the small homoiothermal body during the period of incomplete heat regulation. These nestling downs, also, very often provide excellent cryptic coloration. Often the development of this first generation of feathers is so much shortened that the downy structure appears as the tip of the next generation, the juvenile feather ; it is then termed neoptile. Its nature as the remnant of a first generation has recently been demonstrated by Becker (Fig. 1).

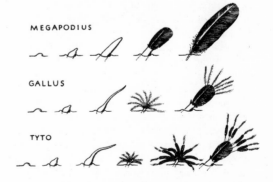

FIG 1. Development of the nestling downs by transformation of the distal part of a feather-germ. *Megapodius* : the feather produces no downy structure at the distal pole. *Gallus* : the distal pole of the feather-germ forms the nestling down. *Tyto* : two sequences of downs are built at the top of each feather.

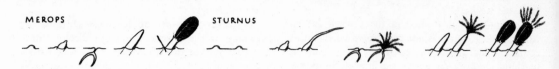

MEROPS   STURNUS

FIG 2. Development of feather germs in extreme nidicolous birds. *Merops* : before hatching, each germ
papilla is protected by a skin fold ; afterwards the
definitive feather is formed. *Sturnus* : all papillae are
protected before hatching but some produce a nestling
down.

In some groups with a nidicolous stage the downs
are suppressed ; the feather development is slow,
all juvenile feathers being enclosed in their sheaths
during the early nestling days, as in kingfishers
(Alcedinidae) and bee-eaters (Meropidae).

In the extreme types of nidicolous development
the feather is arrested after its early growth, the
papillae are surrounded by a wall of growing skin
and disappear beneath the surface. The feather
germs are protected in the same way as the developing eye and ear by an ' amniotic closure ' (Fig. 2).
In strictly limited regions of the dorsal skin some
feathers may continue to grow and develop into
nestling downs. Many of the extreme nidicolous
young seem naked at hatching ; in reality they are
covered with feather germs hidden under a protective
secondary skin.

There are other transitory skin structures limited
to the early nestling stage, e.g. the horny heel-knobs
of young woodpeckers (Picidae).

Sanitation in the Nestling Period. The
hatching bird has only a limited power of regulating
its body temperature (see HEAT REGULATION). In
the extreme nidicolous birds the requisite mechanisms are very slow in developing, and covering by
the adult as well as the insulating properties of the
nest give important help during the early days.
Only if the nest be kept extremely clean can it
provide the necessary thermal insulation and thus
make warming by the parents effective.

In the more highly evolved groups a complicated
sanitation system is developed (see PARENTAL CARE).
The faecal matter of the young is enveloped during
the feeding period by a relatively solid gelatinous
substance, produced by special regulation of the
cloacal secretion during a strictly limited postembryonic period. The parent waits after each
feeding for this conspicuous white packet ; the
young is guided by an inherited behaviour to turn
round after each feeding and to present the shining
faecal packet to the old bird.

In the lyrebirds (Menuridae), the faecal packet
is shot out by the young, caught by the female
outside the nest and transported far away to the
water. In some other passerines the parents help to
pull the packet out of the cloaca. At first, in many
species, the clean white faecal masses are swallowed
by the parent birds. Towards the end of the nestling
period in some species the faecal matter is deposited
by the young at the margin of the nest.

The transitory function of the cloacal epithelium
may work in an opposite way ; in parrakeets and
other parrots (Psittacidae) the cloaca of the nestling
has a drying function. During the whole nestling
period the water is resorbed by the epithelium, so
that a rapidly drying faecal matter is deposited ;
this accumulates in the bottom of the nest-hollow

Plate 11 · Running ; Wading

a *Upper :* Sanderling *Crocethia alba*, in winter
plumage, running along the shore (North America).
This small sandpiper has a circumpolar breeding
range in high latitudes and visits many of the
world's coasts as a migrant. Like other Scolopacidae it is an excellent flier as well as being
addicted to running ; some other sandpipers are
more notable for wading and have relatively long
legs.
*Phot. Gordon S. Smith, from National Audubon
Society, U.S.A.*

b *Lower left :* Whooping Crane *Grus americana* in its
winter-quarters (Gulf States of North America).
The long legs and long neck are characteristic of
the Gruidae and are adapted to wading in search
of food. Formerly more widely distributed at
both seasons, this species now breeds only in the
Mackenzie District of subarctic Canada and winters
only in southern Texas and Louisiana ; the entire
population has been reduced to about 30 birds.
*Phot. Allan D. Cruickshank, from National Audubon
Society, U.S.A.*

c *Lower right :* Spoonbill *Platalea leucorodia* in
breeding dress (Greece). This and other Plataleinae show an adaptation to wading like that of
cranes—an example of convergence, the two
groups not being nearly related. Note also the
specialised form of bill and the nuchal crest
(breeding season only) ; the forward toes are
connected at the base by webs.
Phot. Ilse Makatsch.

(See articles LOCOMOTION ; SANDPIPER ; CRANE ;
VANISHING BIRDS ; SPOONBILL ; ADAPTATION)

Table comparing weights at hatching of nidifugous and nidicolous young.

The total weight in grams is the fresh weight minus the internal yolk-sac. The other weights are expressed as percentages of total weight. The nervous system (brain and eyes) is proportionately heavier in nidifugous types ; the digestive tract is heavier in the nidicolous (in relation to intensified metabolism and parental care).

	Total weight	Brain	Eyes	Digestive tract	Liver
	Grams	Percentages of total weight			
Nidifugous Young					
Vanellus vanellus	13·0	6·05	9·72	6·13	2·95
Chrysolophus pictus	14·08	5·31	5·10	8·77	3·07
Rallus aquaticus	8·85	6·16	4·53	10·51	3·16
Coturnix coturnix	4·58	6·19	5·48	9·66	3·07
Charadrius alexandrinus	4·59	7·21	10·67	6·62	3·29
Nidicolous Young					
Columba livia (dom.)	11·49	2·92	4·94	10·33	3·48
Corvus corone	13·56	3·02	5·06	13·10	2·80
Corvus monedula	7·44	3·57	5·48	13·10	2·51
Sturnus vulgaris	4·66	3·21	4·03	14·09	2·85
Apus melba	4·19	3·11	6·12	14·64	3·05

as a dry powder. Here again this mode of function ceases strictly at the end of the nestling period (see DROPPINGS).

Growth. Reptiles grow slowly ; at hatching the general proportions are very like those of the adult, and the growth-curves of the various organs show only slight differences—growth of the parts is 'isometric'. Birds of ancient lineage, such as the gallinaceous birds, the Ostrich *Struthio camelus*, and the cassowaries (Casuariidae) among others, follow very closely this reptilian rule. In any event,

however, adult dimensions are attained by birds at a relatively early age. Growth in birds comes to a definitive stop very early in life, while in reptiles it may continue for a very long time.

In the more highly evolved groups of birds, the parts of the body show a pronounced divergence in their growth-curves ; sometimes the post-embryonic development of the wings is slowed down (Anseriformes), while in others the growth of feathers is delayed. A striking differential growth may occur in the nervous system and the intestine. The nidifugous type of young shows a marked advance of growth of the brain, corresponding to the early needs of relatively independent behaviour ; the nidicolous type, on the contrary, is characterised by the dominance of intestinal growth, in relation to the intensive feeding by the parents (see Table).

In some highly evolved types of development these differences lead to a remarkable growth-curve ; early in the postembryonic period the nestling attains the adult weight and even surpasses it considerably for a time. This surplus may equal as much as half of the total weight of the adult bird, and it can be due to fat deposits in different organs as well as to a transitory high weight of the liver (Fig. 3). See also GROWTH.

Evolution of Early Feeding Behaviour. The postembryonic surplus of weight demonstrates how intensive the adult feeding of the young must be. This activity of the parents is stimulated by transitory

---

Plate 12 · Swimming; Carrion Feeding

a *Upper :* Rednecked (or Northern) Phalarope *Lobipes lobatus* swimming—a bird in juvenile plumage, during passage (Norfolk, England). This and the other two Phalaropodidae are plover-like birds adapted to a largely aquatic existence ; it is indeed commonly oceanic outside the breeding season. Phalaropes find their food in the surface layer of the water, or in the shallows ; the toes are fringed with lobes, as an aid to swimming.
Phot. C. C. Doncaster.

b *Lower :* Common (or American) Crow *Corvus brachyrhynchos* attracted to carrion in the form of stranded fish (North America).
Phot. Allan D. Cruickshank, from National Audubon Society, U.S.A.

(See articles PHALAROPE ; SWIMMING AND DIVING ; CROW (I) ; FEEDING HABITS)

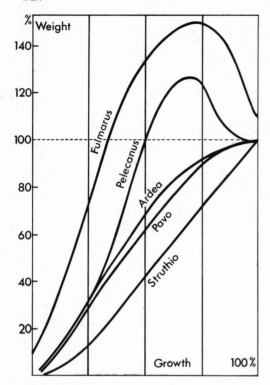

FIG 3. Growth curves of body weight. The mean weight of each species is given by the broken line of 100 per cent. The evolved type of development is often characterised by a surplus weight of the nestling (sometimes more than 25 per cent of the weight of the parents).

structures of the young bird in several groups, particularly in the Passeriformes, where the nestling develops a vividly coloured mouth-cavity enlarged by big white or yellow flanges (see under TONGUE). Combined with the gaping movements of the young, these structures are an effective stimulus for the parents ; the feeding intensity, measured by the number of visits in a day, is related to the development of the mouth flaps (see FEEDING OF YOUNG).

The gaping of the young is undirected in the earliest days ; the head is thrown vertically upwards and the mouth opened. Later on, with the maturation of the nervous system, optical and acoustic stimuli direct the gaping mouth towards the parent's bill. Passerine birds, cuckoos (Cuculidae), woodpeckers (Picidae), and hummingbirds (Trochilidae) show this behaviour in various degrees. In other nidicolous groups, e.g. Pelecaniformes, the young bird actively seeks the mouth of the adult, and the bill of the chick penetrates deeply into the fore-gut. Crossing of bills of adult and young is the method characteristic of the Procellariiformes.

A.P. & W.S.

Becker, R. 1959. Die Strukturanalyse der Gefiederfolgen von *Megapodius freyc. reinw.* und ihre Beziehung der Nestlingsdune der Hühnervögel. Rev. Suisse Zool. 66 : 411–527.
Burckhardt, D. 1954. Beitrag zur embryonalen Pterylose einiger Nesthocker. Rev. Suisse Zool. 61 : 551–632.
Kendeigh, S. C. 1952. Parental Care and its Evolution in Birds. Illinois Biol. Monogr. 22 : 1–356.
Portmann, A. 1955. Die postembryonale Entwicklung der Vögel als Evolutionsproblem. Acta XI Congr. Internat. Orn., Basel 1954 : 138–151.
Sutter, E. 1951. Growth and differentiation of the brain in nidifugous and nidicolous birds. Proc. X Internat. Orn. Congr., Uppsala 1950 : 635–644.

DIABLOTIN : name used in the West Indies for the Black-capped Petrel *Pterodroma hasitata* (see PETREL), and also (Trinidad) for *Steatornis caripensis* (see OILBIRD).

DIACROMYODIAN : see SYRINX

DIAGNOSIS : in taxonomy, see under DESCRIPTION.

DIAL-BIRD : see DAYAL-BIRD

DIAMOND-BIRD : alternative substantive name of *Pardalotus* spp. (see PARDALOTE; and FLOWERPECKER).

DIAPHRAGM : a system of membranes partially dividing the thoraco-abdominal cavity, so that the lungs and cervical air-sacs occupy one chamber and the majority of the air-sacs another, while the heart and abdominal viscera are in the remaining space (see RESPIRATORY SYSTEM). This arrangement in birds contrasts with the complete and more muscular transverse partition between the thoracic and abdominal cavities in mammals.

DIASTATAXIS : see PLUMAGE ; WING

DIATRYMIFORMES : order erected to include such fossil forms as *Diatryma, Omoramphus, Gastornis,* and *Remiornis* (see FOSSIL BIRDS).

DICAEIDAE : a family of the Passeriformes, suborder Oscines (see FLOWERPECKER).

DICHROMATIC : term sometimes used in the sense of dimorphic (see POLYMORPHISM).

DICKCISSEL : *Spiza americana* (see CARDINAL-GROSBEAK).

DICRURIDAE : a family of the Passeriformes, suborder Oscines (see DRONGO).

DIDUNCULINAE : see PIGEON

DIENCEPHALON : part of the forebrain (see NERVOUS SYSTEM).

DIGESTION: see ALIMENTARY SYSTEM; GRIT; NUTRITION; PELLET

DIGIT: a 'finger' or toe (see SKELETON; and LEG; WING). Primary feathers borne on the wing digits are sometimes called 'digitals'.

DIKKOP: see THICKKNEE

DIMORPHISM: see POLYMORPHISM; SEXUAL DIMORPHISM

DINORNITHES; DINORNITHIDAE: see below

DINORNITHIFORMES: an order, alternatively 'Dinornithes', of extinct 'ratite' birds comprising the family Dinornithidae, which some authors divide into Dinornithidae and Anomalopterygidae (see MOA). The order is not recognised in Stresemann's system, wherein the family Dinornithidae is placed in his order Apteryges (Apterygiformes)—see also RATITES, PHYLOGENY OF THE.

DIOCH: substantive name of *Quelea* spp. (see WEAVER).

DIOMEDEIDAE: see under PROCELLARIIFORMES; and ALBATROSS

DIPPER: substantive name of all members of the family Cinclidae (Passeriformes, suborder Oscines); used without qualification in Britain for *Cinclus cinclus*, and in North America for *C. mexicanus*; in the plural, general term for the family. (The alternative name 'Water Ouzel' was formerly used in Britain more often than nowadays, and the common names in some European countries mean 'water blackbird' and 'water starling'.) The Cinclidae are of mainly Palaearctic and New World distribution, in hilly country with rapid streams, and are remarkable—among passerines—for their aquatic, and indeed subaquatic, habits. There are four species in a single genus, and these differ only slightly in size and otherwise little except in plumage coloration; so far as information is available, their habits are closely alike.

The dippers as a group provide an excellent example of the adaptability of a typical passerine bird to an unusual environment without very obvious modifications. It would hardly be suspected from a cursory examination of a dipper, even in the hand, that it is a water bird. Its size and shape are approximately those of a Starling *Sturnus vulgaris*, although its plumage differs in colour and also in being dense and soft in texture. The flight, too, resembles that of the Starling. Whereas most water birds have feet modified in some way for swimming, dippers have feet of the kind normal for a perching bird; and the legs are rather long. When dippers swim on the surface, their unspecialised feet are moved very rapidly because they present only slight resistance to the water.

The following account of habits refers to the Dipper *C. cinclus*, particularly as observed in Britain, but may be taken as characteristic of the family. Under water the Dipper uses its wings for swimming, and they provide a means of propelling the bird powerfully enough to compete with the rushing turbulent currents in which it usually feeds. This is very well shown in Dr J. W. Jones's remarkable film taken through the glass side of a fish-hatchery tank visited by a wild Dipper. It can be seen on the film that, time after time, the wings propel the bird to the bottom within reach of fish ova. It was noted that the bird took only those ova that happened to be exposed and made no attempt whatever to uncover ova that were buried in the usual way. The film shows that each time the bird comes up it rises quickly and easily to the surface, but it gives the impression of requiring sustained effort with its wings to keep down. In the action covered by this film, scarcely any use is made of the feet; on the other hand, many experienced observers have reported seeing the feet used to assist the bird on the bottom. Naturally, the head is lowered when the bird is feeding on the bottom. It has been suggested that, if the bird tilts forward when facing the current, the pressure of water against the bird's back will tend to stabilise it if the legs are used for walking on the bottom. The significance of this has been challenged, and it now seems certain that the Dipper can move in all directions relative to the current, and that it can either walk on the bottom or rely solely on its wings for its under-water activities.

A Dipper is capable of rising straight out of water after a dive and flying off. Conversely, it can fly along a river course and suddenly plunge into the water, diving below from flight. At other times it will dive off a boulder, the wings being opened as it submerges. Usually it simply wades into the water, or it dives from the surface when swimming. The depth to which it usually goes is 1–2 feet, but the writer has seen one repeatedly going down to 3–4 feet.

The Dipper's name presumably refers to the bobbing action of the bird. This movement is often accompanied by blinking; each time the bird tips, it usually closes its white eyelids. The call-note is a strident 'zit', 'zit', which may be given from a boulder or in flight. The song resembles that of the Wren *Troglodytes troglodytes* in being loud and penetrating ; like the call-note, it can be heard above the roar of a cascading torrent.

The territorial behaviour of the Dipper has often been noted. Breeding pairs claim a considerable stretch of river and intruding members of the species are liable to be challenged. When the pair meet after being separated they often engage in a display in which they face each other, with bills pointing upwards, so that the white bib is shown to the best advantage. This is reminiscent of the display of the Robin *Erithacus rubecula*, a bird that also has a striking bib. This greeting ceremony doubtless plays a part in recognition, and it is interesting to note that, in both species, the sexes are so similar that they cannot be distinguished in the field, and that in both there are times when the females may sing. Population studies suggest that a normal British 'Dipper river' may have an average of about three birds for every two miles of its course.

Dipper *Cinclus cinclus*. *C.E.T.K.*

The food of the Dipper consists of many kinds of small water creatures living in fast flowing streams and rivers. The list of prey includes caddis-fly and dragon-fly larvae, small aquatic molluscs and crustaceans, worms, tadpoles, and very small fish. The Dipper ejects pellets of indigestible material through its mouth.

Dippers require sites close to water for their domed nests ; usually there is water immediately below the nest, and a typical site is in a steep river-

bank. Man-made sites are often provided by recesses in bridges, or in walls that face a river. Sometimes a nest is close to, or even under, a waterfall, so that it is constantly wetted by spray. Moss is used for the exterior and much of the rest of the structure. The lining, however, is of dead grass and a few dead oak or beech leaves. The clutch of 4–5 white eggs is laid early as compared with most birds ; in Britain it is usually in April, but sometimes earlier. A second brood is sometimes reared. The young disperse soon after leaving the nest.

The writer has had the opportunity of comparatively observing the behaviour of *C. mexicanus*, of which he watched two families in a remarkably turbulent stretch of water in the Yosemite Valley, California. The flight, the call notes, and the feeding behaviour appeared to be identical with those familiar to him in European birds.

As in the case of the wrens (Troglodytidae), another and probably related group building domed nests, it is possible that the dippers originated in the tropics of the New World and from there spread northwards and then eastwards. Distribution of the family and of separate forms tends to be discontinuous owing to the absence, over wide areas, of suitable habitats. At the present time there are in the Andes several races of the White-capped Dipper *C. leucocephalus*. The North American species, *C. mexicanus*, is found only on the western side of that continent, from Panama to Alaska, and is mainly slate-coloured with a dull brown head. The Palaearctic species (sometimes called the White-breasted Dipper) *C. cinclus* has a discontinuous distribution over much of Europe and eastwards to central Asia, with footholds in north-western Africa and on the southern flank of the Himalayas. Its geographical variation is complex, but according to Vaurie the subspecific forms fall into three groups—a western one, an isolated one in the Urals, and one in Central Asia. The Brown Dipper *C. pallasii*, a sombre bird chocolate-brown all over, is an inhabitant of northern Asia, eastwards to Japan. In the Himalayas, where the distribution of *C. cinclus* and *C. pallasii* overlap, the latter tends to frequent the lower levels (from the foothills to 6000 feet, but sometimes much higher) and the large streams ; the former is found in Kashmir at heights of 8000–14 000 feet. In mountain populations there is some altitudinal shift with the seasons, and in the colder, northern part of its range it may move south in winter. Elsewhere it is non-migratory except that in Germany second-year males have shown a tendency to wander. The habits of *C. mexicanus*, as described by American ornithologists, appear to be much the same as those of *C. cinclus,* and what Whistler says about *C. pallasii* in India is likewise consistent.   H.G.H.

Brownlow, H. G. 1953. Under-water movement of the Dipper. Brit. Birds 46 : 73–74.
Eggebrecht, E. 1937. Brutbiologie der Wasseramsel (*Cinclus cinclus aquaticus* (Bechst.)). J. Orn. 85 : 636–676.
Goodge, W. R. 1959. Locomotion and other behaviour of the Dipper. Condor 61 : 4–17.
Hann, H. W. 1950. Nesting behaviour of the American Dipper in Colorado. Condor 52 : 49–62.
Ingram, G. C. S., Salmon, H. M., & Tucker, B. W. 1938. The movements of the Dipper under water. Brit. Birds 32 : 58–63.
Jones, J. W. & King, G. M. 1952. The underwater activities of the Dipper. Brit. Birds 45 : 400–401.
Richter, H. 1953. Zur Lebensweise der Wasseramsel. Der Ortswechsel. J. Orn. 94 : 68–82.
Robson, R. W. 1956. The breeding of the Dipper in north Westmorland. Bird Study 3 : 170–180.

DIRECTION, SENSE OF: an expression requiring carefully restricted definition (see SENSES; also NAVIGATION).

DISCRIMINANT FUNCTION: see STATISTICAL SIGNIFICANCE

DISEASE: ill health in any of the many forms from which birds, like all other animals, may at times suffer. The causes of disease may be divided into immediate (or exciting) causes and predisposing causes. The chief predisposing factors in bird diseases are bad environmental conditions and adverse changes in the food supply.

Climatic changes and food supply are often linked. The bird's resistance to disease may be lowered by poor nutrition or by sudden changes in the temperature ; thus abnormal heat or abnormal cold may cause heavy losses either directly or by predisposing to infectious disease. Sustained wet and cold weather is liable to bring on diseases of the lungs, which are a common source of trouble in chicks, especially amongst the nidifugous species. The main change is one of acute congestion and oedema of the lungs, and it is probable that the poor heat-regulating mechanism of the young chick is also a factor in the development of this syndrome of 'chilling' (see HEAT REGULATION). Wet weather may increase the food supply by allowing birds to catch more worms and molluscs ; but this may sometimes be a disadvantage, since frequently these animals act as intermediate hosts for many parasites and thus a well-fed nestling may receive a pathogenic burden of parasites, such as the massive infection with trematodes sometimes seen in waders (Charadrii) and gulls (Larinae). Periods of drought may increase the concentration of birds at drinking places and thus facilitate the spread of infectious disease, such as salmonellosis or coccidiosis. Lack of water in very hot or cold weather is frequently a direct cause of death in birds.

Disease may be caused by pathogenic microorganisms—the fungi, bacteria, rickettsiae, and viruses that produce the group of illnesses known as the infectious diseases ; when the latter are spread by contact, direct or indirect, they are called contagious diseases. Disease is sometimes due to poisoning, and a very wide range of toxic substances is deleterious to birds. Ill health and even death may arise from a deficiency of vitamins or minerals, or simply from an insufficient food supply. Overwork of an organ of the body may give rise to disease elsewhere in the body ; thus enlargement of the heart has serious repercussions in many other organs. Infection with protozoan or metazoan parasites is a very frequent cause of disease, which arises when the delicate balance between host and parasite is deranged. Finally, it is probable that direct injury is the commonest cause of disease and death in wild birds.

As a result of disease, from whatever cause, changes occur in the organs and tissues of the bird and these alterations, which may be gross or microscopic, are termed lesions. Sometimes these are very specific to the cause, but more usually several different causes can produce very similar changes and effects. The primary cause of disease may act locally or it may act widely throughout the body ; for example, the cause remains localised in staphylococcal infections, whereas in pasteurellosis the agent gets into the blood and is disseminated widely in the tissues. Frequently the primary lesions have a further causative action in producing secondary disease elsewhere in the body.

The part played by disease in regulating the population of free-living wild birds is not yet clear ; the study of animal ecology in general suggests that numbers are controlled primarily by the food supply, and that predators and disease are of secondary importance (see POPULATION DYNAMICS). In some cases, however, food shortage and disease may act together . A classic example of this is grouse disease, in the Red Grouse *Lagopus scoticus,* where it seems that the critical factor may be malnutrition and that this is followed by a heavy infection with trichostrongyles (see ENDOPARASITE). These outbreaks usually occur in the spring, when the food supply is at its lowest. Dense populations help such outbreaks, since they aid the spread of disease and also reduce the available food. Epidemics with high mortality have occurred in many parts of the world, caused by several different bacterial and viral agents, but the long-term effects on bird numbers are not clear. Isolated cases of disease in wild birds are much more frequently encountered than the large outbreaks, and this is true even of the colonial species of birds.

Some of the more commonly encountered diseases of wild birds, other than those due to metazoan parasites, are described below. These conditions also occur in domestic and caged birds, but the emphasis here has been placed on the free-living wild bird.

Aspergillosis. This disease is due to infection with a mould, usually *Aspergillus fumigatus*, which is commonly present in decaying vegetable matter. Infection occurs when the bird inhales or ingests the spores of the fungus, and thus the lesions are produced chiefly in the lungs and the air sacs. The pulmonary lesions vary in size from pinhead spots to nodules several centimetres across ; the air sacs may be converted into thick-walled sacs with caseo-necrotic centres. Sometimes the disease is widespread in the body, and many organs, including the brain, may be affected. Aspergillosis has been recorded in many species of birds, and occasionally the disease occurs in large outbreaks with heavy mortality. Waterfowl and game-birds are particularly liable to aspergillosis, especially when kept in a semi-wild state. The disease is also frequently seen in penguins (Spheniscidae) kept in captivity.

Botulism. An anaerobic bacterial organism, *Clostridium botulinum* Type C, produces a very powerful exotoxin that is responsible for a serious type of food-poisoning in many species of animals, including birds and man. The toxin is formed outside the body of the bird when the anaerobe grows in stagnant shallow ponds or pools. *C. botulinum* multiplies rapidly in water containing decaying vegetation, dead fish, and particularly large quantities of dead insect matter ; slight alkalinity of the water and high temperatures aid multiplication, so that outbreaks occur most frequently in the summer months. Ducks are most frequently affected, so much so that the disease is called ' duck sickness '. The disease is not, however, confined to ducks, and to date species of birds belonging to 21 families are known to be affected with botulism. Under suitable conditions very large outbreaks of botulism occur, and it has been estimated that in one outbreak in Oregon a million birds died and that between one and three million birds died at Great Salt Lake in 1929.

Candida albicans Infection. This fungus sometimes causes disease of the mouth and crop of birds, a condition called ' thrush ' or ' canker ' by the bird-keeper. In young birds it sometimes causes serious losses.

Coryza. The term is applied to an infection of the upper respiratory tract of birds. It is a common infection in all species of birds and resembles the common cold of man. Droplet infection is the method of spread, and the disease is particularly common where birds are in close contact with each other. Most cases of coryza occur in the winter and spring months, outbreaks being often associated with severe climatic changes. The disease is common in domestic poultry and is commonly seen where game-bird chicks are intensively reared. It is thought that several infective agents may produce the condition and that in nature it is very rarely a single infection. Affected birds have a discharge from the eyes and nares, and the infra-orbital sinus is frequently distended with excess mucus. The disease is usually a mild one ; but it may be severe and spread down into the lungs and air sacs, when the condition may become chronic.

Deficiency Diseases. Lack or imbalance of amino-acids, proteins, carbohydrates, fats, minerals, water, and vitamins may lead to disease. Common signs of a deficiency disease include retarded or stunted growth, poor feathering, certain bone conditions, poor reproduction, and even death. Much is known of this group of diseases in domestic birds but little of the nutritional requirements of wild birds in nature. Young Mallard *Anas platyrhynchos* are sometimes affected with a disease characterised by lack of head feathers, and this appears to be due to a deficiency of vitamins of the B complex. See also NUTRITION.

Encephalitis. Inflammation of the brain occurs in birds, and one specific form of this is due to a virus. In domestic poultry the disease is known as epidemic tremor because of the muscular spasms that shake the body. A form of avian encephalomyelitis sometimes occurs in tits (Paridae) and probably in other birds. Equine encephalitis virus occurs in wild birds in America, especially in pheasants (Phasianidae).

Erysipelas Infection. The micro-organism *Erysipelothrix rhusiopathiae* usually produces a fatal septicaemia. Most species of mammals, birds, and fishes seem to be susceptible to infection with this organism, which can live for long periods in the soil and probably gets into the body through small abrasions and wounds. A closely related organism, *Listeria monocytogenes*, also causes septicaemia, with haemorrhages throughout the body ; or it may produce a chronic condition in which the main changes are confined to the head region, the comb and wattles being particularly affected in the case of the domestic fowl.

Fowl Leucosis. The term 'leucosis complex' refers to a group of diseases characterised by an abnormal production of the white blood cells and consequent changes in the organs and tissues. As a result of the multiplication of the stem cells (primordial germ cells), tumour-like swellings are produced. This group of diseases is of the greatest importance in domestic poultry but little is known of its occurrence in wild birds. A similar neoplastic condition has been seen in partridges (Phasianidae) and owls (Strigiformes) in Britain, but it is not known if the conditions are related.

Fowl-plague. This is a most serious virus infection of domestic fowls, but most other birds are fairly resistant. The disease spreads rapidly in fowls and produces a high mortality. The term 'fowl-pest' embraces both this condition and Newcastle disease (below).

Fowl-pox. This is a virus infection of the skin, especially of the head and feet, of birds. It is a common disease and has been recorded in many species. Amongst wild birds, pigeons (Columbidae) seem to be most frequently affected. Wart-like nodules or scabs appear on the head and on the feet ; sometimes there may be diphtheritic membranes in the mouth and at the back of the throat.

Lead Poisoning. This is common in waterfowl in America and is a serious source of loss. Lead shot falls into the mud of ponds and streams and is then eaten by ducks. The metal is deposited in the tissues and acts as a cumulative poison. See also under GRIT.

Newcastle Disease. Caused by a virus, this is one of the most serious diseases of domestic poultry and has a world-wide distribution. Acute and chronic forms of the disease occur. The virus has been isolated from a very large number of different species of wild birds, many of which appear to harbour the virus without showing any ill effects.

Pasteurellosis. *Pasteurella pseudotuberculosis* is a common pathogen of wild-life. Many species of birds become infected with this organism, which produces white necrotic lesions in various parts of the body. It does not usually cause outbreaks of disease but is responsible for sporadic cases.

Protozoal Infections. Many protozoa parasitise birds, but few of them are pathogenic. They are to be found in many tissues of the body. Genera of the suborder Haemospororina are important pathogens, e.g. members of the genus *Plasmodium* cause malaria in man and birds. These parasites are transmitted by mosquitoes. They undergo compli-

cated life cycles, the details of which differ in man and birds. The parasitised erythrocytes (red cells) break down and hence anaemia is produced. *Plasmodium gallinaceum* causes a serious disease, with a high mortality, in domestic fowls. It is believed that junglefowl (e.g. *Gallus layfetti*) are the natural hosts of this parasite.

Parasites of the genus *Haemoproteus* are transmitted by louse-flies and midges. These blood parasites are common in many species of birds and occasionally they cause disease. Leucocytozoan parasites occur in the white cells of birds (also in the red cells). They are common in wild birds and also cause disease in many species of domestic birds. Leucocytozoan species are transmitted by blackflies (*Simulium*).

Parasites of the order Eucoccidiorida, which includes the coccidia, are of the very greatest importance in domestic poultry. Members of the coccidia family have a single host. The infective oocyst is ingested by a bird and a multiplication cycle then occurs in the parasitised tissue, usually the intestine. Acute disease and death is the usual sequel. See also ENDOPARASITE.

Psittacosis (Ornithosis). This is a disease caused by a very large virus, and epidemics of psittacosis have been described in captive and free-living wild birds. The disease has a world-wide distribution. At least seventy species of birds, including many non-psittacine species, have been proved to be infected with the virus, and man is also susceptible. Infection in birds often takes place in the nest, and adverse changes in the environment of the birds may precipitate an acute outbreak of the disease. There are no characteristic clinical signs, and at post mortem examination an enlarged spleen may be the only lesion.

Quail Disease. Enzootics of a highly fatal disease in the American Bobwhite *Colinus virginianus* and some species of grouse (Tetraonidae) have been described. The disease takes the form of an ulcerative enteritis with a heavy mortality. The exact cause is not known, but a virus has been incriminated.

Salmonellosis. Infections of birds with *Salmonella* organisms are common and important problems in the poultry industry. Wild birds sometimes harbour the organisms and may show lesions at post mortem examination. Acute septicaemic and chronic forms of the disease are encountered, and usually the liver and spleen show lesions in the form of grey or white nodules scattered through the substance of the organ ; there may be translucent nodules in the lungs. *S. pullorum*, *S. gallinarum*, and *S. typhi-murium* are the species most often isolated from wild birds. The organisms are excreted in the droppings, which thus serve as further sources of infection.

Tuberculosis. The avian type of *Mycobaterium tuberculosis* is a common cause of tuberculosis in birds, which become infected by ingestion. Infection with acid-fast bacilli of this or similar species has been recorded from many species, particularly from predators. The disease affects many organs and commonly produces lesions in the liver, intestine, and spleen. These lesions are nodular, white, and cheesy in appearance ; they contain large numbers of the organism. Affected birds frequently excrete the bacilli in vast quantities and so spread the infection.

Tumours. Neoplasms (malignant new growths) are common in birds, and many different forms occur. They may arise from any organ or tissue. Some of them are of virus origin, and in domestic poultry an intensive study has been made of their properties and characters.

Vesicular Dermatitis. This term is applied to a skin disease that is due to one or more viruses and occurs in several species of wild birds, including Manx Shearwater *Puffinus puffinus*, Common Gull *Larus canus*, Blackheaded Gull *L. ridibundus* and Oystercatcher *Haematopus ostralegus*. Blisters or vesicles appear on the webs of the feet and there may be a heavy mortality amongst the young. The disease is contagious, being spread through the medium of infected perching-stones and by contact with infected ground.

See also ECTOPARASITE ; ENDOPARASITE.

A.R.J.

Biester, H. E. & Schwarte, L. H. 1959. Diseases of Poultry. 4th ed. Ames, Iowa.
Committee of Inquiry on Grouse Disease. 1911. The Grouse in Health and Disease. 2 vols. London.
Herman, C. M. 1955. Diseases of birds. *In* Wolfson, A. (ed.). Studies of Avian Biology. Urbana, Ill.
McDiarmid, A. 1960. Diseases of Freeliving Wild Animals. F.A.O. Health Mono. no. 1. Rome.

DISPERSAL: term used variously, in different contexts, with the basic sense of outward spread from a point or area of origin. In respect of long-term distribution it implies range expansion (cf. RADIATION (2); and see RANGE EXPANSION). In respect of seasonal movement it denotes a more or less random centrifugal movement from the breeding locality in the off-season, not amounting to true migration (see MIGRATION). In a quite short-term sense it may be applied to the daily (sometimes longer) sorties from the communal breeding or roosting place in quest of food, if these take place in various directions.

DISPERSION: the state of spatial separation between individuals of a flock, colony, or population ; defined by Wynne-Edwards (in an important book published after the present work was in proof) as ' the placement of individuals or groups of individuals within the habitats they occupy and the processes by which this is brought about '. See TERRITORY ; also AGGREGATION ; ECOLOGY ; FLOCKING.

Wynne-Edwards, V.C. 1962. Animal Dispersion in relation to Social Behaviour. Edinburgh and London.

DISPLACEMENT ACTIVITY: term designating movements that, as regards their causation and their function, seem to occur out of context ; they are in both respects unexpected. For instance, fighting cocks may go through the complete or incomplete movements of feeding even although they are not hungry and do not actually eat anything; a broody gull *Larus* sp. may make building movements even although its dominant urge is to incubate and the nest does not need to be repaired. The following problems are raised by these phenomena : are such unexpected movements caused in the same way as they are when appearing in the usual context, and do the movements serve the same function in both contexts ?

' Displacement activity ' is synonymous with ' substitute activity ', ' displacement reaction ', ' false activity ', ' irrelevant behaviour ', ' extraneous response ', ' sparking-over activity ', and similar terms. The term is used to indicate a phenomenon that has to be explained ; it is not intended as offering an explanation. To label a certain movement a displacement activity is doing no more than to state that a displaying Peacock *Pavo cristatus* performs ' curious antics '—in both cases a phenomenon is pointed out that has to be studied.

It is still a matter of dispute in what respects there are gradations between displacement activities and other examples of one behaviour changing into another and often unexpected movement. For instance, a bird may suddenly interrupt sexual behaviour and attack its mate ; or it may attack another bird preventing it from reaching its food ; or a bird may take a roundabout way to the nest when meeting with an obstacle. The solution depends, of course, on future research ; and naturally the criterion ' unexpected ' is of value only so long as it leads to research and only until an explanation has been found. In spite of this possibility of a graded series, the recognition of such extreme cases as displacement feeding in fighting cocks, displacement preening in male Starlings *Sturnus vulgaris* in a hostile clash, and displacement building in an incubating gull, has been useful by calling attention to important problems of animal behaviour ; these are closely related to the problem of normal motivation, to problems of social communication, and to problems of the origin and evolution of behaviour. The problem of their causation is complicated by the fact that many displacement activities have obviously provided ' raw material' for the secondary evolution of signal movements, and in the process have been ritualised (i.e. secondarily adapted as a signalling device) and perhaps emancipated (i.e. detached from their original motivation) ; for an understanding of the phenomenon, non-ritualised displacement activities thus seem to be the most useful.

Two basic facts have been established. (1) A certain movement, readily recognisable by its form alone (e.g. preening in a gull) occurs in two very different situations, namely (a) when the plumage is wet, dirty, or disarranged, and (b) when the bird is broody and at the same time frightened by a disturbance near the nest. Similarly, Starlings preen when their plumage is wet, dirty, or disarranged, and when they are facing territorial rivals so that they are induced both to attack and to escape. However little we know about the causation of building (or preening), this much is certain, that ' normal' building (or preening) is not dependent on arousal of attack and escape. (2) Such activities appearing in two situations can be shown to be adapted in minute detail to one of the two situations (building serves to construct a nest ; preening to re-arrange and clean the plumage), whereas in the other situation no such adaptedness is evident ; or, in ritualised displacement activities, the function is entirely different (see RITUALISATION).

The first fact shows that one movement may appear as the result of different causal situations. These, it is true, must be supposed to share common causal factors, in fact they must have a ' final common path' since the motor patterns are identical, and the problem is : to what extent is the deeper causation different in the two situations, to what extent similar? The second fact justifies the qualitative distinction between the ' normal', ' usual', or ' autochthonous' movement and the displacement activity ; it implies that the movement has evolved primarily because of its usefulness in the first situation and that its appearance in the second situation is, in a sense, a by-product.

Analysis of the conditions in which displacement activities occur has shown that they often appear when the autochthonous movement (or movements) aroused at the moment is thwarted. From studies of normal behaviour we know that full performance, either once or repeated, of the end acts of behaviour chains normally causes a drop in the readiness to repeat the behaviour (' drive reduction'), and it therefore seems as if incomplete reduction of the thwarted ' drive' is in some way responsible for the occurrence of displacement activity. Study thus forces the investigator to unravel the factors that cause normal drive reduction, in order to understand more fully why in displacement situations reduction of a drive failed to be achieved.

Studies of such situations have suggested several possible causes of incomplete drive reduction. The best known and probably most common cause is the simultaneous arousal of two wholly or partly incompatible behaviour tendencies. Thus the simultaneous arousal of attack and escape, which is common in a territorial boundary clash, gives rise in many animals to a variety of displacement activities. Another conflict situation occurs in pair formation, when sexual tendencies conflict with aggressive and fleeing tendencies. It is also possible, however, that there are situations in which absence of stimuli, necessary for the continuation of the normal behaviour chain, gives rise to displacement activity, although it is becoming increasingly clear that even in such situations the possibility of a conflict cannot be ruled out.

A second aspect of the problem is : why does the animal in such circumstances show behaviour at all ; why, instead of the thwarted movements, does it perform another movement of its repertoire ; and what determines which of the other movements shall be shown?

There are two hypotheses. Earlier investigators (Makkink, Kortlandt, Tinbergen) have assumed, more or less explicitly, that the excitation so to speak ' sparks over' (or finds an outlet) through another channel of the nervous system. As support for this idea it has been considered that a displacement activity is often much more vigorously executed than it ever is when the activity is directly aroused. However, this ' vigour' seems to be due to admixtures of components belonging to one of the systems that are active at the moment ; for instance displacement nest building in fighting Herring Gulls *Larus argentatus* (' grass pulling') includes vigorous pecking into the ground, now recognised as a redirected attack (see REDIRECTION). This argument is therefore no longer valid. Further, the sparking-over idea seems to be in conflict with the generally observed fact that two instincts cannot be fully active at the same time, but tend to suppress each other ; a very hungry animal does not respond readily to predators ; conversely, strong stimulation by a predator may stop all other activities and cause escape. Why should suppression suddenly turn into its opposite, facilitation?

The second hypothesis (Van Iersel, De Ruiter, Weidmann, Sevenster) supposes that a conflict between two antagonistic systems suppresses not only the movements of each of them but also the inhibitory effect which each of them, when aroused, has on all other systems. These are supposed, on good grounds, to be all more or less aroused, although none of them is completely dominant so long as one system dominates them all and, so to speak, claims priority for its movements. But the state of arousal of each of these latent systems is different; usually one is nearer the threshold for release than the others, and this would be the one most easily disinhibited when two dominant tendencies come in conflict with each other. According to this hypothesis, therefore, simultaneous arousal of two incompatible systems would result in disinhibition enabling the 'next dominant' system to produce its movements. Thus, in a broody bird, nest building is supposed to be constantly in a state of mild arousal, but is always suppressed by brooding; and only when brooding is thwarted (and the bird is neither very hungry nor has its plumage disarranged) do nest building movements appear. Two facts are consistent with this idea: (a) the displacement activity is usually incomplete in the same way as a low intensity form of the activity when directly aroused; (b) all stimuli that elicit the movement when directly aroused also seem to facilitate it when it is shown as a displacement activity. Such facilitation may be provided by external stimuli; in certain conflict situations a bird is more ready to make bathing movements when it happens to be in the water than when it is on land. Or it may be provided by the initial posture; thus it seems very probable that the fact that a redirected attack makes a male Herring Gull bend down, in roughly the same posture that it takes up when collecting nest material, facilitates collecting of material rather than any other activity. Whether this is due to external stimuli, to proprioceptive stimuli, or to links between 'central commands' (Van Holst) cannot be decided without further experiments on suitable objects. It may well be that the decision as to which one of a number of more or less available movements will be shown as a displacement activity, in a certain conflict, depends on the imbalance between all the available factors, internal and external, that are present for each of these potentially available movements. Thus, the clarification of the problem consequent on more precise observations and on more concise formulations has led to distinct hypotheses, and accurate experimental work is now in progress in various laboratories.

Displacement activities are further of great interest because they seem to have supplied the raw material for many displays that function as signals. Comparative studies indicate that, once a displacement activity has acquired signal value (or, in other words, is responded to in a new way by other individuals), it may change and acquire all the characters that make a signal effective (see RELEASER; RITUALISATION). How this new function originated can only be surmised, but it is conceivable that the admixture of 'autochthonous' elements (such as a redirected attack) and the quick alternation between the displacement activity and parts of the conflicting behaviour patterns may have contributed to this. The selection pressure towards improved signalling function seems to have promoted such changes as exaggeration of certain components and omission of others, rhythmicity, development of brightly coloured structures, and development of 'typical intensity' (Morris). It seems that ritualisation is often, if not always, accompanied by 'emancipation', i.e. by separation of the mechanism underlying the displacement activity from its original controls and its incorporation into a new major executive system; thus, courtship movements such as may have been derived from threat may now be motivated by sexual rather than by hostile tendencies (see DISPLAY). This possibility alone is enough to demand concentration on non-ritualised displacement activity when the causation of the phenomenon itself is to be studied. N.T.

Iersel, J. J. A. Van & Bol, A. C. A. 1958. Preening of two tern species: a study on displacement activities. Behaviour 13: 1–88.

Morris, D. 1957. 'Typical Intensity' and its relation to the problem of ritualisation. Behav. 11: 1–12.

Sevenster, P. 1961. A causal analysis of a displacement activity (Fanning in Gasterosteus aculeatus L.). Behav. suppl. 9.

Tinbergen, N. 1952. 'Derived' activities; their causation, biological significance, origin and emancipation during evolution. Quart. Rev. Biol. 27: 1–32.

DISPLAY: term denoting movements that have become specialised in the course of evolution to serve as 'signals' in social communication. Although it is usually restricted to visual signals, many primarily visual signals are associated with characteristic calls; and visual and auditory signals may both have a display function. The discussion here is limited to visual signals.

Functional Aspects. Display movements can be roughly classified according to the context in which they appear.

(i) *Threat.* These movements are used in encounters with rivals, and indicate the potential aggressiveness of the displaying individual. Two common types are the 'head forward', in which the body is horizontal and directed towards the rival, and the 'head up', where the bill is pointed upwards and the breast directed towards the opponent. Some species have a repertoire of several different threat postures.

(ii) *Submissive.* These are used between rivals or mates and serve to reduce the aggressiveness of the bird to which the display is directed. Amongst passerines a common submissive posture consists of perching slightly crouched, with the head withdrawn and the body feathers raised. Thus a subordinate bird in a dominance hierarchy will display in this way to a superior, and a receptive female may adopt such a posture at pair formation (see DOMINANCE (2), PAIR FORMATION).

(iii) *Begging.* These are used primarily by juveniles begging for food from their parents, and also in courtship feeding (see COURTSHIP FEEDING).

(iv) *Sexual.* These are used between mates or potential mates ; they serve a variety of functions such as pair formation, maintenance of the pair-bond, reduction of mutual aggressiveness, synchronisation of reproductive rhythms, and facilitation of copulation (see COPULATION).

(v) *Greeting and nest-relief.* This category overlaps the two previous ones. It consists of displays given when two individuals meet after a temporary separation, and thus occurs in the contexts of parent/young and male/female relations. These displays probably function in reducing aggression.

(vi) *Social.* These are without obvious sexual or aggressive significance, and are important, for instance, in flock integration (see FLOCKING).

(vii) *Anti-predator.* This includes a number of displays given to predators—for instance, the 'mobbing' displays given by passerines and others to predators, and distraction displays (see DISTRACTION DISPLAY).

Although displays function as social signals, this does not necessarily imply an immediate response by the partner. Thus the importance of submissive and greeting displays lies not so much in evoking a response as in inhibiting the aggressiveness of the partner. Further, many courtship displays occur at intervals during periods of maintenance activities, and although they may have long-term stimulatory or pacificatory effects they seem to produce no immediate changes in the situation.

Causation. In nearly all cases that have been analysed, display movements are associated with tendencies to behave in incompatible ways. In the case of aggressive displays, these tendencies are attacking and fleeing ; in courtship display, a sexual tendency is involved in addition—although the meaning of 'sexual' here is to be interpreted rather broadly, as many courtship displays are only distantly related to copulation—and sometimes also tendencies to nest-build, preen, etc. In mobbing, the tendencies are to investigate, to attack, and to flee ; and in distraction display, conflicting tendencies to show parental behaviour, to attack, and to flee may be involved.

When any one of these tendencies is present alone, the behaviour is simple—e.g. pure attack, escape, or sexual behaviour may be shown. When two or more incompatible tendencies are present, various types of ambivalent behaviour may occur (see AMBIVALENCE), and some instances of this have been specialised in evolution for a communicatory function and thus may be designated as displays. Most species have a large repertoire of display movements, and each is associated with a particular range of strengths and relative strengths of the conflicting tendencies. Thus, where there are several threat postures, each is associated with different values of attacking and fleeing tendencies. Similarly, as the absolute and relative values of the male's tendencies to attack, to flee from, and to behave sexually towards the female change throughout the reproductive season, there are correlated changes in the courtship displays. Often particular components of a display (e.g. crouching, wing raising) are associated primarily with one of the conflicting tendencies ; the nature of the display then indicates the motivation. Thus, although the displays of any one species usually fall into a number of fairly distinct types, each type shows considerable variability and there may be intermediates between them.

There are some exceptions to this general rule that display movements are associated with conflicting tendencies. Thus the various components of the soliciting posture of most female passerines all fluctuate together ; although the female may change over suddenly from soliciting to aggressive or fleeing behaviour, it may be that the posture itself is purely sexual. Similarly, although the begging displays of young birds may contain aggressive or fleeing components, these may not be essential to the display.

Ontogeny. Display movements characteristic of the species normally appear in individuals on the first occasion that the relevant circumstances arise. Furthermore, the response to display movements made by other individuals is also usually appropriate on the first occasion it arises. See BEHAVIOUR, DEVELOPMENT OF.

Evolution. Display movements are usually characteristic of the species, and are more similar in closely related species than in distantly related ones. The comparative study of display can thus provide evidence about phylogenetic relationships between species. Alternatively, by comparing the displays of species of known phylogenetic relationship, it is possible to form hypotheses about the evolution of the displays.

So far, three evolutionary sources of display movements have been recognised—intention movements (e.g. intention movements of attack, escape, nest building, etc.) ; displacement activities (used here in the sense of a heterogeneous category of activities appearing in contexts in which they appear to be functionally irrelevant) ; and redirection activities (see DISPLACEMENT ACTIVITY ; REDIRECTION). In addition, displays of one type may be evolved from displays originally used in another context—e.g. courtship feeding from parent/juvenile behaviour (see COURTSHIP FEEDING), or sexual from aggressive behaviour. In evolution the display movements have been ritualised—i.e. they have become more adapted for a signal function. The changes involved in ritualisation have resulted in the movement becoming more conspicuous and more different from other signal movements of the same species and from signal movements of other species (see RITUALISATION). They consist in :

(*a*) Changes in the form of the movement itself (e.g. changes in the intensity or co-ordination of the components).

(*b*) Changes in the relations between the associated internal and external causal factors and the movement ; important here is the development of ' typical intensity ', whereby a movement of constant form is given over a wider range of causal factors than that which evoked it initially. In this way variability of the movement is reduced and it becomes more efficient as a signal.

(*c*) The development of conspicuous structures that are shown off by the display movement. Since homologous movements in related species often show off different structures, it would seem that the movements must be evolved first and the structures later ; but there has undoubtedly been much interaction.

(*d*) Recombination of single displays into various rigid sequences.

In general, the threat and anti-predator displays of related species are more similar than are the courtship displays ; and the early courtship displays,

functioning in pair formation, diverge more than those used in copulation. This is to be expected on the view that the early pair-forming displays are important in promoting reproductive isolation (see PAIR FORMATION). There may even be some selective advantage in similarity of the aggressive and anti-predator displays to those of related species. The degree of differentation between the courtship displays of closely related species renders these displays useful as taxonomic characters, and they have been so used with effect in a number of groups (e.g. Anatidae).

It is not possible here to attempt any description of the variety of display types to be found amongst birds. Often the displays are extremely elaborate —as in the manakins (Pipridae), bowerbirds (Ptilonorhynchidae), or birds-of-paradise (Paradisaeidae), or in those sexually monomorphic species that have intricate reciprocal ceremonies between the mates (e.g. Great Crested Grebe *Podiceps cristatus*)—see articles on the groups named. To what extent the principles discussed in the preceding paragraphs, which have been derived from the study of relatively simple cases, can be applied to these highly ritualised and elaborate cases remains to be seen.

See Plates (phot.) 22a, 24ab, 25, 26ab, 27ab, 28abc.

R.A.H.

Andrew, R. J. 1956. The aggressive and courtship behaviour of certain emberizines. Behav. 10 : 255–308.

Andrew, R. J. 1956. Some remarks on behaviour in conflict situations. Brit. J. Anim. Behav. 4 : 41–45.

Andrew, R. J. 1961. The displays given by passerines in courtship and reproductive fighting : a review. Ibis 103a : 315–348 ; 549–579.

Armstrong, E. A. 1947. Bird Display and Behaviour. London.

Heinroth, O. & Heinroth, M. 1928. Die Vögel Mitteleuropas. Berlin.

Hinde, R. A. 1952. The behaviour of the Great Tit (*Parus major*) and some other related species Behav. suppl. 2.

Hinde, R. A. 1955–56. A comparative study of the courtship of certain finches. Ibis 97 : 706–745 ; 98 : 1–23.

Lorenz, K. 1937. The companion in the bird's world. Auk 54 : 245–273.

Lorenz, K. 1941. Vergleichende Bewegungstudien an Anatiden. J. Orn. 89 : 194–294.

Marler, P. 1956. The behaviour of the Chaffinch. Behav. suppl. 5.

Morris, D. 1956. The feather postures of birds and the problem of the origin of social signals. Behav. 9 : 75–113.

Morris, D. 1956. *In* L'instinct dans le comportement des animaux et de l'homme (Symposium Singer Polignac). Paris.

Moynihan, M. 1955. Some aspects of reproductive behaviour in the Black-headed Gull (*Larus ridibundus* L.) and related species. Behav. suppl. 4.

Tinbergen, N. 1948. Social releasers and the experimental method required for their study. Wilson Bull. 60 : 6–52.

Tinbergen, N. 1951. The Study of Instinct. Oxford.

Tinbergen, N. 1952. Derived activities : their causation, biological significance, origin and emancipation during evolution. Quart. Rev. Biol. 27 : 1–32.

Tinbergen, N. 1959. Comparative studies of the behaviour of gulls (Laridae) : a progress report. Behav. 15 : 1–70.

DISTAL : furthest from the centre of the body or from the point of attachment (e.g. of a limb) ; opposite of PROXIMAL.

DISTRACTION DISPLAY : a term that has been used with varying connotations but is most appropriately applied to the elaborate stereotyped activities performed by a parent bird that tend to concentrate the attention of potential predators on it and away from the nest or young. The wider term ' diversionary behaviour ' includes less elaborate and specialised activities functioning to the same effect—such as some of the unritualised movements and calls of disturbed birds ; fluttering which appears slightly abnormal ; and possibly movements such as those of the tail of a motmot *Momotus* sp. as it perches on a branch near the nest. Practically all forms of distraction display, as defined above, may be classified into two types—injury simulation and mammal simulation. Injury simulation denotes ritualised behaviour making a bird appear to be incapacitated to some extent. During some such displays the resemblance of the movements to those of a crippled bird are very realistic (Ringed Plover *Charadrius hiaticula*, Killdeer *C. vociferus*). Mammal simulation gives a striking impression of a small mammal escaping. Forms of these displays grade into less recognisable abnormal or inhibited forms of diversionary display. Distraction display, especially injury simulation, is performed by at least some members of a great number of families. Its incidence and accentuation in a species are closely related to habitat adaptation (especially to ground-nesting).

Motivation. Distraction display and a number of other forms of diversionary display are the outcome of conflicting motivations (see DISPLAY) ; those concerned with parental behaviour involve remaining close to nest or chicks and defending them (see PARENTAL CARE) on the one hand, and the impulse to escape on the other. Distraction display is compromise behaviour that has become ritualised (see RITUALISATION). Displacement, transference, or redirection activities such as incongruous preening or feeding behaviour may occur in close association with distraction display and possibly add to its effectiveness (see DISPLACEMENT ACTIVITY). Distraction display is most usually accentuated about the time when the eggs of species with nidifugous young hatch, or when nidicolous young leave the nest.

Evolution. Diversionary displays in general, and distraction displays in particular, must have evolved through the selective effect of predators. The elaborate verisimilitude of some of them reflects the considerable discriminatory ability of some predators. Where there are very few species of relevant predator or, as in some areas of the Arctic, only one major non-avian predator (Arctic Fox, preying mostly on rodents), specialised selection has resulted in specialised displays, in particular the mammal simulation, or ' rodent-run ', of a few species, such as the Purple Sandpiper *Calidris maritima*. The displays of bush-nesting and tree-nesting species in Australia appear to be particularly adaptive in relation to reptilian predators.

Habitat. The most elaborate distraction displays are performed by birds nesting in open habitats. Distraction display is most adaptive for species with relatively inconspicuous nests in vulnerable situations primarily exposed to ground predators. (Such behaviour in tree-nesting species may sometimes indicate an ancestral tradition of nesting on or near the ground.) While similarities in the character of the display may be noted in closely related species, the elaboration of such behaviour in any species appears to be governed by its effectiveness in protecting the nest or chicks.   E.A.A.

Armstrong, E. A. 1956. Distraction display and the human predator. Ibis 98 : 641–654. (References.)

DISTRIBUTION, FREQUENCY : see STATISTICAL SIGNIFICANCE

DISTRIBUTION, GEOGRAPHICAL : the distribution of species or other categories considered in broad terms of range, as distinct from local distribution within the limits of the range. The latter depends on habitat availability and other ecological factors varying from place to place within an area that is occupied to such extent as these allow (see ECOLOGY). Geographical distribution, on the other hand, is determined by factors, operating on a wider scale, that set limits to the range. Such factors include climate, and its effects on terrain, in relation to the conditions to which particular kinds of birds are adapted (see CLIMATOLOGY) ; the configuration of the land-masses, in relation to the original area of habitation ; and the presence of competitive forms in areas otherwise suitable and accessible.

Zoogeography, as the study of this aspect of animal life is called, may take a static view, recording the facts of distribution as they appear at the present time and relating them to existing conditions. Or it may take a historical view, seeking to derive the present situation from the evolution of the different groups and forms in a changing world. The static approach is of necessity largely descriptive ; the historical approach is more analytical, but highly speculative.

In dealing with birds, especially, one may consider either the gross range or the different seasonal ranges—or the breeding range as distinct from the range occupied outside the breeding season (or possibly by non-breeding individuals at any time). In some instances there is only the gross range, nothing more than local movements taking place. In others, the breeding and non-breeding ranges may be markedly different, in which case the ranges may overlap, adjoin, or be widely separated ; the movements involved constitute migration, thus seen as an essential concomitant of seasonal changes in geographical distribution (see MIGRATION).

Physiography. Most birds live on land ; all must come to land at least for breeding. Land constitutes 29 per cent of the surface of the globe ; considered latitudinally, more than two-thirds lies north of the Equator ; considered longitudinally, about two-thirds of the area is included in the Old World. All birds are to a greater or less extent adapted, notably in respect of food supply, to certain climatic conditions. Taking all these points together, one notes that in the North Temperate and Arctic Zones there are large areas of land, all nearly connected ; that in the tropics also there are large areas, but separated from each other ; and that in the South Temperate Zone (mainly in its subtropical portions) there are smaller areas, very widely separated from each other. Nevertheless, all the main areas are at least indirectly linked, or nearly so, by land connections. There is also the question of altitude above sea level, in that elevated areas—some of great extent—are subject to lower temperatures than would otherwise obtain in their latitudes ; but greater altitude cannot be closely compared with higher latitude, seeing that the alpine zone of equatorial mountain masses is not subject to severe seasonal change as in the arctic.

In addition to temperature, precipitation is the other important climatic factor ; the two together largely determine the type of vegetation predominant in an area (see VEGETATION). Deserts present conditions calling for special adaptations on the part of their inhabitants, and so constitute barriers to the spread of non-adapted forms. The same, at the other extreme, is true of continuous areas

of tropical rain-forest—inhospitable to birds of open country. Great mountain ranges may also be barriers, not only as physical obstacles but also because they often represent the boundaries between areas of differing climate.

Despite the avian powers of flight, even moderate expanses of open sea appear to be effective barriers to the dispersal of many land birds ; the frequency of trans-oceanic wandering by individuals bears little relation to the chances of a viable nucleus of a new population becoming established overseas. Indeed, one of the puzzling things about avian dispersal is that while many kinds of land birds do cross water barriers, others seem to be stopped by them ; thus, there are five independently descended species of land birds on Tristan da Cunha, some 2000 miles from the nearest mainland, while on the other hand many species widespread on the American continents are absent from the West Indies.

It is necessary to qualify the foregoing statement that within the total geographical range of a species its local distribution depends on ecological factors such as habitat availability ; this may be entirely true of migratory species or of others that at least move freely through the area between their scattered breeding localities. It is an over-simplification, however, in respect of sedentary species with such discontinuous ranges that they are at all times restricted to certain widely separated areas (for example, see under MONTANE) ; and in such instances, although ecological factors are of course involved, the discrete distribution should be viewed in the geographical rather than the local sense.

Zonation. This term is used by Darlington to express a broad geographical aspect of distribution. Proceeding northwards from the Equator, he describes the following latitudinal zones : (1) The tropics, where birds (families, genera, and species) are most numerous and most diverse, and include many groups not represented in higher latitudes. (2) The north temperate area, where they are less numerous and less diverse, with few groups different from those found in the tropics. (3) The subarctic and arctic area, where true land birds are very few but there is a unique concentration of water birds and shore-birds, mostly migratory.

Southwards from the Equator there is mainly a diffusion of tropical birds into the land-masses of the South Temperate Zone, more limited in extent than those of the North ; here again, there are few different groups, those localised in the Australian and New Zealand avifaunas being the chief exceptions. Beyond, there is only the sea-bird population of the Antarctic.

Longitudinal zonation is most marked between the Old and New Worlds. It is least distinct in the North Temperate and Arctic Zones, where Eurasia and North America share the few circumpolar families (and many genera) of land birds as well as many of the genera and species of far northern sea birds and shore birds ; but each has many genera of land birds peculiar to itself, and has some representatives of families confined to the Old World or the New. In the equatorial belt, although there are pantropical as well as cosmopolitan groups, there are many that are peculiar to their continents. In the South Temperate Zone there are no peculiar groups common to the tips of the southern continents, and there is probably no direct relation between their land-bird populations.

The effect of migration on distribution is to increase the relation between avifauna from latitude to latitude, while at the same time tending to preserve longitudinal distinctions—especially between the Old and New Worlds.

Regions. It is difficult to give satisfactory expression to the facts of distribution in terms of the continents of conventional geography. It is clear, for instance, that for biological purposes the land-mass of Europe and northern Asia is a unit ; and that, on the other hand, northern and southern Asia are contrasted areas divided on the line of the Himalaya Mountains. Again, the Sahara Desert rather than the Mediterranean Sea constitutes the chief latitudinal barrier to dispersal in the Eur-African continents. In the New World, the northern limit of the tropics is a more important boundary than any provided by the configuration of the continents.

For a century, therefore, zoogeographers have been seeking a notation better suited to their special purpose. It was thus that the concept of faunal regions arose ; and it is of interest that it was in respect of birds, despite their mobility, that this was first enunciated—by P. L. Sclater in 1858 ; it was later adopted by Wallace, in but slightly modified form, for animals generally. At the present time there is some tendency to deprecate the idea, on the ground that the regions are not realities and that geographical ornithology should be properly concerned only with assemblages of bird populations. Nevertheless, although the regions have merely a notional existence, they do approximately correspond with certain broad facts of avian distribution and so provide a convenient tool for descriptive purposes ; for that reason the concept has been retained in this work.

The 'classical' regions of Sclater are six in number. Broadly, the Palaearctic Region com-

prises Europe, North Africa, and northern Asia ; the Ethiopian Region comprises Africa from the Sahara southwards ; the Indian (now usually called Oriental) Region comprises tropical Asia and western Indonesia ; and the Australasian Region comprises eastern Indonesia, Australia, Polynesia, and New Zealand. The New World is divided into the Nearctic Region, comprising North America above the tropics, and the Neotropical Region. See separate articles on the AUSTRALASIAN, ETHIOPIAN, NEARCTIC, NEOTROPICAL, ORIENTAL, and PALAEARCTIC REGIONS.

The Palaearctic and Nearctic Regions (closest together at the Behring Straits) present many avifaunal similarities, although also substantial differences, and are sometimes combined as a Holarctic Region (Heilprin). As an adjective, ' holarctic ' is convenient on occasion ; but the concept of a single region overlooks the essential fact that in each of the components there are very diverse elements derived from its tropical counterpart ; and that, despite many common elements, the distinction between Old World and New World remains the most important of all. Sclater himself alternatively designated his three southern Old World regions as ' Palaeotropical '—Western, Middle and Eastern—but without combining them.

Sclater, from his pre-evolutionary standpoint, grouped his four Old World regions as ' Creatio Palaeogeana ' and his two New World regions as ' Creatio Neogeana '. T. H. Huxley grouped the regions in what have since been called ' realms ', the Nearctic, Palaearctic, Ethiopian, and Oriental Regions constituting ' Arctogaea ' and the Australasian and Neotropical Regions constituting ' Notogaea '. Subsequently, the latter term came to be reserved for the Australasian Region, the Neotropical Region being classed by itself as ' Neogaea '. Darlington has renamed Arctogaea more appropriately as ' Megagea ' (the main part of the world).

Darlington has suggested another arrangement of the regions, emphasising their nature. The Ethiopian and Oriental Regions are the main tropical parts of the Old World ; the Palaearctic and Nearctic Regions are ' climate-limited ' ; the Neotropical and Australasian Regions are ' barrier-limited '. This is consistent with the concept of Megagea, subject to a climatic limitation in the north, and of two more isolated southern ' realms '.

In the main, ornithologists find that Sclater's scheme is still useful for its purpose. There are of course transitional areas, e.g. in Arabia, China, Indonesia, and Mexico, where the boundaries of regions cannot be defined except in an arbitrary way.

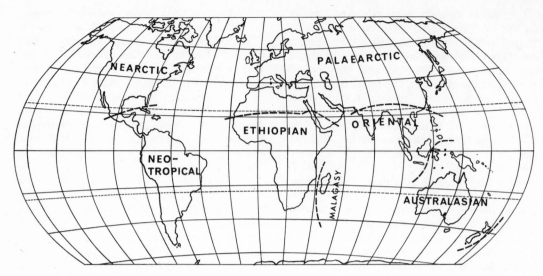

FIG 1.   The six major and one minor zoogeographical regions.   New Zealand is sometimes treated as another minor region, but here as a sub-region.   Antarctica and oceanic islands are not included in any region.   Boundaries are only approximate, and in reality tend to be represented by transitional zones.

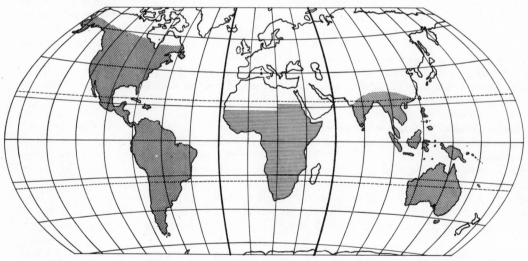

FIG 2.   Some characteristic limited distributions of families.   *Left :* a New World distribution, the tyrant-flycatchers (Tyrannidae).   *Centre :* an Ethiopian distribution, the turacos (Musophagidae).   *Right :* an Oriental-Australasian distribution (but not New Zealand), the wood-swallows (Artamidae).

The chief innovation is the recognition that the scheme is satisfactorily applicable only to the main continents, with their adjacent islands of recent continental origin and fringing archipelagos—not to more isolated islands, single or in groups. Wallace had indeed already separated New Zealand on account of notable peculiarities in its fauna ; but this does not seem to be wholly valid for birds, as the avifauna—although now peculiar in several respects—is clearly derived from that of Australia, and in this work New Zealand is treated as a subregion of the Australasian Region. On the other hand, Madagascar, with its neighbouring island groups, is now regarded as distinct for reasons which seem good to ornithologists ; it is therefore treated here as a minor region additional to the classical six (see MALAGASY REGION). It is also necessary to take some separate account of the

Antarctic continent and its neighbouring islands (see ANTARCTIC). Lesser islands that also cannot well be fitted into a continental scheme are the Celebes (although not distantly isolated, and set apart mainly on other than ornithological evidence), Polynesian elements such as New Caledonia, the Hawaiian Islands, the Galápagos Islands, and various remote islands in the Atlantic Ocean ; so far as land birds are concerned, the respective avifaunas of these islands must be specially considered when occasion demands and may be ignored in a general review.

In addition to all this, the regional concept has only a limited application to sea birds ; the ranges of truly pelagic species, although not of all coastal forms, must be thought of in terms of oceans rather than of continents (see OCEANIC BIRDS).

Systematic Survey. Beginning with the higher taxa of recent birds, one finds that most of the orders are cosmopolitan, in the sense that they are represented in all the main continental regions. The chief exceptions are the small orders of ' ratite ' birds, each of which is confined, or (in one instance)

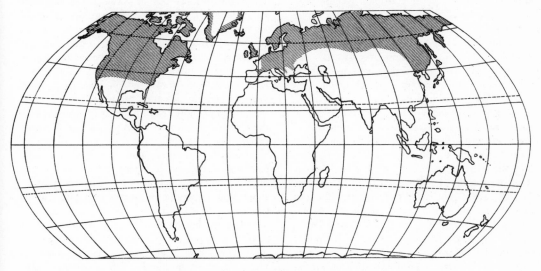

FIG 3. A Northern Hemisphere distribution, the grouse family (Tetraonidae).

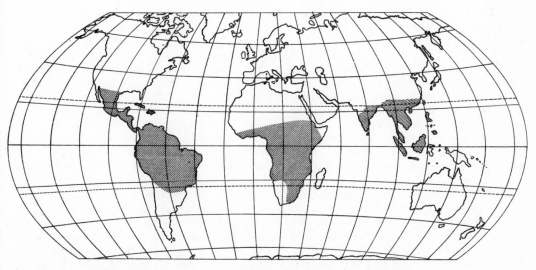

FIG 4. A pantropical distribution (but not Australasian), the trogon family (Trogonidae).

(A Southern Hemisphere distribution, such as that of the penguin family (Spheniscidae), does not lend itself to this type of presentation, being purely coastal.)

almost confined, to a single region ; and the wholly Neotropical Tinamiformes. Partial exceptions are the Sphenisciformes, confined to the Southern Hemisphere but nevertheless represented on the coast of three of the main regions as well as in the Antarctic ; the Gaviiformes, with a circumpolar ('holarctic') distribution in the Northern Hemisphere ; and some orders that can be described as 'pantropical' (or 'tropicopolitan') in that they are absent from the colder latitudes but are otherwise world-wide in their distribution—the Trogoniformes (Ethiopian, Oriental, and Neotropical Regions) and the Psittaciformes (absent from the Palaearctic Region and barely represented in the Nearctic).

Turning next to families (in addition to those that stand alone in their respective orders), one finds again that many are cosmopolitan, pantropical, or otherwise widespread in both Old and New Worlds. There are, however, also many that are restricted to the Old World or to the New, or even to one or two main regions within one of these ; and that a few are restricted to a small part of a main region, to the minor Malagasy Region, or in the extreme case to a small island group. The pattern in detail is best seen from the accompanying Table ; but even this obscures the fact that certain families have a predominant distributional status complicated by a few exceptions— notably the larks (Alaudidae), an Old World family with one species found also in the New World ; and the wrens (Troglodytidae), presenting the same picture in reverse.

It will be noted that all but one of the southern regions, major and minor, have several families not found elsewhere ; and that the Neotropical Region is outstanding in this respect. The exception is the Oriental Region, which shares nearly all its characteristic families with other southern parts of the Old World. The Palaearctic and Nearctic Regions have each a single family almost peculiar to itself ; as already noted, these northern regions share nearly all their families with their respective tropical counterparts. Two families are restricted to oceanic islands—the Drepanididae to the Hawaiian Islands and the Rhynochetidae (one species) to New Caledonia. Of families that have become extinct within historical or almost historical times (not shown in the Table), the Dinornithidae are known only from New Zealand, the Aepyornithidae only from Madagascar, and the Raphidae only from islands of the southern Indian Ocean.

Coming down to genera, very briefly, one not unexpectedly finds that these have more often a relatively restricted distribution—sometimes very restricted indeed. Nevertheless, a few genera are cosmopolitan, or nearly so, examples being *Podiceps*, *Phalacrocorax*, *Ardea*, *Circus*, *Falco*, *Rallus*, *Columba*, *Caprimulgus*, *Anthus*, *Turdus*, and *Corvus*—not to mention a number of sea-bird and shore-bird genera. Even a very few species are almost cosmopolitan, such as the Osprey (or Fish Hawk) *Pandion haliaetus*, the Kentish (or Snowy) Plover *Charadrius alexandrinus*, and the Barn Owl *Tyto alba*, with the Swallow (or Barn Swallow) *Hirundo rustica* as the nearest approach among passerines.

Radiation. Viewed more dynamically, geographical distribution may be considered as the result of a process of radial dispersal of groups or species from the areas in which they originated in the course of evolution. The history of this radiation, however, is largely a matter of speculation and in many respects impossible to unravel. One reason is that the fossil record is too incomplete, both in its taxonomic and in its geographical representation, to be of more than limited help in delineating the distribution of birds in earlier geological times ; reliance on it might indeed be misleading (see FOSSIL BIRDS). Another reason is that the phylogenetic relationship between different groups is itself so often a matter of speculation ; false assumptions about such relationships must inevitably lead to false conclusions about geographical radiation.

A further difficulty is inherent in the problem itself. The process of radiation—doubtless still continuing—must have been extremely complex. The radiation of any group from its original centre may have occurred in multiple and successive phases ; and secondary radiation from the newer areas may have taken place in different or even reverse directions. That genera and species have apparently radiated recently from certain areas does not necessarily imply that the families to which they belong originally did so in the same way.

The rate of dispersal, also, has no doubt been highly variable. On occasion it must be very rapid, a world-wide distribution being attained within the evolutionary span of a single species : the spread of the Cattle Egret *Ardeola ibis* during the last few years exemplifies such rapidity. In other instances a whole family or subfamily has become differentiated into numerous genera and species while remaining restricted to a particular region or island group (Drepanididae ; Geospizinae).

Except where the radiation has been comparatively rapid, its whole history must be interwoven with that of the evolution of the birds and of their adaptations to new conditions ; and with that of the configuration of the land-masses through the relevant periods of geological time and the climates to which they have been successively subject.

An additional complication is that, although some groups may now be at the climax of their radiation —the song-birds (Suborder Oscines) and herons (Ardeidae) are probable examples—others may be in retreat from a former wider distribution. It is therefore conceivable that certain groups of now restricted distribution are merely relict populations, and not necessarily in the areas where they originated. In any event, competition must have been a factor ; and this would itself have been affected by evolutionary adaptations and by changes in condition. As Darlington puts it, ' dispersal has probably involved the rise, diversification, and complex and more or less rapid spread over much or all of the world of a succession of dominant groups, and the complex withdrawal and disappearance of older groups as new ones spread '.

Only a few of the speculations about particular groups can be mentioned. It seems reasonable, on the facts, to suppose that the song-birds (Oscines) originated in the warmer parts of the Old World ; their spread has least affected the Neotropical Region, the only main area where they do not provide the largest number of forms and one in which the suboscine passerines have most greatly developed—a rare example of ' complementarity '. The fact that the parrots (Psittacidae) and pigeons (Columbidae) show their present greatest diversity in the Australasian Region is not sufficient ground, without other evidence, for supposing that to be their area of origin. There is perhaps better reason for thinking that the Phasianidae have spread from an original centre in the Oriental Region. It is probably safe to assume that the kingfishers (Alcedinidae) are by origin an Old World family, with but two genera in the New World and only one of them peculiar to it. Similarly, the owl genus *Tyto* is represented in the New World solely by one almost cosmopolitan species. Much the same is true of the harrier genus *Circus* ; but, on the other hand, the buzzard (hawk) genus *Buteo* has probably radiated from North America.

A.L.T.

Sclater, P. S. 1858. On the general geographical distribution of the members of the Class Aves. J. Proc. Linn. Soc. Lond., Zool. 2 : 130–145. (This is the classical reference, of special interest to ornithologists.)

Wallace, A. R. 1876. The Geographical Distribution of Animals. 2 vols. London. (A more general classical reference.)

Hesse, R., Allee, W. C., & Schmidt, K. 1951. Ecological Animal Geography. 2nd edition.

Darlington, P. J. 1957. Zoogeography : the Geographical Distribution of Animals. New York. (The most recent general work, with abundant references to other literature, and gratefully acknowledged as an important source book for the foregoing article.)

Voous, K. H. 1960. Atlas of European Birds. Edinburgh. (Atlas van de Europese Vogel. Amsterdam. 1960.)

Stresemann, E. & Portenko, L. A. 1960. Atlas der Verbreitung Palaearktischer Vögel. Berlin. (Appearing in parts.)

DISTRIBUTION OF FAMILIES BY REGIONS

The Table is based on the present-day distribution of the families recognised in the classification followed in this work ; it ignores a few minor overlaps into other regions, vagrant occurrences, and the results of modern introduction by human agency. The term ' main regions ' excludes the minor Malagasy Region.

Common to Old and New Worlds:

Cosmopolitan	
(at least five main regions—see notes)	44
Widespread	
(at least three main regions, not all tropical)	4
Pantropical	
(at least three tropical main regions)	8
Northern Hemisphere (see notes)	4
Southern Hemisphere (see notes)	3
	63

Old World Only:

Widespread	
(2 not Australasian ; 1 not Malagasy)	9
Palaearctic only (see notes)	1
Palaeotropical	
(at least the three main tropical regions)	7
Ethiopian (2 also Malagasy)	8
Malagasy only	4
Ethiopian and Oriental (2 also Malagasy)	6
Oriental only	1
Ethiopian and Australasian	1
Oriental and Australasian	5
Australasian :	
Australo-Papuan only	11
New Zealand only	3
Insular (see notes)	1
	57

New World Only:

Widespread (both regions)	9
Nearctic only (see notes)	1
Neotropical only	22
Insular (see notes)	2
	34

Notes. Of the families listed as cosmopolitan, 6 are absent from the Australasian Region, 2 from the Neotropical, one (Burhinidae) from the Nearctic, one (Psittacidae) from the Palaearctic, and one (Diomedeidae) from the North Atlantic ; 9

are absent from the Malagasy Region (in 7 cases also from a main region) ; and one (Phalaropodidae) breeds only in the Northern Hemisphere. Some others, although extending into temperate regions, are mainly pantropical. Several cosmopolitan or widespread families found in the Australasian Region do not extend to the New Zealand Sub-region.

Of the minor overlaps that have been ignored, several relate to Neotropical families extending into the southern Nearctic. The Nearctic family Meleagrididae has a slight southward extension as far as northern Central America. The Palaearctic family Prunellidae has a very slight extension into the Oriental Region at high altitudes.

The families that are restricted to the Northern Hemisphere although widespread therein are the Gaviidae, Tetraonidae, Alcidae, and Certhiidae ; similarly for the Southern Hemisphere there are the Spheniscidae (just reaching the Equator), Pelecanoididae, and Chionididae. The insular families are the Rhynochetidae (New Caledonia), Todidae (West Indies), and Drepanididae (Hawaii).

DIURNAL HABITS: characteristic of the great majority of bird species (for exceptions see NOC-TURNAL HABITS).

DIVER: alternatively ' loon ' (generally used in North America), substantive name of all species of the Gaviidae (Gaviiformes) ; in the plural, general term for the family. (For the question of scientific nomenclature see under COLYMBIDAE.) The divers form a well marked holarctic group of large (26–37½ inches long) aquatic birds, with straight, sharply pointed bills and front toes fully webbed ; they are long-bodied and thick-necked, with relatively small, pointed wings and a well developed but short tail. The tarsi are laterally compressed and the legs are set so far back on the body that progression on land is made extremely difficult and awkward. In the adult stage divers are coloured in strikingly contrasting patterns, mostly black and white, and at all times the sexes present the same general appearance. The body plumage is hard and compact, while feathers of head and neck are soft and velvety. Divers moult their flight feathers simultaneously and thus become flightless for a time. The young have two coats of nestling down, the first coat in which they hatch, and a second set of down that pushes out the first and carries it on its tips, later to be pushed out by the feathers of the first winter plumage. The downy young of all divers are somewhat alike ; they are uniform blackish brown or greyish brown above, changing to white or dull grey on the under parts.

Lakes, ponds, and slow-flowing rivers constitute the summer habitat of all divers. In winter, how-ever, they are essentially marine birds, frequenting inshore waters. They feed chiefly on fish, to a lesser extent on aquatic insects and frogs, and—in salt water—on crustaceans, molluscs, and other marine invertebrates. Divers are noted especially for their skill and swiftness in swimming and diving, and for their weird ' unearthly ' cries. They have a peculiar faculty of submerging gradually without apparent effort and with little or no rippling of the surface of the water. When alarmed they frequently swim with the body submerged and only the head, or even only the bill, showing. They take wing with considerable difficulty, but once in the air their flight is powerful, direct, and rapid (see also FLIGHT ; SWIMMING AND DIVING).

On the whole divers are markedly solitary birds, usually found singly or in pairs. The nests are built on islands and on the shores of lakes and ponds, invariably close to the water's edge. The construction of the nest depends a great deal upon the location ; in some cases it is only a shallow circular depression in the marshy ground, with very little or no nest material at all, while in other cases it may be a substantial structure of water plants and rushes. The eggs are usually two in number. They are elliptical or elongated ovate in shape, olive-brown to olive-green and sparsely spotted with darker brown and black. Both parents share in incubation and in the care of the young. The length of the incubation period is about four weeks, and the fledging period has been estimated at about eight weeks. The young are nidifugous, but during their first few days on the water they are often carried on the back of the parent.

The family is confined to the Northern Hemi-sphere. It consists of a single genus, *Gavia*, composed of 3–5 species, all inhabiting high latitudes of the Northern Hemisphere. In winter they all migrate southward into the temperate regions, especially along the sea coasts. At least some species commonly do so in flocks ; this has been especially noted in *G. arctica*, on southward passage along the Pacific coast of North America. The Great Northern Diver (or Common Loon) *G. immer* and the White-billed Diver (or Yellow-billed Loon) *G. adamsii* are the largest. They are very similar in size and appearance, boldly checked black and white above, white below, and with an essentially black head and neck. The white markings on the upper parts, however, do not appear in young birds or in the winter plumage of the adults. They are geographically repræsen-tative species and by some authors regarded as conspecific. The Great Northern Diver is a Nearctic species inhabiting the northern parts of the United States and much of Canada, ranging eastward to Greenland, Iceland, and Bear Island. The White-billed Diver, on the other hand, is a Palaearctic species with a range extending from the Murman coast along that of northern Siberia to the arctic coast of Alaska. The Black-throated Diver (or Arctic Loon) G. arctica is smaller, but it has a similar colour pattern except that in summer head and neck are grey with a black throat-patch. This is a circumpolar species with an arctic-boreal distribution. It has been split up into three races (G. a. arctica, G. a. viridigularis, and G. a. pacifica), which by some authors are thought to represent two distinct species—the Eurasian G. arctica (including G. a. viridigularis) and the American G. pacifica. The Red-throated Diver (or Red-throated Loon) G. stellata is the smallest diver and is distinguished from other divers by having uniform grey-brown upper parts, which in winter become finely speckled with white ; in breeding plumage the head and neck are grey with a rich chestnut throat-patch. Like the Black-throated Diver, the Red-throated Diver is a circumpolar species with a wide arctic-boreal distribution. See Plate 29 (colour). F.G.

Huxley, J. S. 1923. Courtship activities of the Red-throated Diver (Colymbus stellatus Pontopp.) ; together with a discussion on the evolution of courtship in birds. J. Linn. Soc. Lond., Zool. 35 : 253–292.
Olson, S. T. & Marshall, W. H. 1952. The Common Loon in Minnesota. Minn. Mus. Nat. Hist. Occ. Paper no. 5.
Storer, R. W. 1956. The fossil loon Colymboides minutus. Condor 58 : 413–426.

DIVERSIONARY BEHAVIOUR : agitated movements or sounds that may, for example, serve to divert a predator's attention from nest or young ; in its more elaborate and ritualised form this becomes DISTRACTION DISPLAY.

DIVERSION-LINE : alternative term (proposed by Lack & Williamson 1959 ; deprecated by Thomson 1960) for LEADING LINE (see also MIGRATION).

DIVING : see SWIMMING AND DIVING

DIVING PETREL : substantive name of the species of Pelecanoididae (Procellariiformes) ; in the plural, general term for the family. This is a highly distinctive Southern Hemisphere group of five species in a single genus. For general characters of the order see under PETREL. The structural peculiarity of the diving petrels is that they are of notably compact bodily form, with wings and other members short, thus superficially resembling certain species of the Northern Hemisphere family of auks (Alcidae)—particularly the Little Auk (or Dovekie) Plautus alle—rather than their true relatives. The resemblance is an excellent example of evolutionary convergence, because birds of both groups have a whirring rather than a gliding flight, and both dive rapidly from the air into the sea during feeding manoeuvres and use their wings under water.

In the pattern of their life history diving petrels closely resemble many other small petrels. The single white egg is laid in a burrow in soil soft enough to be excavated by a mated pair ; the birds do not breed in niches of rock, a circumstance sufficient to account for the southern limit of their distribution. Although two species nest on snow-covered and heavily glaciated islands south of the Antarctic Convergence (see ANTARCTIC), such as Heard Island and South Georgia, they can nevertheless find workable peaty soil as thawing advances in the austral spring season.

N.S.

Head of Diving Petrel Pelecanoides urinatrix ; the lower figure shows the frontal region and bill as seen from above. C.E.T.K.

The five species of diving petrels (6½–10 inches in length) are all included within the single genus Pelecanoides. Most forms have a prevailingly drab plumage and are of similar appearance, specific distinctions showing mainly in the form of the bill and the structure of small processes in the nostrils. The southernmost species, P. georgicus, is of circumpolar distribution and, in common with other sea birds belonging to higher southern latitudes, it exhibits no racial variation. P. urinatrix occupies an antiboreal oceanic belt in lower latitudes than that of P. georgicus. It inhabits many subantarctic islands, such as the Falklands, Tristan da Cunha, and Gough Island, and islands to the south of Australia and New Zealand ; it is represented by several mutually isolated forms of subspecific rank. Only very recently (unpublished), it has been learned that restricted breeding populations of this typically antiboreal species have crossed the Antarctic Convergence to South Georgia and Heard Island, where they occupy nesting territory of a different type from that of *P. georgicus*.

Still another species, as yet less well taxonomically defined, is *P. exsul*, which was described from Kerguelen Island in the southern Indian Ocean and is known also from the Crozets and from one or more of the outliers of New Zealand. In the complex of Fuegian islands and waterways of southern South America is a fourth species, *P. magellani*, characterised by a brighter plumage (i.e. more sharply black and white) than any of the others ; it is known only from this very limited continental district. Finally, the coast of western South America influenced by the cool Humboldt Current, from central Chile to northern Peru, is the range of a fifth species, *P. garnotii* (' Potoyunco '), which has nearly double the bulk of any of the other four. This diving petrel formerly nested in the deep guano beds of the rainless Peruvian and Chilean islands and was reputed an important producer of the fertiliser (see GUANO); since the old guano layers have been depleted, suitable soil for its burrows is of limited extent and its population is now probably vastly less than in primitive times.

Diving petrels are mainly crustacean-eaters, but the Peruvian species—and doubtless some of the others—subsists in part upon small schooling fish such as anchovies. Some, if not all, of the diving petrels moult their remiges almost simultaneously and become for a time flightless, but this in no way inhibits their ability to capture food. This is conspicuously true of *P. garnotii*. As pointed out by G. G. Simpson, a peculiarity of this kind in a maritime bird may throw light on the evolution of the penguins (Spheniscidae) from flying forebears. There must have been a point reached by the ancestors of penguins when the advantage of ' flying ' under water outweighed that of flying in air. Assuming the timely appearance of appropriate genetic variation, the development of the penguin type of wing would be readily explicable.

See also ANTARCTIC ; FLIGHT ; SWIMMING AND DIVING.   R.C.M.

Murphy, R. C. 1936. Oceanic Birds of South America. 2 vols. New York.
Richdale, L. E. 1936. The Kuaka or Diving Petrel, *Pelecanoides urinatrix*. Emu 43 : 24–48, 97–107.
Richdale, L. E. 1945. Supplementary notes on the Diving Petrel. Trans. Roy. Soc. N.Z. 75 : 42–53.

DODO : *Raphus cucullatus*, best known member of the Raphidae (Columbiformes, suborder Columbae); in the form ' dodo and solitaires ', general term for the family. This group was peculiar to the Mascarene Islands, in the Indian Ocean east of Madagascar, and its members have become extinct in historic times (see EXTINCT BIRDS). The traditional placing in the Columbiformes has recently been questioned, and an affinity with the Rallidae suggested (Lüttschwager).

The Dodo and its kindred may be regarded as pigeons that had, in the safety of an insular environment, lost the power of flight and grown to great size ; but their peculiarities warrant familial separation. Hachisuka would indeed make two families of them, or at the least divide the Raphidae into two subfamilies—Raphinae and Pezophapinae ; his generic classification also differs from that most usually followed by modern authors, a situation confused by the fact that the two solitaires have the same specific name. Three species are well authenticated ; the Dodo itself was found on Mauritius, while the Réunion Solitaire *Raphus solitarius* (' *Pezophaps solitarius* ') and the Rodriguez Solitaire *Pezophaps solitaria* (' *Ornithaptera solitaria* ') are known from the islands after which they are named. Hachisuka postulates the former existence, on Réunion, of a fourth species, the ' White Dodo ' (as distinct from what he calls the ' Grey or Common Dodo '), and has named it ' *Victoriornis imperialis* ' ; but the evidence for this has not been generally accepted as adequate.

Knowledge of the three recognised species is based largely on contemporary descriptions and pictorial representations of varying degrees of reliability. This evidence is supported by a few museum specimens of the Dodo—one of the best being a mounted one at Cambridge—and fairly abundant osteological remains, including some complete and nearly complete skeletons, of both the Dodo and the Rodriguez Solitaire. There is some reason for believing that living examples of one or more of the species were brought to Europe. None of the species, however, long survived the early visits of European seamen to the islands and the introduction of pigs and other animals. The Dodo appears to have become extinct towards the end of the seventeenth century, the Réunion Solitaire about the same period, and the Rodriguez Solitaire at some point in the eighteenth century.

In size these birds may be equated to a Turkey *Meleagris gallopavo*. They were massively built, with strong feet and bills (with the external nares far out towards the tip of the upper mandible).

The wings were rudimentary and the sterna only slightly keeled. The Dodo was remarkable for its clumsy shape, very large head, heavy hooked bill, short legs, and little tail of a few curly feathers ; the plumage was largely blue-grey. The bird moved slowly and was considered stupid because it had little or no fear of man.

The solitaires were less heavily built, and longer in neck and legs. The Rodriguez Solitaire had a relatively small head, a slender bill, and almost no tail. Their plumage was predominantly brown, except that the female of the Réunion Solitaire is thought to have been white (with yellow legs and bill). Some sexual dimorphism was apparently present in all three species.

Hachisuka, M. 1953. The Dodo and Kindred Birds. London.
Lüttschwager, J. 1959. Zur systematischen Stellung der ausgestorben Drontevögel Raphus und Pezophaps. Zool. Anz. 162 : 127–148.
Lüttschwager, J. 1961. Die Drontevögel. Wittenberg-Lutherstadt.

DOLLARBIRD : *Eurystomus orientalis* (see ROLLER).

DOMESTICATION : the state of animals of which the breeding and maintenance are continuously controlled by man. Further criteria of domestication that stress the economic value of the animal, the morphological and behavioural differences between the domestic animal and its wild progenitor, or its degree of tameness, cannot be applied in their entirety to all domestic species. Some of our domestic species were first domesticated for religious rather than economic reasons ; others are little altered morphologically from the original wild type, while others can scarcely be called tame and indeed are less tame than are some wild birds in rarely frequented places (see TAMENESS). While most domesticated species usually fulfil one or more of these additional criteria, the important implication in the primary definition is that, with control over breeding and maintenance, man can change the animal as far as its genetic potentialities will allow. The number of species that have been domesticated at some time or other is probably very large ; in many cases—perhaps in the majority of cases—domestication has been on only a very small scale and of very short duration.

Most of the avian examples considered here fulfil one or more of the secondary criteria of domestication listed above, and they have been domesticated in relatively large numbers and for considerable periods of time. Cage and aviary birds, together with ornamental waterfowl, have been excluded (see AVICULTURE ; CAGE BIRD). The differences seen in our domestic birds, including the degree of change from the wild progenitor and the amount of intraspecific variation, have developed from the interaction between man's breeding and selection practices and the genetic variability available within a species (see GENETICS). Assuming that mutation rates are approximately equal in our domestic birds, any differences between species in the initial amount of genetic variability available for selection would have depended on the population structure of the ancestral species, on the number and origin of the breeding birds first brought into captivity, and on the introduction of further wild birds from other places and at other times. In general, however, the breeding practices and the amount of conscious or unconscious selection exercised by man have been mainly responsible for the state of our domestic birds today.

Domestication could be facilitated in birds by their possession of a catholic diet, plasticity in reproductive behaviour, and ability to become accustomed to man and the environment supplied by him. Although all these traits are not found in every ancestral species of our domestic birds, domestication of one species might have aided the process with another species ; e.g. the hatching of wild ducks' eggs by domestic hens. As evidence accumulates, it appears that food production was not always the primary object of domesticating what are now important agricultural species ; as will be seen from the histories of many individual species, a species may have had varying functions in societies in different times and places.

Domestic Fowl. This species is usually regarded as a domesticated form of the Red Junglefowl *Gallus gallus*, but some think (Hutt) that it may be descended from any one or more of four species of the *Gallus* inhabiting south-eastern Asia (see under PHEASANT). The date of its domestication is unknown ; it was probably found in India as early as 3200 B.C. and in China it was known as a domesticated bird by 1400 B.C. It reached Persia at a very early date, and appeared in Egypt and Crete in 1500 B.C. However, it may not have become a common domestic animal in Egypt until after the Persian conquest of the country in 525–524 B.C.

The different attitudes of early European societies to the domestic fowl suggest that it entered Europe by two routes ; one through Scythia to the Teutons and Celts, and so from Gaul to Italy ; the other through the Dardanelles to the Aegean. In Asia Minor the cock is first found on coins from the Temple of Artemis at Ephesus of at least 700 B.C. Its arrival in the New World was formerly considered to have been shortly after the voyage of Columbus, but now it seems more likely that it was brought from Asia to the coasts of Peru and Ecuador in pre-Columbian times.

The fowl was popular in many societies as a sacrificial or religious animal, so that this usage and cock-fighting were probably more responsible for its distribution than were its food-producing potentialities. In Persia, for example, it had an exalted position in the Zoroastrian religion. In Greece and Rome it also had religious significance ; but whereas the Greeks valued it primarily as a fighter, the Romans developed its agricultural potentialities as well—a complex poultry industry was formed, together with specialised breeds ; but with the decline of the Roman Empire the industry collapsed, and it was not until the nineteenth century that poultry keeping on a large scale was resumed.

The modern breeds are divided into Mediterranean and Asiatic ; within these two groups numerous breeds and varieties have been developed. In western countries today 37 breeds (including 5 Asiatic breeds) are kept for food production, while there are at least 24 ornamental breeds. The variation produced during domestication includes differences in plumage, body size, shape and size of comb, number of toes, egg-shell colour, skin colour, and osteology. Physiological differences are found in many traits, including egg production, fertility, hatching quality, broodiness, efficiency in food conversion, resistance to certain diseases, and responsiveness to certain hormones. Behavioural dissimilarities are also present. The large-scale breeding methods employed today entail the use of inbred lines derived from a single breed, and many of these lines may differ from one another to an extent comparable to that found between breeds. See also COCK-FIGHTING.

Domestic Duck. All breeds of the common species are descended from the Mallard *Anas platyrhynchos* (see DUCK). It is thought to have first been domesticated in China or south-eastern Asia at a very early date. Ducks were doubtless domesticated elsewhere at later dates, as there are records from Roman times of eggs being collected from the wild and being hatched by domestic hens. Although the wild Mallard does not breed in captivity, its young if hatched by domesticated birds will do so.

The amount of variability in the domestic duck is very small compared with that found in the domestic fowl. There are approximately 12 breeds in the United Kingdom used for meat or egg production or as dual purpose breeds. Morphologically the most striking ones are the Indian Runner, with its upright carriage and cylindrical conform-

ation, and the Crested Duck, which possesses a large globular crest of feathers on the head.

Domestic Goose. The goose was domesticated first in Asia, either in China or south-eastern Asia, some time before the duck. It is generally agreed that it is descended from the Grey Lag Goose *Anser anser* (see under DUCK). The Chinese goose, however, is derived from the Swan Goose *Anser cygnoides* ; it crosses easily with other breeds and the progeny are fully fertile. (For the Egyptian Goose, a not closely related bird, see below.) The domestic goose was already known in Europe by the time of Homer. There are about nine breeds, some of which are very distinctive. The Chinese and African geese both possess large tubercles at the base of the bill ; the Toulouse and the African have ' dewlaps '. The Crested Roman goose, which is of great antiquity, reputedly saved the Capitol in Rome from the Gauls in 390 B.C. by cackling and giving the alarm ; it possesses a large globular crest of feathers on the head. The Sebastopol has curled breast feathers and long plume-like feathers on the back. Little known in western countries is the Russian fighting goose, which is a very old breed (with several sub-breeds) that was for a long time used for gaming in Russia.

Turkey. The Mexican subspecies of the wild Turkey *Meleagris gallopavo gallopavo* (see TURKEY) is considered to be the ancestor of this bird, and domestication probably took place near Oaxaco in Mexico. One authority considers that this occurred at a time culturally equivalent to the Neolithic age in Europe. Its importation into Britain between 1525 and 1532 may have been effected by William Strickland of Boynton-on-the-Would, Yorkshire, for he was allowed to incorporate a turkey cock in his family crest. ' A Dietarie ' published in 1541 by Archbishop Cranmer mentions the Turkey, but during the sixteenth and seventeenth centuries much confusion existed between the Turkey and the Guineafowl, which latter had been called *Meleagris* by the Romans.

Several studies have sought to compare the wild Turkey with domestic birds in the United States of America. In a comparison of the Missouri subspecies *M.g. silvestris* and the domestic Bronze turkey, differences in body conformation, thickness and colour of tarsus, head appendages, plumage colour, and tranquillity were apparent. Also the weights of brain and of the adrenal and pituitary glands, expressed as percentages of body weight, were greater in wild birds. Three varieties are widely bred in Britain today, viz. the Brown, the White, and the Black.

Muscovy Duck. This bird was also domesticated in pre-Columbian times in the New World, where the wild Muscovy Duck *Cairina moschata* is a tropical tree-nesting bird that apparently avoids human habitation (see DUCK). Its name may have come from the Muisca Indians of central Colombia. Apart from the establishment of three varieties differing in colour, there has been no selection for more divergent breeds. The domesticated Muscovy Duck has been introduced into other parts of the world ; it is familiar, for instance, in West African villages. It is sometimes crossed with domestic ducks of Mallard stock, but the progeny are infertile.

Guineafowl. Subspecies of the wild Guineafowl *Numida meleagris* exist in Morocco, and from Senegal to the Red Sea and Kenya (see GUINEAFOWL). The first of these was present as a sacred bird on an Aegean island in the fourth century B.C. The Romans called this subspecies the Numidian fowl, and they kept it as well as the north-east African subspecies which they called *Meleagris* ; both were used for food, but the latter was the more popular. With the decline of the Roman Empire, both forms appear to have been lost to Europe. One reference, however, shows that birds were kept in Athens in the tenth century A.D. After the voyages of the Portuguese navigators in the fifteenth and sixteenth centuries the West African subspecies *N.m. galeata* was brought to Europe. No breeds have been developed.

Domestic Pigeon. Descended from the Rock Pigeon *Columba livia* (see PIGEON) this may well be one of our oldest domesticated animals, for it was a sacred bird in the early cultures of the Near East. It was associated with Astarte, the goddess of love and fertility, and images of pigeons dating from 3100 B.C. have been found. In Egypt it was used as a source of food and was domesticated prior to 2600 B.C. There are records of it in Crete in the second millennium B.C. In classical Greece it became sacred to Aphrodite, and later in Rome it was associated with Venus but was also used for food and as a messenger. After the rise of Islam it was protected on religious grounds in most Mohammedan countries. It arrived in India and China at a very early date, but its role differed from place to place. For the use of pigeons as messengers, and in the sport of pigeon racing, see HOMING PIGEON.

Nearly a century ago Darwin estimated that there were 150 breeds of pigeon, many of which he noted ' differ fully as much from each other in external characters as do the most distinct genera '. He divided the breeds or races into four groups. Group I contains the Pouter pigeons in which the oesophagus is of great size, barely separated from the crop and often inflated ; the body and legs are elongated, and the bill is of moderate dimensions. In Group II the breeds are characterised by bills with the cere swollen and often carunculated or wattled, and the skin round the eyes bare and also carunculated ; the mouth is very wide, and the feet large. Group III contains very divergent breeds, but the type of the group is characterised by the bill being shorter than that of the Rock Pigeon and the bare patch of skin round the eyes not being much developed. The breeds of Group IV resemble the Rock Pigeon in all important points of structure.

Peafowl. Our domesticated birds are descended from the Peafowl *Pavo cristatus* inhabiting parts of India, Assam, and Ceylon (see under PHEASANT). Although the bird was known in ancient Egypt, it was probably not widely known in Europe until the time of Alexander the Great. It is thought to have been introduced into Britain by the Romans, and in medieval times it was a popular bird for banquets. No varieties have been developed under domestication. The other species, the Green Peafowl *P. muticus*, has also been domesticated.

Ostrich. Four subspecies of the Ostrich *Struthio camelus* (see OSTRICH) namely *S.c. camelus*, *S.c. molybdophanes*, *S.c. massaicus* and *S.c. australis*, appear to have been domesticated at some time during the recorded history of man. The greatest incidence of domestication occurred in the latter half of the nineteenth century, when the feathers became fashionable. The main area of ostrich farming was in the Cape Province of South Africa, which is within the range of *S.c. australis*. The first records of birds hatching eggs in captivity at the Cape date from the 1860s. In 1865 there were 80 birds in captivity there, and by 1904 there were 357 000 domesticated birds, the vast majority of which had been hatched by artificial incubation. Ostrich farming was also carried out in North Africa, the United States of America, South Australia, France, Spain, and Italy. In 1914–18 the industry collapsed, but today about 25 000 birds are farmed in South Africa for the production of high-quality leather. Descendants of the imported birds are now feral in South Australian localities.

Little Egret. When the ostrich feather trade was at a maximum, the Little Egret *Egretta garzetta* (see under HERON) was domesticated and farmed on a small scale for its plumes in what is now Pakistan and in Tunisia.

Cormorant. The custom of using Cormorants *Phalacrocorax carbo sinensis* (see CORMORANT) for fishing dates back to the Sung dynasty (A.D. 960–1298) in China, and to the sixth century A.D. in

Japan. The birds are bred by special breeders and sold to fishermen as untrained birds.

Egyptian Goose. In ancient Egypt the Egyptian (or Nile) Goose *Alopochen aegyptiacus* (see under DUCK) was the main domestic bird. Its domestication took place very early, as in the Old Kingdom (which ended in 2300 B.C.) it was very common. Its flesh was widely eaten, although the bird was the sacred bird of the god Geb, but its eggs also had symbolic value and were not eaten. There are very few records of the domesticated bird outside Egypt ; and after the Persian conquest of Egypt in 525-524 B.C. the species ceased to be a domestic animal.

Game-birds. Between the thirteenth and sixteenth centuries pheasants are reported to have been bred domestically for the London markets. Today many enterprises breed game-birds on a very large scale for restocking wild populations and for marketing. The most usual birds include the Pheasant *Phasianus colchicus*, the Partridge *Perdix perdix*, the Bobwhite Quail *Colinus virginianus*, and several species of true quails *Coturnix* spp. (see under PHEASANT). In Italy, China, and Japan the Quail *Coturnix coturnix* is also kept for egg production. A number of aquatic species have also been bred on a large scale for re-stocking. Although no conscious selection has been practised on these birds, and they may not be considered domesticated in the generally used sense of the word, difficulty is often encountered in maintaining wildness in these stocks ; this point again emphasises the difficulty in defining domestication.

D.G.M.W.-G.

Darwin, C. 1868. The Variations of Animals and Plants under Domestication. 2 vols.
Hutt, F. B. 1962. Genetics of the Fowl. London and New York.
Ives, P. P. 1947. Domestic Geese and Ducks. New York.
Roettger, C. R. 1958. Die Haustiere Afrikas. Ihre Herkunft, Bedeutung und Aussichten bei der weiteren wirtschaftlichen Erschliessung des Kontinents. Jena.
Sayer, C. O. 1952. Agricultural Origins and Dispersals. Amer. Geog. Soc.
Wood-Gush, D. G. M. 1959. A history of the domestic chicken from antiquity to the 19th Century. Poultry Science 38 : 321-326.
Zeuner, F. E. 1963. A History of Domesticated Animals, London.

DOMINANCE (1) : see GENETICS

DOMINANCE (2) : term expressing the observed fact that the outcome of aggressive encounters between individual birds is predictable, one of two combatants being regularly victorious and the other defeated ; the bird assured of victory is called the 'dominant' and the other the 'subordinate' bird.

In groups of caged birds a dominance hierarchy is normally established ; at the top is the 'despot' or 'alpha' bird capable of defeating all the others, while below him the other birds are capable of defeating those below them in the hierarchy but not those above. Sometimes complex triangular relationships are found in which, while A dominates B and B dominates C, C dominates A ; such triangles are usually unstable and commonly end in a more normal straight-line arrangement. In a 'peck right' hierarchy of this kind, first studied in domestic fowls (Schjelderup Ebbe 1922), it is sufficient to identify the individuals concerned.

In a so-called 'peck dominance' hierarchy, on the other hand, the locality in which an encounter occurs plays a role in determining the relative dominance of the combatants. Caged pigeons, for example, prefer certain areas of their aviaries, and these they defend ; they are always dominant within them. In the wild, 'peck right' has been described at single feeding-stations of Black-capped Chickadee *Parus atricapillus*, Blue Tit *P. caeruleus*, Great Tit *P. major*, American Tree Sparrow *Spizella arborea*, and Junco *Junco hyemalis*. However, since the observations were confined to single stations, the effect of location was not fully studied, and it seems more likely that, in relatively geographically stable populations, the observed hierarchies may be of the 'peck dominance' type. Marler has recently shown that Chaffinches *Fringilla coelebs* in winter flocks have 'peck right' hierarchies, but that with the setting up of territories in the spring a state of 'peck dominance' takes its place (see TERRITORY).

Once a hierarchy has been set up in a group, it tends to maintain the social order established by the initial encounters and there is a strong resistance to change. Apart from artificial means, changes in dominance occur with failing or improving health and also, in domestic fowls, as a result of mating. Thus, a female of low status mated to a dominant cock rises in rank. Experimentally induced dominance reversals are recorded in groups of domestic fowls and Canaries *Serinus canaria* following injections of the male hormone (testosterone proprionate) into a subdominant bird. Newcomers introduced into established flocks normally cannot enter the hierarchy except from the bottom, whence they have to fight their way up. In an established flock, fights are most frequent between those birds nearest in rank. The winning of contests does not depend entirely on a bird's aggressiveness, health, state of moult, and previous social rank, but also on other psychological factors affecting the birds at the time and in the particular place in which an encounter occurs. A single defeat does not necessarily bring about a change in social position ; several or many engagements are usually necessary for this. Thus, in domestic fowls, the assimilation of an individual into a flock may take between three days and five weeks, and an individual can hold its position without being continually present. Debeaking of chickens did not prevent the formation of a peck order, and the frequency of 'pecking' was actually found to increase on debeaking. Flocks of domestic fowls with well established hierarchies, when compared with those kept in a constant state of changing relations, were found to eat more food, to produce more eggs, and to maintain their body-weight when feeding was restricted. The despots and high-rankers have priority at the food bowls, nests, and roosting places, and generally a greater freedom of movement about the pen.

In caged Chaffinch flocks in winter, the males are normally dominant to the females but are more tolerant of their close approach (at feeding bowls for example) than they are of other males. Marler coloured females artificially so that they resembled males and found that they were tolerated much less than normal females. Females, originally of low social status, also show a rise in rank after colouring. Likewise, when placed with males the coloured females win significantly more fights with them than the ordinary birds.

As the breeding season advances the dominance of the male (in most finches) is gradually reversed in favour of the female (see also PAIR FORMATION). The extent of the reversal does, however, vary between species. It is strongly marked in the Chaffinch, but in some others the tendency of the male to attack the female may be present throughout much of the courtship. Reversal at this time is a consequence primarily of increased fleeing tendencies or reduced attacking tendencies (or both) in the male, associated with his increased tendency to behave sexually. The change is thus at the dictate of the reproductive motivation active at the time, rather than due to a series of combat victories by the female. The aggressiveness of the males towards other males remains high throughout.   J.H.C.

Wood-Gush, D. G. M. 1955. The behaviour of the domestic chicken : a review of the literature. Brit. J. Anim. Behav. 3 : 81–110.

DORSAL: pertaining to the back, or generally to the upper surface of the body (in a more or less horizontal position) ; opposite of VENTRAL.

DOTTEREL: properly *Eudromias morinellus* (see PLOVER (1)) ; also used, particularly in Australia and New Zealand, as substantive name of various *Charadrius* spp., and even of *Peltohyas australis* (Glareolidae—see COURSER.)

DOVE: substantive name of some species of Columbidae (see PIGEON). The names 'dove' and 'pigeon' are to some extent interchangeable. See also CAGE BIRD.

DOVEKIE: alternative name of the Little Auk *Plautus alle* (see AUK).

DOWITCHER: substantive name of *Limnodromus* spp. (see SANDPIPER).

DOWN: see PLUMAGE. The use of down, plucked by the female from her own body, is characteristic of ducks (Anatidae) and lyrebirds *Menura* spp.

DRAKE: special term for a male DUCK.

DREPANIDIDAE: a family of the Passeriformes, suborder Oscines (see HONEYCREEPER (2)). This version of the familial name appears to be more correctly formed than the frequently used 'Drepaniidae'.

DRIFT: displacement of a migrant from its normal route by the wind, irrespective of whether the bird is (a) heading in a constant direction and being laterally displaced, (b) has become disoriented and is flying at random, or (c) is, in certain circumstances, perhaps flying downwind as postulated by Williamson. In this sense the term is purely factual and carries no theoretical implications ; it has been used in the literature for half a century, but more particular attention has been paid to the factor in the last dozen years (see MIGRATION).

DRINKING: a habit subject to considerable differences among birds. Water is an essential constituent of living organisms and must be maintained in certain concentrations for the proper metabolic functioning of the body. Water is lost in excretion, although the amount is reduced by reabsorption from the excreta before their final expulsion from the body ; water is also lost as vapour in respiration, and this is proportionately greater in small than in large birds ; but there is no sweat. Some water intake is therefore necessary, and the question is how much of this must be obtained by drinking and how much can be derived from the food. All foodstuffs contain some free water, and a further amount may be liberated in their metabolism ; it is obvious, however, that the amount obtainable from a diet of dry seeds must be very much less than from succulent vegetable food or from animal food. External conditions such as air temperature and humidity, and also the degree of activity of the bird itself, are factors that must have some effect in varying the requirements (see HEAT REGULATION ; METABOLISM).

Some species show adaptation to conditions that impose minimal water intake. Thus, it has been shown that seed-eating birds such as the Savanna Sparrow *Passerculus sandwichensis* and the Budgerigar *Melopsittacus undulatus*, inhabiting arid country in North America and Australia respectively, can go for long periods without water on their customary dry diet. Other species of similar habits, however, die within a few days if deprived of water, showing that they are not fully adapted to this arid environment but depend on some access to water. Another adaptation is shown by marine and litoral species that are able to use sea-water, having a special physiological mechanism for eliminating excess of salt from the body (see EXCRETION, EXTRARENAL).

As regards the act of drinking, some purely arboreal species, not ordinarily descending to ground level, can do no more than sip from surfaces or small pockets in the foliage after rain, otherwise depending on their food. Many species, however, regularly resort to pools or streams—or sometimes larger stretches of water—specially to drink. In semi-arid areas, some travel long distances daily for this purpose, notably sandgrouse (Pteroclididae) (see SANDGROUSE).

A common method of drinking, in passerine birds for example, is familiar ; the bird repeatedly fills its bill or mouth with water, and each time raises its head to let the liquid run down its throat. On the other hand, pigeons (Columbidae) and sandgrouse imbibe continuously, without raising the head ; so do buttonquails (Turnicidae). Some notably aerial birds, such as swifts (Apodidae), drink in flight, sipping instantaneously from the surface of the water as they pass immediately over it.

Cade, T. J. & Dybas, J. A. 1962. Water economy in the Budgerygah. Auk 79 : 345-364. (General discussion ; references.)

DRIVE: ' the complex of internal and external states and stimuli necessary to the performance of a given course of instinctive behaviour' (Thorpe 1951) ; termed ' internal drive' where external factors are excluded from the definition.

Hinde, R. A. 1959. Motivation. Ibis 101 : 353-357.

DROMADIDAE: see under CHARADRIIFORMES ; and CRAB-PLOVER

DROMADOIDEA: see under CHARADRIIFORMES

DROMAEOGNATHOUS: see PALATE

DROMAIIDAE: see under CASUARIIFORMES ; and EMU. This version of the familial name is preferred to ' Dromiceiidae' by Australian ornithologists, on the ground that *Dromaius* not *Dromiceius* (both of Vieillot 1816) is the proper generic name, the latter having been wrongly formed in the first instance but corrected to the former by the original author a few pages later ; it is understood that application for official recognition of the amended names is being made to the International Commission on Zoological Nomenclature.

DRONGO: substantive name of nearly all species of Dicruridae (Passeriformes, suborder Oscines) ; in the plural (' drongos'), general term for the family. ' Drongo' is the indigenous vernacular name used by the Betsimisarakas and Sakalavas of northern Madagascar for *Dicrurus forficatus*, and from that island it has passed into universal use for the family.

$\frac{1}{2}$

Drongo *Dicrurus adsimilis*, the common species of tropical Africa. *C.E.T.K.*

The drongos, comprising 20 species, are a natural and sharply defined family of the Old World tropics ; but, although there is no difficulty in recognising any member of this family as a drongo, their nearest relatives are a matter of speculation. The muscicapid flycatchers (Muscicapinae), orioles (Oriolidae), shrikes (Laniidae), crows (Corvidae), and birds-of-paradise (Paradisaeidae) have been suggested ; but, in behaviour at least, drongos are most similar to, and are to some extent the ecological counterpart of, the tyrant-flycatchers (Tyrannidae) of the New World, although no relationship is implied in this statement.

General Characteristics. The drongos are solitary, insectivorous, and arboreal birds of medium size, varying in length from 7-8 inches to 14-15 inches, not counting the elongated tips of the tail feathers in some species ; the length reaches a maximum of about 28 inches when the elongated part of the tail is added. The shape and structure of the tail vary enormously, from truncate to very deeply forked ; or the outer tail feathers may be extremely long, curled, or denuded of barbs but ending in racquets. The tail is typically deeply forked, with the tips of the outer feathers curving outwards ; it may be composed of 10 or 12 feathers. The wings are long, pointed, and beautifully tapered, and the combination of these wings with the long and deeply forked tail enables the drongos to manoeuvre with great ease ; the Ashy Drongo *Dicrurus leucophaeus* of India is, according to Whistler, ' a magnificent flier, turning and twisting with extreme speed and skill '. The bill is stout, compressed and arched, hooked and slightly notched ; the rictal bristles are long and very strong. The legs are short, with strong toes and claws. The iris is red as a rule.

The plumage is black, velvety or lustrous, except in two species where it varies from slaty to very pale grey, almost white. In all but the grey species the plumage is more or less glossed with greenish, bluish, or purplish. The intensity of the gloss, which can be brilliant and metallic, and its distribution to certain areas of the plumage or to certain parts of individual feathers, vary from species to species but are constant in each and provide the best systematic character. In some species the gloss forms brilliant spangles on the throat and chest. Some have glossy hackles at the sides of the neck and many are crested, the structure and shape of the crest varying as much as the tail feathers. The crest may consist of only a little brush at the base of the bill, or may extend over its ridge, or may be very full, consisting of webbed feathers that curl over the head and nape. In some species the crest feathers are partly or completely denuded of barbs and vary from a little erect tuft, about two-thirds of an inch, to long filaments that may reach a length of 5 inches. The ornamental modification of some body feathers, the crest, and the tail vary geographically in the same species and are of much interest. A few forms (species or subspecies) are white on the abdomen, upper wing coverts or face,

or have a white spot at the corner of the mouth ; in one found in the Comoro Islands the wings and tail are reddish brown.

Habits. The morphological characters have been stressed here because they are unusual, and to compensate for the lack of data in other respects. The life histories of some drongos are unknown, and none has been thoroughly studied—not even the King-crow *Dicrurus macrocercus*, although it is one of the most abundant and familiar birds of India. In the species of which the nest is known, it is described as a rather shallow cradle or saucer, semi-pendent, and almost invariably fastened in the fork of a slender branch, usually on the outside of a tree, at heights that vary normally from about 15 to 50 feet from the ground. The chief building materials are supple twigs, roots, and grass stems, bound by cobwebs ; the nest looks frail but is said to be very strong. The exact role played by the sexes in nest building, incubation, and care of young is unknown, but one reliable author states merely that ' both sexes share all domestic duties '. The normal clutch varies from 3 to 4 eggs, or 2 to 3 in one or two species. In the case of the Ashy Drongo, an egg is said to have been incubated for 13 days (no further information being supplied) ; and this is the sole incubation record, for this or any other drongo, that is known to the writer.

The voice of the drongos is a jumble of harsh metallic notes and chuckles, interspersed occasionally with musical calls and whistles, but some individuals are accomplished mimics, and the Greater Racket-tailed Drongo *D. paradiseus* is celebrated for this ability. The drongos are reported by all authors to be very pugnacious and fearless, invariably attacking and pursuing certain large birds such as crows (Corvidae) and hawks (Falconiformes) ; but they are apparently not mere bullies, as it is said they do not molest small or harmless birds. It is well known that many species of birds build their nests in the same tree where a drongo has built its own, probably taking advantage of the ' protection ' given by the drongo. Other traits of behaviour worthy of note are that drongos associate with cattle or man, are inquisitive, and (in Africa) follow grass fires and are said to ' play the leading part ' in the mixed bird parties that roam the forest in search of food.

Distribution and Examples. The family is divided into two genera, one of them monotypic. The Papuan Mountain Drongo *Chaetorhynchus papuensis* of the mountains of New Guinea differs from all the others, *Dicrurus* spp., in having 12 tail feathers, and also in some details of structure and colour pattern. The drongos are most numerous in the Oriental Region, with 10 species, one of which ranges to the Solomon Islands and south-eastern Australia ; 3 are endemic in the Ethiopian Region and 4 in Madagascar and neighbouring islands ; and 3 are endemic in the Australo-Papuan area. Three of the Oriental species have penetrated deeply into the Palaearctic Region, to south-eastern Iran in the west and to Manchuria in the north-east, and one of them is reported from the Amur River valley. The ornamental characters are much less evolved in the 7 species of Africa and Madagascar, and these, taken as a group, show only a relatively slight amount of geographical variation ; they appear to be primitive. The most noteworthy of all drongos is the Spangled Drongo *D. hottentottus* of New Guinea, which, with 33 subspecies, is one of the most variable of all birds ; it has freely colonised oceanic islands, some of them by repeated invasions. The systematics and evolution of the drongos have been studied in detail by Mayr & Vaurie and by Vaurie.   C.V.

Mayr, E. & Vaurie, C. 1948. Evolution in the family Dicruridae (Birds). Evolution 2 : 238–265.
Vaurie, C. 1949. A revision of the bird family Dicruridae. Bull. Amer. Mus. Nat. Hist. 93 : 119–342.
Vaurie, C. 1962. Family Dicruridae. In Mayr, E. & Greenway, J. C., Jr. (eds.). Check-list of Birds of the World vol. 15. Cambridge, Mass.

DROPPINGS: the mixture of renal excretion (urine) and intestinal waste matter (faeces) voided through the common exterior orifice, the cloaca (see ALIMENTARY SYSTEM ; EXCRETORY SYSTEM). In the nestlings of many passerine birds each discharge is enclosed in a gelatinous capsule so that it can be removed entire by the parent ('nest sanitation')—see DEVELOPMENT, POST EMBRYONIC ; PARENTAL CARE. Otherwise it tends to be an untidy splash of varying degrees of liquidity ; much of the original water content is reabsorbed through the cloacal wall. The presence of rather insoluble salts in the urine is responsible for the characteristic white appearance, often in the form of a cap on the faecal matter, and for the durable staining of branches or stones at points where birds habitually perch or stand. Where colonially breeding birds congregate in large numbers the material may, under favourable conditions, accumulate to form deep deposits (see GUANO ; GUANO, CAVE).

Sometimes the droppings may be tinged with bright colours, and these can often be recognised as pigments that pass unchanged from the food through the alimentary tract—for example, the purple colour in the droppings of sea birds feeding on mussels (*Mytilus*). In the fasting Adélie Penguin *Pygoscelis adeliae* at its nest the excreta are green,

due to bile pigments ; when a bird has recently come from feeding on crustaceans (*Euphausia*) in the sea, the excreta are pink.

In some circumstances when the excrement is relatively solid and not dropped from a height, it may be less amorphous than a mere splash—for instance, retaining at least in part the cylindrical form imparted to it in passage through the intestine. There may even be a form characteristic of the species or group, a case in point being the long gelatinous 'stool' of, e.g., the Grey Lag Goose *Anser anser*. Notably characteristic are the droppings of grouse (Tetraonidae), well described long ago by MacGillivray in respect of the Black Grouse *Lyrurus tetrix* : 'The faeces in the rectum are comparatively dry, and form a continuous cylinder, in which state, mixed with urine, they are voided, forming a small heap of cylindrical fragments.' The general subject seems to have been little studied. See also PELLET.

DRUMMING: see INSTRUMENTAL SOUNDS

DRYING: see FEATHER MAINTENANCE

DUCK: substantive name of most of the smaller species of Anatidae (Anseriformes, suborder Anseres) ; in the plural, usually in the combination 'ducks, geese, and swans', general term for the family. Apart from a number of ducks that have special names, the other species have the substantive names 'goose' and 'swan'. As the application of 'duck' and 'goose' does not correspond with the taxonomic subdivisions, the whole family is dealt with in this article ; but see also GOOSE ; SWAN ; and COUNT ; DOMESTICATION ; HYBRID.

Ornithologically 'duck' is applied irrespective of sex, but one usage restricts this to the female (even in species with special substantive names, e.g. 'duck Shoveler'), the corresponding term for the male being 'drake' ; in North America 'hen' is often used for the female. The diminutive 'duckling' is used for the young. 'Duck' is often used unchanged in the plural as a collective term—for individuals rather than species.

The members of the family are essentially aquatic, many species obtaining their food principally by diving ; three of the toes are linked by webs (see SWIMMING AND DIVING). All have relatively long necks and blunt. rather spatulate bills. All lay unspotted eggs, mostly nearly white or pale coloured, in nests on the ground, in thick vegetation, or in holes in trees, rocks, or earth, usually lined with down plucked by the female from her breast ; and all have nidifugous down-covered young. All ducks, swans, and most geese moult the flight feathers of the wings simultaneously and pass through a flightless period, lasting from three to four weeks, after the breeding season ; in all the Anatidae the only exceptions to this are the Magpie Goose *Anseranas semipalmata*, and at least some individuals of at least one of the species of sheldgeese of the genus *Chloephaga* (see below).

The classification of the Anatidae now generally accepted is based, with minor modifications, on that proposed by Delacour & Mayr. They used the following special characters in arriving at the new system : the pattern of the scales on the tarsus, the plumage pattern in adults and downy young, the presence or absence of a double moult, the posture and general body proportions, the structure of the trachea and syrinx, and the behaviour, particularly courtship display.

In all, 247 forms, belonging to 147 generally accepted species, have been described. These are placed in 43 genera, grouped in ten tribes and more broadly divided into three sub-families, thus :

Family : Anatidae
  Subfamily : Anseranatinae
    Tribe : Anseranatini   Magpie Goose
  Subfamily : Anserinae
    Tribes : Dendrocygnini   Whistling ducks or tree ducks
            Anserini   Swans and true geese
  Subfamily : Anatinae
    Tribes : Tadornini   Shelducks and sheldgeese
          Anatini   Dabbling ducks
          Aythyini   Pochards
          Cairinini   Perching ducks and geese
          Somateriini   Eiders
          Mergini   Scoters, goldeneyes, and mergansers
          Oxyurini   Stifftails

Of the ten tribes, eight contain species to which the substantive name 'duck' is applied, and the degree to which some ducks may differ in their relationships from other ducks is illustrated by the fact that the single tribe Anserini includes such apparently different birds as swans and geese, while much greater taxonomic differences exist between, say, pochards and stifftails, in spite of their similarities of appearance and habit. Similarly, 'goose' is the substantive name of some species of four of the ten tribes and all three of the subfamilies. 'Swan' is applied only in one tribe, but not to all its members.

Magpie Goose. The subfamily Anseranatinae (and sole tribe Anseranatini) consists of a single species, the aberrant and apparently primitive Magpie Goose *Anseranas semipalmata* of Australia, an untidy black-and-white bird in which the elongated toes are only slightly webbed and in which, unlike almost all other Anatidae, the flight

feathers are moulted progressively instead of simultaneously, so that there is no flightless period. The Magpie Goose seems to form some kind of link with the family Anhimidae, placed in the same order (see SCREAMER).

Whistling Ducks (Tree Ducks). The Dendrocygnini are confined to the tropics. They show no sexual dimorphism, and, as in the Magpie Goose and some swans, both sexes incubate the eggs. They dive freely for food, and they indulge in mutual preening. One species, the Fulvous Whistling Duck *Dendrocygna bicolor*, has a remarkably wide range, occurring (apparently without geographical subspeciation) in North America, South America, Africa, and India.

Swans and 'True Geese'. The Anserini comprise the swans, in the genera *Coscoroba* and *Cygnus*, and the geese of the genera *Anser* and *Branta*. There are nine forms of swan—all large, herbivorous, aquatic birds with notably long necks and powerful, spatulate bills. They show no sexual dimorphism in plumage, and all the species lay pale-coloured eggs in a bulky nest on the ground ; the nidifugous down-covered young ('cygnets') hatch after an incubation period of from 34–40 days. The immature plumage is brownish or greyish.

The Coscoroba Swan *Coscoroba coscoroba*, a South American species, is the smallest of the world's described forms, and has been held to show some affinities with the whistling ducks (Dendrocygnini). The remaining swan species are now generally placed in a single genus, *Cygnus*, and include two Southern Hemisphere forms, the Black-necked Swan *C. melanocoryphus* of South America and the Black Swan *C. atratus* of Australia, and in the Northern Hemisphere five distinct forms in which the adult plumage is white (and a sixth poorly differentiated local race).

The Mute Swan *C. olor*, which has some affinities with *C. atratus*, is an Old World species semi-domesticated in western Europe for about 900 years, originally as a source of food. In England these swans were subject to special legislation and the Crown granted 'royalties' enabling certain noblemen and corporate bodies, such as livery companies of the City of London, to own swans and to mark their bills with registered symbols or 'swan marks'. Any Mute Swans on the River Thames not so marked were the property of the Crown. Annually on the Thames the young Swans were, and still are, captured for marking in a traditional colourful ceremony known as 'swan upping'. The only royalties in Swans still remaining are those granted to the Dyers and Vintners Companies and to the Earl of Ilchester, owner of a famous 'swannery'

THE TEN TRIBES
OF THE FAMILY ANATIDAE

Anseranatini

Dendrocygnini

Anserini

Tadornini

Anatini

Cairinini

Somateriini

Aythyini

Mergini

Oxyurini

or colonial nesting site for Mute Swans at Abbotsbury in Dorset, where in some years more than 100 pairs nest in close company. An albinistic phase of the Mute Swan known as the Polish Swan, in which the legs and feet are pinkish grey instead of black and the first plumage of the cygnets is white instead of the normal brownish grey, is rare in Europe but common among introduced Mute Swans in North America.

In the Palaearctic Region are two rather similar migratory wild swans with yellow patches on their bills—the larger Whooper Swan *C. cygnus cygnus* and the smaller Bewick's Swan *C. columbianus bewickii*, from which an eastern race, Jankowski's Swan *C. columbianus jankowskii*, has been separated. In North America, the largest of the world's swans, the Trumpeter Swan *C. cygnus buccinator* and the smaller Whistling Swan *C. columbianus columbianus* are held to be analogous to the Whooper and Bewick's Swans, although by some not to be respectively conspecific. The Whistling Swan breeds in the Arctic and is migratory, while the remnant populations of the Trumpeter Swan (amounting in 1957 to an estimated 1500) do not apparently migrate far from their breeding grounds in the Rocky Mountains and Alaska.

There are 14 species of 'true geese'—grey geese *Anser* spp. and 'black geese' *Branta* spp. They

are wary birds which graze in flocks or ' gaggles ', fly in ' skeins ', and are confined to the Northern Hemisphere. Most of them breed in Arctic or subarctic latitudes, and many are divided into numerous and well marked geographical races in spite of a strongly migratory habit. In such cases, populations from a particular breeding area preserve a high degree of reproductive isolation because of strong social bonds uniting the families (and probably larger groupings) during the winter migrations. They show no sexual dimorphism in plumage; and they lay unspotted, almost white eggs, which require from 24 to 33 days of incubation before hatching into nidifugous down-covered young. For the most part geese are less aquatic in habit than swans or ducks. Geese have been recorded as living in captivity to an age of at least 42 years.

The typical ' grey goose ' is the Grey Lag Goose *Anser anser*, a widespread Palaearctic species from which, by selective breeding, man has evolved various domestic forms of farmyard geese ; the domestic Chinese Goose was derived (probably more than 2000 years ago) from the Swan Goose *A. cygnoides* breeding in Siberia and wintering in China. The Whitefronted Goose *A. albifrons* has the widest range of all the grey geese, four races spanning the Palaearctic and Nearctic Regions. The Bean Goose *A. fabalis* has a number of distinguishable races, all confined to the Old World. The most westerly form, the Pinkfooted Goose *A. fabalis brachyrhynchus*—the commonest wild goose in Britain in winter—is sometimes regarded as a distinct species. In Europe and Asia these grey geese have been extolled in poetry, prose, and painting as the most romantic of wildfowl, the traditional quarry of particular wariness, the mysterious wanderers whose wild musical cries on migration mark the changing seasons. In many parts of Europe their great assemblies are the finest wild-life spectacle that remains to be seen.

The Bar-headed Goose *A. indicus* is probably the species of which a skein of seventeen was recorded on a photograph of the sun taken at Dehra Dun, India, at a height variously estimated at between 25 000 and 58 000 feet ; it has a slightly larger wing area for its weight than the other grey geese, perhaps because of the high altitudes required for its migrations from breeding grounds in Tibet to the plains of India.

In North America the Snow Goose *A. coerulescens* is dimorphic. In adult plumage one phase is pure white with black primaries, while in the other— the ' Blue Goose '—there is a variable amount of slate grey on the body, most characteristically only

---

Examples of the ten tribes of the Family Anatidae (about $\frac{1}{8}$ natural size) :—

Anseranatini : Magpie Goose *Anseranas semipalmata* (Australo-Papuan area).

Dendrocygnini : Fulvous Whistling Duck *Dendrocygna bicolor* (pantropical).

Anserini : Bewick's Swan *Cygnus columbianus bewickii* (northern Palaearctic), and (in front) Canada Goose *Branta canadensis* (northern Nearctic).

Tadornini : Andean Goose *Chloephaga melanoptera* (western Neotropical), and (on right) Shelduck *Tadorna tadorna* ♂ (Palaearctic).

Anatini : Mallard *Anas platrhynchos* ♂ (Northern Hemisphere), and (behind) Peruvian Torrent Duck *Merganetta armata leucogenis* ♂ (Peru and Ecuador).

Cairinini : wild Muscovy Duck *Cairina moschata* ♂ (Neotropical), and (in front) Mandarin Duck *Aix galericulata* ♂ (eastern Asia).

Somateriini : Eider *Somateria mollissima* ♂ (northern Holarctic).

Aythyini : Pochard *Aythya ferina* ♂ (Palaearctic).

Mergini : Goldeneye *Bucephala clangula* ♂ (northern Holarctic), and (behind) Red-breasted Merganser *Mergus serrator* ♂ (northern Holarctic).

Oxyurini : North American Ruddy Duck *Oxyura jamaicensis jamaicensis* ♂ (North America and West Indies).   *Peter Scott.*

the head and part of the neck being white. This dark plumage, perhaps a recent mutation, appears to be dominant (although the genetics are complex), increasing in its incidence and spreading westwards in the most widespread race of the species, the Lesser Snow Goose *A. c. coerulescens*. No blue phase is known in the larger eastern race, the Greater Snow Goose *A. c. atlanticus*, or in the much smaller Ross's Goose *A. rossii*, which is specifically distinct and confined to a narrow western range in numbers probably not exceeding 12 000–15 000. The handsome Emperor Goose *A. canagicus*, with small heavily loaded wings, has a short migration route from the Alaskan coast along the Aleutian chain ; the white head of this species in the wild state is usually stained to a deep orange yellow by iron deposits in the water, a condition also seen in Snow Geese and in swans. See POLYMORPHISM ; and Plate 20 (colour).

The name *Branta*, like the English 'brent' and the American 'brant', is taken from the rolling call of the bird. Three or possibly four distinguishable races of the Brent Goose (or Brant) *Branta bernicla* breed in the high Arctic in a circumpolar distribution and winter in the intertidal zones of temperate coasts. The failure (probably through disease) of its principal food supply, the sea-grass *Zostera*, caused catastrophic reductions in the numbers all over the world between 1930 and 1940. Unlike other species of geese, wild-caught Brent Geese have only once been known to nest in captivity. The Barnacle Goose *B. leucopsis* is also a high Arctic breeding species but has a very restricted winter range in western Europe. In the Middle Ages it was believed that these geese were hatched from ship barnacles (*Cirripedia*) and were therefore 'fish' rather than 'fowl' ; they were thus permitted as food on Fridays. This belief also extended to the Brent Goose, which was known—particularly in Roman Catholic Ireland—as the 'Barnacle' (or 'Bernicle') ; *B. leucopsis* was called the 'Land Barnacle'.

The most elaborate and striking plumage pattern among the Anserini is that of the Red-breasted Goose *B. ruficollis*, breeding in northern Siberia and wintering near the Caspian and Aral Seas. It is handsomely marked in black and white and chestnut brown and is the smallest of the true geese (although Ross's Goose is scarcely larger).

The Canada Goose *B. canadensis* has been divided into twelve distinguishable geographical races, of which one is believed to be extinct. All have the same black head and neck with white cheek patches, but they vary greatly in size and in the shades of brown of the body plumage. The larger races,

known as 'honkers', provide one of the principal quarry species of the American 'duck-hunter'. The Ne-ne or Hawaiian Goose *B. sandvicensis* is an island species, evidently of common stock with *B. canadensis*, which now has reduced webs to its feet and shorter wings because of its less aquatic and non-migratory habit. In 1950 the total population was believed to be under 50, but intensive captive breeding projects in Hawaii and England had increased the figure to 210 by 1963. The Ne-ne is the 'state bird' of Hawaii.

Shelducks and Sheldgeese. Somewhat goose-like are the shelducks in the tribe Tadornini. The Crested Shelduck *Tadorna cristata* is believed to have become extinct ; it is known only from three specimens, two from Korea and one from near Vladivostok, although it is illustrated in several ancient Japanese prints. The New Zealand Shelduck *T. variegata*, and to a lesser extent the South African Shelduck *T. cana*, exhibit a bright plumage in the female that is evidently analogous to the bright plumage in the males of other duck species ; for example, in *T. variegata* the immature plumage resembles that of the male, in which the head is black, while the adult female assumes a white head and moults annually into a slightly duller post-nuptial 'eclipse' plumage. This sexual inversion is incomplete and, in contrast to the phalaropes (Phalaropodidae) and certain Falconiformes, the male shelduck is larger than the female and dominates the pair.

In Australia the Cape Barren Goose *Cereopsis novaehollandiae*, a large grey bird confined to a very few islands where its numbers are reported to be declining, has been held to link the 'true geese' with the Tadornini although it may more properly belong to the Anserini. The South American genus *Chloephaga* consists of five species of goose-like grazing birds all with a sharply defined mirror or 'speculum' of iridescent colours on the secondary coverts (in contrast to the iridescent secondaries in the 'true ducks' of the tribe Anatini). At least some individuals of one species, the Ruddy-headed Goose *C. rubidiceps*, moult their flight feathers progressively and have no flightless period ; this may be true of other *Chloephaga* species. Two of the species, the maritime Kelp Goose *C. hybrida* and the Upland (or Magellan) Goose *C. picta*, display very marked sexual dimorphism, the males being white or predominantly white, the female predominantly dark brown or reddish brown. In the other three the sexes are scarcely to be distinguished by plumage differences, although in the Andean Goose *C. melanoptera* both are largely white ('male' colour), while in the Ashy-headed

Goose *C. poliocephala* and the Ruddy-headed Goose both are dark ('female' colour). In the Abyssinian Blue-winged Goose *Cyanochen cyanoptera* (which is closely related to *Chloephaga*), there is no sexual dimorphism, and the same applies to the Egyptian Goose *Alopochen aegyptiacus* and the Orinoco Goose *Neochen jubatus*, which seem to link the sheldgeese with the shelducks of the genus *Tadorna*.

Certain further South American species appear to belong to this tribe—the Crested Duck *Lophonetta specularioides*, and the three steamer ducks *Tachyeres* spp. The latter are marine diving ducks of heavy build and plain plumage, and two of them are unable to fly (see FLIGHTLESSNESS).

Dabbling Ducks. The great majority of the Anatini or dabbling ducks have been placed in the large and very various genus *Anas*, which includes the mallards, pintails, wigeon, shovelers, and many different species of teal. In some, especially those frequenting the Northern Hemisphere, there is a sharp sexual dimorphism, the males having a bright nuptial plumage (linked with a more or less elaborate courtship display), which is replaced by a cryptic 'eclipse' plumage (resembling the plumage of the female) during the annual flightless period. The males of most Southern Hemisphere species, however, remain similarly coloured throughout the year; the bright plumage of the males of northern species seems to have been lost (rather than never developed) in sedentary and island races, and the brightness is most marked in the most migratory forms.

Of the dabbling ducks only the Mallard *A. platyrhynchos* has been domesticated, giving rise to various familiar forms (see DOMESTICATION). Aberrant species that have been included in the dabbling duck tribe are the Torrent Duck *Merganetta armata* subspp. of the Andes, the now probably extinct Pink-headed Duck *Rhodonessa caryophyllacea* of India (which may have formed a link with the pochards), the Marbled Teal *Marmaronetta angustirostris* of the Mediterranean and Near East (which almost certainly forms such a link), and two strange species from Australia—the little Pink-eared Duck *Malacorhynchus membranaceus* specially adapted for feeding on blue-green algae, and the Freckled Duck *Stictonetta naevosa* which shows some affinities with the geese and may finally prove to belong to the subfamily Anserinae, perhaps in a tribe of its own. The taxonomic position of the Blue (or Mountain) Duck *Hymenolaimus malacorhynchos* of New Zealand, of which the bill is adapted as a sucker and the principal food is probably green algae sucked from the stones of fast running streams, is still obscure; but the Ringed Teal *Callonetta leucophrys* is now

believed to belong to the tribe Cairinini, perhaps forming a link with the Anatini.

The Pintail *Anas acuta*, which has a wide circumpolar range, is probably the most numerous duck species in the world, and the dabbling ducks of the genus *Anas* provide three-quarters of the quarry for the wildfowler or duck-hunter (see WILDFOWL); most of the other quarter is provided by the next tribe.

See Plate 2b (phot.).

Pochards. The Aythyini include the famous North American sporting bird the Canvasback *Aythya vallisneria*, which is closely related on the one hand to the Pochard *A. ferina* of Europe and on the other to the sympatric American Redhead *A. americana*. The Tufted Duck *A. fuligula* is the most familiar representative in Britain. The Greater Scaup *A. marila*, called in North America 'Bluebill' or 'Broadbill', has a circumpolar breeding range and is found in huge 'rafts', principally on salt water, in many parts of the world. Several of the species share the substantive name 'white-eye'. With the exception of the genus *Netta*, the pochards are all accomplished divers.

Perching Ducks and Geese. The tribe Cairinini shows the widest range in size in the Anatidae. Male Spurwinged Geese weigh up to 22 lb., while the smallest of the Pygmy Geese (or Cotton Teal) *Nettapus* spp. weigh only 8 ounces. The tribe also includes the most brilliantly coloured and fantastically marked of the Anatidae. The drakes of the Mandarin Duck *Aix galericulata* of China, and of the related Wood (or Carolina) Duck *Aix sponsa*, of North America, have patterns of astonishing complexity and beauty. Pairs of caged Mandarin Ducks were formerly given as presents at Chinese weddings as symbols of marital fidelity. The influence of the drake's pattern and colour on Chinese art and culture is demonstrated by the inescapable 'Chinese' appearance of the bird. See Plate 5 (colour).

The large polygamous Muscovy Duck *Cairina moschata* of Central and South America is one of the four species of Anatidae to be domesticated (the others being the Grey Lag Goose *Anser anser*, the Swan Goose *A. cygnoides*, and the Mallard *Anas platyrhynchos*). The wild form of the Muscovy Duck is black, glossed with green, with extensive white patches on the wings. Domestic birds are of increased size (although relatively less so than in some domesticated varieties of the Mallard) and have white, grey, and speckled plumage patterns; the enlarged caruncle on the bill becomes conspicuously scarlet.

The largest of the Cairinini is the Spurwinged Goose *Plectropterus gambensis* of Africa, an untidy bird of dark glossy green with variable amounts of white. Related is the polygamous Comb Duck *Sarkidiornis melanotus* subspp., often called Knob-billed or Knob-nosed Goose, in which the metallic colours of the mantle are very brilliant ; one form is common in Africa and India, while the other is found in South America. The Australian Wood Duck (or Maned Goose) *Chenonetta jubata* is rather closely related to the ducks of the genus *Aix* (above) in spite of its gooselike bill and gait. The three species of Pygmy Geese of the tropical genus *Nettapus* (the smallest of the Anatidae) must have been called 'geese' because of the triangular gooselike bill, apparently adapted for eating the seeds of water lilies, but they are in fact tiny perching ducks.

Eiders. The Somateriini are a tribe consisting of four species of marine ducks all living in the north. The Eider *Somateria mollissima* is divided into five races and commonly nests in colonies, which have been exploited by man for the manufacture of eiderdowns. As in most other species of Anatidae, the female plucks down from her breast in order to line the nest. The best quality down is taken from the Eider's nest, without harmful effect, a few days before hatching, and the second best quality after the eggs are hatched and the young have left the nest. No artificial substitute for this down has been found, and that from a single nest may be worth about ten shillings. Some Eider colonies in Iceland have up to 10 000 nests and are intensively encouraged by their owners by methods that include the spreading of coloured ribbons, musical instruments which play in the wind, and rows of 'semi-detached' artificial nesting sites. The species is common in northern parts of Britain. See Plate 19 (colour) for the King Eider *S. spectabilis.*

Scoters, Goldeneyes, and Mergansers. The tribe Mergini includes a number of ducks which, like those in the Cairinini, do not at first sight appear to be closely related. All are good divers. With the exception of the rare Brazilian Merganser *Mergus octosetaceus* and the now extinct Auckland Island Merganser *M. australis*, the tribe is confined to the Northern Hemisphere. The small extinct Labrador Duck *Camptorhynchus labradorius*, of which the last was shot in 1875, was related to the scoters and may have linked them to the eiders (by way of the small Steller's Eider *Polysticta stelleri*). The three scoters *Melanitta* spp. are largely marine except in the breeding season ; the males are predominantly glossy black.

The affinities of the goldeneyes *Bucephala* spp., Harlequin Duck *Histrionicus histrionicus*, and the Longtailed Duck (or Oldsquaw) *Clangula hyemalis*, are evident ; but the last exhibits an unusual moulting sequence, with contrasting dark summer and light winter plumages in the male, which may or may not be strictly analogous to the 'eclipse' in other species. The Longtailed Duck is one of the fastest fliers among the Anatidae ; a speed of 72 m.p.h. has been reliably recorded in level flight. The little Bufflehead *B. albeola* links the goldeneyes with the scoters, and prehaps also (by way of the Smew *M. albellus*) with the sawbills of the genus *Mergus*, which is held to be rather closely related to the goldeneyes in spite of the long narrow serrated bill adapted for catching fish. See Plate 29 (colour).

Stifftails. The last and rather isolated tribe of the Anatinae is the Oxyurini, a group of extremely aquatic and largely nocturnal freshwater ducks, in most of which the rectrices are long and stiff and evidently have an important underwater control function. The genus *Oxyura* is represented in all six continents by small round diving ducks in which the male in breeding plumage is chestnut red with a brilliant blue bill. The display is elaborate and differs widely in the various species. The male of the very large Musk Duck *Biziura lobata* of Australia carries a large fleshy lobe under the bill. The Blackheaded Duck *Heteronetta atricapilla* of South America lacks the long tail of the tribe and is interesting specially for its apparently parasitic egg-laying habit ; the eggs have been found in nests of coots and rails (Rallidae), herons (Ardeidae), and even of a carrion-eating hawk, one of the caracaras *Polyborus* spp. (see PARASITISM). The African White-backed Duck *Thalassornis leuconotus* appears to be an aberrant stifftail, although its voice, anatomy, and behaviour, and the pattern of the downy young, suggest that the relationship may not be very close.   P.S.

Atkinson-Willes, G. L. (ed.). 1963. Wildfowl in Great Britain. Mono. Nature Conservancy no. 3. London.
Delacour, J. & Mayr, E. 1945. The family Anatidae. Wilson Bull. 57 : 3–55 (and 1946, ibid. 58 : 104–110).
Delacour, J. 1954–64. The Waterfowl of the World. 4 vols. (ill. P. Scott). London.
Hochbaum, A. 1944. The Canvasback on a Prairie Marsh. Washington.
Kortright, F. H. 1942. The Ducks, Geese, and Swans of North America. Washington.
Lorenz, K. 1941. Vergleichende Bewegungsstudien an Anatinae. J. Orn. 89, Sonderheft 3 : 194–284. (And 1953, Comparative Studies on the Behaviour of the Anatinae. London.)
Phillips, J. C. 1922–26. A Natural History of the Ducks 4 vols. Boston and New York.

Scott, P. 1957. A Coloured Key to the Wildfowl of the World. Slimbridge, Glos.

Ticehurst, N. F. 1957. The Mute Swan in England. London.

DUCKLING: special term for a young (not full grown) DUCK.

DUCTLESS GLANDS: see ENDOCRINE SYSTEM

DUETTING: male and female of a pair singing or calling together, or almost together and responsively (see under SINGING).

DUIKER, REED: name, in South Africa, for the Long-tailed Shag *Phalacrocorax africanus* (see CORMORANT).

DULIDAE: a family of the Passeriformes, suborder Oscines (see PALMCHAT ; and under BOMBY-CILLIDAE).

DUNLIN: *Calidris alpina* (see SANDPIPER).

DUNNOCK: alternative and often preferred name of the Hedgesparrow (misnomer) *Prunella modularis* (see ACCENTOR).

DUODENUM: the anterior part of the small intestine (see ALIMENTARY SYSTEM).

DUSTING: see FEATHER MAINTENANCE

E

EAGLE: substantive name of large members of the Accipitrinae (*Aquila*, etc.), Milvinae (*Haliaetus*, etc.) and Circaetinae (harrier-eagles or serpent-eagles)—for all these subfamilies of the Accipitridae see HAWK. See Plates (phot.) 9b, 34a, 45a.

EAR: see HEARING AND BALANCE

EARTHCREEPER: substantive name of *Upucerthia* spp. (see OVENBIRD (1)).

ECDYSIS: see MOULT

ECHO-LOCATION: a means of navigating during flight in dark caves. This has been developed in two widely separated genera of birds—*Steatornis* in the Neotropical Region, and cave swiftlets *Collocalia* spp. in south-eastern Asia (including Ceylon) and parts of Australia (see OILBIRD ; SWIFT). These birds have in common the capacity to fly into dark caves and to nest successfully inside them. The Oilbird *Steatornis caripensis*, flying in the dark, is described as uttering continually a stream of short pulses of sound and, presumably from the delay in the echo, locating and so avoiding the walls of the cave. The swiftlets that nest in dark caves, often in vast numbers (over a million in a single Borneo cave—see EDIBLE NESTS), utter a rapid succession of high clicking notes, and from the rebound echo off rock and other surfaces are similarly able to navigate in total darkness. *Collocalia esculenta*, a swiftlet inhabiting only the daylight mouths of Borneo caves, was found to have no echo technique.

The Oilbird's note has a frequency range of 6–10 kilocycles. *Collocalia maxima*, tested in steady flight at the Sarawak Museum, gave up to six clicks a second, frequencies 1·5 to 5·5 kcs. These birds show much lower frequencies than those established for bats (ca. 70 kcs.) and dolphins using similar devices. In the Oilbird the silent interval between pulses was found to be only about 2–3 milliseconds, indicating a speed of auditory response much greater than that of which the human ear is capable. See also HEARING AND BALANCE ; and under SINGING.

T.H.

Griffin, D. R. 1953. Acoustic orientation in the Oil Bird, *Steatornis*. Proc. Natl. Acad. Sci. U.S. 39 : 884–893.
Griffin, D. R. 1959. Listening in the Dark. Yale.
Medway, Lord. 1959. Echo-location among *Collocalia*. Nature 184 : 1352–1353.

ECLECTUS: former generic name used as English name (otherwise 'Eclectus Parrot') of *Lorius roratus* (see PARROT).

ECLIPSE: a post-nuptial plumage stage occurring in some species (for fuller consideration see under MOULT). It is characterised by being of much shorter duration than the winter (or non-breeding) plumage in most species that show marked seasonal change, as well as by being dull in comparison with a conspicuous breeding dress. Notably, the males of many of the Anatidae are in full breeding plumage for the greater part of the year but have a dull plumage during the latter part of the summer (while a simultaneous moult of the remiges may render them temporarily flightless)—see DUCK ; and Plate 19 (colour). The special point of the term seems to be lost if it is used, as it sometimes appears to be, to cover any relatively dull non-breeding plumage, even although worn throughout the winter or other off-season.

ECOLOGY: the study of plants and animals in relation to their environment ; also spelt 'oecology'. As regards birds, it is well known that each species breeds and spends the winter, respectively, in characteristic areas of the earth ; these areas, which in some instances are the same, form the geographical distribution of the species (see also DISTRIBUTION, GEOGRAPHICAL ; MIGRATION). Within the areas, the species will occupy only certain habitats ; and within the habitats, each species has a characteristic behaviour and abundance. The explanation of these patterns of distribution and abundance is the main problem of avian ecology.

Habitat Preference. It is illuminating to consider a bird about to migrate to its breeding grounds. Each such individual seems to have a behavioural preference for certain habitats and will not breed elsewhere. But there are variations in the habitats chosen by different individuals of the same species. The habitats chosen by the species as a whole are likely to be those in which the individuals have the greatest production of surviving offspring, as these individuals will be preserved by natural selection. The survival of the offspring will depend upon the adaptations of the bird for life in that area, and upon the number and habits of other species already utilising the area. By this habitat selection a species gradually acquires a typical habitat in an area to which its adaptations are appropriate and which is not already saturated with bird-life. But why should species have a preferred habitat at all? The answer seems to be that the presence of other species makes it necessary to specialise. Thus, the few species present on islands such as Bermuda occupy habitats very diverse compared with those occupied by the same species on the adjacent mainland where many additional species are present. The specialisation makes possible a more efficient utilisation of the environment and serves to prevent competition between the species, and together with habitat selection is responsible for much of the pattern of bird distribution and abundance.

Range. A bird's eye is very like a human eye, so that a bird's-eye view of a habitat is probably similar to the botanist's (see VEGETATION). Consequently, the total geographical distribution of a bird species is often most easily described in terms of a vegetation type. Thus, boreal forests that have survived on southern mountains since the last retreat of the glaciers often form southern 'islands' in the distribution of a bird species. The Redpoll *Carduelis flammea* in Europe and the Blackpoll Warbler *Dendroica striata* in North America are examples, while the Ptarmigan *Lagopus mutus* is an outstanding instance of a species remaining on 'islands' of montane tundra. Many species have also extended their ranges by taking advantage of habitats modified by man; in these cases it is reasonably clear that the nature of the vegetation rather than the climate governs the distribution of the species.

In many species, however, only a small geographical portion of what appears to be suitable habitat is occupied, a different species of similar ecological requirements occupying the remainder. It seems probable that the distribution of such species is determined by the presence of the similar species. For example, the Wren (or Winter Wren) *Troglodytes troglodytes* is abundant in diverse habitats in Europe, while in North America (where many other wren species are present) it is confined to boreal forests. Similarly, large-billed fruit-eaters, such as hornbills (Bucerotidae) or toucans (Ramphastidae), are found in most of the wet tropical forests of the world. However, most of the species have relatively restricted ranges and are replaced by others in more distant areas. In these cases, the distribution of the whole family is easily stated in terms of a vegetation type, but the ranges of the individual species are most easily understood in relation to the other species. Other factors acting directly on the species, particularly temperature, play unknown but probably important roles in determining distributions.

Local Distribution. When a plot of land is abandoned by man, or is denuded by natural causes, its vegetation undergoes a regular succession usually leading to vegetation resembling that of undisturbed areas near by. The bird-life undergoes a succession paralleling that of its habitat, some species being present only in early stages of the plant succession and others in later stages. And the abundance of a species generally changes gradually as the succession progresses through habitats that are marginal for it, where the species is present but rare, into optimal habitats where the species is common. The marginal habitats may play an important role in population regulation, there being some evidence that birds spread from optimal habitats under high population pressure. Most civilised areas of the earth are now a patchwork of different stages of succession with their corresponding bird communities. Generally, with knowledge of the bird succession that accompanies the plant succession, one can crudely predict the abundance of each species in any part of the vegetational patchwork. This familiar fact demonstrates that the vegetation plays an important role in determining not only the presence or absence but also the abundance of species.

Food Specialisation. Even within a single habitat—a wood or a field for instance—there are usually many species. This is particularly interesting because of the Volterra-Gause principle, which asserts that two species cannot co-exist indefinitely if they are limited in their population sizes by the same factors. Or, viewed in terms of groups of species in the same habitat, the principle implies that co-existing species are limited by different factors ; this form of expression is weaker in that it does not imply a replacement of one species by another as does the first. Although the differences between co-existing species are well documented, one would expect to witness severe competition only where a mainland form is invading an island or where some resource suddenly becomes short. There are a very few authentic examples of this : the mainland flycatcher of the genus *Elaenia* appears to be driving the West Indian species from the Grenadines, and the Topknot Pigeon *Lopholaimus antarcticus* apparently almost exterminated the White-headed Pigeon *Columba norfolciensis* in Australia when, due to palm-fruit shortage, both were forced to feed on the same camphor laurels. For each such example of competition in action there are vast numbers of examples of species co-existing more or less indefinitely without seeming to harm one another ; and, in every well studied case, marked differences in feeding situation, feeding behaviour, food size, or various combinations of the three have been found. These observations simultaneously reinforce the belief that food is a most important factor in regulating bird numbers, and strengthen the evidence for the validity of the Volterra-Gause principle.

On the other hand, not all of the species that may occur together will necessarily co-exist indefinitely. Some may be 'fugitive' species that lead a more nomadic existence and capitalise on infrequent unusually favourable situations. The wood-warblers (Parulidae) in North American spruce forests provide examples of both kinds of co-existence : the Cape May Warbler *Dendroica tigrina* and the Bay-breasted Warbler *D. castanea* lay extremely large clutches, making possible rapid increases in population where food is superabundant, and shift their breeding grounds to areas where insect outbreaks occur. At the same time, Myrtle, Black-throated Green, Blackburnian, and Magnolia Warblers (all *Dendroica* spp.) may live in the same woods but feed in different situations and with different behaviour.

We have seen that it is possible for several species to persist in one habitat ; but it is not clear how many species can do so. There are astonishing variations in the number of species breeding in single habitats at different latitudes. Thus a few acres of rain-forest in Mexico had 106 species of breeding birds, while a comparable forest in temperate regions would seldom have more than 30 species, and in the high latitudes far fewer species breed in any single habitat. What is the cause of the astonishing diversity of species in the tropics? Basically, there are two possible answers to this question. Either evolution (speciation) has proceeded faster or longer in the tropics and, given enough time, the temperate regions will eventually acquire as many species as the tropics have at present ; or else a limit to the number of species that a habitat can support has been nearly reached—a limit for some reason higher in the tropics. The data available at present are consistent with the second explanation. Presumably the extra species in the tropics, coupled with the resulting decrease in abundance of each, increase the hazards to a species by just as much as do the dangers of migration and unpredictable climate in higher latitudes. The precise details are still quite obscure.

Remote islands have fewer species of land birds than do comparable ones near the mainland, and small islands have fewer than large. In all probability, this pattern is due not to a shortage of time for colonisation but rather to a balance between immigration and extinction. Small islands have greater rates of species extinction, and more distant ones have reduced immigration. In either case, the number of species is lessened. Furthermore, the island of Krakatau, off Sumatra, reconstituted its complete bird fauna within fifty years after it was devastated by the volcanic explosion of 1883, showing the astonishing speed at which the balance between immigration and extinction can be reached.

In any given area, the number of breeding bird species appears to be controlled more by the amount of foliage at different heights above the ground than by the variety of plant species. Thus, for instance, a habitat composed of all sizes of a single tree species will support more bird species than a uniformly mature stand of many tree species.

Migration and Clutch Size. Finally, it is rewarding to consider the pattern of migration (see MIGRATION). It is clear that in the winter months the high latitudes will support only a few birds ; many individuals must spend the winter in warmer climates. But why should an individual migrate out of the tropics in the summer if it can safely winter there? Natural selection provides the simplest answer. If an individual that migrates has a higher reproductive rate than one that remains, the migrating individual will leave more descendants and the migration urge will become more widespread. More specifically, if the migrating individual can increase its clutch size sufficiently to do more than compensate for the inevitable mortality involved in migration, then the migration will be adaptive. Furthermore, for migration to a *higher* latitude to be adaptive it must result in a sufficiently enlarged clutch to overcome the hazards of the extra migration. Thus, for migratory birds at least, the clutch size must increase with latitude at least as fast as the mortality increases with the correspondingly longer migration. That the clutch size increases with latitude is now well established for most migrant species. It increases for many residents too, presumably because mortality is greater in higher latitudes. This does not mean that clutch size is adjusted to mortality, but simply that the difference between the birth rate and the inevitable 'density-independent' death rate tends to be maximum under the influence of natural selection. Thus, a species will not settle to breed in a region where the birth rate is unnecessarily close to the density-independent death rate (see also POPULATION DYNAMICS). Because of the advantage in breeding where the birth rate is high, migrant birds may be expected to breed in the greatest density where the increase in food supply between the winter and the summer is the greatest. This in fact happens ; counting a bird that winters in the tropics as a migrant, the highly seasonal deciduous forest of eastern North America has 80–90 per cent of migrant individuals. The less seasonal forests and west coast maritime forests of Great Britain and North America have fewer migrants ; and the prairies, cultivated regions, and cities with large winter food supplies have practically none.

Summary. It appears that much of the pattern of distribution and abundance can be very crudely explained in terms of specialisation and habitat preference resulting from natural selection. But present knowledge is insufficient to give more than the barest outline.   R.H.M.

Allee, W. C. & Schmidt, K. P. 1951. Ecological Animal Geography. New York. (Based on Hesse's Tier-geographie auf oekologischer Grundlage.)
Lack, D. 1954. The Natural Regulation of Animal Numbers. Oxford.
MacArthur, R. H. 1963. Ecological consequences of natural selection. In Waterman, T. H. (ed.) Theoretical and Mathematical Biology. New York.

ECONOMIC IMPORTANCE: see MAN, BIRDS AND ; UTILISATION BY MAN

ECOSYSTEM: the totality of factors of all kinds that make up a particular environment (see ECOLOGY).

ECOTONE: an area of overlap in environments of different types, and thus in biological communities.

ECOTOPE: a particular kind of habitat within an area.

ECTOPARASITE: a parasite inhabiting the exterior of the host's body, as distinct from an 'endoparasite'. Apart from the nest parasites discussed below and the casual blood-suckers such as mosquitos and leeches, birds are parasitised by the following groups of ectoparasites ; louse-flies (Hippoboscidae), fleas (Siphonaptera), and chewing lice (Mallophaga) belonging to the Insecta, and the ticks and feather-mites belonging to the Arachnida. Of these only the Mallophaga and the feather-mites spend their whole life-cycle, from egg to adult, on the body of the bird.

Hippoboscidae. The louse-flies belong to the pupiparous Diptera. They are blood-suckers and are specialised for a parasitic life by being flattened dorsoventrally and having strong curved claws ; the wings may be fully developed or reduced to a greater or lesser extent. The egg develops, and the larval stages take place, within the body of the female fly ; the fully developed larva is dropped to the ground, where it pupates. There are some 90 species of louse-fly recorded from 18 of the orders of birds. About half of these show some host restriction, but this is mainly ecological, birds in similar habitats being parasitised by the same or related species of fly ; *Olfersia aenescens*, for instance, has been taken from gannets (Sulidae), petrels (Procellariiformes), and terns (Sterninae). The swifts (Apodidae), however, have certain host-specific species that have lost the power of flight and are otherwise adapted to the predominantly aerial habits of their hosts. Mallophaga sometimes attach themselves to louse-flies (22 have been taken from the abdomen of one fly) and may thus be transferred from one host species to another.

Siphonaptera. The fleas are blood-suckers ; they have the body flattened laterally to allow them to move easily through fur or feathers, and their power of jumping enables them to reach a new host or escape capture. The entire pre-adult life is passed away from the host, usually in the nest, where the larva feeds on organic debris. There are about 100 species and subspecies of bird fleas ; these are found on the body of the bird or in nests, in which latter most species are largely resident. As the flea spends part of its life-cycle off the host, it is influenced as much by climatic and other environmental factors as by the host itself. This, together with the fact that in each generation the flea, on emerging from the pupa, may have to find a new host, has prevented widespread host restriction. There are, however, a number of host-specific bird fleas, of which *Ceratophyllus rossittensis* on the Crow *Corvus corone* is an example. Some bird fleas have a restricted geographical distribution ; thus *C. borealis* is found in the British Isles almost exclusively on the outlying islands. Others have an environmental distribution ; for example, *C. garei* is found mainly in damp nests near the ground, while *C. gallinae* is found mainly in loosely built dry nests.

Ixodidae. The ticks are blood-suckers, and some (e.g. *Argas reflexus* found in pigeon lofts) live entirely in the dwelling-place of their host, feeding often and rapidly and remaining on the host for only a short time. Others live a more exposed life ; the eggs are laid in the open and the larva that emerges must attach itself to a passing host for a blood meal ; it then drops to the ground to moult, and after a further blood meal and moult it becomes adult and must once again find a host. These latter species engorge slowly and often spend a considerable time on the host. There are a number of Ixodidae which are confined to birds ; many of these have an ecological not a host distribution ; for instance, *Ixodes uriae* is found in the nests of many sea birds. Others appear to be restricted to one host ; *I. lividus* is probably confined to the Sand Martin (or Bank Swallow) *Riparia riparia*. The immature stages of the common sheep-tick *I. ricinus* are often found on birds, attached to the head.

Mites. The feather-mites (mostly belonging to the Analgesidae) are not blood-suckers, but feed on the feathers and skin debris. They spend the whole of their life-cycle on the host, the eggs being attached to the feathers or laid inside quills. Other mites parasitic on birds are the itch mites (Sarcoptidae) causing scaly leg and de-pluming mange ; the Rhinonyssidae, living in the nasal cavities ; and the red mites (Dermanyssidae), which are blood-suckers and mainly found in nests and roosting places, feeding on the birds at night, but in heavy infestations may remain permanently on the bird.

Mallophaga. These constitute a suborder of the insect order (Phthiraptera) that includes the sucking lice, and spend the whole of their life-cycle on the body of the host. They live amongst the feathers, with the exception of species of one genus that live in the throat pouches of pelicans (Pelecanidae) and cormorants (Phalacrocoracidae). They feed on the feathers and on the blood or other tissue fluids ; blood may be taken by some species from the developing feathers and species of at least one genus live entirely on the fluids ; the lice living inside the calamus of the quill feed on the central pith. The eggs are attached to the feathers or in a few cases are laid inside the quills. The Mallophaga are closely adapted to the environment formed by the feathers of the bird ; their pigmentation, size, and shape and certain morphological characters of the head are, amongst other characters, apparently dependent on feather colour and structure. In size and shape they are adapted to the different ecological niches found on the body of the bird ; thus, for example, on the head and neck is found a short round-bodied type, and on the wings and back a more flattened, elongate type.

The present distribution of the Mallophaga suggests that they became parasitic on the class Aves at an early stage in the evolution of that class and that they evolved with their hosts. Thus, in general, the Mallophaga of related hosts are themselves related ; within the order Charadriiformes, for example, there are a number of mallophagan genera common to the three suborders, and the species of these genera parasitising the Alcae are more closely related to each other than to those on the Charadrii or the Lari. Different species of birds do not normally come into contact with each other, so that there is little opportunity for the interchange of lice populations ; these have, therefore, become strongly isolated. This isolation has led to host restriction, so that in many cases a species of Mallophaga is found on only one host species or a group of related host species.

A bird is usually parasitised by a number of different species of Mallophaga, some of these being adapted to the different ecological niches on the body of the host ; the Rook *Corvus frugilegus*, for example, has six species belonging to five genera, and some of the tinamous (Tinamidae) have as many as 12 species of Mallophaga. Thus, each order of birds is parasitised by species belonging to one or more genera that are frequently peculiar to it, and the relationship between the species of these genera generally reflects the relationship between the hosts within the order. It is, therefore, usually possible to place a bird correctly in its order, and often in a lower category, if the mallophagan genera parasitising it are known, and for this reason the Mallophaga of birds of doubtful affinities may be useful evidence in deciding the relationships of such birds. The affinities of the Mallophaga suggest relationships between the Struthionidae and the Rheidae, between the Phoenicopteridae and the Anseriformes, and between the Musophagidae and the Galliformes. However, many factors such as discontinuous distribution of genera and species, parallel and convergent evolution, secondary infestations, and human error in interpretation of the evidence, may obscure the initial relationship between host and parasite, so that evidence from this source cannot be used as an infallible guide to relationships between the hosts.

Nest Fauna. Birds' nests may contain a great many animals apart from the rightful occupants (see NESTING ASSOCIATION); 529 different kinds, chiefly arthropods, have been taken from 56 nests in Finland. Apart from the obligate parasites (discussed above) that may be found in the nest, probably between 20 and 25 per cent of the nest dwellers are actually dependent on the occupied nest, the rest being casual visitors or those that are also found elsewhere in similar micro-habitats. Included among those dependent on the nest are the bugs, such as the swallow bug *Oeciacus hirundinis*, beetles and their larvae, and the larvae of certain moths and flies. It is the larvae of the flies that form the most dangerous parasites of the young birds and may sometimes be responsible for their deaths. Many of the inhabitants of the nest act as useful scavengers and some feed on the parasites, such as the beetle that feeds on flea larvae. The nidicolous fauna is dependent on the type of the nest; those in burrows and holes, especially when occupied from year to year, have a richer fauna than open nests, such as that of the Wood Pigeon *Columba palumbus*, with little or no lining-material.

Harmful Effects. Apart from being vectors of certain diseases, ectoparasites when present in large numbers may cause the death of young birds through loss of blood; heavy infestations of feather-mites may practically denude a bird of feathers, and some Mallophaga cause damage to the wing feathers by chewing holes in these when in quill. The excessive irritation caused by the presence of large numbers of ectoparasites may cause the host to damage itself by scratching, and may interfere with egg production and fattening in poultry. Ticks may cause death by their poisonous saliva, or blindness when attached near the eye. Preening is known to keep down the numbers of lice, birds with damaged bills usually having excessive populations; dust baths may also help to eliminate some (see FEATHER MAINTENANCE). There is also probably a certain amount of destruction of parasites by each other; some mites are believed to feed entirely on other mites, and some may feed on the eggs of Mallophaga.

T.C.

Ash, J. S. 1960. A study of the Mallophaga of birds with particular reference to their ecology. Ibis 102 : 93-110.
Clay, T. 1951. The Mallophaga as an aid to the classification of birds, with special reference to the structure of the feathers. Proc. X Internat. Orn. Congr., Uppsala 1950 : 207-215.
Rothschild, M. & Clay, T. 1957. Fleas, Flukes and Cuckoos. 3rd edition. London.
Symposium. 1957. Premier Symposium sur la specificité parasitaire des parasites de vertébrés. Neuchâtel.

ECTROPODACTYL: term applied to an unusual arrangement of the toes, found in some Picidae (see LEG).

EDAPHIC: term applied to environmental factors dependent on conditions of the soil or substratum.

EDIBILITY: see PALATABILITY OF BIRDS AND EGGS

EDIBLE NESTS: the material of the most expensive food in Asia, ' caviar of the East ', namely bird's nest soup. This is made from the nests of cave swiftlets *Collocalia* spp. (see SWIFT). Some of these swiftlets may have ' pure ' white nests of salivary secretion, while others have nests of secretion mixed with feathers or vegetable matter, requiring extensive cleaning and therefore lower priced. A few make nests mainly of extraneous materials that render them inedible even by Chinese standards—notably the unfortunately named *C. esculenta* (Linnaeus), least esculent of them all.

Many other swifts (Apodidae) are known to make use of mucoprotein secreted by the sublingual salivary glands—not a proventricular gland as in pigeons (Columbidae), as shown by Marshall & Folley—to cement together the material of their nests; but this habit is developed to the extreme among the *Collocalia* of south-east Asia, in some species to such an extent that the whole nest may be constructed solely of this material. The taxonomy of this genus, one of the most difficult in ornithology, is still far from settled, so that it is hardly possible to list the species known to build nests sufficiently ' spit-rich ' to make collection worth while. Edible nests are collected in India, Burma, Thailand, Malaya, Indochina, and many islands in Indonesia and the Philippines. In Borneo, the largest source of world supply far back into pre-history, the forms concerned are :

Collocalia maxima lowi, the widespread Black-nest Swiftlet, of which the nest is a compound of edible cement and the bird's own plumage; at least 2 000 000 nest in the Great Cave of Niah, Sarawak, probably the largest single site.

Collocalia vestita mearnsi, the more local inland White-nest Swiftlet, of which the nests are almost pure unadulterated edible cement; it favours smaller caves and colonies.

Collocalia francica (' *inexpectata* ') *germani*, the Grey-rumped Swiftlet, found in small sea-caves, building a white nest of unadulterated nest cement.

Although the nest material has been proved to have negligible nutritional value, and eaten alone is a practically tasteless gelatinous substance, Chinese and other Asians esteem it as a tasty, nourishing, and even aphrodisiac food. Birds' nests are therefore always served in soup or jelly mixed with chicken, spices, sauces, or sweets.

Collecting the edible nests in cave darkness is a hazardous occupation. The crevasses, chimneys, and galleries where the swiftlets breed in dense clusters are normally reached by long sets of single poles, pinned or socketed together, and (at Niah) reaching up to 400 feet in height. One man climbs and balances, wielding a long bamboo to which is attached a beeswax candle above a hoe-like blade ('julok') with which he scrapes the nest hinges ; on the floor far below an assistant gathers the falling nests. Throughout south-east Asia this difficult and dangerous work is falling out of favour with the younger generation, so that the number of nests taken is slowly dwindling.

Swiftlets have definite but not yet fully understood breeding cycles. If the nests are collected during the breeding season, the birds at once build again. Incubation and fledging periods are protracted—over 90 days for *C. maxima* at Niah. Eggs are eaten by a cave cricket, and many young die by falling ; but they seldom fail in the final exit flight, their first, sometimes for a quarter of a mile or more out to daylight (see ECHO-LOCATION).

If the nests are not taken, the birds will continue to use and repair old ones until they are of inedible standard. Controlled and organised collecting is therefore desirable ; and in Sarawak this is now done under licence of the Curator of the Museum. But in general the bird's nest industry is falling into disorder, at least temporarily ; this process is assisted by the anti-gourmet spartanism of recent policy in China, for over a thousand years the prime consumer.   T.H.

Johnston, D. W. 1958. Salivary glands of the chimney-swift. Condor 60 : 73–84.

Marshall, A. J. & Folley, S. J. 1956. Nest cement in the edible-nest swiftlets. Proc. Zool. Soc. Lond. 126 : 383–389.

Medway, Lord. 1958. Thunberg's swiftlet (*Collocalia fuciphaga*). Sarawak Mus. J. 12 : 682–689.

EFFERENT: opposite of AFFERENT (see NERVOUS SYSTEM).

EGG: the yolk-laden ovum (female reproductive cell) with surrounding layers added in the oviduct, extruded (laid) by the hen bird and then incubated during development of the embryo within it (see REPRODUCTIVE SYSTEM ; LAYING ; INCUBATION ; DE-VELOPMENT, EMBRYONIC ; HATCHING ; see also under VIVIPARITY). The present article is concerned with structure, except as dealt with under EGGSHELL (for other characteristics see EGGS, NATURAL HISTORY OF).

The avian egg is a complicated structure, which in its design ensures optimum growth and protection of the developing embryo. The essential constituents of the egg are yolk, albumen, and shell, together with membranous structures separating each from the other.

Yolk. The yolk (vitellus) is the main nutritive portion of the egg. It is approximately spherical in shape and varies in colour from light yellow to orange. Enclosed in a thin elastic membrane (membrana vitellina), its physical characteristic is that of a viscous fluid. If an egg is boiled its complex yolk structure is revealed. In its centre is a core of fluid white yolk known as the latebra. This is surrounded by alternating layers of yellow and white yolk. The first yellow layer surrounds the latebra and the last white is in contact with the vitelline membrane. The white layers of yolk are narrower and contain less fat (and pigment) than the yellow. From the latebra there is a thin neck of white yolk extending to the surface of the yolk body, where it expands to form the 'nucleus of Pander'. At this point it is in contact with the germinal spot from which the embryo develops on incubation of the fertilised egg. In the unfertilised egg the germinal spot (or blastodisc) consists of a small, opaque, circular, white area ; the opaque region (periblast) encircles a central portion that frequently has a mottled appearance due to the presence of vacuoles, and these serve to differentiate between the unfertilised and the fertilised egg. In the latter, embryonic development commences before the egg is laid and the germinal spot is then referred to as the blastoderm. In this, two regions can be distinguished—a transparent portion known as the area pellucida, and an outer and wider oval one called the area opaca.

Albumen. The albumen or egg-white forms the rest of the egg complement enclosed within the shell. It exists in two forms ; one is a viscous liquid and the other is gelatinous and semi-solid. The albumen is arranged in concentric layers, of which there are four.

On the long axis of the egg and in contact with the yolk at each side are the chalazae. They are cloudy, spirally twisted, ropelike structures firmly attached to the yolk and spreading over it to form a capsule of mucin-like fibres, firmly attached to the surface of the yolk at its equator. They are formed during the rotation of the egg in the shell gland of the oviduct. At the outer ends of the chalazae they interlace with similar fibres in the albumen. The chalazae themselves, together with the fibrous layer over the yolk which is enveloped by dense albumen, constitutes the membrana chalazifera. External to this is an inner layer of liquid albumen, with no concentration of mucin fibres, in which the yolk floats. The water squeezed out during the twisting of the mucin strands to form the chalazae is responsible for the liquefaction of this inner layer.

This in turn is surrounded by the middle dense layer of albumen, or the albuminous sac. It is the greatest in volume of any of the albumen layers and consists of a structural framework of semi-solid mucin fibres, the interstices of which are filled with liquid albumen. Because it can maintain its shape to some extent, it is an effective protective cushion for the yolk. The middle dense layer is attached to the inner shell membrane at both ends of the egg by the mucin fibres of albumen penetrating and locking with the membrane. The point of attachment is called the ligamentum albuminis, and its area of contact is greater at the broader end of the shell.

Membranes. The shell membranes separating albumen from shell consist of two layers, parchment-like in appearance and attached closely to the shell. The inner membrane (membrana putaminis) is in contact with the outer fluid albumen except in regions of the ligamentum albuminis. The inner and outer membrane layers are firmly apposed except at one point, usually at the broad end of the shell, where they are parted to form the characteristic air-cell. The outer or true shell membrane (membrana testae) is attached closely to the inner surface of the eggshell.

Both membranes consist of matted protein fibres made firm with an albuminous cementing material, and contain pores that are apparently more numerous in the inner layer. Curiously enough, the thickness of the shell membranes in various species seems to relate directly to the size of the egg, the thickness of membranes decreasing as egg size becomes smaller.

In detail, the outer membrane actually consists of three separate layers, each having a network structure. The outermost layer is composed mainly of relatively coarse, unbranched, and flattened fibres of keratin, while the inner layers are of much finer branching fibres of keratin and mucin. The interstices between the fibres are filled with albuminous material.

The air-cell does not appear until the egg is laid. It results from a separation of the inner and outer membranes, is usually to be found at the broad end of the egg, and is sometimes referred to as the air space or air chamber. Its formation is attributed to a cooling effect on extrusion from the maternal body. The size of the air cell increases as embryogenesis proceeds.

Shell ; Cuticle. See separate article on EGG-SHELL.   A.W.G.

Romanoff, A. L. & Romanoff, A. J. 1949. The Avian Egg. New York and London.

EGG MIMICRY : see PARASITISM

EGG PROTEIN : see PROTEINS AS TAXONOMIC CHARACTERS

EGGS AS FOOD : see PALATABILITY OF BIRDS AND EGGS ; UTILISATION BY MAN

EGGSHELL : the calcified layer that surrounds any normal avian egg. It lies immediately external to the two membranes (each consisting of keratin fibres which are perhaps coated with mucin) that enclose the white and yolk and are firmly attached to each other except at the broad end, where they separate to form the air space (see EGG ; and for calcium exchange see NUTRITION ; SKELETON). The inner (mammillary) layer of the shell consists of roughly hemispherical knobs, in the inner end of each of which there is a core of organic matter, chiefly protein. The fibres of the outer membrane pass through these cores and thus the outer membrane is firmly attached to the shell ; indeed, the free end of each mammilla appears to be embedded in the membrane. The diameter of each mammilla increases with distance from the membrane and the mammillae ultimately fuse together. The next outer layer is the spongy layer, in actual fact very compact but given this name because of its appearance in decalcified specimens. The spongy layer is continuous with the mammillary layer, but it is sometimes possible to see the junction of the two when using a microscope and also by special tests. Finally, on the outside of the spongy layer, there is often a cuticle or bloom—a thin coating of an organic nature and of variable appearance ; it may contain some of the shell pigments, but in other cases these also occur in the shell itself. On washing an egg in water, some soluble material may be removed but the true cuticle is unaffected.

Arising from the spaces between the mammillae are numerous channels that traverse the spongy layer and open out on the surface of the egg in small depressions. These are the pores that make possible respiratory and other gaseous exchanges between the egg and its surroundings. The mouths of the pores are covered by the cuticle, but only a very small proportion appear to be blocked with organic matter for any part of their length. In the domestic hen, but not necessarily in all birds, the pores seem to be more prevalent at the broad end of the egg. The general average for the whole shell is 50–200 per sq. cm., and their distribution is not random.

Many chemical analyses of eggshells are misleading because of the inclusion of the whole or part of the membrane with the shell. Complete removal of the membrane leaves the true shell, of which the composition is fairly constant. The organic matter varies from about 1·0 to 2·5 per cent ; and the inorganic matter is almost entirely calcium carbonate present as calcite, with small quantities of magnesium, sodium, potassium, phosphate, chloride, and citric acid making up most of the remainder. Recent work has shown that the organic matter of the true shell consists of a protein, which is *not* collagen, and chondroitin sulphuric acid ; these may play a part in the calcification process. The calcite of the eggshell forms large crystals which traverse the whole thickness of the true shell, and these, in tangential section, appear like the pieces of a jigsaw puzzle. The organic material runs through these crystals and is not merely present between them.

The above description is a generalised one, and eggshells from different families may show considerable variations. In the emus (Dromaiidae) and cassowaries (Casuariidae) for example, there is, above the spongy layer, an extra layer that is richer in protein than the rest of the shell, and covering most but not all of this layer is a granular deposit ; in these shells, the pore channels do not come to the surface but terminate at the protein-rich layer. Similarly, the cuticle is a very variable structure, for in some birds (such as the domestic hen) it is a relatively simple layer, consisting mostly of organic matter, but in the Anatidae it has at least two layers, the outer one being calcified and powdery and the second one being chiefly organic in nature. Other birds, e.g. penguins (Spheniscidae) and gannets (Sulidae), may have a ' chalky ' cuticle of varying degrees of thickness.

The pore channels also exhibit considerable variation. In the Ostrich *Struthio camelus* they are multi-branched, and one such pore system has a number of mouths opening into a common depression. The rheas (Rheidae), emus and cassowaries, and the extinct moas (Dinornithiformes) and elephant-birds (Aepyornithidae), all have a proportion of forked pores, some showing three or more prongs, but the domestic hen and the Turkey *Meleagris gallopavo* usually have simple unbranched channels. When the pore channels are forked, the grooves on the surface of the shell into which the pore-mouths open are generally oriented longitudinally on the surface of the egg.

In the domestic hen, the only species so far examined, there is a considerable variation in shell characteristics such as thickness, pore numbers, and organic matter from one pole of the eggshell to the other, but values for any one latitude are fairly constant.

The term ' shell texture ' is used extensively in the literature, especially in connection with the egg's outward appearance ; but it has so many different meanings that its use is best avoided. It is preferable to make specific reference to each particular characteristic.   C.T.

EGGSHELL DISPOSAL: see PARENTAL CARE

EGGSHELL FORMATION: see METABOLISM ; NUTRITION ; REPRODUCTIVE SYSTEM

EGGS, NATURAL HISTORY OF: external differences serve to distinguish the eggs of various avian species ; individually, no two eggs are exactly alike.

Surface. Most birds lay eggs with a smooth shell ; in some this looks as if it were enamelled or highly polished, but no definite line can be drawn between their structure and that in which the surface is dull. Intermediates, such as matt (finely pitted), are common. The highly coloured eggs of the tinamous (Tinamidae) resemble burnished balls of glazed porcelain. Those of some woodpeckers (Picidae) and babblers (Timaliinae) have a beautiful gloss. There are chalky (powdery) eggs, others oily, some ' soapy ', and those of the emus (Dromaiidae) are ridged.

In many of the ' ratite ' birds the surface is granulated and pitted. There has yet to be determined the reason for the astonishingly hard, thick shell of some of the African francolins, especially the Crested Francolin *Francolinus sephaena*. The eggs of many waterfowl, particularly the ducks and geese (Anatidae), have a greasy or oily exterior that may waterproof the egg. Those of the cormorants (Phalacrocoracidae) and grebes (Podicipitidae) are covered with a chalky film, often of considerable thickness. The powdery outer layer of the egg of flamingos (Phoenicopteridae) is associated with a deposit of fat on the shell immediately below it.

Eggshells vary greatly in thickness ; the tiny eggs of hummingbirds (Trochilidae) have the thinnest, that of the huge extinct elephant-birds (Aepyornithidae) the thickest. Large eggs, as a rule, have proportionately thicker shells than small eggs and are the strongest. For fine structure see EGGSHELL.

Shape. In form eggs vary greatly ; but within a species they are alike, and within each natural group of birds the eggs usually show a resemblance. The shapes, which of course intergrade, are oval, spherical, conical, elliptical, and biconical, each being capable of infinite variety according to the relative position and proportion of the major and minor axis. The eggs of certain owls (Strigiformes)

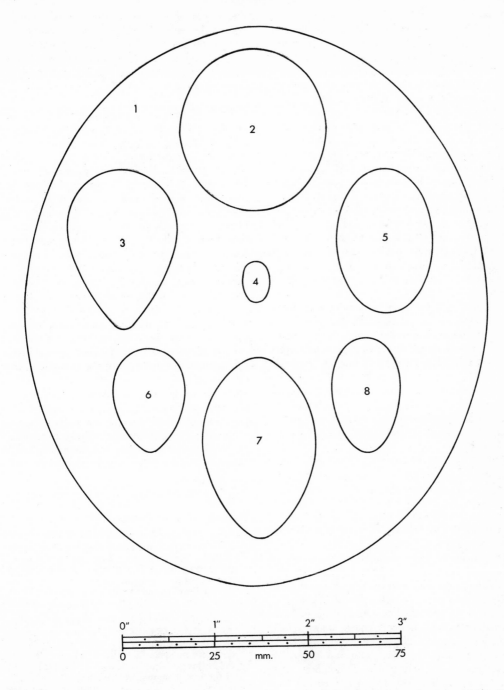

Examples of outlines (or 'profiles') to illustrate some different sizes and shapes of eggs. Shown in natural size; the shapes are here designated in alternative terminologies.

1 Ostrich *Struthio camelus* (largest egg of a living species).
2 Ross's Turaco *Musophaga rossae* (round or spherical).
3 Ruff *Philomachus pugnax* (pyriform or conical).
4 Hummingbird species *Myrmia micrura* (smallest egg).
5 Coroneted Sandgrouse *Pterocles coronatus* (oblong oval or elliptical).
6 African Thrush *Turdus pelios* (oval or ovate).
7 Slavonian (or Horned) Grebe *Podiceps auritus* (biconical, fusiform, or long subelliptical).
8 Alpine Swift *Apus melba* (elliptical ovate or long oval).

A. M. Hughes.

and kingfishers (Alcedinidae), and some others, appear spherical. In nearly all the Charadrii the egg attenuates very rapidly towards the smaller end, sometimes in a slightly convex curve, sometimes without perceptible curvature, and occasionally appreciably concave. Eggs of pyriform shape are mostly those of birds laying four in a nest ; they lie with their points almost meeting in the centre and thus occupy minimal space and are more easily covered by the brooding parent. The eggs of sandgrouse (Pteroclididae) are mostly elongated and almost cylindrical, terminating obtusely at each end. The eggs of grebes have both ends nearly alike but pointed, and are wide in the middle. The egg is shaped during its passage through the oviduct and differences are due to morphological, physiological, and genetic factors (see REPRODUCTIVE SYSTEM). Breadth is usually more constant than length. Eggs abnormal in size or shape are a result of a temporary disturbance or accident to the laying bird, or of disease.

Oologists use a variety of terminologies in designating the shapes, or 'profiles', of eggs. The *Handbook of North American Birds* is using a system, based on Preston, which recognises four principal shapes and three relative lengths of each (taking 'spherical' as the short elliptical), as follows : long elliptical, elliptical, spherical ; long subelliptical, subelliptical, short subelliptical ; long oval, oval, short oval ; long pyriform, pyriform, short pyriform—'ovate' is regarded as a synonym of 'oval', and 'elongate' of 'long'.

Size. The eggs of many nidifugous birds, which are more fully developed at hatching, are relatively large. The number of eggs to be covered at one time also seems to bear some relation to their size —compare, for instance, the Snipe *Gallinago gallinago* with four and the Partridge *Perdix perdix* with up to a dozen or more.

There is an enormous range in size, and a general relationship between the size of the egg and the size of the parent, although the relative egg weight diminishes as the body weight increases. A notable exception is found in the kiwis *Apteryx* spp. of New Zealand, in which the egg equals almost 1/4th of the body weight. This relation varies in a large number of species between 1/9th and 1/15th of body weight ; is 1/28th in quite a number ; and as low as 1/55th in a few of the larger birds. The Guillemot (or Murre) *Uria aalge* and the Raven *Corvus corax* are of about equal size, but egg/body ratio is ten times as great in the former. (See also WEIGHT.)

The egg of the Cuckoo *Cuculus canorus* is only 1/30th of the body weight, possibly an adaptation

due to the bird's parasitic habit of depositing its eggs in the nests of smaller species (see PARASITISM). The Snipe and the Blackbird *Turdus merula* differ only slightly in weight, but their eggs remarkably. Again the eggs of the Guillemot are as big in volume as those of the Golden Eagle *Aquila chrysaetos*, and the eggs of the Snipe equal to those of the Partridge.

The largest present-day egg is that of the Ostrich *Struthio camelus*, measuring 170 by 135 mm. and weighing 1400 grams ; the smallest, that of a hummingbird species, 13 by 8 mm. and 0·5 grams. The weight of the shell of the eggs of small altricial birds, hatched in a very immature condition and living helpless in the nest for some time, may be only 5 per cent of the total weight ; but in the eggs of precocial species, hatched in an advanced state of development and often leaving the nest soon after hatching, it is 10 to 15 per cent of the total. In the parasitic cuckoos (Cuculinae) and honeyguides (Indicatoridae), the weight of the thick shell is relatively great for the size of the egg.

Coloration. There is a great tendency to similarity in the coloration of the eggs of allied species, although there may be striking differences even at subspecific level, as instanced by the immaculate deep terracotta eggs of the nominate race of *Cisticola galactotes* in South Africa and those pinkish-white, darkly but finely speckled, eggs of the race *C.g. nyansae* in Uganda. Egg coloration, in conjunction with other characters, can be of taxonomic value ; thus, each of the several genera of African shrikes (Laniidae), as generally recognised, can be related to a distinctive type of egg. For examples see Plate 43 (colour).

Plate 13 · Tree-climbing

a *Upper :* Golden-backed Woodpecker *Brachypternus benghalensis*—male bird clinging to tree-trunk (India). The zygodactyl feet and the stiff central tail-feathers of the Picidae are adapted to climbing and to resting in positions such as this ; note also the powerful chiselling bill.

Phot. Christina Loke.

b *Lower left :* Nuthatch *Sitta europaea* climbing down a tree (England). The toes are strongly clawed, but arranged as in other passerine birds ; there are no specially stiff tail-feathers. Whether the bird is going up or down, the diagonal placing of the feet, as shown, is characteristic.

Phot. John Markham.

c *Lower right :* Galahs (or Roseate Cockatoos) *Kakatoe roseicapilla* in nesting hole in split tree (Western Australia). *Phot. John Warham.*

(See articles WOODPECKER ; LOCOMOTION ; NUTHATCH ; PARROT ; NEST)

The eggs of the Guillemot exhibit a remarkable range of coloration ; great variety can also be found in the same colony of a single species of African weaver (Ploceidae). More usually these weaver eggs are represented by two predominant types ; but in the Yellow-backed Weaver *Ploceus capitalis* the variation, both light and dark, is bewildering. Reptiles' eggs are white, and it can be assumed that white is the primitive type.

The colours of eggshells are due to two main pigments, red-brown and blue-green, which are responsible for the entire range of hues. The beauty of the coloration and markings of the shells may be enhanced by a glossy surface, by harmonious blending, or by a pleasing contrast of pigments that form markings either regular or irregular. In addition to superimposed markings, there are other more deeply seated stains, which therefore appear of a paler and often altogether different hue, and originate in earlier stages of shell formation. The ground colour varies from white to almost black. There is a tendency to erythrism in the eggs of some species, particularly in Australia and also in certain parts of southern India where the soil is red, and to cyanism in others. The adaptive coloration of some eggs when laid on various soils can be further illustrated by the pale coloration of the eggs of desert-nesting coursers (Cursoriinae) and sand-grouse, or by the predominant black of those, in particular *Cursorius temminckii*, that are laid on burnt ground.

The pigments are usually most plentiful in the cuticle and the superficial layers of the shell, where they determine the egg's colour ; the markings are unevenly distributed over the surface. Shells that appear pure white do, however, contain some underlying pigment. Usually, the bulk of the shell pig-ment or ground colour is in the outermost strata of the spongy layer. Blue-green pigments are probably derived from the bile (biliverdin) and tend to be uniformly distributed as ground colour. Red-brown pigments are probably derived from the haemoglobin of the blood and tend to be deposited, sometimes rather superficially, in a pattern characteristic of the species. Some eggshells also contain porphyrin. See COLOUR.

There is infinite variety in the markings, which includes scrawls as on the eggs of buntings (Emberizinae), the Lilytrotter *Actophilornis africanus*, and some races of *Prinia* ; the marbling on the eggs of nightjars (Caprimulgidae) ; the mottling in varying density of many species ; and the discrete type and the confluent type of blotched eggs. Most remarkable is the wonderful adaptation in certain cuckoos' eggs to those of the fosterer, both in coloration and in size (see PARASITISM).

In different species, pigments are deposited neither in the same concentration nor at the same stage in shell formation. Bands of different colour intensity, due to varying pressure in the oviduct, sometimes encircle the egg. Pigment can be superficial, as in some birds-of-prey (Falconiformes) and certain plovers (Charadriidae), and is then easily rubbed off. The coloration of dry shells tends to fade.

The larger end is commonly protruded first in laying and is often heavily marked ; but if, as sometimes happens, this process is reversed—particularly in the eggs of some of the Falconidae—the narrow end will get the heavy markings. The eggs of those larger birds-of-prey with a normal clutch of two usually differ remarkably, one being well marked and the other poorly, but either type of egg may be laid first. A peculiarity with some species that lay a number of thickly marked eggs is that one egg (more rarely two) diverges widely from the rest in coloration. The variable coloration of birds' eggs has not been satisfactorily explained but is often related to the need for procryptic colouring and pattern. In certain groups there appears to be some correlation between the development of ground colour and markings and the need for protection against solar rays or predators. When completely sheltered, many eggs are white. Egg coloration and markings are distinctive for each female, and probably due to hereditary factors.

Eggs of different species vary greatly in palatability, some being nauseating. Almost without exception the eggs of those species that lay cryptic eggs are the most palatable (see PALATABILITY OF BIRDS AND EGGS).

Clutch Size. According to Lack, clutch size is adjusted by natural selection to that which has the

---

Plate 14 · Feeding Habits

a *Upper left :* Black-necked Stilt *Himantopus himantopus mexicanus* probing mud in shallow water (North America). Note the long legs, neck, and bill of this plover-like bird (placed with the avocets in the Recurvirostridae). For wading, see also Plate 11 (b) and (c). *Phot. Russ Kinne.*

b *Upper right :* Brown Honeyeater *Gliciphila indistincta* feeding on *Grevillea* blossom (Western Australia). This bird is typical of the many species of Meliphagidae. *Phot. John Warham.*

c *Lower :* Nutcracker *Nucifraga caryocatactes* digging in the snow for nuts that it has hidden (Sweden). This member of the crow family is a notable hoarder. *Phot. P. O. Swanberg.*

(See articles AVOCET ; FEEDING HABITS ; HONEYEATER ; CROW (1)) best chance of producing the largest number of fledged young (see POPULATION DYNAMICS). Dependent initially on the degree of protection afforded to the eggs in the nest, and greatly affected by the extremely important factor of food supply, its size is further influenced by whether the species is altricial or precocial. Latitude is another important factor, for where daylight hours are shorter or where insect life is dormant during the mid-day heat, the clutch size is smaller. On the other hand the cormorants (Phalacrocoracidae) in the equatorial lakes region of Africa lay sets on average larger than those of their European counterparts, owing presumably to an abundance of suitable fish that can be caught at any time of the day. As a rule, passerine subspecies lay larger clutches the higher the latitude in which they occur; an exception is the Raven. See also ECOLOGY.

Many nidifugous species, for instance among the Phasianidae (partridges, francolins, pheasants, quail), Tetraonidae (grouse), and Numididae (guineafowl), have large clutches; by contrast, bustards (Otididae), coursers, and thickknees (Burhinidae) lay either one or two eggs. The little migratory Quail *Coturnix coturnix*, for its size, lays an astonishingly large clutch. Habits also have a bearing on clutch size, for wherever they occur the nidicolous nightjars and the nidifugous thickknees (Burhinidae) lay but two eggs, their feeding hours being limited to the night time. Colonial, nidicolous, ground-nesting species that lay but one egg, such as the Gannet *Sula bassana* and the Sooty Tern *Sterna fuscata*, enjoy the general protection of the mass and this ensures a generous degree of juvenile survival. The flamingos, which also lay single eggs in colonies—often large and sometimes vast—and are highly susceptible to disturbance, are protected from man and predatory mammals by the inaccessibility of their breeding grounds. The survival of those penguins (Spheniscidae) that individually brood only one egg under the most adverse climatic conditions is dependent on the protection afforded by the close-packed herd.

Large birds-of-prey rarely lay more than two eggs, but usually only one young bird—survival of the fittest—leaves the nest. In many species first clutches tend to be the largest, but in temperate regions clutches may be larger later in the breeding season when the general conditions are more favourable. They usually decrease, except in those species that normally rear more than one brood, should the original clutch have to be replaced; in double-brooded birds the average clutch size declines as the season progresses.

The number of eggs in a clutch tends towards uniformity in each species but varies greatly from one species to another, from one to a couple of dozen; but there is a tendency in many groups—orders, families, or genera—for the constituent species to lay the same or about the same number of eggs. Under natural conditions many wild species lay only one clutch, but loss of a clutch will stimulate the reproductive cycle, up to eight times. Some normally lay and incubate two or even three clutches in one season. For determinate and indeterminate layers see LAYING.

When food is unusually abundant clutches may be exceptionally large; conversely, in times of scarcity clutches will be small or breeding may even not take place. During a plague of voles in Scotland, Short-eared Owls *Asio flammeus* were laying clutches of 7 to 9 eggs instead of the normal 3 to 5; in lemming years in the Arctic, too, the Snowy Owl *Nyctea scandiaca* and the Rough-legged Buzzard *Buteo lagopus* lay larger clutches. When myxomatosis wiped out rabbits in south-western England, many Buzzards *Buteo buteo* for one year did not breed at all. In drought years in South Africa, the species of bustards normally laying two eggs lay only one, sometimes none. The previous year's nut crop affects the clutch size in the food-storing Nutcracker *Nucifraga caryocatactes*.

C.R.S.P.

EGG-TOOTH: see BILL; DEVELOPMENT, EMBRYONIC

EGRET: substantive name of several species of Ardeidae (see HERON). See Plates 20 (colour), 21 (phot.).

EIDER: substantive name, sometimes 'eider-duck', of *Somateria* spp. and *Polysticta stelleri*; used without qualification for *S. mollissima*; in the plural, general term for the tribe Somateriini (see DUCK). 'Eider-down' is the breast down with which the female *S. mollissima* lines its nest and is in some countries collected commercially. For King Eider *S. spectabilis* see Plate 19 (colour).

ELAENIA: generic name used as substantive common name of *Elaenia* spp. and *Myiopagis* spp. (see FLYCATCHER (2)).

ELANINAE: see HAWK

ELBOW: see under MUSCULATURE; SKELETON; WING

ELECTROPHORESIS: see PROTEINS AS TAXONOMIC CHARACTERS

ELEPAIO: *Chasiempis sandwichensis* of Hawaii (for subfamily see FLYCATCHER (1)).

ELEPHANT-BIRD: in the plural, general term for the extinct Aepyornithidae (Aepyornithiformes), very large flightless running birds of which remains have been found in Madagascar in deposits dating from the Pleistocene to geologically recent times (see FOSSIL BIRDS). The remains, some of which may be classed as merely sub-fossil, consist of bones and eggs, or of fragments of these. The different sizes of corresponding bones indicate that there were several species ; these are referred to the genus *Aepyornis*, but certain of them have been separated under *Mulerornis* by some authors. They all seem to have been tall birds and of particularly massive build, with very stout legs ; it has been estimated that the largest may have weighed 1000 lb. As a generalisation one may say that they had the stature of an Ostrich *Struthio camelus*, although of much greater bulk ; but *A. titan* stood higher (fully 10 feet), about as tall as *Dinornis maximus* (see MOA). Eggs measuring as much as 13 by $9\frac{1}{2}$ inches have been found, and average specimens are estimated to have had a liquid content of two gallons (ca. 9 litres). The egg has been described as the largest known single cell in the Animal Kingdom.

The legend of the Roc (see FABULOUS BIRDS), if it did not originate in Madagascar, subsequently became localised there and may possibly be linked with some persisting tradition of *Aepyornis*. It is very probable that some of these elephant-birds lived at a sufficiently recent date to have given rise to such a tradition ; or the latter may be based on the eggs, of which remarkably well preserved specimens are still uncovered from time to time in the bogs of the island. See also EXTINCT BIRDS.

EMARGINATION: see under WING FORMULA

EMBERIZIDAE: a family of the Passeriformes, suborder Oscines, including—according to the classification used here—the following subfamilies :

Emberizinae	see BUNTING
Pyrrhuloxiinae	
(=Richmondeninae)	see CARDINAL-GROSBEAK
Thraupinae	
(=Tanagrinae)	see TANAGER
Tersininae	see SWALLOW-TANAGER
Coerebinae	see HONEYCREEPER (1)

The first two of these groups have often been assigned to the Fringillidae (see FINCH), while the other three have each been given familial rank by some authors ; and if all these things are done, no such family as the Emberizidae is required (see also under FRINGILLIDAE). A recent view divides the Coerebinae between the Thraupinae (above) and the family Parulidae (see WARBLER (2)).

EMBRYO: the young bird from the earliest stage of its development within the egg until the time of hatching (see DEVELOPMENT, EMBRYONIC).

EMBRYOLOGY: the study of the anatomy and physiology, and particularly the development, of animals during the embryonic stage of life. Much research undertaken from a more general point of view than that of ornithology has used the developing chick as its study material, and hence knowledge of the embryology of birds, or at least of a few types of bird, is notably well advanced (see DEVELOPMENT, EMBRYONIC).

EMEINAE: see MOA

EMERALD: substantive name of *Chlorostilbon* spp., *Elvira* spp., *Ptochoptera iolaima*, and some *Amazilia* spp. (for family see HUMMINGBIRD).

EMIGRATION: migration from an area (see MIGRATION).

EMU: name of the sole surviving member of the Dromaiidae (Casuariiformes) ; in the plural, general term for the family. The Emu *Dromaius novaehollandiae* is the most widespread of the flightless 'ratite' birds of Australia, occurring all over the continent, from sclerophyll forest to open plains. In the dense tropical scrubs of the north-east coast it is replaced by the Australian Cassowary *Casuarius casuarius*, belonging to a related family (see CASSOWARY). From the Pleistocene two other emu-like genera have been described, *Dromornis* and *Genyornis*, but none of the known fossils throw any light on the origins or affinities of the group. The supposed fossil moa from Queensland, ' *Dinornis queenslandiae* ', is now considered to have emu and not moa affinities.

Despite the doleful predictions of John Gould in 1865 when making his plea, ' praying that protection may be afforded to that noble bird, the Emu, in order that it may not be exterminated from the continent ', the Emu has survived surprisingly well the effects of white settlement. Unfortunately the insular forms that had become differentiated in Tasmania, King Island, and Kangaroo Island, were exterminated soon after colonisation, and the mainland birds were driven out of the more densely settled areas in the south-east. But over large parts of Australia the Emu still thrives. It may be seen at times within 20 miles of Perth, Western Australia, and nests in wild bush country 30 miles east of that city. In some areas, furthermore, it has flourished so well that it has become a serious economic pest in the wheat-growing country, knocking down fences and trampling crops. In Western Australia the bird is proscribed under the Vermin Act in these areas, and in the period between 1945 to 1960 (inclusive) bonus payments at the rate of four shillings per bill were made by the State Department of Agriculture for the destruction of 285 000 Emus.

In 1932 the State of Western Australia persuaded the Commonwealth Government to dispatch a machine-gun unit in an attempt to destroy invading Emus on a large scale. The resulting 'Emu War' was a costly failure, but it attracted bizarre notice and the daily press sent correspondents in the field to telegraph daily dispatches on the operations from the front line. The offensive began at Campion on 2 November when a detachment from the Seventh Heavy Battery, Royal Australian Artillery, engaged with the enemy, of which 20 000 were estimated to be operating on the neighbouring farmlands. However, the machine-gunners' dreams of point blank fire into serried masses of Emus were soon dissipated. The Emu command had evidently ordered guerilla tactics, and its unwieldy army soon split into innumerable small units that made the use of the military equipment uneconomic. A crestfallen field force therefore withdrew from the combat area after about a month. Although in succeeding years the use of machine-guns was occasionally requested in dealing with the pest, the authorities were uninterested, and their major activities were directed to more sober measures; the biggest of these was the construction of emu-proof fences to check the seasonal movements of Emus into the marginal wheat-growing country.

The Emu is the second largest of the world's surviving 'ratites', being exceeded in size only by the African Ostrich *Struthio camelus*. It stands between 5 and 6 feet in height and attains a weight of 120 lb.—although most birds are well below that figure, rarely exceeding 100 lb. The plumage is brown or brownish black. The feathers are double, owing to the aftershaft equalling the main shaft in size. The barbs are not hooked together to form a vane and the whole structure is loose and hairlike. Wing and tail quills are not differentiated; the bony wing structure is present but reduced, the manus having only one digit—with three phalanges and a long terminal claw. The sexual differentiation is slight; but the calls are different, the male uttering a series of guttural notes and the female the resonant or booming call. The birds can run at a speed of up to 30 miles per hour and can swim. See Plate 31 (colour).

The nest, large as it is and containing a clutch of 8 to 10 (or sometimes up to 16) massive green-coloured eggs, is surprisingly difficult to find. Thus although the Western Australian Agricultural Department offers a bounty of 6d an egg, no expenditure under this head has been made. Many eggs, however, are retained privately for ornament, as the thick shell can be effectively hand-carved with cameo-like effect. The nest is placed under a tree or bush and consists of a flat bed of trampled-down grasses, bark, and leaves. The average size of the egg is $5\frac{1}{4} \times 3\frac{1}{2}$ inches and the weight $20\frac{1}{2}$ oz. The male alone incubates. The incubation period is 58–61 days, and the male may brood the eggs and newly hatched young for 63 days. The chicks are very pale grey in colour, with conspicuous black longitudinal stripes. Egg-laying takes place in autumn throughout the breeding range of the species. Birds begin to breed in their second year.

The birds feed on a wide variety of native fruits and vegetable matter, including the fruits of *Santalum*, *Casuarina*, *Ficus*, *Podocarpus*, *Eremophila*, and *Macrozamia*. Insects also are eaten, including caterpillars.

Some further anatomical characteristics of the Emu may be mentioned. The Emu has the simplest form of dromaeognathous palate, with a relatively very large prevomer (see PALATE); there is no furcula, the clavicles being vestigial and the coracoids fused with the scapula, and of course, as in all 'ratites', the sternum has no keel; in the pelvis there is no pubic symphysis; the toes are reduced to three (hallux completely absent); there is no oil gland; and although, as in most 'ratites', there is no specially modified syrinx there is an inflatable neck sac communicating with the trachea.

D.L.S.

EMU-WREN: substantive name of *Stipiturus* spp. (see WREN (2)).

ENDASPIDEAN: term applied to the tarsal sheath when that has an anterior scutellated segment extending across the inner side of the tarsus; if, on the other hand, this extends across the outer side, the condition is termed 'exaspidean'.

ENDEMIC: term applied to a species or other taxon in relation to a stated area, meaning that it is restricted thereto; also applied to a disease as the antonym of 'epidemic', meaning that it is always present (see EPIDEMIC).

ENDOCARDIUM: see HEART

ENDOCRINE SYSTEM: comprising the glands of internal secretion, or ductless glands, which secrete specific chemical substances (hormones) of great physiological importance into the blood stream—as distinct from exocrine glands, which secrete through ducts leading, for example, into the alimentary canal or to the surface of the body.

Despite the remarkable pioneer work of John Hunter and A. A. Berthold in the eighteenth and nineteenth centuries, the avian body was in Alfred Newton's day considered to be essentially a group of complicated and little understood organs, the functions of which, however, were probably explicable in terms of the co-ordinating and integrating nervous system. Then, in the early days of this century, there came a general acceptance of the idea of *chemical* reflexes and hormones. Gradually, various structures (most of which had been known to early anatomists) were shown to secrete internally and, in short, to be endocrine glands. Such ductless glands pour their trace substances into the blood stream, which transports them throughout the body. A few hormones probably act on almost every cell in the body, but others influence various specific 'target organs', such as other endocrine glands, structures such as accessory sexual organs (e.g. oviduct), or secondary sexual characters (e.g. display plumes and the like). See also PLUMAGE, ABNORMAL AND ABERRANT ; and MOULT.

When the target organ is another endocrine gland it is stimulated to secrete its own hormone, and this in turn influences other target organs. Sometimes the increased activity of the secondarily stimulated gland results in a hormone 'feed-back' that inhibits the action of the prime mover in the series. Thus, for example, the anterior lobe of the pituitary gland produces gonadotrophic hormones that activate the gonads. These then produce sex hormones which, along with other special effects (e.g. the changes occurring at sexual maturity), to some degree control also the subsequent rate and activity of the anterior pituitary. Again, the hormones of two entirely different glands sometimes operate in a balanced synergism ; for example oestrogen and progestogen, from different ovarian elements, together prepare the avian oviduct for the formation and transmission of the fertilised egg.

However, it must not be thought that a hormone is simply a 'key' to 'unlock' a response. Most tissue reactions (e.g. the formation of brood patches) require a plurality of hormonal influences. Further, alien substances will sometimes bring about endocrine effects (e.g. the advent of comb growth and spermatogenesis after the administration of sulphonamide in fowl disease).

The principal endocrine organs are briefly considered below.

Pituitary Gland (Hypophysis). The pituitary is a compound gland lying in the sella turcica, an excavation of the basisphenoid bone at the base of the skull. A hypophysial portal system connects the hypothalamus (of the brain) with the anterior pituitary gland (see NERVOUS SYSTEM). Blood flow is in the direction of the gland, and it is probable that a chemoregulator is carried down this portal system. The production by the anterior pituitary of hormones influencing other organs stimulated Long's epigram that it is the 'conductor of the glandular orchestra'. But it must be remembered that, as mentioned above, certain target organs within the 'orchestra' have the capacity to modulate the activity of the 'conductor'. Further, after hypophysectomy at least some of them (thyroid, adrenal cortex) continue to function, although at reduced level.

The 'anterior lobe' secretes gonadotrophins, of which the follicle stimulating hormone (F.S.H.) activates ovarian follicles or, as the tubule-ripening hormone (T.R.H.), stimulates spermatogenesis in the testis tubules. The luteinising hormone (L.H.) is also gonadotrophic in function, and in some birds (e.g. the Red-billed Dioch *Quelea quelea*) has a direct effect on the nuptial plumage (Witschi). As the interstitial cell stimulating hormone (I.C.S.H.), it activates the interstitial Leydig cells in the male.

The adrenocorticotrophic hormone (A.C.T.H.) influences the cortical tissue of the adrenal gland (or its homologue), and the thyrotrophic hormone (T.S.H.) stimulates the thyroid gland. The lactogenic hormone influences the mammalian mammary gland (after its initial stimulation by oestrogen) and in birds, as prolactin, it leads to broodiness, the secretion of crop milk in pigeons, and (operating synergetically with oestrogen) the production of brood patches in many widely diverse species (see BROOD PATCH ; INCUBATION ; MILK, PIGEON). A somatotrophic or growth hormone (S.T.H.) has not been proved to exist in birds ; hypophysectomy in birds does cause dwarfism, however, and growth can be restored by prolactin administration.

The 'posterior lobe' of the hypophysis is in direct nervous communication with the brain. Its functions in birds seem to be much the same as in mammals. For example, the factor that causes uterine contractions in mammals has a comparable effect on the avian oviduct.

Thyroid Gland. This gland at the base of the neck contains vesicles lined with specialised epithelium that holds thyroid colloid. The epithelial cells withdraw iodine from the blood stream ; after combination with the amino-acid tyrosine, and further modifications, there is formed the hormone thyroxin ; this has a stimulating effect on body metabolism in general, and also specific effects.

Parathyroid Glands. These minute bodies near the thyroid produce parathormone, which controls the distribution of calcium and phosphate in the blood.

Adrenal Glands. These small paired organs near the kidneys are compound glands of two physiologically and anatomically distinct parts—the medullary (chromaffin) tissue and the cortex. In birds the cortex (of various functions) interdigitates with the medulla. The medulla is under sympathetic nervous control and its hormone, adrenalin, increases cardiac rate and vasoconstriction, elevates blood sugar level, and relaxes the bronchi and so increases lung ventilation (see RESPIRATORY SYSTEM ; VASCULAR SYSTEM).

Sex Glands (Gonads). Leydig (interstitial) cells occur in the testes and produce the steroid testosterone (male sex hormone), which has profound effects on sexual characters and behaviour ; the testes also produce oestrogens. In the ovary, oestrogenic cells of various kinds produce female sex hormones (oestrogens) and these, too, influence sexual characters and behaviour. Oestrogen is concerned also with the formation of ' medullary bone' in the marrow cavities of the long bones, the calcium of which is given up for the production of eggshells (see also SKELETON). Male hormones (androgens), are formed also in the ovary and are (for example) responsible for comb growth in the hen of the domestic fowl. Progesterone, or at least a progestogen, is elaborated in both sexes, probably in the gonads. Work on avian progestogens is in its infancy. For other functions, and anatomy, see REPRODUCTIVE SYSTEM.

Pancreas. Apart from its exocrine function of secreting digestive enzymes (see ALIMENTARY SYSTEM), this compound exocrine and endocrine gland is studded internally with islets of Langerhans ; these produce the hormone insulin that partly controls blood sugar level.

Conclusion. Little is known concerning the precise mode of action of hormones and, more especially, how they influence behaviour. The impressive modern advances in hormone physiology must not tempt us to overstate their influence, nor to underestimate the importance of innate neural patterns (see NERVOUS SYSTEM). It is salutary to recall that pigeons in which testes were congenitally absent exhibited ' complete and emphatic' masculine behaviour. See also BEHAVIOUR, DEVELOPMENT OF.

A.J.M.

Beach, F. A. 1942. Hormones and Behaviour. New York.
Collias, N. 1950. Hormones and behaviour. In Gordon, E. S. (ed.). Symposium on Steroid Hormones. Madison, Wis.
Höhn, E. O. 1950. Physiology of the thyroid gland in birds : a review. Ibis 92 : 464–473.

Höhn, E. O. 1960. The endocrine system. In Marshall, A. J. (ed.). Biology and Comparative Physiology of Birds vol. II. New York and London.
Marshall, A. J. 1960. Reproduction. In Marshall, A. J. (ed.). Biology and Physiology of Birds vol. II. New York and London.
Parkes, A. S. & Marshall, A. J. 1960. The reproductive hormones of birds. In Marshall, F. H. A. Physiology of Reproduction vol. IIB. London.
Witschi, E. 1935. Secondary sex characters in birds and their hormonal control. Wilson Bull. 47 : 177–188.

ENDOPARASITE : a parasite inhabiting the interior of the host's body, as distinct from an ' ectoparasite'. Birds are hosts for an almost infinite variety of endoparasites, but certain genera and families of endoparasites are particularly prevalent, and only these are dealt with here.

With the vast majority of endoparasites there is no direct transmission of infection from one individual of the host species to another such as occurs with bacterial, viral, and fungal infections. In almost every case a period of development outside the bird host is necessary before the parasite can infect another. Similarly, within the host, the parasite undergoes growth and development, passing through various recognisable stages. These two developmental periods, within and outside the host, constitute the life-cycle of the parasite. Development outside the host may be a simple process of growth to an infective stage, in which case the life-cycle is said to be direct. In other cases some other animal must be invaded by the stages outside the main host before development can be completed ; in this case the life-cycle is indirect, and the animal necessary for the outside development is referred to as the intermediate host or vector. In certain cases more than one intermediate host may be necessary, and the second may be a completely different animal from the first. Examples of intermediate hosts are snails, which always act as intermediate hosts for flukes ; and for some flukes fish act as secondary intermediate hosts.

The transmission of infection and the incidence of a particular group of parasites is governed to a great extent by the habitat and the type of food of the bird. Thus fish-eating species acquire parasites that use fish as their intermediate hosts ; and insect-eating birds have a parasite fauna restricted to those species of parasites that develop in insects. Alternatively, birds that feed in groups on the ground are parasitised by organisms having a direct life-cycle.

When extremely heavy burdens of endoparasites occur, then ill health and death can confidently be attributed to such infection. Nevertheless it is often difficult to assess the importance of any given parasitic burden as regards the health consequences.

Limited surveys have shown that generally minimal burdens of parasites exist in the natural state, but seemingly heavy burdens occasionally occur without causing any apparent ill health. However, such burdens may be of importance in so far that they can be a potential menace to the health of the bird if its food supply is curtailed or if other diseases are acquired. There are instances when even a very small number of parasites may result in ill health and death, particularly when a vital organ of the body is incapacitated.

The main groups of endoparasites are roundworms (Nematoda), thornyheaded worms (Acanthocephala), tapeworms (Cestoda), flukes (Trematoda), and unicellular animals (Protozoa). Only the more important pathogenic or commonly occurring genera or species will be mentioned.

Nematoda: Ascaroidea. Ascarids may have a direct or an indirect life-cycle. Of those having a direct life-cycle, the caecal worm *Heterakis* and the intestinal worm *Ascaridia* are extremely common. The caecal worm of domestic poultry, *H. gallinae*, may occur also in a wide range of birds, including ducks (Anatidae), pheasants (Phasianidae), and crows (Corvidae). Infection is acquired by eating infective eggs, which may remain viable on the ground for long periods. Within the caecum of the fowl generally little damage is produced, but nevertheless this parasite is of outstanding importance since it transmits the organism of blackhead, *Histomonas meleagridis*, a severe and frequently fatal disease of domestic fowl, Turkeys *Meleagris gallopavo*, and other birds. Of the other *Heterakis* species, *H. dispar* occurs in ducks, frequently in large numbers and *H. isolonche* is found in pheasants and causes a nodular disease of the caeca.

The genus *Ascaridia* is widely distributed in birds ; *A. galli* in particular has a cosmopolitan distribution in many birds, including domestic poultry and game-birds (Galliformes), while *A. columbae* is a frequent parasite of domestic and wild pigeons (Columbidae). Heavy infections with the genus *Ascaridia* may occur in birds that feed in groups and may be fatal. These worms are some of the largest to be found in birds, and infection can be readily detected without opening the gut.

Of the Ascarids with an indirect life-cycle, the genera *Contracaecum* and *Porrocaecum* are the most common. The larval stages of *Contracaecum* spp. occur in fish, and consequently fish-eating birds (and indeed mammals) are affected by them. *C. spiculigerum* is a very common parasite of the proventriculus and intestine of a variety of sea birds. The genus *Porrocaecum* has a rather wider host distribution. Some are found in birds-of-prey, in which case the intermediate stages occur in moles and shrews. *P. crassum* is particularly common in ducks and requires earthworms as its intermediate host, whilst *P. depressum* and *P. ensicaudatum* are widely distributed in many birds, the latter being particularly common in passerines.

Nematoda: Strongyloidea. The majority of these strongyles have a direct life-cycle. The best-known are the gizzard-worm of geese *Anser* spp., *Amidostomum anseris* ; the gapeworm of poultry, *Syngamus trachea* ; and the small strongyle of grouse (Tetraonidae) and other birds, *Trichostrongylus tenuis*. The gizzard-worm is particularly common in both wild and domestic geese. It is relatively large and lives under the horny coat of the gizzard, causing very marked inflammation and ulceration that frequently ends in death. It tends to affect young birds in particular, and may be responsible for heavy mortality on breeding grounds.

The gapeworm often causes marked mortality in domestic birds, even a few worms leading to respiratory distress. The life-cycle may be direct, or invertebrates such as earthworms and centipedes may act as transport hosts, infection being acquired by eating the latter. Earthworms play another important part in that they make the gapeworms of wild birds, particularly those of Rooks *Corvus frugilegus* and Starlings *Sturnus vulgaris*, more easily transmissible to domestic poultry. It is thought that gapeworms of wild birds—and they occur in many species—are different strains from that found in poultry, but the earthworm can modify them so as to produce infection in domestic birds. A gapeworm, *Cyathostoma bronchialis*, occurs in ducks and geese, and even one or two of these may occlude the trachea of young birds and cause death.

Trichostrongylus tenuis is a very small worm occurring in the caeca and intestine of ducks, poultry, pheasants, grouse, and many other birds. This parasite is of particular importance in the Red Grouse *Lagopus scoticus*, in which it is a well known cause of death (see DISEASE). In ducks, too, it may cause severe inflammation of the intestine.

Nematoda: Spiruroidea. All the parasitic spirurids require an intermediate host to complete their life-cycles, this usually being an arthropod. A wide variety of parasites is included in this group, and they parasitise different sites of the body. One example is the genus *Oxyspirura*, which occurs in the conjunctival cavity of the eye.

One of the most important groups is the Acuari-idae, containing the species *Acuaria uncinata*. This lives in the proventriculus of ducks and geese, causing a great deal of damage and being sometimes responsible for heavy mortality in wildfowl kept in captivity ; the intermediate host is the water-flea *Daphnia pulex*, which is abundant in stagnant and slow-running waters. Other members of the Acuariidae are widely distributed among birds, especially gulls (Larinae), puffins (Fraterculini), and falcons (Falconidae), occurring in the upper digestive tract and also having a marked pathogenic capacity.

A remarkable parasite in the Spiruroidea is *Tetrameres fissispina*, found in waterfowl. The female of this species becomes almost spherical when mature, and since it lives in the glands of the proventriculus it causes marked dilatation and degeneration of glandular tissue.

Nematoda: Filaroidea. Adult filarial worms live in body cavities and inner organs. They produce larvae, microfilariae, which occur in the blood. These, to complete their life-cycle, are taken up by blood-sucking insects and inside these develop to the infective stage. Re-infection occurs with the injection of infective larvae into the body of the bird with saliva from the insect. Blackbirds and thrushes *Turdus* spp. may be infected with such worms in Great Britain.

Nematoda: Trichinelloidea. Capillarids are very thin small worms, difficult to see, but may occur in large numbers in various parts of the digestive tract. One of the commonest is *Capillaria contorta*, which occurs in the crop and oesophagus of domestic and many wild birds.

Acanthocephala. Thornyheaded worms are small, generally sausage-shaped, and have a large retractable proboscis covered with numerous curved spines. This proboscis is used to anchor the worm to the bowel wall, being thrust into the tissues. The most common is *Polymorphus minutus*, occurring in many kinds of waterfowl, sometimes several hundreds or thousands being found and in many cases causing no apparent ill health. This species is readily recognised since it is frequently bright orange in colour and in a heavily infected bird the inside of the bowel may be a continuous orange mass. The intermediate host of *P. minutus* is the fresh-water shrimp, *Gammarus*. The genus *Corynosoma* utilises fish as an intermediate host, in addition to an arthropod, and consequently is found in fish-eating birds (and also in seals). In passerine birds the genera *Prosthorhynchus* and *Centiorhynchus* are commonly found.

Cestoda. Tapeworms have an interesting distribution in birds, in that certain groups of birds possess their own particular fauna of tapeworms. Those of the family Hymenolepididae are perhaps the largest group occurring in birds, being particularly common in the Anatidae. Many species occur, and their identification is a matter of great difficulty. The hymenolepid cestodes require intermediate hosts, and these vary from aquatic arthropods to beetles and annelids. Extremely heavy burdens of *Hymenolepis* spp. may occur in birds and are responsible, at times, for heavy mortality. One of the commonest species, occurring in a wide variety of ducks and other waterfowl, is *H. anatina*.

The tapeworm genus *Raillietina* is common in domestic poultry and in game-birds, also occurring in pigeons, sparrows *Passer* spp., and thrushes. The genus *Anomotaenia* is a large one and occurs in Charadrii, Lari, and Passeriformes. Since even the provisional identification of tapeworms requires staining techniques and microscopic examination, and as they all occur in the intestinal tract and the ill effects produced are much the same with all groups, a diagnosis of heavy tapeworm infection will suffice as a preliminary finding.

Trematoda. Flukes in extremely wide variety occur in birds. Some are extremely small and difficult to see, some may occur in large numbers within a bird without causing any obvious ill health, whilst others may be pathogenic in moderate numbers. All trematodes undergo development within a snail, and in the majority of cases also require a second intermediate host for the infective stage of the fluke (metacercaria), this occurring in a variety of animal life such as fish, snails, insects, crustacea, and annelids. Since many of the intermediate hosts are animals that live in or near water, it is not surprising that waterfowl and sea birds in general are parasitised by flukes.

The fluke family Echinostomatidae is extremely common in waterfowl. It is characterised by a collar of spines round the head, and includes some of the largest trematodes of birds and also some of the most highly pathogenic. *E. revolutum* is a common fluke of the intestines of ducks and geese, whilst the genera *Echinoparyphium*, *Hypoderaeum*, *Echinochasmus*, and *Himasthla* are common groups in water birds.

Members of the family Microphallidae are extremely common in birds feeding on mudflats, saltings, and the seashore. These are very small flukes, and several thousand may be found in the intestine of a single bird. The family Plagiorchidae is chiefly found in sparrows, Starlings, and Rooks and other birds, and one genus, *Prosthogonimus*, is found in the oviduct of such birds. There are other specific sites for flukes than the intestine ; for example, in the gall bladder of passerines *Lyperosomum longicauda* is often found ; the genus *Renicola* occurs in the kidneys of gulls ; the genus *Clinostomum* occurs in the nasal passages of gulls and herons (Ardeidae) ; and even the skin is affected by the genus *Collyriclum*, which causes cysts in such birds as warblers (Sylviinae), wagtails *Motacilla* spp., and sparrows.

One interesting group is the Schistosomatidae, which also contains the pathogenic *Bilharzia* parasites of man in the tropics. Birds in Great Britain such as ducks and swans (Anatidae), grebes (Podicipitidae), and gulls are parasitised by schistosomes, the worms occurring in the veins draining the intestinal circulation. Infection of birds is produced by the infective stages (cercariae) penetrating the skin. (Human bathers may be attacked by these cercariae, when a dermatitis called ' swimmer's itch ' may be produced.)

Protozoa. These are single-celled animals, showing a wide variety of forms. Included in this group are the coccidia, malarial organisms, and trypanosomes. The most important members of the group in Great Britain are the coccidia. It is well known that coccidial parasites of the genus *Eimeria*, especially *E. tenella*, cause enormous economic loss in domestic poultry. Wild birds are also affected by this genus ; geese, Moorhens *Gallinula chloropus*, Kittiwakes *Larus tridactylus*, and cormorants *Phalacrocorax* spp. are among the hosts. Species of the genus *Eimeria* are host-specific, but the related genus *Isospora*, common in passerines, is less so ; thus a commonly found coccidium *Isospora lacazii* occurs in the intestines of Canaries *Serinus canaria*, Goldfinches *Carduelis carduelis*, Skylarks *Alauda arvensis*, wagtails, and Chaffinches *Fringilla coelebs*.

All the coccidia are microscopic and live inside the cells of the intestine. The life-cycle is direct, infection of a bird occurring when it eats the infective stage (oöcyst). These oöcysts may remain infective on the ground for long periods, and large concentrations of them may accumulate around feeding and watering places. Artificial concentration of birds, e.g. due to hand-feeding in winter, may build up sites of marked contamination.

Trichomonads are flagellated protozoa. *Trichomonas gallinae* lives in the crops of birds, and in young pigeons it may cause disease and death, infection of the squabs being by contaminated ' pigeon's milk ' from the parent (see MILK, PIGEON).

Trypanosomes occur in British birds, *Trypanosoma fringillinarum* being found in Chaffinches, and *T. avium* in Rooks and Jackdaws *Corvus monedula*. These trypanosomes are not, however, the cause of serious disease, unlike their relatives the trypanosomes of man and animals in Africa. Other blood organisms are members of the genus *Haemoproteus*, transmitted by blood-sucking flies. This genus is found in thrushes, Blackbirds, Starlings, and birds-of-prey. *H. columbae* is the cause of pigeon malaria, infection being transmitted by the louse-fly of pigeons, *Pseudolynchia canariensis*.

The protozoan *Histomonas meleagridis* is the cause of the severe and often fatal disease of turkeys known as blackhead. It is transmitted from bird to bird by the caecal nematode *Heterakis gallinae* (see above). Initially it causes an inflammation of the bowel, but later it affects the liver and produces marked damage and necrosis. Heavy mortality may occur in turkey poults, and other birds such as domestic fowl, Quail *Coturnix coturnix*, grouse, and partridges *Perdix* etc. may be affected.   E.J.L.S.

Beverley-Burton, M. 1961. Studies on the Trematoda of British freshwater birds. Proc. Zool. Soc. Lond. 137 : 13–39.
Lapage, G. 1961. A list of the Protozoa, Helminths and Arthropoda from species of Anatidae (Ducks, swans and geese). Parasitol. 51 : 1–109.

ENDYSIS: renewal of plumage after moult (ecdysis)—see MOULT.

ENERGY REQUIREMENTS: discussed here in relation to birds in flight (see FLIGHT ; and METABOLISM). Within the last fifty years there have been many attempts to estimate the power output of a bird in flight. The problem is particularly difficult, since no direct approach is practicable. It is possible, for example, to measure the properties of a bird's wing in a wind tunnel, and then to synthesise a theoretical wing-beat cycle based on these properties; this was in effect the method used by Lilienthal to estimate the power consumption of a White Stork *Ciconia ciconia*. The method has large and unpredictable inaccuracies. It is now known that a wing of which the attitude and shape are changing, as happens in flapping flight, may have properties entirely different from the properties of the same wing as predicted from wind-tunnel tests. It is possible, alternatively, to make estimates of the energy output of the metabolism by measurements of oxygen or food consumption ; but one must make some arbitrary assumption on the efficiency of the system in order to find a figure for the energy available for flight. Still approaching the problem from the starting-point of metabolism, one can take the figures for muscle-power output measured in other animals and see whether a reasonable aerodynamic system can be postulated to work with the amount of power to be expected.

The first notable work was that of Lilienthal. This took the form of a point-to-point summation of the forces on a wing in different attitudes. By choosing what he considered to be a suitable series of measurements, he built up a theoretical flapping system with the dimensions of a White Stork. He showed that a bird with similar properties would require a power output, from its flight muscles, of about 0·08 horsepower per pound weight of muscle ($1·3 \times 10^5$ ergs/second/gram) when flying at 30 feet per second. Other workers have tried similar syntheses, using more complex wing shapes and movements, and have suggested values for the energy requirements between 0·5 and $1·0 \times 10^5$ ergs/second/gram.

Straightforward wind-tunnel measurements of the characteristics of birds have given little help. Attempts have been made to fix freshly killed or stuffed birds in flying attitudes and then to measure their aerodynamic properties. Such measurements have shown systems with such poor aerodynamic properties that they would require absurdly large expenditures of energy in flight.

There is a generally accepted figure of 0·01 horsepower per pound weight of muscle ($0·16 \times 10^5$ ergs/second/gram) for the output of mammalian muscle. If the bird is comparable, then even the calculated minimum power required is much too large. If we take this mammalian figure we can calculate, for a particular bird, what are the required characteristics of the physical system for which this power would be sufficient. If this is done, taking a Swallow *Hirundo rustica* as an example, we arrive at a figure for the air resistance which is at least highly improbable. Without further information there is no reason to expect a value of air resistance lower than that found in model experiments, so one must postulate a muscle power output substantially greater than the mammalian figure.

In recent years some information has been obtained that provides at least a partial solution to the problem. Pearson (1950) has measured the metabolic rate of hummingbirds (Trochilidae) at rest and in flight. From these figures, assuming that the difference between the rates at rest and in flight is solely due to the energy release in the flight muscles, he arrives at an output of $5·9 \times 10^5$ ergs/second/gram of muscle —36 times the mammalian figure. Even if this is true, and all the excess metabolism is in the flight muscle, we have no direct information on the power actually available for flight ; but Zeuthen, assuming certain aerodynamic parameters and a transfer efficiency in the muscles of 25 per cent, concluded that a pigeon *Columba* sp. flying at 43 miles per hour needed a comparable rate of energy production in its muscles.

If we accept Zeuthen's figure of 25 per cent power transfer, and Pearson's estimate of the metabolic energy, then we can allow about $1·5 \times 10^5$ ergs/second/gram. This would provide more than enough energy for the type of flight postulated by Lilienthal. But is this level of energy output necessary ? We have only one measurement of the aerodynamic properties of a free-flying bird. In North America, Raspet was able to follow a gliding Black Vulture *Coragyps atratus* in a sailplane (glider) of known performance. By filming the bird with a camera fixed to the machine, he was able to determine the difference between the bird's performance and that of the sailplane. The result was surprising ; the gliding angle was small (22 to 1), and since the wing area was large the lift coefficient was small and the drag very small. The drag (air resistance) was not significantly different from the theoretical minimum drag of a smooth flat plate. Even assuming that a similar drag occurs in flapping flight, the relatively small flight muscles of this bird would need to provide an output of $0·5 \times 10^5$ ergs/second/gram to maintain level flight at 40 feet per second, and of course more during climbing or acceleration. This bird does not provide a good example for such estimates ; it does not undertake powered flights of long duration, so its muscles may be more highly loaded than those of, say, a pigeon. It seems that, even if we assume a highly efficient propulsive mechanism, we must still expect an output from the muscles several times that measured in mammalian muscles. That such an expectation is not unreasonable is confirmed by the observations of Weis-Fogh (1956) on flying insects, where the energy release may be as much as $5·0 \times 10^5$ ergs/second/gram total body weight.

Migration. There are many reliably recorded instances of migration flights of land birds over the sea for distances of 1000 miles and more. The well-known flights of the American Golden Plover *Pluvialis dominica* to Antigua (from Canada) over the Atlantic, and to Hawaii over the Pacific, both involve distances of about 2000 miles. If the birds migrate only in conditions of favourable wind direction, the actual air distance may be less ; even so one must assume a flight range of not less than 1500 miles.

There is the obvious problem of the energy store (fuel) to be carried for such flights. Odum has studied the fat reserves of migrant species, finding that even in short-range migrants the amount of fat before migration is much greater than in sedentary species at the same time of year. In long-range migrants he finds up to 50 per cent wet weight (73 per cent dry weight) of lipids. On the assumption that for a 20-gram bird the 'existence energy' is 0·05 Kcalories per gram, he has calculated the possible flight ranges, at an air speed of 30 miles per hour, if the metabolic rate in flight is twice, three times, or four times the existence level. For a

20-gram bird with 50 per cent of fat he calculates an energy requirement of 0·067 Kcalories per mile at twice the existence level of metabolism, 0·1 Kcalories at three times, and 0·133 Kcalories at four times the minimum. These figures give ranges of 3630, 1755, and 1316 miles respectively.

Lasiewski has repeated Pearson's measurements on a hummingbird and has determined a flight energy figure of about 0·7 Kcalories per hour. With 2 grams of fat this would permit a flight range of 650 miles. This is nearly equivalent to Odum's calculated requirements at three times existence level. Since clearly the heat losses of large birds will be relatively less than those of a very small species (surface/volume ratio—see SIZE) it may be assumed that Odum's minimum figure for the flight duration is conservative.

It seems therefore that the calculations of possible flight ranges of migrating birds agree fairly well with the known distances of migration, and that the fat store of such birds can provide the energy required.   R.H.J.B.

Lasiewski, R. C. 1962. The energetics of migrating hummingbirds. Condor 64 : 324.
Lilienthal, O. 1899. Der Vogelzug als Grundlage der Fliegekunst : ein Beitrag zur Systematik der Flugtechnik. Berlin. (Eng. trans. 1911. Bird Flight as the Basis of Aviation. London.)
Odum, E. P. 1960. Lipid deposition in migrating birds. Proc. XII Internat. Orn. Congr., Helsinki 1958 : 563–575.
Pearson, O. P. 1950. The metabolism of hummingbirds. Condor 52 : 145–152.
Raspet, G. 1950. Performance measurements of a soaring bird. Gliding 6 : 145–151.
Zeuthen, E. 1942. The ventilation of the respiratory tract in birds. Biol. Medd. K. Danske Vidensk. Selskab 17 : 1–51.

ENZYMES, DIGESTIVE: see ALIMENTARY SYSTEM

EPAXIAL: see MUSCULATURE

EPICARDIUM: see HEART

EPIDEICTIC: term applied by Wynne-Edwards to communal manoeuvres and displays, particularly those that occur at special times such as dawn or dusk (see DISPLAY ; FLOCKING ; LEK DISPLAY ; ROOSTING ; SINGING).

EPIDEMIC: as an adjective, applied to diseases meaning that these affect a large number of individuals during a limited period—contrasted with 'endemic' in the primary sense of that term (see ENDEMIC) ; also used as a noun for an outbreak of disease (see DISEASE).

EPIDERMIS: the outer layer of the SKIN.

EPIDIDYMIS: see REPRODUCTIVE SYSTEM

EPIGAMIC: term applied to characters or actions tending to promote reproductive behaviour (see DISPLAY).

EPIGENETICS: the analytical study of the developmental process (ontogeny), a term implying the interaction of genetic factors—see DEVELOPMENT, EMBRYONIC ; DEVELOPMENT, POSTEMBRYONIC.

EPISEMATIC: term applied to appearance or behaviour aiding recognition, applied particularly to coloration. 'Antepisematic' implies a threat ; 'proepisematic' refers to social recognition ; 'pseud-episematic' involves deception, e.g. the eggs of parasitic cuckoos (Cuculinae) may in a sense be protectively coloured in their mimicry, but the role is fundamentally aggressive. Compare APOSE-MATIC ; and in general see COLORATION, ADAPTIVE ; RECOGNITION.

EPITHELIUM: see TISSUE ; and SKIN

EPTHIANURINAE: see under MUSCICAPIDAE

EQUILIBRATION: see HEARING AND BALANCE

EREMOMELA: generic name used as substantive common name of *Eremomela* spp. (for subfamily see WARBLER (1)).

ERNE: archaic and poetic name, in Britain, for the Sea Eagle *Haliaetus albicilla* (see under HAWK).

EROLIINAE: synonym of Calidritinae (see SANDPIPER).

ERROR, STANDARD AND PROBABLE: see STATISTICAL SIGNIFICANCE

ERUPTION: same, but in relation to area of origin, as IRRUPTION (see also MIGRATION).

ERYTHRISM: see PLUMAGE, ABNORMAL AND ABERRANT

ERYTHROCYTE: see BLOOD

ERYTHURINI: see WEAVER-FINCH

ESOPHAGUS: American spelling of OESOPHAGUS (see ALIMENTARY SYSTEM).

ESTRILDIDAE: a family of the Passeriformes, suborder Oscines, now separated from the Ploceidae (see WEAVER-FINCH ; also WHYDAH (1)).

ESTROGEN: same (American usage) as OESTRO-GEN ; see ENDOCRINE SYSTEM.

ETHIOPIAN REGION: one of the classical zoogeographical regions (see DISTRIBUTION, GEOGRA-

PHICAL) ; it consists, broadly, of Africa south of the Sahara. The northern boundary—dividing it from the Palaearctic Region—cannot be defined sharply, since the Sahara itself develops gradually from the less arid country to the south, but for the most part it lies between about 18° and 20° N. lat. (south of the Ahaggar and north of the Aïr and Ennedi massifs) ; in the east it swings northwards to meet the Red Sea at about 22° N. lat. The southwest corner of Arabia has often been regarded as Ethiopian, but although it has strong affinities with the opposite coasts of Eritrea and Somaliland they are balanced by Palaearctic elements. Of islands more than thirty miles off shore, only those in the Gulf of Guinea are typically Ethiopian. Madagascar—originally included as a subregion—is sufficiently different to be regarded as a separate region, while the Comoros are transitional (see MALAGASY REGION). The total area of the Ethiopian Region amounts to about eight million square miles, of which about half a million are south of the tropics, with the extremity at 35° S. lat.

The two main factors that determine the distribution of the Ethiopian birds are the location of the climatic belts, which produce characteristic vegetation types, and of high ground. For a general account of African vegetation see Shantz & Marbut (1923), and for a more modern view of its distribution the *Vegetation Map of Africa*. Chapin (1932) gives descriptions of many African habitats from the ornithologist's point of view.

The Ethiopian Region was divided into 17 avifaunal ' districts ' by Chapin, and subsequently South African ornithologists have been active in subdividing their area further. The divisions thus arrived at are of unequal value, however, and often have only a slight basis of faunistic peculiarity. Actually, the most noteworthy changes in avifauna take place approximately at the boundaries of the main vegetational types, which are as outlined below. An important feature of the avifauna as a whole is the very small number of species that are at home both in evergreen forest and in non-forest vegetation of any sort. Moreover, comparatively few species live at both high and low elevations. Of the approximately 1500 species to which the Ethiopian avifauna is reduced by the application of the modern polytypic species concept, about 250 belong to lowland evergreen forest and another 200 are confined to areas of all kinds above about 5000 feet.

Lowland Rain-forest. Across most of the middle of Africa lies the equatorial rain-belt, where there is no marked dry season. The characteristic vegetation here is tropical evergreen forest, developed in the Congo basin and in the coastal zone of West Africa.

Since the rain is of western (Atlantic) origin, it decreases eastwards ; and the eastern side of the continent is too dry to support typical evergreen forest at low altitudes, even on the Equator itself. Where fully developed, this forest consists of great trees, devoid of side branches below the canopy at 100–150 feet, and with little undergrowth or vegetable food on the heavily shaded ground. On and near the forest floor the main species are galline birds and a variety of thrush-like birds (Turdinae) and babblers (Timaliinae). The higher levels of the forest are far richer, holding especially cuckoos (Cuculidae), turacos (Musophagidae), trogons (Trogonidae), hornbills (Bucerotidae), barbets (Capitonidae), starlings (Sturnidae), and peculiar weavers (Ploceidae). Flycatchers (Muscicapinae) and warblers (Sylviinae) are generally distributed, and bulbuls (Pycnonotidae) are numerous in the undergrowth. Any break in the forest canopy is of great biological importance, whether caused by the fall of a tree, by the passage of a stream, or by human interference. Many plants are specially adapted to take advantage of the access to light and air ; and many animals, including birds, live typically in the resultant secondary growth and in edge conditions. Human clearings, in moderation, increase the abundance of birds in rain-forest areas.

Savannas. To north and south of the equatorial rain-belt, and for the most part within about five degrees of the Equator, the climate changes to a monsoon type, with a long dry season succeeded by a wet season (see CLIMATOLOGY). The typical vegetation is a mixture of deciduous trees and perennial grasses. At their densest the trees form great blocks of ' dry woodland ', especially *Brachystegia* (' miombo ') in the southern tropics ; but elsewhere the formation is usually ' savanna ', where the seasonally leafless trees are scattered through the grassland and are adapted to survive the fierce fires that sweep over it during the dry season. Through these savannas meander drainage channels that often contain no running water but are of importance to birds because of the size of the trees they support, many of which bear fruit. This applies not only nearer the Equator, where in the more humid climates these fringing ' gallery ' woodlands are outliers of the evergreen forest, but also in the dryer savanna, where the gallery becomes thin and the trees more deciduous. The grassland of the savanna is an association of clumps, dense enough to cover the ground and consisting of deep-rooted species that grow several feet high. As a result, during the wet season the ground is largely inaccessible to birds, and again the operations of agriculture, if small-scale, enrich the bird life. The characteristic birds of this heavy grassland are numerous species of grass-warblers *Cisticola* spp. (Sylviinae) and of weavers (Ploceidae and Estrildidae).

Semi-arid Zones. A drier type of country, where the vegetation is reduced to small thorny trees or scrub and only annual herbage, dominates three areas—a belt all along the southern edge of the Sahara, a block in the north-east from the Gulf of Aden to northern Tanganyika, and another block covering South West Africa and the adjoining country. Here the vegetation is so sparse that through most of the year the prevailing hue of the landscape is that of the soil. Characteristic birds are coursers (Cursoriinae), bustards (Otididae), and larks (Alaudidae), but the avifauna of the trees is quite rich. Many of the birds show their adaptation to the severe conditions. They tend to be paler in plumage than their relatives elsewhere, and they are less sedentary. Some species even undertake regular migrations of a thousand miles south fom the dry belt along the edge of the Sahara, e.g Abdim's Stork *Sphenorynchus abdimii* and the Grasshopper Buzzard *Butastur rufipennis*.

Montane Areas. Over most of Africa a great change takes place in the animals and plants above about 5000 feet. The characteristic vegetation of these montane areas is a special type of evergreen forest (with 'alpine' scrub above about 11 000 feet). These conditions are typically developed in (*a*) the small group of highlands at the head of the Gulf of Guinea (especially Cameroon Mountain, 13 000 ft.) ; (*b*) the Abyssinian plateau, much of it at 8000 ft. and over ; (*c*) the Kenya highlands and many isolated mountains in Kenya, Tanganyika (including Kilimanjaro, nearly 20 000 ft.), and Nyasaland ; (*d*) the mountains of central Africa (in the geographical, not the political, sense), especially Ruwenzori (17 000 ft.) and the Kivu volcanos. South of Kenya and the Congo basin, most of Africa is a plateau at least 3000 feet above sea level, but typical montane conditions exist only in a very few localities near the eastern edge.

Isolated though these montane forests are, some of them by particularly dry, hot, thorn country, they to a great extent share a peculiar avifauna that has no close relationship with the birds of the surrounding lowlands. Thus, most of the montane species of Usambara, at 5° S. lat. in Tanganyika, are found also in the mountains of southern Nyasaland, 800 miles away. More remarkable still, Cameroon has many species of birds in common with East African mountains distant more than a thousand miles across the Congo basin ; while the Abyssinian highlands, far less isolated, lack the typical montane forest avifauna.

History. Since hardly any bird fossils are known from the Ethiopian Region, we have to rely on inference. In the first place it seems certain that through most of avian history, the continent of Africa has had very much its present outline and that the present series of climatic belts has existed there, merely changing their location somewhat. Africa must therefore have been a principal scene of continuous evolution of both forest and non-forest birds. Recent geological work has shown particularly that great ecological disruption, no doubt with corresponding influence on extinction and on the later stages of evolution, has taken place in the latter half of the Pleistocene, presumably by no means for the first time. During the last glaciation, as a result of reduced world temperature, a continuous block of montane conditions would have extended from Abyssinia to South Africa, with a connection to the Cameroons, for long periods before about 18 000 years ago. This would have put into communication all those stations of montane birds which are now so widely isolated. Concurrently, birds tolerant only of fully lowland conditions would have been confined to West Africa, the Sudan, the centre of the Congo basin, and a strip all along the coasts. Similar conditions had presumably recurred with each glaciation. Of other considerable changes, not obviously connected with the last glaciation, the most notable are : (1) the distribution of Kalahari sand in the Mid Pleistocene over most of the area now occupied by the great Congo forest, with presumed restriction of the latter's birds to refuges on the eastern and western edges ; (2) the Late Pleistocene fluctuation of the southern edge of the Sahara between 300 miles north and 300 miles south of its present position, the former as lately as 6000 years ago and the latter having severe effects on the evergreen forests of Upper Guinea ; (3) the extension of the Kalahari, eastwards at least to the Victoria Falls, as lately as 10 000 years ago.

Characteristic Forms. Among the birds of the Ethiopian Region there are few endemic groups above the generic level. Less than ten families were claimed by Chapin (1932) as Ethiopian endemics, and of these half consist of only one or two species, while several have been reduced to at most sub-familial rank in recent classifications. The most distinctive birds of the Ethiopian Region are the Hammerhead (Scopidae), Secretary-bird (Sagittariidae), guineafowls (Numididae), mousebirds (Coliidae), turacos (Musophagidae), wood-hoopoes (Phoeniculidae), and, although only by recent extinction elsewhere, the Ostrich (Struthionidae). Africa is also surpassingly rich in certain groups—

francolins (*Francolinus* and *Pternistes* spp.), bustards (Otididae), barbets (Capitonidae), honeyguides (Indicatoridae), larks (Alaudidae), grass-warblers *Cisticola* spp., helmet-shrikes (Prionopidae), shrikes (Laniidae), and weavers (Ploceidae and Estrildidae). Birds of special interest are the two oxpeckers (Buphaginae), evolved as symbionts of the African big game. On the other hand, certain groups, especially the parrots (Psittacidae) and the wood-peckers (Picidae), are represented by fewer species than might have been expected. See Plate 30 (colour).

Besides its resident population, the Ethiopian Region supports an immense number of birds from the Palaearctic during the northern winter. Something like a third of the Palaearctic species, especially the insectivores, winter wholly or mainly south of the Sahara, coming not only from Europe but even from farthest Asia (*Phylloscopus trochilus*, *Oenanthe oenanthe*). The immigrants occupy every part of the Region, except the evergreen forest, as far south as the Cape. See also MIGRATION.

The standard list of the birds of the Ethiopian Region is that of Sclater (1924–30), although many changes now have to be made in it. (White's recent check-list of the passerines is fully polytypic in its treatment.) A more general work, fully illustrated and with descriptions and biological in-formation, has been initiated by Mackworth-Praed & Grant, and the first four (of six) volumes have already appeared. Other works are more restricted in their geographical range.   R.E.M.

Faunistic Works (main areas only)

Bannerman, D. A. 1930–49. Birds of Tropical West Africa. 8 vols. London.

Bannerman, D. A. 1953. Birds of West and Equatorial Africa. 2 vols. Edinburgh and London. (Based on his larger work.)

Chapin, J. P. 1932–54. Birds of the Belgian Congo. Parts 1–4. Bull. Amer. Mus. Nat. Hist. 65, 75, 75A, 75B.

Mackworth-Praed, C. W. & Grant, C. H. B. 1952–55. Birds of Eastern and North-eastern Africa (African Handbook of Birds, Series 1). 2 vols. (2nd ed. 1961). London.

Mackworth-Praed, C. W. & Grant, C. H. B. 1962–63. Birds of the Southern Third of Africa. 2 vols. (African Handbook of Birds, Series 2). London.

McLachlan, G. R. & Liversidge, R. 1957. Roberts' Birds of South Africa. Cape Town.

Reichenow, A. 1900–05. Die Vögel Afrikas. 3 vols. and atlas. Neudamm.

Sclater, W. L. 1924–30. Systema Avium Aethiopicarum. 2 vols. London.

White, C. M. N. 1962a, 1962b, 1963. (Revised check-lists, separately titled, of African passerine families.) Lusaka, N. Rhodesia.

General references

Hall, B. P. & Moreau, R. E. 1962. A study of the rare birds of Africa. Bull. Brit. Mus. (Nat. Hist.) Zool. 8(7) : 315–378.

Moreau, R. E. 1952. Africa since the Mesozoic. Proc. Zool. Soc. Lond. 121 : 869–913.

Moreau, R. E. 1952. The place of Africa in the Palaearctic migration system. J. Anim. Ecol. 21 : 250–271.

Moreau, R. E. 1963. Vicissitudes of the African biomes in the late Pleistocene. Proc. Zool. Soc. Lond. 141 : 395–421.

Schantz, H. L. & Marbut, C. F. 1923. The Vegetation and Soils of Africa. Res. Ser. Amer. Geog. Soc. 13.

Vegetation Map of Africa. 1959. Oxford.

ETHOLOGY: the scientific study of BEHAVIOUR.

ETIOLOGY: see AETIOLOGY

EUPHONIA: discarded generic name used as substantive common name of *Tanagra* spp. (see TANAGER).

EUROPE: see under PALAEARCTIC REGION

EURYLAIMI; EURYLAIMIDAE: see under PASSERIFORMES ; and BROADBILL

EURYOECIOUS: occupying a wide range of the habitats available in an area, i.e. showing 'wide habitat-tolerance'—contrasted with STENOE-CIOUS.

EURYPYGAE; EURYPYGIDAE: see under GRUIFORMES ; and SUNBITTERN

EUSTACHIAN TUBE: see HEARING AND BAL-ANCE ; PALATE ; and under SKELETON

EUSYANTHROPIC: living directly on human habitations—contrasted with 'synanthropic', living near these, particularly on cultivated land ; and with 'exanthropic', living away from human habitations and cultivation.

EUTAXIS: see PLUMAGE ; WING

EVOLUTION: the theory which states that the different kinds of living things have been produced by descent with modification from previously exist-ing forms, not by each one being created separately with its present characters. The theory is now generally accepted by all serious students of biology. Its principal proponents were Lamarck, Darwin, and Alfred Russel Wallace, although various others had put it forward as a speculation.

Under the theory of special creation, formerly generally accepted in Christendom, each sort of animal and plant was created perfect for fulfilling a particular role in the 'economy of nature', so that the world of living things would persist in balance ; each sort was endowed with the power of perpetuating itself. From earliest times, however, certain facts seemed inexplicable on this theory. The existence of rudimentary organs, e.g. wings useless for flight in the Ostrich *Struthio camelus*, could not be explained as necessary to the life of their possessors, precisely because they were rudimentary. Aristotle suggested that Nature, in making animals, had to work to certain plans, the limits of which she could not transcend. Consequently, when forming new sorts (not in an evolutionary manner, in Aristotle's philosophy) she might reduce an organ in one form to a mere rudiment, but could not abolish it if it were an essential feature of the general kind—as wings are an essential feature of birds. Consequently, the rudiments remained as a sign or token of parts of the main plan that had been suppressed. In the Middle Ages and later, God was substituted for Aristotle's rather ill-defined ' Nature ', and His power and wisdom in creating such infinite variations on a few basic plans was a favourite theme with moralists. The study of natural history thus became the following out of the plan of Creation and, in Britain especially, a highly praiseworthy activity on theological grounds.

This idea of the constancy of the essential features of any one kind of animal or plant, and of variation taking place only in inessentials, was characteristic of logic almost until the present century. It had the bad effect of dictating the view that all characters that varied were completely unimportant ; this view was powerfully supported by the practical necessity of finding constant characters by which one could identify and correctly name the enormous diversity of living things that were being discovered. As a consequence of this, and since in a small area of the earth's surface such as western Europe (or . in badly known groups of which little material is available) distinct kinds of animals, with no intermediates between them, can be easily recognised, the idea of the constancy of species and the triviality of variation was all-powerful for centuries. Nobody in Britain who looks at the Raven *Corvus corax*, Carrion Crow *C. corone*, Jackdaw *C. monedula*, Rook *C. frugilegus*, Chough *Pyrrhocorax pyrrhocorax*, Jay *Garrulus glandarius*, and Magpie *Pica pica*, can possibly deny that here are very distinct species with different roles to play and no intermediates between them. The occasional appearance of a black-and-white Jackdaw leaves the specimen an undoubted Jackdaw, not an intermediate between the Jackdaw and Magpie, since the essential features have not been altered. The constancy of species was for many years a thoroughly sensible practical attitude, necessary if the diversity of living things was to be accurately described. Such problems as the relation between the Carrion Crow and the Hooded Crow *C. cornix* were not discovered, or were regarded as not affecting the general picture (see also SPECIATION ; and HYBRIDISATION, ZONE OF SECONDARY).

But there was one practical problem that produced very disturbing results, commented on by Lamarck, Erasmus Darwin, and others. Plant and animal breeders had succeeded, by selecting variant individuals and breeding from them, in producing very different forms, which in a few cases were known to be from the same stock. Here was experimental proof that living things could be modified (artificially, at least), and in some cases to such an extent that the end product could not be classed in the same species as the original stock. Many examples, such as the breeds of dogs, might be explained away as due to hybridisation under artificial conditions between several distinct species. In other cases, it was claimed that the results could persist only under the protection of man and had no natural significance. Charles Darwin was the first to give a serious and detailed discussion of animals under domestication, and he showed conclusively that all the breeds (often fantastically different) of the domestic pigeon were descended from the Rock Dove *Columba livia*, that they had been produced by selecting inheritable variations, and that they were far more different than ' good ' species or even genera—indeed, the fantail breed has far more tail feathers than any other known bird. Since they differed in all sorts of characters, it was impossible to assert that there were essential characters that could not be modified, and therefore equally impossible to set any limit to the amount of modification that could be achieved (given sufficient time).

It was still necessary, however, to show that a process of selection was likely to go on in the wild, without human interference. Darwin and Wallace came to the same idea independently. They observed that variation was almost universal in living things, and that some at least was inherited (although the origin of inheritable variation and its modes of inheritance were not elucidated). They observed also that the number of progeny produced by any pair of animals, or by the seeds of any plant, was vastly in excess of what was required to maintain that species in its existing numbers. Consequently, since the numbers of different sorts of living things do remain nearly constant over long periods, there is an enormous mortality. Their hypothesis was that there must be a continual competition for all the necessities of life, that those individuals which possessed even slightly more helpful variant characters than the average would be favoured automatically, that the less fit would be at a disadvantage and leave fewer progeny, and that the helpful variations would therefore spread through the species. This is the hypothesis of natural selection (see NATURAL SELECTION).

Darwin was also able to show that there was no such rigid sterility barrier between species as had been postulated. It had been claimed that species were endowed with a special sterility barrier so that they could remain distinct, and not dissolve into a general welter of hybrids, while mere varieties were always fertile with their parent species. This was not true ; there were all degrees of fertility and sterility, and the species could therefore be regarded as merely a much more distinct variety. He also showed that once the idea of evolution was granted, rudimentary organs could be well explained as remnants from an ancestral condition that were still being slowly selected out or, being truly useless, were no longer acted on by selection and so still persisted. Moreover, a striking discrepancy between the idea of the perfection of living things and their geographical distribution, which had especially struck him while on the *Beagle*, could be readily explained, although wholly inexplicable on the theory of special creation. If the small marine diving fish-eater in the North Atlantic is the Little Auk *Plautus alle* and it was created perfect for its job, why do we not find it doing exactly that job in the Falkland Islands, where the vacancy for it (so to speak) certainly exists, but instead find a diving petrel, *Pelecanoides urinatrix*, remarkably similar to the Little Auk in every way? Why is it that the large herbivores in Africa are antelopes but in Australia are big kangaroos? Why is it that the extinct animals of which fossils are found in South America are closely related to present day South American forms? The answer is, in every case, that local stocks have evolved to fill all the available niches ; as there are no auks (Alcidae) in the far south, the petrels (Procellariiformes) that are present have taken up the auk niche. In the isolated continent of Australia, marsupials have ' adaptively radiated ' to fill all the niches, while in the formerly isolated continent of South America different mammals, those that happened to get there first, have radiated. Conversely, the same niche (or closely similar ones) can be filled in different regions of the world by very different animals. The Mistle Thrush *Turdus viscivorus* in the Palaearctic is paralleled by cuckoo-shrikes *Coracina* spp. in some of the Pacific Islands, and by a different group again in South America. The honeycreepers (Coerebinae) of South and Central America are small nectar and juice suckers paralleled by the sunbirds (Nectariniidae) of most of the Old World tropics, and the smaller honeyeaters (Meliphagidae) in Australasia. These, therefore, show examples of ' convergence '. Adaptive radiation and convergence can be shown throughout the Animal Kingdom, and

perhaps as well in birds as in any other group (see CONVERGENCE).

Darwin also showed, and Wallace elaborated the theme in several books, that the facts of zoogeography (the great zoogeographical regions of the world, and the special characteristics of oceanic and continental islands) assumed a great significance on the theory of evolution, whereas they remained merely inexplicable on the theory of special creation (see DISTRIBUTION, GEOGRAPHICAL ; SPECIATION).

Darwin was not able, in the *Origin of Species*, to do more with the fossil record than to argue that the reason why no transitions between species had been found in it was that it was far more imperfect than anyone had suspected. But fairly soon afterwards the main stages in the evolution of the horse were recognised, and at the present day the record of evolution of the vertebrates especially is (all things considered) remarkably good. In many groups of invertebrates, beautifully continuous time-series of fossils are known, showing gradual transition from one form to another. Birds are singularly disappointing in this respect ; but this is easily accounted for by their mode of life, which does not conduce to fossilisation of their remains. And yet they include one of the most famous of all links, namely *Archaeopteryx*, which perfectly bridges the gap between modern birds and some small dinosaurs (see ARCHAEOPTERYX ; FOSSIL BIRDS ; ORIGIN OF BIRDS).

Lamarck is often set up in opposition to Darwin as the real founder of evolution. However, anyone who actually reads his works (which form a connected whole) will see that he presents his system deductively from physical and chemical principles that were not in accordance with the science of his day, or of ours, and gives no discussion of his biological evidence at all comparable with that in the *Origin of Species*. He received no fame in his own country until it was necessary to find a rival to Darwin ; this was doubly unjust, since his theory could have been in some part recognised as an

Plate 15 · Feeding—Unique Adaptation

Wrybill *Anarhynchus frontalis*, with two eggs (South Island, New Zealand). This small plover species has the unique adaptation of a laterally curved bill, to the right, as an adaptation to seeking food under stones. The photograph also illustrates the nature of the habitat, ground nesting, and cryptic coloration of eggs and plumage. *Phot. M. F. Soper.*

(See articles BILL ; PLOVER (I) ; COLORATION, ADAPTIVE)

alternative to accepted ones in his own day, and the extreme weakness of its observational basis should have been admitted a century later. No impartial account of Lamarck has yet been written in English.

A.J.C.

Darwin, C. 1859. On the Origin of Species. First edition reprinted, with introduction by C. D. Darlington. London 1950.
de Beer, G. R. 1958. A Handbook on Evolution. British Museum (Natural History). London.
Lack, D. 1947. Darwin's Finches. London.
Simpson, G. G. 1951. The Meaning of Evolution. New York (Mentor Books).
Smith, J. Maynard. 1958. The Theory of Evolution. London (Pelican Books).
The foregoing include the classical reference and three recent explanatory books for the general reader. See also references under NATURAL SELECTION; GENETICS; SPECIATION.

EXANTHROPIC: see under EUSYANTHROPIC

EXASPIDEAN: see under ENDASPIDEAN

EXCREMENT; EXCRETA: see DROPPINGS; GUANO; GUANO, CAVE; and ALIMENTARY SYSTEM; EXCRETORY SYSTEM.

EXCRETION, EXTRARENAL: excretion, particularly of salt in the body fluids, otherwise than by the kidneys and urinary passages. Until

---

Plate 16 · Nocturnal Habit

a *Upper left:* Tawny Frogmouth *Podargus strigoides* at night (Western Australia). Note the large eyes, placed for binocular vision, as in owls.
Phot. John Warham, by flashlight.

b *Upper right:* Short-tailed Shearwaters (or Mutton-birds) *Puffinus tenuirostris* waiting to take off from a vantage point to which they have ascended before dawn (Bass Strait, Australia). Many petrel species have similar nocturnal habits at their breeding stations, the only places where they come to land.   *Phot. John Warham, by flashlight.*

c *Lower left:* Oilbird (or Guacharo) *Steatornis caripensis* in its breeding cave (Trinidad). This species flies out in quest of fruit during the night and otherwise lives in dark caves where it navigates by echo-location.
Phot. Russ Kinne, for New York Zoological Society, by flashlight.

d *Lower right:* Barn Owl *Tyto alba* bringing a vole to its nesting hole in a barn (England). The photograph was taken at night from inside the barn. The large eyes, binocular vision, and soft plumage for silent flight are adaptations to nocturnal activity; the bill and feet are those of a predator.   *Phot. John Markham, by flashlight.*

(See articles NOCTURNAL HABITS; PETREL; FROG-MOUTH; OILBIRD; ECHO-LOCATION; OWL; VISION)

---

recently, it was thought that only the kidneys were responsible for salt excretion in birds (see EXCRETORY SYSTEM). This posed an unsolved problem in respect of marine birds, because the avian kidney was known to be even less efficient at eliminating sodium chloride than its mammalian counterpart. A gull *Larus* sp., for example, would have to eliminate more than two litres of urine to remove the salt derived from one litre of sea water.

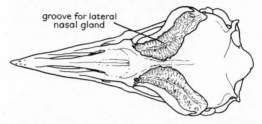

groove for lateral nasal gland

Dorsal view of skull of Adélie Penguin *Pygoscelis adeliae* showing large supraorbital groove for lateral nasal gland. *After Bang, B. G. & Band, F. B. 1959. Bull. John Hopkins Hosp.* 104 (3): 107–149.

In 1957 and 1958 Schmidt-Nielsen and co-workers in the United States discovered, first in the Double-crested Cormorant *Phalacrocorax auritus* and later in the Humboldt Penguin *Spheniscus humboldti*, that salt could be excreted extrarenally in the form of a highly concentrated solution of sodium chloride. The organ responsible for this, a paired structure called the lateral nasal gland (salt gland), is situated on the skull, superior and sometimes anterior to the orbit. Comparative anatomists have long been describing this gland, without knowing its true function (e.g. Matthes). It appears now that the lateral nasal glands are well developed in all marine birds (Schmidt-Nielsen & Ragnar) and also in marine reptiles. The duct of each gland conveys the concentrated salt solution to the nasal cavity, from whence it flows through the external nares to the tip of the bill. In some species of bird (e.g. cormorants *Phalacrocorax* spp. and gannets *Sula* spp.), the external nares are closed in the adult; in such cases the fluid trickles from the internal nares in the roof of the mouth to the tip of the bill. Unlike the kidney, the lateral nasal gland functions only when the need to eliminate salt arises. There are therefore times of intensive activity, such as after feeding at sea, and times of quiescence when no salt will be excreted.

The efficiency of this gland can be tested easily and dramatically. Ten minutes after 5 grams of sodium chloride were given to a Humboldt Penguin weighing 5·8 kilograms, a clear colourless liquid started to drip from the tip of the bill (Schmidt-Nielsen & Sladen). This was shaken away with the characteristic head-shaking movement common to most sea birds. Within four hours a total of 80 millilitres of liquid was collected from the bill. The concentration of sodium chloride averaged 750 m.equiv./litre, and thus two-thirds of the salt fed to the bird had been eliminated through the nose. The kidney proved to be only one-tenth as efficient as the lateral nasal gland during the same period of time.

The gland has many lobes, and these contain several thousand branched tubules radiating from a central duct. Each tubule is surrounded by capillaries through which the blood flows in the opposite direction to the flow of salt secretion. This countercurrent is thought to facilitate the transfer of salt from the blood to the tubule. The lateral nasal gland is a much simpler organ than the kidney. It can do no more than secrete sodium chloride, with a trace of potassium in addition. In fact, if a hypertonic solution of sucrose is injected intravenously into a cormorant, the lateral nasal gland will respond to this osmotic load in the same way as to a salt load, i.e. by eliminating sodium chloride (Schmidt-Nielsen, Jorgensen, & Osaki).

Closely related species of diverse habits show differences in the relative size of the nasal glands, and these differences may be reflected in the shape of the skull ; osteological characters formerly thought to be of primary taxonomic value thus prove to be adaptive (see e.g. under PLOVER).

W.J.L.S.

Schmidt-Nielsen, K., Jorgensen, C. B., & Osaki, H. 1958. Extrarenal salt excretion in birds. Amer. J. Physiol. 193 : 101–107.
Schmidt-Nielsen, K. & Sladen, W. J. L. 1958. Nasal salt secretion in the Humboldt Penguin. Nature 181 : 1217–1218.
Schmidt-Nielsen, K. & Fange, R. 1958. The function of the salt gland in the Brown Pelican. Auk 75 : 282–289.
Matthes, E. 1934. Geruchsorgane. In Bolk, Göppert, Kallius, & Lubosch (eds.). Handbuch der vergleichende Anatomie der Wirbeltiere vol. 2 (2). Vienna.

EXCRETORY SYSTEM: the organs responsible for excreting waste material containing nitrogen from the bird's blood and passing it out of the body, i.e. the paired, elongated kidneys each consisting of three main lobes in most birds ; but four lobes are found in Ciconiiformes and Charadrii, while kiwis *Apteryx* spp. have five. The kidneys lie symmetrically (except in Gaviidae and Podicipitidae) on the dorsal aspect of the body cavity below the synsacrum. The caudal lobes of the two kidneys are fused in the middle line in the Heron *Ardea cinerea*, Chestnut-bellied Heron *Agamia agami*, Puffin *Fratercula arctica* and penguins (Sphenisciidae), and may frequently be so in many other birds. Each kidney lobe is supplied with blood from a renal artery and a branch of the renal-portal vein (see VASCULAR SYSTEM). The subdivisions of the renal-portal veins (the interlobular veins) serve, together with the urine-collecting ducts that accompany them, to subdivide the kidney tissue into numerous lobules ; the vessels run round the periphery of each lobule, and in the central region of each lobule there is a relatively large intralobular vein. The kidney tissue proper consists of a large number of convoluted and looping uriniferous tubules, which at one end join the peripheral urine-collecting ducts and at the other terminate in a Malpighian body or glomerulus, each tubule and its Malpighian body being known as a nephron. The Malpighian bodies encircle the intralobular veins : they are very small and very numerous in birds compared with mammals, varying from 400 per cubic millimetre in some African weavers (Ploceidae) to about 90 per c.mm. in the Rook *Corvus frugilegus*—whereas in mammals there are only about 4–15 per c.mm. The total number of nephrons present in both kidneys may vary from nearly two million in ducks (Anatidae) to some 30 000 in small passerines ; the kidneys tend to be larger in aquatic and marsh birds than in others. The renal arteries break up into fine intralobular arteries that entwine the uriniferous tubules and ultimately join the interlobular veins. Capillaries from these veins also ramify amongst the uriniferous tubules and enter the intralobular veins, which in turn finally unite to form the renal vein (see also VASCULAR SYSTEM ; and DEVELOPMENT, EMBRYONIC).

The fluid extracted from the blood by the nephrons—the urine—passes into collecting ducts that unite to form the ureters, and through them the urine reaches that part of the cloaca known as the urodaeum, to be voided by the bird to the exterior (see ALIMENTARY SYSTEM ; REPRODUCTIVE SYSTEM). There is in birds no urinary bladder as there is in mammals.

Avian urine, although subject to considerable variation, is normally cream-coloured and rich in mucoid substances and urates. The high concentration of urates (uric acid) accounts for over 60 per cent of the total nitrogen excreted and is highly characteristic. After some resorption of water in the cloaca, uric acid is deposited as whitish crystals that are frequently seen mingled with the faeces of birds (see DROPPINGS ; GUANO).

For elimination of salts by the nasal glands of marine birds see EXCRETION, EXTRARENAL.

E.T.B.F.

EXOCCIPITAL: a paired bone of the skull (see SKELETON).

EXOCRINE: see under ENDOCRINE SYSTEM

EXOTIC: applied to species, etc., meaning that these are in the natural course alien to the area under reference.

EXPECTATION OF LIFE: see LIFE, EXPECTATION OF

EXPLOITATION: see UTILISATION BY MAN

EXTERMINATION: see EXTINCT BIRDS

EXTEROCEPTIVE: see SENSES

EXTINCT BIRDS: species or well-defined sub-species (races) that have entirely ceased to exist within historic times. For those that died out in earlier geological periods, see FOSSIL BIRDS ; and for those, still surviving, that seem to be in imminent danger of extinction, see VANISHING BIRDS.

Among the birds that became extinct in geologically recent and historic times are two whole orders of large running birds. These are the Aepyornithiformes (family Aepyornithidae) of Madagascar (see ELEPHANT-BIRD), and the Dinornithiformes (families Dinornithidae and Anomalopterygidae) of New Zealand (see MOA) ; of the former, at least one species is believed to have survived until about 1649 ; and of the latter at least one considerably later (see below). In theses instances abundant sub-fossil remains have provided the basis of our knowledge ; but in the absence of such evidence, species that disappeared before 1600 must be regarded as pre-historic from the ornithological point of view, and thus as palaeospecies. There is no good evidence of the colours of any bird extinct before 1600 ; but three psittacids extinct between 1600 and 1680 have been named on good descriptions, without bones.

Of birds that have become extinct within the span of ornithologically recorded history, the Dodo *Raphus cucullatus* of Mauritius is the proverbial example ; it died out in the seventeenth century, and the remaining members of this family of flight-less pigeons (Raphidae), on other islands of the group, in the eighteenth (see DODO). Another well-known example is the flightless Great Auk *Pinguinus impennis* of the North Atlantic, surviving into the nineteenth century. Most spectacular of all, perhaps, is the Passenger Pigeon *Ectopistes migratorius* of North America, because it existed in millions well into the nineteenth century and yet had become extinct early in the twentieth. At about the same time, the only North American parrot species, the Carolina Parakeet *Conuropsis carolinensis* also ceased to exist. The parrots as a family (Psittacidae) have lost heavily in representation ; so also have the rails (Rallidae), the pigeons (Columbidae), the Hawaiian honey-creepers (Drepanididae), and the ducks (Anatidae). Among the last, the Labrador Duck *Camptorhynchus*

labradorius was known only as a winter visitor farther south, and its former native area is purely conjectural; the Crested Shelduck *Tadorna cristata* of Korea and the Pink-headed Duck *Rhodonessa caryophyllacea* of India are two of the most recent losses of bird species.

The total number of extinctions, however, is much too large to cover here except in summary form. This is done below, in turn systematically, geographically, and chronologically. Finally, the causes of extinction are generally discussed.

Systematic List. Since 1680, which was probably the year before the last Dodo *Raphus cucullatus* lived on Mauritius, 78 full species and 49 well-marked subspecies or races of birds have probably become extinct. In a systematic order by families, and with approximate years of extinction, these are :

(A) Full species

Anomalopterygidae
  1 *Megalapteryx didina* 1773
Hydrobatidae
  2 *Oceanodroma macrodactyla* 1912
Phalacrocoracidae
  3 *Phalacrocorax perspicillatus* 1852
Ardeidae
  4 *Nycticorax megacephalus* 1730
Anatidae
  5 *Tadorna cristata* 1943
  6 *Rhodonessa caryophyllacea* 1944
  7 *Camptorhynchus labradorius* 1875
  8 *Mergus australis* 1905
Falconidae
  9 *Caracara lutosa* 1900
Phasianidae
  10 *Ophyrsia superciliosa* 1868
Rallidae
  11 *Rallus ecaudata* 1925
  12 *R. wakensis* 1945
  13 *R. dieffenbachii* 1840
  14 *R. modestus* 1900
  15 *Tricholimnas lafresnayanus* 1904
  16 *Nesoclopeus poecilopterus* 1890
  17 *Aphanapteryx leguati* 1730
  18 *Porzanula palmeri* 1944
  19 *Pennula sandwichensis* 1893
  20 *Aphanolimnas monasa* 1828
  21 *Pareudiastes pacificus* 1873
Scolopacidae
  22 *Prosobonia leucoptera* 1777
Glareolidae
  23 *Cursorius bitorquatus* 1900
Alcidae
  24 *Pinguinus impennis* 1844
Columbidae
  25 *Alectroenas nitidissima* 1830
  26 *Columba versicolor* 1889
  27 *Ectopistes migratorius* 1914
  28 *Gallicolumba ferruginea* 1774
  29 *Microgoura meeki* 1904
Raphidae
  30 *Raphus cucullatus* 1681
  31 *R. solitarius* 1746
  32 *Pezophaps solitaria* 1791

Psittacidae
33 *Charmosyna diadema* 1860
34 *Geopsittacus occidentalis* 1935
35 *Cyanoramphus zealandicus* 1844
36 *C. ulietanus* 1774
37 *Mascarinus mascarinus* 1834
38 *Necropsittacus rodricanus* 1730
39 *Psittacula exsul* 1875
40 *Amazona violacea* 1722
41 *A. martinicana* 1722
42 *Aratinga labati* 1722
43 *Conuropsis carolinensis* 1914
44 *Ara tricolor* 1885
45 *A. gossei* 1765
46 *A. erythrocephala* 1810
47 *A. guadeloupensis* 1722
48 *A. atwoodi* 1791

Cuculidae
49 *Coua delalandei* 1930

Strigidae
50 *Otus commersoni* 1837
51 *Athene murivora* 1730

Alcedinidae
52 *Halcyon miyakoensis* 1887

Xenicidae
53 *Xenicus lyalli* 1894

Muscicapidae
54 *Turdus ulietensis* 1774
55 *Zoothera terrestris* 1828
56 *Amytornis goyderi* 1875

Zosteropidae
57 *Zosterops semiflava* 1940
58 *Z. strenua* 1918

Meliphagidae
59 *Moho bishopi* 1915
60 *M. nobilis* 1934
61 *M. apicalis* 1837
62 *Chaetoptila angustipluma* 1859

Drepanididae
63 *Loxops sagittirostris* 1900
64 *Hemignathus obscurus* 1895
65 *Psittirostra palmeri* 1896
66 *P. flaviceps* 1891
67 *P. kona* 1894
68 *Ciridops anna* 1892
69 *Drepanis pacifica* 1898
70 *D. funerea* 1907

Fringillidae
71 *Chaunoproctus ferreirostris* 1890

Ploceidae
72 *Neospiza concolor* 1888
73 *Foudia bruante* 1776

Sturnidae
74 *Aplonis corvina* 1828
75 *A. mavornata* 1774
76 *Fregilupus rodericanus* 1832
77 *F. varius* 1862

Callaeidae
78 *Heteralocha acutirostris* 1907

With the loss of these species, 26 genera (19 non-passerine and 7 passerine) have ceased to be represented among living birds ; and likewise the families Anomalopterygidae (see MOA) and Raphidae (see DODO).

(B)   Races of surviving species (some less well-marked or disputed races excluded)

Dromaiidae
1 *Dromaius novaehollandiae diemenensis* 1838
2 *D.n. diemenianus* 1803

Procellariidae
3 *Pterodroma hasitata caribbaea* 1880

Threskiornithidae
4 *Lampribis olivacea rothschildi* 1901

Anatidae
5 *Anas strepera couesi* 1874

Tetraonidae
6 *Tympanuchus cupido cupido* 1926

Phasianidae
7 *Coturnix novaezelandiae novaezelandiae* 1875

Rallidae
8 *Rallus pectoralis muelleri* 1865
9 *Amaurolimnas concolor concolor* 1890
10 *Poliolimnas cinereus brevipes* 1925
11 *Porphyriornis nesiotis nesiotis* 1872
12 *Porphyrio porphyrio albus* 1834

Scolopacidae
13 *Aechmorhynchus cancellatus cancellatus* 1778

Columbidae
14 *Hemiphaga novaeseelandiae spadicea* 1801
15 *Columba vitiensis godmanae* 1790
16 *C. inornata wetmorei* 1927

Psittacidae
17 *Nestor meridionalis productus* 1831
18 *Cyanoramphus novaezelandiae subflavescens* 1869
19 *C.n. erythrotis* 1913
20 *Psittacula eupatria wardi* 1906
21 *Amazona vittata gracilipes* 1899
22 *Aratinga chloroptera maugei* 1892

Strigidae
23 *Sceloglaux albifacies rufifacies* 1890
24 *Speotyto cunicularia amaura* 1890
25 *S.c. guadeloupensis* 1890

Caprimulgidae
26 *Siphonorhis americanus americanus* 1859

Picidae
27 *Colaptes cafer rufipileus* 1906
28 *Campephilus principalis principalis* 1952

Troglodytidae
29 *Thryomanes bewickii brevicauda* 1897
30 *Troglodytes aedon guadeloupensis* 1914
31 *T.a. martinicensis* 1886

Muscicapidae
32 *Phaeornis obscurus lanaiensis* 1931
33 *P.o. rutha* 1936
34 *P.o. oahensis* 1825
35 *Turdus poliocephalus vinitinctus* 1918
36 *Acrocephalus familiaris familiaris* 1923
37 *Gerygone igata insularis* 1919
38 *Pomarea nigra tabuensis* 1773
39 *Rhipidura fuliginosa cervina* 1928

Meliphagidae
40 *Anthornis melanura melanocephala* 1906

Emberizidae
41 *Pipilo erythropthalmus consobrinus* 1897

Fringillidae
42 *Geospiza magnirostris magnirostris* 1835
43 *Loxigilla portoricensis grandis* 1880

Drepanididae
    44 *Loxops maculata montana* 1937
    45 *L.m. flammea* 1949
    46 *Hemignathus lucidus affinis* 1896
    47 *H.l. lucidus* 1860
    48 *Himatione sanguinea freethii* 1923
Sturnidae
    49 *Aplonis fuscus hullianus* 1918

Geographical Review. By faunas, and classifying the last places of extinction of the forms under continental masses, large islands, and small islands (under about 1000 square miles), we have :

HOLARCTIC
(10 spp. + 3 subspp. = 10 per cent of total extinct forms).
NEARCTIC
Continental A 7, 27, 43 ; B 6, 28
PALAEARCTIC
Continental A 5
Small islands
    Eldey, Iceland A 24
    Iwo Jima B 10
    Ryukyu I. A 52
    Bonin I. A 26, 55, 71
    Bering I. A 3

ETHIOPIAN AND MALAGASY
(17 spp. + 2 subspp. = 15 per cent)
ETHIOPIAN
Small islands
    Principe B 4
    São Tomé A 72
MALAGASY
Large island
    Madagascar A 49
Small islands
    Seychelles A 57 ; B 20
    Réunion A 31, 37, 73, 76
    Mauritius A 25, 30, 50
    Rodriguez A 4, 17, 32, 38, 39, 51, 76

ORIENTAL (3 spp. = 2½ per cent)
Continental A 6, 10, 23

AUSTRALASIAN AND POLYNESIAN
(38 spp. + 28 subspp. = 52 per cent)
MAIN FAUNA
Continental A 34, 56
Large islands
    New Caledonia A 15, 33
    Choiseul A 29
    Kangaroo I. B 2
    Tasmania B 1
    Fiji A 16
Small islands
    Tanna, New Hebrides A 28
    Norfolk B 14, 17
    Lord Howe A 58 ; B 12, 15, 18, 35, 37, 39, 49
    Tongatabu B 38
    Savaii (Samoa) A 21
    Tahiti A 11, 22, 35
    Raiatea A 36, 54
    mysterious island, probably in Society I. A 75
    Kusaie (Carolines) A 20, 74
    Wake I. A 12
    Christmas I. (Line I.) B 13
    Washington I. (Fannings) B 5

NEW ZEALAND
Large islands
    Both main islands B 7
    North Island A 78 ; B 23
    South Island A 1
Small islands
    Chatham I. A 13, 14 ; B 40
    Auckland I. A 8 ; B 8
    Stephen I. A 53
    Macquarie B 19
HAWAIIAN
Large island
    Hawaii A 19, 60, 62, 63, 64, 65, 66, 67, 68, 69
Small islands
    Maui B 46
    Lanai B 32, 44
    Molokai A 59, 70 ; B 33, 45
    Oahu A 61 ; B 43, 47
    Laysan B 36, 48
    Midway A 18

NEOTROPICAL (10 spp. + 16 subspp. = 20½ per cent)
Large islands
    Cuba A 44
    Jamaica A 45, 46 ; B 3, 9, 26
    Puerto Rico B 16, 22
Small islands
    Chatham and Charles I. (Galápagos) B 42
    Guadalupe I. (Baja California) A 2, 9 ; B 27, 29, 41
    Culebra I. (Puerto Rico) B 21
    St Christopher B 43
    Antigua B 24
    Guadeloupe, Martinique, and ? Dominica A 47
    Guadeloupe A 40, 42 ; B 25, 30
    Martinique A 41 ; B 31
    Dominica A 48
    Tristan da Cunha (considered in this fauna) B 11

Summary	Species	Races	Total	Per cent
Continental	9	2	11	9
Large islands	20	9	29	23
Small islands	49	38	87	68
	78	49	127	100

More than half the extinctions have been from the Australasian (including Polynesian) fauna. Two-thirds of them have been from islands of under 1000 square miles ; less than a tenth from continents.

Chronology. The chronology of extinction since 1680 can be summarised thus :

	Species	Races	Total	Per cent
1680–1700	1		1	1
1701–1750	9		9	7
1751–1800	10	3	13	10
1801–1850	12	7	19	15
1851–1900	27	19	46	36
1901–1950	19	19	38	30
after 1950		1	1	1
	78	49	127	100

The last full species extinguished was the Wake Island Rail (A 12) in 1945 ; the last race was the U.S. Ivory-billed Woodpecker (B 28) in 1952. The worst period was the 23 years 1885–1907 when 24 species and 14 races, 38 forms in all, became extinct.

What were probably the last survivors of 4 species (A 6, 27, 37, 43) and 2 races (B 11, 17) died in captivity. The last Passenger Pigeon (A 27) died in the Cincinnati Zoo probably at 1 p.m. (local time) on 1 September 1914. Although they were not in captivity, the hour of doom of the last pair of Great Auks (A 24) is known almost as exactly—the afternoon of 3 or, more probably, 4 June 1844.

Of these extinct forms of birds, no skins exist of as many as 14. We have included only those ' skinless wonders ' that are based on reliable field descriptions, pictures, or bones. A few were collected, but their skins have been lost. We have omitted many hypothetical birds from our lists, which are compiled from many sources and involve a re-analysis of the excellent and scholarly work of Greenway (1958). The totals of 78 species and 49 races contain 57 and 45 that have certainly lived and are as certainly extinct as far as zoological certainty can go. The rest can be categorised thus :

(*a*) 5 parrots (Psittacidae) from the West Indies which certainly have not existed since the eighteenth century but which were described in detail and with evident care from first-hand observation by reliable observers, principally Labat and Atwood (A 40, 41, 42, 47, 48).

(*b*) 2 species and 1 race both reliably described and illustrated, but of which no skin survives and with which no bone has yet been identified (A 31, 54 ; B 15).

(*c*) 1 New Zealand moa, known extensively from fossil or sub-fossil bones, of which the survival until the eighteenth century has been determined from archaeological evidence (A 1).

(*d*) 4 Rodriguez species based on descriptions collated with bones (A 4, 32, 38, 51).

(*e*) 1 species, a rail from Rodriguez, based on both descriptions and illustration, collated with bones (A 17). (Another in this category, the Broad-billed Parrot *Lophopsittacus mauritanus*, was last seen on Mauritius in 1638, before the Dodo became extinct).

(*f*) 8 species and 3 races of which the continued survival is faintly possible but in our opinion (and that of others) most unlikely. These are the Guadalupe Storm Petrel (A 2), the Himalayan Mountain Quail (A 10), the New Caledonian Wood Rail (A 15), Jerdon's Courser (A 23), the Night Parrot of Australia (A 34), Delalande's Coucal of Madagascar (A 49), and the Chestnut-flanked White-eye of the Seychelles (A 57) ; also the continental (U.S.) race of the Ivory-billed Woodpecker (B 28), and the Lanai Aauwahio (B 44) and Molokai Aauwahio (B 45) of Hawaii.

There are many other birds, out of at least 100 full species with a present world population of under 2000 (Fisher 1961), that might well figure in this category, such as *Struthio camelus syriacus*, *Athene blewitti*, *Asthenes sclateri* (an oven-bird), *Ramphocinclus brachyurus brachyurus* (a thrasher), *Trichocichla rufa* (a sylviine), *Metabolus rugensis* (a monarchine flycatcher), and the so-called 'Thrush' *Turnagra capensis* of New Zealand. We have been warned, however, by several birds that have been confidently reported as extinct, only to be brought back from the dead by new explorations or more intensive field surveys. Among these the Takahe *Notornis mantelli*, a flightless rail of New Zealand, was widely thought to have died out around 1898 ; it was rediscovered in 1948. The Cahow *Pterodroma cahow*, a petrel species breeding on Bermuda, was rediscovered in 1916, having gone unnoticed since its populous days in the early seventeenth century. The Pink Pigeon *Columba mayeri* of Mauritius, now quite common, was thought to be extinct by Rothschild (1907). The Seychelles Island Owl *Otus insularis* was reported in 1959 after having been last heard in 1906 and marked extinct by Greenway (1958). The Puerto Rican Whip-poor-will *Caprimulgus noctitherus*, described in 1919 from cave bones and subsequently identified with an earlier skin, was not encountered again until 1961, when several were heard, one sound-recorded, and one collected. The Noisy (or Western) Scrubbird *Atrichornis clamosus* of southwestern Australia was last collected in 1889 ; although thought to have been heard in 1920, it was widely believed extinct until rediscovered and sound-recorded in 1961. The Spiny Babbler *Acanthoptila nipalensis* was collected in Nepal in 1948, no other specimen having been taken for over a century.

Of the extinct birds here listed, 16 full species and 6 races were observed or collected on one occasion or at most by one expedition only. The Cook Pacific voyages scored no less than 7 firsts that were also lasts (A 22, 28, 36, 54, 75 ; B 13, 38). Kittlitz got 3 in the Pacific in 1828 (A 20, 55, 74). Darwin got one in the Galápagos in 1835 (B 42). There are scores of other bird species more lately described that have been collected only once ; quite a number are based on unique specimens. Their status can be determined only by history ; but some will surely prove also to be extinct.

(*Postscript.* Two years having elapsed since the numbering of these birds, some changes in the list had occurred by the time of final proof correction at the beginning of 1964. To avoid extensive re-numbering, these are noted separately here ; they but slightly affect the figures in the analysis. (A) 34 and (A) 36 have been proved to be still surviving ; (B) 28 and (B) 45 have also to be deleted, although the evidence for their survival is not fully confirmed. To be added are (A) 28a, a blue dove as yet unnamed which became extinct around 1775 on St Helena ; (B) 1a *Struthio camelus syriacus* 1940, Arabia ; (B) 8a *Rallus philippensis macquariensis* 1894, Macquarie I. ; (B) 20a *Psittacula krameri agnes* 1700, Réunion I. ; and (B) 36a *Bowdleria punctata rufescens* 1900, Chatham I. (A) 57 should be moved to (B) 39a as it is a race of the surviving *Z. mayottensis* of the Comoro Is.)

Causes of Extinction. Before we can discuss how far man has been the agent of destruction of some of the 78 full species of birds, we must examine the rate of natural extinction of birds in an epoch in which man could have played no significant part. Such an epoch is the Pleistocene, a period of about 2 million years, held to end about 10 000 years ago, during which glaciations of varying intensity advanced from the poles towards the Equator, and retreated about a dozen times. Four of the glacia-tions were very severe. On the array of flowering plants upon the surface of the world the Pleistocene had such a catastrophic effect (Good 1953) as ' com-pletely to upset, over much of their range, the balance between plant and habitat '. The number of plant species was fiercely reduced ; and so also, largely in consequence, certainly the number of land mammal species, and probably the number of bird species. Brodkorb (1960) suggests that the avifauna may have been reduced by as much as 25 per cent, and shows that within the avifauna of a particular geological time the average geological longevity of a species is equal to the time needed to replace half the fauna when such longevities are normally distributed, and roughly equal to it when the longevity curve is somewhat skewed ; it approximates to $yn/2e$ where y is the age of the avifauna B.P. (before present), n the number of species identified in it, and e the number of those species now extinct.

Using this formula, Fisher (in press) has examined over ten fossil avifaunas ranging in date from the Blancan (Villefranchian) of North America (about 2 000 000 B.P.) to that of Rancho la Brea (about 14 500 B.P.), has compared them with the post-dodo avifauna, and has found an expectation of species life progressively declining from about 1 500 000 years in the early Pleistocene to about 40 000 at Rancho, at the very end of the Pleistocene. This decline was of course natural. But in the 284 years since 1680 the expectation of species life has become

about 16 000 years, assuming that about 8500 full species were still living in 1962. This suggests that the operations of man in his most civilised period have probably reduced species life by about three-fifths. Put another way, less than half the birds lately extinct may have become extinct naturally, more than half as the consequence of disturbance or destruction of habitat, or direct predation, by man.

An analysis of the certain or probably primary causes of extinction of the 78 lately extinct full species (A group) is as follows :

(a) Extinct by hunting or (in one case, the Great Auk) hunting and collecting : 1, 3, 9, 12, 24, 25, 27, 30, 31, 32, 43, ?44, ?49 (total 13, 2 on continents)

(b) Extinct primarily by human destruction of habitat : 14, 40, 41, 42, 47, ?57, ?60, ?61, ?62, ?63, ?64, ?69, ?70, 78 (total 14)

(c) Extinct by predation of cats, rats, and other human symbiotes : ?2, ?8, ?11, ?13, 18, ?20, 53, ?55, ?58, ?59, ?74 (total 11)

(d) Extinction not, in present knowledge, certainly attributable directly or indirectly to man : 4, 5, 6, 7, 10, 15, 16, 17, 19, 21, 22, 23, 26, 28, 29, 33, 34, 35, 36, 37, 38, 39, 45, 46, 48, 50, 51, 52, 54, 56, 65, 66, 67, 68, 71, 72, 73, 75, 76, 77 (total 40, 7 on continents)

The analysis confirms that there is fairly strong direct proof that nearly half the birds extinct since 1680 were destroyed by man. The rest cannot be formally proved to have been so, although no account has been taken of extinction as a consequence of unsuccessful competition with introduced species, which may have affected a few in category (d), e.g. the Hawaiian species 19, 65, 66, 67, and 68. The result fits that of the faunal analysis quite well. It is interesting to note that man is surely responsible for the end of only 2 of the 9 extinct continental species —the Passenger Pigeon (A 27) and Carolina Parrakeet (A 43) ; and that 88 per cent of the extinctions of full species have been on large and small islands, where the natural evolution rate is probably greater and the expectation of species life lower than that on con-tinents.

A policy of conservation must take note of these evolutionary issues. No bird has provedly become extinct since 1945. We may in future be able to prevent the extinction not only of species dying out because of us, but also of species dying out because of nature, perhaps with the aid of zoos, aviaries, and managed parks. It certainly seems likely that an insurance man can give a better quotation for a species' life now than he could at any time in the last graceless quarter of a millennium.   J.F.

Brodkorb, P. 1960. How many species of birds have existed ? Bull. Fla. State Mus. Biol. Sci. 5 : 41-53.

Fisher, J. 1961. Bird species in danger of extinction. Internat. Zoo Yearbook 2 : 280–287.

Fisher, J. (in press). The expectation of geological life of bird species in and after the Pleistocene.

Good, R. 1953. The Geography of the Flowering Plants. London.

Greenway, J. C., Jr. 1958. Extinct and Vanishing Birds of the World. New York.

Howard, H. 1960. Significance of carbon-14 dates for Rancho la Brea. Science 131 : 712–714.

Rothschild, W. 1907. Extinct Birds. London.

Schorger, A. W. 1955. The Passenger Pigeon, its Natural History and Extinction. Madison, Wis.

Howard, H. 1962. A census of individual pits at Rancho la Brea. Los Angeles Co. Mus. Contrib. Sci. no. 58.

EYAS: special term (also ' eyass ' ; plural ' eyasses ') for a nestling falcon or hawk, used especially of those species taken by falconers for training (see FALCONRY).

EYE: see VISION

EYELASH: a bristle (modified feather) resembling a mammalian eyelash (hair) in situation and appearance ; such eyelashes occur in a few groups of birds, e.g. conspicuously in hornbills (Bucerotidae), many species of cuckoos (Cuculidae), eagle owls *Bubo* spp., and the Ostrich *Struthio camelus*. See also PLUMAGE.

EYREAN: see AUSTRALASIAN REGION

EYRIE: term (also ' eyry ', ' aerie ', ' aery ') for the nest of a bird-of-prey, often an eagle *Aquila* sp., etc. (see also under FALCONRY).

F

FABULOUS BIRDS: kinds of birds that the human imagination has conjured up as religious, magical, or poetic symbols. This is apart from the role played by real species of birds in folklore, heraldry, witchcraft, and totemism (see FOLKLORE; HERALDIC BIRDS; OMENS, BIRDS AS).

The concept of fabulous birds, as of all zoological symbols, originated in primitive man's personification of the forces of nature. As his mind evolved he became increasingly aware of his aloneness in a mysterious and often hostile universe. Abstract concepts of a god or protecting power were at this time beyond his range, and it was thus natural that he should take the familiar creatures of his environment as the basis of elaborate symbols representing the good and evil powers that ruled his life. The more sinister zoological symbols, such as the dragon, belonged to the earth, and especially to the dark subterranean world of evil spirits. Birds, on the other hand, belonged to the sky—an ethereal region of purity and light. Fabulous birds were thus generally symbols of hope and regeneration, representing benevolent forces and the highest aspirations of mankind.

The first fabulous birds of any importance appeared in the Middle and Far East. The chief was Garuda, a gigantic bird-of-prey who, in Hindu mythology, was believed to bear the sun-god Vishnu on his daily journey across the sky. The earliest concepts of Garuda were almost certainly purely avian, and it seems probable that he was a composite symbol derived from observations of such real birds as Pallas's Fishing Eagle *Haliaetus leucoryphus*, the Crested Serpent Eagle *Spilornis cheela*, the Lämmergeier *Gypaetus barbatus*, and the Brahminy Kite *Haliastur indus*. Later, however, he began to be depicted with human arms and legs, the avian characters being restricted to a white face, a golden body, and red wings. Garuda was a relentless enemy of serpents, which were a symbol of evil, and he was also supposed to carry elephants and tortoises to the summits of high mountains to devour them. The cult of Garuda spread eastward from India and he became a much venerated symbol in Indo-China, Siam, and Cambodia. In Malaya he was known as Gerda, and according to Ingersoll the men of Perak still say when a cloud obscures the sun; 'Gerda is spreading his wings to dry.' The cult of Garuda even reached Japan, where he was variously known as Gario, Bingacho, or Karobinga; but here he changed his sex and became half woman, half bird, a sort of feathered angel with the legs of a crane.

Westwards from India several bird-gods and demi-gods shared affinities with Garuda, and many have been descended from him. The most important was the early Persian Senmurv, half bird, half mammal, which was regarded as an elemental connecting link between heaven and earth. The wings, body, and tail of the Senmurv were those of a bird, but it was also supposed to have teeth; and the female of the species was believed to suckle its young. Like Garuda, it was an enemy of serpents and a benefactor of mankind, making its home in a tree of which the seeds would cure all evil. Every time the Senmurv alighted in the tree its branches used to shake and thousands of these seeds were scattered through the world.

In later Persian mythology the Senmurv was replaced by the Simurg. This was a giant bird which made its nest on Mount Alburs, on a peak that touched the sky. It was regarded as a symbol of strength and wisdom, a friend of the sick and the poor, and a comforter of mankind. Some beliefs concerning the Simurg show affinities with the Phoenix legend. For instance, it was reputed to live 1700 years, and when at the end of that time the young was hatched, the parent of the same sex (some versions of the legend say the opposite sex) burnt itself to death. The Simurg may also be identified with the Anka of Arabic lore, and it shares some of the characters of the Rukh or Roc.

The latter was a huge bird which inhabited an island in the Indian Ocean (usually identified with Madagascar), and was reputed to carry off elephants in its claws. The fronds of the exceptionally large palm *Sagus ruffia* were once regarded as the feathers of the Rukh, and the giant eggs of the extinct Madagascan bird *Aepyornis maximus*, each of which will hold over two gallons of liquid (see ELEPHANT-BIRD), may also have played a part in the development of the legend as recounted in the *Thousand and One Nights*, the second and fifth voyages of Es-Sindibad of the Sea.

The most famous and poetic of all fabulous birds is the Phoenix. Pliny describes it as being the size of an eagle, with a gold neck, purple body, azure tail, and crested head. It has been identified by different ornithologists with the Purple Heron *Ardea purpurea*, the Bateleur Eagle *Terathopius ecaudatus*, the Golden Pheasant *Chrysolophus pictus*, or one or other of the various species of parrots (Psittacidae) or birds-of-paradise (Paradisaeidae), but like other fabulous birds it is probably a composite symbol derived from many sources. There was said to be only one Phoenix in the world at a time, and it dwelt in paradise, a land of infinite beauty lying beyond the eastern horizon. Every thousand years (some versions of the legend say 350, 500, or 1461 years) the Phoenix left paradise and flew westwards to die. It collected aromatic plants on the way from the spice groves of Arabia, and built itself a nest in the top of a tall palm tree. Here, on the first dawn after its journey, it sang a song of such surpassing beauty that the sun-god stopped his chariot to listen. When he whipped up his horses again sparks from their hooves set fire to the nest of the Phoenix, and it died on a blazing aromatic funeral pyre. The new Phoenix grew from a worm which was found in the ashes of the nest, and flew back to paradise for its own allotted life span of a thousand years.

The fabulous birds of the west were in general less benevolent than their eastern counterparts. In Greek times the hideous harpies, with their birds' faces and claws, were universally regarded as evil and destructive beings ; even the glamorous sirens, variously depicted as birds with womens' heads or women with birds' legs, used their charms to lure mariners to destruction rather than to succour them in their dangerous calling. More lethal still were the Stymphalian birds, which were dealt with so effectively by Hercules in the sixth of his labours. These were man-eating birds, a mixture of stork, crane, and eagle, armed with arrow-like feathers that wounded all who came within their range.

In conclusion a few less publicised fabulous birds must be briefly mentioned. One of the most magnificent was the Fung-whang, or Feng Huang, the Chinese Phoenix. This was known by the Taoists as the scarlet bird, and was one of the four fabulous creatures symbolising the four quarters of the heavens. Representations of the Fung-whang on Chinese screens and elsewhere suggest that its ancestry owes a good deal to the Peacock *Pavo cristatus*.

In Japan there is still a belief in a race of fabulous birds known as Tengus. The king of the Tengus is said to have the wings and claws of a giant eagle, a long red beak, and exceptionally piercing eyes. The Tengus are nature spirits, not positively evil but decidedly mischievous. They are very skilled in dancing and the use of arms, and sometimes take possession of human victims who, although half-demented, acquire their prowess in these activities while under their influence.

In ancient Sumer a huge divine eagle named Imgig was the royal symbol of Ur. The bird-god Horus of ancient Egypt, almost certainly derived from the Egyptian form of the Black Kite *Milvus migrans aegyptius*, was perhaps the most ancient god of the Egyptian pantheon. In Russia violent winds are still said to be produced by the wings of the colossal eagle-demon Vikhar flying overhead. Similar associations between violent winds and fabulous birds are found in the folklore of many primitive peoples and peasant communities, especially in northern Europe and among the North American Indians.   R.C.

Carrington, R. 1957. Mermaids and Mastodons. London.
Gubernatis, Angelo de. 1872. Zoological Mythology, or Legends of Animals, vol. 2. London.
Hulme, F. E. 1895. Natural History Lore and Legend. London.
Ingersoll, E. 1923. Birds in Legend, Fable and Folklore. New York, London, etc.
Lum, P. 1952. Fabulous Beasts. London.

FACIES : among other meanings in biology, the general appearance of a species without regard to details ; comprises size, shape, posture, or movement, perhaps with general hue and any conspicuous features (see SIZE ; SHAPE AND POSTURE).

FACILITATION : diminution of resistance to a stimulus.

FAECES : see ALIMENTARY SYSTEM ; DROPPINGS ; for nest sanitation see PARENTAL CARE.

FAIRY : substantive name of *Heliothryx* spp. (for family see HUMMINGBIRD).

FAIRY-BLUEBIRD : substantive name of *Irena* spp. (see LEAFBIRD).

FALCON: substantive name of many species of the Falconidae (Falconiformes, suborder Falcones) ; in the plural, general term for *Falco* spp.—or, more loosely, for the whole family. The family has sometimes been divided into three subfamilies—the cosmopolitan Falconinae, and the Neotropical Herpetotherinae and Daptriinae.

Forest Falcons. The Herpetotherinae comprise two genera, *Micrastur* and *Herpetotheres*, the latter monotypic. *Micrastur* has four species, sometimes known as harrier-hawks, in general appearance between a harrier *Circus* sp. and a Goshawk *Accipiter gentilis* (see HAWK)—long-tailed, long-legged, and with a partial facial ruff. They were formerly placed close to the Circinae by some authors on that account, but are in fact primitive falcons which have become adapted for life in dense forests of South America, where they prey on birds. (The term 'harrier-hawk' is also applied to the subfamily Polyboroidinae of the Accipitridae—see HAWK). The Laughing Falcon *Herpetotheres cachinnans* is falcon-like in appearance, dark above with white under parts and a striking white crown set off by a black mask. It inhabits forest in tropical South America, where the birds sit on the tops of trees overlooking open ground and make their presence known by their loud calls, beginning with a single note at short intervals, followed by a more rapid repetition, syllabled by local Indians 'gua-cow' ; several individuals may join in this performance. The bird does not build its own nest.

Caracaras. The Daptriinae, comprising the genera *Milvago*, *Phalcobaenus*, *Daptrius*, and *Polyborus* (including 'Ibycter' and 'Caracara'), are a group of large (buzzard-sized) long-legged birds that look quite unlike falcons. They inhabit open country, forest, or savanna, and are insectivorous or omnivorous, with a strong taste for carrion. Caracaras are very common in parts of Central and South America, and are in general rather sluggish birds, spending much of their time perched, or walking about on the ground ; but they can run swiftly. They associate with vultures (Cathartidae) at carrion and sometimes force these and also other caracaras to disgorge in the same way as skuas (Stercorariidae) will rob gulls (Larinae). Unlike the true falcons, caracaras build their own nests. One species, the Guadeloupe Caracara *Polyborus lutosus*, has become extinct within historical times.

True Falcons. The subfamily Falconinae comprises the genera *Spiziapterx*, *Poliohierax*, *Microhierax*, and *Falco* (including 'Nesierax'). The first three are all very small falcons, the smallest of all the birds-of-prey and represented in the tropics of Old and New Worlds. The Philippine Falconet *Microhierax*

erythrogonys is only 6 inches long, is black above and white below, and hunts insects from the tops of trees in the manner of a flycatcher (*Muscicapa*) ; it breeds in old holes of woodpeckers (Picidae). The African Pygmy Falcon *Poliohierax semitorquatus* is likewise very small, but within its limits it is a bold and dashing little predator, capable of killing small birds as well as the large insects which form the major part of its food. It breeds in the huge communal nests of Sociable Weavers *Philetairus socius* in South Africa, and in East Africa in the thorny nests of buffalo-weavers *Bubalornis* and *Dinemellia* spp. The Sociable Weavers do not object to the presence of the little falcon, which does not molest its hosts.

The genus *Falco*, containing the typical falcons, is the second largest genus in the Falconiformes, being exceeded only by *Accipiter* (see HAWK) in the number of its members. It is, however, a much less homogeneous genus than *Accipiter*, and can be conveniently divided into a number of subgenera on physical characteristics and general habits. Voice consists of screams, squeals, or chattering notes.

The large true falcons are stocky, powerful birds of exceptionally swift flight, the wings being pointed and the tail relatively short. They are among the most accomplished fliers of all birds, and habitually kill their prey, principally birds, in full flight, either striking them dead by a blow of the hind claw or seizing them in the foot and coming to ground with them. Owing to the speed of their attack they rarely kill on the ground, but at times they can. Although they chiefly eat birds they will take occasional mammals, and are fond of flying insects such as termites or locusts when available.

The largest of all falcons, the Gyrfalcon *Falco rusticolus*, is a magnificent species inhabiting Arctic America and Europe and migrating south in winter to temperate latitudes. One of its colour forms is almost pure white, with a few black spots, but more commonly it is grey and white. The Peregrine Falcon *F. peregrinus*, which typifies the larger falcons, could be described as the world's most successful flying bird. Cosmopolitan in distribution, with 17 races, it is a perfect performer in the air, capable of feats of speed and precision flying scarcely to be equalled by any other bird. It is par excellence the falconer's choice, and has been used in all countries where the pursuit is followed (see FALCONRY). In some of its haunts, however, it may not be able to compete with the slightly more powerful and larger Lanner Falcon *Falco biarmicus* of the Mediterranean countries and Africa, which is almost equally swift. Peregrines breed in towns in several countries, no doubt attracted by the large numbers of domestic pigeons found there. Other large falcons of the same general type are the Laggar *F. jugger* of India, the Saker *F. cherrug* of eastern Europe and central Asia, the Prairie Falcon *F. mexicanus* (closely related to the Lanner) and *F. altaicus*. Most of these have been used for falconry to a greater or lesser extent. The Taita Falcon *F. fasciinucha*, a rare inhabitant of Africa, is probably close to the peregrine group although only half the size of a Peregrine.

The hobbies are a group of small, long-winged, exceedingly swift falcons which live largely upon insects but can take some small birds, including swifts (Apodidae), in flight. They catch almost all their prey on the wing and hardly any on the ground. They occur all over the world, and include *Falco subbuteo* of Europe, *F. severus* of India, *F. longipennis* of Australia, *F. cuvieri* of Africa, and *F. albigularis* and *F. femoralis* of South America. Eleanora's Falcon *F. eleanorae* and the Sooty Falcon *F. concolor* are conveniently placed close to hobbies. *F. eleanorae* is a very localised bird, breeding in late summer on certain Mediterranean and other islands, preying on the migrant streams of passerines on southward passage at that time, and thereafter migrating to Madagascar. *F. concolor* inhabits the North African deserts, and preys inter alia on bats, as does *F. albigularis*.

The Merlin *F. columbarius* is a holarctic species, inhabiting open moorland and grassland and preying on small birds caught on the wing. With it may be placed *F. chicquera*, a dashing little falcon inhabiting Africa and India, also feeding on birds, and commonly associated (in Africa at any rate) with the Borassus Palm *Borassus flabellifer*. Both these bold little birds can be trained for falconry, but will not kill anything larger than a small dove. The Merlin is a migratory species throughout its range.

The Grey Kestrel *F. ardosiaceus* and Dickinson's Kestrel *F. dickinsoni* of tropical Africa, and *F. zoniventris* of Madagascar, form another group. They are not true kestrels, having some of the habits of kestrels but being more like merlins in other respects. They kill a good deal of their prey on the ground, and eat small mammals, lizards, and insects as well as birds ; they sometimes hover, but can fly very swiftly also. The Grey Kestrel has the strange habit of appropriating the huge domed nests of the Hammerhead *Scopus umbretta* in which to breed, ejecting the rightful owner. Dickinson's Kestrel breeds in the hollow tops of dead palm trees.

The Red-footed Falcons *F. vespertinus vespertinus* and *F. v. amurensis* are small migrant, insectivorous falcons of striking colouring, with red feet and (in the males) black and grey plumage set off with chestnut under tail coverts. They are highly gregarious both on migration and when breeding, roosting in hundreds together in selected trees, and breeding in colonies in the nests of Rooks *Corvus frugilegus* after the Rooks have flown (*F. v. vespertinus*). In winter they migrate from central Europe and Asia to southern Africa. They are commonly to be found feeding on swarms of flying termites. The Lesser Kestrel *F. naumanni*, although very like the Kestrel *F. tinnunculus* in plumage, is perhaps best placed with these two, being insectivorous and gregarious on migration and breeding in colonies on cliffs and buildings. See Plate 5 (colour).

The kestrels are a large group of small falcons, cosmopolitan in distribution, and having the habit of hovering with gently fanning wings to assist in finding their prey, which is largely small mammals and insects taken on the ground or in long grass. They rarely take birds in flight and are typified by *F. tinnunculus*, which has numerous races occurring all over Europe, Asia, and Africa, and is closely related to *F. sparverius* (unhappily called Sparrowhawk) of America. Other kestrels, *F. moluccensis*, *F. newtoni*, *F. araea*, and *F. punctatus*, inhabit islands in the Pacific and Indian Oceans ; *F. punctatus*, inhabiting Mauritius but reduced to less than 10 pairs, is the rarest of all falcons. *F. cenchroides* is the Australasian representative, and to complete the group there are two rather larger species in Africa—the Fox Kestrel *F. alopex* and the Greater Kestrel *F. rupicoloides*, which are like other kestrels in many of their habits but seldom if ever hover ; they eat small mammals, reptiles, and insects caught on the ground. Many of the kestrels are strongly gregarious when on migration, but breed apart and well separated. In all kestrels the plumage is mainly chestnut and grey in the male, with black spots, and in the female pale reddish-brown with black streaks and bars.

Falco berigora of Australia, known as the Brown Hawk and formerly placed in a separate genus ' Ieracidia ', is one of the commonest, if not the commonest, birds-of-prey on that continent, having many of the habits of kestrels but being much larger and generally darker in colour. It does not hover, but catches most of its prey on the ground (insects, lizards, and small mammals), and is both gregarious and migratory.

In their breeding habits members of the genus *Falco* vary greatly, but none of them seem to build their own nests although they may improve an existing structure. They either breed in a scrape on a rock crag, which may be resorted to year after year, or they appropriate the old nest (and sometimes the occupied nest) of some other bird, such as a large eagle or a buzzard (Accipitridae) or one of the crows (Corvidae). Their eggs are all very handsome, being generally buffish in ground colour, thickly speckled with dark red-brown, sometimes so as to obscure the ground colour completely ; they are very round, and clutches vary from 2 to 5. In the larger species the combined incubation, fledging, and post-fledging periods may occupy 3 months, and the young take some time to become independent of their parents after leaving the nest. Pygmy falcons resemble the typical falcons in that they occupy other birds' nests.   L.H.B.

Beebe, F. L. 1960. The marine Peregrines of the north-west Pacific Coast. Condor 62 : 145–189.

Bent, A. C. 1938. Life histories of North American birds of prey. Part II. U.S. Natl. Mus. Bull. 170 : 1–482.

Cade, T. J. 1960. Ecology of the Peregrine and Gyrfalcon populations in Alaska. Univ. Calif. Publ. Zool. 63 : 151–290.

Horvath, L. 1955. Red-footed Falcons in Ohat Woods. Acta Zool. (Budapest) : 245–287. (In English.)

Thomson, A. L. 1958. The migrations of British falcons (Falconidae) as shown by the results of ringing. Brit. Birds 51 : 179–188.

See also references under HAWK for publications relating to the Falconiformes in general.

FALCONES : see FALCONIFORMES

FALCONET : substantive name of some small species of Falconinae (see FALCON).

FALCONIDAE : see below

FALCONIFORMES : an order, alternatively 'Accipitres', comprising the following suborders and families, the latter dealt with separately as shown :

> Cathartae :
>   Cathartidae   see VULTURE (2).
> Falcones (or Accipitres) :
>   Accipitridae   see HAWK ; VULTURE (1).
>   Falconidae   see FALCON.
> Sagittarii :
>   Sagittariidae   see SECRETARY-BIRD.

The Aegypiinae and Pandioninae, sometimes given separate familial rank, are treated as subfamilies of the Accipitridae ; this follows a recent revision by Stresemann, whose subordinal separation of the Sagittariidae is likewise shown above—instead of having two superfamilies of the Falcones (Falconoidea and Sagittaroidea) as originally in Peters.

The order is a cosmopolitan one, containing the birds-of-prey in the strict sense (see BIRD-OF-PREY). The Cathartidae are confined to the New World and the monotypic Sagittariidae to the Ethiopian Region.

Families based on the fossil type-genera *Neocath-artes* and *Teratornis* are also placed in this order (suborder Cathartae).

FALCONRY : the art of taking wild quarry with birds-of-prey ; also called 'hawking', the terms being synonymous. It is an ancient art, practised in the East as long ago as 1200 B.C. ; and the East, notably China, India, Pakistan, Persia, and Arabia, is still the home of falconry. The art was introduced into England about A.D. 860, and from then until the days of James I falconry was the chief sport of the aristocracy. Thereafter its popularity declined, due partly to the introduction of the art of shooting birds in flight, partly to Puritan influence during the Civil War, and partly to the enclosure of land in the seventeenth and eighteenth centuries. In spite of difficulties, however, the sport has always been pursued in Britain by a small band of devotees, notably the members of the Old Hawking Club in the second half of the nineteenth century and those of the British Falconers' Club today. Similar enthusiasts are to be found on the Continent of Europe, notably in Germany, Holland, and France, and a few kindred spirits practise the art in the United States.

Birds used. Apart from eagles, falconers divide the birds used into two categories, long-winged 'falcons' (e.g. gyrfalcons, peregrines, merlins, sakers, lanners, and laggars) and short-winged 'hawks' (e.g. goshawks, sparrowhawks, shikra, and Cooper's hawk). The Hon. Gerald Lascelles, writing in the Badminton Library series in 1892, thus distinguishes them : ' Falcons or long-winged hawks are distinguished from the true or short-winged hawks by three never failing characteristics, viz. by the tooth on the upper mandible (this in some foreign species is doubled), by the second feather of the wing being either the longest or equal in length to the third (in the short-winged hawks the fourth is the longest feather in the wing), and by the colour of the irides, dark in the case of falcons, yellow in that of hawks.' The term ' falcon ' can, nevertheless, be misleading to the uninitiated, since it is used loosely by falconers to distinguish not only the long-winged birds from the short-winged hawks but, in some cases, such as the Peregrine, the female from the male. In these cases the male, because he is about a third less in size than the female, is known as the ' tiercel '.

The fine-tempered and generous ' falcons ' are birds of the open spaces, moor or marsh, downland or desert. The sky is their playground. Sport with such birds can be obtained only where the country is wide and open, where covert is sparse, and where the falconer, whether afoot or on horseback (or its modern equivalent), can keep up with the flight. To attempt to fly them in close country is at best to court failure, at worst to risk disaster in losing the falcon.

'Hawks', on the other hand, are birds of the woodland and scrub. Threading their way silently through the trees, they take their prey by surprise with a short and headlong dash. They are deadly in their own type of country. When 'in Yarak', that is with a friendly look in her eye, feathers puffed up and crest raised, a Goshawk will fly with a ferocity which never seems satiated with killing. Up to 19 rabbits are known to have been taken in one day by one Goshawk. Two, or at most three flights, are all that could normally be expected of the best Peregrine—but what wonderful flights!

The best birds for sport, and those chiefly used in Britain, are the long-winged Peregrine *Falco peregrinus* and Merlin *F. columbarius*, and the short-winged Goshawk *Accipiter gentilis* and Sparrowhawk *A. nisus*. Kestrels *F. tinnunculus* and Buzzards *Buteo buteo* are easily tamed, and are good birds on which the tyro can practise the art of caring for his charges ; they can, however, be persuaded to take quarry only with the greatest difficulty (or luck), and therefore cannot be regarded as of any practical use for falconry. In recent years, owing to the serious decline in numbers of falcons of native species, British falconers have tended to rely on imported birds, e.g. Saker *Falco cherrug* and Lanner *F. biarmicus*.

All the birds used, whether 'falcons' or 'hawks', are obtained from the wild. Those taken young from the 'eyrie' or nest are known thereafter as 'eyasses'. Those caught when full grown but in their first plumage are called 'passage hawks' or, if in their second plumage, 'haggards'. An 'intermewed' falcon or hawk is one which has moulted in captivity. An eyass is taken at the last possible moment before it can fly ; those taken too young contract the vice of screaming whenever they see a human being. Eyasses, especially long-wings, are generally 'flown at hack' when first taken, i.e. allowed, whilst being highly fed, to fly at complete liberty for some days from a 'hack house' to enable them to develop power of wing.

Equipment. Birds used in falconry are fitted with 'jesses' (short leather straps) on their legs. To the jess is attached, except when the bird is flying, a 'swivel', and through this is run a long leather 'leash'. It is by the leash that birds are secured to the 'block' (the usual resting place in the open of long-wings) or 'perch' (the customary home of short-wings). Indoors, in the 'mews', all birds sit on a 'screen', i.e. a perch from the underside of which hangs a heavy cloth. This cloth prevents a bird which may have 'bated' off the screen from hanging, swinging, head downwards ; aided by the cloth it is able to regain its position.

Bells are attached to the legs by means of leather 'bewits'. By the sound of these bells a falconer can trace his bird if it be lost in covert. By their sound too he can tell at any time what his birds are doing in the 'mews', whether merely shifting their position on the screen, 'rousing' by shaking out their feathers or, unhappily, 'bating'.

The 'hood' is a stiff cap of leather with which a hawk may be blindfolded. To quote Lascelles again : 'What the bridle is to the horse, that the hood is to the falcon ; it is the only means by which she is controlled ; without it, so nervous and excitable is her temperament, that she would, even if trained and fairly tame, dash herself from the perch at every strange sound or sight, and after an exhausting struggle would not, perhaps, recover her equanimity for a whole day. To take her to the field on hand, or travel with her from place to place, among sights and people most alarming to her, would be an impossibility. With the hood on her head she sits like a stuffed bird ; she can be handled, passed from one person to another, carried for hundreds of miles, and taken through streets, railway stations, or where you will, without the slightest trouble and without feeling any alarm or inconvenience to herself.' Sir John Sebright (1828) had this to say : 'It may, perhaps, appear paradoxical to assert that hawks, by being kept hooded, are brought nearer to their natural habits ; but it is undoubtedly the case, for, by this treatment, they are induced to remain at rest when they are not feeding or in the pursuit of game, and such are their habits in the wild state when left undisturbed.' Finally, the late Gilbert Blaine had this to say of hoods : 'No man can claim to be master of hawks until he is a master of hooding ; he who has perfected himself in this art has gained the whole secret of the control of his falcon.'

Methods. Mastery over hawks is obtained largely through playing on the sense of hunger. A hawk that is 'sharp set' or hungry, will fly willingly at quarry or to the 'lure', a bunch of feathers with pieces of raw meat attached, which is swung at the end of a cord or thong. A 'full-gorged' hawk, on the other hand, would, if allowed to fly free, 'rake away' and defy recapture. A good falconer will have his birds in high condition yet keen to fly.

Falcons are flown in different ways according to the type of quarry. When 'game hawking', i.e.

flying at grouse or partridges, a wide-ranging setter or pointer is put down. When game is found, the falconer, having removed her leash, swivel, and hood, puts his falcon in the air. She flies in a spiral, 'ringing' until she has 'gained her pitch' over the dog. The higher she 'mounts' the better. There she will 'wait on' until the falconer 'serves' her by putting up the game, down wind, under her. On sighting the rising game she will 'stoop' at it and either 'bind to' it in mid-air or 'put it in' to covert, over which she will 'make her point' and 'wait on' once more until the falconer can 'put out' the quarry to her again. Having taken the quarry she will be allowed to 'plume' it quietly, that is to pluck or even 'break into' it, before the falconer 'makes into' her and takes her gently on fist again. There, sitting on his glove, she will assuredly be rewarded with a titbit before being 'hooded up' and replaced on the 'cadge', a light wooden framework used to take hawks into the field. Not all flights are successful however. She may 'fly at check' at other quarry, i.e. 'rake away' after, say, a distant pigeon. Then must the falconer, his best foot foremost, follow her and endeavour to 'take her down' with his lure.

When hawking quarry other than game the procedure is different. Instead of the falcon 'waiting on', she is 'flown out of the hood'. Imagine a flock of rooks to have been discovered feeding on an open downland, far from covert. The falconer, preferably mounted, stalks the rooks with his falcon on his fist. He will have already removed her swivel and leash and have 'struck the hood', that is loosened its braces ready for its instant removal. When in a good position, directly down wind and some 250 yards from the rooks, he will 'unhood' her and 'fly her out of the hood' straight at the rooks. A good falcon will drive the rooks upwind whilst climbing steadily over them until she is a hundred feet or more vertically above the whole bunch. Not until then does she select her victim and put in a vertical 'stoop'. This cuts him out from the flock if it does not take him. If he manages to dodge her he may succeed in 'ringing up'. A match in flying will then ensue until the falcon, having 'fetched' her quarry, can force him downwards in a series of stoops. A good falcon, however, will generally maintain the command of the air which she has already obtained. Meanwhile, the hawking party will be galloping hard to keep the flight in sight, hoping that the falcon may 'bind' to the quarry before he can 'make his point' and gain safety among the trees.

The method of flying short-wings is different again. In this case the 'austringer', as the owner

of short-wings is called (see SHAKESPEARE'S BIRDS), will, say when flying a Goshawk at rabbits, carry her 'unhooded' on his fist while the rabbits are being walked up. Though unhooded and held only by her 'jesses', a 'well manned' Goshawk, if 'in Yarak' will sit quietly on fist until a rabbit is put up. Then, like a flash, she will launch herself from her 'austringer's' glove straight at the quarry, which she will seize by the head. Taken thus, the rabbit becomes powerless in her tremendous grip.

A.G.O'C.S.

ap Evans, H. 1960. Falconry for You.
Berners, Dame Juliana. 1486. The Boke of St. Albans. (Facsimile reproduction by William Blades, 1881.)
Bert, Edmund. 1619. An approved treatise of Hawkes and Hawking. (Limited reprinted edition by Harting, 1891).
Blaine, Gilbert. 1936. Falconry.
Lascelles, G. 1892. Falconry (Badminton Library). London.
Latham, Symon. 1658. Faulconry, or The Faulcon's Lure and Cure. 3rd ed.
Mavrogordato, J. G. 1960. A Hawk for the Bush: a treatise on the training of the sparrow-hawks and other short-winged hawks. London.
Mitchell, E. B. 1900. The Art and Practice of Hawking. London.
Salvin, F. H. & Broderick, W. 1873. Falconry in the British Isles. 2nd ed.
Woodford, M. 1960. A Manual of Falconry. London.

FALCUNCULINAE: see under MUSCICAPIDAE

FAMILY: a primary taxonomic category (or a particular example thereof), being a subdivision of an order and a grouping of genera. Secondary categories may be interpolated between these levels when considered necessary—suborder and superfamily as higher divisions of the order, subfamily and tribe as subordinate groupings of genera (see TAXON). Although the category was not used by Linnaeus (whose genera were very wide), it has become one of the most important. It is a level at which the taxonomist demands a high degree of probability that the taxon is monophyletic; it is also one at which he expects to find gaps between the taxon and its neighbours, sufficient in magnitude to make each of them plainly distinctive. The grouping of families in higher taxa tends to become progressively more speculative; the subdivision of a family into subordinate taxa (above species level) comes more and more to depend on points of minute detail.

There are, of course, exceptions. On the one hand there are groups of rather similar families— so little different that some authors regard them as subfamilies of a single family, and that at least ordinal relationship is indisputable. On the other hand, there are families—as at the moment recognised—that include such diverse elements as to raise doubt about their monophyletic character; these groupings can be considered as no more than provisional, pending further evidence. And again, there are families that fail of distinctiveness because they are linked to others by species of apparently intermediate character; in this event, the present tendency is to reduce the families to subfamilial level, where a certain lack of distinctiveness can be more readily accepted—for a case in point see MUSCICAPIDAE. The whole question of familial status and interfamilial relationships is particularly difficult in respect of the passerine birds (see PASSERIFORMES).

Subfamily and Tribe; Superfamily. Secondary categories that are sometimes interpolated between family and genus are subfamily and tribe. These may be useful where the genera within the family are sufficiently diverse and appear to fall into groups. The criteria of degrees of difference are necessarily subjective; so what one author may regard as a number of separate families, another may treat as subfamilies, or even tribes, of a single family. The tribal category is regarded as superfluous by some authors (e.g. Wetmore 1960), but it may help on occasion in breaking up a large family showing relatively little diversity; thus, the Anatidae may be considered as divisible into no more than three subfamilies but can be further subdivided into ten tribes, seven of them in one very large subfamily (see DUCK). In an upward direction, families may be grouped in superfamilies within suborders (see under ORDER).

The names of superfamilies end in '–oidea', those of families in '–idae' (the 'i' is short), those of subfamilies in '–inae', and those of tribes in '–ini'. In all cases the stem of the name is taken from the name of the type-genus. Each of the three higher taxa has a subordinate 'nominate' taxon at the next level below, with the same type-genus and a name identical except for the termination. The names of nominate subfamilies and tribes are not used as separate entry words in this work, as they derive obviously from the name of the higher taxon.

FAMILY-GROUP: with reference to the ranks of taxa, term embracing those taxa that are based on, and are co-ordinate with, the family (see NOMENCLATURE).

FANTAIL: substantive name of *Rhipidura* spp. and related forms (see FLYCATCHER (1)); also the name of a breed of domestic pigeons.

FAP: abbreviation of FIXED ACTION PATTERN.

FASCIA: a sheath of connective tissue.

FASTING: see FEEDING HABITS; PENGUIN; TORPIDITY

FAT DEPOSITION: see METABOLISM; and under MIGRATION. Standard definitions of degrees of fatness, from 'no fat' to 'excessively fat' (in the higher degrees involving abdominal as well as subcutaneous fat), have been proposed by McCabe.

McCabe, T. T. 1943. An aspect of collectors' technique. Auk 60: 550–558.

FAUNA: the total animal life of an area, the vegetable life being the 'flora' and the two together being sometimes known as the 'biota'; the 'avifauna' is the part of the fauna consisting of birds. Faunistic studies are those that deal with the occurrence, prevalence, and distribution of the different forms of birds or other animals in particular geographical areas (see DISTRIBUTION, GEOGRAPHICAL).

FEAR: see BEHAVIOUR, DEVELOPMENT OF; TAMENESS

FEATHER: the component unit of the plumage and a structure outstandingly and uniquely characteristic of birds as a class (see also PLUMAGE; MOULT).

The surface of the body of any vertebrate animal is covered by a skin, a highly organised structure and consisting of two separate parts (see SKIN). These parts are a thick underlying dermis with muscles, blood vessels, and nerves in it, and an overlying epidermis. This epidermis consists, in the adult, of many layers of cells. The deepest of these layers may be distinguished as a single layer of active cells lying upon a basement membrane which is firmly attached to the dermis. This is called the Malpighian or basal layer. Each cell of this layer at intervals divides into two, and the products of these divisions lie, as a rule but not always, one outside the other. The cell remaining in the basal layer divides again, and so also may the one pushed outwards. In this way the products of these divisions generally find themselves progressively farther and farther from the underlying dermis, and so farther and farther away from their only source of nourishment and of oxygen. Thus they die off. As the cells die they become filled with a horny substance called 'keratin' which is a product of their own metabolism in these circumstances. The keratin within any cell may in varying degrees become bonded to that in an adjacent cell. This is the source of the strength of, for instance, the skin on the human hand. By the time an epidermal cell reaches the outer surface of any animal it consists of practically nothing but dead keratin. At the surface these dead cells are constantly being lost through the breaking of the keratin bonds which have been holding them together (Fig. 1). A feather is simply an astonishingly elaborate and specialised product of the epidermis of a bird, and it is made of practically nothing but keratin, certain of the keratinised cells in this case sticking firmly together, instead of falling apart, because of the special bonding of the keratin between adjacent cells.

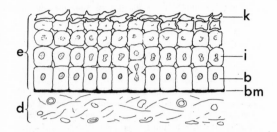

FIG 1. Diagrammatic section through the skin of a vertebrate. One basal layer cell is seen to be dividing into two. *P. G. 'Espinasse.*

b Basal, or malpighian, layer **bm** Basement membrane **d** Dermis **e** Epidermis, of stratified epithelium **i** Immediate products of basal layer **k** Keratinised dead cells

A familiar flight feather is shown in Figure 2A. Keratin is a very strong substance, and the form of a feather is mechanically extremely sound. The result is a wonderfully light and very efficient structure. The parts of it that must be distinguished are labelled in the Figure. The barbs (rami), which together make up the vane on each side of the central spine or rachis, are each provided with barbules (radii) as shown in Figures 2A, B, C. The hooked distal barbules of each barb catch upon the curled proximal barbules (like long pointed spoons) of the barb next more distal, and thus constitute the continuous-looking vane (vexillum). If they come unhooked by accident, they can be made to engage again by stroking the feather from the base towards the tip as is done by the bird in the act of preening (see FEATHER MAINTENANCE).

The rachis, having strong keratin walls, is filled up within by blown-up and keratinised cells looking rather like the pith of some plants, and the barbs (except where they are joined to the rachis) are filled with similar material. This arrangement gives great strength while adding very little to the weight. The aspect of the feather lying against the bird's body in life is called the 'ventral' side, and that presented to the observer in life is called the 'dorsal'.

At about the fifth day of incubation the embryo of a fowl may be seen to have rows of pimples, in well-marked patterns, on its surface. Each pimple is a consequence of an increase in the rate at which epidermal cells are multiplying at that particular site. Here the products of the division of the basal layer cells may some of them extend the area of the basal layer by remaining in it between cells previously there. This local increase in area becomes raised up as a pimple. It is believed that the stimulus causing a local increase in activity of this kind comes from the immediately underlying dermis in which some change has occurred. The dermis here also proliferates and there is thus a finger of dermis pushed out, covered by a thimble of epidermis, as is shown in Figure 3A. This is a feather germ. See also DEVELOPMENT, EMBRYONIC.

Further localised growth now serves to push this feather germ down into a deepening depression. While this is happening, the feather germ continues to lengthen greatly, so that, instead of a pimple on the surface of the embryo, there is now a pit with a long cylinder projecting out of the mouth of a follicle (Fig. 4). The cylinder slopes backwards, so that 'dorsal' and 'ventral' sides can be distinguished.

A 'napkin-ring' of epidermis towards the lower end of the cylinder is distinguished and named the 'collar'. Beneath this again is the persistent papilla. It is within the collar that nearly all the growth leading to the production of a feather takes place. By this growth, which in an adult bird may continue at a high rate for weeks, the cylinder of epidermis is lengthened. The dermal 'pulp' within the cylinder, continuous through the 'inferior umbilicus' and papilla with the rest of the dermis of the bird, dies away some distance up the cylinder; and where it dies the epidermis dies too, having previously keratinised as has been described.

It is clear that if nothing more than this happened there would result, not a familiar feather, but an ever-lengthening hollow cylinder of keratin. In fact, the feather is given form by specialised growth, leading to specialised arrangements among the epidermal cells of the lower part of the cylinder— the region just above the collar. Since the cells so arranged are all fated to die, and in differing degrees to keratinise, and since in differing degrees keratinising cells adjacent to one another may become joined, any arrangement of cells effectively joined together by keratinisation will persist, after the death of the cells, as an arrangement of keratin. Any dead keratinised matrix cells not so joined together will not form part of the pattern but will fall away and be lost as the feather emerges, just as dead keratinised cells are lost from the palms of our hands.

The cells forming the outside of the cylinder, when they keratinise, are joined together to constitute a resistant sheath that holds together everything

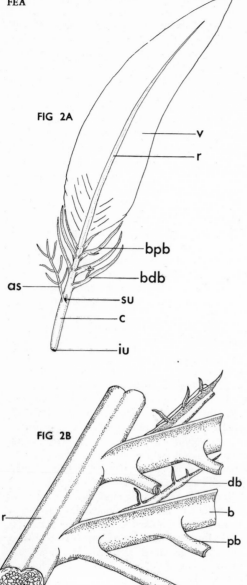

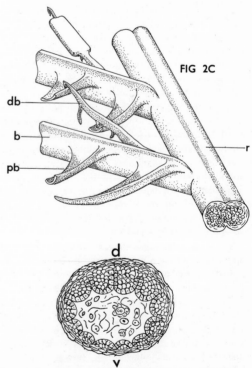

FIG 2A. Diagrammatic representation of the principal parts of a generalised feather, seen from the ventral side, to show the essentials of their relations to one another. Three barbules have been shown much exaggerated in size ; two of them link the two most proximal barbs.

P. G. 'Espinasse.

as Aftershaft **bdb** Barb showing distal barbule **bpb** Barb showing proximal barbule **c** Calamus or quill **iu** Inferior umbilicus **r** Rachis **su** Superior umbilicus **v** One side of the vane

FIG 2B. Enlarged diagrammatic view of a length of rachis in a generalised feather with two barbs attached to it, from the ventral side. Three of the proximal barbules have been cut off short so as to show their curled structure. The upper distal barbule has a flattened and expanded dorsal surface. This is the site of the iridescence seen in some of the feathers in, for instance, a Peacock *Pavo cristatus*. For clarity, the barbules have been drawn much more widely spaced than they are in life.   P. G. 'Espinasse.

b Barb **db** Distal barbule **pb** Proximal barbule **r** Rachis

FIG 2C. A piece of a feather similar to that shown in Figure 2B, but turned over and so viewed from the dorsal side.   P. G. 'Espinasse.

b Barb **db** Distal barbule **pb** Proximal barbule **r** Rachis

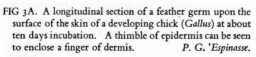

FIG 3A. A longitudinal section of a feather germ upon the surface of the skin of a developing chick (*Gallus*) at about ten days incubation. A thimble of epidermis can be seen to enclose a finger of dermis.   P. G. 'Espinasse.

d Dorsal **v** Ventral

FIG 3B. A transverse section of a feather germ similar to that shown in Figure 3A. Barb-ridges can be seen to be forming as orderly longitudinal thickenings of the epidermal thimble.   P. G. 'Espinasse.

d Dorsal **v** Ventral

inside it. This sheath is destined later to split and to be lost, so freeing everything it had been holding together. It is certain of the epidermal cells within this sheath that, by their specialised growth and keratinisation, become the feather, which is really the persistent pattern, in keratin, dictated by the arrangement they had achieved before their death.

The arrangement of the cells forming the inner aspect of the epidermal pimple described may be seen already in Figure 3B. The inner aspect of the lengthening cylinder becomes longitudinally pleated or ridged. These ridges contain the developing barbs. Within the substance of the barb-ridges many cells fall away individually and take no part in the structure of the finished feather, but some become firmly joined to each other and form the strong hollow barbs, elliptical in section or almost laminar, and filled with pith. Yet others become joined in columns, each column sloping downwards towards its barb, to which proximally it becomes firmly fixed. Two series of such columns are differentiated in each barb-ridge, one series joining the proximal and one the distal aspect of the barb. These columns of single cells, each cell appropriately shaped, will be the barbules when they have become fully keratinised, and processes (barbicels) of these cells formed while they were alive will become keratinised as hooks on the distal set.

After growth has continued for varying periods in different birds, and after the containing sheath has split, all that remains coherent and organised is a short quill (calamus), which is the persistent cylinder below the lowest extent of the barb-ridges, and a group of barbs sticking up from round its upper edge like the spikes on a coronet. On the barbs are arranged the barbules. We now have a first down feather as shown in Figure 5.

From some follicles, series of down feathers are produced throughout the life of the bird, but in most of them the down feather is succeeded sooner or later by a feather having the familiar adult form (see also DEVELOPMENT, POSTEMBRYONIC). The succession of feathers from one follicle is brought about by the occurrence of a new phase of growth following a period in which growth is interrupted. This new phase of growth is initiated, below the old cylinder that gave the old feather, in the persistent papilla (Fig. 4). Growth upwards from this papilla produces a new collar, and this in turn a new and elongating cylinder that pushes the old feather up and out of the follicle, where it drops off. This is the mechanism of the moult.

The difference in form between a first down feather and an adult feather, such as a contour

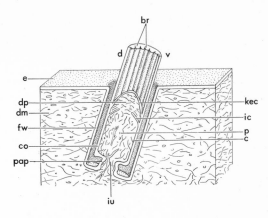

FIG 4. A diagrammatic representation of a block cut from the skin of a bird during its development. The plane of the section nearest the observer cuts a developing feather in half longitudinally. The half of the feather remaining in the block is alone shown. The barb-ridges on the near aspect of the cylinder can be clearly distinguished.

P. G. 'Espinasse.

br Barb-ridges **c** Calamus or Quill **co** Collar **d** Dorsal **dm** Dermis **dp** Dead pulp **e** Epidermis **fw** Follicle wall **ic** Incipient cap **iu** Inferior umbilicus **kec** Keratinised epidermal cap **p** Pulp **pap** Papilla **v** Ventral

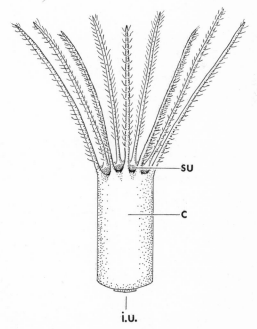

FIG 5. The first product of a feather germ. There is no rachis, and the barbs with small barbules stick up around the top edge of the calamus. *P. G. 'Espinasse.*

c Calamus or quill **iu** Inferior umbilicus **su** Superior umbilicus

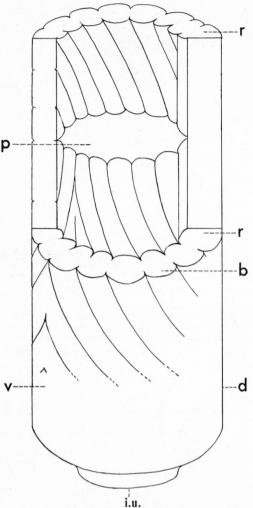

FIG 6. A perspective view of a model of a developing feather. The barb-ridges instead of running straight up and down as in the first down feather can be seen in this to follow a half spiral course, so that each barb-ridge runs into a developing rachis dorsally, thus giving the form of a normal feather.

P. G. 'Espinasse. Reproduced by permission of the Zoological Society of London.

b Barb-ridge **d** Dorsal **iu** Inferior umbilicus **p** Pulp **r** Rachis **v** Ventral

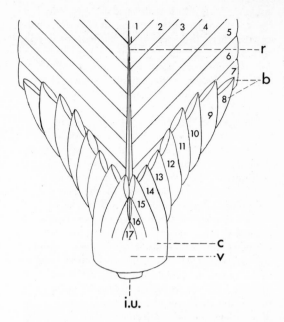

FIG 7. A ventral view of a developing feather. The sheath has been removed. The cylinder is split down its ventral side, thus freeing the tops of opposite barb-ridges from each other. These now open outwards and lie flat in the plane of the paper. No attempt has been made to give the barb-ridges their proper thickness. The numbers are arbitrarily assigned to the barb-ridges from the tip towards the base.

P. G. 'Espinasse. Reproduced by permission of the Zoological Society of London.

b Barb-ridges **c** Calamus or quill **iu** Inferior umbilicus **r** Rachis **v** Ventral

feather of any ordinary bird, is to be understood as deriving essentially from a difference in the arrangement of the barb-ridges on the inner aspect of the developing epidermal cylinder. Whereas in the developing first down feather these ridges were all parallel and straight up and down the walls of the cylinder, in the developing contour feather they each take a half-spiral course. Each pair of barb-ridges is initiated ventrally, and one of them pro-

ceeds, as the cylinder lengthens, to be differentiated downwards and around the cylinder towards the dorsal on one side of the cylinder while its mate goes round the other side. The two fail to meet dorsally, and the strip down the cylinder dorsally thus left intact is the site of the developing rachis (Fig. 6). The sheath, and later the whole wall of the cylinder, splits down the ventral aspect and so the familiar feather is freed (Figs. 7, 8, 9, 10). The aftershaft (hyporachis) is formed by a splitting into two of the originally single ventral line on which barb-ridges are initiated (Fig. 8)—see AFTERSHAFT. When the matrix cells that do not become part of the feather are lost, all that remains (as in the case of the down feather) is the barbs with their barbules bearing hooks in the distal set and being curled up at their edges in the proximal set, but here all firmly attached to the rachis.   P.G.'E.

FEATHER EATING: see under GREBE

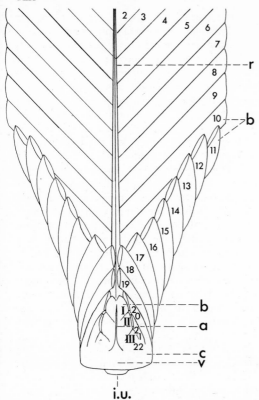

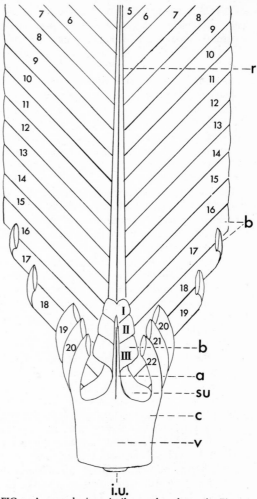

FIG 8. A ventral view similar to that shown in Figure 7, but at a later stage in development. The aftershaft has begun to appear because the ventral split in the cylinder has become doubled instead of single towards the base of the cylinder. *P. G. 'Espinasse. Reproduced by permission of the Zoological Society of London.*

The Roman figures are assigned downwards to the barb-ridges of the aftershaft. **a** Aftershaft **b** Barb-ridges **c** Calamus or quill **iu** Inferior umbilicus **r** Rachis **v** Ventral

FIG 10. A diagrammatic representation in perspective of a block of tissue cut from a developing feather cylinder. It can be taken to be the tissue represented on the top right-hand corner of Figure 6, but here it is viewed from the dorsal aspect. The rachis and barbs 1 and 2 are shown still within the matrix cells as they appear in a transverse section through a developing cylinder. Barb 3, however, is shown after the removal of the sheath and all the matrix cells around it. Its barbules can be seen to be springing away from the barb and assuming positions in which they form a wider angle with their barb than they could assume while held in the matrix cells. When the sheath and all the matrix cells have been lost, the barbs will all lie with their dorsal edges in the plane of the paper and the barbules will assume the positions and angles given to them in Figures 2B and 2C, which should be compared with this drawing. *P. G. 'Espinasse.*

em Epidermal matrix cells **r** Rachis **s** Sheath

FIG 9. A ventral view similar to that shown in Figures 7 and 8, but at a still later stage of development. *P. G. 'Espinasse. Reproduced by permission of the Zoological Society of London.*

Numbers as in Figure 8.

a Aftershaft **b** Barb-ridges **c** Calamus or quill **iu** Inferior umbilicus **r** Rachis **su** Superior umbilicus **v** Ventral

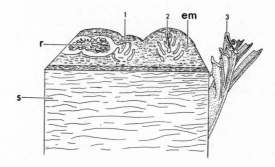

FEATHER MAINTENANCE: term covering a range of highly stereotyped basic movements, together with associated behaviour, most of which are widely distributed in some form throughout the Class Aves. These movements seem to vary little within the larger taxonomic groups, so far as is known. Notwithstanding the pioneer work of Finn, Heinroth, Lorenz, Morris, Nice, and others, the topic has been much neglected and there are great gaps in our knowledge—gaps that tend, of course, to be less apparent in compressed accounts such as the present one. Biochemical investigations are still in their infancy.

The major patterns of feather maintenance include true bathing (in water), oiling, preening, and head scratching ; sunning, dusting, and anting are subsidiary ones. Associated with these are the ' comfort movements ' and the behaviour relevant to the care of the soft parts. Much of all this behaviour is an important source of display and displacement activity. The feather maintenance activities seem to form a homogeneous group. Some have movements in common (e.g. bathing and dusting ; oiling and anting), while they all probably share some motivational and other causal factors and have the same general function. The plumage, especially the all-important wings, can never be in too good a condition ; it is essential that the unique feather covering of birds be in sound order, both for its primary purposes of insulation and flight and for use in display. Hence, natural selection can be expected to have developed any habit, however small its individual contribution, that might help in this important task. Feather maintenance is essentially a combination of individual activities, the total effect being the significant one. In addition to positive maintenance (e.g. repair to the feather structure, dressing with organic liquids), there is the removal of unhygienic substances, both those originating from the external environment (e.g. dirt, ectoparasites) and from the bird itself (e.g. stale preen oil, carbonic and other exudates shed via the feathers). In several cases, special behaviour has been evolved to care for the more inaccessible parts of the plumage, especially the head and the under surface of the primaries. However, the precise functions of most of the individual activities of feather maintenance, particularly of sunning, dusting, and anting, are far from certain, there being little positive, experimental evidence to go on. Of what there is, much is conflicting, in part owing to confusion between causal and functional aspects of the problem. Moreover, too great an effect has been expected from individual activities.

The accounts that follow are mainly descriptive, as it is impossible to cover all aspects here, but some questions of general importance will be briefly mentioned under one or two subheads only (e.g. predator pressure under Bathing ; innate and learned aspects under Sunning and Anting ; taxonomic aspects under Head Scratching). The major activities are dealt with in the order in which they most often occur in nature and in which they presumably achieve their maximum effect—bathing, followed by drying, oiling, and full preening. See also BEHAVIOUR, DEVELOPMENT OF.

Bathing. It seems best to restrict this term to cases of true bathing in water. This involves special movements serving to wet the plumage in order, apparently, that the subsequent oiling or preening, or both, may be more efficiently performed. The cleansing of the feathers and skin appears to be of only secondary importance. Bathing is found in most birds, although absent in certain groups that dust themselves (e.g. Galliformes). The general pattern of typical bathing, i.e. bathing in standing water, consists of movements of the head, the wings, and to a lesser extent the tail, together with the ruffling of the body feathers. There are variations in detail between the bathing methods of different groups, sometimes even between closely related ones. More markedly, the bathing of water birds is usually different from that of land birds. In water birds, most of which bathe while floating in the water, e.g. grebes (Podicipitidae), the activity usually consists of an alternation of two sets of simple movements : (1) the head and shoulders are ducked under the water and raised again rapidly in a scooping motion, sending water on to the back, the head then rubbing sideways along the flanks or folded wings ; (2) the loosely held wings (wrists mainly) are vigorously beaten against the water, splashing it over the plumage. Some species (e.g. geese *Anser* spp., swans *Cygnus* spp.) occasionally turn completely over (somersault) in the water during the first phase of bathing. In land birds (e.g. passerines), most of which bathe while standing in shallow water, bathing is more elaborate although again usually consisting of two alternating groups of movements : (1) the front of the body is lowered, with the tail more or less clear of the surface, the head and often the breast dipped into the water, and the bill vigorously shaken from side to side, while both wings flick up and down together ; (2) the head and forebody are raised, the tail end is lowered into the water, and the wings are flicked extremely rapidly in and out of the water and also over the back transversely—frequently one much more than the other so that the water is sent in spurts first over one side and then over the other. Semi-aquatic birds, such as waders (Charadrii) and rails (Rallidae), bathe while standing in shallow water but otherwise use the method of true water birds. Most birds remain in the water for the duration of the bath, some land birds such as pigeons (Columbidae) even tending to wallow between spells of activity. Land birds of a few groups, e.g. babblers (Timaliinae), nevertheless move repeatedly in and out of the water during bathing, never standing in it for more than a few seconds at a time and performing drying movements in between. Highly aerial birds, such as swallows (Hirundinidae), drongos (Dicruridae), swifts (Apodidae), and terns (Sterninae), bathe from the air, dropping repeatedly into the water, again for a brief moment only ; hummingbirds (Trochilidae), kingfishers (Alcedinidae), and even pigeons and owls (Strigiformes) are among birds that will plunge to bathe.

It will be seen that bathing is not a haphazard affair, but, like most feather maintenance activities, a highly co-ordinated, innate behaviour pattern. When performed completely, its immediate purpose is to wet the plumage, evenly, as much as possible without actually soaking it. It is a controlled wetting, not a drenching. The latter could seriously damage the feathers by rendering them brittle and weak, rob the bird of flight, and, in the case of water birds, destroy waterproofing and buoyancy. When bathing deliberately, birds ruffle the plumage so that the water can reach all the feathers (and, probably, also the skin) ; but when caught in the rain they have a special posture that minimises its effect, sleeking the feathers tightly against the body and standing in a semi-vertical position so that the rain drains off as much as possible. This ' rain posture ' seems to be best developed in tropical species unable to avoid seasonal downpours, and in other species frequenting open habitats. Bathing behaviour may be considered, therefore, as partly a compromise between getting wet and keeping dry (see further below, under Drying). Also, bathing birds are particularly vulnerable to predation ; their movements are conspicuous and their flying (or swimming, or diving) efficiency is reduced ; they need, at any stage in the bathing process, to be able to escape from sudden attack. The ' in-out ' bathing of, for instance, babblers seems especially well adapted to counteract the twin dangers of feather damage and of predation. These selection pressures (along with the irregularity or seasonableness of rain) may also have been responsible for the development, by some species, of dusting as an alternative to true bathing, and also the cause of the special form that bathing takes in those tropical species, especially, that seldom or never bathe in

standing water but mainly in dew or rain-soaked foliage—e.g. hornbills (Bucerotidae), Budgerigar *Melopsittacus undulatus*, Wren-tit *Chamaea fasciata*— or in the rain itself. Specialist rain bathers, e.g. parrots (Psittacidae), have characteristic postures, with feathers ruffled (often especially those in the area of the oil gland), wings fully extended horizontally, and the tail spread. Many species that normally bathe in standing water will sometimes make incomplete, often clumsy, attempts at bathing in rain, in wet vegetation or even, sometimes, in snow (but see under Drying), although their movements are not adapted for this. But pigeons, as well as bathing typically in standing water, also bathe in the rain by lying over to one side with the uppermost wing fully extended and raised to expose the flanks ; they use a similar and probably homologous posture when sunning themselves. Larks (Alaudidae) do not bathe in standing water but lie down in the rain with wings outspread. Some birds, notably surface-feeding ducks *Anas* spp., etc., perform escape reactions when bathing, although no predator is present.

Drying. All birds have special movements to remove moisture, particularly surplus water, from the plumage as quickly as possible. These drying movements, most of which are also used as general comfort movements (see below), occur both during and after deliberate bathing, and also after accidental wetting due to rain, mist, fog, snow, or the like. Indeed, much so-called ' bathing' in these latter conditions is really drying behaviour. Although some water birds, such as cormorants (Phalacrocoracidae) and swans, often leave the water after bathing, most remain in it and dry, oil, and preen there. Among the characteristic drying movements of water birds are ' wing flapping' and the ' ruffle and body shake' (the bird raises and then depresses its contour feathers, at the same time relaxing and then jerking the body forward). Similar movements are shown by semi-aquatic birds and many land birds on firm ground. Some birds, such as ducks (Anatidae) and gulls (Larinae), perform drying movements in flight, and, in most species, normal flight from the bathing to the preening site achieves a similar result. Cormorants, after the normal wing flapping, hold out the wings for long periods to dry after wetting. Passerines do not wing-flap but ruffle and body-shake (see above), ' whirr' (a vigorous vibration of the tail and wing-tips together, producing a loud rustling noise), and ' shuffle' the wings (by drooping and vibrating them) and the tail (by fluttering it sideways). Whirring is especially characteristic of weaver-finches (Estrildidae) and babblers. Also, in passerines, the special wing oiling movements (see below) serve as drying ones, as do various other oiling, preening, head scratching, and comfort movements in most birds.

Oiling. In that majority of species possessing a functioning preen-gland (see OIL GLAND), special anointing movements follow a wetting of the plumage, and by these the fatty secretion of the gland (preen oil) is smeared on the feathers, particularly those of the wings, as quickly as possible. This oiling behaviour is clearly a form of preening, but its exact function is much disputed. Although preen oil is a drying oil, and thus helps to counteract the ill-effects of water on the feather texture, this seems to be of minor importance. It appears that birds, rather than oiling because they are wet, wet themselves on occasion in order to oil and preen more efficiently. In some cases, such as waders (Charadrii) and grebes (Podicipitidae), dry birds will wet the bill during preening bouts. The water on the feathers probably helps to spread the oil quickly over the feathers before it hardens (oxidises) on contact with air. The major (inter-related) functions of oiling probably include the water-proofing and maintenance of the insulating characters of the plumage, especially important in water birds ; this includes keeping them supple, not over brittle, and hence reducing wear and the chances of breakage, a vital factor in the case of the wing feathers. Among subsidiary functions, vitamin production must be mentioned. Upon irradiation in sunlight, preen oil becomes a source of Vitamin D, which is ingested during preening. In addition to preen oil, other organic substances are applied to the feathers by some species : eucalyptus oil by certain parrots (at the same time as preen oil) ; the body secretions of ants by passerines (see below under Anting) ; and, possibly, stomach oil by petrels and their allies (see ALBATROSS).

When oiling typically, most species first stimulate the flow of preen oil from the oil gland with the bill, the tail being characteristically fanned and twisted to one side. They then transfer the oil to various parts of the plumage with the closed bill, using special 'stroking' and 'quivering' preening movements, further spreading of the oil being effected later by the more normal, more leisurely preening that gradually succeeds the true oiling movements. The under surface of the primaries and the head provide particular difficulties for oiling as well as for normal preening. Many non-passerines oil under the wing by turning the head round over the back, lowering the carpus and raising the wing-tip. Toucans (Ramphastidae) flick the wing against the large bill after getting oil. Some species with necks long enough (e.g. grebes, geese)

rub the head directly on the oil gland, and then rub the head on other plumage areas in quick succession, or rub it on previously oiled tracts, or on both. Most passerines, however, have unique methods of anointing these awkward areas, usually dealing with them first after bathing. The head is oiled with the foot, the bird first taking oil with the bill, then scratching the bill with the foot, thus transferring some oil, and immediately after that quickly scratching all over the head, moving it about under the foot as it does so. The under side of the wing is oiled by the bill, and also by the oiled head with rapid quivering motions, the wing being extended sideways and forwards, carpus raised. This co-ordination reaches its peak in babblers, which simultaneously rub the bill and the head on the wing and the wing on the head parts at great speed, alternating quickly from wing to wing and, at maximum intensity, posturing the tail sideways to press against and steady the wing. These wing-anointing movements at times also function as drying ones ; practically identical and homologous movements are used in typical anting (see below). Herons (Ardeinae) and bitterns (Botaurinae), when their necks and heads have been fouled by slime from their fish prey, first rub the affected feathers on the powder-down tracts (see PLUMAGE), next scratch off the slime and the powder with the pectinated claw, and then apply oil and preen.

Preening. This comprises the arrangement, cleansing, and general maintenance of the health and structure of the feathers by the bill—by direct contact between bill and feather and, in many species, by the dressing of the plumage with organic liquids (e.g. preen oil). Preening is the basic and most important single activity in feather care, the bird spending much time over it, preening not only when there is obvious cause (plumage wet, soiled, or disarranged ; irritation amongst the feathers, etc.), but also at other times when external stimulation is at a minimum, especially when the bird is relaxing.

True preening almost invariably follows bathing and oiling, and also occurs in conjunction with other feather-care activities (sunning, dusting, anting). It is, of course, also performed independently. The preening after bathing and oiling appears to be rather haphazard at first ; this is particularly so in passerines, which are very often restless after bathing ; the bird may even cease to preen for a time. Sooner or later, however, full preening develops, the bird then tending to deal thoroughly with specific areas (e.g. breast, wing coverts) before proceeding systematically to others.

There are two main sets of bill actions used in

preening, involving the full movement of both mandibles (e.g. 'nibbling', 'drawing') and the movement of the closed bill only (e.g. 'stroking', 'quivering'). Nibbling (mandibulating) is the most thorough and accurate preening method. The bird deals with the individual feather, seizing it in the tips of the mandibles and passing it between them, working from base to tip with repeated, tiny peckings and, possibly, movements of the tongue. Specks and the like on the feather, feather base, or skin are dealt with by a more restricted, precise nibbling at the very spot, often with a vigorous 'digging' action. Drawing is similar to nibbling, but the bird pulls the feather through the bill in one movement ; many species preen the individual primaries and rectrices in this manner. When preening by stroking, the bird moves the bill rapidly straight down the feather near the shaft, 'stropping' (the vigorous stroking of whole areas of feathers) being a variant of this, especially notice-able in certain water birds (e.g. grebes). Finally, quivering is a trembling action of the bill down the feather. The more important preening move-ments, nibbling and drawing, remove stale and irradiated preen oil, feather exudates, dirt, and ectoparasites directly from the plumage (see ECTO-PARASITE). Some or all of these are consumed, for preening birds make frequent swallowing move-ments. The movements also work in fresh preen oil (and other organic liquids), re-arrange the feathers, and repair breakages in the webbing. They are aided in this by the less skilful preening movements with the closed bill that also function to smooth down the feathers, dry them, and apply oil, and so on, stroking and quivering having special reference to the primaries (at least in passerines).

During preening, the contour feathers are ruffled for better accessibility, the bird bending its head towards the place to be preened, contorting itself to reach the more inaccessible areas. Familiar preening 'contortions' include the straightening of the legs and the tucking down of the head (preening of the belly) ; the sideways posturing of the tail and extreme stretching of the neck (rectrices, rump, and vent) ; the stretching up of the neck and the tucking down of the bill (neck and upper breast), the latter being a particularly awkward one for large-billed birds (e.g. toucans). These various preening postures are stereotyped ; there is little question of a bird 'improvising' movements, even where there seems to be a clear need for doing so. Hence, passerines in dealing with the primaries (especially the almost inaccessible tips) by lifting the wing sideways and forwards (see above, under Oiling), cannot ade-quately nibble-preen them but only hurriedly draw,

stroke, or quiver. But many non-passerines, by keeping the wings at their sides and turning the head round over the back, can preen the primaries more thoroughly and leisurely, the passerines apparently using this co-ordination only to preen part of the upper surface of the wing near the carpus (wing coverts, etc.). The head is preened by scratching (see below) or by being rubbed against other parts of the body ; in some groups, birds preen each others' heads (mutual preening). This reciprocal preening is performed by birds paired together or associating in some other way ; some-times only the dominant bird does the preening (see DOMINANCE (2)). Besides its direct, utilitarian function, mutual preening probably also assists in the establishment and maintenance of social bonds, even although, on occasions at least, it is due to a sublimated tendency to attack. Mutual preening is absent in most groups, but, within the passerines, it occurs in certain crows (Corvidae), babblers, and estrildid weavers, for example ; among non-passerines it occurs in herons, pigeons, parrots, and several other groups. In babblers at least, paired birds also sometimes preen their partner's ventral area. See Plate 21 (phot.).

Head Scratching. The head parts, including the bill, are scratched with one foot while the bird supports itself on the other. There are at least two levels of scratching ; on the basic level (the 'scratch-ing reflex'), it is a simple direct response to irritation or other physical stimulus on the head parts and is, therefore, best classed as a comfort movement (see below) ; on a more extended level, it functions as an important item of feather care. Probably many species use scratching as a means of 'preening' the head, which of course cannot be reached by the bird's own bill. Herons and bitterns scratch off fish slime after treating it with powder-down, while many passerines oil the head by scratching (see above).

There are two main ways in which birds move the foot up to the head for scratching. When scratching 'indirectly' (scratching 'from behind' the wing, 'from over' the wing, and 'from between' wing and body, in older classifications), the bird first makes the positive movement of lowering one wing and then brings up the leg on the same side over the shoulder to the head, the co-ordination being typically two-phase. When scratching 'directly' (scratching 'straight up', 'from under' the wing, and 'from in front of' the wing), the bird lifts the foot straight up to the head without any preceding special movement of the wing.

In the great majority of cases, one head scratching

method only is characteristic of the species and its family and, hence, is often a good auxiliary taxonomic character ; for example, indirect head scratching supports other evidence that oystercatchers (Haematopodidae), and avocets and stilts (Recurvirostridae) are more closely related to the true plovers (Charadriidae) than to other waders. As far as is known, most bird groups—including the more primitive ones—scratch directly. The following are among those that scratch indirectly : the majority of passerines (the most notable exceptions being the babblers) ; swifts and hummingbirds ; nightjars (Caprimulgidae) ; kingfishers, bee-eaters (Meropidae), hoopoes (Upupidae), hornbills, and rollers (Coraciidae) ; several parrot genera ; turacos (Musophagidae) ; sandgrouse (Pteroclididae) ; frigate-birds (Fregatidae) ; and the wader families already mentioned.

The advantage, if any, of one method over the other is much disputed. The direct method is thought by many to be the less primitive and the more efficient of the two ; on the other hand, a recent view is that the indirect method is the more advanced having been evolved to counteract difficulties in balance and accuracy of scratching, particularly in reference to its extended functions in oiling, preening, and so on. The occasional use of the direct method by normally indirect-scratching species, e.g. some American wood-warblers (Parulidae) and nestlings and fledglings of some other passerines, remains to be fully investigated but may be, in part, a temporary reversion to a more primitive method or a wrongly co-ordinated indirect movement, or both.

On the other hand, it is quite possible that neither scratching method is 'primitive', but that both derive from an earlier and cruder method in which birds scratched by bringing the foot straight up to the head while fluttering or lowering the wing in balance. Evolution in scratching then went in two independent directions, involving either a reduction of the wing movement (direct scratching) or its incorporation into the scratching co-ordination (indirect scratching).

Sunning. Behaviour by which the plumage is exposed to the sun by special postures seems to be widespread in birds. As with other feather-care activities, there is controversy over its causation and function. Some workers consider it no more than a simple temperature response. However, it would seem that while inexperienced birds react 'automatically' (purely instinctively) to some quality of the sun (probably its warmth and brilliance), experienced ones also learn to react to it more as an entity ; especially, they respond to the sight of

it, even on cool, windy days. The full function of sunning is obscure, but the exposure of the organic liquids on the feathers (preen oil, etc.) to the sun's ultraviolet rays changes their chemical properties. For one thing, Vitamin D is produced (consumed during preening) ; and there are probably other, as yet unknown, effects more relevant to the good of the feathers. It thus seems that it is the light, at least as much as the warmth, of the sun that is biologically important. Its warmth may well cause ectoparasites to become active in the plumage and even to move from more exposed areas, such as the head (where they are particularly likely to congregate) or under the wings. Preening and head scratching occur commonly during and after spells of sunning.

Sunning birds, like anting ones, are often very incautious and may be closely approached. The sunning may be performed suddenly during other activities (in response to strong stimuli when the sun comes out), or the bird may resort deliberately to a favoured place to rest and bask in the sun. The behaviour occurs in all types of sun conditions (and even in artificial light in the case of captive birds), the form of the sunning postures also partly depending on the position of the sun in the sky and on the mood of the experienced bird. In passerines, the simplest posture involves little more than a slight fluffing up of the feathers as the bird squats with wings drooped at the sides, often with its back to the sun (a similar posture is adopted by many non-passerines also, e.g. gulls, waders, ducks). At fuller intensity, the bird ruffles the feathers well (especially those in the area of the oil gland, and in many cases, those of the head), leans over away from the sun, spreads down the primaries of the wing nearest the sun, and twists round and fans the corresponding half of the tail. This is the most usual form of sunning in passerines. At higher intensity still, the drooped wing is fully raised to expose the under surface and flanks ; while at the very highest intensity, usually when the sun is overhead, the bird lies on the ground with both wings and tail spread right out. When performing the more extreme postures in the full heat of the sun, birds may gape and often appear to have collapsed in distress (see HEAT REGULATION). Although some passerines (e.g. Robin Erithacus rubecula, Dunnock Prunella modularis, Starling Sturnus vulgaris) show more or less the whole range of sunning postures, each species tends to have its own 'typical intensity' form or forms of sunning. In non-passerines, there is considerable variety in sunning method. For example, many groups have only the simplest movements (see above) ; pigeons, somewhat like passerines, lean over and spread one wing and the tail, and also raise one wing vertically as they do when rain-bathing ; owls (Strigiformes) spread-eagle themselves with face turned up towards the sun ; gallinaceous birds lie on one side, or even briefly roll over on their backs, with the wings lifted and spread and the head and neck often outstretched on the ground ; herons (Ardeinae) stand upright facing the sun with the neck stretched up and both wings lowered, shield-like, in front of the body to expose their under surfaces ; frigate-birds sit back on their tails, facing the sun, holding both wings half sideways and twisted so that the under surfaces face forwards and upwards ; boobies *Sula* spp. face away from the sun but stretch both wings backwards, first one and then the other. Some birds, e.g. certain hawks (Accipitridae), herons, and passerines, use what seem to be sunning postures to shield their nestlings from the sun.

Dusting. Behaviour by which ' dust ' (fine dry earth, sand, etc.) is driven into the plumage, and later expelled, occurs in a number of orders but is not nearly so widespread as true bathing. While most characteristic of certain birds living in bare open habitats, and particularly in steppe and desert country, such as larks, sandgrouse, gallinaceous birds, bustards (Otididae), it is also found, for example, in sparrows (Passerinae—but not in other Ploceidae), wrens (Troglodytidae), Wren-tit *Chamaea fasciata*, hoopoes (Upupidae), rollers (Coraciidae), bee-eaters (Meropidae), hornbills (Bucerotidae), motmots (Momotidae), colies (Coliidae), nightjars (Caprimulgidae), seed-snipe (Thinocoracidae), seriamas (Cariamidae), and some owls and hawks. Some species that dust do not bathe in standing water (e.g. larks, gallinaceous birds), but others both dust and bathe (e.g. rollers, bee-eaters, sparrows, wrens). With the exception of the White-winged Chough *Corcorax melanoramphus* (Grallinidae), which has once been recorded as passively anting, no passerine that ants has been reported to dust also. Bathing and dusting have been erroneously equated by some writers, thus implying that they are identical in movements and function, differing only in the medium used. However, birds do not ' bathe ' in dust ; even in those species that both bathe and dust, and perform dusting that contains bathing-like elements, the actions and co-ordinations are usually quite distinctive in the two cases. Moreover, dusting cannot serve precisely the same purpose as true bathing, although its functions are not at all clear. Probably ectoparasites are discouraged and dislodged. Preening and head scratching frequently occur during and after dusting. As with most other feather-care activities, inexperienced birds react at first to dust

instinctively by touch ; later, visual stimuli are equally important to experienced birds.

Most dusting species form hollows of dust, if conditions allow, by squatting or lying down and performing movements of the bill (flicking, pecking), feet (scraping), and body (shuffling, rotating). The dust is driven into the plumage, either directly or indirectly, by movements of the wings (flicking, shuffling, shaking), or feet (scratching as in nest shaping or with one foot only), or of both wings and feet, the bird relaxing or ruffling its contour feathers, especially those of the rump, and often rubbing the head and bill in the dust. After dusting proper, the earth is shaken out of the plumage, often vigorously. Some species (e,g. sparrows) often dust communally, but most do so singly and cautiously (e.g. wrens), frequently raising the head to look for danger, in contrast to the behaviour of solitary sunning or anting birds. The actual form of dusting varies between species and has evidently arisen independently in different groups, even those in the same order (e.g. sparrows, larks). Among the few passerines that dust, sparrows use some water-bathing elements (bill and wing flicking), getting the dust into the feathers mainly by the wing movements, those of the legs chiefly loosening the earth. Wrens dust similarly, but much more quickly and with a different wing movement (also one used in true bathing). Larks do not appear to use any obvious bathing movements but shuffle around with ruffled plumage and drooped wings ; they sometimes dust in snow. The White-winged Chough dusts in a quite unique manner, standing up and actually applying billfuls of dust to various parts of the plumage, dealing with the wings by movements like those used in oiling and anting. Among non-passerines, dusting has been studied most carefully in gallinaceous birds, which scrape earth towards them with the closed bill (often partly burying themselves), scratch up earth into the plumage with the feet, and throw it on the back with movements of the wings. Hoopoes hollow out dusting-holes with flicking movements of the bill, then, while still using the bill, shuffle and rotate slowly in the hole, lying to one side, until half buried. They then shower sand all over and among the ruffled feathers with a series of body-shakes and wing-beats. The Common Rhea *Rhea americana* picks up dust in its bill and throws it over its body.

Anting. This consists of special movements, apparently confined to passerines, whereby the defence and other body fluids of ants (Hymenoptera : Formicidae) are applied to the bird's feathers. The chief organic liquid involved is the formic acid produced by the worker (and queen) caste ants of species of the acid-ejecting Formicinae. Birds will also apply members of the Dolichoderinae, which produce repugnatory anal fluids. Some of these fluids, as also other body secretions of the formicine ants, are essential oils. Stinging ants (Myrmicinae, etc.) are not favoured by anting birds. There are numerous suggested functions for anting, but the evidence points to its being a feather-care activity, its exact functions being linked with the chemical properties of the ant-fluids and their (as yet hardly investigated) effect on the feathers. Formic acid and certain other ant-secretions are known to be insecticidal and would certainly kill or discourage ectoparasites ; further liquids, being essential oils, could serve as an addition or supplement to preen oil anointing. In the majority of anting species, it is the ventral tips of the primaries that are directly dressed with ant fluid, and this may also reach the head when it brushes against the wing. Both are ' inaccessible ' for full preening and are also specially catered for by oiling movements. Bathing, oiling, and preening follow anting.

The anointing of the feathers with ant fluids is effected either directly by the bird applying the ant to its plumage with its bill (active anting), or indirectly by its permitting the ants to swarm on to its plumage, ejecting formic acid (so-called passive anting). In both forms the movements are stereotyped and, although differing somewhat in certain species, otherwise show remarkable uniformity in several passerine families—due either to the ancient origin of anting, or to its ' using ' behaviour patterns already widespread in the order, or to both causes. Birds that ant typically in the direct manner include babblers (Timaliinae), thrushes (Turdinae), weavers (Ploceidae), white-eyes (Zosteropidae), and starlings (Sturnidae) ; they use movements clearly homologous with those used in the highest intensity forms of wing oiling—the wing and tail are postured similarly, and quivering actions are made with the bill and head under one wing at a time. However, as already mentioned, the ventral tips of the primaries, not the whole underwing, are the major target, while the tail posture is more extreme, pressing the rectrices firmly against the wing-tip to make it steady for the anointing. Less commonly, if at all, typically anting birds are alleged to anoint the ventral base of the tail and other areas. Some other species, e.g. some New World orioles (Icteridae) and some crows (Corvidae), habitually practise a more extended anting, applying ants to several feather tracts with oiling-like movements of the bill. A few species, occasionally or habitually, extend both wings when anting actively ; but whereas, for example, the

Blue Jay *Cyanocitta cristata* of America still anoints only one wing at a time, waxbills (Estrildidae) and sugarbirds (Coerebinae) bring the wing-tips together in front of the body and anoint them jointly. In those relatively few species that ant passively as well as actively (chiefly certain crows and larger thrushes), the passive-anting movements are quite different from the active ones, resembling the higher intensity forms of sunning and rain-bathing. The birds squat or lie down among the ants, often while applying them directly or going through the motions of doing so with empty bill, while the wings and tail are partly or wholly spread out. The Jay *Garrulus glandarius* of Europe (which does not normally apply the ants) and a few others of the Corvidae extend both wings forward before the body to facilitate the ants' ascent of the plumage.

There is particular controversy over the causation of anting. While the movements themselves are innate, the bird has to learn that ants are the biologically correct media for anting. Innately, also, it reacts to some simple quality peculiar to the ant. This is thought by some observers to be the acidic, pungent, or thermogenic characters of the ant affecting the taste-buds on the bird's tongue. More probably, in typical active-anting species, this basic stimulus is at least partly a chemical effect (formic acid, etc.) on the nasal organs, while in passive-anting species the touch of the ants upon the bird's legs seems to release anting behaviour instinctively. After experiencing the basic stimulus, the bird comes to associate it with the ant and reacts to the ant as a whole, chiefly visually. Because of this situation, some individuals of anting species never learn to ant, others ant infrequently, while some, particularly those in captivity or other unnatural environment, come to use inappropriate ' substitutes ' with some basic character or characters in common with ants. Such substitutes include smoke, moth-balls, cigarette ends, citrus fruits, and insects other than ants.

Anting in one or both forms has now been recorded in over 200 species of over 30 passerine families. There are, in the writer's opinion, as yet no fully documented or convincing cases of true anting in any non-passerines.

Comfort Movements. Each species has a number of movements that aim to make it more ' comfortable ', e.g. by putting the feathers in order and at ease, by stretching and relaxing muscles, especially those connected with the limbs, and by generally resting the body. Many ' feather settling ' comfort movments are also drying ones (see above), including the ruffling and depression of the contour feathers, body shaking, and, in non-passerines, wing shuffling and wing flapping. The latter movement, although especially characteristic of true water birds, is also well developed in, for example, gallinaceous birds, waders (Charadrii), and gulls (Larinae), which often thresh the wings vigorously. The characteristic stretching movements are often complex, as in many species more than one limb is stretched at a time. Limb stretching co-ordinations would repay careful study, as they are probably useful taxonomic characters in some groups. In passerines, the legs are stretched either both at once, by the straightening of the tarsal joints, or singly, by being extended and straightened sideways and backwards, foot often clenched, as the bird stands on the other leg. Two-leg stretching is often followed by an upward extension of both wings, the carpus being lifted but only the primaries stretched. One-leg stretching is usually accompanied by the full extension of the corresponding wing and sideways fanning of the tail—leg, wing, and tail moving as one. Most non-passerines have somewhat similar movements. Some, such as grebes (Podicipitidae) and bitterns (Botaurinae), raise the wings while stretching the neck forward and the chin upwards. Others, such as ducks and waders, waggle the tail feathers from side to side, or, as in turacos (Musophagidae), slowly fan and relax them. The prolonged 'wing-drying' movements of cormorants, already mentioned, also probably relax the wing muscles, and this seems almost certainly the case with the analogous, briefer 'wing gliding' of grebes. Other comfort movements, relating to the soft parts, are mentioned in the section next following.

Adult birds usually rest and sleep while standing on one or both legs or squatting down ; fully aquatic birds, such as divers (Gaviidae) and grebes, do so floating on the water. Young birds often rest by squatting right down on their breasts ; and this position is sometimes used by adults that feel particularly free from danger, especially in certain groups, such as gallinaceous birds, gulls, and babblers (Timaliinae). When at rest, the bird relaxes and ruffles its contour feathers, those of the flanks often covering the folded wings and, in some species, such as parrots (Psittacidae) and babblers, those of the belly being fluffed over the feet. The head may be retracted into the neck, in the case of some long-necked birds actually resting on the mantle ; or, in the complete posture, it may be turned round backwards and the bill inserted into the scapular feathers (popularly, but erroneously, described as 'under (or behind) the wing'). The majority of grebes do not turn the head back when resting, although the Pied-billed Grebe *Podilymbus podiceps* is said to do so, but tuck the bill away at the side

of the folded neck (the well-known 'pork pie' attitude)—as do several 'ratite' birds. Although some birds (e.g. parrots, babblers, estrildid weaverfinches) rest in bodily contact with their fellows, the majority do not, even communal roosting species such as the Starling (see also ROOSTING). 'Yawning', the opening wide and closing of the free-moving mandible—in most birds the bottom one—together with (according to some authorities) inhalation and expulsion of breath, is widespread in birds.

Care of Skin and Soft Parts. There seem to be no special movements relating to the care of the skin as such ; it is attended to during routine feather maintenance, particularly preening (see above). Several activities, however, function to keep the bill and other 'soft parts' in good order. Many species lubricate the bill and (in the case of passerines at least) the feet with preen oil, more or less incidentally during oiling sessions. Some passerines also deliberately anoint the tarsi, using quivering movements of the bill. Such behaviour probably prevents these parts from becoming dry, rough, and scaly. Bill (and face) wiping is performed frequently after bathing and at other times. The bill and gape-flanges are wiped upon firm objects (branches, the ground) in a characteristic way ; for instance, by stropping the sides alternately with a sharpening-like action or by rubbing one side only at a time. They are also scratched with one foot ; and the bill is cleaned also by seizing or pecking at hard objects. A few birds (e.g. gulls) plunge the bill into the ground. Many water birds dip the bill into the water and shake the head, especially after dealing with prey ; head-shaking is also a widespread reaction to discomfort on or inside the bill or nostrils. Some water birds (e.g. grebes), as well as head shaking, drain surplus water from the bill by touching it against the throat or upper breast. Many preening birds examine the feet and pick off any specks of dirt, while some waders seem to paddle deliberately in water to clean them, especially before incubating the eggs. Many water birds (e.g. grebes) wave the foot to dry it before placing it to rest in the waterproof 'pocket' of flank feathers. Waders do the same, also prior to scratching the head with a mud-soiled foot. The eye is cleaned and also protected during preening, oiling, and like movements, especially by use of the nictitating-membrane (see under VISION), and many birds (e.g. passerines, gallinaceous birds, parrots) have a special 'shoulder-rubbing' movement in response to any dirt or other irritation in or near the eye.

Smoke-bathing. This term is used for a set of

miscellaneous reactions to smoke that require much further study. In some cases, the movements involved are comfort or drying ones (reactions to irritation and foreign bodies on the feathers) ; in others, those of sunning (reaction to heat) or anting (reaction to pungent fumes), as described above. The chemical nature of the smoke, including the degree of acidity, is probably important. In further instances, unrelated to the present general subject, birds are attracted to the smoke by the insects caught up in the rising heat, or by prey driven from grass or ' bush ' by fire.   K.E.L.S.

FEATHERS, HUMAN USE OF: see ORNAMEN-TATION, BIRDS IN HUMAN ; UTILISATION BY MAN

FEEDING HABITS: behaviour exhibited in obtaining and utilising food (see also FOOD SELECTION). In this, few species of birds are so much specialists as to be limited to one prey, or to show a distribution coincident with that of a single food source ; the Everglade Kite *Rostrhamus sociabilis* lives entirely on gastropods of the genus *Pomacea*, the distribution of the Limpkin *Aramus guarauna* in the south-eastern United States is coincident with that of the same mollusc, and the breeding haunts of the Slender-billed Nutcracker *Nucifraga caryocatactes macrorhynchus* are defined by the occurrence of the ' cedar ' *Pinus cembra*. Some species are, in parts of their range, so dependent upon one prey out of many possible foods that a lack of that prey may inhibit breeding or compel migration ; this is the case with Snowy Owls *Nyctea scandiaca* and Long-tailed Skuas *Stercorarius longicaudus* in lemming areas. But many groups—notably the crows (Corvidae) and the gulls (Larinae)—can only be described as omnivorous, perhaps having food preferences but able to subsist upon a startling variety of foods. In some birds there is a marked change in dietary with age—Partridges *Perdix perdix* are almost entirely insec-tivorous when young, but the adult birds are largely vegetarian. In the estrildid finch *Poephila guttata* the two sexes have been shown to have different food preferences, and in the extinct Huia *Heteralocha acutirostris* the marked difference in bill structure was correlated with a difference between the feeding habits of male and female (see BILL ; WATTLEBIRD (2)).

The feeding habits of each species may be divided into two components—the general dietary and hunt-ing methods of the genus, family, or order, and the characteristic specific habits or preferences that give at all times a measure of ecological isolation by ethological means, and enable more than one closely related species to live within a single habitat (see

ECOLOGY). The titmice *Parus* spp., with specific preferences for hunting at different heights, in different trees, and in different parts of those trees, provide a notable example of specific distinctions within the genus. These ethological isolating mechanisms have not necessarily any anatomical basis ; there is nothing structural to indicate that only the Song Thrush *Turdus philomelos* among the British Turdinae possesses the innate capacity to crack open the shells of snails.

Methods of Obtaining Food. Birds have exploited all that grows and moves upon the surface of the earth and in the upper layer of all its waters. The fossorial habit is the only feeding method not represented among birds, although the snow burrows of arctic grouse (Tetraonidae) might be cited as an exception to this statement. Many short-billed species, notably among the Galliformes, will delve a beak's length below the surface, with bill or feet or both, to reach prey beyond direct reach ; and longer-billed species, notably among the Charadrii, probe in the earth, sand, or mud. Fallen leaves, moss, and litter are tossed aside by many birds to reveal preys that lie beneath, and between tide-marks the Turnstone *Arenaria interpres* lives up to its name.

Growing herbage and the leaves of trees are cropped by pigeons (Columbidae), gallinaceous birds (Galliformes), and geese (*Anser*, etc.)—a parrot, the Kakapo *Strigops habroptilus*, is said to ' graze like a rabbit ' ; but in general birds depend more upon fruits, nuts, and seeds—and in humming-birds (Trochilidae) and sunbirds (Nectariniidae), in so far as they may be regarded as vegetarian, upon flowers—rather than upon foliage. The kernels of armoured fruiting bodies are reached by bills adapted for crushing (Hawfinch *Coccothraustes coccothraustes*) or shearing (macaws—Psittacinae), or by the highly specialised crossed tips of the bills of crossbills *Loxia* spp., which first fray, and then probe between, the scales of fir-cones. The large light bills of toucans (Ramphastidae) enable these relatively heavy birds to reach and pluck fruits without performing gymnastic feats or taking wing.

Just as a stout or arched bill usually bespeaks an herbivorous habit, long and light bills can usually be correlated with a dietary in which arthropods, annelids, and other invertebrates predominate. The wide, lamellate bill of flamingos (Phoenicopteridae) and, to a lesser extent, of some surface-feeding ducks (Anatidae) provide filter-feeding mechanisms for very minute food particles.

In the owls (Strigiformes) and the diurnal birds-of-prey (Falconiformes) the taloned feet are used to seize and often to kill the prey ; if the formidable grip or lacerating impact be not sufficient to give the coup-de-grâce the bill comes into action, usually attacking the base of the skull. The long-winged falcons (Falconidae) rely upon speed to secure their prey, the owls, harriers (Circinae), and round-winged hawks (Accipitrinae) more often upon surprise ; the eagles (also Accipitrinae) show a great variety of hunting methods, usually taking their prey upon the ground. The falcons that strike their prey in mid-air will often kill preys larger than themselves ; but in general the birds-of-prey, with their relatively fragile wing feathers, do not risk the rough and tumble with victims larger than themselves so often undertaken by hunting mammals. Among the passerines, the titmice (Paridae) and some of the tyrant flycatchers (Tyrannidae) hold prey with the feet and dismember it with the bill, but the shrikes (Laniidae) rend their impaled prey with bill alone.

The herons (Ardeidae) and all the fish-eaters with the exception of the Osprey *Pandion haliaetus* and fishing-eagles (*Haliaetus*, etc.) use bills alone to secure their prey. But the Reef Heron *Egretta gularis* will reach out a foot to stir tufts of weed and then stab with its bill at bolting fishes.

Among the woodpeckers (Picidae) there is a startling variety of diet and habit—the sap-feeding of the sapsuckers *Sphyrapicus* spp., the ant-eating (with the aid of a long and mobile tongue) of the ground-feeding species, the splitting of hard nuts and the demolition of fir-cones by the pied woodpeckers *Dendrocopos* spp. The kingfishers (Alcedinidae) are also remarkable for the inclusion of many tropical species living far from water and feeding entirely upon insects and small land animals. The fondness of the Palm-nut Vulture *Gypohierax angolensis* for the fruits of the oil-palm, the berry-eating of the Curlew *Numenius arquata*, and the aquatic hunting of the dippers (Cinclidae) are other food preferences and habits scarcely to be suspected on anatomical grounds.

The shallows of the world's waters are worked by a great variety of methods—wading with bill or head submerged to skim or sieve or snatch ; or walking wholly submerged along the bottom, aided by the pressure of the current (and sometimes by the wings), as is the habit of dippers. The phalaropes (Phalaropodidae) and the smaller petrels (Hydrobatidae and Procellariidae), swimming or flitting with paddling feet, feed largely upon organisms from the very surface of the sea. Swimming under water with the wings or feet may follow a leap from the surface, a brisk downward tilt, or a submersion so gradual that it can scarcely be described as a ' dive ' ; and birds that depend upon the impetus of a headlong

plunge to carry them below the surface may dive from forward flight, after a hover, or from a perch (see SWIMMING AND DIVING). The skimmers (Rynchopidae) fish entirely upon the wing, ploughing the surface with the blade-like lower mandible and snapping down upon any small fish which comes in contact with it ; skimmers are said to work back over their own tracks, seeking preys that have been attracted by the disturbance of the surface at the first passage.

In the air, swallows (Hirundinidae), swifts (Apodidae), and nightjars (Caprimulgidae) make many successive captures in the course of sustained flights, while the flycatchers (Muscicapinae) hawk from look-out posts for single victims. Both methods of aerial feeding are used by the bee-eaters (Meropidae).

Preparation of Food. The preparation of prey ranges from bolting the victim whole to a careful plucking (often at some favourite plucking place) or the rejection of some part of the prey—the heads of snakes by the Secretary-bird *Sagittarius serpentarius*, the bills of Starlings *Sturnus vulgaris* by the Sparrowhawk *Accipiter nisus*, and the stings of wasps by shrikes (Laniidae). Such preys as slugs are wiped to and fro in grass by the thrushes (Turdinae), or carried to dusty ground to clear off the slime, which may be toxic ; there is a record of a Mistle Thrush *Turdus viscivorus* treating a hairy caterpillar in the same way.

Some of the straight-billed scavengers, such as the gulls (Larinae) and storks (Ciconiidae), may depend upon a bird with a hooked bill to open up the hide of a carcase. Food invested in a hard shell may be opened by strength of bill or extracted by some other method. The habit of breaking open snails on anvil stones has been evolved at least twice—in the Song Thrush *Turdus philomelos* and in a bowerbird *Scenopoeetes dentirostris*. The Everglade Kite *Rostrhamus sociabilis* extracts the body of *Pomacea* by waiting until the gastropod is partially emerged and then crippling it with a stab of the sharp, slender bill—apparently into a nerve ganglion, showing an innate ' anatomical knowledge ' more reminiscent of a hunting wasp than of a bird ! That tortoises are dropped by the Lämmergeier *Gypaetus barbatus* has been known since classical times, but it has recently been suggested that the victim may not be so much deliberately dropped as let fall during an effort to prise it out in the air. The dropping of bones (presumably for the marrow) has been confirmed in this species. Gulls and crows often drop crustaceans, echinoderms, and molluscs to break them open ; but often it seems to be a matter of chance whether the prey falls on hard or soft ground, although the Pacific Gull *Larus* ('*Gabianus*') *pacificus* is credited with carrying gastropods of the genus *Turbo* to selected dropping places.

The employment of an 'anvil' whereon prey is hammered or dropped may perhaps be regarded as the use of a 'tool' in feeding, as also may be the wedging of nuts into cracks in trees by the Great Spotted Woodpecker *Dendrocopos major* and the impaling of victims by shrikes (Laniidae). There is one truly remarkable use of a tool in feeding (but in obtaining rather than in preparing food), namely in the Woodpecker Finch *Camarhynchus pallidus* of the Galápagos, which probes with a thorn into crevices in the bark of trees and thereby disturbs insects beyond the reach of the somewhat short bill. A Heron *Ardea cinerea* that has caught a large eel will quickly carry its victim some distance back from the water's edge, to dispatch its prey in a place whence escape is difficult.

Frequency. The frequency of feeding activity ranges from the almost uninterrupted hunting by small passerines throughout the hours of daylight, and the three meals a day of thrushes *Turdus* spp. during a super-abundant fruit harvest, to the one meal a day of the Red Grouse *Lagopus scoticus*, the one meal in 48 hours of Great Blackbacked Gulls *Larus marinus* during the East Anglian herring fishery, and the fantastic, week-long fasts of some marine and gallinaceous birds in the breeding season —months long in some penguins (Spheniscidae). Blackbirds *Turdus merula* in autumn and Starlings *Sturnus vulgaris* in spring seek earthworms early in the morning and other foods later in the day. The meal-times of birds-of-prey that can obtain a day's supply in one or two kills often show a clock-like regularity. Night and day dictate the major rhythm of most feeding routines, but in some herons (Ardeidae) and ducks (Anatidae), and many wading birds (Charadriiformes), the ebb and flow of the tide is a more important influence upon feeding times than the alternation of light and darkness.

In feeding routines two components may be detected—the drive to forage and actual appetite. Hunger may be appeased before the drive to hunt is exhausted ; when this occurs a bird will capture and at once abandon prey. The unsatisfied drive to forage may be responsible for 'food storage' in many species—Jays *Garrulus glandarius*, woodpeckers (Picidae), titmice (Paridae), and shrikes (Laniidae). Very little is known of the frequency with which hidden foods are recovered, but in the Nutcracker *Nucifraga caryocatactes* the accumulation of stored food is of real biological importance, birds of this species relying for the bulk of the winter food, and

of supplies for the young, upon hazel nuts garnered in the previous autumn.

Interrelations. The robbing of birds of other species of their prey (piracy or kleptoparasitism) is the regular custom of the skuas (Stercorariidae) and Frigatebirds (Fregatidae) ; Blackheaded Gulls *Larus ridibundus* frequently harry Lapwings *Vanellus vanellus* when feeding on pasture and ploughland, and most species of birds will at times attempt to rob others of their food (see PIRACY). In the titmice there is an inter-specific order of dominance, although in the relations between Great Tits *Parus major* and Blue Tits *P. caeruleus* much depends upon the élan of the displacing attack. In the thrushes, the Song Thrush *Turdus philomelos* is always subordinate to the Blackbird *T. merula*, and may lose up to 9 per cent of its worm harvest to the bigger species.

It has been suggested that within a mixed feeding flock each bird acts unwittingly as a beater for the other members. Parties of members of a single species of pelicans *Pelecanus* spp. or cormorants *Phalacrocorax* spp. will make concerted hunting movements, fishing strung out in line across a creek or over a shoal, or (pelicans) dipping their heads in unison while swimming in compact formation.

Commensalism is most often practised by the use of some larger species as 'beaters' for the disturbance of insects and such small prey—horses, cattle, large game of all kinds, and even railway trains are thus exploited. The Cattle Egret *Ardeola ibis* is an outstanding example, but there are many others. Robins *Erithacus rubecula* are the commensals of wild boars, moles, and man. The use of foraging troops of monkeys as 'beaters' has been described for such different birds as hornbills (Bucerotidae) in Africa, drongos (Dicruridae) in Asia, fairy bluebirds (Irenidae) in the Philippines, and trogons (Trogonidae) in Panama. For the association of some species with crocodiles see CROCODILE-BIRD. Off the south coasts of Arabia the driving of 'sardines' into close packs by tunny and sharks is the signal for the assembly of a screaming company of terns (Sterninae) to swoop and plunge in the turmoil of spray and fish, and all over the world fishing vessels are followed by gulls (Larinae) and other snappers-up of unconsidered trifles. Indeed, it has been advanced that the refuse of the whaling and fishing industries has been responsible for the great increase of the Fulmar *Fulmarus glacialis* within the last century. The strange relationship between the honeyguides (Indicatoridae) and ratels or man is symbiotic rather than commensal (see HONEYGUIDE).

Commensalisms between birds are less common than these relations between birds and members of other classes. The most delightful avian commensalism is that of the Carmine Bee-eater *Merops nubicus* riding upon Abdim's Storks *Sphenorynchus abdimii* and Kori Bustards *Ardeotis kori* and swooping in pursuit of insects disturbed by the mounts. Chaffinches *Fringilla coelebs* will eat the seeds of crab-apples hacked open by Fieldfares *Turdus pilaris* ; and House Sparrows *Passer domesticus* will collect the legs knocked off cockchafers by Blackbirds and Song Thrushes.

The only birds that show a parasitic feeding habit (in the usual sense of the word) are the oxpeckers *Buphagus* spp., which take blood and perhaps tissue from wounds that they keep open on cattle and some large game animals, in addition to eating the ticks initially causing some of the sores. For further detail see OXPECKER.

Study Techniques. Until comparatively recent times the usual and, indeed, almost the only method of studying bird foods was by the examination of gut contents. The value of this technique remains as great as ever, but it has been supplemented by other methods that are especially necessary when the rarity of a species forbids the collection of adequate samples ; in the Hawaiian Goose (or Nene) *Branta sandvicensis*, for example, much has been learned by the examination of droppings. The examination of pellets has long been of use in the study of hawks and owls, but is of very limited value in the study of such birds as herons which have very great powers of digestion (see PELLET). Feathers, fur, and bones at plucking places have yielded much data. Direct observations of easily identified foods, such as wild fruits, and more recently photography, have provided valuable results, both qualitative and quantitative.

The food of nestling birds has been studied by direct observation from hides ; by retrieving samples from young fitted with collars tight enough to prevent the swallowing of meals ; by inducing young herons, cormorants, and hawks to disgorge by fright or massage ; and by persuading parent birds of hole-nesting species to feed an ' artificial nestling '. See below ; also BEHAVIOUR, DEVELOPMENT OF.

See Plates (phot.) 12b, 14, 15. P.H.T.H.

Hartley, P. H. T. 1948. The assessment of the food of birds. Ibis 90 : 361–381.
Meinertzhagen, R. 1959. Pirates and Predators. Edinburgh & London.

FEEDING OF YOUNG: a special aspect of parental behaviour (see PARENTAL CARE ; also DEVELOPMENT, POSTEMBRYONIC). Among nidifugous birds, some species, e.g. ducks *Anas* spp. etc., lead their young but do not directly assist their feeding ; others, e.g. the domestic hen, call their young to food but do not actually give it to them ; while yet others, e.g. gulls (Larinae), actively bring food to their young. Young which remain in the nest are invariably brought food by their parents, or foster-parents in the case of parasitic birds. This may be brought in the claws, e.g. birds-of-prey, or in the bill, e.g. tits *Parus* spp. ; or it may be given by regurgitation, e.g. finches (Fringillidae) or penguins (Spheniscidae). Most young nidicolous birds are also fed for some time after they leave the nest, but there are exceptions ; the young Swift *Apus apus* is not cared for by its parents once it has left the nest hole, and the young Fulmar *Fulmarus glacialis* is abandoned at the nest by its parents and left to enter the wider world alone (as in other petrels). (See also YOUNG BIRD.)

Where the young are actively fed by the parents, the former usually have a begging display. In several cases the stimuli which release begging in the young bird have been analysed. These vary according to the species and with the stage of development of the young, and may be auditory, vibratory, tactile, or visual—or of more than one kind. At present the most detailed analyses of the begging response have been made on finches (Prechtl) and gulls (Weidmann ; Tinbergen & Perdeck). The young of hole-nesting passerines and near-passerines show greatly developed, conspicuous flanges round the beak that were thought to be highly sensitive, so that when the parents touched them the young would beg ; but Wackernagel has now shown that this ' Schnabelwulst' is not well supplied with sensory structures. It has often been suggested that the various components of the begging behaviour shown by the young, and especially the conspicuous gapes which most passerines display, act as releasers of the parents' feeding behaviour, but this has not yet been experimentally examined. However, Betts has found that Pied Flycatchers *Ficedula hypoleuca*, tits *Parus* spp., and Wrens *Troglodytes troglodytes* would offer food to a crude model of a nestling's gape provided that it was moved in a naturalistic way and that the young were calling at the same time ; but the food was then withdrawn unless it was firmly grasped by the model similarly to the way in which nestlings grasp food between the tongue and the upper mandible.

The details of parental behaviour vary greatly from species to species. The males of some birds take no part whatsoever in the care of the young. In other species the male does not participate in incubating eggs or brooding, but does bring food to the nest ; in these cases there is the problem of how the male 'knows there are young in the nest' (Skutch) if he does not regularly visit the nest during the incubation period. In many species male and female share in the care and feeding of the young more or less equally.

The food given to the young may be identical with that used by the adults themselves, or a special diet may be selected. Further, the food given may differ according to the age of the chick ; this sometimes depends upon changes in the availability of different foods in the environment, but often represents an active change in selection by the parents (see FOOD SELECTION). The pigeons and doves (Columbidae) are extraordinary in feeding their young, for the first days after hatching, on a special product of the crop-sacs, known as pigeon's milk, the formation of which is known to be controlled by the hormone prolactin (see MILK, PIGEON).

It has been thought that prolactin is generally of great importance in the control of parental behaviour, but there is insufficient evidence for any such generalisation. The only relevant work specifically on parental feeding is Lehrman's study of the Ring Dove *Streptopelia* 'risoria': adults which have been treated with prolactin will normally feed young squabs placed with them, but are much less likely to do so if their crops are anaesthetised. It seems as if, in this case, prolactin induces development of the crop, and stimulation from the crop then enhances responsiveness to young, rather than that there is any direct effect of prolactin upon the nervous mechanisms controlling feeding behaviour. Much more information, on a variety of species, is needed.

The rate at which young birds are fed and the amount of food which they consume are matters of considerable ecological interest, but it is extremely difficult to obtain adequate data. Mechanical recording gives good information on the rate of visiting the nest, but this is not necessarily equivalent to the feeding frequency : the proportion of visits on which food is given can be determined only by direct observation, and even then there remains the difficulty of assessing the amount of food given. One of the points of special interest, in view of Lack's clutch-size hypothesis, is how the rate of feeding is related to the number of young in the nest, and whether the young in large broods get less food each than do those in smaller broods (see POPULATION DYNAMICS). The evidence so far available suggests that this is not necessarily the case under normal conditions, but that there may be selection against larger broods when there is scarcity of food.

Asynchronous hatching of chicks may possibly be an adaptive device in this context in some species, for example in the Swift and the birds-of-prey ; the younger, smaller chicks tend to die quickly when there is insufficient food, thus leaving more for the elder ones. Sometimes associated with this asynchronous hatching there may be a non-random feeding of the several chicks in the nest. Thus Lockie has shown in Rooks *Corvus frugilegus* and Jackdaws *C. monedula* that the most vigorous chick in the nest tends to get fed first, and the smaller chicks get fed only when there is sufficient food first to satiate the larger ones. Such behaviour is clearly adaptive where there may be shortage of food at times. It would be interesting to know how general such mechanisms are, and whether they are correlated with a likelihood of food shortage. Further, it would be desirable to know how generally the availability of food appears to be the main limiting factor on the size of the brood, and where that is not the case—as seems quite possible, especially for tropical birds—what other factors limit this and whether they act by controlling the rate of feeding the young. Valuable critical studies on the ecological aspects of feeding the young include those of Moreau on Tanganyikan birds, von Haartman on the Pied Flycatcher, Dunnet on the Starling *Sturnus vulgaris*, Gibb on the Great Tit *Parus major*, and Lack on the Swift.

See Plate 45ab (phot.).   E.E.

Dunnet, G. M. 1955. The breeding of the Starling in relation to its food supply. Ibis 97 : 619–662.
Gibb, J. 1955. Feeding rates of Great Tits. Brit. Birds 48 : 49–58.
Haartman, L. von. 1954. Der Trauerfliegenschnäpper. III. Die Nahrungsbiologie. Acta Zool. Fenn. 83 : 1–96.
Lack, D. 1954. The Natural Regulation of Animal Numbers. Oxford.
Lehrman, D. S. 1955. The physiological basis of parental feeding in the Ring Dove. Behav. 7 : 241–286.
Lockie, J. D. 1955. The breeding and feeding of Jackdaws and Rooks. Ibis 97 : 341–369.
Moreau, R. E. 1947. Relations between number in brood, feeding rate and nestling period in nine species of birds in Tanganyika Territory. J. Anim. Ecol. 16 : 205–209.

FEET : (plural of ' foot ')—see under LEG ; SKELETON

FEIGNING INJURY : see DISTRACTION DISPLAY

FEMUR : the ' thigh-bone ' (see SKELETON ; and LEG).

FERAL : literally ' wild ', but applied only to populations of domesticated species that have reverted to a free existence.

FERNBIRD : *Bowdleria punctata* (see WARBLER (1)).

FERTILISATION : the union of the male gamete (spermatozoon, or spermatozoid) with the female gamete (ovum), taking place in the upper part of the oviduct following copulation (see REPRODUCTIVE SYSTEM ; and COPULATION ; DEVELOPMENT, EMBRYONIC ; EGG).

FERTILITY : see HYBRID ; ISOLATING MECHANISM ; REPRODUCTIVE ISOLATION

FIBULA : a bone of the leg (see SKELETON ; and LEG).

FIELDFARE : *Turdus pilaris* (see THRUSH).

FIGBIRD : substantive name of *Sphecotheres* spp. (see ORIOLE (1)). See also BECCAFICO.

FIGHTING : see under AGGRESSION ; TERRITORY ; and DOMINANCE (2) ; also COCK–FIGHTING

FILOPLUME : a hair-like feather (see PLUMAGE).

FILTRATION FEEDING : see FLAMINGO

FINCH : substantive name (or part of compound name) of many species of Fringillidae (Passeriformes, suborder Oscines) ; in the plural, general term for the family. The finches are a heterogeneous group and have been divided into a number of subfamilies. Many authors recognise the following : Fringillinae ; Carduelinae ; Pyrrhuloxinae or Richmondeninae (see CARDINAL-GROSBEAK) ; and Geospizinae (see DARWIN'S FINCHES) ; some also include the Emberizinae (see BUNTING). Some authors do not join these subfamilies as members of the same family, and in the classification followed in this work both the Pyrrhuloxinae and the Emberizinae are placed in a separate family, the Emberizidae. Note should also be made that many weaver-finches (Estrildidae), chiefly from Australia and southeastern Asia, are called 'finches' (see WEAVER-FINCH). The present article is restricted to the Fringillinae and Carduelinae, and only these will hereafter be referred to as finches, the other groups being discussed in separate articles. At the outset, however, it should be made clear that the systematic position of the Fringillinae is controversial ; but the writer agrees with the great majority in considering them to be more closely related to the cardueline finches than to any other group (see also under FRINGILLIDAE).

General Characteristics. The finches can be characterised as being primarily arboreal, 'seed-eating' birds, with nine primaries and twelve tail feathers. The outermost of the ten primaries is vestigial and hidden, except in *Urocynchramus*, where it is very well developed and, apparently, functional. Coloration varies in different genera (see below) ; sexual dimorphism may be slight or strong.

The bill is adapted for extracting or shelling seeds and is very hard, swollen at the base and more or less conical in shape, but nevertheless varies so enormously that these variations are worthy of comment. The two extremes among living species are represented by the Goldfinch *Carduelis carduelis*, in which most of the bill is slender and becomes extremely attenuated and needlelike at the tip, and by the grosbeaks *Mycerobas* spp., in which it is very massive, pyramidal in appearance. The extinct *Chaunoproctus ferreorostris* had an even larger and blunter bill than *Mycerobas*, the bill being about the size of the skull. The birds with these big bills have very large heads, as might be expected, and thick 'bull-necks', and look very stocky. These birds are able to exert great strength to secure the kernels of the fruits on which they feed. Recent studies of the Hawfinch *Coccothraustes coccothraustes* by Sims (1955) and Mountfort and his associates (1957) have shown that in this bird (in which the bill is only about half the size of that of *Mycerobas* or of hawfinches of the genus *Eophona*) the adductor muscles are enormously developed, and that crushing loads varying from 60 to 159 lb., on an area equivalent to that applied by the bird's bill, are required to crush the stones of cherries and olives that the bird cracks so easily to extract their kernels. This is the more astonishing when one considers that the Hawfinch weighs only 55 grams. The most curious adaptation of all is shown, however, by the crossbills *Loxia* spp., in which the tips of the bill cross at oblique angles to extract seeds from the cones of pines and other conifers.

The voice of the finches varies according to territorial or other needs and can be loud, vigorous, and musical, or 'rudimentary', but can be trained to high musical levels as in the Canary *Serinus canaria*. Most species have a well developed flight song and are gregarious and social, as compared with most other passerines. The eating of salt and the lack of nest sanitation have been mentioned as typical traits of the cardueline finches, but all species keep their nests clean during the first few days, and some permanently (e.g. the Bullfinch *Pyrrhula pyrrhula*).

Breeding. The nest of the finches is cup-shaped, and is well and compactly built by the hen alone, although the male may be in close attendance. Twigs, grasses, roots, and, in some species, moss and lichens, are the chief building materials, but bark fibres may be used also. Fine roots, hair, wool, down, and a few feathers, or various combinations of these materials, are added to the lining. Many carduelines nest in loose 'colonies' with weak territories. In 18 species that breed or occur in the British Isles and represent 7 typical genera and *Fringilla*, the nest can be built close to or actually on the ground (Twite *Acanthis flavirostris*) or, because of the lack of taller vegetation, in very low dwarf willows and birches or in rock crevices sheltered by willows (Arctic Redpoll *A. hornemanni*). In the other species it is built at levels varying from about 4 to 80 feet up in bushes, hedgerows, and trees. The eggs are blue or bluish, more or less spotted or streaked with brown or with reddish ; or the ground colour varies from pale greenish to bluish (*Loxia*), and from bluish to brown or olive (*Fringilla*). The normal clutch is 4–6 in most of the 78 species, 3–4 in the crossbills, and 6–7 in the Brambling *Fringilla montifringilla*. The eggs are small in relation to body size. Incubation is performed almost invariably by the female alone, but in the Bullfinch the male is said to take a small part. The incubation period varies from 10 to 14 days, with an average of 12 or 13 in most of the 18 British species ; exact information is lacking (or was not available to the writer) in the case of the Citril Finch *Serinus citrinella* and White-winged Crossbill *Loxia leucoptera*. The young are usually fed by regurgitation.

Distribution. Most finches inhabit the temperate regions of Eurasia, Africa, and the Americas, but a few are found in the arctic and subarctic, in deserts, and in tropical or subtropical regions. Some are restricted to high mountains, the Rose-breasted Rose Finch *Carpodacus puniceus* of Asia breeding well over the tree-line at altitudes which may reach 18 000 feet, perhaps higher than any other song-bird.

There are only 3 species of Fringillinae—the well-known Chaffinch *Fringilla coelebs*, the Canary Islands Chaffinch *F. teydea*, and the Brambling *F. montifringilla*. The Carduelinae include 122 species. Together they constitute an Old World group that has spread to the New World, where only one genus, ' *Spinus* ' (=*Carduelis*), has shown much adaptive radiation. The Fringillinae are restricted to the Palaearctic Region ; and the Carduelinae are best represented there, with 21 genera and 68 species. The cardueliness are well represented also in the Ethiopian Region, with 9 genera and 36 species, and, seemingly, in the New World with 8 genera and 25 species. An analysis of the three contingents shows, however, that the relatively large number in the New World is somewhat misleading, as 6 of its 25 species, in 4 genera, are also very widely distributed in the Palaearctic Region and are conspecific with its populations. These are 2 redpolls *Acanthis* spp., 2 crossbills *Loxia* spp., the Rosy Finch *Leucosticte arctoa*, and the Pine Grosbeak *Pinicola enucleator*. Of the remaining 4 genera in the New World, only 2 are endemic, as against 6 endemic out of 9

for the Ethiopian Region, and 13 endemic out of 20 for the Palaearctic Region (not counting *Fringilla*, but merging ' *Spinus* ' with *Carduelis*). Furthermore, the 2 endemic genera of the New World, *Hesperiphona* (e.g. the Evening Grosbeak *H. vespertina*) and *Loximitris*, are closely related to and weakly differentiated from, respectively, *Eophona* of eastern Asia and the widely distributed *Carduelis* (or ' *Spinus* '). *Hesperiphona* consists of 2 North American species, 1 of which ranges south to Guatemala, and *Loximitris* is monotypic and restricted to Hispaniola. *Carpodacus* (e.g. the Purple Finch *C. purpureus*) is represented by 3 species in the New World, and ' *Spinus* ' by 13 in North and South America.

The cardueline finches have not spread to Madagascar, the Australo-Papuan area, or the islands of the south Pacific, and they are represented in the Oriental Region by only two endemic and a few Palaearctic species, the breeding ranges of which extend to that region. The two endemic species are a bullfinch in the Philippines and a goldfinch in Sumatra and Java.

Fringillinae. The 3 species of Fringillinae differ from the Carduelinae by having no crop, in some other slight anatomical details, and in aspects of their behaviour, and for these reasons are placed in a separate subfamily. The chaffinches are bluish and green with chestnut areas in the male ; the Brambling, of northern Eurasia, is black and white with rusty tinges and is one of the most highly migratory of all finches.

Carduelinae. The serins *Serinus* spp. are yellowish and green, or greyish and nearly white, with a streaked plumage ; some have black areas in the plumage, or little touches of gold. They number 15 species and are best represented in the Ethiopian Region, ranging north to the Azores, Madeira, the Canaries, the Mediterranean area, and other southern parts of the Palaearctic Region, a distribution which suggests an African origin. *Carduelis*, *Acanthis*, and ' *Spinus* ' group 30 species of goldfinches (e.g. the Goldfinch *C. carduelis* of the Palaearctic Region), greenfinches (e.g. the Oriental Greenfinch *C. sinica* of E. Asia), siskins (e.g. the Pine Siskin *C. pinus* of N. America), redpolls *Acanthis* spp., and the Linnet *A. cannabina* and Twite *A. flavirostris*. Most species are streaked, and as a rule sexual dimorphism is slight. The plumage shows various combinations of yellow, green, grey, brown, black, white, red, and gold. The rosy finches *Leucosticte* spp., are restricted to high mountains, and the three species have a rather dull plumage of grey, brown, and almost black, beautifully relieved, however, by rose and silver.

The 4 species of *Rhodopechys* inhabit the desert or very predominantly arid areas and are brownish, greyish, and rosy with black and white areas; to name an example, the Trumpeter Finch *R. githaginea* ranges from the Canary Islands to north-west India.

Carpodacus is the largest genus, with 20 species of rose and purple finches; these are brownish or greyish and, usually, heavily streaked sparrow-like birds, the male being more or less extensively washed with various shades of red from vinaceous and purplish-red to rose, and adorned in some species with silvery feathers about the head and throat; the females lack these feathers and the red pigment. It is the most interesting genus, and some of its species, such as the Common Rose Finch *Carpodacus erythrinus*, are rapidly extending their range; others seem to be dwindling, as in the case of the Sinai Rose Finch *C. synoicus*, which now comprises only four very widely separated populations in the Sinai Peninsula and neighbouring Jordan, Afghanistan, the region of Yarkand in Chinese Turkestan, and Kansu. The crossbills *Loxia* spp. are curious birds that inhabit coniferous forests where they are more or less nomadic, shifting their breeding ground in correlation with the success or failure of the cone crops. Their migratory movements are also very erratic and they are famous for their 'irruptions' into regions where they may have been absent for some years (see IRRUPTION). They are greyish-brown, tinged with greenish, washed more or less extensively with red or orange in the male; the mandibles cross at the tip of the bill of the adult. The bullfinches *Pyrrhula* spp. are a well characterised group of 6 species. They are very gentle birds with a pleasing coloration consisting of soft shades of brown, blue, grey, orange, and red. The grosbeak group (*Coccothraustes*, *Eophona*, *Hesperiphona*, and *Mycerobas*) are noted for their very powerful and massive bills, discussed above.

A salient characteristic of the cardueline finches of the Old World is their relatively large number of well differentiated monotypic genera. Most of these are localised species, some of which are extremely rare in collections. The most interesting is probably Przevalski's Rose Finch *Urocynchramus pylzowi*, which differs from all other Fringillidae by having the outermost of the ten primaries long; its habits and life history are unknown, and this is true of several of the monotypic genera.

See Plates (colour) 6, 29, 43 (egg). C.V.

Marler, P. 1956. The Behaviour of the Chaffinch, *Fringilla coelebs*. Leiden.
Mountfort, G. R. 1957. The Hawfinch. London.

Skutch, A. F. 1954. Life histories of Central American birds. Pt. I. Pacific Coast Avifauna no. 31. Berkeley, Cal.

FINCH-LARK: substantive name of *Eremopterix* spp. (see LARK).

FINCH, PLUSHCAPPED: *Catamblyrhynchus diadema*, a species that some authors place in a family of its own, the Catamblyrhynchidae (Passeriformes, suborder Oscines), and others treat as belonging to the Thraupinae (see TANAGER). The allocation is in either event provisional, as not enough is known about the possible relationships of this peculiar bird. It is found in South America, from Venezuela to Bolivia, and almost nothing is known of its habits. It is a finch-like bird about 6 inches long, mostly dark grey above, with black markings on the head, and reddish below. The fore part of the crown carries golden-brown feathers that are erect and stiff to the touch, like plush.

FINCH, SNOW-: substantive name of *Montifringilla* spp. (see SPARROW (1)).

FINCH, WEAVER: see WEAVER-FINCH

FINFOOT: name of all 3 species of Heliornithidae (Gruiformes, suborder Heliornithes); in the plural (finfoots), general term for the family; they are also called 'sungrebes'. The family is confined to tropical and subtropical zones. In structure, appearance, and habits its members combine characters of grebes (Podicipitidae), cormorants (Phalacrocoracidae), darters (Anhingidae), ducks (Anatidae), and coots (Fulicinae), but they are most nearly allied to the rails (Rallidae); they are distinguished by several anatomical features, and generally by a long, thin head and neck, very broadly lobed toes, and strongly graduated tail. Mainly aquatic, they have a peculiar forward-leaning gait on land.

Pale brown plumage, with a varying admixture of green, grey, black, and white, contrasting with brightly coloured bill and feet, would make a finfoot conspicuous but for its habitat. This is confined to the margins of rivers and creeks, occasionally lakes, bordered or overhung by forest or thick vegetation. Still or slow-running water is preferred, but the bird has no difficulty in adapting itself on occasions to rapids, spate, or flood. In the secluded and inaccessible surroundings of its choice, pairs or family parties swim swiftly or clamber expertly over fallen branches in pursuit of the insects, aquatic and terrestrial, that form their main diet. Well adapted for diving, they have seldom been observed to do so; and records of fish being taken are unreliable, although frogs, crustaceans, and molluscs have often been noted in stomach contents. Leaves have been found in the stomach of one species, and all seem to swallow a quantity of mud and grit. When disturbed the birds prefer to make for thick cover rather than to escape by diving or flying, the long wings seeming seldom to be used except for coot-like 'scuttering' to the nearest bank.

Finfoot *Podica senegalensis*, the African species. *C.E.T.K.*

Nests are built on horizontal branches or fallen trees, often in refuse left by floods, although breeding seems usually to coincide with the earlier half of the rainy season. The eggs, which are remarkably spherical but generally ralline in appearance, are cream-coloured with reddish-brown or purple markings and number from 2 to 5, occasionally 7 ; those of the smallest species still remain to be described.

Three widely separate species now represent the family. The distinctions between them are less remarkable than similarities that suggest an ancient origin and a once far more widespread and continuous distribution. Smallest and least specialised is *Heliornis fulica*, found from southern Mexico to north-eastern Argentina and typically a bird of the Guiana rivers. It is less than a foot in length, looking no larger than a Dabchick *Podiceps ruficollis*, but more slender, and has remarkable black and yellow striped toes. The olive-brown of its general coloration is an exact match of that of *Heliopais personata*, found in south-eastern Asia, from Assam to Malaya, which is twice as long and three or four times as bulky. In the largest species, *Podica senegalensis*, attaining over 2 feet in length, the brown of the plumage lacks any olive tinge but, in the adult, is washed to a greater or lesser extent with peacock green or blue. *Podica*, of which 4 races are recognised (mainly on size) from West Africa

to the 'tropical corridor' of eastern Cape Province, shares with *Heliornis* the white striping on the side of the head, and with *Heliopais* the peculiar feature of having a brighter, yellow iris in the female as compared with the dark brown eye of the male. Indeed, the females of all species tend to be more conspicuously marked.

Due to the extreme difficulty of observation, many peculiarities of the species are unexplained. The stiff shafts of the tail feathers of *Podica*, and a knob on the carpal joint of the wing, may indicate that it is more of a climber than the other two species. A knife-like ridge at the base of the culmen in *Heliopais* appears to develop only in the breeding season. All species are sexually dimorphic in size and also in colour, the rufous cheeks of the female *Heliornis* being noteworthy, although in the African and perhaps the Asian species this colour difference may be largely seasonal ; certainly adult males of the latter two species, which tend to dark grey and black about the head and neck, are comparatively rare in collections. The significance of the zebra-striped feet of *Heliornis*, the bright red feet of *Podica*, or the pea-green yellow-lobed feet of *Heliopais* is unknown ; but in the muddy waters frequented recognition factors rather than aid to the capture of prey seem to be indicated. With its long pointed but slightly decurved bill, the finfoot has even been recorded as catching butterflies.

Little is known of the voices of the three species. To *Podica* are variously attributed hoarse croaks, growls, shrill screams, and a booming note ; *Heliopais* is believed to be the author of a 'water-bottle' bubbling sound ; and *Heliornis* is recorded as emitting a double or triple bark. H.F.I.E.

Pitman, C. R. S. 1962. Notes on the African Finfoot *Podica senegalensis* (Vieillot) with particular reference to Uganda. Bull. Brit. Orn. Cl. 82 : 156–160. (References.)

FIREBACK: substantive name of some *Lophura* spp. (see PHEASANT).

FIRECREST: *Regulus ignicapillus* (see WARBLER (1)).

FIRECROWN: substantive name of *Sephanoides* spp. (for family see HUMMINGBIRD).

FIRE-EYE: substantive name of *Pyriglena* spp. (see ANTBIRD).

FIREFINCH: substantive name of some waxbills *Estrilda* spp. (see WEAVER-FINCH).

FIRETAIL: name popularly applied to various red-tailed species in different parts of the world ;

in Australia one of the recognised names for *Zonaeginthus* spp. (for family see WEAVER-FINCH).

FIREWOOD-GATHERER: *Anumbius annumbi* (see OVENBIRD (1)).

FISCAL: substantive name, alternatively 'fiscal shrike', of some African *Lanius* spp. ; used without qualification for *L. collaris* (see SHRIKE).

FISH-HAWK: American name for the Osprey *Pandion haliaetus* (see HAWK).

FISHING: see FEEDING HABITS

FISSIPALMATE: term applied to a foot that is discontinuously webbed, with lobes or fringes on the separate toes.

FIXATION: general term in nomenclature for all methods of determining the type-species of a genus or subgenus (see TYPE-SPECIES).

FIXED ACTION PATTERN: the presently accepted translation, abbreviated to 'FAP', of the term 'Erbkoordination'; a behaviour pattern which, as defined by Lorenz, (i) is invariant ; (ii) is relatively independent of external stimuli once started ; (iii) has its own specific motivation revealed in vacuum performances ; and (iv) shows specific exhaustion, in that one performance makes an immediately subsequent performance less likely.

A FAP is always associated with a taxis component which steers the invariant FAP relative to the environment, rather as a man might steer a mower with automatically revolving blades to cut particular clumps of grass (see TAXIS). The first behaviour pattern to be considered in this way was the egg rolling of the Grey Lag Goose *Anser anser* (Lorenz & Tinbergen 1938). Here the FAP consists of the goose putting the bill over an egg and then drawing its bill towards its breast, and the taxis component consists of slight lateral balancing movements. The dependence of the taxis component on environmental cues can be shown by substituting a model that is more difficult to roll, when such movements increase ; and the relative independence of the FAP can be shown by removing the egg half-way through the movement, when the bill is drawn steadily back without balancing movements. The taxis component of a FAP may change during development, which confirms that it is correct to separate the two. Thus the gaping response of young Blackbirds *Turdus merula* is at first gravity controlled (they gape upwards) ; later they direct the gape at an optical stimulus.

A second component always associated with a FAP is the releasing mechanism ; that is, the per-ceptual neural mechanism which ensures that one particular pattern of stimuli releases a particular FAP (see SIGN STIMULUS ; also RECOGNITION ; RELEASER). Egg rolling, for example, is released by roughly egg-shaped objects within a particular range of size. A FAP is not usually given in the absence of appropriate releasing stimuli even although the tendency to give it (measured, for example, by the frequency and intensity of other FAPs with which it is usually associated) may be high.

Characteristics. Some qualifications of the characteristics first used to define the FAP must be made in the light of later work.

1. *Invariance.* This remains in practice the best distinguishing feature ; nearly all the FAPs listed by ethologists as components of displays have been recognised in this way. If the behavioural components treated as FAPs are to be really invariant, they must be simple. It has been suggested that such terms be used only of components of behaviour that are not readily divisible into other components ; thus the wing shivering of the Great Tit *Parus major* in courtship could be divided into a FAP of up and down movement, and one of extension and flexion. The problem is, on the whole, one of convenience.

2. *Relative independence of environmental cues.* When FAPs were first discussed it was emphasised that, once released, they were 'independent of the animal's receptors as well as of further external stimulation' (Lorenz & Tinbergen 1938). Experimental evidence is scanty, but it seems likely that proprioceptors are important in co-ordinating the movements of a FAP, although stepping of limbs completely deprived of afferent nerves can occur (see NERVOUS SYSTEM). It may, therefore, be impossible to strip away the last orienting and taxis components to leave a pure FAP. The relative independence of external cues is, of course, true. It is, however, also possible that in some cases a FAP comes to a stop because certain stimuli have been perceived rather than because of changes within itself. Some FAPs are certainly maintained by particular stimuli ; in the Blackheaded Gull *Larus ridibundus* the attitude of brooding is maintained continuously only in the presence of stimuli from a full clutch of eggs.

3. *Specific motivation.* FAPs sometimes occur spontaneously when, because of a lack of the correct releasing stimuli, they have not been performed for a long time. This has been observed for nest-building and hunting movements. The various manipulative and hunting activities shown in play by birds, e.g. tossing objects by hornbills (Bucerotidae), appear also to occur in the absence of other

motivations. Lorenz (1951) believes that a FAP acquires specific motivation in proportion as it becomes ritualised (see RITUALISATION) ; specific appetitive behaviour also develops. The FAP is then said to possess 'reaction specific energy'. A distinction should be drawn between lowering of the threshold of a group of FAPs during an increase in the drive that they express, due to their non-performance (e.g. in hunger), and a lowering of the threshold of a particular FAP during non-performance. Evidence for the latter effect is scanty, and it is not clear that such 'accumulation of reaction specific energy' can occur when appropriate motivating stimuli are absent during the period of non-performance.

4. *Specific exhaustion.* If a FAP is repeatedly elicited by the same stimulus, its threshold may rise until it can no longer be produced. If, for example, mobbing is elicited in a Chaffinch *Fringilla coelebs* by a particular model of an owl (Strigiformes sp.), it will wane and cease ; that is to say, a number of FAPs (calls, tail movements, etc.) will become less frequent and cease. If a new model is presented, mobbing will begin again, but at reduced intensity. Here, then, exhaustion can be divided into response-specific and stimulus-specific effects. Response-specific exhaustion has been regarded as due to the exhaustion of 'response-specific energy', that is, due to the reverse of the changes producing the threshold lowerings discussed in the previous section.

However, the exhaustion of a response consisting of a single FAP (gaping in young passerines) has proved to be entirely stimulus-specific. If gaping to an acoustic stimulus is exhausted, it will nevertheless be immediately given at full strength as soon as the acoustic stimulus is replaced by an optical one, and vice versa. Similar results hold for the gobbling call of the Turkey *Meleagris gallopavo*, elicited by pure notes of various pitches. Thus, these studies of a single FAP have produced no evidence of exhaustion of the FAP as such. It may be significant that changes in the strength of hunger had no effect on the rate of exhaustion of gaping, so that in this case, at least, the FAP was relatively free of the influence of other behaviour patterns. The distinction between stimulus-specific and response-specific exhaustion may well be meaningless for FAPs aroused only by a single simple releaser.

Relation to other terms. 1. *Reflex.* A reflex is repeatedly elicitable without exhaustion, unlike a FAP ; however, we have seen above that, in some cases at least, exhaustion affects the releasing mechanism rather than the FAP itself. It is hard to make other distinctions. Both a FAP and a reflex may show a 'warming up' period during which individually inadequate stimuli summate to produce the reaction (e.g. turkey gobbling and postural reflexes, respectively). Both show threshold changes ; that is, when the 'central excitatory state' of a reflex, or the 'reaction specific energy' of a FAP are high, the reaction may be given to stimuli that in other states would be inadequate. Lorenz suggested that reactions showing long-term threshold changes due to changes in internal stimuli might none the less be considered as reflexes (e.g. micturition following urine accumulation), but that where such changes were purely nervous a FAP is involved. Very many long-term changes in drive-level (affecting the threshold of FAPs) are controlled by changes in internal stimuli, and an attempt to draw a line merely confirms the difficulty of distinguishing FAP and reflex.

2. *Appetitive behaviour and Werkzeugreaktionen.* The taxis component of an instinctive act has from the first been recognised as intergrading with appetitive behaviour (i.e. variable behaviour that brings an animal towards the goal object or situation appropriate to its motivation). The invariant motor patterns that are used in locomotion and manipulation (e.g. in tits *Parus* spp., such hunting movements as leaf turning), and that as a result occur in the appetitive behaviour expressing various different drives, were distinguished as 'Werkzeugreaktionen' (Lorenz 1937), even although, as they were recognised to occur spontaneously at times (e.g. spontaneous attempts to fly in young birds), it would not have been possible otherwise to distinguish them from FAPs. The recent tendency has been to emphasise the resemblances between 'Werkzeugreaktionen' and FAPs, and to suggest that appetitive behaviour may show exhaustion phenomena similar to that shown by a FAP (Hinde 1953). Appetitive behaviour excluding obvious 'Werkzeugreaktionen' (i.e. variable goal-directed behaviour involving only locomotion) certainly shows a phenomenon very like exhaustion in 'extinction' (e.g. the number of unrewarded approaches to a food-pan appears to be the critical factor determining when a conditioned lever-pressing response in rats will cease to be elicitable, i.e. be extinguished).

Modern usage. As noted above, the characteristics that theoretically most definitely distinguish a FAP are invariance and relative independence of environmental cues. In practice these have been the characteristics almost always used to identify FAPs, and it would probably be in best accord with modern usage if the term FAP were redefined in respect of these two characteristics alone, excluding any generalisations about motivation. It also seems best to restrict the term to behaviour patterns that cannot be readily broken up into simpler units. The puffed-run courtship display of a male Yellow-hammer *Emberiza citrinella* involves, for instance, such FAPS as feather raising, crouching, bill lowering, and so on.

Innateness. When a FAP is said to be innate it is in general meant that it appears in animals reared in isolation, and that it seems to require no preliminary practice before it appears as a co-ordinated act. Strictly speaking, an innate behaviour pattern would be one for which the neural basis develops independently of any overt performances of the pattern or parts of the pattern ; thus salamanders developing in anaesthesia show co-ordinated swimming when the anaesthetic is removed. Naturally, such evidence is rarely available. Evidence is accumulating for nest building, both in rats and in birds, that early manipulative experience with material like that used in the nest may be needed if normal nest building is to occur. Nevertheless, the term innate remains useful to express the fact that the causal factors determining the development of a FAP, in the form characteristic of a particular species, are present in all individuals of that species even if reared in isolation. See also BEHAVIOUR, DEVELOPMENT OF.

Evolutionary Study. Attention was first paid to FAPS when it was found that there were differences between the invariant behaviour patterns making up the displays of related species of pigeons (Whitman) and ducks (Heinroth). Later comparative studies have attempted to determine the course of evolution of such FAPS, using (i) the retained resemblances to the ancestral pattern, (ii) the retention of the motivation appropriate to the ancestral pattern, and, (iii) the existence of intermediate stages in related species.

Some of the most fertile sources for the FAPS of displays appear to have been toilet movements given in conflict situations (e.g. 'grunt-whistle' of Mallard *Anas platyrhynchos* courtship), intention movements of flight, such as tail and wing movements or crouches (e.g. courtship in pigeons (Columbidae), fringillids, ducks (Anatidae), cormorants (Phalacrocoracidae), and others) ; in passerine aggressive displays ; in begging, and behaviour due to autonomic activity in conflicts. A fuller account is given under RITUALISATION.

FAPS used in manipulation (e.g. pecking) or locomotion, unlike those of displays, have remained relatively unchanged over a wide range of avian species. This is probably because some displays are important in specific recognition (e.g. at pairing),

and so there would be a strong selective pressure towards distinctiveness to prevent interbreeding.

Such a state of affairs is, however, exceptionally favourable to convergence between more distantly related groups. The sources for components of passerine courtship display, for instance, are relatively limited, so that where hybridisation is impossible the possibility of the evolution of similar displays by chance is appreciable. Some FAPS, such as tail flicks and other intention movements of flight, appear to be selected for conspicuousness alone, so that their form is of secondary importance. As a result, form seems to have been determined by origin alone. Tail-flicking of wagtail type has appeared separately in several groups of ground-feeding insectivores ; a synchronising of leg movements, in running, with tail movements may be the cause.

Differences in FAPS must therefore be used with as much caution in taxonomy as differences in any other characteristic. It would be preferable to use the present systematic classification to study the evolution of FAPS, rather than to use differences in FAPS to amend the classification.   R.J.A.

Hinde, R. A. 1953. Appetitive behaviour, consummatory act and the hierarchical organisation of behaviour—with special reference to the Great Tit (*Parus major*). Behaviour 5 : 189–224.

Lorenz, K. 1937. Über den Begriff der Instinkthandlung. Folia Biotheor. 2 : 17–50.

Lorenz, K. 1951. Über die Entstehung auslösender 'Zeremonien'. Vogelwarte 16 : 9–13.

Lorenz, K. & Tinbergen, N. 1938. Taxis und Instinkthandlung in der Eirollbewegung der Graugans. Z. Tierpsychol. 2 : L 1–29.

Tinbergen, N. 1951. The Study of Instinct. Oxford.

Tinbergen, N. & Kuenen, D. J. 1939. Über die auslösenden und die richtunggebenden Reizsituationen der Sperrbewegung von jungen Drosseln (*Turdus m. merula* L. und *T. e. ericetorum* Turton). Z. Tierpsychol. 3 : 37–60.

Thorpe, W. H. 1956. Learning and Instinct in Animals. London.

FLAMINGO: substantive name of the species of Phoenicopteridae ; in the plural (–gos), general term for the family and suborder (Phoenicopteri). In the classification followed in this work the flamingos are assigned to the Ciconiiformes, but they are by some placed in a separate order Phoenicopteriformes. They are a remarkable group of birds found in specialised habitats in the Old and New Worlds. They are characteristically large (3–6 feet in length), with long sinuous necks and long legs terminating in webbed feet. The unique feature is the large bill, sharply decurved in the middle ' with the lower jaw large and trough-like and the upper small and lid-like ' (Jenkin). In adult plumage they are invariably pink and red in colour, with the strongest hues on the upper wing-coverts and with black flight feathers ; the face is bare, and the bill and legs are usually bright red or yellow and the eye orange. Their bodies contain large amounts of stored red fat. They can both swim and fly with ease, and in flight the neck is held extended. Some species undertake considerable migratory movements, chiefly at night.

Their systematic position is obscure. On the basis of field habits and Mallophaga they seem most akin to the ducks and geese (Anseriformes) ; on some anatomical evidence they have affinities with storks (Ciconiidae) and ibises (Threskiornithidae), while recent work with egg-white proteins places them close to herons (Ardeidae). The ' honking ', gabbling, and other notes are decidedly goose-like.

The group contains three genera ; *Phoenicopterus*, *Phoeniconaias*, and *Phoenicoparrus*. The first has been divided by some authors into three species *P. ruber*, *P. chilensis*, and *P. roseus* (' antiquorum '), but as the bill structure and habits of all these are essentially similar it seems preferable to regard them as races of *P. ruber*, sometimes collectively called the Greater Flamingo. *Phoeniconaias* is monotypic, and *Phoenicoparrus*, distinguished from the other genera by the absence of a hind toe, has two species both inhabiting alkaline lakes in the high Andes up to 14 000 feet above sea level.

All flamingos are highly gregarious and sometimes occur in huge numbers together, when they form possibly the most impressive and colourful of all bird spectacles. It has been estimated that there may be 6 000 000 flamingos, of which the vast majority, perhaps 4 500 000, are Lesser Flamingos *Phoeniconaias minor* inhabiting parts of Africa and India. *Phoenicopterus ruber* follows it in numbers ; and the rarest is *Phoenicoparrus jamesi*, which was believed to be almost extinct between 1924 and 1957 but has been recently rediscovered in the Andes of Bolivia.

Flamingos are invariably associated with brackish or salt-water lakes or lagoons, usually with warm climates and often with high altitudes. They obtain their food from the water and mud by means of highly specialised filtering structures (described in detail by Jenkin) in the bill, which is held upside down. The tongue, which is thick and fleshy, lies in a groove in the lower mandible and works to and fro like a piston. Water is taken into the bill, either by simple suction of the tongue or by vigorous gobbling movements of the tongue and throat, and is expelled again three to four times a second. Coarse particles of food are kept out by stiff excluder hairs, and the finer particles (chiefly blue-green

algae and diatoms) are caught on the fine hair-like lamellae which cover the inside of the mandibles. The food masses are worked on to the tongue and thence swallowed. This description applies to *Phoenicoparrus* and *Phoeniconaias*, which have what are termed ' deep keeled ' bills, with the upper mandible triangular in section, fitting closely into a groove in the lower mandible, and the inside surfaces of both entirely covered with an expanse of fine lamellae. *Phoenicopterus ruber* has the upper mandible ' shallow keeled ', and only small parts of the interior of the bill are covered with filtering lamellae. Its diet is more varied than that of the other species, including small molluscs, crustacea, and the organic particles in mud as well as algae and diatoms. It is essentially a bottom-feeder, whereas *Phoeniconaias* can obtain its food by sweeping its head from side to side near the water surface. The difference in feeding habits between *Phoenicopterus ruber roseus* and *Phoeniconaias minor* probably accounts for their ability to co-exist, as in some localities they do in great numbers. It has been pointed out, further, that in the highly alkaline or saline waters where all these birds live they must extract their food practically dry, as the water itself, if consumed in large quantities, could be toxic.

All flamingos breed in colonies, sometimes in enormous numbers. In East Africa individual colonies of over 900 000 pairs have been seen, and more than 1 000 000 pairs on one lake. The nests are truncated cones of mud about 6–14 inches high with a shallow depression on top, scooped up by the bird's bill. Differences in water level may affect the suitability of the site for a colony, and this may account for seemingly capricious changes in locality and for complete absence of breeding in some years. On the other hand, *P. ruber* has been known to breed on small rocky islands, making a nest of grasses, feathers, and gravel in the absence of suitable mud. The clutch is normally one, less than one per cent of nests containing two eggs. The eggs of all species are chalky white overlaying a bluish shell, and the yolk is blood-red. Contrary to popular belief, the flamingo incubates on top of the nest with its long legs folded beneath it, and not hanging down at the sides. Incubation periods are about 28 days. See Plate 37a (phot.).

The young when first hatched are grey and, in *P. ruber* and *P. minor* at least, have red bills and red swollen legs, both of which turn black within a few days. For 2–3 days they do not leave the nest, but they can swim at 10 days if required. They form, thereafter, into huge herds attended by a few adults. The bill at first is straight and unspecialised (as in ancestral forms from the Miocene), and the young are dependent on their parents for food until the filtering structure is properly formed and they can fly, at about 65-70 days. They are fed throughout this time on food of fluid consistency regurgitated by the parents. The parent is apparently able to recognise its own chick in spite of the seeming impossibility of this when the young are gathered in huge tight-packed herds. The first immature plumage of young flamingos is grey with a varying amount of brown markings and little pink colour ; the bill and legs are then black. They moult into adult plumage apparently between one year and one and a half years of age, but it seems probable that they do not breed for several years.

Jenkin has remarked that the filtration feeding of flamingos is comparable with that of whale-bone whales (Mysticeti) and otherwise unique among adult vertebrates. She has pointed out that the apparatus gives the birds a choice of the size but not the kind of food particles. The food requirements of large flocks is enormous, and the distribution of flamingos is thus influenced by the availability of habitats where certain food organisms can multiply in great abundance—localities with brackish or alkaline water such as are especially found in arid regions with high evaporation.

The Old World form of the Greater Flamingo *Phoenicopterus ruber roseus* breeds in the Camargue in southern France and (possibly) in southern Spain ; otherwise it is native to the Caspian Sea and Persian Gulf area of Asia (including north-west India) and to some widely separated parts of Africa. The American Flamingo *P. r. ruber* is found, less widely than formerly, on the Atlantic seaboard and islands of subtropical and tropical America ; and *P. r. chilensis* inhabits temperate South America ; the Lesser Flamingo *Phoeniconaias minor* is found in East and South Africa, Madagascar, and north-west India. As already mentioned, *Phoenicoparrus andinus* and *Phoenicoparrus jamesi* are purely Andean.

L.H.B.

Allen, R. P. 1956. The Flamingos : their natural history and survival. Natl. Audubon Soc. Res. Rep. no. 5 : 1–285.
Brown, L. H. 1959. The Mystery of the Flamingos. London.
Jenkin, P. M. 1951. The filter-feeding and food of flamingos. (Phoenicopteri). Phil. Trans. Roy. Soc. 240B : 401–493.

FLANK : see TOPOGRAPHY

FLAPPING FLIGHT : see FLIGHT

FLATBILL : substantive name of *Rhynchocyclus* spp., sometimes applied also to other genera (see FLYCATCHER (2)).

FLAVOUR : see PALATABILITY OF BIRDS AND EGGS

FLEAS : see ECTOPARASITE

FLEDGING : term usually applied to the acquisition by a young bird of its first true feathers ; when the process is complete the bird is ' fledged ', and may for a short time be described as a ' fledgling ' (see PLUMAGE ; YOUNG BIRD).

FLICKER : substantive name of *Colaptes* spp. (see WOODPECKER).

FLIGHT : the form of locomotion especially characteristic of birds as a class and determining their main adaptations, these largely persisting even in the small minority that have lost the power (see AVES ; FLIGHTLESSNESS ; LOCOMOTION). The primary adaptation to this purpose lies in the modification of the forelimbs as organs of flight (see WING) ; the wings are used to provide both upward lift against gravity and forward propulsion through the air, being capable also of various special movements required for purposes of manoeuvre. Other parts of the body surface play a more passive part ; but to a greater or lesser extent the tail feathers are moved or spread to assist in braking or turning or to increase area (see PLUMAGE ; SHAPE AND POSTURE ; TAIL). The internal mechanisms concerned are for the most part considered elsewhere; see especially HEART ; MUSCULATURE ; PNEUMATISATION OF BONE ; RESPIRATORY SYSTEM ; SKELETON. See also ENERGY REQUIREMENTS ; HEARING AND BALANCE ; MOULT ; WINGS, COMPARATIVE ANATOMY OF.

Lift and Drag. Although it is possible to get lift with flat surfaces, curved ones give far better results. A bird's wing is convex on the top surface, and concave below, and is thick near the ' leading edge ' and thin at the ' trailing edge ' ; aircraft designers have found no other shape to be better. This shape is very easily evolved from a forelimb, the thick edge holding the bones and muscles while the thin edge is made up of the feathers projecting backwards. Such a wing is called an ' aerofoil '. Fast fliers such as divers (Gaviiformes) have flatter wings than slow fliers such as owls (Strigiformes).

Although the wing moves forward through the air, it is much easier to think of it as stationary with the air flowing past it. This air-flow produces a force that is nearly vertical, the ' reaction '. It is usual to resolve it into two components, the ' lift ' and the ' drag '. The point X (Fig. 1) where the reaction acts is the ' centre of lift '. The angle that the wing makes with the horizontal is called the ' angle of attack '.

The reaction is proportional to the square of the velocity, to the wing area, and roughly to the angle of attack (for small angles). If the angle of attack is increased, the reaction increases until a point is reached when the smooth flow of air over the wing breaks down and becomes turbulent ; the wing is then said to be ' stalled '. With further increase of angle of attack the drag increases very rapidly. Birds' wings are so very flexible that they do not stall very easily. Also, part of the wing may be stalled while the rest is unstalled.

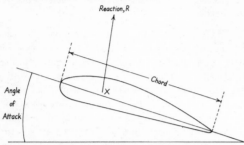

FIG 1. Reaction of air on wing. Angle of attack.

It is necessary for the lift to be equal to the weight. As a bird slows down it increases the angle of attack to near stalling, and with further decrease of speed it increases the area by opening the wings more fully and then the tail. At high speed the bird decreases the area by sweeping back its wing-tips, and is thus able to keep the angle of attack at its best value.

Stalling may be prevented or delayed by the use of slots on the wing's leading edge, formed by the lifting of the alula. This may be seen especially while the bird is landing, when stalling is often to be detected by the raising of upper wing coverts.

Much of the size of the drag component is due to the formation of wing-tip vortices. These are reduced by the use of long narrow wings, and by the action of wing-tip slots. Wing-tip vortices are increased during flapping flight. Some birds fly in V-formation to make use of these vortices ; each one, except the leader, has one wing partly supported by the upward part of the vortex caused by the bird in front. The drag just mentioned is called the ' induced drag ' ; there is also ' form drag ', proportional to the frontal area, and ' skin friction ', proportional to the surface area. Induced drag is inversely proportional to the square of the velocity ; form drag and skin friction are directly proportional to the square of the velocity.

The ' aspect ratio ' of a wing is a figure obtained by dividing the wing-span by the average chord. Wings with high aspect ratios are found in birds that glide, because such wings are aerodynamically so much more efficient ; they are, however, more difficult to flap efficiently. Low aspect ratios are

found in birds, such as pigeons (Columbidae), that are strong flappers.

Skin friction in aircraft is reduced by highly polishing all the surfaces. In birds it is believed that both form drag and skin friction are very low owing to the ability of the bird to change the contours of its surfaces. Possibly the effect of turbulence on the nerve-endings at the base of the feathers can cause a reflex action that alters the shape of the surface until turbulence is minimal.

Gliding. When a bird is gliding *horizontally* in still air, the forces on it are as shown in Figure 2.

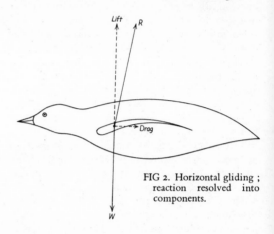

FIG 2. Horizontal gliding ; reaction resolved into components.

The glide can continue only with loss of speed, when drag multiplied by distance gone will equal loss of kinetic energy : $\dfrac{WV^2}{2g}$. Since the bird must keep the lift equal to its weight, it must increase the supporting surfaces (wings and tail) or the angle of attack in order to produce lift at slower and slower speed. The area cannot be increased beyond its limits, and increase in angle of attack eventually causes stalling ; the bird must therefore either flap, or dive to get up speed, or land. The whole sequence of increase of area and angle of attack, followed by stalling, can be seen when a heavy bird comes in to land on water ; as the bird finally stalls it puts in a couple of quick flaps, against the direction of motion, to lose the last of its speed.

If a bird wants to glide without loss of speed it can do so only with loss of height, when drag multiplied by distance gone will equal loss of potential energy (i.e. weight multiplied by loss in height) :

$$\frac{\text{Weight}}{\text{Drag}} = \frac{\text{Distance gone}}{\text{Height lost}}$$

Weight divided by drag is usually called the ' lift-drag ratio' (lift being equal to weight). The height lost divided by the time is called the 'rate of sink'. The forces on a bird gliding at constant speed will be as shown in Figure 3.

An aerodynamically 'clean' bird, such as an albatross *Diomedea* sp., can reduce its wing area by sweeping back its wing-tips in order to glide at increased speed. Therefore, instead of having to reduce its angle of attack, like an aeroplane, it can keep its lift constant at increased speed with the same angle of attack. Thus lift/drag can remain constant, and the gliding angle need not be increased to give increased speed. This is what is called 'having good penetration'.

A slow bird, with a relatively poor gliding angle, may have a lower rate of sink than a fast glider with a flatter gliding angle (Fig. 4). Albatrosses get farther in a given time, but vultures (Aegypiinae or Cathartidae) lose less height. To get this low rate of sink, vultures have very large deeply cambered wings, with many deep slots.

Soaring. If a bird glides in air that is rising at a speed greater than the bird's rate of sink, then the bird will rise relatively to the earth, even although it is sinking relatively to the surrounding air. It is not necessary for the air to be rising vertically, so long as its velocity has a vertical component greater than the bird's rate of sink.

Birds soar in rising columns of hot air, called thermals, above deserts, parade grounds, and even corrugated iron roofs. When air is deflected by hills, buildings, waves on the sea, or other obstacles, if there is a vertical component large enough birds will take advantage of it (Fig. 5). The Fulmar *Fulmarus glacialis* can glide in eddies below cliff edges when there is an offshore wind (Fig. 6), while the Gannet *Sula bassana* and cliff-nesting gulls (Larinae) regularly use the standing waves found to the leeward of their breeding places (Fig. 7).

Raspet (1950) studied the performance of the Black Vulture (or 'Buzzard') *Coragyps atratus* (Cathartidae) soaring in thermals, by the unusual method of following the birds in a sailplane. He found that the bird was able to 'control the air-flow over his body and wing so that it is laminar over its entire surface'. If this be true, this bird, and presumably other similar birds, have achieved boundary layer control by some as yet unexplained means. There is good evidence that porpoises have managed to get a similar non-turbulent flow of water over their surfaces.

When a vulture or a buzzard *Buteo* sp. is soaring, its wings are fully extended with wing-tip slots open ; in this attitude the rate of sink is minimal, allowing the bird to soar in weak thermals.

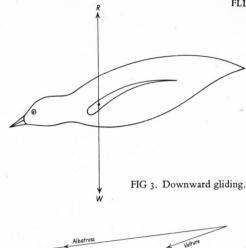

FIG 3. Downward gliding.

FIG 4. Speed and gliding angle.

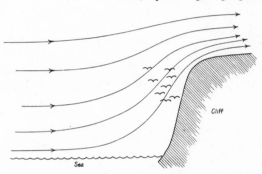

FIG 5. Soaring in rising air.

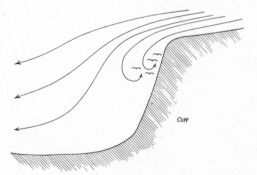

FIG 6. Gliding in air eddies.

FIG 7. Distribution of Gannets *Sula bassana* slope-soaring to windward, and soaring in standing waves to leeward, of the Bass Rock.

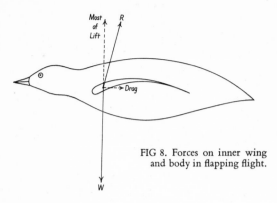

FIG 8. Forces on inner wing and body in flapping flight.

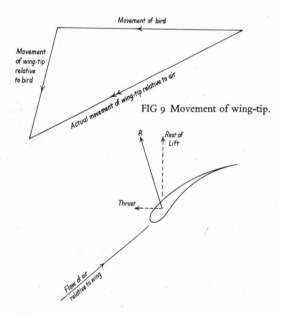

FIG 9 Movement of wing-tip.

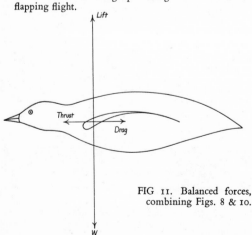

FIG 10. Forces on wing-tip during down stroke in flapping flight.

FIG 11. Balanced forces, combining Figs. 8 & 10.

Flapping Flight. Figure 2 shows all the forces so far mentioned. The lift is equal and opposite to the weight, but the drag is not balanced. The bird cannot continue to fly straight and level unless some other force is brought in to balance the drag. This force is the ' thrust ', caused by the flapping of the bird's wings.

The thrust is caused mainly by the wing-tips, so one may divide the bird and consider the forces on each part. Take first the forces on the inner wing and the body (Fig. 8). The inner wing does not move very fast, and continues to act as an aerofoil exactly as when the bird was gliding.

The forces on the wing-tips are easy to understand, once it is seen that they have two motions that have to be added together. The tips are moving forward with the bird, and at the same time they are moving roughly downwards relative to the bird. Combining these two motions one gets the motion shown in Figure 9.

If the wing-tip were not flexible it would have a very large angle of attack and would stall ; but the forces on the tip cause it to twist, and so one gets a force diagram as in Figure 10.

Long narrow wings twist easily enough, but short broad wings work in a different way. The primary feathers are emarginated so as to make deep slots. Since the feathers have their shafts close to the leading edges, the forces on them cause them to twist, and each acts like a twisted wing, giving a highly efficient method of getting a forwardly directed reaction. This method is seen at its greatest development in the Galliformes, which need to get great thrust from very short wings. When the forces on the two parts of the bird are combined one gets a force diagram as in Figure 11.

During the downbeat the thrust is greater than the drag and the bird accelerates. During the upstroke the thrust disappears and the bird decelerates. These accelerations and decelerations are small, and to the human eye the bird appears to be moving at steady speed.

The above description of flapping flight applies to a bird at full speed, but at take-off there may not be enough flow over the inner wing to give the requisite lift, and so another method is used until full speed is reached. This has been demonstrated by R. H. J. Brown in his films of a pigeon taking off. There is a much more complex movement, the thrust being obtained by a backward flick during the upstroke, and the lift is got during the powerful downstroke.

During level flapping flight the downstroke is produced by a contraction of the pectoralis major (see MUSCULATURE) ; and the upstroke is produced by the reaction of the air, the pectoralis major relaxing and controlling the movement.

When a bird is taking off steeply, the powered upstroke is caused by a contraction of the supra-coracoideus, helped by the deltoid. These two muscles are small and of low endurance. The ratio of the weights of the pectoralis major and the supracoracoideus is a very good indication of the flight action of the bird concerned ; for example, the weight of the pectoralis major is 3–6 times that of the supracoracoideus for birds that take off steeply, and up to 20 or even more times for birds that 'taxi' into the wind.

The total weight of the flight muscles is revealing, varying from over 30 per cent of the total weight for a strong flier such as a pigeon down to less than 10 per cent for an owl. Some birds have surprisingly little muscle ; the Black-throated Diver *Gavia arctica*—a strong flier—has only 10 per cent, while the Razorbill *Alca torda*, in some ways a very similar bird, has 25 per cent.

Hovering. Many birds can hover by reducing their speed to that of the wind, and flying with air speed above that of stalling, and ground speed nil. Another method is to glide in a wind which is being deflected upwards ; gulls (Larinae) are especially adept at this method. When a bird hovers in still air, it has to take up an almost vertical body attitude and beat its wings backwards and forwards in a horizontal plane, both strokes being powered. This puts a great strain on the supracoracoideus muscle, which tires quickly unless it has been specially developed for this work as in the humming-birds (Trochilidae). Hovering in search of prey on the ground or in the water is exemplified by such birds as the Kestrel (' Windhover ') *Falco tinnunculus* and species of shrikes (Laniidae), terns (Sterninae), and kingfishers (Alcedinidae).

Manoeuvres. Consider a bird gliding at a steady speed in a straight line. It is acted on by two forces only—the reaction of the air (R) and the force of gravity, i.e. its own weight (W). These two forces are equal and opposite, and the bird is said to be in equilibrium (Fig. 3).

If the bird wishes to change its attitude it can do so by arranging for these two forces not to be on the same straight line. They then form a couple and produce a turning effect, although they do not deflect the bird from its straight line path. How-ever, the change of attitude will cause a change in the reaction of the air, and *this* will cause a change of course.

The first necessity is a change of attitude. The force of gravity will continue to act at the centre of gravity, come what may, but the reaction (R)

can be moved backwards or forwards or to one side, by an adjustment of wing or tail or both. If the wings are moved forward the head will lift and the tail drop (Fig. 12). Partially folding one wing or increasing the angle of attack of the other will make the bird bank (Fig. 13). Any change of attitude produced in one of these ways will change the angle with which the wind strikes wing or tail, and will cause the reaction to change its size and direction, thus producing an unbalanced force. This unbalanced force is produced either by passive deflection of air by wings, tail, or feet, or by the active driving of air by the wings. For a given size of bird, therefore, manoeuvrability is roughly proportional to the wing and tail area, and highly muscled birds such as pigeons (Columbidae) have an advantage over less muscled birds.

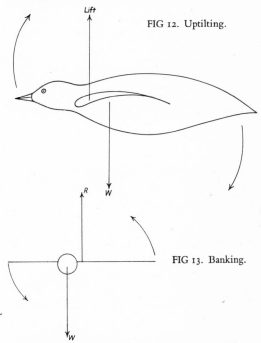

FIG 12. Uptilting.

FIG 13. Banking.

The force produced by a deflecting surface is proportional to its area, and to the square of its speed through the air, so high-speed birds which need a small area for lift likewise need small control surfaces. The greatest manoeuvrability is seen where a bird has a large extra area not used in normal flight. A falcon *Falco* sp. cruising along with its tail fully closed and its wings only partly opened has great reserves of area, while a diver *Gavia* sp. flies with its wings fully open and has little or no tail ; no wonder the diver's flight is so direct. In general, high manoeuvrability has been evolved by birds that fly among trees, and by those that pursue flying prey, and is least developed in aquatic birds. Birds that have extra area available can fly at a large range of speeds; the speed range of a diver is negligible.

The effect of a force depends on how far its line of action is from the axis about which the bird is rotating. Large forked tails and high aspect ratio wings all give greater manoeuvrability.

When an unbalanced force has been produced, a change in velocity follows. If the force acts along the line of the bird's motion, all that happens is that the bird accelerates or slows down. If the force is at right angles to the bird's path, then there will be a change of direction without change of speed. Usually both effects are seen, the force being in such a direction that it can be resolved into two components, one along the line of flight and one at right angles.

Consider a bird which by change of attitude has made the air strike it in such a way that there is a force at right angles to the flight path. The bird will turn in a circle, the force (centripetal) pulling it towards the centre of the circle. The size of the force can be calculated; for example, a bird weighing 2 lb. moving round a circle of radius 5 feet, at 40 feet per second, will have a force of 20 lb. acting on it—a force of 'log' as an airman would say.

A diagram showing the forces on the bird, from a position right ahead, shows how the force acts (Fig. 14). The reaction is very large, and has been resolved into two components, one equal and opposite to the weight, and the other, the centripetal force, acting towards the centre of the circle. With such a large reaction on the wings, no wonder they bend so much. To spread the load, the tail is

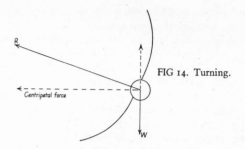

FIG 14. Turning.

opened fully, and the wings also. Any movement of the centre of lift caused by the opening of the tail can be balanced by the swinging forward of the wings as they open to their full extent.

Landing. It is in landing that the extra wing and tail area is most needed. The bird comes in below its landing place if possible, and glides up to it. As height is gained, speed is lost. The bird maintains its lift by opening its wings and tail fully, and by increasing the angle of attack. Finally, when just about to stall, it loses the last of its speed by flapping against the direction of motion and drops gently on to its perch.

Measurements. In the study of bird flight some measurements are necessary, including the following:

Weight. The weight of an individual bird varies from month to month during the year, and even from hour to hour during the day. If possible it is best to take the average of as many specimens as possible.

Wing area. There is less variation here. The maximum area is easier to measure than the working area, which changes during the wing beat. Lay the bird on its back with one wing on a sheet of

---

ca. ⅜ nat. size

Plate 17 · Permanent Bright Plumage (Sexes Alike)
by D. M. REID-HENRY

The species shown are characterised by bright plumage alike in both sexes and worn at all seasons. They contrast with those in Plates 5–8, in which marked sexual or seasonal differences are depicted. See article PLUMAGE.

1   Rainbow Lorikeet *Trichoglossus haematod* (Australasian Region)

2   Kiskadee Flycatcher (Great Kiskadee) *Pitangus sulphuratus* (Texas to Argentina)

3   Cuban Trogon *Priotelus temnurus* (Cuba)

4   Indian Roller *Coracias benghalensis* (southern Asia)

5   Ceylon Blue Magpie *Urocissa ornata* (Ceylon)

6   Southern Carmine Bee-eater *Merops nubicoides* (southern Africa)

7   Blackheaded Oriole *Oriolus xanthornus* (India and southeastern Asia)

8   Lesser Purple Gallinule *Porphyria alleni* (tropical Africa)

9   Red-bibbed Fruit Pigeon *Ptilinopus viridis* (Moluccas)

D.M.H.

graph paper, and pin out the wing into a natural position ; it is best to have the leading edge at 90° to the main axis of the body, although the tip will be swept back somewhat. Draw a line carefully round the wing, and the area can be found quickly by counting the squares enclosed.

Wing span. Wing-tip to wing-tip at full extent.

Wing shape. Slots, sweep-back, aerofoil section, and dihedral angle are among features to be noted.

Wing muscles. It would be a considerable task to dissect out all the wing muscles, but a very good idea of their size and proportions can be got by weighing the two breast muscles, the pectoralis major and the supracoracoideus, which are very easy to dissect out.

Other points. Many other details may be relevant, such as the size of the heart, the colour of the muscles, the degree of development of the air-sacs, and so on.

Calculations. From the above measurements the following can be calculated :

Wing loading. Weight divided by wing area. This is not strictly comparable if the birds differ markedly in size, for weight varies with the cube of the linear dimensions, while wing area varies as the square. Where it is wished to compare many birds of various sizes, the square root of the area can be divided by the cube root of the weight, giving a coefficient of similarity.

Aspect ratio. This is very important, since the induced drag is inversely proportional to the aspect ratio. A very easy way of calculating the aspect ratio is to divide the wing area into the square of the span. Aspect ratios vary from about 5 for gallinaceous birds to about 20 for an albatross.

' *Power-weight ratio* '. The weight of the wing muscles expressed as a percentage of the total body weight. It varies from about 30 per cent for a pigeon to less than 10 per cent for some owls. The figure obtained by dividing the weight of the pectoralis major by the weight of the supracoracoideus can tell us much, varying as it does from about 2–3 for gallinaceous birds to 20 or more for soaring birds.

Gliding angle. This is said to be a function of the span loading i.e. weight divided by span. The span loading is easy to measure, but to get an accurate measurement of the gliding angle would be very difficult.

Specialised Flying Types. Much more can be learned from study of the really good and the definitely poor fliers than from the average ones. A number of types have been chosen that are specialised in one way or another, and the following notes made about them.

Albatrosses. The Wandering Albatross *Diomedea exulans*, for example, is a bird evolved for ' dynamic soaring ' in a region of very strong winds. This flight method is possible only if there is a pronounced wind-gradient—the lower layers of air being retarded by friction, and full wind speed not being found below about 50 feet. The bird glides down-wind with great increase of ground speed, and then, close to the surface, turns and gains height into the wind—the loss of air speed being not as great as the loss of ground speed since the bird is flying into winds of greater and greater speed as it rises. At about 50 feet the bird again turns down-wind and the cycle is repeated.

Such a method is possible only to a bird of great weight and ' penetration '. This species weighs up to 27 lb. and has a wing-span of about 11 feet. The wings are remarkable for their high aspect ratio,

---

Plate 18 : Age Differences in Plumage by MICHAEL YULE

For each species an adult is shown in front and an immature bird behind. The species have been chosen from among those with a marked difference in respect of age, but relatively little difference between adults in respect of sex or season. Where the adults do in fact differ, the bird depicted is a male in breeding plumage ; in the Great Spotted Woodpecker the adult female lacks the crimson band on the nape, and in the Common Gull the adults of both sexes have fine grey streaks on the crown, nape, and sides of neck in winter. Noteworthy are the bright crown in the young Woodpecker although dark in the adult, and the bright plumage but lack of long tail feathers in the young Flycatcher. See article PLUMAGE.

ca. $\frac{1}{5}$ nat. size

1 Great Spotted Woodpecker *Dendrocopos major* (Palaearctic Region)

2 Gray Jay *Perisoreus canadensis* (northern North America)

3 Scissor-tailed Flycatcher *Muscivora forficata* (southern U.S.A.)

4 Scarlet Ibis *Eudocimus ruber* (northern South America)

5 Night (or Black-crowned Night) Heron *Nycticorax nycticorax* (tropics and subtropics, except Australasia)

6 Common (or Mew) Gull *Larus canus* (northern Palaearctic and northwestern North America)

quoted as up to 25—by far the greatest found among birds. The wings are very flat and have no slots. The wing muscles are not well developed, and so the bird can take off only by 'taxiing' into the wind. Owing to the small wing area and streamlined form, the bird glides at high speed, although it is not very manoeuvrable. By partly closing its wings it can glide at even higher speeds, with its wings still at their most efficient angle of attack.

Vultures. In both Old World vultures (Aegypiinae) and New World vultures (Cathartidae) the wings are long and wide, giving a large area and a low aspect ratio. This gives a low wing loading. The wings are deeply cambered and have wing-tip slots more highly developed than in any other birds except the Galliformes. This special development gives good lift at very low speeds.

The angle of glide is not remarkably good, but the very slow stalling speed gives a very low rate of sink, enabling the bird to maintain height when gliding in weak upcurrents caused by the rising of hot air. The flight muscles are poorly developed, and so the bird has difficulty in maintaining itself in still air. Many vultures stay grounded till the sun has heated the ground sufficiently to give strong enough thermals. The tail is very large and is used as an accessory lifting device. This type of flight has been developed mainly among carrion-eating birds, for owing to the long periods that may elapse between their meals, their flight has to be economical in power.

Gallinaceous Birds. The Pheasant *Phasianus colchicus*, for an example of the Galliformes, is a heavy bird with very broad small wings which show the extreme development of wing-tip slots for propulsion. Each primary feather acts like a separate reciprocating air-screw as it twists during the wing-beat. The flight muscles are greatly developed, allowing the bird to make an explosive steep take-off, after which it glides for a short distance, wings at a marked anhedral angle, before landing again. The great development of the supracoracoideus muscle enables the wing to be recovered quickly after each down-stroke. If possible, the Pheasant prefers to escape by running and flies only as a last resort.

Gallinaceous species living in woodlands have larger tails than those living in the open, presumably to help them to steer through twigs and branches. Although the Pheasant is slow and has very little endurance, this does not mean that it is poorly adapted or degenerate. In its own way the Pheasant is a specialist, no other bird having its powers of gaining height so rapidly.

Pigeons. The pigeons (Columbidae) have wings of low aspect ratio and medium area, with extremely large muscles, for continuous fast flapping. The supracoracoideus is greatly developed, chiefly for the take-off. The wings have considerable emargination, to allow the individual primaries to act as propellors. The wrist-slot also is large, and so the bird has a rather low stalling speed (partly owing to this and partly owing to the large tail). Pigeons are highly manoeuvrable, and their small wing span allows them to fly among trees. They have high endurance and a wide range of speeds.

Divers (Loons). Divers (Gaviidae) are highly streamlined, heavy birds with small wings of high aspect ratio. There are no slots on the wings and there is no tail to speak of. Thus they have high wing loading with very little drag.

The wing muscles are very small, especially the supracoracoideus, and so the bird takes off by 'taxiing', using its great leg-power to help. Since the bird spends so much of its time swimming, the concentration of muscles in the legs rather than in the wings is understandable. Landing must always be on water, since the stalling speed is high.

Once the bird is air-borne, the flight must be fast since the wings are so small, and the low drag allows this with a low expenditure of power. Thus the divers show that fast flight in itself does not demand a great deal of power, but that lack of power (and wing area) prevents slow flying. Naturally, manoeuvrability is small—no disadvantage to a bird living in large open spaces.

Auks. The auks (Alcidae) are heavy birds with small wings. A high aspect ratio and lack of slots gives low drag, but, unlike the divers, which they otherwise resemble, they have extremely large and well developed breast muscles. This difference has evolved as a result of the auks' use of their wings for swimming under water ; here, owing to the density of the medium, high power is needed for fast movement.

Auks have poor manoeuvrability, due to high wing-loading and small area of tail. Their difficulty in taking off is due to small wing area rather than to lack of power. Their flight is fast and direct, with a high flapping rate, and looks (and probably is) inefficient. Extreme specialisation for swimming under water has thus led to inefficient flight, and in one species to flightlessness. The diving petrels (Pelecanoididae) of the Southern Hemisphere have evolved to almost exactly the same type by convergence ; not only do they have muscles of the same kind and size, but their wing shape is exactly the same.

Hummingbirds. In the Trochilidae the inner part of the wing has been reduced by the shortening of the bones, so that the wings are made up of primary feathers only. The great development of breast muscles gives a rapid beat for fast flight and for hovering, and the large tails give great manoeuvrability (for further details see HUMMINGBIRD).

When the bird hovers, with head up and tail lowered, the wings beat in a horizontal plane, both the upstroke and the downstroke being powered ; hence the supracoracoideus muscle is highly developed. The expenditure of energy is so great that the birds have to economise by loss of temperature control at night (see TORPIDITY). Despite their small size, certain hummingbirds make long migrations, in some cases over hundreds of miles of open sea.

Swifts. In the Apodidae one finds the ultimate in high-speed types. Drag has been reduced to a minimum owing to streamlining, flat camber of wings, high aspect ratio, great sweep-back, and lack of slots. The muscles are well developed, the supracoracoideus especially so. Since the latter is not needed for taking off there is a strong presumption that it is used for powered wing raising—giving thrust on the upstroke as well as on the downstroke. The tail is very small, for at the speed at which swifts fly control surfaces need not be very big.

Owls. The Strigiformes have extremely large wings for their weight. They are able to fly very slowly, with a slow flapping rate. Their breast muscles are proportionately smaller than in any other group of birds, giving great economy in energy.

Frigatebirds. In the Fregatidae, low wing loading and high aspect ratio enable the birds to soar. By partly closing the wings and sweeping them back, the frigatebirds can transform themselves into high-speed types, with great manoeuvrability. Most birds can do this to a certain extent, but the frigatebirds carry the process very far. One would expect their breast muscles to be well developed.

Early Flight. For the beginnings of flight in young birds see under BEHAVIOUR, DEVELOPMENT OF ; FLIGHT, PRECOCIOUS.

See Plates (phot.) 1, 2, 3, 4, 9, 16c, 47a.   J.B.

Brown, R. H. J. 1951. Flapping flight. Ibis 93 : 333–359.
Brown, R. H. J. 1961. Flight. *In* Marshall, A. J. (ed.). Biology and Comparative Physiology of Birds vol. 2. New York and London.
Graham, R. R. 1930. Safety devices in wings. Brit. Birds 24 : 2–21, 34–47, 58–65.
Hartman, F. A. 1961. Locomotor mechanisms of birds. Smiths. Misc. Coll. 143 (1) : 1–91.
Odum, E. P., Connell, C. E. & Stoddard, H. L. 1961. Flight energy and estimated flight ranges of some migratory birds. Auk 78 : 515–527.
Raspet, A. 1950. Performance measurements of a soaring bird. Gliding 1 : 145–151.
Raspet, A. 1960. The biophysics of bird flight. Science 132 : 191–200.
Slipjer, E. J. 1950. De Vliegkunst in het Dierenrijk. Leiden.
Steinbacher, J. 1960. Der Flug der Vögel. *In* Schmidt, H. (ed.). Der Flug der Tiere. Frankfurt.
Stolpe, M. & Zimmer, K. 1939. Der Vogelflug. Leipzig.
Storer, J. H. 1948. The flight of birds analysed through slow-motion photography. Bull. Cranbrook Inst. Sci., Bloomfield Hills, Michigan, no. 28 : 1–94 (176 figs.).

FLIGHTLESSNESS : a condition so relatively unusual in birds as to make it an outstanding character of those in which it is found. Nearly all young birds are unable to fly until practically full grown (for exceptions see FLIGHT, PRECOCIOUS). The adults of some species are temporarily rendered nearly or wholly incapable of flight by simultaneous moult of the remiges, as is common among the Anatidae (see MOULT). Individual birds, also, may be incapable of flight owing to disease or abnormality (see PLUMAGE, ABNORMAL AND ABERRANT). The condition here to be considered, however, is total loss of the power of flight in certain species, and indeed throughout certain taxonomic groups. Loss of flight in domesticated varieties of some flying species need be no more than mentioned (see DOMESTICATION).

Birds as a class are comprehensively adapted for flying (see AVES), and only a little of this general adaptation is ever lost. It is now usually believed that flightlessness in recent birds is always secondary, i.e. that these species had flying ancestors ; but the earliest known bird was unable to do more than glide, although many of the distinctive characters of flying birds were already present (see ARCHAEOPTERYX ; ORIGIN OF BIRDS).

Apart from some forms long extinct (see FOSSIL BIRDS), the most notable examples of flightless birds are two—the large running birds of the so-called 'ratite' orders on the one hand, and the essentially aquatic penguins (Spheniscidae) on the other. The power of flight has, however, been lost also in some small taxonomic groups or single species in a variety of different orders. Others again have such poor powers of flying as to make them seem well on the way to flightlessness. In addition, there are groups and species in which the power of flight has been retained but is little used, the birds' mode of life tending to a preference for running, swimming, or hiding. Whatever may be the relationship of the various 'ratite' groups (see RATITES, PHYLOGENY OF THE), they have evolved in the direction of large size, very strong legs, and a wholly terrestrial mode of life (see CASSOWARY ; ELEPHANT-BIRD ; EMU ; MOA ; OSTRICH ; RHEA) ; the Apertygidae are exceptional in having attained only moderate size and in having developed nocturnal habits instead of relying on fleetness of foot for safety (see KIWI). The positive adaptation has been accompanied by loss of the power of flight, the wings being much reduced—quite rudimentary in the Apterygidae—and the small size of the pectoral muscles correlated with a flat sternum, lacking a keel.

The case of the Spheniscidae is quite different. Here evolution has led to adaptation for a largely marine existence, with modification of the wings as flippers for swimming (see PENGUIN ; SWIMMING AND DIVING). This use of the wings requires strong pectoral muscles and a carinate sternum, as in the case of flying birds.

In the other and more sporadic examples, the power of flight seems to have been lost as something unnecessary rather than as a concomitant of any high degree of specialisation in another direction. They are, of course, ground-dwelling or aquatic birds. Many of them are insular forms that had at one time few enemies ; but the arrival of man, and of mammalian predators introduced by him, has often ended their viability (see EXTINCT BIRDS ; VANISHING BIRDS). It has been suggested that on a small island, as yet free from predators, the power of flight was not only unnecessary but also positively disadvantageous owing to the risk of being blown out to sea.

The power of flight has been lost in two whole families of recent birds, in addition to those already mentioned. The Raphidae of the Mascarene Islands, the three known species of which have become extinct within historic times, were insular birds that had evolved in the direction of large size, with much reduced and functionless wings (see DODO.) None of the three species of Mesitornithidae, a gruiform family of ground-dwelling birds peculiar to Madagascar, is known to fly ; although they have fair-sized wings the clavicles are much reduced (see MESITE). In addition, the Kagu Rhynochetos jubatus of New Caledonia, sole member of the gruiform family Rhynochetidae, is apparently flightless (see KAGU).

In some ways even more interesting are the exceptional flightless species in families of which the great majority of members can fly, and often do fly readily and strongly. Such was the now extinct Great Auk Pinguinus impennis, large for its family (Alcidae) and with much reduced wings but a strongly carinate sternum (see AUK). Among the Podicipitidae there is the Flightless Grebe Centropelma micropterum of Lake Titicaca (see GREBE) ; and among the Phalacrocoracidae the Flightless Cormorant Nannopterum harrisi of the Galápagos Islands (see CORMORANT).

There are several flightless species, some recently extinct and others still surviving, among the Rallidae (see RAIL). They include the wekas Gallirallus spp. of New Zealand, the Takahe Notornis mantelli (at one time believed to be extinct) of the same country, Porzanula palmeri of Laysan Island, Gallinula nesiotis of Tristan da Cunha (subspecies extinct) and Gough Island, and the very small Atlantisia rogersi of Inaccessible Island.

Among the Anatidae, two of the three steamer ducks Tachyeres spp. are flightless. They are more heavily built birds than their flying congener ; when speed is necessary, the wings are flapped to aid progress over the surface of the water (see DUCK).

The Owl Parrot (or Kakapo) Strigops habroptilus of New Zealand is flightless, although it sometimes opens its wings when pressed or while climbing in trees ; the Ground Parrot Pezoporus wallicus and Night Parrot Geopsittacus occidentalis of Australia are nearly flightless (see PARROT).

Among the Passeriformes one can cite only the Stephen Island Wren Xenicus lyalli of New Zealand, probably now extinct and believed to have been flightless (see WREN (3)). Some of the wattle-birds (Callaeidae) of the same country are, however, very nearly flightless (see WATTLE-BIRD (2)).

See Plates (phot.) 10ab, 25, 38ab.   A.L.T.

Lowe, P. R. 1928. A description of *Atlantisia rogersi*, the diminutive and flightless rail of Inaccessible Island (South Atlantic), with some notes on flightless rails. Ibis (12) 4 : 99–131.

Lowe, P. R. 1934. On the evidence for the existence of two species of Steamer Duck (*Tachyeres*), and primary and secondary flightlessness in birds. Ibis (13) 4 : 467–495.

Stresemann, E. 1932. La structure des rémiges chez quelques râles physiologiquement aptères. Alauda 1932 : 1–5.

FLIGHT, PRECOCIOUS: flying by young birds well before they have attained full size. The general rule is that a bird does not fly until it is practically full grown, which is usually at a very early age ; and it is clear that the flight feathers appropriate to an adult would, in the partly grown bird, be out of proportion to the other factors involved in flying (see FLIGHT). It is, however, characteristic of the Galliformes that a miniature set of remiges is grown by the chicks so that they can fly when quite small. This is no doubt a useful safety-device for ground-living birds ; on the other hand, it may on occasion lead to undue scattering of the brood while its members are still of an age to need parental protection. Precocious flight reaches its extreme in the Megapodiidae (where the question of scattering does not arise) ; for instance, the chick of the Mallee-fowl *Leipoa ocellata* can fly almost as soon as it leaves the egg (see MEGAPODE). More often, in other families of the Galliformes, flying does not begin until later, e.g. 3–4 days in curassows (Cracidae) and 12–14 days in the Pheasant *Phasianus colchicus*. Precocious flight is also found in the gruiform family Turnicidae (see BUTTONQUAIL).

FLIPPER: term applied to the modified wing in Spheniscidae (see PENGUIN ; SWIMMING AND DIVING).

FLOCK: see ASSEMBLY, NOUN OF

FLOCKING: term for the positive social behaviour of individual birds that results in their congregation into groups (flocks), as distinguished from aggregations of animals resulting from the influence of ecological factors alone.

Nature of Gregariousness. It has been generally assumed that some kind of social 'instinct' was responsible for flock formation, but Tinbergen (1951) denied this by concluding that social activities always formed a part of some other instinctive behaviour : 'An animal is called social when it strives to be in the neighbourhood of fellow members of its species when performing some or all of its instinctive activities . . . in other words when these instincts are active the fellow member of the species is part of the adequate stimulus situation which the animal tries to find through its appetitive behaviour.' Recently several workers have demonstrated that this latter view was mistaken. Studies on the Spice Finch *Lonchura punctulata* and the Black-faced Dioch *Quelea quelea*, as well as on fishes, indicate that gregarious behaviour is more than an aspect of other instinctive behaviour sequences. The stereotyped nature of the schooling behaviour of fishes has been considered indirect evidence for mechanisms controlling the behaviour in the central nervous system, and thus for the existence of a separate schooling instinct. It seems, then, that both in birds and fishes there is a strong motivation, producing gregariousness, that can be considered as independent from other activities.

There is, however, some evidence that gregarious behaviour develops in part by a learning process, and it is difficult to distinguish this from the possible maturation of an inborn recognition of certain social 'releasers'. It would, therefore, not be wise to call flocking behaviour instinctive in the early sense of Tinbergen. Recent use of the term 'tendency', defined by Hinde as 'the readiness to show a particular behaviour . . . under natural conditions', allows analysis of the subject while avoiding the complex dispute between those emphasising learning and those emphasising innateness of activities. The flocking behaviour can, therefore, be said to be a manifestation of the 'social tendency' widely found in birds and animals.

Types of Flock. There are several different kinds of flocks that can be classified, for example, according to their temporal duration :

Bad Weather Flocks. In certain species territories are held throughout the winter, yet in most of these cases the birds form flocks under conditions of exceptional hardship (e.g. Blackbird *Turdus merula*). Bad weather flocks often migrate from the most difficult conditions.

Seasonal Flocks. A large number of passerine species, particularly in the temperate zone, form flocks in winter following a breeding season in which individual pairs are dispersed in territories throughout the breeding habitat. Cardueline finches (Carduelinae) and the Chaffinch *Fringilla coelebs* show behaviour of this kind.

Permanent Flocks. Some species are gregarious throughout the year, breeding in colonies within which small individual territories for each pair are found. Many sea birds and some finches (Fringillidae), icterids (Icteridae), and weavers (Ploceidae) are examples. In the anis (Crotophaginae) pair territories have disappeared and a communal territory is defended by the flock against neighbouring flocks ; in some of these birds the eggs are normally placed by all the females in a single nest.

Flocks may be monospecific or composed of several species—often of species having different feeding habits. In African forests mixed foraging parties commonly occur, and it is said that the flycatching species feed on insects disturbed by other birds. In other cases, for instance where tits (Paridae) of several species feed with Treecreepers *Certhia familiaris*, Nuthatches *Sitta europaea*, and sometimes warblers (Sylviinae), or in limicoline flocks (Charadrii) composed of species of widely divergent bill-size, or in mixed parties of surface-feeding and diving ducks (Anatidae), there seems no direct food-finding advantage in the association (see below).

See also ROOSTING.

Social Structure. The internal social structure of flocks varies chiefly in the extent to which family ties are retained. In flocks of geese (*Anser*, etc.), complex individual relations may be distinguished within groups of individuals based largely on family or sexual bonds retained from the previous breeding season. Tits and finches form flocks in autumn through the congregation of young birds after separation from their parents, which join them after the moult ; the individuals then show no discriminatory relations with others. The social behaviour consists almost entirely of the gregarious responses that maintain the flock and, probably only in small flocks of stable composition, a constant or somewhat variable 'peck right' hierarchy (see DOMINANCE (2)). At the onset of the breeding season, pairing may occur within the flock (e.g. Great Tit *Parus major*), the pairs then drifting off to their territories ; or the male birds may leave the flocks and find territories to which the females later come (e.g. Chaffinch *Frinigilla coelebs*). In permanent flocks, pair bonds may be formed on special pairing grounds, or the males may temporarily leave the flock in groups to found their territories in a colony site (e.g. Ploceinae).

Hediger has pointed out that social animals may be divided into two types : 'contact' animals, which maintain touch contact with one another particularly when resting, and 'distance' animals, which even when resting rarely come into contact but maintain 'individual distances'—each individual maintaining an area around itself within which the approach of another is reacted to either with attack or by avoidance (see also AGGRESSION). Flocks of contact species are recorded in the Artamidae, Coliidae, Hemiprocninae, and Estrildidae, for example. Distance species occur in many families, including the Laridae, Scolopacidae, Paridae, Fringillidae, and Ploceidae.

Flock Behaviour. The behaviour of flocks has three main characteristics : synchronisation of activities, cohesion of the flock during movement, and the maintenance of a roughly constant dispersion of individuals within the area covered by the flock (Crook 1961).

Synchronisation. Stationary flocks normally show some degree of synchronisation of maintenance activities such as feeding, drinking, sleeping, hopping about, washing, and preening. Two factors contributing to this have been recognised :

(i) The 'following reactions' whereby one bird follows the movements of others and thus moves from one place to another more or less synchronously with them.

(ii) 'Social facilitation', the immediate copying of the behaviour of one individual by another.

It might be said that the 'following reaction' is a special case of 'social facilitation', in that the following bird is copying the flying away behaviour of another bird ; but it seems that, apart from any tendency to copy, the tendency to keep close to other individuals (i.e. the social tendency) is operating. In addition, the 'following reaction' is normally directionally oriented and is usually a direct reaction to a precise pattern of stimuli, such as the sudden exposure of wing flashes or the sound of flight cries. In stationary flocks social facilitation

plays the major role in synchronisation, whereas in group movements it is the following reaction that plays the predominant role.

Cohesion. In spite of frequently different activities of component members, cohesion of the flock is maintained during passage from one area to another. It may be measured in terms of the 'following reactions' that bring it about. The time interval between the movement of one bird and that of another may be recorded, and measurements giving an indication of the strength of the social bonds in the flock obtained. This is in effect a measure of the strength of the social tendency during the flock movement concerned.

Constant State of Spatial Dispersion. Members of bird flocks are dispersed within their environment less than they would be if dispersed at random. Within their flocks, however, 'distance' birds are normally distributed more evenly than they would be at random. This even distribution is maintained by the 'individual distance' behaviour in opposition to the social tendency, the two forces varying somewhat in strength with the mood of the birds and resulting in differences in dispersion. During activities such as sitting alert or hopping about in an aviary, both the tendency to approach other birds and the converse, to reject approach on infringement of the individual distance, are about equally 'active', the birds being highly responsive to the behaviour of their fellows. The result is a very even spatial distribution. During both rest and extreme activity, for instance when quartering the ground for food, the birds are less aware of their neighbours and a more variable spacing of the flock results. During fright, individual distance aggression is absent because the attention of every individual is focused on the source of danger ; extreme concentration of the birds then results. In 'contact' species very little aggression is seen and the birds clump close together during rest, dispersing a little while active in group movements and food searching. These differences in flocking behaviour demand much further investigation.

Flock Movements. The movements of flocks of passerine birds have been classified under several headings : (i) drifting movements ; (ii) synchronised or integrated movements ; and (iii) escape movements. In 'drifting movements' a group moves slowly over the feeding ground by the independent short flights or hops of individuals. The flock moves slowly forward, and the main element in the advance are the repeated flights of the birds left behind over the heads of their fellows to land in the van. The movement is made without calls or noisy flight. 'Synchronised movements', however, entail the synchronous 'take off' of all the individuals at approximately the same time. Such movements usually occur when the birds pass from one feeding area to another. Movement is often initiated by flight calls from a few birds, whereupon others join them in calling until the sudden movement of the group occurs. In some species the sudden whirr of wings of a few birds flying up may serve as a stimulus. If danger threatens, 'escape' movements occur in which the flock flies up as a unit with a rush of wings but without calling. Small birds frequently rush for cover after such an alarm.

Value of Flocking. The survival value of flocking may lie partly in the rapid concentration of individuals at sources of abundant food. This argument appears relevant particularly to sea birds and granivorous passerines, as well as to those species that form bad weather flocks (see above); species that feed solitarily in the non-breeding season seek prey of such a nature, or in such a way, that the presence of other individuals would evidently not be advantageous. In addition, flocking gives an increased awareness of the approach of predators; thus, Lack (1954) has remarked that solitarily feeding birds are less likely to notice approaching predators than flocking feeders, or may have to spend relatively more time on the alert and less time in feeding and resting. Many gregarious species have special alarm notes which denote the approach of a predator and to which other individuals respond appropriately. Birds may also combine to prevent a possible attack by a predator by 'mobbing' it. Moynihan has recently suggested that in mixed-species flocks of Central American forests certain species show adaptations in both colour and behaviour that function in maintaining the cohesion of groups.

See Plate 48b (phot.).   J.H.C.

FLORA: the total plant life of an area (contrasted with FAUNA); see VEGETATION.

FLORICAN: substantive name (also spelt 'floriken') of two Indian species of Otididae (see BUSTARD).

FLOWERPECKER: substantive name of some species of Dicaeidae (Passeriformes, suborder Oscines); in the plural, general term for the family. This is a group of small or (rarely) medium-sized arboreal birds (3 to 7½ inches long) of Oriental and Australasian distribution.

General Characteristics. Most (40 out of 55 species) are grouped within the two widely distributed genera *Prionochilus* and *Dicaeum*. These typical flowerpeckers are small birds, with a wing length in adult individuals of 40–76 mm. (1½–3

inches), and with short, stumpy tails. The bill, in which the edges of the distal third are serrated, is short, varying in structure between a stout and blunt type like that of tits (Paridae) and a thin, attenuated, more or less decurved type like that of warblers (Sylviinae) or short-billed sunbirds (Nectariniidae). The short tongue has, in its deeply cleft distal half, the edges curled to form two slender semitubular tips; this somewhat resembles the tongue structure in sunbirds and is probably an adaptation to nectar feeding. The plumage coloration in some species is plain, similar in both sexes; in other species the males are brightly coloured, often with contrasting patches of red and with glossy areas, the females as a rule being more dully coloured. The outermost (tenth) primary is well-developed in *Prionochilus*, but vestigial in *Dicaeum* except in *D. melanoxanthum*.

Mistletoe-bird *Dicaeum hirundinaceum*.   Natural size.
C.E.T.K.

The New Guinean genera *Melanocharis* (with 5 species) and *Rhamphocharis* (monotypic) are more primitive and have a rather simple structure of the tongue, but in many ways show relationship to *Prionochilus*. The New Guinean monotypic genera *Oreocharis* and *Paramythia*, as well as the genus *Pardalotus* (pardalotes or diamond-birds) with 7 species inhabiting the Australian continent and Tasmania, are more aberrant, and their relationship with the typical flowerpeckers is obviously more remote. They share with *Dicaeum* the vestigial outer primary, but differ in having a simple tongue structure and in lacking the serration of the bill; even in habits they differ strikingly. The pardalotes come nearest to the typical flowerpeckers in appearance. They are small birds with short tails, tit-like bills, and a variegated plumage in which a guttate pattern is very conspicuous and has given rise to the common names. The Arfak Flowerpecker *Oreocharis arfaki* resembles a large tit, while the Crested Mountain Flowerpecker *Paramythia montium* is of the size of a thrush *Turdus* sp.

Habits. The typical flowerpeckers resemble sunbirds in appearance and general habits. They usually frequent high trees, where they fly restlessly around in search of food, their favourite hunting grounds being flowering epiphytes, strangling figs, or, particularly, clumps of parasitic plants growing high up in the branches. They are energetic and noisy birds that turn and twist about in every kind of attitude and constantly twitter when feeding. During flight they utter rather sharp call notes that can be rendered as ' chip, chip '. Some species have modest warbled songs. The flowerpeckers are not especially gregarious, but appear in pairs or family parties.

The habitat selection is very varied. Some species frequent lowland rain-forest, others the montane mossy forests, and *Paramythia montium* ascends even to the stunted trees of the timberline. Many species prefer second growth, bamboo groves, and cultivated areas, and may, as in the case of the Scarlet-backed Flowerpecker *Dicaeum cruentatum* of Burma and Malaya, be a common inhabitant of village and town gardens.

The food of the typical flowerpeckers consists of berries (chiefly those of the family Loranthaceae), nectar, and insects. The pardalotes are almost entirely insectivorous, while the four New Guinean endemic genera are fruit-eaters. All flowerpeckers are sedentary in high degree, except the Mistletoe-bird *Dicaeum hirundinaceum* of Australia, which has nomadic habits and is a powerful flyer with long swallow-like wings.

Breeding. The pendant, domed nests of the typical flowerpeckers are similar to those of sunbirds. They are pear-shaped structures, suspended by the stalk from a twig, with the entrance high on one side, built of vegetable fibres, rootlets, grass, and cobweb, lined with silky down. The nest of the Thick-billed Flowerpecker *Dicaeum agile* (Indo-Malayan) differs in its peculiar felt-like fabric. The pardalotes place their nests in holes in trees or hollows or crevices in the ground, or in a tunnel excavated by the birds themselves, usually in the side of a bank. The nest itself is elaborately built of bark and grass, and is usually cup-shaped—but domed in some species. The only nest known of the New Guinean endemic genera is that of *Para-*

mythia ; it is cup-shaped and placed in dense bushes. Most flowerpeckers lay white eggs, only *Paramythia* and a few species of *Dicaeum* have spotted eggs. The clutch is in *Dicaeum* and *Prionochilus* 1-4, usually 2 ; in *Pardalotus* 2-5, usually 4 ; while *Paramythia* has only one egg. In the species investigated the female alone builds the nest and incubates the eggs, while both sexes participate in the feeding of the young. In *Pardalotus* it is known that the excavating of the nesting tunnel is shared by both sexes.

Distribution. The distribution of the family covers the whole Oriental Region westwards to the drier parts of India, and the Australasian Region (not New Zealand) eastwards to the Solomon Islands. Two species, *Dicaeum ignipectus* and *D. melanoxanthum*, range into the Palaearctic parts of the Himalayan area and south-western China. Richest in species are the Philippines (13 species, of which 11 are endemic) and New Guinea (11 species, all endemic).

Ecological Relations. A close association exists between certain flowerpeckers and the mistletoes (mainly the genera *Loranthus*, *Viscum*, and *Amyema*, belonging to the Loranthaceae). Many species among the typical flowerpeckers feed almost exclusively on the fruits of these plants (apart from insects), and at the same time they constitute by far the most effective disseminators of the mistletoe seeds. In this way a mutual dependency, highly specialised, has evolved between the plants and the birds. In spreading these harmful parasitic plants, which are a serious pest in many areas, the flowerpeckers become important birds from an economic point of view.

The method of eating the mistletoe berries differs according to the structure of the bill. The thick-billed species, such as the above-mentioned *Dicaeum agile*, use the bill to separate the fleshy epicarp from the seed, swallowing the former and getting rid of the latter by scraping it off on a twig. The thin-billed species, such as Tickell's Flowerpecker *Dicaeum erythrorhynchos* of India, swallow the berries whole and void the viscous seeds after an astonishingly short time, usually a few minutes. The seeds are able to germinate in both cases, i.e. whether they have passed through the alimentary canal of the birds or not. The extraordinary rapidity with which the mistletoe fruits pass through the intestines is due partly to the laxative effect of the berries, but mainly to a special structure of the stomach. The muscular stomach has developed into a blind sac with a sphincter at its opening, which construction allows the easily digestible berries to pass directly from the oesophagus to the intestine without entering the stomach ; on the other hand, insects and spiders, which need grinding and a more thorough treatment before the digestible parts can be assimilated, are not prevented from entering the muscular stomach. The alimentary canal of *Melanocharis* and *Paramythia* is not so specialised, but more closely resembles that in other fruit-eating passerines.

Owing to their nectar feeding, many flower-peckers are of importance as pollinators of various flowers, but in this respect play a lesser role than honeyeaters (Meliphagidae), sunbirds (Nectari-niidae), and some other groups (see POLLINATORS AND DISTRIBUTORS).   F.S.

Keast, A. 1958. The influence of ecology on variation in the Mistletoe-bird *Dicaeum hirundinaceum*. Emu 58 : 195–206.

Leeuwen, W. M. van. 1954. On the biology of some Javanese Loranthaceae and the role the birds play in their life histories. Beaufortia 4 : 105–205.

Mayr, E. & Amadon D. 1947. A review of the Dicaeidae. Amer. Mus. Novit. no. 1360 : 1–32.

Sálim Ali. 1931. The role of sunbirds and flower-peckers in the propagation and distribution of the tree-parasite, *Loranthus longiflorus* Dest., in the Konkan (W. India). J. Bombay Nat. Hist. Soc. 35 : 114–149.

Salomonsen, F. 1960–61. Notes on flowerpeckers (Aves, Dicaeidae). 1–6. Amer. Mus. Novitates : nos. 1990 : 1–28 ; 1991 : 1–38 ; 2016 : 1–36 ; 2057 : 1–35 ; 2067 : 1–24 ; 2068 : 1–31.

FLOWER-PIERCER : substantive name of *Diglossa* spp. (see HONEYCREEPER (1)).

FLUKES : see ENDOPARASITE

FLUTTERER : *Klais guimeti* (for family see HUMMINGBIRD).

FLYCATCHER (1) : substantive name of many species of the subfamily Muscicapinae of the Muscicapidae (Passeriformes, suborder Oscines) ; in the plural, general term for the subfamily. The word was originally used for small Old World songbirds having a flat broad bill surrounded by long bristles, and with a short tarsus, preying on insects either caught in the air during repeated sallies from a chosen look-out perch or found by hunting in dense foliage. In this sense the Pied Flycatcher *Ficedula hypoleuca* of Europe and its congeners are typical members of the subfamily Muscicapinae. These species, however, represent merely one of numerous branches of a 'bush' of forms, with many off-shoots in tropical areas, which can be separated only arbitrarily from neighbouring 'bushes' that Mayr & Amadon have termed Turdinae, Timaliinae, Pachycephalinae, Sylviinae, and Malurinae (see MUSCICAPIDAE). Many of the more than 50 species of Muscicapinae breeding in

New Guinea, for instance, are more like warblers (Sylviinae), chats (Turdinae), or even shrikes (Laniidae), than they are like any of the European flycatchers—this in respect of habits, shape of bill, rictal bristles, and relative length of tarsus.

$\frac{2}{3}$

Collared Flycatcher *Ficedula albicollis*, of eastern Europe. C.E.T.K.

Flycatchers may be as tiny as a kinglet *Regulus* sp., e.g. *Abrornis*, or as large as a thrush *Turdus* sp., e.g. *Bradornis*. The plumage is often brightly coloured, and many forms are sexually dimorphic. The tail is generally truncate ; but it may be fan-shaped, as in the fantails *Rhipidura* spp. of the Oriental and Australasian Regions ; or it may be more than twice the length of the body, as in adult males of some of the paradise flycatchers *Terpsiphone* spp. found in countries bordering the Indian Ocean. Ornamental wattles of emerald green, turquoise blue, purple, or red are characteristic of the puff-back flycatchers *Batis* spp. and the wattle-eyes *Platysteira* spp. and *Diaphorophyia* spp. of Africa, and also of *Terpsiphone* spp. ; so likewise are fleshy eye-rings characteristic of *Arses telescopophthalmus* of New Guinea and *Zeocephus rufus* of the Philippines.

Some 110 species of the diversified subfamily Muscicapinae are united by Vaurie in a tribe 'Muscicapini', the limits of which are not sharply defined. Although these are more or less closely related to the European species, some nevertheless show considerable differences. Thus *Muscicapella* ('*Nitidula*') spp. of tropical Asia, among others, have slender bills and quite short bristles ; they pick up insects from twigs and leaves. The large grey flycatchers *Bradornis* spp. of Africa dart down on insects moving on the ground, after the manner of shrikes (Laniidae). Others live sociably like tits (Paridae) in the foliage, e.g. *Newtonia* spp. of

Madagascar ; or like a robin *Erithacus* sp. keep near the ground in the dim shadow of the forest undergrowth, e.g. members of the south-east Asian genera *Anthipes* and *Dendrobiastes*. *Namibornis* of South West Africa has a position on the borderline between the Muscicapinae and the Turdinae.

The manner of life and, especially, the breeding biology of few of the Muscicapini are nearly as well known as those of the several European species. Some breed in holes in trees (*Ficedula* spp.), others in crevices (Spotted Flycatcher *Muscicapa striata* ; Blue-and-white Flycatcher *Cyanoptila cyanomelana* of the eastern Palaearctic). Many species construct solid, open, cup-shaped nests (*Terpsiphone, Batis, Rhipidura*) ; in some Australian *Microeca* spp. the nest is so minute that there is room for only one nestling. *Dendrobiastes* spp. and the Black-and-orange Flycatcher *Ochromela nigrorufa* of southern India build enclosed nests of moss, with a side entrance, in ground moss or under tree-roots on the forest floor. Some African species lay their eggs in the deserted nests of other birds—Boehm's Flycatcher *Myopornis boehmi*, the Dusky Blue Flycatcher *Pedilorhynchus comitatus*, and the Swamp Flycatcher *Alseonax aquaticus* in those of weavers (Ploceidae) ; Cassin's Grey Flycatcher *Alseonax cassini* occasionally in those of swallows (Hirundinidae), although commonly in a cavity or fork.

Among Palaearctic species, the Pied Flycatcher *Ficedula hypoleuca* and the Collared Flycatcher *F. albicollis* have very similar habits. They are hole-breeders and they catch insects on the wing or in the foliage. The male defends several territories and is polygamous ; either he leaves the first female and helps the second one to rear the brood, or he returns for this purpose to his first companion. The Red-breasted Flycatcher *F. parva* breeds in crevices and shallow holes in the trunks of trees in mixed woods. The male of this graceful species has, when over two years old, an orange-red throat. All these and related species show a characteristic flicking of the tail and wings when alarmed.

In contrast, the Spotted Flycatcher *Muscicapa striata*, inhabiting nearly the whole of Europe and part of Asia, has no territorial song. This and related species are specialised to hunt flying insects from a perch. The female builds the nest in a niche in a wall or tree and incubates the clutch of (commonly) 6 eggs.

In general, the eggs of flycatchers are bluish, reddish, yellowish, or white, and more or less spotted or mottled ; but in the Mariqua Flycatcher *Bradornis mariquensis* of South West Africa they are uniformly olive-green. In tropical and subtropical forms the clutch usually consists of 2 or 3 eggs. Two

Australian *Microeca* spp. lay only a single egg. The Palaearctic forms have large clutches ; the Pied Flycatcher lays up to 9 eggs, but on the average 6. In some forms only the female incubates (*Ficedula* spp., the Puff-back Flycatcher *Batis capensis*), in others the male shares the duties of incubation as well (Korean Flycatcher *Ficedula xanthopygia*, eastern Palaearctic Region ; Pied Fantail *Rhipidura rufifrons*, New Zealand ; *Terpsiphone* spp.). Both parents feed the young.

The Muscicapinae are distributed over the whole eastern hemisphere, and have even colonised New Zealand (*Rhipidura*) and the Hawaiian archipelago (*Chasiempis*). They are confined to the Old World ; in the New World their ecological niche is occupied by the tyrant-flycatchers of the family Tyrannidae, among which there are species looking like Muscicapini but having a different vocal apparatus (see FLYCATCHER (2)).

All the Palaearctic species winter in the tropics. Among the European ones the Spotted Flycatcher and the black-and-white *Ficedula* spp. migrate to Africa, whereas *F. parva* winters in western India. The Grey-spotted Flycatcher *Muscicapa griseisticta* migrates from Ussuriland to Celebes and the Moluccas.

See Plates 6 (colour), 35a and 39a (phot.).

E.S. & E.C.

Campbell, B.   1955. A population of Pied Flycatcher (*Muscicapa hypoleuca*). Acta XI Congr. Internat. Orn., Basel 1954 : 428–434.

Curio, E.   1959. Verhaltensstudien am Trauerschnäpper. Z. Tierpsychol., Beiheft 3 : 1–118.

Haartman, L. v.   1949. 1951, 1954. Der Trauerfliegenschnäpper. I, II, III. Acta Zool. Fenn. no. 56 : 1–104 ; no. 67 : 1–60 ; no. 83 : 1–96.

Ripley, S. D.   1955. Some comments on Vaurie's revision of the Muscicapini. Auk 72 : 86–88.

Vaurie, C.   1953. A generic revision of flycatchers of the tribe Muscicapini. Bull. Amer. Mus. Nat. Hist. 100 : 453–538.

FLYCATCHER (2): substantive name of many species of Tyrannidae (Passeriformes, suborder Tyranni) ; in the form ' tyrant-flycatchers ', general term for the family. Other substantive names used in different genera include ' tyrant ', ' kingbird ', ' phoebe ', and ' pewee '. According to some authors there are two subfamilies, Tyranninae and Oxyruncinae, the latter monotypic ; according to others *Oxyruncus cristatus* should be placed in a family of its own (see SHARPBILL).

The family of tyrant-flycatchers, comprising over three hundred species, is confined to the Americas ; there it replaces, and in many respects resembles, the Old World flycatchers (Muscicapinae) (see FLYCATCHER (1)), being superficially separable from that family merely on the pattern of the primaries and on tarsal characters. Like the Muscicapinae, they show a wide variety of form and an even wider range of habitat and behaviour ; but on the whole they have not adopted such brightly coloured plumage, nor are they usually such capable songsters —belonging, as they do, to the non-singing division of the Passeriformes.

The largest size attained is about 9 inches in length, apart from those few species with elongated tails, and the smallest 3–4 inches. Generalisation on plumage pattern and colour is impossible in view of the great variety, although there is a tendency to adopt protective colours in shades of green, brown, yellow, grey, white, or almost black ; red is unusual, and blue almost unknown. Usually there is no or very slight sexual dimorphism, but

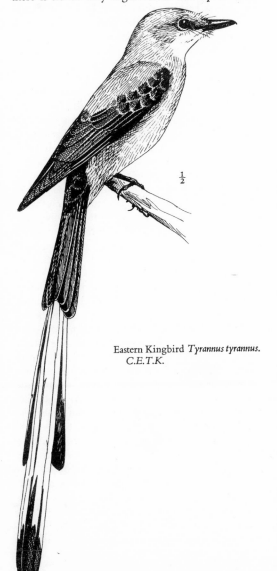

$\frac{1}{2}$

Eastern Kingbird *Tyrannus tyrannus.*
C.E.T.K.

exceptions are the wide-ranging Vermilion Flycatcher *Pyrocephalus rubinus* and the Spectacled Tyrant (or Silverbill) *Lichenops perspicillata* of Chile and Argentina. The kingbirds *Tyrannus* spp. exemplify a rather characteristic plumage pattern that is more or less common to other prominent and often aggressive genera. This is nearly black or rufous, grey, or olive on the upper parts ; often has prominent eye, superciliary, or crown stripes ; is usually darkest on crown, wings, and tail, and is white, grey, or yellow on the under parts. Yet many tropical species (e.g. *Euscarthmus meloryphus,* but doubtfully placed in the family) are extremely drab. Exceptionally brightly coloured species are the Vermilion Flycatcher, in which the male has bright red crown and under parts, the rest of the plumage being dark brownish or almost black ; and the Argentine-Chilean Many-coloured Tyrant *Tachuris rubrigastra,* of which the colours are black, white, green, orange, scarlet, and (most unusually) blue. Many species are more or less crested, and this may or may not be accompanied by a concealed or partly concealed crown-patch of bright yellow, orange, red, or white, this feature being the most outstanding plumage character of the family although not possessed by all genera. Its extreme development is seen in the Northern Royal Flycatcher *Onychorhynchus mexicanus,* which has an erectile, fan-shaped crest of long orange-vermilion feathers, tipped with violet. The wing varies from long and pointed in certain migratory species, e.g. the Chocolate Tyrant *Neoxolmis rufiventris* of Argentina, to short and rounded as in many small species of the tropical forests. The tail is usually of normal length for the size of the head and square-ended, although very short in some small species and somewhat rounded in a few others. The Scissor-tailed Flycatcher *Muscivora forficata* and Swallow-tailed (or Fork-tailed) Flycatcher *M. tyrannus* are exceptional in having long, deeply forked tails. Rictal bristles are normally well developed, better than in cotingas (Cotingidae) and manakins (Pipridae), and the bill, although sometimes as long as the head, is usually shorter, broader at the base than it is high, strong, and hooked. It reaches its biggest in the Boat-billed Flycatcher *Megarhynchus pitangua,* with a distinctly curved ridge. Variations are also seen in the flatbills *Rhynchocyclus* spp. and spadebills *Platyrinchus* spp., which have remarkably broad, flattened, and triangular bills, and the tody-flycatchers *Todirostrum* spp., which have bills that are rather long, much flattened and often scarcely tapered. Others, e.g. the tyrannulets *Camptostoma* spp. and the bentbills *Oncostoma* spp., have compressed bills with arched culmina. The legs and feet are normally developed in most genera, but stronger, longer, and more powerful in species that have adopted a terrestrial way of life, such as the Short-tailed Ground Tyrant *Muscigralla brevicauda*.

The habits of included species are very variable. Larger species, such as the kingbirds, characteristically live in more open country, use conspicuous perches, are aggressive towards other birds, especially raptors, and generally behave much as typical Old World flycatchers (Muscicapinae). Smaller species often inhabit better wooded or forested areas and may then behave more like leaf-warblers *Phylloscopus* spp. (Sylviinae). Others are intermediate or have become essentially terrestrial species. The latter may behave like shrikes (Laniidae) or ground-feeding kingfishers (Alcedinidae), e.g. the Grey Pepoaza *Xolmis cinerea*, sitting on conspicuous perches and dropping down to catch and eat their prey on the ground, or fill the niche of Old World stonechats *Saxicola* spp. and wheatears *Oenanthe* spp. (e.g. *Muscisaxicola* spp. and the Short-tailed Ground Tyrant).

The members of the family are probably dominantly insectivorous birds, but some larger species with shrike-like or terrestrial habits, such as the Kiskadee Flycatcher (or Great Kiskadee) *Pitangus sulphuratus* and Kittlitz Ground Tyrant *Agriornis livida*, take lizards, frogs, mice, and small birds ; also many species are liable to eat fruit and berries, so that perhaps few are exclusively either insectivorous or vegetarian. The flight is not strong, especially among smaller sorts, and is rarely sustained (except, no doubt, in migratory species) ; the kingbirds may be mentioned in particular, since characteristically they have a rather weak, fluttering action and often do not fully withdraw the legs and feet. Special song-flights, associated with territorial activities, have been evolved in some species inhabiting open country, such as the Vermilion Flycatcher, the Short-tailed Ground Tyrant, and the Spectacled Tyrant. Generally the song is poor to unpleasant, either an undistinguished twittering or a rasping and irregular grating ; but some have sweet songs or clear mellow calls, as in *Pitangus sulphuratus* and in the Black-crowned Pepoaza *Xolmis coronata* of Argentina, with low whistles of such human quality as regularly to deceive dogs. The phoebes *Sayornis* spp. have the characteristic habit of twitching the tail when at rest, while the Torrent Flycatcher *Serpophaga cinerea* and its congeners incessantly open and spread the tail like a fan when perched.

As would be expected, the breeding habits vary considerably. Probably most species build open, cup-shaped nests in forks and on the branches of trees and bushes ; but these may be rather large and untidy on the outside in kingbirds, as neat as those of hummingbirds (Trochilidae) in some species of *Elaenia*, or very frail and transparent in *Euscarthmus*. Some phoebes line their nests with mud. Other genera (*Tolmomyias, Pitangus, Fluvicola, Arundiricola, Camptostoma*) make enclosed, ball-shaped nests (with a side entrance), while the tody-tyrants construct long pendant masses of grass and plant fibres in which a nest cavity is worked. Species such as the Pied Water-tyrant *Fluvicola pica*, *Arundiricola leucocephala*, and the Many-coloured Tyrant, being marsh or water-frequenting birds, invariably nest over water. Hole nesting has been adopted by the crested flycatchers *Myiarchus* spp. and Baird's Flycatcher *Myiodynastes bairdii* ; ground nesting is common among terrestrial species, e.g. *Muscisaxicola* spp. nest under stones and in crevices, and the Short-tailed Ground Tyrant makes partly domed nests in more open places. Some species of *Tolmomyias* and *Camptostoma* have a tendency to nest in proximity to aggressive social hymenoptera (see NESTING ASSOCIATION).

Clutch size in most tropical forms is 2–3, but species in higher latitudes more usually lay 4 eggs (as do some tropical species). Laying is probably usually every day, but the tyrannulets *Camptostoma* spp. and some other genera lay at intervals of 48 hours. Eggs vary from pure white, cream, or buff (e.g. Short-tailed Ground Tyrant, *Phaeomyias murina, Elaenia leucospodia*) to spotted and blotched eggs of all sorts, although the ground-colour is always white to creamy, sometimes with a greenish or olive tinge but never blue. The incubation period is known for a good many species, and it is interesting that, although most incubate for 14–18 days (elaenias, kingbirds, pewees *Contopus* ('*Myiochanes*') spp., *Myiozetetes* spp., and many others), the Black-tailed Flycatcher *Myiobius atricaudus*, the Sulphur-rumped Flycatcher *M. sulphureipygius*, and the Ochre-bellied Flycatcher *Pipromorpha oleaginea* have periods of at least 19–23 days. Similarly, the nestling period varies, since the Vermilion Flycatcher has a normal period of 13–14 days in Ecuador, which is probably representative of many species, but the Short-billed Flatbill *Rhynchocyclus brevirostris*, the Boat-billed Flycatcher of Mexico, *Myiobius* spp., and *Myiozetetes* spp. have periods of at least $3-3\frac{1}{2}$ weeks in the nest ; and a continuous series between these two extremes is known. The territorial habit is usually well developed, territories often being defended with display, song-flights, and much general singing and squabbling.

The family is listed by Hellmayr as having 115 genera and 361 species, but these figures include many monospecific genera and also species that are probably better regarded as mere races ; when it is critically reviewed, the number of both genera and species will probably be reduced. The family is confined to the Americas, from Canada to Tierra del Fuego, and is represented in the Galápagos Islands ; the Neotropical Region has by far the larger number of forms. Its members inhabit all sorts of country from tropical rain-forest to desert and open pampa, and are absent only from the highest Andean peaks. In the higher latitudes, on both sides of the Equator, several species are migratory. For instance, in Argentina the Vermilion Flycatcher, elsewhere sedentary, only comes to breed in the southern summer, while the Chocolate Tyrant is migratory to southern Patagonia, as are also the Black Tyrant *Knipolegus aterrimus*, the Mouse-brown Pepoaza *Xolmis murina*, and the Spectacled Tyrant or Silverbill. Almost all North American species are also migratory, and such well-known birds as kingbirds, phoebes, and pewees are involved, as well as species of other genera such as *Muscivora, Myiarchus, Empidonax, Contopus,* and *Nuttallornis.* It may be mentioned that few of these migrants move farther south than the northern coasts of South America and thus do not cross the Equator in their travels.

See Plate 17 (colour).   S.M.

Marchant, S. 1960. The breeding of some S. W. Ecuadorian birds. Ibis 102 : 349–382, 584–589.
Skutch, A. F. 1960. Life Histories of Central American Birds. Part II. Pacific Coast Avifauna no. 34. Los Angeles.

FLYCATCHER-SHRIKE : alternative substantive name of some species of Campephagidae (see CUCKOO-SHRIKE).

FLYCATCHER, SILKY : see SILKY FLYCATCHER

FLYCATCHER-WARBLER : name given to *Seicercus* spp. (see WARBLER (1)).

FLYEATER : substantive name of *Gerygone* spp. (see WREN (2)).

FODI ; FODY : substantive name of *Foudia* spp. (see WEAVER).

FOLIAGE-GLEANER : substantive name of species in several genera (e.g. *Automolus*) of Furnariidae (see OVENBIRD (1)).

FOLKLORE : a branch of social anthropology dealing with data in which birds figure, including local names, proverbs, legends, myths, folktales, rituals, and symbols (see also FABULOUS BIRDS). Aspects of the human exploitation of birds, such as devices for trapping them and the use of their plumage as adornments or parts of their bodies as medicine, are also relevant (see ORNAMENTATION, BIRDS IN HUMAN). Hunting and fowling were the mainstay of life in Palaeolithic times, and traces of beliefs and rituals concerned with increasing the fertility and vulnerability of prehistoric man's quarry survive in extant traditions. Thus folklore is indispensable as one of the few sources of information concerning the modes of thought and spiritual life of earlier communities. The importance which pre-literate peoples attached to birds as beings possessing supernatural powers is attested by cave art, wherein men are represented with bird-like heads—probably masks, and by the myths in which birds participate in creation or have vital cultural roles attributed to them. Thus in a number of Asian creation myths an animal, often a bird, brings up mud from the primaeval waters.

Three avian characteristics have been influential in giving birds a place in the folklore of most human societies. (1) Being winged and agile they come and go mysteriously ; migratory species appear and disappear unaccountably. Their ability to fly up into the heavens suggests that they may be in touch with, or be emissaries of, sky powers. Affinities have been perceived between the precarious stay and departure of the human soul and the movements of birds. (2) Men have been impressed by likenesses between themselves and birds, particularly their bipedal gait and their singing, dancing, and building activities. Owls (Strigiformes), because of their binocular vision and the human quality of their calls, have been regarded as uncanny because creatures which seem partly human arouse disquieting emotions. Shamans have sometimes decorated themselves with feathers or other parts of birds, seeking thereby to acquire and wield some of their powers. (3) The colours of their adornments and other structural characteristics have inspired aetiological explanations or beliefs associating birds with supernatural beings or mythical events. Some black species, such as the Raven *Corvus corax* and Swift *Apus apus*, have been associated with the devil. The Raven is said to have been blackened by smoke, and the Robin *Erithacus rubecula* to have had its breast singed in fetching the primaeval fire. In Cornwall the red bill of the Chough *Pyrrhocorax pyrrhocorax* has given rise to the notion that it is an incendiary ; but this belief is not linked with the origin of fire, although myths concerning other fire-birds may have contributed to its formulation. According to a legend of comparatively recent origin, the peculiar mandibles and red breast of the Crossbill *Loxia curvirostra* witness to the bird's efforts to draw the nails from the Cross.

Birds that figure in ritual or are protected by public

opinion for all or most of the year are usually species which possessed magico-religious significance in earlier times. Some of them were ceremonially sacrificed. Bird ritual performed at a regular time each year may be assumed to be ancient. Many bird beliefs are concerned with prosperity and, basically, fertility, or, on the other hand, with warding off evil—dominating motivations in human life. Birds may be thought of as participating in impregnating women, as in the Siberian shaman's ritual of dangling a model bird over a barren woman and in the myth of Jupiter and Leda, or as rain-makers bringing fertility to the crops. Possibly some migratory birds, such as geese *Anser* spp., on their northward passage were considered to be not merely heralding the spring but inaugurating it. In decay, beliefs concerning the magical activities of birds are apt to become vague associations between them and good or bad luck.

Ominous birds, such as owls and various corvine species, are often believed to bring or foretell disaster, but inconsistent beliefs concerning birds may prevail in neighbouring communities or even contemporaneously in the same community ; in Athens, owls were regarded as beneficent. The inconsistent or ambivalent notions attaching to such birds are commonly attributable to the merging of two culture streams or to the peculiar thought-forms of unsophisticated people. A frightening object or creature may be used to intimidate other alarming beings or powers or to frustrate untoward events. The bodies of owls, or representations of the birds, were hung or set up in Europe and China to avert the thunderbolt. Moreover, while the appearance of a benevolent creature heralds good fortune, its departure may presage disaster. Casuistry enters into the interpretation of bird omens (see OMENS, BIRDS AS). Contrary inferences may be drawn according as a bird flies to right or left, and in the familiar rhyme (with several variants) about the Magpie *Pica pica*, ' One for sorrow, two for mirth . . .', we have an example of significance depending on numbers.

Many bird traditions have originated through unsophisticated people mistaking conjunction for causation. Woodpeckers (Picidae) drumming as the rain began to fall were assumed to be rain-makers, as many primitive peoples drum for rain. Where there is more sophistication, a strange apparition may be thought of as foretelling rather than causing some blessing or calamity. A cormorant *Phalacrocorax* sp. perching on a church tower may be associated with a shipwreck should one occur about the same time. The belief that a bird tapping at a window foretells illness or death still persists because some-

times an incident of this kind coincides with a family tragedy. Almost any species of bird may at some time or another be considered to possess mysterious significance because of such chance conjunctions. Associations based on sympathetic magic are responsible for a number of bird traditions. For example, eagles *Aquila* spp. being powerful, parts of their bodies were considered to be potent medicines.

Some traditions concerning birds are shared by more than one species. Thus it would be gratuitous to attempt an exact differentiation of raven and crow traditions. When a myth travels beyond the area in which a bird figuring in it occurs, another species may be substituted—either because it bears some similarity or by virtue of its already possessing supernatural associations. In parts of north-eastern Asia and north-western America the Raven is the bringer of fire although it has no red adornments like other fire-birds. The cranes (Gruidae) are held to be propitious birds in the Far East, as the White Stork *Ciconia ciconia* is in Europe.

Associations between a god, goddess, saint, or culture hero have arisen in various ways and each must be considered on its merits. Cú Chulainn's ' scald-crow ' and Odin's Raven appear to have survived from times when the supernatural powers of animals were viewed with awe and fear ; but most of the birds in Christian art, such as doves (Columbidae) and the Goldfinch *Carduelis carduelis*, were deliberately introduced because of the conventional symbolism they had acquired (see ART, BIRDS IN).

Not many birds have major significance in European folk beliefs. Owl and raven traditions are very ancient, and beliefs concerning solar birds, such as eagles and geese, are also old. The woodpeckers' association with rain goes back to prehistoric times. The Wren *Troglodytes troglodytes*, like the Robin and Swallow *Hirundo rustica*, is connected with fire-bringing, but originally it may have been a chthonic being in league with the powers lurking in the earth. The ' Hunting of the Wren ', which still persists in most of the Republic of Ireland, is the most elaborate bird ritual surviving in Europe. The Cuckoo *Cuculus canorus*, endowed with a voice of human timbre, is associated with luck and fertility.

Ornithologists, especially those working in the less industrialised regions of the world, should regard the collection of folklore as important. The mapping of the distribution of customs and beliefs before folklore disappears or its boundaries become blurred is urgent. In some societies bird beliefs connected with totemism, ancestor worship, and reincarnation have to be evaluated. Those trained in the physical or biological sciences should bear in mind that they must sometimes apply to folklore different criteria and principles of interpretation from those to which they are accustomed. Thus a multiplicity of irreconcilable explanations of a custom such as the eating of the Michaelmas goose, indicates, not that the ceremony is of little importance, but on the contrary that it has ancient antecedents. The occurrence of nonsense in a folktale may be evidence that the version is old and authentic. Apparent trivialities are often of vital significance. Since bird beliefs and ceremonial are most adequately integrated into the life of the less industrialised communities it is desirable to evaluate their functions in the societies preserving them. The student of folklore is concerned with current changes in folklore no less than with past beliefs and customs. E.A.A.

Armstrong, E. A. 1958. The Folklore of Birds. London.
Swainson, C. 1885. Provincial Names and Folk Lore of British Birds. London.
Thomas, N. W. 1908. Animals. In Encyclopaedia of Religion and Ethics 1 : 483–535.

FOLLICLE, FEATHER: see FEATHER

FOLLICLE, OVARIAN: see REPRODUCTIVE SYSTEM

FOLLOWING RESPONSE: see under IMPRINTING

FOOD: see FEEDING HABITS ; FEEDING OF YOUNG ; FOOD SELECTION ; PIRACY ; PREDATION ; also ALIMENTARY SYSTEM ; GRIT ; METABOLISM ; NUTRITION ; PELLET

FOOD, BIRDS AS HUMAN: see UTILISATION BY MAN

FOOD DEFICIENCY: see DISEASE

FOOD SELECTION: an aspect of behaviour (see FEEDING HABITS), of interest also from the evolutionary and ecological points of view in that closely related species living in the same habitat do not compete for food (as shown by various authors). Although some avian species are specialised for taking a particular type of food, e.g. the seed-eating finches (Fringillidae), many are rather catholic in their taste and take a wide variety of food items. This wide range of objects taken by many species is apparently due to an initial responsiveness to a few generalised stimulus situations, each characteristic of a variety of objects. The effective stimuli are later narrowed by learning. The course taken by this learning is determined not only by the food within the environment, but also by the behaviour patterns and structures available for finding it.

Each species has its own repertoire of stereotyped motor patterns used in feeding. Although usually common to all members of the species and appearing in characteristic form when first used, they may depend on learning for their full effectiveness. This learning may affect the co-ordination of the movement, the stimuli that elicit it, or both. Thus the first appearance of pecking in young chicks appears to be independent of learning ; initially anything on the ground that is small and contrasts with its background is pecked at (Spalding). Should the object be edible it is swallowed ; the sequence provides a reinforcement, and the animal comes to distinguish edible from inedible objects.

The ability of many birds—including Jays *Garrulus glandarius*, Magpies *Pica pica*, some finches and tits *Parus* spp.—to use the foot in conjunction with the bill while feeding is often characteristic of the species, but learning enters into its perfection. It enables sources of food to be tapped that would otherwise be unavailable ; thus Magpies pull down and stand on grass stems while they peck out the seeds, and Goldfinches *Carduelis carduelis* combine bill and foot to feed on thistle heads. Even although the perfection and use of such motor patterns may involve learnt modifications to eliciting stimuli and to the movement itself, differences between species in their repertoire of motor patterns must ultimately be genetic.

Although the stimuli eliciting feeding responses prior to learning may be very generalised, some stimulus situations tend to produce greater response than others, and differences between the species have been demonstrated. For example, Engelmann showed that adult domestic hens, raised without any form of grain, pecked at rye more than peas or wheat ; later their choice changed to wheat, which is preferred by normally reared adult birds under similar conditions. These experiments, and others with artificial seeds of varying shapes and sizes, indicated an initial preference for a longish shape and for a size that could be dealt with most easily.

Newly-hatched birds with little visual experience and no opportunity for direct learning have been tested for their differential response to colour. It is known that closely-related species tend to show similar colour preferences, and in many cases these preferences have selective advantages. Hence, gulls and terns peck at red and orange, and these colours often, but not always, appear on the parent's bill (N. Tinbergen & Perdeck, and others). The Moorhen *Gallinula chloropus* also selects red ; so does the Coot *Fulica atra*, although here the adult's bill is white. In studies of young Anatidae and Phasianidae, which obtain their own food from the start, Kear found that almost all species preferred green. It is supposed that these differences are innate.

In species where the initial responsiveness is to a very wide range of objects, trial-and-error learning later limits the effective stimuli (see LEARNING). The importance of trial-and-error learning varies, of course, between species, and nowhere is it the only factor limiting the range of effective stimuli. Often there are short-term changes in responsiveness, dependent on an encounter with an edible object such that the bird 'searches for' similar objects and ignores others. L. Tinbergen described this as a change in the 'specific search image'.

Parental example and local experience are also important, the latter especially in flocking species. Further, dietary conditions may also play a role, for hens can learn to select food in such a way as to correct for some deficiencies. The complexity of the problem of food selection is illustrated by L. Tinbergen's study of the Great Tit *Parus major*, dealing with food preferences shown by the birds feeding their young and by individual variations in diet. Trial-and-error learning is not the only factor influencing food selection, for the bird does not always concentrate on the most readily available food, but takes a variety. Thus, although captive finches prefer certain seeds over others, small amounts of all seeds offered are taken at times, provided that the birds are physically capable of dealing with them. Birds fed on one seed only for a short time will often reject that seed upon a return to a choice situation, although the original scale of preference may reappear later (Kear). This 'dietary fatigue' requires definition and analysis.

Some species are known to change their diet with the seasons coinciding with the onset of breeding, the feeding of the young, the moult, and the changing climatic conditions. To some extent this is probably a matter of availability, but preferences may also be governed by internal changes.

Distantly related species may have marked innate differences in the stimuli that elicit their feeding responses. Between closely related species, however, such innate differences are often inconspicuous. The problem of how inter-specific differences in food selection arise is acute—especially when the stimuli eliciting feeding behaviour are diverse. Sometimes competition is avoided by differences in habitat selection or in the selection of the feeding niche within the habitat. In other cases, overlap in diet is prevented because the course of learning that takes place is governed by the range of motor patterns or structures available for feeding. Thus tits, but few other species, learn to open milk bottles because they have the motor patterns necessary to do so (Hinde & Fisher) ; and the size of seeds taken by finches is determined in large part by the size of the bill—each species learns to take those seeds that it can deal with most efficiently. The bill and other structures used in feeding are usually adapted to feeding conditions in the localities inhabited by the species (Snow). Populations adapted to different conditions and meeting later may therefore select different diets not because of innate differences in responsiveness but because they learn to eat those foods to which they are structurally adapted (Hinde). See also TASTE.

J.K.

Engelmann, C. 1943. Über den Geschmackssinn des Huhns. VI. Über angeborene Formvorliebe bei Hühnern. Z. Tierpsychol. 5 : 42–59.

Hinde, R. A. 1959. Behaviour and speciation in birds and lower vertebrates. Biol. Rev. 34 : 85–128 (at pp. 103–110).

Hinde, R. A. & Fisher, J. 1952. Further observations on the opening of milk bottle tops by birds. Brit. Birds 44 : 393–396.

Kear, J. 1962. Food selection in finches with special reference to interspecific differences. Proc. Zool. Soc. Lond. 138 : 164–204.

Kear, J. (in press). Colour selection and preference in young Anatidae. Ibis 106.

Plate 19 · Plumages of a Single Species by PETER SCOTT

KING EIDER *Somateria spectabilis* (Arctic, circumpolar)

1 Nest and eggs, showing nest down   **2** Adult female   **3** Ducklings 3 days old

4 Duckling 3 weeks old   **5** Female 3 months old   **6** Male 4 months old

7 Male in first winter   **8** Adult male in full plumage   **9** Same, displaying

10 Adult female, reddish phase (commoner than the duller phase depicted in 2)

11 Adult male in full eclipse   **12** Adult male losing full plumage (stage between 8 and 11)   **13** Adult male coming into full plumage   The birds shown in flight are all adults

See articles DUCK ; MOULT ; PLUMAGE.

Foreground birds approx. $\frac{1}{6}$ nat. size

Spalding, D. 1872. Instinct, with original observations on young animals. Reprinted 1954, Brit. J. Anim. Behav. 2 : 2–11.

Snow, D. W. 1954. The habitats of Eurasian tits (*Parus* spp.). Ibis 96 : 565–585.

Tinbergen, L. 1949. Bosvogels en insecten. Nederl. Boschbouw Tijds. 4 : 91–105.

Tinbergen, N. & Perdeck, A. C. 1950. On the stimulus situation releasing the begging response in the newly-hatched Herrring Gull chick (*Larus a. argentatus*). Behav. 3 : 1–38.

FOOL HEN : popular name for the Spruce Grouse *Canachites canadensis* (see GROUSE).

FOOT : see under LEG ; SKELETON

FOOTEDNESS : a physiological dominance of one foot over the other, comparable with right-handedness or lefthandedness in human beings. There is some evidence of this in domestic pigeons. It was found that birds alighting on a perch usually landed with one foot first, and seldom with both together. Of 11 birds (in 7259 landings), 3 used the right foot on more than 90 per cent of occasions ; none showed such a significantly preponderate use of the left foot.

It has been noticed (Dobie 1936, and others) that in the Crossbill *Loxia curvirostra* the use of a particular foot to hold a cone is correlated with the direction of crossing of the mandibles. A cone is usually held in one foot ; and if the lower mandible twists to the right, then the left foot is used—and vice versa. When the cone is held with both feet, if the lower mandible twists to the right the base of the cone lies under the left foot and its tip under the right foot—and, again, vice versa. The effect is that the tip of the lower mandible presses towards the central axis of the cone, while the scale is raised mainly by the tip of the upper mandible. Which foot is used is presumably learnt by a young bird according to its bill structure. Sometimes, but not always, the tarsus of the foot used for holding is markedly thicker than the other (I. Newton, personal communication 1963).

Dobie, W. H. 1936. Crossbills' method of feeding. Brit. Birds 30 : 43-44.

Fisher, H. J. 1957. Footedness in domestic pigeons. Wilson Bull. 69 : 170-178.

FORAMEN : an aperture (plural ' foramina ') in a bone or other bodily structure (see SKELETON).

FOREHEAD : see TOPOGRAPHY

FOREST : country closely covered by trees and classified according to whether these have (1) broad thin leaves, either (a) evergreen, e.g. tropical rain-forest, or (b) deciduous, varying in character with prevailing humidity and temperature ; (2) broad thick leaves, e.g. sclerophyll forests in regions of winter rain ; or (3) narrow thick leaves, e.g. coniferous forest. These forests severally provide different types of bird habitat ; if continuous for great distances they may also be important, notably rain-forest, as distributional barriers (see RAIN-FOREST ; TAIGA).

FORKTAIL : substantive name of *Enicurus* spp. (see THRUSH).

FORM : in taxonomy, a loose or deliberately neutral term for a species or a subdivision thereof, non-committal as regards the rank or status to be assigned to it ; sometimes used more precisely to embrace subspecies and monotypic species, e.g. in giving the total number of ' forms ' included in a genus or found in an area. For nomenclatural purposes, however, it is now (after 1960) assumed that a ' form ' or ' variety ' designated as such is infrasubspecific (presumably where the context admits).

FORMALISING : term used earlier (Selous), in respect of behaviour, for RITUALISATION.

Plate 20 : **Polymorphism** by MICHAEL YULE

The species shown are characterised by the presence in their populations of two or more ' morphs '—plumage phases differing markedly from each other independently of sex, age, season, or geographical race. See article POLYMORPHISM.

1 Screech Owl *Otus asio* (North America) Red-brown and grey morphs

2 Many-coloured Bush-shrike *Chlorophoneus multicolor batesi* (tropical Africa) Three of the several morphs (see article)

3 Reddish Egret *Hydranassa rufescens* (southern North America) White and reddish morphs

4 Ruff *Philomachus pugnax* (Palaearctic) Four examples of the polymorphic nuptial plumes of the male

5 Lesser Snow (or Blue) Goose *Anser coerulescens coerulescens* (Arctic North America) Downy goslings of the blue and white morphs

6 Arctic Skua (or Parasitic Jaeger) *Stercorarius parasiticus* (circumpolar) Dark and light morphs

Upper row ca. $\frac{1}{3}$ nat. size ; remainder ca. $\frac{1}{4}$ nat. size

FORMENKREIS: term introduced by Klein-schmidt in 1900 for a taxonomic grouping between the wide Linnean genus and the narrowly defined species of his own day ; the nearest equivalent in current parlance is ' superspecies'. The author's views, although based on theoretical considerations that are unacceptable, had a useful influence on the development of taxonomic thought. See also SUPERSPECIES.

Stresemann, E. 1936. The Formenkreis-theory. Auk 53 : 150-153.

FORMICARIIDAE: see under PASSERIFORMES ; and ANTBIRD

FOSSA: a depression in a bone, e.g. temporal fossa, tympanic fossa (see SKELETON).

FOSSIL BIRDS: forms of the Class Aves extant in earlier geological epochs and preserved as fossils in rocks dating from these various times. The first fossil bird in the geological record is *Archaeopteryx*, the subject of a separate article (see ARCHAEOPTERYX). It is Kimmeridgian (Upper Jurassic) in date and thus it was a member of a living environment about 160 million years ago. Three skeletons of this bird have been found, the last of them being discovered only in 1956. The three skeletons are of the same species, two of the examples being probably adults, the other a younger bird. What is important is that, for a brief time at least, *Archaeopteryx* was a well-established form.

Geological Time-Scale

System		Age (million years)
Quaternary	Recent	
	Pleistocene	up to 1
Tertiary	Pliocene	1– 11
	Miocene	11– 25
	Oligocene	25– 40
	Eocene	40– 70
Mesozoic	Cretaceous	70–135
	Jurassic	135–180
	Triassic	180–225
Palaeozoic	Permian	225–270
	Carboniferous, etc.	270–350
		350–

(First Reptiles in Carboniferous ; first Mammals in Triassic ; *Archaeopteryx* in Jurassic ; first Neornithes in Cretaceous ; first Man in Pliocene.)

The geological record, despite old speculations in print, has no evidence as yet of any bird before *Archaeopteryx* (see ORIGIN OF BIRDS) ; the so-called Triassic and Jurassic bird footprints have turned out to be those of dinosaurs, the bones to belong to pterodactyls. And, after the first remains in the Jurassic, there is no other certain bird skeleton or fragment until the Cretaceous, a gap of some 30 million years. What had transpired in that long intervening period is uncertain, except that when we come to the Cretaceous the birds are well established.

Cretaceous. It has lately become apparent that the history of birds in this Cretaceous aspect is much more complicated than had usually been thought. Earlier, one had been led to believe that there were two principal lines of evolution, so far as birds are concerned, in the Cretaceous. They are represented by *Ichthyornis*, a flying sea bird, and by *Hesperornis*, another sea bird but already so much at home in the water that it had abandoned flight. As befitted supposed direct descendants of the toothed *Archaeopteryx*, these two birds were said to bear teeth in their relatively long jaws.

In fact the picture is very different. There are in all over a dozen different genera, and two dozen species, from North and South America and from Europe (including England). All of them except one are remains of aquatic birds, and this is to be expected, seeing that it is only when the remains have fallen into the sedimentary deposits of gently running water, or in the waters of quiet lakes or seas, that there is much chance of the materials being covered up by sands and muds almost at once and thus being put on the way to permanent preservation by fossilisation. Birds that died on land, like their counterparts today, fell a prey to scavengers and to the processes of decay (see also EVOLUTION).

A survey of these forms yields the following results. Next in geological succession after the Upper Jurassic *Archaeopteryx* is the thigh bone from Auxerre in the Lower Cretaceous of France, that may belong to a goose (Anatidae), although it is obviously difficult to be sure of identity on such slender evidence. Other hind limb bones, from Transylvania, have been given the name *Elopteryx* and are thought to belong to an ancestral form related to the cormorants (Phalacrocoracidae). Then, from the Cambridge Greensand in England, there came many years ago several bones that have been examined in great detail and given the name *Enaliornis*, although their relationships are not at all clear ; they must have been bones of a sea bird about the size of a pigeon *Columba* sp.

Next comes a collection of well-known names, although even yet full details of the structure of the birds are not known. Most of the specimens are bones from a fine-grained deposit that was laid down in a large inland sea in what is now the United States. Here, in Kansas, are the yellowish deposits of Niobrara chalk laid down in Upper Cretaceous water. *Ichthyornis* is known by 7 species, and although most of these are founded on little material, this series contains the almost complete skeletons of *Ichthyornis victor*, one of the best-known fossil birds. *Ichthyornis* (' fish-bird ') was superficially rather like a tern (*Sterna*) and was about 8 inches in height. Its skeleton is much like that of a modern bird and shows a very strong keel on the sternum, so that powers of flight must have been well developed. It was long famous for the fact that its jaws were toothed, but recent examination of all the available material in America has shown that what were presumed to be the jaw bones were, in fact, bones of a swimming reptile, and there is no actual evidence that *Ichthyornis* had teeth. *Apatornis*, a close relative of *Ichthyornis* and of the same age, was not so powerful a flier.

Hesperornis (' western bird ') from the same Niobrara Chalk formation of Kansas, was quite definitely unable to fly at all. It, too, is known by several skeletons, which reveal many details of the body and limbs but are rather unsatisfactory as regards the skull. The bird was large, over 6 feet long from bill to tail, and the feet and legs were so highly adapted for swimming that it is improbable that they could have been used on land. The shoulder girdle is, however, weak, and there is no keel on the breast bone, indicating that the power of flight had already been lost. More convincing on this point is the fact that the lower arm bones were never developed, and it is probable that there was no visible vestige of a wing at all on the living bird. *Hesperornis* is another of the traditionally toothed birds and there are many illustrations clearly showing the dental arrangement. Today this is much in question. At least one specimen in an American Museum seems to have teeth, although arranged on a rather different plan, but most of the others have the jaw bones so entangled with other bones that it is very difficult to say whether the bird can be credited with teeth. Also found in the Niobrara is *Hargeria*, which is closely related to *Hesperornis* and which certainly has no teeth.

Other bird remains of similar age to these well-known forms are *Neogaeornis* from southern Chile, which appears to have been a swimming bird but of which the only specimen is a tarso-metatarsus; *Scaniornis*, of which the humerus, scapula, and coracoid are known ; and *Parascaniornis*, of which there is only a vertebra. These latter two birds come from Sweden and appear to have been related to the flamingos (Phoenicopteri). As already mentioned, bones from the leg of an ancestral cormorant have come from the Upper Cretaceous of Transylvania and are named *Elopteryx*. Finally there are two species of *Cimolopteryx*, from Wyoming and known only by shoulder bones, of which the relationships are obscure ; they seem to have been about the size of a pigeon.

Another Cretaceous bird, this time from Canada, has been described from a very fine lower jaw 9 inches long. It came from Alberta and was named *Caenagnathus*. While it has one or two bird-like features, it seems more likely that this is the jaw of a small running dinosaur, but further remains might establish its avian position. This bone is in any event remarkable, for, of all the Cretaceous bird or bird-like remains, it alone is clearly of a terrestrial animal.

Tertiary. The Cretaceous geological period marks the end of one of the greatest of evolutionary times, and although its known record of bird fossils is relatively poor it is clear that enormous advances must have been made during it. This is certainly the case, for even if the Cretaceous proves to be more prolific of birds than has generally been suspected, the next epoch—the Tertiary—even in its earliest part (Eocene) emerges with a great number of forms, among which many of the modern families of birds are represented. For example, in the Eocene London Clay, formed about 60 million years ago, there is *Proherodius*, a heron (Ardeidae), and *Lithornis*, the oldest known vulture (Aegypiinae). *Halcyornis*, also from the London Clay, is thought to be related to the kingfishers (Alcedinidae).

From the Eocene beds of the Paris Basin, slightly younger than the deposits in the London Clay, there has also come interesting evidence of the antiquity of certain groups. *Agnopterus* is a flamingo (Phoenicopteri) ; *Romainvillea*, an ancestral goose (Anatidae) ; *Gypsornis* is a rail (Rallidae) ; and *Paraortyx* and *Palaeortyx*, also from France, are thought to be relations of the partridges (Phasianidae). Eocene deposits in America have produced *Neocathartes*, related to the New World vultures (Cathartidae), from Wyoming ; *Gallinuloides* and *Palaeophasianus*, which may be related to the pheasants (Phasianidae) ; and several rails (Rallidae) from New Jersey, Wyoming, and Colorado.

In the time of this widespread and ancient formation the birds were truly set ; and we have to remember that, as in the case of the Cretaceous birds, these are all the remains of birds which fell into favourable circumstances for fossilisation. Animals of the woods and forests must have perished without trace, so that the fossil picture of bird evolution is necessarily rather one-sided. Even so, it is possible to say something of the descent of other main avian groups, although they do not achieve the antiquity of those already listed. The herons, bitterns, and storks (Ciconiiformes) stem from the Eocene, with representatives in the Eocene of England, France, Wyoming, and Patagonia. Ducks and geese (Anatidae), with the representative in the Cretaceous already mentioned, also occur in the Eocene of France and Utah, but true geese (*Anser*) are in Europe in Miocene times, spreading from there around the world and arriving in America during the Pleistocene.

As we have seen, the vultures have a long history around the world, as have the pheasants (Phasianidae) and their allies. Cranes (Gruidae) and rails (Rallidae) are also Eocene in origin. Associated with them are the bustards (Otididae), and also the cariamas (Cariamidae) of South America. One of these last, the large and powerful *Phororhacos* of the Miocene of Patagonia, was quite flightless ; but with a skull 18 inches long, a skeleton 5 feet high, and very powerful limbs, it was well endowed for looking after itself on the ground.

Gulls (Larinae), terns (Sterninae), auks (Alcidae), sandpipers (Scolopacidae), are all known from Eocene times onwards ; in the Pliocene period there were several auks. Pigeons (Columbidae) are largely debarred from fossilisation by their occurrence in situations where the remains are most likely to be destroyed by scavengers ; although there are said to be Miocene forms, pigeons do not become common until the Pleistocene.

Parrots (Psittacidae) and cuckoos (Cuculidae) date from the Oligocene, but the owls (Strigiformes) are more ancient and are to be found (*Protostrix*) in the Eocene of Wyoming. The nightjars (Caprimulgidae) and the swifts (Apodidae) are Oligocene in history, as are the trogons (Trogonidae). Woodpeckers (Picidae) are more ancient, their first representative being *Uintornis* from the Eocene of Wyoming. Most of the Passeriformes are of very modern development, and their mode of life and the fragility of their skeletons render them unlikely to be fossilised. Toucans (Ramphastidae), colies (Coliidae), and hummingbirds (Trochilidae) are, as yet, unknown as fossils. Divers (Gaviidae) and grebes (Podicipitidae) seem to date from the Oligocene, as do the albatrosses (Diomedeidae) ; pelicans (Pelecanidae) and tropicbirds (Phaethontidae) date from the Eocene.

A fine series of penguins (Spheniscidae) extends from Eocene times, one of their characteristics being a continuous decrease in size since the Miocene, when *Pachydyptes* and *Anthropornis* were 5 feet high as compared with the smaller penguins of today.

During the long course of this avian history, birds of many kinds have abandoned flight where and when they could adequately maintain themselves upon the ground (see FLIGHTLESSNESS). Today the classic examples are the ' ratites ' (see RATITE) ; these are of much antiquity, for by the Eocene such flightless running birds had already emerged as separate from those which fly.

Of these early forms there is little fossil evidence, although *Eremopezus* from the Eocene of the Fayum may represent an ancestor of *Aepyornis*, itself known only from Madagascar although it may have been more widely distributed in earlier times (its bones in Madagascar being mainly of Pleistocene and recent date). Most of its skeletons indicate large and massive birds reaching their climax in *Aepyornis titan*, which was over 10 feet high (see ELEPHANT-BIRD).

The moas (Dinornithidae) of New Zealand, although not of great antiquity, have long had an extensive literature (see MOA). Complete skeletons, feathers, tracheal rings, traces of skin, and eggs have all been found in caves, swamps, and Maori refuse dumps. Moas were completely flightless, for they had no wing bones at all and but little shoulder girdle from which a wing could have depended ; they compensated for this by having very stout and well-developed legs. There are many forms included in the general title, but the largest of them all was *Dinornis maximus*, about 10 feet high.

The emus (Dromaiidae) of Australia and the rheas (Rheidae) of South America are doubtfully late Pliocene and mainly Pleistocene in antiquity. Ostriches (Struthionidae) were once much more widely spread than in recent times and a Pliocene ostrich from India is known.

The large flightless *Diatryma*, from the Eocene of Wyoming, was 7 feet high and is an early example of the abandonment of flight, but it is not an ancestor of the ' ratites ' (of which the early origins and evolution are still controversial subjects). See RATITES, PHYLOGENY OF THE.   W.E.S.

Howard, H. 1950. Fossil evidence of avian evolution. Ibis 92 : 1–21.
Lambrecht, K. 1933. Handbuch der Palaeornithologie. Berlin.
Swinton, W. E. 1958. Fossil Birds. British Museum (Natural History). London.
Wetmore, A. 1952. Recent additions to our knowledge of prehistoric birds. Proc. X Internat. Orn. Congr., Uppsala 1950 : 51–74.
Wetmore, A. 1955. Palaeontology. *In* Wolfson, A. (ed.). Recent Studies in Avian Biology. Urbana, Ill.

See also references under ARCHAEOPTERYX ; MOA.

FOSSORIAL : term applied to the habit of digging (not just scratching or probing) or burrowing in the soil, exhibited by various birds in preparing nesting holes (see NEST).

FOSTER PARENTS : see PARASITISM

FOUNDER PRINCIPLE : the thesis that the

founders of a new population (e.g. breeding colony) contain only a small fraction of the total genetic variation of the parental population.

FOVEA: part of the retina of the eye (see VISION).

FOWL, DOMESTIC: see DOMESTICATION

FOWL LEUCOSIS; FOWL PLAGUE; FOWL POX: see DISEASE

FRANCOLIN: substantive name of *Francolinus* and *Pternistis* spp. (see under PHEASANT).

FRATERCULINI: see AUK

FREGATAE; FREGATIDAE: see under PELE-CANIFORMES ; and FRIGATEBIRD

FREQUENCY DISTRIBUTION: see STATISTICAL SIGNIFICANCE

FRIARBIRD: substantive name, alternatively ' leatherhead ', of *Philemon* spp. (see HONEYEATER).

FRIGATEBIRD: substantive name of the species of Fregatidae (Pelecaniformes, suborder Fregatae) ; in the plural, general term for the family. There is a single genus, *Fregata*. Frigatebirds (or man-of-war-birds) are found in tropical and subtropical oceanic areas, particularly where flying-fish are abundant. Unlike most other sea birds, they tend to remain close to their breeding grounds throughout the year ; although wanderers have been reported well over 500 miles from the nearest land, the presence of several frigatebirds together has for long been recognised as a sign that land is near.

The breeding colonies are usually situated close to large groups of boobies (Sulidae) or other sea birds, on which the frigatebirds depend for a considerable part of their food supply. Their skill in chasing home-coming boobies, forcing them to disgorge and then catching the food in mid-air, has been described by many observers. Frigatebirds are, however, capable of fishing for themselves. They seldom settle on the water, as their oil glands are small and the plumage rapidly becomes saturated ; instead they fly above shoals of hunting tuna and other fish and catch on the wing the flying-fish which leap out of the water to escape their pursuers. They also snap up refuse from the surface of the sea ; and they may swoop low over breeding colonies of terns (Sterninae) or other relatively small birds, taking unwary chicks. The enormous black wings (spanning 7 feet in the larger species), long hooked bill, and forked tail provide an unmistakable flight silhouette. Frigatebirds soar effortlessly, taking advantage of rising currents of air to gain height and remaining semi-motionless on the wing for

hours at a time (see also FLIGHT). In pursuit of prey they are capable of speedy and highly manoeuvrable flight, in which the large tail is used to great advantage for steering and braking. The wings become an encumbrance on the ground, and in strong winds the birds have difficulty in landing. The legs are small, and the feet, with reduced webbing and sharp claws, are appropriate for perching more than for swimming.

Ascension Frigatebird *Fregata aquila*, breeding on Ascension Island, South Atlantic. *C.E.T.K.*

$\frac{1}{16}$

Typically, frigatebirds nest in trees or low shrubs, but in the absence of vegetation they breed successfully on the ground. There is a marked sexual dimorphism in all species ; females are generally larger than males, and at the courtship season the males develop a crimson inflatable gular sac, which is used during the display. In splendid black and iridescent plumage, the males take up a nest site on the colony ; with wings spread and sac inflated like a balloon they posture to females flying overhead, shivering violently and rattling bill and quills as potential partners approach. There is strong competition for sites in the crowded colonies. The nest material, which is accumulated by both partners before and during incubation, includes sticks, feathers, and bones. A single large white egg is laid, and both parents incubate. The chick is hatched after 40–50 days of incubation, and is closely brooded for the first two weeks until covered with pale grey down. The chicks defend themselves from the intrusions of neighbours while both parents search for food. Although fully feathered after 4–5 months, the juveniles (which in all species are distinguished by a white head) remain dependent on their parents for a further 2–6 months, augmenting their food by scavenging on the colony. They fly together in small bands, picking up feathers and seaweed from the surface of the sea, snatching small unattended chicks of their own species, occasionally turning their attention to boobies and other flying birds, and gradually acquiring the skill necessary for catching food on the wing.

Resting adults and chicks seek shade from the strong tropical sun. In exposed places they take up a remarkable ' sunning ' posture, extending the wings and turning them so that the concave undersurface lies uppermost. This probably exposes the bare flanks to the air and helps the birds to remain cool.

Both the taxonomics and the distribution of frigatebirds require further study. The sedentary habit has led to the formation of many small, isolated populations ; although 5 species and some 14 subspecies are listed, there is considerable confusion in the literature over diagnostic characters and measurements, particularly from those localities (e.g. South Trinidad and the Galápagos Islands) where two similar species are found living side by side. The Ascension Frigatebird *Fregata aquila* is apparently peculiar to Ascension Island, where at present the population numbers between two and three thousand birds. The Christmas Island Frigatebird *F. andrewsi* is found on Christmas Island and in the eastern Indian Ocean ; and the Magnificent Frigatebird *F. magnificens*, the largest member of the genus, ranges from the Galápagos Islands and eastern Pacific Ocean to the Caribbean Sea, the Cape Verde Islands, and the coast of West Africa. The Lesser Frigatebird *F. ariel* and the Great Frigatebird *F. minor* are found in the Indian and Pacific Oceans, appearing also at South Trinidad in the southern Atlantic Ocean. On some of the archipelagos in the central Pacific Ocean frigatebirds are tamed and used, like homing pigeons, to carry messages from island to island.   B.S.

Stonehouse, B. & S. 1963. The Frigate Bird *Fregata aquila* of Ascension Island. (B.O.U. Centenary Expedition). Ibis 103b : 409–422.

FRIGATE-PETREL : substantive name of *Pelagodroma* (' *Fregatta* ') spp. (see PETREL).

FRINGILLIDAE : a family of the Passeriformes, suborder Oscines (see FINCH). In the classification here followed it consists of 3 subfamilies : the Fringillinae (3 species of *Fringilla*, confined to the Palaearctic Region) ; the Carduelinae (numerous genera and species, nearly cosmopolitan but not in the Australasian or Malagasy Regions) ; and the Geospizinae (a peculiar group restricted to the Galápagos Islands) treated in a separate article (see DARWIN'S FINCHES).

In addition, both the Emberizinae (see BUNTING), and the Pyrrhuloxiinae or ' Richmondeninae ' (see CARDINAL-GROSBEAK) were in the past usually placed in this family ; but they now tend to be placed, with others, in a separate family (see EMBERIZIDAE). The Passerinae were also formerly included in the Fringillidae but are now accepted as belonging to the Ploceidae (see SPARROW (I) ; WEAVER).

The taxonomic position is still very fluid, with some authors placing the Carduelinae in the Ploceidae and also tending to redistribute the elements of the Emberizidae. Differing views are reflected in the following Table. Of the two arrangements of families, A is that followed in this work and B represents one permutation of alternative views that have advocates at the present time.

Families (A)	Subfamilies	Families (B)
Estrildidae	Estrildinae	Estrildidae
Incertae sedis	' Viduinae '	
Ploceidae	Bubalornithinae	Ploceidae
	Ploceinae	
	Passerinae	
	Carduelinae	
Fringillidae	Fringillinae	Fringillidae
	Geospizinae	
	Pyrrhuloxiinae	
	Emberizinae	
Emberizidae	Tersininae	Tersinidae
	Thraupinae	Thraupidae
	Coerebinae	(part Thraupidae, part Parulidae)

FROGMOUTH : substantive name of the species of Podargidae (Caprimulgiformes, suborder Caprimulgi) ; in the plural, general term for the family. This is a group of large ' nightjars ' (in the ordinal sense) confined to the Oriental and Australasian Regions (not New Zealand) ; it comprises 2 genera : *Podargus* (3 species), restricted to Australia, New Guinea, and the Solomon Islands, and *Batrachostomus* (9 species), occurring from India to Malaya. Frogmouths have the same marbled grey-brown and rufous cryptic colouring and soft plumage as true nightjars (Caprimulgidae), but differ considerably in some of their habits and structural characters.

They are arboreal, nest-building creatures, laying white eggs and having to a large extent lost the aerial feeding habit. The bills are wide and boat-like, so that earlier naturalists surmised that they were superbly adapted for hawking after nocturnal flying insects. However, it has been demonstrated that frogmouths capture most of their prey on the ground or from branches, short flights being made from a sally point to take a resting beetle, scorpion, centipede, snail, or frog. Mice and small birds, and occasionally fruits, are also eaten. Such terrestrial feeding habits have been adopted independently to some extent by other nightjar groups, but in none so completely as in this family. This has resulted in some structural modifications. Thus, although the frogmouths are still comparatively fast fliers for short distances, they are inferior to the Nightjar *Caprimulgus europaeus* for sustained flight owing to their lower aspect-ratio. Manoeuvring ability, as judged by relative tail area, has been lost by *Podargus* in greater degree than by *Batrachostomus*.

Podargus builds a flimsy stick nest in the horizontal fork of a tree, *Batrachostomus* a pad-like structure made up of its own down and with an external covering of spider-web and lichens. The latter lays one white egg ; the clutch in *Podargus* is 2, occasionally 3. Both the incubation and fledgling periods are about 30 days. The young are covered with long white down. Probably only the female broods, but both parents share in the feeding of the young.

Podargus has a characteristic alarm posture in daylight ; the bird stretches out, with its bill pointed obliquely upward, and the resemblance to a broken branch is remarkable. It freezes into this rigid ' broken branch ' stance only if flushed unawares by day and does not adopt the attitude at night. The birds are active after dusk and before dawn. The call note is a repeated ' oom-oom-oom '. Frogmouths occur in pairs in forested country ; they are nowhere particularly numerous, and, in the Australasian Region, are never seen in the great densities reported of nightjars in Africa and tropical America.

Anatomical peculiarities, as compared with true nightjars, include a desmognathous instead of an aegithognathous palate, no functional basipterygoid processes, 13 instead of 14 cervical vertebrae, sternum double-notched on each side, outer toe with 5 phalanges, a single carotid, and a bronchial syrinx. The tongue is large and paper-like. In both genera there is a pair of remarkably well-developed powder-down tufts arranged on either side of the rump. *Podargus* lacks an oil gland, while *Batrachostomus* possesses a very small one.

See Plate 16a (phot.).   D.L.S.

FROGMOUTH, OWLET: see OWLET-FROG-MOUTH

FRONTAL: pertaining to the forehead (for the frontal bones see SKELETON); also used on occasion (e.g. aerodynamically) in its ordinary more general sense of entire forward-facing aspect.

FRONTED: refers to the forehead (in such combinations as ' white-fronted ').

FRUITCROW: substantive name of species of *Querula* and *Pyroderus* (for family see COTINGA).

FULICINAE: see under RAIL

FULMAR: substantive name of *Fulmarus* spp. and *Macronectes giganteus*, and often applied without qualification to *F. glacialis* ; in the plural, a general term for these and allied genera of the Procellariidae (see PETREL). See Plate 29 (colour).

FURCULA: bony structure (' wishbone ' or ' merrythought ') formed by the fusion, in birds, of the right and left clavicles (see SKELETON).

FURNARIIDAE: see under PASSERIFORMES ; and OVENBIRD (I)

FURNARIOIDEA: see under PASSERIFORMES

G

GADWALL: *Anas strepera* (see DUCK).

GAGGLE: see ASSEMBLY, NOUN OF

GAIT: see LOCOMOTION

GALAH: alternative name of the Roseate Cockatoo *Kakatoe roseicapilla* (for family see PARROT). See Plate 13C (phot.).

GALÁPAGOS FINCHES: see DARWIN'S FINCHES

GALBULAE; GALBULIDAE: see under PICIFORMES; and JACAMAR

GALBULOIDEA: see under PICIFORMES

GALL-BLADDER: not always present in birds (see LIVER).

GALLI: see below

GALLIFORMES: an order, alternatively 'Galli' (also used as subordinal, see below), comprising the following suborders and families, the latter dealt with separately as shown:

Galli:
  Superfamily Cracoidea
    Megapodiidae   see MEGAPODE
    Cracidae   see CURASSOW

  Superfamily Phasianoidea
    Tetraonidae   see GROUSE
    Phasianidae   see PHEASANT
    Numididae   see GUINEAFOWL
    Meleagrididae   see TURKEY
Opisthocomi:
    Opisthocomidae   see HOATZIN

The last named is sometimes treated as a separate order, in which event suborders disappear.

This is an order of mainly ground-feeding but often partly arboreal birds, for the most part of medium size. They are often referred to as 'gallinaceous birds', the domestic fowl being a characteristic member; and they are sometimes loosely called 'game-birds', which some of the most familiar species notably are. The order is a cosmopolitan one, but the Megapodiidae and Numididae have restricted distributions in the Old World and the Cracidae, Meleagrididae, and Opisthocomidae in the New; the Tetraonidae are confined to the Northern Hemisphere. Several species have been domesticated and others are often kept in captivity as ornamental birds (see DOMESTICATION).

A family based on the fossil type-genus *Gallinuloides* is also placed in this order (suborder Galli, superfamily Cracoidea).

GALLINACEOUS: resembling a domestic fowl (see above).

GALLINAE: the fifth avian order of Linnaeus, equivalent to the Galliformes.

GALLINULE: substantive name of species of *Porphyrio*, *Porphyrula*, and sometimes (alternatively to 'moorhen') *Gallinula* (see RAIL). See Plate 17 (colour).

GALLITO: substantive name of *Rhinocrypta lanceolata* (see TAPACULO).

GALLOPHEASANT: in the plural, term for *Lophura* spp. (see PHEASANT).

GAME-BIRDS: sometimes used ornithologically to denote the Galliformes, but properly a general term for certain quarry species belonging for the most part to the families Tetraonidae and Phasianidae (see GROUSE; PHEASANT). In certain parts of the world other families of the Galliformes are included, such as turkeys (Meleagrididae), guineafowl (Numididae), megapodes (Megapodiidae) and guans (Cracidae). Bustards (Otididae) of the order Gruiformes, tinamous (Tinamiformes), and certain 'waders' (Charadrii)—notably snipe and woodcock (Scolopacidae)—are usually regarded as game-birds, although the ducks, geese, and swans (Anatidae) are not (see WILDFOWL); but in New Zealand the introduced Black Swan *Cygnus atratus* and Canada Goose *Branta canadensis* are sometimes referred to as ' game ', and ' game ducks ' was formerly used for dabbling ducks of the tribe Anatini (see DUCK).

The term ' game ' has a legal connotation in Britain, and a game licence is required to shoot Partridge *Perdix perdix*, Pheasant *Phasianus colchicus*, grouse (Red Grouse *Lagopus scoticus* and Ptarmigan *L. mutus*), and ' black game ' (Black Grouse *Lyrurus tetrix*); bustards *Otis* spp. were also included, anachronistically, in this list until 1954. In addition, the Woodcock *Scolopax rusticola* and snipe *Gallinago* spp., etc., have a more limited status under the game laws, and until 1954 this was true also of the Quail *Coturnix coturnix* and the Landrail (or Corncrake) *Crex crex*. The need for special game laws to protect sporting rights originated from the fact that in the common law of England (not Scotland) wild animals in general were nobody's property until brought into possession by killing or capture. In America, game laws have had the object of protecting the birds rather than of preserving enclosure rights (see PROTECTION).

The shooting of game-birds in most parts of the world consists of ' walking-up ' (' jump shooting ' is the American phrase), and dogs—setters and pointers—have been bred specially for giving advance warning of crouching game-birds. A more complicated system known as ' driving ' was evolved and brought to a high pitch of efficiency in Britain at the end of the nineteenth century; grouse, pheasant, and partridge ' drives ' became and have remained a feature of British country life, and are conducted strictly in accordance with tradition. The breeding and training of dogs for ' pointing ', ' setting ', and particularly for ' retrieving ' wounded birds, is regarded by devotees of the sport as one of the most satisfying aspects of game shooting.

P.S.

GAMETE: general term for a germ-cell, whether spermatozoon or ovum (see REPRODUCTIVE SYSTEM; and GENETICS).

GAMOSEMATIC: term for appearance or behaviour that helps members of a pair to find each other.

GANDER: special term for a male GOOSE (1).

GANNET: substantive name of some species of Sulidae (Pelecaniformes, suborder Pelecani); commonly used without qualification in the British Isles for the species found there; in the plural, general term for the family. The other substantive name used for members of the family is ' booby ', generally applied to the tropical species. This family of large sea birds is represented on the coasts of all the continents except Antarctica. A score of forms are usually regarded as constituting 9 species in a single genus, although the latter is sometimes rather unnecessarily split into two.

Gannets are 26–40 inches long, some species being smaller than others; they are heavily built birds, with thick necks of moderate length and large heads. A characteristic feature is the stout and moderately long bill, tapering towards the slightly decurved tip; the skin at the base of the bill, including that of the small throat pouch, is bare. The external nares are imperforate (for method of breathing see under RESPIRATORY SYSTEM). The totipalmate feet are large, the legs short and stout. The wedge-shaped tail is long, and the wings are long and pointed.

The adult plumage is commonly white for the most part, but with black or at least dark primaries; or more of the wing and the whole or part of the tail may be dark. In two species dark colour predominates. Also in the adult, the bill, the facial skin, and the feet may have a bright colour characteristic of the species—and the sexes may differ in this respect, although they are otherwise similar. Immature birds tend to be brownish with pale spots, and they gradually acquire adult plumage over a few years.

Gannets are ungainly birds on land, but they have little occasion to come there except to their nests. They are magnificent fliers, and they are at home in the water. They are exclusively marine, but offshore rather than oceanic birds. They live mainly on fish of species found near the surface, but squids are also taken. The birds fly or soar over the sea, sometimes as high as 100 feet above the water, and then, with partly closed wings, drop like plummets. They strike the water with considerable force and may remain submerged for several seconds. They can in fact also dive from the surface; and they swim under water, but it is not believed that they descend to a great depth (see SWIMMING AND DIVING). The prey is not speared, as might be imagined from the shape of the bill and from the plunging action; rather do the birds get under the fish and grasp it with the bill while coming up to the surface. They habitually sleep on the water. They are on the whole silent birds at sea, although there is much grunting and croaking at the nests.

Nesting is in colonies, often closely packed and of vast size, at sites to which the species tenaciously adhere. Some species nest on the ledges of cliffs, or on the flat tops of steep-sided islands. Others nest on more accessible ground and even in bushes or trees. The nest may be a bulky structure of seaweed and herbage on a ledge, or a mere hollow in the ground surrounded by such materials; arboreal nests may be built of sticks. The eggs are pale bluish or greenish under an outer chalky layer. Some species usually have only a single egg, others 2–3; but often when there are two eggs only one chick is reared. In the incubation of the single egg of *S. bassana* the webbed feet, one above the other, are applied to it. Both parents take part in incubation and in the care of the young. The latter are naked on hatching, with dark skin, but quickly acquire a down plumage. The young of *S. bassana* are fed in the nest for two months or so and are then starved for about ten days before they are able to descend to the sea; thereafter they are for some time unable to rise from the water or to catch food, so they must live on their reserves—they are very fat—for some weeks. (See Plate 37b (phot.).)

Three species of gannet may be regarded as constituting a superspecies (or may perhaps even be conspecific)—which is more to the point than placing them in a separate genus. They have a white adult plumage, with black primaries and pale yellow on the head. The Gannet *Sula* ('*Morus*') *bassana* of the North Atlantic (the alternative name of 'Solan Goose', a misnomer, is obsolescent) is in a world context called the Northern Gannet. It has its European breeding stations on islands off Iceland, in the Faeroes, and round the coasts of the British Isles, with minor ones of slight age in Brittany, the Channel Islands, and Norway. Scotland has six main colonies, that on St Kilda being the largest in the world; the Bass Rock in the Firth of Forth is the classical location, while Sule Stack (Orkney) and Sulasgeir (Outer Hebrides) have significant names. Wales has one and Ireland two. On the American side there are half a dozen stations on islands in the Gulf of St Lawrence and off Newfoundland. The total breeding population is known with some accuracy (Fisher & Vevers): there were approximately 82 000 nests on the eastern side of the Atlantic in 1949, and there had been approximately 13 000 on the western side ten years earlier (not recounted). In the British Isles, and notably on Grassholm off Pembrokeshire, young gannets have been ringed in large numbers. Although home waters are by no means entirely deserted, many of the birds travel south as far as the coast of tropical West Africa; and the ringing results have shown that this movement is made by a much higher proportion of birds in their first year than of birds of greater age (Thomson).

The closely related forms are the Cape Gannet (or Malagash) *S. capensis* (with dark tail), breeding off South Africa and migrating northwards up both coasts of the continent; and the Australian Gannet *S. serrator* (with the central tail-feathers dark), breeding in the Bass Strait and off Tasmania, with another population on the coast of North Island, New Zealand. Ringing of the New Zealand birds has shown that some of them visit Australian waters and, again, that the movement is more pronounced in the first year than later.

Blue-faced Booby *Sula dactylatra, based partly on a photograph by Philip Ashmole (B.O.U. Centenary Expedition to Ascension Island). M.Y.*

Three species of booby are widely distributed in tropical seas, and each has a number of subspecific forms; they have the characters indicated by their common names. The Brown Booby *S. leucogaster* is found in the Caribbean and the tropical Atlantic, and westwards through the Pacific to northern Australia. Its head and upper parts are mainly dark; the bare facial skin is dark blue in the male, bright yellow in the female. Both the Red-footed Booby *S. sula* (colour of feet not visible in flight) and the Masked (or Blue-faced or White) Booby *S. dactylatra* are found in the tropical parts of the Atlantic, Pacific, and Indian Oceans. All three breed on Ascension, although the Red-footed Booby (which elsewhere commonly nests on bushes or trees) only in small numbers. The other two species provided the B.O.U. Centenary Expedition with abundant opportunities for study, interesting differences in behaviour being noted (Dorward). Thus, the Masked Booby did its fishing farther out to sea than the Brown Booby, and the proportions of various fish species in the diet was found to be different. The Masked Booby nested on flat areas and the

Brown Booby on cliffs. The peaks of the respective breeding seasons were also different, and there was some evidence that the cycle in the Brown Booby was less than annual. The Red-footed Booby, at least in some areas, commonly nests in a plumage apparently intermediate between the immature and the adult, but this may be a dimorphic brown phase (see POLYMORPHISM).

Three other boobies have more restricted ranges—the Blue-footed Booby *S. nebouxii* from Mexico to Peru and the Galápagos; the Peruvian Booby *S. variegata* off Peru and Chile; and Abbott's Booby *S. abbotti* in the tropical part of the Indian Ocean. The Peruvian Booby is the 'Piquero' of the guano islands (see GUANO), whereas Abbott's Booby is a tree-nester; both species are characterised by the chequered black-and-white plumage of the lower back. A.L.T.

Dorward, D. F. 1962. Comparative biology of the White Booby and the Brown Booby *Sula* spp. at Ascension. Ibis 103b : 174–220 (B.O.U. Centenary Expedition).
Dorward, D. F. 1962. Behaviour of boobies *Sula* spp. Ibis 103b : 221–234 (B.O.U. Centenary Expedition).
Fisher, J. & Vevers, H. G. 1943–44. The breeding distribution, history and population of the North Atlantic Gannet (*Sula bassana*). J. Animal Ecol. 12 : 173–213 ; 13 : 49–62.
Gurney, J. H. 1913. The Gannet. London.
Thomson, A. L. 1939. The migrations of the Gannet : results of marking in the British Isles. Brit. Birds 32 : 282–289.

GAPE; GAPE FLANGES: see BILL ; FEEDING OF YOUNG

GAPING: see BEHAVIOUR, DEVELOPMENT OF

GARDENER: substantive name of *Amblyornis* spp. (see BOWERBIRD).

GAREFOWL: alternative name of the extinct Great Auk *Pinguinus impennis* (see AUK ; EXTINCT BIRDS).

GARGANEY: *Anas querquedula* (see DUCK).

GARROD'S FORMULA: see MUSCULATURE

GARRULINAE: see CROW (1)

GARUDA: see FABULOUS BIRDS

GASTRULATION: see DEVELOPMENT, EMBRYONIC

GAUSE'S RULE: for Volterra-Gause Principle see ECOLOGY

GAVIAE: alternative ordinal name (see below) ; but 'almost from the beginning of systematic Ornithology the word *Gavia* has been used in several senses' (Newton) ; one of the more recent usages of 'Gaviae' was for an order equivalent to the present suborder Lari of the Charadriiformes.

GAVIIDAE: see below

GAVIIFORMES: an order, alternatively 'Gaviae' (but see above), comprising only the Holarctic family Gaviidae (see DIVER). For the question of nomenclature see under COLYMBIDAE.

GEESE: plural of GOOSE.

GENE: see GENETICS

GENERA: plural of GENUS.

GENETICS: a study of which the subject matter is how characters are passed on from parent to offspring ; therefore one of the fundamental subsciences of biology. Its rise can be dated from 1900, when the work of the Abbot Mendel (1822–84) was rediscovered.

Simple Mendelian Inheritance. Perhaps the simplest example, and a quite common one, is that of a pair of contrasted characters inherited as simple alternatives. For example, in the Budgerigar *Melopsittacus undulatus*, we might have one pure-bred wild-type (green and yellow) and one pure-bred white parent, and cross them. We find that all the offspring are wild-type ; but if these are mated together (brother to sister) and a large number of progeny obtained, there will be both wild-type and white birds among them, but no intermediates. Moreover, the proportion of wild-type to white birds will be approximately 3 : 1 (the more nearly so as the total number of the progeny increases).

This example is explained as follows. The wild-type parent, being pure-bred, had only wild-type ancestors. It received equal contributions from both parents of the factors controlling its colour, and its genetic constitution in respect of the alternative wild-type (W) and white (w) can be represented as WW. Similarly the pure-bred white is ww. When these mate, they produce ova or sperms each carrying one single factor for colour, and the constitution of all their offspring must therefore be Ww (since each is formed from the fusion of a sperm with an ovum). In this example, and many others, these individuals carrying different alternatives are wholly like one of the parents, not intermediate between them. This is expressed by saying that the character wild-type plumage is 'dominant' to white plumage, and white is 'recessive' to wild-type. The hereditary factors responsible for their development, and transmitted in the ovum or sperm, are nowadays called 'genes'. In the example given, a gene controlling some features of the colour pattern can exist in two alternative states, one giving wild-type, the other white. Such alternatives (there may be very many of them) are called 'allelomorphs' of the same gene. Any one bird can carry only two of them. When the two allelomorphs in an individual are of the same sort, as in the two parents (WW and ww) the individual is said to be 'homozygous' for the allelomorph; when they are different, as in the offspring of the two pre-bred parents (Ww), they are 'heterozygous'. Now, when the heterozygous offspring were mated, each parent in a mating could produce two sorts of ova or sperm in equal numbers, one sort carrying W and the other w. The ova and sperms are taken as mating at random (this is usually very nearly true), and however many sperms (or ova) a bird produces, half of them will carry W and the other half w.

In the F_2 (second filial) generation, therefore, we have three different 'genotypes' (genetic constitutions) in respect of these two allelomorphs. And since wild-type was found in the F_1 generation to be dominant to white, both the WW offspring in the F_2 (which are exactly the same as the wild-type original parent, genetically) and the heterozygous Ww will appear with wild-type coloration. But the individuals with ww, the homozygous recessives, are the same as their white grandparent and will be white. By this second mating, therefore, the white character which was lost in the F_1 generation, has been extracted again—in fact, both grandparental types have segregated out without contamination.

The results of the whole experiment can be shown as in Figure 1:

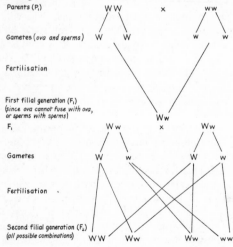

Segregation is one of the most fundamental discoveries of genetics. It seems that a recessive character may disappear, but its allelomorph may still exist in the population, hiding (so to speak) in heterozygous individuals, and able to reproduce the recessive character whenever two heterozygous individuals (heterozygotes) mate and produce offspring. The genetic basis of variation can therefore be conserved, although the visible amount may seem to decrease.

From the example just given, it is easy to see what would happen if a heterozygote and a recessive homozygote were crossed ('back-crossing'). The mating would be as shown in Figure 2:

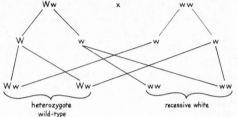

The result would be equal numbers of wild-type heterozygotes and whites, and no wild-type homozygotes. (Of course, if only two or three offspring were obtained, by chance they might all be wild-type or all white.) If however, we had mated a wild-type homozygote to a white, which is exactly the same mating as the first one given above, all the offspring would be wild-type (heterozygotes). A mating of an individual with a dominant character to one homozygous for its recessive alternative is a test-mating showing whether the dominant was heterozygous or homozygous.

It is known that the bodies of most animals are made up of many cells, each with a nucleus within which are carried minute thread-like bodies, the chromosomes. It is on these that the genes are carried, each gene being associated with a particular place or 'locus' on a particular chromosome. A complete set of chromosomes is carried both in the ovum and the sperm, so that the fertilised egg carries a double set in which there are two (one from each parent) of each kind of chromosome, except for the sex-chromosomes (see later). Normally, all the cells produced by division from the egg during development have a double set each. When the sex-cells (gametes) are to be produced, there is a special 'reduction-division' or 'meiosis' whereby only a single complete set (with one from each pair of chromosomes) is put into each ripe sperm or ovum. (The ordinary division used to produce all other cells is called 'mitosis', and involves no reduction in chromosome number.)

When we have *two* pairs of contrasted characters in a mating, we are dealing with two allelomorphs each of *different* genes—genes, that is to say, at different loci. If the loci are on different chromosome-pairs, then the inheritance of the two pairs of allelomorphs proceeds independently of each other. Suppose we have characters A, a and B, b, and the first parents have the constitution AA, BB and aa, bb, i.e. they are homozygous dominant and recessive respectively. Then all the F_1 will be Aa, Bb. When these are mated, we have *two* crosses simultaneously of the same kind as was made in the F_1 of the first example. The genes will assort independently, and the best way to work out the combinations is to tabulate the constitutions of the possible gametes. Obviously, one individual can produce gametes with A and B, A and b, a and B, and a and b, since either B or b can occur with a or A. All these will be sperms from a cock, or ova from a hen, and all types can therefore fuse with each other, as in Figure 3:

	OVA			
	AB	aB	Ab	ab
AB	AA BB	Aa BB	AA Bb	Aa Bb
aB	aA BB	aa BB	aA Bb	aa Bb
Ab	AA bB	Aa bB	AA bb	Aa bb
ab	aA bB	aa bB	aA bb	aa bb

(SPERMS)

This gives many possible constitutions; but if only the constitutions for A and a are listed (B and b being disregarded), a ratio of 1 AA : 2 Aa : 1 aa will be found, as in the first example, and similarly if only B and b are taken. With A and B dominant, the resulting 'phenotypes' (the sums of characters shown by each individual, in contrast to the sum of the genes carried by it) of the double cross can be worked out from the table, and come to a proportion of :—

9 A and B : 3 a and B : 3 A and b : 1 a and b
As will be seen from the Table, some of those showing A will be homozygous for it, and others will be heterozygous—in fact there are four sorts of phenotypes (just listed) but nine different genotypes. Only the double recessive (a and b) can be known at sight to be homozygous.

Often a single character, e.g. size, is affected by very many genes at many different loci. A large individual may well be heterozygous for many loci, and so may a small one. At some loci the allelomorph reducing size may be the recessive, at others it may be the dominant. When two such individuals are crossed, an enormous number of possible genotypes will be produced ; a few will happen to have all the characters for large size, a few all those for small, but most will have a mixture producing some intermediate state. Consequently, there will be much variation in the progeny, but the commonest size class will be intermediate between those of the two parents. This is a very common observation, and led to the belief in blending inheritance, namely that the contributions of the two parents were blended in the offspring.

For many hundreds of years it was believed (and still is by a few) that the blood was the basis of inheritance, and that the bloods from the parents actually mingled, and of course could never be separated. This is the basis for the wrong idea that if a pedigree hen (or bitch, or cow, for example) has been accidentally served by a cock (dog, bull) of a different breed or no breed at all, she is therefore 'contaminated' and will never breed 'pure-blooded' offspring again. Many useful animals have been destroyed because of this belief.

It is easy to work out crosses involving more than two allelomorphs along the same lines as in the examples given above. If we have a cross with A_1, A_2, and a, in which A_1 is dominant to A_2, and both to a, the parents being, for example, A_1a and A_2a, then the result of a simple cross is as shown in Figure 4:

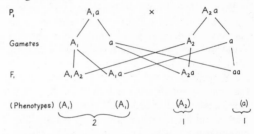

P_1 A_1a × A_2a

Gametes A_1 a A_2 a

F_1 A_1A_2 A_1a A_2a aa

(Phenotypes) (A_1) (A_1) (A_2) (a)

     2   1   1

Linkage. It often happens that we are dealing with two or more loci which are on the *same* chromosomes. These are then said to be linked, and the rule that the genes will assort independently will *not* hold. If the two chromosomes of a particular pair in some individual are carrying A, a and B, b as shown in Figure 5 :

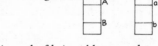

then instead of being able to produce gametes with all the possible genotypes (AB, Ab, aB, ab), it can produce only AB and ab, and these will be transmitted as single units. If the chromosomes were as in Figure 6 :

then it could produce only Ab and aB. In the first case, since the two dominants (A and B) are on the same individual chromosome, they are said to be linked in 'coupling'; in the second case they are on different chromosomes of the same pair and are linked in 'repulsion'. Linkage is seldom perfect, however, and during the production of the gametes the chromosomes in the nucleus of their precursor-cells come close together in pairs (they have, of course, a double set like almost all other cells in the body) and actually exchange corresponding pieces of their own material—in some chromosome-pairs very frequently, in others very rarely if at all. Consequently, even in the example of linkage in repulsion given just above, in the production of a few of the ova or sperm this process of 'crossing-over' may occur, and a few (or perhaps many) of the cross-over classes of gametes (in this case AB or ab) may be obtained. The closer the two loci are on the same chromosome, the less likely it is that crossing-over will occur between them. Maps of the chromosomes in a few animals have been prepared by observing cross-over values and working out in what order particular loci are strung out along a chromosome.

Sex and Linkage. The control of sex in most vertebrates is by means of the sex-chromosomes. In the female of birds (but in the male of mammals and many other vertebrates) the members of one chromosome-pair are not identical in appearance; in the other sex, one of these is absent, while the other is represented twice. The odd chromosome is called the Y, the other the X chromosome, so that in birds the constitution of females is XY (or XO, the Y being absent) and of males XX (while it is the other way round for mammals, including man). The Y chromosome carries very few genes, and is often largely inert. Since males can mate only with females, *every* mating in respect of the sex-chromosomes is between a heterozygote and a homozygote that differs from it as in the mating Ww × ww given above; consequently a 1 : 1 ratio of phenotypes is always produced genetically (although this may be modified somewhat by other factors). The X chromosome carries genes that affect other characters besides the purely sexual ones, and these are then said to be 'sex-linked'. A very few are known on the Y chromosome. Such genes may be useful to breeders, if their effects are seen very early in life, for sexing young chicks.

Significance of Sexual Reproduction. The whole point of sexual reproduction seems to be to pass on to the offspring, linked groups of genes in particular allelomorphic states that have been favoured by natural selection; these work together harmoniously to build up the enormously complex system that any organism is, and to adapt it for its role in nature; but at the same time a limited amount of trying out of different combinations of the allelomorphs of different genes is allowed by crossing-

over, so that new combinations, perhaps better fitted for changing conditions, can be produced. Also there can be apparently spontaneous changes in the genes themselves by which wholly new allelomorphs are very occasionally produced. The production of a new inheritable variation is called 'mutation'. New arrangements, whether of genes or of chromosomes, are not likely to be advantageous if at all considerable; the chances of a sudden large random change in a very delicate and complex organism being actually beneficial are very slight. Consequently the mutation rate must be kept low (it is one of the dangers of atomic radiation that it raises it) or the race may break down internally. But a thin trickle of small changes is necessary to maintain variability, with which to cope with changing conditions.

Modification of Dominance. It was implied above that a gene may control a character. This, however, is really an over-simplification. The genes most easy to work with in genetical investigations are those that always have a definite effect on a particular character, virtually irrespective of all the other genes present in the genotype. But, in fact, even this apparent independence is achieved by a careful adjustment of the other genes. There is often very considerable modification by genes of each other's action. Dominance has been shown in some cases (including fowl) not to be a property residing in a particular allelomorph, but a result of modifiers acting on it. It has been possible to take a stock segregating for two allelomorphs, in which the heterozygote was intermediate between the two homozygotes—i.e. there was *no* dominance—and, by selecting in two different lines, to make the same allelomorph dominant to its partner in one line and recessive to it in the other. Dominance, whether brought about by the action of modifiers or in other ways, is a device for allowing a useful allelomorph to express itself even in single dose, while suppressing a less useful one (except, of course, when it is by itself). There is no doubt that the properties of genes, and of genetic mechanisms such as meiosis, or sex, have all been evolved by natural selection.

Genetical Study in the Field. Birds are unsatisfactory material for genetical research because of the length of their generations and because maintaining a breeding stock in captivity entails much trouble, space, and expense. Nevertheless, much information has now accumulated about species in domestication and in aviaries.

In the field, recent research has mainly concentrated upon analysis of phenotypic variation between populations without troubling about its genetic basis. Most of this variation, especially that used in discriminating between subspecies, is more or less continuous (e.g. size and colour differences) and controlled by many genes. This is best studied at the phenotypic level. However, distinct characters, controlled by one or a few genes, occur in small ratios in all wild populations, and the study of the geographical pattern of these ratios can illuminate the evolution of a species or species-group. Since most birds lay a fair number of eggs, it is possible to determine the genetic control of these distinct characters from field observations of matings and progeny without excessive labour.

These distinct characters can also occur in substantial ratios in some populations, and the study of this type of polymorphism gives useful information upon the degree of isolation existing between populations, and upon the alterations of ratios with environmental change (see POLYMORPHISM).

See also under BLOOD ; PLUMAGE, ABNORMAL AND ABERRANT.   A.J.C.

Ford, E. B. 1957. Mendelism and Evolution. London.
George, W. 1951. Elementary Genetics. London.
Sheppard, P. M. 1959. Natural Selection and Heredity. London (Hutchinson University Library).
Sinnott, E. W., Dunn, L. C., & Dobzhansky, T. 1958. Principles of Genetics. New York.
Srb, A. M. & Owen, R. D. 1957. General Genetics. New York.

The foregoing are general works of various degrees of technicality or simplification.

GENITAL SYSTEM: see REPRODUCTIVE SYSTEM

GENOTYPE: the group in which an individual falls by reason of its genetic constitution (compare PHENOTYPE). The term was at one time misapplied (also ' generitype ', ' generotype ') in ornithological nomenclature to the type-species of a genus (see TYPE-SPECIES).

GENS: literally ' race ' (plural ' gentes ') ; has been used in various contexts for infrasubspecific categories ; also ' a chronological series of populations forming a single evolutionary lineage (divisible into palaeospecies) and biospecifically separated at any time from its closest relatives ' (Cain)—see EVOLUTION.

GENUS: a taxonomic category representing a grouping of species ; also a particular example or (plural ' genera ') examples of that category. In Mayr's words, a genus is ' a systematic category including one species or a group of species of presumably common phylogenetic origin, which is separated from other similar units by a decided gap '. The category is a primary one in nomenclature, in that it is obligatory that every species should be placed in a genus. If there is only one species in the genus, the latter is ' monotypic ' ; if there are two or more species, these are said to be ' congeneric '. The name of the genus (which must be unique in the Animal Kingdom, a matter in which the *Nomenclator Zoologicus* is helpful) constitutes the first word of the scientific name (binomen or trinomen) of an included species or subspecies. Every genus has a ' type-species ' ; and a genus may itself be the type of a higher taxon. See NOMENCLATURE ; SPECIES ; TAXON ; TYPE-GENUS ; TYPE-SPECIES.

The genus is a purely subjective concept, and taxonomists vary widely in the standards of difference that they regard as calling for generic separation. The original Linnean genus was a broad category ; and the general tendency now seems to be a swing back for some distance in that direction. This follows an era during which many authors have indulged in a great deal of splitting of genera in accordance with their own standards of difference and ideas of relationship. Apart from this, but accentuated by it, has been the transfer of species from one genus to another in the light of new information or changing views. Unfortunately, all these revisions involve changes in the naming of species—a notable defect of the binominal system. For this reason it is sometimes necessary to show a discarded but familiar generic name in parenthesis (using an equal sign or quotation marks, in distinction from the convention regarding subgeneric names).

Subgenus. A genus may be divided into subgenera where the included species appear to fall into well-marked groups ; but the subgenus is not a primary category. Taxonomists who use narrow genera naturally have little occasion for such subdivision ; in wider genera it serves to express ideas about interspecific relationships, with the advantage that it does not affect the names of species. For particular purposes, however, a subgeneric name may be shown in parenthesis after the generic name in a binomen or trinomen. In each divided genus, one of the subgenera is ' nominate ', having the same type-species as the genus and a name identical with the generic name. A category of ' superspecies ' may be interpolated between subgenus and species, but this has no nomenclatural status (see SUPERSPECIES ; also SPECIES-GROUP (2)).

Neave, S. A. 1939-40, 1950. Nomenclator Zoologicus (Index of generic and subgeneric names in the Animal Kingdom proposed from 1758 onwards), vols. 1-4 and 5. Zoological Society of London. Vol. 6, covering 1946-55, in press (1964).

GENUS-GROUP: with reference to the ranks of taxa, term embracing genus and subgenus (see NOMENCLATURE).

GEOGRAPHICAL DISTRIBUTION: see DIS-
TRIBUTION, GEOGRAPHICAL

GEOGRAPHICAL VARIATION: see SUB-
SPECIES ; and CLINE ; also Plate 42 (colour)

GEOLOGICAL FACTORS: those relating to the
formation and composition of the earth's surface that
play a part in determining the environmental conditions under which birds live. Geological events
have produced the physiographical characters that
constitute the basis of past and present environments
and that also affect their climates (see CLIMATOLOGY).
The mineral composition of rocks governs the nature
of the soil and thus, to some extent, that of the
vegetable element in the environment (see VEGETA-
TION) ; influences attributable to the condition of
the soil are known as ' edaphic '.

History of the Land-masses. The stages in the
emergence of the present pattern of land and sea must
obviously have influenced, during the relevant
periods, the distribution—and indeed the evolution
—of birds (see DISTRIBUTION, GEOGRAPHICAL ;
NEARCTIC REGION ; etc.). Although the first known
birds lived in the Jurassic Period, it would be unprofitable to push speculation so far back as the time
when the continent of ' Atlantis ' occupied much of
the present place of the North Atlantic Ocean and
North America, when the great area of ' Gondwana-
land ' unified all the southern continents as we know
them, and when the ' Tethys Sea '—lying from east
to west—separated the northern from the southern
land-masses ; or even to the Cretaceous Period,
before the end of which Australia became separated
from southeastern Asia. At the beginning of the
Tertiary Era, in the Eocene Period, the Tethys Sea
was still large ; what are now Europe and northern
Asia were separate—likewise North and South
America ; the location of the Indonesian-Papuan
islands was covered by sea ; and a land-mass
(' Lemuria ') extended from Madagascar towards
India.

A long period of tectonic calm, during which at
least the continents of Africa and Australia were
reduced to vast peneplains, came to an end in the
Miocene. All the great mountain masses of the
world, e.g. the Himalaya, have been raised since that
time ; this has had the direct effect of providing
areas of cool climate at low latitudes, and a secondary
effect—in some places—of accentuating aridity in the
lee of the rising massifs. By the end of the Tertiary,
in the Pliocene Period, the geographical pattern of
the earth's surface was beginning to resemble that
of the present day. Such are the hypothetical recon-
structions that geologists make (for table of geological time see under FOSSIL BIRDS).

The Pleistocene Period still saw major changes in
the levels of land and sea, in addition to the great
climatic fluctuations to be mentioned below. There
was a continuing gradual upheaval of lands, with
raising of great mountain chains ; and at one time
or another land-bridges existed between various
masses now separated by straits, e.g. continental
connections with such present islands or island-
groups as the British Isles, Japan, Indonesia, Ceylon,
and Tasmania. In ' recent ' times, the last 10 000
years or so (by some called the Holocene Period,
while others prefer to regard the Pleistocene as still
with us), the changes have continued on a smaller
scale ; for instance, Britain probably became separated from the continental land-mass no more than
8000 years ago. The processes doubtless continue—
' this telluric symphony, in several movements, is
still being played ' (Flint).

Glaciation. There is some evidence of glaciation
in remote geological ages, but the record is dim and
there were, anyhow, no birds then. In the Cretaceous Period and through the Tertiary Era, mild
climatic conditions seem to have been widespread,
ranging from tropical to temperate. On the other
hand, the Pleistocene Period was marked by intermittent severe glaciation of large parts of the earth's
surface. According to authorities, there were at
least four distinct glaciations and three interglacial
periods ; and on this main cycle, minor fluctuations
were imposed. At the greatest intensity of glaciation,
thick ice-sheets covered large parts of northern
Europe and northern North America, and likewise
high montane regions elsewhere, and Antarctica.
The weight of the ice-sheets tended to depress the
earth's crust beneath them, and this is still rising
again in places.

With so much of the total amount of terrestrial
water locked in solid form, the level of the ocean fell
with the intensity of glaciation, rising again when
melting of glaciers took place on a large scale. In
opposite phase, large lakes developed in formerly
arid regions owing to decreased evaporation in the
cooler climate of the world induced by glaciation,
and greater rainfall produced a pluvial instead of a
dry climate ; with diminished glaciation, the aridity
returned and the lakes shrank (while the level of the
ocean was rising)—the Caspian-Aral system of inland
seas (saline because having no outlet) is an example
that has been particularly studied.

As the last severe phase of the most recent glaciation began to give way only about 18 000 years ago,
it seems reasonable to assume that the drastic changes
associated with it have been of paramount importance, among factors in geological history, in shaping
the geographical pattern of bird life as we see it

today. In recent times—say, again, the last 10 000 years—the remains of glaciation have been still further reduced (subject to minor fluctuations), with spread of forests in formerly barren boreal zones, and with increasingly arid conditions in North Africa, the Middle East, and elsewhere.

The potential distribution and necessary migrations of birds of different ecological requirements may be inferred from what we know (largely on the evidence of palaeobotany) of environmental conditions at various points in geological time, and particularly during and since the last glaciation. From this it is possible to make inferences regarding the more recent development of the existing pattern of avian distribution and the seasonal migrations that constitute an essential aspect of it (see MIGRATION).

Palaeontology. A factor of much importance, not in bird-life but in ornithology, is the formation of fossils (see ARCHAEOPTERYX ; EVOLUTION ; FOSSIL BIRDS ; ORIGIN OF BIRDS).

Flint, R. F. 1957. Glacial and Pleistocene Geology. New York and London.
Oakley, K. P. & Muir-Wood, H. M. 1962. The Succession of Life. 5th ed. British Museum (Natural History), London.
Moreau, R. E. 1954. The main vicissitudes of the European avifauna since the Pliocene. Ibis 96 : 411–431.
Moreau, R. E. 1963. Vicissitudes of the African biomes in the late Pleistocene. Proc. Zool. Soc. Lond. 141 : 395–421.
Zeuner, F. E. 1945. The Pleistocene Period, its Climate, Chronology, and Faunal Succession. London.

GEOSPIZINAE : see DARWIN'S FINCHES

GERM-CELL : a gamete (see REPRODUCTIVE SYSTEM).

GERMINAL VESICLE : the nucleus of the ovum (see DEVELOPMENT, EMBRYONIC ; EGG).

GILL-SLIT : see DEVELOPMENT, EMBRYONIC

GIZZARD : the ventriculus (see ALIMENTARY SYSTEM).

GLACIATION : see GEOLOGICAL FACTORS

GLADIATOR : name, alternatively 'Gladiator Shrike', of *Malaconotus blanchoti*, and also of the rare *M. gladiator* (see SHRIKE).

GLAND : a secretory organ. Some glands discharge their secretions through openings or ducts, e.g. those associated with digestion—see ALIMENTARY SYSTEM ; the secretions of others are internal, i.e. absorbed into the blood stream (hormones)—see ENDOCRINE SYSTEM. The body-surface in birds has few glands (see OIL GLAND ; SKIN).

GLAND, SALIVARY : see ALIMENTARY SYSTEM ; PALATE ; TONGUE

GLAREOLIDAE : see under CHARADRIIFORMES. There are two subfamilies, Glareolinae (see PRATINCOLE), and Cursoriinae (see COURSER).

GLAREOLOIDEA : see under CHARADRIIFORMES

GLEDE : old name (also spelt 'glead' and 'gled') in Britain for the Kite *Milvus milvus* (see under HAWK).

GLENOID CAVITY : articulation of the head of the humerus with the pectoral girdle (see SKELETON).

GLIDING : see FLIGHT

GLOGER'S RULE : that, in a given species, races in warm and humid areas are apt to be more heavily pigmented than those in cool and dry areas.

GLOMERULUS : part of a nephron (excretory unit of a kidney)—see EXCRETORY SYSTEM.

GLOTTIS : see RESPIRATORY SYSTEM

GLYCOGEN : see LIVER ; METABOLISM

GNATCATCHER : substantive name of some species of the subfamily Polioptilinae of the Muscicapidae (Passeriformes, suborder Oscines) ; in the plural, general term for the subfamily. Other species have the name 'gnatwren'. This is a New World group closely related to the Old World warblers (Sylviinae). They are tiny birds with long tails, which they switch about continually. In colour they are pale blue-grey above and white below. The central tail feathers are dark brown or black, the outer ones white. The male (in spring and summer) has a black band across the forehead, which females and young lack. The song is soft, high pitched, and of little volume. The call is a high metallic 'zee' note. They are usually to be found near marshes or swamps, breeding in the United States from about 41° N. lat., south to Mexico and the Bahama Islands.

The nests are usually woven about branch-forks of bushes or trees. They are carefully made of soft grasses and plant fibres, all bound together with the webs of spiders and insects, to which lichens are attached. They are lined with various soft materials. Both sexes assist in nest building, incubation of eggs, and feeding of young, although there is said to be some individual variation among males in this respect. The 4-5 eggs have a blue ground colour, spotted with reddish brown.

Of the dozen species, the Blue-grey Gnatcatcher *Polioptila caerulea* is widely distributed in the United States (and even to southern Ontario), although commonest in the warmer parts. The Half-collared Gnatwren *Microbates cinereiventris* and the Long-billed Gnatwren *Ramphocaenus rufiventris* are inhabitants of Middle America. The precise systematic position of these last two genera has been the subject of differences in opinion.   J.C.G., Jr.

Rand, A. L. & Traylor, M. A. 1953. The systematic position of the genera *Ramphocaenus* and *Microbates*. Auk 70 : 334–337.

GNATEATER: alternative substantive name of the species of Conopophagidae ; in the plural, alternative general term for the family (see ANTPIPIT).

GNATHOTHECA: term sometimes applied to the part of the rhamphotheca covering the lower mandible (see BILL).

GNATWREN: see under GNATCATCHER

GOAL-ORIENTATION: term proposed by Lack & Williamson (1959) for the directing of flight to compensate for lateral displacement, so that the normal goal is reached ; distinguished from ' one-directional navigation ', in which flight is directed on a constant heading without compensating for drift, diversion, or artificial displacement (see MIGRATION ; NAVIGATION).

GOATSUCKER: now mainly in American usage, in the plural, an alternative general term for the Caprimulgidae and more particularly for the nominate subfamily (see NIGHTJAR).

GO-AWAY-BIRD: substantive name of some species of Musophagidae (see TURACO).

GOBBLING GROUND: special term in North America for the social display ground of the Lesser Prairie Chicken *Tympanuchus pallidicinctus* (see GROUSE ; LEK DISPLAY).

GODWIT: substantive name of *Limosa* spp. (see under SANDPIPER).

GOLDCREST: name (formerly ' Golden-crested Wren ', a misnomer) of *Regulus regulus* (see WARBLER (1)).

GOLDENEYE: substantive name of *Bucephala* spp. ; used without qualification, in Britain, for *B. clangula* (see DUCK).

GOLDENTAIL: *Hylocharis eliciae* (for family see HUMMINGBIRD).

GOLDENTHROAT: substantive name of *Polytmus guainumbi* and *Smaragdites theresiae* (for family see HUMMINGBIRD).

GOLDFINCH: substantive name of some *Carduelis* or ' *Spinus* ' spp. ; used without qualification, in Britain, for *C. carduelis* (see FINCH).

GONAD: general term for the primary sex organs, testes (paired) in the male and ovary (single) in the female (see REPRODUCTIVE SYSTEM ; and ENDOCRINE SYSTEM).

GONOLEK: substantive name of some *Laniarius* spp. (see SHRIKE).

GONYS: the ridge formed by the junction of the two rami of the lower mandible near its tip (see BILL).

GOOSANDER: name used in Britain for *Mergus merganser*, in North America called ' Common Merganser ' (see DUCK).

GOOSE (1): substantive name (plural ' geese ') of many species of Anatidae ; the ' true geese ' are placed, with the swans, in the tribe Anserini of the subfamily Anserinae, but the name is also used in three other tribes (and both other subfamilies) in such a way that ' ducks ' and ' geese ' cannot be taxonomically separated (see DUCK). Ornithologically, ' goose ' is applied irrespective of sex, but one usage restricts it to the female in contradistinction to the ' gander ' or male ; the diminutive ' gosling ' is used for the young.

GOOSE (2): misnomer sometimes (not in current ornithological usage) applied to certain large sea birds unrelated to the geese, as ' Solan Goose ' for *Sula bassana* (see GANNET), and ' Ember Goose ' or ' Immer Goose ' for *Gavia immer* (see DIVER).

GORGET: a band of colour, in some plumage patterns, on the throat or upper breast.

GOSHAWK: substantive name of *Accipiter gentilis* and nearly related congeners ; also of the chanting goshawks *Melierax* spp. and the Gabar Goshawk *Micronisus gabar* (see HAWK).

GOSLING: special term for a young (not full-grown) GOOSE (1).

GOURINAE: see PIGEON

GRACKLE: substantive name of species in several genera (*Quiscalus*, etc.) of Icteridae (see ORIOLE (2)) ; also, sometimes applied in Asia to mynahs of the genus *Gracula* (see STARLING).

GRALLAE: the fourth avian order of Linnaeus, but later used in a restricted sense for an order approximating to the Gruiformes.

GRANDALA: generic name used as substantive

name of *Grandala coelicolor* (for subfamily see
THRUSH).

GRANDRY'S CORPUSCLES: see TOUCH

GRANULATE: covered with small tubercles, as
on the podothecae of some birds (see LEG).

GRASSBIRD: substantive name, in Australia, of
Megalurus spp. (see WREN (2)).

GRASSFINCH: in the plural, general term for a
tribe (Erythurini) of the Estrildidae (see WEAVER-
FINCH). Also, 'Grass-finch' is used in America as
substantive name of *Sicalis* spp. (for family see FINCH).

GRASSQUIT: substantive name of species of
Tiaris, Volatinia, Loxipasser, et al. (for family see
FINCH).

GREBE: substantive name of all species of Podicipitidae (Podicipitiformes or Podicipediformes); in
the plural, general term for the family. The latter
is an isolated group of foot-propelled diving birds
with no known relatives, modern or fossil, which
constitutes the order Podicipediformes (for nomenclature see under COLYMBIDAE; PODICIPITIDAE).
Grebes are of world-wide distribution, but absent
from the high Arctic, the Antarctic areas, and some
oceanic islands. Characteristically, at least in the
breeding season, they inhabit fresh standing water,
particularly lakes and the like, although in some cases
nesting takes place on slow-running streams and
rivers—even, rarely, in sheltered coastal inlets.
Outside the breeding season some populations move
to the sea in the immediate vicinity of the coast,
especially when forced to do so by cold weather or
drought, while more northerly populations are truly
migratory. Movement on the wing is chiefly at
night (especially by moonlight), while by day the
birds travel by swimming close to shore, feeding as
they go.

Grebes are medium-sized to quite large birds ($8\frac{3}{4}$-
29 inches long), greyish, nearly black, or brownish
above, with pure white satiny under parts in many
species (some of which were formerly hunted for
their breast pelts), although others—at least in nuptial
plumage—are shaded, mottled or spotted below to
a greater or lesser extent, some showing no white at
all. Head ornamentation, usually lost or much
reduced in non-breeding plumage, is well developed
in many species, being linked with elaborate courtship behaviour. Most species show an appreciable
amount of white on the upper surface of the wing.
The sexes are alike in plumage but may differ in size.

Grebes are highly adapted for diving and an
almost exclusively aquatic life. Their feet, with
lobed and partially webbed toes and laterally compressed tarsi (the hind edges of which are curiously

serrated), are placed at the very rear of the body.
The tail is vestigial, with no stiff rectrices, and this—
together with the arrangement of the feet and the
inclusion of all but the distal ends of the tibiotarsi
within the main body mass—gives the birds their
characteristic blunt-ended appearance. The wings
are relatively small, with the quill feathers curved to
fit the contour of the back closely. One species is
definitely known to be permanently flightless, and
the flying powers of some others are in doubt; the
wing-beats of the rest are very rapid because of the
high loading. The flight outline is distinctive, with
the neck extended in front and the feet projecting
behind. The lengths of the bill and of the neck, as
well as the degree of streamlining of the body, tend
to vary with overall size and main type of food. The
smaller grebes, with a diet in which the bulk of
aquatic invertebrates probably equals or exceeds
that of fish, tend to be the most rotund, with fairly
short necks and bills (very stout and hooked in
Podilymbus for dealing with crustaceans). The larger,
principally fish-eating grebes are more streamlined
with proportionately longer necks and bills (rapier-
like in *Aechmophorus*, which apparently alone among
grebes spears fish under water). Most grebes have
the unique habit of eating their own feathers and of
feeding them to the young, the ball of many whole
and disintegrating feathers in the stomach apparently
aiding digestion in more than one way.

Courtship in grebes is 'mutual', i.e. performed
by both sexes together and with the roles either
identical or different but interchangeable. In some
grebes, at least, courtship occurs at night (especially
by moonlight) as well as by day. Although some
of the larger species are highly vocal, it is the smaller
less ornamented species that tend to specialise more
in vocal display (trilling duets etc.), with simpler
visual elements. Multiform and highly ritualised
visual ceremonies reach their peak in the more
ornamented 'typical' grebes and in *Aechmophorus*
with its plainer (but very strikingly conspicuous)
black and white plumage. These displays include
head shaking, weed holding, habit preening, and
wing showing, some of which (depending on the
species) are performed in upright 'penguin' dances
or in rushes over the water. Copulation occurs out
of the water, usually on a weed platform; reversed
mounting has been recorded.

Nests are built in the water, being made of aquatic,
often sodden plants and tethered to growing vegetation or piled up from the bed, sometimes actually
floating. The 2–8 eggs are usually elliptical with a
white, bluish, or greenish shell, entirely or partially
covered by a chalky layer which becomes stained to
shades of brown. Both sexes incubate; the sitting

bird, when disturbed, often hides the eggs with nest material. Many grebes are solitary nesters (territorial to a greater or lesser degree) while some are colonial (*Aechmophorus* greatly so). The young are more or less conspicuously striped, particularly on the head and neck (although the young of *Aechmophorus* are totally unstriped), and during the first 2–3 weeks of life are often carried on the backs of the parents.

The taxonomy of the Podicipitidae needs modern revision at all levels; work on this problem has already been started (Simmons; Storer), but in the meantime it seems best to follow established trends, based chiefly on Peters (1931). On these lines, there are 21 distinctive forms of grebe, classifiable into 17–21 species in 4–5 genera. The largest of these genera, *Podiceps*, is cosmopolitan; the remainder are monotypic (with one possible exception) and confined to the New World. Of the latter, the very large Western Grebe *Aechmophorus occidentalis* (slightly crested only)—already mentioned several times—is solely North American, but the Pied-billed Grebe *Podilymbus podiceps* (unornamented grey head, with black throat and black stripe on bill) is widely distributed in North, Central, and South America, with the very similar, possibly conspecific Giant Pied-billed (or Atitlan) Grebe *P. gigas* confined to Lake Atitlan in Guatemala. The flightless Short-winged Grebe *Centropelma micropterum* (with ragged crest, white face, and a red and yellow bill) occurs mainly in the area of Lake Titicaca (Peru/Bolivia) at 12 500 feet above sea-level; in both sexes the feet are bright yellow above, black below.

Of the so-called 'dabchicks' in the genus *Podiceps*, two species range widely; the Least Grebe *P. dominicus* (unornamented grey head with black crown and throat) from southern tropical North America southwards through most of South America and the Little Grebe *P. ruficollis* (unornamented chestnut and black head, with greenish stripe at base of bill) extensively in the Palaearctic, Ethiopian, and Oriental Regions. In Australia the latter is replaced by the very closely related and very similar Black-throated Little Grebe *P. novaehollandiae*, previously thought to be conspecific but overlapping with it on several Australasian islands (Mayr). In Madagascar, as well as *P. ruficollis* (the local status of which seems uncertain), there are two closely related, endemic dabchicks—Delacour's Little Grebe *P. rufolavatus* confined to Lake Aloatra (with black cap, face rusty-buff to a varying extent, and the green stripe on the bill), and Hartlaub's Little Grebe *P. pelzelnii* (elaborate head pattern, with black cap and the rest of the head grey, white, and red). Both these species, and particularly *P. rufolavatus*, have a better developed head ornamentation than other dabchicks, with the feathers on crown and face somewhat elongated. Also called 'dabchicks' are the two 'hoary headed' species of the Antipodes—the New Zealand Dabchick *P. rufopectus* and the Hoary-headed Grebe *P. poliocephalus* of Australia, both with long, hair-like filaments on the head.

Of the typical ornamented grebes in the genus *Podiceps*, several species are indigenous to South America. Three range widely—the Silver Grebe *P. occipitalis* (grey head with black nape patch and long, golden, auricular fan), the Lesser Golden Grebe *P. chilensis* (white auricular patch on black head), and the very large Great Grebe *P. major* (dark grey facial disc, rest of head black with short crest). All three occur throughout most of the southern half of the continent, including Tierra del Fuego, with *P. chilensis* extending west to Peru and *P. occipitalis* even farther to southern Colombia. The latter also reaches the Falkland Islands, where *P. chilensis* is replaced by the almost identical but much larger Rolland's Golden (or Brown) Grebe *P. 'rolland'*, with which it may be considered conspecific. Taczanowsky's Silver Grebe *P. taczanowskii* (almost identical with, but larger than, *P. occipitalis*) is confined to Lake Junin in Peru, where the smaller bird also occurs. A sixth, newly described, grebe, the Colombian Eared Grebe *P. andinus* (similar to and possibly conspecific with *P. nigricollis*, but with chestnut foreneck and upper breast and darker auricular fan), is known only from the east Andean lakes in Colombia (de Schauensee).

All three North American species of ornamented grebes occur also in the Old World. Both the Slavonian (or Horned) Grebe *P. auritus* (black head and tippet, yellowish horn-like auricular tuft) and the large Red-necked Grebe *P. grisegena* (grey facial disc, black head with small crest, contrasting area of yellow on the bill) have a Holarctic, virtually circumpolar, breeding distribution, in the case of the former including Scotland and Iceland. The Black-necked (or Eared) Grebe *P. nigricollis* (black head, marked crest peak, golden auricular fan) has a larger but more discontinuous and capricious range, reaching Great Britain, Africa, and far eastern Asia, and being replaced in South America by the closely related, possibly conspecific, *P. andinus* (above). Finally, the large Great Crested Grebe *P. cristatus* (black crest, tippet of chestnut fringed with black on white face) is found solely in the Old World, occurring discontinuously in the Palaearctic, Ethiopian, Oriental, and Australasian Regions (including New Zealand).

See Plates 8 (colour) and 34d (phot.).

K.E.L.S.

Delacour, J. (1933) Les grèbes de Madagascar. Oiseau 3 : 4–7.

de Schauensee, R. M. 1959. Additions to the ' Birds of the republic of Colombia '. Proc. Acad. Nat. Sci. Philadelphia 111 : 53–75.

Huxley, J. S. 1914. The courtship-habits of the Great Crested Grebe (*Podiceps cristatus*) ; with an addition to the theory of sexual selection. Proc. Zool. Soc. Lond. 1914 : 491–562.

Mayr, E. 1943. Notes on Australian birds, 2. Emu 43 : 3–17.

Munro, J. A. 1941. The grebes. Studies of waterfowl in British Columbia. Brit. Columb. Prov. Mus. Occ. Paper no. 3 : 1–77.

Peters, J. L. 1931. Check-list of Birds of the World vol. 1. Cambridge, Mass.

Simmons, K. E. L. 1955. Studies on Great Crested Grebes. Avic. Mag. 61 : 3–13, etc. (six parts).

Simmons, K. E. L. 1962. Some recommendations for a revised check-list of the genera and species of grebes (Podicipitidae). Bull. Brit. Orn. Club 82 : 109–116.

Storer, R. W. 1960. Evolution in the diving birds. Proc. XII Internat. Orn. Congr., Helsinki 1958 : 694–707.

Storer, R. W. 1963. Courtship and mating behaviour and the phylogeny of the grebes. Proc. XIII Internat. Orn. Congr., Ithaca, N.Y., 1962 : 562–569.

Storer, R. W. 1963. Observations on the Great Grebe. Condor 65 : 279–288.

Wobus, U. 1964. Der Rothalstaucher. Wittenburg-Lutherstadt.

GREBE, SUN-: see FINFOOT

GREENBUL: substantive name of species of Pycnonotidae in several genera (see BULBUL).

GREENFINCH: substantive name of some *Carduelis* spp. ; used without qualification, in Britain, for *Carduelis* (' *Chloris* ') *chloris* (see FINCH).

GREENHEAD: a name in North America for the Mallard *Anas platyrhynchos* (see DUCK).

GREENHEART-BIRD: *Lipaugus cineraceus*, a species of PIHA (for family see COTINGA).

GREENLET: substantive name now restricted to *Hylophilus* spp. (see VIREO).

GREENSHANK: *Tringa nebularia* (see SAND-PIPER).

GREGARIOUSNESS: see FLOCKING ; and under MIGRATION

GRENADIER: alternative substantive name of one or two waxbills *Estrilda* (' *Granatina* ') spp. (see WEAVER-FINCH).

GRESSORES: see CICONIIFORMES

GREYBIRD: alternative substantive name of some *Coracina* spp. (see CUCKOO-SHRIKE).

GREYHEN: see under BLACKCOCK

GREYLAG: colloquial short name for the Grey Lag Goose *Anser anser* (see under DUCK).

GRID, NATIONAL: see MAPPING

GRIFFON: substantive name of *Gyps* spp.; used without qualification for *G. fulvus* (see VULTURE (1)).

GRIT: particles of stone of varying coarseness taken in by birds that eat vegetable matter, to grind their food to pulp through the action of the powerful stomach muscles (see ALIMENTARY SYSTEM). Grit taken passes direct to the stomach through the crop, by-passing food in the crop. Serviceable grit is not evacuated from the stomach with digested food, and is seldom found in faeces. Birds with stomachs completely free of food, such as specimens taken on migration, retain their quota of grit or sand.

Diving ducks (Anatidae) that eat molluscs and crustacea do not take grit but use the hard outer coverings of their food in like manner to reduce it to digestible form. Starlings *Sturnus vulgaris* and Dippers *Cinclus cinclus*, when eating vegetable matter, use small shells to aid digestion instead of grit. Fruit-eating birds such as some pigeons (Columbidae), do not take grit, the stones of the fruit acting as grit ; but when eating grain they will take in grit. The Brambling *Fringilla montifringilla* when eating soft fruit and berries in autumn takes no grit, but in winter when eating hard seeds it will take in much grit. For birds swallowing their feathers see GREBE.

Birds resort to regular places at regular times for grit ; the Red Grouse *Lagopus scoticus*, very dependent on coarse grit, will undertake mass movement after heavy snow when their grit supply is covered. The size of grit is in direct relation to the coarseness of food. Birds such as the Capercaillie *Tetrao urogallus* and some Himalayan pheasants (Phasianidae) that eat very coarse food consume large quantities of coarse grit, whilst swans *Cygnus* spp. and geese *Anser* etc., eating soft vegetable matter, take in little but coarse sand. The Flamingo *Phoenicopterus ruber*, eating gastropods among other things, takes a fairly coarse grit ; whilst the Lesser Flamingo *Phoeniconaias minor*, eating algae and diatoms, takes a very fine sand. The Ostrich *Struthio camelus*, eating very coarse vegetable matter, takes in up to two pounds of grit composed of pebbles sometimes an inch in diameter. It is known that the Moas (Dinornithidae) of New Zealand consumed coarse vegetable matter ; in one stomach as many as 200 stones have been found, weighing $5\frac{1}{2}$ pounds. The regular occurrence of small pebbles in the stomachs of adult divers *Gavia* spp. and nestling Cormorants *Phalacrocorax* spp. has never been satisfactorily explained.

Seed-eating birds are the least effective seed distributors, as the seeds are destroyed by grit. Fruit-

eating birds and the raptors are the best seed distributors, the latter eating the crops and stomachs of seed-
eating birds and evacuating seeds ripe for germination
(see POLLINATORS AND DISTRIBUTORS).

Bright-coloured grit is preferred to dull. The
discovery of the famous ruby mines in Burma
originated with the finding of a ruby in the stomach
of a pheasant. The nature of grit can determine the
source whence migratory birds commence their
flight. Both Whooper Swans *Cygnus cygnus* and
Pink-footed Geese *Anser arvensis brachyrhynchus* shot
in Scotland have been found to contain black lava
grit that can have derived only from Iceland.

There are many parts of Britain where duck have
been shot for generations. This naturally produces
a high proportion of lead pellets in the ground where
ducks consume grit. In South Uist eight lead pellets
have been taken from the stomach of a Shoveller
Anas clypeata ; and a Mallard, *A. platyrhynchos* shot
in Suffolk had seven pellets of lead. A Mallard
picked up dead in Suffolk had a number of lead
pellets in the stomach, the cause of death being
diagnosed by a pathologist as ' chronic lead poisoning ' (see DISEASE). A similar pollution of soil
exists in the neighbourhood of grouse-butts that
have stood in the same position for many years.

R.M.

GROSBEAK: substantive name of species of
Carduelinae (Fringillidae) in the genera *Mycerobas*,
Chaunoproctus, *Pinicola*, and *Hesperiphona*, and sometimes (as a poor alternative to ' rose finch ') *Carpodacus* (see FINCH) ; also of species of Pyrrhuloxiinae
(Emberizidae)—see CARDINAL-GROSBEAK ; and sometimes of certain of the Ploceidae—see WEAVER.

GROUND-CUCKOO: general term for most
members of the subfamily Neomorphinae (see
CUCKOO).

GROUND-ROLLER: substantive name of the
species of the subfamily Brachypteraciinae of the
Coraciidae (Coraciiformes, suborder Coracii) ; in
the plural, general term for the subfamily. The
group, which is restricted to Madagascar, is here
treated as a subfamily of the Coraciidae (see ROLLER),
but by Wetmore and others as a separate family
(Brachypteraciidae) of the Coraciiformes. There
are 5 species, placed in 3 genera. All are stout-bodied
ground birds, about 10–18 inches long ; characters
are a large stout bill, large head, large eyes, short
wings, a moderate to long tail, and moderate to long
legs. The colours are soft and rich, variously
patterned ; the sexes are alike.

Four species live on the floor of the rain-forest
where the foliage above casts a continual shade and
the ground is nearly bare of vegetation. Uncon-
firmed native reports say that some of these ground-
rollers are nocturnal. They are stolid birds ; when
alarmed they may walk a few steps or stand motionless, then fly with whirring flight to a low perch.
They are not noisy, and the calls that the writer has
occasionally heard are either low and soft, or chuck-
ling notes, but natives report loud cries from them.
The food of these birds is composed of insects and
of small reptiles and amphibians, taken on the
ground. The data on breeding seem to be all from
native sources, which claim that the eggs, either
white (probably) or spotted (unverified), are laid
in a hole dug by the bird in the ground or in a bank,
or in a hole in a tree. The caution with which
native evidence should be accepted is indicated by
its including statements about the birds hibernating
for some months.

Long-tailed Ground-roller *Uratelornis chimaera*. *C.E.T.K.*

The fifth species lives not in the forest, but in the
dry scrub of the sandy sub-desert country of the
south-western part of Madagascar. There it walks
on the ground ; when alarmed it runs and bounds to
the shelter of a nearby shrub and then stands quietly,
often with head up and tail raised, or may fly to a low
perch. This species, too, feeds on insects and is said
by natives to nest in a hole in the ground.

The four rain-forest species, 10–12 inches long and
with moderate length of tail and legs, are the Short-
legged Ground-roller *Brachypteracias leptosomus*, with
crown chestnut, nape washed deep blue, most of
upper parts olive green, rump blue green, breast
and flanks buffish with brown and black barring ;
the Scaled Ground-roller *B. squamigera*, with under
parts and head buffish, heavily barred or marked with
dark crescents on each feather, the head having a
black median stripe and another stripe behind each
eye, the upper back being rufous and the rest of
upper parts mostly green ; the Blue-headed Ground-
roller *Atelornis pittoides*, with crown blue, mantle
green, chin and throat-patch white surrounded with

blue, breast and flanks pale rufous; and Crossley's Ground-roller *A. crossleyi*, with head and under parts mostly rufous with a black, white-streaked patch on the lower throat, and with the mantle, rump, and tail deep green.

The desert species, the Long-tailed Ground-roller *Uratelornis chimaera*, is about 18 inches long, and has a very long tail and long legs; the upper parts are dull rufous brown variegated with greyish and blackish brown in a complicated pattern; the under parts are white with a dark brown breast band.

A.L.R.

Dresser, H. E. 1893. A Monograph of the Coraciidae. Farnborough, Kent. (See pp. 87–98, pls. 22–25.)
Rand, A. L. 1936. The distribution and habits of Madagascar birds. Bull. Amer. Mus. Nat. Hist. 72 : 143–499. (See pp. 418–421; habits.)

GROUND-THRUSH: see QUAIL-THRUSH; RAIL-BABBLER

GROUP (1): in nomenclature, 'an assemblage of co-ordinate categories' (see FAMILY-GROUP; GENUS-GROUP; SPECIES-GROUP (1); and NOMENCLATURE).

GROUP (2): in taxonomy, a loose or deliberately neutral term for a taxon or collection of taxa, non-committal as regards the precise rank or status to be assigned to it.

GROUSE: substantive name of many species of Tetraonidae (Galliformes, suborder Galli); in the plural (unchanged), general term for the family. The other substantive names used are 'ptarmigan', 'prairie chicken', and 'capercaillie'; there are also various popular alternative names, particularly for American species. The family is a circumpolar one, confined to the Northern Hemisphere north of about 26°N. lat. There are 18 recognised species, some with numerous subspecific forms; they are referred to one Holarctic, 6 Nearctic, and 4 Palaearctic genera.

Grouse are fowl-like birds ranging in length from 12 to 35 inches and in weight from about $1\frac{1}{4}$ to $14\frac{1}{2}$ pounds, with most between $1\frac{1}{4}$ and 4 pounds. They differ from other gallinaceous birds in having the nostrils hidden by feathers, the hind toe considerably raised above the other three and the tarsi at least partially (in most cases fully) feathered; there are no spurs. In keeping with their northern habitats, grouse have 'snowshoes' in winter—a dense mat of stiff feathers on the toes of the ptarmigan, and a row of pectinations 2–3 mm. long on each side of the toes of other grouse; the most southerly forms, Attwater's Prairie Chicken *Tympanuchus cupido attwateri* and the Lesser Prairie Chicken *T. pallidicinctus* have poorly developed snowshoes or none. The bill is short and strong. The wings are short and rounded, the flight being strong but not sustained. The tail, sometimes large, takes various forms.

Grouse are mainly terrestrial birds, but some are partly arboreal in habit. They are adapted to many ecological niches. There are two circumpolar species in the arctic and subarctic regions, the Rock Ptarmigan *Lagopus mutus* and the Willow Ptarmigan (or Willow Grouse) *L. lagopus*. Farther south, the White-tailed Ptarmigan *L. leucurus* breeds on the mountain tundras of western North America; and the Red Grouse *L. scoticus* lives on the upland moors and lower peat-bogs and mosses of the British Isles, to which it is restricted except for some artificial introductions on the European continent. Curiously enough, there are no ptarmigan on the high mountains of southern central Asia, where one finds instead the Snow Partridge *Lerwa lerwa* and the snow-cocks *Tetraogallus* spp. (Phasianidae).

The open parts of North America have several species of grouse. The mid-continental grasslands are the home of the Greater Prairie Chicken *Tympanuchus cupido* and the Lesser Prairie Chicken *T. pallidicinctus*. There are no desert grouse, but the Sage Grouse *Centrocercus urophasianus* lives under semi-desert conditions in the sagebrush plains of the West. Sharptailed Grouse *Pedioecetes phasianellus* are found in open grasslands, the brushy zone between grassland and forest, and in openings in the forest. The Black Grouse *Lyrurus tetrix* of northern Europe and *L. mlokosiewiczi* of Eurasia similarly span a number of habitat types.

In forests, the Hazel Grouse *Tetrastes bonasia* of Europe, *T. sewerzowi* of Asia, and the Ruffed Grouse *Bonasa umbellus* of North America do best in young to middle-aged broad-leaved stands characterised by mixed species and age classes. The Sharp-winged Grouse *Falcipennis falcipennis* of Siberia and the Spruce Grouse *Canachites canadensis* (from which *C. c. franklinii* is sometimes specifically separated) of North America prefer coniferous forests, commonly spruce, of middle age and older. The Capercaillie *Tetrao urogallus* of Europe (and *T. parvirostris* of Siberia) corresponds with the Blue Grouse *Dendragapus obscurus* of western North America in their choice of coniferous forests—especially in winter, when the same tree may be fed upon for days on end; summer habitats are more varied but less strictly comparable, as the Blue Grouse rears its young in cover which is considerably more open than that used by the Capercaillie.

Grouse tend to be soberly dressed. Forest grouse show mostly dark browns, greys, and black; the grouse of open country are paler, with light browns, buff, and grey predominating. Ptarmigan *Lagopus* spp. are especially well camouflaged, being the colour of rock and lichen in summer and snow-white in winter; but the Red Grouse, in this genus, has no white winter coat. Strong sexual dimorphism in plumage occurs only in the Capercaillie and Black Grouse, in which the hens are mottled brown while the cocks are iridescent blue, black, greenish, and (Capercaillie) brown. The sexes differ less in the Red, Blue, Spruce, Sharp-winged, Hazel, and Sage Grouse, and in the summer plumage of the ptarmigans. In the Ruffed and Sharptailed Grouse, and in the prairie chickens, such plumage differences are subtle. Sexual differences among all species are accentuated by special characters and especially by behaviour during the breeding season. Cocks have wattles, generally red or orange, above the eyes; hens have smaller wattles if any. In spring, Blue and Sharptailed Grouse and prairie chickens have inflatable orange or lavender cervical air-sacs which figure prominently in display. The Sage Grouse cock has greenish-yellow air sacs and wattles.

Spectacular types of display occur within the family. Some species are solitary, e.g. Spruce, Hazel, and Ruffed Grouse. Some have a highly organised social display (see LEK), as Black, Sage, and Sharptailed Grouse and prairie chickens, in which a few to several hundred (Sage Grouse) cocks gather each morning and often in the evening through the spring. (In North America there are special names for the display grounds of the different grouse: 'strutting ground' for Sage Grouse, 'dancing ground' for Sharptailed Grouse, 'booming ground' for Greater Prairie Chicken, 'gobbling ground' for Lesser Prairie Chicken.) The same group-display grounds are used day after day and often year after year. Ptarmigans begin to display in loose aggregations before the winter packs have broken up. When the packs disperse the cocks take up individual territories, some close enough together to meet and fight occasionally. This, indeed, suggests a way in which social display may have originated.

In all of the social grouse one sometimes sees a single cock displaying wholly apart from any group. Capercaillie customarily display singly in trees, especially on the European continent, as well as in groups on the ground. Blue Grouse of the coastal coniferous forests display singly, while those of the interior, breeding in thinner cover, show a tendency toward social display.

With exceptions, then, social display occurs mainly in open country habitats and solitary display in forests. The grouse with social displays are all polygamous or promiscuous. So are the Capercaillie and Blue Grouse, and the solitary Ruffed Grouse. The highly territorial and solitary Hazel Grouse is monogamous, as are the ptarmigans (including Red Grouse) and the Spruce Grouse.

The nests are shallow scrapes on the ground, generally with little lining. Clutch size varies from species to species, but averages roughly from 6 to 12 eggs; in a number of species early clutches are on the average larger than later ones. The female incubates the eggs and cares for the precocial young. Research in Sweden has shown that Capercaillie chicks have a poor temperature-regulating mechanism for some time after hatching, and food reserves for only 3–5 days. In persistent cold and wet weather chicks die of starvation because they cannot leave the warmth of the brooding hen; alternatively, those that do go out to feed become chilled and die of exposure. Herein may lie a population-limiting factor of major and widespread importance.

Grouse are primarily browsers and grazers, although many eat cultivated grains when opportunity offers. There is a close connection between grouse and plants of the heath family, for example heather, blueberry and its relatives, and crowberry. Fruits and such greens as clover, strawberry, and sorrel are relished. Insects and ant pupae are major foods of the chicks; adults are less insectivorous. Buds and catkins are the main winter diet, with willow, birch, and hazel everywhere of importance. The buds and needles of conifers are eaten in quantity by the Capercaillie and by the Blue, Spruce, and Sharp-winged Grouse. The Greater Prairie Chicken is granivorous.

Seasonal movements of some extent are not unusual, and indeed some grouse are semi-migratory. Rock and Willow Ptarmigan in many areas move to less inclement winter-quarters to the south, or downslope from mountain habitats. Blue Grouse generally move upslope for the winter, almost to the timberline. Both ptarmigans and Blue Grouse make large parts of these journeys on foot. Capercaillie and Black Grouse often winter some miles from their breeding areas. Sharptailed Grouse shift to denser woody cover for the winter, sometimes a matter of a few hundred yards and sometimes as far as 10–15 miles. The Greater Prairie Chicken in the north moves to the neighbourhood of grainfields for the winter, and formerly migrated along the Mississippi Valley. Sage Grouse are known to move as far as 100 miles to wintering grounds. By comparison the Spruce, Ruffed, and Hazel Grouse are more sedentary.

Most grouse are first class game-birds. Many lie well to dogs, some are driven, and practically all are excellent for stalking. Capercaillie and Black Grouse are in some places shot in display in spring; the sport is to find and select a trophy bird, which alone is shot. Spruce Grouse are exceptional in being so unwary as to be popularly called 'Fool Hen'. The meat of most grouse is dark and delicious, although old Sage Grouse and the conifer-eaters tend to be bitter. Some, as the prairie chickens, have light meat until the end of the post-juvenile moult. There is a considerable literature on game management relating to species of grouse, particularly in America. Earlier, a comprehensive study was made in Britain of the habits, food, parasites, and numerical fluctuations of the Red Grouse, the results being embodied in a classical report.

Grouse have felt the hand of man in other ways. Ruffed and Blue Grouse have gained habitat through timber cutting, and both have lost range where forests have been wholly converted to farmland. The Black Grouse throve on the fire agriculture practised in Finland for hundreds of years, and logging followed by fire encouraged Sharptailed, Blue, and Ruffed Grouse and Prairie Chicken in North America. Such fires are a thing of the past. Tree planting has wiped out countless forest openings in both the Old and New Worlds, openings without which grouse and many other forest animals cannot live. The grassland grouse—prairie chickens, some Sharptailed Grouse, and Sage Grouse—have suffered the greatest losses through expropriation of habitat. Habitat destruction has had far more effect than the levy for food and sport.

The increasing human population puts increasing pressure on the land. The 'Heath Hen' (nominate form of the Greater Prairie Chicken) is extinct; Hazel Grouse are virtually gone from the intensively managed forests of central Europe. On the other hand, the Red Grouse clearly shows that grouse can be maintained and increased by deliberate effort. The British stock of the Capercaillie had become extinct by 1760, but the introduction of Continental birds in and after 1837 has led to re-establishment of the species in Scotland (see NATURALISED BIRDS). The conclusion is inescapable ; how we use the land is a matter of life and death for most kinds of wild-life, and grouse are no exception.

See Plates 5, 8 and 29 (colour), and 24a (phot.).

F.H. & F.H.

Ammann, G. A. 1957. The prairie grouse of Michigan. Tech. Bull., Mich. Dept. Conservation, Lansing.
Bump, G., Darrow, R. W., Edminster, F. C. & Crissey, W. F. 1947. The Ruffed Grouse—Life History, Propagation, Management. Buffalo.
Committee of Inquiry on Grouse Disease. 1911. The Grouse in Health and Disease. 2 vols. London.
Elliot, D. G. 1865. A Monograph of the Tetraonidae, or Family of the Grouse. New York.
Fuschlberger, R. H. 1956. Das Hahnenbuch. München.
Hamerstrom, F. & Hamerstrom, F. 1960. Comparability of some social displays of grouse. Proc. XII Internat. Orn. Congr., Helsinki 1958 : 274-293.
Lumsden, H. G. 1961. The display of the Capercaillie. Brit. Birds 54 : 257-272.
Patterson, R. L. 1952. The Sage Grouse in Wyoming. Denver.

GROUSE, SAND-: see SANDGROUSE

GROWTH: increase in the size of the body or of its parts, as distinguished from development ; the latter term implies some change in form as a result of differentiation of tissues, commonly in the direction of greater specialisation, but growth and development are so largely synchronous and so intimately related that they are not sharply separable (see DEVELOPMENT, EMBRYONIC ; and particularly DEVELOPMENT, POST-EMBRYONIC). Mere time differentials in the growth of the several dimensions of an organ may affect its shape ; and the formation of the proportions of the growing body is a space-time process that, equally with purely spatial relations, is species-specific in its characteristics (Dinnendahl & Kramer).

Growth is finite in birds, which are not among those animals that continue to increase in size with age. Moreover, full size is attained by young birds very rapidly. In most species, except those that have precocious flight or are flightless, this is by about the time that they are able to fly (see FLIGHT, PRECOCIOUS ; FLIGHTLESSNESS). That usually means a matter of a few weeks after hatching, and two weeks or less in the case of many small species (see YOUNG BIRD). An exceptional phenomenon is the arrested growth, until the following spring, of such young King Penguins *Aptenodytes patagonica* as are hatched too late to be more than about three-quarters grown by the onset of winter (see PENGUIN). Young Emus *Dromaius novaehollandiae* do not, at least in areas of poor food supply, attain full size for nearly 18 months.

Where no significant change in shape is involved, growth is subject to the mathematical law that surface area increases in proportion to the square of the linear dimensions, and volume—and therefore weight (assuming specific gravity to be constant)—in proportion to the cube. The implications of this, in respect of species of similar shape but different sizes, are mentioned elsewhere (see SIZE ; WEIGHT) ; they are of particular importance for a flying animal (see FLIGHT). In the case of the growing bird, however, there is an important change in shape due to the growth of the flight feathers and rectrices ; surface area, especially when the wings are extended, is in this way greatly increased out of all proportion to the linear increase in other parts, and with little effect on weight.

Kramer, G. 1953. Uber Wachstum und Entwicklung der Vögel. J. Orn. 94 : 194-199.

Dinnendahl, L. & Kramer, G. 1957. Über grössenab-
hängige Anderung von Körperproportionen bei
Möwen (*Larus ridibundus, L. canus, L. argentatus,
L. marinus*). J. Orn. 98 : 282–313.

GRUES ; GRUIDAE : see below

GRUIFORMES : an order comprising the following suborders and families, the latter dealt with
separately as shown :

Mesoenatides :
Mesitornithidae	see MESITE

Turnices :
Turnicidae	see BUTTONQUAIL
Pedionomidae	see PLAINS-WANDERER

Grues :
Superfamily Gruoidea
Gruidae	see CRANE
Aramidae	see LIMPKIN
Psophiidae	see TRUMPETER

Superfamily Ralloidea
Rallidae	see RAIL

Heliornithes :
Heliornithidae	see FINFOOT

Rhynocheti :
Rhynochetidae	see KAGU

Eurypygae :
Eurypygidae	see SUNBITTERN

Cariamae :
Cariamidae	see SERIEMA

Otides :
Otididae	see BUSTARD

In Stresemann's system all the above suborders are
treated as separate orders (the first as ' Mesoenades '),
with orders Psophiae and Ralli in addition (leaving
the Aramidae in the Grues).

Of the assemblage as a whole, it may be said that
it consists essentially of ground-living birds—
ground-feeding and mainly ground-nesting ; many
of them seldom fly, and a few never. The Heliornithidae and some of the Rallidae, e.g. coots (Fulicinae)
and gallinules of various genera, are adapted to an
aquatic life ; many others frequent marshes or the
margins of water. Of the families, the Rallidae
include a large number of genera ; four of the
families are monotypic. Only the Gruidae and
Rallidae are cosmopolitan, although the Turnicidae
and Otididae are widespread in the Old World ; the
others have restricted distributions.

Families based on the following fossil type-genera
are also placed in this order (involving an additional
suborder : suborder Grues—*Geranoides, Eogrus,
Orthocnemus* (provisional placing) ; suborder Phoror-
rhaci—*Phororhacos, Psilopterus, Brontornis, Opistho-
dactylus, Cunampaia* ; suborder Cariamae—*Bathornis,
Hermosiornis*. Wetmore (1960), however, now
treats the Phororhaci as one of two superfamilies of

the Cariamae (Phororhacoidea and Cariamoidea)
(see FOSSIL BIRDS).

GRUOIDEA : see above

GUACHARO : alternative name of *Steatornis
caripensis* (see OILBIRD).

GUAN : substantive name of some species of
Cracidae (see CURASSOW).

GUANO : the naturally desiccated, nitrogenous
dung of fish-eating sea fowl—a word of Quechua
(Inca) origin adopted into most European languages ;
secondarily, the same term has been applied to other
animal excreta, such as ' bat guano ' from caves (see
also GUANO, CAVE). Guano has been extensively
sought as the best of organic fertilisers.

Wherever masses of bird droppings are subject to
moisture and leaching, they undergo chemical
changes leading to loss of nitrogen and phosphatisa-
tion of the substrate ; the material thus loses much
of its efficacy as plant food. Nevertheless, phosphatic
guano is exploited as a commercial product on
certain oceanic islands. On the other hand, high-
grade nitrogenous guano, characteristic of the
virtually rainless central west coast of South America
and of a corresponding area in South West Africa,
is of the greatest worth ; its market value has at times
exceeded £20 per ton.

Such guano consists largely of ammonium urate
or uric acid. Ammonium or calcium oxalate and
phosphate are also important constituents, and
sulphates are present in significant quantities. This
composition is characteristic of the fresh excreta of
sea birds in general. The following analyses of
guano from the Mejillones Peninsula, Chile, and
Santa Rosa Island, Peru, both of which have a slightly
richer proportion of nitrogen than is common, are
cited by Hutchinson.

	Mejillones	Santa Rosa
	Per cent	Per cent
H_2O	22·28	20·40
Organic (ign. loss)	56·03	50·30
Insol. (SiO_2 etc.)	1·47	1·78
Na_2O	3·51	—
K_2O	2·51	2·48
CaO	3·67	10·93
MgO	0·50	—
P_2O_5	7·14	11·17
(Al, Fe)PO_4	0·85	—
Cl	2·16	—
SO_3	0·30	—
N total	17·41	14·64
N organic	—	9·84
$N \cdot NH_3$	—	4·73
$N \cdot NO_3$	—	0·07

Conditions for the deposition and preservation of nitrogenous guano in nature are determined by climatic and geographical factors. Aridity is essential, as are also an abundant food supply of schooling fish, and nesting grounds sufficiently free from predatory animals to favour large concentrations of sea birds. Numerous rocky islands on the continental shelf of Peru and northern Chile fulfil these requirements. Nevertheless, the guano that has accumulated in this region is not of great age, in a geological sense. Artifacts found in deep layers of the beds date from as early as the ninth century of our era. Although the rate of accretion has varied in different periods, as determined by measurement of the laminae, average growth is of the order of 8 cm. a year. From these and other data it is estimated that formation of the present or recent Peruvian guano caps began about 500 B.C. Radio-carbon (C^{14}) techniques, applied to guano from at least one small cryptic deposit, indicate considerably greater age and suggest that there may have been earlier guano 'cycles' during or since the Pleistocene. A mere century of rainy climate would eliminate the previous accumulations of millennia.

So far as known, guano was extracted and applied to crops by prehistoric people only in Peru; the highly organised aboriginal industry is described by Garcilaso de la Vega in *The Royal Commentaries of the Yncas* (1609). Although guano was continuously used throughout Spanish colonial times, more than two centuries passed before Alexander von Humboldt made its existence and properties known to the modern world.

Recognition of guano as a major product of international trade commenced about 1840. Unfortunately, the substance was then viewed in Peru in the same light as coal or metals, rather than as a renewable natural resource. Whereas Incaic decrees had rigorously protected the birds, and annual withdrawals had probably been less than the increment, resulting in a steady state, the new exploitation became a process of unlimited 'mining' and no thought was given to the welfare of the sea fowl. The single aim was to excavate guano, load it into vessels, and export it to various world ports. The sole function of the ancient beds, in the eyes of most Peruvians, was to eliminate taxation and to supply funds with which to run the Government. Between the years 1848 and 1875 more than 20 000 000 tons of guano were shipped from Peru to Europe, the United States, and elsewhere. The total exports were never fully recorded, but one by one the coastal islands (beginning with the famous Chinchas) were levelled down to bedrock.

After the turn of the present century, Peruvian agriculture was threatened with disaster for want of fertiliser. An enlightened point of view was needed to follow the spendthrift debauch which Peruvians term the 'Saturnalia'. In 1909 the semi-official Compañia Administradora del Guano was founded and the process of restoration began. All the islands are sanctuaries, and the annual production of guano is treated as a crop. Nesting grounds for sea birds have been extended to the mainland, since 1946, by the erection of pest-proof walls across the bases of certain salients of the coast; these peninsulas are thus converted into additional 'islands'.

The graph of rising production has not been smooth, because periodic changes in oceanic circulation bring about 'crashes' in the bird population at intervals of years, but the long-term trend has been upward. Production of about 20 000 tons per annum in early years of the present century had before 1960 climbed to 300 000 tons.

At present a possible new danger threatens the guano industry. Within a very few seasons Peru has become the largest producer in the world of fish-meal, made from a species of anchovy (*Engraulis*). This fish, which feeds upon minute plankton, is the key organism in the Peru coastal current and the principal food of the guano birds. Recent legislation now limits the manufacture of anchovy meal from Peruvian waters to 600 000 tons annually.

The guano-producing birds in South America, and in the few other areas where nitrogenous deposits are forming, are chiefly members of the order Pelecaniformes. In former times the Peruvian Penguin *Spheniscus humboldti* and Peruvian Diving Petrel *Pelecanoides garnotii* may also have held high rank; both of these nested in burrows dug into the guano, and, since removal of the old beds, both have suffered great reduction in numbers. Today the three most important species are the Peruvian Cormorant (or Guanay) *Phalacrocorax bougainvillei*, the Peruvian Booby *Sula variegata*, and the Brown Pelican *Pelecanus occidentalis thagus*. All of these are endemic in the desert littoral of Pacific South America. In South Africa, where the guano islands are likewise well managed after earlier frantic and wasteful exploitation, the chief producers are the Cape Cormorant *Phalacrocorax capensis*, the Cape Gannet *Sula* ('*Morus*') *capensis*, and the Jackass (or Black-footed) Penguin *Spheniscus demersus*. These, too, are endemic in the area.

Typical guano birds form some of the largest and densest of nesting populations. The Peruvian Cormorant or Guanay covers all favourable rock surfaces of many islands, the nests averaging three per square metre. After the young have hatched, there may be several million birds in a single colony. Guano birds are also voracious eaters. A Guanay deposits on land throughout its life a minimum dry weight of one kilogramme of guano per month. Very little defecation takes place in the sea, at least among the pelecaniform birds, a serviceable reason for this being that guano itself forms the substance of the deep-bowled nests. As to the efficiency of conversion by weight from live fish to dry guano, the ratio for the Guanay has been determined as approximately 9·7 : 1. Human methods can convert fish into meal in a ratio of about 5 : 1. Birds, however, produce a better and vastly cheaper product. Furthermore, they cannot make more guano from their prey than is consistent with survival of all parts of the ecosystem involved. (See also DROPPINGS ; EXCRETORY SYSTEM.)   R.C.M.

Principal sources, listed chronologically, include bibliographies.

Murphy, R. C. 1936. Oceanic Birds of South America. 2 vols. New York.

Meise, W. 1938. Guano und anderer Vogeldung. *In* Die Rohstoffe des Tierreichs. 1(2) : 2113–2172. Berlin.

Hutchinson, G. E. 1950. Survey of contemporary knowledge of biogeochemistry. 3. The biogeochemistry of vertebrate excretion. Bull. Amer. Mus. Nat. Hist. 96 : i–xviii, 1–544.

Levin, J. V. 1960. The Export Economies : Peru in the Guano Age. Cambridge, Mass.

GUANO, CAVE : a subsidiary but appreciable source of guano (see above), very rich in nitrogen content, deposited as faeces by swiftlets *Collocalia* spp. in the scattered groups of limestone caves where they nest, often in great numbers, through Burma, Indo-China, Thailand, and Malaya, into the Indonesian Archipelago (see EDIBLE NESTS). In recent times, under pressure of increasing population, this has proved a local source of fertiliser for peasant farmers and latterly for organised Chinese pepper-gardening and similar cash crops. Conditions of extraction are primitive and sometimes dangerous. The filthy, stinking, black, slimy product, composed mainly of decaying insect remains, retails for between $6 and $12 (Straits) a sack, or around £1 per hundredweight, varying according to distance from source. A large proportion of all accessible cave-floor deposits in south-east Asia have now been stripped down to bedrock.   T.H.

GUIDING : see HONEYGUIDE

GUIDING LINE : less appropriate alternative term (translating ' Leitlinie ') for LEADING LINE.

GUILLEMOT : substantive name of *Uria* spp. (' murre ' in American usage) and *Cepphus* spp. (also called ' tystie ')—see AUK. Although originally a French word, it is now pronounced in English with the final syllable as in ' hot '.

GUINEAFOWL : substantive name of species of Numididae (Galliformes, suborder Galli) ; in the plural (sometimes unchanged), general term for the family. This group of gallinaceous birds is often included in the Phasianidae but is worthy of family rank. The members are restricted to Africa, Madagascar, the Comoro Islands, and a small part of Arabia. The guineahen of our poultry yards is descended from an introduced species, *Numida meleagris* (see DOMESTICATION) ; it may be instanced as approximating to the size that most of the family attain, one species being smaller and one larger.

Well known as sporting birds, the 8–10 species of guineafowl are grouped in 4 genera. Most widely distributed of the family are the so-called helmet-guineafowls and the bristle-nosed guineafowls, the latter distinguished by the tuft of bristles at the base of the culmen ; they are usually ranked as subspecies of *Numida meleagris*. The head and neck are bare of feathers, except for scattered hair-like plumes on the neck ; a naked bony helmet surmounts the crown, the bill is heavy and arched, the nostrils are exposed, and coloured wattles depend from the gape ; the legs and feet are exceptionally strong, as becomes birds given to running and to scratching in the soil ; the tarsus is bare and the hind toe raised above the level of the front toes. With one exception, male guineafowl are not provided with spurs like the francolins (Phasianidae). The wing is rounded, despite which all the species are powerful fliers ; they have well-developed tails. The plumage varies a good deal. In the *Numida* group, the body plumage below the breast and mantle, which are usually grey, is black covered with round white spots. Members of this genus range over the dry bush-country and the tree-savanna belt ; they are particularly addicted to the ironstone country in Senegambia. The nominate form is found from Lake Chad eastwards to the Sudan and Ethiopia, with a foothold (possibly as a result of introduction at some remote date) in south-western Arabia. Many races have been described on minor characters. The Grey-breasted Guineafowl *N. m. galeata* occurs widely in West Africa north of the Equatorial Forest. In South West Africa lives the Wattle-nosed Guineafowl *N. m. damarensis*, a native also of Angola and Damaraland. On the other side of the continent, the Helmeted Guineafowl *N. m. mitrata* (sometimes specifically separated), is remarkable for its long, elevated, and compressed helmet, varying in development and height ; it ranges from Zanzibar to the coast of Kenya, and is represented in Madagascar and the

Comoro Islands by what are probably the descendants of introduced birds.

Closely allied to *Numida* but very different in its headdress is the Crested Guineafowl *Guttera edouardi*, with a conspicuous bunch of black curly feathers on the crown, a naked face, but black instead of grey collar; the body is covered with much smaller white spots surrounded with pale blue on a black ground. It is more of a dense bush or even forest bird than *Numida*. Crested Guineafowl in several forms range over a wide area of Africa, from the Rift Valley to the Zambesi and beyond, with a well-known representative *G. e. verreauxi* in West Africa.

Very striking is the Plumed Guineafowl *G. plumifera*, in the same genus as the last and very similar in its body plumage but with the head surmounted by a crown of straight stiff plumes, not curly as in the 'crested' bird. It lives in the depths of the primitive forest and was discovered in 1856 by the explorer Paul du Chaillu in Gaboon. Yet another member of this genus, described as very local, is the Kenya Crested Guineafowl *G. pucherani*, the bare skin of the throat and round the eyes being red while the rest of the head and neck is cobalt-blue; it is a bird of dense thickets but not found in true forest.

Perhaps rarest of all is the White-breasted Guineafowl *Agelastes meleagrides*, which is specially remarkable for having a completely bald red head without any bony helmet. It has a white breast and mantle, and dark unspotted body plumage. A native of Ghana and Liberia, it has seldom been encountered by Europeans. Sometimes described as turkey-like in appearance, it has been seen in parties of four to five but is extremely wary.

Smallest of the family is the Black Guineafowl *Agelastes niger*, all black except for the light-red naked skin on the head and the pinkish-grey naked throat; a strip of short velvety black feathers extends from the forehead almost to the occiput. It is a bird of Lower Guinea, where it keeps to the remotest parts of the virgin forest and is reputed to be excessively shy. It is not gregarious, but the cock wanders in the dark forest accompanied by one or two hens. Its affinities with the guineafowls has been disputed, so chicken-like is it in appearance, but examination of its metacarpus has finally settled its position. Few Europeans have seen it alive. This bird was formerly placed in a genus ('*Phasidus*') of its own, until Hall gave reasons against this separation of what are evidently two closely related species.

Finally, the most attractive of all the family is the Vulturine Guineafowl *Acryllium vulturinum*, the sole representative of its genus and the only highly decorative member of the family. It has been well depicted in colour by Lodge in Jackson's *Birds of Kenya Colony and the Uganda Protectorate*. The bare skin of the head and neck is greyish-blue, a horseshoe band of downy chestnut feathers ornaments the nape, the breast and abdomen are cobalt-blue; long pointed hackles, black with white shafts and margined with cobalt, fall from the lower neck and mantle, while the rest of the plumage is black, spotted with white. Very characteristic is the tail of 16 feathers, the middle ones considerably elongated and pointed. The crimson eye lends a wicked look to this truly magnificent member of the family. It is an inhabitant of the desert belt—'the dry, arid, scorching and most uninviting bush-velt, which it shares with the Dik-diks'. Living in little bands amidst these arid surroundings, the birds must depend for many months of the year on drops of dew for their water supply.

Guineafowl feed on insects (favouring white ants), vegetable matter of all kinds, seeds, leaves, and bulbs; much of such food they obtain by scratching. Molluscs and small frogs are also eaten. Guineafowl lay many eggs, 10 to 20 being not uncommon in the more widely spread species, usually in a scrape in the ground. The eggs are cream or buff, some closely speckled, but those of both *Agelastes* species are apparently unknown. Except in the nesting season, the species that inhabit the more open country are highly gregarious, forming into packs before and after the breeding season. The life-history of the two rarest forms is still wrapt in mystery.

See Plate 30 (colour).   D.A.B.

Boetticher, H. von. 1954. Die Perl-hühner. Wittenburg-Lutherstadt.

Ghigi, A. 1927. Monografia delle Gallie di Faronen (Numididae). Pubbl. Staz. Sper. Pollicolt. Rovigo 2: 1–84.

Hall, B. P. 1961. The relationship of the guinea-fowls *Agelastes meleagrides* Bonaparte and *Phasidus niger* Cassin. Bull. Brit. Orn. Cl. 81: 132.

Skead, C. J. 1962. A Study of the Crowned Guinea Fowl *Numida meleagris coronata* Gurney. Ostrich 33: 51–65.

GUIRA: *Guira guira* (see CUCKOO).

GULAR: pertaining to the throat (see TOPOGRAPHY).

GULL: substantive name of nearly all the species of the subfamily Larinae of the Laridae (Charadriiformes, suborder Lari); in the plural, general term for the subfamily. The other subfamily is the Sterninae (see TERN), but some authors reduce both to tribal status, with the Rynchopidae as well (see SKIMMER). These authors include Moynihan, whose revision is followed here as regards generic and subgeneric taxonomy. The other substantive name used is ' kittiwake ', for two species.

The gulls are cosmopolitan and the most familiar of sea birds. They are popularly known as ' sea gulls ' (poetically as ' sea mews '), but they are coastal rather than oceanic ; many species indeed frequent inland waters and marshes, and they may at times be found far from such haunts. A few species are small but many are rather large birds (8–30 inches in length). They are stoutly built, with long and pointed wings. The tail is of moderate length, usually almost square. The bill is stout and slightly hooked. The front toes are webbed, the hind toe small or (in a few) vestigial.

The plumage is characteristically white with pale grey or darker colour on the back and wings (the tips of the latter black in most species). In a few species the general appearance, even of the adult, is much darker, e.g. *Larus fuliginosus* of the Galápagos Islands (described as being of the ' colour of lava ') and the Sooty Gull (see below). Many have a dark hood or mask in the breeding season. The bill and legs are bright red or yellow in some, but there are seasonal and age differences. The sexes are alike. Immature birds are darker, often largely mottled brown, and full adult dress may not be attained for several years.

Gulls fly strongly, with slow wing-beats, and are adept at gliding and soaring. They swim buoyantly, but seldom dive below the surface. The calls are harsh or yelping. Some gulls catch fish, but many are largely scavengers and eat a variety of animal and vegetable food. The birds are gregarious at all times, roosting in flocks on water or land and breeding in colonies that are sometimes of great size. There is elaborate hostile and sexual behaviour of various types, which has been intensively studied in some species.

The nest is characteristically a bulky, untidy structure of grasses or the like. It may be placed on a cliff, the usual site for some coastal species (with a building as an occasional substitute), or sometimes in a tree ; or it may be on a tussock in a marsh or floating among reeds ; or it may be on dry, level ground. The usual clutch is 2–3 ; the eggs are either pale or deep brownish or greenish, with heavy mottling ; the chicks are downy and alert when hatched but are fed at the nest until well grown. Both parents incubate the eggs and care for the young.

Moynihan places all the species in the genus *Larus*, where most of them already were ; this suppresses some small genera that have formerly been distinguished on such characters as shape of tail and virtual absence of the hallux—the latter not even

constant among individuals. He divides the genus into three subgenera and a number of subordinate groups, largely on ethological grounds. The subfamily (or tribe) has a worldwide distribution, including Antarctica ; but the greater number of forms is found in the Northern Hemisphere, some being native to the high Arctic.

Large Whiteheaded Gulls. A familiar example of the subgenus *Larus* is the Herring Gull *Larus argentatus* of northern North America and north-western Europe. Very like it but for the dark mantle and yellow legs is the Lesser Blackbacked Gull *L. fuscus* of the Palaearctic Region ; the two species are sympatric in Europe but are connected by inter-grading subspecific forms elsewhere (see RING SPECIES). One of the largest species is the Great Blackbacked Gull *L. marinus* of the North Atlantic ; another, with light grey back, is the circumpolar Glaucous Gull *L. hyperboreus*. Smaller than any of those yet mentioned is the Common Gull *L. canus* of the Palaearctic Region and parts of western North America ; the English name is unfortunate, as the species is nearly everywhere outnumbered by others —in American usage it is called Mew Gull. Other members of this extensive group of rather similar species include the Ring-billed Gull *L. delawarensis* of North America, the Black-tailed Gull *L. crassirostris* of north-eastern Asia, and the Pacific Gull *Larus* (' *Gabianus* ') *pacificus* of southern Australia.

Standing rather apart from the above main group is the Dolphin Gull *Larus* (' *Gabianus* ') *scoresbii* of Tierra del Fuego and the Falkland Islands. It is a relatively dark bird of medium size, with bright red bill and legs, and has a display behaviour which is peculiar in some respects.

Hooded Gulls. The subgenus *Xema* constitutes the other large assemblage, and most of its species fall into two groups. There are the ' primitive ' hooded gulls (Moynihan), such as the Laughing Gull *L. atricilla* and Franklin's Gull *L. pipixcan* of America, the Sooty Gull *L. hemprichi* of the western Indian Ocean, and the very large Great Blackheaded Gull *L. melanocephalus* of the Mediterranean and central Asia. Contrasted with these are the ' masked gulls ', of which the Blackheaded Gull *L. ridibundus* is a familiar Palaearctic example. Others in this group are Bonaparte's Gull *L. philadelphiae* of North America, the Greyheaded Gull *L. cirrocephalus* of the great lakes of Africa, the Silver (or Redbilled) Gull *L. novaehollandiae* of Australia, and the Blackbilled Gull *L. bulleri* of New Zealand.

Although they have traces of a dark hood only in juvenile and winter plumage, the kittiwakes may be placed in this subgenus on other grounds. The almost circumpolar, cliff-nesting Kittiwake *Larus* ('*Rissa*') *tridactylus* is, unlike most gulls, often seen in mid-ocean, and there are numerous records of ringed birds crossing the Atlantic. The related species is the Redlegged Kittiwake *L. brevirostris* of the Bering Sea. The hallux is vestigial in these forms.

In two species there is a white hood in nuptial plumage, contrasting with a darker neck and body—Heermann's Gull *L. heermanni* of the California Current and *L. modestus* of the Humboldt Current. The behaviour of Saunders' Gull *L. saundersi*, an inland species of Mongolia and northern China, is little known. The Little Gull *L. minutus* is a small blackheaded species of the Palaearctic Region. Near it may perhaps be placed the Rosy (or Ross's) Gull *Larus* ('*Rhodostethia*') *roseus* of northern Siberia; it has only a black collar to represent the hood, and it is otherwise peculiar in the roseate suffusion of the white plumage and in having a graduated tail. Finally, there are two fork-tailed species—the Swallow-tailed Gull *Larus* ('*Creagrus*') *furcatus* of the Galápagos Islands and Sabine's Gull *Larus* ('*Xema*') *sabini* of the high Arctic; these may or may not be closely related—the behaviour of the former is in some respects peculiar, that of the latter scarcely known.

Ivory Gull. By itself in the subgenus *Pagophila* is placed the Ivory Gull *Larus* ('*Pagophila*') *eburneus*. It has the unique character, among gulls, of an entirely white plumage. It breeds only in the high Arctic and little is known of its behaviour.

See Plates 8 (colour) and 34b (phot.).

A.L.T.

Bateson, P. P. G. & Plowright, R. C. 1959. Some aspects of the reproductive behaviour of the Ivory Gull. Ardea 47 : 157-176.
Coulson, J. C. & White, E. 1956. A study of colonies of the Kittiwake *Rissa tridactyla*. Ibis 98 : 63-79.
Coulson, J. C. & White, E. 1960. The effect of age and density of breeding birds on the time of breeding of the Kittiwake *Rissa tridactyla*. Ibis 102 : 71-86.
Cullen, E. 1957. Adaptations in the Kittiwake to cliff-nesting. Ibis 99 : 275-302.
Dwight, J. 1925. The gulls (Laridae) of the world ; their plumages, moults, variations, relationships and distribution. Bull. Amer. Mus. Nat. Hist. 52 : 63-401.
Moynihan, M. 1955. Some aspects of reproductive behaviour in the Black-headed Gull (*Larus ridibundus ridibundus* L.) and related species. Behav. suppl. 4 : 1-201.
Moynihan, M. 1956-58. Notes on the behaviour of some North American gulls. Behav. 10 : 126-178; 12: 95-182 ; 13 : 113-130.
Moynihan, M. 1959. A revision of the family Laridae (Aves). Amer. Mus. Novit. no. 1928 : 1-42.
Noble, G. K. & Wurm, M. 1943. The social behaviour of the Laughing Gull. Ann. New York Acad. Sci. 45 : 179-220.
Thomson, A. L. 1924. The migrations of the Herring Gull and Lesser Black-backed Gull ; results of the marking method. Brit. Birds 18 : 34-44.
Tinbergen, N. 1953. The Herring Gull's World. London.
Tinbergen, N. 1960. Comparative studies of the behaviour of gulls (Laridae) : a progress report. Behav. 15 : 1-70.
Weidmann, U. 1955. Some reproductive activities of the Common Gull, *Larus canus* L. Ardea 43 : 85-132.

GULLET: the anterior part of the oesophagus (see ALIMENTARY SYSTEM).

GUSTATORY SENSE: see TASTE

GUT: the alimentary tract, from mouth to cloaca (see ALIMENTARY SYSTEM).

GYMNORHINAL: see NARIS

GYNANDROMORPHISM: see PLUMAGE, AB-NORMAL AND ABERRANT

GYPAETINAE: see VULTURE (1).

GYRFALCON: *Falco rusticolus* (see FALCON).

H

HABITAT PREFERENCE: see ECOLOGY

HABITUATION: see LEARNING

HACK: term used in FALCONRY.

HACKLE: a long slender feather on the neck; such feathers are found, especially, in various species of Galliformes.

HADADA: *Hagedashia hagedash* (see IBIS).

HAEMATOPODIDAE: see under CHARADRI-IFORMES; and OYSTERCATCHER

HAEMOGLOBIN: see BLOOD

HAGGARD: term for a hawk caught as an adult and trained (one caught as full-grown but in its first plumage is a 'passage hawk')—see FALCONRY.

HALCYON: poetic name for KINGFISHER.

HALCYONES: see CORACIIFORMES

HALLUX: the first toe, usually 'opposed' (i.e. directed backwards) in birds and often much reduced (sometimes absent)—see SKELETON; and LEG.

HAMMERHEAD: name, alternatively 'Hammer-kop', 'Hammer-headed Stork', or 'Anvil-head', of *Scopus umbretta*, sole species of the Scopidae (Ciconiiformes, suborder Ciconiae). It is a rather heavy-looking bird of medium size (about 20 inches in length), with rather short legs and a moderately long bill that is laterally compressed and slightly hooked. The wings and tail are rather long. The conspicuous feature is a long backward-pointing crest, so to speak balancing the bill and giving the bird its common names; in flight, however, the crest lies along the neck and ceases to be obvious. The plumage is brown with some streaks and bars of lighter and darker colour; the bill and legs being black, the general appearance is sombre. The sexes are alike. Powder-down patches are lacking, but the middle toe is pectinated as in Ardeidae. The

three forward toes are connected by a partial web; the hind toe is on the same level.

Hammerhead *Scopus umbretta*, sole species. *C.E.T.K.*

The species has a wide range in tropical Africa, and this extends also to Madagascar and south-western Arabia; the birds inhabiting part of the coastal area of West Africa, from Sierra Leone to Nigeria, belong to a dwarf race. The Hammerhead frequents marshes, mangrove swamps, and tidal creeks, but seldom far from trees. It is usually found singly or in pairs. The flight is slow, with the neck only slightly retracted. The birds utter harsh croaks, often when flying, and tend to be particularly active at twilight.

The Hammerhead often stands on the backs of hippopotamus in shallow wallows, and from there catches frogs; these and other aquatic animals form its principal food. A 'dancing' courtship display, with bowing and wing-flapping, has been described.

The nest is a remarkable affair—an enormous structure of sticks and other vegetation, lined with mud or dung. It may be 3–4 feet in diameter and forms a closed chamber, with an entrance tunnel in the side. This is placed in a tree, at varying height from the ground. The 3–6 eggs are white and slightly chalky. The nidicolous young are downy; they are tended by both parents.   A.L.T.

HAMULUS: a hooked barbicel (see FEATHER).

HANDSAW: see HERNSHAW; SHAKESPEARE'S BIRDS

HANGNEST: name sometimes applied, in North America, to *Icterus* spp. (for family see ORIOLE (2)).

HAPLOOPHONAE: see under PASSERIFORMES; SYRINX

HAREM POLYGAMY: see POLYGAMY

HARLEQUIN: sometimes used by itself for the Harlequin Duck *Histrionicus histrionicus* (see DUCK).

HARPY: sometimes, at least formerly, used alone for the Harpy Eagle *Harpia harpyja* (see under HAWK). See also FABULOUS BIRDS.

HARRIER: substantive name of *Circus* spp.; in the plural, general term for the subfamily Circinae of the Accipitridae.

HARRIER EAGLE: substantive name, alternatively 'serpent eagle', of species of Circaetinae (Accipitridae); in the plural, general term for the subfamily (see HAWK).

HARRIER-HAWK (1): substantive name of species of Polyboroidinae (Accipitridae); in the plural, general term for the subfamily (see HAWK).

HARRIER-HAWK (2): sometimes used as the substantive name, alternatively 'forest falcon' (Brown & Amadon), of *Micrastur* spp.; in the plural, serves as a general term for the Herpetotherinae (see FALCON).

HATCHING: the emergence of the developed chick from the egg after incubation; the term is applied both to the egg and to the chick—e.g. the eggs 'hatch', the young 'are hatched' or 'hatch out'. The process and its physiological implications are described in the final section of the article DEVELOPMENT, EMBRYONIC. The hatching of the different eggs in a clutch may be almost synchronous, or there may be a considerable interval between first and last. In many species with nidicolous young the broken pieces of eggshell are removed from the nest by the parent or parents. See also BEHAVIOUR, DEVELOPMENT OF; EGG; EGG-TOOTH; INCUBATION; PARENTAL CARE. For the condition of the young immediately after hatching see DEVELOPMENT, POST-EMBRYONIC; YOUNG BIRD.

HATCHLING: term sometimes applied to a newly hatched bird (see YOUNG BIRD).

HAWAIIAN HONEYCREEPER: see HONEY-CREEPER (2)

HAWAIIAN ISLANDS: a mid-oceanic archipelago having an avifauna largely related to the Nearctic Region but with elements of Australasian affinities (see AUSTRALASIAN REGION; DISTRIBUTION, GEOGRAPHICAL; and HONEYCREEPER (2)).

Peterson, R. T. 1961. A Field Guide to Western Birds. 2nd ed. Boston, Mass. (Section on Hawaiian birds.)

HAWFINCH: substantive name of *Coccothraustes coccothraustes* and of *Eophona* spp.; used without qualification for the first mentioned (see FINCH).

HAWK: substantive name, or part of the substantive name, of many members of the Accipitridae (Falconiformes, suborder Falcones (or Accipitres)) —in American usage the name is given to species of Accipitridae that in British usage have special substantive names (e.g. 'buzzard', 'harrier'), and is even applied to some species of Falconidae (see FALCON); in the plural, general term for the Accipitridae, the subject of this article except that the several genera of Old World vultures are separately treated (see VULTURE (1)). Apart from the vultures, the family is often divided into subfamilies: the Accipitrinae (true hawks, including 'bird hawks', buzzards, and eagles), Circaetinae (harrier eagles or serpent eagles), Circinae (harriers), Polyboroidinae (harrier-hawks in one sense), Milvinae (true kites and fish eagles), Perninae (honey-buzzard etc.), Elaninae (white-tailed kites), Machae-rhamphinae (Bat-hawk), and Pandioninae (Osprey or Fish-hawk)—the last two being monotypic. For convenience this grouping is followed here, but the writer considers it probably preferable to regard all but one of these suggested subfamilies as united in a single group constituting the Accipitridae, with Pandionidae as a separate family.

General Characters. The birds in this large and varied assemblage range from minute sparrowhawks *Accipiter* spp. to huge and powerful eagles, those of the genera *Harpia*, *Pithecophaga*, and *Haliaetus* being the largest and strongest birds-of-prey in the world and among the largest of flying birds. In almost all birds-of-prey the female of the species is larger than the male, sometimes much larger; she is often duller and browner in colour, and immature birds may be quite different in appearance from the adults.

The family has the characteristics of the order, of which the most obvious are the decurved and pointed bill, with base covered by a cere in which the external nares are situated, and the powerful gripping feet with strong claws. Leaving aside the carrion-eating Old World vultures, they are—with some exceptions—hunters of live prey ; the latter ranges from birds in flight to fish, and from sizeable mammals to insects. Unlike many of the owls (Strigiformes), which have similar adaptations of bill and foot by convergence, they are diurnal in their habits—occasionally crepuscular (*Machaerhamphus*). Different species have screaming, yelping, mewing, whistling, or cackling cries.

Most of the birds here discussed breed in trees, either making their own nests or sometimes adopting the nests of others ; some eagles and buzzards breed on crags. The nests are built of sticks and are often lined with green leaves, sometimes with grass, rags, and oddments. The larger species build huge structures to which they return year after year. Small clutches of 1–2 eggs are typical of large eagles, but the smaller species may lay 3–5 or even more. Incubation times vary from about 28 days in small sparrowhawks to 49 days in large eagles, and fledging periods from 30 days to 130 days. The whole cycle from nest repair to independence of the young, 2–3 months or more after leaving the nest, may be so long as to prevent breeding in successive years ; the largest species are long-lived, slow-breeding birds.

True Hawks and Eagles. The Accipitrinae are the largest and most varied subfamily, containing most of the world's hawks (in the strict sense), buzzards, and eagles. It may conveniently be divided into several smaller groupings. First, the genera *Accipiter*, *Melierax*, and *Urotriorchis* are small to medium-sized hawks of swift flight, generally inhabiting woodlands or forests, and preying upon birds, small mammals, and reptiles. Of these only *Accipiter* occurs in the New World, while the others (*Urotriorchis* being monotypic) are confined to the Ethiopian Region. Three other genera, to be mentioned later, also belong to this group.

The genus *Accipiter* contains the true sparrowhawks and is the largest of all the genera of the birds-of-prey, cosmopolitan in distribution, and with representative members in any woodland ecotype, from the pine forests of the far north to the most luxuriant tropical rain-forests and the thorn-scrub of Africa. All are broad-winged, long-tailed hawks, with rather long thin legs ; they fly from tree to tree in the forest, and when hunting adopt methods of stealthy approach behind cover, culminating in a sudden pounce. Few of them can fly down birds in the open, but they are adept at catching them in thick vegetation. The largest member of the genus, the Goshawk *Accipiter gentilis*, is about 19–23 inches

long, grey above and white barred grey below, with a fierce yellow eye ; it has been trained for falconry, as have several others of the genus, and is capable of killing birds as large as a Pheasant *Phasianus colchicus* and mammals up to the size of a rabbit (see FAL-CONRY). At the other extreme is the tiny African Little Sparrowhawk *Accipiter minullus*, about the size of a thrush *Turdus* sp. and living to a considerable extent on insects ; these it catches in twirling flights after the manner of a flycatcher (Muscicapinae). Between these two extremes are hawks of every intermediate size, but all bold and aggressive, all inhabiting woodlands, and all living mainly on birds, with mammals and reptiles as side-lines. Close to the genus *Accipiter* is *Melierax* (including ' *Micronisus* ') ; these are birds of the open African thorn-bush, grey above, with white under sides barred with grey. The two Chanting Goshawks *Melierax* spp. are large birds capable of killing guineafowl (Numididae), but living chiefly on insects and lizards, which they often catch on the ground, running about like small editions of the Secretary-bird *Sagittarius serpentarius*. The Gabar Goshawk *Melierax gabar* is like a sparrowhawk in its habits. Finally there are the Long-tailed Hawk *Urotriorchis macrourus*, a strange dark-coloured hawk, black above with chestnut below and a long tail ornamented with white dots, which inhabits dense forests in West Africa and lives chiefly on arboreal squirrels and birds ; two Australasian genera, *Erythrotriorchis* and *Megatriorchis*, of large and powerful hawks ; and the Lizard Buzzard *Kaupifalco monogrammicus*, which is systematically more closely akin to the next group but has the habits of a small *Accipiter* and preys chiefly on lizards.

The next subdivision of the Accipitrinae comprises large hawks with soaring flight, inhabiting woodlands or open country, and preying upon mammals and reptiles caught on the ground, with birds forming a minor part of the diet. The genus *Buteo* (including ' *Rupornis* ' and ' *Asturina* '), containing the true buzzards, is the largest of this group, and is cosmopolitan in distribution save for Australasia and Malaysia. The genera *Heterospizias*, *Leucopternis*, ' *Asturina* ', ' *Rupornis* ', *Parabuteo*, *Buteogallus* (including ' *Urubitinga* '), and *Busarellus* are confined to Central and South America, and *Butastur* to Africa, India, and the East. *Butastur* spp. (e.g. the Grasshopper Buzzard *B. rufipennis* of Africa) are the least like buzzards of the whole group, having more the habits of harriers (Circinae) in some ways. All these birds are large, with a wing-spread of 3–5 feet. They all can soar, but they perch a great deal on trees, telegraph posts, or rocks, and catch their prey on the ground. Some frequent lowland swamps, others mountainous country ; the Augur Buzzard *Buteo rufofuscus* occurs in Africa up to 17 000 feet above sea-level, and the Mexican Black Hawk *Buteogallus anthracinus* is found in swampy areas or tropical forest regions at low altitudes. They are mainly brown in colour in immature plumage, but in the adult dress often develop handsome plumages of brown, white, and red-brown, or black and white. Females are generally only slightly larger than males. Some are migratory, e.g. the Rough-legged Buzzard *Buteo lagopus*, which is also one of the few members of the group with the tarsus feathered to the toes. Others remain in their haunts all the year round, the tendency being for those that live in the far north to migrate, while most tropical and subtropical species do not.

The third subdivision of the Accipitrinae consists of large or very large birds-of-prey, with wingspread of 4–8 feet and weight of $2\frac{1}{2}$–16 lbs. (1000–7000 grams), generally called eagles. They include the following American genera : *Harpyhaliaetus, Spizastur, Oroaetus, Morphnus,* and *Harpia. Stephanoaetus* and *Polemaetus* inhabit Africa, and *Ictinaetus, Harpyopsis,* and *Pithecophaga* occur only in India and the Far East. The genera *Aquila, Spizaetus,* and *Hieraaetus* are of wider distribution. *Aquila* in particular is found in all regions of the world except South America and the Malaysian area, being represented in Australia by *Aquila* ('*Uroaetus*') *audax.* All these birds are both large and aggressive, preying on large and small mammals, birds, and reptiles. Some eagles, especially *Aquila* spp., eat carrion ; the Tawny Eagle *A. rapax* pursues and robs other raptors of their prey. Although some are hardly bigger than buzzards, they are in general fiercer and more active than the birds of that group. They vary in size from small, active hawk-eagles of the genera *Spizaetus* and *Hieraaetus* to huge and powerful birds-of-prey (*Stephanoaetus, Polemaetus, Aquila, Harpyopsis, Pithecophaga,* and *Harpia*). *Aquila, Spizaetus, Spizastur, Hieraaetus, Stephanoaetus, Polemaetus, Oroaetus,* and *Ictinaetus* have feathered tarsi, the rest bare tarsi. The largest and most powerful of all is the Harpy Eagle *Harpia harpyja,* inhabiting tropical South America ; and scarcely smaller is the Philippine Monkey-eating Eagle *Pithecophaga jefferyi,* which has unusual blue eyes. The smaller members of the group include Ayres' Hawk-eagle *Hieraaetus ayresi,* a rare bird of Africa which is like a sparrowhawk in its habits in that it lives on birds of the tree-tops, and the very handsome *Hieraaetus kieneri* of India. Those that live in open country (*Aquila, Polemaetus*) tend to live principally on mammals and gallinaceous birds, caught upon the ground but often seized in spectacular fashion. All these birds are capable of beautiful soaring flight, and some of them are probably as fast as or, faster than, any other birds-of-prey, although they may appear, by reason of their large size, to move more slowly than some falcons. Their plumage varies from dull brown (*Aquila*) through various patterns of grey and white and black and white to very rich and beautiful combinations of black, buff, chestnut, and white (*Stephanoaetus* and *Spizaetus ornatus*). Two, Verreaux's Eagle *Aquila verreauxi* and the Black Eagle *Ictinaetus malayensis,* are mainly black, with white on the rump ; the latter species has the peculiar habit of feeding upon the eggs of other birds, taken in the nest.

Snake Eagles. The snake eagles, serpent eagles and harrier eagles are sometimes placed in a subfamily Circaetinae ; they live principally on snakes and other reptiles and have feet specially adapted, with short rough toes of immense power, to grasping and holding this prey. *Circaetus, Terathopius,* and *Dryotriorchis* are African genera, the latter two monotypic and the first with one of its species, the Short-toed Eagle *C. gallicus* of Europe, extending over the warmer parts of Europe, Asia, and Africa. The crested serpent eagles *Spilornis* spp. occur from India to the Philippines, and *Eutriorchis astur* inhabits Madagascar. The habits of these birds in the field are much like those of other large eagles. They are given to soaring for long periods, or to perching on outstanding trees and rocks whence they can see their prey ; the Short-toed Eagle can hover like a Kestrel *Falco tinnunculus,* although relatively huge (see FALCON). They drop on their prey and either snatch it into the air or kill it on the ground. When eating snakes they crush the head first, afterwards swallowing the rest of the body whole. They inhabit open country, forests, and bushland. The most remarkable of the whole group is the Bateleur *Terathopius ecaudatus* of Africa, which has exceptionally long wings and a very short tail. Birds of this species fly perhaps 200 miles on most days of their lives, canting from side to side and occasionally performing astonishing aerobatics ; they eat carrion and mammals as well as reptiles, and at carrion will pursue and attack other carrion birds in the hope of making them disgorge. The Serpent Eagle *Dryotriorchis spectabilis* of West Africa is a strange bird of dense tropical forests and has large eyes that perhaps help it to see in poor light.

Harriers. The subfamily Circinae, cosmopolitan in distribution, contains the harriers *Circus* spp., a very characteristic genus inhabiting open country, cultivation, or swampy land. They are either mainly brown in colour or, in some species, the males are grey and the females and juveniles brown ; two species, *Circus maurus* of South Africa and *C. melano-*

leucus breeding in north-eastern Asia, are black and white. All harriers are slender, long-winged, long-tailed birds with long legs, and rather owlish heads. They spend most of the day on the wing but also perch on posts, hillocks, and so on. Their habits are similar all over the world, in that they fly low over the ground, systematically quartering to and fro, and dropping on prey in the grass. Unlike most birds-of-prey, they both roost and breed on the ground ; and the male, when bringing prey to the nest, characteristically passes it to the female in flight, a little way from it. Some of the species are migratory, the Palaearctic Pallid Harrier *C. macrourus* being one of the commonest birds-of-prey in the plains of Africa and India in winter. On migration they tend to be gregarious, and they roost in company in ' forms ' in the grass (Pallid Harrier and Marsh Harrier *C. aeruginosus*). Some tend to concentrate in swampy localities and others in dry open plains or steppe, but they never frequent woodland country for long. They live on small mammals, frogs, and some insects and reptiles, but occasionally also take birds on the ground ; they cannot catch birds on the wing.

Harrier-hawks. The subfamily Polyboroidinae contains the harrier-hawks, curious long-tailed, long-legged birds the size of a buzzard, grey and black in plumage with yellow legs and bare skin on the face ; they inhabit Africa and Madagascar, usually in wooded country. The South American genus *Geranospiza* is probably closely related. The African continental species is the Harrier-hawk *Polyboroides* (' *Gymnogenys* ') *typicus*. They are unable to kill any large prey, and they have buoyant, rather erratic flight. They feed largely on the young of other birds, and in attacking weaver-birds (Ploceidae) frequently hang head downwards with flapping wings. They are also fond of the fruits of the Oil Palm *Elaeis guineensis*. The term ' harrier-hawks ' is also applied to certain Neotropical Falconidae (see FALCON).

True Kites and Fish Eagles. The Milvinae are a large and varied subfamily of cosmopolitan distribution, containing the genera *Milvus*, *Lopho-ictinia*, *Hamirostra*, *Haliaetus*, *Ichthyophaga*, *Haliastur*, *Rostrhamus*, *Harpagus*, and *Ictinia*. The Black Kite *Milvus migrans*, in its many races, is one of the commonest and most obvious birds-of-prey in the warmer parts of the Old World, scavenging in thousands in towns and villages of the East. It is migratory throughout its range to a greater or lesser extent, and decidedly gregarious on migration. However, it was apparently the Red Kite *M. milvus* that was formerly a common scavenger in London.

Haliaetus and *Ichthyophaga* are two genera of large

or very large birds-of-prey living largely on fish. *Haliaetus*, comprising the fish eagles and sea eagles, is nearly cosmopolitan in distribution and contains some of the largest and finest of all birds-of-prey, among them the European Sea Eagle *H. albicilla*, the American Bald Eagle *H. leucocephalus*, Steller's Sea Eagle *H. pelagicus* of north-eastern Asia and the Fish Eagle *Haliaetus* (' *Cuncuma* ') *vocifer* of tropical Africa. The fishing eagles *Ichthyophaga* spp. inhabit inland lakes, rivers, and ponds in southern Asia and live on fish amongst other food. *Haliastur* is a genus of two species, inhabiting India, the Far East, and Australia, and in places very common ; the Brahminy Kite *H. indus*, regarded as sacred in India, inhabits swampy areas, and lives on frogs and offal.

The American genera *Rostrhamus*, *Harpagus*, and *Ictinia* are rather unlike the Old World kites in their general habits. The Everglade Kite *R. sociabilis* breeds in colonies and feeds exclusively on snails, which it extracts from the shell with the long point of its upper mandible. *Rostrhamus* (' *Helicolestes* ') *hamatus* also has a remarkably long and sickle-shaped bill. The genus *Ictinia* contains small grey kites, in appearance very unlike the typical *Milvus* spp. of Europe and Asia ; they live in open country, feed largely on insects, spend a great deal of time on the wing, and are capable of remarkable aerial evolutions ; they are migratory and tend to be gregarious on migration.

Honey-buzzards. The subfamily Perninae contains a variety of genera difficult to relate to others—*Leptodon*, *Chondohierax*, and *Elanoides* in America, *Pernis* and *Aviceda* in Europe, Asia, and Africa, and *Henicopernis* in New Guinea and nearby islands. The Honey-buzzard *Pernis apivorus* of Europe and Asia is a medium-sized buzzard-like bird which feeds chiefly on the grubs and honey in bees' and wasps' nests. It is a migrant, moving south from Europe in numbers to Africa, and from northern Asia to India and farther east. The Swallow-tailed Kite *Elanoides forficatus* of America (not to be confused with the African bird of the same English name, mentioned below) is a very beautiful bird, with black back, tail, and wings, the rest of the plumage being white ; it has remarkable powers of flight, and on account of its beauty has been much persecuted and reduced in numbers. The so-called cuckoo-falcons *Aviceda* spp. are widespread in Africa, India, and the Far East, one reaching Australia. Superficially rather like sparrowhawks, but distinguished by having two notches on the upper mandible, they are crested and generally conspicuously patterned in plumage ; the Black Baza *A. leuphotes* of north-eastern India and Malaysia is a very striking black-and-white bird, while other members of the genus are grey or brown above and often handsomely barred below. They are generally insectivorous, and in most parts of their range rather rare. They were formerly placed close to *Harpagus*, to which they have certain similarities.

White-tailed Kites. The Elaninae are a nearly cosmopolitan subfamily of small or very small birds-of-prey, inhabiting open country. *Elanus* spp. occur in America and the warmer parts of Europe, southern Asia, Africa, and Australia ; examples are theWhite-tailed Kite *E. leucurus* of America and the Black-shouldered Kite *E. caeruleus* widespread in the Old World. All members of the genus are small grey-and-white hawks, superficially like falcons, with black markings at the fore edge of the wing. They are attractive and useful birds, perching constantly on telegraph posts or tall trees, dropping on insects and small mammals in the grass. They can hover very gracefully, like the Kestrel.

The other two members of the subfamily are very small and beautiful birds-of-prey in monotypic genera, the Pearl Kite *Gampsonyx swainsoni* of America and the Swallow-tailed Kite *Chelictinia riocourii* of northern tropical Africa. The Pearl Kite is one of the smallest birds-of-prey, and is blackish above, with rufous on head and back, and white below ; it has well developed powder-down tracts. *Chelictinia* is an exquisitely graceful little bird with swallow-like forked tail, grey and white plumage, and a flight so buoyant that it resembles a tern *Sterna* sp. rather than a bird-of-prey. It is gregarious, migratory, and breeds in small colonies, sometimes associated with larger birds-of-prey; it feeds on insects.

Bat-hawk. The subfamily Machaerhamphinae contains a single species, the Bat-hawk *Machaerhamphus alcinus*, which inhabits Africa and parts of the Far East and has the remarkable habit of catching bats as they emerge from caves or buildings at dusk ; this prey is commonly swallowed in flight. In general appearance like a large falcon, it has a wide gape and very large eyes adapted to its habits ; it flies extremely swiftly, looking up, down, and sideways when hunting. It requires an open space such as a large pool in a river, a station platform, or an open lawn to be successful, and in addition to bats it eats swallows and martins (Hirundinidae) ; it spends the day in shady trees, and it is a rare bird, solitary in habit, throughout its range.

Osprey. The Pandioninae (or Pandionidae) comprise only the Osprey *Pandion haliaetus*, a bird of almost cosmopolitan distribution, absent only from South America as a breeding species but occurring even there on migration. It feeds exclusively on fish, catching them with a tremendous headlong

dive in which it often completely submerges, throwing its feet forward at the last moment before entering the water so as to grasp the prey. The feet are specially adapted, with a spiny rough surface, for holding such prey. Where it is common it breeds in colonies, notably on the coasts of North America (where it is known as the ' Fish-hawk ') and northeast Africa. It is commoner on sea coasts but occurs also on inland lakes. It is frequently robbed of its prey by eagles of the genus *Haliaetus*.

See Plates 2a, 9a b, 34a, 45a, 48a (phot.).

L.H.B.

Amadon, D. & Brown, L. H. (in prep.). Handbook of the World's Birds of Prey. London.
Bent. A. C. 1937. Life histories of North American birds of prey. Part I. U.S. Natl. Mus. Bull. 167 : 1–409.
Broley, C. L. 1947. Migration and nesting of Florida Bald Eagles. Wilson Bull. 59 : 3–20.
Brown, L. 1955. Eagles. London.
Brown, L. H. 1952, 1953, 1955. On the biology of the large birds of prey of the Embu District, Kenya Colony. Ibis 94 : 577–620 ; 95 : 74–114 ; 97 : 38–65, 183–221.
Brown, L. H. 1960. The African Fish Eagle *Haliaetus vocifer* especially in the Kavirondo Gulf. Ibis 102 : 285–297.
Brüll, H. 1937. Das Leben deutscher Greifvögel. Jena.
Compton, L. V. 1938. The pterylosis of the Falconiformes with special reference to the taxonomic position of the Osprey. Univ. Calif. Publ. Zool. 42, no. 3.
Craighead, J. J. & Craighead, F. C. 1956. Hawks, Owls and Wildlife. Harrisburg, Pa.
Gordon, S. 1955. The Golden Eagle. London.
Herrick, F. H. 1934. The American Eagle. New York.
Holstein, V. 1942. Duehøgen, *Astur gentilis dubius* (Sparrman). Biol. Stud. Danske Rovfugle 1 (English summary). Copenhagen.
May, J. B. 1935. The Hawks of North America. New York.
Moreau, R. E. 1945. On the Bateleur, especially at the nest. Ibis 87 : 224–249.
Rowe, E. G. 1947. The breeding biology of *Aquila verreauxi* Lesson. Ibis 89 : 387–410, 576–606.
Swann, H. K. 1924–45 (ed. Wetmore, A.). Monograph of the Birds of Prey (Order Accipitres). 2 vols (1930, 1945). London. (Coloured plates.)
Sievert, H. 1933. Die Brutbiologie des Hühnerhabichts. J. Orn. 81 : 44–94.
Sievert, H. 1941. Zur Brutbiologie des Fischadlers (*Pandion h. haliaetus* (L.)). J. Orn. suppl. 3 : 145–193.
Stresemann, V. & E. 1960. Die Handschwingenmauser der Tagraubvögel. J. Orn. 101 : 373–403.
Thomson, A. L. 1958. The migrations of British hawks (Accipitridae) as shown by ringing results. Brit. Birds 51 : 85–93.

HAWK-EAGLE: substantive name of species of *Spizaetus*, *Hieraaetus*, and allied genera (Accipitrinae) —see HAWK.

HAWKING: synonymous with FALCONRY ; also used to describe the behaviour of a bird of any kind flying in search or pursuit of prey.

HEAD: see TOPOGRAPHY; also BILL

HEADING: the direction in which a bird is flying

through the air, as distinct (in a wind) from its 'track' relative to the earth's surface (see MIGRATION ; TRACK).

HEARING AND BALANCE: senses here treated together because in both cases the sensory apparatus is in the ear.

Ear. The avian ear conforms to the general plan of terrestrial vertebrates in being divisible into outer, middle, and inner parts. The outer ear is generally a short simple feather-covered tube (meatus) leading from the exterior to the eardrum, lacking the pinna characteristic of mammals and situated just behind the angle of the jaw. In some birds, e.g. vultures (Aegypiinae) and the Ostrich *Struthio camelus*, the feather covering is lacking and the external opening is exposed. In owls (Strigiformes) the meatus is usually enlarged and considerably complicated, the structure often including a well developed operculum or concha (on the anterior margin) that lies over the orifice but can be erected ; moreover, the left and right sides may differ (Pycraft 1898). In some of the Scolopacidae the external opening is below instead of behind the orbit (Pycraft 1908).

The middle ear is an air-filled cavity derived from the spiracular gill-cleft and communicating with the pharynx by the Eustachian tube. Sound energy is transmitted across it from the eardrum to the fenestra ovalis of the inner ear by the columella, a rod composed partly of bone and partly of cartilage and held in position by a number of radial processes. The bony end of the columella is continuous with the 'footplate' that almost fills the fenestra ovalis, to the margin of which it is attached by a flexible but impervious annular ligament.

The upper part of the inner ear (membranous labyrinth) consists of the utricle and semicircular canals, which are exclusively concerned with the appreciation of the orientation and acceleration of the head in space. The lower part consists of sacculus, cochlea, and lagena. Of these, the sacculus probably and the lagena possibly are also exclusively concerned with orientation. The auditory part is the cochlea, which resembles that of mammals in the number and general arrangement of its parts but is proportionately smaller and apparently simpler and less spacious in design. It is straight or slightly curved instead of being coiled in a tight spiral. Corti's organ is the receptive part of the cochlea, consisting of the basilar membrane, hair cells, and tectorial membrane ; it is much shorter and somewhat broader than in mammals, and it lacks the rods of Corti that are characteristic of the latter. The differences are consistent with the shorter auditory spectrum and the quicker rate of response in birds, as compared with

mammals, that has been inferred on other grounds. See also DEVELOPMENT, POST-EMBRYONIC.

Hearing. Birds closely approach man in the precision of all the auditory functions that have been measured, e.g. absolute sensitivity at the optimum frequency, pitch discrimination, ability to locate a source of sound. It is probable, however, that the range of frequencies over which birds have a useful sensitivity is generally less than the human range by one or two octaves at each end. Possible exceptions are the parrots (Psittacidae) and owls, with a sensitivity at the high-frequency end of the spectrum that may equal man's. All attempts to demonstrate ultra-sonic sensitivity in birds have been unsuccessful, and it is noteworthy that those birds which have been shown to employ an echo-location system resembling in principle that of bats (see ECHO-LOCATION) use frequencies that, unlike bats' signals, are well within the human auditory range. The practical disadvantages of employing such relatively low frequencies for echo-location are so considerable as to suggest that the bird's ear is incapable of being readily modified in the direction of increasing sensitivity to ultra-sonic frequencies. The frequently alleged auditory sensitivity of birds to very low frequencies, e.g. from distant explosions, has been explained as due to the presence in the legs of very sensitive receptors (corpuscles of Herbst), which might be excited in a standing bird either by earth-borne waves or by infra-sonic waves of large amplitude in the air (see TOUCH). Although more limited in its frequency range than the human ear, the bird's ear is probably very substantially faster in its response, and birds are capable of recognising as distinct sounds some which succeed each other so rapidly that to the human ear they are inextricably fused.

A high speed of response and a high differential sensitivity to loudness are properties that must be assumed in order to account for the ability of birds to locate a sound source in the horizontal plane with an accuracy at least equal to man's, although their external ear-openings are much closer together than his. Marler has shown that the same physical characteristics make a sound difficult of location for both birds and man, which suggests that the mechanism of location is the same in both. Pumphrey has pointed out that, in theory, the asymmetry of the external ears of owls could permit these birds to make rapid assessments of the direction of sound sources not in the horizontal plane.

See also SINGING.

Balance. The parts of a bird's labyrinth concerned with balance differ structurally in no essential way from those of other vertebrates and there is no reason to suppose a difference in function. The upper part of the labyrinth consists of devices for detecting angular (semi-circular canals) and rectilinear (utricle and probably sacculus) accelerations of the head. Information about them, fed into the vestibular nucleus, results in appropriate 'instructions' to (in a bird in flight) the muscles actuating wings and tail, movements of which promptly counteract any tendency to roll, pitch, yaw, or stall detected by the labyrinth (see FLIGHT ; NERVOUS SYSTEM). The whole arrangement is clearly a feedback circuit, although much complicated by postural reflexes regulating the position of the head in relation to the body. Like every other feed-back circuit, its efficacy depends on its rate of response (time constant) being appropriate to the rate of change of the forces to which it has to respond. No information is available for birds, but the stability maintained by a hovering Kestrel *Falco tinnunculus* in a gusty wind, and the speed with which the tail feathers continually change their position, do suggest that the time constant is very short—shorter perhaps than in any mammal of comparable size.   R.J.P.

Marler, P. 1955. Characteristics of some animal calls. Nature 176 : 6–8.
Portmann, A. 1961. Sensory organs : equilibration. *In* Marshall, A. J. (ed.). Biology and Comparative Physiology of Birds vol. 2. New York and London.
Pumphrey, R. J. 1948. The sense organs of birds. Ibis 90 : 171–199.
Pumphrey, R. J. 1961. Sensory organs : hearing. *In* Marshall, A. J. (ed.). Biology and Comparative Physiology of Birds vol. 2. New York and London.
Pycraft, W. P. 1898. A contribution towards our knowledge of the morphology of owls. Trans. Linn. Soc. 7 : 223–275.
Pycraft, W. P. 1908. On the position of the ear in the Woodcock (*Scolopax rusticola*). Ibis (9th. ser.) 2 : 551–558.
Retzius, G. 1884. Das Gehörorgan der Wirbelthiere. Stockholm.
Schwartzkopf, J. 1955. Schallsinnesorgane, ihre Funktion und biologische Bedeutung bei Vögeln. Acta XI Congr. Internat. Orn., Basel 1954 : 189–208.
Schwartzkopf, J. & Winter, P. 1960. Zur Anatomie der Vogel-Cochlea unter naturlichen Bedingungen. Biol. Zbl. 79 : 607–625.
Schwartzkopf, J. 1963. Morphological and physiological properties of the auditory system in birds. Proc. XIII Internat. Orn. Congr., Ithaca, N.Y., 1962 : 1059–1068.

HEART : in birds, lies in the median plane of the thoracic cavity and serves the usual purpose of a pump maintaining the circulation (see VASCULAR SYSTEM ; also DEVELOPMENT, EMBRYONIC).

It is essentially a muscular (myocardial) tube, covered externally by a serous membrane (epicardium) and lined by another (endocardium). It lies within a serous cavity, the pericardium. The heart muscle fibres are striated (see MUSCULATURE), and

are intrinsically endowed with the property of rhythmical contraction so that heart-beats may continue independently of external stimuli.

As in mammals, there are four essential chambers (two atria—formerly often called 'auricles'—and two ventricles) in the avian heart, and the circulation of the blood through the lungs is independent of that round the body. Blood passes through the heart in the following sequence : systemic veins—right atrium—right ventricle—pulmonary artery—lungs —pulmonary vein—left atrium—left ventricle— systemic arteries (see Fig.; also Fig. under VASCULAR SYSTEM).

Atria. In 'ratite' birds the sinus venosus—a chamber formed at the confluence of the main veins entering the heart—persists in an undivided condition and its oval opening into the right atrium is guarded by a pair of sinu-atrial membranous valves (see Fig., inset C). In, e.g., crows (Corvidae), finches (Fringillidae), and the domestic fowl a horizontal septum separates the opening of the left anterior vena cava (see VASCULAR SYSTEM) from the remainder of the sinus ; the posterior vena cava opens immediately cranial to this septum, and the right anterior vena cava still further anterior ; the left cusp of the S-A (sinu-atrial) valve is mainly united with the atrial septum, while the right cusp (equivalent to the Thesbian valve of mammals) shows some reduction (see Fig., inset A). In most birds each vein has its own independent opening, the right anterior vena cava being separated from the posterior vena cava by a transverse ridge ; in the region of this ridge the left cusp of the S-A valve is well developed, while the right cusp becomes progressively smaller in the series Columbidae—Passeriformes—Falconiformes (see Fig., inset B).

Two pulmonary veins unite to enter the left atrium through an opening guarded by a single membranous valve (much reduced in passerines) passing across the atrial wall from the atrial septum towards the atrio-ventricular opening, thus delimiting the right caudal angle of the left atrium as a separate chamber containing the opening of the pulmonary vein. The atrial septum is very thin ; in passerines and storks (Ciconiidae) it is quite transparent.

Ventricles. The left atrio-ventricular orifice is guarded by a membranous valve consisting of a septal and a marginal cusp, the free edge of each cusp being anchored to papillary muscles by chordae tendineae. The septal cusp of the right atrio-ventricular orifice, however, has been absorbed into the ventricular septum to form the cranial portion of it, the pars membranacea septi. Further, the marginal cusp is not membranous but muscular—

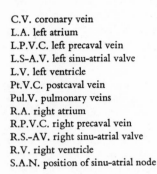

C.V. coronary vein
L.A. left atrium
L.P.V.C. left precaval vein
L.S-A.V. left sinu-atrial valve
L.V. left ventricle
Pt.V.C. postcaval vein
Pul.V. pulmonary veins
R.A. right atrium
R.P.V.C. right precaval vein
R.S.-AV. right sinu-atrial valve
R.V. right ventricle
S.A.N. position of sinu-atrial node

Dorsal view of the heart of a bird (e.g. *Gallus*) to show the entry of the great veins (arteries omitted for sake of clearness). Insets (semi-diagrammatic and not to scale) :

A. The area outlined by the dotted parallelogram in the main figure excised and turned over to the right to show the interior surface. The valvular arrangement shown here is found in e.g. Corvidae, Fringillidae, and *Gallus*.

B. Similar to inset A. This figure illustrates the condition found in most birds, where each vena cava has its own separate valved opening into the right atrium.

C. Similar to inset A. This illustrates the primitive, undivided sinus venosus as in ' ratites '. *E. T. B. Francis*

formed mainly by an inflexion of the ventricular wall.

The inner surface of each ventricle is corrugated, due to the presence of muscular bands—trabeculae carneae. The vessel leading from the right ventricle is the pulmonary arch, and that from the left the carotico-systemic arch (see VASCULAR SYSTEM).

Myocardium. The muscular walls of the several chambers vary in thickness and density—the atria being thin-walled, the right ventricle intermediate, and the left ventricle thick and dense. These walls have their own blood supply from a pair of coronary arteries arising from the base of the aorta, the right coronary artery being the larger.

Contraction. The autonomic rhythmicity of the heart achieves its highest rate in a mass of specialised muscle fibres situated beneath the epicardium near the sinu-atrial opening at the base of the right S-A valve ; this is the S-A node, and since the stimulus for contraction spreads thence throughout the muscle fibres of the atria, causing them to contract, it is known as the ' pace-maker '. The stimulus for contraction is conducted to a second

mass of nodal tissue situated at the dorsal and caudal end of the atrial septum—the A-V (atrio-ventricular) node—either through the atrial muscle or at a faster rate through specialised fibres (Purkinje fibres) found in the atrial walls of many birds. From this node—the stimulus is conveyed by a bundle of specialised muscle fibres—the A-V bundle—which runs ventralwards embedded in the muscular ventricular septum to a point slightly below and to the right of the septal attachment of the right A-V valve. Here the bundle divides into right and left limbs, which pass on either side of the septum ; these in turn communicate with a network of Purkinje fibres that ramify beneath the endocardium of both ventricles and around the branches of the coronary arteries and veins, ultimately joining the ordinary ventricular muscle fibres and transmitting the stimulus to them, thus causing them to contract. Peculiar to birds is a ' recurrent branch ' which leaves the A-V bundle just before it bifurcates into right and left limbs, and enters the musculature of the right A-V valve, thus causing the valve to contract and close the orifice before the ventricles contract. By means of this specialised system the various chambers of the heart always contract in the right sequence for each contraction wave.

Although autonomic in action, the heart-rate can be influenced by the vagus nerve ; stimulation of the nerve tends to slow the heart, and blocking or section of the nerve to accelerate it. The heart-rate of birds is very high and may vary from say 60–70 beats per minute in the Ostrich *Struthio camelus* and 93 per minute in the male Turkey *Meleagris gallopavo* to over 1000 per minute in the hummingbirds (Trochilidae). These figures are for the resting animal ; they are much higher in flight.

Heart Weight. The heart weight (H.W.) may be as much as 2·75 per cent of the body weight (B.W.) in some hummingbirds, but it is more usually in the region of 1·0–1·5 per cent amongst carinate birds. Leaving the smallest birds out of account, the 'heart ratio' $\left(\dfrac{H.W. \times 100}{B.W.} \right)$ shows a positive correlation with the speed of flight (or running) and the loudness of song or call (Löer).

As Hartman has recently shown, the ratio of heart size to body weight is of great significance to the maintenance of sustained flight ; birds with only a modest equipment of flight muscles can fly for long periods if they possess large hearts. Thus, although the tinamous (Tinamidae) have extremely large flight muscles (37–40 per cent of body weight) and powerful leg muscles, they are capable only of explosive flight over short distances since they possess relatively the smallest heart of all birds (0·19–0·25 per cent of body weight), making prolonged effort impossible. Compare this with the pigeons (Columbidae), in which the flight muscles are of about the same size as those of the tinamous (31–44 per cent), while the heart ratio is from 0·93–1·29 per cent.

Other factors affecting heart size are as follows. Sex : in general, males have heavier hearts than females. Altitude : individuals living at high altitudes tend to have larger hearts than those of the same species living at lower altitudes—e.g. the Common Ani *Crotophaga ani* and the Squirrel Cuckoo *Piaya cayana* from 4500 feet have larger hearts than those from sea level (P < 0·01). Latitude : more northerly specimens have larger hearts than more southerly ones. Seasons : a difference in heart size has been noted in certain Florida birds collected in spring compared with those in winter (P < 0·01).

E.T.B.F.

Hartman, F. A. 1961. Locomotor mechanisms of birds. Smiths. Misc. Coll. 143 (1) : 1–91.
Löer, F. 1911. Vergleichende Untersuchungen über die Maase und Proportionalgewicht des Vogelherzens. Pflüg. Arch. ges. Physiol. 140 : 293–324.

Simons, J. R. 1960. The blood-vascular system. *In* Marshall, A. J. (ed.). Biology and Comparative Physiology of Birds vol. 1. New York and London.

HEATH FOWL : antique term (in British game laws) for Black Grouse *Lyrurus tetrix*—contrasted with 'Moor Fowl' for Red Grouse *Lagopus scoticus* (see GROUSE).

HEATH HEN : name of the now extinct nominate· race of the Greater Prairie Chicken *Tympanuchus cupido* (see GROUSE ; EXTINCT BIRDS).

HEAT REGULATION : the process by which correct body temperature is maintained ; also called 'thermoregulation'.

Birds belong to the group of animals called 'homoiothermal' (or 'warm-blooded'). The difference between these and 'poikilothermal' ('cold-blooded') animals is that they are able to maintain the body cavity and brain at a nearly constant temperature (called the body temperature) by internal physiological mechanisms, although the temperature of the limbs is variable. Cold-blooded animals, which in some situations are by no means cold, can regulate their temperature only by suitable behaviour, e.g. basking in the sun ; this may help some species to maintain a fairly constant temperature in periods when they are active, but, when inactive, they are at the mercy of the climate. Homoiotherms can also regulate their body temperature by appropriate behaviour.

Homoiothermy has evolved twice, once for mammals (or perhaps for their immediate reptilian ancestors) and once for birds and their ancestors. The physiology of heat regulation of mammals and of birds is remarkably similar and is a striking case of parallel evolution.

All warm-blooded animals have a comparatively high body temperature, in most circumstances above that of the atmosphere. Their heat production is many times that of cold-blooded animals of the same size. The body temperature is maintained both by regulation of the heat production and by heat dissipation. Heat is dissipated by conduction and convection to the air, by radiation to the surroundings, and by the evaporation of water. It is conserved by an insulating layer of hair, feathers, or subcutaneous fat.

The body temperature of all species of birds is about 106° F (41° C) when they are awake but inactive, being some 6° F above that of most mammals. In birds that sleep at night it is 2–3° F lower at night than in the day ; on the other hand, nocturnal birds have a higher body temperature at night. The temperature rises during periods of intense activity even in a cool environment and can exceed 110° F (43° C) in active birds. It is not adapted to habitat, being on an average no higher in tropical than in arctic species.

Hibernation is almost unknown in birds, but in California the Poor-will *Phalaenoptilus nuttallii* sometimes hibernates. Its body temperature under these conditions is close to air temperature. Hummingbirds (Trochilidae), like bats, often cool at night but warm again in the early morning. Fledgling Swifts *Apus apus* behave in the same way when starved (see TORPIDITY).

Most birds rely mainly on their feathers for conservation of heat, but in such birds as penguins (Spheniscidae), marine ducks (Anatidae), and petrels (Procellariiformes), subcutaneous fat is also important. Feathers insulate by stabilising a layer of air next to the skin, for still air is a poor conductor of heat. The dispersal of this still air by the wind is prevented by the ends of the contour feathers curving over the down. The amount of insulation depends on the depth of feathering and it can be increased by fluffing out the feathers, especially when a bird is standing or sitting still. The secretion of the preen gland makes the feathers waterproof, thereby preserving the insulation in rain, and for aquatic birds during swimming (see OIL GLAND ; and FEATHER MAINTENANCE). Adaptation of a species to its native climate is probably mainly in its insulation. There is also seasonal adaptation ; summer plumage is lighter than winter plumage, and in those birds that moult only once a year the plumage becomes thinner in summer by attrition (see MOULT).

Heat can also be conserved by the circulation. For example, in cold conditions the circulation of the legs can be adjusted so that very little heat is conducted down them ; in consequence they dissipate little heat and become cold, and some arctic birds are adapted to tolerate leg temperatures near freezing point. On the other hand, in warm weather the circulation is adjusted to conduct the maximum amount of heat down the legs and, since the legs of most species are unfeathered, they are able to dissipate heat efficiently.

When the environmental temperature falls, the heat production of birds rises. This heat is produced by the metabolism of absorbed nutrients, of glycogen, and of the fat reserves (see METABOLISM). In very cold conditions the body temperature may fall in spite of the rise in heat production. If this fall proceeds beyond a certain point, heat production is progressively reduced and finally the bird will die of cold. In warm conditions there is an environmental temperature at which the heat production is minimal, and this is called the critical temperature ;

it is low in well insulated birds. At very high environmental temperatures the heat production rises, and this rise works against heat regulation. To continue producing enough heat to keep warm in the cold, a bird must have enough to eat ; in small birds even a few hours starvation can impair resistance to cold, and the high mortality of birds in cold winters is due to starvation more than to cold itself.

When the environmental temperature is close to body temperature, a bird cannot dissipate all its heat production by radiation and convection. It must evaporate water to keep itself cool. Birds, unlike most mammals, do not have sweat glands (see SKIN). The small amount of water vapour diffused through the skin (insensible perspiration) cannot be increased in heat stress. The increase must, therefore, come from the respiratory passages by rapid panting ; the rate can reach as much as 300 respirations per minute in domestic hens. When the atmosphere is humid, less water can be evaporated than when it is dry. The lack of sweating in birds is the only important difference between their heat regulation and that of the mammals. Nevertheless, many mammals also have to rely mainly on panting to evaporate moisture because their sweating is poorly developed. See also RESPIRATORY SYSTEM.

Birds are skilled in the regulation of body temperature by suitable behaviour. For instance, many species roost in sheltered places (see ROOSTING), and migration is in part an evasion of cold climates, although mainly related to food supply. It is in the care of the young that behavioural heat regulation is most highly developed. The control of egg temperature during incubation is in some species as exact as the control of body temperature in the adult. This temperature is below the adult body temperature and to some extent adapted to the climate and the type of nest—penguins, for instance, have a lower egg temperature than domestic fowls. Control is achieved by heat supplied by the incubating adult and retained by the insulation of the nest. The eggs are frequently moved and turned to ensure that none are permanently in a cool or warm spot. To facilitate heat transfer most species develop a bare patch on the breast at incubation time. The Mallee-fowl *Leipoa ocellata* and a few other species provide the heat for incubation by the fermentation of a pile of litter (see MEGAPODE).

Young birds that are precocial, with down on hatching, have a well developed system of heat regulation, although they usually need some brooding. The altricial birds, naked at hatching, have no heat regulation at this stage ; they are entirely dependent on the parents to keep them at a fairly constant temperature, and their heat regulation begins to develop only when the feathers appear. At hatching, the body temperature of both classes of young is a few degrees below that of the parents ; it rises to the adult value during the first few weeks of life (see also DEVELOPMENT, POSTEMBRYONIC).

J.C.D.H.

Howell, T. R. & Bartholemew, G. A. 1962. Temperature regulation in the Sooty Tern *Sterna fuscata*. Ibis 104 : 98–105. (References to earlier papers by the same authors on other species.)

Hutchinson, J. C. D. 1954. *In* Hammond, J. (ed.). Progress in the Physiology of Farm Animals vol. 1. London.

King, J. R. & Farner, D. S. 1961. Energy metabolism, thermoregulation, and body temperature. *In* Marshall, A. J. (ed.). Biology and Comparative Physiology of Birds vol. 2. New York and London.

HEDGESPARROW : name (misnomer), alternatively ' Dunnock ', of *Prunella modularis* (see ACCENTOR).

HEEL PAD : a callosity behind the intertarsal joint in nestlings of some piciform and other birds (see LEG).

HELIORNITHES ; HELIORNITHIDAE : see under GRUIFORMES ; and FINFOOT

HELL-DIVER : popular American name for the Pied-billed Grebe *Podilymbus podiceps* (see GREBE).

HELMET : an ornament, usually composed of feathers, on the top of the head, as in helmet-shrikes (Prionopinae)—compare CASQUE.

HELMETBIRD : *Aerocharis prevostii* (see VANGA).

HELMETCREST : *Oxypogon guerinii* (for family see HUMMINGBIRD).

HELMET-SHRIKE : substantive name of species of Prionopinae ; in the plural, general term for the subfamily (family of some authors)—see SHRIKE.

HEMIPODE : alternative substantive name of species of Turnicidae and Pedionomidae, and also used as a general term for the suborder Turnices (see BUTTONQUAIL ; PLAINS-WANDERER).

HEMIPROCNIDAE : see APODIFORMES ; and SWIFT

HEN : a female bird ; applied without qualification to the female of the domestic fowl (compare COCK). Special terms apply to the females of some species, e.g. PEN, GREYHEN, PEAHEN, REEVE. The names of certain species have also a special use as terms for the female, e.g. DUCK, GOOSE, FALCON ; but note that in North America the female of any duck species is the ' hen '.

HERALDIC BIRDS : avian symbols used as charges in armorial bearings. In heraldry the animals fall into roughly the same classes as in zoology, but with the addition of heraldic monsters. The four main classes are beasts, monsters, fishes, and birds. Most books on heraldry deal fairly fully with beasts ; monsters can be studied in the many excellent beastiaries and books of monsters ; Thomas Moule's *Heraldry of Fish* (1842) is the last word on that subject ; but birds have been neglected. It is, therefore, particularly pleasant to be able to remedy here, if only in some slight measure, this deficiency.

Heraldry is a form of hereditary personal symbolism in which the basic medium for the display of the devices used is the shield. It is European in conception and application, just post-Conquest in time of origin and, to a great extent, dependent for much of its early symbolism and many of its conventions on the Crusades, jousts, and tournaments. Two symbols are used, the arms borne upon the shield and the crest. The crest is a device which was originally modelled on top of the helmet and which, together with the mantling which flows from it, is often shown in pictorial representations of arms. That heraldry was from its inception at once utilitarian and also pictorial and decorative accounts for the fact that crests are often absurdly impracticable and could never have been in actual use, but only engraved upon seals and otherwise used pictorially.

It is not surprising that birds are early to be found in heraldic symbolism, when it is considered how frequently they appear in more ancient symbolisms. The eagle on the standard of a Roman legion is well known ; perhaps less familiar in this regard is the owl, which in a most heraldic form graced, inter alios locos, the reverse of an Athenian tetradrachmon minted about the time of the Persian Wars.

In Christian symbolism the dove holds pride of place as a symbol of the Holy Spirit and His attributes of peace (see also ART, BIRDS IN). If only for this reason, it has always been a favourite heraldic charge, whilst the pelican as a type of Christ is popular in the heraldry of ecclesiastics. In early heraldry she is often drawn more like an eagle, and is almost invariably depicted ' in her piety ', i.e. on a nest and pecking her breast to feed her young with her own blood. The origin of this fable of self-wounding may lie in the habit of resting the pouched bill upon the breast. A well known example of the pelican in heraldry occurs in the arms of Richard Foxe, Bishop of Winchester, *Azure a Pelican wings elevated and addorsed Or vulning herself proper*. Foxe, who died in 1528, founded Corpus Christi College, Oxford, in 1515, and his arms still form part of the cumbersome coat borne by his foundation.

An early arrival in the heraldic aviary was the

martlet (see also SHAKESPEARE'S BIRDS). This bird has always been shown *sans* legs and looking perhaps rather more like a fat swallow than anything else. Indeed, to preserve the obvious pun, it is described as an *hirondelle* (swallow) in the arms of Arundell (*Sable six hirondelles 3, 2, and 1 Argent*) : variants of these arms are used by both the East Sussex and West Sussex County Councils. Most heraldic writers state that 'martlet' is a synonym for 'martin', a bird which has such short legs that it relies upon them but little, and is therefore always depicted heraldically without legs, albeit it is almost invariably shown 'close' and not in flight. Other writers assert that it represents a swift, for these birds are found in great numbers in the Holy Land and crusaders may have come to associate these elegant yet sturdy (and apparently legless) creatures with their own exploits in the Near East and adopted them as symbols of speed and endurance, as well as a reminder to others that the bearers had fought for the Faith. It is amusing to note that the martlet is used to denote a fourth son in heraldry. The story is that the first son inherited, the second became a soldier, and the third entered the church ; but for the fourth there was nothing, so he flew away to seek his fortune. That the martlet is of great antiquity in heraldry is borne out by its presence in a great many of the coats depicted in 'Glover's Roll' (ca. 1255).

It was a common mediaeval practice to show in arms not only military but also sporting symbols. Thus one finds hunting horns, greyhounds, and, of course, hawks. These last are usually shown belled and jessed, and sometimes hooded. The hawk is drawn in a somewhat stylised way and indifferently called a 'hawk' or 'falcon', except where a pun is required or where for some special reason a particular species was chosen for a charge. Then the hawk may be found looking much like any other, but blazoned a 'goss-hawk', 'sparrowhawk', 'gerfalcon', 'marlion', or 'hobbey'. See also FALCONRY.

The birds so far mentioned are to be found in heraldry principally owing to the qualities which they symbolise. Very many other kinds of bird grace armorial bearings, but principally because they pun on the name of the bearer of the arms. There is no need to mention what birds are to be found in the arms of Larkins, Bustard, Sparrow, Hancock, Cobbe, and Storke, to mention but a few.

Whilst it is often apparent why a certain bird appears in a certain coat of arms, as the pheasant which is found in the crest of the Worshipful Company of Cooks, this is not always the case. In 1550 one William Strickland, of Yorkshire, was granted arms and a crest, the latter consisting of *A Turkey Cock Argent beaked and legged Sable combed and*

FIG 1. Pelican ; in the arms of Richard Foxe (as Bishop of Bath and Wells), from College of Arms Ms. L. 10.

FIG 2. Turkey ; an early drawing in the records of the College of Arms.

wattled Gules. The reason for this grant is that William Strickland was said to have introduced turkeys into England from North America ; the sketch which is part of the docquet of this grant must therefore be one of the first ever made of a turkey in Britain—indeed, one look at the sketch lends support to this view ! The arms of the Worshipful Company of Musicians are full of royal emblems, and this might suggest that the swan in the arms is a royal swan ; however, the reason for its appearance is almost certainly an allusion to the legend that the soul of Apollo, the god of music, passed into a swan when it was at the point of death, thus enabling the bird to sing a beautiful song before it died.

The swan deserves particular mention as it was the famous badge of the powerful family of Bohun, Earls of Hereford and Essex, and the crest of the Beauchamps, Earls of Warwick, and from these families it percolated through to many others. Why these and other families adopted the swan is uncertain. It has been suggested that the reason is to be found in the fact that they can all trace descent from the house of Boulogne, connected in legend with the Knight of the Swan. This theory is carefully examined by A. R. Wagner in his essay 'The Swan Badge and the Swan Knight' (*Archaeologia* 97 : 127). It is interesting to consider how legend and romance were mirrored in an heraldic charge which, because it was adopted by one or two powerful families, soon found its way into the heraldry of smaller families, as representing either consanguinity with, or feudal dependence upon, these early magnates.

Although birds are seen to best advantage as crests and charges in arms they are also used as supporters. It is a privilege of peers and certain grades of knight to have supporters on either side of the shield. Although a bird is a rather unsteady supporter, compared with a beast or a human being, it is becoming increasingly popular.

Whilst it would probably not be correct to state that birds as heraldic charges have never been so popular as they are today, yet one can truly say that during the past sixty years more new species of birds have been admitted to the heraldic aviary than in the preceding six hundred years.

When the Zoological Society of London was granted arms in 1959, it was desired to represent different classes of animal. Therefore, to the principal charge of a lion was added a crest consisting of an osprey with a fish in its talons—as suggested by the editor of the present work and effected by the writer of this article.   J.P.B.-L.

HERBST'S CORPUSCLES : see TOUCH

HEREDITY : see GENETICS

HERMIT : substantive name of *Glaucis hirsuta*, *Phaethornis* spp., and sometimes *Threnetes* spp. (see HUMMINGBIRD).

HERN ; HERNSHAW : obsolete or dialect names, in Britain, for the Heron *Ardea cinerea*—the latter variously spelt, including 'handsaw' in Shakespeare.

HERODIONES : see CICONIIFORMES

HERON : substantive name of most species of the Ardeinae, a subfamily of the Ardeidae (Ciconiiformes, suborder Ardeae) ; in Britain commonly used without qualification for the sole native species ; in the plural, general term for the Ardeinae and sometimes extended to cover the whole family. The substantive name 'egret' is used for some species. The other subfamily is the Botaurinae (see BITTERN). The 'Cochleariidae', sometimes treated as a separate (monotypic) family, are here merged with the

Ardeinae. Internal classification and scientific nomenclature follow the most recent critical revision (Bock 1956).

Herons are birds of from moderate to large size—up to 56 inches long, but bill and neck account for much of this dimension. Typically, the body is slim and the neck long. The legs are moderately or very long, with all four toes long and slender, and the tibia is partly bare ; there is no web, and the middle toe is pectinated. With a few exceptions, the bill is rather long, strong, straight, and pointed. The lores are bare. The tail is short and the wings broad ; the flight—with neck retracted and legs extended behind—is strong, although it may seem laboured. The carriage is upright in most species, and the neck is commonly retracted when the bird is at rest—but is instantly extended on alarm or in seizing prey, a swift movement to which the structure of the cervical vertebrae is adapted.

The plumage is loose in texture and simple in its colour pattern in some combination of grey, blue, greenish, purple, rufous, or white ; several species are entirely white. Many have long plumes on head, neck, breast, or back, but usually only in breeding dress. Apart from this and some changes in the colour of the 'soft parts' to be mentioned later, there are no conspicuous seasonal differences. The sexes are generally alike, but often with the colours more intense in the male. Only in some species are the immature birds strikingly different in appearance. On the other hand, several species are dimorphic or polymorphic and have different colour phases, of which some have been regarded as distinct species or are even now in doubt (see POLYMORPHISM). Patches of powder-down are characteristic of the plumage of herons, and the disintegrating material is used in preening to remove fish slime and oil (see PLUMAGE ; FEATHER MAINTENANCE). Two pairs of patches, on breast and rump, are found in all members of the family, but in the Ardeinae there is also an inguinal pair and a few species have others on the back.

Herons are adapted for wading, and most of them are found in the vicinity of water, usually rivers and lakes but also quiet bays of the sea. The food consists of fish and other forms of animal life, including insects in some cases. A characteristic method of feeding is for a solitary bird to stand motionless at the water's edge or in the shallows until the prey comes within striking distance—but the spear-like bill is commonly used to grasp, not to impale. The food is swallowed whole and pellets of undigested material are disgorged. Food may also be sought by more active wading, or by walking on marshy or even dry ground. Wading in quest of food may be a slow walk, or it may consist of quick dashes in various directions ; sometimes the bottom is stirred up with the feet, and sometimes the wings are held extended or are rapidly flicked open and closed again. The difference in method depends partly on species, but some use a variety. A particularly interesting method is commonly used by the Black Heron *Hydranassa ardesiaca* of Africa ; the bird stands motionless in the shallows, with bill directed downwards, while the wings are held extended in a forward position so that they form a canopy over the head. The tips of the wing feathers may be in the water, if the latter is deep enough, as some published photographs show. It is thought that the patch of shade constitutes a false refuge into which the fish are lured ; it has also been suggested that the bird's vision is helped by the cutting out of reflections from the surface in a bright light. The Reddish Egret *H. rufescens* of the New World, like some other species, also raises its wings when feeding ; but it does so in the course of a characteristic rapid dashing about, with sudden turns, in the shallows. Still another method is among those used by the short-legged species that can wade only in very shallow water ; thus, for example, the Green Heron *Butorides virescens* of America often dives for its food from a mangrove root or a floating log.

All herons are highly or mainly gregarious in the breeding season. Some remain so throughout the year, but others become solitary or at most ' semi-social ' when not breeding. Flocks may become dispersed when feeding, but they tend to reassemble for flight to communal roosts in trees. Some species, however, are largely nocturnal in their activity. The notes are mostly harsh croaking or ' yelping ' sounds, but a few exceptions will be mentioned later.

Sexual display performances are varied and elaborate ; they include aerial and non-aerial, vocal and non-vocal elements. Those of four North American species have recently been studied in detail by Meyerriecks (1960) ; those of a few other species were already well known. In many species the period of sexual display is marked by changes in the colour of the ' soft parts '—bill, buccal cavity, orbital skin, irides, bare lores, legs, and feet. The brighter colours last for only a short time in some cases and are poorly described in most textbooks (but see Palmer) ; they may fade even during the egg-laying period, but there can be a recrudescence if the first nest or clutch is destroyed. The change is usually from a yellowish to a reddish hue, less often to bluish or a shiny black. Thus, the iris of the Green Heron *Butorides virescens* turns from yellow to orange and its legs and feet from yellowish to brilliant coral-orange ; the distal part of the yellow

bill of some Old World subspecies of the Great (or ' Common ') Egret *Egretta alba* turns black ; and the proximal part of the bill of the Squacco Heron *Ardeola ralloides* turns from yellowish-green (distal part nearly black) to cobalt blue, the bare loral area changing from yellowish-green to a vivid emerald. There is experimental evidence that the process is, not surprisingly, under hormonal control (see ENDOCRINE SYSTEM). The colour change is due partly to the deposition of pigments (carotenoids and melanins (see COLOUR) ; and partly to increased vascularisation, particularly of the integument of the legs. Furthermore, the intensity of the reddish colour can be momentarily increased under the influence of some form of excitement or alarm, which apparently produces a flushing of blood-vessels near the surface ; this has been observed in the iris of the Green Heron, in the lores of the Snowy Egret *Egretta thula*, in the bill and legs of the Grey Heron *Ardea cinerea*, and in the legs of various species including the Cattle Egret *Ardeola ibis*.

Most herons nest in colonies ; these are sometimes of very large size and may include birds of several ardeine and other ciconiiform species. The nests are ordinarily platforms of sticks placed in trees, often at a considerable height. The 3–7 eggs are usually unmarked, the ground colour being white, buff, or pale blue. Both sexes incubate. The downy young are nidicolous and are cared for by both parents. The young are fed with regurgitated prey ; the old bird's bill is gripped crosswise by the chick and the food extruded sideways from between the mandibles.

The size and breeding habits of herons make them suitable for population studies in developed countries, where few colonies can be overlooked. In Britain a census of the breeding pairs of *Ardea cinerea* has been maintained for many years, whereby the fluctuations in numbers have been made apparent (Nicholson). Incidentally, herons do well in captivity and make good exhibits in zoological gardens.

The herons are a truly cosmopolitan group, represented in all the continents, and in Madagascar, New Zealand, and various oceanic islands. The majority of the species are tropical and subtropical, but a few extend throughout the North Temperate Zone. In temperate latitudes the birds tend to be migratory, although in Britain the native species is found throughout the year. In several species a dispersal before migration proper brings many of the birds as late summer visitors to localities well north of the breeding range.

Bock recognises 64 species in the subfamily ; these he places in 15 genera (all of which find mention in this article), tentatively grouped in three tribes—

Tigriornithini (tiger herons), Nycticoracini (night herons), and Ardeini (typical or 'day' herons).

Tiger Herons. The Tigriornithini are regarded as the most primitive group, nearest to the putative ancestral stock of the family. They have also been called 'tiger bitterns' because of some resemblances to the other subfamily ; relatively to typical herons, they are shorter in the leg and stouter in shape —moreover, they have booming calls. A barred pattern of plumage is characteristic. They are secretive birds and solitary nesters, usually building in trees.

The group has a relict distribution—wide but markedly discontinuous. There are four genera, of which three are monotypic. The genus *Tigrisoma* has three species, all in the Neotropical Region, the Lined (or Banded) Tiger Heron *T. lineatum* being an example. The White-crested Tiger Heron *Tigriornis leucolophus* is found in the forests of West Africa, and the New Guinea Tiger Heron *Zonerodius heliosylus* in the Papuan area. The Zigzag Heron *Zebrilus undulatus* is found in the Guianas and Brazil ; it is peculiar in its small size and in having quite a short bill, but little is known of its habits.

Night Herons. The Nycticoracini are herons of medium size and with nocturnal feeding habits. Compared with typical herons, they are short-legged, short-necked, and rather squat in shape—but still upright in carriage ; and the bill is shorter and heavier. The genus *Nycticorax* has an almost world-wide distribution. The Black-crowned Night Heron *N. nycticorax* is found from Canada to Tierra del Fuego and the Falkland Islands, also in Hawaii, and from southern Europe through Africa and southern Asia ; this range is continued by the Nankeen Night Heron *N. caledonicus* from the Philippines to Australia and Polynesia. The Black-crowned Night Heron is migratory in the northern parts of its breeding range ; it nests in low bushes or even reed-beds, as well as in trees. The other three species are American ; they include the Whistling Heron *N. sibilatrix* of southern tropical South America, which is unique in uttering a high-pitched whistle (and was formerly placed alone in a genus 'Syrigma').

The genus *Gorsachius* is confined to the Old World, with one species in tropical Africa and three in eastern Asia. They resemble the tiger herons in being solitary nesters and in booming after the manner of bitterns. The Magnificent Night Heron *G. magnificus* is confined to the mountains of Hainan Island and Fukien.

The Boat-billed Heron (or Boatbill) *Cochlearius cochlearius* differs markedly only in the peculiar bill, flattened into a broad scoop (about 3 inches long and 2 inches wide), with correlated changes in the skull. Such an obviously adaptive character does not seem to warrant more than generic separation. The bird stands some 20 inches high and is restricted to Middle America and northern South America. Wetmore (who adheres to separate familial status, 1960) states that boatbills roost and nest in trees and are mainly nocturnal. He has found them feeding in shallow water, scooping in their prey.

Typical Herons. The Ardeini are the well known day-feeding herons and egrets, a large and cosmopolitan group. Some of the genera show the greatest development of such characters as slim body, long neck, long slender bill, and long legs ; others are more compactly built, with relatively short neck and legs. Plumes are highly developed in the breeding plumage of all ; it seems probable that the specific differences in these serve as isolating mechanisms by facilitating recognition. They are gregarious birds and given to nesting in large mixed colonies comprising several species.

The Grey (or Common) Heron *Ardea cinerea* is widely distributed in the Palaearctic Region and breeds also in parts of Africa and in Madagascar. Closely related to it is the Great Blue Heron *A. herodias* of North America, the West Indies, and the Galápagos Islands ; and probably conspecific with this is the Great White Heron *A.* 'occidentalis' of Florida, which may be no more than a local population of a colour phase. The Purple Heron *A. purpurea*, widely distributed in the Old World, is exceptional in that it normally rests in reed-beds or marsh vegetation. Among the other species, the Goliath Heron *A. goliath* of tropical Africa is one of three forms notable for very large size.

The Little Egret *Egretta garzetta*, distributed from southern Europe to Australia, is a small heron of graceful build and pure white plumage ; it has a black bill, black legs, and yellow toes. It holds its head high on its long neck and steps daintily. In the breeding season the adults of both sexes have long plumes depending from the nape and elongating the scapulars ; these feathers, of which the barbs are long and free, are the 'aigrettes' of fashion (absurdly mistranslated 'osprey' in the feather trade). In some part of its range, such as eastern Africa, this species has colour phases ranging through various greys to almost black. Bigger—almost the size of a Grey Heron—is the Large White (or Great) Egret *Egretta* ('Casmerodius') *alba*, ranging from south-eastern Europe to Madagascar and New Zealand and from the United States to Patagonia ; there are several variants of its English name, of which the least happy is 'Great White Heron' (applicable to another species, as already noted), and in North

America it is called 'Common Egret' as well as 'Great Egret'. Among the other (and smaller) species in this genus are the Snowy Egret Egretta ('Leucophoyx') thula, confined to the New World, and the Reef Heron Egretta ('Demigretta') sacra, ranging from Burma to New Zealand ; the latter species is mainly of a dark slate colour, but pure white and inter-mediate phases occur.

The Squacco Heron Ardeola ralloides is a small, compactly built heron with relatively short legs, found in southern Europe and throughout Africa. The upper parts are buffish and the bird is incon-spicuous when perched, only to 'explode' into white when the wings are unfolded on taking off. There are several closely related species, including the Madagascar Squacco Heron A. idae (with all-white breeding plumage) and the Indian Pond Heron (or Paddy-bird) A. grayii. Congeners also include the Cattle Egret Ardeola ('Bubulcus') ibis—sometimes called the 'Buff-backed Heron' in books, but the name has no real currency and is only seasonally appropriate. The bird is mainly white but in breeding dress has pale buff plumes on crown, breast, and back. There may be some geographical or other variations, but the legs appear to be dark in immature birds, dull yellow in winter adults, becoming brighter and eventually reddish in the breeding season, the bill also becoming mostly red. The species is distributed from the Iberian Peninsula southwards to Madagascar and eastwards through central and southern Asia ; in recent years it has expanded this range by establishing itself first in South America and then in North America, and likewise in Australia (although there also artificially introduced). It is commonly to be seen in parties or flocks walking about among grazing cattle and feeding on insects disturbed by these ; it has a similar relation with large wild mammals where these exist, and the birds may often be seen perched on their backs—from elephants downwards.

The Green Heron Butorides virescens of subtropical North America and Middle America has already been mentioned. Races of the related Green-backed (or Little Green or Mangrove) Heron B. striatus are found through much of South America, tropical Africa, southern Asia, Australia, and Polynesia. It is a small, compact, short-legged species with a dark crest and greenish upper parts. The third member of the genus, B. sundevalli, is confined to the Galá-pagos Archipelago. The genus Hydranassa, of small to medium-sized herons, is also pantropical. It includes the Reddish Egret Hydranassa ('Dichroman-assa') rufescens and the Little Blue Heron Hydranassa ('Florida') caerulea, both of tropical and subtropical America, and the Black Heron Hydranassa ('Melano-phoyx') ardesiaca of tropical Africa. This last has bright orange toes ; its 'canopy feeding' habit has already been mentioned.

The Agami (or Chestnut-bellied Heron) Agamia agami is an aberrant species in a monotypic genus, and is found from southern Mexico to Brazil and Peru. Although its legs are short, the neck is very long ; the bill is long and thin. The plumage of the adult is brilliantly coloured—blue on the back, pale blue on the crown, neck, and scapular plumes, and bright chestnut below. The plumes on crown and back are particularly broad ; those on the back are, uniquely, sickle-shaped.

See Plates 18 and 20 (colour) ; 1, 21, 36, 40a (phot.). A.L.T.

Bock, W. J. 1956. A generic review of the family Ardeidae (Aves). Amer. Mus. Novit. no. 1779 : 1–49.

Lowe, F. A. 1954. The Heron. London.

Meyerreicks, A. J. 1960. Comparative breeding behaviour of four species of North American herons. Publ. Nuttall Orn. Club no. 2 : i–viii, 1–158.

Palmer, R. S. (ed.). 1962. Handbook of North American Birds vol. 1. New Haven and London. (Colour plates of seasonal changes in soft parts of some species.)

Percy, W. 1951. Three Studies in Bird Character. Bitterns, Herons and Water Rails (63 pp., 82 pls.). London.

Nicholson, E. M. 1928. Report on the 'British Birds' census of heronries, 1928. Brit. Birds 22 : 270–323 ; 334–372 (and subsequent reports by the same and other authors).

Rydzewski, W. 1956. The nomadic movements and migrations of the European Common Heron Ardea cinerea L. Ardea 44 : 71–188.

Schüz, E. 1927. Beitrag zur Kenntnis der Puderbildung bei den Vögeln. J. Orn. 75 : 86–224.

Verwey, J. 1930. Die Paarungsbiologie des Fischreihers. Zool. Jahrb., Abt. Allg. Zool. Physiol. 48 : 1–120.

Wetmore, A. 1960. A classification for the birds of the world. Smithsonian Misc. Coll. 139 (11) : 1–37. (For Cochlearius.)

HERPETOTHERINAE : see FALCON

HESPERORNITHIFORMES : order erected to include such fossil forms as Hesperornis, Hargeria, Enaliornis (provisional placing) and Baptornis (see FOSSIL BIRDS).

HETEROCHROISM : see PLUMAGE, ABNORMAL AND ABERRANT

Plate 21 · Preening

Large (or Great) Egret Egretta alba standing on its nest and preening under the wing (Hungary). Note also the nuptial plumes on the back, and the two small chicks. This heron species is widely distributed in tropical and subtropical parts of Old and New Worlds.
                                              Phot. Eric Hosking.

(See articles FEATHER MAINTENANCE ; HERON)

HETEROCOELOUS: term for a type of vertebra (see SKELETON).

HETERODACTYL: see under ZYGODACTYL

HETEROGYNISM: term introduced by Hellmayr for a situation in which the taxonomic characters distinguishing closely related species (often geographically replacing each other) are more strongly marked in the females than in the males.

HETEROSIS: see under HYBRID

HETEROZYGOUS: see GENETICS

HIBERNATION: spending the winter in a state of reduced animation. (The term is sometimes wrongly used, in foreign publications in English, as a synonym of 'wintering', i.e. living in a winter area reached by migration.) It is common in some classes of animals; but it is scarcely known to occur in birds, although formerly fabled to do so as a regular event. Some avian species nevertheless have the capacity to survive inclement conditions in a state of reduced animation and body temperature, usually for relatively short periods but for at least three months in the Poor-will *Phalaenoptilus nuttallii* of western North America (see TORPIDITY; also HEAT REGULATION).

HILL: special term for the display ground (court) of the Ruff *Philomachus pugnax* (see LEK DISPLAY).

HILLSTAR: substantive name of *Oreotrochilus* spp. and *Urochroa bougueri* (for family see HUMMINGBIRD).

HIND LIMB: see LEG; LOCOMOTION; SKELETON

Plate 22 · Threat; Fighting; Singing

a   *Upper:* Cape Dikkop (or Spotted Thickknee) *Burhinus capensis* in medium intensity 'open-wing threat' posture (South Africa). In this posture the tail is nearly horizontal and only partly spread; at higher intensity, the tail is spread and cocked.
Phot. G. J. Broekhuysen.

b   *Lower left:* Blue Tit *Parus caeruleus* and Great Tit *P. major* fighting (England). These are two common European species; the Blue Tit is the one above. *Phot. Eric Hosking.*

c   *Lower right:* Robin *Erithacus rubecula* singing (England). This familiar Palaearctic member of the thrush subfamily (Turdinae) has the breast, throat, and forehead orange-red in adults of both sexes. *Phot. John Markham.*

(See articles AGGRESSION; DISPLAY; THICKKNEE; TIT; THRUSH; SINGING)

HIRUNDINIDAE: a family of the Passeriformes, suborder Oscines (see SWALLOW).

HISTOGRAM: see STATISTICAL SIGNIFICANCE

HOARDING: see FEEDING HABITS

HOATZIN: *Opisthocomus hoazin*, sole member of the Opisthocomidae (Galliformes, suborder Opisthocomi). It is an inhabitant of high marsh vegetation in some localities of the hottest parts of South America, being called 'Cigana' (gypsy) or 'Catingueiro' (smelling like a Negro) in Brazil, and 'Canje Pheasant' in Guiana. It is a slenderly built bird, in general appearance resembling the chachalacas (Cracidae)—see CURASSOW. It has a total length of 25 inches but weighs little more than $1\frac{3}{4}$ lbs. (810 grams) as the body is quite small. The sexes are almost alike. The remarkably small head bears a long, erect, and bristly crest; this, together with the long thin neck, makes for an appearance—seen from the front—like that of a peacock *Pavo* sp. The short curved bill is operated by strong muscles; the upper mandible is articulated with the skull, a peculiarity found also in parrots (Psittacidae), turacos (Musophagidae), and some other birds (see BILL). The wings are large in relation to the body, but they are weak owing to reduction of the flight muscles. The tail is both long and broad; the legs and toes are stoutly built. The plumage of the upper part of the body is dark brown, spotted with white in places; the crest is reddish brown, and the bare skin on the face is blue. The under parts are reddish yellow, with the belly rust-coloured.

Systematically the Hoatzin is unique in many respects and has therefore often been placed in an order by itself; there is not only similarity to the gallinaceous birds but links with other orders such as the pigeons (Columbiformes). On the one hand, the Hoatzin has characteristics that seem to connect it with primitive and extinct birds. Thus, the wing structure in the young Hoatzin recalls that of *Archaeopteryx*; the first and second digits carry large claws movable by special muscles, and these aid the bird in grasping branches after the manner of climbing reptiles. Correspondingly, the development of the flight feathers is retarded—contrary to what obtains in gallinaceous birds generally. Mature birds lose their claws and show a normal development of flight feathers; but they use their wings to help in climbing about in the branches, often breaking their primaries in the process.

On the other hand, the Hoatzin shows specialisation equal to that of the most advanced of living birds; and in this respect the digestive tract is particularly remarkable. While in all other vegetarian birds the food is broken up in the gizzard, in the Hoatzin this function is performed by the crop ; the latter is of unusual size and consists of a number of separate sections which squeeze out and break up the food. To perform this function, the crop has thick muscular walls and a horny internal layer, whereas the true gizzard is much reduced. The size and resultant weight of the filled crop is such as to make the bird top-heavy, and when the Hoatzin crouches on a branch it preserves its balance by leaning on its sternum, covering which a special callosity has been developed. Peculiarities in the bones of the pectoral girdle can also be related to the size of the crop. When the bird jumps from branch to branch it maintains its equilibrium by spreading its wings and flapping its tail. The feet do not provide a sufficient grip on the branches—compare curassows (Cracidae), which can cling firmly even to thin branches.

Hoatzin *Opisthocomus hoazin*, sole species. *C.E.T.K.*

Hoatzins live in permanently flooded forests along the overgrown shores of some of the big rivers and their tributaries. The birds can exist only where certain marshy plant foods are available ; these include the great Araceae *Montrichardia* and the arboreal White Mangrove *Avicennia*. The birds feed on the tough leaves, flowers, and fruit of these plants. Occasionally they also take small animals, including fish and small crabs, which they capture in the mud or in the shallow water under the brush. While so occupied they sometimes fall into the water, or even jump into it.

Hoatzins are quite sedentary and rather lazy. They live in flocks of 10–20 individuals ; larger groups of 30, 40, or more have also been noted. Their loud hoarse cries and hissing sounds make their presence known from afar. The name 'Hoatzin' is said to be of Aztekion origin, supposedly resembling some of their utterances. When calling, the birds usually spread wings and tail. They are most active in the morning and evening and on moonlight nights. They like to climb to the tops of the trees along the shore, from where they look about them and fly clumsily across small bays and creeks. During the hot part of the day they rest hidden in the shadow of the dense brushwoods and are difficult to find.

Hoatzins remain in flocks even during the breeding period, which occasionally appears to extend throughout the year. They often breed in colonies and make their nests in the entangled branches 6–16 feet above the water. The nest is flat and made of dry twigs loosely entwined. There are 2–4 eggs, relatively small, yellowish with pink spots ; egg-shape varies considerably, and average size is 46 × 33 mm. The young have two successive down plumages. Although the young stay in the nest for a considerable time, they soon become adventurous and start making excursions ; that they use their wings as hands has already been mentioned. As they also have a good grip with their feet and bill, as in parrots, they are able to clamber about without mishap. This manner of locomotion appears excellently adapted to the mangrove jungles. When danger threatens, the young let themselves fall into the water, where they dive and swim off, using both wings and legs ; afterwards they climb out again, continuing their way through the branches.

The old feed the young from the crop, the young bird putting its head well into the widely gaping bill of the parent. As at times there are more than two mature birds visiting a nest, and as females exceed males in collections, some observers have suspected polygamy.

Hoatzins have a musky odour that varies in intensity with the individual and season. It has been falsely asserted that this odour is always quite strong and can be noted from afar (hence the name 'stinking bird'). There is also a widespread notion that the flesh, too, has this odour, which has caused the natives to leave the birds generally alone, although occasionally they are used for medicinal purposes. The eggs, however, are much in demand.

The sole species occurs from Guiana and Brazil to Colombia and Bolivia. The birds have been observed in widely separated localities, but these are connected by rivers and their tributaries. The Amazon may be considered as the centre of distribution.

H.S.

Beebe, W. 1909. A contribution to the ecology of the adult Hoatzin. Zoologica (N.Y.) 1 : 45–66.
Goeldi, E. 1886. *Opisthocomus cristatus:* a Cigana. Bol. Mus. Pará 1 : 1–4.

HOBBY: substantive name of certain small *Falco* spp. ; used without qualification, in Britain, for *F. subbuteo* (see FALCON).

HOLARCTIC REGION: the Palaearctic and Nearctic Regions combined (Heilprin 1887)—see DISTRIBUTION, GEOGRAPHICAL ; NEARCTIC REGION ; PALAEARCTIC REGION. For some characteristic birds see Plate 29 (colour).

HOLDING: using the feet to grasp food or other objects (except perches—see PERCHING). Most birds do not use the feet in this way, 'manual' functions devolving entirely on the bill (see BILL). Some birds indeed have feet obviously incapable of a prehensile function, e.g. when adapted to running or swimming (see LEG). Among the exceptions, parrots (Psittacidae) are specially notable, often using a foot very much as a hand when feeding. Birds-of-prey (Falconiformes) and owls (Strigiformes) make much use of the feet in seizing, killing, holding, and dismembering their food. To some extent this is true also of some of the 'minor raptors', such as figure prominently in the list of families given below. Tits *Parus* spp. not only hold food with the foot but can learn to pull up a hanging string with food at the end of it, the pulling being done with the bill but the successive lengths being secured on the perch with the feet. Further examples of use of the feet for holding food and so on are to be found among the toucans (Ramphastidae), tyrant-flycatchers (Tyrannidae), nuthatches (Sittidae), shrikes (Laniidae), pepper-shrikes (Cyclarhinae), shrike-vireos (Vireolaniinae), drongos (Dicruridae), wattle-birds (Callaeidae), bell-magpies (Cracticidae), and crows (Corvidae) ; this list is not necessarily exhaustive—the Purple Gallinule *Porphyrio alba* (in Africa) is, rather unexpectedly, described as holding food up to its bill while it bites pieces off. In at least some of these cases the held object may be carried in flight (see CARRYING).

HOLORHINAL: see NARIS

HOLOTHECAL: see BOOTED ; LEG

HOLOTYPE: see TYPE-SPECIMEN

HOMALOGONATAE: birds with an ambiens muscle (Garrod)—see MUSCULATURE.

HOMING PIGEON: a domestic pigeon *Columba livia* var. used for 'homing', either as a carrier of messages or in the sport of pigeon racing. Pigeons have been used to convey messages since the days of the ancient Egyptians, and were much used by the Greeks and in the Roman Empire and generally throughout the Middle East. Regular pigeon-posts were established and military operations were supported. The most famous siege use of pigeons was in Paris in 1870–71, when 150 000 official and a million private messages (microphotographed) were passed. With the advent of telegraphy and wireless the civilian use of pigeon-post disappeared, but in both World Wars much use was made of them. In the 1939–45 war some 200 000 birds were supplied by private breeders to the British Services and 50 000 were reared by the U.S. Army ; nearly 17 000 were parachuted to the Resistance in German-occupied Europe and 2000 returned safely. Many airmen owed their lives to the S.O.S. messages carried by pigeons released as the aircraft crash-landed on the sea.

To fit pigeons for close support of modern warfare, birds were trained to home to mobile lofts, moved a short distance each day ; only moderate success was obtained with intense training, and the birds were particularly likely to go astray if they were required to cross old flight lines, as in a retreat. Attempts were also made to establish a two-way message service by feeding the birds in one place and giving them grit, water, and roosts in another ; this was useful only over short distances. Drastic selection provided pigeons that would fly short distances at night, up to 20 miles. All these specialised techniques of training laid heavy emphasis on the birds being given an intimate knowledge of the country in which they were to fly. Pigeons sent long distances and returning to an established base were trained by a series of releases, at increasing distances, in the direction from which they would eventually have to return.

Directional training of that kind is also the basis of pigeon racing. This is an important sport and there are perhaps 100 000 pigeon fanciers in Britain alone, with something like two million pigeons in their lofts. The sport developed with the advent of the railways, which provided swift transport to distant release points. The first pigeon race over 100 miles was held in 1818 in Belgium, and similar races had been established in England by 1875. Such distances are nowadays considered suitable for young birds of the year ; yearlings will fly races of 300 miles, and older birds up to 500 miles. Because of heavier losses at sea-crossings the longer races, 700–800 miles from the Faeroe Islands in the north and from San Sebastian (Spain) in the south, are seldom flown. In continental North America races of 1000 miles are often flown, although no birds return in one day.

Only a small fraction, perhaps one in twenty, of pigeons come through all the initial stages and return from the long-distance races.

Elaborate precautions are taken to ensure correct timing and to eliminate fraud. Before release a temporary rubber leg-band with a code number is put on each bird by officials. On its return the owner removes the band and drops it into a sealed time-check clock which marks the hour and minute of arrival. The distance from the release point to the home loft is measured to the nearest yard on a great circle, and the speed of the bird expressed in yards per minute. In good conditions homing speeds of 1200 y.p.m. are common, while with tail winds they may be in excess of 2000 y.p.m. Birds may, apparently, fly for up to 16 hours a day. Competition is within clubs and within area federations ; prize money is relatively modest but is increased by systems of ' pooling ' for the big national races. Birds that have been successful in such races are much in demand as breeders and can, in Britain, command £50–£100 ; and up to £500 has been paid for quite exceptional birds. Much attention is paid to pedigrees, but there is general agreement that the only real test of an individual is its performance in races. Various fads about body shape and colour come and go ; at present there is a school of thought that stresses ' eye-sign ', the configuration of the ciliary muscle of the pupil, and in view of the over-riding importance of the eye it is not impossible that there may be something in this idea. There are also numerous techniques that are supposed to increase the speed of homing, but little agreement as to whether, for instance, cocks or hens home faster or whether they should preferably be incubating eggs or feeding young. The ' widowhood ' system seeks to send cocks off to a race in a frenzy of sexual passion.

Although pigeon races are essentially one-directional, the direction selected being that which gives the longest runs to the area, it is well known that good homers can return, although not so swiftly or certainly, from other than the training direction. This indication of a more advanced form of navigational ability has been seized upon in testing theories of bird navigation (see NAVIGATION). The pigeon is certainly a bird readily amenable to experimental treatment, but a great deal of confusion has resulted from the use of birds of inferior stock. There is a wide range of individual variation in homing ability.

Other species have been used for message carrying. The Romans used swallows (Hirundinidae) to convey the winning colours of chariot-races, but these were wild birds caught at their nests on the day required.

Pacific islanders, however, have tamed frigatebirds *Fregata* sp. and use them for inter-island communication.

In a different category were the ' shore-sighting ' birds carried by ships of olden times. The technique was known in countries as far apart as Scandinavia and Ceylon. Ravens *Corvus corax* were particularly favoured and were released when land should be near ; if the bird made off, it not only confirmed the presence of land but indicated its direction.

G.V.T.M.

Levi, W. M. 1951. The Pigeon. Columbia, S.C.

HOMOIOTHERMAL: ' warm-blooded ', as contrasted with ' poikilothermal ' or ' cold-blooded ' ; other spellings and alternative terminations are sometimes used (see HEAT REGULATION).

HOMOLOGUE: a structure basically equivalent to another (but possibly adapted in a different way)—compare ANALOGUE.

HOMONYM: see NOMENCLATURE

HOMOTHERMA: term embracing birds and mammals (see ANIMAL KINGDOM).

HOMOZYGOUS: see GENETICS

HONEY-BUZZARD: name of *Pernis apivorus* and allies (see HAWK).

HONEYCREEPER (1): substantive name of some species of Coerebinae ; in the plural, general term for the subfamily. Many of the species are alternatively named ' sugarbird ', particularly by aviculturists, and other names are used for some as shown below. In the classification here followed, this purely Neotropical group is placed in the Emberizidae (Passeriformes, suborder Oscines), but it is sometimes given independent familial rank. In any event, it is now almost certain that it is a composite assemblage, consisting of birds of tanager (Thraupinae) and wood-warbler (Parulidae) stock that have converged as a result of adaptation to a nectar diet.

General Characteristics. Honeycreepers are small birds with rather thin decurved bills. In many species the males are brilliantly coloured, with unrivalled shades of deep blue, turquoise-blue, and blue-green, and the females much duller, predominantly greenish ; but in the flower-piercers *Diglossa* spp. both sexes are dully coloured. The male Blue (or Red-legged) Honeycreeper *Cyanerpes cyaneus* is peculiar in moulting, at least in parts of its range, into a female-like plumage during the non-breeding season. The chief morphological feature

Blue Dacnis *Dacnis cayana*.
Natural size. *C.E.T.K.*

of the family is the structure of the tongue, which shows a fine series of modifications, involving curling up and fraying of the lateral edges and splitting of the anterior end, leading up to the double tubular tongues of *Coereba* and *Diglossa*, and paralleling the condition found in some Meliphagidae (see HONEY-EATER). The species are distributed throughout the West Indies, Central America, and South America except for the extreme south.

Habits. Honeycreepers are mainly sedentary and, outside the breeding season, most species are more or less gregarious. Song is poorly developed in the family, all their utterances being high pitched and of feeble volume. They are typically birds of the forest and forest-edge, doing most of their foraging in the forest canopy ; cultivation with trees, however, forms a habitat suitable for several species. The Bananaquit *Coereba flaveola* has a far wider habitat tolerance than the others : an extraordinarily successful species, it is probably the most abundant bird in many parts of the West Indies and has come to live in close association with man.

Most honeycreepers suck nectar from flowers in the usual way, by inserting the bill into the corolla opening from a perched position. The flower-piercers, however, as their name implies, pierce a hole in the side of the corolla tube with a bill that is beautifully adapted for the purpose. The upper mandible has a sharply hooked tip and is notched along the cutting edge, while the lower mandible, which is a little shorter, ends in a very sharp point.

The bird holds the corolla tube in position by hooking the upper mandible round it, pierces it with the lower mandible, and inserts its tongue, which is unusually long, into the hole. In spite of their specialised tongues, honeycreepers have a varied diet. The larger species, such as the Blue Dacnis *Dacnis cayana* and the Green Honeycreeper *Chlorophanes spiza*, supplement their diet with a wide variety of fruits ; the smaller Bananaquit and flower-piercers supplement theirs especially with insects.

Breeding. Most honeycreepers build cup-shaped nests, placing them in forks of trees and bushes. The Bananaquit is exceptional in building a globular covered nest with a downward-pointing entrance at the bottom and to one side. Unlike the other species, the Bananaquit also builds nests that it uses only for roosting in ; only a fraction of all the nests built are used for breeding purposes, and these are usually more substantial than the dormitory nests. The eggs—2 in most species, 2 or 3 in the Bananaquit—are usually white or pale blue, speckled with brown.

There has been some controversy over the nest and eggs of the Blue Honeycreeper. In Guiana and Trinidad a covered pensile nest of tough black fibres, with the hole at one side at the top, has been attributed to this species, with eggs so thickly spotted with very dark brown as to appear virtually black—the only ' black ' egg known. But in Central America the species is known with certainty to build a cup-shaped nest and to lay white eggs speckled with brown, and a Blue Honeycreeper nest recently found in Trinidad was of this type. Hence it is possible that the covered nest and black egg have been incorrectly attributed to this species.

In the Bananaquit and flower-piercers the nestlings are fed by regurgitation, apparently on boluses of small insects ; the nestling flower-piercer receives the food into an enlarged protuberant crop, in which respect they resemble the hummingbirds (Trochilidae). In the other species food is brought to the young in the bill.

Taxonomy. If the group be taxonomically disintegrated as the work of Beecher suggests, of the genera mentioned above *Dacnis*, *Diglossa*, *Chlorophanes*, and *Cyanerpes* are retained in the Emberizidae near the tanagers and *Coereba* is assigned to the Parulidae. *Certhidea olivacea*, formerly placed in the Coerebinae, is now accepted as belonging to the Fringillidae. D.W.S.

Beecher, W. J. 1951. Convergence in the Coerebidae. Wilson Bull. 63 : 274–287.
Skutch, A. F. 1962. Life histories of honeycreepers. Condor 64 : 92–116.

HONEYCREEPER (2) : substantive name of some species of Drepanididae (Passeriformes, suborder

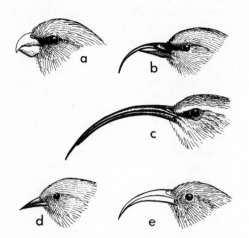

Adaptive radiation in form of bill among Hawaiian honeycreepers (Drepanididae): **a** Palila *Psittirostra bailleui* **b** Akaipolaau *Hemignathus wilsoni* **c** Kauai Akialoa *H. procerus* **d** Akepa *Loxops coccinea* **e** Iiwi *Vestiaria coccinea*

Oscines); in the plural, usually in the form 'Hawaiian honeycreepers', general term for the family. The group is confined to the Hawaiian Islands, and the native names of the species have been largely adopted. The species vary in colour and in form of bill, but the family appears to be separable into two subfamilies: the Drepanidinae are characterised by curved bills for extracting nectar; bills of the Psittirostriinae resemble those of finches (Fringillidae), being adapted for cracking seeds.

In relation to other song-birds they are small to medium sized, about 4 to 8 inches in length, the males rather larger than the females. The colour of the plumage may be green, yellow, red (*Loxops*, *Hemignathus*), or black (*Drepanis*); the Crested Honeycreeper *Palmeria dolei* is grey, streaked and spotted with red, and has a frontal crest. The sexes are alike in some species, unlike in others; immature birds are duller in colour than adults. The birds may be found singly or in small, scattered flocks. The songs vary in quality: some are described as 'sweet little songs' (*Loxops*), others 'like a creaking wheel' (*Vestiaria*). The nests are simply constructed of grass and twigs. They are sometimes lined with soft material, and are built in trees or bushes, but sometimes in grass. The 2 or 3 eggs are laid in the spring; they are spotted on a white background.

Such great diversity of form of bill and colour of plumage caused ornithologists of the last century to assign 69 known forms to 4 families and 18 genera. Even reduction to a minimum leaves 9 genera, 5 of these containing but a single species—making about 22 species in all.

Diverse as they are in colour and bill, however,

the birds are generally similar in form and habit. Certain genera (*Pseudonestor*, *Hemignathus*) are intermediate between the two subfamilies in the shape of bill and tongue; and these characteristics, together with a strong musky odour that is unique in the family and characteristic of all its members, has led to the conclusion that all had ancestors in common. For this reason they provide a favourite example of adaptive radiation.

The species are non-migratory and are variously distributed among the islands of the Hawaiian archipelago, some being restricted to a single island. Those for which native names are used include the Iiwi *Vestiaria coccinea*, the Apapane *Himatione sanguinea*, the Akepa *Loxops. coccinea*, the Anianiau *L. parva*, and the Akialoa *Hemignathus procerus*—the last also being called Sicklebill, a name used differently elsewhere.

It is a deplorable fact that 24 per cent of all known species and subspecies are now probably extinct. This is thought to have been the result of destruction of habitat by human beings and by other animals introduced by them.   J.C.G., Jr.

Amadon, D. 1950. The Hawaiian Honeycreepers (Aves, Drepaniidae). Bull. Amer. Mus. Nat. Hist. 95: 151–262.
Baldwin, P. H. 1952. Annual cycle, environment and evolution in the Hawaiian honeycreepers (Aves: Drepaniidae). Univ. Calif. Publ. Zool. 52: 285–398.
Munro, G. C. 1944. Birds of Hawaii. Honolulu.
Perkins, R. C. L. 1901. An introduction to the study of the Drepaniidae. Ibis (8) 1: 562–585.

HONEYEATER: substantive name of many species of Meliphagidae (Passeriformes, suborder Oscines); in the plural, general term for the family. This is a group of arboreal, mainly nectar-eating and fruit-eating, birds of Australasian distribution (with one genus in South Africa).

General Characteristics. The most striking family character is the brush-tongue, an adaptation to nectar feeding but in its structure notably different from that in other groups of birds with similar habits. The tongue is prolonged and protrusible; the basal part is curled up on each side, forming two long grooves; the distal part is deeply cleft into four parts, which on their edges are delicately frayed and together form the 'brush' which licks up the nectar. In spite of much variation and secondary changes, the basic characters of the tongue are present in all members of the family.

Other characters widespread in the family are the pervious nostrils, and the tendency to absence of feathers from parts of the face, on which develop bare spaces, or even lobes, wattles, or other appendages. The plumage is in most species rather dull, greenish, greyish brown, or streaked, the sexes being similar. The most notable exception to this is in several species of *Myzomela*, which possess contrasting patches of sanguineous red in the plumage and display a pronounced sexual dimorphism. In many honeyeaters there is a conspicuous yellow, golden, or white patch on the posterior part of the ear region ; this character is particularly well developed in the members of the large genus *Meliphaga*.

The honeyeaters display extraordinary variation in structure, bill form, body proportions, and even mode of life. They include birds resembling goldcrests *Regulus* spp., other warblers (Sylviinae), and thrushes (Turdinae) ; species that could be mistaken for sunbirds (Nectariniidae) or hummingbirds (Trochilidae) ; species with falcate bills like Hawaiian honeycreepers (Drepanididae) or bee-eaters (Meropidae) ; larger species approaching the appearance of orioles (Oriolidae), jays and magpies (Corvidae) ; and even birds looking very similar to tits (Paridae), nuthatches (Sittidae), and flycatchers (Muscicapinae). This extreme variation has been compared with that of the marsupials among mammals ; and, although this may be exaggerated, there is obviously a striking parallelism in history and evolution in these two groups.

Habits. In such a large and diversified group as the honeyeaters, ecology and habits of life are of course extremely varied. Common to all honeyeaters is their arboreal habit. Only a few descend to the ground for feeding ; and not a single species places the nest on the ground, although a few make use of high grass tussocks as nesting sites. They are mainly birds of the forests, where they frequent tree-tops and flowering trees. Several species, most of them inhabiting the continent of Australia, have become adapted to the open non-forested areas. No species can exist in completely treeless country, however, but a single species—the Singing Honeyeater *Meliphaga virescens*—ranges right to the coastal sand-dunes and also inhabits the small islands off the barren south and west coasts of Australia. Many species are attached to the mangrove swamps, savannas, heathland, and mallee, a few even to the mulga scrub, while in the spinifex country in the interior of Australia only one species, the Pied Honeyeater *Certhionyx variegatus*, is occasionally encountered. Several species are restricted to the high mountains of New Guinea, while some, most of them belonging to the genera *Myzomela* and *Lichmera*, are inhabitants of small oceanic islands.

Honeyeaters are more or less gregarious ; no species are solitary. Outside the breeding season they generally move around in small parties, and these under certain conditions can increase to large swarms. Some open-country species are markedly nomadic ; a few subtropical—temperate species make regular seasonal movements. In most species the flight is undulating, but some of the larger species have a more clumsy flight like that of a Magpie *Pica pica*.

The diet of the majority of honeyeaters consists of a mixture of nectar, pollen, and insects. In addition, many honeyeaters feed also on fruits and berries and may do some damage in Australian orchards.

The vocal utterances differ widely. Many of the smaller species are excellent songsters, while the larger ones are not so musical and utter various harsh and noisy babbling sounds, usually characteristic of the genus. A few species frequenting open country have song-flights. Some of the species inhabiting dense rain-forests are very silent.

Breeding. The nest is a cup-shaped, sometimes pendulous, structure, differing considerably in composition and situation ; it is placed in trees or bushes, usually high up. In several species the nests are placed on branches overhanging water, along rivers or lake borders. Group nesting, in colonies up to twenty or more, is a rather frequent phenomenon, at least in Australian species. A peculiar habit is developed in some species of *Melithreptus* and *Meliphaga* ; in order to obtain nest material they habitually pull hairs off cows, larger marsupials (possums), and even man. The species of *Ramsayornis* are unique among honeyeaters in building closed nests, dome-shaped with a side entrance. The Bluefaced Honeyeater *Entomyzon cyanotis* of Australia differs from all other honeyeaters in using deserted nests of babblers (Timaliinae), preferably those of *Pomatostomus temporalis*, and it is known sometimes to oust the legitimate owners by force.

The eggs are spotted, most often with reddish brown. The clutch consists in the tropical species, so far known, of only one egg ; in the subtropical ones of 2, occasionally 3 eggs ; in the larger species often of 4 eggs ; and in the temperate species (in New Zealand) also usually of 4 eggs. The participation of the male in nest building and incubation differs widely, and in many species the female alone performs these duties. On the other hand, both sexes share in feeding the young.

Distribution. Apart from the isolated South African genus *Promerops* (see separate article on SUGAR-BIRD (I)) the honeyeaters belong to the Australasian Region, where they are widely distributed and form one of the most characteristic bird groups. Only one species, the Brown Honeyeater *Lichmera indistincta*, has crossed Wallace's Line and settled on Bali ; another species, *Apalopteron familiaris*, inhabits the Bonin Islands, which are regarded as belonging to the Palaearctic Region. To the east the range of the honeyeaters includes the greater part of Micronesia, Melanesia, Polynesia (east to Samoa and Tonga), the Hawaiian Islands, and the New Zealand islands.

The 167 species of honeyeaters (including a total of about 450 subspecies) are divided among 38 genera, of which 14 are monotypic. The largest genera are *Meliphaga* (36 species), *Myzomela* (24 species), and *Philemon* (16 species). New Guinea and the Australian mainland form the centre of distribution and are inhabitad by an almost equal number of species—New Guinea (with satellite islands) by 63 species, Australia (with Tasmania) by 67 species. The New Guinea honeyeaters are generally more primitive and unspecialised, while the Australian (and New Zealand) forms include a great number of specialised and derivative types.

Ecological Relation. Blossoms of trees and shrubs constitute the main feeding place of most honeyeaters. Owing to this fact they are very efficient pollinators ; in fact they form, together with certain parrots (Psittacidae), the most important agents in the fertilisation of the greater part of the indigenous Australian tree and shrub flora, such as the Myrtaceae, Proteaceae, and Epacridaceae (see POLLINATORS AND DISTRIBUTORS). An intimate connection exists between these plants and the honeyeaters, and the ornithophilous flowers have developed a number of adaptations to bird visits, just as the honeyeaters in their anatomy demonstrate striking adaptations to nectar feeding ; this is true of the tongue, as mentioned above, and also of the alimentary tract. The intestinal canal is rather short and wide, the opening of the oesophagus into the stomach and that of the intestinal canal (pylorus) are placed very closely together, in a little chamber partly separated from the stomach proper. This structure permits nectar and other easily digestible matters to pass directly from the oesophagus to the intestines, while insect food can be retained in the stomach for the necessary period of digestion there.

The members of the New Guinean genus *Melipotes* have given up nectar feeding and have become fruit-eaters ; their tongue structure has been secondarily simplified. Even the species belonging to the Australian genus *Conopophila* have mostly given up nectar feeding and are mainly insectivorous, capturing their prey in the air like flycatchers (Muscicapinae). One of the species, the Painted Honeyeater *C. picta*, has specialised on mistletoe berries, apart from insects. The six species of *Melithreptus* are tit-like, active birds, of which the Strong-billed Honeyeater *M. validirostris* of Tasmania

has developed food habits and even a bill form almost like those of a nuthatch *Sitta* sp. It runs up trunks, taking insects from under the bark, which it pulls off with its powerful bill. The O-o-aa *Moho braccatus* of Hawaii is predominantly insectivorous and searches for food by climbing the boles of trees like a woodpecker (Picidae), aided by its stiff tail-feathers. The spinebills *Acanthorhynchus* spp. of Australia have long and extremely thin decurved bills, and during nectar feeding are able to hover in front of the blossoms like hummingbirds (Trochilidae). The four miners *Manorina* spp. are jay-like, noisy, and inquisitive birds with babbling notes. The Bell Miner *M. melanophrys* is more musical and has a peculiar song, resembling the tinkling of a silver bell ; the New Zealand Bell-bird *Anthornis melanura*, which is a distant ally, has a somewhat similar song. The strange Tui *Prosthemadera novaeseelandiae* of New Zealand is a glossy bluish-green bird like a starling *Sturnus* sp., with two tufts of white curled feathers on the lower throat ; it is known to be an excellent mimic of other birds' songs. The friar-birds or leatherheads *Philemon* spp. generally resemble jays or jackdaws (Corvidae) but have parts of the head naked and inky black, and in many species with a horny protuberance on the bill. They are strange in appearance and utter loud and querulous chatterings. The wattle-birds *Anthochaera* spp. have on each side of the head a pendant wattle, longest and most conspicuous in the Yellow Wattle-Bird *A. paradoxa* of Tasmania ; they utter peculiar guttural notes, resembling coughing or barking.

Sugarbirds. The two sugarbirds *Promerops* spp. of South Africa, which are characterised by a long, curved bill and a prolonged, drooping tail, agree with the honeyeaters in the structure of the tongue and of the alimentary canal, in plumage pattern, in nest and eggs, and in feeding habits. The genus therefore must, in spite of its remote breeding range, be incorporated in the Meliphagidae (see SUGARBIRD (1)).

See Plates 6 and 31 (colour) ; 14b (phot.).

F.S.

Barrett, C. 1947. Australian Bird Life. Melbourne.
Deignan, H. G. 1958. The systematic position of the bird genus *Apalopteron*. Proc. U.S. Natl. Mus. 108 : 133–136.
Gilliard, E. T. 1959. The ecology of hybridisation in New Guinea honeyeaters (Aves). Amer. Mus. Novit. no. 1937 : 1–26.
Hindwood, K. A. 1944. Honeyeaters of the Sydney District (County of Cumberland), New South Wales. Australian Zoologist 10 : 231–251.
Koopman, K. F. 1957. Evolution in the genus *Myzomela* (Aves : Meliphagidae). Auk 74 : 49–72.
Mathews, G. M. 1923–27 : The Birds of Australia vols. 11 and 12. London.
Mayr, E. 1941. List of New Guinea Birds. New York.

HONEYGUIDE: substantive name of the species of Indicatoridae (Piciformes, suborder Galbulae) ; in the plural, general term for the family. The honeyguides are small birds, 4½ to 8 inches in length,

Black-throated Honeyguide *Indicator indicator*. *C.E.T.K.*

and not conspicuously coloured—although there is sexual dimorphism in some species. The plumage is generally brown, olivaceous or grey above and lighter below ; there are various markings, notably white spots on the tail, and there are yellow wing-patches in two species, while one species has patches of orange on the forehead and rump. The bill is short, stout, and blunted, with raised rims round the nostrils ; and in the nestlings of some species both mandibles are hooked. The legs are short, the toes zygodactyl, and the claws strong and hooked. The wings are relatively pointed ; the flight is rapid. The tail tends to be graduated (lyre-shaped in one species), with the outermost pair of rectrices always shorter than the next. The skin is notably thick, probably serving as a defence against insect stings.

Honeyguides are inhabitants of tropical forest and deciduous woodland, arboreal in their habits. They tend to be solitary ; and they have a variety of calls, some of them harsh. Some species feed on insects, often caught on the wing, and also on bee larvae, honey, and particularly on beeswax ; such ' cerophagy ' appears to imply a metabolic use of wax unique among birds. Others, *Prodotiscus* spp., feed on waxy scale insects.

This beeswax feeding habit is associated with the ' guiding ' of man and other mammals which gives the birds their name, although it is definitely known only for two of the species. For instance, the Black-throated Honeyguide *Indicator indicator*, which is widely distributed in tropical and southern Africa, although absent from the dense forest belts, guides man and ratels (honey-badgers) to the nests of wild honeybees and, after a nest has been robbed, feeds on the remains and especially on the wax of the broken comb. This behaviour was doubtless first developed, before the advent of man, in association with ratels,

while the African human has deliberately made himself a substitute for the ratel as far as the bird is concerned. The bird, usually alone, begins by coming to a person or animal, uttering repeated churring notes, fanning its tail and otherwise making itself conspicuous ; in this manner it leads the way towards the bees' nest, keeping some 15-20 feet ahead. When the bird hears or sees swarming bees, which is usually near a bees' nest, it perches silently and patiently until the robber has broken into the hive, taken his loot, and departed. The ' guiding ' behaviour is purely instinctive and unplanned. The species is not solely dependent on this behaviour for its food, as it also catches insects. There is indeed evidence that guiding of humans is becoming less frequent in some areas, because the diminished interest in the honey of wild bees on the part of sophisticated Africans has caused the birds to disregard humans as potential foraging symbionts.

So far as the habits of different species are known, honeyguides are parasitic in their breeding habits. A white egg—how many in all has not been ascertained—is laid in the nest of some hole-nesting or burrowing species, often one of the barbets (Capitonidae). *Prodotiscus insignis* is parasitic on open-nesting passerines such as white-eyes *Zosterops* spp. Incubation and parental care are then left to the hosts (see PARASITISM).

The family includes about a dozen species, in four genera, most of them being found in Africa south of the Sahara and the rest in southern Asia ; none lives in Madagascar. Most of the species, including the two Asian forms, are placed in the genus *Indicator*, of which one example has been mentioned at some length above. The remaining small genera are *Prodotiscus*, *Melignomon*, and *Melichneutes*. The sole species in the last named is the Lyre-tailed Honeyguide *M. robustus*, a bird of the Guinean rain-forest noteworthy for complicated aerial evolutions in the course of which a non-vocal sound is produced—apparently (as in the ' bleating ' of the Snipe *Gallinago gallinago*) by the outer tail-feathers ; this species is not known to guide, and about its breeding habits there is no information.   H.F.

Friedmann, H. 1955. The honey-guides. U.S. Natl. Mus. Bull. 208 : 1–292.

HONKER: name applied in North America to the Canada Goose *Branta canadensis* (see under DUCK).

HOOD: an area of distinctive colour, in some plumage patterns, covering a large part of the head (see TOPOGRAPHY).

HOOKBILL: *Ancistrops strigilatus* (see OVENBIRD (1)).

HOOPOE: *Upupa epops*, sole species of the Old World family Upupidae (Coraciiformes, suborder Coracii), the various geographical representatives being now usually accorded no more than subspecific rank. The related wood-hoopoes (or 'tree-hoopoes') are placed in a separate family, Phoeniculidae (see WOOD-HOOPOE). The Hoopoe has a long pedigree in human culture—used as a hieroglyph in ancient Egypt, occurring widely in folklore, and figuring prominently in *The Birds* of Aristophanes.

The Hoopoe is a strikingly beautiful bird, and quite unmistakable—all the more because it permits close approach. It measures 10½–12 inches from tip to tip, and the predominant hues of the plumage range from pinkish, through cinnamon to chestnut. Alternating black and white bars on the wings and tail form a distinctive pattern, even more conspicuous in a back view of the bird in flight. The crown carries an erectile crest of pinkish brown feathers with black tips. The sexes are similar in appearance, although the female is sometimes slightly duller or smaller. The newly fledged young have the same general pattern, already including the crest. The bill is rather long, slender, and decurved ; the tongue is short. The tarsi are short ; the four toes are long, with the 3rd and 4th united in their basal portions.

Except on migration, when small parties may be formed, the Hoopoe is not very sociable. The name is derived from the cry—'hoop, hoop, hoop' ; there are also mewing and chattering notes. The ordinary flight is slow and undulating, often erratic like that of a butterfly. The birds spend much of their time on the ground, but they roost in trees and often perch on these or other vantage points. The food consists of large insects and their larvae, spiders, worms, and small vertebrate animals such as lizards. Although insects are sometimes taken in flight, most of the food is obtained on the ground, the bird's bill being well adapted to removing its prey from cracks and crevices and from among soft earth.

The Hoopoe shows a preference for a warm dry environment, and for the rather open type of woodland that provides for its respective habits of feeding on the ground and perching in trees ; gardens, orchards, vineyards, forest clearings, and palm groves are all favoured. The nest is in a hole in a tree, wall, rock, bank, termitary, or the like ; the cavity is usually unlined, although sticks, leaves, and so on are sometimes added. The eggs, 4–6 or considerably more on occasion, vary from pale blue to olivaceous in ground colour and are usually unspotted. The female alone incubates but is fed by the male—as, earlier, during courtship. Both parents care for the young, which are nidicolous and have only sparse down at the time of hatching. The nest becomes very foul, as sanitation is apparently imperfectly practised and sometimes not at all. It is also apt to acquire a highly offensive musky odour, due to an excretion of the oil gland (by the nestlings as well as by the sitting female) as a defence measure in reaction to fear ; in addition, in these circumstances, the young birds eject faeces within the nest (Sutter).

The distribution is somewhat sporadic, but it extends from middle latitudes in the Palaearctic Region (in Europe, from the English Channel and the Baltic) to South Africa, Madagascar, India, Ceylon, Malaya, and Sumatra. In the northern parts of this range the birds are migratory, those breeding in Europe withdrawing to Africa for the winter. Britain is just outside the normal breeding range ; but the species is an annual visitor in small numbers, particularly in the southern counties of England in spring, and has occasionally nested. In Europe generally it seems to be less common than formerly.

In Africa, the species is absent from the two extremes of environment, the utter desert areas of the Sahara and the central belt of continuous rain-forest. The race *U. e. senegalensis*, more or less resident in the northern tropics, is more rufous in coloration than the nominate race breeding in the Palaearctic Region ; and this is still more true of *U. e. africanus* in the southern part of the African continent. The same tendency to richer coloration is seen in *U. e. ceylonensis*, resident in southern India and Ceylon. Some authors have accorded full specific rank to these and other allopatric forms.

See Plate 4a (phot.).   A.L.T.

Skead, C. J. 1950. A study of the African Hoopoe. Ibis 92 : 434–463.
Sutter, E. 1946. Das Abwehrhalten nestjunger Weide-hopfe. Orn. Beob. 43 : 72–81.

HOOTING: term applied, where appropriate, to the calling of certain birds, especially owls (Strigiformes).

HOPPING: see LOCOMOTION ; LEG

HORMONES: internal secretions having specific physiological actions (see ENDOCRINE SYSTEM ; REPRODUCTIVE SYSTEM).

HORNBILL: substantive name of all species of Bucerotidae (Coraciiformes, suborder Bucerotes) ; in the plural, general term for the family. (Stresemann places the family in a suborder Upupae—see CORACIIFORMES.) It is a family of the Old World tropics, from Africa to the Solomon Islands.

Hornbills are so called by reason of the enormous bill, which in some of the 45 species is surmounted by a large casque ; an anatomical peculiarity is that the first two vertebrae (atlas and axis) are fused into a single bone. They are indeed birds of remarkable appearance, seemingly top-heavy, but the casque is in reality an extremely light structure as a rule—a horny shell supported internally by a cellular bony tissue, sponge-like in appearance and of extreme delicacy (an exception will be mentioned). The casque may be of various shapes and is much smaller and less prominent in the female than in the male. In the Black-casqued Hornbill *Ceratogymna atrata* of the West African forests the casque is cylindrical and in the male is so greatly developed as almost to dwarf the huge mandibles above which it rests ; this bird is one of the largest of the arboreal species, measuring about 3 feet from bill to tail. The mandibles are very large in all but the smallest members of the family ; they are generally coarsely serrated and in some species transversely furrowed. In most species the eyelids have stiff black lashes, very highly developed in the ground hornbills *Bucorvus* spp. The legs are short and stout, but longer—and with a very thick tarsus—in the ground hornbills. The feet in all species have very broad soles, the 2nd, 3rd, and 4th toes being united ; the hind toe is free and well developed, with an equally broad sole. See also SEXUAL DIMORPHISM (Fig.).

In many species, but not all, the sexes are alike in plumage, but the bill of the male is often very different from that of the female. Many species are crested or have elongated feathers on the nape. The tail is moderately long in most, but in the monotypic genus *Tropicranus* (which Peters merges with the Malayan genus *Berenicornis*) it is greatly elongated and strongly graduated. In size hornbills vary very much; the Ground Hornbill *Bucorvus leadbeateri* of southern Africa is a bird as large as a Turkey *Meleagris gallopavo*, over 40 inches in length with a wing span of 5 feet, while the Red-billed Dwarf Hornbill *Tockus* ('*Lophoceros*') *camurus* of that continent measures but 15 inches from bill to tail. The large species in Africa and Asia are noted for the extraordinary rushing noise made by their wings when in flight, likened to the roar of a train ; it is probable that this noise is produced, or at least accentuated, by the absence of feathers covering the bases of the remiges, which enables the air to pass through more easily.

The family is by some taxonomists divided into two subfamilies, the one (Bucoracinae) restricted to the two ground hornbills of Africa *Bucorvus* spp., and the other (Bucerotinae) including all the remaining genera. So specialised are the hornbills in certain structural characters and in their pterylosis that they are commonly ranked as a separate suborder of the Coraciiformes. The number of genera into which the arboreal members of the family are divided is largely a matter of opinion.

Hornbills are distributed widely in the tropics of the Old World, ranging through Africa south of the Sahara (but not Madagascar) and southern Asia, in which latter we find them in India, Burma, Siam, Indo-China, Malaya, Sumatra, Java, Borneo, the Celebes, the Moluccas and Solomon Islands, and even reaching the Philippines ; but they do not occur in Australia. Since the days of Pliny these strange-looking birds have attracted the attention of travellers, who have brought back wondrous tales concerning them. Their breeding habits are indeed among the most interesting of any birds. The eggs in some genera number 3–5, but are more usually 2 or even only one in the larger species. They are laid in a hole or hollow of a tree up to 100 feet from the ground, although sometimes quite low, and the female then walls herself in, sometimes with material brought by her mate, the aperture being filled in with dung or clay so as to leave only a slit through which food can be passed by the male. While in the hole the hen bird undergoes an extensive moult, shedding her flight and tail feathers. Throughout this period the male attends her assiduously ; in the White-thighed Hornbill *Bycanistes albotibialis* a male was seen to make 18 visits in less than $10\frac{1}{2}$ hours (Chapin), and this is frequently exceeded in *B. brevis* with up to 24 visits in a like period—one male being recorded as bringing about 24 000 fruits in all ; up to 50 or more small fruits may be brought at a time but are regurgitated individually (Moreau).

See Plate 33 (phot.).

The Moreaus' fine studies of the Silvery-cheeked Hornbill *Bycanistes brevis* have made known the habits of this species probably more thoroughly than those of any other in the group. Among other facts, it was discovered that these hornbills roost communally in high trees, sometimes a hundred or two together ; they congregate in flocks for feeding purposes—as do many other species—and daily go long distances for food. This is the common highland form of East Africa, in forests around 7500 feet above sea level. The birds are believed to pair for life. The nest-hole is plastered up from the inside entirely by the female, using mud (earth and saliva mixed) brought by the male and regurgitated to her in pellets. Towards the end of the incubation period the male passes in a considerable amount of bark, the use of which is unknown ; and among other objects brought to the immured female, in addition to fruits and berries, are flowers !

The unique nesting behaviour of hornbills raises several questions of great interest. The female's habit of walling herself in (with some help from her mate in certain species) is sufficiently remarkable in itself, but it also involves adaptations to the prolonged sojourn in the hole. Incubation periods are about 30 days in *Tockus* and 50 in *Bycanistes*, fledging periods fully 50 and about 45 respectively ; *Bycanistes* females are known to have been in their holes for 108 and 112 days altogether. The problem of nest sanitation, concerning the female as well as the young, is dealt with by high-velocity defaecation out through the slit, by 'casting' fruit stones and so on by mouth, and by the symbiotic presence of a scavenging insect fauna. It is not known at what age the young become capable of defaecation through the slit, or how the parent deals with their excreta until then.

There is also the correlation of the accelerated moult of the female with the nesting habits. In some *Tockus* spp. the moult takes place so quickly, within a few days of her settling in the hole, that she is utterly incapable of flight if taken out. (The proximate factor controlling the onset of this moult is not known, and Moreau suggests that it would be an interesting subject for experiment.) In at least some *Tockus* spp., where the female has an accelerated moult, the clutch is 3–5, and the food is mainly animal ; in these cases the female knocks her way out as soon as she has renewed her plumage and proceeds to help the male with feeding the young, still in the nest. The young then re-plaster the hole, using dung and food remnants ; they do this without parental help—a most remarkable technique on the part of half-fledged nestlings. In larger, frugivorous species of hornbill that have only one or two young and obtain food more easily than the *Tockus* spp., the female does not break out until the young are ready to fly ; in such cases all the feeding at the nest is done by the male.

Young hornbills in the cramped quarters of the nesting hole sit with their tails raised vertically ; they retain this position, huddled closely together, even if they are taken out and placed in the open.

The ground hornbills *Bucorvus* spp., are, it would appear the only members of the family in which the female is not walled-in during the incubation period. These great birds nest in hollow trees or stumps, exceptionally in a hole in a cliff-side, the female laying one or two eggs but not becoming imprisoned in so far as our present knowledge admits. There are even accounts of young being reared in stick nests. In South Africa the male will occasionally relieve his mate when incubating (Roberts).

Hornbills of various species inhabit wooded country of every kind, from dense rain-forest to sparse acacia. The ground hornbills, in particular, live in open savanna country, where they may be seen in pairs or small parties of six or eight walking about in search of food. All across the Sudan is found the custom of a stuffed head of a ground hornbill being tied on that of a native hunter while he crawls through the grass when stalking game, the apparent proximity of the bird reassuring the unsuspecting quarry. Hornbills feed on a great variety of fruit and berries and on insects of all kinds ; the White-crested Hornbill *Tropicranus albocristatus* lives mainly on an insect diet, often procured on the wing. This bird is well known, in West Africa and the Ituri, to follow bands of monkeys as these progress through the forest and to feed on the insects which the monkeys disturb—an association for mutual benefit shared by a large squirrel. Some of the larger hornbills *Ceratogymna* spp. will swallow palm-nuts. Termites are a favourite food of some species ; small mammals, reptiles, and birds are also captured and eaten ; one Malayan species is reported to capture fish (H. C. Robinson), but so unlikely a diet requires confirmation. A bird of one of the smaller species is known to have eaten a chameleon, and one of a Burmese species has been seen with a bat (which escaped) in its bill. The ground hornbills are omnivorous : from the stomach of one Abyssinian Ground Hornbill *Bucorvus abyssinicus* were taken a piece of the hoof of an antelope, many small feathers, a lizard, a frog, many dung beetles, a large waterbug, a caterpillar, a millipede, many insect eggs, and two bean pods ; large snakes are attacked by several of these birds banding together.

In the Ethiopian Region 25 species are listed in the *Systema Avium*, grouped in 5 genera. Great diversity in size is shown ; the plumage is for the most part dull, the colours being restricted to the bare patches of skin or wattles in some of the larger species, and to the colour of the bill and casque. Black and white or brown predominates in the plumage. Very ornamental is the White-crested Hornbill of Ghana and the Congo, already mentioned, with its graduated tail nearly 18 inches long and an ample crest of white plumes with black shaft streaks.

In the Malay Peninsula, in which about 12 species are known, all are birds of the heavy forest, with the exception of the two local pied hornbills *Anthracoceros* spp. that are birds of the sea-coasts—but not of the mangrove swamps, preferring the banks of large rivers and never found in old jungle. Most striking of the Malay species is the Great Hornbill *Buceros bicornis*, which occurs from India to Sumatra and measures 52 inches in length. This black-and-white bird has an enormous bill and casque, yellow, tinged with red at the tip and with orange in the middle. The Helmeted Hornbill

Rhinoplax vigil, has been described as 'a perfect nightmare of a bird'; this Malayan species has a call that begins with a series of whoops, uttered at first at half-minute intervals but gradually becoming faster until it ends with a harsh quacking laugh.

Of Indian species the Rufous-necked Hornbill *Aceros nipalensis* is some 45–48 inches in length, the sexes differing markedly in the shape of the deeply grooved bill; the absence of a casque, the bright blue facial skin, the bright scarlet skin of the throat, the rufous head and neck, and the black-and-white tail, are distinctive characters. In striking contrast is the Great Hornbill, already mentioned, with its immense casque. A purely Indian species is the Grey Hornbill *Tockus birostris*, some 24 inches in length, light brownish grey with white tips to the long graduated tail; it is found from the base of the Himalaya throughout the better-wooded parts of India. In Burma, from which country 9 species are listed, hornbill feathers are valued for ceremonial head-dresses, the Chins also hanging them round their graves. The Helmeted Hornbill, already mentioned, has a solid-fronted casque which is commercially valued in the East (see IVORY, HORNBILL).

In the Far East, hornbills are found in many of the Pacific Islands. There are at least 4 genera to be found in the Philippine Islands—*Penelopides*, *Buceros*, *Anthracoceros*, and *Aceros* (or 'Rhyticeros'). Representative races of Blyth's Hornbill *Aceros plicatus* extend from Burma through Malaya, Borneo, the Moluccas, and New Guinea to reach the Goodenough Islands and the Bismarck Archipelago.

Various superstitions surround certain species, which in consequence are never molested by the native inhabitants of the forests in which they live (see OMENS, BIRDS AS). The White-thighed Hornbill of the Ituri forest, already mentioned, is said to be of prime importance in the superstitious customs of Walabi and Bandako, only boys being allowed to eat it; it shares this taboo with the black-and-white monkey.

The full life history of many of the hornbills is but imperfectly known, and no group would better reward further investigation; the habits of the family are difficult to study, as so many of its members spend much of their life in the tree-tops. There is of course no relationship between the hornbills of the Old World and the toucans (Ramphastidae) of the New World with their likewise enormous bills.

D.A.B.

Elliot, D. G. 1877–82. A Monograph of the Bucerotidae. London. (Finely illustrated.)
Moreau, R. E. 1937. The comparative breeding biology of the African hornbills (Bucerotidae). Proc. Zool. Soc. Lond. 107A : 331–346.
Moreau, R. E. & W. M. 1941. Breeding biology of the Silvery-cheeked Hornbill. Auk 58 : 13–27.
Peters, J. L. 1945. Check-list of Birds of the World vol. 5. Cambridge, Mass.
Sanft, K. 1960. Bucerotidae (Aves/Upupae). *In* Mertens, R. & Hennig, W. (eds.). Das Tierreich 76 : 1–176. Berlin.

HORNERO: South American substantive name of the true ovenbirds *Furnarius* spp., especially *F. leucopus* (see OVENBIRD (1)).

HOUBARA: sometimes used alone as the name of the Houbara Bustard *Chlamydotis undulata* (see BUSTARD).

HOVERING: see FLIGHT

HUET-HUET: *Pteroptochos tarnii* (see TAPACULO).

HUIA: *Heteralocha acutirostris* (see WATTLEBIRD (2); and EXTINCT BIRDS).

HUMERUS: a bone of the fore-limb (see SKELETON; WING). The flight feathers ('tertials') borne on this part of the limb are sometimes called 'humerals'.

HUMIDITY: see CLIMATOLOGY; METEOROLOGY

HUMMINGBIRD: substantive name of many species of Trochilidae (Apodiformes); in the plural, general term for the family. The name derives from the peculiar sound made by the vibration of the wings during flight; many of the species, however, are known by special names that in most instances refer to the plumage. To this group of birds belong the smallest of the higher vertebrates, and probably also the most brightly coloured.

The hummingbirds, of which more than 450 well defined forms (over 300 species) are known, constitute one of the most homogeneous and highly specialised groups in the whole bird world. Their mostly very diminutive size, the brilliance and peculiar iridescence of their plumage, and the speed and singularities of their flight are among the chief characteristics which have made them so popular, and have also led to their being frequently compared with insects. They do not show close affinities with any other family of birds; but they are generally associated systematically, by modern authors, with the swifts (Apodidae) in the same order.

The skeleton of hummingbirds reveals some peculiarities closely related to their mode of life. The development of the sternal keel, greater in comparison to the whole size than in any other bird, and the shortness of the humerus explain their powerful and vibrating flight, to which the peculiar shape of the wings is also related. As in the fore-limbs, the hind limbs also have very short bones, and they invariably possess four digits, mostly armed with sharp claws ; the disposition and the muscle-formula of these digits are similar to those in the passerine birds. In some species, such as the White-booted Rackettail *Ocreatus underwoodi* of northern South America, the legs are covered by long downy feathers.

If the characters of the limbs, with the consequent inability to walk on the ground, recall those of the swifts, the cranial characters differ widely and show close similarity to those of the woodpeckers (Picidae), especially in the development and position of the hyoid bone. The latter is connected with a very long, protractile, and bitubular tongue, which itself moves inside an invariably thin and sharply pointed bill ; but the external appearance neverthe-less varies greatly, in length and shape, among the numerous genera.

Most species of hummingbirds are of smaller size than a Wren *Troglodytes troglodytes*. Some are larger, notably the Giant Hummingbird *Patagona gigas* of the Andes, with an overall length of about 8½ inches. Some are much smaller ; the smallest of all (and of all birds) is the Bee Hummingbird *Mellisuga helenae* of Cuba—comparable in size with a common bumble-bee, having a total length of little more than 2 inches, of which about half is accounted for by the bill and tail.

The bill is generally elongated and is either quite or nearly straight, or decurved (often), or even in a few cases curved upwards : the Sword-billed Hummingbird *Ensifera ensifera* has a bill as long as the whole head and body together, thus presenting the proportionately largest development of this organ among birds. The wings are rather oar-shaped and have 10 primaries, of which the first, or in a very few species the second, is the longest. The secondaries are few and short. There are almost invariably 10 rectrices, the disposition of which varies widely so that the tail may be anything from deeply scissor-like to long-pointed cuneate, with all intermediates—forked, square, rounded, with some-times quite an unusual shape and strangely formed feathers. Thus, in the White-booted Rackettail, already mentioned, the outer pair of rectrices are like long wires, each ending in a 'racket' of black feathers. Still more remarkable is the very small and little known Spatuletail *Loddigesia mirabilis* of Peru ; it is exceptional in having only 4 rectrices, of which the outer pair are much elongated, wire-like, curved so that they overlap midway, and ending in purple 'rackets'. The Graceful Trainbearer *Lesbia nuna* of the Andes has the outer tail feathers 4 inches long or more ; in the Sappho Comet *Sappho sparganura* of South America the tail is a long streamer of cop-

pery hue ; and the tiny body of Gould's Heavenly Sylph *Cyanolesbia coelestis* of the Andes carries a purplish tail more than 5 inches long.

The body plumage, growing from a notably tough skin, consists mainly of not very numerous feathers that are rather scale-like in appearance and that in most cases possess a highly differentiated iridescence. Of the pigments commonly present in bird plumages, the hummingbirds never have other than the two most primitive ones, black and rufous ; there are often pure white areas largely devoid of pigment. The metallic lustre and iridescent colour-ing, resulting from the diffraction of light through the peculiar microstructure of the pigmented feathers, produce a brilliancy and a variety of tints unrivalled in any other group of birds. These shiny colours are often localised on small areas of the plumage, in a pattern which has often been compared to precious stones or gems ; hence the colourful and descriptive names which have been applied to many species by early authors, using words such as ' topaz ', ' ruby ', and ' sapphire '.

The sexes are sometimes more or less alike in external appearance, e.g. in most of the dully coloured ' hermits ' in the widely distributed genus *Phaethornis*. In the majority of species, however, male and female differ noticeably either in colour or in ornamentation. In a few species both sexes are brilliantly coloured in equal degree. In no case does the female possess more than rudiments of the pecul-iar ornamentation of supplementary or unusually developed feathers which occurs frequently in the male sex. These ornaments include crests, as in Delalande's Plovercrest *Stephanoxis delalandei* of Brazil. The Frilled Coquette *Lophornis magnifica*, also of Brazil, has a chestnut crest and also long white plumes on the sides of the neck ; these adorn a tiny body of burnished bronze with a coral-red bill. As a rule the females are more or less noticeably smaller than the males ; but among the most diminutive species they tend, on the contrary, to be slightly larger.

In addition to the humming noise made by the wings, there is a variety of vocal sounds. These are mostly described as squeaking or twittering notes. There is sometimes, however, a distinct song with a pleasant cadence although too high to sound melo-dious to the human ear.

The flight consists almost invariably of an uninter-rupted succession of wing-beats at a very high frequency, attaining 50 or more per second for the smallest species, and presenting a mere blur to the human eye. (Greenewalt records 80 beats for *Calliphlox amethystina* of tropical South America, a bird weighing about one tenth of an ounce.) But this number decreases in proportion to increase of size, and the largest species is even said to be capable of sometimes using some other type of flight. In any event the flight may attain a considerable speed, and the hummingbirds are to be considered as among the fastest of all known birds. They can also ' hover ' so that they remain stationary in the air, as they commonly do when feeding. Through their peculiar mode of vibrating flight, they are the only birds that can fly backwards. On the whole, most of them are excellent flyers and, especially when considering their very small size, the very long distances which they can cover are remarkable (see FLIGHT).

The diet of hummingbirds consists of both animal and vegetable food, in fact from very small arthropods to flower secretions ; tiny soft insects are the chief element of this diet and in some cases even the only one. The peculiar shape and extreme mobility of the tongue are closely related with the manner of feeding : through their powerful flight, the birds often catch insects on the wing, but still more frequently they are accustomed to take their food, both nectar and insects, by hovering in front of a flower and introducing the bill into the mouth of the corolla ; this allows the protractile tongue to reach the nectar at the bottom. When the corolla is long the side of it may be pierced by the bill. Spiders, as an animal food, and the juice of altered fruits, as a vegetable one, are often appreciated. As a general rule, hummingbirds are also very fond of water, and for drinking and for wetting their plumage most of the species need frequent and close contact with some source of humidity, such as rain, mist, or spray.

The sexual and nesting habits are remarkable. Generally speaking, although a few recent observations are at variance with this commonly accepted rule, the sexes live quite independently of each other except during the mating season and may even sometimes congregate in different areas widely apart. In the case of Longuemare's Hermit *Phaethornis longuemareus*, Skutch has described courtship assemblies of males, usually amidst dense second-growth, where each has his favourite perch and performs throughout the day ; he also observed a courtship display consisting of an intricate aerial dance by the male immediately above the perched female. Such habits are, as a rule, extremely difficult to observe with any continuity owing to the restless darting movements of the birds and the density of the cover in which they often live.

At least in the great majority of species that have been at all adequately observed, the females undertake the whole duties of building the nest, incubating the eggs, and rearing the chicks. The nests are in most cases very delicate and elaborate open structures, more or less deeply cup-shaped, placed on twigs or among foliage, and built with both animal and vegetable matter such as cotton, moss, lichens, and spiders' webs. The clutch is almost invariably composed of two eggs (seldom one only), which are of elliptical shape and uniformly white coloration. The young are at first blind and practically naked ; their growth is rapid, but they do not leave the nest until their wing feathers are fully grown, about 22–24 days after hatching. There is no downy stage in their feathering, and their first plumage resembles more or less, except for duller colouring and lack of ornamentation in the males, that of the adult stage.

Owing to the high rate of their metabolism; hummingbirds are, during the day, in frequent need of food among the flowers ; and their pugnacious and intolerant temper, together with their great power of flight, contribute to give them a great vivacity and mobility. After dusk, however, they remain quietly perched on some twig, losing their activity—and they may even, in certain circumstances, fall into a kind of hibernation, with diminished body temperature (see TORPIDITY). They live a mostly solitary existence ; and, although certain species may sometimes show a tendency to aggregate in small parties, they seldom tolerate the propinquity of intruders either of their own kind or of others. They are even bold and aggressive, and many cases are recorded where they attack with their sharp bills much larger and more powerful birds than themselves, such as birds-of-prey.

The family is strictly confined to the New World, where it is represented in all continental and insular territories from Alaska and Labrador in the north to Tierra del Fuego in the south, except the Galápagos Archipelago. However, owing to their perpetual need of animal food, the life of hummingbirds is closely dependent on an abundance of insect life and, although to a lesser extent, of flowers. They may be encountered wherever and whenever minute arthropods, at least, are to be found in sufficient numbers ; but they are of course, by far, much more numerous in the tropical countries than anywhere else, and especially so in the subtropical zone of the Andes in South America, where heavy moisture and luxuriant vegetation seem to afford them the best conditions of life. Nevertheless, some species are perfectly adapted to live, amid a surprising scarcity of food, in semi-arid areas along the Pacific coast of both North and South America, while others inhabit the almost as poor páramo zone of the highest Andes. The area which possesses the greatest number of species is Ecuador and its neighbouring countries, Colombia and Peru.

The several species that extend their breeding habitat into the temperate countries, both in the north and in the extreme south (Patagonia), are all migratory and spend the winter months in warmer latitudes. Thus, the Ruby-throated Hummingbird *Archilochus colubris* is a well known summer visitor in eastern North America, as far as southern Canada ; while on the western side the Calliope Hummingbird *Stellula calliope* reaches British Columbia and the Rufous Hummingbird *Selasphorus rufus* breeds as far north as south-eastern Alaska. Even many tropical species are known to make regular movements, related to local conditions of food supply as affected by the alternation of wet and dry seasons or the flowering of certain plants. Generally speaking, the lowland species are often widely distributed, sometimes over enormous areas, while most of the mountain birds remain characteristic of a single climatic zone and are sometimes even narrowly localised.

Subject to their feeding and nesting requirements, hummingbirds—owing to their small size and their entire lack of fear—can adapt themselves readily to the vicinity of man ; they thus become generally numerous, or at least frequent visitors, where gardens, parks, and cultivation are widely spread.

The word 'hummingbird' is omitted (regularly or alternatively) from the names of many species, so that other terms—mostly invented by Gould but still widely used—become substantive. In addition to some already mentioned, the following are examples : the Andean Rainbow *Coeligena iris*, the Comte de Paris' Starfrontlet *C. lutetiae* of Ecuador and Columbia, Temminck's Sapphirewing *Pterophanes cyanopterus* of the Andes, and the Sunangel *Heliangelus strophianus* also of the Andes. These and others are given separate entries.   J.B. (2)

Some Observations on Living Hummingbirds.

The repeated assertion that the tongue of hummingbirds is used, like that of the woodpeckers and wrynecks (Picidae), for catching insects is not borne out by close observation of a score or so of species of Trochilidae in captivity. It appears to be a highly specialised organ adapted for drinking liquids only. The tip does not remain inert in the liquid as would the proboscis of a moth, but is rapidly thrust in and out ; nor is it as flexible as in the woodpeckers and their allies. No insects, however small, have been seen to be collected or sucked up by it. On the other hand, hummingbirds of some genera (notably *Glaucis* and *Androdon*) are probably able to extract insects and spiders from flowers *with the bill*, and to swallow them without having to drop and catch them.

However, most hummingbirds—unlike the passerine sunbirds (Nectariniidae)—are incapable of manipulating an insect held in the bill. Indeed, none of the species observed was able to grip live food with the mandibles for more than a second or two. Flying insects were caught in the air, and spiders taken while floating from gossamer ; they were rushed at with gaping bill, forced into the gullet by the bird's air speed, and then swallowed. Sometimes a small spider was poked out of its web and then engulfed before it reached the ground.

All the hummingbirds rested from flight by gripping the perch with both feet, except for an individual of *Boissonneaua flavescens tinochlora* that rested on one leg with the other tucked up in the manner common among passerines.

All the individuals observed practised indirect head and neck scratching, but this was carried out more deliberately and with a less rapid foot movement than is usual with passerines. Sometimes, while being cleaned, the bill was gripped and held for a moment, almost parrot-fashion, by a claw.

All the species made occasional sharp claps with the wings during flight, particularly after bathing. At this time, too, a somewhat awkward attempt at oil-gland operating and head scratching often took place while a bird hovered in mid-air. The wing-clapping sound seems to be caused by an irregular flick of the wing-beats rather than by an actual slapping together of the wing tips.

The phenomenon of torpidity in these birds, including reference to the present writer's published observations (Chaplin 1933), is dealt with in the article on that subject (see TORPIDITY). It may be relevant that members of the Trochilidae, unlike the majority of birds (Apodidae, Caprimulgidae, Meropidae, and Alcedinidae are among other exceptions), do not sleep with the bill turned back and the nostrils buried among the feathers (commonly puffed out, but smooth in some species) of the mantle. The head is not turned back, but retracted between the shoulders ; the bill points forward and slightly

---

Plate 23 · Cryptic Attitude

Yellow Bittern *Ixobrychus sinensis* on its nest in cryptic attitude (Penang, Malaysia). In this pose, characteristic of all bitterns when alarmed, the body is held rigidly upright, with neck and bill extended and wings drooping ; the lines of its shape and plumage markings thus run parallel with the surrounding reeds, and the colour of the environment is also well matched. The neck is slowly twisted so that the source of danger is kept in view.   *Phot. Loke Wan Tho.*

(See articles COLORATION, ADAPTIVE ; BITTERN)

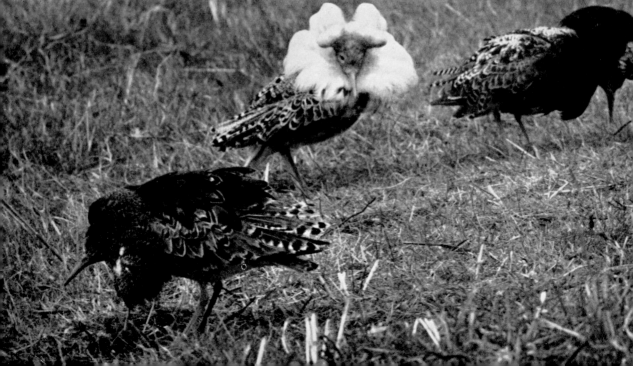

upward. It seems possible that the reduced metabolism of hummingbirds makes superfluous the
nostril protection that presumably diminishes heat
loss through the lungs in the other position.

See Plate 44a (colour phot.).   C.

Banks, R. C. & Johnson, N. K. 1961. A review of North
    American hybrid hummingbirds. Condor 63 :
    3–28.
Berlioz, J. 1944. La Vie des Colibris. Paris.
Dorst, J. 1962. Nouvelles recherches biologiques sur les
    trochilidés des hautes Andes péruviènnes (Oreo-
    trochilus estella). Oiseau 32 : 95–125.
Gould, J. 1861 (2nd ed. and supplements 1880–85).
    Monograph of the Trochilidae. London.
Greenewalt, C. H. 1960. Hummingbirds. New York.
    (Colour photographs of 70 spp. in natural size,
    mostly in flight.)
Martin, A. & Musy, A. 1959. La Vie des Colibris—Les
    Trochilidés. Neuchâtel.
Peters, J. L. 1945. Check-list of Birds of the World vol. 5.
    Cambridge, Mass.
Simon, E. 1921. Histoire Naturelle des Trochilidae.
    Paris.
Skutch, A. F. 1951. Life history of Longuemare's Hum-
    mingbird. Ibis 93 : 180–195.
Wagner, H. O. 1946. Food and feeding habits of Mexican
    hummingbirds. Wilson Bull. 58 : 69–93.

HUNTING : see FEEDING HABITS

HWAMEI : *Garrulax canorus* (see BABBLER).

HYBRID : term often used loosely to denote any
cross between individuals of unlike genetic constitution, but in its more restricted sense applied only to
the first generation cross between individuals of
different species. Interspecific hybrids are relatively

Plate 24 · Display ; Lek

a *Upper :* Sage Grouse *Centrocercus urophasianus*
strutting in sexual display, with external air sacs
on the breast and sides of neck at peak of inflation
(North America). The Tetraonidae, confined to
the northern parts of the Northern Hemisphere,
are polygamous birds and the males of various
species have remarkable visual and auditory
courtship displays. This particularly large species
is found in south-western Canada and north-
western U.S.A., but now in reduced numbers.
*Phot. Joe Van Wormer, from National Audubon
Society, U.S.A.*

b *Lower :* Ruffs *Philomachus pugnax*—males performing 'lek' display on their 'hill' (Denmark).
This Palaearctic sandpiper species is notable for
the ruff that forms part of the nuptial plumage of
the males and is polymorphic in its coloration.
The white-ruffed bird in the photograph is an
intruder and has its tufts well raised ; the bird in
the foreground shows the 'beak-stabbing'
reaction. For colours see Plate 20.
              Phot. C. C. Doncaster.

(See articles DISPLAY ; GROUSE ; POLYGAMY ;
SANDPIPER ; LEK DISPLAY ; POLYMORPHISM)

---

rare under natural conditions, although intermediates
are sometimes found in regions where the ranges of
two closely related species overlap (see SPECIATION ;
HYBRIDISATION, ZONE OF SECONDARY). Most of the
authentic cases of hybridisation have occurred in
captivity or semi-captivity, where the choice of
mates is necessarily limited and where a mate of the
same species is often not available. The chances of
hybridisation are usually greater in the case of species
that stand close to each other phylogenetically, but
close relationship is no guarantee of crossing ability
(see also PAIR FORMATION).

The percentage of fertile eggs laid by females
paired with males of another species is usually well
below the average for pure-bred birds of either
parental species, and many of the embryos die in
shell. Male avian hybrids have been reported more
often than females, and it seems probable that, in
general, males are more likely to hatch and to
survive to maturity than are females. However, as
anomalies can often be detected more easily in cock
than in hen birds (owing to their frequently more
distinctive coloration), and as sterile females sometimes assume male-like plumage, it is possible that
some of the hybrids reported as males might have
been genetic females (see also PLUMAGE VARIATION).

Hybrids vary greatly in degree of viability. In
some cases the embryos die during incubation (often
at a very early stage), while in others the hybrids
are exceptionally hardy and long-lived. Most
hybrids show characters that are intermediate between
the parental species, but heterosis or 'hybrid vigour'
is not uncommon. Many hybrids show extreme
rapidity of growth and some eventually surpass their
parents in body size.

Interspecific hybrids are usually less fertile than
birds of the parental species, and in some cases they
are completely sterile ; the degree of fertility is not
correlated in any way with the presence or absence
of heterosis. In a surprisingly large number of bird
hybrids there is at least partial fertility in both sexes.
Many species of duck, for example, not only interbreed fairly freely, but their hybrids are fertile with
other species of *Anas*, so that 'multiple hybrids'
involving as many as 5 or 6 species sometimes occur.
This may be an indication that under the present
taxonomic system there has been excessive splitting
up of genera into so-called species that may deserve
no more than subspecific rank : fertile hybrids
seem to be particularly frequent in certain orders.
Where the sexes differ in fertility, the more fertile
sex (in birds) is usually the male. Occasionally,
infertile females are capable of laying small eggs,
and males showing complete functional sterility may
exhibit normal or supernormal libido. In some

hybrids inter-sexuality has been observed. Complete sterility in both sexes tends to be most frequent among the hybrid progeny of species that are not closely related taxonomically (e.g. birds placed in different genera).

In certain cases it has been possible to produce interspecific hybrids by means of artificial insemination where natural mating has failed, but in general the degree of success achieved has been very limited. However, with improved techniques, better results may be expected in cases where failure to produce progeny is due primarily to difficulties in mating.

Differences between reciprocal crosses, where they exist, are not necessarily confined to the percentage of eggs fertilised and the number of young hatched : they may also be evident in the appearance of the hybrid birds and in their reproductive capacity when adult. Female hybrids of domestic drake × Muscovy duck parentage, for example, are often good layers, even in their first year (although the eggs are small and incapable of fertilisation), whereas females from the reciprocal cross (Muscovy drake × domestic duck) rarely lay, even in their second year. Although there are exceptions, most of the data obtained so far appear to fit Haldane's hypothesis that in inter-specific hybrids the heterogametic sex (in birds, the female) is more often absent, rare, or sterile than is the homogametic (male) sex ; but no reliable conclusions on this point can be drawn in the absence of detailed investigations (see GENETICS).

The problem of hybridisation between species has aroused great interest for many years. One of the largest books ever published on the subject is that of Suchetet, which deals exclusively and in some detail with reports of hybrids, or presumed hybrids, found in the wild. The most recent work of a comprehensive nature is Gray's check-list, containing data on hybrids produced in captivity as well as in the wild ; it is much less detailed but includes references to a greater number of hybrids.   A.P.G.

Gray, A. P. 1958. Bird Hybrids : a check-list with bibliography. Farnham Royal, Buckinghamshire.
Suchetet, A. 1896. Des hybrides à l'état sauvage. Vol. 1 —Classe des Oiseaux. Lille.

HYBRIDISATION, ZONE OF SECONDARY:

an area in which two closely related forms make contact and freely interbreed, having earlier differentiated under conditions of geographical (or ecological) isolation (see SPECIATION). This seems to be the only way in which such a situation could arise, as without a period of isolation the gene flow would either prevent differentiation or would limit it to clinal variation (see CLINE). One must therefore postulate the earlier existence of a barrier that has since broken down or been surmounted.

This may sometimes be due to human activity, e.g. in cutting virgin forest or in planting trees at intervals across open prairie. The disappearance of a barrier would, broadly speaking, create one of three types of situation according to the extent to which differentiation had meanwhile proceeded. At one extreme, contact between the two forms would not result in any regular interbreeding—there would in fact be no zone of hybridisation at all, and the two forms would obviously have become ' good ' species. At the other extreme, if there was no selection against the hybrid forms, the genetic results of interbreeding would spread in both directions from the area of contact, so that the two forms would ultimately be merged again in a single cline in which the two previously differentiated forms would lose their identity ; this would be proof that the two stocks had not become irrevocably committed to separate lines of evolution (see SPECIES).

Between these extremes there is the situation in which there is selection against the hybrids, which are in some way at a disadvantage as compared with the parent stocks. In these circumstances the two forms retain their identity in their main areas, and intermediates are restricted to the zone of contact ; the genetic results of interbreeding are prevented from spreading into the two main populations. Theoretically, the conditions of natural selection might alter in some way and the situation is thus not absolutely stable ; apart from that possibility, the two stocks have clearly established a good measure of evolutionary independence and could be regarded as separate species notwithstanding the regular occurrence of intermediates in a limited zone.

A classical case is that of the Carrion Crow *Corvus corone* and the Hooded Crow *C. ' cornix '*, two closely similar birds with a striking plumage difference. In their breeding areas they more or less divide the Palaearctic Region between them, with contact along a line across the Highlands of Scotland, along a line approximating to that of the River Elbe, and along lines in central and eastern Asia. These lines correspond with zones of hybridisation, in which obvious intermediates are common ; elsewhere each kind preserves its distinctive character, although further divisible into geographical races (see also under SPECIATION). Similarly, in North America, the Blue-winged Warbler *Vermivora pinus* and the Golden-winged Warbler *V. chrysoptera* regularly interbreed where their ranges overlap.

A much more complex situation has been described by Sibley and his associates in respect of the Rufous-sided Towhee *Pipilo erythrophthalmus* and the Collared Towhee *P. ocai*. These two otherwise similar emberizids are strikingly different in plumage (in both sexes). Both are widespread in Mexico (and the former also north to southern Canada) but are there altitudinally and ecologically separated in their breeding distribution. Local areas of contact are therefore numerous, but the situation differs from one to another. In some localities the two forms exist together without interbreeding, while elsewhere interbreeding is the rule. Certain areas are thus inhabited wholly by intermediates, of which some populations show a preponderance of this or that element while others show a more or less equal balance. Others are inhabited by pure stocks of one species or the other—and in a few places, as already noted, by pure stocks of both. There is thus in some localities an instability in the reproductive isolating mechanisms that in others suffice to keep the two forms distinct.

As Sibley points out, the result of selection against hybrids is to eliminate the descendants of those members of the parental stocks in which the reproductive isolating mechanisms are weakest ; there is thus, in effect, a 'reinforcement' of the isolating mechanisms, which may lead to a reduction in the number of hybrids produced. This may happen quite rapidly, so that a new situation due to the breakdown of a barrier may soon become stabilised. Vaurie has described how the Azure Tit *Parus cyanus*, in the latter part of the nineteenth century, extended its range rapidly from Siberia into the range of the Blue Tit *P. caeruleus* in Europe. The two species interbred freely at first, but the incidence of hybridisation soon waned. Although—the Siberian Tit having in part retracted its range—there is still an area of overlap, hybridisation is now only occasional.

The whole question is one of great interest ; and when the process of evolution is as rapid as in some of the instances cited, the opportunities for study are invaluable.   A.L.T.

Sibley, C. G. 1954. Hybridization in the Red-eyed Towhees of Mexico. Evolution 8 : 252–290.
Sibley, C. G. & West, D. A. 1958. Hybridization in the Red-eyed Towhees of Mexico : the Eastern Plateau population. Condor 60 : 85–104.
Vaurie, C. 1957. Systematic notes on Palaearctic birds no. 26. Paridae : the *Parus caeruleus* complex. Amer. Mus. Novit. no. 1833 : 1–15.

HYDROBATIDAE : see under PROCELLARI-IFORMES ; and PETREL

HYOID : see SKELETON ; TONGUE ; and MUSCU-LATURE

HYPAXIAL : see MUSCULATURE

HYPERSTRIATUM : part of the forebrain (see NERVOUS SYSTEM).

HYPHENS : as regards their use in vernacular or scientific names of birds, see NAME, ENGLISH ; NOMENCLATURE.

HYPOCOLIINAE : see BOMBYCILLIDAE ; and below

HYPOCOLIUS : generic name used as common name of *Hypocolius ampelinus*, sole member of the subfamily Hypocoliinae of the Bombycillidae (Passeriformes, suborder Oscines). This is an aberrant species placed thus near the waxwings (Bombycillinae) by recent investigators (see under BOMBYCILLIDAE). Its home is in south-western Asia,

Hypocolius *Hypocolius ampelinus*, sole species.   C.E.T.K.

from where irregular migrations take place to north-western India and perhaps casually to north-eastern Africa.

The plumage is pale grey, tinged with blue on the back and with buff on the forehead and (to a lesser extent) the under parts. A black band, beginning at the base of the bill, extends through the lores and the region of the eyes and ears, round the back of the neck ; this band can be erected, at the back of the neck, into a small crest. Primary flight feathers are black, tipped with white ; the tail is grey, tipped with black. Females are grey, not black, about the face and neck. Juveniles are buffy-brown, without black markings except for the tips of the tail feathers ; the tips of the flight feathers are marked with buff as well as white.

In comparison with waxwings, the size is slightly smaller ; the bill is similar, being short, broad at the gape, and slightly hooked ; the feet and legs are short and strong ; the wings are relatively shorter and more rounded, with a tenth primary relatively slightly longer. Rictal bristles are absent. Structure of the palate is similar to that of the waxwings (Bombycillinae) and silky flycatchers (Ptilogonatinae).

Nests have been found in the Tigris-Euphrates Valley of Iraq and in south-western Arabia. These are large and loosely constructed of twigs, lined with soft vegetable matter and sometimes hair (resembling nests of waxwings). They are usually in palm trees and are well concealed among the leaves, but other bushy trees are sometimes chosen. Both this species and the waxwings are prone to desert their nests. Eggs (4–5) are laid in mid-June. They are very pale slaty grey, with darker blotches and spots at the larger end ; occasionally these form a ring or even cover the whole egg.

Generally, the behaviour resembles that of waxwings. The birds are sluggish, shy, and sociable except in the breeding season. Their flight is strong, swift, and direct (not undulating). Fruits and berries are staple foods, although insects are also taken. Only a squeaking note (no song) is recorded.

J.C.G., Jr.

Delacour, J. & Amadon, D. 1949. The relationships of *Hypocolius*. Ibis 91 : 427–429.
Meinertzhagen, R. 1954. Birds of Arabia. Edinburgh and London.

HYPOPHYSIS: the pituitary gland (see ENDO-CRINE SYSTEM).

HYPORACHIS: AFTERSHAFT.

HYPOSITTIDAE: a monotypic family separated by some authors, but of doubtful affinities and now provisionally merged with the Sittidae (see NUT-HATCH).

HYPOTHALAMUS: part of the forebrain (see NERVOUS SYSTEM).

I

IBIS: substantive name of most species of the subfamily Threskiornithinae of the Threskiornithidae (Ciconiiformes, suborder Ciconiae) ; in the plural (ibises), general term for the subfamily. The other subfamily is the Plataleinae (see SPOONBILL). The wood-ibises belong to a different family (see STORK) ; and note that the generic name *Ibis* is used in the latter, and that the specific name *ibis* occurs both in that genus and in the Ardeidae.

Ibises are birds of the size of a Curlew *Numenius arquata* or markedly larger (about 22–30 inches in length) and likewise have the distinctive feature of a long, thin, and decurved bill. The neck is long, extended in flight, and the rather long legs have the tibiae partly bare ; the toes are of moderate length, the forward three connected at their bases by a small web. The tail is rather short. In some the face, or the whole of the head and neck, is unfeathered, showing black or brightly coloured skin. A few species have short dependent crests at the back of the head. The plumage is sometimes mainly white, but is scarlet in one species ; in others it is mainly dark, but often with a metallic sheen of purple, bronze, or green. The sexes are nearly alike, but immature birds tend to be darker and to have feathered heads and necks in species in which these parts are bare in the adults.

The most usual habitat of ibises is the vicinity of fresh water, and they are found particularly in tropical and subtropical countries. The food consists of crustaceans, fish, reptiles, worms, insects, and some vegetable matter. The birds are more or less gregarious. They utter various harsh croaking notes—loud yelps in some.

Breeding is colonial. The nests are built of sticks or rushes and placed in trees or bushes, or among reeds, or on cliffs, or on the ground on rocky islands ; even for the same species the site may vary according to local conditions. The eggs are usually 3–4 in number, from nearly white to blue in colour, marked in some species and immaculate in others. The nidicolous young have two successive down plumages (as in Ciconiidae). Both parents incubate the eggs and tend the young.

The subfamily is widely distributed in the warmer parts of the world ; apart from accidental occurrences, it is not represented in New Zealand. About 26 species have been recognised, but some of those that replace each other geographically may be merely subspecific forms. They have been placed in as many as 17 genera, about half of them monotypic, but a modern revision would probably reduce the number. Of these genera, 10 are restricted to the Old World and 6 to the New World, only *Plegadis* being cosmopolitan.

The Sacred Ibis *Threskiornis aethiopica* (emblem of the British Ornithologists' Union) was revered by the ancient Egyptians and must have been abundant in their country, judging from frequent mummified specimens and from mural paintings showing the birds with eggs and young ; but the species has been extinct in Egypt for nearly a century. It is still today a familiar bird in Africa south of the Sahara, and the range extends to southern Arabia and to Madagascar. It is a striking bird, with pure white plumage except for the dark wing-tips, noticeable in flight, and dark ornamental plumes on the lower back. In the adult the head and neck are bare of feathers, with black skin ; the bill is black and the legs are very dark red. It is gregarious, companies being seen feeding along the rivers or on cultivated land ; flight is commonly in V-formation. The nests may be on trees or on the ground ; the eggs are chalky, pale bluish with red blotches near the broad end. The White Ibis *T. melanocephala* of southern Asia and the White Ibis (or Sicklebill) *T. molucca* of Indonesia and Australia are similar forms. The Straw-necked Ibis *Threskiornis* ('*Carphibis*') *spinicollis* of Australia has stiff buffish plumes on the front of the lower neck.

Another species found in Africa is the Hadada *Hagedashia hagedash*, which has olive-brown plumage with a green metallic sheen on the wing coverts ; it is often a noisy bird, with a loud yelping cry.

Also African are the Olive (or Green) Ibis *Lampribis olivacea* (various races) and the Spotted-breasted Ibis *L. rara* ; these are crested species. Also olivaceous is the Wattled Ibis *Bostrychia carunculata* of Ethiopia, with a wattle depending from the throat. The crested *Lophotibis cristata* is found in Madagascar.

The Hermit Ibis (or Waldrapp) *Geronticus eremita* formerly bred in central Europe but became extinct there in the seventeenth century. It is now found only in North Africa and the Middle East, where it is a bird of dry country, feeding largely on beetles and nesting in colonies on cliffs. The plumage is mostly metallic bronze-green and purple, with the bill and the bare face and crown dull crimson ; the bird has a strong unpleasant odour. Its congener, *G. calvus*, inhabits mountain areas in southern Africa. The remaining Old World species are the Giant Ibis *Thaumatibis gigantea* of Indo-China ; *Nipponia nippon* of Japan and (probably no longer) China ; the Black (or Warty-headed) Ibis *Pseudibis papillosa* of India, and its congener *P. davisoni* of south-eastern Asia. *P. papillosa* has a patch of red papillae on the bare black skin of the crown, and brick-red legs. The Japanese Ibis, now on the verge of extinction, is a white bird with a red face and has the habit, unusual in the group, of nesting in pine trees.

.In southern North America there is the White Ibis *Eudocimus* ('*Guara*') *albus*, popularly misnamed ' white curlew'. The young are mainly dark in plumage, but the adults are white with dark wing-tips, pink legs, and bare reddish skin on the face. Its range extends from the southern United States to northern South America. The related Scarlet Ibis *E. ruber* of tropical South America (mainly known from the northern coastal belt) has, in the adult, the entire plumage bright scarlet—a most gorgeous bird.

In South America there are also the Buff-necked Ibis *Thersiticus caudatus* and two related forms, which together cover the continent ; the Green (or Cayenne) Ibis *Mesembrinibis cayennensis*, found from Panama to the northern Argentine ; *Harpiprion caerulescens* of central Brazil and the northern Argentine ; *Phimosus infuscatus*, widely distributed in tropical parts ; and *Cercibis oxycerca*, found from the Orinoco to the Rio Negro.

In the sole cosmopolitan genus, the Glossy Ibis *Plegadis falcinellus* has a wide distribution. Its races are found from southern Europe (occasionally wandering to the British Isles) to Australia and to Africa, and also over much of the Americas. It is a bird of dark plumage, looking black at a distance but in a good light showing much purplish-brown, with a metallic gloss of bronze and green. The

eggs are dark greenish-blue. The White-faced Ibis *P. chichi* is purely American, ranging from the western United States to the Argentine ; the *Handbook of North American Birds* (unlike the *A.O.U. Check-list*) treats it as a subspecies of *P. falcinellus*.

See Plate 18 (colour). A.L.T.

IBISBILL : *Ibidorhyncha struthersii* (see under AVOCET).

IBIS, WOOD : see STORK ; WOOD-IBIS

ICE-BIRD : sailors' name for some prions *Pachyptila* spp. (see PETREL). Note, however, that the German name ' Eisvogel' applies to the Kingfisher *Alcedo atthis*.

ICHTHYORNITHES : a superorder of extinct birds (see under CLASS ; FOSSIL BIRDS).

ICHTHYORNITHIFORMES : order erected to include such fossil forms as *Ichthyornis* and *Apatornis* (see FOSSIL BIRDS).

ICTERIDAE : a family of the Passeriformes, suborder Oscines (see ORIOLE (2)).

IDEATION : see LEARNING

IIWI : *Vestiaria coccinea* (see HONEYCREEPER (2)).

ILEUM : the posterior part of the small intestine (see ALIMENTARY SYSTEM).

ILIUM : a paired bone of the pelvic girdle, partly fused with the other elements (see SKELETON).

ILLUSTRATION, BIRD : the pictorial representation of birds in the illustration of books, and more particularly of books dealing wholly or partly with birds as a main subject. If by ' illustration ' we mean ' the pictorial elucidation of any subject ' (O.E.D.), then book illustration is of venerable antiquity. It was probably derived from Egypt, and some authorities hold that the illustration of books began in earnest at the time when the papyrus roll gave way to the codex on parchment, bound in book form—a form which came into general use in the fourth century A.D. It seems likely that technical works, or text-books as we should now call them, have always been illustrated ; but we must recognise that in addition to illustrations that explain and amplify the text there are illustrations that are solely or very largely decorative. The line between these two types of illustration is not always very clearly drawn—we can instance the woodcuts of Thomas Bewick—but the distinction has to be kept in mind for a proper understanding of the subject.

If we pass over the imaginative and didactic portrayals of birds to be found in the medieval bestiaries, and also the excellent marginal decorations in such manuscripts as that of 'De Arte Venandi cum Avibus' (ca 1248) of the Emperor Frederick II, then any account of bird illustration may conveniently begin with the invention of printing and the first use of the woodcut.

Paradoxically, it would seem that the standard of accurate observation deteriorates with the advent of printing, although in the work attributed to Konrad von Megenburg, the *Pùch der Natur* (Augsburg 1475), the woodcuts seem to have been prepared not merely for decorative purposes but with some intention of illustrating the text. Certainly this work was one of the first printed books to contain illustrations of birds, although there are better portrayals in the *De Proprietatibus Rerum* of Bartholomaeus Anglicus, printed by Wynkyn de Worde (ca 1495) and containing one of the earliest illustrations of birds in a book printed in England.

In 1491 Jacob Meydenbach printed at Mainz the richly illustrated *Hortus Sanitatis*, the third part of which, 'Tractatus de Avibus', contains about 103 figures of birds. Among these is a fine frontispiece depicting a number of birds, and two 'ornithologists' in deep discussion.

During the sixteenth century much progress seems to have been made in book illustration, doubtless due in part to the influence exerted by the woodcuts of Dürer, and the beautiful plant drawings of Leonardo da Vinci ; and with Pierre Belon, of Le Mans, direct observation of birds may be said to have begun. Belon's *Histoire de la nature des oiseaux* (Paris 1555) may be noted as the first ornithological treatise in which the 160 figures were described by the author as 'simple portraits of the birds, the nature of which no one else had illustrated before'.

Also in 1555, Conrad Gesner, of Zürich, published the third volume, devoted to birds, of his famous encyclopaedia, the *Historia Animalium*. Gesner, like Belon, used original drawings for his woodcuts ; but it must be admitted that the figures in Gesner's work are superior to those in Belon. They are, for the most part, the work of a Strasbourg artist, one Lukas Schan, whom Gesner himself describes as equally skilled both in painting and in fowling. Gesner also borrowed some pictures from Belon, as did Aldrovandi, in a somewhat similar three-volume work published at Bologna from 1559 to 1603.

By the end of the sixteenth century engraving on metal had begun to supersede the art of woodcutting. One of the earliest bird books to be illustrated by the new process was the *Uccelliera* of Giovanni Olina, published at Rome, in 1622, with plates by A. Tempesta and F. Villamena.

During the seventeenth century artists were often employed to portray the denizens of royal menageries and aviaries. Such, for example, were Georg and Jakob Hoefnagel, and Roelant Savery, who worked in this way for the Emperor Rudolf II ; or Nicolas Robert, the founder of the famous *Collection des Vélins*, who between 1673 and 1676 produced three sets of bird plates.

A definite step forward was marked by the publication, in 1676, of Francis Willughby's 'Ornithologiae libri tres,' brought out, after Willughby's death in 1672, by John Ray. Willughby may be accounted the founder of British ornithology, and his work, perhaps one of the first standard illustrated 'textbooks' on birds, contains 77 plates, some signed W. Faithorne, F. H. van Hove, and W. Sherwin.

During the seventeenth and eighteenth centuries the many voyages of discovery gave rise to books illustrated with magnificent plates, many coloured, of which we may cite as a well-known example Mark Catesby's *Natural History of Carolina* (2 vols., London 1731-43). In this work, the birds occupy 109 out of the 220 plates, and the figures are so true to nature that the book 'has long been treasured as a model representation of subjects of natural history' (Nissen). Catesby himself engraved the plates and also coloured the first copies.

The enormous interest provoked by the work of Buffon in France was helped on by the publication of the collection of plates of animals drawn and engraved under Buffon's supervision by F. N. Martinet, who began work in 1765. By about 1783 some 1000 plates had been published, 973 of which contained figures of birds. This comprehensive ornithological iconography, of significance even today, is usually referred to as the *Planches enluminées, exécutées par Daubenton le jeune*, or simply as Buffon's *Planches enluminées*.

This was also the period of the de luxe monograph in France. Such works as J. B. Audebert's *Oiseaux dorés* (2 vols., Paris 1800-02) ; F. Levaillant's *Histoire naturelle des Perroquets* (2 vols., 1801-05), with figures drawn by J. Barraband ; A. G. Desmarest's *Histoire naturelle des Tangaras* (1805-07), with 72 coloured plates by Barraband's pupil Pauline de Courcelles (later Mme Knip)—all these works, of superlative beauty, made this the golden age of ornithological illustration in France.

The eighteenth century marks the beginning of coloured engravings in scientific works, and perhaps the earliest work of this kind devoted to British birds was Eleazer Albin's *Natural History of Birds* (1731-38), which is full of examples of what the late Iolo Williams used to call the 'magpie and stump' manner of bird illustration. In England, Thomas Pennant's *British Zoology* (1761-66), with 121 bird plates engraved by Mazell and coloured by Peter Paillou, marked a new departure in the study of British birds.

But the most famous name in England at this time is undoubtedly that of Thomas Bewick, who by 1800 was rediscovering the woodblock, but with a modification 'so great as to make a new thing of it. . . .' He made wood give the delicacy of shadowing which only intaglio copperplates could give before ; and his wood could be printed at one and the same impression with the type instead of on a separate 'plate'. The 'white-line' engraving of his silhouettes influenced English and Continental work for two centuries' (F. Meynell, *English Printed Books*, 1936).

The climax of illustrated bird books is undoubtedly the four-volume 'elephant folio' work of J. J. Audubon, *The Birds of America*, published in London from 1827 to 1838, and illustrated with 435 aquatint engravings of great splendour. The huge format of the plates is due to the fact that the birds are represented in their natural size, and in this connection we should mention P. J. Selby's *Illustrations of British Ornithology* (1831–34), in which the life-size figures were engraved by W. H. Lizars in hand-coloured reproductions, made for the most part from Selby's own drawings.

The close of the eighteenth century brought with it the invention of lithography, and among the pioneers of the use of this process was Edward Lear, whose *Illustrations of the Family of Psittacidae* (1830–32) contains 42 lithographic plates 'drawn from life, and on stone'. These plates were coloured by hand.

In 1832 appeared the first of John Gould's famous series of illustrated folio works, *A Century of Birds from the Himalaya Mountains*. In the preparation of the lithographic plates for all his works, Gould received much assistance, from his wife first of all, and from such artists as Edward Lear, H. C. Richter, Joseph Wolf, and others. Gould died in 1881, with more than forty volumes to his account, and with the death of this dominant figure in the ornithological world of the time the series of great bird books of the Victorian era came to an end. The high standard of his illustrative work was carried on by Wolf, one of the greatest animal painters of his time, J. G. Keulemans, and Joseph Smit, to mention only three.

Keulemans, who died in 1912, illustrated a large number of ornithological works, including G. E. Shelley's *Monograph of the Nectariniidae* (1876–80), and also made drawings for the *Ibis* between 1869 and 1909, and for the lithographs in the British Museum's great *Catalogue of Birds*. Perhaps the most important illustrated work of this period is Baron Lilford's *Coloured Figures of the Birds of the British Islands* (1891–98), for which the chromo-lithographs were made from drawings by Keulemans and Archibald Thorburn, with some by G. E. Lodge and W. Foster.

With Thorburn a new era of bird illustration began, in which H. Grönvold, J. G. Millais, and G. E. Lodge were among the leading artists. Thorburn himself is considered by some to be the greatest of bird artists, and it is certainly true that his beautiful and accurate paintings mark him out as the most notable illustrator since the days of Gould. Grönvold, who died in 1940, is well known for his contributions to many works ; we may give, for example, his contributions to W. Beebe's *Monograph of the Pheasants* (4 vols., 1918–22), perhaps the last bird book to be illustrated in the 'grand manner', by chromolithography and collotype. Lodge died in 1954 at the age of 94. His published memoirs are full of historical interest for the subject, with many precious counsels on field observation and drawing from life.

This great tradition of bird illustration has been worthily carried on in Britain by such artists as Roland Green, J. C. Harrison, Winifred Austen, Peter Scott, D. M. Reid-Henry, and C. E. Talbot Kelly, to mention only a few names. We have earlier referred to the revival by Bewick of the art of wood-engraving, which had declined rapidly from about the middle of the sixteenth century and had fallen almost entirely into disuse by the end of the seventeenth. In the present century, such artists as E. Fitch Daglish, Robert Gibbings, and C. F. Tunnicliffe, have successfully re-introduced this art, which both illustrates the text and also, as has been said, 'shows respect for the printed page'.

Among Continental artists of recent date, mention should be made of the Swedes J. Larsen and B. Liljefors ; of the Germans O. Kleinschmidt, E. Aichele, and F. Murr ; of the Frenchman Paul Barruel, whose delightful water-colours illustrate the three fascicles of the *Iconographie des Oiseaux de France*, published by the Société Ornithologique de France in 1953–55 ; and of the Swiss Robert Hainard, an original artist working in the entomological field as well as in that of birds, whose coloured wood-engravings are much esteemed.

In the United States the work of L. A. Fuertes (1874–1927) is perhaps seen at its best in his posthumously published *Abyssinian Birds and Mammals* (1930), with its delightful chromolithograph reproductions. Allan Brooks, an accomplished naturalist, as well as illustrating a number of books also contributed many drawings to the *National Geographic Magazine* ; and George M. Sutton, himself an ornithologist of note, illustrated his *Birds in the Wilderness* (1936) with his own pencil drawings and sketches in colour. One very recent work, illustrated by an American artist of distinction, is James Bond's *Birds of the West Indies* (1960), with illustrations by Don R. Eckelberry—a worthy successor to the foregoing.

How far will photography and especially colour-photography (see PHOTOGRAPHY), of the excellent kind seen, say, in such productions as Walt Disney's 'Living Desert' (1954), supersede the work of the bird painter? Before attempting to answer this question it is necessary to compare the best colour-photographs of birds with the plates, not only in the great classic works that we have been briefly considering, but also with those in such comparatively recent productions as Barruel's *Iconographie*, mentioned above, or Peterson, Mountfort, and Hollom's *Field Guide to the Birds of Europe*, where the pictures by Roger Tory Peterson (as in his own American *Field Guides*) aid identification so tremendously. There can be no doubt that the craftsmanship and intuition of the bird artist, assisted by all the modern methods of photo-lithographic reproduction, can provide descriptive qualities and convey the essential nature of the bird and its habitat in a way that no photograph, however excellent, can entirely achieve.   A.C.T.

The following publications deal generally with the subject or with certain aspects of it.

Alexander, W. B. 1953. Ornithological illustration. Endeavour 12 : 144–153.

Anker, J. 1938. Bird Books and Bird Art. Copenhagen.

Harris, H. 1926. Examples of recent American bird art. Condor 28 : 191–206.

Lodge, G. E. 1946. Memoirs of an Artist-Naturalist. London.

Nissen, C. 1953. Die illustrierten Vogelbücher : ihre Geschichte und Bibliographie. Stuttgart.

Ronsil, R. 1957. L'Art français dans le Livre d'Oiseaux. Mem. Soc. Ornith. France no. 6.

Schäfer, W. 1949. Das wissenschaftliche Tierbild. Frankfurt a/M.

Sitwell, S., Buchanan, H., & Fisher, J. 1953. Fine Bird Books 1700–1900. London.

IMITATION: see under LEARNING ; MIMICRY, VOCAL

IMMATURITY: see under YOUNG BIRD

IMMIGRATION: migration into an area (see MIGRATION ; and IRRUPTION).

IMPENNES: a superorder recognised by some authorities (see under CLASS ; and PENGUIN).

IMPERVIOUS: as applied to nostrils, see NARIS.

IMPRINTING: a special case of exploratory or latent learning that has particular relevance for the student of ornithology (see also LEARNING). Like latent learning and insight learning, it is characterised by the absence of any reward in the usual sense of something which satisfies one of the primary physiological needs of the animal. The name 'imprinting' ('Prägung' in German) was originally given to a type of learning characteristic of the development of the following response of the young of nidifugous birds such as geese and ducks (Anatidae) and rails (Rallidae). Heinroth, in 1910, found that young geese reared from the egg in isolation reacted to their human keepers, or to the first relatively large moving objects that they saw, by following them as they would their parents. In extreme cases it seems that this need happen perhaps for only a few minutes for the young bird to come to accept a human being as its proper associate and to retain for the rest of its life a tendency to regard human beings as fellow-members of its species. Thus a bird, as a result of this first experience, may when it becomes mature—months or years later—be found to be irreversibly fixated sexually to human beings ; and Lorenz assumed from his work on geese that this was characteristic of imprinting. Subsequent investigation seems to show that such fixations based solely on the experience of the first few hours or days of life are extremely rare. Although many examples have been reported, it is evident that in almost all cases there has been a long subsequent history of rearing and attending by human keepers, so that there has been continual opportunity for the bird to learn to respond to human beings as a result of other types of learning (see LEARNING). The important point emerges, however, that when the young bird first follows the parent or substitute parent the attachment is not to an individual (although this will usually come later as a result of conditioning) but to the 'species' in a very general manner. Thus, we can sum up the characteristics of the process of imprinting, in the sense originally proposed by Lorenz, as :

(1) A learning process confined to a very definite and brief period of the individual life.

(2) One that, once accomplished, is often very stable and perhaps in some rare cases irreversible.

(3) A process that is often completed long before the various specific reactions to which the imprinted pattern will ultimately become linked are established.

(4) Learning that is generalised in the sense of leading to an ability to respond to the broad characteristics of the species.

On the whole, subsequent research has tended to emphasise the importance of conclusions (1) and (4) and to suggest that (2) and (3) apply only in exceptional cases.

As regards the first point, it has been shown that the critical age for imprinting Mallard *Anas platyrhynchos* ducklings, by the process of following, is between 13 and 16 hours ; and that if the first experience is delayed beyond the latter age then the percentage of ducklings that can be imprinted falls rapidly to zero (Figure). It is known, however, that by holding the birds in complete isolation, or by giving doses of drugs such as meprobamate that reduce metabolism and act as muscle relaxants, the critical age for imprinting can be extended (Hess). Similar evidence for the existence of a critical period early in life has been found in chicks and goslings, as well as in the young of Tufted Duck *Aythya fuligula*, Moorhen *Gallinula chloropus*, Coot *Fulica atra*, and others.

Further light on the question as to how far imprinting is supra-individual learning has been provided by work on the following response both of rails (Coot and Moorhen) and ducklings (Mallard). Hinde, Thorpe, & Vince found that if a young Moorhen shows a following tendency at all, when tested under controlled conditions with a model drawn along a wire, it matters little what characteristics the first model possesses. Having learnt to follow one model (say a black wooden box or a carved model of a Moorhen) it will, at least in the same experimental environment or situation, subsequently follow models as different from this as a yellow football bladder or a canvas-covered ' hide ' $6 \times 2 \times 2$ feet. Experiments of this kind emphasise that in these species the period during which young birds can learn to follow moving objects as such is strictly limited. Once a bird has learnt to follow models, however, the ability to transfer from one type to another can be demonstrated in birds as young as 3 days and as old as 60 days, although when first presented with a new model they will show a slight diminution in response, indicating that they perceive a difference and that the new model is not at first quite as acceptable as the old. With the Coot and Moorhen it appears that in the early days of life the following response is stronger than the tendency, which is also present, to flee from strange objects. The result is that in the course of following experiments the young bird gets used to a number of strange objects and so its fleeing tendency is weakened by ' habituation ' (see LEARNING). Later, the fleeing drive becomes stronger and more difficult to habituate ; and consequently, with age, a strange object becomes less likely to elicit following. In the Coot practically all the waning of a following response with age can be attributed to this growth in the fleeing drive, and in this species no evidence has so far been obtained suggesting that any per-

manent and irreversible effect is produced, such as will become linked to instinctive behaviour patterns that are to mature later. In species such as the Mallard, however, there seems little doubt that the termination of the imprinting period cannot be due solely to the development of a competing fleeing drive, but that there is an internally controlled waning of the following tendency independent of the development of fear responses.

It is evident that the following response is in some way ' its own reward '. All that the bird is doing in the first instance is giving rein to a need to maintain itself, by its own efforts, in a constant spatial relationship with a moving object. This moving object can be almost anything that is not too large or too small, and that does not move too fast or too slowly. To this extent at least imprinting can be regarded as a special case of exploratory learning, the ' exploration ' being restricted to a certain class of moving objects. Experiments have shown quite clearly that the actual following is the essential basis of the learning process, and that any subsequent reinforcement by feeding, brooding, protection, and the like is not essential for learning as it occurs under these experimental conditions. Hess has evidence that, with Mallards, the imprinting strength increases with the distance travelled by the animal in following the imprinting model during the imprinting process. His results indicate that it is the distance travelled and the amount of effort put into the travelling, rather than the time taken in travelling, that is the effective factor. Thus, for imprinting to take place there must be an initial tendency to orient and move towards an object, in other words to ' investigate ' it ; and, subsequent to this, energy must be expended in the attempt to reach or keep up with it.

To sum up this work on imprinting in birds, we can say tentatively that the imprinting period is initiated primarily by the maturation of an internally motivated appetitive behaviour system which is in readiness, at the time of hatching or very soon after, to express itself in the following response. The time during which this internally controlled tendency can find its *first* expression in action is limited, by internal factors, to a matter of a few hours or at most days ; but during this time the response is ready to appear as soon as the circumstances permit it to do so. The termination of the ability to make that first response is, as we have seen, very largely influenced by the development of competing fleeing responses. On the other hand, of course, once the following behaviour has had a chance to establish itself, it will continue towards those models that have become associated with the achievement of the consummatory situation resulting from successful following, and may be yet further generalised to others. Nevertheless, the evidence that, in some species at least, an internal change directly reduces the appetitive following drive with age remains very strong.

If, however, we regard imprinting as simply the ability to learn—during a very short period of the early life—the visual characteristics of certain classes of moving objects, we shall miss some very important implications of the phenomenon. Birds are primarily visual animals and the following response is, of course, primarily the result of seeing the parent or parent-substitute ; but it is quite clear that there is no justification for restricting the idea of imprinting to the following situation or to visual stimuli. Any instance of a sensitive period for learning a response to a particular kind of stimulus can be reasonably regarded as an example of the same phenomenon. Thus there is no doubt that acoustic stimulation can play a very important part in the imprinting process. With young ducklings and rails it is not necessary, for the achievement of efficient following, that the model should emit any sound, although there is no doubt that if a sound is produced (particularly an intermittent sound) the model is thereby rendered more attractive and easier to follow. There seems little doubt that certain species may recognise instinctively the characteristic call of the parent, and when this happens the utterance of the appropriate call will enormously enhance and reinforce the imprinting process. It has been shown by Klopfer, however, that surface-nesting species of waterfowl can learn the appropriate sound signal involved in the maintenance of the brood-parent relationship as a consequence of visual imprinting. No unlearned preference for any particular auditory signal appeared to exist, and it was not found possible to obtain auditory imprinting in the absence of visual stimulation. With the cavity-nesting Wood Duck *Aix sponsa*, however, the reverse situation was found—although apparently not in the hole-nesting Shelduck *Tadorna tadorna* : exposure to sound signals alone could, in the Wood Duck, produce subsequent preference for that sound, thus demonstrating auditory imprinting ; and this imprinted response to sound was not reinforced or altered in any way by following or by a visual stimulus. This experimental conclusion, of course, fits the facts of the natural life of the Wood Duck, since the first response of the young ducklings to their mother must be based on auditory stimuli. There is no doubt that the following response, in addition to being important in establishing the parent-young link, is also an essential element in the process of family integration in birds such as ducks and geese.

In nidicolous birds, naturally, this particular type of following response cannot operate. Nevertheless there is in certain song-birds good evidence for something very suggestive of imprinting in the process of learning characteristic song (see SINGING). In the Chaffinch *Fringilla coelebs*, for instance, the hand-reared isolated bird produces extremely simple songs representing the inborn component of the specific song. In the early weeks and months of life, the young birds can learn from their parents, or other adults of the species, some of the characteristic features of the normal song, such as its division into phrases, that it should end with a flourish, and that it should have certain restrictions as to pitch. There is good evidence that this learning can take place, both in the wild and under experimental conditions, without any immediate practice on the part of the learner—a fact that again suggests similarity to imprinting. When the bird comes to compete with neighbouring territory-holders in its first breeding season, it then sings in competition with them and as a result rapidly learns the finer details, especially those of the end phrase, of one or a number of different songs. This period during the first breeding season thus appears to be a period of special sensitivity to a particular kind of auditory stimulation. It is, however, brought to an abrupt close by internal factors, presumably hormonal, and by the time the young Chaffinch is at the most 13 months old its ability to learn songs is at an end ;

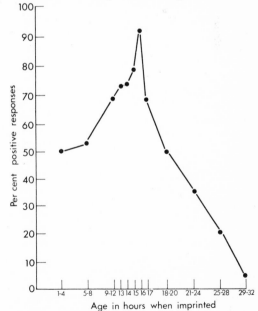

Critical age for imprinting in Mallards *Anas platyrhynchos* expressed as a percentage of positive responses.

Redrawn from Hess 1957.

and, however long it may live, the song or songs it has acquired during its first year remain its characteristic song or songs for the rest of its life.

W.H.T.

Heinroth, O. 1910. Beiträge zur Biologie, namentlich Ethologie und Physiologie der Anatiden. Verhl. V Internat. Orn. Kongr., Berlin 1910 : 589–702.

Hess, E. H. 1957. Effects of meprobamate on imprinting in waterfowl. Ann. N.Y. Acad. Sci. 67 : 724–732.

Hinde, R. A., Thorpe, W. H. & Vince, M. A. 1956. The following response of young Coots and Moorhens. Behav. 9 : 214–242.

Klopfer, P. 1959. The development of sound-signal preferences in ducks. Wilson Bull. 71 : 262–266.

Lorenz, K. 1935. Der Kumpan in der Umwelt des Vogels. J. Orn. 83 : 137–214 ; 289–413.

Thorpe, W. H. 1956. Learning and Instinct in Animals. London. (2nd ed. 1963.)

Thorpe, W. H. 1958. The learning of song patterns by birds, with especial reference to the song of the Chaffinch Fringilla coelebs. Ibis 100 : 535–570.

Thorpe, W. H. 1961. Bird Song : the biology of vocal communication and expression in birds. Cambridge.

Thorpe, W. H. & Zangwill, O. L. (editors) 1959. Current Problems in the Behaviour of Animals and Men. Cambridge.

INCA : substantive name of some *Coeligena* spp. (for family see HUMMINGBIRD).

INCERTAE SEDIS : term used in taxonomy to mean ' of uncertain taxonomic position '.

INCUBATION : the process by which the heat necessary for embryonic development is applied to an egg after it has been laid. Such heat is usually derived from the bodies of one or both of the parent birds. There are two aspects from which this process may be viewed ; that of the egg in its passive role, and that of the adult bird in its active role. Study of the egg involves details of the time and temperature required for successful hatching ; this leads to a consideration of the development rate of the embryo, which determines the incubation time and is determined by the incubation temperature. Study of the parent birds involves reference to the special behaviour associated with the warming of eggs or newly hatched young (see also DEVELOPMENT, EMBRYONIC ; HEAT REGULATION).

Incubation Period and Temperature. Some confusion has arisen in the literature through failure to distinguish between these two aspects. This is particularly evident in the recording of incubation periods ; these have sometimes been given in terms of the time between laying and hatching of an egg or eggs, and sometimes as the length of time that parents spend sitting on the nest. Further, various beginning and end points have been used in estimating the incubation time of an egg and these have not always been clearly stated, with the result that there is often some difficulty in comparing the records of different observers. The best practical definition of incubation time, as applied to the egg, seems to be that given by Heinroth—the time from laying of the last egg of a clutch to hatching of that egg. The problem has been reviewed by Swanberg.

Incubation times range from about 80 days in the Royal Albatross *Diomedea epomophora* to about 10 days in some of the smaller passerines. Relatively long periods occur in Strigiformes (*Bubo bubo*, 35 days), Falconiformes (*Gypaetus barbatus*, 55), Procellariiformes (*Puffinus puffinus*, 52–54), Spheniciformes (*Aptenodytes forsteri*, 53), Struthiiformes (42), Casuariiformes (*Dromaius novaehollandiae*, 56–60), Apterygiformes (75–80) ; relatively short periods occur in Picidae (*Dendrocopos major*, 12–13), Turnicidae (12–13), Columbidae (*Columba palumbus*, 15), and Passeriformes (most less than 15). For other examples see Kendeigh and Nice. A number of factors have been suggested to account for the differences of incubation times in different species. The size of the bird or egg, the length of the bird's life, the stage of the chick's development at hatching, climate, season, and food supply, are some of them. Nice, reviewing these theories, concluded that the crucial factor is the rate of development of the embryo ; this being a product of natural selection, ultimate causes may be located in the bird's ecological relationships.

Little has been done to test the direct effect of environmental factors on incubation times. Nice states that in the incubator eggs usually hatch a quarter or half a day sooner than they would in the nest, which means that it has not been possible to increase the rate of development much beyond that found in nature, although this may be considerably retarded by keeping the eggs at a temperature lower than that to which they would normally be subject. It seems, then, that birds usually maintain their eggs near a temperature which promotes the most rapid development ; but there are exceptions.

This temperature at which the eggs are normally kept in nature is the ' incubation temperature ', although the term may also be used to refer to the temperature range within which development of the embryo is possible. Huggins gives egg temperatures for 37 species of 11 orders, measured by inserting thermocouples into the eggs. He found the average temperature for all his birds to be in the vicinity of 34° C. Atmospheric conditions tend to influence the temperature at which the eggs are kept ; to counteract this, birds may sit tighter in cold adverse weather, and may spend longer periods off the nest, sometimes actively shading the eggs, when the weather is hot.

Parental Behaviour ; Brood Patches. Incubation behaviour comprises the special movements and organisation of daily activities shown by birds when they have eggs or newly hatched young. Kendeigh has surveyed a large body of data, collected from all groups, on such points as the division of labour between the parents and the patterns of attentiveness and inattentiveness, i.e. intervals spent on and off the nest. Almost all the possible arrangements are exemplified, from equal sharing of incubation between the sexes to either male or female taking sole charge, and there are numerous examples of adaptive specialisation. For instance, species in which only one member of a pair broods are, in many cases, sexually dimorphic ; the incubating bird is coloured cryptically, and its mate conspicuously. In male passerines there is a general correlation between the presence of brood-patches and the occurrence of incubation (Skutch).

The brood-patch or brood-patches, when present, consist of one or more areas of the ventral surface that become denuded of feathers, oedematous, and richly supplied with blood vessels, an adaptation facilitating the transfer of heat from parents to eggs (Tucker). There is some evidence, from birds that sit from the start of laying, that the maximum incubation temperature is not attained until brood-patch development is completed, which may not be until near the end of the laying period (Swanberg ; Paludan ; Ytreberg). There are birds, such as the cormorants (Phalacrocoracidae) and gannets (Sulidae), in which brood-patches do not occur : in gannets their function seems to be performed by the highly vascularised webbed feet (Tucker).

The movements performed when a bird sits on eggs usually include ruffling or lowering of the abdominal feathers to expose the brood-patches, and a waggling or quivering action as or after the bird lowers itself. This ' settling ' probably serves to bring the brood-patches into the closest contact with the surfaces of the eggs (Beer 1961). It may be preceded by a movement, called ' shifting ', in which the standing bird bends its head down and moves the eggs about by rolling them with the underside of its bill. A further movement, normally confined to the incubation period, is ' retrieving ' ; this is performed by various birds that build shallow nests on the ground (Poulsen), and it consists of rolling or shifting a displaced egg until it is again inside the nest. In some cases the bird shifts and settles on the egg outside the nest several times, which results in the egg being moved closer to the nest. In other species the retrieving bird bends over the egg and moves its bill towards its feet while standing in the nest or, if the egg is too far away for this, combines the shifting movement with walking backwards.

To analyse the causal mechanisms underlying this behaviour, a distinction must be made between the influence of external stimuli and the internal physiological condition of the bird. One method used to test the role of environmental stimuli has been the presentation of standard stimulus situations throughout the season and the recording of fluctuations in the readiness of the bird to respond to them (Beer 1963). From such tests it has been found that, in some birds, the period during which incubation movements are released by eggs can be extended into the pre-incubation phase, but this can be achieved only within fairly fixed limits (about 7 days in the Herring Gull *Larus argentatus* according to Paludan). Similarly, the incubation behaviour period can be shortened or entirely eliminated by substituting begging chicks for a bird's own eggs (Emlen), and it can be extended through failure of the eggs (or substitute models) to hatch (Paludan).

Changes in responsiveness to standard stimulation must be the result of internal changes, probably associated with hormone secretions from the pituitary and the gonads, although little can be said that is supported by evidence from a large number of species. Most of the investigations of physiological factors have been carried out on domestic pigeons and fowls, and these are in many respects highly atypical of the Class Aves as a whole. An example of such work carried out on passerines is that described by Bailey, who presents evidence to show that the brood-patches result from the synergistic effect of two hormones—oestrogen, which gives rise to increased vascularity of the dermis, and prolactin, which causes moulting and dermal oedema but only in the presence of oestrogen (see ENDOCRINE SYSTEM). The relation between structural change in the brood-patches and the associated behaviour is, of course, another problem. The activities of the endocrine glands may depend directly or indirectly on external conditions such as changing photoperiod, stimuli received during courtship, and visual or tactile stimuli from the eggs. An example of interaction between external and internal factors is presented by evidence of a type of mechanism controlling the number of eggs laid. In at least some indeterminate layers, this seems to involve inhibitory processes set in motion by stimuli received from the first-laid eggs at the start of incubation (Paludan ; Weidmann)—see LAYING. Reviews bearing on the physiology of incubation are those of Brenemann and Marshall. Recent reviews of the roles of hormones have been made by Eisener and Lehrman.

Special Cases. Species in several groups, e.g. cuckoos (Cuculinae), do not themselves incubate but parasitise other birds (see PARASITISM). The Megapodiidae also do not incubate but utilise natural sources of heat such as solar radiation, heat of fermentation of decaying organic matter, or volcanoes ; by altering the rate of fermentation in their mound nests or the depth at which the eggs are buried in mound or sand (Frith), the birds are to some extent capable of regulating the temperature at which the eggs are kept (see MEGAPODE).

See Plate 38A (phot.).   C.G.B.

Bailey, R. E. 1952. The incubation patch of passerine birds. Condor 54 : 121–136.
Beer, C. G. 1961, 1963. Incubation and nest building behaviour of Black-headed Gulls I : incubation behaviour in the incubation period. III : the pre-laying period. Behav. 18 : 62–106 ; 21 : 13–77.
Brenemann, W. R. 1955. Reproduction in birds : the female. Mem. Soc. Endocrin. 4 : 94–113.
Eisner, E. 1960. The relationship of hormones to the reproductive behaviour of birds, referring especially to parental behaviour : a review. Brit. J. Anim. Behav. 8 : 155–179.
Heinroth, O. 1922. Die Beziehungen zwischen Vogelge-wicht, Eigewicht, Gelegegewicht und Brutdauer. J. Orn. 70 : 172–285.
Huggins, R. A. 1941. Egg temperature of wild birds under natural conditions. Ecology 22 : 148–157.
Kendeigh, S. C. 1952. Parental care and its evolution in birds. Illinois Biol. Monog. 22 (1–3) : 1–356.
Lehrman, D. S. 1961. Hormonal regulation of parental behaviour in birds and infrahuman mammals. In Young, W. C. (ed.). Sex and Internal Secretions. 3rd. ed. Baltimore.
Marshall, A. J. 1955. Reproduction in birds : the male. Mem. Soc. Endocrin. 4 : 75–93.
Nice, M. M. 1954. Problems of incubation in North American birds. Condor 56 : 173–197.
Poulsen, H. 1953. A study of incubation responses and some other behaviour patterns in birds. Vidensk. Medd. Dansk Naturh. Foren. 115 : 1–131.
Skutch, A. F. 1957. The incubation patterns of birds. Ibis 99 : 69–93.
Swanberg, P. O. 1950. On the concept of ' incubation period '. Vår Fågelv. 9 : 63–80.

INCUBATOR BIRD : see MEGAPODE

INDEX : term sometimes applied to the second digit of the manus, but by a few authors to the first (see WING).

INDIAN REGION : alternative name for ORIENTAL REGION.

INDICATORIDAE : see under PICIFORMES ; and HONEYGUIDE

INDIGENOUS : term applied to species, etc., meaning native to the area under reference.

INDIGO-BIRD : substantive name, alternatively ' indigo-finch ' or ' combassou ', of *Hypochera* spp. (see WHYDAH (1)). There is also the Indigo Bunting *Passerina cyanea* of North America (see BUNTING).

INDIVIDUAL VARIATION : differences between one individual and another within the same population of a single species, excluding such as are directly related to age, sex, seasonal condition, definite polymorphism, ill-health, or gross abnormality (for excluded factors see DISEASE ; PLUMAGE, ABNORMAL AND ABERRANT ; POLYMOR-PHISM ; SEASONAL CHANGE ; SEXUAL DIMORPHISM ; YOUNG BIRD ; WEIGHT ; for geographical variation see CLINE ; SUBSPECIES).

Morphologically, the occurrence of small differ-ences is to be expected, in that variability is a charac-teristic of living organisms and provides the material for natural selection (see EVOLUTION ; NATURAL SELECTION). The most apparent differences, within the limits of the above definition, are in dimensions (small departures from the mean) and in the colour tone or the pattern detail of the plumage ; for the most part, these can be accurately determined only with the bird in hand.

In respect of behaviour, everyone who has observed birds closely is aware of the existence of ' individual-ity '—although it is sometimes hailed as a surprising discovery, and even as something that ornithologists tend to ignore or deny. Differences in this regard are even more to be expected than morphological variations, as they may represent either innate varia-tions of a ' temperamental ' kind, or the effect of a bird's particular experience ; in practice, the dis-tinction may be hard to draw. When birds are very intimately studied, even in the free-living state, the observer himself may become a factor permanently influencing behaviour (see also TAMENESS). Such considerations must be given weight in making an objective assessment.

INFECTION : see DISEASE

INFESTATION : see ECTOPARASITE ; ENDOPARA-SITE

INGLUVIES : the crop (see ALIMENTARY SYSTEM).

INHAMBU : name used in Latin America for *Crypturellus* spp. (see TINAMOU).

INHERITANCE : see GENETICS

INJURY FEIGNING : see DISTRACTION DISPLAY

INNATE BEHAVIOUR : see FIXED ACTION PATTERN

INSECTICIDES : see TOXIC CHEMICALS

INSESSORES : former ordinal name, applied to an assemblage of so-called ' perching birds ' comprising the Passeriformes of today and various other groups.

INSHORE HABITAT: see under OCEANIC BIRDS

INSIGHT: see LEARNING

INSTINCT: an innate capacity for forms of behaviour that do not have to be learnt by the individual—a word falling into disuse as a scientific term because it represents an over-simplified concept and has acquired a variety of meanings.

INSTRUMENTAL SOUNDS: non-vocal sounds, made respectively by the bill, wings, or tail, as contrasted with vocal utterances (see SINGING). The three types may be considered separately.

Bill Sounds. Some of these, perhaps to be regarded as adventitious, are made by two birds together. Various clattering noises are made in the course of bill-fencing and bill-sparring in a wide range of birds, such as grebes (Podicipitidae), herons (Ardeidae), auks (Alcidae), pigeons (Columbidae), kingfishers (Alcedinidae), woodpeckers (Picidae), waxwings (Bombycillinae), thrushes (Turdinae), crows (Corvidae), and some finches (Fringillidae). Bill-crossing and bill-tapping are common in the sexual display of albatrosses (Diomedeidae) ; the whetting together of the bills of a pair of Laysan Albatross *Diomedea immutabilis* has been described as producing a whistling sound (G. W. K. Fisher 1902).

Bill-rattling, producing a noise like that of a nutmeg-grater, occurs among frigate-birds (Fregatidae) as an alarm note, and also as an entreaty for food on the part of the chicks. The bill-clappering of storks (Ciconiidae) is well known. In the White Stork *Ciconia ciconia* it is a sign of recognition between members of a pair or group ; the head is thrown right back between the legs, to the accompaniment of raising and flapping of wings and spreading of tail. The chick, when sufficiently strong, exhibits similar behaviour towards its parents, recognising them and soliciting food. Other species of stork also clapper, but less loudly. The Shoebill *Balaeniceps rex* clatters its massive mandibles, but without posturing, as a note of alarm and an entreaty for food.

Bill-snapping as a defensive threatening sound is made by most owls (Strigiformes) and is particularly loud in such large species as the Eagle Owl *Bubo bubo* and the Snowy Owl *Nyctea scandiaca*.

In a different category are sounds made by the bill in contact with various objects. Some of these are adventitious effects of feeding or nesting actions, for example among tits (Paridae), nuthatches (Sittidae), and woodpeckers (Picidae). On the other hand, specialised bill-drumming—beating a tattoo on the wood of a tree—is practised by many woodpeckers (Picidae) and has been most studied in the Greater Spotted Woodpecker *Dendrocopos major*. In this species both sexes produce a loud, harsh, vibrating sound by an extremely rapid rain of blows at a selected point, most commonly near the end of a broken or dead branch but exceptionally on some quite different sort of sounding-board such as the lead-covered top of a wireless mast. The pitch of the sound is in due proportion to the diameter of the branch ; the normal duration is about a second, and the normal frequency is estimated at 8–10 (sometimes as low as 3–5) blows per second. The strength diminishes after the first or second blow, so that the sounds run together and die out in a short continuous vibration. The sound may be audible (to the human ear) at distances of up to a quarter of a mile. The drumming period extends, in Britain, from the end of February to the first week in May ; the sound serves to attract mates, and both birds drum before coition. In the Lesser Spotted Woodpecker *D. minor*, the sound tends to be less powerful and higher in pitch, and may last for 2 seconds at a frequency of 14–15 blows per second ; both sexes drum before performing the sexual 'butterfly dance'. The Flicker *Colaptes auratus* of North America beats a rolling tattoo on dead branches in spring, and sometimes uses metal telegraph poles for the purpose.

Wing Sounds. Whereas the normal flight of some birds, such as owls (Strigiformes), is notably silent, and that of others is inaudible except when there is a dense flock within close range, that of others makes considerable noise. Ducks (Anatidae) are foremost among wildfowl in producing more or less musical sounds with their wings when flighting ; the audible intensity of the sound depends to a great extent on atmospheric conditions and wildfowlers are agreed that it reaches its maximum effect on still, frosty mornings. Teal *Anas crecca*, especially in planing down, make a metallic-sounding 'swoop', and among other surface-feeding species the Shoveller *Spatula clypeata* stands out for the amount of sound emitted during level flight—as, in a different group, does the Shelduck *Tadorna tadorna*. On the whole, however, it is the diving ducks that make most sound, and notably the Goldeneye *Bucephala clangula*—commonly known in America as the 'Whistler' because of the penetrating sound made by its wings, especially in the case of old drakes. The Mute Swan *Cygnus olor*, alone among its kind, produces a high-pitched harp-like note as the primaries on the downbeat strike the air.

Various gallinaceous birds (Galliformes) have noisy flight. Pheasants *Phasianus colchicus* flying to roost create a musical high-pitched whistle with their wings ; and the 'whirr' of wings of Red Grouse

Lagopus scoticus and Partridge *Perdix perdix* are familiar. The American Wood-ibis *Mycteria americana* makes a most amazing noise as the air rushes through the wings when it dives from a height to its feeding grounds. The Rhinoceros Hornbill *Buceros rhinoceros* has been described as making a sound ' like that of a chugging steam locomotive ' with its wings.

Hummingbirds (Trochilidae) are so called because of the sound made by the extremely rapid vibration of their wings ; it reminded Salvin of a piece of machinery actuated by a powerful spring. The humming sound is produced by wing-beats as fast as 50 to the second (although the largest species, the Giant Hummingbird *Patagona gigas*, beats its wings only 8–10 times per second). As originally noted by Darwin, different species produce a different ' hum '. In the male Broadtail *Selasphorus platycercus* the primary feathers taper at the tips and the air filtering through the openings produces a distinctive rattling whistle, whereas the female has normally shaped feathers and flies with the usual sort of buzzing sound.

The foregoing examples relate to ordinary flight, although the sounds are in some cases not heard under all conditions. There are other instances where a characteristic sound is emitted only at special times, and usually as an element of display ; these include cases where the sound is the result of wing-clapping, although that can happen also in other circumstances. This last point is particularly relevant to the pigeons (Columbidae) ; wing-clapping is common in domestic pigeons, notably tumblers, and many wild species start with a few clapping strokes when taking off—the sound varies considerably from one species to another. In the Wood Pigeon *Columba palumbus* the male, near the top of its display flight, makes 1–3 vigorous claps with its wings ; the sound has been attributed to forcible downstrokes analogous to the crack of a whip. In other cases the clapping sound is due to the wings striking each other.

Even the silent-flying owls do this. In the breeding season the Shorteared Owl *Asio flammeus* will circle on extended wings with only occasional beats, and from time to time will drop like a stone for some distance clapping its wings 4–6 times in rapid succession beneath its body ; the wing-tips appear to meet only at the first clap, but contact at the carpal region is said to take place throughout the clapping (Christoleit). The clapping is also used when the nest is threatened. The Longeared Owl *A. otus* performs zig-zag flights between the tree-trunks, and then rises above the tree-tops clapping its wings beneath the body at the end of each beat ; both sexes do this, the female less frequently, and again the action is

also used when the nest is threatened. Similar habits have been described for other owls.

In the breeding season the male Nightjar *Caprimulgus europaeus* produces a series of wing-claps ; the tips do not appear to meet, but possibly the carpal joints do. The male may clap as many as 25 times in succession while gliding with tail spread and wings raised obliquely. The female also claps, and apart from the mating season has been observed to do so (by the present writer) when accompanied in flight by her two young in early September. In America the Nighthawk *Chordeiles virginianus* indulges in ' sky-coasting ', and when the bird makes the turn the air rushing through the primaries produces a booming sound such as one might imitate by blowing across the bung-hole of an empty barrel.

The Ruffed Grouse *Bonasa umbellus* of North America ' booms ', while at rest, by striking its wings against its breast. It is a great performer in the mating season, and both sexes ' boom ' before coition. The sound is described by Forbush as a deep-toned thump, like the muffled beating of a great heart, followed by a quickly accelerating drumming roll like distant thunder. Various other gallinaceous birds have similar, if less notable, performances ; for instance, the crowing of the cock Pheasant *Phasianus colchicus* in spring is associated with flapping and thumping.

Both sexes of the Redthroated Diver *Gavia stellatus* produce a noise like an express train with their wings when, in May and June, they volplane down to the loch uttering wild raucous cries. The American Woodcock *Philohela minor* has the first three primaries modified and attenuated as a musical instrument used during the nuptial flight ; the writer observed this at twilight in March, when the birds produced a cadence of musical whistling during the rapid descent following the upward spiral. Various plovers (Charadriidae) in the breeding-season make wing noises during flight ; thus the male Lapwing *Vanellus vanellus* makes a ' zooming ' noise.

Among the passerines, mention may be made of the birds-of-paradise (Paradisaeidae) ; those species with specialised wings and drooping tails, such as Princess Stephanie's Bird-of-paradise *Astrapia stephaniae* produce an attractive sound comparable with rustling silk. The Neotropical manakins (Pipridae) perform peculiar dances with both buzzing sounds and clashes that resemble loud thumb-snappings ; their wings, notably those of the Yellow-thighed Manakin *Pipra mentalis*, show a peculiar modification presumably for the production of mechanical sounds, but just how this is done has not been settled for any species. Other examples include the wing sounds made by clapper larks *Mirafra* spp. and todies *Todus* spp.

Finally, a case of wing-sound made by two birds : in courtship flight the drake Pintail *Anas acuta* passes beneath the duck so closely that their wings clatter together with a loud noise like a watchman's rattle.

Tail Sounds. Of these the chief are the 'drum-mings' or 'bleatings' of snipe *Gallinago* ('*Capel-la*') spp. during aerial evolutions in the breeding season. The Common Snipe *G. gallinago* produces a resonant, tremulous sound lasting about a couple of seconds and sometimes frequently repeated ; both sexes do it, but chiefly the male. The sound accompanies a rapid descent at an angle from a considerable height. Experiments (Meves ; Roh-weder ; Bahr) have provided definite proof that the sound is a result of vibration of the outer pair of rectrices, which—when the tail is spread fanwise—are detached from the remaining six pairs ; but that the wavering element is due to the action of the wings in intermittently deflecting air against the tail. The sound can be artificially reproduced by various devices, such as attaching the musical feathers in the appropriate position to a cork and whirling it at the end of a string ; the latter imparts a vibratory motion and serves (as a rigid stick will not) to simulate the tremulous effect naturally derived from wing movements.

The musical feathers, the outermost rectrices (7th pair), show a specialised structure, the essential features of which are comparable with those of a harp. The outer web is narrow and formed of stiff rami that can be easily separated. The inner web is very broad and formed of long, stiff rami making an acute angle with the shaft and having radii and hamuli so arranged that the whole web is strongly locked together. The adjacent feathers (6th pair) show something approaching the same structure, whereas the five central pairs are soft and unmusical.

In some other species of snipe that make similar sounds the total number of rectrices is greater—16, 18, 20, or even 26-28 ; this last occurs in the Pintail Snipe *G. stenura* of Asia, in which 8-9 on each side are attenuated, the outermost so much so that they resemble pins. The number showing specialisation varies considerably with species, thus in *G. nobilis* of northern South America there are three on each side. The quality of the sound also varies ; thus in Latham's Snipe *G. australis* it is more voluminous—a tremendous rushing noise—and in the Auckland Island Snipe *Coenocorypha aucklandica* the bleat is high-pitched. The Great Snipe *Gallinago media* and the Jack Snipe *Lymnocryptes minimus* possess no musical feathers, and the same is true of the European

Woodcock *Scolopax rusticola* and the American Woodcock *Philohela minor*.

A sound made by the Lyre-tailed Honeyguide *Melichneutes robustus*, in the course of elaborate flying evolutions, is thought to be produced by vibration of the outer rectrices, as in the Snipe.

P.M.-B.

INSULIN : see ENDOCRINE SYSTEM ; also NUTRITION

INTEGUMENTARY STRUCTURES : out-growths from the skin (see SKIN). Of these the chief are feathers (see FEATHER ; PLUMAGE), the rhamphotheca covering the bill, sometimes with horny excrescences or extensions such as casques and frontal shields (see BILL), the podothecae cover-ing the feet (see LEG), and the oil gland (see OIL GLAND) ; these are dealt with elsewhere, as indi-cated. So also are the claws growing on the toes and sometimes on the digits of the manus, and the spurs that are present on the tarsus or on the carpal joint in some species (see LEG ; WING). There remain to be considered various accessory structures found in certain species, especially about the head and neck ; these are of several kinds.

Combs, Wattles, and Lappets. These are unfeathered flaps or appendages, usually of a fleshy texture and brightly coloured. Their function must lie in display and recognition ; they often show sexual dimorphism ; and their state may be subject to hormonal control. They are included in the general term 'caruncle'. A familiar example of a comb—an erect process situated longitudinally on the crown—is that of the domestic fowl, largest in the cock ; the name derives from the serrated margin. Wattles are often pendulous from the angles of the mouth ('rictal lappets'), and there may be more than one on each side. Or they may be harder, more warty excrescences, variously situated —rictally, frontally, near the eye, or anywhere on the patches of bare skin found in some species, chiefly on the face and neck. Some of these, as with others adorning the bill, are moulted seasonally (see MOULT). Wattles are found in many species, particularly among the pheasants (Phasianidae), turkeys (Melea-grididae), plovers (Charadriidae), jacanas (Jacanidae), cotingas (Cotingidae), honeyeaters (Meliphagidae), starlings (Sturnidae), and wattle-birds (Callaeidae). The Turkey *Meleagris gallopavo* has a varied assort-ment, comprising a distensible frontal caruncle, tubercles on head and neck, and a throat wattle.

Pouches and Sacs. These are of different kinds. The gular pouches of pelicans (Pelecanidae) and, less markedly, of cormorants (Phalacrocoracidae) play a part in the capture and swallowing of prey. Others are ornamental, such as the long red pouch depending from the almost naked neck of the Marabou *Leptoptilos crumeniferus* ; or the inflatable sac, covered with bright red skin on the front of the throat, in male frigatebirds *Fregata* spp. Others again are concealed by feathers and are used in the production of booming calls, such as that uttered in spring by the male Prairie Chicken *Tympanuchus cupido* with the aid of two inflatable sacs on the sides of the neck.

INTELLIGENCE: a term without precise connotation for the study of bird behaviour, its place being taken by 'insight learning' (see LEARNING ; also NERVOUS SYSTEM).

INTENTION MOVEMENTS: movements, e.g. the assumption of a posture, preparatory to the action of a fully developed 'drive'.

INTERBREEDING: see GENETICS ; HYBRID ; HYBRIDISATION, ZONE OF SECONDARY ; ISOLATING MECHANISM ; REPRODUCTIVE ISOLATION ; SPECIATION

INTERMEWED: term used in FALCONRY

INTERNATIONAL CODE; INTERNAT-IONAL COMMISSION: see NOMENCLATURE

INTESTINE: the posterior part of the gut or digestive tract, comprising the small intestine (duodenum and ileum) and the large intestine (rectum)—see ALIMENTARY SYSTEM. The intestine as a whole is disposed in the body cavity in a series of three or four loops, and these form a variety of patterns that are characteristic of particular groups and thus of some taxonomic value. The character is little used nowadays, probably because of its practical inconvenience in being ascertainable only by dissection of complete specimens in good condition ; but the results of its taxonomic application run reasonably parallel with those obtained by other methods. A terminology of the different patterns was introduced by Gadow (1889) but need be only briefly summarised here.

The first or duodenal loop is always 'closed', i.e. with its two branches united externally by membranes, and has the pancreas within it ; the descending branch lies to the right of the ascending branch when viewed from the ventral aspect—this is termed a 'right-handed loop'. When all the loops run parallel with the long axis of the body, the pattern is termed 'orthocoelous' ; when some form spirals it is 'cyclocoelous'. Gadow named four main orthocoelous patterns, grouping cyclocoelous patterns under a fifth head :

1. Isocoelous—second and subsequent loops closed and left-handed.

2. Anticoelous—second loop closed and left-handed, third loop closed and right-handed.

3. Plagiocoelous—at least the second loop (generally open) doubled over in horseshoe form.

4. Pericoelous—second loop left-handed, open, and surrounding the third loop (which is generally straight and closed).

5. Cyclocoelous—loops forming spirals (as mentioned above).

Variations of these main types have also been given names, e.g. antipericoelous and isopericoelous among the orthocoelous, and mesogyrous and telogyrous among the cyclocoelous.

INTRODUCTION, ARTIFICIAL: see NATU-RALISED BIRDS

INVASION: term best reserved for an expansion of range into a new area ; but sometimes used as synonymous with IRRUPTION.

IORA: substantive name of *Aegithina* spp. (see LEAFBIRD).

IRENIDAE: a family of the Passeriformes, sub-order Oscines (see LEAFBIRD).

IRIS: a thin, opaque membrane in front of the lens of the eye, which by its state of contraction determines the size of the aperture (pupil) in its centre (plural 'irides' ; see VISION).

IRIS COLORATION: often a noticeable character of the living bird at close range or of the newly dead specimen, but of course lost in the museum skin and not always accurately represented by the artificial eyes of mounted exhibits ; the character may show sexual dimorphism, and changes with age and sometimes with season. A brown pigmentation of the iris, resembling that found in many mammals, is very common among birds ; in others, brilliant lipochrome pigments are present, especially yellow, green, and blue (see COLOUR). Red or reddish eyes are also common, but the appearance may be due (as in the Rock Dove *Columba livia*) more to richness of the superficial blood-vessels than to pigmentation of the iris itself. Iris coloration, on close examination, may often be seen to be variegated.

Some examples of birds showing various colours other than brown may be mentioned. Yellow irides are found, for instance, in most owls (Strigiformes), some 'waders' (Charadrii), some pigeons (Columbidae), and some herons (Ardeidae), but also in many other groups. The Jackdaw *Corvus monedula* is a familiar example of a species in which the iris is almost white (pearl-grey in the adult). In adult

Budgerigars *Melopsittacus undulatus* the iris is white peripherally, and chocolate-brown with white concentric lines in the pupillary part. In the Honey-buzzard *Pernis apivorus* a layer of guanine-containing cells in the yellow iris makes the latter appear brilliant white in reflected light.

An example of a bird in which the irides are green—a relatively infrequent colour—is the Cormorant *Phalacrocorax carbo*. Blue irides are found in, for example, the Oilbird *Steatornis caripensis*, the Blue-eyed Shag *Phalacrocorax atriceps*, the Ariel Toucan *Ramphastos ariel*, and the Monkey-eating Eagle *Pithecophaga jefferyi*.

Many groups include red-eyed birds, e.g. rails (Rallidae), pigeons (Columbidae), grebes (Podicipitidae), herons (Ardeidae), coucals (Centropinae), barbets (Capitonidae), puffbirds (Bucconidae), vireos (Vireonidae), and mocking-birds (Mimidae) ; the White-winged Chough *Corcorax melanoramphos* (Grallinidae) has a bright red eye.

Sexual dimorphism in iris coloration is not infrequent. In Brewer's Blackbird *Euphagus cyanocephalus* (Icteridae), the iris is white in the male, dark in the female ; whereas in two species of finfoots (Heliornithidae) it is dark brown in the male and bright yellow in the female. In the Carolina Wood Duck *Aix sponsa* the iris is orange-red in the male, dark brown in the female. A striking case is that of the Saddlebill *Ephippiorhynchus senegalensis* (Ciconiidae) ; the brown eye of the male tones with the dark plumage of the head, while the 'chrome yellow' (Chapin) iris of the female is a conspicuous character.

Iris coloration may change with age ; in a number of instances, brown in the immature bird is succeeded by yellow in the adult. In the Gannet *Sula bassana*, the iris is dark brown in the nestling, grey-blue in the juvenile, and nearly white—with a fine black outer ring—in the adult (Lockley). There may sometimes be seasonal change ; for instance in the Rockhopper Penguin *Eudyptes crestatus* the colour of the iris, with that of the bill, varies from red to yellow with the seasons (see also HERON).

To be distinguished from iris coloration is the colour of the orbital ring of bare (sometimes hardened) skin round the eye in some species, e.g. among the cormorants (Phalacrocoracidae), or any circular pattern in the plumage in that position. The white-eyes (Zosteropidae) take their name from a white ring round the eye.

Duke-Elder, W. S. 1958. System of Ophthalmology. Vol. I. The Eye in Evolution. London. (Chap. XIV. The eyes of birds.)

IRRADIATION: see RADIATION (3)

IRRUPTION: a type of irregular migratory movement, the characteristics of which are here described. Most migrations are regular, taking place at the same seasons each year between the same breeding and wintering areas (see MIGRATION). But some are irregular in both time and space, occurring only occasionally and in unpredictable places. These latter are usually known as 'irruptions', but this is not a wholly satisfactory term since it describes the movements only from the point of view of the receiving areas ; they are equally 'eruptions' from the areas that are abandoned. The term irruption also implies movement on a massive scale, the occasional spectacular mass-movements having doubtless caught the imagination and led to the adoption of the term ; but these are exceptional, and many more modest movements occur. The term 'irregular migration' is to be preferred, since irregularity is the most distinctive character. The term 'invasion', sometimes used in this sense, is better reserved for rapid expansions of range into new areas of settlement (see INVASION ; RANGE EXPANSION).

The birds best known for irregular migration in the Northern Hemisphere are shown in the Table ; but many other species behave in this way. Svärdson claims that some 40 Swedish birds have displayed tendencies to it.

The irregular migrants are native to two main kinds of habitat, arid steppes and the northern forests. Those of the northern forests may be further subdivided into birds of the taiga (conifer) and birds of broad-leaved forests (often with a mixture of conifers). Both kinds of habitat are subject to extremes of climate, prolonged drought in the one and low temperatures coupled with heavy snowfall in the other, at times producing conditions that will not support bird life.

The majority of irregular migrants, especially those in which the behaviour is most marked, are food specialists. The foods on which each is principally dependent in winter are shown in the Table. In the birds of the broad-leaved forests this food specialisation is less marked and irregular migrations are less common, occurring chiefly among the northernmost populations.

Furthermore, the trees on which the forest birds depend are themselves irregular in their production of food-providing fruits. This irregularity is caused partly by variations in the weather at flowering time, high temperature during a few critical weeks favouring the production of fruits, and partly because a heavy fruiting exhausts the trees' productive powers and is invariably followed by a year of low yield. This tends to set up a rhythm in the produc-

The Commonest Irregular Migrants in the Northern Hemisphere

Species	Preferred Food	Distribution
1. *Steppe Birds*		
Pallas's Sandgrouse *Syrrhaptes paradoxus*	*Agriophyllum gobicum*	Central Asia
Rosy Pastor *Sturnus* ('*Pastor*') *roseus*	Locusts (in breeding season)	Turkestan
2. *Birds of Northern Conifer Forests* [1]		
Crossbill *Loxia curvirostra*	Spruce	Holarctic
Two-barred Crossbill *L. leucoptera*	Larch	Holarctic
Pine Grosbeak *Pinicola enucleator*	Conifer seeds, berries	Holarctic
Thick-billed Nutcracker *Nucifraga caryocatactes macrorhynchos*	Hazel	Scandinavia
Thin-billed Nutcracker *N. c. caryocatactes*	Arolla Pine	Siberia
Clark's Nutcracker *N. columbiana*	Conifer seeds	Nearctic
Siskin *Carduelis spinus*	Birch, Alder	Palaearctic
Nuthatch *Sitta europaea* (Siberian populations)	Spruce	Siberia
Red-breasted Nuthatch *S. canadensis*	Pine, Spruce	Nearctic
Coal Tit *Parus ater*	Spruce, insects	Palaearctic
Waxwing *Bombycilla garrulus*	Berries, especially Rowan	Holarctic
Cedar Waxwing *B. cedrorum*	Berries	Nearctic
Thick-billed Parrot *Rhynchopsitta pachyrhyncha* [2]	*Pinus chihuahuana*	Mexico
3. *Birds of broad-leaved forests* [1]		
Jay *Garrulus glandarius*	Oak	Palaearctic
Fieldfare *Turdus iliacus*	Berries	Palaearctic
Black-capped and Acadian Chickadees *Parus atricapillus* and *P. hudsonicus littoralis*	Insects	Nearctic
Purple Finch *Carpodacus purpureus*	Seeds	Nearctic
Evening Grosbeak *Hesperiphona vespertina*	Ash-leaved Maple	Nearctic
Brambling *Fringilla montifringilla*	Beech	Palaearctic
Redpoll *Acanthis flammea*	Birch	Holarctic
Great Spotted Woodpecker *Dendrocopos major*	Spruce, Scots Pine, nuts	Palaearctic
4. *Raptors and other predators*		
Goshawk *Accipiter gentilis gentilis*	Lemming	Palaearctic
American Goshawk *A. g. atricapillus*	Varying Hare	Nearctic
Rough-legged Buzzard *Buteo lagopus*	Lemming, Vole	Holarctic
Snowy Owl *Nyctea scandiaca*	Lemming, Vole, Varying Hare	Holarctic
Eagle Owl *Bubo bubo*	Lemming	Palaearctic
Horned Owl *B. virginianus*	Varying Hare	Nearctic
Long-tailed Skua (or Jaeger) *Stercorarius longicaudus*	Lemming	Holarctic
Great Grey (or Northern) Shrike *Lanius excubitor*	Vole	Holarctic

[1] Some of the birds in 2 and 3 live in both habitats.

[2] The last species has a more southerly but montane distribution ; it wanders northward sporadically into Arizona.

tivity of the trees ; and Swedish records show clearly that a heavy crop of spruce cones may be expected every third or fourth year in the south of the country, although this rhythm is less marked farther north where the weather at flowering time is more irregular. The fruiting of other trees shows similar fluctuations, a fact well-known to hard fruit growers in Britain.

These three—climatic extremes, food specialisation by the birds, and irregular fruiting—combine to cause acute imbalance at times between the level of the birds' populations and the supply of their special foods. This is often reinforced by the fact that fine weather at flowering time favours a successful nesting season, and the following heavy fruit crop favours survival during that winter. In the following autumn, when the food supply is low through ' tiredness ' of the trees, bird populations are at peak and the imbalance is at its most acute. In this situation the irregular migrants fly in search of more plentiful food supplies.

We are used to thinking of migration as basically a north-and-south movement. It is important to appreciate that the irregular migrations of the northern forest birds are essentially explorations within the birds' natural vegetation zones and are therefore basically east-to-west or west-to-east ; extensions southwards occur only when the imbalance between population and food supply is at its height and over a wide area, so that these latitudinal migrations fail to solve the birds' problem. But, since ornithological reporting is greatest in north-western Europe, overspills there have tended to be most fully described and westerly movements have been over-emphasised at the expense of easterly ones that have gone unreported.

Much remains to be discovered about these movements. We do not know, for instance, whether they are entirely random in direction or whether some populations have a westerly or easterly (or even southerly) preference. Two interesting ringing returns—a Waxwing ringed in Poland in February 1937 and recovered in the following winter some 3000 miles farther east in Siberia, and a Cedar Waxwing ringed in central California in April 1935 and recovered two years later in Alabama 2000 miles to the east—suggest that birds may travel randomly in entirely different directions in different winters. It has been suggested, however, that the known stimulus to migration of anticyclonic weather may favour westerly rather than easterly movements.

We do not know whether the whole of the population moves at once. A high proportion of juveniles has been noted in irruptions of Jays, Great Spotted Woodpeckers *Dendrocopos major*, Crossbills, Two-barred Crossbills, and Nutcrackers, which suggests that they may move more readily than adults. This is known, of course, in such partial regular migrants as the British Robin *Erithacus rubecula melophilus*. It does not, however, seem to occur with Waxwings.

Nor do we know to what extent the birds regain their breeding areas. Whole populations of Crossbills are known to settle down and breed for one or sometimes more seasons in an area into which they have irrupted. They may thus be nomadic over a very wide range, an example being one that was ringed as a nestling in Denmark and found breeding two years later in Czecho-Slovakia. In other species ringing recoveries (which are few) show that at any rate some birds regain their normal breeding area ; but it is also known that many breed beyond the normal range in the year following a big exodus. They may, indeed, do so in the spring preceding one, overcrowding in the normal range at a time of peak population causing them to move out at this season. With these, competition for nesting sites and for territories is probably a more important cause for movement than lack of food. At times large numbers ' wander until death ' if they fail to find a sufficient food supply ; this certainly happened during the irruption of Waxwings to Britain in 1937.

Some authors have suggested a cyclic rhythm in these movements. A ten-year cycle for irruptions of the Waxwing into western Europe has been proposed, for instance. Close examination of the records, however, does not bear this out, and it seems clear that movements of irregular size and distance take place every year in some part of the birds' range. Cyclic fluctuations do take place, however, in the numbers of predators on mammals in which a cyclic rhythm is well-established (four-year cycles in lemmings and voles, a ten-year cycle in the Varying Hare). In phase with these are cyclic variations in the numbers of Willow Grouse *Lagopus lagopus* and Ptarmigan *L. mutus*, since they are alternative foods for the predators and so suffer extra heavy predation at the time when the mammal populations have ' crashed '. When a sharp imbalance between the predators and their prey occurs, the former may wander far beyond their normal ranges and these movements may occasionally attain the scale of irruptions.

With some species, notably the Brambling and Redpoll, the line of demarcation between regular and irregular migration is faint. These certainly migrate regularly every year, although in fluctuating numbers, but the extent of their movements is governed by where they find their preferred foods in greatest abundance. They are birds of the broad-leaved forests where the pressures of climatic extremes and food-supply fluctuation are less, and there is a more southerly component in their movements, since this vegetation zone is broad and extends well to the south. How the birds locate feeding areas is not known, but they may have developed the ability to recognise subtle visual signs such as differences in colour of woods that are rich in food.

Much less is known about the steppe species. The Rosy Pastor is a regular migrant to India from the Asiatic steppes. It feeds its young on locusts, and its irregular migrations occur in spring, presumably on occasions when it returns on its normal spring migration to find a failure of the locust hatch. The movements of Pallas's Sandgrouse are probably caused by prolonged drought (for particulars of the major irruptions see SANDGROUSE).

From the foregoing it is clear that the ultimate cause of this behaviour lies in food supply. Just as regular migrants are solving the problem of a food supply that fails regularly every year, these irregular migrants are solving the problem of a food supply that fails irregularly. It is probable, moreover, that this kind of behaviour has an added value for the survival of those species that live in an environment subject to catastrophic extremes of climate and so of food supply. It provides a source of pioneers to repopulate the range after a disaster has brought numbers to a dangerously low level. And it enables the birds, which are opportunist rather than conventional in their behaviour, to search out and make use of supplies outside the disaster area.

The proximal causes of these irregular movements are more open to question. Svärdson has suggested that irregular migrants in fact start to migrate every year and that the proximal factors releasing the flight are exactly the same as those operating for regular migrants ('1. hormonal change, acting through metabolism, anchored by photoperiodism ; and 2. temperature, visibility, stability of air, and time of day'). But the irregular migrants differ from the regular ones in that their flight is arrested when they find abundant food.

Lack, on the other hand, suggests that high numbers in themselves act as the proximal stimulus. Certainly the birds are unusually excited and restless before a big movement, and the big movements usually occur earlier in the season than lesser ones. This, he suggests, is of advantage in causing the birds to move well in advance of failure of the food supply. Probably both explanations are right, the physiological and environmental stimuli operating every year and being reinforced at times of peak population by the added stimulus of high numbers as such.

Certainly, if Lack is right, it helps to explain why species that are normally considered sedentary occasionally show behaviour closely akin to irruption. Cramp et al. attributed the mass movements in Britain and western Europe of Blue Tits *Parus caeruleus* and Great Tits *P. major* in 1957 to high population following unusually good survival during the preceding mild winter ; and they cited the outbreak of ' paper-tearing ', and so on, as evidence of unusual excitement in the birds. The fine dry summer of 1959, when breeding success was outstanding, was also followed by some unusual events. There was a quite unprecedented number of foreign recoveries of British-ringed Linnets *Acanthis cannabina* and Goldfinches *Carduelis carduelis*, both of which are normally sedentary, and irruptions of tits were again recorded.

It seems probable that irregular migration is far more widespread than is generally supposed and that many species that are not normally migratory at all respond to an unusual situation of high population by this kind of behaviour. In these it is rare because a situation of population–food imbalance is rare ; in the birds noted for it, it is common because they live in a habitat where imbalance is common.

R.K.C.

Cramp, S., Pattet, A. & Sharrock, J. T. R. 1963. The irruption of tits in autumn 1957. Brit. Birds 53 : 176–192.

Lack, D. 1954. The Natural Regulation of Animal Numbers. Oxford.

Svärdson, G. 1957. The ' invasion' type of bird migration. Brit. Birds 50 : 314–343.

ISCHIUM : a paired bone of the pelvic girdle, partly fused with the other elements (see SKELETON).

ISOBAR : a line connecting points of equal atmospheric pressure (see METEOROLOGY).

ISOCHRONAL LINE : a line joining geographical localities at which the same event occurs simultaneously ; applied, notably, to the mean date of arrival of a given migratory species (see MIGRATION).

ISOCOELOUS : see INTESTINE

ISOHYET : a line connecting points of equal rainfall (commonly in terms of mean annual rainfall or the mean for some stated period of the year)—see CLIMATOLOGY.

ISOLATING MECHANISM : a difference between species, or populations of a species, that tends to prevent cross-mating and so to maintain reproductive isolation ; such differences are often in factors concerned in recognition, i.e. in appearance (plumage) or behaviour (display, voice). An isolating mechanism is said to be 'specific' when it is adaptively built up between two populations that are genetically capable of interbreeding and of producing fertile hybrids ; this can occur only when there is some contact between the two populations, with the production of hybrids that are at a selective disadvantage as compared with the parent stocks. Such specific isolating mechanisms often play an important part in speciation (see SPECIATION ; also HYBRID ; HYBRIDISATION, ZONE OF SECONDARY ; RECOGNITION ; REPRODUCTIVE ISOLATION ; SINGING).

ISOPHENE: a geographical line along which a character of a polytypic species has the same value ; 'a line of equal phenotype'. Isophenes run roughly at right angles to the direction of a CLINE.

ISOPIPTESIS: a term that has been used in the past, with regard to the dates of arrival of migratory species, in the sense of ISOCHRONAL LINE.

ISOTHERM: a line connecting points of equal air temperature (commonly in terms of the mean temperature for a stated day or month of the year)— see CLIMATOLOGY ; METEOROLOGY.

ITALICS: as regards their use in printing scientific names of birds (represented by single underlining in manuscript or typescript), see NOMENCLATURE.

IVORY, HORNBILL: from the casque at the base of the upper mandible of the huge Helmeted Hornbill *Rhinoplax vigil*, which provides a block ($3 \times 1\frac{1}{2} \times 1$ inches) of a very hard substance, deep red on the outside, golden yellow within. In appearance something between amber and yellow jade, in consistency similar to elephant ivory, this became one of the prized imports from the Indonesian islands to China in ancient times. Prepared pieces have been found as far back as the early metal age in excavations at Niah caves, Sarawak (1959). 'Ho-ting', as it was called, was far more valuable than jade, gold, or ivory by weight ; and only the finest craftsmen could work it. The Chinese developed a method of heat-treating and pressing the casque, both to preserve the esteemed red outer layer and to enable artists to carve it in small flat strips—especially for the belt-buckles of high-ranking mandarins. Only this species of hornbill, mainly found now in Borneo and confined to virgin rain-forest in hilly country, has a sufficiently solid, large casque for the purpose. Museum pieces sometimes classified as 'toucan' and 'crane's bill' are nearly always 'ho-ting'. Less than forty perfect specimens are known to survive in existing collections, including three in Philadelphia, one (inferior) in the British Museum, and eighteen—including two whole casques carved with magical scenes and a set of sacred horses —in the collection of T. Harrisson, Sarawak.

A local craft of making floral jewellery from hornbill ivory developed in Sumatra and continued until recently ; and some inland tribes of Borneo still carve the raw beak into fine pendant ear-rings and belt-toggles. The Kelabits of the Borneo uplands have discovered that, by applying the oil of the bird's own uropygial gland, the red sheath colouring is preserved from natural fading. The Helmeted Hornbill is also characterised by elongated central tail feathers, held semi-sacred in parts of Borneo (see ORNAMENTATION, BIRDS IN). T.H.

Smythies, B. E. 1960. Birds of Borneo. Edinburgh. (Two plates of Sarawak ho-ting pieces.)

J

JABIRU : *Jabiru mycteria* of South America (not, as stated by Newton with a wrongly titled figure, *Mycteria americana*) ; in the Old World the name is sometimes applied to the Saddlebill *Ephipporhynchus senegalensis* or the Blacknecked Stork *Xenorhynchus asiaticus*. For all these species of Ciconiidae see STORK.

JACAMAR : substantive name of species of Galbulidae (Piciformes, suborder Galbulae) ; in the plural, general term for the family. This consists of 5 genera and about 15 species of small or medium-sized birds (5–11 inches long) confined to the wooded portions of continental tropical America, chiefly at low altitudes. Jacamars have long, pointed, usually slender bills. Their legs are short, and in four-toed species two toes are directed backwards ; but in the genus *Jacamaralcyon* only three toes are present, the inner hind toe having been lost. The more typical species have glittering metallic plumage and, with their long thin bills, remind one of overgrown hummingbirds (Trochilidae). Perhaps even more than hummingbirds, they seem charged with intense vitality. They are among the most exciting of all birds to meet.

A widespread and familiar member of the family is the Rufous-tailed Jacamar *Galbula ruficauda*, which ranges from southern Mexico to Ecuador, Brazil, and Trinidad. The upper plumage, including the wings and central feathers of the long tail, is glittering metallic green, over which play golden, coppery, and bronzy glints ; there is a broad green band across the chest, separating the white throat from the rufous-tawny of the posterior under parts and the outer tail feathers. The female differs from the male only in having the throat pale buff instead of white. In both sexes, the long sharp bill is black.

The largest member of the family is the Great Jacamar *Jacamerops aurea*, a long-tailed bird (in all nearly a foot in length) ranging from Costa Rica to the Amazon valley. In the male, the top of the head is bright metallic green, which merges into rich metallic golden or reddish bronze on the back and shoulders, this in turn becoming bright golden-green on the rump and central tail feathers. The outer feathers of the tail are violet-blue. The sides of the head and the upper throat are metallic green, the lower throat is pure white, and the remaining under plumage is rufous-tawny. The female is like the male except that her lower throat is tawny like the rest of the ventral surface. The bill, which is only moderately long and slightly curved, is black.

A less graceful and glittering representative of the family is the White-eared Jacamar *Galbalcyrhynchus leucotis* of Amazonia. Its plumage is largely chestnut and, as the name implies, there is a white patch behind each eye. A long, thick, almost white bill and a short tail give it a top-heavy aspect.

Jacamars appear to be wholly insectivorous and, at least in the best known genus, *Galbula*, their prey is captured on the wing. The bird rests on an exposed perch, turning its head from side to side, until it espies a suitable flying insect ; this it then overtakes by means of a rapid sally, making a fine display, especially if the victim is a large, brightly coloured butterfly or a wide-winged dragonfly. Morphos and large swallow-tails *Papilio*, which most flycatching birds eschew, are favourite fare of the jacamars. With the victim fluttering in its slender bill, the captor returns to its perch, against which it beats the insect long and loudly until the brilliant wings flutter earthward, after which the body is eaten. Despite a predilection for large and showy insects, jacamars capture many that are small and inconspicuous.

Although jacamars are closely related to the puff-birds (Bucconidae), their loquacity contrasts with the latter's taciturnity no less than their graceful slenderness with the puffbirds' chunkiness. The Rufous-tailed Jacamar is a noisy bird, and its sharp calls, sounding afar through the woodland, suggest that it lives at a high pitch of excitement. When mated birds are together, and especially when two males compete for a female, their animated vocal performances include an accelerated series of high-pitched notes that may merge into a long-drawn, clear, soft trill. At its best, the jacamar's song is delightfully melodious.

Jacamars nest chiefly in burrows, which they dig in roadside or streamside banks, in steep wooded hillsides, or in the wall-like mass of clay raised up by the roots of a great tree that has fallen before the wind. Breeding in cavities in termites' nests has been reported for several species of *Galbula*; these include the Rufous-tailed Jacamar, which usually nests in burrows, and this suggests that a termitary is chosen when a suitable site for digging a tunnel is not available. In this species, the burrow is excavated by both sexes. They loosen the earth with their fine-pointed bills, seemingly little fitted for this task, and remove it from the tunnel by kicking vigorously backward as they enter. At one nest, the female did the larger share of the digging, but she was often fed by her mate. The burrows of this species range from about 11 to 18 inches in length, and at the mouth they are from $1\frac{3}{4}$ to 2 inches in transverse diameter and slightly less in height. At the inner end, the burrow dilates into a chamber, which the jacamars do not line. The same burrow may be used in successive years.

The Rufous-tailed Jacamar lays 2–4 white, glossy eggs; few records are available for other species. The female incubates through the night, while by day she and her mate sit alternately, taking sessions that usually exceed an hour and may last for over three hours. Intervals of neglect are short and the eggs are almost constantly attended. The sitting parents regurgitate many shards of beetles and other chitinous parts of insects, and these accumulate on the floor of the chamber. The period of incubation ranges from 20 to 23 days.

In contrast to the perfectly naked nestlings of most piciform birds, newly hatched jacamars bear copious long whitish down. They are equipped with prominent heel pads that are nearly smooth instead of strongly papillate like those of woodpeckers (Picidae), toucans (Ramphastidae), and other birds that breed in unlined holes in trees. Both parents bring the young a variety of insects, but they fail to remove droppings. As they grow older, the nestlings become noisy, and while they await their meals repeat weak-voiced imitations of their parents' calls, including pleasant little trills. They leave the burrow when 21–26 days of age, wearing plumage much like that of adults of the same sex.

See Plate 32 (colour).   A.F.S.

Peters, J. L. 1948. Check-list of Birds of the World vol. 6. Cambridge, Mass.

Sclater, P. L. 1882. A Monograph of the Jacamars and Puff-birds, or Families Galbulidae and Bucconidae. London.
Skutch, A. F. 1937. Life-history of the Black-chinned Jacamar. Auk 54 : 135–146.
Skutch, A. F. 1963. Life history of the Rufous-tailed Jacamar *Galbula ruficauda* in Costa Rica. Ibis 105 : 354–368.

JACANA: substantive name (alternatively ' lily-trotter', especially for the African forms) of the species of Jacanidae (Charadriiformes, suborder Charadrii) ; in the plural, general term for the family. The name is derived from a Brazilian word and should strictly be pronounced ' jaçaná '. The jacanas constitute a tropical and subtropical family of which the precise systematic position is still obscure. They are extraordinary, long-legged waterfowl of moderate size—mostly 10–13 inches in length, not including the tail plumes in the breeding dress of one species. The length of leg is accentuated by the bareness of much of the tibia. The foot is remarkable—excessively elongated toes and straight claws, with the claw of the hind toe much longer than the toe and tapering to a fine point ; this formation of the feet enables the birds to move easily over floating vegetation, the spread ensuring the best distribution of the weight. The sexes are alike, but the females are usually the larger. Rufous coloration or dark bronze tints predominate ; the juveniles are rufous-brown above and nearly white below. The adult plumage is usually assumed after two years and, except in *Hydrophasianus*, there is no special off-season plumage. Most species have a frontal shield—red, yellow, or blue ; in the juveniles it is rudimentary. The bill is moderately long, straight, and compressed, with the culmen curved at the tip. The wings are rather long, and the tail is short except in *Hydrophasianus*. On the carpal joint there is a small spur or blunt knob ; this is sometimes exaggerated into an inch-long spine. During the annual moult *Actophilornis* is flightless for a while, as it sheds its flight feathers simultaneously. In flight some species display a conspicuous light wing-patch.

Insects and all manner of aquatic life, animal and vegetable, form the food, which is taken while the birds move actively over the water plants. The jacanas' walk is rail-like, a deliberate high-stepping action with an accompanying jerk of the tail at each step, but they can run at considerable speed. When skipping from one piece of floating vegetation to another, or when alighting, they momentarily raise their wings perpendicularly, butterfly-wise, above the back. Over short distances the flight appears slow and laboured, although the wing-beats are rapid, and is much hampered by the long hanging

$\frac{1}{3}$

African Jacana (or Lily-trotter) *Actophilornis africanus.*
C.E.T.K.

legs ; on longer flights they fly more strongly, with the legs extending out behind. Jacanas are agile swimmers and divers ; they submerge to conceal themselves, and at this the downy chicks are expert. *Metopidius,* to hide, will flatten motionless with outstretched neck on water-weed. Jacanas are usually seen in pairs, many being found where suitable areas are sufficiently extensive ; but sometimes they congregate in hundreds and even thousands when not breeding. Although not strictly migratory, they may indulge in extended local movements. Except in the breeding season, jacanas are to a great extent silent ; but they have a variety of cries, such as plaintive piping, attractive mewing (*Hydrophasianus*), cackling, clucking, churring, grunting, and a persistent scolding ' chittering' when alarmed. The courtship display includes raising and flirting the wings, bowing, and weed carrying. In defence of their young, the parents resort to spectacular distraction antics. They threaten their own kind with upraised wings.

Like most species of waterfowl, jacanas breed at the end or in the latter part of the rainy season. The nest is a scanty pad of aquatic vegetation, usually placed on floating plants. Both sexes may incubate and both take part in nest building. When the parent is brooding, it sometimes seems that the eggs must be partially submerged (as they certainly often are immediately after the bird has left the nest) ; on the other hand, *Actophilornis* has been described as holding the eggs against its sides by the wings, with which it appears to scoop them up as it sits down. The normal set of eggs is four, although fewer (mostly as the result of misadventure), but rarely more, are found. In shape pyriform or ovate, they are hard-shelled ; in *Actophilornis* the yolks are rich reddish orange. The highly polished eggs, as if varnished, are unmistakable ; the cuticle waterproofs the shell. In most the ground colour varies from buff to brown, scrolled and criss-crossed— sometimes so thickly as almost to obscure the ground —with bold, irregular, twisted lines of blackish or brown, and underlying finer pencillings of light or bright brown. The eggs of *Hydrophasianus* show various shades of immaculate bronze. The chicks are precocious and leave the nest soon after hatching to run about the water plants ; the pronounced striping of the downy chick is atypical for the suborder.

There are 7 species in 6 genera : the Lily-trotter *Actophilornis africana* throughout the Ethiopian Region, its congener *A. albinucha* in Madagascar, the Lesser Lily-trotter *Microparra capensis* in eastern Africa, the Pheasant-tailed Jacana *Hydrophasianus chirurgus* and the Bronze-winged Jacana *Metopidius indicus* in India and south-eastern Asia, the Lotus-bird *Irediparra gallinacea* in Indonesia and Australia, and the American Jacana *Jacana spinosa* in tropical America (several races). In *Jacana* the frontal shield is small ; in *Hydrophasianus* and *Microparra* it is absent ; and in *Irediparra* it has an erect central comb. *Jacana* (there is a melanistic variety) and *Actophilornis* have rufous plumage ; the former has a greenish-yellow wing-bar which is conspicuous in flight, and the Malagasy species of the latter has a broad white nuchal patch. *Microparra capensis,* in coloration and size, resembles juvenile *Actophilornis. Metopidius indicus* and *Irediparra gallinacea* (3 races) are bronze coloured, the latter with white throat and abdomen, golden forehead, cheeks, and parts of neck, and black breast. *Hydrophasianus* is the only jacana to assume a distinct and striking nuptial plumage ; this is alike in male and female, the general effect being very dark brown, with excessively elongated black tail feathers and conspicuous white wing coverts, throat, cheeks, and forehead ; the off-season plumage is dull brown above, the wings vermiculated with black, the under parts and tail white, the sides of neck golden and separated from the white throat by a broad black band.

Jacanas are found from sea level to about 8000 feet (Kenya), in the open, on aquatic vegetation in the sheltered shallows of inland waters. It is unusual for these birds to enter cover.

See Plate 43 (egg).   C.R.S.P.

Hoffmann, A. 1949. Über die Brutpflege des polyandrischen Wasserphasans, *Hydrophasianus chirurgus* (Scop.). Zool. Jahrb. (Syst.) 78 : 367–403.

JACANAE; JACANIDAE: see under CHARADRIIFORMES ; and JACANA.

JACANOIDEA: see under CHARADRIIFORMES.

JACKASS, LAUGHING: alternative name of the Kookaburra *Dacelo novaeguineae*, while the Blue-winged Kookaburra *D. leachii* is sometimes called the ' Howling Jackass ' (see KINGFISHER).

JACKDAW: *Corvus monedula* ; also applied to one related species (see CROW (1)).

JACOBIN: substantive name of *Florisuga mellivora* and *Melanotrochilus fuscus* (for family see HUMMINGBIRD).

JAEGER: substantive name, in American usage, for skuas of the genus *Stercorarius* (as contrasted with *Catharacta*—not separated by all authors)—see SKUA.

JAW: see SKELETON ; and BILL.

JAY: substantive name of many species of Corvidae, in various genera ; used without qualification, in Britain, for *Garrulus glandarius* (see CROW (1)). ' Blue Jay ' is a misnomer in India for *Coracias benghalensis* (see ROLLER). For ' jay-thrushes ' see BABBLER. See Plates 18 and 42 (colour), 40b (phot.).

JERY: substantive name of *Neomixis* spp. (see BABBLER).

JESS: term (plural ' jesses ') used in FALCONRY.

JOINT: see SKELETON

JUGAL: a paired bone of the skull (see SKELETON).

JUGULUM: the foreneck (see TOPOGRAPHY).

JUNCO: substantive name of *Junco* spp. (see BUNTING).

JUNGLEFOWL (1): substantive name of *Gallus* spp. (see PHEASANT ; DOMESTICATION).

JUNGLEFOWL (2): name used in Australia for *Megapodius freycinet* ; in the plural, serves as a general term for this and allied genera (some also called ' scrubfowl ')—see MEGAPODE.

JUVENAL ; JUVENILE: term of which the first spelling is usual in America, the second in Britain (see under YOUNG BIRD).

JYNGINAE: see under WOODPECKER

K

KAGU: native name, adopted as English, for *Rhynochetos* ('*Rhinochetus*') *jubatus*, sole member of the Rhynochetidae (Gruiformes, suborder Rhynocheti). This bird is thought to be a primitive form, and affinities to various groups have been suggested ; the nearest are probably to the Eurypygidae (see SUNBITTERN). The body is rather larger than that of a domestic fowl, but the legs are longer. The rather loose plumage is pale slaty grey with darker bars, but when the broad, rounded wings are spread these are seen to have a conspicuous pattern of white, reddish, and black markings. The head has a long loose crest that is usually pendant but can be erected. The strong and slightly decurved bill is bright red, as are the legs.

Kagu *Rhynochetos jubatus*, sole species. *C.E.T.K.*

The Kagu is found only in New Caledonia, where it was formerly widespread but now has a precarious existence in the remoter mountainous parts. It is largely a nocturnal bird, living on the forest floor, scarcely flying at all, and finding worms, insects, and other animal food on or in the ground. It has a characteristic habit of running rapidly and then standing motionless ; it has also been observed to perform peculiar antics, whirling round while holding the tip of its tail or of a wing in its bill ; and the wings are spread in display. It has a loud rattling call. The sexes are similar to each other in appearance. Both take part in building and incubation. The nest of twigs and leaves is on the ground ; the single rusty egg resembles those of the rails (Rallidae), and the chick has an abundant dark down.

Warner, W. D. 1948. The present status of the Kagu, *Rhynochetos jubatus*, on New Caledonia. Auk 65 : 287–288.

KAKA: Maori name used for *Nestor meridionalis* (see PARROT).

KAKAPO: alternative name (Maori) of the Owl Parrot *Strigops habroptilus* (see PARROT).

KAKATOEINAE: see PARROT

KAKELAAR: alternative name of *Phoeniculus purpureus* (see WOOD-HOOPOE).

KALIJ: substantive name of some *Lophura* spp. (see PHEASANT).

KASPAR HAUSER: see SINGING

KATABOLISM: see METABOLISM

KEA: Maori name used for *Nestor notabilis* (see PARROT).

KEEL: the carina of the sternum (see SKELETON ; and CARINATE).

KESTREL: substantive name of certain *Falco* spp. ; used without qualification, in Britain, for *F. tinnunculus* (see FALCON).

KIDNEY: see EXCRETORY SYSTEM

KILLDEER: *Charadrius vociferus* (see PLOVER (1)).

KINESIS (1): movement of the upper mandible in relation to the skull (see BILL ; SKELETON).

KINESIS (2): 'locomotory behaviour not involving a steering reaction but in which there may be turning, random in direction' (Thorpe 1951)—compare TAXIS.

KINGBIRD: substantive name of *Tyrannus* spp. (see FLYCATCHER (2)).

KING-CROW: *Dicrurus macrocercus* (see DRONGO).

KINGFISHER: substantive name of all species of Alcedinidae (Coraciiformes, suborder Alcedines) except the few known as 'kookaburras'; applied without qualification, in Britain, to *Alcedo atthis*; in the plural, general term for the family. This cosmopolitan group includes over 80 species, some of them with numerous subspecific forms, and these are nowadays placed in about 12 genera. They are grouped in three subfamilies—Cerylinae, Alcedininae, and Daceloninae; the validity of the original morphological basis for this division has recently been confirmed by V. & E. Stresemann, working on the mode of moulting the primaries. It is nevertheless rather a homogeneous family, in that all its members show an unmistakable general similarity.

General Characters. In size, kingfishers range from 4 to 18 inches long. They have compact bodies, short necks, and large heads; they perch in an upright posture. The bill is long and notably massive, straight, and usually ending in a sharp point; in some it is narrow (laterally compressed), in others relatively broad. The legs are very short; the toes are syndactyl, the 3rd and 4th being united through most of their length and the 2nd and 3rd basally—and in some the 2nd is much reduced or absent. The wings tend to be short and rounded. The tail is variable, from stumpy to very long; the greatest lengths are due to extension of the central rectrices (sometimes with racket-shaped ends).

The plumage is commonly of bright colours, often of metallic brilliance; greens, blues, purple, and reddish tones predominate, often with white patches and dark markings. The bill and feet are often brightly coloured, especially red; in some species the upper mandible is bright red while the lower is dark brownish. The sexes are very often alike, but when they are dissimilar it is not always the male that is the more colourful.

Habits. They are in the main solitary birds. The flight is direct and rapid; on the ground the birds hop; they habitually perch on branches or stumps, the first toe being directed backwards. The calls range from plaintive pipings to harsh rattling notes and outbursts of demoniac 'laughter'.

Many kingfishers are mainly piscivorous, catching their prey (which may include crustaceans, aquatic insects, etc.) by plunging headlong into the water, often from no great height—commonly from a perch above the stream, but in some species often from flight and sometimes into salt water as well as fresh. Unlike most plungers (see SWIMMING AND DIVING), they are not otherwise aquatic in the ordinary course. It is tempting to regard the form of the bill as an adaptation to this mode of fishing, comparing it with the bills of gannets (Sulidae), tropicbirds (Phaethontidae), and terns (Sterninae). The fact is, however, that the majority of species do not fish, and many of them indeed live far from water. Such birds live largely on insects, but also take other invertebrates (including crustaceans) and small vertebrates (sometimes including birds and rodents). The method of catching, nevertheless, is similar—a sudden swoop, usually from a perch, to the ground or into the herbage. The distinction is not quite sharp, as some terrestrial feeders will occasionally fish, and some fish-eaters will dart at passing insects. The aberrant *Clytoceyx rex*, a very large New Guinea species, digs in the soil for earthworms and has a bill flattened for the purpose.

The correspondence between feeding habits and taxonomic status likewise does not seem to be exact; the Cerylinae are fishing species, the Daceloninae are in the main 'tree' (or 'wood' or 'bush') kingfishers, while the Alcedininae are divided—*Alcedo* spp. being fishers and the others mostly not. It is generally considered that the terrestrial feeders are primitive, and one must therefore suppose the form of bill to have been first evolved in adaptation to that habit; if this be correct, fishing may be regarded as a later behavioural development that exploited a remarkable 'pre-adaptation' of the bill (see PRE-ADAPTATION).

Kingfishers are hole-nesters, and add no lining to the chamber. There is a certain correlation with feeding habits, in that the fish-eaters burrow in river banks, while the terrestrial feeders more often burrow in termite nests (including arboreal ones) or make use of cavities in trees. The eggs, 2–7 according to species, are pure white. The nidicolous young are at first either naked or have slight down; the subsequent feathers remain encased in their sheaths until the birds are about ready to fly. Both parents take part in incubation and in care of the young.

Distribution. Although the family is a cosmopolitan one, absent only from high latitudes and some remote islands, the great majority of its members belong to tropical parts of the Old World. Of the three subfamilies, only the Cerylinae are represented in the New World, with only one species widespread in North America. There is also only one species of kingfisher that is widespread in the Palaearctic Region and found in Europe. In Africa species are numerous—much less so in Madagascar. There are also many species in the Oriental Region, and the greatest concentration is attained in the islands of south-eastern Asia and the Pacific Ocean. Several are found in Australia and one is found in New Zealand. Most are sedentary (although, especially in the higher latitudes inhabited, some are migratory or partially so) ; it is therefore not surprising to find a great diversity of insular forms, specific and subspecific : of one species in the Pacific area about 50 races have been described.

Cerylinae. The Belted Kingfisher *Megaceryle alcyon* of North America, with eastern and western races, is one of the larger kingfishers and has a ragged crest ; the plumage is mainly blue-grey above, with a pectoral band of the same colour, and white below (with rufous markings in the female only) ; it fishes from hovering flight and has a loud rattling call. The mainly Neotropical genus *Chloroceryle* is the only one in the entire family peculiar to the New World. Of its 4 species, the Texas Kingfisher *C. americana* has a range extending north into the southern United States ; it is a much smaller bird than *M. alcyon*, without a crest and with greenish upper parts, and has a rufous breast-band in the male only. The crested Amazon Kingfisher *C. amazona*, with a generally similar plumage pattern and the same sexual dimorphism, is the largest of the genus.

Among the Cerylinae of the Old World the Pied Kingfisher *Ceryle rudis*, in a monotypic genus (if *Megaceryle* be kept separate), is a familiar bird throughout Africa south of the Sahara and in some south-western parts of Asia. It measures some 10 inches in length and has a perceptible crest. Although lacking the bright colours usual in the family, its plumage of contrasted black and white is conspicuous. Moreover, it shows little fear of man and is a noisy bird, often encountered in small chattering parties although solitary and silent when fishing. This it usually does by plunging from flight, and often after hovering for a moment in one spot ; it can be seen doing this over shallows off the sea-shore as well as on great rivers and on inland waters of all sorts. The Giant Kingfisher *Megaceryle maxima* of tropical Africa, a handsomely coloured bird about 18 inches long, seems to fish only from a perch.

Alcedininae. This group is exemplified by the Kingfisher *Alcedo atthis* of Europe, widely distributed (many races) over all but the most northerly parts of the Palaearctic Region, and through the Oriental Region, east to the Solomon Islands. A stumpy, bobbing little bird, brilliant blue-green above,

chestnut below, and red-legged, it can for colour stand comparison with tropical species, such as the not very dissimilar Shining-blue Kingfisher *A. quadribrachys* of West Africa. There are 7 other members of the genus in Africa and the Oriental Region (although certain of them, with others, are placed by some authors in a genus ' *Corythornis* ').

The foregoing are fishers, but the remaining members of the subfamily are mainly insectivorous. They include the Dwarf Kingfisher *Myioceyx lecontei* and the Pigmy Kingfisher *Ispidina picta* of tropical Africa, which are no more than 4 inches long (counting a one-inch bill) ; the former genus is monotypic, while the latter has a second species, *I. madagascariensis*, that is peculiar to Madagascar and distinctive in being wholly rufous above. Then there are 10 or 11 three-toed kingfishers *Ceyx* (including ' *Alcyone* ' and ' *Ceycopsis* ') spp., mostly inhabiting south-eastern Asia, Indonesia, and the Australo-Papuan area. They are small brightly coloured birds, mostly insectivorous, although some apparently fish. The range of 2 species extends to Australia ; 3 are peculiar to the Philippines.

Revisions of the generic taxonomy of the subfamily have been proposed by Delacour and (as regards African species) by Traylor, but need not be assessed here. Difficulties are that the number of toes— formerly stressed—is probably an unreliable character, as a tendency towards suppression of the 2nd digit is general in the group ; and that the laterally compressed form of bill in fishing species may be acquired by convergence.

Daceloninae. The third subfamily comprises ' tree ' kingfishers, mostly of arboreal habit and catching insects in the air like flycatchers (Muscicapinae) or pouncing on ground prey after the manner of shrikes (Laniidae). They include the well-known Kookaburra (or Laughing Jackass) *Dacelo novaeguineae* (' *gigas* ') of Australia, found naturally in most parts of that continent and introduced in others. It is a large bird, without great brilliance of plumage but notorious for its weird calls—often uttered in chorus ; it has three congeners, all in the Australo-Papuan area. The Stork-billed Kingfisher *Pelargopsis capensis* of southern Asia is a large species that is both a fisher and a predaceous terrestrial feeder, being also aggressive even towards birds very much larger than itself ; it has two congeners.

There are also four species in monotypic genera— the Banded Kingfisher *Lacedo pulchella*, found from Burma to Borneo ; the Earthworm-eating Kingfisher *Clytoceyx rex*, already mentioned ; the Hook-billed Kingfisher *Melidora macrorrhina*, also of New Guinea ; and the Blue-eared Kingfisher *Cittura cyanotis* of the Celebes. The genus *Tanysiptera* has 7 species, all in the Austral-Papuan area, including the Racket-tailed (or Galatea) Kingfisher *T. galatea* of the Moluccas and New Guinea ; all have in fact racket-shaped ends to the much elongated tail feathers.

Finally, there are the very numerous forms of *Halcyon* (including ' *Syma* ', etc.)—nearly 40 species, some of them with many subspecies—distributed in the Ethiopian, Oriental, and Australasian Regions. These are mainly terrestrial feeders. Tropical Africa has, among others, the Senegal Kingfisher *H. senegalensis* and the Striped Kingfisher *H. chelicuti*. The White-breasted Kingfisher *H. smyrnensis* is found from Asia Minor to the Philippines, the migratory Black-capped Kingfisher *H. pileata* from China to Indonesia, and so on. The White-collared Kingfisher *H. chloris*, although not a fisher, frequents muddy coastal areas from the Red Sea to Samoa. Again one notes the great number of insular species, from Indonesia eastwards into the Pacific Ocean. The Sacred Kingfisher *H. sancta*, with much yellow in its plumage, is widely distributed in Australia and is the sole representative of the family in New Zealand.   A.L.T.

See Plate 41 (colour).

Delacour, J. 1951. The significance of the number of toes in some woodpeckers and kingfishers. Auk 68 : 49–51.
Peters, J. L. 1945. Check-list of Birds of the World vol. 5. Cambridge, Mass.
Sharpe, R. B. 1868–71. A monograph of the Alcedinidae, or Family of the Kingfishers. 3 vols. London. (Colour plates.)
Skutch, A. F. 1957. Life history of the Amazon Kingfisher. Condor 59 : 217–229.
Stresemann, V. & E. 1961. Die Handschwingen-Mauser der Eisvögel (Alcedinidae). J. Orn. 102 : 439–455.
Traylor, M. A. T. 1960. Genera *Corythornis*, *Ispidina* and *Myioceyx*. Bull. Brit. Orn. Cl. 80 : 144–146.

KINGLET : in American usage, substantive name of *Regulus* spp. (see WARBLER (1)).

KISKADEE : substantive name (alternatively ' kiskadee flycatcher ') of *Pitangus* spp. (see FLY-CATCHER (2)). See Plate 32 (colour).

KITE : substantive name of species of Milvinae, and used also for members of the Elaninae (for both these subfamilies of the Accipitridae see HAWK).

KITTIWAKE : substantive name of two species of Larinae ; used without qualification, on both sides of the Atlantic, for *Larus* (' *Rissa* ') *tridactylus*, the other species being the Redlegged Kittiwake *L. brevirostris* of the Bering Sea (see GULL). See Plate 34b (phot.).

KIWI : substantive name of the three species of Apterygidae (Apterygiformes) ; in the plural,

general term for the family. This is a ' ratite ' group peculiar to New Zealand and is usually placed in an order by itself, but is by others placed alongside the moas (Dinornithidae). Accumulating evidence for the polyphyletic origin of ' ratites ', and a formidable list of respects in which kiwis do not conform with a general ratite pattern, suggest that their relationships might well be examined more critically (see RATITES, PHYLOGENY OF THE) ; at least it can be agreed that they are decidedly anomalous.

After a century and a half of study directed mainly to osteology and the morphology of soft parts, including recent studies of the brain, the gross anatomy may be regarded as fairly well known. There is a considerable scattered literature about kiwis, and good summaries of what was known at the time appeared in Newton's *Dictionary of Birds* (1896) and in the *Cambridge Natural History* (Evans 1909). No field studies comparable in critical standards with the anatomical work have ever been made, and most of what has been written about life history and habits is sketchy and anecdotal, or else it has been based on the observation of captive birds. In a country where the variety and density of ever-green vegetation makes it difficult to see more than a small proportion of the common birds, it is not surprising that the unobtrusive nocturnal kiwis remained unnoticed during the first forty years of European contacts with New Zealand. Today, in a much reduced habitat, kiwis are still plentiful in suitable localities ; but very few of New Zealand's two million human inhabitants, including ' outdoor types ' living in kiwi country, have ever seen a live kiwi except in a zoo.

Adult kiwis range in size, according to species and to sex, through about the same scale as domestic fowls, say from bantam to Orpington ; in weight the range is from 3 to 9 pounds. Females in all forms are larger than males. Distinctive are the powerful, muscular, but rather short legs ; the tarsus is bare, the hallux is small and elevated, the claws are sharp and strong. Distinctive also is the sharp taper of the trunk (due to small pectoral development) to a strong neck. The skull is small and compressed ; the bill is long and flexible, with nostril apertures at the tip. The extraordinary feathers, lacking aftershafts, are weakly barbed and lie without any firm contouring ; that is to say, they are permanently ruffled in appearance and almost hair-like. This texture is uniform over the whole body, even on the tips of the primary quills of the vestigial and hidden wings. There is no tail. The eyes are small, and sight cannot be a strongly developed sense ; the ear aperture is large and suggests a good sense of hearing ; tactile sense seems to be well served by the bill and facial bristles ; and olfactory efficiency can be inferred from the long nasal passages and the terminal position of the nostrils. Normal food includes earthworms, insects, and fallen berries. The voice, thin and reedy in the male and somewhat hoarse in the female, is used to produce a two-note call, heard only at night.

The foregoing description applies equally to all the known forms. There are three closely similar races of the Common (or Brown) Kiwi, which Rothschild more aptly called the striated kiwis, one each on the three main islands, viz. *Apteryx australis mantelli*, North Island ; *A. a. australia*, South Island ; and *A. a. lawryi*, Stewart Island. Also in the west and south of the South Island are two fairly distinct spotted kiwis, both with soft barred plumage. The larger and darker is the Great Spotted (or Large Grey) Kiwi *Apteryx haasti*, the smaller and paler is the Little Spotted (or Little Grey) Kiwi *A. oweni*. Both show a considerable size range clinally, and some doubtful subspecies have been described.

Some random field observations and some study of captive birds have revealed an outline of an interesting life history. The egg is large, elongated, and white. Of *A. australis* the average weight of an egg (dimensions 135 × 84 mm.) is about one pound. There have been speculative assertions that this is roughly one quarter of the weight of an adult bird, without due reference to the age and sex of the adult quoted ; this was checked recently at the Dominion Museum, Wellington, and a female *A. a. mantelli* killed when on the point of laying, was found to weigh eight pounds including the weight of her one-pound egg. In the North Island, *A. a. mantelli* lays two eggs in a hole under roots or in a well covered hole in a bank. In several observed nestings in captivity, no female has been known to sit after the laying of the second egg, the incubation being done by the diminutive male, a task requiring 75–77 days. During the first 6 days in the nest the chicks are not fed ; when they do emerge they pick up their own food, with some assistance from the male parent clearing the ground. Nothing precise is recorded about rate of growth to maturity or of moult sequence. The first feathers, developed within the egg, are superficially similar to the adult structure and are at no stage downy. Much more precise field and aviary study is needed to provide an adequate account of life history, physiology, and behaviour patterns of kiwis. It is at least gratifying that none of the species seems to be in any danger of extinction.

See Plate 10b (Phot.).   R.A.F.

Classical references

Owen, R. 1841. On the Anatomy of the Southern Apteryx (*Apteryx australis* Shaw). Trans. Zool. Soc. Lond. 182 : 257–309.

Parker, T. J. 1891. Observations of the Anatomy and Development of *Apteryx*. Phil. Trans. Roy. Soc. 182 : 25–134

Fürbringer, M. 1888. Untersuchungen zur Morphologie und Systematik der Vögel, zugleich ein Beitrag zur Anatomie der Stütz- und Bewegungsorgane. Bijdr. Dierk. K. Zool. Genostschap XV. 2 vols. Amsterdam (vol. 2, pp. 1567 et seq.).

Rothschild, W. 1899. The Genus *Apteryx*. Novit. Zool. 6 : 361–402.

Recent references

Gibbings, R. 1947. Kiwis in Captivity (as told by F. D. Robson). Wellington.

Krabbe, K. H. 1959. Studies on the brain development of the kiwi *Apteryx mantelli*. Morphogenesis of the Vertebrate Brain 8. Copenhagen.

Verheyen, R. 1957. Les kiwis (Apterygiformes) dans les systèmes de classification. Bull. Soc. Roy. Zool. d'Anvers 15.

See also works on New Zealand birds.

KLEPTOPARASITISM: see PIRACY ; also FEEDING HABITS

KNEE: for both the true knee and for a popular misconception on the subject see LEG.

KNOT: substantive name of *Calidris canutus* and one congener (see SANDPIPER). See Plates 29 (colour), 48b (phot.).

KOEL: *Eudynamys scolopacea* (see CUCKOO). See Plate 5 (colour).

KOKAKO: *Callaeas cinerea* (see WATTLEBIRD (2)).

KOKLAS: *Pucrasia macrolopha* (see PHEASANT).

KOLOA: alternative name (indigenous) for the Hawaiian Duck *Anas platyrhynchos wyvilliana* (see DUCK).

KOOKABURRA: substantive name of *Dacelo* spp. (see KINGFISHER).

KORHAAN: substantive name of some South African species of *Eupodotis* (see BUSTARD).

KORI: alternative name of the Giant Bustard *Ardeotis kori* (see BUSTARD).

KRONISMUS: term ('cronism' if anglicised) proposed by Schüz for the actual or attempted swallowing by parents of their own dead or sickly young.

Schüz, E. 1957. Der Verschlingen eigener Junger ('*Kronismus*') bei Vögeln und seine Bedeutung. Vogelwarte 19: 1–15.

L

LABYRINTH: part of the ear (semicircular canals)—see HEARING AND BALANCE.

LAGENA: part of the cochlea, in the inner ear (see HEARING AND BALANCE).

LAGGAR: *Falco jugger* (see FALCON).

LAMARCKISM: see EVOLUTION

LAMINIPLANTAR: having the horny sheath of the tarsus undivided on its posterior surface, although scutellate on the anterior surface (see LEG) ; compare BOOTED.

LÄMMERGEIER: name, alternatively ' Bearded Vulture ', of *Gypaetus barbatus* (see VULTURE (I)).

LANCEBILL: substantive name of *Doryfera* spp. (for family see HUMMINGBIRD).

LAND-BRIDGES: see GEOLOGICAL FACTORS

LANDRAIL: alternative name (probably obsolescent) for the Corncrake *Crex crex* (see RAIL).

LANGERHANS, ISLETS OF: see ENDOCRINE SYSTEM

LANIIDAE: a family of the Passeriformes, suborder Oscines (see SHRIKE).

LANNER: *Falco biarmicus* (see FALCON).

LAPPET: a wattle, particularly one at the gape (see INTEGUMENTARY STRUCTURES).

LAPWING: substantive name of some *Vanellus* spp., others being called ' plover ' ; used without qualification for *V. vanellus* ; in the plural, general term for plovers of this genus (split by some authors into several genera constituting a subfamily Vanellinae)—see PLOVER (I).

LARI: see under CHARADRIIFORMES.

LARIDAE: see under CHARADRIIFORMES. There are two subfamilies, in the classification followed here, Larinae (see GULL), and Sterninae (see TERN).

LARK: substantive name (sometimes in a compounded form) of the species of Alaudidae (Passeriformes, suborder Oscines) ; in the plural, general term for the family.

Characters. The larks are a well defined group, among the Oscines, in having the posterior surface of the tarsus covered with scutes and not with an unbroken lamina, and in lacking an ossified pessulus in the syrinx. Sexes are more or less alike in colour, and the juveniles are slightly more variegated by spotting. On the whole the larks are quietly coloured birds, with the exception of the brighter coloration in the Shore Lark *Eremophila alpestris* and finch-larks *Eremopterix* spp. Most species have a single annual moult, whilst a few have a double moult. The hind claw may be longer or shorter than the hind toe, and much curved or nearly straight.

The variation in size and shape of the mandibles accords with the purposes which they serve. The proportionately huge finch-like bill of *Rhamphocoris clotbey* for crushing desert insects and hard seeds, the long slender bill of the Bifasciated Lark *Alaemon alaudipes* used for digging, and the tiny cone-shaped bills of the smaller *Calandrella* spp. and *Eremopterix* spp. used for crushing seeds, are beautiful adaptations.

The weights and wing areas of larks are interesting, as shewn by two examples of measurements from resident populations, in southern Israel and Sinai respectively:

	weight gr.	wing length mm.	wing area sq. mm.
Melanocorypha calandra	60–70	120–135	18 000–22 000
Alaemon alaudipes	38–44	124–136	24 000–29 000

Here we have two larks of about equal wing length but with quite different weights and wing areas. The flight of *Alaemon* is buoyant, almost butterfly-like, and not used for long distances. The flight of *Melanocorypha* is accompanied by rapid wing-beats and is sometimes, when the bird is going to water, sustained over considerable distances.

The family contains both residents with nomadic habits and long-distance migrants, and it offers a good example of the development of the wing feathers for the purpose for which they are used. Development has not followed the lines that one might have expected. One would think that a migrant should have a larger wing area than that of a resident, but the opposite is the case ; shape of wing and length of fully grown primaries are more important than wing area. The Skylark *Alauda arvensis* and the Crested Lark *Galerida cristata* are of about the same size, weighing between 30 and 45 gr. The wings of Skylarks vary from 106 to 120 mm. in length, and those of Crested Larks from 99 to 115 mm. But the wing areas of Skylarks vary from 15 000 to 19 000 sq. mm., those of Crested Larks from 15 400 to 20 500 sq. mm.

General Habits. Larks prefer open country, whether it be Arctic tundra, the Tibetan Plateau, dry meadow or crop-land, or the deserts of North Africa and Arabia ; but many species also live in thin ' bush ' ; there are no larks in forest or near-forest. Larks walk and run ; they never hop. When alarmed they squat or run, but a few desert-loving species stand bolt upright and quite still. Some, such as *Mirafra africana* and *Chersophilus duponti*, can run at five miles an hour, and it is with the greatest difficulty that they can be persuaded to fly even a short distance. Many other species of *Mirafra* perch habitually in trees, as does the Woodlark *Lullula arborea*. Some *Mirafra* spp. clap their wings in courtship flight and have become known as ' clapper larks ' or ' flappet larks '.

The food of all larks except the Shorelark (or Horned Lark) *Eremophila alpestris* is about half vegetable and half insect. The Shorelark freely eats seeds and buds in summer, but from autumn to spring it eats mainly insects with some molluscs and crustaceans. Many of the long-billed larks are great diggers after larvae. *Alaemon alaudipes* has been seen to excavate a hole two inches deep for Orthoptera—the exact spot being located by listening, as is done by the thrushes (Turdinae). Other species are just scrapers, or simply browsers on insects and seeds.

During the non-breeding season flocking is usual and is preparatory for migration among those species living in the higher northern latitudes. But in the desert, and even in tropical Africa, many species flock in the non-breeding season. Even the Crested Lark, usually solitary and sedentary, has been observed in a close-packed flock in Arabia ; and *Rhamphocoris*, usually found singly or in pairs, has been seen in flocks of 50 and more in Morocco, drawn together by an abundance of food (migrating caterpillars). Calandra Larks *Melanocorypha calandra* often flock in winter, especially where a long flight to water is essential, as many as 400 being seen close-packed in Sinai in November at a water-hole.

Singing. A most characteristic feature of the family is their exquisite song, which serves both for courtship and for territorial defence. Most of the group enjoy a high standard of song, poured out sometimes from a small stone or eminence, or from a post or bush, but reaching perfection when delivered in the air. The Skylark, usually singing in flight, will sing equally well when confined in a cage. The song of the Skylark is one of the delights of the British countryside but is surpassed in excellence by the song of the Bifasciated Lark *Alaemon alaudipes*. This song comprises a series of pipes and melodious whistles in perfect harmony and continuous for about two minutes ; it is poured forth either in the air or from a desert bush or rock ; when in the air it is followed by a slow spiral sail-down with outstretched fluttering wings, the piping and whistling continuing until the final plummet to earth with closed wings, the drop being checked only at the last moment. In the clear desert air and with an audience of silence, solitude, and space, the music of that lark attains a rare perfection.

Breeding. All larks make their nests on the ground, sometimes a mere scraping, sometimes thinly lined with grass, and many African species of *Mirafra* have a grass dome over the nest. The eggs, varying from 3 in hot climates to as many as 5 elsewhere, are dull white or very pale blue, blotched and thinly spotted with browns and often zoned.

A peculiarity of the sand larks *Ammomanes* spp. and *Eremopterix* spp. is that a rampart of small pebbles is placed on the windward side of the nest and can be as high as 20 mm. (four-fifths of an inch).

Distribution. The Alaudidae are a predominantly Old World group, only the Shorelark *Eremophila alpestris* being found in the Americas, where it is known as the Horned Lark. In the Old World the family is distributed from high northern latitudes to southern Africa, Madagascar, and southern Asia, with one representative in New Guinea and Australia. No member of the family has established itself on an oceanic island.

The similar cryptic coloration and the lack of diagnostic specific character in the larks, combined with the fact that many populations are isolated by considerable distances from their nearest relatives, make this a difficult family for systematists, and no two workers will be found to agree on the limits of every genus, or on which of several isolated populations can be regarded as conspecific. Peters (whose nomenclature is followed here) recognised 15 genera, substantially fewer than earlier authors ; of these 5 are monotypic, and 3 others each comprise only 2 species. The largest genus is *Mirafra*, a group of diverse habits ; some dwell in scrub or 'bush' and have been termed bush larks, while others are essentially ground birds and some of them inhabit semi-desert. Of the 25 species, 21 are confined to Africa, 1 to Madagascar, and 2 to Asia, while the Singing Bush Lark *M. javanica* ranges from north-eastern Africa, through parts of Asia to Australia. Other examples are the Flappet Lark *M. rufocinnamomea* of much of Africa, the Clapper Lark *M. apiata* of southern Africa, and the Bush Lark *M. assamica* of southern Asia. The genus *Heteromirafra* has its sole species in two isolated communities in north-eastern and southern Africa, and *Certhilauda* its 3 species in southern Africa ; the latter include the Longbilled Lark *C. curvirostris*.

The finch-larks of the genus *Eremopterix* are distributed in 6 species over Africa south of the Sahara, except in rain-forest and montane areas, and one of them, *E. nigriceps*, has a range extending from the Cape Verde Islands to central India. A seventh species, *E. grisea*, occupies most of India and also Ceylon.

The genera *Ammomanes* (6 spp.), *Alaemon* (2 spp.), and *Ramphocoris* (1 sp.) are distributed in Africa and parts of Asia, but particularly in the arid areas of northern Africa and Arabia. The Sand Lark *Ammomanes deserti* ranges from Morocco to western India. The genus *Melanocorypha* is distributed in 6 species from the Mediterranean countries to the steppes and deserts of Asia.

The genus *Calandrella* has 8 species confined to Africa, 1 in Africa and Asia, 2 in Asia only, and a twelfth—the Short-toed Lark *C. cinerea*—distributed from southern Europe eastwards to Mongolia and southwards to Cape Colony. *Chersophilus* and *Pseudalaemon* are monotypic genera confined to northern Africa. The Crested Lark *Galerida cristata* ranges from the Iberian Peninsula to Korea ; of its 5 congeners, 2 are African and 2 are Indian, while *G. theklae* occupies much of the same range as *G. cristata* in southern Europe, North Africa, and parts of Asia.

The Skylark *Alauda arvensis*, to be mentioned more fully below, is the well-known Palaearctic species for which the name 'lark' is often used without qualification ; *A. gulgula* of southern Asia is closely related. The Wood Lark *Lullula arborea*,

in a monotypic genus, is also a Palaearctic species but is absent from the more easterly parts.

As already mentioned, the Shore (or Horned) Lark *Eremophila alpestris* is the sole representative of the family in the New World ; it ranges there from the Arctic coasts of North America southwards to Mexico, with an isolated population, *E. a. peregrina*, in the Andes of Colombia. It has, however, a circumpolar distribution and in the Old World ranges from the mountains of northern Europe and Asia to Japan and the deserts of North Africa and the Near East. *E. bilopha* of the Sahara and south-western Asia is now regarded as a distinct species.

Colour Adaptability. Few groups of birds display better than larks the effect of natural selection and modification to suit habit and environment. The variation in size and shape of the mandibles in relation to food has already been mentioned. Another remarkable, and almost unique, feature of the family is the colour adaptability of the mantle plumage to the soil on which the birds live. Since the group is largely terrestrial, survival from attacks by predators depends very much on being inconspicuous on the ground. Those that feed in cultivated areas or on grass-land, such as *Alauda* and *Calandrella*, do not require so much protection as those that live in total exposure in desert. In the case of *Ammomanes* the likeness between mantle plumage and soil is absolute. In Central Arabia we find patches of black lava closely adjacent to areas of almost white sand, the former being the habitat of a very dark race of the Desert Lark *A. deserti annae*, and the latter of a pale sandy race. And yet nothing will induce the pale race to stray on to the lava, nor will the dark race be driven on to the pale sand. Three species of *Ammomanes* occur in the deserts of North Africa and Arabia and east to north-western India, whilst there are two species in south-western Africa and another in the Indian peninsula. *Ammomanes* is the best example of soil and plumage correlation among birds ; the result is a mosaic distribution, the same coloured plumage occurring where the same coloured rock or sand occurs, whether in Africa, Arabia, or farther east. See Plate 42 (colour).

Another soil/plumage resemblance occurs in *Mirafra somalica*, the reddest of all larks and living on red sand exactly matching its mantle plumage. In South West Africa and the Kalahari the larks also tend to resemble the soil on which they live.

The genus *Alauda* (Skylark) displays a different reaction to environment to that of *Ammomanes*. Sharpe seventy years ago gave a concise introduction to this group : 'The difference in intensity of plumage of Skylarks must be studied by the light of their habitats and conditions of life, and probably the increase of rainfall may have something to do with modification of colour.'

Skylark. The breeding range of the Skylark *Alauda arvensis* extends from about the Arctic Circle to the British Isles and Morocco, and throughout Europe and Palaearctic Asia (except Arabia) to Kamchatka and Japan. The Skylark is a regular migrant in the northern part of its range ; the birds migrate by night, flying low, but wintering individuals seldom pass beyond the Mediterranean area. It has been introduced to Long Island near New York, and into New Zealand. The Long Island colony disappeared about 1913, but the species has since been introduced into Kermadec, Hawaii, and the Chatham Islands.

The plumage of the Skylark does not show violent changes in relation to either soil or climate, there being a certain degree of natural cover, either grass or bush, in the habitat. But the species affords an ideal example of a north to south cline in size, and a cline in colour running east and west from East Persia, races becoming darker and more richly coloured as they reach the periphery of the distribution. Aridity and humidity appear to exert a greater influence than the colour of the soil. But this influence is neither great nor entirely constant, with the result that no series from one locality is uniform ; this has led to many races being described, only a few of which can be accepted as valid.

In the last century larks were a common form of food in Britain, between 20 000 and 30 000 larks at once being sometimes brought to the London market, where they were sold to the value of £2000 annually. During the winter 1867–68, 1 000 255 larks valued at £2260 were taken into the town of Dieppe.

Misnomers. The name 'lark' has often been misapplied ; the Titlark of Britain is a pipit, the Meadowlark of America is an icterid, and the Magpie-lark or Mudlark of Australia is a grallinid (and a 'mudlark' is also a dirty little street urchin !). The term 'skylarking' by children derives from the joy of the combination of song and movement, a pleasure to all who watch.

See Plate 42 (colour). R.M.

Meinertzhagen, R. 1951. Review of the Alaudidae. Proc. Zool. Soc. Lond. 121 : 81–132.
Peters, J. L. 1960. Family Alaudidae. *In* Mayr, E. & Greenway, J. C., Jr. (eds.). Check-list of Birds of the World vol. 9. Cambridge, Mass.
Vaurie, C. 1951. A study of Asiatic larks. Bull. Amer. Mus. Nat. Hist. 97 : 438–526.
White, C. M. N. 1961. A Revised Check List of African Broadbills, Pittas, Larks, Swallows, Wagtails and Pipits. Lusaka, N. Rhodesia.

LARK, MAGPIE : see MAGPIE-LARK.

LARK, MEADOW : see MEADOWLARK ; and ORIOLE (2)

LARK-QUAIL : name, alternatively 'quail-plover' (misnomer), of *Ortyxelos meiffrenii* (see BUTTONQUAIL).

LARK, SONG- : see SONGLARK

LARO-LIMICOLAE : Stresemann's order equivalent, in the classification here followed, to the order Charadriiformes less the families Jacanidae, Thinocoridae, and Alcidae.

LARYNX : see RESPIRATORY SYSTEM ; SYRINX ; TRACHEA

LATEBRA : see EGG

LATENT LEARNING : see LEARNING

LATEROSPHENOID : a paired bone of the skull (see SKELETON).

LATIPLANTAR : having the hinder aspect of the tarsus flat (applied to oscine Passeriformes) ; opposite of ACUTIPLANTAR (in general, see LEG).

LATITUDE : see MAPPING

LAVEROCK : archaic name for the Skylark *Alauda arvensis* (see LARK).

LAYING : the deposition of the egg ; the act of oviposition itself and various attendant circumstances are considered here (see also EGG).

Oviposition. At ovulation the ovary releases a yolk (ovum) into the body cavity. Within half an hour it is engulfed by the upper end of the oviduct, the infundibulum, and it then passes through three further regions of the oviduct (see REPRODUCTIVE SYSTEM). In the 'magnum', the chalazae and the thick albumen are added ; in the 'isthmus', inner and outer shell membranes are formed ; and in the 'uterus' or shell-gland, where the egg remains for 20–24 hours, it undergoes a 25 per cent osmotic increase in volume, the chalky shell is deposited, and (mainly in the last hour before laying) the pigment may be formed. The times given apply to the domestic hen, in which the whole process from ovulation till laying takes about 24–27 hours.

The method by which the egg is carried through the oviduct has not been demonstrated conclusively. Some maintain that it is moved entirely by ciliary action, and others that it is propelled by peristaltic movements of the oviduct. In the oviduct the egg lies with its pointed end towards the cloaca and in many species, e.g. domestic pigeon, eggs are correspondingly laid pointed pole first. In other species, e.g. Blackheaded Gull *Larus ridibundus*, domestic hens and ducks, eggs are quite often laid blunt end first ; this happens in 29 per cent of the eggs of Khaki-Campbell domestic ducks. By using X-rays, it has been shown that such eggs undergo a quick 180° rotation (in a horizontal plane) an hour before they are laid. On rare occasions this rotation precedes the formation of pigment spots ; the latter then collect round the pointed pole of the egg. Rotation is more frequent in some individuals than in others, and its incidence increases with age, presumably because the uterus wall becomes more stretched with repeated layings.

How the egg is actually released from the body has for long been a matter of controversy. Some maintained that the whole uterus (with contained egg) prolapses through vagina and cloaca to the exterior, where the uterine wall everts, thus unwrapping the egg and leaving it outside. Recently, however, Sykes observed, in laparotomised hens, that the uterus is not everted during oviposition ; instead, the egg passes from the uterus into the vagina and is then pushed out by peristaltic action of the vaginal muscles. In intact birds he showed, also, that the distension of the vagina by the egg evokes a ventroflexion of the legs and erection of the feathers surrounding the vent, as well as ' bearing down ' contractions of the abdominal muscles and increased respiratory movements causing a rise in the abdominal pressure. The egg may be expelled after a period of bearing down lasting 1–3 minutes. In social parasites, e.g. cowbirds Molothrus spp. and cuckoos (Cuculinae), the process is a matter of seconds. A Bobwhite Quail Colinus virginianus needs from 3–10 minutes at the nest to lay an egg, whereas Turkeys Meleagris gallopavo and geese Anser sp. are reported to labour for 1–2 hours. A bird that cannot lay its egg is called egg-bound ; this condition may be caused by inflammation, stricture, or tumour in the oviduct ; sometimes a malformed, oversized, or soft-shelled egg may be responsible.

An egg that is ready for laying can be held back ; a Cuckoo Cuculus canorus is thus able to wait until the nest-owner has left the nest (see PARASITISM). Many song-birds postpone laying while quickly constructing a new nest when the old one has been damaged or removed.

Age of Bird. Captive Quail Coturnix coturnix reproduce at 6 weeks of age, some individuals laying as early as 38 days (Science 129 : 267). Most breeds of domestic hen begin laying at 5–7 months ; most passerines, pigeons (Columbidae), and ducks Anas spp. etc., many gallinaceous birds, and some owls (Strigiformes) at one year ; geese (Anser spp. etc.), many gulls (Larinae), and birds-of-prey (Falconiformes), some waders (Charadrii), and a few passerines at 2 years ; cormorants (Phalacrocoracidae), divers (Gaviidae), and the larger gulls at 3 years; the large birds-of-prey and storks (Ciconiidae) when 4–6 years old, and the Royal Albatross Diomedea epomophora not until it is at least 8 years old. In many of these species the age at which breeding first occurs may vary with the individual. These differences are often explained by stating that larger birds require longer to mature than those of smaller size. More convincing is Lack's suggestion that breeding imposes a strain on the parents that may have been too great for the young individuals in some species, thus leading to an adaptive retardation of the breeding age.

Time of Year. Like other reproductive activities, egg-laying is restricted to particular seasons of the year in most birds (see BREEDING SEASON). In general it is so timed that the young grow up when their food is most abundant. In temperate and cold climates the proximate factors controlling the time of egg-laying are increase in day-length in late winter and warm temperatures in early spring (Kluyver, for Great Tit Parus major). In the tropics the rainy season determines the onset of breeding in many passerines. In special cases other factors and adaptations may be involved ; thus the Great Crested Grebe Podiceps cristatus does not normally breed until the vegetation supporting its floating nest has grown up. Eiders Somateria mollissima, Common Gulls Larus canus, and Herring Gulls L. argentatus in the arctic are reported to postpone breeding on islets until the surrounding ice has melted, which may be an adaptation against robbing by arctic foxes. The date of laying of the first egg varies somewhat from year to year and between individuals ; in many species, birds laying for the first time tend to do so a few days later than older ones. According to Darling, birds of a colony influence one another's reproductive activities in such a way that bigger colonies lay earlier in the season and within fewer days, i.e. are more closely synchronised, than small ones. Recent studies (e.g. Coulson & White) do not support either statement, but it appears that small colonies may lay later in the season because they include a larger proportion of young birds than bigger colonies.

Time of Day. Some birds lay only at a particular time of day ; many song-birds such as finches (Fringillidae), wrens (Troglodytidae), tanagers (Thraupinae), wood-warblers (Parulidae), and hummingbirds (Trochilidae) around sunrise ; pigeons (Columbidae) early in the afternoon ; pheasants (Phasianidae) in the evening. In a flock of domestic hens, 56 per cent of the eggs were laid between 9 a.m. and 1 p.m.

Successive eggs may not be laid at the same time of day ; in the domestic pigeon the second egg appears 44–46 hours after the first and is thus laid earlier in the afternoon. The laying pattern, i.e. the time interval between the laying of successive eggs, is characteristic for a species. This interval is 20–24 hours for most but not all passerines and for many ducks ; 24–28 hours for the domestic hen ; 24–72 hours, with an average of 40 hours, for the Blackheaded Gull ; 2 days for the Raven *Corvus corax*, Ostrich *Struthio camelus*, and Rhea *Rhea americana* ; 3 days for cassowaries *Casuarius* spp. ; 5 days for the Condor *Vultur gryphus* ; and for the Masked ('Blue-faced') Booby *Sula dactylatra* a 6–7 days' interval has been reported. The interval probably corresponds to the time necessary for the formation of the various layers of the egg. It is known that in the domestic hen ovulation usually follows the laying of the previous egg within about 30 minutes, except when the previous egg is laid late in the afternoon—in which case ovulation is delayed until the next morning.

Number of Eggs. Most birds lay eggs in a clutch—they lay a few eggs in sequence, then stop and brood. The domestic hen is a notable exception, laying continuously for a large part of the year. Here cycles of 3, 4, or more days of uninterrupted laying are separated from one another by one or a few days of non-laying. The annual output declines steadily with increasing age and so does the length of the laying season : 351 eggs in one year and 1515 eggs laid within 8 years by a single hen have been recorded.

The number of eggs in a clutch (clutch size) varies with the species. Some lay only one egg ; others regularly have clutches of 2, 3, or 4 ; others show more variability, especially where the number is large (such as 10–20 for the Partridge *Perdix perdix*). In many species clutch size varies between populations, with the individuals of a population, and even for one individual in different years. The average clutch size of a population has been shown to be delicately adjusted so as to yield the maximal number of successfully reared young. It is influenced by such factors as the age of the parents, seasonal influences responsible for the availability of food later in the year, and population density (see EGGS, NATURAL HISTORY OF ; POPULATION DYNAMICS).

Determinate and Indeterminate Layers. Little is known about how the regulation takes place— what are the climatic (or other) indicators of abundance of food later in the season, and by what means do they affect the activity of the ovary? A further complication arises from the fact that two different types of egg-laying mechanism may have

to be distinguished (Cole 1917) ; in some birds (indeterminate layers) the number of eggs laid can be changed by adding or removing eggs during or just before the time of laying ; in other birds (determinate layers) this has no influence. In the latter case, presumably, the ovary produces only as many yolks as eggs will be laid. Experimental addition of eggs to the first egg of the clutch may reduce the number of eggs laid subsequently, e.g. in the Tricoloured Blackbird *Agelaius tricolor* of North America. In many other species, e.g. the Swallow *Hirundo rustica*, pigeons (Columbidae), gulls (Larinae), and the Lapwing *Vanellus vanellus*, this has no effect ; but if eggs are presented a few days earlier in some of these, egg-laying may be suppressed fully or partially —thus a Blackheaded Gull sitting on model eggs for 2–8 days before laying its first egg may lay only 2 or 1. Removal of eggs, so as to leave only one or a few in the nest, increases the number to be laid in many species. Such protracted laying occurs e.g. in the Yellow-shafted Flicker *Colaptes auratus* (where one female laid 71 eggs within 73 days) and in other woodpeckers (Picidae) ; a Mallard *Anas platyrhynchos* is reported to have laid 80–100 eggs when one was removed daily, and a Sparrow *Passer domesticus* laid up to 50 eggs in succession (of which 12–19 were laid on consecutive days) instead of the usual clutch of 4–5. These and many other birds thus qualify as indeterminate layers. In a few others, e.g. Swallow, Magpie *Pica pica*, Gentoo Penguin *Pygoscelis papua*, Lapwing, and gulls, this procedure has no influence on the number of eggs laid. Nevertheless some of these have been shown to be indeterminate layers ; they will lay additional eggs at normal intervals if the first egg is taken as well, i.e. if all eggs are removed as soon as they are laid. In these circumstances the Lapwing and Gentoo Penguin will lay one and gulls 3 or more additional eggs (Paludan and others). In pigeons, egg-laying could not be protracted in this way (Poulsen).

In the ovary of an indeterminate layer more oocytes may enter the final phase of growth (Stieve) than are normally laid, and tactile or visual stimuli from the eggs in the nest are responsible for the cessation of laying. In some species, e.g. gulls, the end of laying is determined not by a definite number of eggs in the nest but by the opportunity for the bird to incubate. Only a limited number of eggs are laid after the onset of incubation, which causes all oocytes under a critical size in the ovary to degenerate. In species that do not incubate before the clutch is complete this explanation cannot apply. Here it is the critical number of eggs in the nest that stops the growth or causes the degeneration of superfluous oocytes. In neither case can laying be protracted once the reserve follicles have started to degenerate, i.e. one or more days after the onset of incubation.

Number of Clutches. Most wild birds normally lay only one clutch in each year, but there are others that have two or more broods in a season. The domestic pigeon may lay up to ten clutches a year. In most species (but not the domestic pigeon) the number of eggs tends to decrease with each successive clutch.

In Megapodiidae there may be no clutch in the ordinary sense ; the eggs, often very numerous, are laid at intervals throughout several months, and there is no synchronisation of incubation and hatching (see MEGAPODE).

Most birds with only one brood annually, and all of those with more than one, are able to replace the clutch when it is lost (repeat laying) ; a Black-headed Gull *Larus ridibundus* will lay again 8–12 days after the loss. Exceptions are some big vultures (Aegypiinae) and most Procellariiformes. Repeat clutches tend to be smaller than the first one.

U.W.

Conrad, R. M. & Scott, H. M. 1938. The formation of the egg of the domestic fowl. Physiol. Rev. 18 : 481–494.
Davis, D. E. 1955. Determinate laying in Barn Swallows and Black-billed Magpies. Condor 57 : 81–87.
Ottow, B. 1955. Die Lage des Vogeleies im Uterus und damit zusammenhängende physiologische Fragen. J. Orn. 96 : 15–23.
Poulsen, H. 1953. A study of incubation responses and some other behaviour patterns in birds. Vidensk. Medd. Dansk Naturh. Foren. 115 : 1–131.
Romanoff, A. I. & A. J. 1949. The Avian Egg. New York.
Skutch, A. F. 1952. On the hour of laying and hatching of birds' eggs. Ibis 94 : 49–61.
Sykes, A. H. 1953. Some observations on oviposition in the fowl. Quart. J. Exp. Physiol. 38 : 61–68.
Weidmann, U. 1956. Observations and experiments on egg-laying in the Black-headed Gull (*Larus ridibundus* L.). Brit. J. Anim. Behav. 4 : 150–161.

LEADING LINE: see MIGRATION

LEAFBIRD : substantive name of species in one genus of Irenidae (Passeriformes, suborder Oscines); in the plural, general term for the family. Other names used are ' iora ' and ' fairy-bluebird '. This is a small Oriental group of three very distinct genera. They are characterised by short, thick legs and small feet, a fairly long, rather slender, slightly curved or hooked bill, moderately sized wings and tail. The plumage is long, thick, and fluffy, particularly abundant on the rump, recalling in texture that of the bulbuls (Pycnonotidae), probably their nearest relatives, and also of the drongos (Dicruridae) and the cuckoo-shrikes (Campephagidae). The sexes are more or less dissimilar, with a very few exceptions.

Leafbirds have a bright, whistling or chattering voice ; their calls are varied and striking. They are purely arboreal in habits, frequenting forests, second growth, and sometimes gardens. The majority of them feed on fruit and berries, with the addition of insects. They build neat, cup-shaped nests, and they lay 3 or 4 eggs that are lined and speckled with reddish and brown on a grey, cream, or pink background.

Blue-backed Fairy-bluebird *Irena puella*. *C.E.T.K.*

Leafbirds are found in the Oriental Region, including southern China and the Philippines ; they are particularly numerous in Malaysia. The three genera differ much in size and in colours. The smallest in size (from $4\frac{3}{4}$ inches long), the ioras *Aegithina* spp., are yellow or olive-green and black, with some white ; the males have a non-breeding plumage, similar to the female plumage, as well as a brighter breeding dress. Their legs are relatively longer and their bills straighter, and they are more insectivorous, than the birds of the two larger genera. One species, the Common Iora *A. tiphia*, is widespread and common, even in gardens, throughout the range of the family ; there are many local subspecies. It has an acrobatic aerial courtship display. Another, *A. nigrolutea*, is closely similar but confined to north-central India ; a much greener one, *A. viridissima*, is strictly Malaysian. The fourth species, *A. lafresnayei*, is a good deal larger and is found in Burma, Indo-China, and Malaya ; it resembles *A. tiphia* in colour.

The leafbirds proper, *Chloropsis* spp., are larger, with a slightly curved and pointed bill ; their main colour is a bright, light green. To their diet of fruit, berries, and insects, they add flower nectar and pollen. The voice is strong and bright, and some sing really well. They are not shy by nature and can often be observed feeding in wild fruit trees, chattering and moving about happily. The dress of the males mostly differs from that of the females in having more black, orange, or blue on the face and throat. The Philippine species, *C. flavipennis*, is the most uniform, while the Orange-bellied Leafbird *C. hardwickii*, from northern India, Burma, Indo-China, southern China, and Malaya, is the largest and most brilliantly marked, with much orange, black, and blue in the plumage. The Golden-fronted Leafbird *A. aurifrons*, from India and Indo-China, is the best known ; it is often exported, being a very popular cage-bird. The smallest and most beautiful species is the rare Blue-masked Leafbird *C. venusta*, from Sumatra, in which the male is deep olive-green with a blue and black head, a blue tail, and a yellow breast. There are in all 8 species of *Chloropsis*, several of them with many subspecies.

The third genus, *Irena*, is composed of the two species of Fairy-bluebird, the size of a Starling *Sturnus vulgaris*. In the Indo-Malaysian species, the Blue-backed Fairy-bluebird *I. puella*, the males are clad in light, iridescent blue and velvety black, while the females are verditer blue ; it is found in India, Burma, Siam, Indo-China, Malaysia, and Palawan. The sexes are more or less similar, blue and black, in the Philippine species *I. cyanogaster* ; the eyes are ruby red, the bill and the small legs are black. Each species has several subspecies. Fairy-bluebirds live on forest trees and eat mostly berries, particularly the small wild figs of banyans ; it is not unusual to observe small flocks thus feeding and chattering. They are in fact rather common in suitable habitats.

Wetmore places *Irena* in a special subfamily of the Oriolidae, and treats the other two genera as constituting a family Chloropseidae.   J.D.

Delacour, J. 1960. Family Irenidae. *In* Mayr, E. & Greenway, J. C., Jr. (eds.). Check-list of Birds of the World vol. 9. Cambridge, Mass.

LEAFLOVE: used as a substantive name for some species of Pycnonotidae (see BULBUL).

LEAFSCRAPER: substantive name of *Sclerurus* spp. (see OVENBIRD (1)).

LEARNING: best defined as ' the production of adaptive changes in individual behaviour as a result of experience'. It is contrasted with innate or instinctive behaviour, which does not depend on such individual experience to bring it forth or develop it but is so fully under the control of the hereditary mechanism that it appears at the appropriate time in the individual life cycle irrespective of special experience. There has been considerable difference of opinion as to whether the term ' adaptive' should be included in the definition (Thorpe 1956) ; the word is used here in order to

prevent the term ' learning ' from including such changes in behaviour as those resulting from fatigue, sensory adaptation, and the effects of injury (surgical or otherwise). This is important, because it is generally agreed that learned behaviour is to be carefully distinguished from changes in behaviour caused by physiological or structural damage to the system.

Many workers have considered that a more or less frequent repetition of a stimulus or of a changed situation is necessary for learning, but so many examples are now known of learning as a result of a single experience that this contention can no longer be maintained. There are six different categories of learning that are found to be useful in describing behaviour of birds and the higher vertebrates generally, one of which is discussed in a separate article (see IMPRINTING). See also BEHAVIOUR, DEVELOPMENT OF.

Habituation. This is, in some respects, the simplest type of learning found in the Animal Kingdom. It consists of ' the waning of a pre-existing response as a result of repeated stimulation when this is not followed by any kind of reward or punishment' (Reinforcement). It is most evident in nature in relation to avoiding action to more generalised and simple stimuli such as loud sounds, sudden movements, any stimulus or situation that is strange, and any familiar stimulus at an unusually high intensity. Many species of birds, also, have the inborn ability to recognise, and immediately take appropriate avoiding action or other response in regard to, certain types of predator, such as hawks (Falconiformes) and owls (Strigiformes), that are particularly dangerous to their species ; but such an inherited response is hardly likely to have been evolved except in response to dangers that are of primary significance to the particular species. To have such an instinctive response to every kind of predator, and to every and any danger, would be out of the question. Therefore instead of, or in addition to, such specific responses, practically all animals show this ability to become habituated to stimuli that experience shows to be harmless. Obviously, if the response to such stimuli as sudden movements and sounds were completely automatic and unvarying, the life of the animal would become impossible since it would be continually taking cover from the flicker of a leaf and from every passing shadow. Habituation is thus that very simple form of learning which saves an animal from wasting its energies in response to stimuli that experience shows to be of no significance. Habituation is obviously of prime importance in the process of taming birds and other animals, constituting as it does the first step in accepting the abnormal conditions of captivity. The term 'habituation' is used in a general way for any type of response decrement shown by animals ; not many examples have been sufficiently fully analysed for us to go further than this. It is, however, now clear (see Hinde 1954 ab, 1960 ; Thorpe 1956, pp. 299–300) that there are at least four types of response decrement included under the general term, and it has become of considerable practical and theoretical importance to distinguish these where possible. They are as follows :

1. Short-term waning of the response irrespective of the nature of the stimulus—a kind of localised fatigue of short duration (e.g. the waning of the pecking responses of the young Herring Gull *Larus argentatus* after frequent repetition).

2. Long-term waning of the response irrespective of the nature of the stimulus, e.g. some examples of inhibition of sexual behaviour in long-deprived birds. (As yet comparatively little studied.)

3. Short-term waning of the response to a specific stimulus. This type of behaviour may be observed in the changed intensity of the begging response of nestling passerines and may be evidence of some transitory changes in the releasing mechanism, giving rise to a passing lack of attention to the stimulus.

4. Long-term response-waning specific to the stimulus. This is habituation in the strict sense and, when information warrants it, the term is best reserved for this kind of phenomenon. It is an effect that endures for weeks or months rather than seconds or minutes. Examples specifically studied include the long-term nystagmus (rapid involuntary oscillation of the eyeballs) of both young and adult pigeons *Columba* sp. produced as a result of repeated rotation ; similarly, habituation can be shown in the reduction of the number of head movements correlated with the nystagmus habituation to sound signals, which has also been studied in pigeons and domestic chicks.

Finally, the term 'habituation' is most useful if it is restricted to processes depending on changes in the central nervous system, as distinct from changes in the level of response of the sense organs themselves. This is one of the reasons why it is important to distinguish No. 1 type of response from No. 4 above, since the former is much more likely to be due to temporary change in responsiveness of the sense organ concerned.

Conditioning. In the strict Pavlovian sense this may be defined as ' the process of acquisition by an animal of the capacity to respond to a given stimulus with the reflex reaction appropriate to another stimulus (Reinforcement) when two stimuli are applied concurrently for a number of times '.

Conditioning in the strict physiological sense is a most important element in habit formation, but it cannot usually be discriminated from other conditioning factors in the free-living bird. Nevertheless it is of immense importance as being a means by which the releasing mechanism is elaborated or modified to fit the environmental situation more exactly. It consists of the linking of a pre-existing response to a new stimulus without changing the response. Pavlov and his pupils were the pioneers in the laboratory study of the conditioned responses not only of mammals but also of birds ; the domestic pigeon has been the species mainly used. Just as with the dog used in salivary conditioning experiments, so the bird has to be trained to stand in a specially devised ' coat ' with openings to allow the free movement of the head and one leg only. When this phase of preliminary habituation is completed, the application of a mild electric shock can be used as conditioning stimulus on the presentation of food. A great variety of auditory, visual, tactile, and ampullar stimulations have been successfully used as conditioning stimuli. The conditioning method is of great importance in investigating the range of abilities of the sense organs. The conditioned reflex is not the sole element through which learning is achieved ; but, historically, it constituted one of the first ways in which the learning process of animals could be quantitatively and precisely studied in the laboratory, and it remains an invaluable tool for the investigation of the senses of animals.

Trial-and-error Learning (Instrumental Conditioning). Trial-and-error learning is the term used to designate the essential process in the acquisition or specialisation of habits. There are many synonyms, such as ' Conditioned reflex type 2 ', ' Conditioned reflex type R ', ' Instrumental conditioning ', ' Thorndykian conditioning ', ' Action conditioning ', ' Instrumental learning ', ' Escape-and-avoidance training '. Of these, perhaps ' Instrumental conditioning ' and ' Action conditioning ' are the two most appropriate for the phenomena likely to be encountered in the laboratory. Whereas the strict reflex conditioning consists of the linking of a pre-existing response to a new stimulus without change in that response, instrumental conditioning consists of the modification of the response itself or the production of a new response. Thus, whereas classical conditioning is relatively passive, instrumental conditioning involves active motor or appetitive behaviour on the part of the animal. In order to demonstrate instrumental or action conditioning, the generalised appetitive behaviour of the animal is allowed to take place or deliberately invoked (instead of being suppressed, as in the

Pavlovian experiment), and this behaviour comprises a number of possible acts. Thus the learning consists in selecting the most appropriate form of these various items of behaviour as a result of the reward that follows them. Strictly, then, reflex conditioning is restricted to the acceptance of a new stimulus, instrumental conditioning to the development of a new act. In fact, *the two together* make up what could be called trial-and-error learning, which is an expressive name for the behaviour as seen in the normal animal learning in its natural environment. It can now be more precisely defined as ' the development of an association as a result of reinforcement, during appetitive behaviour, between a stimulus or situation and an independent motor action as an item in that behaviour, when both stimulus and motor action precede the reinforcement in time and the motor action is not the inevitable inherited response to the reinforcement '. A particularly good example of trial-and-error learning is the improvement in the co-ordination and control of pecking movements in a bird as the result of experience. Pecking and drinking are based on innate unlearned reflexes and responses, but much of the fine adjustment of both results from trial-and-error learning. Similarly with ' learning to fly ' ; it has been shown that the essential movements of flight are innately co-ordinated and do not require practice for their development, but once the young bird has taken its first flight it achieves fine adjustments of the flight movements and learns to control alighting and take-off under varying wind conditions as a result of trial-and-error learning. In the same way, trial-and-error learning plays an important part in the improvement of many examples of nest-building ; many birds appear to be born equipped with latent nest-building motions, but they have to learn, at any rate to some extent, what materials are appropriate for nest building and how to manipulate them.

The trial-and-error learning ability of pigeons has been used on a very large scale by Ferster & Skinner (1957) for the fundamental study of the effect of different systems and schedules of reward on learning ability. In this immense study, involving many hundreds of experiments, the pecking response of the pigeon is used as a special instance, the result of which can be applied to human learning systems. While the work in itself is in no sense ornithological, it provides a number of results of great interest to the student of the behaviour of birds and other animals. In particular it reveals one of the most important distinctions between classical conditioning and trial-and-error learning. In the former the response has to be rewarded for a high proportion of the occasions

on which it occurs if it is to be maintained with its full intensity and efficiency. With instrumental conditioning ' partial reinforcement ', that is, the giving of only an occasional reward, may be as effective as, or even more effective than, unfailing reward at every performance. With pigeons under schedules of intermittent reinforcement, Ferster & Skinner describe two birds which were able to respond in a sustained manner when only 1 in every 875 pecks was rewarded by obtaining food. Again, when reward ceases on completion of conditioning, as many as 10 000 pecking responses may appear in the absence of reward before the pecking response has completely subsided. Considering bird behaviour as a whole, trial-and-error learning is infinitely the most important process involved in adjusting voluntary actions to the circumstances of the environment. For it to take place one must first have appetite motivation (e.g. the drive of the pecking response), often governed by ' curiosity ' relating to the external environment or some particular part of it. Trial-and-error learning enters into every positive example of individual adaptation and mode of behaviour, and there is no instance of adaptive modification of actions, however ' intelligent ' it may appear, that does not contain trial-and-error learning in at least some degree. All training of birds and mammals for whatever purpose depends upon it at some stage, if not at every stage, and there is nothing that can be called ' habit ' which lacks it altogether.

It is through trial-and-error learning that play serves its function as a means of acquiring knowledge and skill appropriate to better performance in all the varied activities of the bird's life. It was for long believed that young birds, in contrast with young mammals such as kittens and badger and fox cubs, do not play. This conclusion seems to have been based on insufficient evidence, for there are now so many examples on record of playful behaviour in a great variety of young birds that one must conclude that it is general (Thorpe 1956, pp. 321-323)—see PLAY. This playful behaviour consists in tilting and sparring matches between young birds, the playful hunting of inanimate objects by young raptors (e.g. the Kestrel *Falco tinnunculus*), and the playing with sticks, stones, and other material objects which may be regarded as potential nest material. More elaborate examples of behaviour that can probably be regarded, at any rate provisionally, as play are the soaring and tumbling in rising air currents by Rooks *Corvus frugilegus* and other birds, and the play of birds such as Eiders *Somateria mollissima* and Black Guillemots *Cepphus grylle* in torrents and tide races. The most extreme development of what appears to be play is found in the bowerbirds (Ptilonorhyn-chidae) where the bower displays and 'games' seem to have passed far beyond the limits of utilitarianism (see BOWERBIRD).

To sum up, we see that classical conditioning is the establishment of an association between a normal reward or reinforcement (which can usually be regarded as involving a consummatory act) and a new external or exteroceptive stimulus, which is initially indifferent in the sense that it does not innately release any specific responses and so does not originally have any 'meaning' for the animal. Instrumental conditioning, on the other hand, is the establishment of an association between a voluntary mator act as part of appetitive behaviour, primarily as perceived by the animal's proprioceptive organs, and the normal reward or reinforcement—the natural reinforcement thus involving a consummatory act or a consummatory situation or both. Thus classical conditioning and instrumental conditioning combine together to make up the full normal process of trial-and-error learning—the first by conditioning the external stimulus to the 'innate releasing mechanism', the second by conditioning a voluntary movement (the motor act) of the appetitive behaviour to the 'innate motor mechanism' of the consummatory act. Thus :

1. Exteroceptive stimulus + Innate releasing mechanism = Reflex conditioning.
2. Proprioceptive stimulus + Innate motor mechanism = Instrumental (Action) conditioning.
3. Reflex conditioning + Instrumental conditioning = Trial-and-error learning.

Both components of learning are regarded as essentially anticipatory in the sense of having prospective reference to an ensuing reinforcement in the form of a reward or a consummatory act, but whereas the first component is essentially passive, the second involves active trial—or appetitive behaviour.

Latent Learning. In the types of learning so far described the performance is established or stereotyped as a result of the attainment of some kind of reward, e.g. food, drink, effective nest building, or control of flight movements. It has long been recognised that in some animals another type of learning can be discerned which is independent of reward in the ordinary physiological sense of the term. The classical experiment is as follows : a litter of young rats is divided into two groups, one of which is placed for a period every day for ten days in a particular maze of a particular pattern and allowed to explore this maze at random ; the others are given no such experience. If, then, both groups of rats

are given identical training in such a maze by being rewarded in the normal manner by finding food in the food box on completion of the run, it will be found that those rats which had had the chance to explore the maze previously (but without being rewarded in it) had, in fact, learnt a great deal about its layout and show a striking decrease both in errors and time of running as compared with the control group. A simple maze may in this way be entirely mastered through random exploration, but this learning is latent in that it cannot be demonstrated until the introduction of a reward. Latent learning can thus be defined as 'the association of indifferent stimuli or situations (i.e. situations without reward)'. One cannot conveniently train pigeons in mazes, but there is little doubt that latent learning is a laboratory version of what is a very general feature of animals that in nature have to find their way about. There is no doubt that a great deal of the learning displayed by birds in getting to know territory, individual habitat, migration routes, and so on, resembles latent learning in that the learning achieved is not immediately rewarded in the ordinary physiological sense. Also, like latent learning, it implies a tendency to explore the environment and to learn as a result the characteristic features and their special relation to one another.

Insight and Insight Learning. The term 'intelligence' has no precise connotation for students of animal behaviour and is best avoided. Its place is taken by the term 'insight learning' which is defined as 'sudden adaptive re-organisation of experience' or 'the sudden production of a new adaptive response not arrived at by overt trial-and-error behaviour'. In mammals the precise evidence for insight is provided chiefly by the ability to learn a special kind of maze or detour problem such that when the animal has learnt one roundabout way through a maze it is able to 'see' that there is another shorter way that can be taken, and can show its insight into the maze situation by taking this short cut as soon as it is allowed to do so, without having actually traversed the path before. The sudden production of a completely new response such as is shown by the tool-using behaviour of the higher mammals also comes under this category. With birds the existence of insight and learning of this fully developed kind is difficult to establish, although there are many observations suggesting that it may well occur. Evidence for insight can, however, also be obtained from experiments in which the animal shows evidence of ideation. Ideation may be defined as the occurrence of perceptions, in the absence of the corresponding external stimulus, in the form of images that are in some degree abstract or generalised and that can be the subject of further ' mental ' comparison and reorganisation by learning processes. Some promising lines of investigation such as those which have led to the demonstration of the phenomenon of ' reminiscence ' in rats, have not yet been attempted with birds. With birds the ability to deal with number and to abstract a numerical quantity from a given number of specific objects provides perhaps the best evidence available for ideational processes (see COUNTING).   W.H.T.

Ferster, C. B. & Skinner, B. F. 1957. Schedules of Reinforcement. New York.
Hinde, R. A. 1954a ; 1960. Factors governing the changes in strength of a partially inborn response, as shown by the mobbing behaviour of the chaffinch (*Fringilla coelebs*). I, II, and III. Proc. Roy. Soc. B. 142 : 306-331, 331-358 ; 153 : 398-420.
Hinde, R. A. 1954 b. Changes in responsiveness to a constant stimulus. Brit. J. Anim. Behav. 2 : 41-55.
Thorpe, W. H. 1956. Learning and Instinct in Animals. London. (2nd ed. 1963.)
Thorpe, W. H. 1959. Learning. Ibis 101 : 337-353.

LEATHERHEAD: substantive name, alternatively ' friar-bird ', of *Philemon* spp. (see HONEY-EATER).

LECTOTYPE: see TYPE-SPECIMEN

LEG: the paired hind limb ; but the term ' leg ' is variously used, in different contexts, for the whole limb or for the ordinarily visible part of it and to include or exclude the ' foot ', itself an inexact term for the extremity. The main components are the thigh, the lower leg (equivalent to shin), the so-called tarsus, and the toes—corresponding osteologically with the femur, the tibiotarsus plus fibula, the fused tarsometatarsus (with one free metatarsal where there are four toes), and the digit phalanges (see SKELETON). The joints between these components are the knee, the inter-tarsal joint or ankle, and the joints of the toes ; as most birds stand on their toes, the raised ankle is often popularly mistaken for a knee (the real knee being concealed in the plumage) although it bends in the reverse direction.

Birds are dependent upon their limbs for locomotion on land or on water, and there are a number of adaptations to meet these varying conditions. When the bird is standing, the leg is situated just behind the bird's centre of gravity, balance being maintained by the toes. The legs are set farther back in swimming species ; this is particularly true of the divers (Gaviidae), in which walking becomes almost impossible, so that on land they rest on their tarsi and wriggle on their stomachs—as sometimes do penguins (Spheniscidae), although these can also walk or hop in the upright position ; the grebes

(Podicipitidae) can run on their toes in emergency.

The thigh, knee, and upper part of the lower leg are completely hidden by the flank feathers and it is only the lower part of the lower leg, the ankle joint, the tarsus, and the toes that are visible. The relative length of the limb is extremely variable. Birds that walk or run, such as the Ostrich *Struthio camelus*, have long legs, whereas most small birds hop and have relatively shorter legs (see LOCOMOTION). In passerine birds that run, e.g. larks (Alaudidae) and wagtails (Motacillidae), the young initially hop. Similarly, wading birds, particularly flamingos (Phoenicopteridae) and the Stilt *Himantopus himantopus*, have long legs and can thus go far into the water without wetting their plumage. The Secretary-bird *Sagittarius serpentarius* is an example of a long-legged hawk-like bird that both evades snakes and preys on them by springing in the air and killing them by striking. The shortest legs are seen in those species that seldom walk, such as the swifts (Apodidae) and the kingfishers (Alcedinidae) ; but such short legs are capable of digging—the Bee-eater *Merops apiaster* leans on its wings while it digs with its feet.

Relative strength depends upon function. Birds-of-prey possess powerful limbs for striking and holding their quarry ; swimming species, particularly those that are not assisted in the water by their wings, possess massive thighs (see SWIMMING AND DIVING) ; whereas those that scratch the ground for food, such as the gallinaceous birds, have heavy tarsi and toes. See also CARRYING ; HOLDING ; PERCHING.

Covering of Tarsi and Toes. In some birds, the tarsi and even the toes are covered with feathers or bristles. This may be protective against the cold, e.g. Pallas's Sandgrouse *Syrrhaptes paradoxus*, in which the feathers extend to the upper surface of the toes only, and the Ptarmigan *Lagopus mutus*, in which the under surface of the toes is also feathered. Feathering in other species, including the owls (Strigiformes) and the House Martin *Delichon urbica*, cannot be accounted for in this way. Feathering may therefore be primitive, a scaly covering being a secondary transformation of feathers. These scales may be shed annually (see MOULT), and occasional variants of the Buzzard *Buteo buteo* possess feathered tarsi, similar to those of the Rough-legged Buzzard *Buteo lagopus*. Man has produced feathered tarsi by selective breeding in domestic pigeons and fowls.

The part of the limb lacking feathers is covered with a thickened, hardened structure, the podotheca. This may be corneous (horny) as in land birds or softer and more ' leathery ' as in water birds. The surface may be scutellate (scaly), reticulate (covered

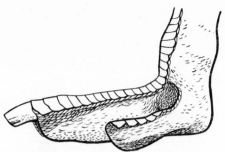

FIG 1. Foot (right) of Ostrich *Struthio camelus*, with toes uniquely reduced to two. $\frac{1}{5}$ nat. size. *M.Y.*

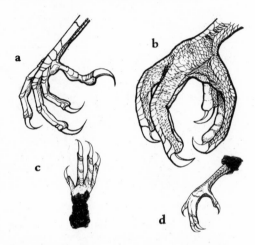

FIG 2. Some perching and clinging feet (right): **a** Starling *Sturnus vulgaris:* anisodactyl; **b** Senegal Parrot *Poicephalus senegalensis*, zygodactyl; **c** Swift *Apus apus*, with all four toes directed forwards; **d** Kingfisher *Alcedo atthis*, syndactyl. Natural size. *M.Y.*

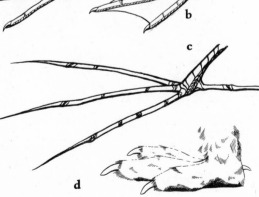

with polygonal plates), granulate (covered with small tubercules), cancellate (covered with cross lines, as on the webs of water birds). If the podotheca is undivided or has only a few scales close to the toes, the bird is said to be 'booted' or holothecal, a condition found in most passerines (but when young these have scutellae that disappear by fusion). The young of certain Piciformes, Coraciiformes, and Trogonidae possess 'heel' pads, at the back of the intertarsal joint, that are shed when the birds leave the nest. These pads are in most cases strongly papillate, but smooth in Galbulidae. In some grouse (Tetraonidae) with unfeathered toes these are laterally pectinated (for pectinate claws see below).

Tarsal Shape. In most species the tarsus is rounded in cross section, but in many swimming species it is compressed laterally to reduce water friction when the leg is brought forward, the foot folding neatly to the same shape. This is most highly developed in divers and grebes, where the tarsus resembles a knife blade.

Spurs. These consist of a bony core covered with a pointed horny sheath and are situated on the posterior and inner surface of the tarsus. They are used with skill in battles that can well prove fatal, and are possessed by cock birds of polygamous species such as pheasants and peacocks (Phasianidae) and turkeys (Meleagrididae). The peacock-pheasants *Polyplectron* spp. have up to four full-sized spurs on each leg. See also COCK-FIGHTING.

Number and Arrangement of Toes. No bird has more than 4 toes; some have only 3, the hallux having been lost (vestigial in some others); and one species has only 2, as noted below. Their arrangement depends upon function. The majority have 3 forward toes and one, the 1st toe or hallux, behind (anisodactyl). This was the position in *Archaeopteryx* of the Jurassic period (see ARCHAEOPTERYX). Exceptions are as follows:

(*a*) All 4 toes may point forwards, as in the swifts (Apodidae), an adaptation for climbing vertically and clinging to the nest.

(*b*) The 1st toe may be capable of turning backwards or forwards, as in the mousebirds (Coliidae); this and the preceding case have been termed the pamprodactyl foot.

FIG 3. Some walking and wading feet (right): **a** Lapwing *Vanellus vanellus*; **b** Avocet *Recurvirostra avosetta*, webbed; **c** Lesser Lilytrotter *Microparra capensis*; **d** Ptarmigan *Lagopus mutus*, in winter plumage with feathered toes ('snowshoes'). $\frac{2}{3}$ nat. size. *M.Y.*

(*c*) The outer forward toe (4th) may be capable of turning backwards or forwards, as in most owls (Strigiformes) and the Osprey *Pandion haliaetus*.

(*d*) The toes may be permanently in pairs, 2 in front and 2 behind—the zygodactyl or ' yoke-toed ' foot. This occurs in woodpeckers (Picidae), toucans (Ramphastidae), cuckoos (Cuculidae), parrots (Psittacidae), and others. These have the 1st and 4th toes pointing backwards, but in the trogons (Trogonidae) it is the 1st and 2nd that do so (sometimes called ' heterodactyl '). In some Picidae, e.g. the Three-toed Woodpecker *Picoides tridactylus*, the 1st toe has been lost ; in a few others (*Campephilus* etc.) the 1st and 4th toes are, during climbing, rotated into an external lateral position (ectropodactyl).

(*e*) The 3rd and 4th toes may be partly united, with a single broad sole—the syndactyl foot of the kingfishers, hornbills (Bucerotidae), and the Cock-of-the-rock *Rupicola rupicola*.

In swift-running species it may be advantageous to lessen the surface of contact with the ground. Thus the 1st toe becomes raised and tends to disappear, as in some plovers (Charadriidae). The extreme is seen in the Ostrich, which has only 2 forward toes, one poorly developed and both possessing a soft elastic cushion on the sole to prevent sinking into soft sand. In sandgrouse (Pteroclididae) the 3 forward toes are united by a membrane holding them close together.

Claws. Claws are specialised scales, and in grouse *Lagopus* spp. are moulted in winter. Their shape is variable ; sharp, well curved claws are used for gripping firmly and are seen in such birds as the treecreepers (Certhiidae), the Wallcreeper *Tichodroma muraria*, woodpeckers, and the birds-of-prey (excepting the carrion-feeding vultures (Aegypiinae) and the Honey-buzzard *Pernis apivorus*, in which the claws are weaker and straighter). The claws of oxpeckers *Buphagus* spp. are extremely sharp. Strong, blunt claws are associated with species that scratch the ground in search of food, while exceptionally long claws, such as the hind claws of some larks and pipits *Anthus* spp., and the long 2nd claw of the One-wattled Cassowary *Casuarius unappendiculatus*, may be concerned with balance when running. In the jacanas (Jacanidae) all 4 claws are long, in association with long thin toes ; this remarkable adaptation enables the birds to walk over floating vegetation. In grebes the claw is flattened and is incorporated into the paddle.

The herons (Ardeidae), nightjars (Caprimulgidae), and pratincoles *Glareola* spp., have a serrated edge or ' comb ' on the inner border of the 3rd claw ; the function of this pectinate claw is unknown.

Types of Foot. Although there are many

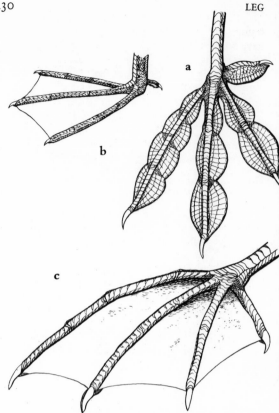

FIG 4. Some swimming feet (right) : **a** Coot *Fulica atra*, lobate ; **b** Mallard *Anas platyrhynchos*, palmate ; **c** Cormorant *Phalacrocorax carbo*, totipalmate. $\frac{1}{2}$ nat. size. *M.Y.*

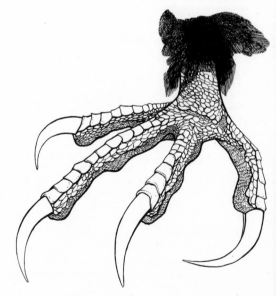

FIG 5. Foot (right) of Golden Eagle *Aquila chrysaetos*, adapted for grasping. $\frac{1}{2}$ nat. size. *M.Y.*

transitional forms, three main functional patterns have been evolved.

1. *Perching*

(*a*) In the passerine foot all the toes are free and mobile, the hind toe being highly developed and 'opposable' to produce a firm grip. (For an exception see PARROTBILL (1).)

(*b*) The zygodactyl foot with 2 'opposable' toes provides an even surer grip. Parrots use the foot like a hand in feeding. The 'semi-zygodactyl' variant, typified in *Turacus fischeri*, has been defined by Moreau ' as having a fourth (outside) toe that can be brought back to form an angle of about seventy degrees with the first toe, and forward until it almost touches the third toe, but normally is held at right angles to the main axis of the foot '.

(*c*) In the raptorial foot the toes are widely spread and possess sharp, highly curved claws. The under surface of the toes has bulbous and roughened pads, which in the Osprey carry spines to fix the slippery fish. This type of foot has great grasping and holding powers.

2. *Walking and wading.* In general the foot has tended to lose its power of gripping. The hind toe may become elevated to lose contact with the ground and has become reduced in size—or it may be lost, as in the Kittiwake *Larus* ('*Rissa*') *tridactylus*. In some wading birds the toes are partially or completely webbed, for example the flamingos, storks (Ciconiidae), and avocets *Recurvirostra* spp. ; walking over soft ground is thus facilitated, and such species can swim well on occasion.

The rails (Rallidae) have developed long toes and claws as an adaptation for walking over soft ground ; this type reaches its extreme form, as already mentioned, in the jacanas, which are thus able to distribute their weight over a large surface area.

The feathered foot of the Ptarmigan increases the weight-bearing surface when walking on snow in winter. The American Ruffed Grouse *Bonasia umbellata* in winter develops 'snow shoes' in the form of a row of scales along each side of the toes.

3. *Swimming.* Many unrelated birds such as the petrels (Procellariiformes), gulls (Laridae), auks (Alcidae), ducks and geese (Anatidae), have developed along similar lines to transform the foot into a paddle.

In the lobate variation, each toe carries independent webs, examples being the coots *Fulica* spp., phalaropes (Phalaropodidae), the grebes, and the three remarkably grebe-like species of finfoot (Heliornithidae), thought to be of gruiform evolution. In grebes, the tibiotarsus is held in extreme external rotation when the bird is swimming ; the foot is pale on its inner surface and dark on its outer surface, so that, as the latter is uppermost in swimming, the normal countershading is maintained.

In the palmate variation the 3 forward toes are united by a web, typical examples being the gulls, petrels, and ducks. The hind toe is free, poorly developed, and unmodified except in diving ducks, in which it is lobulate. The Hawaiian Goose *Branta sandvicensis* possesses a partially palmate foot and is an example of a goose that has reverted to a more terrestrial life.

In the totipalmate variation characteristic of the Pelecaniformes, all 4 toes are webbed to provide the perfect swimming foot, the outer toe being the longest and the hind toe pointing slightly forward.

Unfeathered legs and feet, particularly webbed feet, are a potential source of heat loss. Irvine & Krog have shown in gulls *Larus* spp., however, that there is not only a reduced blood flow at low external temperatures but also some kind of vascular heat exchange, so that blood flowing into the unfeathered part of the leg does so at a very low temperature. This can be appreciated by feeling the cold web of any water bird. Serious heat loss is thus eliminated ; and, in extremes, loss can be further reduced if the bird sits on its legs, covering them with its feathers (see also HEAT REGULATION).

Abnormalities. Supernumerary limbs and toes occur as genetic variants (except in domestication, the Dorking Fowl possessing a constant supernumerary toe on each foot). Very rarely a toe may be missing due to a congenital defect ; frequently the toes are crooked, in association with inbreeding. Survival has been recorded in a wild Pheasant *Phasianus colchicus* after both feet had been accidentally amputated through the tarsi. Partial or total loss of one or both feet is not uncommon in water or wading birds and there is evidence that this is caused by fishes and molluscs. Loss of toes in a Moorhen *Gallinula chloropus* has followed a tuberculous arthritis. Normal embryonic development may be altered by radiation or drug administration.

J.G.H.

Beebe, C. W. 1907. The Bird—its Form and Function. New York.
Bock, W. J. & Miller, W. D. 1959. The scansorial foot of the woodpeckers, with comments on the evolution of perching and climbing feet in birds. Amer. Mus. Novit. no. 1931 : 1–45.
Thomson, J. A. 1923. The Biology of Birds. London.

LEITLINIE: original German term, best translated as 'leading line' (see MIGRATION).

LEK DISPLAY: term originally accepted to denote the assemblies of the Blackcock *Lyrurus* *tetrix* and now extended to cover other displays in which male birds take up stances and posture in small areas, generally called ' courts', usually on arenas or display grounds. (' Lek' seems to be derived from Swedish ' leka', ' to play', which can have a sexual connotation.) The arenas of the Ruff *Philomachus pugnax* are called ' hills', and other terms are applied to the arenas of some American Tetraonidae (see GROUSE). The court is essentially a non-nesting territory (see TERRITORY); it is a rendezvous resorted to by females in condition for sexual stimulation and coition. The lek is usually maintained at the arena for considerable periods of time and many species revive the performance at the same display-ground year after year.

Lek displays may be graded according to the degree to which courts are separated from one another. They may be located widely apart but not so far as to prevent the males from hearing each other's loud calls (Argus Pheasant *Argusianus argus*, Capercaillie *Tetrao urogallus*); or, at the other extreme, two males may display together before a female (Blue-backed Manakin *Chiroxiphia pareola*). The Magnificent Bird-of-paradise *Diphyllodes magnificus* makes courts in the jungle, each bird out of sight of the others; Greater Birds-of-paradise *Paradisaea apoda* posture on neighbouring tree-boughs. Some of the courts of the Black-and-white Manakin *Manacus manacus* are practically contiguous; while as many as 40 courts of the Cock-of-the-rock *Rupicola rupicola* may be situated on an arena 80 feet in length.

Lek displays, being performed by species belonging to the Galliformes, Gruiformes, Charadriiformes, Apodiformes, and Passeriformes, exemplify convergence in behaviour. There are forms of lek display that have affinities with other forms of display and pair relationship (see PAIR FORMATION). The Lyrebird *Menura novaehollandiae* makes several courts in his territory, where he displays and sings an elaborate song (see LYREBIRD; SINGING). The bowers of bowerbirds (Ptilonorhynchidae) may be regarded as display-courts which have acquired special significance (see BOWERBIRD). Cock Great Bustards *Otis tarda* separate from the flock and posture here and there on their range, becoming particularly active when approached by a female. Soon after dawn wild Turkeys *Meleagris gallopavo* fly to the flock territory and strut; there is strong competition between the cocks, and the dominant male attracts and copulates with a number of females. This is a form of ' harem polygamy' (see POLYGAMY). The aquatic group-displays of some ducks (Anatidae) have features in common with lek behaviour. In some species of grouse and other lek birds

dominant males are most successful with the females. Among Ruffs relationships that have been styled monogamous, polygamous, polyandrous, and homosexual occur, but probably the sexual relationships in this species, as in most other lek birds, are best considered as forms of transient multiple pairing (see POLYGAMY). Male lek birds tend to be highly sexed and some may copulate frequently in a brief period.

Nearly all cock lek birds are equipped with striking adornments or unusual adaptations for sound production, or both. The latter enable them to signal their location to females; in Gould's Manakin *Manacus vitellinus* there are thickened wing-quills with which a snapping sound is produced, and the Lesser Prairie Chicken *Tympanuchus pallidicinctus* has air-sacs which give resonance to the booming call. The Ruff is exceptional in being silent at the ' hill', but the courts are only a foot or two from each other, the arena is open and frequented year after year, and conspicuousness is increased by corporate flights. The delicate structure and detailed pattern of feathers exhibited in lek posturing indicate that the adornments are effective in close-up display, and this suggests that sexual selection has played an important part in their evolution. The females are less conspicuous than the males, for they undertake all domestic responsibilities (see PARENTAL CARE), and in accordance with the general principles of adaptive coloration they tend to be cryptically coloured (see COLORATION, ADAPTIVE). While the males of lek birds that display beneath foliage often sport bright adornments, the plumage of those frequenting arenas in open spaces is less conspicuous. In species in which the female rears the young and the male differs in appearance, the extravagant adornments of the male facilitate identification by females without breeding experience, but even so hybridisation occurs more frequently in some lek species than in normally territorial birds (see HYBRID).

During lek displays the birds tend to stimulate one another and posturing activities are often socially facilitated. Vigorous movements are performed in a small space, static poses are adopted from time to time, leaves and twigs on the floor of the court

---

Plate 25 · Display

Chinstrap (or Ringed) Penguin *Pygoscelis antarctica* in ecstatic display posture while brooding two small chicks (South Orkneys, Antarctic). The sexes are alike in plumage, and share parental duties. Note that this bird has been flipper-banded, a form of ' ringing'.   *Phot. W. J. L. Sladen.*

(See articles DISPLAY; PENGUIN; RINGING)

are removed—although with the larger species, such as the Blackcock and Ruff, the vegetation is trampled down by the birds' feet. These convergences are due to lek procedure often involving strict localisation of display to a small area, a high ritualisation of pugnacious impulses (see RITUALISATION), and the inhibition or thwarting of coitional motivation. Some aspects of the displays, such as whetting the bill on twigs and picking up leaves, may have originated as displacement or transference (redirection) activities derived from ancestral nest-building movements (see DISPLACEMENT ACTIVITY).

In spite of the hazards from predators entailed in regular display at a fixed site by relatively conspicuous birds, most lek species successfully maintain their numbers where undisturbed by man ; but they are increasingly menaced by his activities, particularly in causing large-scale alterations of habitat. The destruction of ancestral display arenas tends to disrupt the breeding cycle. As in no other birds is such beauty combined with exceptionally interesting behaviour, special efforts for the protection of lek species are desirable.

See Plates 20 (colour), 24 (phot.).   E.A.A.

Armstrong, E. A. 1949. Bird Display and Behaviour. London. (New ed. in press, New York).
Gilliard, E. T. 1962. On the breeding behaviour of the Cock-of-the-rock (Aves, *Rupicola rupicola*). Bull. Amer. Mus. Nat. Hist. 124 : 35-68.
Snow, D. W. 1962. A field study of the Black and White Manakin, *Manacus manacus*, in Trinidad. Zoologica (N.Y.) 47 : 65-104.
Snow, D. W. 1963. The evolution of manakin displays. Proc. XIII Internat. Orn. Congr., Ithaca, N.Y., 1962 : 552-561.

LENS : part of the eye (see VISION).

LEPTOSOMATIDAE : see CORACIIFORMES ; and CUCKOO-ROLLER

Plate 26 · Display

a   *Upper :* Superb Lyrebird *Menura superba*—male in sexual display (south-eastern Australia). The birds breed in winter in heavy forest, and this photograph (which needed a fast exposure because of the shimmering of the tail-plumes) was taken in dim light at midday.

Phot. R. P. Cooper, by flashlight.

b   *Lower :* Spotted Bowerbird *Chlamydera maculata*—male at the entrance of his bower (Australia). The display-objects that this bird has collected in the foreground are bleached bones, mostly vertebrae of sheep.   *Phot. R. P. Cooper.*

(See articles DISPLAY ; LYREBIRD ; BOWERBIRD)

LEUCISM : see PLUMAGE, ABNORMAL AND ABERRANT

LEUCOCYTE : see BLOOD

LEYDIG CELLS : see REPRODUCTIVE SYSTEM

LICE : see ECTOPARASITE

LIFE, EXPECTATION OF : the average further period for which birds of a specified age will live under the conditions of mortality prevailing. Since in all the birds so far studied the adult death-rate is constant with respect to age, up to an age when extremely few individuals are left alive, the average expectation of further life is sufficiently given by the formula $\dfrac{2-m}{2m}$, where 'm' is the annual mortality expressed as a fraction of unity. The average further life for adult song-birds (Oscines) is 1–2 years, for various wading birds and gulls (Charadriiformes) 2–3 years, for Swifts *Apus apus* 4–5 years, and for the Yellow-eyed Penguin *Megadyptes antipodes* 9–10 years ; while, if figures for a small population can be trusted, adult Royal Albatrosses *Diomedea epomophora* may live 30–40 years on average. Since the mortality rate is higher in the juvenile than in the adult bird, the life-expectancy is lower for a juvenile than for an adult, and the figure calculated from the egg stage is far lower still, owing to the big losses among eggs, nestlings, and chicks (see also POPULATION DYNAMICS).

The above figures refer to the average further life of adult birds in the wild state and subject to natural mortality. Individual birds can live much longer, both in the wild and in captivity, small passerines often for 10–15 years and sometimes longer, and various large birds from 20 to well over 50 years (see LONGEVITY). This 'potential age' should be clearly distinguished from the average age to which birds may be expected to live in the wild. D.L.

Lack, D. 1954. The Natural Regulation of Animal Numbers. Oxford. (See chap. 9—average age.)

LIFE ZONE : an area defined, for ecological purposes, in terms of temperature and humidity rather than of nature of ground and vegetation (contrast BIOME).

LIGAMENT : band of connective tissue, tough and flexible, uniting two bones (see SKELETON) or supporting an organ.

LIGHT : considered as an environmental factor—see PHOTOPERIODISM ; also under BREEDING SEASON ; MIGRATION ; NOCTURNAL HABITS ; RHYTHM ; ROOSTING ; VISION.

LILACTHROAT : substantive name of some *Heliodoxa rubinoides* subspp. (see HUMMINGBIRD).

LILY-TROTTER: substantive name most commonly used for African species of Jacanidae (see JACANA).

LIMB: see LEG ; WING ; also SKELETON ; and FLIGHT ; LOCOMOTION ; SWIMMING AND DIVING

LIME, BIRD: a viscous substance (made from holly bark, etc.) used for smearing on twigs or other perches in order to catch small birds. The term is sometimes popularly misapplied to the residual excrement adhering to trees, rocks, buildings, and the like much frequented by birds.

LIMICOLAE: formerly used as the name of an order equivalent to the suborder Charadrii of the Charadriiformes (see also LARO-LIMICOLAE).

LIMPKIN: *Aramus guarauna*, the sole species in the New World family Aramidae (Gruiformes, suborder Grues). It has certain osteological and pterylographical characters that are crane-like (i.e. as in Gruidae) and a digestive system like that of the rails (Rallidae). In general appearance it is like a very large rail (length 23–28 inches). The sexes are similar in size and appearance. The bill is long, laterally compressed, and slightly decurved. The neck is long and slender ; the wings are very broad and rounded ; the tail is short and broad ; the legs are long, with tibiae partly bare. The general coloration is glossy brownish olive, quite finely streaked with white on the neck and with broader broken streaks on the body. Fledged young closely resemble adults, but have shorter bills. Nestlings are dark brownish, evenly coloured.

Although it is a wading bird, usually occurring in wooded swamps or shaded places where there is a lush growth of woody or herbaceous vegetation, it has been found in areas of arid brush in the West Indies. It stands on the ground or perches at any height, including the tops of tall trees. The feet are not webbed, but it is an efficient swimmer. It is seldom seen in flight. Although, where not protected, it is considered to be crepuscular and nocturnal in its habits, it is notably unwary and diurnal (as well as nocturnal) at certain localities in Florida where it is responding to full protection.

The Limpkin feeds almost exclusively on large snails, mainly *Pomacea* ('*Ampullaria*'), obtained in water of wading depth. The bird walks ashore or to very shallow water with its prey, extracts the snail, and discards the undamaged shell ; a perching place is sometimes littered with these. The young out of the nest, even for some weeks after they have attained flight, approach from behind and reach forward between a parent's legs for food ; the snail (in shell)

is taken from the bill of the parent and the whole thing swallowed. (For colour photographs of the birds and their staple food, see especially : 1958, *Natl. Geographic Mag.* 113 (1) : 114–121.)

Relatively little is known about its breeding habits. The rather flimsy shallow nest, of sticks and dry vegetation, is built in a shaded spot on the ground near water or even as high as a few yards up in a bush or tree. The 4–8 eggs are pale buff, spotted or blotched with various light browns. Incubation is by the sexes in turn, period unknown. Both parents tend the precocial young for an unknown length of time.

Limpkin *Aramus guarauna*, sole species. *C.E.T.K.*

The Limpkin is best known for its voice and is often called 'wailing bird' or 'crying bird'. Its varied wailing, screaming, and assorted clucking notes are heard most frequently at night. This sedentary species occurs from southern Georgia and in Florida, through Central America and on various islands, south in South America east of the Andes to central Argentina. Four subspecies are recognised.

R.S.P.

LINCOLN INDEX: the formula of a sampling method used in population studies (and see PREDATION), viz. :

$$\text{Population} = \frac{M \times S}{m}$$

where 'M' is the number of marked animals released in a given area ; 'S' is the number of animals captured in a sample taken after the dispersal of the marked animals from the release point ; and 'm' is the number of marked animals in the sample S.

Lincoln, F. C. 1930. Calculating waterfowl abundance on the basis of banding returns. Circ. U.S. Dept. Agric. no. 118 : 1–4.

LINKAGE: see GENETICS

LINNET: *Acanthis cannabina* (see FINCH).

LIVER: a large unpaired organ associated with the digestive tract (see ALIMENTARY SYSTEM). In addition to secreting bile into the duodenum by way of the hepatic duct or ducts (gall-bladder present or absent), it is the site of important metabolic changes in substances brought to it by the portal vessels (see VASCULAR SYSTEM) and also to some extent a storage depot, e.g. of glycogen (see METABOLISM).

LIVER (with long 'i' as in 'diver'): name derived from that of the city of Liverpool and applied since the seventeenth century to a bird imaginatively portrayed in the municipal coat-of-arms, originally intended to be the eagle of St John the Ecclesiastic but now changed out of recognition (see, in general, HERALDIC BIRDS).

LLANO: an environment of savanna type characteristic of parts of tropical South America (see SAVANNA).

LOBATE; LOBED: having the toes separately fringed by lobes, as distinct from webs connecting the toes (see LEG).

LOCOMOTION: in this article restricted to terrestrial locomotion, i.e. movement on the ground or other solid surfaces ; for aerial locomotion see FLIGHT (and for exceptions FLIGHTLESSNESS), and for aquatic locomotion see SWIMMING AND DIVING. Pedal locomotion involves flexing the legs, at the various joints, to a greater or lesser extent ; it varies in details with the proportions of the legs and the structure of the feet (see LEG)—see also TRACKS.

Walking and Running. Most non-passerine birds, and some passerines, usually proceed on the ground by walking—that is, by advancing the feet alternately. When this is done with sufficient rapidity, it may be termed 'running'. Many birds can run with great speed relative to their size, e.g. small plovers (Charadriidae) and sandpipers (Scolopacidae) ; other strong runners include various gamebirds (Galliformes), the bustards (Otididae), and the tinamous (Tinamidae). Running reaches its extreme development among the flightless 'ratite' birds ; the Ostrich *Struthio camelus* is said to be capable of a speed of about 40 miles per hour. See Plate 11 (phot.).

Among the Passeriformes, most of the crows (Corvidae) walk, and other examples include starlings (Sturnidae), larks (Alaudidae), waterthrushes (Parulidae), and wagtails (Motacillidae). The last named are among the smallest passerine birds that walk and run ; Delalande's Gnateater

Corythopis delalandei (Conopophagidae), $4\frac{3}{4}$ inches long, is an example of a very small species that walks.

Some birds that have relatively short legs can do little more than waddle, and many of these take to the air or to water whenever speed is necessary ; examples can be found in such groups as the pigeons (Columbidae) and the ducks (Anatidae), among others. Some of those that are highly adapted for swimming have the legs set so far back that they cannot for long maintain an upright position ; divers (Gaviidae), which traverse only minimal distances on land, push themselves forward on their breasts. Penguins (Spheniscidae) normally stand or walk upright, but they can attain more speed on snow by 'tobogganning' in a horizontal position, sometimes using their 'flippers' (wings) as well as their legs for propulsion.

Hopping. A succession of jumps, with the feet together is the common form of terrestrial locomotion among small passerine species ; some exceptions have been mentioned above. It is also used by some of the larger species, such as the Jay *Garrulus glandarius* (unlike most of the Corvidae). The pittas (Pittidae) have developed it highly, proceeding in a series of immense bounds (described as 'kangaroo-like leaps'), repeated at high speed if necessary. The rockfowl *Picathartes* spp. show at least as much exaggeration of this mode of progression.

Birds that habitually hop do not necessarily use this method of terrestrial locomotion exclusively ; some hop or walk, e.g. American Robin *Turdus migratorius*. Although larks and wagtails walk, as already mentioned, the young birds hop (see also BEHAVIOUR, DEVELOPMENT OF).

Climbing. Progress in trees or other vegetation presents a special case. Some birds of arboreal habit move about in trees very little without practically flying, although it may be for only a stroke or two. They may nevertheless hop from twig to twig, or walk or sidle along a branch ; a Goldfinch *Carduelis carduelis* will climb the stem of a plant. On the other hand, species in certain groups are specially adapted to walking more or less vertically up the trunks of trees (or a rock, as in the Wallcreeper *Tichodroma muraria*), clinging with their strong feet and bracing themselves with their stiff tails—e.g. woodpeckers (Picidae), wood-hoopoes (Phoeniculidae), woodcreepers (Dendrocolaptidae), treecreepers (Certhiidae), and some ovenbirds (Furnariidae). Nuthatches *Sitta* spp. climb tree-trunks obliquely, with one foot up to hang from and one down for support, and can also walk down head first in the same manner ; the tail is not used. See Plate 13 (phot.).

Various nidicolous young make some play with

their wings in crawling about the nest. In the Hoatzin *Opisthocomus hoazin* the young climb among the branches by aid of the claws on their wings (see HOATZIN). Some parrots (Psittacidae) use the bill as an aid to climbing—at least when caged.

General. The highest development of terrestrial locomotion is found, as one would expect, among those birds that neither fly nor swim, e.g. the Ostrich. The poorest development is among birds that are largely aquatic or aerial in their mode of life. Examples of the former have been given above ; the latter include swifts (Apodidae), with feet adapted for clinging to a vertical surface and with no occasion to move on a horizontal one except within the nesting hole. Most nightjars (Caprimulgidae) likewise have little power of walking, but the Pauraque *Nyctidromus albicollis* is an exception.

Nevertheless some birds excel in two or even three of the main forms of locomotion. Thus, plovers and their allies (Charadrii) are both swift runners and strong fliers ; and they can swim well on occasion, as indeed the phalaropes (Phalaropodidae) do habitually. Some aquatic birds, unlike others mentioned above, can also run rapidly ; this is true of various rails and gallinules (Rallidae). A.L.T.

Hartman, F. A. 1961. Locomotor mechanisms of birds. Smiths. Misc. Coll. 143 (1) : 1-91.

LOCUS : of a gene (plural ' loci ')—see GENETICS.

LOCUST-BIRD : name applied in parts of Africa to various species of birds that congregate to feed on locust swarms, e.g. the Black-winged Pratincole *Glareola nordmanni* as an off-season visitor to South Africa.

LOGGERHEAD : name applied in the Falkland Islands to steamer ducks *Tachyeres* spp. ; and in North America to the Loggerhead Shrike *Lanius ludovicianus*.

LOGRUNNER : substantive name of *Orthonyx* spp. (see RAIL-BABBLER).

LONGCLAW : substantive name of *Macronyx* spp. (see under WAGTAIL).

LONGEVITY : duration of life, with a connotation of substantial age. Although the potential life-span of different species of birds is a matter of some interest, it has little to do with the actual length of life of average members of these species under natural conditions (see LIFE, EXPECTATION OF). In all but the largest birds, relatively secure from predators, the actual life-span is so short in comparison with the potential life-span that the mortality rate of any species in the wild is often constant in successive

years of individual age, after the dangerous juvenile stage, and may even decline with age. In other words, senescence is not usually a factor ; this state may possibly be attained by some individuals of large species such as gannets (Sulidae) and albatrosses (Diomedeidae). Comfort (1962) has illustrated the general point by showing that only 25 per cent of captive Night Herons *Nycticorax nycticorax* in the Zoological Gardens in London had died at an age when less than one per cent of Grey Herons *Ardea cinerea* (the nearest available comparison) survive in the wild.

The ages attained by birds in captivity are not necessarily a close index of even potential life-span under natural conditions, but some authenticated figures may be cited. Flower was able to record 41 species of birds as living to over 30 years of age, and these included the following 6 living to over 50 years ; Eagle Owl *Bubo bubo* (68), Great Sulphur-crested Cockatoo *Kakatoe galerita* (56), Bateleur *Terathopius ecaudatus* (55), Vasa Parrot *Coracopsis vasa* (54), Andean Condor *Vultur gryphus* (52), and White Pelican *Pelecanus onocrotalus* (52). His study, based on a substantial body of evidence, suffices to give the general picture of longevity among captive birds, although there may be individual records of greater ages.

Equivalent information about longevity under natural conditions is obtainable only from the records of ringed birds (see RINGING). These records, in respect of species for which they are numerous, give a picture of the ages to which birds quite commonly live, with indications of the greater ages that may be attained by a small minority of individuals. Rydzewski has published a list, from all available sources (which unfortunately do not include much of the vast American material), giving the longest periods for which wild birds of various species have been known to carry rings. Some of these birds were ringed as adults (A), so that their actual life-spans were longer to an uncertain degree ; others were ringed as pulli (P) or juvenile (J), and the recorded period thus approximates either very or fairly closely to the whole length of life.

The following are the species in Rydzewski's list for which periods in excess of 18 years are recorded (omitting *Larus* spp. and *Sterna* spp. after the first three in each genus).

Herring Gull *Larus argentatus*	$31\frac{11}{12}$	(P)
Curlew *Numenius arquata*	$31\frac{6}{12}$	(P)
Blackheaded Gull *Larus ridibundus*	$30\frac{3}{12}$	(P)
Oystercatcher *Haematopus ostralegus*	$28\frac{5}{12}$	(P)
Arctic Tern *Sterna paradisaea*	27	(J)
Lesser Blackbacked Gull *Larus fuscus*	$26\frac{1}{12}$	(P)

Caspian Tern *Sterna caspia*	26
Kite *Milvus milvus*	$25\frac{8}{12}$ (P)
Common Tern *Sterna hirundo*	$24\frac{11}{12}$ (P)
Heron *Ardea cinerea*	$24\frac{6}{12}$ (P)
Buzzard *Buteo buteo*	$23\frac{9}{12}$ (J)
Redthroated Diver *Gavia stellata*	$23\frac{8}{12}$ (J)
Swift *Apus apus*	21 (P)
Osprey *Pandion haliaetus*	$20\frac{11}{12}$ (P)
Woodcock *Scolopax rusticola*	$20\frac{9}{12}$ (P)
Shoveller *Spatula clypeata*	$20\frac{5}{12}$
Mallard *Anas platyrhynchos*	$20\frac{1}{12}$
Starling *Sturnus vulgaris*	20 (A)
Rook *Corvus frugilegus*	$19\frac{11}{12}$ (P)
Glossy Ibis *Plegadis falcinellus*	$19\frac{10}{12}$ (P)
Turnstone *Arenaria interpres*	$19\frac{8}{12}$ (P)
Mute Swan *Cygnus olor*	$19\frac{5}{12}$ (J)
White Stork *Ciconia ciconia*	$19\frac{2}{12}$ (P)
Redwing *Turdus iliacus*	$18\frac{9}{12}$
Coot *Fulica atra*	$18\frac{3}{12}$ (A)
Cormorant *Phalacrocorax carbo*	$18\frac{2}{12}$ (J)

The following is a selected list of small passerine species from the other end of the scale.

Swallow *Hirundo rustica*	$15\frac{11}{12}$ (J)
Siskin *Carduelis spinus*	$10\frac{11}{12}$ (A)
Tree Sparrow *Passer montanus*	10 (A)
Pied Flycatcher *Ficedula hypoleuca*	$9\frac{2}{12}$ (P)
Blue Tit *Parus caeruleus*	$8\frac{7}{12}$ (A)
Reed Warbler *Acrocephalus scirpaceus*	$8\frac{1}{12}$ (A)

As a generalisation, one can say that potential life-span in birds is roughly, very roughly, correlated with size.

Comfort, A. 1962. Survival curves of some birds in the London Zoo. Ibis 104 : 115–117.
Flower, S. S. 1938. Further notes on the duration of life in animals. IV. Birds. Proc. Zool. Soc. Lond. 108 (Ser. A) : 195–235.
Rydzewski, W. 1962. Longevity of ringed birds. The Ring 3 (33) : 147–152.

LONGITUDE: see MAPPING

LONGSPUR: substantive name, in North America, of *Calcarius* spp., including the Lapland Bunting *C. lapponicus* (see BUNTING).

LONGTAIL: substantive name of *Urolais epichlora*, and an alternative substantive name for prinias *Prinia* spp. (see WARBLER (1)).

LOOMERY: term which has been applied to breeding colonies of guillemots (*lomvia*)—see AUK.

LOON: substantive name used in North America for all the species of Gaviidae (see DIVER).

LORE: the area between the base of the upper mandible and the eye, on each side (plural 'lores'; adjective 'loral')—see TOPOGRAPHY.

LORIINAE: see PARROT

LORIKEET: substantive name of some small species of LORY.

LORY: substantive name of species of Loriinae; in the plural ('lories'), general term for the subfamily (see PARROT).

LOTUS-BIRD: name in Australia for *Irediparra gallinacea* (see JACANA).

LOURIE: alternative substantive name of some species of Musophagidae (see TURACO).

LOUSE-FLIES: see ECTOPARASITE

LOVEBIRD: substantive name of *Agapornis* spp. (Africa), and sometimes applied to the Budgerigar *Melopsittacus undulatus* (Australia). See PARROT.

LOWAN: name, alternatively 'Mallee Fowl', of *Leipoa ocellata* (see MEGAPODE).

LUMBAR: pertaining to the lower back.

LUNG: see RESPIRATORY SYSTEM

LURE: instrument used in imitating bird-calls to attract birds of the particular species within range; also a form of bait used by falconers to recover their charges (see FALCONRY).

LYMPHATIC VESSELS: see VASCULAR SYSTEM

LYREBIRD: substantive name of the two species of Menuridae (Passeriformes, suborder Menurae); in the plural, general term for the family. Both species are placed in the genus *Menura*, and the birds are remarkable for their appearance and behaviour. The group is restricted to eastern Australia and has no near relatives anywhere. Its systematic position has been the subject of varying opinions over a lengthy period, but there is now general agreement that the genus has some distant relationship with *Atrichornis*, and the two genera are placed together in a suborder of their own, each with familial rank (see SCRUB-BIRD).

The first specimens were taken in 1798, by an ex-convict and a youth who were exploring a rugged region some sixty miles south-west of Sydney. The bird was then regarded as a form of pheasant (Phasianidae) or, alternatively, a bird-of-paradise (Paradisaeidae), and so the species became known as the 'Native Pheasant', 'Botany Bay Pheasant', and 'New South Wales Bird-of-paradise'. The name 'Lyrebird', which dates from the 1820s, was based on the supposed resemblance of the tail to a Greek lyre, and indeed this resemblance sometimes occurs, although only momentarily, when the bird is displaying.

Specimens having been sent to London by Governor Hunter of New South Wales, one of them was seen, in the possession of Lady Mary Howe, by Major-General T. Davies in 1799, and was by him figured and described (*Trans. Linn. Soc.* 1802) as *Menura superba*. Latham, for no clear reason, changed the specific name to *novaehollandiae*, and because of doubt regarding publication dates this amendment has sometimes been accepted ; it is now considered, however, that Davies's name has priority over that of Latham, as well as over numbers of other names, some of them fantastic, that were published by British and other European writers who discussed and figured the spectacular bird in the early years of the nineteenth century.

The cause of the keen interest at once aroused by the Superb Lyrebird was, almost entirely, the decorative tail of the species. This feature comprises 12 filamentary feathers, 2 wire-like plumes that are usually termed 'feelers', and 2 equally long but more substantial feathers (about 30 inches in length and $1\frac{1}{2}$ inches wide) that are silvery-mauve beneath and each carry crescent-shaped markings of golden-brown, with black at the curved tip. In contrast, the body of the bird, which approximates to that of an average domestic fowl in size, is plain brown ; it was doubtless this fact, combined with consideration of the strong legs and feet, relatively small wings, and terrestrial habits, that caused some ornithologists for many years to regard the species as gallinaceous. Their chief difficulty in this respect, and one that they countered by disbelief, was a report regarding the male bird's alleged accomplishments—a statement made by David Collins (early colonial official at Sydney), in his *Account of the English Colony in New South Wales* (1802), to the effect that the bird was not only impressive in display but brilliant as a singer and vocal mimic.

Support for the belief that the species was gallinaceous had been given by a claim that a large number of eggs, coloured white, were laid in a rudimentary nest on the ground. That idle claim was dispelled, and the gallinaceous theory collapsed when, after many years of searching by men of various nationalities, the breeding habits of the bird became known. It was learned then that the nest is a large, domed structure of sticks and is placed on the ground, on a rock-ledge, on a stump, or in a tree-fork ; that a single egg, purplish-brown spotted with slaty-grey, constitutes a clutch ; and that the chick at birth is sightless and scantily clothed in black down. More recently, the Superb Lyrebird has been closely studied, mainly near Sydney and in Sherbrooke Forest near Melbourne, where members of the species are fairly numerous and have become

relatively tame through the frequency of human visits. Research, including study of tape-recordings has also been undertaken near Canberra.

The second species of the genus, Prince Albert's Lyrebird *M. alberti*, is less known, partly because of its limited range and partly because of its dense environment in subtropical rain-forest. This bird, not discovered until 1849, differs from its relative in being rather smaller, in having a strong wash of rufous in the plumage, and in having a considerably less substantial tail.

In each species the female is similar to the male in body plumage, but the tail, while sturdy, is not decorative. In each species, too, the female is a competent vocal mimic, although the talent is exercised much more mildly than it is by the male bird. Vocalisation on the part of the growing chick is mainly a loud scream, uttered when it is disturbed in the nest. Flight, with both species, resolves chiefly into skimming descents of hillsides, wing-aided jumps from rock to rock, and flying leaps upward from branch to branch. Although they are terrestrial feeders, the birds are quite at home in trees, and at times a nest may be placed in a fork as much as 60 or 70 feet from the ground.

Lyrebirds breed in winter, this choice being doubtless governed by the fact that worms, crustaceans, and other animal-life on which they feed are then most abundant. Courtship begins in mid-autumn and the nests are built in May or June. The nest, which is made of sticks cleverly interlaced and given a roof of moss, has a chamber sufficiently commodious to allow the chick to stand almost erect. Construction is solely the work of the female. She, too, alone broods the egg, which at an early stage she surrounds, either for warmth or as a screen, with a mass of downy feathers plucked from her own flanks. Incubation normally occupies about 6 weeks, including a period of several days when the egg is neglected immediately after being laid.

Possibly the large tail of the male would not allow him to enter the nest—the tail of the female, indeed, acquires a distinct twist through being turned to one side during brooding—but he also leaves to the female a further 6 weeks of duty in caring for the nestling. It has been suggested that his conduct may be affected by polygamy, but if this practice obtains it is not constant. What stands out in the bird's behaviour, very definitely, is his devotion to display and song.

During the courtship and breeding seasons a number of circular clearings, each about 3 feet in diameter and slightly raised, are constructed by the male on the forest floor. One bird may have as many as 10 or more, and upon these mounds remarkable performances are rendered. Extending the lyrate feathers laterally, and swinging the filamentary plumes upward and over his head in the form of a fairy parasol, the bird presents a beautiful sight ; and as he does this he sings most spiritedly, mingling his own resonant notes with imitations of a wide variety of calls of other birds, at the same time dancing, or at least prancing, to the rhythm of his own melody. Given suitable conditions, performances of the kind are rendered several times a day, by each male bird, during the season ; and, moreover, it is not uncommon for strong singing to be heard, and mild displays to be seen, after the spring moult. Nor is vocalisation restricted to the mounds ; it is sometimes exercised on logs and the branches of trees.

Whether or not vocal mimicry has any practical value, which seems doubtful, it has been developed to an extraordinary degree by both species of lyrebird. Their talents extend in some instances to imitations of the noise of parrots (Psittacidae) in a flock, to the calls of migratory birds (heard only in the mimic's non-breeding season), to the cries of nocturnal birds and mammals, and occasionally to 'artificial' sounds. Mimicry has sometimes been heard from specimens kept in captivity ; neither species, however, makes an attractive exhibit in confinement, since display is not practised in such circumstances, and there is only one instance (achieved on the Blue Mountains of New South Wales in 1936) of a pair having bred in an aviary.

During almost one hundred years, from about 1815, male Superb Lyrebirds were ruthlessly slaughtered for the sake of their tails, which were marketed as articles of household adornment both in Australia and elsewhere. That traffic, which caused the death of thousands of the birds, was checked just in time, and now both species of *Menura* are rigidly safeguarded. Consequently, they are holding their own

reasonably well, although in many areas they have been seriously affected by the spread of settlement. Other detrimental factors are forest fires, predatory native mammals, and introduced pests such as the fox and the feral cat.

The range of the Superb Lyrebird extends, discontinuously, throughout well wooded and mainly rugged country from immediately east of Melbourne up the coast to the north-east of New South Wales, whence it turns north-west to enter a granitic area in southern Queensland ; in this latter area it has differentiated into what was originally described as a species, M. ' *edwardi* ' (Prince Edward's Lyrebird) but is now regarded as a subspecies. In addition, the Superb Lyrebird appears to have become established in Tasmania, where examples were introduced at intervals from 1934 onward.

The smaller species, Prince Albert's Lyrebird, is known for the most part only as a voice, being very shy and not building definite display mounds ; moreover, it is curiously restricted in its distribution, being confined to a relatively small area of heavy rain-forest in the north-east of New South Wales and the south-east of Queensland.

The Superb Lyrebird, more than other members of Australia's avifauna, has been made the subject of numerous articles, books and booklets, broadcasts, films, and voice-recordings. All of these, no doubt, have tended to promote popular appreciation and have assisted to support the view, expressed by John Gould in the 1840s, that this distinctive bird should be regarded as an emblem of Australia.

See Plates 26a (phot.), 31 (colour).   A.H.C.

Chisholm, A. H. 1960. The Romance of the Lyrebird. Sydney.
Littlejohns, R. T. 1938. The Lyre-bird : Australia's Wonder-songster. Melbourne.
Smith, L. H. 1951. The Lyrebirds of Sherbrooke. Melbourne.

M

MACAW: substantive name of *Ara* and *Anodorhynchus* spp. (see PARROT).

MACHAERAMPHINAE: see HAWK

MACROCHIRES: see APODIFORMES

MACROSMATIC: having a highly developed olfactory sense (see. SMELL).

MADAGASCAR: see MALAGASY REGION

MAGNETIC SENSE: a faculty sometimes hypothetically invoked, but not known to exist (see SENSES ; also NAVIGATION).

MAGPIE (1): substantive name of species in several genera of Corvidae ; used without qualification, in Britain, for *Pica pica* (the ' Black-billed Magpie ' of North America)—see CROW (1) ; and Plate 17 (colour).

MAGPIE (2): substantive name of *Gymnorhina* spp. in the family Cracticidae (Passeriformes, suborder Oscines) ; in the form ' Australian magpies ' or ' bell-magpies ', sometimes used as a general term for the whole group. There is in fact no satisfactory single term for the family, *Strepera* spp. being known as ' currawongs ', ' piping-crows ', or ' crow-shrikes ', and *Cracticus* spp. as ' Australian butcher-birds ' ; one or other generic appellation may be used in a wider sense, or a triple designation may be given, but ' song-shrikes ' seems to be gaining currency as a general term.

The Cracticidae are birds ranging from 10 to 23 inches in length and showing some superficial resemblance to crows (Corvidae) and shrikes (Laniidae). They are stoutly built birds with large heads and large, strong bills, usually hooked and in some species markedly so. There is a tendency to black or pied plumage. The legs are strong, and rather long in some species. There are considerable differences in shape of wing, but they are all birds of strong flight. They are noisy and gregarious for the most part, and largely arboreal ; the notes are loud and metallic. The family is restricted to Australia (including Tasmania), New Guinea, and adjacent islands, although one or two species have been introduced into New Zealand. The birds are non-migratory.

Currawongs. The currawongs *Strepera* spp. are large birds (about 20 inches in length) having a long tenth primary, tarsi almost completely sheathed in scales arranged in a kind of boot, and the bill long and straight with a sharp, slightly hooked point. The plumage is black, grey, and white. The birds frequent all types of forest country, from coastal brushes to montane lightly-timbered grasslands and inland mallee scrubs. Their food consists of insects, fruits, and small reptiles, mammals, and birds, and also birds' eggs. Flocking is characteristic during the winter months, but in spring and summer the birds mostly revert to breeding pairs, defending territorial areas. The nest is usually placed high in a tree-fork and is composed of sticks, with a lining of bark-fibre. The eggs are 2–5, usually buffy-brown spotted and streaked with darker shades. Currawongs are found in eastern and southern Australia, Tasmania, and Lord Howe Island.

Six species used to be recognised, but Amadon has grouped the forms in two. The Pied Currawong *Strepera graculina graculina* of eastern Australia and Lord Howe Island and the Black Currawong *S.g. fuliginosa* of Tasmania utter ' rollicking-type ' calls, the origin of the name ' currawong ', while the forms in the Grey Currawong *S. versicolor* group have ' bell-type ' notes. Although the Black Currawong appears to be the Tasmanian representative of *S. graculina*, it is possible that it originated from an earlier insular invasion by *S. versicolor*. The larger Clinking Currawong *S. v. arguta* of Tasmania, pied in plumage but obviously more closely related to the Grey Currawong of south-eastern Australia, could be a more recent immigrant.

A peculiarity of the *S. versicolor* group is the number of isolated forms and the tendency to an inconsistency in plumage characters where some other forms have come secondarily in contact. Thus, there are currawongs with greyish plumage and white wing specula, and others which are black and white, or greyish-brown and white, in varying degrees ; but no clear-cut colour characters separate the two groups. On the other hand, call-notes and geographical dispersion clearly divide the genus into two species or superspecies.

Bell-magpies. The use of 'magpie' for the conspicuous black and white *Gymnorhina* spp. is long established in Australia, and various attempts made to popularise other names have failed. Anyone travelling through any of the more settled areas of Australia and Tasmania must consider them probably the most prominent birds. Although three species are currently accepted, it is seldom that more than one occurs in any area, and possibly only one widely-ranging variable species is involved. The White-backed Magpie *G. hypoleuca* occurs from Tasmania and south-eastern Australia, usually south of the Great Dividing Range, to South Australia, although many scattered records are known as far north as south-eastern Queensland. North of this general line the Black-backed Magpie *G. tibicen* is predominant, extending to some localities in northern and north-western Australia, and a small population is restricted to southern New Guinea. The Western Magpie *G. dorsalis* is confined to the south-west of Australia. The White-backed Magpie has become well established as an introduced species in New Zealand.

Magpies are more terrestrial than are their near relatives, the butcher-birds and currawongs, and are intermediate in size between these two groups. The legs are long and strong, the tail is rather short, the wings are long and somewhat pointed, and the plumage is always black and white, with greyish tones in immature birds. Most of the food is secured on the ground, consisting mainly of large insects and of small reptiles and mammals. The nests are made of sticks, and well lined with grasses and soft material. Usually they are placed high in trees, and during the breeding season pairs defend their respective territories resolutely, even attacking human beings at times although this is believed to be done only by the older 'rogue' birds. The 3–5 eggs are very variable in colour but mostly greenish-blue with numerous brownish streaks. The gay carolling call-notes of Australian magpies, often given by many birds in chorus, are among the best-known sounds of the Australian bush and are especially pleasant at early dawn.

Butcher-birds. The genus *Cracticus*, which includes 6–7 species, is considered to be the most primitive of the 3 genera. These Australian butcher-birds, although not allied to the true shrikes (Laniidae), at times show the shrike-like habit of impaling their prey on thorns or wedging it in tree-forks. Their food consists mainly of large insects, reptiles, small mammals, and young birds. Although smaller than the species of the allied genera, they are rather large song-birds, with stocky bodies and large heads. Their plumage is mostly black, white, and grey. Some species show a striking parallelism in colour pattern with another Australian bird, the Magpie-lark *Grallina cyanoleuca*. The nests are constructed of sticks, lined usually with grasses, and are built in trees, usually at no great height from the ground. The 3–5 eggs are greyish-green with spots and markings of darker tones. Although the birds are generally arboreal in habits, food is often taken from the ground. They are beautiful songsters, early morning notes being particularly pleasing. The Pied Butcher-bird *C. nigrogularis* must be considered one of the world's best songsters, especially when rendering its full repertoire in a subdued undertone. Territorial behaviour is very marked, and during the breeding period older birds may become very pugnacious, often attacking human beings.

The Grey Butcher-bird *C. torquatus* extends over most of Australia and Tasmania ; the Silver-backed Butcher-bird *C. argenteus* of north-eastern Australia is often considered a geographical race of it. The Black-backed Butcher-bird *C. mentalis* of Cape York and New Guinea, and the Black Butcher-bird *C. quoyi* of northern coastal Australia and of New Guinea, are the only two occurring in both countries. A rufous-brown colour phase of the last-mentioned species, which is normally wholly black, is intriguing. The Pied Butcher-bird ranges widely in Australia, generally inland. Two species, the Black-headed Butcher-bird *C. cassicus* and the White-rumped Butcher-bird *C. louisiadensis*, are restricted to New Guinea, the latter being found only on Tagula (Sudest) Island.

See Plate 31 (colour). A.R.M.

Amadon, D. 1951. Taxonomic notes on the Australian butcher-birds (Family Cracticidae). Amer. Mus. Novit. no. 1504 : 1–33.

Amadon, D. 1962. Family Cracticidae. *In* Mayr, E. & Greenway, J. C., Jr. (eds.). Check-list of Birds of the World vol. 15. Cambridge, Mass.

Ashby, E. 1926. A review of the Australian species of *Strepera* (crow-shrikes). Emu 25 : 199–203.

Campbell, A. G. 1929. Australian magpies of the genus *Gymnorhina*. Emu 28 : 165–176.

Iredale, T. 1956. Birds of New Guinea vol. 2. Melbourne.

McGill, A. R. 1956. The Black-winged Currawong. Emu 55 : 129–134. (Distribution map.)

Robinson, A. 1956. The annual reproductive cycle of the Magpie, *Gymnorhina dorsalis* Campbell, in south-western Australia. Emu 56 : 233–336.

Wilson, H. 1945. The life history of the Western Magpie. Emu 46 : 233–244, 271–286.

MAGPIE-LARK : substantive name of two of the four species of Grallinidae (Passeriformes, suborder Oscines) ; the present most usual general term for the family is ' mudnest-builders '. The other names for species are ' apostlebird ' and ' chough '. The family (Mayr & Amadon 1951) is restricted to the Australo-Papuan area, and comprises the genus *Grallina*, with 2 species, and the monotypic genera *Struthidea* and *Corcorax* ; the 2 latter are distinctive both morphologically and in behaviour, so that they stand apart from the much less aberrant and non-colonial *Grallina* spp. Thus, 2 subfamilies are involved—the Grallininae and the Corcoracinae.

Grallininae. The Magpie-lark (or Mudlark) *Grallina cyanoleuca*, a black-and-white bird, is a prominent feature in the Australian countryside. It has the general body proportions of an American Robin *Turdus migratorius* or European Blackbird *T. merula*, and the typical individual is $11\frac{3}{4}$ inches long. Most of the head, back, wings, tail, throat, and breast are gleaming black ; the eyebrow, a large patch below and behind the eye, the base of the tail, the shoulder, the lower breast, and the abdomen are white. In the female the throat is white, and the white eyebrow is lacking.

Magpie-larks are ground feeders, taking insects of various kinds, earthworms, and fresh-water snails from open fields, roadsides, gardens, and particularly along the water's edge of lakes and dams. This liking for the nearness of water, necessary because the nest is made of mud, is further reflected in the common choice of nest site—a large tree on a river bank or lakeside. Magpie-larks are aggressive and ever ready to attack a passing bird-of-prey, uttering shrill alarm calls as they pursue it through the air. Their continent-wide distribution, their conspicuousness, and the readiness with which they have adapted themselves to city suburbs, have made them amongst the best-known Australian birds.

Serventy & Whittell have described a typical example of the bowl-shaped mud nest of *G. cyanoleuca* as 6 inches across, $3\frac{1}{2}$ inches deep, having walls $\frac{3}{4}$ inch thick, and weighing 2 lb. $1\frac{3}{4}$ oz. The nests are placed on bare horizontal branches, or in bare forks, in tall trees. Strength is given by strands of grass being freely mixed with the mud during construction. The need for mud is a direct limiting factor on breeding, which is commonly stopped or interrupted in dry years. Again, if there is rain, the species will nest in autumn. The eggs are usually 3–4 in number, white with violet and purplish-brown blotches.

Robinson has made a detailed study of the life history of the Magpie-lark in south-western Australia. The birds pair for life and retain the same territory (15–20 acres per pair in this section) in successive seasons, although some join flocks in winter. Flocks of up to 500 individuals, obviously most of them immature, may occur at this time. In eastern New South Wales, P. A. Gilbert recorded winter flocks running into a couple of thousand birds ; notwithstanding this, the present writer has found that, over most of New South Wales, adults remain spread out in pairs over the countryside throughout the year. Robinson found that nest building takes 2–20 days, that the eggs are laid on consecutive days, and that the whole of the nesting is shared by both parents. Immature birds assume adult plumage at the end of three months.

In contrast with the Australian species, which dwells in open country, the smaller *Grallina* (' *Pomareopsis* ') *bruijni* of New Guinea is a montane species. Gilliard records that it occurs thinly scattered along the mountain streams, feeding about and amongst the slippery rocks. It lacks the engaging manner of *G. cyanoleuca*, and it is described as fearless but wary.

Corcoracinae. The Apostlebird *Struthidea cinerea* and the White-winged Chough *Corcorax melanorhamphus* differ from the Magpie-lark in having the sexes alike in plumage, and *Corcorax* differs from both in having a bright red iris in contrast to the pearly-white or cream-yellow irides of the other two species. The Apostlebird is rather larger than the Magpie-lark, being about 13 inches in length ; it is of grey plumage, with the individual feathers tipped lighter, and has a short, stout bill. It gets its name from its habit of going about in parties of about twelve. The bird lives in the drier parts of eastern Australia, westward of the Great Dividing Range, from northern Queensland to north-western Victoria, and frequents open country, feeding mainly on the ground on both insects and seeds. It does not usually fly far, but tends to ascend a tree by a series of leaps. The cries are very harsh. Apostlebirds nest communally. Each nest is an open cup made of mud, reinforced and lined with grass ; it is usually placed on a horizontal branch high above the ground. The 4–5 or more eggs are pale bluish with dark brown and purplish markings.

The White-winged Chough, 17–18 inches long, is the largest member of the family. It has a slender decurved bill of moderate length ; the plumage is mainly glossy black, with a white patch on each wing. It is most plentiful in the open forests of inland south-eastern Australia, from southern Queensland to southern South Australia, and in fewer numbers on the tablelands and coastal areas. Its habits are generally similar to those of the Apostlebird. It is an omnivorous feeder and eats insects, tadpoles, seeds of various native and exotic plants, and fruits, sometimes invading orchards and gardens to feed on soft fruits and grapes. The eggs are creamy white, boldly marked with brown blotches and submerged ones of slate-grey.

No studies comparable with those on the Magpie-lark have been made on either the Apostlebird or the White-winged Chough, but some interesting general observations have been published by Sharland. He states that the communal nesting behaviour of each follows much the same pattern. In the White-winged Chough, which is the one he discusses in more detail, the community may consist of from 8 to 20 individuals, and the clutch size in the single nest varies from 2 to 8. Four eggs were the average, and Sharland thought that any one female contributed only 2 eggs to the combined clutch. The component individuals in the flock shared in the work of nest construction, incubation, and tending of the young ; but only 'dominant' females laid the eggs. This type of social behaviour did not, however, lead to high nesting success ; it was unusual to find more than two young reared to maturity, although the nest might originally have contained 6 eggs, all of which hatched. Many nestlings were trampled to death in the various change-overs made by different birds desirous of mothering them.

See Plate 31 (colour).   A.K.

Amadon, D. 1950. Australian mud nest builders. Emu 50 : 123–127.
Mayr, E. 1962. Family Grallinidae. In Mayr, E. & Greenway, J. C., Jr. (eds.). Check-list of Birds of the World vol. 15. Cambridge, Mass.
Robinson, A. 1947. Magpie-larks—a study in behaviour. Emu 46 : 265–281, 382–391 ; 47 : 11–28, 147–153.
Serventy, D. L. & Whittell, H. M. 1962. Birds of Western Australia. 3rd ed. Perth, W.A.
Sharland, M. S. R. 1944. Social breeding birds. North Queensland Nat. 12 (73) : 1–3.

MAGPIE-ROBIN: substantive name of *Copsychus* spp. (see THRUSH).

MALACONOTINAE: see SHRIKE

MALAGASH: alternative name of the Cape Gannet *Sula capensis* (see GANNET).

MALAGASY REGION: the zoogeographical region formed by Madagascar and its off-lying islands, classically regarded as a subregion of the Ethiopian Region (see DISTRIBUTION, GEOGRAPHICAL ; ETHIOPIAN REGION). Opinions have differed on the question of regional or subregional rank. The view favouring the lower status has probably been influenced by the nearness of Madagascar to Africa, and by reluctance to treat a relatively small land-surface (some 240 000 square miles) as entirely separate. Nevertheless, the Malagasy fauna shows a higher proportion of peculiarity than does either the Ethiopian or the Indian.

It has often been stated that Madagascar has been isolated since the Miocene, but it appears that this was no more than an inference from equivocal zoogeographical data and that there is no evidence for any land connection later than the Secondary. The Mascarenes (Mauritius, Réunion, and Rodriguez) are small oceanic islands ; so are the Comoros, with an avifauna transitional to the Ethiopian (Benson 1960). The Seychelles, although on geological grounds probably a continental relict, are oceanic from the ornithological point of view. Purely on geographical grounds the probability is overwhelming that the greater part of the Madagascar avifaunal stock came from Africa, and some of the existing birds indicate that immigrant stock has continued to establish itself at long intervals. The best evidence is provided by the few passerine species that may belong to African superspecies. There are, however, 3 genera in the Madagascar fauna that are typically eastern and unknown in Africa today.

Apart from the extinct Aepyornithidae of Madagascar and Raphidae of the Mascarenes (see ELEPHANT-BIRD ; DODO), the Madagascar avifauna includes 3 endemic families, so rated by universal consent— the rail-like, dry-country Mesitornithidae (3 species), the suboscine Philepittidae (4 species), and the passerine Vangidae (ca. 11 species) which resemble shrikes (see MESITE ; ASITY ; VANGA). There are 3 other endemic groups rated by some authorities as families but by others only as subfamilies, the Leptosomatidae (1 species) and Brachypteraciinae (5 species) in or near the Coraciidae (see CUCKOO-ROLLER ; GROUND-ROLLER), and the Hyposittinae (1 species) in the Sittidae (see NUTHATCH). Of the 182 species 65 per cent are endemic, the proportion actually rising to 95 per cent in the passerines. Furthermore, specific differentiation has been so marked that the genera average only 1·3 species each ; but at the same time, except to a limited extent in *Coua* (see CUCKOO) and the Vangidae, there has been no evolutionary radiation in Madagascar of any particular stock.

Madagascar has a wide range of habitats : the east side of the island is very wet and still carries some 1200 square miles of evergreen forest ; the south-western corner is arid and has been so sufficiently long for its own typical species of plants to develop ; while most of the island is covered with more or less wooded savanna, which degenerates into eroded grassland on the central plateau (where habitat destruction has been worst). The surface relief is simple, with a single line of highland running down the island west of centre ; it reaches an altitude of 9000 feet, but little land lies above 5000 feet and no typical montane avifauna is developed. Given these conditions, and on the postulate that geographical isolation is needed for the achievement of the genetical isolation essential to speciation, it is extremely difficult to understand how evolution to specific level, of which the results are obvious in Madagascar today, can have proceeded in the island, especially as dissection by the sea is ruled out. It is true that cases of subspeciation are numerous, but there are hardly any isolates.

With all its prolonged evolution and replenishment by immigration, the balance of the Madagascar avifauna remains odd. One-third of all its species belong to water-bird families, compared with one-thirteenth in the Ethiopian avifauna ; but the fact that one in three of the Madagascar water birds are endemic species shows that the rich variety of the group in the island is not merely because birds of these types find it easier than others to get there. By contrast with the water birds, the Madagascar passerines account for only one-third of the avifauna, compared with three-fifths in the Ethiopian Region. The Madagascar passerines are unexpectedly deficient in fruit-eaters, of which there are only one starling (Sturnidae) and one bulbul (Pycnonotidae), and in seed-eaters, which are limited to one lark (Alaudidae), three ploceid weavers and one estrildid. It is noteworthy, also, that individual species tend to show a wider ecological tolerance in Madagascar than in Africa, for in the island nearly half the species occurring in forest also inhabit the savanna, many of them even the arid southwest also. Nothing comparable is found in Africa.

The avifauna of the Mascarene islands has of course suffered most grievously from extinctions since Europeans began to live there around the beginning of the sixteenth century. Hachisuka has amassed all the available information about the extinct species. Apart from the Raphidae, he lists 37 species, among which owls (Strigiformes), rails (Rallidae), pigeons (Columbidae), parrots (Psittacidae), and starlings bulk largest. The present miserable remnants of the insular avifaunas, further confounded by introductions, have been listed most recently by Berlioz and by Milon for Réunion and by Rountree et al. for Mauritius. For the Seychelles there is no evidence that any such outstandingly remarkable birds

as those on the Mascarenes ever existed, but some extinctions have occurred in the last hundred years and several other species, confined to one or two islets, are among the rarest birds in the world. The latest account of them is by Loustau-Lalanne.

R.E.M.

Benson, C. W. 1960. The birds of the Comoro Islands : results of the British Ornithologists' Union Centenary Expedition 1958. Ibis 103B : 5–106.
Berlioz, J. 1946. Oiseaux de la Réunion. Paris.
Hachisuka, M. 1953. The Dodo and Kindred Birds, or the Extinct Birds of the Mascarene Islands. London.
Loustau-Lalanne, P. 1962. Land-birds of the granitic islands of the Seychelles. Seychelles Soc. Occas. Publ. 1. Seychelles.
Milon, P. 1951. Notes sur l'avifaune actuelle de l'île de la Réunion. Terre et Vie 98 : 129–178.
Rountree, F. R. G., Guérin, R., Pelte, S. & Vinson, J. 1952. Catalogue of the birds of Mauritius. Mauritius Inst. Bull. 3 : 155–217.
Rand, A. L. 1936. The habits and distribution of Madagascar birds. Bull. Amer. Mus. Nat. Hist. 72 : 143–499.
Sclater, W. L. 1924–30. Systema Avium Aethiopicarum. 2 vols. London.

MALAR : pertaining to the area on the side of the throat immediately below the base of the lower mandible (see TOPOGRAPHY).

MALEO : Dutch name (sometimes used as English) in Indonesia for *Megacephalon maleo* (see MEGAPODE).

MALIMBE : sometimes used as substantive name of certain *Malimbus* spp. (see WEAVER).

MALKOHA : substantive name of *Rhopodytes* spp. (see CUCKOO).

MALLARD : *Anas platyrhynchos*, the common ' wild-duck ', but originally applied only to the male (a usage now obsolete)—see DUCK ; and Plate 2b (phot.).

MALLEE : an environment, consisting of *Eucalyptus* scrub, characteristic of Australia.

MALLEE FOWL : name, alternatively ' Lowan ', of *Leipoa ocellata* (see MEGAPODE). See Plates 31 (colour), 33b (phot.).

MALLOPHAGA : see ECTOPARASITE

MALPIGHIAN BODY : see EXCRETORY SYSTEM

MALPIGHIAN LAYER : the basal layer of the epidermis (see SKIN).

MALURINAE : see MUSCICAPIDAE ; and WREN (2).

MAMMALS, ASSOCIATION WITH : occurs, as a regular habit of various avian species, chiefly in relation to the quest for food (see FEEDING HABITS). The most frequent role of the mammal, wild or domesticated, is that of a beater, disturbing insects or other prey of the birds as it moves through the herbage ; and often the attendant birds will perch on the mammal, although only in a few cases do they commonly find any part of their food on the beast itself. The habit is particularly characteristic of the Cattle Egret *Ardeola ibis*, widely distributed in tropical parts of the world. It is shown, however, by such familiar birds as the Starling *Sturnus vulgaris*, associating with cattle in Europe. A similar association is that of the Piapiac *Ptilostomus afer* with domestic stock and wild grazing mammals in tropical Africa ; its habit of perching on Elephants *Loxodonta africana* is well known, and the more remarkable because that mammal does not tolerate the attentions of oxpeckers *Buphagus* spp. Examples of such associations between birds of many species with grazing or browsing mammalian species, in various parts of the world, are much too numerous to cite at length.

Aquatic and wading birds of many species habitually perch on the backs of almost submerged Hippopotamus *Hippopotamus amphibius* ; cormorants (*Phalacrocorax* spp.) are characteristic in this role— and it has been recorded even of the Crab-plover *Dromas ardeola* on ' hippos ' in the sea. Sometimes the bird may find small particles of food on the hippo's hide, as the Common Sandpiper *Actitis hypoleuca* appears to do ; sometimes the beast's back provides a vantage point for fishing, as in the case of the Hammerhead *Scopus umbretta* on the look-out for frogs ; in other instances it may be no more than a convenient resting-place.

Roving troops of monkeys, in different parts of the world, are followed by parties of birds—hornbills (Bucerotidae), drongos (Dicruridae), trogons (Trogonidae), and so on—for the prey that they disturb (see FEEDING HABITS).

The two oxpeckers *Buphagus* spp. have a closer, rather symbiotic, relation with the mammals that they frequent to feed upon the ticks in the hide (see OXPECKER). Another special case is the strange association on the part of the honeyguides (Indicatoridae) with ratels and man (see HONEYGUIDE).

Nesting associations with mammals are rare. The only perfect case seems to be that of the Minera *Geositta cunicularia* of South America, which nests only in the burrows of the Vizcacha *Lagostromus trichodactylus* (see NESTING ASSOCIATION).

For associations with mankind see MAN, BIRDS AND ; also TAMENESS.

MAMMAL SIMULATION: also ' rodent run ' (see DISTRACTION DISPLAY).

MANAKIN: substantive name of species of Pipridae (Passeriformes, suborder Tyranni)—not to be confused with MANNIKIN ; in the plural, general term for the family. This Neotropical group of some 59 species is allied to the cotingas (Cotingidae) and, less closely, to the tyrant-flycatchers (Tyrannidae). Manakins are small, stocky birds the size of tits (Paridae), usually with short wings and tail, and with short bills rather broad at the base and slightly hooked at the tip. In most species the sexes are strikingly different, the males being predominantly black with patches of brilliant red, orange, blue, and other colours, and the females greenish. In several species the males have some of the flight feathers modified for making mechanical sounds. In one species, *Teleonema filicauda*, the male's tail feathers are prolonged into curved wire-like structures. In a few species, supposed to be primitive, the sexes are alike and mainly green or brown. It is, however, doubtful whether some of these, for example the Thrush-like Manakin *Schiffornis turdinus*, are really closely related to the typical manakins.

$\frac{2}{3}$

Gould's Manakin *Manacus vitellinus*. C.E.T.K.

Manakins are distributed throughout the forested regions of tropical South and Central America. Most are birds of primary forest, but some species are regular in second growth. They feed mainly on small fruits, plucked by the birds on the wing ; insects are also taken in small quantities. The nest is a thinly woven hammock slung in a horizontal fork of a sapling or fern, usually at no great height and often over water. The two eggs are of a pale ground-colour mottled and spotted with brown. In the species for which the facts are known, the female alone builds, incubates, and cares for the young.

Manakins are especially notable for their elaborate courtship behaviour, which appears to have evolved under conditions of intense sexual selection. In Gould's Manakin *Manacus vitellinus*, and others of this genus, the males display in 'leks' (see LEK DISPLAY). Each clears for itself a small 'court' on the floor of the forest, taking away all leaves and twigs that are small enough to be carried, and dropping them a few feet away. Each court contains one vertical sapling that serves as the main display perch, and usually one or more other saplings. On and around his court the male executes astonishing jumps and other evolutions of a highly stereotyped nature. Various loud snapping and whirring noises are made with the wing feathers, the secondaries having much thickened shafts and a special musculature, while the outer primaries are thin, stiff, and curved. The females visit the males at their courts and take part in a joint dance with them. Mating in this genus, as in the other species studied, takes place on the main display perch. The four species of *Pipra* that have been studied display on horizontal perches 30 or more feet up in trees, below the main forest canopy. Their display consists of various elements ; a swift flight to the perch from a distance, a sliding movement along the perch, raising of the wings and spreading of the tail, vibrating of the whole body, rapid to and fro flights between the main perch and an adjacent perch, the last accompanied by mechanical wing-noises. In two species of *Machaeropterus* the male perches head downwards on a vertical perch and rapidly turns the body from side to side while making a grasshopper-like reeling sound. It is noteworthy that, in *Machaeropterus* and some other species, observers have found it extremely difficult to determine whether certain sounds accompanying the displays are vocal or mechanical in origin. In *Corapipo gutturalis* the male is described as crouching on the ground and, with wings fully spread, moving towards the female in a laboured undulating crawl, an action strikingly like that described for the bowerbird *Archboldia sanfordi* (see BOWERBIRD).

Species of *Chiroxiphia* have perhaps the most remarkable displays in that two or more males co-operate in a joint dance. In *C. pareola* two males jump up alternately, side by side, in a rhythmic dance accompanied by a curious rhythmic whining call. When a female comes to the display perch they face her and jump up in 'catherine wheel' formation in front of her ; the front bird first jumps up and, hovering, moves backwards through the air while the other bird hops up into his place and jumps as the first bird lands. In *C. caudata* several males have been described as dancing, perched in a row on a horizontal twig, before one female.   D.W.S.

Gilliard, E. T. 1959. Notes on the courtship of the Blue-backed Manakin (*Chiroxiphia pareola*). Amer. Mus. Novit. no. 1942 : 1–19.

Skutch, A. F. 1949. Life history of the Yellow-thighed Manakin (*Pipra mentalis*). Auk 66 : 1–24.
Snow, D. W. 1962. A field study of the Black and White Manakin, *Manacus manacus*, in Trinidad. Zoologica (N.Y.) 47 : 65–104.
Snow, D. W. 1963. The evolution of manakin displays. Proc. XIII Internat. Orn. Congr., Ithaca, N.Y., 1962 : 553–561.
Wagner, H. 1946. Observaciones sobre el comportamiento de *Chiroxiphia linearis* durante su propagacion. Anales Inst. Biol. Mex. 16 : 539–546.

MAN, BIRDS AND: a relationship with two aspects, the impact of mankind on bird-life and the part played by birds in human activities. The human impact on birds is partly direct and partly indirect. In the first place there are frank predation by man and also other forms of exploitation for human purposes (see UTILISATION BY MAN). There is also some deliberate destruction of birds that are thought, with or without good reason, to be harmful to human interests or to be excessively numerous (see, for example, QUELEA CONTROL). There is sometimes, also, negligent or wanton slaughter. Against this may be set the growing human effort to conserve and protect wild birds (see CONSERVATION ; PROTECTION).

The indirect impact on bird-life is very much greater. With the immense increase in human populations and in man's powers of action, the natural habitats of many bird species have been destroyed on a huge scale ; drainage, cultivation, and afforestation change the character of the land in a way that is inimical to some species, while industrial and urban development may ruin it for most. Even the ocean is not immune (see OIL POLLUTION). Apart from damage to a habitat, human intervention may alter the balance of nature by deliberate elimination of predators or by the introduction of additional animal species from elsewhere. The bird life of remote islands has been devastated by man's introduction, deliberate or accidental, of domestic or other animals (see EXTINCT BIRDS ; VANISHING BIRDS).

To a great extent the destruction or alteration of natural habitats is an inevitable process. It can be mitigated only to a limited, albeit desirable, degree by the creation of nature reserves, sanctuaries, and refuges (see CONSERVATION). At the same time, where some species have lost, others have gained ; the more sophisticated environments resulting from human enterprise—tended woods, fields, gardens, and even buildings—have their own avifauna, often enjoying greater security than under more natural conditions. Birds are indeed sometimes actively encouraged, by intentional or incidental augmentation of their food supply, and by the artificial provision of nesting facilities (see NESTBOX). Species have also been introduced by men, but often unhappily, into parts of the world to which they were not native (see NATURALISED BIRDS).

The other aspect of the relationship between birds and man is largely the converse of what has already been described. Birds are utilised by man in various ways. They also play a part in the ecology of human environments—notably insectivorous species on cultivated land, but a few vegetarian species themselves become pests. From the ornithological standpoint, great interest attaches to the way in which many species of birds have so thoroughly adapted themselves to living in largely man-made habitats and often in close association with man himself. In particular, several species now nest mainly or exclusively on buildings, so that in some instances it is difficult to be sure about the natural sites that must have been largely used only a few thousand years ago. And the adaptation to living close to human beings includes the remarkable degree of tameness that is quickly acquired by many species where birds are never molested (see TAMENESS).

For the relation to man of other than wild birds under natural conditions, see AVICULTURE ; CAGE BIRD ; DOMESTICATION ; HOMING PIGEON.

In addition to material considerations, birds have contributed outstandingly to man's aesthetic enjoyment, as well as providing material for his scientific interest. Evidence of this is to be found in the important role played by birds in various aspects of human culture (see ART, BIRDS IN ; BIBLE, BIRDS OF THE ; FABULOUS BIRDS ; FOLKLORE ; HERALDIC BIRDS ; MUSIC, BIRDS IN ; OMENS, BIRDS AS ; POETRY, BIRDS IN ; SHAKESPEARE'S BIRDS.)

MANDIBLE: term sometimes used without qualification for the lower jaw (compounded of several bones—see SKELETON) and its horny covering (see BILL), and in this sense contrasted with 'maxilla' ; in another usage applied to either jaw, with the adjective 'upper' or 'lower' (see also MAXILLA ; MUSCULATURE).

MANGO: substantive name of *Anthracothorax* spp. (for family see HUMMINGBIRD).

MANGROVE SWAMP: a specialised type of environment widely distributed in tropical parts of the world and bordering arms of the sea, tidal rivers, or saline marshes ; it consists of mangrove trees (several species) growing closely together out of water and liquid mud, presenting a most formidable obstacle to human ingress.

MANNIKIN: substantive name of various *Lonchura* spp. ; in the plural, general term for a tribe (Amadini) of the Estrildidae (see WEAVER-FINCH). Not to be confused with MANAKIN.

MAN O' WAR HAWK: sailors' name for *Fregata* spp. (see FRIGATEBIRD).

MANTLE: see TOPOGRAPHY

MANUBRIUM: forward process of the sternum (see SKELETON).

MANUCODE: substantive name of species of *Manucodia* and *Phonygammus* (see BIRD-OF-PARADISE).

MANUS: the 'hand' (see SKELETON ; WING).

MAPPING: of importance in the study of geographical aspects of bird life ; (see DISTRIBUTION, GEOGRAPHICAL ; MIGRATION). There are some facts concerning it that cannot be repeated too often for the benefit of both map users and map makers. The first is that while the world is round, the map is flat. Therefore, to transfer information from the globe to paper involves : knowledge of the shape of the world ; some graticule of reference ; the scale of the map ; and the principle of transferring data from a three-dimensional to a two-dimensional surface (projection).

Shape of the World. Although we are on the threshold of a more precise knowledge of the shape of our planet, to be derived from space examination, at present for all practical purposes we assume the shape to be that of an ellipsoid with its flattening ratio from a hemisphere of $\frac{1}{293}$ (app.) according to Clarke (1880), or $\frac{1}{297}$ according to the International Ellipsoid (Hayford 1910).

Graticule of Reference. The graticule that has been in general use for a long time, and was standardised at the International Meridian Conference in Washington, D.C., in 1884, consists of a net of latitudes and longitudes. The northern latitudes number from the Equator (0° lat.) to 90° N. at the North Pole, and the southern latitudes similarly in the southern half of the globe, the Equator being the great circle and all other latitudes being of constantly decreasing circumferences from the Equator to the Poles. The longitudes divide the globe by a set of great circles with the prime meridian (0° long.) going through the old Observatory at Greenwich and all others named from 0° to 180° westwards and eastwards respectively ; all meridians go through the Poles. There are four latitudes of special significance : 23° 27' N. (Tropic of Cancer) ; 66° 32' N. (Arctic Circle) ; 23° 27' S. (Tropic of Capricorn) ; 66° 32' S. (Antarctic Circle). Both the latitude and longitude of any point on the world are easily established with the help of instruments which allow the measuring of angles subtended from the given point to the sun or some selected stars and with exact knowledge of the time of day. Therefore, this gives an excellent grid of reference, in which any

MAP   448   MAP

value of latitude and longitude refers only to one point on the globe.

Scale. The scale of a map is nothing more than the ratio of the distances on the map to those on the geoid. This can be expressed on a map in four ways :

(*a*) Descriptive, e.g. so many miles to one inch.

(*b*) Numerical (Representative Fraction), e.g. 1 : 1 000 000 ;

(*c*) Graphical, e.g. in the form of a line subdivided into miles, kilometres, or any other specific unit of linear measurement.

(*d*) Comparative, giving the scale in the form of an inset of a known area on the same scale, e.g. England on a map of Australia.

The larger the scale, the smaller the area covered by a given size of map, but the larger the amount of information. It is, however, often not understood among map users that the scale is very seldom uniform throughout a map. The lack of uniformity increases with the decrease in scale, and it is also governed by the kind of projection used, e.g. on maps drawn on Mercator projection the change in scale going south or north from the central latitude is very rapid.

The measuring of distances on large-scale maps is quite in order, but when it comes to small-scale maps, especially those that cover the whole of a hemisphere or the world, the situation is quite different. Apart from the fact that the scale throughout the map will not be uniform, the shortest straight line between two points will not necessarily coincide with the shortest route between the same points on the globe.

On the globe the shortest route between two points is that which lies on the great circle (arc of the great circle, or orthodrome). Although special graphic solutions for different projections are to be found, the simplest way of determining the distances is, of course, by taking them off a reliable globe of a fair scale (say 20 inches in diameter), using a piece of strong string or a flexible measuring tape.

There are also trigonometric formulae that allow the shortest distances between two points to be calculated from their known latitude or longitude.

Projections. The term ' projection ' in cartography refers to the system of relating the ellipsoid to the plan (map). There is one important fact concerning all projections used, namely, that one cannot re-create all the characteristics of the curved surface of the globe or ellipsoid on the plan. As an example, take a slice of the surface of a perfect sphere with two meridians bounding it and intersected by parallels of latitude. On the curved surface the meridians are intersected by parallels at right angles (spherical). To retain the same angular character-

istic, we have to construct our meridians on the map as two parallel lines, thus stretching the original distance between them more and more as we progress north or south of the Equator (cylindrical projection). In this way, we are able to retain a similarity of angles (conformity) while sacrificing the equality of areas. Hence the necessity for different projections, each designed to preserve on the map one of the conflicting characteristics existing on the curved surface : concerning area (equivalence), shape (orthomorphism), scale (equidistance), and bearing (conformity).

All map projections can be classified into many groups depending on the point of view, e.g. construction (plane, conical, cylindrical) or relationship of the projection surface to the ellipsoid (tangent, secant, polysuperficial, direct, transverse, or oblique). However, the most important classification of projections, at least from the point of view of the map user, is according to their property : equidistant, equivalent, orthomorphic, conformal, or others.

In the case of distribution maps, the right choice of projection is an equivalent one (equal area). Such projections can be found in all classes of projections classified according to their constructions.

Cylindrical—Transverse cylindrical equal area ; cylindrical equal area.

Conical—Equal area conical ; Alber's conical ; Bonne.

Zenithal—Lambert azimuthal equal area ; zenithal equal area.

Others—Sinusoidal equal area (or Sanson-Flamstead's) ; Mollweide ; Bartholomew's Atlantis ; Goode's homolographic ; Eckert.

When it comes to maps of the whole world, the equivalent (equal area) projections retain their characteristic at the cost of serious distortion of shapes, giving rather unfamiliar portrayal of some parts of

---

Plate 27 · Mutual Display

a *Upper :* Wandering Albatrosses *Diomedea exulans* in courtship dance (South Georgia). At this stage in the mutual performance, when excitement mounts, the male raises his wings and shrieks, usually pointing his neck vertically upwards (as shown). The female is on the right ; an interested spectator in the background. Later, the female also raises her wings ; and both birds slowly approach each other until their bills almost touch.
Phot. Niall Rankin.

b *Lower :* Avocets *Recurvirostra avosetta* in courtship dance (Hungary). The sexes are alike. The recurved bill characteristic of the genus is well seen
Phot. Zoltán Tildy.

(See articles DISPLAY ; ALBATROSS ; AVOCET)

MAP 449 MAR

the world. The least distorting projection is, of course, one that eliminates certain areas of the globe from it. These are sometimes called interrupted projections, good examples being sinusoidal and Goode's homolographic. The disadvantages of these interrupted projections are the missing links, chosen in the sea areas for distribution on land, or on land for distribution on the sea.

For that reason, and especially in the case of a very small scale for maps of the world, a compromise is introduced by using projections that are neither of equal area nor orthomorphic, but are fairly equal area and at the same time give a satisfactory likeness of the continents. Hence the choice, in this work (p. 208), of the Winkel projection of the world ; this is a combination of azimuthal and cylindrical projections and has neither equivalence nor conformity but portrays the world reasonably well. As all the maps are of small scale, it is hoped that users will not try to measure the areas for making comparisons.

British National Reference Grid. A further fact concerns additional aid to users of the larger-scale maps of Great Britain. The national reference systems are the successors of the military grid introduced on maps for the use of the artillery ; the metric reference system grid was introduced to facilitate the determination of the target, where the grid not only permits quick finding of the target but at the same time gives the distance in metres.

Plate 28 · Caressing ; Courtship Feeding ; Greeting Ceremony

a *Upper :* Wood Pigeons *Columba palumbus* caressing on nest (England). In this case the nest was empty, before laying. Caressing and similar display acts serve to bring the pair into full breeding condition and to synchronise their sequence of physiological changes. *Phot. R. K. Murton.*

b *Lower left :* Little (or Least) Terns *Sterna albifrons* engaged in courtship feeding (England). The farther away bird has just alighted to offer a small fish to its mate, the latter standing over two eggs in the scrape that serves as a nest. This species has an almost world-wide distribution on coasts and rivers, except in the higher latitudes.
Phot. Eric Hosking.

c *Lower right :* Openbill Stork *Anastomus oscitans* performing the greeting ceremony while standing above young in the nest—presumably because its mate is approaching (India). This display action, with the head laid back, is characteristic of the Ciconiidae. The remarkable gap left between the mandibles of the closed bill, in this species, is seen in the photograph. *Phot. Loke Wan Tho.*

(See articles DISPLAY ; PIGEON ; TERN ; COURTSHIP FEEDING ; STORK)

The National Reference System used in Great Britain facilitates the finding of any place in the country without having to use the more cumbersome reference to the geographical latitude and longitude. This system was introduced by the Ordnance Survey on the recommendation of the Davidson Committee (1935). It is based on the international metre and it consists of lines drawn parallel to and at right angles to the central meridian of the projection of the map (2° W.). The origin of the National Grid is located about 132 km. west of Land's End and about 8 km. south of Lizard Point, and therefore always gives positive values. It extends 1300 km. to the north and 700 km. to the east.

Each square of 100 km. in each direction is given two letters ; the first letter refers to the whole of a larger square 500 km. in each direction, and the second refers to the further subdivision to 100 km. units. Within the 100 km. squares the numbers of kilometres are used and the spacing of the grid lines is adapted to the scale of the map ; e.g. for 1 : 62 500, quarter-inch, and half-inch maps, the lines are shown at intervals of 10 km. and the reference is given in the form of the two letters of the 100 km. square plus four figures (kilometres). The first two figures refer to the value of easting to be read on southern or northern margins of the map, and the second two figures refer to the northing to be read on the eastern or western margins of the map. On the one inch, 1 : 25 000, and six-inch maps, the lines of the grid are drawn at intervals of 1 km. and the values of northing and easting are increased to three figures (reading to nearest 100 metres). For plans on 1 : 2500 and 1 : 1250 scales the grid lines are spaced at intervals of 100 metres and the figures of easting and northing are increased to four for each (reading to nearest 10 metres). By using this system, every point in Great Britain has its own specific reference.

J.J.K.

MAP, WEATHER : see METEOROLOGY

MARABOU : also ' Marabou Stork ', *Leptoptilos crumeniferus* (see STORK).

MARGARORNITHINAE : see OVENBIRD (1)

MARISMA : Spanish word applied to marshy country, notably in the delta of the Guadalquivir (an important bird habitat).

MARKING : see RINGING

MARROW : see BLOOD ; SKELETON

MARSH : see SWAMP ; also DAMBO

MARTIN : substantive name of some species of Hirundinidae (see SWALLOW).

MARTLET: archaic and heraldic name for a bird which may have been either the House Martin *Delichon urbica* (or other hirundine) or the Swift *Apus apus*, perhaps used for both (see HERALDIC BIRDS ; SHAKESPEARE'S BIRDS).

MATE: either member of a pair in relation to the other (see PAIR).

MATING: same as PAIRING.

MATURATION: literally 'ripening' ; in physiology, applied particularly to completion of the development of the germ-cells (see REPRODUCTIVE SYSTEM) ; in ethology, the development of a behaviour pattern in a young bird without performance, i.e. without learning through practice (see BEHAVIOUR, DEVELOPMENT OF).

MATURITY: Attainment of the age at which the bird is capable of reproduction (although actual breeding condition is a seasonal phenomenon) ; in practice, the criterion is usually the acquisition of full adult plumage (for immaturity see under YOUNG BIRD). Many species, especially of small birds, breed when a year old or just under ; in an environment where there is not a closely limited breeding season they may do so when several months younger than that. Many others do not usually breed until about two years old. Other species again, particularly among the larger birds, take several years to reach breeding age. (In captivity some species may lay at a very early age, e.g. Quail *Coturnix coturnix* at 7 weeks.)

The term is sometimes used in a more restricted sense for the age when maximum breeding capacity is attained (Richdale—see PENGUIN). In some long-lived species this may apparently be several years after first breeding ; and there are reasons for supposing that it may in many others be at least one year after first breeding (or after the year in which some individuals of the age-group first breed).

MAVIS: popular name, in Britain, for the Song Thrush *Turdus philomelos* (see THRUSH).

MAXILLA: osteologically, a slender paired bone of the skull, between the jugal and the premaxilla (see SKELETON) ; sometimes used more generally as a term for what is otherwise called the 'upper mandible', i.e. the upper jaw (of which the premaxillae are the chief bones) and its horny covering (see BILL) ; in the latter usage the term mandible is restricted to the lower part (see MANDIBLE).

MEADOWLARK: substantive name of *Sturnella* spp. (see ORIOLE (2)).

MEAN, ARITHMETIC: equivalent to 'average' in the sense in which the latter word is most exactly used—the sum of the recorded values divided by the number of observations. For the reliability of the mean of a sample, especially for comparison with other means, see STATISTICAL SIGNIFICANCE. Two other forms of average have their statistical uses : the 'median' is the middle value in a series arranged in order, half of the values lying below it and half above ; the 'mode' is the value that occurs most often in a series (the peak of the frequency curve—when there are two peaks, the curve is 'bimodal'). In a perfectly symmetrical distribution, the median and mode coincide with the mean.

MEASUREMENT: as applied to birds, relates particularly to certain dimensions that are most commonly used as general indications of size or for taxonomic purposes. See SIZE ; WEIGHT.

General Indications. For this purpose the most commonly cited dimension is total length—measured in a straight line from the tip of the longest tail feather to the tip of the bill, when a fresh specimen is laid on its back (without undue stretching) and the bill is in line with the body. This measurement (in inches) is frequently cited in the present work, among others, to give the reader a rough idea of the comparative size of a species and of the range of size within a group. It has the disadvantage, however, of being affected by the shape of the bird, giving an exaggerated impression when the bill, neck, body, or tail is relatively long, and of course especially when two or more of these parts are elongated. The measurement cannot be made, with any accuracy, on a prepared skin.

'Span' (also 'expanse', 'spread') is sometimes cited—the distance between the wing-tips (ends of the longest primaries) when both wings are fully extended ; here, likewise, the shape and relative length of the wing is a factor as well as the general size of the bird (see also FLIGHT). It occasionally helps, in conveying an impression, to cite the standing height of a large, long-legged bird ; this can be only an estimate from life, probably in captivity, of the vertical distance from the crown of the head (when the neck is erect) to the ground or perch on which the bird stands.

Precise Measurements. These are of dimensions that can be measured accurately, with dividers, either on the live bird in the hand or on the museum skin ; they are customarily expressed in millimetres. Some cannot be reliably taken when critical feathers are not fully grown after moult. The most usual are :

Wing. The minimum chord between the carpal joint (of the folded wing) and the tip of the longest primary, with the concavity pressed flat but the normal lateral curvature of the primaries undisturbed.

Tail. Length from the base of the central pair of rectrices to the tip of the longest feather in its natural position.

Bill. The length of the upper mandible in a straight line (chord of the culmen) from its tip to the edge of the feathering at the base of the skull, or (if so stated) to the edge of the cere where one is present.

Tarsus. Length from the angle (posterior) of the intertarsal joint to the base of the last complete scale (anterior) before the divergence of the toes.

Egg Measurements. These are of necessity taken with callipers ; they are customarily expressed in millimetres. The usual dimensions cited are length (diameter from pole to pole on the long axis) and breadth (greatest diameter at right angles to the long axis).

Variations. In citing any measurement, as applicable to a species, one has to remember that there may be differences relating to age, sex, or population; there will also be a certain range of individual variation among birds that are the same in these respects. Age, sex, and population are matters to be considered and noted in selecting the material. Individual variation is discounted by using the average (mean) of measurements of a sample (see MEAN, ARITHMETIC) ; but sometimes the range of variation may itself be a fact of importance. As regards the adequacy of samples and related matters, see STATISTICAL SIGNIFICANCE. For factors for converting measurements between British and metric systems, see CONVERSION TABLES at the end of the volume.

MEATUS: an opening, particularly of the ear (see HEARING AND BALANCE).

MEDIAN: see under MEAN, ARITHMETIC ; STATISTICAL SIGNIFICANCE

MEDICAL USES: see GASTRONOMIC AND MEDICAL USES

MEDULLA: for that of the adrenal glands see ENDOCRINE SYSTEM.

MEDULLA OBLONGATA: part of the hindbrain (see NERVOUS SYSTEM).

MEGAGEA: see under ARCTOGAEA ; DISTRIBUTION, GEOGRAPHICAL

MEGAPODE: substantive name of species of Megapodiidae (Galliformes, suborder Galli) ; in the plural, general term for the family. Alternative English names, given to species found in Australia, are ' junglefowl ' (more properly used in the

Phasianidae), ' scrubfowl ', ' brush-turkey '—and in one instance ' Mallee-Fowl ' (sometimes ' Mallee-hen ') or ' Lowan '. Such general terms as ' mound-birds ', ' mound-builders ', and ' incubator birds '—this last a common American usage—have been applied to the group. The family is a small one and, except for one species with a rather wider range, is confined to eastern Indonesia, Polynesia, New Guinea, and Australia. The members are characterised by their habit of not brooding their eggs. Instead they lay them in holes in the ground or in mounds of rotting vegetable matter and leave them to be incubated by natural heat.

The family comprises 7 genera, which can be divided into 3 ecological groups, viz. junglefowl (*Megacephalon, Eulipoa,* and *Megapodius*), brush-turkeys (*Alectura, Aepypodius,* and *Talegalla*), and the Mallee Fowl (*Leipoa*). Of these *Megacephalon, Eulipoa, Alectura,* and *Leipoa* are monotypic, the species being *M. maleo, E. wallacei, A. lathami,* and *L. ocellata*. The genus *Aepypodius* includes 2 species, *A. arfakianus* and *A. bruijnii* ; and *Talegalla* includes 3, *T. cuvieri, T. fuscirostris,* and *T. jobiensis*. Peters recognised 9 species, including 28 subspecies, of *Megapodius,* but Mayr & Amadon have recently reviewed the genus and reduced these to 3 species—*M. freycinet, M. laperouse,* and *M. pritchardii*.

Range and Habitat. Of the brush-turkeys, *Aepypodius* spp. and *Talegalla* spp. are confined to New Guinea, and *Alectura lathami* to the eastern coast of the Australian mainland. They are generally restricted to dense tropical rain-forests, but in a few places *Alectura* extends into more arid inland scrubs.

The junglefowl are relatively widespread, particularly *Megapodius freycinet,* called ' Junglefowl ' in Australia ; the latter species, with many subspecies, extends from the Nicobar Islands in the west to central Polynesia in the east, and from the Philippines in the north to the tropical northern coasts of Australia. Included in this range are coral islands with little vegetation, heavily vegetated continental islands, and mainland jungles. The birds are found in all these habitats but rarely extend far inland. *M. pritchardii* and *M. laperouse* have a similar habitat but more restricted ranges, in central Polynesia and the Mariana Islands respectively. *Eulipoa wallacei* and the Maleo *Megacephalon maleo* are found in the Molucca Islands and Celebes respectively. They usually inhabit the inland forests, but they visit the shore during the breeding season.

The Mallee Fowl (or Lowan) *Leipoa ocellata* is unique in inhabiting a semi-arid environment. It is confined to the dry scrubs of inland Australia ; it is characteristic of, but by no means confined to, mallee scrub, which consists of several species of dwarf eucalyptus. The only extension of its range from the inland area occurs in Western Australia, where it is found in a narrow strip of heathland on the south-western coastline.

General Appearance and Habits. Megapodes are ground-living birds. Junglefowl and brush-turkeys are very active, although secretive, birds and seldom fly unless hard pressed. They are quite vocal, particularly in the evenings. According to K. H. Bennett, the Mallee Fowl's 'actions are suggestive of melancholy, for it has none of the liveliness that characterises almost all other birds, but it stalks along in a solemn manner as if the dreary nature of its surroundings and its solitary life weighed heavily on its spirits'. The male possesses a very loud booming call and the female a high-pitched crow.

With the exception of *Megacephalon maleo* and *Eulipoa wallacei*, which are more colourful, junglefowl are dull brownish birds with sombre plumage and small crests. *M. maleo* is distinguished by having a black tail, black wings, and pink under parts, and its head bears a prominent casque. All are about 20 inches in total length.

The brush-turkeys are black, with vertically folded tails, and are longer than junglefowl, being 26–28 inches in total length. Their heads and necks are bare, except for numerous coarse hairs. Similar in size to the brush-turkeys, the Mallee Fowl is coloured brown in keeping with the red-brown soils of its habitat, and each feather of the wing coverts bears a prominent white spot edged with black.

The food of megapodes consists of insects, small animals, seeds, and fruits. The food of the Mallee Fowl is better known than that of other members of the family and consists largely of the seeds of the *Acacia, Cassia,* and *Beyeria,* and the flowers of several ephemeral herbs. The birds are apparently independent of free water, but will drink if water is available.

Nesting Mounds. The simplest type of incubation is found in *Megacephalon, Eulipoa,* and some individuals of *Megapodius freycinet.* The birds simply lay each egg in a pit dug on a beach or in sandy soil exposed to the sun. The hole is filled in, and the eggs are hatched by heat conducted from the soil surface. The site is not visited again, and so no temperature control is exercised. A suitable incubation temperature is apparently achieved by careful selection of the location of each egg-pit. On some islands, notably Savo and Simbo in the Solomons, and near Rabaul in New Britain, the egg-pits are dug into soil through which volcanic steam percolates, the eggs being incubated by that agency. On Dunk Island, off the Queensland coast, some junglefowl lay their eggs in fissures in rocks exposed to the sun, the heat-retaining capacity of the rock

ensuring a relatively constant temperature by day and night.

In other places, particularly in denser jungles, *Megapodius freycinet* constructs large mounds of earth up to 35 feet in diameter and 15 feet high, including a variable amount of vegetable material which, by fermentation, supplements the heat of the sun. The eggs are laid in tunnels up to 3 feet long dug into the mound. The amount of vegetable material in the mound varies according to its location. Some mounds are built of almost pure soil and others of almost pure vegetable material, and all intermediate stages exist. Several pairs of birds probably participate in the construction of these mounds. Apparently the exact composition is determined by the local air temperature and amount of insolation ; heavily shaded mounds require a greater supplement of heat of fermentation than those exposed to direct sunlight.

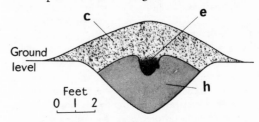

Cross section of mound of the Lowan (or Mallee-fowl)
Leipoa ocellata (Australia).   H. J. Frith.

c covering of loose sandy soil ; **e** egg chamber (filled with mixture of sandy soil and vegetable material) and eggs ; **h** hotbed of fermenting vegetable material

There is no such variation in the nesting mounds of the brush-turkeys, all of which construct mounds composed mainly of plant material ; these are commonly about 12 feet in diameter and 3 feet high. In the warm moist jungles the mound ferments rapidly and generates much heat. The males regularly test the temperature of the mound by probing with their bills ; the temperature-perceiving organ is not known but is possibly the tongue. In the first burst of fermentation the temperature of mounds rises to a high level, and the males exercise some control over it by digging into the top and turning over and mixing the material. Not until the temperature is declining does he permit the female to approach and lay eggs. Throughout the incubation period the male remains in charge of the mound and exercises some control over its temperature. The details of this process are, however, not known.

In its arid inland habitat the Mallee Fowl must adopt more complicated methods to secure a suitable incubation temperature. The air temperature fluctuates widely during the day and the year ; accordingly the soil does not keep a suitable constant temperature. Leaf mould does not form on the ground, litter is sparse, and fallen leaves dry and wither and do not ferment.

In order to overcome these obstacles and to provide the proper constant temperature the birds dig a hole in the ground up to 15 feet in diameter and 3 or 4 feet deep. During the winter they fill the hole with vegetable material swept up from the ground over a radius of some 50 yards, and when it is moistened by a shower of rain the whole is covered by a layer of sandy soil 2 feet thick. Sealed from the dry air, the vegetable material ferments and generates heat, which later in the season is supplemented by solar heat.

The male Mallee Fowl tends the mound throughout the breeding season and regulates its temperature, testing it by probing with the bill, in the same manner as the brush-turkeys. It has been found that in the spring the buried vegetable material ferments very rapidly. At that time of the year most of the heat reaching the eggs, which are placed in a pit in the central part of the mound, comes from fermentation. The amount of heat is so great that the male finds it necessary to cool the eggs, which he does by digging into the top of the mound in the very early morning and allowing some of the heat to escape. In midsummer some heat is still available from the vegetable material and much is also conducted downwards from the sun, and the eggs tend to overheat. The male is able to control this by increasing the thickness of the insulating soil layer and by digging out and occasionally scattering the whole mound in the very early morning, rebuilding it when the soil has cooled in the morning air.

In autumn the eggs might suffer from a lack of heat, the fermentation having finished and the sun's heat declining. In that season, however, the eggs are warmed by scooping the mound out into the form of a saucer during the heat of the day, allowing the sun's rays to penetrate its interior. Throughout the day the male turns the soil over in the sun, warming it, and intermittently returns portions to the mound, until by mid-afternoon the mound is fully restored with heated soil. The combined effect of these operations is that the eggs are maintained at a temperature very close to 92° F throughout the incubation period, which extends from September until March or April (at Griffith, New South Wales). The male is engaged in either building or maintaining the mound for eleven months of the year.

Egg Laying. Details of egg laying have been recorded for only one megapode, the Mallee Fowl. The number of eggs laid varies from 5 to 35.

Variation in clutch size is very great, both between different females in one year and in the same female in different years. The eggs are laid at intervals of several days, the length of the interval being apparently determined by the nutritional state of the female.

In the megapodes each egg begins to incubate as soon as it is laid, and as the eggs are laid throughout a period of several months the first eggs are hatched and the chicks have left the mound long before the last eggs are laid. The chicks on hatching dig their way unaided to the surface of the mound and run into the scrub. They are capable of running very swiftly within a few hours of hatching and can fly within 24 hours. They never see their parents and live completely independent and solitary lives.

See Plates 31 (colour), 33b (phot.). H.J.F.

Frith, H. J. 1956. Breeding habits in the family Megapodiidae. Ibis 98 : 620–640.
Frith, H. J. 1956. Temperature regulation in the nesting mounds of the Mallee Fowl *Leipoa ocellata* Gould. C.S.I.R.O. Wildl. Res. 1 : 79–95.
Frith, H. J. 1959. Breeding of the Mallee Fowl *Leipoa ocellata* Gould. C.S.I.R.O. Wildl. Res. 4 : 31–60.
Frith, H. J. 1962. The Mallee-fowl : the bird that builds an incubator. Sydney.
Oustalet, E. 1880–81. Monographie des oiseaux de la famille Megapodiides. Ann. Sci. Nat. (6) 10 : 1–60 ; 11 : 1–182.
Fleay, D. H. 1937. Nesting habits of the Brush Turkey. Emu 36 : 153–63.

MEGAPODIIDAE: see under GALLIFORMES ; and MEGAPODE

MEIOSIS: division of a germ-cell involving reduction in the number of chromosomes (see CELL ; GENETICS).

MELANIN: see COLOUR

MELANISM: see PLUMAGE, ABNORMAL AND ABERRANT

MELEAGRIDIDAE: see under GALLIFORMES ; and TURKEY

MELIPHAGIDAE: a family of the Passeriformes, suborder Oscines (see HONEYEATER ; SUGAR-BIRD (1)).

MEMBRANE BONE: one that, in the course of development, ossifies directly without going through a cartilaginous stage (see SKELETON).

MEMBRANES, FOETAL: see DEVELOPMENT, EMBRYONIC

MEMBRANES, SHELL: see EGG

MENDELIAN INHERITANCE: see GENETICS

MENTUM: chin (see TOPOGRAPHY).

MENURAE; MENURIDAE: see PASSERIFORMES; and LYREBIRD

MERGANSER: substantive name of *Mergus* spp. (see DUCK).

MERGINI: see DUCK

MERISTIC: statistical term for values that vary in whole units, e.g. number of eggs in clutch; opposed to 'linear', where the variation is continuous (e.g. in wing length) so that in constructing a frequency distribution the values must be arbitrarily grouped (e.g. to the nearest millimetre)—see STATISTICAL SIGNIFICANCE.

MERLIN: *Falco columbarius* (see FALCON).

MEROBLASTIC: the type of embryonic development found in birds (see DEVELOPMENT, EMBRYONIC).

MEROPES; MEROPIDAE: see CORACIIFORMES; and BEE-EATER

MERRYTHOUGHT: the FURCULA; and see SKELETON

MESENTERY: a fold of peritoneum in the abdominal cavity, enclosing part of the intestine together with blood vessels and nerves supplying it (see ALIMENTARY SYSTEM; INTESTINE).

MESETHMOID: bony interorbial septum (see SKELETON).

MESIA: substantive nume of the Silver-eared Mesia *Leiothrix argentauris* (see BABBLER).

MESITE: native name for one species used as an English substantive name for two of the three species of Mesitornithidae (Gruiformes, suborder Mesoenatides or Mesitornithes); in the plural, alternatively 'roatelos', serves as a general term for the family. For scientific nomenclature, and also for orthography of the English name, see under MESITORNITHIDAE.

The group is restricted to the island of Madagascar. The birds are the size of large thrushes *Turdus* spp. (12–13 inches long), with long full tails, short wings, moderate-sized feet, and the bill either short, straight, and fairly slender, or as long as the head and curved. The birds are plainly coloured in soft browns, or brown above and brown and white below. The most striking external feature is the possession of five pairs of powder-down patches.

Birds of ancient and isolated lineage, they recall no other group closely enough to suggest relationships. There is a striking similarity in specimens to ground babblers of the genus *Eupetes*; their gait is pigeon-like, rather than skulking or quick running; they have even been classified with the gallinaceous birds.

However, the sum of their structures seems to indicate that they belong near the rather heterogeneous crane-rail assemblage, the Gruiformes.

Mesite *Mesitornis unicolor. C.E.T.K.*

$\frac{1}{3}$

One species, *Mesitornis* ('Mesoenas') *unicolor*, lives in the rain-forest of eastern Madagascar; one, *Mesitornis variegata*, in the dry forests of the north-west; and one, *Monias benschi*, in the arid brushlands of the south-west part of the island. (For the last, 'Monias' may be used as an English name, in preference to the inappropriate 'Bensch's Rail'.) They live entirely on the ground, where they walk and run with quick, pigeon-like steps, bobbing the head and depressing the tail at each step. Some data indicate that they are flightless despite having well-developed wings. Certainly, when alarmed they run rather than fly, although some authors have said that they 'fly poorly'. When disturbed, *Monias benschi* utters short, slightly explosive calls 'nak—nak . . .' repeated at short intervals. Their diet is a mixed one of insects and seeds picked up from the ground, where they go about in couples or small parties.

The nest is placed in a shrub or small tree a yard or two above the ground and in such a situation that it could be reached without flying. The nest is a flat, thin platform of twigs with a small amount of lining of grass, leaves, and other soft material. Some data indicate that a single egg is the rule, but the clutch size has been given as two or three eggs. The eggs are nearly oval and have a slight gloss, a nearly white ground colour, and small and medium-sized spots of brown which may form a wreath near one end. The young are down-covered at hatching and are nidifugous, accompanying the parent. In *M. benschi* the downy chick is plain brown above and white below, tinged with rufous on throat and breast. The first plumage resembles that of the adult.

The scant data on breeding biology indicate that it may be unusual. In *Mesitornis unicolor* the female has been recorded as incubating. In *Monias benschi* the small bands in which this bird was found at breeding time usually had more males than females ; there is evidence that the male incubates and cares for the young, suggesting that this species may be poly-androus.   A.L.R.

Rand, A. L. 1951. The nest and eggs of *Mesoenas unicolor* of Madagascar. Auk 68 : 23–26. (Habits, bibliography.)

MESITORNITHIDAE : see under GRUIFORMES ; and MESITE. The familial name was until recently 'Mesoenatidae', and earlier, 'Mesitidae' ; this is because the generic name 'Mesites' Geoffroy 1838 was preoccupied in Insecta, and now *Mesitornis* Bonaparte 1855 has been found to have priority over 'Mesoenas' Reichenbach 1862. The subordinal name can be changed at will

As regards orthography of the English term (see preceding entry), the original generic name 'Mesites' is a classical word, although of irrelevant meaning, and some have considered that it should be anglicised in that form, i.e. with the singular written 'mesites' and pronounced in three syllables ; in that event the plural would be 'mesitae', as the English term for the family. On the other hand, 'mesite' is stated to be a native name in Madagascar, and so it is properly anglicised as 'mesite' in the singular and 'mesites' in the plural, both disyllabic. The name has presumably come to English through the French, in which it is at least as old as the original scientific name ; Geoffroy referred to the bird as 'la Mésite variée' in naming it 'Mesites variegata.'

MESOBLAST : the middle layer of the embryo, developing between the epiblast and endoblast that are formed at a very early stage (gastrulation)—see DEVELOPMENT, EMBRYONIC.

MESOENATIDES : alternatively 'Mesoenades' and 'Mesitornithes' (see under GRUIFORMES ; and MESITORNITHIDAE).

MESOGYROUS : see INTESTINE

MESOMYODI : see PASSERIFORMES ; SYRINX

MESOPTILE : term applied to the second of two nestling down plumages, in cases where there is such a sequence, the first then being called 'protoptile' (see PLUMAGE).

METABOLISM : term derived from a Greek word meaning change and covering the many chemical changes that take place in the cells and tissues of the body, but excluding those occurring in the digestive tract (see ALIMENTARY SYSTEM). The word is sometimes loosely used to mean the relation between the intake and excretion of an element together with its movement in the body, as for example in the term 'sodium metabolism'. However, the metabolism of an element (as in the term 'nitrogen metabolism') usually means the chemical changes of its compounds in the body.

The cells and tissues are provided with numerous catalytic agents, particularly enzymes, which accelerate and control the chemical reactions. These are of two kinds ; anabolism means those processes that increase the complexity of the starting material ; katabolism refers to those changes that result in chemical simplification. Katabolic reactions are usually associated with the liberation of part of the energy content of the starting material. Anabolic reactions, on the other hand, are usually attended by uptake of energy, which is obtained by simultaneous reactions of a katabolic nature.

The katabolism of fat and carbohydrate to carbon dioxide and water, together with the breakdown of nitrogeneous compounds, produces the heat that maintains the body temperature above that of the environment (see HEAT REGULATION). This heat production, or the oxygen consumption associated with it, is often called loosely the metabolism or the metabolic rate. The resting metabolic rate at the critical temperature of a bird starved till no further nutrients are absorbed from the digestive tract, is called the basal or post-absorptive metabolism. This is the lowest rate of metabolism normally observed. But in hummingbirds (Trochilidae), when the body temperature falls to a low level at night, or in a 'hibernating' Poor Will it would be much lower, (see under HEAT REGULATION ; TORPIDITY). The basal metabolism is roughly proportional to the surface area of a bird.

The katabolism of nitrogenous compounds in birds is of special interest. The most important end product is uric acid, which is excreted in the urine in place of the urea excreted by mammals. The reason for this difference is supposed to be related to the shortage of water in the egg. Once it is laid, the egg receives no more water and loses part of what it has by evaporation ; it must eke out the initial supply both to form the tissues of the growing embryo and to accommodate the waste products of metabolism. If urea were produced a toxic concentration would accumulate in the tissues or, if the urea were excreted in solution, the embryo would become dehydrated. Uric acid, however, is nearly insoluble, and most of it is deposited as a solid in the allantois, a membranous bag (see EGG). The solid white matter seen in avian excreta is the precipitated uric acid or ammonium urate. Many reptiles also excrete uric acid in place of part or all of the urea.

The growth of a bird is the result of anabolic processes. The amino-acids absorbed into the blood-stream from the digestive tract are joined together to form the proteins of the tissues. Similarly, many other complex compounds are synthesised from simple precursors. The conversion of glucose to glycogen and fat, and the synthesis of egg proteins, are other examples of anabolic processes.

When an atom or molecule has been built into the structure of the body, it does not remain there for the lifetime of the animal. There is an equilibrium within the cell between anabolism and katabolism, so that, although the structure may not change, the materials of which it is made are continuously on the move. This is true even of bone, especially in breed-ing birds ; in the formation of the eggshell calcium is required at a much greater rate than it can be absorbed from the gut and is therefore provided by mobilisation from the bones ; the calcium of the bones is ultimately replenished from the diet.

The source of the energy of muscular contraction is adenosine triphosphate. This compound is also the source of energy for anabolic reactions. One of the phosphate radicals can be transferred to another compound with a considerable amount of energy. For example, the synthesis of glycogen from glucose requires the absorption of energy. To provide this energy, the enzyme hexokinase transfers one phos-phate radical from adenosine triphosphate to glucose to form glucose-6-phosphate ; the remaining stages of the synthesis can then take place without further energy absorption. The energy given by adeno-sine triphosphate is a property of the bond attaching the phosphate radical to the rest of the molecule. After this energy donation, adenosine diphosphate is left ; the triphosphate is regenerated from this by other katabolic reactions.

The metabolic reactions of birds are adapted to the seasonal stresses that they encounter. Thus in tem-perate climates there is considerable deposition of fat in the autumn as a defence against temporary starvation and low temperatures in winter. At the time of migration, there is a considerable mobilisation of fat from the fatty tissues into the blood, presum-ably to make fat readily available for metabolic processes. The energy of the oxidation of this fat will be used ultimately for the regeneration of adenosine triphosphate consumed in the muscular work of flying.   J.C.D.H.

METACARPAL: name of certain bones of the 'hand' (see SKELETON ; WING).

METAPATAGIUM: a membranous fold of skin between the body and the posterior margin of the upper wing (see MUSCULATURE ; WING).

METAPTILE: obsolete term (see PLUMAGE).

METATARSAL: name of bones of the foot, three of them fused together in birds, and at their upper ends with the distal row of tarsals, to form the TARSOMETATARSUS (see also SKELETON ; and LEG).

METEOROLOGY: the study of the atmo-sphere in motion, the physical processes that occur in it, and the effects of both in terms of weather. Whereas climate (see CLIMATOLOGY) influences the distribution of birds and the seasonal cycle of their lives, weather is responsible for day-to-day variations in their environment that affect their behaviour, not least in respect of migration (see MIGRATION). Likewise, the ordinary flying performance of birds is affected by local air movements, such as eddies and thermal up-currents (see FLIGHT).

Air movements and eddies range in scale from a few metres or less to thousands of kilometres. The largest-scale wind circulations and certain well-marked geographical regimes of more local nature are described elsewhere (see CLIMATOLOGY). The semi-permanent climatic features (sometimes called 'centres of action') of the general atmospheric circulation, such as the Iceland depression and the Azores anticyclone, are in reality statistical entities that respectively represent the successions of travel-ling low and high pressure systems largely respon-sible for the day-to-day variations of weather ; the individual travelling 'lows' and 'highs' repeatedly slow up and linger in certain regions such as those mentioned.

Pressure and Wind Systems. 'Depressions' are areas of low atmospheric pressure around which the wind circulates counter-clockwise in the North-ern Hemisphere, clockwise in the Southern. The winds in the free atmosphere blow nearly along the lines of equal pressure ('isobars') but near the surface have a component of motion across the isobars to-wards the low pressure side as a result of surface friction. Most of the change of direction takes place within the bottom 300 to 500 metres (1000-1500 feet) above the ground. Most depressions of middle and high latitudes form in association with the 'polar front', where airstreams of polar and tropical origin meet, or on subsidiary fronts between airmasses of contrasting temperature, moisture, and density. Frontal depressions normally pass through a life cycle of 2 to 3 days, beginning with a slight wave on the

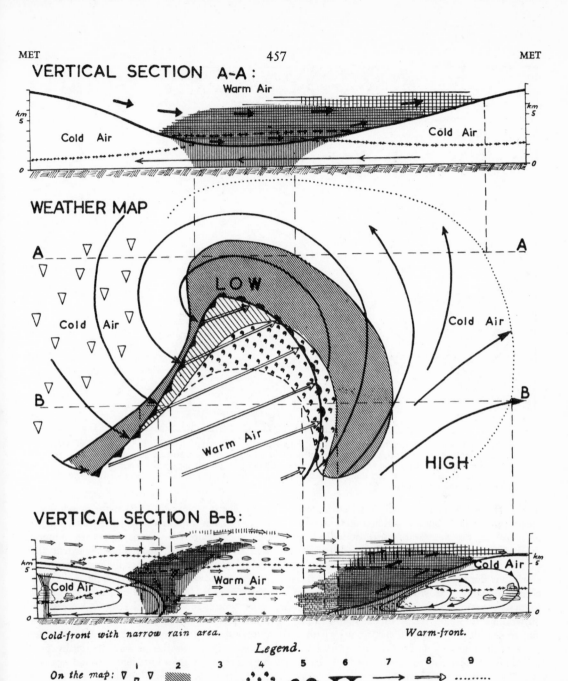

VERTICAL SECTION A-A:

Warm Air

Cold Air   Cold Air

WEATHER MAP

LOW

Cold Air

Cold Air

Warm Air

HIGH

VERTICAL SECTION B-B:

Cold Air   Warm Air   Cold Air

Cold-front with narrow rain area.   *Warm-front.*

Legend.

On the map:

1 Showers   2 Rain area in the cold air   3 Rain area in the warm air   4 Area of drizzle   5 Warm front
6 Cold front   7 Stream-lines of cold air   8 Stream-lines of warm air   9 Fore limit of Cirrostratus cloudsheet
10 Frontal surface   11 Other surface of discontinuity   12 Motion of the cold air relative to the centre
13 Motion of the warm air relative to the centre   14 Falling ice-needles   15 Floating cloud particles   16 Lower
limit of ice nuclei   17 Snowfall or rain   18 Drizzle

FIG 1.   Model of the structure of a depression, showing also cross-sections through the fronts along the lines
A–A and B–B, north and south of the centre (*after Bergeron*).
     For the Southern Hemisphere the weather map should be inverted so that the easterly winds blow on the
south side of the centre and the westerly winds on the north side of the centre.

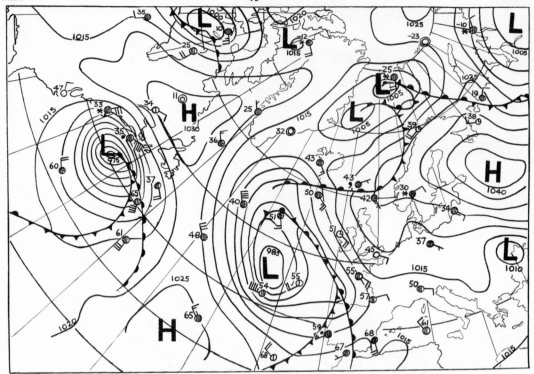

FIG 2. *Situation at* 12h. G.M.T., *2nd April* 1958. This depicts a rather cold, dry easterly wind situation with high pressure over the British Isles extending from an anticyclone over Russia and Scandinavia. There are strong winds around two depressions in rather low latitudes over the Atlantic ; the warm sectors of these 'lows' are seen over Spain and south of the Newfoundland Banks. In the inner Arctic it is still winter and very low temperatures prevail.

front. The wave travels, usually eastwards, along the front, gains in amplitude, and becomes cusped as the narrowing tongue of warm air is 'occluded', i.e. lifted off the surface by the undercutting denser cold air. The kinetic energy of the system increases to a maximum during the occlusion process and then declines. Figure 1 shows a typical frontal (warm sector) depression at a fairly young stage of its growth and illustrates the accompanying weather. The front is described as a 'warm front' where its passage brings the arrival of the warmer airmass, and a 'cold front' where its passage brings in the colder air. The strongest winds and the most extensive rain are commonly just ahead of the warm and cold fronts, but not invariably in these positions. Fully developed depressions in the higher latitudes have dimensions of the order of 2000 km. (1000 to 1500 miles) across. By contrast, the occasional intense 'cyclones' and more sluggish depressions of the tropics and subtropics are seldom more than 500 to 600 km. (300–400 miles) across.

'Anticyclones' are areas of high atmospheric pressure around which the wind circulates clockwise in the Northern, counter-clockwise in the Southern Hemisphere. Near the surface the winds have a component of motion across the isobars away from the high pressure side. Anticyclones are commonly well over 3000 km. (2000 miles) in extent along the major axis (being generally oval shaped and sometimes consisting of several 'cells' joined by a long 'ridge'). A life cycle of 4 to 5 days appears to be typical for individual cells, and occasionally much longer periods pass without any important disturbance in the central part of the high pressure system. Quiet weather prevails, especially in the central region of the anticyclone. Subsidence of the lower atmosphere, general within 5 to 10 km. (3–6 miles) of the surface in anticyclonic conditions, inhibits the vertical growth of cloud and holds dust, smoke, and other impurities low, as a gradually thickening haze—especially in the bottom 1000 to 3000 feet (1 km.). Cloudless skies are common, especially in summer and in the lower latitudes. But in winter, especially in regions with considerable humidity sources, surface cooling is liable to produce extensive fog or overcast skies (characteristic stratus or stratocumulus cloud from 1000 feet, or less, to 3000 feet above ground level) ; the weak surface

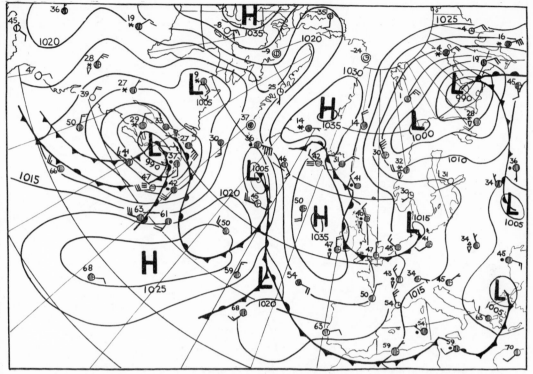

FIG 3. *Situation at 12h. G.M.T., 8th April 1958.* Northerly weather type over the British Isles and western Europe, bringing 'April showers' in the cold airstream which is rendered thermally unstable by rapid heating from below as it comes to lower and lower latitudes. On the Riviera the mistral is blowing (though not specially strong). There is fog in the warm airstreams south of Newfoundland and approaching southwest Iceland. A strong gale (Beaufort Force 9) is reported between south Greenland and the depression over the Atlantic : this is in the cold Arctic airstream constrained to pass between the Greenland mountains and the occluded front of the depression.

winds and gathering haze beneath the cloud-sheet lead to conditions of reduced light and persistent gloom, whereas on high mountains rising above the fog and cloud brilliantly clear sunny weather and relatively high temperatures prevail. The regions of rather less high pressure between the anticyclone cells are areas of relative weakness in a high pressure regime. Being, as it were, saddle points in the pattern of pressure levels defined by the isobars, these regions are known by the mountaineering term 'col' (German 'Sattel'). They are liable to sluggish disturbances and, in summer, are frequently places where thunderstorms develop.

When and where the large-scale atmospheric circulation is weak, local effects of the topography upon the wind flow are most clearly seen. In some topographical channels quite gentle winds may be 'funnelled' into winds of some strength, and moderate winds may be increased to produce a local gale. (When the general circulation produces a widespread gale from the same quarter, violent winds are liable to occur in such topographical channels.)

Diurnal land and sea breezes and katabatic (downslope) and anabatic (upslope) winds are regular features, respectively, of coastal climates (including, on a smaller scale, those of lake shores) and of the local climates of valley and mountain (see CLIMATOLOGY). Zones up to 15 or 20 miles (30 km.) from the coast or mountain foot are commonly affected, depending upon the strength of the circulation developed.

Frictionally produced eddies may extend up to several times the height of the mountain, cliff, or other object producing them and travel many times this distance to leeward, causing winds to be turbulent and gusty. The duration of the gusts depends upon the size of the eddies, but periods of ten seconds to a minute are characteristic. The ascent of air blowing up a windward cliff affords conditions for soaring flight. Downward eddies over leeward cliffs may be equally abrupt. Here and there a rugged terrain may give rise to local back eddies (air drifting back towards the hill) in the lower levels on the lee side. Mountains also produce trains of

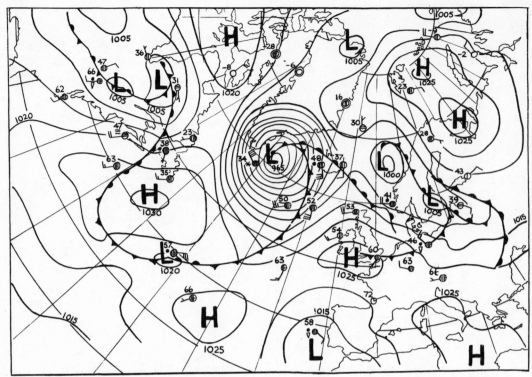

FIG 4. *Situation at 12h. G.M.T., 21st April 1958.* This illustrates the type of anti-cyclonic situation over the British Isles which gives genial warm, spring sunshine. There is also a warm southwesterly airstream over the eastern seaboard of North America, though with some fog over the cold water. Temperatures are still very low over the Arctic, though a rapid rise normally occurs in the twenty-four hour daylight during May (in the next four to five weeks after the date of this map).

waves down-wind (i.e. to leeward), sometimes marked by lens-shaped clouds in the crests of the waves ; these waves also cause a pattern of up-draughts and down-draughts and variations of horizontal wind speed.

Vertical convection is set up by strong surface heating of the air—for instance in hot weather and in outbreaks of polar air advancing rapidly over warm oceans. The thermal up-currents also afford conditions for soaring.

See also CLIMATOLOGY, for ' prevailing winds '.

Wind Force. The strength of the wind increases with the pressure gradient (cf. wind strengths and isobar spacing on the sample weather maps, Figs. 2–6). This is best seen over the sea and open flat country. The wind speed normally increases with height above the ground (as the effect of friction disappears). Wind force is commonly given on the scale originally defined by Admiral Beaufort in terms of the effect of the wind upon a man-of-war of the period 1800–50. Specifications suitable for use on land have also been defined (see *Meteorological Glossary*), and the scale is internationally recognised.

Approximate speed equivalents at a height of 10 metres (33 feet) above open ground are given in the Table below :

' Beaufort Force '	Speeds in knots
0	Less than 1
1	1– 3
2	4– 6
3	7–10
4	11–15
5	16–21
6	22–27
7	28–33
8	34–40
9	41–47
10	48–55
11	56–63
12	64 and over

A gale is defined as a wind of Beaufort force 8 or over. (A knot is a speed of one nautical mile (6080 feet) per hour.)

Local Winds. In addition to the land and sea breezes occurring on most coasts and the equally general mountain and valley winds (anabatic and katabatic), many local winds with special character-istics and special names are known to meteorology.

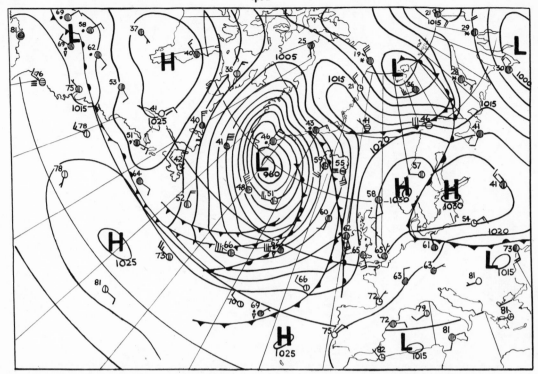

FIG 5. *Situation at 12h.* G.M.T., *17th September* 1958. This shows a vigorous, warm southerly windstream over the eastern North Atlantic, including western parts of the British Isles, and an anticyclone giving late summer weather over most of Europe and neighbouring parts of the Atlantic. The very deep depression south of Greenland bears witness to the autumn intensification of the atmospheric circulation over the Atlantic (the increased energy being derived from the seasonal increase of temperature gradients which are much weaker in summer than at other times). Temperatures in the Arctic are still much higher than in April, but cold air is able to spread south over Canada and northern Asia.

Of these the most important is the Alpine föhn wind, because it has given its name to a process of universal occurrence. This is the name given in the Alps to a warm wind descending the northern valleys from the south, its high temperature being partly attributable to latent heat of condensation liberated during ascent on the windward side of the mountains ('föhn effect'). This is a leeside wind characterised by dryness, warmth, turbulent descent, bright skies, and 'lenticular' (lens-shaped) cloud forms. The name is applied in meteorology to similar conditions in the lee of any mountain range, e.g. the 'Chinook' winds crossing the Rocky Mountains in Alberta and the prevailing south-west winds in Aberdeenshire and Moray in Scotland.

Examples of other well known local winds are :

Mistral. The lower Rhône Valley acts as a funnel to northerly winds that acquire great strength in being constricted into the narrow channel between the Alps and the Massif Central. The strength of the (cold) wind persists over the French Riviera and far out to sea over the Mediterranean.

Bora. The cold, squally, katabatic easterly winds that descend from the mountains of Yugoslavia to the Adriatic, especially when the pressure distribution favours easterly winds. In many respects similar to the mistral.

Scirocco. The warm, relaxing south wind of the Mediterranean (especially central Mediterranean). Very hot, dust-laden, and dry when it leaves the coast of Africa, it quickly picks up moisture over the sea and arrives in Malta and Italy as a warm, excessively humid breeze. Sea fog and low cloud, especially on windward coasts, are characteristic.

Khamsin. The name given to the hot southerly winds that blow in North Africa, the Red Sea area, Arabia, and nearer parts of Asia before depressions advancing from the west and south-west, most commonly in spring and early summer. In Libya the same wind is called 'Ghibli'. The highest temperatures ever recorded occur in this wind, which also produces blowing dust when the wind is strong. The dust and the highest temperatures, as well as the strongest winds from the desert interior, are liable

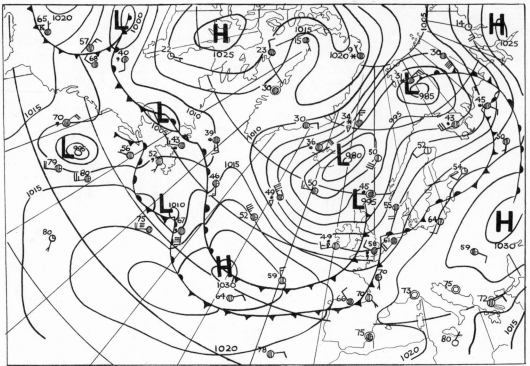

FIG 6. *Situation at 12h.* G.M.T., *10th October* 1958. This illustrates a typically unsettled 'westerly situation' over Britain and the Atlantic, such as frequently occurs at all times of the year. There are several depressions all travelling east or east-north-east and successive warm and cold airmasses pass east with them across the temperate zone of America, the Atlantic and Europe. Wind strength and direction vary greatly as the sequence passes across any given place. A feature which is by no means unusual in late summer and early autumn is the tropical cyclone seen between Bermuda and the coast of America, moving north into the belt of westerlies where such storms draw in the fronts near their path and then travel swiftly northeast and deepen as normal, but often particularly intense, depressions of the subpolar zone. Temperatures in the Arctic have fallen notably since the September situation depicted in Figure 5, but in the subtropical zone (e.g. Bermuda, Mediterranean) summer temperatures still prevail.

to be experienced over a belt just a hundred miles or so in width immediately ahead of the cold front advancing from the west.

Harmattan. The dust-laden, dry, east or north-east wind of West Africa. Commonest, and penetrating farthest south, during the northern winter. Both the Scirocco and the Harmattan sometimes transport and deposit Saharan dust over distances of a thousand miles and more from the desert.

Thermal Effects and Convection Phenomena. The lower atmosphere receives almost all its heat from the Earth's surface and suffers a net loss of heat at higher levels, particularly by radiation to space from cloud tops. Hence there is generally a fall of temperature with height, the average 'lapse rate' being about 3° F/1000 feet (0·6° C/100 m.). Over strongly heated dry ground, lapse rates up to double these figures may be observed. However, under clear skies at night the ground cools rapidly by radiation to space, especially where the surface is

covered with snow or ice. At such times the air is chilled from below and an 'inversion of temperature' may occur, the temperatures being higher aloft (and up the hillsides) than near the (lowest) ground.

The prevailing lapse of temperature with height determines the 'thermal stability' or 'thermal instability' of the air, conditions which respectively lessen or accelerate vertical motions. Elements of locally over-heated and uplifted air undergo expansion, and as they rise their temperature drops at a fixed rate. This temperature drop during 'adiabatic expansion' is familiar as the principle of the refrigerator. The temperature of rising air falls about 5·4° F per 1000 feet (1° C/100 m.), known as the 'adiabatic lapse rate', or 2·6° F per 1000 feet (0·5° C/100 m.) if cloud forms. Thus the bigger the lapse rate in the surrounding air, the more the rising air is liable to become warmer (and less dense) than its environment at each level ; this liability is greatly increased when condensation occurs. The result is acceleration of vertical currents. By contrast, vertical motion is discouraged by small or inverted lapse rates. Inversions are particularly characterised by smooth, horizontal flow of the air, which may be completely halted or turned aside by topographical and smaller barriers ; any clouds present are correspondingly smooth in texture and liable to form a uniform overcast.

Strongly heated air is unstable for vertical motion, turbulent in its flow (gusts and squalls), and much more readily surmounts barriers. Heat is transported upwards throughout the airmass in a pattern of convection cells, each usually marked by vertical growth of clouds (cumulus or cumulonimbus) separated by clear spaces where the compensating down-currents of air are found. Such convection cells are commonly 5 to 25 miles (say 10–50 km.) across, depending on the vertical scale of development, and are fed by converging surface winds. The variations of surface wind as a succession of convection cells passes over a given spot appear as squalls and lulls, each lasting from several minutes to half an hour or more, depending upon the scale of development and rate of travel. The associated convection clouds range from the small, harmless cumulus of fair weather to scattered shower or thunderstorm clouds (cumulonimbus). The vertical and horizontal scales of development increase together. Squalls of 50 knots or more may be experienced beneath thunder clouds, and in extreme cases the vertical current is fed by a swiftly rotating system of convergent surface winds ('tornado', 'waterspout') capable of destroying buildings and lifting heavy objects. Such revolving storms have a diameter of only a few metres to a hundred metres or so. Their incidence shows geographical concentrations, especially in the American Middle West and in parts of Europe near great rivers and in flat or undulating country. They occur chiefly at times of the year and times of the day when there is most liability for a cold air supply to become moist and strongly heated.

Diurnal changes of temperature over land and the associated vertical movements of air generally tend to produce the strongest (and gustiest) surface winds in the afternoon, dropping about nightfall.

Atmospheric Moisture and Precipitation. The air's capacity to hold moisture in vapour form depends upon its temperature, the amount required to saturate it being about six times as great at tropical temperatures (30° C, 86° F) as at the freezing point. 'Relative humidity' is the ratio, expressed as a percentage, of the water vapour actually present in a given volume of air to that required to saturate it. Any particular moisture content determines the temperature, called the 'dew point', at which the air would become saturated on cooling and condensation would begin.

Evaporation occurs wherever unsaturated air passes over water, ice, snow, wet ground, or vegetation. Condensation occurs wherever air is chilled below its dew point. Fog is formed in this way over cold surfaces and cloud occurs similarly in rising air.

The three principal forms of cloud—sheet clouds (stratiform), ripple clouds (stratocumulus, altocumulus), and heap clouds (cumuliform)—correspond to the three principal types of vertical motion producing the necessary adiabatic cooling—respectively, gliding of one air layer over another (either smoothly or with small-scale turbulence), turbulent wave motion, and nearly vertical up-currents in convection cells. Additionally, clouds consisting of ice crystals may be readily distinguished by their fibrous texture (cirrus, also cirro-stratus, cirrocumulus, and cumulonimbus anvils). More details of cloud types are given, with illustrations, in *Cloud Forms* (see also Ludlam and Scorer).

Condensation occurs initially on minute hygroscopic nuclei such as sea-salt particles, of diameter 0·001 to 0·002 millimetres, suspended in the air. Actual cloud droplets are commonly about 0·04 millimetres in diameter. Drizzle occurs when the drops reach sizes approaching 0·5 mm. Growth into raindrops of sizes up to 5·5 mm. diameter depends upon the presence of ice crystals (on which supercooled water sublimes) or suitable electrical charges on the drops. In temperate and higher latitudes most rain is believed to originate as snow in clouds where ice crystals are present and sublimation is at work at temperatures below the freezing point. Once temperatures underneath the cloud fall to near the freezing point, snow may reach the ground without melting. (Snow-cover over continental terrains more than 1000 to 2000 miles (say 3000 km.) in longitudinal extent affects the large-scale atmospheric circulation in such a way as to tend to maintain the cold regime by steering depressions with their warm sectors along tracks near the periphery of the snow-covered land.) Sleet is a mixture of rain and snow produced by partial melting of snow before reaching the surface. Hail is formed by rain drops being carried up above the freezing level in vigorous vertical convection currents where they collide with ice particles in the cloud and freeze to form concentric shells of ice encasing the original ice crystals. The largest raindrops (up to 5·5 mm.) and hailstones (which may attain diameters of several centimetres) occur where vertical currents are strong enough to delay their fall during the final stages of growth ; their occurence is indicative of violent up-currents of the order of 5 to 8 m./second (1000 to 1500 feet/minute) such as occur in thunderclouds.

Condensation also takes place in the form of dew on cold surfaces, particularly at the sharp edges and tips of blades of grass, leaves, and the like. Some of the moisture is exuded by the vegetation itself. At temperatures below the freezing point hoar frost is similarly formed. 'Rime' is the name given to the thicker deposits of ice crystals growing out to windward on exposed objects over which fogs and clouds of supercooled droplets pass at temperatures below the freezing point. Deposition by a persistent cloud drift lasting several days may produce heavy deposits which are liable to break under their own weight.

Visibility. The transparency of pure, dry air is seen in the Arctic and Antarctic, where visibility sometimes exceeds 200 miles (over 300 km.) in fine weather (although optical distortions—mirages and related phenomena—are common and may make landscape recognition difficult). Condensation of atmospheric moisture and suspended solid impurities (sea-salt, fine desert sand, smoke, and ash) in the air reduces visibility. 'Mist' is defined as visibility 1–2 km. due to suspended (minute) water droplets ; 'haze' is spoken of with a similar range produced by suspended solid particles. 'Fog' is defined by the meteorologist as visibility less than 1 km. due to condensed moisture, smoke, or solid particles. Laymen, except those concerned with aviation, seldom speak of fog until visibility falls to about 200 metres (technically 'Thick Fog') or less. Visibility may be reduced to less than 1 km. also in severe 'blizzards' (drifting snow raised by a wind), in sandstorms, and in falling snow (particularly when the flakes are large).

The Freezing over of Water Bodies. The temperature of water surfaces falls more slowly than that of neighbouring dry land under conditions of cooling by radiation or wind. This is partly because of vertical circulations developed within the water and partly because of its large specific heat. Moreover, the freezing point of salt ocean water is about $-2°$ C ($28·6°$ F).

Salt water is denser than fresh water, other things being equal. The density of water changes with its temperature, fresh water having maximum density about $+4°$ C ($39°$ F) and sea water about its freezing point. As long as the surface temperature is higher than that corresponding to greatest density, cooling of the surface causes the water to sink and be replaced from underneath by less cold water until the entire depth reaches its maximum density. From then on, or in circumstances where fresh water overlies saline, cooling leaves the coldest water on top and the temperature of the surface can fall much more rapidly.

Evaporation assists cooling owing to the latent heat abstracted. But strong winds cause stirring of the surface layers by waves, and the formation of ice may thus be delayed ; in these circumstances the first ice appears as 'pancakes' or 'sludge' globules of rapidly increasing thickness, instead of the thin sheets of ice which quickly cover the whole surface of still water. In all cases shallow water is likely to freeze over sooner than deep, and fresh water before salt water.

Sample Weather Maps. Since lateral wind drift, particularly at night or under overcast skies, affects bird migration, and as most meteorological services publish 'daily weather reports' containing weather maps (in some cases covering most of the Northern Hemisphere), it is desirable for ornithologists to be able to read such maps. A few sample situations, chosen from the transition seasons when there is most migration, are illustrated here (Figs. 2–6). For fuller instruction and explanation of symbols the reader is recommended to consult *Weather Map.*

Units used on Figures 2–6 are as follows :

Pressure. Millibars. 'Isobars' (lines of equal pressure) spaced at 5 mb. intervals. 1000 mb.$= 750·1$ mm. or $29·53$ in. mercury.

Temperature. Degrees Fahrenheit. The simpler Centigrade scale is used on the Daily Weather Reports published by the Meteorological Office since January 1962 and on the corresponding publications of most other meteorological services. The following scale of equivalents may be found useful :

$+40°$ C	$= 104°$ F	$-10°$ C	$= +14°$ F
$+30°$ C	$= 86°$ F	$-20°$ C	$= -4°$ F
$+20°$ C	$= 68°$ F	$-30°$ C	$= -22°$ F
$+10°$ C	$= 50°$ F	$-40°$ C	$= -40°$ F
$0°$ C	$= 32°$ F (freezing point)		

Wind. Beaufort force. Each whole fleck on the tail of the plotted wind arrows corresponds to two units of Beaufort force.

Cloud cover. Each whole stroke inside the position circles plotted corresponds to approximately two-eighths of the sky covered with cloud.

Weather symbols illustrated have the following meanings :

• Rain	Rain shower	☰ Fog
Drizzle	Snow shower	
✳ Snow	Hail shower	

Warm front   Cold front   Occlusion

The charts depict types of weather situation and circulation pattern which are specially common in spring and autumn. In reading the temperatures on Figures 2–6 it is to be noted that the time of the chart is noon on the Greenwich meridian, local 6 a.m. in 90° W. and 6 p.m. in 90° E. Although the winds and temperatures are mostly typical of the airstreams in which the observations were made, some effects of local shelter and maritime or continental influence may be discerned.   H.H.L.

Ludlam, F. H. & Scorer, R. S. 1957. Cloud Study, a pictorial guide. London.
Meteorological Office 1939. The Meteorological Glossary. 3rd ed. London (H.M.S.O.—M.O. 225).
Meteorological Office 1956. Weather Map. 4th ed. London (H.M.S.O.—M.O. 595).
Meteorological Office 1949. Cloud Forms. 6th ed. London (H.M.S.O.—M.O. 233).

MEW: archaic or poetic name, also ' sea-mew ', for a gull (Larinae sp.), cf. German ' Möwe ' ; also, in American usage, adjectival name of *Larus canus* (see GULL).

MEWS: term used in FALCONRY

MICROPODIFORMES: see APODIFORMES

MICROPSITTINAE: see PARROT

MICROSMATIC: with poorly developed olfactory sense (see SMELL).

MIGRATION: regular movement of birds between alternate areas inhabited by them at different times of year, one area being that in which the birds breed and the other being an area better suited to support them at the opposite season ; the term is also used for any movement or series of movements forming part of the general phenomenon, e.g. at a particular time or place, or of a given species or an individual bird. The range in the breeding season may sometimes be more extensive than the actual breeding area, owing to wider distribution of non-breeding individuals. The birds do not normally breed in the second area, although in some instances other members of the same species may do so. Migration can be regarded as an alternative to the adaptation to the conditions of the breeding area throughout the year shown by sedentary species (see ECOLOGY). From the distributional point of view, a migratory species may be said to have a gross range within which there are seasonal ranges (see DISTRIBUTION, GEOGRAPHICAL).

Sources of Information. The broad fact of bird migration has been known from ancient times ; yet the phenomena have, for the most part, been so difficult to observe that other explanations of the seasonal disappearances and reappearances of familiar species have often been accepted (see HIBERNATION). Modern knowledge, although still far from complete, rests securely on information from the following main sources.

1. The now extensive data on the distribution of particular species, and even subspecific forms, at different times of year—with records, abundant for some countries, of the dates of arrival in, or departure from, seasonally occupied areas.

2. Direct observation of ' visible migration ' by day, or of resting birds temporarily present in unusual numbers, especially at favourable localities such as headlands and small islands (see OBSERVATORY).

3. Nocturnal observation of birds attracted to lighthouses and lightships, or heard calling overhead, or seen by telescope while crossing the face of the moon, this last method having been notably developed in North America in recent years (see MOON WATCHING).

4. Observation of migrants in flight (by day or by night) by means of radar, a very recent development (see RADAR).

5. The results of marking individual birds, usually with numbered metal rings on the legs (see RINGING).

6. Experiments on birds under controlled conditions, chiefly in studies of pre-migratory restlessness and of orientation (see NAVIGATION).

Nature and Extent. Very many species of birds, widely representative of orders and families, are migratory in some degree ; and although migration reaches its greatest development among birds breeding in the higher latitudes, migratory species include not a few that are wholly confined to the tropics. Other species—also widely representative—are sedentary, including some that are found in high latitudes. Among the migratory species there are great differences in the extent of the movements performed and in the degree to which these are definite and regular. In some instances there are marked differences between populations of a single species, or even between individuals or age-groups within a single population.

Local Movements. There is every gradation between migrations involving only short journeys and those involving journeys of great length. In some instances the movement may be merely from an inland breeding area to winter feeding grounds near the coast. Again, there are migrations that show a more obvious directional trend but are limited to journeys of a few hundreds of miles and involve no extensive sea-crossing. Such short movements may be termed ' local ', without implying any qualitative peculiarity.

Vertical Displacement. A special case of local movement is that in which the displacement is principally a matter of altitude. There are many instances of birds breeding on high mountain slopes and descending to the valleys or foothills for the winter. The reverse happens in the area of the Dead

Sea, where some birds breeding in the hot valley about 1000 feet *below* sea level seek a colder climate in the adjacent hill country for the winter. On some steep islands Wallace's Megapode *Eulipoa wallacei* is usually found only above about 2500 feet (although on others at sea level), but the females descend to lay and leave their eggs on the shore, whence the young ascend when able to do so (Ripley).

Distance Migration. Although the difference is in degree rather than in kind, migration is more clearly recognisable when it involves journeys of many hundreds or some thousands of miles. Thus, there is much migration from breeding areas in high latitudes to winter quarters in much lower latitudes —say, from northern Europe to the Mediterranean basin or even to the tropics. Or the movement may be extensive while involving little or no change in latitude—say, from the interior of the European continent westwards to the Atlantic seaboard. In this last case, and also where migration is only from a high to a rather less high latitude, one is dealing with the 'hardy migrants' able to tolerate a winter of moderate severity. In the British Isles, for example, such birds appear as 'winter visitors' from farther north or farther east—but this and analogous terms represent only the geographical viewpoint of the observer.

Transequatorial Migration. In its extreme development, migration does much more than bring the birds to a lower latitude in the same hemisphere for a milder winter; it brings them across the Equator to temperate latitudes in the other hemisphere, where they 'winter' in the local summer while the native birds are breeding. Thus, many species breeding in Europe spend their off-season in the summer of South Africa; and the same holds good of North America and southern South America on the one hand, and of northern Asia and Australasia on the other. Journeys of several thousands of miles are involved; the Arctic Tern *Sterna paradisaea*, which breeds up to 82° N. lat. in the Arctic and reaches 74° S. lat. in Antarctic seas in its off season, presents a unique latitudinal range of about 11 000 miles, and some individual journeys that cannot be less (and will often be more) than 8000 miles in each direction. The phenomenon of transequatorial migration seems to import an additional quality, in that the birds are for part of the year exposed to the seasonal influences of a differently phased climatic cycle.

Although many birds native to the Southern Hemisphere migrate northwards as far as the tropics, there is no instance of a southern species of land bird migrating to the North Temperate Zone. That the transequatorial migration of some northern land birds has no full counterpart is doubtless related to the distribution of the landmasses; there are in the Southern Hemisphere no important areas of land, other than Antarctica, lying in latitudes equivalent to those to which the really long-distance northern migrants are mainly native. It is only among sea birds, notably petrels (Procellariiformes), that there are species native to the Southern Hemisphere that 'winter' in the northern temperate summer.

Some migrations are not only transequatorial but also transoceanic, as witness the numerous records from the Atlantic coast of southern South America of Manx Shearwaters *Puffinus puffinus* ringed at their breeding places in the British Isles (with one exceptional record from South Australia).

Dispersal. Not in conformity with the strict definition of migration are certain annual movements that are more in the nature of dispersals. The characteristic of a dispersal is that the statistical focal point of the population remains relatively constant, the numbers of dispersed individuals tending to diminish with distance outwards; and there may be no directional bias apart from any limitations imposed by topography. When dispersal tends to be more in one direction than in others, and especially if the centre of gravity of the population shows a shift in that direction, one may suspect the existence of some degree of true migration on the part of at least a proportion of the birds. See also DISPERSAL.

Oceanic Nomadism. Certain species, particularly of sea birds, appear to be nomadic throughout the part of the year when they are not breeding; but the wanderings are not necessarily random, and there may be a substantial shift in the centre of gravity of the population from its breeding area, the latter being often completely deserted. Some such movements follow a seasonal pattern; and others may perhaps be classed as true migration by modifying the concept of an alternative area to denote merely the limits of nomadism. These limits may be wide; ringing records have shewn that various species of sea birds commonly cross the North Atlantic, and many of the Procellariiformes breeding in the Southern Hemisphere regularly visit northern seas (see OCEANIC BIRDS; also ANTARCTIC).

Partial Migrants. This term is applied to species of which, in a given breeding area, some individuals are migratory while others are not. The Song Thrush *Turdus philomelos* and the Lapwing *Vanellus vanellus* are examples, in respect of their British native populations. To what extent the behaviour of individuals of like age is constant from year to year cannot readily be ascertained; but it is known for several species that the tendency to migrate is shown by a greater proportion of young birds in their first year than by older members of the same population—the Gannet *Sula bassana* in the British Isles is a case in point, and likewise the Australasian Gannet *S. serrator* in New Zealand (Wodzicki & Stein). The theoretical implications of this variability in the exhibition of innate behaviour are important.

Pre-migratory Movements. Many migrants, especially the young of the year, show a tendency to dispersal or nomadism in the period between the end of the breeding season and departure on migration proper ; the journeys are sometimes of substantial length, and if there is a bias in favour of a particular direction the latter may be different from —even opposite to—that ultimately to be taken. In the case of long-distance migrants, these movements are clearly separable from true migration (for terminology see ZWISCHENZUG).

Weather Movements. Under stress of unusually severe weather during the winter in the North Temperate Zone there may be further movements on the part of hardy migrants. These movements differ from true migration in showing no regularity from year to year either in their extent or in the dates of their occurrence. They are, in fact, much more closely linked with current meteorological events than is migration proper.

Reversed Migration. This term is applied to weather movements that in some years supervene after the inception of the normal spring return of hardy migrants towards their breeding area. On a local scale, reverse movements may occur at any time when adverse conditions are encountered during a stage of migration or possibly when there is a waning of the migratory urge late in the day.

Irruptions. These, also called ' eruptions ' (according to the observer's viewpoint), are irregular movements occurring only in certain years, whereas in other years they are either absent or much less pronounced (see IRRUPTION).

Seasons. In temperate or still higher latitudes the breeding season is of course in summer, with very few exceptions ; and winter is the season that is avoided by migration—in favour of a milder winter, often in a tropical environment, or of the summer of the opposite hemisphere. Spring and autumn, as known outside the tropics, are thus the seasons of migration. There are, however, wide differences between species as regards actual dates ; some are early and some are late—and, as a general rule, those that are early in spring tend to be late in autumn. There are also considerable variations between the populations of a species native to different parts of its total range. Even for a single population, immigration or emigration is spread over a period, apart from the time spent on the journey.

Tropical Seasons. Among migratory species living entirely within the tropics, the contrast is usually between a rainy season and a dry season of the year. For the majority, the breeding area is suitable during the rains, but some species breed in the dry season (see BREEDING SEASON). Similarly, the alternative habitat tends to be one that is favourable to the feeding habits of the species during the other part of the year.

The complexity of some of the movements taking place entirely within the tropics is exemplified by the migrations of various African species of Caprimulgidae (Chapin). The Plain Nightjar *Caprimulgus inornatus* and the Standard-winged Nightjar *Macrodipterix longipennis* both inhabit the area between the Sahara desert and the Congo forest, and are both found in the northern part of this in the rainy season and in the southern part from December to June, but the latter species breeding in the southern and the former in the northern. In the same region, between March and August the Pennant-winged Nightjar *Semeiophorus vexillarius* is found as a visitor from its breeding area south of the forest belt ; and the European Nightjar *Semeiophorus europaeus* also traverses the area on its transequatorial journeys— nor do these exhaust the list of members of this group known as migrants in that part of Africa. Another interesting case is that of the nominate race of the Broad-billed Roller *Eurystomus glaucurus*, which breeds only in Madagascar but migrates north-westwards into East Africa, so that some visit the Congo between June and November.

Dates. For any species or population of a species the dates of migration are, as a rule, remarkably constant. It is only within narrow limits, apart from weather movements of hardy migrants, that the dates vary in accord with the meteorological characteristics of particular years.

Weather Influences. Migration is obviously related to climate, in that it is a form of behaviour adapted to seasonal changes in the environment (see CLIMATOLOGY). The relation to weather, the meteorological events of the particular year (see METEOROLOGY), is, within narrow limits of time, more direct. Weather influences are of two kinds—those that affect the inception of a movement or of a stage of one, and those that affect migrants during flight.

Effect on Inception. Good weather, such as occurs during anticyclonic conditions, is in general conducive to the inception of a migratory movement that birds are in a state of readiness to make ; a relatively low (or perhaps falling) temperature in autumn and a relatively high (or perhaps rising) temperature in spring also appear to be influential. There is no evidence that high barometric pressure is more than a concomitant, or that the direction of the winds associated with the anticyclone is important. Settled weather and clear skies may be of more significance, the general result being that the flight has a good chance of being accomplished under favourable conditions—although on occasion a quite different weather situation may be encountered before completion, possibly with unfortunate results. Bad weather, on the other hand, is a deterrent to the inception of a movement. The greatest manifestations of migratory activity—so-called ' rushes '— often occur when movement has been held up for a period and favourable weather then suddenly supervenes. It is of course the weather situation at the starting point that is effective as regards inception.

Effect on Performance. Storms encountered during flight, especially in the case of sea-crossings, can be disastrous. Very strong head-winds hamper progress, sometimes to an equally serious extent. Dense fog tends to bring movements to a standstill. When birds are flying without landmarks, particularly at night, the effect of a side-wind is to cause lateral drift ; this can have an important effect on the direction actually attained, with the result that the pattern of the movement may be greatly changed (see below). Drift taking migrants far out to sea may end either in disaster to the birds or in their arrival at abnormal destinations.

Directions. Migration in its more extensive forms involves essentially a change in latitude ; the general trend is therefore north and south. As already mentioned, however, this is in many instances modified by circumstances of geography and climate ; much migration thus takes place in directions diagonal to the north and south line, and some of it even on an east to west line or even with a slight element contrary to the general trend. This statement applies to the journeys performed ; the direction of flight during parts of these journeys shows still greater differences. Moreover, the general directions of the movements may differ between one species and another or even between populations of a single species. From these various causes, simultaneous movements—sometimes even of the same species—may locally follow different and sometimes opposite directions.

Routes. At one time, students of migration were much influenced by the idea that birds followed certain definite routes, corresponding with important topographical features such as coastlines and great rivers. It was supposed that an inherited knowledge of these routes must form part of the migration instinct, and theoretical fancy sought to attribute the use of certain sea-crossings to the existence of land-bridges in earlier geological times.

Apparent exceptions to this type of behaviour were explained by assuming that there were two types of migration—one taking place on a broad front across land or sea, and the other on a narrow front along definite routes. Now one thinks in terms of a single type of migration, in which individual lines of flight may or may not become concentrated along topographical features according to whether such features lie suitably to the general trend of the movement. Nevertheless, different methods of orientation do seem to be involved.

Standard Direction. There is indeed good reason for believing that migrants possess an innate capacity to head constantly in a particular compass direction without the aid of landmarks. This direction, for any species or population of a species, is usually known as its ' standard direction ' (equivalent to Geyr von Schweppenburg's original term ' Normalrichtung ', which he subsequently replaced by ' Primärrichtung ' ; the term ' preferred direction ' has also been used). There is some evidence that, even for the individual bird, the standard direction may be different in successive stages of a journey.

Leading Lines. Nevertheless, there is no doubt that certain topographical features are commonly followed by day during parts of migratory journeys, and often so closely that orientation is patently visual. Such features are known as ' leading lines ' (the ' Leitlinie ' of Geyr von Schweppenburg, less appropriately translated as ' guiding lines ' or ' diversion lines '). It seems that they have a strong attraction for many migrants and tend to divert them from their standard direction. This is notably true of coasts ; an inhibition against venturing over open water may play a part in the case of some land birds, but the diversionary effect has also been noted when a coastline is approached from the sea. When a leading line diverges too far from the standard direction (sometimes producing local ' retromigration '), it tends to be abandoned, the preference for the standard direction then apparently overcoming the attraction of the leading line. It is probable that flight with the aid of landmarks has a safety advantage, outweighing the disadvantage of a moderate but not excessive diversion from the essential direction of the whole journey. The question of orientation without landmarks is discussed elsewhere (see NAVIGATION).

Drift. Migrants following leading lines or having other landmarks available can correct their flight for the effect of wind (' goal-orientation '). On the other hand, birds flying without such visual help (' onedirectional migration ')—at night, above cloud, or over the sea—are subject to lateral drift under the influence of wind, as already mentioned. The evidence is that the 'track' actually achieved in relation to the earth's surface is the resultant of the bird's heading (in its presumed standard direction) and the effect of the wind upon its body ; but sometimes the birds seem to become disorientated. Notable variations in migratory movements occur because of drift, and these have been particularly studied in the North Sea area (Williamson et al.). 'Redetermined migration', at the next stage of the journey, can apparently often restore drifted birds to their proper route. On the other hand, we do not know how it is possible for, say, the Bronze Cuckoo *Chalcites lucidus* to overcome the hazard of drift on its transoceanic migration to its breeding place in New Zealand, its off-season being spent in the Solomon and Bismarck Islands.

Seasonal Differences. Although spring migration is broadly the counterpart of autumn migration, there are cases in which the two journeys do not closely correspond. Thus, it has been pointed out that the Subalpine Warbler *Sylvia cantillans* is abundant in Egypt on spring passage but unknown there in autumn ; and a recent study by Moreau (1961) suggests that this species does in fact perform a 'loop migration' in that area, travelling much farther east in spring than in autumn. An even more striking case is that of the Redbacked Shrike *Lanius collurio*. The birds breeding in western Europe migrate at first southeastwards in autumn, cross the Mediterranean, and mostly strike the northern coast of Africa on a front of about 600 miles from Cyrenaica to Egypt. Returning in spring from eastern and southern Africa, the birds pass the Mediterranean zone much farther to the east, by the Levant and Asia Minor (Moreau 1961 and sources cited by him). These instances are well authenticated, but in some cases apparent differences of this kind may be due to conditions affecting the extent to which the birds come under observation at one season or the other—for instance, feeding opportunities may induce a pause in the movement in one direction but not at the other time of year. There may also be differences in the extent of lateral displacement caused by drift, according to the prevailing winds, or in the amount of concentration produced by convergence of leading lines—so noticeable, for instance, at the southern tip of Sweden in autumn.

Some oceanic species, lacking a fixed wintering location, also apparently follow a kind of circuit. Thus, the Short-tailed Shearwater *Puffinus tenuirostris*, breeding on the southern coast of Australia, migrates northwards on the western side of the Pacific Ocean, moves eastwards in the Bering Sea during its off-season, and returns southwards at first on the American side—according to the indications of ringing records (Marshall & Serventy).

Return. It is obvious that a migratory population returns to its native area in successive breeding seasons, the range of a species at that season remaining practically constant ; in many instances the same can be said of the off-season distribution. The results of ringing have shewn for many species that accurate return of the individual to its former breeding locality is normal, although aberrant exceptions inevitably occur. In some cases it has been noted that the first return of a bird to its native locality may be less precise—merely to the same district—whereas the return of an older bird may be to the exact nesting spot. There is a smaller body of ringing evidence for exact return to the same wintering locality in successive years ; this certainly occurs in many instances.

Abmigration. This term was introduced by the present writer (1923) to denote a spring migration on the part of a bird that had remained in its native area during the winter. This abnormality, as ringing has shewn, occurs with some frequency among ducks (Anatidae) in particular and is probably due to early pairing between a member of a sedentary population of the species and a winter visitor to the area. It is to be distinguished from the 'aberrant return'—possibly arising in the same manner—of a winter visitant individual migrating in spring to a breeding area other than that from which it had come in autumn.

Performance. Various aspects of the actual performance of migration can be only briefly mentioned.

Diurnal and Nocturnal Flight. Some species migrate by day, some migrate by night, and some do one or the other according to circumstances (or both in the course of a long flight). Diurnal migrants include such large birds as crows (Corvidae) and such persistent fliers as swallows (Hirundinidae). Most of the small song-birds are nocturnal migrants, although at other times they are wholly diurnal in habit and usually seem to be helpless in the dark ; this is doubtless an adaptation for safety from attack by birds-of-prey on the part of weak species ordinarily unaccustomed to making sustained flights away from cover.

Gregariousness. There is a general tendency for birds to migrate in flocks, sometimes of very large size and sometimes consisting of more than one species (see also FLOCKING). This is true of some species that are much less markedly gregarious at other times ; but other species are solitary travellers as a rule. Many nocturnal migrants call incessantly during the flight, which no doubt helps to preserve the coherence of flocks ; some diurnal migrants are likewise vociferous, but other species are noticeably silent on passage. See Plate 48b (phot.).

Age and Sex. Flocks of autumn migrants sometimes consist wholly of young birds of the year and sometimes wholly of adults ; at other times—and ordinarily in some species—they may consist of a mixture. There is indeed much separate migration of young birds, leaving the breeding area in the late summer or early autumn while their parents await completion of the post-nuptial moult (see MOULT). On the other hand, for instance, adult Cuckoos *Cuculus canorus* depart early, while their young are still being tended by foster-parents (see PARASITISM) ; and the adults of some migratory shearwaters (Puffininae) desert their breeding localities before the young are able to leave the nest (see PARENTAL CARE). The males of many species reach the breeding grounds in spring slightly in advance of the females of the same population.

Altitude. Some migration takes place within a height of a few hundreds of feet of ground or sea, but perhaps most at heights 3000–5000 feet above the surface, with some migration at much greater heights. This statement takes account of the new evidence beginning to become available from radar observations, but in the main this confirms what was already believed ; on the other hand, radar observations show that ordinarily visible migration tends to give an incomplete and sometimes unrepresentative picture of the total movement at a particular place and time. Height above sea level, where the land surface is itself elevated, is of course another matter, and much greater altitudes are necessarily attained when migrants are crossing mountainous country.

Radar observations have shewn that the common passerine winter visitors to Britain tend to fly higher in spring than in autumn, and higher by night than by day ; and they have on occasion recorded small birds at heights of up to 21 000 feet (Lack). Another finding has been that waders (mainly Lapwings *Vanellus vanellus*) travel at a more constant height than passerines, nearly all the echoes on any one movement being within 2000 feet of each other (instead of being spread over a greater altitudinal range) and in all mostly at 3000–6000 feet.

Velocity. Birds migrate at the steady speed of their ordinary flight, not at the accelerated rate of which they are capable over short distances in emergency. It may be little over 20 m.p.h. for many small passerines ; but speeds of up to about 50 m.p.h. are attained by stronger fliers, and speeds in excess of that by a few species. These are of course air speeds, and the actual speed in relation to the ground will be greater or less according to the wind—the body of air of which the flying bird in effect forms a part, and within which it can feel only the head-on resistance to its own passage.

Duration of Flight. Most birds migrate during only part of the day or night, say six to eight hours. One may therefore deduce that the stage of a journey accomplished in a single flight is commonly of the order of 200–400 miles. Many sea-crossings that are regularly made, however, somewhat exceed that in length and a few greatly exceed it. It has been estimated that crossings of the Gulf of Mexico may, for some species, involve at least 24–36 hours of continuous flying, and sometimes substantially more, for, when Yucatan is avoided, the distance is about 1000 miles. Moreau (1961), estimates that migration across the Sahara in spring, when the winds are as a rule unfavourable, may involve flights of 50–60 hours without 'refuelling'. An extreme case is that of the American Golden Plover (Pacific race) *Pluvialis dominica fulva*, which in migrating from the Bering Sea area to Hawaii apparently makes an uninterrupted flight of at least 2000 miles. See also ENERGY REQUIREMENTS.

There is not much definite evidence about the intervals between stages of a journey ; but, at least in autumn, halts of several days are common for some species, although a single day may suffice. This refers to true migration ; dispersals and wanderings are probably more leisurely.

There is a recent record of a Knot *Calidris canutus* ringed in England and recovered eight days later in Liberia, a distance of about 3500 miles.

Rate of Advance. Apart from the speed of flight and the total period occupied by all the stages of an individual journey, there is the question of the rate at which the migration of a species spreads over the seasonal range to be occupied. In the spring migration of many species, the warmer parts are occupied first and the birds bound for higher latitudes come through later. For some species the advance keeps pace with that of the isotherms, but in others it is faster or slower. Moreover, even for a single species the rate may not be uniform but tends to accelerate towards the limit of the range.

Pre-migratory State. The inception of migration is preceded by a period during which restlessness ('Zugunruhe') is exhibited ; one deduces that the birds are in or nearing a state of readiness for departure and perhaps awaiting only the appropriate external stimulus. The well-known autumn flocking of the Swallow *Hirundo rustica* is an example. The state of restlessness has also been demonstrated, by mechanical recording, in caged birds of several species ; and this has formed the basis of experiments in which external conditions have been varied or hormone preparations have been administered. Another sign of physiological readiness is the deposition of subcutaneous fat, which is drawn upon as a source of energy during the journey.

Theoretical Problems. Migration is immense in its manifestations, highly complicated in its performance, and yet on the whole remarkably regular in its annual repetition : such a phenomenon obviously presents problems of great biological interest. First, a form of behaviour so expensive in energy and so hazardous to life must serve a useful purpose, i.e. have a ' survival value ' for the species, or it would not persist. Secondly, there is the question of causation ; merely that migration is useful does not explain its happening, nor can it be imagined as a rational course of action. Thirdly, there is the question of method : how is migration accomplished ?

Utility. Migration enables birds to exploit opportunities that would otherwise not be available. The breeding area provides the conditions best suited to the reproduction of the species—appropriate nesting sites and an abundant food supply at the time when it is most needed, and in higher latitudes long days in which to collect food for the young. Yet at the other time of year it may be incapable of supporting even non-reproductive life : unavailability of suitable food is probably more important than the direct effects of climatic conditions.

That birds breed at a particular time of year is itself largely an adaptation to the seasonal availability of a maximum (or qualitatively optimum) supply of food while the young have to be fed (see BREEDING SEASON) ; and migration is clearly related to this. The whole annual cycle of a bird's life can be seen as an alternation between reproductive and non-reproductive states—geared to seasonal fluctuations in food supply, with migration as an accessory adaptation and with the necessary periods of moult appropriately interpolated.

Causation. Not only is it inconceivable that birds should by conscious deliberation (if they were capable of that) avoid conditions that they have never experienced, but they cannot be regarded as migrating under the compulsion of immediate external forces (except in the case of certain weather movements already mentioned). Migration from the breeding area often begins before the need is apparent, proceeds farther than the minimum necessity requires, and displays greater regularity than do the seasonal changes of climate. Migration must be regarded as an innate form of adaptive behaviour ; one has therefore to look for an ultimate cause that originated the capacity for this behaviour, and also for a proximate stimulus bringing it into

play year after year. This distinction between evolutionary and immediate factors in causation is essential to any understanding of the problem.

The origin of the migration instinct doubtless lies in the evolution of each species, in the history of its distribution, and in the long-term changes in the geographical and climatic conditions to which it has been subject. The various speculative theories cannot be discussed here ; but it may be noted that migration must have originated many times, and probably in various ways for different species. The process is doubtless still continuing, and perhaps sometimes in a retrograde direction so that certain species or populations may be less migratory than they once were ; there is possibly a clue here to the fact, already noted, that in some species the adults show less tendency to migrate than do the young of the year.

In respect of the evolution of migratory habits, it is of interest that some species cling to what are apparently ancestral directions of travel, best explained on the assumption that they have extended their breeding range at some relatively recent date. While the common trend of autumn migration from northern Europe is south-westerly, some species that have probably spread there from Asia show a south-easterly trend ; an example is the Rustic Bunting *Emberiza rustica*, a predominantly Asian species breeding as far west as Finland but no more than a casual vagrant to southern Europe. Again, the Red-eyed Vireo *Vireo olivaceus* breeds as a summer visitor right across Canada, but the birds from the western part of that country do not ordinarily appear as migrants farther down the Pacific seaboard ; and Kennicott's Willow Warbler *Phylloscopus borealis kennicotti* breeds in Alaska—and has done so for long enough to have become subspecifically distinct (although it belongs to an otherwise purely Palae-arctic genus)—but in autumn apparently crosses the Bering Sea to go south on the Asian side. Nevertheless, it would be rash to suppose that, in the course of evolution, a new way can never be found from a new area.

The recurring proximate stimuli that evoke the behaviour twice a year appear to be of two kinds. There must be endogenous factors in the annual cycle of the bird's life that are concerned in building up the state of readiness for migration ; and exogenous factors that thereafter act as releasers, triggering off the activity. There is evidence that the physiological readiness is linked with the changing condition of the reproductive organs and is, in fact, influenced by hormones (see ENDOCRINE SYSTEM). The classical experiments of Rowan showed that these changes are in turn, in some instances, responsive to decrease or increase in the length of day—the most regular of all the changes in the environment, but of diminishing amplitude towards the Equator. Further work, however, has disclosed various complications warning us against accepting any over-simplified explanation, and it may well be true that ' the total physiological and psychological state of the bird is important in inducing its migratory and breeding behaviour, and not the physiological condition of one organ alone' (Wolfson) ; one has certainly to bear in mind the interrelations of the different organs and the dominant part that the pituitary may play in determining the total state.

It remains to say that the nature of the external stimulus is not necessarily the same for all species, and for any one species not necessarily the same (or counterpart) in autumn and in spring. A bird breeding in high latitudes is subject to very different environmental conditions when ' wintering ' in the tropics ; and a transequatorial migrant is subject to the conditions of spring at the outset of both its journeys. Again, a bird migrating wholly within the tropics is subject to influences peculiar to that environment. It is possible that a bird's physiological cycle is, at least in some instances, synchronised with the seasonal cycle of the environment only at one time in the year, and that its migratory behaviour at the other time is the expression of an inherent rhythm (see RHYTHM). There is indeed some evidence, in the case of birds ' wintering ' in the tropics, that the timing of northward departure is determined by the latitude, i.e. climate, of the breeding area of the particular population concerned (Curry-Lindahl). A further point is that a social stimulus can apparently spread through a flock from the individuals earliest influenced by endogenous factors.

Method. The primary question under this head is how migrants find their way ; this is the problem of orientation, discussed elsewhere (see NAVIGATION). It has already been noted that two separate processes are involved. The simple one is visual orientation in following topographical features. The difficult one to understand is heading in a constant direction without the aid of landmarks, as described earlier.

There remains the deeper question of how migrants ' know' what way to find ; what determines the standard direction in which particular birds, on particular occasions, instinctively head ? And again, especially in the case of a first autumnal migration, what brings the journey to an end when the appropriate goal is reached ? Here one is brought back to the nature of the behaviour and can assume only that the pattern of a bird's migration is somehow a part of the innate capacity for undertaking it.

A.L.T.

Only a few modern general works, and papers giving references to the vast literature, are listed chronologically below.

Thomson, A. Landsborough. 1926. Problems of Bird Migration. London and Boston.

Rowan, W. 1931. The Riddle of Migration. Baltimore.

Thomson, A. Landsborough. 1936. Recent progress in the study of bird-migration : a review of the literature, 1926–35. Ibis (13 ser.) 6 : 472–530.

Thomson, A. Landsborough. 1949. Bird Migration : a short account. 3rd ed. London.

Drost, R. 1951. Study of bird-migration 1938–50. Proc. X Internat. Orn. Congr., Uppsala 1950 : 216–240.

Various authors. 1953. Series of papers on visible migration. Ibis 95 : 165–364.

Farmer, D. S. 1955. The annual stimulus for migration : experimental and physiologic aspects. *In* Wolfson, A. (ed.). Recent Studies in Avian Biology. Urbana, Ill.

Lack, D. 1960. The influence of weather on passerine migration. A review. Auk 77 : 171–209.

Marshall, A. J. 1961. Breeding seasons and migration. *In* Marshall, A. J. (ed.). Biology and Comparative Physiology of Birds vol. 2. New York and London.

Moreau, R. E. 1961. Problems of Mediterranean—Saharan migration. Ibis 103a : 373–427, 580–623.

Dorst, J. 1963. The Migrations of Birds. London (U.S.A. 1961 ; Les Migrations des oiseaux. Paris, 1956).

See also references under IRRUPTION ; MOON WATCHING ; NAVIGATION ; RADAR ; RINGING.

MILK, PIGEON :

a secretion of the adult crop on which the nestlings of all pigeons (Columbidae), so far as known, are fed at least for their first few days of life. In pigeons and doves the crop is a very well developed two-chambered sac used for food storage. In both sexes, during the last days of incubation, the stratified pavement epithelium lining the two dorso-lateral planes of the crop enlarges so that a honeycomb appearance results. From this region cells are sloughed off that contain the milk, a substance that looks and smells like cheese and is, in fact, rather similar in composition to mammalian milk, being very rich in proteins and fats. (Water 65–81%, protein 13·3–18·6%, fat 6·9–12·7%, ash 1·5% ; the milk has no carbohydrate but has active amylase and invertase and is rich in vitamins A, B, and B_2 ; the ash is rich in sodium but lacks calcium as compared with mammalian milk.)

Furthermore, as with mammals, milk production is controlled by the pituitary hormone prolactin (see ENDOCRINE SYSTEM). A subcutaneous injection of as little as 0·1 micrograms of prolactin, in the region of the crop sac, is sufficient to cause a response, with proliferation of cells of the crop gland. Prolactin injection also results in a marked hyperglycemia and produces an antigonadal action causing the gonads of sexually mature pigeons to regress. When follicle-stimulating hormone is simultaneously injected, this gonad regression can be prevented ; thus prolactin suppresses the formation of follicle-stimulating hormone. Injection of testosterone and progesterone, which are claimed to release prolactin from the pituitary, brings about broodiness in pigeons. Oestrogen terminates broodiness, and it is claimed that it acts by preventing the release of prolactin.

For the first few days of life nestlings receive nothing except milk, but from about the fourth day they are given increasing amounts of whatever else the adults are collecting. As the nestlings grow, more food is given to them but the amount of milk in the mixture remains constant. Most pigeons are grain-eaters, but unlike those of many other seed-eating species the young are not fed on appreciable quantities of animal food. Milk production seems to be an adaptation ensuring that the nestlings receive adequate supplies of protein during their maximum growth period.

It is known that hunger in pigeons produces considerable crop activity with muscular contractions. These vary, depending on the degree of hunger and amount of food in the crop. Thus, in hungry birds milk intended for the young can be used by the adult. In the Wood Pigeon *Columba palumbus*, and probably in all species under wild conditions, there is a marked rhythm of feeding activity. Throughout incubation the male Wood Pigeon attends the eggs during the middle part of the day—about 1000–1700 hours B.S.T. in August in Britain ; and the female incubates for the rest of the day. The adults feed during the off-nest periods ; and in August, when food supplies are at a peak and grain is taken, enough food can be collected in less than one hour. This same situation applies for the first few days after the eggs hatch. The off-duty bird feeds itself and returns to the nest with the crop empty or with only a little food. When this is used and the crop is empty, milk cells are sloughed off and these are regurgitated to the small young at frequent intervals. It is important that during this time the milk is not contaminated by other foods, and this is partially achieved by the parents brooding the young for long periods without themselves feeding. When the young are very small—up to three days—milk is not liberated until the crop is cleared, but the physiological mechanism by which this is achieved is not known. Work is required to determine whether there are changes in the level of hormones throughout the day. As already mentioned, there is a link between broodiness and prolactin level, which in turn affects milk production.

After the third or fourth day, with increasing amounts of other food being regurgitated, milk production is still confined to those periods when the adults tend the young (nestlings are continuously brooded until about the tenth day). With very large young, milk production drops and both adults return to the nest around 1000 and 1700 hours to feed the nestlings. At this time, physiological changes occur, and females may lose most of their broodiness drive and begin to build new nests and even to lay eggs. The routine for feeding young can be upset if Wood Pigeons have nestlings at times when food is scarce. Under these conditions the adults may require much more time to collect food for themselves, e.g. when feeding on clovers, and as a result the rhythmic feeding of themselves or their young is affected. Adults may then leave small young unattended and unfed, and a high nestling mortality can occur ; adults may also leave eggs unattended for the same reason. The production of crop milk does not make pigeons more independent of their environment but rather enables them to thrive in situations that would otherwise be untenable. At the same time, this method of feeding their young seems to have fixed at two, sometimes one, the maximum number of young that can be reared, and hence the low clutch size.

Further controlled experiments linking the physiological changes in the adults with field observations are required, as most work done so far relates to domestic birds under artificial conditions. Comparative studies to establish the nature of feeding rhythms in other members of the Columbidae are also needed. R.K.M.

MILLERBIRD : *Acrocephalus familiaris* of the Hawaiian Islands (for subfamily see WARBLER (I)).

MILVINAE : see HAWK

MIMESIS : same as MIMICRY (adjective ' mimetic ').

MIMICRY : advantageous resemblance of one species to another. ' In Batesian mimicry a relatively scarce, palatable and unprotected species resembles an abundant, relatively unpalatable or well-protected species, and so becomes disguised. In Müllerian mimicry, on the other hand, a number of different species, all possessing aposematic attributes and appearance, resemble one another, and so become more easily recognised' (Cott 1940) ; in the first case the enemy is tricked by a sham warning (pseudaposematic), in the second educated by a real one common to many (synaposematic). Only the former type of mimicry is found among birds, and only in a small number of instances that are mostly associated with breeding parasitism (see PARASITISM ; also NATURAL SELECTION).

Some of the reported cases may be due to coincidence rather than to adaptation, especially where the two species belong to the same taxonomic group ; adequate information on the behavioural aspect is often lacking. It is thought that some predators are more easily able to approach their prey through resemblance to species, related or not, of innocuous habits—Batesian mimicry in reverse, so to speak. This would seem to be possible only where the latter species is much the commoner of the two ; and certain parallelisms between carnivorous and insectivorous birds-of-prey inhabiting the same area should be examined from that point of view. An instance of resemblance of a predator to an unrelated inoffensive species is that of the Curassow Hawk *Ibycter americanus*, one of the caracaras of South America, which is partly predatory and partly carrion-eating and resembles a curassow of the genus *Ortalis*.

In other instances, ranking as true Batesian mimicry, a weak species may derive advantage from resembling a pugnacious one. Wallace pointed out long ago the resemblance of certain orioles *Oriolus* spp. in the eastern Indonesian area to the pugnacious friar-birds *Philemon* spp., large honeyeaters found in the same part of the world ; these orioles are dull-hued birds, unlike most of their family, but have coloured head adornments superficially like those of the local friar-birds, island species for island species.

The general resemblance of the Cuckoo *Cuculus canorus* to the Sparrowhawk *Accipiter nisus* is familiar, and this is more striking—also extending to immature plumage—in the case of the Hawk Cuckoo (or Brainfever-bird) *C. varius* of India and the Shikra *A. badius*. Similarly, the black Drongo Cuckoo *Surniculus lugubris* of Asia resembles the pugnacious drongo *Dicrurus ater* known as the ' King Crow ' ; and it victimises the latter, and related species, in its parasitism. In another Asian cuckoo, the Koel *Eudynamys scolopacea*, the male is black and the female brown, but the nestlings of both sexes are coloured like the male and so resemble the young of such usual foster-parents as the House Crow *Corvus splendens*. Black nestling plumage is found in other *Eudynamys*, and also *Clamator*, species parasitising various members of the Corvidae and Sturnidae.

See also COLORATION, ADAPTIVE ; for egg mimicry see PARASITISM.

Cott, H. B. 1940. Adaptive Coloration in Animals, London.
Armstrong, E. A. 1951. The nature and function of animal mimesis. Bull. Anim. Behav. no. 9 : 46–58.

MIMICRY, VOCAL: imitation by birds of sounds outside their specifically characteristic vocalisations. The place that the ability to imitate sounds plays in the development of the vocalisations of a species is dealt with to a certain extent elsewhere (see LEARNING ; SINGING). However, the vocal performances of those birds that can not merely imitate sounds characteristic of their own species or of other species of birds but can even imitate the human voice and other sounds of non-avian origin, pose problems of quite a different order for students of animal behaviour and of phonetics .

Consonant and Vowel Sounds. Roughly speaking, there are two types of consonant sound in human speech, the plosives (of which *p*, *b*, *t*, and *d* are examples) and the fricatives (which include *f*, *v*, and varieties of *s*, *z*, and *ch* sounds, all on the whole of relatively high frequency). The first group, the plosives, really involve different ways of stopping and starting sounds more or less suddenly, with more or less explosive force, and with greater or less infusion of high frequencies. Since birds in the course of producing their normal vocalisations are obviously capable of stopping and starting their sounds with extreme suddenness, we should expect them to be able to produce something like our consonants ; but since the tongue, larynx, and mouth cavity are so different from ours, and since the overall size of the vocal organs of most birds is so much smaller than ours, we should not expect sound-spectrograms of birds' voices to show more than a slight and very general resemblance between the stopped sounds of birds and those which we ourselves produce. Thus we find that the sound-spectrograms of normal bird voices do not give us any very clear evidence of distinguishing between, say, *p* and *b*, or *t* and *d*. When we come to the fricatives we find that the resemblances are a good deal closer, and we can distinguish in bird vocalisations sounds that are closely similar to a number of our own fricative consonants ; it is for this reason that when we attempt to represent the sounds of small birds in words, we find ourselves making such lavish use of the letters *f*, *v*, *s*, *x*, and *z*. Thus, the closest similarities between human consonants and the sounds made by birds as part of their normal repertoire are found amongst those that depend on the range and relative intensity of the higher frequencies present.

When we come to the vowels, the problems posed by bird vocalisations are of peculiar interest to the phonetician. Twenty-three different vowels or vowel-like sounds are recognised in human speech. These are the incidental result of the fact that we have more than one resonator. Vowels occur whenever our throats and mouth cavities are stirred into resonance simultaneously, whether this is due to vocal cords (as in speech and song, when the sound is said to be ' voiced ') or whether it is merely due to the airstream passing through both cavities, as in whispering. Four types of modulation occur in speech : (i) start-stop, (ii) vocal cord, (iii) frictional, and (iv) cavity modulation. Of these, (i) and (iii) affect the flow of air from our lungs, (ii) and (iii) convert it into audible sound waves, while (iv), broadly speaking, varies the quality of the sound. The different types of consonants discussed above are produced by differing combinations of these types of modulation but always contain (i) or (iii) or both. When pure vowels or vowel-like sounds are produced in ordinary speech, only (ii) and (iv) occur. The vocal resonances that give the vowel sounds their characteristic qualities are determined by the shapes and sizes of the resonators and are under very precise control by the movements of the lips, jaw, tongue, and soft palate ; but it stands to reason that this cavity modulation will affect the sounds produced by the vocal cords very much more than those produced by frictional modulation, since the sounds produced by the vocal cords arise behind the cavities concerned whereas those produced frictionally arise in front.

Talking Birds. At first sight the vocal equipment of birds does not appear to have the cavities necessary to enable them to produce anything at all similar to our vowels, and examination of sound-spectrograms of bird vocalisations often shows that when we think we hear a particular vowel we may be deceiving ourselves. In some cases all that the bird seems to be doing is to change the overall pitch of the sound in the same general manner as we may change pitch during vowel production, but without producing the characteristic human resonance patterns. However, there is no doubt that some species of birds, particularly those such as parrots (Psittacidae) and mynahs (*Acridotheres* spp., etc.), which can be taught to produce plausible imitations of human speech, do in fact do something more than this and can, in a manner not yet by any means understood, produce a surprisingly accurate copy of the vocal resonances hitherto regarded as peculiar to human speech. A great deal more anatomical and physiological research will be necessary before it will be possible to account fully for the talking abilities of birds, and until this further knowledge is available speculation is apt to be profitless.

Quite apart from the physiological problems arising in connection with bird imitation of human speech, there are other questions concerning the evolution and biological function of this mimetic ability. Talking birds are so familiar to us that the significance of the performance has often been overlooked. No satisfactory evidence is available that either parrots or mynahs ever use their remarkable powers of imitation in the wild ; these seem to lie completely latent. Within the primates we find a great variety of vocal mechanisms which, it would seem, should enable some of these apes to produce

excellent imitations of human speech, yet not even the chimpanzee can be taught to do this. That the birds with their entirely different and apparently much inferior vocal equipment can on occasion overcome almost perfectly the problems of phonation posed by human speech is indeed mysterious.

Why these birds should learn to imitate human speech when kept in captivity is perhaps a little more understandable. Many birds such as Budgerigars *Melopsittacus undulatus* and mynahs learn to talk best when they are kept in close contact with human beings but away from their own kind. This is probably because, as they develop a social attachment to their human keepers, they learn that vocalisations on their part tend to retain and increase the attention that they get, and as a result vocal production, and particularly good vocal imitation, is quickly rewarded by social contact. This seems an obvious explanation of the fact that a parrot when learning will tend to talk more when its owner is out of the room or just after he has gone out—as if he is attempting, by his talking, to bring him back. If this theory about the psychology of talking birds is correct, it makes their process of learning appear very similar to that of the human infant in its first attempts to talk. Mowrer, in advancing this hypothesis, has suggested that birds and babies make their first efforts at reproducing words and other sounds because these sounds seem good to them—they are, in fact, self-stimulatory. Mothers often talk or croon to babies when attending to them, and so the sound of the mother's voice has become associated with comfort-giving measures. So it is to be expected that when the child, alone and uncomfortable, hears its own voice this will likewise have a consoling, comforting effect. In this way Mowrer supposes that the human infant will be rewarded for his own first babbling and jabbering without any necessary reference to the effects that these sounds produce upon others. Before long, however, he will learn that if he succeeds in making the kind of sound his mother makes he will get more interest, affection, and attention in return ; and so the stage is set for the first steps in the learning of human language. In spite of all the differences, it seems hard not to believe that something of the same sort is happening in the learning of human speech by pet birds.

Mimicry in Wild Birds. While many birds learn their songs, or at least some phrases of them, by imitation from others of their own species, it is well known that some species incorporate into their songs sounds copied from completely alien species or even sounds of non-avian origin. This tendency to mimic a wide variety of sounds can probably be regarded as a special development of the ability to learn songs from the parents or other conspecifics. It has been shown that some species that show no traces of imitation of alien sounds in their songs nevertheless include quite a number of such sounds in their sub-songs. When these sub-songs are transformed at the beginning of the breeding season into the true songs, all the sounds of alien origin are omitted. This fact will perhaps give a clue to the development of this faculty of general mimicry, for it is significant that sub-songs seem to have little or no communicatory function, whereas the songs themselves, at least in territorial species and probably in many others too, are important in transmitting information to other members of the species about the circumstances of the singer, e.g. whether mated or not, whether established in a territory, and sometimes also constituting an individual recognition mark. It seems not improbable that in those species which have become general mimics the song has lost some of its advertising functions in the territorial situation and no longer has to serve as a highly specific recognition mark.

There is no doubt that a very large number of species occasionally imitate alien sounds, but only very few species are good general mimics. Even in those which are renowned for their mimicry, such as the Starling *Sturnus vulgaris*, the Marsh Warbler *Acrocephalus palustris*, and the Mockingbird *Mimus polyglottos*, it is far from easy to make any estimate of how much of the vocal repertoire has been picked up in this way. The longer and more varied the natural song, the easier it is to imagine resemblances, as in the Marsh Warbler, to the notes of other birds. While some imitation in all these species is undoubted, we cannot say how much—even with the most famous of them, the Mockingbird. It certainly seems that in some individuals of this species a great deal of imitation is taking place, and Borror & Reese provide much evidence that Mockingbirds can acquire many of the songs of the Carolina Wren *Thryothorus ludovicianus*. On the other hand, Loye Miller provided evidence that only about ten per cent of the Mockingbird's song was copied.

The robin chats *Cossypha* spp. are said to include some of the best mimics among African birds, and here it is again possible that mimicry is a feature of sub-song rather than of the full song ; the full song in this species seems to have very clearly defined territorial and advertising functions. In Australia, the bowerbirds (Ptilonorhynchidae), the lyrebirds (Menuridae), and the scrub-birds (Atrichornithidae) are all renowned as mimics ; and Chisholm has pointed out that it is the ground-living members of these and a number of other families in

Australia that are most skilled and persistent in their mimicry. Marshall points out that most vocal mimics in Australia are strongly territorial (although not necessarily using their vocalisations in territorial defence), and that most of them carry out much of their mimicry near the ground in wooded country where visibility is limited. He suggests that the lack of visibility places a premium on communication by sound, and that it is biologically advantageous for individuals to make more and more sound in order that conspecifics—perhaps territorial rivals, and certainly members of the opposite sex—shall be constantly aware of their presence. This argument is, however, not very easy to follow ; it is not necessary for a bird to be imitative in order to make plenty of noise, and making a loud and persistent noise will not avail the species at all unless that noise is recognised as a specific signal by other birds. Only if—which is perhaps the case—the vocal quality is such that the species is recognisable *whatever* the song pattern it utters, would mimicry seem to be biologically useful. But even if the vocal quality is recognisable, that does not of itself seem to suggest any advantage to the bird in declaiming the song patterns of others rather than of its own species—although it might be an easy way of increasing the individual character of a bird's song, since no two birds are likely to copy the same model in the same way or sequence. Thus, mimicry by birds living in the dense vegetation described by Marshall might, in the end, make it easier for birds to recognise their mates as individuals by their vocal utterances than would otherwise be the case. W.H.T.

Borror, D. J. & Reese, C. R. 1959. Mocking Bird imitations of Carolina Wren. Bull. Mass. Audubon Soc. 16 pp.
Chisholm, A. H. 1932. Vocal mimicry among Australian birds. Ibis (13 ser.) 2 : 605–624.
Chisholm, A. H. 1937. The problem of vocal mimicry Ibis (14 ser.) 1 : 703–721.
Marshall, A. J. 1950. The function of vocal mimicry in birds. Emu 50 : 5–16.
Mowrer, O. H. 1950. Learning Theory and Personality Dynamics. New York. (Ch. 24 : The psychology of talking birds : a contribution to language and personality theory.)
Thorpe, W. H. 1961. Bird Song : the biology of vocal communication and expression. Cambridge.

MIMICS: sometimes used as a general term for the Mimidae.

MIMIDAE: a family of the Passeriformes, suborder Oscines (see MOCKINGBIRD).

MINER: substantive name of *Manorina* spp. (see HONEYEATER); and see below.

MINERA: sometimes ' miner ', substantive name

of *Geobates poecilopterus* and *Geositta* spp. (see OVENBIRD (1)).

MINERAL REQUIREMENTS: see NUTRITION

MINIVET: substantive name of *Pericrocotus* spp. (see CUCKOO-SHRIKE).

MIOMBO: an environment, consisting of sparse leguminous woodland (*Brachystegia*), characteristic of large parts of East Africa.

MISTLETOE-BIRD: *Dicaeum hirundinaceum* (see FLOWERPECKER).

MITES: see ECTOPARASITE

MITOSIS: ordinary cell-division, without reduction in the number of chromosomes (see CELL).

MOA: substantive name of the species of the extinct order Dinornithiformes (in the sense used in this work—i.e. excluding the Apterygidae, merged by some authorities) ; in the plural, general term for the order. The moas are variously regarded as constituting a single family, Dinornithidae, or two families (see later). They were running birds, of from large to very large size, inhabiting New Zealand ; supposed remains found in Australia are not now accepted as correctly attributed. The abundant material discovered in New Zealand is of no great antiquity : the living birds were well known to the Maoris ; and extinction became complete only within the last few centuries. Examples of the largest species, *Dinornis maximus* (including *D. 'robustus'*), are estimated as standing about 10 feet high.

Discovery. The name has its origin in the Polynesian languages and was supplied by the Maoris when asked for a name for birds of which the first European settlers in New Zealand found only sub-fossil or sub-recent bones. Specimens of these bones were first exhibited and described by Richard Owen, who showed in 1839 the shaft of a femur brought to England by Dr John Rule. Owen's verdict was that that the femur indicated the existence in New Zealand of a large struthious bird, probably as large as the Ostrich *Struthio camelus*. With more material received in the next few years, he was soon able to elaborate his descriptions and referred to his genus, *Dinornis*, 6 distinct species. These descriptions were elaborated over a period of nearly forty years, the combined papers being issued in collected form in 1879. There were subsequent monographic reviews by zoologists working in New Zealand, notably that of F. W. Hutton ; by this time the described species had increased to 26, but two

later monographs in the twentieth century are more conservative. Full treatment and bibliographical references to the subject are given by Gilbert Archey (1941) and by W. R. B. Oliver (1949). All classifications have agreed in regarding the moas as ' ratite ' birds, and this assumption has not been challenged except by theoretical inference (see RATITES, PHYLOGENY OF THE). It would still be possible to regard many of the structural characters found in this group as secondary modifications associated with increase in size and decline of function of many parts of the bony structure. This hypothesis has not been seriously advanced with any supporting data, however, although Mayr & Amadon (1951) have indeed suggested that the group may possibly be polyphyletic.

Evolution. More than a century of study in the field has disposed of some of the elements of mystery surrounding the large deposits of moa bones, and has answered some of the questions about time and causes of extinction. For one thing, the moas have no well documented fossil history. The supposed earliest bone to be described is not in very satisfactory condition and has been tentatively regarded as mid-Pliocene. In the absence of adequate fossil record, it is reasonable to assume that moas developed as a group of large flightless birds in a comparatively short time from volant ancestors. Such explosive radiation in evolution has been suggested for several elements of the fauna of the larger oceanic land-masses of the Southern Hemisphere ; conditions in Madagascar, the Mascarene Islands, and New Zealand seem to have much in common. In New Zealand, contemporary with the moas, were large representatives of such recognisable families as rails (Rallidae) and geese (Anatidae), and while it is perhaps not justifiable to assume that a similar explosive evolution of birds of galline stock produced the moas, the theory should not be ruled out as a possible line of investigation. It is fairly clear that divergent evolution in the group proceeded in an extremely favourable niche, unimpeded by congestion or competition. It may well be that the conditions that favoured rapid development were those that brought about almost equally rapid extinction, for there is much evidence of climatic and resultant instability in both landforms and vegetation in New Zealand during the late Pleistocene and early Recent. During this period, the whole balance, and some of the composition, of the flora is known to have changed ; and when the same process affected the fauna it included some spectacular extinctions.

Human Impact. A final factor not yet fully assessed was the influence of man. Polynesian immigrants arrived not much more than one thousand years ago, and the early waves of human migration developed a culture that has been described by archaeologists as the moa-hunter period. The evidence gradually assembled has shown beyond all doubt that in both North and South Islands the human inhabitants made good use of flesh of moas for food, and of their bones to some extent for ornaments. This activity was much more extensive, and probably continued later, in the South Island ; radio-carbon dating estimations have been made there of moa bones from undoubted association with human occupation sites. If their accuracy is accepted, they place the date of final extinction as some time in the seventeenth century. In spite of the fact that representatives of all the genera of moas have now been recorded in varying quantity from moa-hunter sites, it remains true that the largest deposits of surviving bones are found in situations that indicate death from natural causes, accumulated over a long period, and in a few cases possible disasters.

Deposits. The richest deposits have been found in swamps, and some of the classical localities referred to in the literature are Glenmark, Waikouaiti, Hamilton (Otago), Te Aute, and Enfield. In these deposits, huge mixtures of bones prevented much identification of individual skeletons, and the attempts to assemble them resulted in many mistakes in the early descriptions of supposed species. A much more useful swamp deposit found in the twentieth century at Pyramid Valley, Canterbury, has provided individual skeletons to a much more satisfactory extent. Sand dune deposits have also been useful, especially when skeletons uncovered by dune movement have been found intact ; they have the disadvantage of not lasting long and of being easily scattered. Cave deposits have varied in quality, but they have been marked by the excellent state of preservation of some of the specimens and for a high proportion of individual skeletons. Such caves occur in limestone districts, and those in drier regions have produced not only bones but dried integument and feathers. Notable cave discoveries have been Earnscleugh, Knobby Range, Queenstown, Castle Rock, and others, all in Southland and Otago. North Island limestone caves have produced only bones, but they have made an important contribution to the defining of species peculiar to the North Island. Some of the localities are Waikaremoana, Coonoor, and Martinborough. Apart from Maori camp sites, swamps, sandhills, and caves, there have been numerous finds in river deposits ; and in the early days of European settlement, when a good deal of forest and scrub land was being cleared, skeletons were found on the open surface of the ground. From the mass of material that has thus found its way into museums and other institutions, it is likely that all the species formerly existing are now known, although there may be disagreement as to their classification. The early Maori rock-paintings of moas at Craigmore, Pareora, South Island, may also be mentioned.

Possible Survival into the Nineteenth Century. On the controversial topic of whether or not early European visitors are likely to have met with living specimens of moas of any kind, it must be admitted that the only available evidence is circumstantial. It is quite clear that none of the largest species were ever seen by Europeans, but there is a strong probability that at least one of the smaller ones, the South Island Bush Moa *Megalapteryx hectori*, still survived in the southern province of Otago into the early part of the nineteenth century. Sealers from Foveaux Strait were in the habit of spending many months in the south-western fiords and living off the land. They seldom had occasion to report natural history observations, but when some of them were questioned by F. Strange, a naturalist who accompanied H.M.S. ‘Acheron’ on survey in 1852, they described various birds upon which they depended for food. Most of the birds described are recognisable, except one referred to as a large bird and called by the sealers ‘the fireman’. The reference here was to a rattling call reminiscent of the sound made by the wooden rattles carried by firemen on duty. Maori informants about the same time frequently referred to kiwis and to a larger bird which they called the Roa. European lexicographers have since attached this name to one of the larger kiwis, *Apteryx haasti*, but this species does not and apparently did not occur in the south-western area, and there is a strong probability that Roa, although described as like a large kiwi, was, in fact, not a kiwi at all.

Among reported direct observations by Europeans, one of the most arresting is that given in her later years by a Mrs Alice McKenzie who was born and spent her childhood at Martins Bay. Throughout her life she retained a vivid recollection of an incident when, as a child of seven, about the year 1880, she had been waiting for her brother who was mustering cattle. As she sat on a coastal sand dune adjacent to forest, she was surprised to see a large bird of dark bluish plumage standing close to her. It was about $3\frac{1}{2}$ feet in height, and her clearest recollection was of its large protruding eyes, broad beak, and powerful scaly legs which she remembered as being about the same thickness as her own forearm and wrist. After she had published this description in a book of reminiscences, Mrs McKenzie was cross-questioned by many people and interviewed for radio broadcast.

She continued to give convincing and good descriptive answers. It goes some way to confirm the possibility that *Megalapteryx* still survived in small numbers when we consider the excellent state of preservation of bones of one individual *Megalapteryx* found in an open hunter's fireplace in the Takahe Valley near Lake Te Anau. In limestone dust against an adjacent cliff, the well preserved feathers of *Notornis*, kiwis *Apteryx* spp., Weka *Gallirallus greyi*, Kakapo *Strigops habroptilus*, and moas were found by investigators in 1949, and the bones of birds of the same species were mixed up with the cooking stones. Plaited sandals, flax nooses, fire-making sticks, and other artifacts were also lying about in a good state of preservation, and as it is known that hunters from Maori settlements at Te Anau and near Riverton on Foveaux Strait were still visiting this area between 1840 and 1860, it is not beyond the realm of possibility that an occasional *Megalapteryx* found its way into the bag. Contemporary European interest in moas and the search for them was, at that time, centred on looking for birds standing 8 feet or more in height ; a bird not much larger than a sizable turkey would undoubtedly have been regarded as a satisfactory catch, but not otherwise 'newsworthy'.

Reconstruction. When all speculation has had its say, however, the reconstruction of moas as birds depends on the interpretation of plentiful bones, quantities of eggshell, a few unbroken eggs, a few feathers and pieces of skin, and some gizzard contents. These remains, and careful consideration of the situations in which they have been found, provide some clues. Superficially the birds must have had the looped neck stance of emus and cassowaries (Casuariiformes) rather than the erect carriage of Ostrich and rheas (Rheidae). Surviving feathers, at least of *Megalapteryx*, are much less 'degenerate' than the norm of struthious birds, with enough vane structure to show some pigmentation (purplish black centres and golden buff edges). Eggshell, which is usually white and occasionally pale green, is not abnormally thick for the size of the eggs, and has been found by Tyler (1957) to be not very different in texture, composition, and mechanical properties from normal avian eggs. Moas appear to have been entirely herbivorous, cropping heavily from grasses and from the twigs and leaves of a wide range of accessible shrubs. Berries and seeds also are plentiful in crop remains, and when such were from tall forest trees they must have been picked up from the ground. All in all, the 'browsing and grazing pressure' exerted in early New Zealand by flocks of moas must have been considerable.

Their distribution appears to have been of greatest density in foothills adjacent to low country. Except in plateau areas the remains of the largest forms are not at all plentiful at high altitudes or in steep country, but the more agile *Megalapteryx* in the South Island and the somewhat similar *Anomalopteryx* in both islands, smaller birds both, were montane species. Of their nidification nothing is known except for the findings of the late W. H. Hartree, who discovered many nest sites of *Anomalopteryx* in two North Island districts. Without exception they contained remains of only single eggs or single chicks in scoop nests on small sheltered ledges and cavities in what had once been forested country. From other sketchy evidence it seems likely that females were larger than males, and possibly that incubation duties were carried out by males.

Classification. The following classification of the Dinornithiformes, adapted from Archey (1941) and Oliver (1949), represents a conservative diagnosis of relationships :

Family Dinornithidae
  Genus *Dinornis* Owen—Six species ; three species in each island, separated by differences in height.
Family Anomalopterygidae
  Subfamily Anomalopteryginae
  Genus *Anomalopteryx* Reichenbach—Two species, separated by size ; the larger in both islands, the smaller in South Island.
  Genus *Megalapteryx* Haast—One species in three size-groups ; probably confined to South Island.
  Genus *Pachyornis* Lydekker—Four species, separated by size and relative stoutness ; two in each island.
  Subfamily Emeinae
  Genus *Emeus* Reichenbach—Two species ; in both islands, but rare in North Island.
  Genus *Euryapteryx* Haast—Four species, separated by size ; the largest in South Island, the others in North Island.   R.A.F.

Owen, R. 1879. Memoirs on the Extinct Wingless Birds of New Zealand. 2 vols. London. (Collected papers of 1843 et seq.)
Hutton, F. W. 1892. The moas of New Zealand. Trans. N.Z. Inst. 24 : 93–172.
Archey, G. 1941. The Moa, a study of the Dinornithiformes. Bull. Auckland Inst. Mus. no. 1 : 1–119.
Oliver, W. R. B. 1949. The moas of Australia and New Zealand. Bull. Dominion Mus. no. 15.
Tyler, C. 1957. Some chemical, physical, and structural properties of moa egg shells. J. Polynesian Soc. 66 : 110–130.

MOBBING: see DISPLAY ; FLOCKING ; and under SCARING ; SINGING

MOCKINGBIRD: substantive name of about half the species of Mimidae (Passeriformes, suborder Oscines) ; in the plural, general term for the family.

The name 'thrasher' is used for many of the other members of the group, and 'catbird' for a few. The members of this New World family are in appearance suggestive both of thrushes (Turdinae) and the larger wrens (Troglodytidae). They are long-tailed birds, with rounded or short wings, either largely terrestrial or dwellers in dense brush or low trees. The bill is strong, medium to long, and slightly to strongly decurved. Most of the species are gray, brown, or nearly white, with or without dark spots and streaks ventrally ; many have white areas in the wings and on the tips of the lateral tail feathers. Ground-dwelling invertebrates and various fruits are the foods of most members of the group.

The family is renowned for its vigorous and versatile song, which does not adhere to fixed patterns although notes are often repeated several times in succession and are used again subsequently. The variety of sounds produced leads to many fortuitous resemblances to the notes of other species, a circumstance that has led to false claims concerning the degree of mimicry. True and perfect mimesis does occur, however, but the best estimates are that it constitutes little over ten per cent of the units of the song performance (L. Miller) even in the well studied Northern Mockingbird *Mimus polyglottos*. Usually, mimicry involves no more than three or four copies within the hearing range of any one singer (see MIMICRY, VOCAL). Many species sing in the non-breeding season, as well as during nesting, and females of several of the species may sing at that time. Night singing is prominent in the nuptial season, and in the members of the genus *Mimus* song may continue as the bird flies up above its song perch. The Sage Thrasher *Oreoscoptes montanus*, in a monotypic genus, sings on the wing as it circles low over its sage-brush habitat.

Nests are placed chiefly in bushes or dense trees and are open cup-like structures, often bulky. The eggs number 2–5, rarely more, the greater numbers occurring only in some individuals of species living in high latitudes ; sets of but 2 or 3 are regularly laid in or near the tropics. The ground colour of the eggs ranges from buff to blue or pale green and spotting is heavy, light, or absent. Incubation is performed by the female, but also by the male in some thrashers. Both parents feed the young. Mockingbirds are often extremely aggressive, and they frequently defend the area about the nest with vigour and strike persistently at people or dogs and cats in efforts to drive them away.

Territorial behaviour is conspicuous, and territories may be maintained in the non-breeding season by pairs or by single individuals (Michener). No social flocks are formed. Migration is well developed only in the species that breed in the northern and middle United States and southern Canada. The California Thrasher *Toxostoma redivivum* shows an unusual ability to nest in the autumn, as well as in the normal spring period.

The family Mimidae ranges from southern Canada through Central America, the West Indies, and South America to southern Argentina and Chile. The greatest number and diversity of kinds are found in the arid south-western United States. There is a total of 34 species in the family ; these are placed in 13 genera, of which 9 are monotypic. The mockingbirds of the genus *Mimus* comprise 9 species, spread throughout the range of the family. The mockingbirds of the Galápagos Islands belong to an endemic superspecies, *Nesomimus trifasciatus* et al., with 9 forms that reflect the influence of isolation within this archipelago in fostering the evolution of species and subspecies.

Catbird *Dumetella carolinensis* (mockingbird family). *C.E.T.K.*

$\frac{1}{3}$

The thrashers of the genus *Toxostoma* constitute an array of 10 species confined to the United States and Mexico in which a series of stages in evolution has been demonstrated leading to augmentation of running ability, reduction of wings, and lengthening and increased curvature of the bill. The most extreme of these are the Le Conte Thrasher *T. lecontei*, the Crissal Thrasher *T. dorsale*, and the California Thrasher *T. redivivum* ; they are weak flyers specialised to feed by digging for insects in the soft soil and leaf litter of their desert and chaparral habitats. Extensive adjustments of the structure of the head and neck entailed in these adaptations have been reported by Engels.

The Blue Mockingbird *Melanotis caerulescens* and the Blue-and-white Mockingbird *M. hypoleucus* of Mexico and Central America (sole members of the genus) are aberrant in coloration in the family ; so also is the Black Catbird *Melanoptila glabrirostris* of Yucatan, which is distinguished by the iridescent black of its plumage but resembles in structure the

Common Catbird *Dumetella carolinensis* of the United States. A strongly isolated monotypic genus is represented by the Socorro Thrasher *Mimodes graysoni* of Socorro Island in the Revillagigedo Archipelago off the west coast of Mexico. Confined to the West Indies are the tremblers *Cinclocerthia ruficauda* and *Ramphocinclus brachyurus*, and also the Scaly-breasted Thrasher *Allenia fusca* and Pearly-eyed Thrasher *Margarops fuscatus*, the last two suggesting thrushes (Turdinae) in general appearance. The Brown Trembler *C. ruficauda* derives its name from its habit of violently trembling the wings and body, a characteristic serving readily to distinguish it in the field.

One of the most aberrant members of the family is the Black-capped Mockingthrush *Donacobius atricapillus* of tropical South America, possessing a bright yellow patch of thickened skin in the apterium on the side of the neck. This is a loud-voiced species with clear whistles, elaborate song, and a harsh whirring chatter. The latter note and the bird's skulking habits suggest relationships with the wrens (Troglodytidae).   A.H.M.

Davis, J. & Miller, A. H. 1960. Family Mimidae. *In* Mayr, E. & Greenway, J. C., Jr. (eds.). Check-list of Birds of the World vol. 9. Cambridge, Mass.
Engels, W. L. 1940. Structural adaptations in Thrashers (Mimidae : Genus *Toxostoma*) with comments on interspecific relationships. Univ. Calif. Publ. Zool. 42 : 341–400.
Michener, H. & Michener, J. R. 1935. Mockingbirds, their territories and individualities. Condor 37 : 97–140.
Miller, L. 1938. The singing of the Mockingbird. Condor 40 : 216–219.
Swarth, H. S. 1931. The avifauna of the Galápagos Islands. Calif. Acad. Sci. Occas. Papers no. 18.

MOCKINGTHRUSH: *Donacobius atricapillus* (see MOCKINGBIRD).

MODE: see under MEAN, ARITHMETIC ; STATISTICAL SIGNIFICANCE

MOHO: alternative name of the Oriole Babbler *Hypergerus atriceps* (for subfamily see BABBLER).

MOLLYMAUK: sailors' name, with several variants, for the smaller species of Diomedeidae (see ALBATROSS) ; also applied to some other sea birds.

MOLT: American spelling of MOULT.

MOMOTIDAE: see CORACIIFORMES ; and MOTMOT

MOMOTOIDEA: see under CORACIIFORMES

MONAL: substantive name of *Lophophorus* spp. (see PHEASANT).

MONARCHINAE: see under MUSCICAPIDAE

MONIAS: *Monias benschi*, sometimes misnamed ' Bensch's Rail ' (see MESITE).

MONKLET: substantive name of *Micromonacha lanceolata* (see PUFFBIRD).

MONOPHYLETIC: of a single evolutionary ancestry (contrasted with POLYPHYLETIC).

MONOTYPIC: term applied to a taxon that has only one unit in the immediately subordinate category, e.g. a genus comprising only one species, or a species not divisible into subspecies—contrasted with POLYTYPIC.

MONOTYPY: see under TYPE-SPECIES

MONSOON: see CLIMATOLOGY

MONSTROSITY: any gross abnormality of structure such as the possession of two heads, or of supernumerary bills, wings, legs, or toes ; more rarely the absence of a normal part. Monsters are more frequently noted in domesticated than in wild birds, and may usually be ascribed to accidents during embryonic development. Abnormal eggs, e.g. with two or three yolks, also occur.

MONTANE: appertaining to mountains ; term applied particularly to the avifaunas of elevated areas in which the bird-life is strikingly different from that of adjacent areas of less altitude. The contrast tends to be especially pronounced at high levels in low latitudes ; and it has been one of the puzzles of ornithology that particular sedentary species, sometimes not even showing subspecific differentiation, are found on isolated tropical mountain ranges separated by wide areas of unsuitable country in which such birds are never encountered (see ETHIOPIAN REGION).

MOOD: ' the preliminary state of " charge " or " readiness for action " necessary to the performance of a given course of instinctive behaviour ' (Thorpe 1951).

MOON WATCHING: a means of migration study. When a telescope is trained on the moon, passing birds are visible as silhouettes against the lunar disc. This fact, made known long ago through accounts from the United States, Great Britain, Syria, and Australia, was not systematically exploited until the middle 1940s, when American investigators at Louisiana State University worked out ways of using such observations to measure quantities and directional trends of migration.

The details of the observational method have been the main subject of a 49-page booklet (Newman

1952). The basic field procedure typically employed is fairly simple. The instrument most commonly used is a 20-power prism spotting telescope mounted on a tripod with a pan-tilt head and legs that can be spread far enough apart to straddle an adjustable lawn chair. Although an experienced operator can carry on profitable watches on at least 15 nights of a lunation, most of the work has been done during the period when the lunar disc is nearly round (from 2 nights before to 2 nights after the night of the full moon). The observer visualises the disc as an upright clock-face with 12 o'clock uppermost and the other hours and half-hours spaced around the rim accordingly. He identifies the slants of the pathways of passing birds in terms of the imaginary numbers on the clock-face (e.g. 4.30 to 9.00). This information is noted, together with the time of each observation and other accessory data, such as the image size.

The difficulties of making sense of the results are several. The moon's movement, both in altitude and azimuth, continually changes not only the directional meaning of the clock co-ordinates but also the theoretical size of the effective observation space, which even at a given time has different dimensions for birds approaching from different directions. The method currently in use is to compute the horizontal breadths of the observation cone at the appropriate lunar altitude and azimuth as they apply to birds in 16 directional sectors, each with a spread of $22\frac{1}{2}°$, and then to express the amount of migration as the proportionate quantity per hour per sector per mile of front. The mathematical principles underlying this rather intricate translation have been explained in greatest detail by Rense (1946). The Louisiana State University processing centre now does the work with specially constructed calculating boards, using sliding scales and incorporating precomputed solutions. A modification, adapted to the resources of the individual observer, has been described by Nisbet (1959). Tests have shown that the Nisbet method is comparable in directional accuracy to the standard method, but its quantitative aspects appear less satisfactory. An even more concise graphic method of decoding the data has been devised by Newman.

More than 2500 ornithologists and astronomers have devoted some 20 000 hours to lunar observations of bird migration. Two papers (Lowery 1951; Lowery & Newman 1955) have recorded some of the results; but a great deal more is about to be published, particularly regarding autumn movement. Tentative conclusions, some already in print, have been many: night-migrating passerines do not travel in compact flocks, although loose aggregation may be somewhat greater in the fall than in spring;

the amount of night migration in the United States varies considerably from region to region; the tendency of nocturnal migrants to follow major river courses is demonstrable but slight, although the birds may to a greater extent accept the borders of the sea as 'lines of influence' (Leitlinien); crossings of the Gulf of Mexico are an important reality and for the most part conform to a typical 'timetable'; the greatest volume of migration occurs with northerly winds in autumn and southerly winds in spring, i.e. more or less downwind; nevertheless, some silhouettes clearly demonstrate lateral drift, and strong adverse winds can turn a considerable part of nocturnal migration in a direction opposite to its proper seasonal trend. The computed amount of migration most commonly reaches its maximum volume at 11 p.m. in spring and 10 p.m. in autumn; the time of the peak seems to be influenced by the time of twilight, while the steepness of rise and descent of the density curves seems to be accentuated on nights when migration is heaviest; purely local results frequently show marked deviation from the general hour-to-hour pattern, yet the general similarity of curves for the various geographical sections, even those largely represented by different species, suggest that most nocturnal migrants behave temporally in a similar way.

Moon watching and radar produce migration data of much the same type (see RADAR). But, since the uncertainties in the methods themselves differ, each provides a check on the other. Moon watching and radar working in concert can yield much more dependable results than either method employed alone.   G.H.L. & R.J.N.

Lowery, G. H., Jr. 1951. A quantitative study of the nocturnal migration of birds. Univ. Kansas Publ., Mus. Nat. Hist. 3 : 361–472.

Lowery, G. H., Jr., & Newman, R. J. 1955. Direct studies of nocturnal bird migration. *In* Wolfson, A. (ed.), Recent Studies in Avian Biology. Urbana, Ill.

Newman, R. J. 1952. Studying Nocturnal Bird Migration by Means of the Moon. Special publ. Mus. Zool., Louisiana State University, Baton Rouge.

Rense, W. A. 1946. Astronomy and ornithology. Popular Astronomy 54 : 55–73.

Nisbet, I. C. T. 1959. Calculation of flight directions of birds observed crossing the face of the moon. Wilson Bull. 71 : 237–243.

MOOR FOWL: antique term (in British game laws) for the Red Grouse *Lagopus scoticus* ; cf. HEATH FOWL.

MOORHEN: substantive name of *Gallinula* spp. ; applied without qualification, in Britain, to *G. chloropus* (see RAIL).

MOORUK: native name in New Guinea, sometimes used as English, for Bennett's Cassowary *Casuarius bennetti* (see CASSOWARY).

MOPOKE: popular name, also written 'morepork', used in Australia for *Podargus strigoides* (see FROGMOUTH), and both there and in New Zealand for subspecies (or related forms) of *Ninox novaeseelandiae* (see OWL). The name purports to represent the call.

MORILLON: British fowler's name (probably obsolescent) for immature Goldeneye *Bucephala clangula*, once thought to be a different species (see DUCK).

MORPH: term introduced (J. S. Huxley 1955) to replace the less precise 'phase', denoting any one of the different forms of a species population subject to polymorphism (including dimorphism, where there are only two morphs)—see POLYMORPHISM.

MORPHOLOGY: literally, the science of form or shape ; nowadays commonly extended to cover all external characters, including coloration, or even used synonymously with 'anatomy' (literally, internal structure as revealed by dissection) ; and it may be applied not only to the study but to its subject matter, as a collective term for the 'morphological' characters of a taxon.

MORPHOSPECIES: see under SPECIES

MORTALITY: see LIFE, EXPECTATION OF ; LONGEVITY ; POPULATION DYNAMICS ; PREDATION

MOSAIC EVOLUTION: see under ARCHAEOPTERYX

MOSSIE : or Cape Sparrow, *Passer melanurus* (see SPARROW (1)).

MOTACILLIDAE: a family of the Passeriformes, suborder Oscines (see WAGTAIL).

MOTHER CAREY'S CHICKEN: sailors' name (from 'Mater cara') for storm-petrels of various species (Hydrobatidae)—see PETREL.

MOTIVATION: see DRIVE ; and AMBIVALENCE

MOTMOT: substantive name of species of Momotidae (Coraciiformes, suborder Alcedines) ; in the plural, general term for the family. The motmots are allied to the kingfishers (Alcedinidae) and even more closely to the todies (Todidae). The 6 genera and 8 species (*Momotus* and *Electron* have 2 apiece) are confined to continental tropical America, chiefly at low altitudes. The family is best represented in northern Central America and southern Mexico, where in certain regions of lighter vegetation motmots are abundant and conspicuous. Among the noteworthy structural peculiarities of the motmots are the serrated edges of their broad bills, which are

about as long as their heads and decurved at the end ; and their feet, in which the outer toe is united to the middle one for most of its length and only one toe is directed backwards, as in kingfishers.

These beautiful birds ($6\frac{1}{2}$ to $19\frac{3}{4}$ inches in total length) are clad in softly blended shades of green, olive-green, and rufous rather than in brilliant spectral colours, although the head is often adorned with bright blue and a black patch is usually present on the chest or throat. The most striking feature of motmots is the tail, which is long and strongly graduated. In typical motmots, the central rectrices far exceed the others in length, and when they first expand the vanes may be narrower in the subterminal region than elsewhere. In this subterminal portion the barbs are loosely attached and fall away as the bird preens, and probably also in consequence of rubbing against the vegetation through which it moves, leaving a length of naked shaft supporting a spatulate or racquet-like tip where the vanes remain intact. The length of denuded shaft varies considerably from genus to genus, and in some genera it is lacking. While perching, motmots often swing their tails, pendulum-wise, from side to side and sometimes hold them tilted sideways. When they about-face on a perch, they lift the tail over it with a graceful flourish.

One of the most beautiful members of the family is the Turquoise-browed Motmot *Eumomota superciliosa*, which is found from southern Mexico to northern Costa Rica in semi-arid country and in clearings in the rain-forest. Well over half of its 14 inches is accounted for by its long tail. As in other motmots, the sexes are alike in coloration. The upper plumage is largely bright olive-green, with a patch of cinnamon-rufous in the centre of the back. Above each eye is a broad band of pale turquoise, the bird's brightest colour. The lores and ear-tufts are black, and on the throat is an elongated, wedge-shaped patch of black bordered on each side with turquoise. The remaining under plumage is greenish-olive and cinnamon-rufous. The middle feathers of the greenish-blue tail have a much greater length of denuded shaft than in other motmots, so that the spatulate, blue and black ends hardly appear to be connected with the rest of the bird ; this makes the Turquoise-browed Motmot more airily graceful than its relatives.

The largest member of the family is the Rufous Motmot *Baryphthengus ruficapillus*, which inhabits heavy forests from Nicaragua to Amazonia. This 18-inch bird has the head, neck, and most of the under parts tawny, the back and rump and under tail coverts green. There is a black patch on each side of the head and one in the centre of the chest. Each of the central tail feathers has a short length of naked shaft. At the other extreme of size is the Tody Motmot *Hylomanes momotula*, an elusive and little-known inhabitant of forests from southern Mexico to north-western Colombia. About 6½ inches long, clad in dull green and rufous with black ear-tufts, this small motmot has a short tail without racquet tips.

An aberrant member of the family is the Blue-throated Motmot *Aspatha gularis*, which in northern Central America and extreme southern Mexico inhabits forests of oaks, pines, and cypresses from about 4000 to 10 000 feet above sea level, where it resides throughout the year, despite the severe frosts of the winter months. About 11 inches long, this motmot is almost wholly clad in green, but it has black ear-tufts and a black patch in the centre of the foreneck. The feathers of the long tail are strongly graduated, but the central ones have continuous webs rather than racquet tips.

When foraging, motmots perch motionless until their keen eyes detect a beetle, a caterpillar, a spider, a butterfly, or a lizard on the foliage, on the ground or (as regards some of these) in the air. Then they make a swift dart, seize the victim, and carry it back to the perch, against which they usually beat it before gulping it down. Small fruits, plucked while the bird hovers on the wing, vary the diet of some species.

Although the utterances of motmots are all structurally simple, they vary immensely in tone from species to species. The Turquoise-browed Motmot voices a dull, wooden 'cawaak cawaak'. The call of the widespread Blue-diademed Motmot *Momotus momota* is a full, frog-like, not unmelodious 'coot coot'. At dawn, the rain-forest of Panama is filled with the hollow hooting of the Rufous Motmot, a mysterious, ghost-like sound difficult to trace to its source. The most melodious species is the Blue-throated Motmot, of which the delightfully clear and mellow notes are heard chiefly at dawn, when the members of a pair often sing in unison.

Motmots nest chiefly in burrows, which are dug by both sexes (in the species for which information is available). The earth is loosened with the bill and removed by kicking backwards with the feet each time a bird enters to resume digging. In the Turquoise-browed Motmot, the female seems to perform the greater share of the work, but the male sometimes gives her an insect. Often the burrow is in the vertical bank of a watercourse or road, but the Blue-diademed Motmot may dig its tunnel in the side of a mammal's burrow or of a narrow pit in level ground, which makes its nests very difficult to find. In this species, as in the Blue-throated Motmot, the burrow may be crooked, with one or several sharp turns ; but that of the Turquoise-browed Motmot is as a rule only slightly curved. Motmots' tunnels up to 14 feet in length have been recorded, but most are much shorter. Along the bottom of an occupied tunnel are two distinct parallel grooves, made by the birds' short legs as they shuffle in and out. In limestone regions, motmots sometimes nest in caverns or in niches in the sides of wells.

Three or four (rarely more) broad, roundish, pure white eggs are laid on the bare floor of the enlarged chamber at the end of the burrow. They are incubated by both parents, who sit for long periods (up to 6 hours continuously in the Blue-throated Motmot). While incubating, motmots regurgitate many chitinous pieces from their insect food and an occasional seed, all of which are trampled into the floor of their chamber. In the Blue-throated Motmot, the incubation period is 21 or 22 days. Nestling motmots, hatched blind and with no trace of down on their pink skin, are brooded and fed by both parents ; but no attempt is made to keep the nest clean. In the Blue-throated Motmot and the Turquoise-browed Motmot, the young leave the burrow when 28–31 days of age ; they are then well feathered, much in the pattern of the adults, and fly well, but their stubby tails of course still lack the racquet tips.

Blue-diademed Motmots may begin in autumn to dig the burrows in which they will breed 4–7 months later. Blue-throated Motmots dig their burrows even earlier, in June or July, soon after their young are fledged. These tunnels are soon finished and are then used as dormitories by the constantly mated pair throughout the winter months, when nights are cold and frosty. Even after the eggs are laid in these old burrows in the following spring, both parents continue to sleep with them, as they do with the nestlings. After the latter are fledged, they do not return to sleep in the burrow, but the parents sometimes continue to lodge in it until the new burrow is completed. The motmots of the lowlands, however, appear not to use their burrows as dormitories, and only one parent sleeps with the eggs or young.　　　　　　　　　　A.F.S.

See Plate 32 (colour).

Peters, J. L. 1945. Check-list of Birds of the World vol. 5. Cambridge, Mass.
Skutch, A. F. 1945. Life history of the Blue-throated Green Motmot. Auk 62 : 489–517.
Skutch, A. F. 1947. Life history of the Turquoise-browed Motmot. Auk 64 : 201–217.

MOULT: or 'molt' in American usage, the periodic shedding (ecdysis) and renewal (endysis) of plumage, and in some species of certain accessory structures of epidermal origin (see FEATHER ;

PLUMAGE ; and BILL) ; the term is also loosely applied to the period during which moulting occurs. In the usually annual cycle of the bird's life, the events of moult are adaptively timed in relation to the seasons of breeding and of migration (if any)—see BREEDING SEASON ; MIGRATION.

Determination. The cyclical occurrence of moult is determined by intrinsic (physiological) factors in which the thyroid and hypothalamic-pituitary-gonadal systems are principally concerned (see ENDOCRINE SYSTEM), activated also by extrinsic (physical) influences. Of the latter, light appears to be the most important, but temperature also contributes. As recent research has demonstrated the importance of the thyroid, the following points may be noted :

(*a*) Thyroid hormone (thyroxin) stimulates the developing feather papillae, causing cell-division (mitosis) and thereby accelerating moult. Progesterone acts synergistically with thyroxin, possibly by androgen/oestrogen inhibition.

(*b*) Failure of thyroid secretion suppresses moult, i.e. feather growth ; this has been established both experimentally and in cases of demonstrable pathology of the thyroid in nature.

(*c*) Thyroid acts selectively on different areas of the body surface ; the head and neck, wings, and tail are little affected, but the body feathering is profoundly so.

(*d*) The response to thyroid varies with species, for reasons that are uncertain. It is strongly marked in pigeons (Columbidae), and also in the Peacock *Pavo cristatus*, and in the domestic fowl. A less intense response is noted in the Partridge *Perdix perdix*, Kestrel *Falco tinnunculus*, Tawny Owl *Strix aluco*, Bullfinch *Pyrrhula pyrrhula*, and Jay *Garrulus glandarius*. Some crows (Corvidae) are extremely resistant to thyroid administration, e.g. the Jackdaw *Corvus monedula*.

(*e*) Administration of thyroid does not affect the order in which the feathers are moulted (see later).

(*f*) The latent period of a thyroid-induced moult is 5–7 days ; the intensity of the moult depends upon dosage. Repeated administration evokes a progressively diminishing response, presumably from exhaustion of proliferation of the cells of the papillae through over-stimulation. Repeated small doses at frequent intervals are more effective than larger doses at longer intervals ; but a massive single dose produces a very intense response.

(*g*) Extirpation of the thyroid in the Starling *Sturnus vulgaris* in April suppresses the postnuptial moult ; extirpation in May delays the moult by 15 days ; if extirpation be not performed until June, then a normal postnuptial moult ensues. This indicates that the thyroid is effective as an activator of moult only during a specific period. However, inactivation of the thyroid by administration of thiouracil—although it lowers metabolism—does not invariably suppress moult ; in fact in certain dosage thiouracil will provoke a moult. While the above important functions of the thyroid are to be noted, it is now believed that, in the main, control of moult is gonadal ; and the specific variability in response to thyroxin seems to support this assumption. Thyroxin as a pacemaker exerting a powerful influence upon general metabolism is doubtless responsible for the increase of up to 25 per cent in the metabolic rate which has been recorded during the moulting period, especially during that of the flight feathers.

The normal periodicity can be upset by disorders of endocrine balance, either experimentally induced (e.g. by ablation of organs or by administration of certain hormones) or occurring naturally in frank pathological states. Castration favours the loss of feathers, suggesting that the sex hormones inhibit moult. This hypothesis finds support in the 'eclipse' plumage of Anatidae (see later), assumed at the end of the reproductive period when gonadal activity is waning. There is no evidence that adrenalin has any effect on moult, although an injection of desoxycorticosterone will precipitate a moult, possibly through inhibition of gonadal hormones. Hypophysectomy provokes an unseasonable moult. Enheptin, growth factor (2—amino—m, 5 nitrothiazole), inhibits gonadotropins and thyroid stimulating hormone, and brings on a moult with gonadal regression. Castration in Brown Leghorns causes irregular ecdysis, the common factor being the inhibition or reduction of gonadotropin. Extrinsic factors influencing breeding and therefore moult are photoperiodicity, as well as rainfall and humidity with their effects upon environment.

The influence of temperature, in conjunction with the level of nutrition (fat deposition), has been demonstrated in experimental work on the Scarlet Tanager *Piranga erythromelas* and the Bobolink *Dolichonyx oryzivorus*. In these species, by enriching the diet and increasing fat deposition, the postnuptial moult was suppressed indefinitely. In *Piranga* the birds continued to moult from one red nuptial plumage into the same plumage again, the usual green non-breeding dress being missed in the sequence. By raising the temperature, body weight was decreased and the postnuptial moult ensued. As it is well known that the thyroid influences metabolism, these results may depend on activation of thyroid function. See Plate 7 (colour).

Purposes. Renewal of feathers is essential for the

maintenance of health, and of the functions of temperature regulation, protection of the body, and (in the vast majority of birds) flight—therefore for survival. It also subserves intraspecific recognition and accentuates secondary sexual characters, thereby enhancing display and so favouring the perpetuation of the species.

Frequency. All birds moult at least once a year, many species twice, and a few thrice. The main function of the postnuptial moult is the renewal of worn and faded plumage ; it is therefore general and almost always complete. In some groups, such as birds-of-prey (Falconiformes) and swallows (Hirundinidae), the moult of the remiges and rectrices may be delayed until mid-winter. This adaptation seems to be correlated with migration, during which birds of the two named groups are often in close association.

The prenuptial moult, when present, is usually partial. It intensifies the secondary sexual characters by brighter colours or by adding plumes or other adornments (e.g. the facial warty excrescences in the Ruff *Philomachus pugnax*). This moult tends to be more evident in males than in females, exceptions including the phalaropes (Phalaropodidae), the godwits *Limosa* spp., and the Dotterel *Eudromias morinellus*. Part of the colour change apparent at this season is in some species due to abrasion of the edges of feathers (see later). Miller (1961) states that the Andean Sparrow *Zonotrichia capensis* has two complete adult-type moults annually, each of two months' duration.

In the cranes (Gruidae) the remiges are moulted only every other year. In the cock of the Longtailed Yokohama Fowl (a domestic breed), after it has undergone two moults of the rectrices and tail-coverts during immaturity, these feathers are then retained for life, a matter of twelve years, the tail often attaining a length of over 25 feet.

In the Ptarmigan *Lagopus mutus* there is a partial moult during the late summer and autumn, when an admixture of the grey breeding dress and the brownish autumn plumage is observable before the birds pass into the white plumage of winter. Assumption of this winter plumage has been shown to depend on a fall in temperature ; this, by responsively increasing metabolism and acting through the endocrine system, suppresses melanin production (Salomonsen). The prenuptial moult in spring, later in males than in females, brings the birds into breeding dress (see also COLORATION, ADAPTIVE). Another example of a triple moult is provided by the Longtailed Duck *Clangula hyemalis*, which has—unusually among ducks—a breeding dress distinct from that worn through the winter.

The moult can be a purely local and normal condition, as in the case of defeathering of the incubation patch area which is initiated by the hormone prolactin, prior to the increased vascularity, epithelial hypertrophy, and oedema in preparation for incubation (Bayley 1952).

Sequences. At hatching, birds are variously covered, some being psilopaedic (bare except for the scantiest of neossoptile down) and altricial (fed by their parents in the nest), while others are ptilopaedic (well covered with down) and precocial (soon able to find their own food) ; this distinction, however, is only broadly true and there are exceptions (see YOUNG BIRD). The natal or nestling down plumage, such as it may be, gives place to the first covering of definite feathers. This juvenile plumage is, in turn, soon superseded by the first winter plumage, except that the remiges and tail feathers tend to be retained. This plumage may closely resemble the ' adult ' winter dress, but it commonly shows differences characteristic of immaturity. In the following spring many species acquire a first nuptial plumage (so called although they may or may not breed) not readily distinguishable from that of the adults ; the same is true of the second winter plumage ; and from the second nuptial plumage onwards the sequence in very many species is merely repetitive from year to year.

The foregoing is broadly true of the majority of passerine birds (the young being psilopaedic), and the typical sequence may be set out schematically as follows (terminology based on Dwight) :

    Neossoptile down plumage
      Postnatal moult
    Juvenile plumage
      Postjuvenile moult
    First winter (or non-nuptial) plumage
      First prenuptial moult
    First nuptial plumage
      First postnuptial moult
    Second (sometimes ' adult ') winter
      (or non-nuptial) plumage
      Second prenuptial moult
    Second (often ' adult ') nuptial plumage
      And so on.

The term ' second ' is scarcely applicable where there is no observable distinction from subsequent adult plumages and moults. In a few instances this may even be true of the term ' first ' ; thus, the Shore (or Horned) Lark *Eremophila alpestris* goes straight into apparently adult plumage at its postjuvenile moult, while in various species the distinction between yearlings and older birds is lost at the first prenuptial moult, i.e. well within the first year of life.

(The new *Handbook of North American Birds* is using a different terminology, slightly adapted from that of Humphrey & Parkes. In this, the term 'basic' is applied to a plumage that is the only one in the annual cycle, or to the non-nuptial plumage when there are 2 or 3; 'alternate' is applied to a second (nuptial) plumage; and 'supplementary' to a third plumage, whether it comes before or after the alternate. The sequence following the postnatal moult, in species with 2 plumages per cycle, is thus named as follows: 'Juvenal plumage; Prebasic I molt; Basic I plumage; Prealternate I molt; Alternate I plumage; Prebasic II molt'; and so on.)

The usual passerine pattern thus consists of 3 plumages and 5 moults in rather less than the first 2 years of life; there are exceptions (e.g. the White-throat *Sylvia communis*, in which the moult is annual). From the second nuptial ('Alternate II') plumage, if not sooner, the repetition of definitive sequences merely marks the individual's increasing maturity, with or without visible enhancement of adult characteristics.

Some other species, however, take several years to acquire the adult characteristics in full, and the age of the bird may be shown in the successive plumages, e.g. gulls (Larinae). The period for complete development may be as long as 7 years (Twelve-wired Bird-of-paradise *Seleucidis melanoleuca*) — or even 10 (Baldheaded Eagle *Haliaetus leucocephalus*), at least in captivity.

There are also substantial differences at the beginning of the sequences, apart from the broad distinction between psilopaedic and ptilopaedic young. In some psilopaedic species there is no neossoptile down at all; thus kingfishers (Alcedinidae) and woodpeckers (Picidae) are hatched completely naked and later acquire a first plumage of true feathers; more commonly there is a scanty down plumage, at hatching or later in nestling life, on the future pterylae. In the Pelecaniformes the young are altricial, but although hatched naked acquire a thick covering of down within a few days. In a few groups, e.g. penguins (Spheniscidae), divers (Gaviidae), and some owls (Strigiformes), there are two successive plumages of neossoptile down, termed protoptile and mesoptile respectively. In a few species a postjuvenile plumage is interpolated between the juvenile plumage proper, lost very early, and the first winter plumage.

In the Galliformes the young become air-borne in a matter of two weeks (see FLIGHT, PRECOCIOUS). They are enabled to do so by having small pre-juvenile remiges, which are moulted between the sixth and fourteenth weeks, when the true juvenile remiges are acquired. In the extreme case of the megapodes (Megapodiidae), the downy young have prejuvenile remiges at the time of hatching and are able to fly almost at once.

Eclipse Plumage. In some groups the full adult plumage, in which the birds breed, is replaced at the end of the reproductive season by a dull 'eclipse' plumage that is worn for only a short time before a fresh adult plumage is acquired; this is found among the ducks (Anatidae), bee-eaters (Meropidae), cuckoo-shrikes (Campephagidae), sunbirds (Nectariniidae), and weavers (Ploceidae). It is particularly striking in the males of typical duck species, which lose their very distinctive plumage early in the breeding season and become more like the cryptically coloured females. As they shed all the remiges simultaneously, the birds are rendered temporarily flightless; they accordingly take no part in parental duties, but remain out on the open sea or in thick cover until they emerge with flight restored and in full plumage again. This very early moult of the drakes does not occur in all the Anatidae, in some of which the males share parental responsibilities (e.g. the Shelduck *Tadorna tadorna*, geese *Anser* spp. etc., swans *Cygnus* spp.). An exception to the temporary total loss of the flight feathers is the Magpie Goose *Anseranas semipalmata*. The moults of the two sexes of a species do not always coincide — in the Mallard *Anas platyrhynchos* the drake is through the moult a month ahead of the duck.

Two theories have been advanced to explain eclipse plumage. One is that it represents a dull plumage such as might be worn throughout the winter, but is in fact replaced by a rapidly assumed nuptial dress. The other regards it as a specialised interpolated plumage serving a protective function and so having a survival value.

Order of Moult. The common pattern of a complete postnuptial moult is that of a symmetrical loss of a few feathers from homologous pterylae on the two sides of the body; in this way, feather loss and gain are nicely balanced to maintain function. Most usually, the primaries are the first to begin moulting, followed by the secondaries and the tail feathers, and then by the body feathers generally; the moults of these different groups of feathers usually overlap. There are, however, many anomalies and exceptions.

The primaries are usually shed in a definite order, fixed for the species; this apparently non-adaptive character has been used for taxonomic purposes in some groups (Stresemann). Most often, the primaries are moulted in succession from the innermost outwards; in other cases the moult may begin with two feathers simultaneously, say the first and seventh primaries, proceeding outwards from each. In other cases, however, the order appears to be irregular. The secondaries are commonly moulted from the outermost inwards.

Diesselhorst (1961) and Stresemann (1963) draw attention to the fact that in *Muscicapa striata*, in contrast to all other passerines, the moult of the primaries is in ascending order, while the rectrices are moulted centripetally. Diesselhorst further notes, in regard to the moult of the secondaries and tail feathers, that in these feather tracts the ordinary passerine sequence is reversed ; this reversal it is thought may have been originated by a single mutation. V. & E. Stresemann (1961), referring to the Alcedinidae, state that a grouping of the genera in accordance with the order of the moult of the primaries corresponds exactly with the 3 sub-families Daceloninae, Alcedininae, and Cerylinae established on morphological grounds by W. Miller in 1912.

Simultaneous moult of all the flight feathers has already been mentioned in respect of species of Anatidae going into eclipse. In these cases the moult of the remiges is rapid, but the body moult is slow. In the smaller Anatidae replacement of the remiges takes about 21 days. The Shelduck is flightless for 25–31 days, the average for drakes being 29 days and for ducks 27 days ; the actual time for shedding the remiges is believed to be 3 days. Flight is again possible long before the full length of the remiges is achieved. In swans a flightless period persists for 42–49 days.

It may be remarked that the Shelduck undertakes a 'moult migration' at the end of the breeding season. The main body of birds from the British Isles resorts to the sandbanks in the Bight of Heligoland to spend the flightless period, and some to the Bridgwater Bay area in the west of England.

Simultaneous moult of the remiges is also found in flamingos (Phoenicopteridae), grebes (Podicipitidae), divers (Gaviidae), and darters (Anhingidae).

The tail feathers are moulted in symmetrical pairs. The moult commonly begins with the central pair and proceeds centrifugally ; but it may begin with the outermost pair and proceed centripetally ; or, sometimes, it may begin with an intermediate pair and proceed both outwards and inwards in each half of the tail. Small owls (Strigiformes) tend to moult all the rectrices at once, whereas in the larger species of owls these feathers are replaced more gradually. In woodpeckers (Picidae) and treecreepers (Certhiidae) the two central rectrices—used for support in climbing—are retained until the new rectrices of the other pairs are grown.

A most remarkable moult pattern is found in some of the hornbills (Bucerotidae), for in them the females moult all the remiges and rectrices in extremely accelerated sequence (so that all the quills are absent at once), and in some species the body feathers as well, during the time that they are incubating and are walled up in the nesting cavity (Moreau)—see HORNBILL. In some crows (Corvidae), such as the Magpie *Pica pica*, all the feathers of the head and neck are moulted almost simultaneously.

In the petrels (Procellariidae) and in the Pelecaniformes (except the Anhingidae) full power of flight is maintained throughout, and the moult is consequently protracted. Moulting is also prolonged in the Falconiformes and in swifts *Apus* spp. ; its presence is observable in some large eagles *Aquila* spp. at all times of year.

Among flightless birds, the Ostrich *Struthio camelus* is an example of a species with a protracted moult. In the penguins (Spheniscidae) the moult is general, and as a rule rapid, the feathers being shed irregularly in patches. In Humboldt's Penguin *Spheniscus humboldti* moult occupies about 12 days, and in the Emperor Penguin *Aptenodytes forsteri* 20 days.

Intraspecific Differences. Several instances in which the moult sequence or pattern of a species differs according to the sex of the bird have already been mentioned. Another is the Black Grouse *Lyrurus tetrix*, in which the cock moults twice a year but the hen only once.

There may also be differences depending on age. Thus, in some shrikes *Lanius* spp. and orioles *Oriolus* spp. there are two moults annually during the early years of life, but thereafter only one. The duration of a full moult varies much, according to the species ; in the Shore (or Horned) Lark *Eremophila alpestris* the adult type of plumage is acquired in 3 months.

Cases are known in which there are differences in moulting between geographical races of a single species, presumably in adaptation to climatic or other conditions of the respective areas. Johnston (1961) cites the accelerated tempo of the breeding and moulting cycles in Northern Alaska in several species, e.g. in *Larus hyperboreus* where moult commences soon after the eggs are laid in order to complete both breeding and moult in an abbreviated summer period.

Accidental Moult. When feathers are lost by accidental causes, those lost are generally regenerated before the next normal moult. If breast feathers are plucked from the immatures of the Bullfinch *Pyrrhula pyrrhula* or the Golden Pheasant *Chrysolophus pictus*, the regenerated feathers are those of the first prenuptial plumage ; doubtless this applies to other species also.

Missed Moult. Failure or retardation of the moult can occur in circumstances causing diminished vigour or in actual disease. This may be general but is more often localised and symmetrical, the feathers of the affected regions showing excessive wear and fading. Retardation of endysis can be purely local as a result of disease, and has been seen in association with the occurrence of a neoplasm (sarcoma) of the humerus in a Muscovy Duck *Cairina moschata* in which feather growth had proceeded to only approximately 50 per cent of that of the healthy wing.

Abrasive or Substractive Moult. Certain species, such as the Linnet *Acanthis cannabina*, the Reed-Bunting *Emberiza schoeniclus*, the Starling *Sturnus vulgaris*, and many other passerines, by abrasion accompanying the prenuptial moult become more contrasting and colourful as the pale edges of the feathers wear off. It is possible that the actual colour of the remaining part of the feathers also becomes intensified, since the red of the breast of the cock Linnet becomes brilliantly scarlet as the breeding season advances.

Aptosochromatosis. In support of the hypothesis that colour change can occur without moult, otherwise than by abrasion, a measure of fresh evidence has been brought forward that deserves close study (Staples & Harrison 1949). For 'cosmetic coloration' see COLOUR.

Moult of Accessory Structures. These cases can be divided into three classes. First, there are those that come under the heading of secondary sexual characters accompanying and supplementing the prenuptial moult, being developed expressly for the breeding season and being discarded at the end of the reproductive period. Typical examples are found in the auks (Alcidae), the Puffin *Fratercula arctica* providing a familiar instance ; in this species the highly coloured parts of the bill, the two small supraorbicular excrescences, and the puffy 'rosettes' at the angles of the gape are shed. Also, the Horn-billed Auk *Cerorhinca* ('*Ceratirhina*') *monocerata* moults the internaral protuberance. A further example is the 'bill-horn' of the males of the American White Pelican *Pelecanus erythrorhynchus*, the horn falling off at the end of the breeding season.

Secondly to be mentioned is the moulting of the claws in ptarmigan *Lagopus* spp. It is very probable that the tarsal scutellae are also moulted regularly ; evidence in support of this is provided by the case of a Song Thrush *Turdus philomelos* with abnormal cutaneous horns on its head and on one leg, these being cast each time the bird moulted. Probably this applies to all pathological structures arising from tissues of epidermal origin, including those of the uropygeal gland (which in certain circumstances can produce a 'horn' that is moulted regularly).

The third category consists of structures that serve a temporary function only. In the Hoatzin *Opisthocomus hoazin* the young have functional claws on the 1st and 2nd digits of the manus for the first week of life only ; these are shed and during after life the claws are represented by minute callosities. A further instance of structures of this nature is afforded by the 'heel' pads of woodpeckers and wrynecks (Picidae), toucans (Ramphastidae), scansorial barbets (Capitonidae), and others, this structure falling off when the birds leave the nest.

See Plates 7, 8, 18, 19 (colour).   J.M.H.

Dwight, J. 1900. The sequence of plumages and moults of the passerine birds of New York. Annals N.Y. Acad. Sci. 13 : 73–360.
Humphrey, P. S. & Parkes, K. C. 1959. An approach to the study of molts and plumages. Auk 76 : 1–31.
Miller, A. H. 1961. Molt cycles in equatorial Andean Sparrows. Condor 63 : 143–161.
Moreau, R. E. 1937. The comparative breeding biology of the African hornbills (Bucerotidae). Proc. Zool. Soc. Lond. 107A : 331–346.
Palmer, R. S. (ed.) 1962. Handbook of North American Birds vol. 1. New Haven and London.
Salomonsen, F. 1939. Moults and sequence of plumages in the Rock Ptarmigan (*Lagopus mutus* (Montin.)). Videns. Medd. Naturh. Foren. Kjöb. 103 : 1–491.
Staples, C. P. & Harrison, J. G. 1949. Further to colour change without moult. Bull. Brit. Orn. Cl. 69 : 33–37.
Stresemann, V. & E. 1961. Die Handschwingen-Mauser der Eisvögel (Alcedinidae). J. Orn. 122 : 439–455. (And similar studies of other groups.)
Stresemann, E. 1963. Taxonomic significance of wing moult. Proc. XIII Internat. Orn. Congr., Ithaca, N.Y., 1962 : 171–175.

MOUND-BIRDS; MOUND-BUILDER: see MEGAPODE

MOUNTAINEER: *Oreonympha nobilis* (for family see HUMMINGBIRD).

MOUNTAINGEM: substantive name of *Lampornis* spp. (for family see HUMMINGBIRD).

MOURNER: substantive name of species of *Laniocera*, *Rhytipterna*, and allied genera (for family see COTINGA).

MOUSEBIRD: substantive name, alternatively 'coly', of the species of Coliidae (sole family of the Coliiformes) ; in the plural ('mousebirds', 'colies'), general term for the family. They are birds of such specialised character that modern taxonomists have placed the family in an order of its own, and structurally they have many peculiarities to justify that course. The species all much resemble one another in appearance, and in each the sexes are alike. The body is small, approximating to that of a House

Sparrow *Passer domesticus*, but the tail of 10 feathers with very stiff shafts is long in proportion, in some species 10 inches in length ; in all members of the family it is strikingly graduated. Another distinctive feature is that all are crested. The bill is short, curved, and rather powerful. The feet are very strong ; the toes, which are remarkable for the fact that all four may exceptionally be directed forwards, are provided with long sharp claws. The supposed resemblance to mice, in the way that colies creep about within a bush, may be fanciful ; but they do use their adaptable feet for perching or clinging in all kinds of positions. The note of some species is described as 'twittering', but the Blue-naped Mousebird *Colius macrourus* has a long-drawn clear whistle which is uttered on the wing. The plumage is exceptionally soft and the feathers are loosely attached to the skin. Colies are sombrely dressed in grey or brown, relieved in *C. macrourus* with a blue nape patch, in the Red-faced Mousebird *C. indicus* with red cheeks, in the White-headed Mousebird *C. leucocephalus* with a white head, and in the Bar-breasted (or Speckled) Mousebird *C. striatus* with barred or speckled breast ; all of these show subspecific variation, but the White-backed Mousebird *C. colius* and the Chestnut-backed Mousebird *C. castanotus* do not.

Colies are extremely sociable and are usually seen in small parties ; and several may roost huddled together. Both sexes take part in incubation, and each parent, on relief by its mate, may join a flock that probably includes members of other sitting pairs not engaged in domestic duties at the moment (*C. striatus* in Tanganyika—E. G. Rowe, personal communication). The flight is sometimes undulating—a sail, and then a series of quick wing-beats—and the birds are apt to fly straight into the heart of a bush. More often the flight from bush to bush is direct and rapid, and when they are flushed they tend to leave in quick succession rather than all at once. Occasionally, perhaps when performing local movements, they fly in a compact flock.

Mousebirds normally eat fruit and other vegetable matter, but one has been known to rip open the nest of a sunbird (Nectariniidae sp.) and carry off the young. The nest may be a shallow cup of fibrous material lined with bits of grass (*C. macrourus*) or a platform of fine twigs and rootlets lined with leaves (*C. striatus*). Eggs number 2–4, either plain cream or white, or speckled and scrawled with shades of brown or sepia. Breeding occurs from the orchard-bush country at a comparatively low level to an altitude of at least 6000 feet in the Cameroon montane district and probably higher in Abyssinia.

The family is confined to the Ethiopian Region

¼

Blue-naped Mousebird or Coly
Colius macrourus, of tropical Africa. *C.E.T.K.*

and is not represented in Madagascar. The 6 species in a single genus, all mentioned above, among them cover the greater part of Africa from the French Sudan and Abyssinia south to Cape Province, in which huge area they are confined to the savanna and acacia steppe. D.A.B.

See Plate 30 (colour).

MOUSTACHIAL : applied to a streak, in some plumage patterns, running back from the base of the bill.

MOUTH : see BILL ; TONGUE ; also ALIMENTARY SYSTEM ; RESPIRATORY SYSTEM

MOUTH MARKINGS : signals inside the mouth of a nestling, often on the tongue (see TONGUE).

MUD-HEN : popular name for the American Coot *Fulica americana* (see RAIL).

MUDLARK : see MAGPIE-LARK

MUDNEST-BUILDERS : general term for the Grallinidae (see under MAGPIE-LARK).

MULE : see CAGE BIRD

MULGA : name for a type of bush country in Australia, characterised by *Acacia aneura*.

MÜLLERIAN DUCTS : see REPRODUCTIVE SYSTEM

MUNIA : substantive name in Asia of various species of Estrildidae ; in the plural, sometimes used as a general term for the group (see WEAVER-FINCH).

MURRE : alternative substantive name (preferred in American usage) of guillemots of the genus *Uria* (Alcidae)—see AUK.

MURRELET : substantive name of species of *Brachyramphus*, *Endomychura*, and *Synthliboramphus* (see AUK).

MUSCICAPIDAE : a family of the Passeriformes, suborder Oscines, now commonly regarded as embracing a great assemblage of mainly Old World, largely insectivorous, ten-primaried song-birds ; these may be grouped in the following subfamilies (of which several were earlier accorded familial rank) :

Turdinae : thrushes, robins, chats, wren-thrush (*Zeledonia*)—see THRUSH (1).

Timaliinae : babblers, wren-tit (*Chamaea*), rockfowl (*Picathartes*)—see BABBLER.

Cinclosomatinae (Orthonychinae) : rail-babblers, quail-thrushes, logrunners—see RAIL-BABBLER.

Paradoxornithinae : parrotbills, reedling (*Panurus*) —see PARROTBILL (1).

Polioptilinae : gnatcatchers, gnatwrens (*Ramphocaenus*, *Microbates*)—see GNATCATCHER.

Sylviinae : Old World warblers, kinglets (*Regulus*), tit-warblers (*Leptopoecile*), fern-bird (*Bowdleria*)—see WARBLER (1).

Malurinae : Australian ' wrens ' or warblers—see WREN (2).

Muscicapinae : Old World flycatchers, fantails (*Rhipidura*, etc.)—see FLYCATCHER (1).

Pachycephalinae : thickheads or whistlers—see THICKHEAD.

The editors of Peters's *Check-List of Birds of the World* recognise another subfamily, the Monarchinae, mainly for the paradise flycatchers and for the oceanic island genera *Monarcha* and *Myiagra*, but these are regarded as included in the Muscicapinae for the purposes of the present work. Others separate the fantails from the Muscicapinae as the Rhipidurinae, or the shrike-tits from the Pachycephalinae as the Falcunculinae, or the Australian chats from the Malurinae as the Epthianurinae ; others again include the Paradoxornithinae in the Timaliinae. Not all taxonomists follow the author of the articles here in separating the rail-babblers from the Timaliinae as the Cinclosomatinae. The fact is that sharp boundaries cannot be drawn at subfamilial level and that taxonomic groupings within the assemblage are largely arbitrary. The purely European ornithologist, who finds no difficulty in separating thrushes, warblers, and flycatchers, may regret the downgrading of traditional families

and the inconvenience of so large a single one ; but consideration of all the tropical forms of intermediate character or doubtful affinity seems to exclude any other course in the present state of knowledge. According to Vaurie, the flycatcher species *Rhinomyias gularis* in its geographical variation completely bridges the gap between the flycatchers and the thrushes, so that if the conspecificity were not certain a taxonomist might be tempted to place some of the subspecies in the one group and some in the other.

Vaurie, C. 1952. A review of the bird genus Rhinomyias (Muscicapidae). Amer. Mus. Novit. no. 1570: 1-36

MUSCLE : see MUSCULATURE

MUSCULAR CONTRACTION : see METABOLISM

MUSCULATURE : the system of muscles, which are the specialised organs for effecting movement. Collectively these form the ' flesh ', which in an average bird constitutes almost half the total body weight, being highly developed in relation to the power of flight. Muscular tissue is one of the four fundamental bodily tissues and constitutes the major part of most muscles ; but in every muscular organ connective tissue is an important component, e.g. the tendons, attaching the fleshy parts to fixed points, and the fasciae, serving as a harness within which the contractile elements perform their work. Sometimes, as in the limb muscles of gallinaceous birds (Galliformes), bone is a component of a muscle, some of the tendons in old birds being replaced by bone.

Characters of Muscular Tissue. The essential feature of muscular tissue is its specialisation for the function of contraction, whereon it becomes shortened in one dimension, thereby drawing the attached ends closer together. Contractility is a fundamental property of all protoplasm, but in muscular tissue this power is enhanced by the development of fibrillar contractile material within the cell protoplasm. Muscular tissue consists principally of so-called muscle fibres, but (unlike connective tissue fibres, which are by-products of cell activity and located extracellularly) muscle fibres are themselves elongated cells, containing nuclei and other bodies similar to those found in ordinary cells but with the addition of contractile fibrils arranged longitudinally.

Muscular tissue occurs in two principal forms : (i) the so-called plain, unstriped, or involuntary muscle, and (ii) the striped or voluntary muscle. The epithet ' striped ' refers to a cross-striped pattern seen when the fibres are viewed microscopically.

All fibres possess the longitudinal striping produced by the contained contractile fibrils, but a cross-striped appearance is superadded in the second category of fibres by virtue of alternate pale and dark bands on individual fibrils, and this is rendered still more evident by the fact that neighbouring fibrils are arranged with their alternating bands in accurate register.

Unstriped muscle fibres are short, fusiform cells with few fibrils. They occur especially in the walls of hollow organs, blood-vessels, glandular ducts, and in association with feathers. They are principally concerned with slow, rhythmic movements, e.g. the intestinal movements that are not under control of the will. They are, therefore, referred to as visceral muscles, being nowhere connected to the skeleton.

Striped muscle fibres are much more complicated in structure ; they are immensely longer and are connected, at least by one end, with the skeleton, upon which they exert lever-like actions determined by the will of the animal—exerted from the brain through the nervous system, every muscle fibre being the terminus for a motor nerve fibre (see NERVOUS SYSTEM).

A third category, somewhat intermediate in structure between the two others, is found in the heart and hence known as cardiac muscle (see HEART). Its fibres consist of short, broad inter-communicating cells with longitudinal fibrillae, but also marked by cross-bands or discs albeit these lack the alternating light and dark pattern and are spaced remotely. Cardiac muscle is a highly specialised tissue, developed from unstriped muscle, to which it is more closely allied than to the cross-striped variety. It is concerned with the continued rhythmic contraction of the cardiac chambers and is highly developed in rapidly beating hearts, e.g. those of hummingbirds (Trochilidae).

The rest of this article is concerned solely with the category of striped or skeletal muscle. This occurs in two varieties, called ' pale ' (or ' white ') and ' red '. The difference is of some physiological moment in that the red variety is concerned with somewhat heavier and often more prolonged duties ; thus it occurs in the pectoral muscles of, e.g. the Kestrel *Falco tinnunculus*, whereas those of the domestic fowl, with waning powers of flight, are ' white '. Conversely, certain leg muscles of running birds, such as the fowl, contain a large proportion of ' red ' fibres. The two varieties differ profoundly in their microscopic appearances, the red (among other features) having specialised arrangements in respect of its blood supply.

Parts of a Muscle. The part of a skeletal muscle of greatest functional importance is its ' belly '—the portion where the contractile fibres are concentrated. This may be a spindle-shaped structure, a flat sheet, or some intermediate form. Some muscles have more than one belly, located either side by side or end to end, separated by an intermediate tendon or a connective tissue intersection. At either end the belly typically becomes partly or wholly replaced by connective tissue in the form of a tendon or (in the case of flat muscles) an aponeurosis. By means of these the muscle gains its attachments to the skeleton. The more fixed attachment from which the muscle normally acts is called the origin ; the more movable (usually more distal) attachment is its insertion ; but in certain circumstances the functions may be reversed. The skeletal attachments when mediated by connective tissue, as they usually are, leave their impress on the bone in the form of lines, crests, ridges, or tubercles, which are characteristic for each bone. In other words, bone structure is determined largely by local musculature (see SKELETON).

Naming of Muscles. Muscles are named in various ways, e.g. according to shape (cucullaris), attachments (ilio–tibialis), position (supracoracoideus), or action (expansor secundariorum). Unfortunately, avian myological nomenclature is very confusing, different writers having adopted different names for the same muscle. Confusion has also arisen from mistaken homology, i.e. by misinterpreting avian muscles as equivalents of muscles occupying similar positions in human anatomy. Although not infallible, the best guide to muscular homologies lies in their nerve supply, which in the long run depends on their embryological history.

On the basis of their nerve supply, skeletal muscles are primarily divided into those supplied by the motor divisions of cranial nerves and those similarly supplied by nerves from the spinal cord. Of the former group there are two subgroups : (a) those derived, like the spinal muscles, from embryonic pre-muscle masses called myotomes, and (b) those related to the so-called visceral arches and supplied by the nerves of those arches (which correspond with the gill arches of fishes). The former group comprises the ocular muscles and the latter the muscles associated with the jaws, throat, and related structures. Muscles supplied by spinal nerves are further grouped according to their relations to the skeleton ; axial muscles are those aligned along the spinal column and associated with the ribs ; appendicular muscles are those connected with the limbs and include also those that bind the limb girdles to the trunk.

Schematically, this grouping may be shown as follows :

I. Cranial muscles

  (a) Derived from myotomes (somatic)
    1. Ocular muscles
    2. Hypoglossal musculature
  (b) Derived from visceral arch mesenchyme
    1. Muscles of the mandibular arch
    2. Muscles of hyoidean arch
    3. Muscles of posterior arches

II. Spinal muscles (derived from trunk myotomes)

  (a) Axial muscles
    1. Epaxial (dorsal to spinal column)
    2. Hypaxial (ventral to spinal column)
  (b) Appendicular muscles

Cranial Muscles. 1. *Ocular muscles* (supplied by the 3rd, 4th, and 6th cranial nerves). These are the small muscles concerned in moving the eyeball and differ not at all in birds from those in other vertebrates, performing the same functions throughout, and therefore of little import in taxonomy. Included here is also the levator muscle of the upper eyelid, and the muscles (M. pyramidalis and M. quadratus) responsible for the movements of the nictitating membrane (see VISION).

2. *Hypoglossal musculature.* This is a small but varied muscular group supplied by the 12th cranial nerve ; it includes certain tongue muscles and fibres which migrate to the neck even as far as the sternum (e.g. the sterno-hyoideus in *Apteryx*). These may be represented by laryngo-hyoideus, tracheo-hyoideus, or sterno-trachealis and so forth, according to species. In ducks (Anatidae) a clavicular attachment occurs spanning the trachea (ypsilo-trachealis). In front of the tongue and serving as protractors thereof are the genio-glossi. Other elements connect the various parts of the hyoid apparatus.

3. *Muscles of the mandibular arch* (supplied by 5th cranial nerve). Following Lakjer, these fall into two groups on developmental grounds, namely those derived from the first dorsal constrictor mass and those developed from the adductor mandibulae, as shown in the table.

Constrictor I dorsalis

M. protractor pterygoidei	M. protractor pterygoidei proper
	M. protractor quadrati
M. levator bulbi	M. tensor periorbitae
	M. depressor palpebrae inferioris
Add. mandibulae externus	*a* superficial
	b medial
	c deep

Adductor mandibulae

Add. mandibulae posterior	
Add. mandibulae internus	M. pseudotemporalis
	M. pterygoideus

It will be noted that some derivatives of the constrictor become associated with the orbital floor and on contraction serve to raise the eyeball, whilst another element is a depressor of the lower eyelid. On the contrary, the derivatives of the adductor mandibulae correspond closely with what in mammals are termed the muscles of mastication ; they effect movements of the lower jaw in closing the bill and in such side to side movements as are necessary, e.g. in seed cracking. The most important here are the pterygoid muscles and the pseudotemporalis. The former arises from the ventral surface of the pterygoid and palatine bones, sometimes from the maxilla also ; it inserts on the medial surface of the mandible. Their action is to close the bill, or, when the mouth is open, to flex the upper mandible when the latter is provided, as in parrots (Psittacidae) and ducks, with a hinge-like articulation with the cranium.

The pseudotemporalis consists of a variable number of parts, the most important being a bundle that springs from the postorbital process and the quadrate and passes to the mandible in front of the joint, deep to the jugal arch. This corresponds rather to the mammalian masseter than to the temporal muscle, the latter being represented by two or three small slips arising from the lower part of the orbit and interorbital septum and inserting on the palatine and pterygoid bones.

Also supplied by the 5th nerve is the mylohyoideus, which forms the fleshy floor of the mouth, connecting the two halves of the mandible. It is developed from the ventral constrictor of the first arch. For further details and taxonomic implications concerning the mandibular musculature see Starck & Barnikol and Fiedler.

4. *Muscles of the hyoid arch* (supplied by 7th cranial nerve). These comprise the so-called facialis musculature because, in mammals, a large element of it migrates beneath the skin of the face to differentiate into the muscles of expression—these are lacking in birds. Chief representatives here are the depressor mandibulae, which corresponds with the posterior belly of the mammalian digastric, and a mylohyoideus posterior. The latter is continuous with the mylohyoideus anterior in front, but it arises on the outer surface of the hinder part of the mandible and sometimes spreads to the occiput. It inserts in the angle between the hyoid horn and the forward projection of the hyoid into the tongue. It elevates the

tongue and larynx, drawing them backwards. When the tongue is elongated and extraordinarily pro-tractile, as in woodpeckers (Picidae) and humming-birds (Trochilidae), it may differentiate into two parts, a serpi-hyoideus and a stylo-hyoideus, the former from the serpiform process of the mandible, the latter from the occiput (see TONGUE).

The depressor mandibulae is a large and often compound muscle. It arises from the occiput later-ally and inserts on the inner process of the angle of the mandible and therefore acts as antagonist to the pterygoideus and pseudotemporalis.

5. *Muscles of the posterior arches* (supplied by 9th and 10th cranial nerves). These comprise the con-strictor muscles of the pharynx, the laryngeal muscles that close the glottis during swallowing, and the tiny syringeal muscles (see SYRINX).

Spinal Muscles. A. *Axial Musculature* : 1. *Epaxial*. This is comprised principally by fibres connecting the vertebrae together dorsally, acting therefore as extensors of the spine. It also includes fibres connecting the occiput with the anterior cervical vertebrae (e.g. biventer cervicis, splenius, rectus capitis dorsalis). All are supplied by dorsal divisions of the spinal nerves.

2. *Hypaxial*. These may be divided topographi-cally into three groups, a sub-vertebral system, a lateral series of superimposed flank muscles, and a ventral or rectus sheet closing the body-wall below. All are innervated by ventral primary divisions of spinal nerves. The subvertebral series constitutes a ventral counterpart of the epaxial system, but less continuous, being developed chiefly in the neck, though also represented in the tail. They serve as flexors of the vertebrae, and of the head upon the neck. The lateral system is largely supported by the ribs and fills the interspaces between them ; but in the abdominal region, where ribs are lacking, the musculature provides the external and internal oblique and transversalis muscles, in that order from without inwards. Inferiorly, the rectus abdominis in birds is short, passing from the pelvis forwards to the hinder edge of the sternum.

B. *Appendicular Musculature*. Muscles of the limb and limb-girdles are historically derived in the main from the lateral system of hypaxial somatic musculature and are supplied by the lateral branches of the ventral primary divisions of the spinal nerves, the filaments of which invade the limb-buds in the embryo at the time when the core of the buds is becoming differentiated into muscular tissue (see DEVELOPMENT, EMBRYONIC). Each limb-bud is a product of that district of the skin (over several segments) normally supplied by these lateral nerves. In total bulk the appendicular muscles far exceed

all the rest, and among them are many of taxonomic importance—more, however, in the hind limb than in the fore limb, as the wing is similarly constructed and performs much the same function in all birds except penguins (Spheniscidae), so that there is little reason for profound modification in adaptation to function. The very reverse holds good in the hind limb, where profound changes occur in correlation with the divergent foot structure adapted for multi-farious purposes in the different avian groups (see LEG).

Musculature of the fore limb. In view of the above remarks, this will be dealt with only briefly (see also FLIGHT). The largest, most powerful, and most characteristic muscle is the pectoralis, which forms the bulk of the fleshy mass on the breast. Its fibres arise from the body and keel of the sternum in a U-shaped field of attachment and converge for-wards and laterally to a stout tendon inserting on a tuberosity at the upper end of the humerus. Its action is to depress the wing.

Deep to the preceding is a smaller pectoralis termed supracoracoideus. It springs also from the keel and body of the sternum, with additional fibres from the coraco-clavicular membrane. Its stout tendon passes through the foramen triosseum and then over the shoulder-joint to insert on the upper tubercle of the humerus. Its action is to abduct and rotate the humerus. In ' ratite ' birds it is reduced, springing almost solely from the coracoid (see SKELETON).

Fleshy tissue over the shoulder prominence is pro-vided by the deltoideus muscle. This is often com-pound and also sends off slips (sometimes reinforced by fibres from other muscles) to the propatagium. Thus the propatagialis longus (tensor patagii longus) forms the support for the free margin of the propa-tagium. It is composed of slips from deltoid, pectoralis, cucullaris, and biceps, and it is always present. Its long elastic tendon attaches to the carpus. Contrariwise, the propatagialis brevis, although similarly composed, is absent in *Apteryx* and some other ' ratites ' and in penguins ; but elsewhere it is often complex. In woodpeckers (Picidae), where it is simplest, it shows a belly and a strong tendon along the antero-lateral side of the upper arm attaching itself to the proximal tendon of the forearm muscle, extensor metacarpi radialis longus, just beyond the lateral condyle of the hum-erus. In other birds it usually divides and may receive slips from the long propatagial muscle. In some cases, as in petrels (Procellariiformes) there are sesa-moid bones in these inserting slips. Garrod con-sidered the various arrangements to be of taxonomic significance.

On the dorsal side the most important muscles are the cucullaris (equivalent to the combined mammalian trapezius and sterno-mastoid) and posteriorly, the latissimus dorsi. Cucullaris has a linear origin extending from the occiput along the spines of all the cervical vertebrae and inserts mainly on the clavicle, but also sends fibres to the skin of the shoulder. The latissimus dorsi, a broad triangular sheet, arises by aponeurosis from the vertebral column in the mid-line, behind the cucullaris as far back as the pelvis. It inserts along a line on the upper part of the humeral shaft and also sends fibres to the metapatagium, which, together with contributions from another deeper muscle, the serratus superficialis, constitute the metapatagialis muscle. The serratus contribution comes from the ribs and connects not only with skin but also with the proximal cubital quills. The latissimus portion acts indirectly on the metapatagium by joining the anconeus longus.

The upper arm is provided with flexor and extensor groups as in other land vertebrates, the former including biceps and brachialis and the latter a triceps (= anconeus). From the last mentioned is derived in part an important expansor secundariorum, which inserts by fleshy slips on the bases of the proximal two or three secondary quills. Proximally it comprises an elastic tendinous band with connections on the sterno-scapular ligament and often by means of a fibrous pulley with the axillary region. This muscle is lacking in penguins, auks (Alcidae), petrels, owls (Strigiformes), parrots (Psittacidae), and several other groups, but complicated in anserines and gallinaceous birds (for details see especially Berger, who proved its presence in passerines, where it had formerly been stated to be absent, and also that the muscle is comprised wholly or partly of unstriped fibres).

Musculature of the hind limb. Following Stresemann, these muscles may be considered in ten groups :

1. *Dorsal group of ilio-femoral muscles* passing from the dorsal surface of the ilium to the great trochanter of the femur, or beyond. Here are included the gluteal muscles—abductors of the thigh.

2. *Ilio-femoralis internus*—a single muscle corresponding to the iliacus of mammals, serving as an abductor and medial rotator.

3. *Ambiens*—an important muscle inherited by the more primitive birds from reptiles, but lost in the higher groups, whence Garrod divided the Class Aves into Homalogonatae (those with the muscle) and the Anomalogonatae (see AMBIENS). When present it is a long, fusiform, subcutaneous structure arising on the ilium just in front of the acetabulum (pectineal process or ilio-pubic spine). Its tendon of insertion passes over the knee joint laterally and

ends in a complex fashion. It perforates the lateral head of the peroneus longus and forms one of the heads of the deep flexor muscle of the second and third toes. In action it assists in flexion of the toes whilst the knee is flexed in perching, but it is evidently not essential to this mechanism as it is absent in ' perching birds ' (Passeriformes).

4. *Sartorius* (= ilio-tibialis medialis)—an offshoot of the reptilian ilio-tibialis ; not homologous with the mammalian sartorius, but with the rectus femoris. In action it flexes the thigh, at the same time extending the knee.

5. *Adductor group*—a fleshy mass on the medial side of the thigh differentiated variously into several distinct muscles.

6. *A group of femoro-tibial muscles* serving as knee extensors.

7. *Caud-ilio-femoralis*—usually bipartite, consisting of an ilio-femoral and a caudo-femoral component, the former sometimes referred to as the accessory part of femoro-caudal. The two parts converge to a single band-like tendon inserting on the lower part of the back of the femur.

8. *A group of tibial adductors* including the ischio-flexorius (= semimembranosus), caud-ilio-flexorius (= semitendinosus), and ilio-fibularis (= biceps). These muscles, together with the preceding, were discovered by Garrod to be exceptionally variable. He considered them of great value taxonomically, and accordingly set up a formula based upon a simple notation, using letters as symbols indicating the presence of the muscles concerned. His notation is as follows :

A = caudi-femoralis part of caud-ilio-femoralis
B = accessory = pars ilio-femoralis of same
X = semitendinosus = caud-ilio-flexorius
Y = accessory part of semitendinosus (= flexor cruris lateralis)

Subsequent research revealed a number of inadequacies in the system, although the notation is still used in combination with other anatomical findings. Hudson has, moreover, supplemented Garrod's categories by new symbols thus :

C = ilio-trochantericus medius
D = glutaeus medius + minimus (= pyriformis of some authors)
Am = Ambiens
V = Vinculum between inserting tendons of flexor perforatus digiti III and f. perforans et perforatus digiti II (see below).

In Garrod's scheme the formula ABXY, all four muscles being present, represents a primitive condition ; ABX, AXY, and BXY are derived conditions, further reduction produces formulae AX, BX, XY, whilst A is the most specialised condition (occurring in owls, swifts (Apodidae), frigatebirds *Fregata* spp., and some birds-of-prey (Falconiformes)).

9. *Extensor group of the shank.* Pertaining here are the tibialis anterior, an elevator of the foot ; the extensor of digits I, III, and IV, the abductor of digit II, and the two peronaei (p. longus or superficialis and p. brevis or profundus).

10. *Flexors of the foot and toes.* Superficially there is a fleshy, three-headed gastrocnemius ending distally in a stout tendon, often calcified, which passes over the mid-tarsal joint, to which it is bound by fibrous tissue, widens to double its previous diameter as it passes the tarsometatarsus, and thereafter, again becoming thin, it fades into the plantar fascia.

Deeply lie the long flexors of the toes. These are diverse in their arrangement, especially the disposition of their inserting tendons, the various patterns being of some taxonomic significance. There are 3 principal sets of long flexors each of which may be represented by several muscles, the hallux having but one, the 2nd and 3rd digits three each, the 4th toe two. Inserting tendons pass to the bases of 1st, 2nd, and 3rd and terminal phalanges of the toes. Those inserting on the proximal phalanx are perforated, just prior to insertion, by tendons inserting on the 2nd and 3rd phalanges and these, in turn, are perforated by the tendons to the terminal phalanges, so that we speak of flexores perforati, flexores perforantes et perforati, and flexores perforantes.

Flexores perforati digitorum II, III, and IV arise in various fashions, separately or partly fused, either from the intercondylar region of the femur or more distally from ligaments around the knee, or the upper part of the tibia and fibula, and from the tendon of the ambiens. In this last contingency the muscle supplying III is a direct continuation of ambiens fibres. The same muscle also receives, at the ankle region, fibres from the peronaeus superficialis.

Flexores perforantes et perforati digitorum II and III arise in similar fashion, except for the connection with the ambiens. In many cases the tendon to the 3rd digit receives a slip or vinculum from that of the flexor perforatus.

Flexor perforans or profundus is the deepest

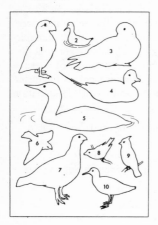

ca. ⅖ *nat. size*

Plate 29 · Characteristic Northern Birds by C. F. TUNNICLIFFE, R.A.

All the species shown are confined, as breeding birds, to the Holarctic area ; and all of them, ignoring any subspecific differences, are common to both its components—the Palaearctic Region (Europe, North Africa, and northern Asia) and the Nearctic Region (North America except tropical parts). Of the families represented, the Alcidae, Phalaropodidae, Gaviidae, and Tetraonidae consist of birds breeding only in the Northern Hemisphere ; this is true also of the monotypic genera *Clangula* and *Plectrophenax*, and of the genera *Loxia, Bombycilla,* and *Calidris*—and indeed true of the whole subfamilies Bombycillinae and Calidritinae, and nearly true of the tribe Mergini (to which *Clangula* belongs). The migrations of the phalaropes and of the Knot take them far into the Southern Hemisphere. Where alternative English names are given, the second represents North American usage. See articles PALAEARCTIC REGION ; NEARCTIC REGION.

1 Puffin or Common (Atlantic) Puffin *Fratercula arctica* (Alcidae)

2 Red-Necked Phalarope or Northern Phalarope *Lobipes lobatus* (Phalaropodidae)

3 Fulmar *Fulmarus glacialis* (Procellariidae)

4 Longtailed Duck or Oldsquaw *Clangula hyemalis* (Anatidae)

5 Red-throated Diver or Red-throated Loon *Gavia stellata* (Gaviidae)

6 Snow Bunting *Plectrophenax nivalis* (Emberizidae)

7 Willow Grouse or Willow Ptarmigan *Lagopus lagopus* (Tetraonidae)

8 Crossbill or Red Crossbill *Loxia curvirostra* (Fringillidae)

9 Waxwing or Bohemian Waxwing *Bombycilla garrulus* (Bombycillidae)

10 Knot *Calidris canutus* (Scolopacidae)

Where there are sexual or seasonal differences, the plumage depicted is that of the breeding bird, and of the male except in the case of the phalarope species (in which the female is the brighter and larger of the two).

C.F.Tunnicliffe

K3 1963

stratum arising from the greater part of the back of tibia and fibula. Its stout tendon passes deep to the preceding tendons over the tarsometatarsal joint and divides into 3 slips that proceed to the 3 anterior toes. The hallux or hind toe has its own deep flexor, the flexor hallucis longus, which arises from the intercondylar area of the femur ; its belly lies upon, and to the fibular side of, that of the last muscle, but its tendon accompanies the flexor perforans tendon, coming to lie on its posterior face in the metatarsal region. In this region it bifurcates, one part forming a vinculum to the perforans tendon and the other (stronger) portion continuing to an insertion in the base of the terminal phalanx of the hind toe. The vinculum ensures that flexion of the hind toe is automatically accompanied by flexion of the other toes, whereas these can, through their own deep flexors, contract without involving the hind toe. Loss of the hind toe is not accompanied by loss of its deep flexor, in view of the persistence of its vinculum.

Many modifications occur in the tendons in correlation with the various disposition of the toes in zygodactyl, anisodactyl, pamprodactyl, and other types of foot structure (see LEG).   W.C.O.H.

Berger, A. J. 1956. The expansor secundariorum muscle, with special reference to passerine birds. J. Morphol. 99 : 137-163.

Berger, A. J. 1960. The musculature. In Marshall, A. J. (ed.). Biology and Comparative Physiology of Birds vol. 1. New York and London.
Fiedler, W. 1951. Beiträge zur Morphologie der Kiefermuskulatur der Oscines. Zool. Jb. 71 (Abt. Anat.) : 235-288.
Hudson, G. E. 1937. Studies on the muscles of the pelvic appendage in birds. Amer. Midl. Nat. 18 : 1-108.
Lakjer, T. 1926. Studien über die Trigeminus-versorgte Kaumuskulatur der Sauropsiden. Copenhagen.
Starck, D. & Barnikol, A. 1954. Beiträge zur Morphologie der Trigeminusmuskulatur der Vögel. Morph. Jb. 94 : 1-64.
Stresemann, E. 1927-34. Aves. In Kukenthal, W. & Krumbach, T. (eds.). Handbuch der Zoologie vol. 7 : pt. 2. Berlin and Leipzig.

MUSEUM: an institution having nowadays the main function of preserving, for study and display, collections of specimens relating to a particular range of subjects ; when the subject is birds, the specimens are usually to be found in museums of natural history. The size of the museum determines the scope of its functions. In national museums, for instance, the aim may be to preserve specimens as representative as possible of the world's birds, and to display every aspect of bird biology susceptible of illustration by exhibits ; whereas in small museums the object may be no more than to show local species, mounted and displayed in some semblance of nature. The latter fill in many details that cannot be included in the former.

ca. ¼ nat. size

Plate 30 · Characteristic African Birds by KEITH SHACKLETON

All the species shown are confined to the Ethiopian Region, i.e. tropical and southern Africa, except that the Ostrich survived in south-western Asia into the present century and still has a precarious remnant in North Africa. The families Struthionidae, Balaenicipitidae, and Sagittariidae each include only the one species ; and the families Numididae, Phoeniculidae, Musophagidae, and Coliidae are represented only in the Ethiopian Region, except that one species of guineafowl has races in North Africa, south-western Arabia, and the Malagasy Region. The three other birds belong to subordinate groups—subfamilies or tribes—restricted to the Ethiopian Region. See article ETHIOPIAN REGION.

1   Crowned Crane *Balearica pavonina* (Gruidae)

2   Ostrich *Struthio camelus* (Struthionidae)

3   Green Wood-hoopoe *Phoeniculus erythrorhynchus* (Phoeniculidae)

4   Shoebill *Balaeniceps rex* (Balaenicipitidae)

5   Redbilled Oxpecker *Buphagus erythrorhynchus* (Sturnidae)

6   Secretary-bird *Sagittarius serpentarius* (Sagittariidae)

7   Lady Ross's Turaco *Musophaga rossae* (Musophagidae)

8   Blue-naped Mousebird *Colius macrourus* (Coliidae)

9   Vulturine Guineafowl *Acryllium vulturinum* (Numididae)

10   Bareheaded Rockfowl *Picathartes gymnocephalus* (Muscicapidae, Timaliinae)

Where there are sexual or seasonal differences, the plumage depicted is that of the breeding male.

Casual public interest in things outside personal experience is now catered for by the educational side of a museum's functions. One aspect is self-teaching by means of exhibits with explanatory labels displayed in public galleries ; mechanically recorded vocal explanations, to which members of the public can listen through ear-phones, are now used in some large institutions. These methods may be supplemented by lectures on particular themes given by professional teachers and specialists, either in the exhibition galleries themselves or in lecture rooms where specimens, slides, and films are shown. There may also be special facilities for elementary teaching, and series of portable exhibits for circulation to schools.

Exhibits and lectures reflect current knowledge of ornithology, allowing for the inevitable time-lag necessary for assimilation and presentation. Much of this knowledge is derived from a study of the specimens stored in parts of the museum specially designed for that purpose ; these specimens are not freely accessible to the public but are available for the use of accredited students. The foundations of study series—specimens stored in cabinet drawers—were the birds obtained by people who could indulge in the once popular habit of collecting, either as an end in itself or for some special purpose. Growth of the collections can be attributed to more purposeful collecting, for example by the student in the field who wants certain specimens to be identified, by other students who have completed particular studies and deposit their specimens for preservation, and by expeditions organised with the object of determining the avifauna of little-known regions. The orderly arrangement of specimens, a prime necessity in a large collection, gave rise to the science of taxonomy, the grouping of like with like in a manner reflecting their natural affinities (see CLASSIFICATION ; SYSTEMATICS ; TAXONOMY). Investigation of the taxonomy of birds by study of their morphology is one of the principal subjects of research in museums, both by the staff and by visiting students, although the former have to devote some of their time to the problems of storage and preservation ; these problems themselves become subjects for research, as precautions have to be taken against attacks by insect pests and moulds, and also against deterioriation due to chemical and physical changes.

The usual preserved specimen consists of a ' skin ' —the skin and feathers, with bill (and part of skull) and legs attached ; it is dried, lightly stuffed with cottonwool or tow, and moulded so that it lies flat. The preservation of skins in the field and their transport to museums are simple ; and the general opinion is that such specimens provide a reasonable sample of morphological characters for taxonomic study. Much bird taxonomy is based on skin specimens, and the additional study of other anatomical features has so far done little to alter conclusions arrived at from their examination. This is especially true as regards species and genera, but it is possible that many groupings above that level are more arbitrary than natural, and that comprehensive studies of morphology should be more largely developed. To this end collections are made, where possible, of whole specimens in preserving fluids, and various parts of birds, such as dried skeletons, gonads, and eggshells, each of which add to the sum total of knowledge of the material aspects of a bird's biology. They also add to the many curatorial problems.

The determinations of affinities and the arrangement of specimens in a classified series for reference purposes requires that certain units should have distinctive names. The basic unit of a museum study collection, as indeed of all present taxonomy, is the species (see SPECIES). When a new unit is distinguished, its significance can become widely known only by the publication of an adequate description attached to a new name. It is usual, also, that the main part of the description should be of a single specimen, which consequently becomes the type-specimen. Types are preserved with particular care because they are the ultimate standards for identification purposes ; they are the key-stones of nomenclature and as such are important, but they have little scientific value beyond that (see NOMENCLATURE ; TYPE-SPECIMEN).

The morphological limits of each named form are determined by the variants that can be associated with the type. The main kinds of variation are : individual (the amount of variation in a sample of the same sex and age from one locality), sexual, seasonal, developmental, and geographical (but see also POLYMORPHISM). Also to be considered is evolutionary variation, or variation over long periods of time, which is becoming increasingly important to students of modern birds as well as to palaeontologists. Variation of these kinds can be extensive, so that the series required to illustrate a single species may amount to many hundreds of specimens ; even then the student of some special aspect of a bird's biology may find that number inadequate. There is a point where preservation of further specimens can be replaced by recorded data, and some museums make provision for storing such information.

The museum most appropriate to mention in the present context is the British Museum (Natural

History) in London. Others in Britain are the Royal Scottish Museum in Edinburgh and the National Museum of Wales in Cardiff; but there are also numerous civic, university, school, and private museums, some of which have outstanding exhibits or very fine study series of certain groups. Most countries possess national museums of some importance in world ornithology, and sometimes also private museums. Examples of the latter are the American Museum of Natural History in New York and the Chicago Natural History Museum, which provide exhibits and collections in addition to those held nationally at the Smithsonian Institution in Washington, D.C. On the Continent of Europe there are museums of ornithological importance in Paris, Brussels, Leiden, Copenhagen, Stockholm, Berlin, Moscow, Leningrad, to mention but a few; and farther afield in Bombay, Calcutta, Singapore, Melbourne, Wellington, Cape Town, Pretoria, Nairobi, and in many cities and towns in South and Central America.   J.D.M.

Berlioz, J. 1960. Le rôle capital des musées dans l'avenir de l'ornithologie. (Presidential address.) Proc. XII Internat. Orn. Congr., Helsinki 1958: 44–49.

MUSIC, BIRDS IN: regarded here as an avian element in human culture. There is a varied and well-stocked aviary in musical literature which divides itself into three main classes. First, a few birds whose song is sufficiently melodious to go into musical notation, correct as to pitch and rhythm, so that they can appear in their proper persons in quotation. Of such the Cuckoo is the most obvious in spite of the variation in his interval; the Blackbird, which however is inclined to get its top notes a little sharp, and the Nightingale with its coloratura, are common in orchestral, keyboard, and vocal music; Beethoven's Pastoral Symphony (second movement) is the locus classicus for Nightingale, Quail, and Cuckoo (which sings a major third). Secondly, birds which fill the air with unspecified song may be less realistically represented by trills and motifs played on wind instruments, as in Respighi's tone-poem The Fountains of Rome and pervasively in the music of Dvorak, or by any other means of suggestion such as the human voice. Bishop's song with flute obbligato 'Lo! here the gentle lark' and Vaughan Williams's piece for violin and orchestra 'The Lark Ascending' are not realistic, although the bird is specified. In Siegfried, Wagner merely calls his intelligent bird, which reveals to the hero the secret of his birth and parentage, 'Waldvogel', without further designation of its species; perhaps it was a Wood Warbler! Thirdly, there are birds which have inspired composers, whether by their legendary exploits, by their physical appearance, or by their symbolism. Of these the leader is the Mute Swan, 'which living hath no note', as Gibbons's madrigal 'The Silver Swan' puts it. This disillusioned bird, when she unlocked her silent throat, expressed the view that 'more geese than swans now live, more fools than wise'.

The unmusical Swan has had far the best deal from composers. In Lohengrin Wagner gave his hero an apostrophe to his 'lieber Schwann', that had conveyed him by boat on the Scheldt; when the spell is broken the Swan's place is taken by a dove. In Sibelius's Swan of Tuonela it is a bird of the Finnish equivalent of the River Styx—was the bird black like the waters on which it floated, or was it red as depicted in a picture well known in Finland? The cor anglais is its instrument. In Tchaikovsky's ballet Le Lac des Cygnes it is the oboe; the theme it plays is astonishingly suggestive:

Ex. 1
Oboe

Once heard, the association is ineffaceable. In Saint-Saens's Carnival des Animaux the Swan is a cello, which floats on arpeggios provided by the pianos. Pavlova devised her most famous dance to this music, although there is nothing to suggest death in Saint-Saens's predominantly humourous suite. Grieg's song 'The Swan' has a text by Ibsen on the same theme of the dying Swan, and the breaking of its silence is portrayed by the sudden descent of the piano to its bass octave. In Orff's Carmina Burana a roasted Swan laments in a tenor solo its change from an elegant water-fowl into a table bird.

The Nightingale, which infests German lieder, might be expected to have his song literally reproduced or at any rate openly imitated with such modification of its intervals as did not fit our scales; but when Respighi in his other Roman tone-poem, The Pines of Rome, needed the song of a Nightingale he did not give it to the piccolo but prescribed a gramophone record of an actual bird; this is a device which some people regard as cheating, the realistic truth thus becoming artistic falsehood. There is a Nightingale in Granados's Goyescas that is given a little cadenza at the end of an exquisite nocturne, which is suggestion not quotation, for its shifts, compass, and harmonic implications are beyond avian capacity. German songs are mostly invocations to the bird to sing or be silent, and only the slightest hint of bird-song, perhaps a grace note in the accompaniment, is used by Schubert and

Brahms. Similarly, the Curlew in Peter Warlock's song-sequence with string quartet and wind sings a suggestive but synthetic song on the flute. The Cuckoo is really the only musician safe enough to be entrusted by composers with a specific part, as Delius has done in his orchestral idyll ' On Hearing the First Cuckoo in Spring ', where the clarinet plays a minor third. Daquin's harpsichord piece called ' The Cuckoo ' uses the same interval.

There are some bird-calls, not songs, that obtain more or less realistic representation in music. Perhaps the most important are the cockcrows in Bach's *Passions*. After Peter's denial, immediately the cock crew thus :

Ex.2

in the ' St John Passion ' played by the cello of the continuo ; and in the ' St Matthew Passion ' the tenor Evangelist incorporates it thus :

Ex.3

E- he der Hahn krä — hen wird

Compare the rise and fall of this German bird with the Russian in Rimsky-Korsakov's opera *Coq d'Or*, where the golden cockerel after his cry :

Ex.4

warns the King that all is well if his next phrase goes down and up, but that he must beware if it goes up and down. Another cock, this one roasted, appears in a Christmas carol and crows to King Herod in testimony to the Nativity, but this naturally has no musical representation in a strophic tune. One of Haydn's symphonies is nicknamed ' La Poule ', and one of Mozart's unfinished operas is about a goose in Cairo (*L'Oca del Cairo*). The side-drum roll at the beginning of Rossini's overture *La Gazza Ladra* is an orchestral ' stunt ', but it may also be an imitation of the Magpie's dry croak. There is a duck nicely characterised by a squawking oboe in Prokofiev's pleasant musical conte, *Peter and the Wolf*, as well as a bird (species unspecified) represented by the flute, which helps to secure the capture of the wolf.

By way of a round-up—Dvorak wrote a symphonic poem called ' Der Waldtaube ', Vautor a madrigal called ' Sweet Suffolk Owl ', Cyril Scott a piano piece called ' Waterwagtail ' ; there are many songs about linnets and blackbirds. Two pet sparrows, both named Philip, occur in Tudor poems by John Skelton and George Gascoigne, which are the subjects of musical setting : Jane Scroop's ' Lament for Philip Sparrow ' makes one of Vaughan Williams's *Five Tudor Portraits*, and ' Philip my Sparrow ' is the subject of a song, ' Of all the birds that I do know ', in John Bartlett's *A Book of Ayres* (1606), which is however said to be a skit on Philip Sparrow the poet. The funeral of little Jane's pet sparrow is attended by all the fowls of the air, who are orchestrally accompanied by copious suggestions of bird-song. The old Spanish dance-form ' Canaries ' has no connection with the bird other than the place of origin in the islands of that name. The Lyrebird of Australia has given its name to an edition of music and gramophone records financed by a patron from Australia.

Such a category-defying catalogue of the fowls of the air cannot be exhaustive : mention of one bird will evoke memory of another, or of a further instance of its appearance in a different musical context. Much nature music in operas and orchestral tone-poems contains writing for wood-wind to suggest the birds' contribution to dawns or forests, but the modern French composer, Olivier Messiaen, has used bird-song as an ingredient, part thematic, part colouristic, in his gigantic ' Turangalila Symphony ', of which he writes, ' a part for pianoforte solo, which is extremely difficult, is designed to point up (' diamanter ') the orchestra with brilliance, with chord clusters and bird songs '. Authentic bird-song, however, presents too many difficulties of intonation, less of rhythm, to induce composers to make much use of it thematically.   F.S.H.

MUSKEG : an environment, consisting of grassy bog, characteristic of much of northern Canada.

MUSOPHAGI : a suborder of the Cuculiformes comprising only the family Musophagidae (see TURACO) ; in Stresemann's system treated as a separate order (' Musophagae ').

MUSOPHAGIDAE : see above; and TURACO

MUTATION : see GENETICS

MUTTON-BIRD : local name for various species of petrel (Procellariidae) ; applied in New Zealand to the Sooty Shearwater *Procellaria grisea*, and on the southern coasts and islands of Australia to the Short-tailed Shearwater *P. tenuirostris* (see PETREL). The young of both species are in these areas collected commercially in large numbers for human consumption. The latter species is known as the Whalebird in Alaska, which it visits during the northern summer.

MYCTERIINAE: see STORK

MYIASIS, WOUND: the presence of maggots in a wound on a living bird.

MYNAH: substantive name of various Asian species of *Acridotheres, Gracula,* and *Sturnus* (see STARLING).

MYOCARDIUM: see HEART

MYOLOGY: the scientific study of muscles (see MUSCULATURE).

MYTHICAL BIRDS: see FABULOUS BIRDS

N

NAME, COLLECTIVE: see ASSEMBLY, NOUN OF

NAME, COMMON: sometimes used as an equivalent of 'vernacular name' or 'popular name' (see NAME, VERNACULAR). 'Common name' is subject to the slight ambiguity that it is also the translation of the *nomen triviale* of Linnaeus, which had the meaning of 'specific name' (see NOMEN-CLATURE).

NAME, ENGLISH: the name ('vernacular name', 'popular name') of a species or category of birds in the English language. English names, especially those of familiar birds, are part of the living language; as with other words, they are thus governed by usage, and this may change with time or differ between one English-speaking country and another. Unlike scientific names, which are based on international agreement among zoologists to accept certain conventions (see NOMENCLATURE), English names can be subject to no fixed rules, and their application may cut across taxonomic boundaries; also, they are usually not of international significance apart from the English-speaking world.

Nevertheless, it is expedient that there should be some approach to uniformity—by consensus of opinion—in the practice of ornithologists with regard to English names, at least during one period of time and in the same country. Clearly, a standard should be sought along the lines of determining the best current usage and of encouraging general adherence to it on the part of ornithologists. Some of these may have strong minority views that it would be improper to stigmatise as necessarily incorrect; but it seems probable that most of the diversity of practice is accidental rather than deliberate. Admittedly, there are in many cases alternative names to those given greatest acceptance by ornithologists—names that have also had substantial currency, and may even have been preferred at earlier dates, or that may be found in poetry or literary prose. There are also dialect names, locally or widely used, that have a place in the popular speech of the countryside and in writings embodying that.

Some ornithologists and others actively seek to influence usage by reviving older names or by introducing new ones because these are considered to be more pleasing or more appropriate. One may think that such attempts to change English names, widely used outside the realm of ornithology, may lead to confusion. On the other hand, it would be unreasonable to deny some latitude in the use of alternative names for which a case can be made (e.g. 'Dunnock').

There are certain tendencies in common usage that may well be encouraged by ornithologists. There is, notably, a welcome trend in the direction of shortening cumbersome compound names, such as the 'Golden-crested Wren' (a misnomer at that) of a few decades ago, now 'Goldcrest'. The prefix 'Common' likewise now tends to be omitted in many instances where it is really unnecessary, and the redundant second term to be dropped in 'Fulmar Petrel', 'Eider Duck', and others. Similarly, ornithologists may help to mould general usage by showing preference for the more appropriate of alternative names both in common use, e.g. 'Willow Warbler' rather than 'Willow Wren'.

In the case of birds familiar on both sides of the Atlantic, it is impracticable in the face of differing common usage to secure complete uniformity in English names as between the British Isles and North America, two areas with many birds in common (see below). Similar considerations apply to names used by English-speaking people in various other parts of the world. On the other hand, many English names have been invented by British ornithologists for birds that are not ordinarily found in their country and that are therefore nameless in common speech. Such names, if unsatisfactory, are more susceptible of deliberate change. In particular, it seems to be good practice to displace such a name in favour of one that is widely current in some part of the world where the bird is well-known ; thus the 'Buff-backed Heron' of British bird books is known to English-speaking people in Africa and Asia, and more appropriately, as 'Cattle Egret'. Again, in the British Isles, the English names used in North America may well be preferred for species that are merely stragglers from that continent.

Names for Species and Subspecies. English names are primarily the names of species. This follows naturally from the fact that subspecific forms are usually indistinguishable in the field, except in some cases by skilled observers ; they can therefore have no names in common speech. Where it is desired to refer to a subspecies (or race) by an English name, this should consist of the name of the species prefaced by a qualifying adjective or adjectival phrase. Such compounded names for races are nearly all of comparatively recent origin ; and indeed the desirable occasions for using them seem to be much fewer than some current practice would suggest. Subspecies can be referred to either by their scientific names, as befits a technical concept, or by such expressions as 'Northern race' in relation with the English name of the species.

There are a few inevitable exceptions, where subspecies are so distinct in appearance that they have acquired separate English names in common speech. If such names are firmly embedded in the language, as where two races of *Motacilla alba* are known respectively as 'Pied Wagtail' and 'White Wagtail', it seems impossible to do otherwise than accept the situation. Unfortunately, this means that there is no English name covering the species as a whole ; and this in turn involves the invention of additional English names for any forms of it other than the two in question.

Initial Capitals. Whether or not to use capitals for the initial letters of the English names of species is a controversial point. Ordinary literary usage would prefer small letters, and some ornithological publications follow this. More commonly it is felt that, for scientific purposes, there are advantages in the use of capital letters. For one thing, references to particular species can be more easily picked out on a page. For another, certain ambiguities are avoided ; thus, 'a Little Gull' can refer only to *Larus minutus*, whereas 'a little gull' might mean a gull of any small species.

When initial capital letters are preferred, they are used for each main term of the name but not for the second element of a hyphenated compound. Capital letters are in any event not given to English names when these are used in a general rather than a specific sense, e.g. 'gulls'.

Hyphenation. It has in the past been a frequent practice in ornithological publications to hyphenate two elements of a name where this consists of a noun preceded by a noun used as an adjective ; but not to insert a hyphen between a true adjective and a following noun. This is a tiresome convention, because it involves e.g., for various tits *Parus* spp., writing 'Marsh-Tit' on the one hand and 'Blue Tit' on the other. Moreover, an exception tends to be made when the adjectival noun is the proper name of a place, as in 'Sandwich Tern', and this further complicates the procedure.

There seems to be nothing in ordinary English usage of the present day to demand such a rule as that mentioned above. 'The hyphen is not an ornament ; it should never be placed between two words that do not require uniting and can do their work equally well separate' (Fowler). The present tendency happily seems to favour the suppression of all unnecessary hyphens, including especially those that have been inserted merely because the word before it, used adjectivally, happens to be a noun. A hyphen is unnecessary between any two words of which the second would naturally be used for indexing.

On the other hand, some hyphens are made necessary by the sense, unless the two elements can be written as a single word ; 'Oyster-catcher' is a case in point, as 'catcher' here means nothing by itself. Other necessary hyphens are those between elements of a compound adjective, e.g. 'Black-headed'. It seems desirable, however, to encourage a tendency to go further and to make single words out of properly hyphenated pairs when the sense allows. 'The conversion of a hyphenated word into an unhyphenated single one is desirable as soon as the novelty of the combination has worn off, if there are no obstacles in the way of awkward spelling, obscurity or the like' (Fowler). We already have many compound names such as 'Redpoll', 'Bullfinch', and 'Blackbird' that are always spelt as single words ; and others that usually or sometimes are, such as 'Oystercatcher', 'Yellowhammer', and 'Hedgesparrow'. There also seems to be no reason against adjectives such as 'Blackheaded' being written as single words ; but there are instances where the result would be aesthetically disagreeable or not immediately intelligible.

A few hyphens are inescapable on account of awkward spelling, notably 'Bee-eater'—to write 'Bee Eater' (indexing as 'Eater, Bee' !) would be wrong ; to write 'Beeeater' would be absurd.

Fabricated Names. Where common usage does not operate, ornithologists are free to invent English names (if these are considered necessary in the circumstances) ; Eisenmann & Poor have suggested certain principles, as follows. There should be an appropriate name for every species, applicable to the whole species and forming the latter part of the name of each included subspecies. A name should give no false impression of taxonomic relationship. The name of a species should not be formed from a geographical name, or any name from a personal one. The adjectives 'common' (at best of only local relevance), 'least' (or 'little'), and 'great', should be used with extreme care. A name should not be given that is identical with one already well established elsewhere for another species.

American Usage. The English names used in the United States and Canada, even without going beyond those currently recognised by the American Ornithologists' Union, show some unavoidable differences from British ornithological practice. The same name may be differently applied; or different names may be used for the same species or group. It may be convenient to draw attention here to the instances over which confusion is most likely to arise.

The following collective names are applied in the respective hemispheres to birds that have superficial features in common but belong to different taxonomic groups: 'vulture', 'quail', 'flycatcher', 'warbler', 'oriole', and 'sparrow'—see entries under the several names and others to be mentioned below. The names 'hawk' and 'bunting' have a wider application in the New World.

Among names for species, applied quite differently, the following are outstanding examples:

	British Application	American Application
Blackbird	*Turdus merula*	*Agelaius* spp.
Sparrow Hawk	*Accipiter nisus*	*Falco sparverius*
Robin	*Erithacus rubecula*	*Turdus migratorius*
Redstart	*Phoenicurus* spp.	*Setophaga* spp.
Tree Sparrow	*Passer montanus*	*Spizella arborea*

The name 'Great White Heron' is given to *Ardea occidentalis* in America but was until recently applied in British bird books to *Egretta alba*, now designated an 'egret' with varying adjectives. There are of course many instances in which the same name is applied to closely related birds, with or without distinguishing adjectives apt to be omitted in ordinary use. Among unofficial American names, there are such uses as 'buzzard' for vulture (New World family) and 'yellowhammer' for a species of woodpecker.

Special American names for groups include 'loon' instead of 'diver', 'jaeger' instead of 'skua' for *Stercorarius* spp. (not *Catharacta*), 'murre' instead of 'guillemot' for *Uria* spp. (not *Cepphus*), and 'goat-sucker' instead of 'nightjar'.

The most important instances of different substantive names for the same species are:

British Usage	American Usage
Longtailed Duck	Oldsquaw
Goosander	Common Merganser
Hen Harrier	Marsh Hawk
Moorhen	Common Gallinule
Little Auk	Dovekie
Sand Martin	Bank Swallow
Lapland Bunting	Lapland Longspur

There are many other instances in which a different adjectival name is used although the birds are at most subspecifically distinct, e.g. 'Kentish Plover' becomes 'Snowy Plover' in America, 'Grey Phalarope' becomes 'Red Phalarope' (refers to breeding plumage), and 'Common Gull' becomes 'Mew Gull'. Some American names such as 'Duck Hawk' for 'Peregrine' and 'Pigeon Hawk' for 'Merlin' are no longer the official preferences.

Finally, there are many cases in which a species is known in Britain by its substantive name without qualification, but an adjective is added in America for distinction from related species there, e.g. 'Rock Ptarmigan', 'Barn Swallow', 'Winter Wren'.

Other Usages. In the more widely divergent avifaunas of Australia and New Zealand, differences arise chiefly from the use of names familiar in Britain for birds that are not even closely related, e.g. 'chough', 'magpie', 'robin', 'treecreeper', 'warbler', and 'wren'—again see entries under the several names. In other parts of the world, even where English is largely spoken, this tendency is less noticeable; on the other hand, many compound names are merely ornithological fabrications, without roots in common speech and often varying from author to author. Sometimes a name from an indigenous language is adopted and more or less anglicised; or a scientific generic name (currently used or obsolete) does duty as an English substantive name.   A.L.T.

Macleod, R. D. 1954. Key to the Names of British Birds. London.
Swann, H. Kirke. 1913. A Dictionary of English and Folk Names of British Birds. London.
American Ornithologists' Union. 1957. Check-list of North American Birds. 5th. ed. Baltimore.
Eisenmann, E. 1955. The species of Middle American birds. Trans. Linn. Soc. N.Y. 7 : 1–128.
Eisenmann, E. & Poor, H. H. 1946. Suggested principles of vernacular nomenclature. Wilson Bull. 58 : 210–215.

NAME, POPULAR: recognised equivalent of NAME, VERNACULAR.

NAME, SCIENTIFIC: see NOMENCLATURE

NAME, SUBSTANTIVE: term used throughout this work for a noun that is the chief element in the

English name of a number of species distinguished from each other by qualifying adjectives (including nouns and participles used adjectivally). Either or both elements of the full name may be compound, and each of them, unless written as a single word, should preferably be hyphenated (being indissoluble) ; on the other hand, the adjectival and substantive names should not be joined by a hyphen. For a few species a single word serves as a complete name, e.g. Brambling, Dodo. In other cases the substantive name may ordinarily be used alone where there is no other species with the same substantive name in the area, but in a wider context an adjectival name must be added. Occasionally there may be two independent (not hyphenated) qualifying names, e.g. Great Crested Grebe, Grey Lag Goose. There is a certain analogy between an English substantive name and a scientific generic name, but this must not be pressed ; unrelated species may have the same substantive name, and closely related species may have different ones. See NAME, ENGLISH.

NAME, TRIVIAL: see NOMENCLATURE—but also sometimes used in the sense of NAME, VERNACULAR.

NAME, VERNACULAR: ' the name of a taxon in any language other than the language of zoological nomenclature' (International Code)—see NOMENCLATURE ; ' popular name' is a recognised equivalent. ' Vernacular name', however, is sometimes used in the restricted sense of a name in a local dialect or in the native language of a country foreign to the writer or speaker ; this ambiguity can be avoided by using an adjective denoting the particular language. The vernacular names given in this work are, unless otherwise indicated, ' English names' (see NAME, ENGLISH). For names in other European languages see the work cited below.

Jørgensen, H. I. 1958. Nomina Avium Europaearum. (Revised edition.) Copenhagen.

NANDU: alternative name for species of Rheidae (see RHEA).

NAPE: see TOPOGRAPHY

NARIS: usually in the plural (' nares '), for the paired openings of the nasal cavities in the skull (see SKELETON). The anterior or external nares (nostrils) pierce the rhamphotheca of the upper mandible at varying distances from its base (uniquely at the tip in kiwis Apteryx spp.)—see BILL ; the passages continue through apertures in the bones (premaxillae) into the nasal cavities. The posterior or internal nares (also called ' choanae ') lead from the nasal

cavities into the buccal cavity. For the nasal cavities and their functions see RESPIRATORY SYSTEM and SMELL ; for the nasal glands see EXCRETION, EXTRA-RENAL.

The external nares are of various shapes, from round to linear ; sometimes there is a central tubercle in each naris. Usually they are exposed (gymno-rhinal) ; but in some birds they are concealed by frontal feathers, e.g. in crows (Corvidae) and grouse (Tetraonidae). Sometimes each naris is protected by a flap (operculum), which in tapaculos (Rhino-cryptidae) is movable. In the Procellariiformes (Tubinares) the nostrils are carried in a double horny tube on top of the bill. The internasal septum, separating the right and left passages, is imperforate in most birds but perforate in a few. Although the nostrils remain open (pervious) in most birds, they are or become secondarily closed (impervious) in some Pelecaniformes (see RESPIRATORY SYSTEM) ; in such cases, entry to the nasal cavities is only from the mouth through the choanae, which may be quite large, and respiration is through ' secondary external' nares at the angle of the mouth (Macdonald).

The shape of the *bony* aperture of the nostril has been used as a taxonomic character (Garrod). It is ' holorhinal' when the posterior margin is rounded, ' schizorhinal' when it forms a slit ; ' pseudoschi-zorhinal' is a term applied to a modification of the holorhinal type ; and ' amphirhinal' signifies that there are two bony apertures (one behind the other) on each side. In Sulidae (see above) even the bony aperture is blocked.

NASAL: a paired bone of the skull (see SKELETON).

NASAL CAVITY: see NARIS ; PALATE ; RES-PIRATORY SYSTEM ; SKELETON ; SMELL ; and EXCRETION, EXTRARENAL

NATIVE COMPANION: alternative name for the Australian Crane *Grus rubicunda* (see CRANE).

NATIVE HEN: substantive name, in Australia, of *Tribonyx* spp. including the flightless Tasmanian Native Hen *T. mortieri* (for family see RAIL).

NATURALISED BIRDS: species that have been introduced by human agency, direct or indirect, into areas where they either had not yet spread by natural means or had become extinct, and that have successfully established themselves and are now breeding regularly as wild birds. Mere acclimatisation in captivity, or even the casual escape of captive individuals, is excluded from the definition.

Extensive man-made changes have taken place in the world distribution of certain bird species within the past hundred years or so. The House Sparrow *Passer domesticus*, for instance, was a native of Europe and parts of Asia and North Africa but has been spread to the remaining continents by human agency. It now occupies almost the whole of North America, large parts of South America and Australia, and a substantial part of South Africa, as well as New Zealand, Cuba, Hawaii, New Caledonia, the Falklands, and many other islands. It has been estimated that within the past century largely man-made extensions have doubled the natural world range of the House Sparrow, which was six million square miles, so that it now occupies one-quarter of the earth's surface. The Starling *Sturnus vulgaris* has been artificially spread almost as widely, as will be further mentioned.

Introductions may be either deliberate or more or less accidental. Deliberate introductions have been made for three main reasons. In western Europe and in North America, excessive shooting of game stocks has led to widespread and prolonged introductions of game-birds ; this has sometimes, as with the Partridge *Perdix perdix* from Hungary to Britain, been to supplement stocks of native species, but more often, as with the Pheasant *Phasianus colchicus* in both Europe and North America, to diversify the native game stocks with completely alien birds. Nostalgia for the sights and sounds of the home country led to large-scale and often highly successful introductions of western European song-birds into North America, South Africa, Australia, and New Zealand. In the British Isles especially, the desire to increase the amenities of country estates led to the importation of large numbers of ornamental waterfowl, the progeny of which have sometimes been neither pinioned nor wing-clipped and have thus escaped to found feral populations. Some more or less domesticated birds have also been able to escape from captivity and establish themselves in the wild.

In the British Isles, despite attempts to introduce upwards of 100 bird species (mostly during the past hundred years), only four completely alien birds have become thoroughly naturalised over a wide area ; the Pheasant from various parts of Asia, the Red-legged Partridge *Alectoris rufa* from southern Europe, the Little Owl *Athene noctua* from western Europe, and the Canada Goose *Branta canadensis* from North America. In addition, the Mandarin Duck *Aix galericulata* and the Golden Pheasant *Chrysolophus pictus*, both from China, are naturalised in limited areas : the Capercaillie *Tetrao urogallus*, after becoming extinct in the Scottish Highlands about 1785, was successfully reintroduced there from Sweden in 1837–39 ; the Gadwall *Anas strepera* became

naturalised in two small areas in south-eastern England at the same time as an apparently natural colonisation from the Continent took place in Scotland ; and the widespread present-day populations of both the Mute Swan *Cygnus olor* and the feral domestic pigeon *Columba livia* var. represent escapes from more or less domesticated stocks. Of these ten species, four were introduced to supplement game stocks, three were ornamental waterfowl, two were formerly kept for food, and the Little Owl was introduced as an aesthetic whim of a handful of bird-loving nineteenth-century landowners.

In France, on the other hand, the numerous introductions of birds over the past hundred years have resulted in only one additional species becoming established—Reeves's Pheasant *Syrmaticus reevesi* joining the already naturalised *Phasianus colchicus*. This is no doubt largely due to the fact that a continental area tends to have fewer vacant ecological niches than an island.

In North America the two most successful and widespread naturalised birds have been the House Sparrow and the Starling from Europe. The House Sparrow has now occupied the whole of the cultivated area of the United States and Canada. The Starling has spread, since 1870, over the whole continent north to the Gulf of St Lawrence and west to the Rocky Mountains ; it also occurs in Jamaica as a result of a separate introduction in 1903. Small local populations of naturalised Partridges, Pheasants, Goldfinches *Carduelis carduelis*, and Tree Sparrows *Passer montanus* from Europe, have also been added to the avifauna of North America. The Greater Bird-of-paradise *Paradisaea apoda*, of the Aru Islands and New Guinea, was introduced into Little Tobago, West Indies, in 1909.

Of the numerous European song-birds introduced into Australia and New Zealand by homesick emigrants, mainly in the 1860s, eight are now naturalised in Australia and thirteen in New Zealand. The Skylark *Alauda arvensis*, Song Thrush *Turdus philomelos*, Blackbird *T. merula*, Greenfinch *Carduelis chloris*, Goldfinch, House Sparrow, and Starling are found in both countries today. In New Zealand an interesting by-product has been the interbreeding of subspecies of the Redpoll *Acanthis flammea* from different parts of Europe, and perhaps also of the Yellowhammer *Emberiza citrinella*.

Asiatic birds naturalised in Australia include the Indian Spotted Dove *Streptopelia chinensis suratensis*, the Common Myna *Acridotheres tristis* (also naturalised in Hawaii and New Zealand), and the Red-whiskered Bulbul *Pycnonotus jocosus*. All the birds of the latter species now at large in New South Wales and Victoria are said to derive from some that either escaped or were liberated from an aviary in Sydney, a city where they are now plentiful in the parks and threaten to become a pest to fruit-growers. From Africa, the Ostrich *Struthio camelus* was introduced into South Australia under domesti-cation and has become feral in one or two areas. Non-European birds naturalised in New Zealand, in addition to the Common Myna, include the Cali-fornia Quail *Lophortyx californica*, the Black Swan *Cygnus atratus* from Australia, and the White-backed Magpie *Gymnorhina hypoleuca* (Cracticidae) also from Australia.

Success in deliberate attempts at naturalisation is quite haphazard, as the British record shows. Animal species are well adapted to their native en-vironment, but if they are to establish themselves firmly in a completely different part of the world a whole complex of factors, such as climate, food supply, and cover for both nesting and roosting, must be suited to them ; nor must pressure from predators be too great. A. C. Twomey has pointed out that imported European birds became naturalised in the United States only in regions with temperature and rainfall corresponding to those in their native breeding places. In New Zealand the introduced European species have completely supplanted native birds over most of the cultivated area, being for the most part pre-adapted to the habitat created by the destruction of the native vegetation and the sub-stitution of imported crop plants. No doubt the native New Zealand birds would in time have adapted themselves to the areas cultivated by man, but the presence of the European birds has deprived them of the chance.

Theoretically, its own fecundity is the only limit to the increase of an introduced bird population in a suitable new habitat, until it comes up against the natural ceiling that the environment imposes on it. The expansion of the Starling and House Sparrow populations in North America bears this out well ; so does the increase, from 2 cocks and 6 hens to 1898 birds in five years, of a population of Pheasants on a small island off the western coast of North America.

When populations build up to their natural ceiling on an island, the surplus may attempt to spread oversea, as is suggested by the fact that, as G. R. Williams has shown, many of the small birds natura-lised in Australia and New Zealand began to appear by the end of the century on the small islands that lie mostly 200–550 miles to the southward of the two main landmasses. There can be little doubt that most of them were blown there by the wind. Campbell Island, for instance, 450 miles south of Dunedin, now has breeding Blackbirds, Song

Thrushes, Starlings, Redpolls, Chaffinches *Fringilla coelebs*, and Hedgesparrows *Prunella modularis*, all almost certainly self-introduced—but from stocks naturalised in a secondary area.

No highly migratory species have succeeded in keeping their migratory habit while becoming naturalised in a new country. Most of the European birds that have been so successful in other parts of the world are at most partial migrants in Europe. The Canada Goose in Britain, however, provides an instance of a migratory bird population that has lost its urge to migrate during a period of captivity and has become wholly sedentary in its secondary home. The Pheasant, on the other hand, is normally a wholly sedentary bird but has shown some signs of acquiring a migratory habit in the harsher climate of Sweden.

Bird introductions have on the whole proved less disastrous than introductions of mammals and insects, but the examples of the Starling in North America and perhaps of the Red-whiskered Bulbul in Australia are there to point the dangers of irresponsible introductions.   R.S.R.F.

Etchécopar, R. D.   1955.   L'Acclimation des oiseaux en France au cours des 100 dernières années.   Terre et Vie 102 : 42–53.
Fitter, R. S. R.   1959.   The Ark in our Midst.   London.
Gabhardt, E.   1959.   Europäische Vögel in überseeischen Ländern.   Bonn. Zool. Beitr. 3/4 : 310–342.
Niethammer, G.   1963.   Die Einbürgerung von Saugetieren und Vögeln in Europa.   Hamburg and Berlin.
Williams, G. R.   1953.   The dispersal from New Zealand and Australia of some introduced European passe-rines.   Ibis 95 : 676–692.

NATURAL SELECTION: the process suggested by Darwin and Wallace as the mechanism producing evolution (see EVOLUTION). From the observations that plants and animals produce far more young than are needed to maintain their numbers, and that all organisms show considerable variation of which much is inheritable, they inferred that there must be competition, both between individuals of the same species and between those of different species, for the necessities of life. Then those that carried variations improving their means of obtaining food, or mates, or shelter, or other necessities, would tend to leave more offspring than the others ; thus, favourable variations would spread through popula-tions, and less favourable ones would be eliminated.

Natural selection has now been confirmed as the means of evolution, by observation in the field, experiment, and mathematical analysis. It was much attacked by those who thought it degraded the ' economy of nature ' to a mere blind struggle. More important objections were that most mortality was due to accident, and selection could have very little to work on ; that such organs as the electric apparatus of the electric eel, or the eye, or the wing of a bird, could not be evolved since their more primitive stages would be useless ; that inheritance was by blending the characters of the parents, so that varieties could not be perpetuated ; and, later, when genetics first began to develop, that species could appear in one jump by changes in the hereditary mechanism, so that no intermediates were produced.

It may be agreed that a great deal of mortality is due to purely random happenings that will have no selective effect ; nevertheless, very strong selection has been demonstrated in the wild, which is the important point. The difficulty over primitive stages of organs is a real one ; it must be shown that intermediate stages of development could be selected for. In the case of the wing, the development of gliding surfaces to aid arboreal jumping forms will account for the first stages, and the subsequent use of them for flapping flight (probably first developed as a device for landing on vertical tree-trunks) for the remainder. In the Molluscs, all sorts of eyes, ranging from mere groups of sensory cells up to the amazing eyes of squids, are found, giving a delicacy of perception suited to the mode of life of the possessor. A. D. Blest has shown experimentally that even mere blotches of colour on a moth's wings, if suddenly displayed, can be intimidating to birds ; but that the more they are like large eye-spots, the more effective they are. It has also been shown that weak electric pulses emitted by various sorts of fish living in muddy water are of great use in radio-location of obstacles or prey ; an intensification of these for greater radar range could secondarily be used as a defensive or offensive mechanism. The difficulty over blending inheritance has been removed by the advance of genetics (see GENETICS). The suggestion that species arise by a single mutation is certainly wrong for many animals, the species of which differ in very many genes as a rule and arise by a slow process of accumulation of many small differences (see SPECIATION).

Birds have been much used in direct studies on natural selection, but mainly as predators. Sumner used diving birds to predate small fishes, some of which had been made pale by keeping them in the dark, and showed that the fishes that least resembled the colour of the background against which they were seen by the birds were taken more frequently than the others. Kettlewell has shown that many common birds in England predate the Peppered Moth *Biston betularia* and, by highly selective predation, are responsible for the enormous proportion of melanic forms in and near industrial areas. The melanics well resemble smoke-blackened bark, whereas the normal form is almost invisible on lichen-covered trunks ; lichens disappear in industrial areas, but where they are present it is the melanic form that is conspicuous against them and is very heavily predated. Cain and Sheppard have shown that thrushes *Turdus* spp. and other birds exert visual selection on the different colour-forms and banding-forms of the snail *Cepaea nemoralis*, removing preferentially those that resemble the background least. Other studies have been made in Germany and North America (see also PREDATION). An example of selection acting on birds themselves is given by Lack's study of the adaptive significance of clutch size. He has shown that birds laying larger clutches than normal for their species usually lose some of the young because they cannot get enough food for all of them ; those laying fewer than normal will of course leave less offspring than others ; consequently there is an optimum clutch size for each species under given environmental conditions, and selection will act to enforce it (see also POPULATION DYNAMICS).

Although much selection is exerted by conditions external to the individuals of a population (e.g. by weather, predators, or each other), much is also produced internally by variation. An animal is so complicated a system that many genetic changes in it are highly deleterious and may even be fatal. Thus, if a mutation occurs that renders its possessor sterile, although perfectly healthy, no offspring can be produced by it ; this is equivalent to the highest possible selection against this variety, even if it should happen to be able to obtain abundant food and other necessities and undergo no struggle or competition at all.

The selection coefficient in respect of two forms of a species is measured, in the most general way possible, by the ratio of offspring they produce in the next generation. Thus if form A leaves only 90 offspring to every 100 of form B, the selection coefficient of A is —10 per cent in respect of B, and in a population where the two occur together A will rapidly vanish. It will be noted that nothing is specified as to what selective forces (e.g. predators, disease, starvation, etc.), or how many of them, are acting, and at what stage in the life history. The selection coefficient gives the net advantage or disadvantage of one form relative to another. This being so, it can be used to study all forms of selection, and one of the great recent advances in evolutionary theory has been made with it. Mathematical geneticists, especially R. A. Fisher, J. B. S. Haldane, and Sewall Wright, have shown that in large populations even a selection coefficient as low as +1 per cent is sufficient to cause a particular form to spread through that population in remarkably few generations. In very small populations chance may play some part in determining the frequency of forms with low selection coefficients. Only a few selection co-efficients have been measured as yet, but these, although usually referring to apparently quite trivial variations, are often about 10–20 per cent or more, which is huge. This means that, however trivial we may think a character is, we are not in a position to say that selection (indeed, even violent selection) cannot be acting on it. Many, perhaps most, genes exert many different effects over the body, and a trivial but easily observed effect may be only a single one among very deep-seated influences caused by a single gene.

Now, since the process of sexual reproduction is continually producing variation by dealing out in each generation different combinations of alternatives, and new variations are constantly being produced by mutation (see GENETICS), a character that is not being held constant by selection is liable to considerable variation from individual to individual. (Perhaps an example is the variation of human finger-prints: provided sufficient ridges are present and orientated in all directions for grasping, it may not matter much exactly what patterns occur.) Consequently, if we find a character, however trivial it may seem to us, that is constant in a population of more than a few thousand (perhaps even a few hundred) breeding individuals, it is infinitely more likely to be constant for some good selective reason than to be of no selective value at all. This conclusion is entirely confirmed by the experimental investigations mentioned above ; and from the work of Lorenz and of Tinbergen it is now known how exceedingly important in the lives of birds apparently very ' trivial ' plumage marks may be.

A clear distinction between selection and adaptation must be made. The term ' adaptation ' is used (a) for the production of fitness for some particular function, and (b) for a structure, piece of behaviour, or the like, that adapts an organism to do some particular thing—thus the wing of an albatross *Diomedea* sp. is an adaptation for rapid gliding flight. Selection is the means whereby adaptation is brought about, and adaptive structures or behaviour are produced. The selection coefficient, measured by proportion of progeny in the next generation, gives only the net effect of all the different selective pressures, producing different adaptations, that act on individuals. It does not necessarily measure the production of any one adaptation. Only when the exact selective pressure can be identified, as in the examples given above of birds selecting out the more conspicuous

varieties of moth or snail against a given background, can a special selection coefficient be obtained that measures how well adapted the varieties are for one particular function (in this case, escape by means of cryptic coloration).

If natural selection is so powerful, it has been asked, why are not all animals perfectly cryptic in their coloration, or brilliantly coloured to advertise their distastefulness to intending predators ? The answer appears to be that every animal has to fulfil very many different functions in order to persist, and that nearly every feature is a compromise between different demands, a compromise that will vary in its terms from species to species according as their habits differ. It should also be noted that the acquisition of a high degree of specialisation need be of no great importance to a species. In the Moluccas there is an oriole (*Oriolus bouroensis* and allies) that flies with and mimics a noisy and aggressive friar-bird (*Philemon*), even varying geographically from island to island as its model varies (see also MIMICRY). As long as hawks occasionally make the mistake of avoiding these orioles because they look like friar-birds, there will be selection maintaining and even improving the mimicry. But it is quite possible that if the friar-birds were to vanish overnight, the orioles might persist in much the same numbers as before ; an increase in predation of the adults might well be compensated for by a reduced mortality of juveniles (say, with fewer juveniles, some disease might be less readily transmitted by flies from nest to nest). The evolution of mimetic patterns in this species, therefore, need have no effect on its population size, and no significance for its likelihood of persistence.

Selection always acts here and now, so to speak ; it cannot produce organs now to be used only in the far distant future. A population cannot be selected to withstand varying conditions unless conditions are actually varying. No doubt there are many examples of organs produced for one purpose that by sheer good luck are found later to be useful for something else—the electric organs of the electric eel appear to be an example. Such pre-adaptation, however, must be coincidental. Selection may even act to produce an immediate short-term advantage that in the long run will produce serious disadvantages and even, if conditions change, lead to the extinction of the species (one possible example is known in plants).

The power of natural selection, although immense, has therefore definite limitations. But that it is the force acting to produce evolutionary change need not be doubted. The identification of selection pressures, their measurement where possible, and the interpretation of structure, physiology, and behaviour in terms of them, is one of the principal tasks of biology.   A.J.C.

Fisher, R. A. 1929. The Genetical Theory of Natural Selection. (Revised edition 1958, Dover Books, New York.)
Sheppard, P. M. 1959. Natural Selection and Heredity. London (Hutchinson University Library).

One technical and one explanatory work are cited above ; all the references given under GENETICS and SPECIATION are also relevant.

NAVIGATION: here used in the sense that a bird may be considered to have navigational ability if it is able to orientate itself in the absence of landmarks known previously to it ; visual following of topographical 'leading lines' is not considered (see MIGRATION), nor is the very different question of steering in dark caves (see ECHO LOCATION). The orientation may be simple, unidirectional (orientation in one compass direction), or complex, directed to a point or area (true navigation, 'goal orientation', homing).

'Compass' orientation serves as the basis for migration in many birds that shuttle directly back and forth between summer and winter quarters, for instance on a north-east and south-west line. If young birds are released after all adults have left, they will proceed in the normal ('primary', 'standard') direction and for approximately the right distance. The latter is probably determined by the duration of the physiological migratory urge, coupled with suitable proximate stimuli. Similarly, if young birds actually on migration are caught and displaced to one side of their appropriate track, they will continue in the same direction, on a parallel course, and for much the same distance.

Simple compass orientation on release from captivity and without relevance to the migration direction has been observed in a number of species, including the non-migratory domestic pigeon *Columba livia* and Mallard *Anas platyrhynchos*. The orientation is short-lived and its biological significance is obscure, although certainly related to stress conditions—a form of escape reaction. Different species have different 'nonsense' orientations, and even within a species discrete populations show radically different tendencies. These appear to be fixed at an early age, if not actually innate. Birds can also be trained to fly in one certain direction, and this has been used as the basis of pigeon-racing (see HOMING PIGEON).

Birds placed in circular cages hop and flutter while in the state of migratory restlessness and their movements are orientated in the migration direction. Learned compass orientation can also

be studied in cages by training birds to select one from a circle of identical containers, the one actually with food always being in the same compass direction. The ability to orientate and to select the migration direction proves to be congenital, being shown by birds hand-reared from hatching, under wholly artificial conditions.

With caged birds the physical basis of the orientation can be studied in detail. If the sky is completely excluded by heavy overcast or by artificial cover, there is no orientation. By day the sun is the guide to orientation, for if its apparent position is altered by mirrors the bird changes direction through an equivalent angle. The bird is, however, able to take into account the sun's 'movement' through the day, implying some form of internal 'chronometer'. Indeed this can easily be altered by keeping the birds in an artificial day some hours in advance or behind the natural day ; on seeing the natural sun again the birds turn, as appropriate, through a greater or less angle in taking up their direction. Alternatively, if they are shown a stationary artificial sun they will orientate at different angles to it according to the time of day, behaving as if the artificial sun *did* move. (See also TIME MEASUREMENT.)

Sun-compass orientation is shown by several nocturnal migrants, and for a time it was thought that they would have to rely upon directions obtained at sunset to serve them through the night. However, 'nonsense' orientation has been shown at night by ducks equipped with leg lamps, and migratory orientation has been observed in caged warblers (Sylviinae) set out under a starry sky. Further, orientation was obtained under the artificial stars on the dome of a planetarium. If the spring star pattern was shown in autumn, the birds alternated between the autumn direction and the reciprocal spring direction ; but if star patterns appropriate to non-migratory seasons were shown the birds were completely confused and headed in all directions.

Observations under field conditions confirm that compass orientation breaks down under periods of heavy overcast ; indeed, the start of a migratory movement is often delayed in such circumstances. If a movement is under way when overcast is encountered the birds, particularly at night, are liable to be disorientated. In any event, they are subject to lateral drift under the influence of beam winds. the actual track being the resultant of the compass heading and wind direction. This has been observed over the sea by means of radar and may result in the arrival on the east coasts of Britain of birds of Continental origin migrating southwards (see RADAR).

There are many cases known in which such drifted

migrants have re-orientated themselves and regained their normal winter quarters. In the migrants displaced experimentally, it would appear that it is the adults, with at least one season's experience of the winter quarters, which show this 'homing' to an area. Most homing experiments have been carried out with breeding birds, since their urge to return is strong and only a small area need be kept under observation. Colonial breeding birds have been favoured as a matter of convenience.

Non-migratory birds have seldom returned home from more than a few miles, but many migratory species have shown remarkable homing abilities. The longest flights on record are those of a Manx Shearwater *Puffinus puffinus* which homed 3050 miles in $12\frac{1}{2}$ days, and of Laysan Albatrosses *Diomedea immutabilis* which covered 3200 miles in 10 days and 4120 miles in 32 days. These, and many shorter journeys done in times indicative of straight-line flight, do not suggest that the birds wandered at random in search of known landmarks. Such suggestions followed earlier work that had given rise to slow returns, with the proportion of successful birds falling steeply as the distance of release increased. Attempts were made to follow homing birds with aircraft, or to plot the distance flown by means of a radioactive recorder attached to the bird's wings. However, such exotic methods are not needed when homeward orientation is apparent a very few minutes after release, while the birds are still in sight of the observer at the release point. Such evidence is acceptable only when the birds (and preferably the same individuals) have orientated homewards from several different directions. Otherwise, for example, a simple congenital northward tendency might appear as homeward orientation in birds released to the south. Definite evidence that birds can determine where they are on the earth's surface relative to home has been obtained only with pigeons and shearwaters.

Not unnaturally such a remarkable ability has attracted the attention of people with many different interests and has given rise to a multitude of hypotheses. The latter fall into two mutually exclusive groups, those suggesting that the bird maintains a sensory contact with home and those requiring it to react to quantitative differences between stimuli present at release and at home.

Direct visual contact is ruled out by reason of the immense distances involved and the low height at which the birds fly; nor is the bird's eye especially sensitive to the more penetrating infra-red rays. Various other 'radiations', real or imaginary, have been proposed and dismissed. Another form of sensory contact proposed has been a 'thread of Ariadne' whereby the surroundings at release are recognised as the last link in a series of such features. This has been disproved by detour experiments in which birds taken to the release point by a long and devious route flew straight home. Another version of this type of theory is the suggestion that the bird is able, through its inner-ear mechanism, to record every change of direction and acceleration during the outward journey and to integrate the results to give the overall angular displacement from home. This 'inertial navigation' is used in man-made vehicles and certainly cannot be dismissed out of hand; but birds have shown unimpaired orientation after being taken to the release point in irregularly revolving drums.

Against contact and retracement theories in general is the evidence that orientation and homing are *not* better the closer to home the birds are when released. Indeed, there is evidence that good homeward orientation, independent of known landmarks, will occur only over a certain minimum distance. This is more in accord with theories of 'grid' navigation. These visualise at least two physical factors (X and Y) varying quantitatively in a regular way across the earth's surface, but with the gradient of X crossing the gradient of Y at an angle. The values of X and Y at the release point will be different from those at home and so indicate their relative positions on the 'grid'. The closer the home and release points are to each other, the more similar will be the values of X and Y and, it is supposed, the more difficult for the relevant sense organ to discriminate between them. The bird would also have to be able to determine the orientation of the 'grid' with reference to the surroundings of the release point, much as we set a map by coinciding its northing line with a compass needle.

The forces resulting from the earth's rotation could, in theory, provide one set of grid lines, since they vary regularly with latitude. However, their effects on a bird are extremely small and it is most unlikely that they could be detected with anything approaching the necessary accuracy, say by the semicircular canals of the ear (see HEARING AND BALANCE). Similar considerations weigh against detecting and measuring the earth's magnetic field, either directly, or indirectly by the minute voltages set up when moving through that field. Numerous tests have been made with magnets attached in various positions on the birds' bodies without impairing their homing. Massive experiments designed to show homing to an anomalous point, with the same magnetic and latitudinal characteristics as the true home, were completely negative.

The weight of evidence is that homing, like simple

compass orientation, is based on celestial clues, probably using the sun or stars to provide a navigational 'grid'. Homing or homeward orientation has not yet been demonstrated under a night sky, and the evidence for a true bi-coordinate navigation based on the star pattern rests on the behaviour of a few caged warblers in a planetarium. When these were shown star patterns corresponding to lower latitudes they shifted their 'migration' direction slightly, just as they would have done in the normal circumstances. One bird, exposed to a star pattern some hours in advance of the home situation, apparently treated this as being due to its having been transported in longitude, for it reacted by orientation strongly to the west. There is controversy over the interpretation of these laboratory experiments, and they should be treated with caution for the present.

There is general agreement that homing by day breaks down in cloudy conditions. It has been suggested that only a compass element, needed to set a grid map, is involved, the grid itself being based on non-celestial (and unspecified) factors. However, simple compass orientation is shown to persist with overcast, provided that very general localisation of the sun is possible, whereas true homeward orientation is disrupted even when cloud cover is not complete.

It is not impossible that the bird could see sufficient of the star pattern to navigate by it during daylight. But, in the absence of any direct evidence for this, attention has focused on methods by which the bird could utilise detailed observation of the sun to determine its own position. The simplest method would be to observe when the sun is at its highest point (local noon) enabling a time comparison to be made to give, in effect, the change in longitude; and to measure its angle of elevation at that time, when comparison with the home value would give, in effect, the change in latitude. This—and any other method of celestial navigation—requires the bird to have an accurate time-keeping mechanism, geared to the home time. While birds undoubtedly do have physiological chronometers there is little evidence as to their accuracy.

Since birds have been shown to orientate towards home at various times of day, such *direct* observation of the sun's noon position cannot be the basis for navigation. Theoretically, at any instant of time the sun's height and the rate at which this is increasing (or decreasing), if compared with the values at home, would reveal the displacement from home. But for much of the day the sun paths for two places, say, 50 miles apart (from which distance homing orientation has been observed) run very close together and actually cross over early and late in the day. Thus gross misinterpretations are possible, and for

---

Plate 31 · **Characteristic Australian Birds** by BETTY TEMPLE WATTS

ca. ⅛ nat. size

All the species shown are Australian, except that the bird-of-paradise depicted belongs to New Guinea. The families represented are confined to the Australasian Region (including New Zealand) and islands of the Pacific Ocean. See article AUSTRALASIAN REGION.

1 Australian Cassowary *Casuarius casuarius* (Casuariidae)

2 Blue-faced Honeyeater *Entomyzon cyanotis* (Meliphagidae)

3 Emu *Dromaius novaehollandiae* (Dromaiidae)

4 Pied Butcherbird *Cracticus nigrogularis* (Cracticidae)

5 Lesser Bird-of-paradise *Paradisaea minor* (Paradisaeidae)

6 Golden Bowerbird *Prionodura newtoniana* (Ptilinorhynchidae)

7 Plains-wanderer *Pedionomus torquatus* (Pedionomidae)

8 Mallee-fowl *Leipoa ocellata* (Megapodiidae)

9 Superb Lyrebird *Menura superba* (Menuridae)

10 Noisy Scrub-bird *Atrichornis clamosus* (Atrichornithidae)

11 Magpie-lark *Grallina cyanoleuca* (Grallinidae)

Where there are sexual or seasonal differences, the plumage depicted is that of the breeding male (but in the Plains-wanderer the female is in fact somewhat brighter and larger).

The artist, not having seen the cassowary or the bird-of-paradise in life, gratefully acknowledges having based the postures on photographs by, respectively, A. W. Ambler and E. T. Gilliard in the latter's *Living Birds of the World*, by permission of the publishers, Hamish Hamilton Ltd., London.

B.T.W. 1963

D.M.H.

much of the day the feat of distinguishing one sun arc from another would seem impossible even for the superlative eye of the bird. This is the more so since the bird is not distinguishing between two observed arcs ; one of them must be memorised—and memorised in every detail throughout its entire length and for each day of the year.

A much lesser demand on the bird's visual memory is made by the hypothesis of sun-arc extrapolation. Here the bird is required only to remember the height of the sun at noon at home the previous day. Then on release it is required to observe the sun's movement along a small portion of its arc and to extrapolate from this to obtain an estimate of the highest elevation it reaches at the release point, and when. Comparisons could thus be made between the sun arcs for home and release point when they are at their most separate.

The detection of the sun's movement lies within the known capacity of the avian eye, and the ability to extrapolate is necessary to any animal capable of swift movement or living on moving prey. It would be impossible for a human being to measure the sun's movement whilst in flight, as the bird is on this hypothesis required to do ; but there are many indications that in flight the bird's whole system of postural stabilisation is of a different order from our own. Certainly much more research is needed on this point.

There is some experimental evidence in favour of this hypothesis. Pigeons kept out of sight of the sky for many days at the autumn equinox, when the noon height of the sun is changing relatively rapidly from day to day, showed confusion, if not re-orientation (in the predicted false direction), on release. Attempts to alter the internal chronometer by exposure to a simple artificial out-of-phase day were unsuccessful. After more elaborate treatment to disrupt and then reset the 'chronometer', dis-orientation, and probably re-orientation as if to the false shift in longitude, was observed in pigeons. Contrary evidence, also obtained with pigeons, now appears to have been due to the particular birds showing a simple (northward) direction tendency. Their near-immediate orientation (allowing no time for observation of sun movement), the failure of sun occlusion to alter their orientation, and their ready reaction to out-of-phase days to give a simple angular deviation, are all results such as would be expected in the case of simple compass orientation, as opposed to true bi-coordinate navigation.

In summary, therefore, it now appears that two main types of navigation are shown by birds ; a simple distance-and-bearing type and a more complex form of grid navigation. Both appear to be based on celestial clues, using either the sun position or the star pattern. These conclusions appear certain in the case of the simple compass orientation and plausible but 'not proven' so far as true navigation is concerned.   G.V.T.M.

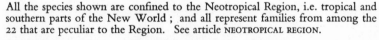

Plate 32 · Characteristic Neotropical Birds by D. M. REID-HENRY

All the species shown are confined to the Neotropical Region, i.e. tropical and southern parts of the New World ; and all represent families from among the 22 that are peculiar to the Region. See article NEOTROPICAL REGION.

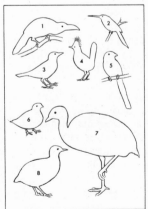

ca. $\frac{3}{10}$ nat. size

1   Emerald Toucanet *Aularhynchus prasinus* (Ramphastidae) (subsp. *cyanolaemus*)

2   Rufous-tailed Jacamar *Galbula ruficauda* (Galbulidae)

3   Atacama Cinclodes *Cinclodes atacamensis* (Furnariidae)

4   Grey Gallito *Rhinocrypta lanceolata* (Rhinocryptidae)

5   Blue-throated Motmot *Aspatha gularis* (Momotidae)

6   D'Orbigny's Seed-snipe *Thinocorus orbignyianus* (Thinocoridae)

7   Common Trumpeter *Psophia crepitans* (Psophiidae)

8   Red-footed Tinamou *Crypturellus noctivagus* (Tinamidae) (subsp. *dissimilis*)

Where there are sexual or seasonal differences, the plumage depicted is that of the breeding male.

Griffin, D. R. 1955. Bird navigation. *In* Wolfson, A. (ed.). Recent Studies in Avian Biology. Urbana, Ill.

Kramer, G. 1959. Recent experiments on bird orientation. Ibis 101 : 399–416.

Kramer, G. 1961. Long-distance orientation. *In* Marshall, A. J. (ed.). Biology and Comparative Physiology of Birds vol. 2. New York and London.

Matthews, G. V. T. 1955. Bird Navigation. Cambridge.

Matthews, G. V. T. 1963. The astronomical bases of 'nonsense' orientation. Proc. XIII Internat. Orn. Congr., Ithaca, N.Y., 1962 : 415–429.

Sauer, F. 1957. Die Sternorientierung nächtlich ziehender Grässmücken (*Sylvia atricapilla, borin* und *curruca*). Z. Tierpsychol. 14 : 29–70.

Sauer, F. & Sauer, E. 1960. Orientation of nocturnal bird migrants by the stars. Proc. XII Internat. Orn. Congr., Helsinki 1958 : 645–648.

NEARCTIC REGION: the usual designation in zoogeography for North America north of the tropics (see DISTRIBUTION, GEOGRAPHICAL). The borders are the Arctic Ocean in the north, the Bering Straits and the Pacific Ocean in the west, and the Atlantic Ocean in the east. A border in the south is more difficult to draw ; it is usually placed through Mexico, along the northern edge of the tropical rain-forest (see NEOTROPICAL REGION). Thus defined, the Nearctic Region extends from about 83° N. lat. to about 20° N. lat.

Physiography. In this vast area almost the entire range of possible climates is encountered. The major geographical features of North America, in contrast to Europe, extend longitudinally. The west consists of parallel mountains, the Rocky Mountains and related chains, extending from Alaska southward into Mexico and Central America and continuing into the Andes of South America. The interior of North America is occupied by plains extending from the Gulf of Mexico northward into Canada, where they comprise the vast Canadian Shield. In the east a minor chain of mountains, the Appalachians, extends from Georgia and Alabama into Pennsylvania and continues in several more or less isolated mountain ranges in New York, Vermont, New Hampshire, Maine, and the Maritime Provinces of Canada. This essentially longitudinal arrangement of the major geographical features is, to a large extent, responsible for some of the otherwise puzzling features of the North American bird-life.

Many attempts have been made to subdivide the Nearctic Region into local provinces, beginning with the life zones of Merriam to the biotic provinces of recent authors. Since all these zones intergrade insensibly, none of the attempts can be considered fully successful. On the whole, bird-life and landscape change latitudinally, with the climatic and vegetational belts becoming increasingly better defined northward. A circumpolar tundra belt north of the tree-line is well defined. A ' Canadian ' coniferous belt with its characteristic avifauna is fairly well defined. Both extend southwards along the mountains. Farther south there is a less well defined series of belts of deciduous forest, limited to areas of higher rainfall. Between the Mississippi Valley and the Rocky Mountains lie extensive plains ('prairies'); and in northern Mexico and the south-western states are extensive arid areas, some of them true deserts. The bird-life of each of these vegetational areas differs more or less drastically from that of other areas.

History of the Avifauna. The composition of the North American bird fauna is best understood in the light of its history. The North American continent was apparently separated from Europe by the Atlantic Ocean for the entire Tertiary Period (70 million years) or longer. It has had intermittent connections with Asia across the Bering Straits bridge ; and it was separated from South America, at least from the early Eocene to the late Pliocene, by a series of Central American water-gaps cutting through what are now Nicaragua, Panama, and north-western Colombia. This history of the North American landmass explains the composition of its avifauna. On the whole, the fauna has evolved in isolation from both Eurasia and South America, but there has been opportunity for a limited amount of faunal exchange across the Bering Straits bridge and the ' stepping-stones ' in the Panamanian gap.

During the first half of the Tertiary the southern half of North America was humid and tropical as far north as latitudes 38°–40°, as shown by the palaeobotanical records. This permitted the evolution of a tropical North American fauna rather distinct from the tropical fauna of South America. The two tropical faunas intermingled when the Panamanian land-bridge was established near the end of the Tertiary (late Pliocene). In the meantime there had been a steady process of cooling and reduction of rainfall in North America, in part caused by the rising of the mountain ranges in the western parts. This resulted in the development of deserts, subsequently populated by invaders from the adjacent, more humid habitats.

In addition to sea birds and world-wide elements, the North American avifauna consists essentially of three elements. (1) An indigenous element that evolved during the Tertiary isolation ; (2) immigrants from South America ; and (3) immigrants from Eurasia. The fauna as a whole is thus somewhat intermediate between that of South America and that of Asia. Even though there is some ambiguity in any faunal analysis, it is fairly easy to determine to which of the three stated faunas most genera and families of North American birds belong.

Indigenous Elements. Five families of songbirds can be considered indigenous North American elements. The wrens (Troglodytidae) have far more species and genera north of the Tertiary gap through Central America than they have in South America. The large number of endemic species and genera in the arid, subtropical zone of Mexico and the southwestern United States is further proof. A single species, the well-known Winter Wren *Troglodytes troglodytes*, has crossed into Eurasia. Other well-known North and Central American species are the House Wren *Troglodytes aedon*, the Carolina Wren *Thryothorus ludovicianus*, the Long-billed Marsh Wren *Telmatodytes palustris*, and the Rock Wren *Salpinctes obsoletus*. Wrens are found in nearly every habitat from the most desolate desert to marshes and the tropical rain-forest.

The mocking-bird family (Mimidae) contains many well-known North American birds of gardens, woodlands, and open country, such as the Catbird *Dumetella carolinensis*, the Brown Thrasher *Toxostoma rufum*, and the Mocking-bird *Mimus polyglottos* ; the family is restricted essentially to the areas south of the coniferous forest belt. The vireos (Vireonidae), a family of small, mostly greenish, insect-eating birds of the leafy canopy of trees and bushes, are particularly well represented in the southern United States, Central America, and the West Indies ; the Red-eyed Vireo *Vireo olivaceus* is perhaps the most common North American woodland bird, the polytypic species extending as far south as southern South America. The American wood-warblers (Parulidae) are a group of colourful but structurally little diversified warbler-like birds well represented also in the northern coniferous belt, and two species have indeed crossed over into eastern Siberia ; the northern species are highly migratory, and their passing through the United States in spring and fall, in enormous numbers, is one of the most spectacular aspects of bird-life in North America. Considering that these four families are so well represented in North and Central America and in the West Indies, it is astonishing how few genera have crossed the Tertiary water-gap into South America. Some of those that did cross have, however, evolved secondarily a considerable number of species in South America.

The fifth family consists of the buntings or American sparrows (Emberizidae). This family is highly diversified in the New World, so much so that it is difficult to delimit it against the tanagers (Thraupinae) and other finch-like birds, for instance the cardinals (Pyrrhuloxiinae). Well-known North American species are the Song Sparrow *Melospiza melodia* with over thirty subspecies extending from the Aleutians and Alaska south to Mexico, the Field Sparrow *Spizella pusilla*, the White-throated Sparrow *Zonotrichia albicollis*, and the Towhee *Pipilo erythrophthalmus*. These buntings, like their Eurasian counterparts, are largely birds of the open country, from deserts to prairies and marshes ; but several species are typical for the undergrowth of the forest, particularly in the tropics.

Some small families or subfamilies that are presumably indigenous North American elements are the dippers (Cinclidae), the gnatcatchers (Polioptilinae), the waxwings (Bombycillinae), the silky flycatchers (Ptilogonatinae), the mostly tropical motmots (Momotidae), the West Indian todies (Todidae), and the Palmchat (Dulidae). Several families of non-passerine birds are perhaps indigenous North American elements, such as the New World vultures (Cathartidae) represented by the Turkey Vulture *Cathartes aura*, Black Vulture *C. atratus*, and California Condor *Gymnogyps californianus*, and the grouse family (Tetraonidae) with numerous woodland species but also birds of the open country such as the extinct Heath Hen (an eastern subspecies of the surviving Prairie Chicken *Tympanuchus cupido*) and the spectacular Sage Grouse *Centrocercus urophasianus*. The American quails (Odontophorinae) take the place of the pheasants and partridges (Phasianinae) of the Old World. Two species of turkey (Meleagrididae) are the most spectacular gallinaceous birds of the New World.

Old World Element. In view of the continued inflow of Old World elements through the Tertiary, it is not surprising that some of the earlier immigrants have evolved separate evolutionary lines. Among the earlier elements are the cranes (Gruidae), pigeons (Columbidae), cuckoos (Cuculidae), owls (Strigidae), crows (Corvidae), and thrushes (Turdinae). Only a few pigeons of the *Columba* type occur in North America, although this group is richly represented in South America. A close relative of the extinct Passenger Pigeon *Ectopistes migratorius*, the Mourning Dove *Zenaidura macroura*, is one of the most widespread North American birds. Cuckoos are represented by several genera, none of them parasitic ; the roadrunner *Geococcyx californianus* is characteristic of the more arid areas of the west and south-west. Many genera of owls are the same as those found in Eurasia, but there are some special types, such as the Burrowing Owl *Speotyto cunicularia* and the Elf Owl *Micrathene whitneyi*.

See Plate 30 (colour).   E.M.

American Ornithologists' Union. 1957. Check-list of North American Birds. Baltimore.
Blake, E. R. 1953. Birds of Mexico. Chicago.
Palmer, R. S. (ed.) 1962 et seq. Handbook of North

American Birds. New Haven, Conn. (To be completed in about 6 vols.).

Peterson, R. T. 1947. A Field Guide to the Birds. 2nd ed. Boston, Mass.

Peterson, R. T. 1961. A Field Guide to Western Birds. 2nd ed. Boston, Mass.

Snyder, L. L. 1957. Arctic Birds of Canada. Toronto.

NECK: see SHAPE AND POSTURE ; TOPOGRAPHY

NECTAR-FEEDERS: birds that feed on the sugary liquid in the calyces of some flowers and on the insects found in or with this. The habit has been evolved in several unrelated families in different parts, mainly tropical, of the world. The principal groups are the hummingbirds (Trochilidae) and honeycreepers (Coerebinae) of the New World, the sunbirds (Nectariniidae) of Africa and southern Asia, the honeyeaters (Meliphagidae) and flowerpeckers (Dicaeidae) found chiefly in Australasia, and the Hawaiian honeycreepers (Drepanididae).

NECTARINIIDAE: a family of the Passeriformes, suborder Oscines (see SUNBIRD).

NEDDICKY: name, in South Africa, of *Cisticola fulvicapilla* (for subfamily see WARBLER (1)).

NEGRO-FINCH: substantive name of *Nigrita* spp. (see WEAVER-FINCH).

NE-NE: Hawaiian vernacular name, widely adopted, for the Hawaiian Goose *Branta sandvicensis* (see under DUCK).

NEOGAEA: see under ARCTOGAEA ; DISTRIBUTION, GEOGRAPHICAL

NEOGNATHAE: a superorder (see under CLASS).

NEOGNATHOUS: see PALATE ; SKELETON

NEOMORPHINAE: see CUCKOO

NEONTOLOGY: the study of geologically recent forms of life (contrasted with PALAEONTOLOGY).

NEORNITHES: a subclass (see under CLASS).

NEOSITTIDAE: a family separated by some authors but now usually merged with the Sittidae (see NUTHATCH).

NEOSSOPTILE: term applied to the natal down plumage (where present), as contrasted with ' teleoptile ' (see PLUMAGE).

NEOTENY: persistence of embryonic characters into adult life (see DEVELOPMENT, POSTEMBRYONIC ; SKELETON).

NEOTROPICAL REGION: the usual designation in zoogeography for tropical America and the non-tropical parts of South America, together with the West Indies and other islands near South America (see DISTRIBUTION, GEOGRAPHICAL). South America

is the real home of the Neotropical fauna, while Central America and the West Indies occupy a special position discussed below. The Neotropical Region extends from the northern edge of the tropical rain-forest in Mexico, about 20° N. lat. (see NEARCTIC REGION), south to Cape Horn, in about 57° S. lat.

Physiography. South America is characterised by numerous geographical superlatives. The Andes, forming the western edge of the continent throughout its length, are the greatest mountain range in the world, extending through eighty degrees of latitude. The Amazon is the world's greatest river. The region is dominated by tropics and subtropics, and the southern third of the continent is so narrow that it leaves only little space for a temperate zone fauna. There are two areas of mountains east of the Andes —the isolated Guiana-Venezuela highlands (with Mt Roraima and Mt Duida), and the eastern Brazilian mountains. There are extensive savannas (' llanos ') north of the River Amazon, particularly in the upper Orinoco basin of Venezuela and north-eastern Colombia, and more extensive ones from the Matto Grosso south into Patagonia. Very arid country, some of it true desert, extends from the Pacific coast of southern Ecuador south through coastal Peru and Chile to about Valparaiso, southwards extending increasingly far into the mountains and encroaching in northern Argentina beyond the foot of the eastern Andes. As Wallace said, the Neotropical Region ' is distinguished from all the other great Zoological divisions of the globe by the small proportion of its surface occupied by deserts, by the large proportion of its lowlands, and by the altogether unequalled extent and luxuriance of its tropical forests '.

History of the Avifauna. The avifauna of South America not only is the richest in the world but is also remarkably uniform throughout the continent. There are no latitudinal barriers anywhere east of the Andes, and the Andes themselves have served as a distributional pathway, permitting the colonisation of the lower latitudes by many temperate zone elements. The south temperate avifauna is characterised more by the paucity of its elements than by its distinctiveness. There are, however, a number of endemic genera, some of them, such as the seedsnipe (Thinocoridae), forming an endemic family.

Although South America is now in land connection with North America across the isthmus of Panama, it was an isolated continent for most of the Tertiary Period and perhaps for much longer. Three major water-gaps (' portals ') are known to have existed during this period ; one across Nicaragua, one across Panama, and the third across north-western Colombia. These water-gaps were separated by insular 'stepping-stones' for those faunal elements capable of island-hopping. The last of the portals did not close until the end of the Pliocene, perhaps not more than two million years ago. There is no ornithological evidence for any land connection with either Africa or Australia (across Antarctica) : some of the formerly cited evidence was based on faulty classification ('ratites') ; some is explained by recent transoceanic colonisation such as that demonstrated by the Cattle Egret *Ardeola ibis*, the Green Heron *Butorides striatus*, two whistling ducks *Dendrocygna* spp., and a pochard *Netta erythroph-thalma* ; and finally some is explained by colonisation across the Bering Straits land-bridge—parrots (Psittacidae) and trogons (Trogonidae).

Indigenous Element. The old indigenous South American element includes a number of small families (the number of included species is indicated in parentheses), such as the rheas (Rheidae) (2), screamers (Anhimidae) (3), hoatzin (Opistho-comidae) (1), trumpeters (Psophiidae) (3), sun-bittern (Eurypygidae) (1), seed-snipe (Thinocoridae) (4), potoos (Nyctibiidae) (5), and oilbird (Steator-nithidae) (1). Fossil rheas are known as far back as the Eocene, while for the eight other families the assumption of a South American origin is based on inference (absence from all other continents, either living or as fossils). Five other non-passerine families are much richer in species in South America than anywhere else, and for them a South American origin is hardly in doubt : tinamous (Tinamidae) (35–40), hummingbirds (Trochilidae) (319), puff-birds (Bucconidae) (32), jacamars (Galbulidae) (14), and toucans (Ramphastidae) (37). They include some of the most characteristic elements of the South American avifauna.

South America is characterised, even better than by these non-passerines, as the home of the Clama-tores (= Suborder Tyranni) the true mesomyodean passerines. All the families of this suborder are Neotropical (except for a few Old World genera with simplified syringeal musculature, probably not at all related to the South American families). The South American Clamatores are divisible into two main branches, the Tracheophonae (= Superfamily Furnarioidea) and the Haploophonae (= Super-family Tyrannoidea). The Tracheophonae, in which the syrinx is entirely tracheal, consists of the tapaculos (Rhinocryptidae) (26), antpipits (Conopophagidae) (10), antbirds (Formicariidae) (221), (ovenbirds (Furnariidae) (212), and woodhewers (Dendroco-laptidae) (47). This group, including more than 500 species, forms a dominant element in the South American avifauna. The antbirds are particularly characteristic of the undergrowth in the tropical rain-forest, while some of the genera of ovenbirds contribute conspicuous species to the temperate zone fauna of the continent, both in the southern latitudes and at the higher altitudes of the Andes.

In the haploophone Clamatores, the syrinx muscles are tracheobronchial, but are attached only at one end of the bronchial rings. This includes the tyrant-flycatchers (Tyrannidae) (366), the manakins (Pip-ridae) (59), cotingas (Cotingidae) (90), and the plantcutters (Phytotomidae) (3). This group also comprises more than 500 species. Indeed, the two groups of Clamatores combined contain nearly one-eighth of all the known species of birds of the world.

Most of the indigenous South American bird families, like their mammalian counterparts, have been poor colonisers. Only the hummingbirds and the tyrant-flycatchers, among the truly South American elements, seem to have colonised North America across the Central American stepping-stones to develop subtropical and temperate zone representatives in the North American fauna. The other families crossed into Central America late in the Tertiary, most of them apparently only after a complete land connection had been established.

Nearctic Element. The stepping-stones between North and South America were used much more actively by North American elements to carry on a steady colonisation. The earliest of these immi-grants—the tanagers (Thraupinae), cardinals (Pyr-rhuloxiinae), honeycreepers (Coerebinae), and trou-pials (Icteridae)—settled there such a long time ago that, except for their evident relationships to North American elements, they have acquired all the characteristics of South American families ; the Emberizidae should perhaps be included in this group. Much of the adaptive radiation of these families took place in South America.

Other immigrants radiating secondarily in South America were contributed by such pantropical groups as the parrots, the trogons, and one or two smaller groups. Other rather early arrivals from North America include the guans (Cracidae), the American quail (Odontophorinae), pigeons (Colum-bidae), jays (Corvidae), and thrushes (Turdinae). Typically North American families, such as the wrens (Troglodytidae), vireos (Vireonidae), wood warblers (Parulidae), and motmots (Momotidae), invaded South America prior to the closing of the water-gap, and certain genera speciated there quite actively. The Andean chain, through Central America in almost continuous mountainous con-nection with the North American Rocky Mountains, has permitted the immigration of some typically holarctic elements into South America, such as pipits *Anthus* spp., the Horned (or Shore) Lark

Eremophila alpestris, and the Short-eared Owl *Asio flammeus.*

Needless to say, the South American continent has a rich fauna of fresh-water birds, consisting essentially of cosmopolitan families but with many endemic genera and species. Among the more characteristic of these the following may be mentioned : torrent ducks *Merganetta* spp., the Coscoroba *Coscoroba coscoroba*, the South American sheld-geese *Chloephaga* spp., and the steamer ducks *Tachyeres* spp. (mostly salt water).

Subdivisions and Islands. Attempts to sub-divide the Neotropical Region into subregions have been unsuccessful as far as the area south of Panama is concerned. The 'Guianan' and 'Brazilian' districts are occupied by some different species and genera, but the total character of the local faunas depends more on climate and vegetation than on historical features.

Central America, 'tropical North America' as Wallace quite rightly called it, contains a strongly mixed fauna—an old indigenous element and numerous post-Pliocene invaders from South America. The West Indies have an unbalanced and impoverished avifauna, indicating that they received their fauna by transoceanic dispersal ; this is con-firmed by studies of mammals, reptiles, fishes, and insects. Most of the avian immigrants came from tropical Central America, for a long period before and after the closing of the Panamanian gap. Typical for the West Indies are certain thrushes, mocking-birds (Mimidae), vireos, wood warblers, tanagers, finches (Fringillidae), icterids, and the peculiar Palm Chat *Dulus dominicus*, some tyrant flycatchers, the endemic family Todidae, some trogons, some hum-mingbirds (including the smallest bird in the world), some parrots, pigeons, and some hawks (Falconi-formes), to mention the more important. Other islands, such as the Galápagos, the Falklands, and the Juan Fernandez group, received most of their fauna from the adjacent parts of South America.

See Plate 32 (colour).   E.M.

Alrog, C. C. 1959. Las Aves Argentinas. Tucumán.
Bond, J. 1960. Birds of the West Indies. London.
Cory, B. 1918–19 ; and Hellmayr, C. E. & Conover, B. 1929–49. Catalogue of the Birds of the Americas and the Adjacent Islands. Field Mus. Nat. Hist. Zool. Ser. 13. Chicago.
Peters, J. L. 1951. Suborder Tyranni, Superfamily Fur-narioidea. *In* Check-list of Birds of the World vol. 7. Cambridge, Mass.
de Schaunsee, R. M. 1964. Birds of Colombia. Nar-berth, Penn.

NEOTYPE : see TYPE-SPECIMEN

NEPHRON : an excretory unit of the kidney (see EXCRETORY SYSTEM).

NERVOUS SYSTEM : in birds, built on the same plan as in vertebrates generally ; it resembles that of reptiles, especially the Crocodilia and certain lizards, very closely. The difference from reptiles is chiefly one of relative size ; in a bird the brain is ten or more times larger than the brain of a reptile of similar body weight. See also DEVELOPMENT, EM-BRYONIC ; DEVELOPMENT, POSTEMBRYONIC.

Central and Peripheral Systems. The nervous system consists of a central nervous system (C.N.S., the brain and spinal cord) and a peripheral nervous system (the cranial and spinal nerves, and the visceral or autonomic nerves and ganglia). The peripheral nerves are made up of nerve fibres that can be divided into two main categories ; those that conduct impulses from the special sense organs such as eyes or from the skin and deeper tissues to the C.N.S. (afferent or sensory fibres) ; and others that conduct impulses from the C.N.S. to the muscles, causing them to contract and produce movements (efferent or motor fibres)—see also MUSCULATURE. Viscera such as the heart, blood-vessels, glands, and the alimentary canal are supplied by efferent nerve fibres that are classed as autonomic or visceral and are further subdivided into sympathetic and para-sympathetic. Viscera usually have a double nerve supply, sympathetic and parasympathetic ; these are functionally antagonistic—for example, parasym-pathetic stimulation slows the rate of the heart beat, whereas sympathetic causes acceleration. Viscera are also supplied by many afferent fibres.

Functions. It is the general function of the C.N.S. to integrate the information reaching it in the form of afferent or sensory impulses from all parts of the body and from the outside world, into patterns significant in the life of the animal. It must also be capable of storing this information selectively, so that it can form the basis of memory and learning ; but the physical form in which information is stored in the C.N.S. is not known. The C.N.S. must also have motor functions ; on the basis of the informa-tion reaching it at any particular time, combined with what has been stored from previous experiences, it must integrate or co-ordinate outgoing efferent impulses to the muscles and viscera so that useful movements and patterns of behaviour result.

To a large extent the particular kind of behaviour that can be integrated by the nervous system depends on its intrinsic structure, its 'built-in' characteristics (which are inherited). Such behaviour is activated automatically in response to appropriate sensory stimuli and is called reflex or instinctive. The extent to which it can be modified or added to as a result of experience varies in different vertebrates (see LEARNING). In birds it is very limited, and much

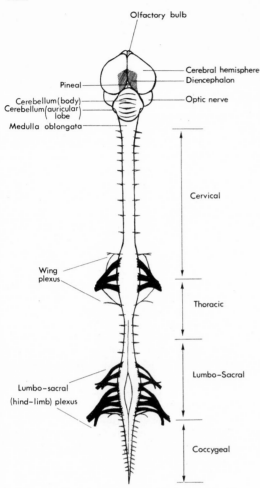

FIG 1. Diagram of the nervous system of a bird (*Columba*). *Modified from Kappers, Huber & Crosby 1936.*

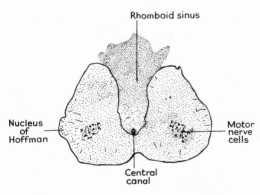

FIG 2. Transverse section through lumbo-sacral region of the spinal cord of a pigeon *Columba* to show the rhomboid sinus.

Modified from Kappers, Huber & Crosby 1936.

avian behaviour consists of complex but relatively stereotyped patterns, as is well seen in the reproductive cycle (mating, nest building, and so on). Patterns of behaviour depending on inherited structure are not so conspicuous in mammals, where the nervous system is less rigidly organised and shows greater plasticity in its functions : behaviour in consequence depends to a larger extent on learning and the storage of information. These differences between birds and mammals are reflected in fundamental differences in the structure of the nervous system, particularly in the part called the fore-brain (see below).

The functions of the nervous system in co-ordinating and activating patterns of behaviour can also be strongly influenced by chemical substances, hormones, circulating in the blood. These are produced by the endocrine glands (see ENDOCRINE SYSTEM), some of which (the pituitary and the suprarenal glands) are closely associated anatomically with the nervous system. The effect is well illustrated in sexual behaviour. When, as in the male animal, male sex hormones are predominant, the behaviour integrated by the nervous system will be that appropriate for the male ; experimentally the same nervous system can be shown to be capable of integrating female sexual behaviour under the influence of female sex hormones. Although such effects can be demonstrated in mammals, they are particularly characteristic of birds, where 'built-in' mechanisms form a more important part of the nervous system.

Spinal Cord. The spinal cord (Fig. 1) is co-extensive with the vertebral column, as in most other vertebrates except mammals, and contains a narrow channel throughout its length known as the 'central canal'. The cervical and lumbo-sacral regions are long, the thoracic and coccygeal relatively short ; there are well marked cervico-thoracic and lumbo-sacral enlargements where the nerves to the wings and legs arise. A feature peculiar to birds is the 'rhomboid sinus' ; this is a mass of gelatinous tissue, rich in lipids and glycogen, which separates the dorsal parts of the lumbo-sacral region of the spinal cord (Fig. 2) ; its function is unknown. In the same region collections of nerve cells situated superficially on the lateral aspects of the cord form the 'nuclei of Hoffmann'. Somewhat similar but less conspicuous marginal nuclei are present in reptiles. The spinal cord is connected by well developed ascending and descending tracts with the cerebellum ; the latter is largely concerned with the maintenance of equilibrium, a particularly important function during flight. Other connections with the brain are much less well developed, and the spinal cord possesses considerable autonomy. It is able to co-

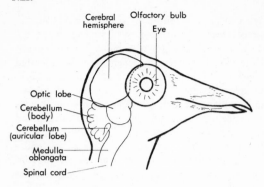

FIG 3. Lateral aspect of the brain of a bird, shown in relation to the eye and the outline of the head.

ordinate the movements of the wings in flight, or the legs in running, with little assistance from the brain ; it is well known that movements of this kind are often carried out actively for a short time after decapitation.

Brain Stem. As the spinal cord enters the skull it enlarges to form the medulla oblongata, from which most of the cranial nerves arise (Figs. 1, 3, and 4). In the same region the central canal enlarges to form a cavity called the 4th ventricle. The parts of the brain stem surrounding this ventricle belong to a subdivision of the vertebrate nervous system known as the hind-brain ; it includes the pons in mammals (absent in birds) and the cerebellum (see below) as well as the medulla oblongata. Except in detail the medulla oblongata of birds does not differ markedly from the usual vertebrate pattern. Its expanded cranial end is continuous with the next part of the brain stem, the mid-brain, which is characteristically specialised. It possesses two more or less spherical swellings, the optic lobes, which develop on its dorsal aspect and remain in that situation in all other vertebrates ; in birds they are displaced laterally and ventrally by the backward enlargement of the cerebral hemispheres (Figs. 1, 3, and 4).

Cerebellum. The cerebellum (Figs. 1 and 3) is large, and situated on the dorsal aspect of the hind-brain. The main part, the corpus or body, is somewhat compressed from side to side and elongated cranio-caudally ; it corresponds with the vermis in mammals and there is only rudimentary representation of the lateral extensions that form the mammalian cerebellar hemispheres. The body is divided by transverse furrows into anterior, middle, and posterior lobes, corresponding closely with the same subdivisions in mammals. These lobes are further divided by secondary furrows into folia ; the most caudal of these is the nodule, and, strictly speaking,

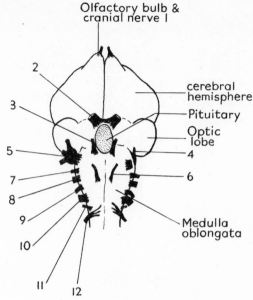

FIG 4. Ventral aspect of the brain of a pigeon, to show the roots of the cranial nerves.

should not be included in the body of the cerebellum. On each side the nodule gives rise to a lateral extension which varies in size in different birds. This is the auricular lobe (Fig. 3), corresponding to the flocculus of mammals. The whole complex (the nodule with its lateral extension) is called the flocculo-nodular lobe, and is a primitive part of the cerebellum that receives many connections from the vestibular division of the 8th cranial nerve.

Functionally the cerebellum is essential for the maintenance of posture and equilibrium and for regulating the range and force of movements. It may be thought of as acting like an 'automatic pilot', maintaining stability and direction during flight, and it is noteworthy that the tracts connecting it with the centres in the spinal cord through which bodily movements are controlled are well developed in birds. The absence of cerebellar hemispheres is also understandable ; they are a characteristic feature of the mammalian brain, where they are concerned in the regulation of learnt and skilled movements, particularly of the limbs, and movements of this kind play little part in the behaviour of birds.

Fore-brain. The cranial end of the brain stem, the mid-brain, is continuous with a complex mass of nervous tissue, the fore-brain. This consists of a median part, the diencephalon, directly continuous with the mid-brain, and bilateral expansions forming the cerebral hemispheres (Fig. 1). The whole fore-brain is hollow, the median cavity of the diencephalon being called the 3rd ventricle. It is continuous caudally through the mid-brain and the 4th ventricle of the hind-brain with the central canal of the spinal cord. On each side the cavity of the 3rd ventricle extends into the cerebral hemisphere to form small lateral ventricles (Fig. 4).

The median diencephalic part of the fore-brain is concealed from view by the cerebral hemispheres (Fig. 1). On each side it contains complex masses of nerve cells, the thalami, which are similar in their organisation to the same parts in reptiles. Ventral to the thalami and forming the floor of the 3rd ventricle is the hypothalamus, another complex of nuclei, connected by a thin stalk to the pituitary gland (Fig. 4). On the dorsal aspect of the diencephalon the pineal apparatus is found ; it is vestigial, and no parietal eye is present as in some reptiles.

The cerebral hemispheres are rounded and smooth, lacking the convolutions characteristic of the mammalian brain. The olfactory bulbs (Figs. 1 and 4) attached to the anterior poles of the hemispheres are generally small and sometimes fused together. The olfactory sense is correspondingly poorly developed, so that most birds are classed as microsmatic ; most vertebrates have a well developed sense of smell and are classed as macrosmatic. In a number of avian species, however, e.g. ducks (Anatidae), the domestic fowl, and most markedly the kiwis *Apteryx* spp., the bulbs are quite well developed ; but, with the possible exception of the kiwis, it is doubtful if any birds could be described as macrosmatic (see SMELL).

In all vertebrates the cerebral hemispheres are divided into dorsal and ventral parts forming the roof and floor respectively of the lateral ventricles. In the dorsal part the extensive superficial cortex so characteristic of mammals is formed ; the ventral part forms the massive basal ganglia of the hemisphere, of which the principal constituent is a mass of nerve cells called the corpus striatum. In birds the most striking features are the small extent and rudimentary character of the cortex, and the relatively enormous development and complex differentiation of the basal ganglia (Fig. 5). In this way birds resemble reptiles, but they have carried much further the reptilian trend towards reduction of cortex and enlargement of the basal ganglia ; mammals have developed in an opposite direction, acquiring an extensive cortex and retaining relatively small basal ganglia. In birds the basal ganglia are further increased in size and complexity by the addition of a hyperstriatum, present only in rudimentary form, if at all, in reptiles ; this is developed from the dorso-lateral part of the hemisphere where cerebral cortex is formed in mammals. There is no doubt that the large basal ganglia are functionally

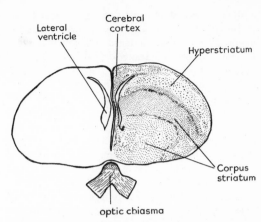

FIG 5. Transverse section through the cerebral hemispheres of a sparrow *Passer. Based on Kappers, Huber & Crosby* 1936.

concerned with the integration of the instinctive behaviour of birds, and it is probable that the hyperstriatum is of particular importance in relation to the activities of the breeding cycle. These neural mechanisms are very sensitive to facilitation or inhibition by hormones.

The functions of the diencephalon are not well understood. The thalami are connected to many other parts of the brain, particularly to the basal ganglia of the hemispheres, and probably co-operate with these structures in the integration of instinctive behaviour. By analogy with mammals (where, however, they are very differently organised), one would expect the thalami to be largely responsible for the reception of sensory information from lower levels of the nervous system, with its integration, and with its relay to the cerebral hemispheres. The hypothalamus is closely associated with the pituitary gland. It is mainly concerned in the integration of visceral and metabolic activities and has been described as the head ganglion of the autonomic nervous system. In mammals its functions are not purely neural, and it can secrete hormones that pass down the stalk to the pituitary, so that it is very closely associated with the endocrine system ; it probably has similar functions in birds. Centres for the regulation of the excretion or retention of water, for temperature regulation, for a general inhibition resulting in sleep, and a number of other functions have been identified in the hypothalamus, which is a very important part of all vertebrate brains.

Cranial Nerves. The twelve pairs of cranial nerves (Fig. 4) characteristic of higher vertebrates are all present in birds. The 1st (olfactory) are slender (see above). The 2nd (optic) are particularly large and decussate completely in a chiasma or crossing. They discharge to the optic lobes of the mid-brain, which contain what is probably the most highly differentiated neural tissue in the avian nervous system. The size of the nerves and the complexity of the optic lobes is associated with the great importance and high degree of development of the visual sense in birds (see VISION). The organisation of the visual system, however, is very different from that of mammals, where the decussation at the chiasma is incomplete and the nerves discharge principally to the fore-brain. In birds, although the main visual centres are undoubtedly in the mid-brain, a few optic fibres end in the diencephalon. There is evidence that the appreciation of the nature of objects seen requires the co-operation of this part of the fore-brain and probably of the cerebral hemispheres as well. The 3rd (oculomotor), 4th (trochlear), and 6th (abducens) nerves are all purely efferent and supply the ocular muscles as in vertebrates generally. The 12th (hypoglossal) is also efferent and supplies the tongue muscles ; it gives a branch to the muscles of the syrinx, which are therefore not comparable with laryngeal muscles (supplied by the vagus)—see SYRINX. The 5th (trigeminal), 7th (facial), 9th (glossopharyngeal), 10th (vagus), and 11th (accessory) form the usual series of branchial or visceral arch nerves. They contain, of course, no component from lateral line organs as in aquatic vertebrates, and only a few special avian features need be mentioned. The 5th nerve is well developed and supplies complex sensory corpuscles, such as those of Grandry and Herbst, which are often associated with the bill ; while usually considered to be tactile, their function is not fully understood (see TOUCH). Fibres serving the sensation of taste are present in the 7th and possibly in the 9th nerves, but are very few in number on account of the poor development of this particular sense in birds (see TASTE). The 11th nerve (accessory) is small and constitutes one of the caudal roots of the vagus ; there is no spinal component as in mammals. There remains only the 8th nerve, which has both auditory and vestibular divisions with connections in the brain stem resembling those of mammals rather closely. The auditory division (from the lagena) is comparatively small, but the vestibular is well developed, as would be expected in animals where the maintenance of equilibrium is a particularly important function (see HEARING AND BALANCE).

Spinal and Autonomic (Sympathetic and Parasympathetic) Nerves. These are arranged on the same general plan as in mammals and reptiles, but there are many detailed differences related to the different proportions of the parts and organs of the body.

The roots of the spinal nerves are shown attached in series to the spinal cord in Figure 1. They are enlarged opposite the wing and the hind limb, where they form the brachial (wing) plexus and the lumbo-sacral plexus respectively, as in all tetrapoda. Autonomic nerves are not shown : they arise from ganglia (collections of nerve cells), outside the C.N.S., that are classified in two categories, sympathetic and parasympathetic (see above). The former are arranged in two regular chains, approximately one pair of ganglia for each segment of the body, on each side of the vertebral column ; the latter are more irregularly scattered, usually close to the viscera they supply. Both sympathetic and parasympathetic ganglia are connected to the C.N.S. through spinal or cranial nerves, so that their activity is centrally regulated and integrated.

Differences among Birds. There are great variations among birds in the size of the brain and in the proportions between its parts. In general the gallinaceous birds (Galliformes) show primitive characteristics, with relatively small cerebral hemispheres and well developed olfactory bulbs, and the same may be said of pigeons (Columbidae) and plovers (Charadrii). Crows (Corvidae), owls (Strigiformes), and parrots (Psittacidae) are at the opposite extreme, with particularly large cerebral hemispheres. The ' ratite ' birds tend to have relatively large olfactory bulbs, and among them the kiwis have already been mentioned as possibly macrosmatic ; these birds also have the large cerebellum typical of birds generally, suggesting that they are descended from ancestors able to fly (see RATITES, PHYLOGENY OF THE). In the fossil *Archaeopteryx*, the earliest known bird, the endocranial cast indicates that the brain was essentially reptilian in form ; the cerebral hemispheres were elongated, possibly with long olfactory peduncles as in a typical lacertilian brain, and there is no evidence of enlargement of the cerebellum or of ventral displacement of the optic lobes (see ARCHAEOPTERYX). The evidence from endocranial casts of fossil forms is always to be accepted with caution, since it cannot be known with certainty how completely the cranial cavity was filled by the brain. In modern birds (unlike reptiles) the cranium does in fact fit closely around the brain, so that a cast gives an accurate representation of its form and proportions. It is of interest that in the fossil flying reptiles (Pterosauria) there seems to have been a similar close relationship between the cranium and the brain, which is shown by endocranial casts to resemble that of modern birds closely, perhaps more closely than is the case with *Archaeopteryx*.

Some small birds, notably the hummingbirds

(Trochilidae), have a particularly large brain/body weight ratio. In spite of this, the cerebral hemispheres are very primitive and reptile-like, so that their claim to be neurologically advanced depends chiefly on the cerebellum and mid-brain. Most of the differences between the brains of different birds can be related to differences in their mode of life ; they do not seem to have much systematic relationship to taxonomic subdivisions, since quite large differences may be found between birds not widely separated in taxonomy.   F.G. (2)

Portmann, A. 1950. Système nerveux. In Grassé, P-P. (ed.). Traité de Zoologie vol. 15. Paris. (Good general account of avian nervous system, with many references.)
Portmann, A. & Stingelin, W. 1961. Central nervous system. In Marshall, A. J. (ed.). Biology and Comparative Physiology of Birds vol. 2. New York and London.
Kappers, C. U. A., Huber, C. C. & Crosby, E. C. 1936. The Comparative Anatomy of the Nervous System in Vertebrates. New York. (Details of fibre tracts and cellular structure, with full references to the older literature.)
Edinger, T. 1929. Die fossilen Gehirne. Berlin. (Accounts of endocranial casts—also same author, 1941, Amer. J. Sci. 239a : 665–682).

NEST: popularly a term implying a structure, made by a bird, in which eggs are laid and incubated, and perhaps usually thought of as shaped like an open bowl ; but to the ornithologist this meaning is inadequate. Many birds make no nest ; others excavate or use holes without nest material ; still others make structures but do not incubate the eggs. Further, although eggs are normally incubated in one spot till they hatch, the Black Vulture *Cathartes aura* of the New World may move its eggs for appreciable distances during incubation, although how this is done has never been satisfactorily observed. Thus a comprehensive definition would be : either a structure built or excavated by the birds or already in existence, or a spot or area, in which eggs are laid and remain till they hatch (after incubation by the species concerned or, so to speak, artificially). The only exceptions are parasites, such as Old World cuckoos (Cuculidae), the Blackheaded Duck *Heteronetta atricapilla* of southern South America, and various others that have no nests of their own (see PARASITISM), and the Emperor and King Penguins *Aptenodytes forsteri* and *A. patagonica*, which incubate the single egg between belly and tarsi or feet and may move about with it thus held, so having nothing that can be called a nest. See also NEST BUILDING ; NEST SITE SELECTION ; NESTING ASSOCIATION ; and NESTBOX.

Nests are often specifically distinct in respect of materials or site or both, as with the tyrant-flycatcher *Cyanotis azarae* of the Argentine, which makes beautifully felted cups of yellow plant down attached to a single reed ; or characteristic decorations may be used, as a discarded snake-skin by the Paradise Rifle-bird *Ptiloris paradiseus* of Australia. Moreover, closely related birds tend to have similar habits of nesting, and so the nest has some practical value in taxonomy ; thus the woodpeckers (Picidae) excavate holes and make no nest inside, the anis *Crotophaga* spp. line their nests with fresh green leaves, and buzzards *Buteo* spp. decorate theirs with some fresh material. One may therefore surmise that, although perhaps the nests of the majority of species of birds in the world are still unknown to science, entirely novel nest forms are unlikely to be awaiting discovery, nests of some members of all the larger groups of birds having been already described.

The greatest complexity and variation of construction occur among passerine birds. The nonpasserines nearly all build simple structures of sticks, reeds, and the like, or else place their eggs on the ground or in natural holes, or make holes for themselves, without adding nest material. In contrast, passerines which nest on the ground or in holes all make more or less substantial nests. Thus, probably the earliest birds had the simplest nest-making habits, at first placing their eggs on the ground, in cavities or on ledges without any material, and later building simple structures or excavating holes for themselves. Presumably ground-nesting and hole-nesting passerines adopted these habits secondarily.

Non-passerine Birds. Although these usually have relatively crude nests, they provide interesting contrasts and exceptions. Some hummingbirds (Trochilidae) build the smallest known nests, 2 cm. across and 2–3 cm. high, whereas a much-used nest of the Osprey *Pandion haliaetus* may be about a yard in diameter and two yards high. Further, the hummingbirds, which are among the neatest nest-builders and make perfectly felted cups of plant down and cobwebs, contrast with pigeons (Columbidae), which usually make very imperfect platforms of sticks. In some of the latter (*Columbigallina* spp.) the original structure is modified by the growing young, whose excreta accumulate round the nest and ultimately form a much larger shallow cup, able to contain them.

Incubation Mounds. The Australasian megapodes (Megapodiidae) have the remarkable habit of 'artificial' incubation. Various species make mounds of sand and leaves in which the eggs are put and in which they hatch by the heat of the decaying vegetable matter, while in New Britain *Megapodius freycinet* may lay in holes in ground heated by subterranean emanations near volcanoes ; in some species, notably the Mallee Fowl *Leipoa ocellata*, the temperature is carefully controlled by the birds (see MEGAPODE).

Use of Saliva. The swifts (Apodidae) are interesting in that many species use saliva for building and stick their half-cups on the sides of caves, in hollow trees, or elsewhere. One extreme is shown by the Palm Swift *Cypsiurus parvus* of Africa, which sticks its nest to the under-side of palm leaves ; the other is found in species of *Collocalia* in the Far East, which provide edible nests and are the only birds of economic importance in this respect : they nest in caves, and probably different species build nests with different amounts of moss and plant material mixed into the saliva, the best quality commercially being those of pure saliva (see EDIBLE NESTS). The Cayenne Swift *Panyptila cayennensis* makes a most remarkable nest—a cylinder up to 60–70 cm. long, open at the bottom, of feathery plant material and a few feathers felted together with saliva, the outside being left rough and plastering being done only from the inside. About half-way up inside the tube a small shelf is made on which the eggs are laid. The whole may be a pendant tube fastened at the top to a ceiling or the under-side of a branch ; or it may be built against a tree-trunk or wall, in which case only half the cylinder is constructed and the support forms the other wall of the nest. Thus, like most other swifts, the bird nests in a hole—but it constructs its own hole.

Aquatic nests. The grebes (Podicipitidae) make nests which are pads of vegetation floating on water, but attached to a plant ; the jacanas (Jacanidae) often make nests of rushes on floating water-lily roots or lotus leaves ; while some rails (Rallidae) and some terns *Sterna* ('*Chlidonias*') spp. may make simple nests of reeds and water plants over water, but usually in less open situations and not truly floating.

Ground nesting. Other non-passerines may be broadly divided into ground-nesters, hole-nesters, and the builders of simple nests in trees. Simple ground nesting without any material is characteristic of the Ostrich *Struthio camelus*, sand-plovers *Charadrius* spp., thickknees (Burhinidae), sandgrouse (Pteroclididae), and nightjars (Caprimulgidae) ; and an interesting example is the Egyptian Plover *Pluvianus aegyptius* (Glareolidae), which partly or entirely buries its eggs in sand and certainly covers them with sand when leaving the nest. Many auks (Alcidae) nest on ledges on sea-cliffs without material, but most other Charadriiformes make some nest of plant material on the ground, sometimes a substantial one, as in the Stilt *Himantopus himantopus* and many gulls (Larinae). Albatrosses (Diomedeidae) build big mounds of soil and vegetation, and flamingos (Phoenicopteridae) make mounds of mud. Other ground-nesters are some penguins (e.g. the Adélie and Chinstrap Penguins *Pygoscelis adeliae* and *P. antarctica*), making a scrape lined with stones ; most ducks and geese (Anatidae), which are unique in using their own down in addition to grasses and other material as lining ; the pheasants, grouse, and turkeys (Galliformes), which usually line their scrapes with leaves and grass ; and the cranes and rails (Gruiformes), which make substantial structures of plant material.

Hole nesting. Birds nesting in holes in the ground include shearwaters (Puffininae), storm-petrels (Hydrobatidae), kingfishers (Alcedinidae), motmots (Momotidae), and bee-eaters (Meropidae), the last three making their own burrows (often of considerable length) in banks or on flat ground, while the others are less liable to dig their own holes. Some groups which generally use existing holes in cliffs, trees, or buildings are parrots (Psittaciformes), owls (Strigiformes), trogons (Trogonidae), rollers (Coraciidae), and hoopoes (Upupidae). Hornbills (Bucerotidae) also do so, with the interesting modification that the entrance is usually restricted with plaster of some sort, the female helping to immure herself. The potoos (Nyctibiidae) are specialised nesters, placing the single egg on top of a stump, where the bird incubates in an upright position. Woodpeckers (Picidae) and barbets (Capitonidae) mostly make their own holes in trees, but some do so in ants' or termites' nests, and one woodpecker lays on the ground.

Simple structures. The Pelecaniformes (cormorants, pelicans, frigatebirds), Ciconiiformes (herons, storks), Falconiformes, Cuculiformes (cuckoos, turacos), and pigeons (Columbidae) mostly make simple, if large, nests in trees, but many—especially among the birds-of-prey—use the old nests of other species, nest on ledges, or nest on the ground. Among the Ciconiiformes, a notable exception is the Hammerhead *Scopus umbretta* of Africa, which makes a large dome of sticks cemented with mud, 3–4 feet high and with the entrance in the side.

Passeriformes. In spite of great variety of form and building skill, most passerines make simple cup-shaped nests. The range of size and materials may be represented by the Raven *Corvus corax* with a big nest of sticks or heather-stems lined with finer plant material and wool, and many small birds (e.g. *Rhipidura* spp. of the Muscicapinae) which use the finest plant fibres and cobwebs to make small neat cups. Nevertheless, small birds may make huge nests, the Firewood Gatherer *Anumbius annumbi* (Furnariidae) of the Argentine being the classical example ; it makes a nest two feet deep and one foot across of big sticks obliquely resting in the branches of a tree, with the entrance at the top and a crooked passage leading down to the nest cavity. On the other hand some species make such flimsy unlined nests that the contents are visible from below, e.g. the Ecuadorian finch *Neorhynchus peruvianus*, the nest of which is a mere network of plant tendrils. Most simple nests are supported in forks or on branches, but some open cups are slung from supporting twigs by the rim, e.g. antbirds (Formicariidae), vireos (Vireonidae), and the crombecs (*Sylvietta* spp.) of Africa, while others may be bound to two or three upright supports, e.g. reed warblers *Acrocephalus* spp.

Enclosed nests. Enclosed ball-type nests of various sorts are common. Normally built nests of interlaced plant material with a large side entrance are characteristic of such low nesters as warblers of the genus *Phylloscopus* (Sylviinae), pittas (Pittidae), lyrebirds (Menuridae), and some of the Icteridae (e.g. the Military Starling *Pezites militaris*). Others are neater, more felted structures of fine plant material and moss with small entrances at the side, as in some wrens (Troglodytidae), tyrant-flycatchers (*Camptostoma* spp.), and becards (Cotingidae), although the last typically make flat tops to the nest. Some warblers of the genus *Cisticola* achieve a similar result by binding in growing grass as a partial dome. Perfect ovoid nests with a small side entrance towards the top are built of moss and lichen by the Long-tailed Tit *Aegithalos caudatus*, but an even more perfect nest, felted together of the finest material to the texture of surgical lint and with a top entrance of two flaps which have to be pressed apart for entry, is made by the penduline tits *Anthoscopus* spp. of Africa. Untidy pendant structures, more or less purse-shaped, up to five feet long and often with a beard of material hanging down from the bottom and a projecting porch over the entrance, are made by some sunbirds (Nectariniidae). The African broadbills *Smithornis* spp. also make nests with a beard from the bottom, and the Tody-tyrant *Todirostrum cinereum* of America first constructs a long streamer of material, in the centre of which it later works an aperture for the nest cavity. Ovoid, retort-shaped, or bottle-shaped nests, occasionally on the ground, are made by weaver-finches (Estrildidae) of interlaced grasses, but individuals of some species (*Estrilda melpoda, E. troglodytes, E. atricapilla*) attach a semi-covered upper storey or extension, apparently used for roosting. More striking are the large retort-shaped nests of spinetails *Synallaxis* spp. (Furnariidae), which make big spheres of thorny twigs measuring about 18 by 12 inches, enclosing a large nest cavity, with a long winding narrow tunnel as an entrance. Finally, the tailor-birds (Sylviinae of the genus

Orthotomus in Asia and allied forms in Africa) bind leaves together with cobweb or other material and build a nest in the pocket so formed.

Woven nests. Woven nests, made by the weavers (Ploceidae) of the Old World and the Icteridae of the New, are another interesting type. Among the former are various sorts from the globular nest with entrance near the top, covered with a slight porch and rather carelessly woven strips of palm leaf (Village Weaver *Ploceus cucullatus*), to the neatly woven, inverted sock with long tubular entrance, 2 feet by 4 inches, made of the sheathing of palm fruit (Red-vented Weaver *Malimbus scutatus*). The culmination of such habits is in the Social Weaver *Philetairus socius* (Passerinae) of South West Africa, which first constructs a roof of coarse straws in some large tree, and then makes many nest chambers below, the whole forming a large single mass. The Icteridae (oropendolas, caciques, and New World orioles), however, weave pendant bags rather than globular nests, with entrance through a slit at or near the top. These bags may be several feet long in the larger species, and as the birds are usually colonial, a nesting tree may seem to be laden with monstrous fruit ; but some of these orioles (*Icterus mesomelas* and *I. graceannae*) make much smaller, more conventional woven cups open at the top, but also pendant.

Mud nests. Among passerine birds there are nests made of mud. The most remarkable is that of the Ovenbird *Furnarius leucopus* of America, which makes a thick-walled domed nest on tree branches with an entrance at the side leading round by a corridor into the nest chamber. The rockfowl *Picathartes* spp. of West Africa make mud structures plastered on rock faces. Simple neat mud-cups on branches are made by the Magpie-lark (or Mudlark) *Grallina cyanoleuca* and the White-winged Chough *Corcorax melanorhamphus* (both of the Australian family Grallinidae), while some thrushes (e.g. Song Thrush *Turdus philomelos*) use mud as a lining or foundation in more conventional nests. Many swallows (Hirundinidae) also use mud either for simple half-cups plastered to some support, or for more complex flask-shaped nests.

Hole nesting and ground nesting. The passerines with these habits need no special mention, since the peculiarities of their nests are more often those of site rather than structure ; but it may be said that nuthatches *Sitta* spp. tend to restrict the entrance to the nest with a mud plaster. The Sand Martin (or Bank Swallow) *Riparia riparia* is notable for the length of the burrows that it makes.

See Plates 4, 9, 33, 34, 35, 36, 37, 39, 40, 45 (phot.).

S.M.

NESTBOX: term used broadly to describe any artificial structure designed to attract species normally breeding in holes and cavities ; some more open structures to encourage the nesting of other birds may also be mentioned under this heading. The nestbox derives originally from the clay flasks first recorded in the late Middle Ages in Holland—they can be seen in F. van Valkenborch's *Kirchmessfest* (1597)—and from wooden cistulae (flasks) used in Silesia. Both were utilitarian : the first broods of sparrows *Passer* spp. and Starlings *Sturnus vulgaris* hatched in them were taken for food ; so were the eggs of the Goldeneye *Bucephala clangula* 'farmed' in Lapland, at first by means of improved natural sites and later in boxes. Charles Waterton, the early nineteenth-century Yorkshire squire, is believed to have been the first naturalist to put up boxes simply to encourage birds, and their use for this purpose developed during the century ; by 1897 J. R. B. Masefield knew of 20 species that had occupied boxes or artificial platforms in Britain. Nestboxes were first applied on a large scale to attract and increase the numbers of 'beneficial' insectivorous birds in forests by Baron von Berlepsch in Germany ; by about 1907 all the 300 boxes in his park, and 90 per cent of some 2000 boxes in his woods, were occupied by birds of 14 different species. Soon afterwards it was realised that whole populations of certain species could be induced to use nestboxes if enough were provided, and could thus be studied in many aspects of their population structure. Pioneer studies were those of S. P. Baldwin and W. W. Bowen on the House Wren *Troglodytes aedon* in the U.S.A., begun in 1915, and of K. Wolda and his associates on the Great Tit *Parus major* in Holland, begun in 1920. But the species most suited to nestbox studies is probably the Pied Flycatcher *Ficedula hypoleuca* ; since L. von Haartman began work on it in Finland in 1941, populations have been 'emboxed' in all the European countries where it breeds commonly, and tens of thousands of birds have been ringed.

The nineteenth-century nestbox was made of wood, with a round entrance hole and a fixed lid, and was designed primarily to attract titmice (Paridae), Nuthatches *Sitta europaea*, redstarts *Phoenicurus* spp., and Pied Flycatchers. Von Berlepsch favoured a hollowed-out section of log, resembling as closely as possible the nest-hole of the Greater Spotted Woodpecker *Dendrocopos major* which these small birds were accustomed to use under natural conditions. It has since been found, however, that the shape and external appearance of the box matter very little and that those made of planed boards are quite as effective as 'rustic' boxes with bark-covered

sides. Certain rules nevertheless govern the correct construction and maintenance of safe and durable nestboxes, and these have been described in a field guide published by the British Trust for Ornithology. For example, the entrance hole should be sufficiently high up the side or front panels of the box to make it hard for the larger predators to reach the contents of the nest ; the roof or lid should overlap the sides to keep off raindrops ; and there should be no perches or ledges on which predators can get a grip.

Towards the middle of the twentieth century nestboxes in materials other than wood were developed ; plastics, cement and sawdust, cement bricks, hardboard, and tin all found advocates. Their advantage over wood lies in superior resistance to weather and to attacks by squirrels and Greater Spotted Woodpeckers which became increasingly a nuisance in Britain in the 1950s. Their disadvantages include expense, brittleness, liability to overheating in exposed sites, and in some instances weight. The Russians have experimented with bottle gourds as the cheapest form of artificial nest cavity ; but it is apparently not possible to inspect the contents.

Nestboxes should normally be sited on the side of a tree or wall away from the hottest sun. H. N. Kluijver pointed out that on trees in western Europe this makes them vulnerable to the maximum flow of water after a rainstorm, but some compromise position can usually be found. In woods the main consideration is to site boxes away from twigs and branches which can be used by predators ; an open approach for the nesting bird is also important. Provided that they are securely attached to a trunk or branch, nestboxes need not be rigid ; in closed canopy woodland they can be fixed to branch snags by a wire loop and lifted down by the loop for inspection. In Britain, the Nature Conservancy has conducted an experiment to find out the height preferred by small birds using nestboxes, but the results after five years were inconclusive ; it seems probable that most species have little or no preference. However, boxes in most localities have to be sited at least ten feet above the ground to avoid human damage.

Ideally, a nestbox should have a fixed roof and open at the front for inspection ; but where it is desired to catch the parent birds in the box for ringing and examination, a movable lid is preferable. Various devices have been developed for retaining adult birds in the box, from small external spring nets to internal treadles that release a shutter. In Britain, J. A. Gibb adapted the automatic swinging door used by racing pigeon owners in their lofts. This was followed by non-automatic shutters remotely operated by means of a fishing line passing under the lid and over the side of the box ; J. H. Jenkins and P. A. Banks were responsible for ingenious variations of this idea. After capture in the box, the birds are most easily removed through a detachable version of the sleeve used in the catching boxes of Heligoland and other large traps (see TRAPPING).

The traditional design of nestbox has been adapted to attract various species : there have been boxes with narrow entrances and with entrances at the back, both intended for treecreepers *Certhia* spp. ; multiple boxes for the Purple Martin *Progne subis* ; boxes filled with chips for Chickadees *Parus atricapillus* to excavate. D. Lack evolved elongated boxes with holes opening downward to embox a colony of Swifts *Apus apus* ; others have taken this idea further to counterfeit the burrows of Sand Martins *Riparia riparia* and Madeiran Petrels *Oceanodroma castro* ; while artificial nests for Swallows *Hirundo rustica* and House Martins *Delichon urbica* have been successful in Switzerland. Removal of half the front panel converts the traditional nestbox into a covered tray or ledge suitable for Spotted Flycatchers *Muscicapa striata*, Robins *Erithacus rubecula*, and many other species. By increasing the size, owls (Strigiformes), Kestrels *Falco tinnunculus*, Jackdaws *Corvus monedula*, Stock Doves *Columba oenas*, and ducks (Anatidae) can be attracted. For the Tawny Owl *Strix aluco* a quite distinct chimney design was used most successfully by H. N. Southern, who slung it by wire bands under an upward sloping bough ; an inspection mirror was fastened to the mouth of the chimney and a perforated floor allowed drainage.

As well as nestboxes and their obvious derivatives, many other artificial means have been used to encourage nesting ; the cart-wheels or platforms put up on houses in Holland and elsewhere for the White Stork *Ciconia ciconia* are one of the oldest devices and have been copied in the U.S.A. to attract Ospreys *Pandion haliaetus*. Woven baskets for Mallards *Anas platyrhynchos* are another Dutch idea, while in Iceland stone ' houses ' are built for Eiders *Somateria mollissima*. Egg collectors used to ' farm ' Greenshanks *Tringa nebularia* in Scotland by providing ideal sites for them, and other ground-nesting birds have been catered for in the same way. Von Berlepsch suggested tying twigs together to make better than natural forks for bush-nesting birds, and ' nesting substrates ' have been used by several species in America.

The main development of the nestbox up to the middle of the twentieth century took place in Europe and North America, although it was still not proved that large concentrations of boxes did more than concentrate the birds using them. For example, in the Forest of Dean (Gloucestershire, England) as many as 189 out of 200 nestboxes spread over 60 acres were occupied in 1949 ; but no control data are available for the area before boxes were first put up there in 1942. In Russia, large-scale attempts to attract birds to forests involved over 10 000 nestboxes in nine areas in 1953 ; they were occupied by nearly 4000 pairs of 18 species . Partially successful attempts were also made to transfer both adults and nestlings to newly afforested areas. Foresters in India began putting up boxes in the 1950s, but the great variety of tropical species nesting in holes and cavities still offer further opportunities for nestbox techniques.

B.C.

Büttiker, W. 1960. Artificial nesting devices in southern Africa. Ostrich 31 : 39–48.
Cohen, E. 1961. Nestboxes. (British Trust for Ornithology Field Guide no. 3, revised edition.) Oxford.
Hiesemann, M. 1908. How to Attract and Protect Wild Birds (English edition). London.
Masefield, J. R. B. 1897. Wild Bird Protection and Nesting Boxes. Leeds.
Mason, C. R. & Reed, P. C. 1950. Provide your birds a nesting place. Bull. Massachusetts Audubon Soc. 34 : 1–16.
Stresemann, E. 1948. Geschichte des Starenkastens. Ornithologische Beobachter 45 : 169–179.

NEST BUILDING: behaviour concerned with the excavation or construction of nests. Most species of birds lay their eggs in a previously constructed nest, which may be anything from a mere scrape in the ground to a high elaborate structure the building of which involves complex patterns of behaviour and the use of many different materials (see NEST). Construction is usually by the female, but the male often helps and in some polygamous species he may do nearly all the work (see POLYGAMY).

Nest building may involve the selection of a site (see NEST SITE SELECTION), its preparation, the collection of material, the carrying of that material to the site, and the actual construction of the nest. Preparation of the site is usually unnecessary in species which build open cup-nests, but in hole-nesters it may involve excavation or the cleaning out of a pre-existing cavity. Many ground-nesting birds first make a depression in the earth or sand.

In most simple nests, and in some complex ones, only one type of material is employed ; but usually there are a number, some being used for the outside and some for the lining. Thus the Longtailed Tit *Aegithalos caudatus* uses mainly moss, spiders' silk, lichen, and feathers (Tinbergen). If more than one type of material is used, which type is brought to the nest may be dictated either by the internal state of the female or by stimuli from the partially completed nest. In domesticated Canaries *Serinus canarius* the change-over from collecting grass for the cup to feathers for the lining depends in part on stimuli from the partially constructed nest, and in part on an internal, possibly hormonal, change in the female (Hinde). A variety of relatively stereotyped patterns of behaviour may be used in collecting the material and preparing it for use. Thus weavers (Ploceidae) tear up grass leaves longitudinally (Crook) and Canaries sometimes mandibulate material in water. Nest building in the Wren *Troglodytes troglodytes* is stimulated by rain, the function of this apparently lying in the increased flexibility of the material (Armstrong).

The material is usually carried in the bill ; in some cases special movements make it more easily transportable (e.g. *Parus* spp.). Some love-birds *Agapornis* spp. carry material in the rump feathers (Moreau).

Nest construction involves the integration of a number of stereotyped movements characteristic of the species. Closely similar movements are often characteristic of a wide range of related species. Amongst passerines, common movements are 'pulling and weaving', in which loose strands projecting from the rim are pulled towards the breast and pushed down into the cup ; 'scrabbling', in which the female presses down into the cup and pushes back hard with each leg alternately ; and 'turning', in which she turns round while sitting in the nest and thus shapes the cup. Sometimes quite complex movement patterns appear ; thus some weavers knot strands round twigs with half-hitches.

The appearance of each activity involved in nest building depends both on a certain internal state and on external stimuli. Thus all the nest-building activities of Canaries are increased by injections of oestrogen (Warren & Hinde) and each is elicited by a particular stimulus situation (e.g. collecting by stimuli from the material, scrabbling by stimuli from the nest cup).

For the construction of a nest, these various patterns of behaviour may be integrated into functional sequences. The principal processes involved are :

(i) The various behaviour patterns of nest building share common causal factors, e.g. certain hormonal states.

(ii) Nevertheless, the various activities may appear at different threshold levels of these factors : thus as a female passerine comes into reproductive condition, she first shows gathering, then carrying, and then the stereotyped movements of nest construction.

(iii) Often each activity brings the bird into the stimulus situation where the next one is evoked ; thus, gathering leads to carrying, carrying to placing material in the nest, and so on.

(iv) The performance of each activity is associated with a decreased tendency to continue or repeat that activity ; thus the change-over from gathering to carrying, or from sitting building in the nest-cup to gathering again, depends not only on the stimuli presented as a consequence of the first activity, but also on a decreased internal tendency to continue it.

(v) Stimuli from the partially constructed nest may influence subsequent behaviour ; thus a decrease in the size of the nest-cup may cause canaries to bring a high proportion of lining material, and to bring material less often. In this way stimuli from the near-completed nest are instrumental in causing building to cease.

(vi) Although, in all species so far studied, the various constituent activities appear in individuals reared away from their parents and even away from the species-characteristic nest, learning may play an important role in nest construction. Thus the location of suitable sources of material must be learnt : Canaries kept without material learn to pull out their own feathers.

(vii) Thorpe has suggested that learning plays an essential role in the fine integration of the activities of nest building. Thus he suggests that, while building, the bird is responsive to stimuli similar to those which would be provided by a perfect nest ; actions which make the existing structure approximate more closely to a finished nest are reinforced and thus repeated.

Existing evidence shows (*a*) that the performance of the constituent activities of nest building has some reinforcing value (e.g. the Canaries deprived of material, cited above, whose abnormal behaviour involved the movements of nest building but never led to the construction of a nest) ; (*b*) since the abnormal patterns seen in Canaries deprived of material do not appear in undeprived birds, it seems that the construction of the species-characteristic nest is learnt in preference to the mere performance of constituent activities which do not lead to a completed nest ; (*c*) stimuli characteristic of the finished nest produce a decrease in building behaviour. All these points are in harmony with Thorpe's view, but experimental evidence in support of it is still lacking.

The hormonal basis of nest building probably differs between species. Oestrogens are primarily responsible in Canaries, but in some species androgens may be important (Noble & Wurm). In many species there is a close link between nest building and courtship, and the peaks of nest building and copulation may coincide.

The nest is of obvious functional significance : the differences even between the nests of closely related species may be adaptive. Thus the nest form amongst West African weavers is more closely related to habitat than to systematic relationships, and each nest type has special protective functions in its environment (Crook). Some species decorate their nests ; thus tits place fragments of torn leaves round the nest cup, and Starlings *Sturnus vulgaris* gather flowers ; the significance of this is not understood.

Little is known of the evolution of nest building. It has been suggested that some of the shaping movements are derived from copulatory movements, and the collection of material from aggressive movements redirected on to grass stems, but there is no evidence to support these views. See also BEHAVIOUR, DEVELOPMENT OF.

See Plate 36ab (phot.).   R.A.H.

Armstrong, E. A. 1955. The Wren. London.

Crook, J. H. 1960. Nest form and construction in certain West African weaver-birds. Ibis 102 : 1–25.

Hinde, R. A. 1958. The nest-building behaviour of domesticated canaries. Proc. Zool. Soc. Lond. 131 : 1–48.

Moreau, R. E. 1948. Aspects of evolution in the parrot genus *Agapornis*. Ibis 90 : 206–239.

Noble, G. K. & Wurm, M. 1940. The effect of testosterone propionate on the Black-crowned Night Heron. Endocrinology 26 : 837–850.

Stresemann, E. 1927–34. In Kükenthal W., & Krumbach, T. (eds.), Handbuch der Zoologie vol. 7 Pt. 2. Berlin and Leipzig.

Thorpe, W. H. 1956. Learning and Instinct in Animals. London.

Tinbergen, N. 1953. Specialists in nest-building. Country Life, 30 Jan. 1953 : 270–271.

Warren, R. P. & Hinde, R. A. 1959. The effect of oestrogen and progesterone on the nest-building of domesticated canaries. Anim. Behav. 7 : 209–213.

NEST, COCK : term sometimes applied to extra nests, or nest-like structures, not used for laying eggs in, although the birds may roost in them. In particular, the male Wren *Troglodytes troglodytes* is well known to build such nests ; these are unlined, while lining the nest used for laying in is exclusively an activity of the female.

NESTING ASSOCIATION : an example of symbiosis, including all instances of one bird species often or habitually placing its nests, singly or in colonies, near those of other bird species or near the habitations or structures of other living organisms ; and all instances of other organisms often or habitually living in birds' nests. The following different types of association are known :

1. *With other birds.*

(*a*) Mixed colonies of two or more, often related species, e.g. in herons (Ardeidae), gulls and terns (Laridae), auks (Alcidae).

(*b*) One species nesting (singly, in scattered pairs or in colonies) among pure or mixed colonies of other birds, e.g. in Scandinavia the Tufted Duck *Nyroca fuligula* and Turnstone *Arenaria interpres* among Laridae, and the Black-necked Grebe *Podiceps nigricollis* moving its colonies yearly with those of the Black-headed Gull *Larus ridibundus*.

(*c*) Colonies of non-aggressive birds round a nest of a more aggressive, usually raptorial, species, e.g. many African species of weaver (Ploceidae) in the same tree as a Black Kite *Milvus migrans*, Red-tailed Buzzard *Buteo auguralis*, Pied Crow *Corvus albus*, or Marabou Stork *Leptoptilus crumeniferus*; in the Arctic, geese with Snowy Owl *Nyctea scandiaca* or falcons (Falconidae), and Fieldfares *Turdus pilaris* with the Merlin *Falco columbarius*.

(*d*) Single pairs of different species, e.g. Barred Warbler *Sylvia nisoria* with Red-backed Shrike *Lanius collurio*, and White Wagtail *Motacilla alba* with Osprey *Pandion haliaetus*, in Scandinavia ; other examples in Australia.

2. *With insects.*

(*a*) Cavity in a structure made by insects adopted or excavated as nest chamber, e.g. ant-chats *Myrmecocichla* spp. and barbets *Trachyphonus* spp. in Africa using holes in ground termitaria, as casual nest parasitism : but other occurrences in South America, Africa, Asia, and Australia are of parrots (Psittacidae), jacamars (Galbulidae), trogons (Trogonidae), kingfishers (Alcedinidae), woodpeckers (Picidae), and cotingas (Cotingidae) using arboreal ants' or termites' nests. For many of the species, the behaviour has not been sufficiently studied to decide whether it is habitual or whether active or dead insect nests are used ; but in some (Buff-spotted Woodpecker *Campethera nivosa* of Africa, the parrot *Aratinga canicularis* of South America) it appears to be habitual and relating to live nests.

(*b*) More or less true symbiosis when insects live and feed in a bird's nest, helping to keep it clean, as noted particularly in such Australian parrots as *Psephotus chrysopterygius* and *Platycercus eximius*, and in the African Silvery-cheeked Hornbill *Bycanistes brevis*, where nests have contained large faunae of dipterous and lepidopterous larvae with chalcid and beetle parasites.

(*c*) Nests near more or less aggressive social insects (aculeate Hymenoptera or ants), as is well-known in South America, Africa, and Australia and recorded in Asia, mostly within the tropics. This involves large birds such as raptors and storks (Ciconiidae) among which it is poorly known, and small, mostly passerine, birds of several families (Tyrannidae, Muscicapidae, Troglodytidae, Nectariniidae, Icteridae, Ploceidae, Fringillidae, etc.).

3. *With spiders.* This is recorded for sunbirds (Nectariniidae) and for the Little Grey Flycatcher *Alseonax epulatus* (Muscicapinae) in Africa.

4. *With vertebrates.*

(*a*) Probably the only regular association with reptiles is that of the Tuatara lizard *Sphenodon punctatum* in the burrows of the New Zealand shearwaters *Puffinus carneipes* and *P. bulleri*, although small lizards and geckos often hide in woodpeckers' holes.

(*b*) In the Argentine pampa the Minera *Geositta cunicularia* nests exclusively in the burrows of a mammal, the Vizcacha *Lagostromus trichodactylus*, making its own holes in the sides of these. (Abandoned holes made by the Minera are occupied by the swallow *Notiochelidon cyanoleuca*, which otherwise would find no nest sites in such flat land.) This is probably the only association with mammals, excluding man.

(*c*) With man, e.g. various swallow species (Hirundinidae) which simply take advantage of buildings as nest sites ; but certain weavers (Ploceidae) and Abdim's Stork *Sphenorhynchus abdimii* in Africa are among other birds that often or usually nest near houses without actually using them.

Clearly the causes of these associations are not always the same, but there is much still to be found out about all types and some are so little known (types 2*a* and 3 and to a lesser extent 1*c* and *d*) that they cannot be further discussed here. Type 2*b* is apparently simple symbiosis, and types 4*a*, *b*, and in part *c* are merely cases of birds or their associates using suitable artificial sites. Similarity of habitat preference probably explains type 1*a*, but sociability may play a part. These reasons cannot be the complete answer for type 1*b*, since the Tufted Duck is a good associate in Scandinavia but not at all in Britain. Types 1*c* and *d* may be for protection in some cases, as are presumably some of the human associations 4*c* ; but Ospreys' nests may provide the only available nest sites for White Wagtails 1*d*, and availability of food may bring about the association of predators with colonial nesters 1*c*. Some of the single associations 1*d* are just not understood.

Type 2*c* (with aggressive social insects) is the most interesting and best studied category. Associations by large birds are too poorly known for discussion here, since in some parts of Africa where they have been recorded so many suitable nesting trees are insect-infested that association may have no significance ; yet possibly sometimes the association may be on the part of the insects, seeking protection from bee-eaters (Meropidae) and honeyguides (Indicatoridae). The Bronze Mannikin *Spermestes cucullatus* has been found statistically to have a definite preference for nesting near 'protective' associates (Maclaren) ; in Africa among a sea of acacias certain bird species will choose only those infested by wasps ; and in Ecuador *Camptostoma obsoletum*

has been observed to build first and repeat nests alongside the same wasps' nest. For small birds there is a body of evidence which shows that the birds deliberately choose the association. Such cases are characterised by the facts that nearly all associating birds build domed or enclosed nests ; that the nests of both associates are conspicuously placed ; and that, if not nesting near insects, the species concerned either conceals its nest more carefully or uses other methods of apparent protection (in thorns, at the end of slender boughs, over water, or near raptors or man). The Village Weaver *Ploceus cucullatus* is interesting since in Africa it habitually nests with raptors or man and not with insects, but in Haiti (where it was introduced about 300 years ago) it associates with insects. Some species which are notorious associates, e.g. the Yellow-rumped Cacique *Cacicus cela* (Icteridae) of America, are aposematically coloured, but this is not universal or even common among such birds, e.g. some tyrant-flycatchers (Tyrannidae) and wrens (Troglodytidae) which are dull-coloured birds. So far as has been observed the insects tolerate the birds, but are immediately roused by human interference ; yet some of the associating Hymenoptera are not adequate deterrents. If, as seems most likely, the birds seek protection by the association, there are unexplained problems. Why do the insects tolerate the birds, and how do they distinguish their activities from those of potential predators ? How can the birds have begun to recognise the protective value of the insects ? Against what predators is the association effective? Certainly man, monkeys, and rodents could be driven off by the insects, but these are probably not important enemies in many cases ; predatory birds might be deterred, but this is uncertain ; perhaps snakes are especially susceptible, but again there is no evidence. Consequently it has been suggested that the association is not for protection, but merely due to similar habitat preferences, because in addition to the difficulties just mentioned protection is not complete and 'protected' nests are said to be no more successful than 'unprotected' ones. However, such a suggestion disregards the evidence for protective association. It is too much to expect that protection is ever complete ; and as no quantitative studies have been made the suggested similarity in success is a mere guess. In view of the evidence for deliberate choice by some associating species, any satisfactory explanation must include the idea of protection.   S.M.

Durango, S. 1947. Om vanan hos vissa fåglav att bosätta sig intill insektssamhällen eller andra fågelaåter Fauna och Flora : 185–205, 249–259.
Maclaren, P. I. R. 1950. Bird-ant nesting associations. Ibis 92 : 564–566.

Moreau, R. E. 1942. The nesting of African birds in association with other living things. Ibis (14 ser.) 6 : 240-263.

NESTLING: see under YOUNG BIRD

NEST PARASITISM: see PARASITISM

NEST RECORDS: see under BIRD-WATCHING

NEST SANITATION: see PARENTAL CARE

NEST SITE SELECTION: an aspect of behaviour of which the study involves such considerations as the season when birds select their nest sites, the interval between nest site selection and the start of building, the share of the sexes, and the factors that may influence birds in selecting nest sites. For the variety of sites used see NEST.

Many birds occupy the same site and nest in successive years ; eyries of the Golden Eagle *Aquila chrysaetos*, for instance, may be occupied (by succeeding generations) for centuries, although the birds probably ring the changes on two or three alternative sites. The initial selection of a fresh site is rarely observed in such species, mainly because the final selection may be preceded by so long a period of reconnaissance, perhaps over several years, that the process cannot easily be seen as a whole. At the other extreme, summer migrants may select a nest site and begin building on the same day—which is equally difficult to observe. Between these extremes are the majority of birds which select their nest sites over a period of some days or weeks shortly before they start building ; these can be observed more readily, and knowledge of them forms the basis of this article.

Seasons. The selection of a nest site does not necessarily mean that the birds are ready to build. Even in those species which select a fresh nest site each year there is often an appreciable interval between selection and building, the length of which may range from several weeks or even months down to a day or less, depending largely on the bird's drive to breed. A mild spell in late winter can initiate song, courtship, and even nest site selection, in species that will not begin to build until several weeks later ; these activities will cease with the return of colder weather. Alternatively, a bird that has lost an early nest, or is proceeding to a second brood, may condense its nest site selection and building, which earlier in the season may have lasted a week or more, into two or three days in the urgency to breed.

Share of Sexes. A survey of some 170 representative British breeding species (C. & D. Nethersole-Thompson) included none in which the male, and about 30 in which the female, normally takes sole charge in nest-site selection ; in the remaining species both sexes participate, with males taking the initiative rather less often than females. This pattern is repeated in most orders of birds, although in the Anatidae and Galliformes the males evidently take little or no active part. The suggestion, based on observations at other stages in the breeding cycle, that in species in which the males take the initiative they are more brightly plumaged than the females, seems not to hold for males taking an active part in nest site selection.

Hole-nesters. In general, the birds' routine tends to be more elaborate in species with specialised requirements. Thus titmice *Parus* spp. mostly nest in holes, of which there is often a shortage ; and they may frequently be seen inspecting holes from September to April. It has been recorded (Hinde) that they are most active in March and April, just before they start to build ; but that there is also a lesser peak of activity in October and November. Since tits also roost in holes in winter, their activity in autumn could equally be roost site selection ; but as winter roosts are often used later for breeding, this distinction may be unimportant (see ROOSTING). In spring, hole inspection is most frequent in the morning and tails off markedly in mid-afternoon. When several equally suitable sites are available, the final decision may be left literally to the last minute before building begins—indeed later, for tits commonly deposit nest material in several holes before eventually lining and laying in one of them.

In a typical hole inspection by the Great Tit *Parus major*, the male flies to the hole, leaving the female near by, and peers inside, turning its head sideways to display its white cheeks ; it may also tap at the entrance. Probably both the head turning and tapping have special meaning to the female, which may or may not respond by approaching the hole. If she does, she shivers her wings, increasingly the nearer she comes, and then normally enters the hole, sometimes preceded by the male ; she may remain inside for two or three minutes. If the female does not respond, the male usually returns to her and shortly repeats the performance at the same or another hole. Thus he suggests a number of sites to the female, one of which she is likely to accept. Other members of the genus *Parus*, as well as such hole-nesters as the Redstart *Phoenicurus phoenicurus* and Pied Flycatcher *Ficedula hypoleuca*, behave rather similarly.

Ground-nesters. Contrasting with the elaborate routine of hole-nesters is the nest site selection (N. Tinbergen) of the Herring Gull *Larus argentatus*. At first the pair indulges in frequent preliminaries to nest building, moving from one possible site to another. As the season advances these bouts become both more frequent and more intense, until one culminates in the beginning of an actual nest at one or other of the sites, the selection of which is evidently quite haphazard.

The same author has described nest site selection by the Red-necked Phalarope *Lobipes lobatus*, in which species the female takes the initiative in courting, territorial disputes, and nest site selection, while the male alone incubates the eggs and tends the young. Before the eggs are laid both sexes go together for several days making scrapes in the soil more or at less at random through the territory. Then, about an hour before laying, the female revisits many of the scrapes and apparently lays in whichever scrape she happens to be at when the egg appears.

Once gulls (Larinae) and waders (Charadrii), for instance, have selected a suitable territory, there is probably no shortage of nest sites (see TERRITORY) ; hence their seemingly casual nest site selection. There are exceptions, of course, such as the discriminating nest site selection of the Greenshank *Tringa nebularia*, which prefers to nest close to some small landmark such as a log or large stone on the otherwise rather featureless landscape, individual pairs returning to these sites in successive years (C. & D. Nethersole-Thomson).

Open-nesting Song-birds. Nest site selection by the majority of these comes somewhere between the elaborate procedure of the hole-nesters and the casual choice of most gulls and waders. In Scottish Crossbills *Loxia curvirostra scotica*, for example, the nest site is usually chosen in a distinctive tour by both sexes, during which the female broods in various crotches ; this is accompanied by frequent snatches of such irrelevant behaviour as bill-wiping, 'false feeding', and preening (see DISPLACEMENT ACTIVITY). The final choice of site is the female's ; but one male unsuccessfully attempted to initiate a nest by placing a twig in a crotch, which was declined by the female. Spells of brooding in possible sites are often mentioned in the literature on nest site selection in other birds ; likewise the intrusion of seemingly irrelevant behaviour, which is typical of birds and other animals in times of emotional stress.

Competition. The considerations that influence a bird in selecting its nest site are little known, except indirectly through descriptions of the sites used. Competition for nest sites is generally keenest among birds with specialised requirements ; in the Swift *Apus apus*, for example, exceptionally prolonged struggles for the possession of nestboxes have been described (Lack). Competition between members of the same species may be to some extent avoided by the territorial system of some birds. Competition for nesting space is especially marked in' densely colonial species ; among sea birds, for instance, each species demands a special type of ledge or other support for its nest, the presence of which may govern the birds' local distribution in the breeding season. In the van of the spread of the Fulmar *Fulmarus glacialis* round the British coast, incipient colonies are commonly frequented for several years before breeding takes place, by birds which appear to be prospecting for suitable nest sites.

Appropriation. Many birds, notably birds-of-prey, appropriate old nests of other species for themselves ; and the Green Sandpiper *Tringa ochropus* is remarkable among waders for laying in old nests, mostly of the Song Thrush *Turdus philomelos*. Some birds appropriate freshly completed or occupied nests of other species ; thus the House Sparrow *Passer domesticus* habitually evicts the House Martin *Delichon urbica* ; and a pair of the American Parasitic Flycatcher *Legatus leucophalus* sometimes causes the rightful owners of several occupied nests to desert before settling on one of them. Nest appropriation has evolved independently in a number of different groups of birds throughout the world ; it has perhaps reached its most refined form in wholly parasitic species such as the Cuckoo *Cuculus canorus* (see PARASITISM).

Associations. Presumably for protection against predators, certain tropical birds nest in close association with wasps' nests ; and for the same reason Bramblings *Fringilla montifringilla* often nest in colonies of Fieldfares *Turdus pilaris*, which are especially active in defence of their nesting area, and Tufted Ducks *Aythya fuligula* likewise in mixed colonies of terns and gulls (Laridae)—see NESTING ASSOCIATION. J.A.G.

Nethersole-Thompson, C. & D. 1943–44. Nest-site selection by birds. Brit. Birds 37 : 70–74, 88–94 108–113.

NESTORINAE: see PARROT

NETTING: see TRAPPING

NEUROMUSCULAR SENSE: see SENSES

NEUTRAL CATEGORIES: in taxonomy, categories that can be used as terms without commitment to a view of the status of the subject matter, e.g. FORM; GROUP; COMPLEX.

NEW GUINEA SUBREGION: see AUSTRALASIAN REGION

NEW ZEALAND SUBREGION: a division of the Australasian Region, but by some zoogeographers regarded as a separate minor region (see AUSTRALASIAN REGION ; DISTRIBUTION, GEOGRAPHICAL).

NICHE: place in the total community that a species is enabled to occupy by virtue of its adaptations.

NICTITATING MEMBRANE: also called 'third eyelid' (see VISION).

NIDICOLOUS: see under YOUNG BIRD

NIDIFICATION: see NEST BUILDING

NIDIFUGOUS: see under YOUNG BIRD

NIGHTHAWK: substantive name of various New World species of Caprimulgidae; in the plural, general term for the subfamily Chordeilinae (see NIGHTJAR).

NIGHTINGALE: substantive name of some *Luscinia* spp.; used without qualification, in Britain, for *L. megarhynchos* (see under THRUSH).

NIGHTJAR: substantive name of the Old World species of Caprimulgidae (Caprimulgiformes, suborder Caprimulgi); in the plural, a general term for the family, but American usage prefers 'goatsuckers and nighthawks'; some species have special names derived from the calls. This homogeneous family has a nearly world-wide distribution, but it is not represented in the most northern parts of America and Eurasia, in southern South America, or in New Zealand and many oceanic islands. The North Temperate Zone species migrate southwards for the winter. The plumage is soft and is buffish, rufous, greyish, or nearly black. The upper parts are in general strongly mottled and vermiculated; the under parts are mostly barred or spotted and often with white patches on chin and throat, on the wings and on the tips of the tail feathers. In some species both a grey and a more rufous phase occur (see POLYMORPHISM). The sexes are normally somewhat different in colour. The tail is rather long; the wings are long and pointed; and the flight is silent and easy. The skull is flattened, with the bill short and weak. The gape, which is extremely wide, and in most species provided with strong bristles, enables the bird to catch insects (the main food) during flight. The eyes are large. The feet are commonly very short, with a feathered tarsus in some species; the toes are small, the middle toe possessing a pectinated claw.

Most species are crepuscular or nocturnal in habit. During the day the birds lie up closely and are difficult to detect owing to their cryptic coloration. Normally the birds perch on the ground or lengthwise on a branch. Some species frequent desert areas, others are inhabitants of open spaces in wooded districts, and some of forests.

Generally no nest is made, the eggs being laid on the bare ground. These number 1 or 2, rarely 3.

They are white to pinkish buff, beautifully marbled or blotched with black, brown, or violet. Both parents incubate and care for the young, which are nidicolous and covered with protective (buff or greyish) down.

About 70 species are known, generally grouped in 18 genera. On the basis of anatomical differences the family can be divided into two subfamilies, the Chordeilinae (nighthawks) and the Caprimulginae (goatsuckers).

Chordeilinae. The nighthawks are restricted to the New World; the species lack rictal bristles. In North America the Common Nighthawk *Chordeiles minor* and the very similar Lesser Nighthawk *C. acutipennis* are well-known representatives. The first frequents open country or forest borders and is also found in the Greater Antilles; the latter, which is somewhat smaller and darker, ranges also over the greater part of tropical South America and is an inhabitant of desert areas or open sandy savannas. In both species the males are slightly larger than the females, and they have a white wing-patch and a subterminal tail-bar that are absent or smaller in the other sex. Both species are known to breed sometimes on the flat roofs of houses. The Lesser Nighthawk prefers to roost on the horizontal branches of low bushes.

Other species are the white-bellied Sand-coloured Nighthawk *C. rupestris* and the small Least Nighthawk *C. pusillus*. Both are distributed in the northern part of South America. The remaining three genera, which are monotypic, are likewise found in South America. The Nacunda Nighthawk *Podager nacunda* has a white belly and throat-patch, rather long unfeathered tarsi, and a melancholy voice; it is an inhabitant of the savannas and is known to migrate northwards.

Caprimulginae. More than half of the known species in the whole family belong to the typical genus *Caprimulgus*, of which many species are rather alike in plumage. The European Nightjar *Caprimulgus europaeus* is found from Great Britain and northern Africa far into Asia, and in winter migrants reach South Africa; the 'churring' or jarring note is the origin of the name. In eastern Asia the related Jungle Nightjar *C. indicus* occurs, and it is also distributed over India, in winter reaching the Greater Sunda Islands; the males differ from the European Nightjar in having subterminal white spots on the outer four pairs of tail feathers instead of on the outer two only. In the same area, from India and southern China through Indonesia to northern Australia, the Large-tailed Nightjar *C. macrurus* is widely distributed; it is distinguished from *C. europaeus* by the fact that the four, instead of the three outer primaries show a white spot. In southern Europe and the western parts of North Africa, the Red-necked Nightjar *C. ruficollis*, with a yellow rufous collar, is found. The paler and sandier coloured Egyptian Nightjar *C. aegyptius* inhabits the desert areas of south-western Asia and northern Africa. Different species occur in Africa, but the habits of many are not yet very well known, although mostly these seem not to differ greatly from those of the other members of the family. Some perform regular intertropical migrations (see MIGRATION). Some species, such as the Fiery-necked Nightjar *C. fervidus*, inhabiting the southern part of Africa, hunt from a fixed perch during the night instead of hawking over longer distances as do most of the other species. Different types of churring sounds are made by various species, while others have whistling calls.

Fiery-necked Nightjar *Caprimulgus pectoralis fervidus*, of southern Africa. *C.E.T.K.*

North American representatives include the Whip-poor-will *Caprimulgus vociferus*, ranging from northern North America to well into Middle America ; the closely related *C. noctitherus* from Puerto Rico has long been regarded as extinct, but has recently been rediscovered. Another species named from the call is the Chuck-will's-widow *C. carolinensis* ; it is a somewhat larger species frequenting wooded marshes and rocky hills in the western parts of the United States and wintering in the West Indies and Middle America. Other species inhabit South America, such as the beautiful Cayenne Nightjar *C. cayennensis* with throat white, and sides of face and abdomen and the lateral tail feathers mainly white ; another is the Dark Nightjar *C. nigrescens*, also found in northern South America.

The species of the genus *Eurostopodus* are distributed from south-eastern Asia through the Philippine and Indonesian archipelagoes to Australia. They lack the rictal bristles and have ear-tufts. Most species are rather large and dark, showing much black and dark brown but with a white throat-patch.

The White-necked Nighthawk *Nyctidromus albicollis* is an inhabitant of Middle and South America ; it breeds under the cover of bushes, and the eggs are deposited on a thick layer of dead leaves. The Poorwill *Phalaenoptilus nuttallii* is a rather small species with a relatively short tail, occurring in North America. Recently it has been discovered

that during winter birds of this species hibernate in rock niches and may return to the same hole every winter. During this winter dormancy the birds remain in a state of torpidity with an exceedingly low body temperature, 18°–19° C (64°–66° F) as against 40°–41° C (104°–106° F) normally (see TORPIDITY).

In some species the males show a remarkable elongation of certain feathers of wings or tail. In middle Africa the Standard-winged Nightjar *Macrodipteryx longipennis* is found ; it is a rather dark species, in which the males have, during the breeding season, the shaft of one of the feathers of each wing greatly elongated, with the terminal portion vaned. In the southern part of Africa occurs the rather large Pennant-winged Nightjar *Semeiophorus vexillarius* ; here it is the inner primaries that are extraordinarily prolonged. In the small Long-tailed Nightjar *Scotornis climacurus*, inhabiting middle Africa, the central tail feathers are greatly elongated. The males of the South American genera *Uropsalis* and *Macropsalis* are distinguished by a forked tail with much elongated lateral feathers. In *Hydropsalis*, from South America, the outermost as well as the central tail feathers are prolonged.

See Plates 3b, 44b (phot.). G.C.A.J.

NIGHTJAR, OWLET: see OWLET-FROGMOUTH

NIGHTJAR, TREE-: see POTOO

NITROGEN METABOLISM: see EXCRETORY SYSTEM ; METABOLISM

NOCTURNAL HABITS: characteristic of a minority of bird species, the great majority being entirely diurnal. Outstanding examples of special adaptations to activity in minimal light intensities are found in the Strigiformes, Steatornithidae, and the Apterygidae (see, respectively, OWL ; OILBIRD ; KIWI) ; but some of the owls—although all show the main adaptations to nocturnal habits—are in fact diurnal, or largely so. Other birds, notably the Caprimulgidae (see NIGHTJAR), are crepuscular in habits, being active in the dim light of dusk and dawn rather than in full night or day ; the Bat-hawk *Machaerhamphus alcinus* is a special case (see HAWK). Others again are nocturnal in their nesting activities but to a large extent diurnal in their search for food ; examples are many of the petrels (Procellariiformes), e.g. Manx Shearwater *Puffinus puffinus*, and a few penguins (Spheniscidae), e.g. Little Penguin *Eudyptula minor* (see PETREL ; PENGUIN). Further, many aquatic and wading birds (e.g. Anatidae and Charadrii), in particular, are partly nocturnal as well as mainly diurnal, showing considerable activity on nights that are not too dark on the water or open ground. Even among birds that are as a rule strictly diurnal, many migrate by night, e.g. numerous small species of the Passeriformes (see MIGRATION). This may be largely or wholly an adaptation to the need for using the day for feeding.

As the counterpart of nocturnal activity, quiescence during the day calls for concealment. This may be achieved in dense foliage or ground vegetation, or by virtue of cryptic coloration in more open situations. In many instances, however, the birds spend the day in holes or burrows used for nesting, and sometimes also for roosting outside the breeding season. This is true of various owls. Petrels that nest in burrows tend to have their comings and goings during the hours of darkness, and in the daytime are either underground or out at sea. The Little Penguin, mentioned above, is similarly nocturnal to a large extent when ashore at its breeding places. The Oilbird *Steatornis caripensis* nests, and has its daytime roosts, in the utter darkness far inside great caves, where it finds its way by echo location ; similar nesting and navigational habits are found in certain swiftlets *Collocalia* spp., but these birds are otherwise diurnal.

Nocturnal habits constitute a form of concealment, and like other forms may be either defensive or aggressive. The flightless kiwis feed at night ; and the oceanic petrels safeguard their unavoidable visits to land, for breeding, by resort there to nocturnal habits. On the other hand, owls use darkness—and their silent flight—for hunting ; at the same time they exploit a particular source of food in animals that are themselves nocturnal. Likewise, the crepuscular nightjars feed on insects that fly in the twilight ; and the case of the Bat-hawk is self-explanatory. In contrast, the Oilbird is frugivorous —the only nocturnal bird that is. The activities of shore birds are often governed more by the state of the tide than by the alternation of night and day.

For the sensory adaptations to nocturnal activity see VISION ; also HEARING AND BALANCE ; SMELL ; and ECHO-LOCATION.

See Plates 10b, 16 (phot.).

Hosking, E. J. & Smith S. G. 1945. Birds of the Night. London.

NODDY: substantive name (plural ' noddies ') of *Anous* spp. (see TERN).

NOMADISM: see MIGRATION

NOMEN: with adjectives conservandum, dubium, novum, nudum, oblitum, and triviale (see below).

NOMENCLATURE: the scientific naming of species and subspecies, and of the genera, families, and other categories in which species may be classified (see TAXON). Scientific names are necessary because there must be names that are internationally understood, and also because vernacular names, where such indeed exist in common speech, are governed by popular usage and are thus liable to be inexact in their application or to change in meaning with the passage of time (see NAME, various entries). In practice, scientific nomenclature has fallen short of the ideal, for reasons partly inevitable and partly arising from human wilfulness and negligence. The only hope of uniformity lies in the subordination of individual views or prejudices to the generally accepted code and authority ; to regard nomenclature as more than a means to an end is pedantry, and to take a minority course in a matter of convention is merely a nuisance.

International Code. So far as the Animal Kingdom is concerned, the practice of scientific naming is governed by the International Code of Zoological Nomenclature, and no other code has validity in any branch of zoology. The International Code is a system of rules and recommendations authorised by the International Congresses of Zoology. The current edition of the Code (formerly ' Rules ') is that adopted by the XV International Congress of Zoology (London, 1958) and published in 1961. ' The object of the Code is to promote stability and universality in the scientific names of animals, and to ensure that each name is unique and distinct. All its provisions are subservient to these ends, and none restricts the freedom of taxonomic thought or action.'

Two points in the earlier history of international rules are of particular ornithological interest. The first set of rules to be generally accepted was that adopted by the V International Congress of Zoology in 1901 ; the British representative on the small drafting committee was an ornithologist, P. L. Sclater. Among earlier codes was that prepared, with special reference to birds, by the American Ornithologists' Union in 1885. Notable predecessors were the Strickland Code adopted by the British Association for the Advancement of Science in 1842, and the Dall Code published by an American zoologist in 1877.

Binominal System. The Code embodies in legislative form the methods used by Linnaeus (Linné) and first consistently applied in the Tenth Edition of his *Systema Naturae*. These constitute the Binominal System (sometimes ' binomial' or ' binary ') ; and this has as its temporal starting point 1 January 1758, the year in which the edition was published. The essence is that every species is placed in a genus, and that the name of a species is a binominal combination, or ' binomen ' (plural, ' bi-nomina '), consisting of the name of the genus and a second word denoting the particular member of it ; the first term of the binomen is the ' generic name ', the second the ' specific name ' (formerly ' specific trivial name '—the nomen triviale of Linnaeus him-self). The name of a genus is used alone to designate that taxon as such. The specific name of a species has no meaning in isolation.

Trinominal System. This is a more recent ex-tension (Schlegel 1844) of the Binominal System and is covered by the same rules. Where a species is divisible into subspecies (sometimes called ' races '), the binomen constituting the name of the species is for each of them extended by a third term, the ' subspecific name ' ; the ' trinomen ' thus formed is the name of the subspecies. The species as a whole is nevertheless still referred to by its binomen. The subspecies that corresponds to the original descrip-tion and type locality of its species is the ' nominate subspecies ', and the third term of its name is a repetition of the second.

The International Code expressly does not provide for the nomenclature of infrasubspecific forms, e.g. ' varieties ' ; nor does it extend to the naming of hybrids, as such (see HYBRID). Further, when a num-ber of geographical populations described as separate subspecies are found to intergrade, more or less con-tinuously, this ' cline ' (although of great importance in reality) is not itself a nomenclatural entity (see CLINE).

Groups of Categories. The Code in its most recent form recognises three basic taxa—the species, the genus, and the family. On these it founds what it calls (for purely nomenclatural purposes) the ' species-group ' of taxa, comprising species and subspecies ; the ' genus-group ' of taxa, comprising genus and subgenus ; and the ' family-group ' of taxa, comprising superfamily, family, subfamily, tribe, ' and any supplementary categories required '. The names used for taxa within each group are ' co-ordinate ', and are subject to the same particular rules (additional to the general rules applicable to all names). The names of taxa in the genus-group and family-group are single words. (For the other meaning of the term see SPECIES-GROUP (1)).

The Code expressly excludes provision for the nomenclature of taxa above the rank of superfamily. This is ' because the practice of zoologists in regard to them is not sufficiently uniform to permit the formulation of rules covering them at this time '. The taxa most commonly used at this level are class, subclass, superorder, order, and suborder ; of these, class and order may be regarded as basic (see TAXON).

Availability of Names. The first requirement of a name is that it should be made ' available ' for the purposes of nomenclature. This is done by pro-posing it, for a particular use, in a publication. The form of the name, the information about its proposed use, the circumstances of proposal, and the method of publication must be in accordance with the conditions laid down in the Code. These conditions have been made progressively more stringent in respect of names proposed after certain dates—1930, 1950, 1960 ; the conditions applied to names pro-posed earlier (from 1758 onwards) are necessarily in more general terms. A name once duly made available, even if it is or becomes invalid for reasons mentioned later, retains a permanent status in nomenclature ; generally speaking, it can be used (at the same group level) only for its original purpose—except that the availability of a specific or subspecific name in one genus does not affect the use of an identical name in another. A name proposed in a manner or circumstances that do not make it ' available ' acquires no such status and is not thereby barred for the future ; such a name is called a nomen nudum or (if it failed in respect of uncertain application) nomen dubium.

Priority; Validity of Names. ' Priority is the basic principle of zoological nomenclature. Its application, however, under conditions specified in the Code, may be moderated to preserve a long-accepted name in its accustomed meaning.' Accord-ingly, the valid name of a taxon is the oldest available name applied to it, provided (i) that it is not invali-dated by any provision of the International Code, e.g. those relating to homonymity (next section) ; (ii) that it has not been suppressed by the Interna-tional Commission (mentioned later) ; (iii) that it has not become a nomen oblitum (defined below) ; and (iv) that it has not been superseded by the Commission's express validation of some other name (which thereby becomes what is sometimes called a nomen conservandum). The exceptional use of what are known as ' plenary powers ' by the Com-mission, in the suppression and validation of names, is no new thing ; but the more automatic provision in respect of *nomina oblita* is effective only from 1961. Such a ' forgotten name ' is one that ' has remained unused as a senior synonym in the primary zoological literature for more than fifty years ', and it cannot be brought into use except by direction of the Com-mission. This provision should discourage the kind of antiquarian research that has too often led to instability of nomenclature by reviving names of overlooked priority discovered in old works, some-times of indifferent merit.

Preoccupation; Homonyms. A name that has been made available is automatically invalidated if found to be preoccupied by an earlier use, either in the identical form or in some very close approximation to it (as defined in the Code). The rule is that a name of supraspecific rank must be unique in the Animal Kingdom ; a name of specific or subspecific rank must be unique in the particular genus. Identical or very nearly identical names for different taxa are 'homonyms' of each other ; a difference of a single letter, except where dependent on a variable spelling of the original word, is sufficient distinction (i.e. 'Apus' and 'Apis' are not homonyms). The name in its oldest use is the 'senior homonym', in any other use a 'junior homonym'. The 'law of priority' operates here also ; the senior homonym is valid, if other conditions are satisfied, while junior homonyms are invalid.

'Primary homonyms' are those that were in fact homonymous from the outset, although possibly not detected as such until later. 'Secondary homonyms' are those that have become so as the result of taxonomic change—identical specific names may properly exist in related genera, but if these genera are later merged the two specific names become homonyms and one is invalidated ; similarly, the splitting of a genus may validate a name that had hitherto been a junior homonym.

Synonyms. Whereas 'homonyms' are identical names proposed for different purposes, 'synonyms' are different names proposed for the same purpose. The operation of the 'law of priority' in respect of synonyms has already been noted, but some points of terminology remain to be mentioned. The oldest of a set of synonyms is the 'senior synonym', and is the valid name if other conditions are satisfied ; the remainder are 'junior synonyms' and are invalid, except that the next in order of priority will be promoted if for any reason the existing senior synonym is invalidated (e.g. through being or becoming a junior homonym). When there is no available name to promote, a 'replacement name' or nomen novum must be proposed—the term does not apply to a name for a new species.

Synonyms are 'objective' (sometimes 'absolute' or 'nomenclatural') when they expressly refer to the same 'type' (see later), so that there can be no doubt about the identity of their meaning ; they are 'subjective' (sometimes 'conditional' or 'zoological') when the identity of meaning is a matter of opinion and could thus be disputed. Loosely, 'synonym' without qualification is often applied to any junior synonym, as distinct from the valid name. A list of the names given by various authors to a particular taxon is known as the latter's 'synonymy'; this includes authors' names and publication dates, sometimes with full bibliographical references. The term may also be used for the relationship between different names for the same taxon.

The Type Concept. It has become a fundamental principle of nomenclature that a name is firmly attached to a 'type'. However the subjective limits of a nominal taxon may be altered, the name stays with the objective type, i.e. with the part of the original taxon that includes it. 'The type affords the standard of reference that determines the application of the scientific name.'

The type of a species-group taxon is a 'type-specimen', originating from a 'type-locality' (see TYPE-SPECIMEN ; and TYPE-LOCALITY). The type of a genus-group taxon is a 'type-species'. The type of a family-group taxon is a 'type-genus'. Within a group, the type of any taxon is also the type of its nominate subordinate taxon, if any.

A type-species must nowadays be expressly designated by the author of the name of a genus-group taxon ; for older nominal taxa there are various methods of selecting a type for a genus if no designation was originally made (see TYPE-SPECIES). A type-genus is that on which the name of a family-group taxon is based—the names of such taxa are purely derivative, not invented ad hoc. The type-genus is not necessarily the one with the oldest name ; and there are provisions to obviate changes in the names of the family-group taxa with changes in generic names.

Form of Names. Scientific names must be either Latin or properly latinised ; they are often derived from classical Greek, or formed from modern personal and geographical names or the like—and may even be arbitrary fabrications (thus, e.g., 'Dacelo' is an anagram of 'Alcedo'). They must be single words—two single words in a binomen, three in a trinomen ; if a compound word is used, the parts must be united without a hyphen (subject to one rare exception probably not occurring in ornithology). Names must be written entirely in Latin or neo-Latin letters ; and no figure, diacritic mark, apostrophe, or diaeresis may be used. The printing of linked vowels as diphthongs is now deprecated.

Pre-existing names that do not conform with the requirements are to be treated as incorrect original spellings and (like inadvertent errors) amended wherever found ; the corrected form keeps the date and authorship of the original. If the name consisted of two parts, these are to be united and any hyphen or apostrophe eliminated ; if one part was in contracted form, the implication is that this should be written in full to make union possible. Diacritic marks are simply omitted, except that when the German umlaut sign is deleted the letter 'e' is to be inserted after the vowel that was modified. To give examples: *novae hollandiae, clot-bey, l'herminieri, st. thomae, aëdon,* and *rüppellii* respectively become *novaehollandiae, clotbey, lherminieri, sanctaethomae, aedon,* and *rueppellii* ; to some extent usage had been tending in this direction before the 1961 Code made the changes mandatory. Certain recommendations concerning the formation of new names are appended to the Code.

Species-group Names. A specific or subspecific name ('species-group' name in this sense—see SPECIES-GROUP (1)) must be an adjective in the nominative singular agreeing in gender with the generic name, and changing in this respect if necessary ; or a noun in the nominative singular standing in apposition to the generic name ; or a noun (or, in some circumstances, an adjective used as a noun) in the genitive case. The genders and proper declension of non-classical names may often be difficult to determine, but the Code gives detailed guidance. A specific or subspecific name is always spelt with a small (lower case) initial letter.

Genus-group Names. A generic or subgeneric name must be a noun in the nominative singular or be treated as such. It is always spelt with a capital initial letter. A subgeneric name does not form part of the binomen or trinomen, and except in taxonomic works it need not usually be shown at all ; when required, however, the subgeneric name is given in parenthesis between the generic name and the specific name. (This practice must not be confused with that of showing a familiar but discarded generic name in parenthesis after the generic name actually used ; such a name is usually distinguished, within its parenthesis, by the equal sign or by quotation marks.)

Use of Italics. Generic, subgeneric, specific, and subspecific names are preferably printed in a typeface different from that of the text, usually in italics. This does not apply to the names of higher taxa.

Family-group Names. The names of family-group taxa are nouns in the nominative plural, and are always spelt with initial capital letters. They are formed from the name of the type-genus, with the termination '-idae' (the 'i' is short) in the case of families and '-inae' in the case of subfamilies ; the terminations '-oidea' and '-ini' are recommended in the case of superfamilies and tribes respectively.

Names of Higher Taxa. As already mentioned, the names of taxa above the level of superfamilies are not governed by the International Code, and even within the ornithological field there is variation of practice. One convention (followed in the present work) is to derive the name of an order or suborder from that of an included family, adding the

termination '-iformes' in an ordinal name, and using a normal Latin plural for a subordinal name ; when this is not done, there may be confusing identity between an ordinal name of one author and a subordinal name of another (see ORDER). In a different convention, ordinal names may be independent fabrications, e.g. 'Tubinares'. The type concept does not, in any event, apply at these higher levels.

Emendations. A scientific name, once established, cannot be rejected or altered simply because it is found to be inappropriate or even misleading. The stability of the conventional labels of which the system consists is more important than the accuracy of the meanings that prompted their adoption, e.g. than whether *maximus* is indeed the largest, or *sinensis* is characteristically Chinese. Further, a specific name cannot be rejected because it is a tautonym of the generic name, at one time thought by some to be objectionable.

It is, however, permissible to correct a lapsus calami or a copyist's or printer's error in a name as originally proposed (and mandatory to remedy defects in form such as the intrusion of a hyphen or apostrophe). Otherwise, the original spelling must be retained even if it is demonstrably erroneous in some respect. Subsequent misspellings of an original name—as distinct from deliberate 'emendations' within the permitted limits—have no nomenclatural significance.

Authorship. When the name of a genus (or subgenus) is mentioned by itself, the name of the author who first proposed it may be added ; it is not usual to do this in respect of names of higher taxa. When the binomen constituting the name of a species is given, the name of the author who first proposed the specific name may be added ; if he originally named the species in a different nominal genus, his own name is placed within brackets to denote that he did not use the present combination in its entirety. A similar convention applies to the names of the authors of subspecific names, shown after trinominal combinations. The year of publication, or even the complete reference, may follow the author's name if the nature of the subject calls for this. Unless there is special reason to fear ambiguity in the use of a scientific name, however, authors' names are seldom necessary except in systematic publications.

International Commission. The International Commission on Zoological Nomenclature is a permanent body deriving its powers from the International Congresses of Zoology. It makes recommendations to successive Congresses for the clarification or modification of the Code. Between

Congresses it makes provisional amendments to the Code in the form of 'Declarations', and it gives 'Opinions' and 'Directions' on nomenclatural matters not involving changes in the Code. It exercises 'plenary powers' to suspend the application of provisions of the Code in particular cases where stability or universality seems likely to be disturbed ; among other things, it can annul or validate any name. On the basis of the Opinions rendered, it compiles 'Official Lists' of accepted, and 'Official Indices' of rejected, names and works. The International Trust for Zoological Nomenclature is an administrative body acting for the Commission in matters of property and publication. The Standing Committee on Ornithological Nomenclature, appointed by the International Ornithological Congresses, has no powers of decision but makes recommendations to the International Commission with regard to names in the Class Aves.

A.L.T.

Salomonsen, F. 1960. Report of the Standing Committee on Ornithological Nomenclature. Proc. XII Internat. Orn Congr., Helsinki 1958 : 30–43.
Stoll, N. R. et al. (Editorial Committee). 1961. Code International de Nomenclature Zoologique adopté par le XVe Congrès International de Zoologie. International Code of Zoological Nomenclature adopted by the XV International Congress of Zoology. London. (The French and English texts, printed in parallel, are 'equivalent in force, meaning and authority'.)

NOMINAL TAXON: the taxon, as objectively defined by its type, to which a given name applies (see NOMENCLATURE). A nominal taxon persists as a nomenclatural entity even if it has ceased to correspond with any taxon currently recognised for other purposes.

NOMINATE: adjective applied to a subordinate taxon, denoting that it contains the type of a subdivided higher taxon and bears the same name as that taxon (amended in suffix in family-group names, according to rank). Thus, every subdivided species has a nominate subspecies, in the trinomen of which the second and third terms are identical ; every genus subdivided into subgenera has a subgenus with the same name as itself ; and (for example) every family divided into subfamilies has a subfamily with the same name as itself (apart from ending in '-inae' instead of '-idae'). On the other hand, the definition (by its reference to types) excludes a species of which the specific name *happens* to be a tautonym of the generic name, and a genus with a name providing the stem of family-group names. It should be noted that the concept is purely nomenclatural ; a nominate subspecies has no inherent pre-eminence over its fellows, and the term 'typical

subspecies' is ambiguous as an equivalent. See NOMENCLATURE ; TAUTONYMY ; TYPE.

NOMINOTYPICAL: obsolete equivalent of NOMINATE.

NONPAREIL: cage-bird dealers' name for the Painted Bunting *Passerina ciris* (see BUNTING).

NON-VOCAL SOUNDS: see INSTRUMENTAL SOUNDS

NOSTRIL: see NARIS

NOTES: see SINGING ; and BEHAVIOUR, DEVELOPMENT OF

NOTOCHORD: see DEVELOPMENT, EMBRYONIC

NOTOGAEA: see under ARCTOGAEA ; DISTRIBUTION, GEOGRAPHICAL

NUCHAL: pertaining to the nape (see TOPOGRAPHY).

NUCLEUS: see CELL

NUKTA: name used in India for the Comb Duck *Sarkidiornis melanotos* (see DUCK).

NUKUPUU: *Hemignathus lucidus* (for family see HONEYCREEPER (2)).

NULL HYPOTHESIS: see STATISTICAL SIGNIFICANCE

NUMBERS: the number of different kinds of birds in the world, and their distribution by main regions ; the number of individual birds of any one kind in the world or, failing that, in some stated part of it ; the number of birds of all kinds in a given area of habitat of a certain type, and the grand total (so far as even an intelligent guess is practicable) of birds of all kinds in the whole world ; also the number of individual birds (of one or more species) constituting spectacular assemblies or taking part in great migratory movements. For number of eggs in a clutch (young in brood) see EGGS, NATURAL HISTORY OF.

Number of Species. Mayr (1963) estimates that there are about 8600 species of birds known to exist at the present time. It seems unlikely that the number of new species remaining to be discovered is substantial ; there is also, apart from extinctions, the countervailing process of determining that some supposedly distinct species are no more than subspecific forms (see SPECIES ; SUBSPECIES).

Subspecies. The same authority estimates that there are about 28 500 subspecies, making an average of 3·3 per species. Many species are of course monotypic (reckoned as one subspecies for average), while others may include from 2 to a large number of subspecies. In the highly insular Indo-Australian area, the Golden Whistler *Pachycephala pectoralis* has more than 70 subspecies ; and even in the continental area of North America the Song Sparrow *Melospiza melodia* has about 30.

Taxonomic Incidence. The grouping of species in higher taxonomic categories is an essentially subjective process ; the numbers of such categories are thus of relatively little interest and vary from authority to authority. The classification followed in this work comprises 154 families (of living birds) grouped in 27 orders. There is actually a fair measure of agreement about families (although one man's family tends to be another man's subfamily), but the number of orders is much greater in some modern systems (e.g. Stresemann) than in others— Linnaeus recognised only 7 (see ORDER). Several families and even one order consist of only a single species, while others include only a very few. At the other extreme there are families with several hundreds of species ; and more than half of the total number of species belong to a single order, the Passeriformes.

Geographical Incidence. There are no readily available estimates, on a uniform basis, for the numbers of species in the different continents or zoogeographical regions (see DISTRIBUTION, GEOGRAPHICAL) ; such as have been published for these areas separately were made at different dates and used varying definitions. Except in a comprehensive study it is not possible to deal with the overlapping of area boundaries by many species ; and there is also the question of reckoning sea birds, more readily grouped by oceans than by land-masses.

Bearing these reservations in mind, a few very rough general indications can be given. The number of species occurring in the Palaearctic Region is about 950 (see PALAEARCTIC REGION) ; and the corresponding figure for the Nearctic Region is about 750. Moreau (personal communication) has recently estimated, ' using the most polytypic concepts that have been suggested ', that the Ethiopian Region has about 1520 species of land birds ; and that the Malagasy Region has about 200 species.

Keast has recently published some exact figures for the Australasian Region. He states that Australia has 531 breeding land and freshwater species, plus 37 breeding sea birds. He gives the corresponding figure for New Guinea as 566—allowing for overlap, 906 for Australia and New Guinea combined. New Zealand has 215 species. See AUSTRALASIAN REGION. No total figures seem to be available for the oceanic islands, of which some in the Pacific are particularly rich, nor for the Oriental Region considered as a whole.

There remains the Neotropical Region, which has the richest avifauna of all—South America has indeed been called ' the bird continent ' and credited with some 2500 species. In the present work it is stated that the Region has more than 1000 species of suboscine passerines alone. See NEOTROPICAL REGION.

Size of Species Populations. In some contexts a widespread species is considered as a group of local populations, which may be discontinuous in their distribution and in some cases subspecifically distinct ; for the purposes of this article it will be convenient to speak of total population, meaning the number of individuals belonging to a particular species. There are reasonably accurate figures for some of the smallest species populations ; one can but guess at some of the largest. In between, there are good estimates of the world populations of some moderately numerous species, especially birds of large size with breeding colonies in only a few localities. There are other species for which the populations in particular countries can be estimated with some confidence, but extrapolation of the figures to cover the whole range is a precarious process. Some of the methods used in making population estimates are discussed elsewhere (see CENSUS ; COUNT), as are the natural factors governing the size of populations (see ECOLOGY ; POPULATION DYNAMICS).

Small Populations. The smallest even theoretically viable population of a species is obviously a pair capable of breeding ; and in the process of becoming extinct a species may briefly linger at this point. There are in fact instances in which the last survivor of a species has been known either in the wild or in captivity and the exact date of its death is on record. During the last three centuries a considerable number of species have been brought to or near this endpoint directly or indirectly by human agency (see EXTINCT BIRDS ; VANISHING BIRDS). It is however also a natural process that some species should become ' biological failures ' unable to readapt themselves to changes in their physical environment or to meet new forms of competition. Thus for one reason or another species may come to be represented only by relict populations which in some instances may be very small. The latter may even benefit from human interference, when deliberate measures to save the remnant are taken (see CONSERVATON ; PROTECTION).

Fisher (1960) has listed nearly 100 species that are in danger of extinction or are known to have total populations of less than 2000 birds. Many of these are relicts and need not be further considered in this article (which is not concerned with the process of extermination) beyond mention of a few examples.

Thus the total population of the Whooping Crane *Grus americana* has in recent years, under all protection that can be given, fluctuated around 30 birds. Again, the remaining population of the California Condor *Gymnogyps californianus* is estimated at about 60. That of the Hawaiian Goose (or Nene) *Branta sandvicensis* has been brought from a very low ebb to more than 200 birds, including those in captivity and those returned to the wild from captivity (see AVICULTURE).

More relevant to the present discussion are those populations that have probably always been small, on account of natural limitations. They are of course highly vulnerable to intensive human predation or to destruction of habitat, but in the absence of these the species cannot be rated as unsuccessful. Many of them are insular forms, and one can make a long list of species of such families as the rails (Rallidae), pigeons (Columbidae), and parrots (Psittacidae) that have evolved on islands, notably in south-eastern Asia and in the tropics of the Pacific Ocean ; their populations can never have been very large, but it may be only where the island is quite small or when other factors have supervened that they become dangerously reduced. Some passerine examples are the Grand Cayman Thrush *Turdus* ('*Mimocichla*') *ravidus*, found only on the small West Indies island of that name ; the Seychelles Warbler *Bebrornis sechellensis*, now restricted to an area of 60 acres, on Cousin Island, where 30 birds were counted in 1960 ; and the Chatham Island Robin *Petroica* ('*Miro*') *traversi*, of which a population estimated at 40–70 birds appears to survive on a single acre—an astonishing density—of habitat provided by one islet of the group (formerly also on a larger island).

Not all the species that have limited insular breeding places are sedentary. Thus, the Waved Albatross *Diomedea irrorata* breeds only on Hood Island in the Galápagos Archipelago, the Short-tailed Albatross *D. albatrus* only on one of the Bonin Islands (formerly also on Wake Island), and Abbott's Booby *Sula abbotti* at present date only on Christmas Island. All these have populations of less than 2000 adults. There are also very restricted breeding areas other than islands ; e.g. Delacour's Little Grebe *Podiceps rufolavatus* is known only from Lake Alotra in Madagascar and has a small total population. This opens up a further aspect of the subject.

Hall & Moreau have recently analysed the status of nearly 100 species of African birds, mainly passerines, that are ' rare ' in the arbitrary sense (in most cases) that they are restricted to ranges measuring not more than 250 miles in any direction ; for about 15–20 of them the total population may

consist of less than a few thousand individuals, and sometimes of no more than a few hundred. These inhabit ecological islands, especially of montane forest and much less often of open upland, relict lowland forest, or swamp. The populations of most of them are limited by natural factors, just as in the case of species restricted to geographical islands. They are not ' vanishing birds ' in present circumstances, although their survival is certainly bound up with the integrity of the forest or other habitat.

The same authors point out that the topography of Africa south of the Sahara lends itself to this kind of situation, which seems to have arisen less often in most other parts of the world. In North America there is the well-known case of Kirtland's Warbler *Dendroica kirtlandii*, which breeds almost exclusively in a habitat characterised by young jack pines *Pinus banksiana* and within an area of 60 × 100 miles in central Michigan ; in 1961 the population of breeding adults was about 1000 (Mayfield). Incidentally, this parulid is migratory, and winters only in the Bahamas. There are a few other North American examples, mostly in the subtropical promontories (Florida and Baja California) or in the Arctic northwest.

The few Palaearctic examples of ' rare ' species in the above sense are mostly found in the Far East, notably in the semi-deserts and mountains on the borders of China and Tibet. The only clear western case is that of the finch *Serinus syriacus* of the mountains of Syria and the Lebanon. Australia also provides a few examples, some of which are probably relict species, while others appear to have evolved in relation to the peculiar environments where they are found. The latter include the Rock Warbler *Origma rubecula* of the Sydney limestone, and four rather similar species—each in an ecological island—of the widely distributed grass-wren genus *Amytornis*.

Some Larger Populations. The possibilities of closely estimating the total populations of more abundant and widespread species are practically limited to large or otherwise conspicuous birds that concentrate their breeding activities at a few places. This requirement is met mainly by certain sea birds. Fisher & Vevers made an estimate of the population of the Gannet *Sula bassana* of the North Atlantic based on the number of occupied nests ; allowing for some moderate increase known to have occurred since then, it may be taken that there are about 280 000 breeding adults, but without data on mortality rates one cannot calculate what number should be added for birds in their years of immaturity.

Lockley has estimated, on slighter evidence, that the Puffin *Fratercula arctica* of the North Atlantic may have a total population of about 15 million breeding adults (the majority divided fairly equally between Iceland, the Faeroe Islands, and the British Isles). The Greater Shearwater *Puffinus gravis*, although ranging widely, breeds only in the Tristan da Cunha group in the South Atlantic ; Rowan has estimated that the main colony, on Nightingale Island, has 4 million birds—making 5 million breeding adults in all.

Calculations based on wildfowl counts in Great Britain and elsewhere, coupled with ringing statistics, suggest that the total population of the Barnacle Goose *Branta leucopsis* is about 50 000, and that the western Palaearctic population (possibly about half the total) of the White-fronted Goose *Anser albifrons* is of similar magnitude.

When one considers small land birds of widely distributed species, it becomes obvious that they must vary much in abundance. Figures are lacking for total ranges, but, when it can be estimated that a single country has 10 million birds of a particular species, there may often be grounds for assuming that the world population of the species runs into hundreds of millions. A total population of this order can be postulated for the Red-billed Dioch *Quelea quelea* of Africa on the basis of figures relating to its destruction as an agricultural pest (see QUELEA CONTROL). There are estimates suggesting a similar abundance, early in the nineteenth century, of the now extinct Passenger Pigeon *Ectopistes migratorius* of North America (see EXTINCT BIRDS). Fisher has suggested that the most numerous sea bird may be Wilson's Petrel *Oceanites oceanicus*, which breeds in ' fantastic ' numbers in the Antarctic and roams the seas of much of the world ; but no estimates have been given.

Some Local Populations. Although it is difficult to make any useful estimate of the total population of a widespread and diffusely breeding species, it may be quite practicable to estimate the population of that species in a particular country, especially a country where adequate ornithological manpower and organisation is available. Fisher (1940) calculated that the most numerous species in England and Wales were the Chaffinch *Fringilla coelebs* and the Blackbird *Turdus merula*, each with about 10 million individuals, followed by the Starling *Sturnus vulgaris* and the Robin *Erithacus rubecula*, with 7 million each. The House Sparrow *Passer domesticus* has much more localised abundance and comes in the next group, with 3 million. In all, 14 species have populations, in England and Wales, exceeding a million, and 15 more are of 350 000 or over. These species contribute about 75 per cent of the total bird population of the country.

Such estimates as the foregoing have obviously to be based on sample censuses in representative types of country. Species that have relatively small populations, but that are large in body and concentrated in their breeding places, lend themselves to more direct counting. Thus, the population of the Heron *Ardea cinerea* in Great Britain was found in a comprehensive census in 1928 to consist of about 8000 breeding adults, and annual fluctuations have since been recorded by sampling methods (Nicholson). A similar study was made of the Great Crested Grebe *Podiceps cristatus* in 1931 (Harrisson & Hollom) ; on the basis of this census, and of more recent sample checks showing some increase, the population in Great Britain appears to consist of rather more than 3000 adults.

The organisation of such studies in the United Kingdom has been particularly an activity of the British Trust for Ornithology. Similarly, the Wildfowl Trust has organised counts of Anatidae that have brought winter visitants into reckoning, and a few figures may be quoted from a recent report (Atkinson-Willes). The population of the Mute Swan *Cygnus olor* in Great Britain, where the birds are resident, numbers about 18 000 adults. The Pink-footed Goose *Anser brachyrhynchus* does not breed in Great Britain but arrives in autumn to the number of 45–60 000. The population of the Mallard *Anas platyrhynchos* at its winter peak, when native birds are greatly reinforced by visitors, is guessed at 500 000 ; and corresponding estimates for the Wigeon *A. penelope* and the Teal *A. crecca* are 250 000 and 150 000 respectively. While probably not more than 2000 breeding adults and some non-breeding individuals make up the summer population of the Tufted Duck *Aythya fuligula*, this may increase in winter to about 30 000. The resident population of the Eider *Somateria mollissima* is perhaps 30–40 000 (mainly in Scotland).

Merikallio (1958) made a comprehensive study of the numbers of birds of all species in Finland. This was done by actual counts along a survey line in the sum of its parts more than 1000 km. long, carefully selected to give a true sample of the different types of habitat. The results gave the following figures for the total number of breeding adults (expressed in pairs in the original) in the country, limited here to the top 7 species :

Willow Warbler	*Phylloscopus trochilus*	11 400 000
Chaffinch	*Fringilla coelebs*	10 600 000
Tree Pipit	*Anthus trivialis*	3 300 000
Willow Tit	*Parus montanus*	2 800 000
Spotted Flycatcher	*Muscicapa striata*	1 980 000
Yellowhammer	*Emberiza citrinella*	1 940 000
Brambling	*Fringilla montifringilla*	1 740 000

It was further noted that the 2 commonest species accounted for 10 per cent of the total avifauna.

Total Density of Bird-life. Lack (1937), reviewing the data of census work available at that time, gave some figures for the density of birds of all kinds in different types of country. In terms of numbers of adult birds per 10 acres (he used the now less common unit of 100 acres) the answers ranged from 13 to 28 in English agricultural land, and from 13 to 200 in English woodlands. Much higher figures, up to 1180, were given by 'islands' of particularly favourable habitat, especially gardens. On the basis of this and similar information, Fisher (1940) conjectured that there might be about 120 million land birds in Great Britain.

Low figures are naturally found in barren environments ; Lack cites under 3 per 10 acres for Arctic tundra, for instance. High figures are characteristic of richly vegetated tropical country. Very high figures, locally, are yielded by some of the great breeding colonies of sea birds ; but these represent temporary concentrations of birds effectively inhabiting (obtaining food from) more extensive areas.

Fisher has made the further suggestion, based on known density figures and various guesses, that the total number of all birds in the world may perhaps be something like 100 000 million. His calculation was admittedly no more than an exercise in extrapolation ; but it is conceivable that the actual total may be of that order of magnitude—'give or take' some tens of thousands of millions !

Assemblies and Movements. Some of the most spectacular manifestations of bird-life are to be found at the breeding places of colonial nesters, notably sea birds. When the species are of large size, a few hundreds or thousands may provide spectacle enough ; but much greater numbers occur. The colony of Gannets on the island of Grassholm off the coast of Wales (see Plate 37b (phot.)) has more than 20 000 breeding birds ; and the three colonies in the St Kilda group, off the west coast of Scotland, together have nearly twice that total. Such figures, however, are greatly exceeded by other species. Some of the Antarctic 'rookeries' of the Adélie Penguin *Pygoscelis adeliae* have over a million breeding birds. One island of the Seychelles group was believed to have about 10 million adults of the Sooty Tern (or Wideawake) *Sterna fuscata* some thirty years ago ; the recent British Ornithologists' Union expedition to Ascension Island, in the South Atlantic, found between 750 000 and 1 million of these birds ('wideawake fair') on the slightly discontinuous breeding grounds there. Some of the petrels (Procellariiformes) nest in enormous colonies —one example has already been given. The Little

Auk *Plautus alle* breeds in extremely large colonies on Arctic cliffs. Among land and freshwater birds, the greatest spectacle of the kind is presented by flamingos (Phoenicopteridae) in some of their chief concentrations for breeding or feeding ; breeding colonies in tropical Africa (*Phoenicopterus ruber* and *Phoeniconaias minor* together) have been estimated to contain nearly 2 million birds, with more than that number on a single lake.

Other large assemblies are for roosting purposes, and dramatic aerial movements of huge flocks are sometimes involved—as in the case of the Starling *Sturnus vulgaris*. Other well-known passerines that sometimes roost together in very large numbers include the Sand Martin (or Bank Swallow) *Riparia riparia* and the White Wagtail *Motacilla alba* ; the number of birds in such a roost may exceed a million. In the United States one of the many mixed winter roosts—predominantly of the Redwinged Blackbird *Agelaius phoeniceus* and the naturalised Starling— may contain millions of birds (estimates up to 10–15 million birds, and densities as high as 1 million birds per acre). Birds may also congregate in large numbers where food is specially abundant, or where water is available in an arid area. Meinertzhagen reports hundreds of thousands of sandgrouse (Pteroclididae), of four species, at watering places in Bikanir (see SANDGROUSE).

Birds on migration often travel in vast flocks, not necessarily of a single species, or in an almost continuous succession of flocks. Here again the size of the bird is a factor in the spectacle. To see 30 000 Hooded Crows *Corvus corone cornix* pass along a coastline in a day is a memorable experience, as the writer can testify. Relatively small migrating flocks of species as large as the White Stork *Ciconia ciconia* are impressive, and this is true of pelicans (Pelecanidae), cranes (Gruidae), and swans *Cygnus* spp. or geese *Anser* spp., among others. The flocks of some of the smaller migrants (although many of these more often travel at night) may be very large.

Of the total number of birds of all species involved in a particular migration, spread over a season, one example may be given. Moreau has stated reasons for supposing that about 600 million European birds perform the Mediterranean—Saharan transmigration each autumn. This means that 250 000 birds per mile of longitude enter North Africa, or an average of 4000 per mile daily over two months.

A.L.T.

Atkinson-Willes, G. L. (ed.). 1963. Wildfowl in Great Britain. (Nature Conservancy Mon. no. 3.) London.
Fisher, J. 1940. Watching Birds. (Pelican Books.) Harmondsworth, Middlesex and New York.

Fisher, J. 1960. Bird species in danger of extinction. *In* Jarvis, C. & Morris, D. (eds.). Internat. Zoo Yearbook vol. 2 : 280–287. London.

Fisher, J. & Vevers, H. G. 1943–44. The breeding distribution, history and population of the North Atlantic Gannet (*Sula bassana*). J. Anim. Ecol. 12 : 173–213 ; 13 : 49–62.

Hall, P. B. & Moreau, R. E. 1962. A study of the rare birds of Africa. Bull. Brit. Mus. (Nat. Hist.), Zool. 8 (no. 7) : 313–378.

Harrisson, T. H. & Hollom, P. A. D. 1932. The Great Crested Grebe Enquiry 1932. Brit. Birds 26 : 62–92, 102–131, 142–155, 174–195. (And subsequent papers by the same authors or by the second alone.)

Keast, A. 1961. Bird speciation on the Australian continent. Bull. Mus. Comp. Zool., Harvard 128 : 305–495.

Lack, D. 1937. A review of bird census work and bird population problems. Ibis (14 ser.) 1 : 369–395.

Lockley, R. M. 1953. Puffins. London.

Mayfield, H. 1962. 1961 decennial census of the Kirtland's Warbler. Auk 79 : 173–182.

Mayr, E. 1963. Animal Species and Evolution. Cambridge, Mass., and London.

Merikallio, E. 1958. Finnish Birds, their Distribution and Numbers. (Fauna Fennica no. 5.) Helsinki.

Moreau, R. E. 1961. Problems of Mediterranean—Saharan migration. Ibis 103a : 373–427, 580–623.

Nicholson, E. M. 1928. Report on the 'British Birds' census of heronries, 1928. Brit. Birds 22 : 270–323, 334–372. (And subsequent reports by the same and other authors.)

Rowan, M. K. 1952. The Greater Shearwater *Puffinus gravis* at its breeding grounds. Ibis 94 : 97–121.

NUMBER SENSE: see COUNTING

NUMIDIDAE: see under GALLIFORMES ; and GUINEAFOWL

NUN: substantive name of some mannikins *Lonchura* spp. (see WEAVER-FINCH).

NUNBIRD: substantive name of *Monasa* spp. (see PUFFBIRD).

NUNLET: substantive name of *Nonnula* spp. (see PUFFBIRD).

NUPTIAL: pertaining to the breeding season, a term applied especially to plumage and display.

NUTCRACKER: substantive name of the two species of *Nucifraga* ; used without qualification, in Britain, for *N. caryocatactes* (see CROW (1)). See Plate 14c (phot.).

NUTHATCH: substantive name of the more typical species of Sittidae (Passeriformes, suborder Oscines) ; used in Britain without qualification for the common European species ; in the plural, general term for the family. Other substantive names used in the family (as at present recognised) are 'sitella' and 'creeper', the latter applying to species formerly placed elsewhere (Certhiidae, etc.). There is still considerable doubt about the position of some species which it is at present convenient to include, and the attempt to divide the Sittidae into subfamilies is therefore unprofitable. The family is widely distributed.

General Characters. Nuthatches are small birds, the 31 species being mostly about 4½ inches long, but ranging from 3¾ to 7½ inches. They are all similar in form—a compact body with a short tail, very long sturdy toes and claws, and a long symmetrically tapered bill. In many species a black stripe runs through the eye, and some have a black cap. The upper surface is blue-grey in most of the typical species, blue-green in 3 found in southern Asia. The under parts are white, grey, reddish brown, or chestnut. Sexual dimorphism is already evident in the juvenile plumage of some species.

Habits. All members of the family are climbing birds that seek their food on trees, or in a few cases on rocks. Instead of using the tail for support when clinging to a tree-trunk, as done by woodpeckers (Picidae) or treecreepers (Certhiidae), they climb obliquely, with one foot high to hang from and the other low for support. They can climb down a tree, head foremost, by the same method.

The food consists of insects, spiders, and other small animals. The birds inhabiting northern or mountainous areas feed largely on seeds in winter, and some small species are specialised for eating the seeds of conifers. Seeds and all larger prey species are hammered into cracks and are there either broken into small pieces or opened up by strong pecks. The European species is in this way able to open even hazel-nuts, hence the 'nuthatch' (nut hack). Many species store food, especially seeds, by hiding them singly in cracks or under bark, if possible covering them so that they are not visible.

The voices of the Sittidae are various, but the song mostly consists of repeated single notes that often sound like a trill. The songs of several species can be imitated by whistling. Nuthatches are strongly territorial, and some defend territory even in winter. At the latter season, however, some are social and form flocks.

Breeding. Members of the genus *Sitta* mostly nest in natural hollows in trees, but some small species make holes for themselves in dead wood ; 2 species nest in crevices in rocks. Several species reduce the size of the entrance with earth and fill up all cracks ; the rock nuthatches wall up a semi-enclosed hollow and construct an entrance tube. *Neositta* spp. build unsheltered nests ; *Salpornis* builds in tree cavities and *Tichodroma* nests in rock crevices. The 4–10 eggs are white with reddish spots. The young usually remain in the nest for 22–24 days (26 in *Tichodroma*) and when fledged are fully capable of flying and climbing ; in a further 8–12 days they are independent.

Distribution. The family is predominantly holarctic in distribution, most species of *Sitta* inhabiting Asia and Europe and 4 of them North America. *Neositta* spp. are confined to Australia and New Guinea ; *Daphoenositta* lives only in New Guinea, and *Hypositta* only in Madagascar. *Salpornis* is found in Africa and India, and *Rhabdornis* spp. in the Philippines. *Tichodroma* inhabits the high mountain ranges of Europe and Asia. The family is not represented in South America or New Zealand. So far as known the birds are non-migratory, except for some individuals of *Sitta canadensis*.

True Nuthatches. Of the 18 species of *Sitta* the most widely distributed is the Nuthatch *S. europaea*, of which the many races range through the whole of Europe and northern Asia as far as the limit of trees ; it is also the sole member of the genus to reach Africa, where it is found in a small north-western area across from Gibraltar. This species is particularly adaptable, not specialised but capable of utilising most kinds of trees and of seeds, making caches of the latter in autumn. The Chestnut-bellied Nuthatch *S. castanea* of southern Asia is similar, but differs in voice and in showing marked sexual dimorphism. The Rock Nuthatch *S. tephronota*, specialised as regards habitat, is found in the warmer parts of Asia ; in Persia it occurs along with Neumayer's Rock Nuthatch *S. neumayer*, which reaches its western limit at the Adriatic. The Giant Nuthatch *S. magna* is restricted to the mountains of central Burma, northern Thailand, and Yunnan ; it is as large as a Great Spotted Woodpecker *Dendrocopos major* and flies like a member of that family (Picidae). Other species in eastern Asia are the White-tailed Nuthatch *S. himalayensis*, the Yunnan Nuthatch, *S. yunnanensis*, and the Chinese Nuthatch *S. villosa*. Very similar is the Corsican Nuthatch *S. whiteheadi*, once thought to be conspecific with the Red-breasted Nuthatch *S. canadensis* widely distributed in North America. In the Near East is found the rather unusually coloured Krüper's Nuthatch *S. krueperi*. In the southern part of North America are found two closely related forms, the Pigmy Nuthatch *S. pygmaea* and the Brown-headed Nuthatch *S. pusilla*. In the mountain ranges of Afghanistan and Kashmir dwells the White-cheeked Nuthatch *S. leucopsis* ; very similar but somewhat larger is the White-breasted Nuthatch *S. carolinensis* of North America. In southern Asia there are three brightly coloured species : the Velvet-fronted Nuthatch *S. frontalis* (coral-red bill in some races), the Azure Nuthatch *S. azurea* (confined to Indonesia), and the Beautiful Nuthatch *S. formosa* (Sikkim to eastern Assam).

Treerunners. Six species of *Neositta*, the so-called 'treerunners' or 'sitellas', are widely distributed in Australia ; they are similar in body form to *Sitta* spp. but more brightly coloured. They have sometimes been placed in a family of their own (Neosittidae) but do not seem to require more than generic separation. The species are the Orange-winged Sitella *N. chrysoptera*, the White-headed Sitella *N. leucocephala*, the Black-capped Sitella *N. pileata*, the White-winged Sitella *S. leucoptera*, the Pied Sitella *N. albata*, and the Striated Sitella *N. striata*. In New Guinea, 5 races of a seventh species, the Papuan Sitella *N. papuensis*, occur in close proximity to the systematically isolated Wonder Treerunner *Daphoenositta miranda*.

Wallcreeper, etc. One of the most beautiful of birds is the Wallcreeper *Tichodroma muraria*, found only among rocks in the high mountains of Europe and Asia. This bird does not climb in the usual way but rather flies upwards in short jumps, when the striking red markings on the wings become conspicuous. Apart from this the plumage is principally like that of a nuthatch ; the bill is thinner and curved, the feet are weaker, and the wings are notably round. There are no congeners.

In another monotypic genus, the Spotted Creeper *Salpornis spilonotus*, of Africa and southern Asia, shows certain similarities in form to the Wallcreeper. The two species of *Rhabdornis*, the Stripe-headed Creeper *R. mystacalis*, and the Plain Creeper *R. inornatus*, live in the Philippines and feed upon nectar and insects in flowers.

Coral-billed Nuthatch. Finally, *Hypositta corallirostris* of Madagascar has sometimes been placed in a family by itself (Hyposittidae), having no near relatives. It is here provisionally included in the Sittidae, but its affinities are obscure ; it has been suggested that it may even be an aberrant member of the Vangidae. Rand found it in the humid eastern forests from about sea level to nearly 6000 feet ; he described it as an active bird, very 'creeper-like' in its feeding habits—not seen head down.

See Plate 13b (phot.). H.L.

Löhrl, H. 1958. Das Verhalten des Kleibers (*Sitta europaea caesia* Wolf). Z. Tierpsychol. 15 : 191–252.

Löhrl, H. 1960–61. Vergleichende Studien über Brutbiologie und Verhalten der Kleiber *Sitta whiteheadi* Sharpe und *Sitta canadensis* L. J. Orn. 101 : 245–264 ; 102 : 111–132.

Norris, R. A. 1958. Comparative biosystematics and life history of the Nuthatches *Sitta pygmaea* and *Sitta pusilla*. Univ. Calif. Pub. Zool. 56 : 119–300.

Voous, K. H. & van Marle, J. G. 1953. The distributional history of the Nuthatch *Sitta europaea* L. Ardea 41 : 1–68.

NUTRITION: the qualitative and quantitative food requirements of birds, a subject on which it is difficult to generalise ; although the nutritional requirements of domesticated species of economic importance have received much attention, for other birds little more than food and feeding habits have been studied (see FEEDING HABITS ; FEEDING OF YOUNG ; FOOD SELECTION).

The high body temperature and large surface area of birds, coupled with their great activity, demand a high energy intake and relatively rapid absorption from the gut (see METABOLISM). Relative to body length, the avian gut is shorter than that of mammals, and food passes quickly from mouth to cloaca (see ALIMENTARY SYSTEM). A shrike *Lanius* sp. is said to digest a mouse in about three hours, and domestic hens require only about two hours for the passage of mash through the gut. The ratio of surface area to body volume is higher for small birds, so that a higher rate of heat production is required to maintain the same body temperature (see HEAT REGULATION). This is reflected in the high food intake of small birds, relative to their weight ; the small Goldcrest *Regulus regulus* requires one-third of its body weight in food per day, this figure falling to one-eighth for the larger Starling *Sturnus vulgaris*, and tending to decrease for still larger birds.

The digestion of starch and sugars in the avian gut involves basically the same reactions as carbohydrate digestion in mammals. Birds metabolise carbohydrates rapidly and show a marked ability to convert carbohydrates into fats. Blood-sugar levels are generally high in birds, and although insulin appears in avian sugar metabolism, it plays a less vital role than it does in mammals ; in birds, insulin is apparently partially replaced by other hormones as yet unidentified (see ENDOCRINE SYSTEM).

Protein requirements vary widely with specialisation in feeding habit. In very general terms, the amino-acid patterns of avian and mammalian tissues are comparable ; commonly a bird requires in its diet a greater number of essential amino-acids. Certain basic differences in nitrogen metabolism, between the avian and mammalian systems, are being elucidated. The specialised features of the avian nitrogen metabolism will probably be ultimately referable to the characteristic excretion product, uric acid, which is in turn related to the demands of embryonic excretion within the cleidoic egg (i.e. one enclosed in a shell or membrane).

Fibre is not readily digested by birds, although the intestinal caeca, where present, break down certain types of fibre by both bacterial and enzymatic means.

For the species investigated, fibre digestibility appears to be related to caecal size.

Birds are known to require the same range of vitamins as mammals ; beri-beri (polyneuritis), due to vitamin B_1 deficiency, was first demonstrated in domestic pigeons and fowls and suggested the search for other vitamins. The vast majority of birds can probably synthesise vitamin C and do not require a dietary supply.

The commoner mineral elements required by the avian system include sodium, chlorine, calcium, magnesium, phosphorus, iron, and sulphur. These may be termed major minerals, being required in amounts that are relatively large when compared with the trace elements, such as iodine, manganese, cobalt, and zinc. Dietary requirements for minerals are known with some accuracy in the case of the domestic fowl ; but the fact that breed differences are now being encountered indicates the futility of generalising on the needs of birds as a class. The secretion of calcium (largely as calcium carbonate) by the female bird in the production of the eggshell is associated with a calcium metabolism differing from that of the mammal (see REPRODUCTIVE SYSTEM). It is known that up to one-third of the skeletal calcium can be mobilised by domestic fowls in full lay, but a more normal estimation, for both domestic and wild birds, shows that each egg receives about 25 per cent of its calcium from the body stores. The amounts of phosphorus, manganese, and vitamin D ingested can affect the deposition of the shell, and insufficiencies result also in malformed embryos.

Bone deposition requires magnesium and phosphorus in addition to calcium. The dietary sulphur appears in certain amino-acids, found notably in the feathers. Iron and cobalt are required for the production of red blood-cells. Iodine is employed in the elaboration of thyroid hormone by the thyroid. In egg-yolks, relatively high concentrations of zinc are found, combined with a protein known as vitellin ; associated with an enzyme, the element is probably important in carbon dioxide metabolism and bone deposition.   A.N.W.

Simkiss, K. 1961. Calcium metabolism and avian reproduction. Biol. Rev. 36 : 321-367.

NYCTIBIIDAE: see under CAPRIMULGIFORMES ; and POTOO

NYCTICORACINI: see HERON

NYE: see ASSEMBLY, NOUN OF

O

OBSERVATORY, BIRD: a station more or less permanently maintained at some favourable place, usually a small island or a headland, for the continuous observation of bird migration ; observatories may be manned throughout the year or only during the main seasons of migration, and this may be achieved either by a regular staff or by relays of volunteers. Apart from observational work, these stations are important centres of ringing (see RINGING ; TRAPPING) ; and the opportunity of handling large numbers of birds caught for this purpose is used for various associated studies.

The prototype was established a century ago when Heinrich Gätke began to devote himself to the study of migration problems on the North Sea island of Heligoland. In addition to collecting specimens, which included many extra-limital forms previously unknown in western Europe, Gätke introduced a daily survey and estimation of numbers of migrant birds, which he carried on down to 1887. This 'daily census' of birds present is now standard practice at all British bird observatories and at many on the Continent. The modern bird observatory at Heligoland was established by Weigold in 1909, when large-scale trapping and ringing of migrants in specially designed wire-netting traps (still universally known as 'Heligoland traps') largely replaced the collecting of specimens. Today this observatory is organised from the Institut für Vogelforschung at Wilhelmshavn, and in the famous trapping-garden on Heligoland and on the beaches of nearby Dune Island over 15000 birds a year are ringed, while on some days of autumn migration an estimated 100 000 birds alight on the island (Feeny 1959).

In the early years of the present century, observations of bird migration were made in the British Isles by Eagle Clarke, who spent substantial periods at such vantage points as Fair Isle, St Kilda, the Kentish Knock Lightship, and the Eddystone Lighthouse ; the repeated visits of the Misses Baxter and Rintoul to the Isle of May (Firth of Forth), and of Patten to various Irish lightstations, were in the same tradition. Regular observatories came later, and their development has been a marked feature of non-professional ornithological endeavour since the end of the war in 1945.

In Britain only two observatories were in operation before the war, on the island of Skokholm (Pembrokeshire) under R. M. Lockley and later the West Wales Field Society, and the Isle of May under the Midlothian Ornithological Club. Studies were interrupted by the war, but afterwards both stations reopened and others quickly sprang up under the aegis of local societies or as private ventures, often at places where ornithologists of an earlier generation had found observation and collecting profitable. Such places were Spurn Point at the mouth of the Humber (1947), Fair Isle between Orkney and Shetland (1948), Cley and Blakeney on the north coast of Norfolk (1949), and Dungeness in Kent (1952), where the North Sea and English Channel meet. Today about a score of stations report regularly to the Migration Research Officer of the British Trust for Ornithology, part of whose work is to co-ordinate research at the observatories and to analyse their results ; and bird observatory methods (fully described by Williamson 1960) are used intermittently as opportunities arise at a number of other localities. The issue of *Bird Migration* for December 1959 gave autumn reports from twenty-six sites forming an effective network covering the North Sea, the English Channel, the Irish Sea basin, and the north-western approach between Co. Donegal and Fair Isle.

Elsewhere in western Europe, Rossitten (on the isthmus known as the Kurische Nehrung) at the south-eastern corner of the Baltic has a long history as a ringing station and migration study centre, having been established under Thienemann in 1903 and continued while the locality remained German. Today regular observations on ' visible migration ' are made between mid-September and mid-October each year in the east Baltic area and reported to the Zoological Institute of the Estonian Academy of Sciences. In addition to Heligoland, West Germany has an observatory (successor to that at Rossitten) at Radolfzell on the Bodensee (Lake of Constance). In Sweden the Sveriges Ornitologiska Förening started a bird observatory near Ottenby at the southern tip of Öland in 1946, where a vast amount of data on visible migration has since been accumulated, while the grand total of birds ringed exceeded 100 000 in the first ten years. Similar observational work, mainly on birds-of-prey, has been done at Falsterbo Bird Observatory by members of the Skånes Ornitologiska Förening since 1949 (Rudebeck 1950 ; Ulfstrand 1960). In Norway the only regularly manned ringing station, concentrating on migrant waders, is at Revtangen, but bird observatory methods have been employed from time to time on the island of Utsira and at the south-western peninsula of Lista (Griffin, Harrison, & Swales 1956). In Denmark similar activities have taken place at Blaavandshuk (west Jutland) intermittently since 1954. In the Netherlands the 'fowling yards' have been the inspiration of large-scale ringing activity, coupled with valuable experiments on navigation involving the displacement of large numbers of ringed Starlings *Sturnus vulgaris* and Chaffinches *Fringilla coelebs* ; whilst at Vogeltrekstations Leiden and Texel, and elsewhere, considerable research has been undertaken on the effects of coastal 'leading lines' on migrating birds (see MIGRATION). K.W.

Clarke, W. Eagle. 1912. Studies in Bird Migration. 2 vols. London & Edinburgh.
Danielsson, G. & Edelstam, C. (1947). Ottenby Fågelstation, dess tillkomst och verksamhet år 1946. Vår Fågelvärld 1947 : 38–51.
Gätke, H. 1895. Heligoland as an Ornithological Observatory. Eng. trans. Edinburgh.
Griffin, D. M., Harrison, C. J. O. and Swales, M. K. 1956. A review of ornithological observations at Lista, south Norway. Sterna no. 23.
Rudebeck, G. 1950. Studies on bird migration based on field studies in southern Sweden. Vår Fågelvärld Suppl. 1 : 1–48.
Ulfstrand, S. 1960. Studies in visible migration at Falsterbo Bird Station. Bird Migration 1 : 183–187.
Williamson, K. 1960. The work of the British bird observatories. Proc. XII Internat. Orn. Congr., Helsinki 1958 : 749–757.

OCCIPUT : the back of the head (adjective 'occipital')—see TOPOGRAPHY.

OCEANIC BIRDS : insusceptible of rigid definition, but usually taken to include any species capable of living for long periods away from land and habitually obtaining food from the open sea. The degree of emancipation of different sea birds from land varies greatly ; most gulls (Larinae) and the cormorants (Phalacrocoracidae), for example, have geographical ranges that are essentially continental, and rather easily interrupted by oceanic barriers ; whereas the distribution of petrels and their allies (Procellariiformes) is broadly related to the particular oceans on the shores and islands of which they breed, and they are just as easily halted by any land barriers that cannot be circumvented. Many of the birds in the former group habitually extend to inland habitats as well as coastal ones, and are more accurately described as aquatic rather than as marine. All salt-water birds have very large nasal glands, which are of the greatest physiological importance in that their secretions rid the body of excess salt (see EXCRETION, EXTRARENAL).

A rough but helpful ecological distinction can be made between (1) inshore, (2) offshore, and (3) pelagic birds. The first group includes most cormorants, marine species of duck (Anatidae), and gulls. In general these keep within sight of the shore and neighbouring islands ; many of them roost ashore at night, although some of the sea-ducks and divers (Gaviidae) do not in fact come on land except to nest : the members of this group have no real claim to be classed as oceanic birds, and they need not therefore be further considered here. The second group is best marked in regions where the continental shelf is most extensive, as along both coasts of the North Atlantic ; it contains many predominantly fish-eating species such as the gannets (Sulidae), tropicbirds (Phaethontidae), and auks (Alcidae) ; these live continuously at sea when not attending their breeding places, but nevertheless they seldom wander much beyond the continental edge, into the outermost or pelagic habitat. The latter is the home of the true deep-sea birds, which may often depend for food more on squids or planktonic organisms such as crustaceans than on fish ; the great order of the Procellariiformes contains by far the largest number and variety of its inhabitants (see ALBATROSS ; DIVING PETREL ; PETREL).

We distinguish these three groups by the distance to which they habitually work out to sea ; but in fact the pelagic birds not infrequently work in from seaward to the waters of the continental shelf—although generally remaining out of sight of land. It must be noted also that some birds, such as the Arctic Tern *Sterna paradisaea*, become pelagic only during migration ; similar seasonal changes in ecology are common.

Effects of Wind. Oceanic birds at sea have no haven of shelter in storms, nor any means of anchoring themselves when afloat. The smallest kinds of storm petrels (Hydrobatidae) weigh roughly the same as a House Sparrow *Passer domesticus* (25-45 gm. in the Fork-tailed Petrel *Oceanodroma leucorrhoa*, which is actually not the smallest), but have a considerably larger wing area ; and they are liable to be whipped off the wave-crests during gales, like spindrift, and driven far to leeward. Normally, high-latitude storm petrels migrate to calm waters in the tropics or the opposite hemisphere and thus escape the fury of autumn and winter storms ; but sometimes they are caught and 'wrecked' in immense numbers when swept ashore by persistent autumn gales. The Little Auk *Plautus alle* appears sometimes to suffer a rather similar disaster.

The wind affects much larger species also. The Greater Shearwater *Puffinus gravis* breeds on Tristan da Cunha and then crosses the Equator in late April and May to spend the non-breeding season in the North Atlantic ; it has been ascertained that migrants to the north appear earliest on the west side of the ocean and tend gradually to pile up nearer the European side as the summer wears on, presumably as a result of leeway not made good. The Slender-billed Shearwater *P. tenuirostris* follows a similar migratory loop or figure-of-eight in the Pacific, breeding in Australia and wintering north to the Aleutians and Bering Sea ; other similar cases are known. In the Southern Ocean there is evidence that the Wandering Albatross *Diomedea exulans* habitually traverses the globe downwind from west to east—possibly more or less continuously all the time it is at sea in the latitude of the westerlies—and some other species may prove to do the same (see also ANTARCTIC ; CLIMATOLOGY). The prolonged calms and absence of high waves in the tropical Atlantic, on the other hand, may have barred the entry of any albatrosses into the Northern Hemisphere in this sector, since these huge birds are able to sail through the air only by obtaining lift from the up-draft on the windward side of waves : their flight movements consequently, like those of the shearwaters and petrels, are practically confined to the 10 metres or so next to the surface, within which they continually rise and fall, bank and veer.

Conditions of Life. Contrary to expectation, the pelagic habitat is a comparatively safe one for such highly adapted birds. Long life is the general rule, coupled with a low reproductive rate ; it is common in several oceanic families to lay only a single egg, e.g. in some penguins (Spheniscidae), in all Procellariiformes, tropicbirds, frigatebirds (Fregatidae), and gannets, and in most auks ; and in some of them it is not replaced if lost. Adolescence may be prolonged (5-7 years in the King Penguin *Aptenodytes patagonica*, Slender-billed Shear-

water, and Fulmar *Fulmarus glacialis*, 9 years or more in the Royal Albatross *Diomedea epomophora*) ; and this is partly responsible for the large numbers of non-breeding birds that remain at sea throughout the year. All oceanic birds without exception are colonial breeders. It may be noted that the high seas are devoid of avian predators (as distinct from ' pirates ' (see PIRACY)).

Planktonic food is not by any means uniformly abundant in all parts of the sea's surface ; and Jespersen demonstrated a very close correlation between the densities per unit area of macroplankton and oceanic birds. The greatest concentrations of both occur in southern and northern temperate and subarctic latitudes, and off the western coasts of continents where up-welling water greatly enhances productivity, for example in the great Humboldt Current west of South America. Regions of up-welling occurring in the tropics, as off Peru and West Africa, are among the favoured wintering grounds of the three smaller skuas *Stercorarius* spp. and the sea-going phalaropes *Phalaropus fulicarius* and *Lobipes lobatus* (see PHALAROPE ; SKUA). For the same reason, concentrations of many other marine birds are found there.

Distribution. It is scarcely surprising that oceanic birds reach their greatest variety and development in the Southern Hemisphere ; thus out of about 100 species of the Procellariiformes with known distributions, only about 30 breed north of the Equator. A number of the southern breeders migrate northwards to overwinter in the North Temperate Zone, chiefly between May and October ; these include the Greater Shearwater, Sooty Shearwater *P. griseus*, and Wilson's Petrel *Oceanites oceanicus* in the Atlantic sector, and, in the Pacific, the Slender-billed Shearwater, Pink-footed Shearwater *P. creatopus*, and Pale-footed Shearwater *P. carneipes*, besides the Sooty Shearwater (which is possibly more abundant in the Pacific than in the Atlantic).

Whereas a few of the major groups of oceanic birds have world-wide distributions, others are confined to low latitudes or to one hemisphere, and some have a disrupted ' bipolar ' type of range. The typical shearwaters (Puffininae) and storm petrels are cosmopolitan. The auks are wholly northern, and so are the phalaropes and smaller skuas in the breeding season. The Southern Hemisphere contains all the penguins, except the Galápagos Penguin *Spheniscus mendiculus* which just reaches the Equator, and all the diving petrels (Pelecanoididae) ; all but three of the albatrosses (Diomedeidae) are exclusively southern also, the exceptions being the Laysan Albatross *D. immuta-*

bilis, Short-tailed Albatross *D. albatrus*, and Black-footed Albatross *D. nigripes*, which breed in the North Pacific. Examples of bipolar distribution are found in the fulmars *Fulmarus glacialis* and *Fulmarus* ('*Priocella*') *antarctica*, gannets of the subgenus *Morus*, and the Great Skua *Catharacta skua* subspp.; and of pan-tropical distribution in the tropicbirds, frigatebirds, and boobies (subgenus *Sula*), among others. Not all individual species of oceanic birds are necessarily wide-ranging; some in fact have very restricted breeding areas. But it is the general rule that their distributions can be much more easily ascribed to particular sea areas than to the customary continental regions of zoogeography (see DISTRIBUTION, GEOGRAPHICAL).

All the families or different types of oceanic birds have now been mentioned, except for the kittiwakes *Larus* ('*Rissa*') *tridactylus* and *L.* ('*R.*') *brevirostris*, which, alone among the gulls (Larinae), are truly pelagic in the non-breeding season; they inhabit the north temperate and arctic waters of the Atlantic and Pacific Oceans.   V.C.W.-E.

Bourne, W. R. P. 1963. A review of oceanic studies of the biology of seabirds. Proc. XIII Internat. Orn. Congr., Ithaca, N.Y., 1962 : 831–854. (Numerous references.)
Murphy, R. C. 1936. Oceanic Birds of South America. 2 vols. New York. (Important for general biology and bibliography.)
Fisher, J. & Lockley, R. M. 1954. Sea Birds. London.
Alexander, W. B. 1955. Birds of the Ocean. 2nd ed. London. (Field book.)

OCELLA: eye-like pattern on plumage, e.g. in the tail of a Peacock *Pavo* sp.

OCREATE: same as 'holothecal' (see BOOTED).

ODONTOGLOSSAE: former ordinal name of the Phoenicopteri (see under CICONIIFORMES; and FLAMINGO).

ODONTOGNATHAE: a superorder of extinct birds (see under CLASS; FOSSIL BIRDS).

ODONTOPHORINAE: see PHEASANT

ODONTOPTERYGES: see under PELECANIFORMES

ODOUR: not very noticeable in most birds, but some species give off a characteristic smell. The latter is often, for widely unrelated species, described as 'musky'; but in the absence of any systematic study, and of objective standards in description, it cannot be assumed that the realities so named are identical or very closely similar. Among birds in which a characteristic odour is commonly remarked are the Musk Duck *Biziura lobata*, Muscovy Duck *Cairina moschata*, Magpie Goose *Anseranas semipalmata*, Hoatzin *Opisthocomus hoazin*, Hermit Ibis (or Waldrapp) *Geronticus eremita*. Puffin *Fratercula arctica*, Hoopoe *Upupa epops*, species of Hawaiian honeycreeper (Drepanididae), and even a weaver, *Ploceus thomae* (Ploceidae); also, most or all species of the Procellariiformes. Regarding *Geronticus*, Meinertzhagen writes of a 'smell like putrid carrion, which is not lost after several years in the dried skin'; and adds that 'the flesh tastes as it smells'. The comparatively odourless state of the intact body of most birds, as contrasted with mammals, can be related to the absence of cutaneous secretions other than that of the oil gland; when a characteristic odour is present, it can usually be ascribed to the latter (see OIL GLAND; SKIN). On the other hand, the bill plates of the Crested Auklet *Aethia cristatella* have been described as giving out an odour like that of tangerine oranges (see AUK).

Offensive odours may be emitted by ejecta from either end of the alimentary canal, both vomiting and defaecation being common reactions to threat of danger. To what extent these have ever more than incidentally a repellent role it is difficult to judge, although the human observer is certainly anxious to avoid, say, a squirt of stomach oil from one of the Procellariiformes (see ALBATROSS). Incubating Anatidae, in particular, are apt to defaecate over or near their eggs when suddenly flushed, and in the case of the Eider *Somateria mollissima* the faecal matter is notably offensive in odour. This latter characteristic may, however, be simply due to the fact that the caecal contents are evacuated in such circumstances; these probably always smell strongly, and possibly more so than usual in the case of a fasting bird (such as incubating Eider females are said to be) that has retained its faeces for some time. That the foul odour gives the eggs any protection against egg-eating mammals, as has often been thought, is doubtful; it has indeed been suggested that the scent may even aid the mammal's search. Anyhow, the objectionable odour lasts only while the faeces remain wet, which may be for as little as ten minutes.

The nesting or roosting places of some species become highly odorous through the accumulation of droppings and food refuse. The nests of many sea birds, raptors, and coraciiform species are cases in point.

For the olfactory sense of birds, see SMELL; see also PALATABILITY OF BIRDS AND EGGS.

Kear J. 1963. The production of offensive excreta by nesting wildfowl. Fourteenth Ann. Rep. Wildfowl Trust 1961–62 : 162–164.

OECOLOGY: see ECOLOGY

OESOPHAGUS: consisting of the gullet and, where present, the crop (see ALIMENTARY SYSTEM).

OESTROGEN: see ENDOCRINE SYSTEM

OFFICIAL INDICES AND LISTS: see NOMEN-CLATURE

OFFSHORE HABITAT: see OCEANIC BIRDS

OILBIRD: *Steatornis caripensis*, sole member of the Neotropical family Steatornithidae (Caprimulgiformes, suborder Steatornithes). It is known also as 'Guacharo' and, in Trinidad, 'Diablotin'. Although the Oilbird is generally placed in the order Caprimulgiformes, usually in a suborder of its own, its affinities are still not clear ; in any event it occupies a very isolated position. Anatomically it is in general closest to the caprimulgiform birds, but in some characters it resembles the owls (Strigiformes) more closely. In its ecology and behaviour it differs strikingly from the other caprimulgiform birds, and indeed from all other birds. It is the only nocturnal fruit-eating bird.

The Oilbird is in appearance something between a large nightjar (Caprimulgidae sp.) and a hawk (Accipitridae sp.). It has a powerful hooked bill surrounded by long vibrissae, long wings with a span of just over 3 feet, an ample tail, and short weak legs. The plumage is rich brown, barred with black and with a scattering of white spots that are especially conspicuous on the wing coverts. Oilbirds are gregarious, cave-living, nocturnal birds ; they spend all the day crouched on ledges in the caves that they inhabit, flying out at night to feed on the fruit of various forest trees, chiefly palms and members of the Lauraceae. The fruit is plucked on the wing by means of the strong hooked bill ; in intervals between feeding the birds have been reported to perch on bare branches, but so far very little is known about their behaviour outside the caves. Fruit is brought back whole to the caves, apparently in the stomach (as there is no crop), and digested there during the day. The seeds are regurgitated and fall on the lower ledges and floor of the caves, forming a deep rich humus in which etiolated seedlings sprout but soon wither through lack of light.

In addition to the clicking sounds which enable Oilbirds to navigate in pitch-dark caves (see ECHO LOCATION), they utter extremely loud screaming and snarling calls, which from a chorus of several hundred birds in a large cave become almost deafening. When flying at night outside the caves they utter occasional harsh cries, but not the echo-locating clicks. As their eyes are rather large and very sensitive to light, it seems probable that it is by sight that they orientate themselves outside the caves.

It is probable that scent plays an important part in the locating of food trees. Many of them are notably spicy or aromatic, and the Oilbird's olfactory apparatus is very well developed.

The nest is a bulky structure with a shallow saucer-shaped depression, placed on a ledge usually high up on the cave wall. It is made predominantly of regurgitated fruit of paste-like consistency applied directly from the side of the bill, but disgorged seeds and to a lesser extent the bird's own excreta also contribute to the structure. Nests are used year after year and grow in height as more material accumulates. The tempo of breeding is extremely slow. The eggs, usually 2–4 in a clutch, are laid at intervals of several days ; incubation lasts about 33 days ; and the young remain in the nest for up to 120 days. Both parents incubate the eggs. The young are hatched with a little sparse down, grow a second coat of down after about three weeks, and then the adult plumage. They become very fat, reaching a weight half as great again as the adult's by about the seventieth day and then gradually losing the excess weight as the feathers grow. Because of the great amount of fat, which when boiled down yields an odourless and durable oil, young Oilbirds used to be, and to some extent still are, collected by the natives of the regions where they occur—hence their name. In Trinidad, eggs may be found at any time ; but most clutches are laid in the early months of the year.

Oilbirds occur from western British Guiana through Venezuela and Colombia, to Ecuador and Peru, and in Trinidad. They are everywhere very local, depending on the presence of suitable caves. Most of these are in mountainous country, but in Trinidad there are some colonies in sea-caves along the rocky north coast.

See Plate 16c (phot.). D.W.S.

Snow, D. W. 1961–62. The natural history of the Oilbird, *Steatornis caripensis*, in Trinidad, W. I. Zoologica (N.Y.) 46 : 27–48 ; 47 : 199–221.

OIL GLAND: an externally secreting organ situated dorsally on the rump, above the root of the tail ; also called 'preen gland' or 'uropygial gland'. It is basically a paired organ, having two halves, more or less united, symmetrical round the mid-line of the body. The interior consists mainly of secretory tubules leading into a cavity that opens to the surface by orifices, in some birds taking the form of a nipple. The number of orifices differs. There are as many as five in some groups in;

others (e.g. Anseriformes) there is one for each half of the gland, but these may be united into one—although then usually divided by a septum (but not in the Hoopoe *Upupa epops*). The exterior of the gland, although of course concealed by overlapping plumage, may be bare but surrounded by a circlet of small feathers, or it may have a covering of down.

The gland is found in the great majority of birds, but it is absent in the Ostrich *Struthio camelus*, emus and cassowaries (Casuariiformes), bustards (Otididae), frogmouths (Podargidae), and some others (see below). In others again, e.g. pigeons (Columbidae) and nightjars (Caprimulgidae), it seems to be scarcely functional. The greatest development occurs among aquatic birds, notably the Procellariiformes and Pelecaniformes. The large size in the Osprey *Pandion haliaetus* may likewise be related to a partly aquatic mode of life ; but this cannot be true of the Oilbird *Steatornis caripensis*, in which the organ is also large.

Except for some small glands in the external ear passages, the uropygium is the only cutaneous gland in birds, in strong contrast with mammals (see SKIN). The oily secretion contains fatty acids and the like. In the incubating females and the nestlings of the Hoopoe the secretion has a strong offensive smell ; it is also odorous in the Musk Duck *Biziura lobata* and in petrels (Procellariiformes)—see ODOUR.

The function of the gland has been much debated. It seems certain that in many birds it is used in preening, the secretion being expressed by means of the bill and with the latter applied to the plumage to keep the feathers in condition and waterproof ; that the gland tends to be especially well developed in aquatic birds is noteworthy (see FEATHER MAINTENANCE). It has also been suggested that the secretion helps to maintain the condition of the horny sheath of the bill itself. On the other hand, some birds possessing oil glands have bills of a form that appears to make the act physically impossible (see BILL) ; or, again, some species of which the preening has been closely observed have not been seen to perform the act. There is the further point that species that do not possess an oil gland nevertheless succeed in keeping their plumage in good condition. Other functions have been suggested, such as that the oil gland may serve some purpose as a scent organ, although only in a few does the secretion smell strongly to the human nose and birds in general are not credited with any acute olfactory sense (see SMELL). There is experimental evidence that in some birds the secretion applied to the plumage may have an antirachitic function, enabling Vitamin D to be synthesised under the influence of sunlight (and presumably either absorbed

through the skin or orally ingested in subsequent preening) ; extirpation in certain species has induced rickets, a sign of Vitamin D deficiency, but in others the results have been negative. The truth may well be that the function is not identical for all birds.

The oil gland is unsatisfactory as a taxonomic character, although there have been attempts to use it as such. The feathering of the gland is constant in its nature throughout some families, but in others there are considerable differences between species. Likewise, as already noted, the gland is absent in certain families (some of which there is no reason for regarding as related) ; but in others it is generally present but absent in some of the species—as among pigeons (Columbidae), parrots (Psittacidae), and woodpeckers (Picidae).

OILING : see FEATHER MAINTENANCE ; OIL GLAND

OIL POLLUTION : results of the discharge of fuel oil into the sea, considered here as affecting bird-life. The change-over from coal-burning to oil-burning ships during the second decade of the twentieth century resulted in a new and appalling hazard to birds. Oil-carrying ships, or tankers, clean out their tanks periodically and discharge the resultant sludge into the sea, where it floats until it is washed ashore, polluting everything in its train. Dry-cargo ships cause similar pollution when they get rid of the water used as ballast in their empty bunker fuel tanks. Sea birds coming in contact with this oily waste are doomed ; their feathers become clogged with the thick tarry filth, they can neither fly nor swim, and they are buffeted about by the waves or struggle ashore till death from starvation or exposure ends their sufferings.

The United Kingdom in 1922 passed legislation prohibiting the discharge of waste oil in territorial waters. Many other countries took similar action to protect their coasts, but it was soon realised that this was an international problem. An international conference was held in Washington in 1926 at which two points of view were put forward : entire prohibition of discharge, and 'zoning'. Finally, a system of zones in which discharge of waste oil was prohibited was agreed upon ; but unfortunately this Convention was never ratified although it was observed voluntarily by a number of shipping companies.

The destruction of sea birds continued, resolutions deploring the situation were passed at international conferences, and the matter was taken up by the League of Nations ; but nothing practical resulted.

After the Second World War refineries were established in Europe, and crude oil, previously refined in the country of origin, was shipped to that continent ; tanker fleets consequently increased enormously and the problem of oil pollution became even more acute. In Sweden, during the spring of 1952, 30 000 oiled birds were washed ashore along the coast of Gotland in a single month; and from a survey during the preceding winter it was estimated that the number of birds destroyed round the coasts of the British Isles was between 50 000 and a quarter of a million. Some years later it was reported that in the area of Newfoundland hundreds of thousands of sea birds are killed annually.

In 1952, on the initiative of the British Section, International Council for Bird Preservation, a committee was set up on which all the interests affected by oil pollution were represented, and means of concerted effort was thus achieved. An international conference organised by this committee in 1953 was followed by an inter-governmental conference called by the United Kingdom in 1954. A Convention was then drawn up containing many measures to abate pollution of the sea, such as the provision in ports of facilities for the reception of waste oil, installation of oil separators on ships, and extensive zones of prohibition. After having been accepted by 10 nations this Convention came into force for tankers in 1958 and for dry-cargo ships in 1961, by which latter date the number of supporting countries had increased to 15.

In 1962 a further inter-governmental conference, attended by representatives of 55 countries, was convened in London by the Inter-governmental Maritime Consultative Organisation (IMCO). Many amendments were made to the 1954 Convention, one of the most important points being acceptance of the principle that ships shall in no circumstances discharge persistent oil into the sea. The realisation of this principle has been the goal of bird conservationists for over forty years, since only by such a measure can the mass destruction of sea birds be brought to an end.   P.B.-S.

OIL, STOMACH: see under ALBATROSS

OLDSQUAW: American name (spelt as one word in A. O. U. list) for the Longtailed Duck *Clangula hyemalis* (see DUCK). See Plate 29 (colour).

OLFACTION: see SMELL

OLFACTORY BULBS: parts of the forebrain (see NERVOUS SYSTEM ; SMELL).

OLIGOMYODIAN: see SYRINX

OLIVE-BACK: alternative substantive name of some waxbills *Estrilda* spp. (see WEAVER-FINCH).

OMAO : or Hawaiian Thrush, *Phaeornis obscurus*, (for subfamily see THRUSH).

OMENS, BIRDS AS: the use of birds in augury (ornithomancy) or, more loosely, as omens individually. This can be traced back into ancient Rome, e.g. geese *Anser* spp., and Greece, e.g. owls (Strigiformes), and ancient China—see FOLKLORE. In recent historical times, organised omenist systems have survived in vigorous form only within southeastern Asia, where in some places they remain paramount and can constitute a full-scale 'animist pagan' system of ethics. This system is vestigial among some hill tribes of the mainland, but is strongest among the inland peoples of Borneo, all of whom have versions of belief by which actions of a few selected species of mammals, reptiles, and especially birds are taken to indicate metaphysical conditions favourable or otherwise to current or intended enterprises. Birds generally form between half and three-quarters of the animist code. Identification between birds and man is easy enough, in a pre-Darwinian context where man seldom *feels* superior and often regards other life around him, e.g. the munias (Estrildidae) which threaten his rice crops each year, as nearly co-equal.

The position of the bird in relation to the observer, and its movements or calls in flight, are the principal factors in interpreting the augury. A bird crossing one's path from left to right may be dangerous, from right to left very encouraging. Variants are innumerable, methods of propitiation numerous. In extreme conditions of persistent bad omen a group may even abandon their whole longhouse village ; among the remote Sabans and Muruts of central north Borneo, to abandon a ricefield painfully cleaned from virgin jungle is not at all uncommon.

To Western logical minds it may seem strange that flying from right to left is good, vice versa bad. But any simple code likes to have a yes-and-no balance ; few get it, but bird augury *appears* to have it. Exactly the same principles of fortune decide the Chinese temple observance of tossing mangrove corms until both fall one way up ; or the Australian national game of 'two-up', played with three pennies.

Elaborate bird usages have lately disappeared in all but the remotest areas. Bird beliefs remain deeply engrained, however, associated with the part omen and other birds play in folklore, notably as ancestral demi-gods and mighty warriors. Bird augury was based largely on fertility and associated beliefs linked to head-hunting and war, and augurs were deliberately consulted before any such operations could be undertaken. The cessation of headhunting in this century invalidated some of the basic premises. Yet the greatest ceremony over a large part of Borneo today is still 'Gawai Burong', the Feast of the Birds, with elaborate avian and omenist associations, now in effect a peaceful secular continuation of a once blood-marked rite of rejuvenation and continuity, symbolised in the great birds.

A feature of bird augury is the variability of the birds selected. Thus the Sea Dayaks of south Borneo use as bird augurs one of the medium-sized woodpeckers and a tiny one *Sasia abnormis*, a rare jungle kingfisher *Lacedo pulchella*, the noisy Crested Jay *Platylophus galericulatus*, two rather uncommon and quiet trogons (Trogonidae), and a beautifully songed shama *Copsychus* sp. The immediately adjacent Land Dayak, Maloh, Kenyah, and Kayan people, however, put dominant emphasis on noisy, small, very common spider-hunters *Arachnothera* spp., and determine much of their daily and nightly lives thereby—whereas the Sea Dayaks ignore these, only saying of such ubiquitous birds : 'Nobody will take heed of your words.'

The Sea Dayak omen birds are all regarded as interchangeable bird-man deputies of their ancestor hero and warrior—Sengalang Burong (Hornbill-Kite) and his brave sons-in-law, living in an eight-roomed long-house with Himself at the centre. Related ideas were held in ancient Greece, northern India, and modern Africa ; Sir James Frazer wrote in *The Golden Bough* : 'When the Nandi men are away on a foray, nobody at home may pronouce the names of the absent warriors ; they must be referred to as birds. Should a child so far forget itself as to mention one of the distant ones by name, the mother would rebuke it, saying, "Don't talk of the birds who are in the heavens".'

All the Borneo omen birds are resident species ; but it does not follow that all were originally so in the lands whence these peoples came in proto-historical times. Certainly, there is another important sequence of thought in the Far East—notably in China and Borneo—centred on migratory birds. It is not difficult to see how this could, in another context, lead directly to an omenist system. In ancient China such beliefs persist even under Communism. The 'Red Bird of the South' ('teng huang'), a frequent phoenix-like form in Chinese ceramic, jade, and scroll art for over two thousand years, is a symbolic bisexual conglomerate of several birds—the quail, coming to north China from the south as a portent of summer all along the mighty Yellow River, the peafowl, pheasant, junglefowl, eagle, and flying dragon. At the other end of the scale, in the remotest hinterland of central Borneo, the Kelabits determine their crucial rice-planting cycle by the arrival of a series of migrating birds

reaching the Equator from the far north, indicating to man the sequence of clearing and planting, bedding, weeding, protecting, and harvesting the vital rice padi. These birds, which give their names to the months, are an eastern race of the Yellow Wagtail *Motacilla flava*, Brown Shrike *Lanius cristatus*, Japanese Lesser Sparrowhawk *Accipiter gularis*, and Siberian Pale Thrush *Turdus pallidus*; all 'winter' above 3000 feet in the Bornean uplands and return north during March–April, after the rice crop has been gathered in.   T.H.

ONTOGENY: the developmental history of the individual (see DEVELOPMENT, EMBRYONIC ; DEVELOPMENT, POSTEMBRYONIC ; also BEHAVIOUR, DEVELOPMENT OF). This is contrasted with the evolutionary history of the species (or other taxon)—see PHYLOGENY.

OOAA : *Moho braccatus* of the Hawaiian Islands (for family see HONEYEATER)

OOCYTE: a cell in the sequence leading to the formation of an ovum (see REPRODUCTIVE SYSTEM ; and LAYING).

OOLOGY: the scientific study of the eggs of birds, with particular reference to external characteristics such as shape and size, texture and coloration of shell, and number in clutch (see EGGS, NATURAL HISTORY OF ; and EGGSHELL). Extension of interest beyond this overlaps the more general field of reproductive physiology and behaviour (see, for example, BREEDING SEASON ; INCUBATION ; LAYING ; PARASITISM). The study of the contents of the egg, and of the developing chick within it, is a different subject (see DEVELOPMENT, EMBRYONIC; EGG).

In the main, oology is a form of systematic work (see SYSTEMATICS). In its broad descriptive phase it is now worked out in so far as most parts of Europe and North America are concerned, and new observations relate mainly to local differences, unusual variations, and the like ; but in some parts of the world there is still very much to be learnt, the eggs of many species being as yet either wholly unknown or the subject of only meagre information. Regrettably, the proper scientific study is obscured by controversy over egg collecting, some of which seems to spring from a desire merely to amass collections and often betrays its nature by a false emphasis on rarities.

OPENBILL: also 'Open-billed Stork', *Anastomus* spp. (see STORK).

OPERCULUM: a covering flap, as over the anterior nares or the external auditory meatus in some birds (see BILL ; HEARING AND BALANCE ; NARIS ; OWL).

OPISTHOCOMI ; OPISTHOCOMIDAE : see under GALLIFORMES ; and HOATZIN

OPTIC LOBES : parts of the brain (see NERVOUS SYSTEM).

OPTIC NERVE : see VISION ; and NERVOUS SYSTEM

ORANGEQUIT : *Euneornis campestris* (for sub-family see HONEYCREEPER (I)).

ORANGETHROAT : *Luscinia pectardens* (for sub-family see THRUSH).

ORBIT : see SKELETON

ORBITAL : applied to a distinctive area, in some plumage patterns, round the eye.

ORBITOSPHENOID : a paired bone of the skull (see SKELETON).

ORDER : a primary taxonomic category, a sub-division of a class—here the Class Aves—and a grouping of families ; other categories may be interpolated between these primary ones to build up a more elaborate hierarchical system, especially sub-class and superorder on the one hand, suborder and superfamily on the other (see CLASSIFICATION ; TAXON). The system followed in this work is among those that use the convention of making every ordinal name end in ' -iformes ' ; an earlier convention favoured ' -morphae '.

Whereas the family is the convenient group for most general purposes, the aim of ordinal grouping is to express the supposed phylogenetic relation-ships between families. At this level, however, the suppositions tend to become very uncertain and highly speculative ; the content of orders has there-fore not only changed greatly with advancing knowledge but is also the subject of differing views at the present time. Authorities who are sceptical about evidence of relationships naturally tend to preserve a greater number of separate orders of limited content ; those who are bolder place more families together and thus reduce the number of orders.

Nevertheless, many orders are not in serious dis-pute. Some of these comprise only a single family, and the ordinal rank merely expresses the view that the family does not appear to have any near relation-ships ; others comprise a few families that are generally accepted as being related. Even the Order Passeriformes, comprising a very large number of families, is also accepted as having ordinal charac-teristics clearly separating these from all other groups. The greatest difference of opinion concerns the large assemblages of families regarded by some as gruiform and coraciiform respectively.

The classification followed by Peters and used in the present work is based on that of Wetmore, which fundamentally goes back to Fürbringer and Gadow. The chief alternative is that of Stresemann, which differs mainly in recognising a larger number of orders and so keeping an open mind on the question of the phylogenetic relationships of many of the families. Allowing for this difference in approach, there is no serious inconsistency between them. The same cannot be said of certain other views, notably those recently put forward by Verheyen and those earlier published by P. R. Lowe, but as these have found little acceptance they can be disregarded here.

The differences between the ordinal systems of Wetmore and of Stresemann (revised 1959)—apart from mere differences in the names of equivalent orders—may be summarised as follows.

WETMORE	STRESEMANN
Dinornithiformes ⎫ Apterygiformes ⎭	Apteryges
Galliformes	⎰ Galli ⎱ Opisthocomi
Gruiformes	⎧ Turnices ⎪ Ralli ⎪ Heliornithes ⎪ Mesoenades ⎪ Rhynocheti ⎬ Eurypygae ⎪ Cariamae ⎪ Psophiae ⎪ Grues ⎩ Otides
Columbiformes	⎰ Columbae ⎱ Pterocletes
Charadriiformes	⎧ Jacanae ⎪ Thinocori ⎨ Laro-Limicolae ⎩ Alcae
Anseriformes	⎰ Anseres ⎱ Anhimae
Ciconiiformes	⎰ Phoenicopteri ⎱ Gressores
Cuculiformes	⎰ Musophagae ⎱ Cuculi

Coraciiformes
$\begin{cases} \text{Coracii} \\ \text{Halcyones} \\ \text{Meropes} \\ \text{Momoti} \\ \text{Todi} \\ \text{Upupae} \\ \text{Bucerotes} \end{cases}$

Apodiformes
$\begin{cases} \text{Apodes} \\ \text{Trochili} \end{cases}$

(For familial composition see separate entries under the names of all orders—for the latter see Table of Classification at the beginning of this work.)

In listing orders, it is customary to begin with those that are believed to be most primitive and to proceed towards the most highly developed—the Passeriformes. In British works the proceeding used commonly to be reversed, and sometimes still is, but that is a mere matter of convention. The placing of the orders is obviously speculative in high degree ; any list must also be arbitrary in that no linear arrangement could adequately express relationships of the kind involved.

Suborder. The suborder is a secondary taxonomic category, a subdivision of an order and a grouping of superfamilies (if any) and families. Not all orders are divided into suborders, the category being used only when required. It represents an important level in a system of classification such as that followed in the present work, in which many orders are wide. In other systems, where what are suborders here tend to be given independent ordinal rank, the occasion for subdivision may disappear.

The names of suborders end in ordinary Latin plural form (' -i ', ' -ae ', ' -es '). As some authors end their ordinal names in the same way, these can be identical with subordinal names of others. The International Code of Zoological Nomenclature does not apply at this level.

For superorder see under CLASS ; for superfamily see under FAMILY.

Stresemann, E. 1959. The status of avian systematics and its unsolved problems. Auk 76 : 269–280.
Wetmore, A. 1960. A classification for the birds of the world. Smithsonian Misc. Coll. 139 (11) : 1–37.

ORIENTAL REGION: one of the main zoo-geographical divisions of the Earth (see DISTRIBUTION, GEOGRAPHICAL) ; also known as the Indian Region, although that adjective is better retained for the sub-region covering the greater part of continental and peninsular India, with Ceylon.

Boundaries. The Oriental Region lies mainly between 68° and 135° E. long. and between 10° S. and 32° N. lat., therefore largely within the tropics. Its northern boundary, dividing it from the Palae-

arctic Region, runs from the Hindu Kush Mountains in the west along the entire length of the Himalaya, and farther east to include Yunnan and Szechuan. It continues roughly south of the basin of the Yangtze Kiang to form an indeterminate frontier with the Manchurian Subregion of the Palaearctic till it reaches the East China Sea in the neighbourhood of Ning-po in ca. 30° N. lat. From its western extremity the boundary trends south-west, excluding Afghanistan and Baluchistan, and may conveniently be taken as the valley of the Indus down to its mouth near Karachi in West Pakistan.

South of the Asiatic mainland, the Oriental Region includes the continental islands of Formosa and Hainan as well as the greater part of the Indonesian Archipelago, the Philippines, Borneo, the Celebes, and the Greater and Lesser Sunda Islands east to Timor. There are curious clear-cut divisions as well as close intermingling between the characteristic Oriental and Australian faunas on many of the islands in this area, and the line of demarcation from the Australasian Region is not easy. In the last eighty years or so, since Wallace first postulated the boundary between the islands with a mainly Indo-Malayan fauna and those with the Australo-Papuan type, a succession of investigators (including many ornithologists) have conducted intensive faunal studies on the islands to determine their correct biogeographical status. The demarcation originally proposed by Wallace—' Wallace's Line ' as Huxley named it—on the basis of the presence or absence of certain typical bird and other animal groups of the Oriental and Australasian Regions at first enjoyed a wide measure of acceptance from zoologists on account of the truly remarkable examples of clear-cut divergence which it showed, e.g. as between the islands of Bali and Lombok, separated by a deep and narrow strait (only 15–20 miles wide), and as between Borneo and Celebes. Many dominant Oriental bird groups, e.g. the barbets (Capitonidae), range as far east as Bali and then suddenly break off, being completely absent from Lombok and beyond. Woodpeckers (Picidae), abundant in the Oriental Region as far east as Borneo, Java, and Bali, are very poorly represented (by only 4 or 5 species) in Lombok, Celebes, and eastward up to the Moluccas, being absent over the rest of the Australasian Region. On the other hand, many typically Australian groups, e.g. honeyeaters (Meliphagidae) and cockatoos (Kakatoeinae), reach westward as far as Lombok, but there end abruptly. The faunal differences on the opposite sides of the Strait of Macassar, between Borneo and Celebes, are superficially even more striking ; they are not confined to birds but extend to mammals and other animal groups.

The line, as postulated by Wallace, passed between Bali and Lombok in a north-easterly direction, through the Macassar Strait separating Celebes from Borneo, and then on ENE. between Mindanao and Sangi Islands, passing west of the Marianas or Ladrones group. Huxley's proposed modification, by drawing it north from the Macassar Strait to pass between Palawan and Mindoro Islands, excluded the Philippines from the Indo-Malayan Subregion.

On statistical analyses of the extensive data accumulated by investigators since Wallace's time, on a percentage basis of typically Oriental and typically Australasian faunal elements present or absent on the various islands, it was realised that a more rational boundary between the two regions would be one that showed a faunal balance, i.e. with the Oriental and Australasian elements in more or less equal proportions. A line of this nature can of course be only arbitrary, since the 50:50 balance does not hold good for all taxonomic groups. Such a line of faunal balance between the Oriental and Australasian faunas was first demonstrated by Weber, in 1902, to exist much farther east than Wallace's Line. As modified by subsequent investigations, Weber's Line runs roughly along the Molucca Passage between Celebes and the northern Moluccas, southward between Sulu Islands in the west and Obi Islands in the east, swings west of Buru, and, leaving Timorlaut Islands on its east, curves WSW. along the edge of the Sahul Shelf to include Timor in the Indo-Malayan Subregion. Thus, on consensus of current view, all the islands in the intermediate zone between Wallace's Line and its eastern counterpart —the 'Wallacea' of some zoologists—belong to the Indo-Malayan Subregion.

Characteristic Groups. One bird family is peculiar to the Oriental Region, the leaf birds (Irenidae), and is in fact confined chiefly to the Indo-Chinese Subregion. The Oriental Region shares with the Ethiopian Region, either exclusively or overwhelmingly, the passerine families Eurylaimidae, Pycnonotidae, Nectariniidae, and Ploceidae. The typical Ethiopian family of the honeyguides (Indicatoridae) is represented here (but in no other region) by the common genus *Indicator*. Many genera, e.g. *Harpactes* (Trogonidae), *Nyctiornis* (Meropidae), *Psittacula* and *Loriculus* (Psittacidae), *Acridotheres* and *Gracula* (Sturnidae), and *Pericrocotus* (Campephagidae), are confined to it and do not occur at all outside its limits. The family Phasianidae is particularly well developed in the Oriental Region, the spectacular genera *Pavo*, *Gallus*, *Lophura*, *Pucrasia*, *Catreus*, *Argusianus*, *Polyplectron*, and *Rollulus* being peculiar to it.

Subregions. The region is readily divisible into the following three main subregions upon the general spectrum of their avifauna and other animal groups:

1. The Indo-Chinese Subregion (='Himalo-Chinese' of Elwes and Blanford)
2. The Indo-Malayan or Malaysian Subregion (='Malayan' of above authors)
3. The Indian Subregion

The first two are essentially very similar in regard to their physiography, being covered largely with tropical and subtropical vegetation, the result of heavy monsoon rainfall and high humidity. Nevertheless, they each exhibit marked peculiarities in many of their plant and animal manifestations, the first subregion showing an affinity with the Palaearctic in its temperate zone forms, e.g. the Fringillidae, while the second possesses elements with distinctly Australo-Papuan affiliations.

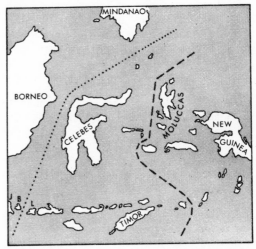

Transitional zone at boundary with the Australasian Region. The classical Wallace's Line (dots) approximates to the western limit of this zone—**J** = Java (part), **B** = Bali, **L** = Lombok ; Weber's Line (dashes) represents its median, where the two faunas are more nearly balanced. The islands between Wallace's Line and New Guinea are sometimes collectively termed 'Wallacea'.

The Indo-Chinese Subregion. This includes the southern aspect of the entire Himalayan Range (up to the tree-line—9000 to 12000 feet elevation), particularly the section that lies east of the Arun-Kosi River in eastern Nepal. Beyond, its boundary extends into north-western and eastern China, marching with the Palaearctic Region. Many typically eastern genera, e.g. *Paradoxornis*, terminate in Sikkim and Nepal, but the avifauna of the Himalaya westward of the division indicated retains its overall Indo-Chinese character in diminishing degree. This tendency is well illustrated by many other timaliine genera, e.g. *Garrulax*, abundantly represented in Yunnan and the eastern Himalaya, but sparsely in the western.

Besides the Himalaya, this subregion includes Assam, Burma, Thailand, and Indo-China (Vietnam), i.e. the entire portion of the Oriental Region lying on the Asiatic mainland east of the Ganges delta, with the exception of the Malay Peninsula. It also includes the islands of the Andamans group, as well as Formosa and Hainan.

The Indo-Malayan or Malaysian Subregion. This lies for the most part within a tropical belt 10 degrees on either side of the Equator and includes the Malay Peninsula south of the Isthmus of Kra, together with all the islands of the Archipelago west of Weber's Line. The Nicobar Islands, off the western tip of Sumatra, show closer avifaunal affinities with this subregion than with the Andamans, which are spatially nearer to Burma. This subregion is more exclusively tropical and forested than either of the others. Its avifauna lacks all traces of Ethiopian affinities, so noticeable in the Indian Subregion. It also lacks temperate zone forms of the Himalaya with Palaearctic affiliations, such as the rose finches (Fringillidae).

The Indian Subregion. This stretches southward from the foot of the Himalaya to include the entire peninsula and Ceylon. Its western boundary is that of the Oriental Region—the Indus Valley—while on the east the deltas of the Ganges and Brahmaputra rivers demarcate it from the Indo-Chinese Subregion. Two clear-cut 'provinces' are recognisable which, for convenience, may be termed

(*a*) The Peninsular Province, covering all India and Ceylon except the portions under (*b*);

(*b*) The South-western Province, the tropical humid, heavy-rainfall zone commencing at the northern extremity of the Western Ghats in Khandesh and the Surat Dangs, but more properly south from about Goa (ca. 15° 30′ N. lat.) including western Mysore, the Nilgiri and Palni Hills, and Kerala, together with its virtual extension in south-western Ceylon—the so-called 'Low-country Wet' and 'Central Hill' zones.

The avifaunal character of the Peninsular Province is largely Palaearctic and Ethiopian. A typical example of the latter is the cursorid genus *Rhinoptilus* (sometimes merged in *Cursorius*) with several species in Africa but only a single one, *R. bitorquatus*, in peninsular India. There is an almost complete absence of characteristic east-oriental genera of birds in this province, as there also is in the Ethiopian Region.

The South-western Province, although much smaller, is one of the most interesting areas, from the biogeographical point of view, by virtue of the very striking similarities and parallelisms its fauna and flora exhibit with those of the far-flung Indo-Chinese and Malaysian subregions. It constitutes the western terminal of what is known as the 'Indo-Malayan Arc' or 'Horseshoe' of animal distribution: Malaya–Burma–eastern Himalaya–Ceylon. Several typical sedentary birds inhabiting its two extremities (e.g. *Chrysocolaptes lucidus*, *Buceros bicornis*) are morphologically inseparable, even at subspecific level. These remarkable 'relict populations' of south-western India, now cut off from their nearest neighbours in the Himalaya by 1000 to 1500 miles, have received special attention from zoologists in recent years. Much interest has been aroused by the very attractive 'Satpura hypothesis' of the Indian zoologist, S. L. Hora, which seeks to explain the history, route, and mechanics by which freshwater hill-stream fishes, and other specialised hygrophilous fauna of the Indo-Chinese Subregion, reached Travancore and Ceylon. This hypothesis postulates a once continuous mountain trend from the eastern Himalaya and Garo Hills, across peninsular India over the Rajmahal Hills and the Satpura Mountains, and then southward over the Sahyadris or Western Ghats to Kerala and Ceylon. Ceylon, which was alternately joined to and separated from peninsular India during various geological epochs, bears evidence of having received distributional faunal waves from the mainland. Under periods of prolonged isolation, many endemic races (or species, as some ornithologists consider them) have developed on the island.

The avifauna of the humid South-western Province contains one monotypical muscicapine genus, *Ochromela*, peculiar to its mainland section. Numerous examples can be cited of birds not occurring in the adjoining Peninsular Province, but having close affinity, or even identity, with forms living in the eastern Himalaya and in the Indo-Chinese and Indo-Malayan Subregions generally. Prominent among such are laughing thrushes *Garrulax* spp., Fairy Bluebird *Irena puella*, woodpeckers of the genera *Dinopium*, *Hemicircus*, *Dryocopus*, and *Picumnus*, Great Hornbill *Buceros bicornis*, spinetail swifts *Chaetura* spp., Broadbilled Roller *Eurystomus orientalis*, Malabar Trogon *Harpactes fasciatus*, Frogmouth *Batrachostomus moniliger*, and the falconid genus *Aviceda*. Some of these birds, e.g. *Dryocopus*, *Hemicircus*, *Picumnus*, *Buceros*, curiously enough, are not found in Ceylon : the complete absence of vultures *Gyps* spp., so common and abundant on the Indian mainland, is another anomaly not easily explained considering the powerful flight and far-ranging capabilities of these birds.

S.A.

Zoogeographical references

Abdulali, Humayun. 1949. Some peculiarities of avifaunal distribution in peninsular India. Proc. Natl. Inst. Sci. India 15 : 387–393.

Ali, Sálim. 1949. The Satpura Trend as an ornithogeographical highway. Proc. Natl. Inst. Sci. India 15 : 379–386.

Blanford, W. T. 1901. The distribution of vertebrate animals in India, Ceylon, and Burma. Phil. Trans. Roy. Soc. 194 : 335–436.

Mayr, E. 1944. Wallace's Line in the light of recent zoogeographical studies. Quart. Rev. Biol. 19 : 1–14.

Rensch, B. 1936. Die Geschichte des Sundabogens. Eine tiergeographische Untersuchung. Berlin.

Ripley, S. D. 1959. Zoogeographical considerations in the Indian avifauna. J. Bombay Nat. Hist. Soc. 56 : 72–81.

Scrivenor, J. B. 1942. Review of a symposium on the biogeographic division of the Indo-Australian Archipelago. Nature 149 : 556–557.

Stresemann, E. 1939. Die Vögel von Celebes. Zoogeographie. J. Orn. 87 : 312–425.

Faunistic Works

Ali, Sálim. 1941 (and later editions). The Book of Indian Birds. Bombay.

Ali, Sálim. 1962. Birds of Sikkim. Madras.

Baker, E. C. Stuart. 1922–30. The Fauna of British India, including Ceylon and Burma. Birds. 8 vols. London.

Deignan, H. G. 1945. The birds of Northern Thailand. Bull. U.S. Natl. Mus. no. 186 : 1–615.

Delacour, J. 1947. The Birds of Malaysia. New York.

Delacour, J. & Jabouille, P. 1931. Les Oiseaux de l'Indochine française. 4 vols. Paris.

Delacour, J. & Mayr, E. 1946. Birds of the Philippines. New York.

Gibson-Hill, C. A. 1949. An annotated Check-List of the Birds of Malaya. Bull. Raffles Mus. Singapore no. 20 : 1–300.

Hachisuka, M. 1931–35. The Birds of the Philippine Islands. 4 vols. London.

Henry, G. M. 1955. A Guide to the Birds of Ceylon. London.

Herklots, G. A. C. 1946 (and later edition). The Birds of Hong Kong. Hong Kong.

La Touche, J. D. D. 1925–34. Birds of Eastern China. 2 vols. London.

Phillips, W. W. A. 1953. Revised Check-List of the Birds of Ceylon. Colombo.

Ripley, S. D. 1961. A Synopsis of the Birds of India and Pakistan, together with those of Nepal, Sikkim, Bhutan, and Ceylon. Bombay.

Smythies, B. E. 1953. The Birds of Burma. 2nd ed. Edinburgh.

Smythies, B. E. 1960. The Birds of Borneo. Edinburgh.

Whistler, H. 1923. Popular Handbook of Indian Birds. London. (4th ed., revised N. B. Kinnear, 1949.)

ORIENTATION : see NAVIGATION ; also HEARING AND BALANCE

ORIGIN OF BIRDS : the evolution of birds as a class from some ancestral form of animal (see EVOLUTION). On this there is little direct evidence from fossils, as we have no continuous series of transitional forms such as exists for certain other classes of animals. Our knowledge, or our estimation, of how this particular evolution was accomplished must rest mainly on deduction made from three fixed points from which we can work backwards. These points are the three specimens of *Archaeopteryx* that have been discovered in the last hundred years, and the reader should consult the separate article upon that bird (see ARCHAEOPTERYX). This is essential, because it is upon the characters of the skeleton of that primitive bird, the earliest that the geological record has revealed, that we must base our initial deductions.

Despite its feathers and its wings, formed on a plan that still exists, *Archaeopteryx* was an anomaly ; although it looked like a bird, its skeleton was that of a reptile. If this seems to be odd, let us consider a modern bird. It has a toothless bill or beak ; *Archaeopteryx* had reptilian jaws and well-developed teeth. The modern bird has a few short tufted feathers that serve as a tail ; *Archaeopteryx* had a long reptilian tail with twenty vertebrae, even if on the outside there was a pair of feathers at the level of each vertebra. Then the breathing and heat-control systems of modern birds call for many air spaces in the body, and even the limb bones are hollow and have thin walls (see HEAT REGULATION ; PNEUMATICITY OF BONE ; RESPIRATORY SYSTEM ; SKELETON). All the bones of every specimen of *Archaeopteryx* are more or less solid and quite like the bones of reptiles.

In brief, if *Archaeopteryx* had been discovered without the imprint of its wings and feathers it could have been classified without much difficulty as a reptile ; and, as a matter of fact, it was. Now, this can be interpreted as meaning that the relations between birds and reptiles in ancient days were very close, and that birds are very probably descended from a reptilian ancestor. If this is true, we must ask from what kind of reptiles they can have come ; and if we analyse the reptilian characters of *Archaeopteryx* we are able to get some clues.

The skull of *Archaeopteryx* is small and has a large socket for the eye. In front of each eye is a long opening in the skull ; and behind each eye, and separated from it by a bar of bone (the postorbital), are another two openings in the skull, one on top and the other on the side. Now, these openings are very important to the student of fossils, for they at once suggest that this skull is 'diapsid' (two-arched) and that it is therefore related to the skulls of the pterodactyls (flying reptiles), the crocodiles, and the dinosaurs ; but, of course, they do not imply that it is from one of these kinds of animals that birds have come. It has already been said that the jaws of *Archaeopteryx* are unlike those of any other kind of bird in having small and sharp teeth. Then again, if we look at the backbone of the primitive bird we see that each of the vertebrae has flat-faced ends, like those of many reptiles but quite unlike those of any other bird, living or extinct, where the vertebrae have saddle-shaped ends. Similarly the lower leg bones (tibia and fibula) are as in reptiles and not as in birds. We can fit these reptilian characters too into the subclass that contains the dinosaurs, crocodiles, and flying reptiles.

The problem then is to find a small reptile, about the size of a crow *Corvus* sp., that was able to walk or run mainly on its hind legs but that must have had quite well-developed front legs as well, for birds have strong fore limbs covered by their feathers. Clearly the crocodiles do not seem likely to be the answer, for although there have been many small and streamlined species of crocodile, their sprawling gait is quite unlike what we require. Pterodactyls were reptilian gliders with a certain capacity for flight, so much so that their limbs were hollow like those of modern birds, but the proportions of their limb bones were quite unlike those of *Archaeopteryx* or the ancestral reptile that we are seeking. Dinosaurs were land-living reptiles often of great size, but many of them were small and able to run swiftly and gracefully on their hind legs ; some, indeed, were able to run or walk along the branches of trees. But dinosaurs have in their history lost certain shoulder bones that all birds retain, so that a dinosaur ancestry is not possible.

The closest similarities of all between *Archaeopteryx* and reptiles, whether in general characters or in size, lie in a small group of extinct reptiles known as Thecodonts. They too are Archosaurs, the overall group that includes the dinosaurs, crocodiles, and pterodactyls. The name Thecodont means 'teeth in sockets' and it can be seen that the Thecodont skeleton contains many primitive features that have been lost in the other groups mentioned ; and that they have a general skeleton plan from which, after some important changes, the skeleton of *Archaeopteryx* could undoubtedly be derived.

Amongst the Thecodonts there is a group of small bipedal reptiles called the Pseudosuchia which lived in the Triassic geological period (about 225 million years ago) in Scotland, in Germany, and in South Africa (so far as the record shows). Even by that time they were becoming specialised, and it may well be that it is even among their ancestors, of Permian age, that the original bird ancestor may be found. Certainly the skulls of these reptiles bear all the characters seen later in birds in modified form. The accompanying text figure shows the skull of a Pseudosuchian *Euparkeria capensis*, from the Triassic of South Africa. From this it is seen that the principal differences are in the height of the snout

of the reptile, its stronger jaws, and the smaller size of the eye socket. It can also be inferred from the bulk of the back of the two skulls that *Archaeopteryx* had a larger brain. It is really a question of proportion, for all the same bony elements are there. How could this modification come about ?

Whether the origin of the birds is to be sought in a Triassic Pseudosuchian or in the Permian ancestors of these must remain for the time being an unsettled question ; but what is perfectly clear is that, over 200 million years ago, there were a considerable number of small bipedal reptiles of the *Euparkeria*

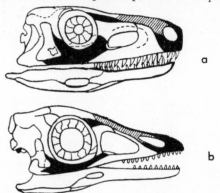

Skulls of (**a**) the fossil reptile *Euparkeria capensis* and (**b**) *Archaeopteryx*. Dark areas are the premaxilla and the lacrimal and jugal bones ; the nasals are diagonally shaded.

kind about, living in daily contact with a great many related forms and, of course, among other reptiles of small and large size. In other words, there must have been a good deal of competition for both food and space. The situation is not unique ; it had

---

Plate 33 · Nesting—Special Adaptations

a *Upper :* Grey Hornbills *Tockus birostris*—male visiting the nesting hole where the female is walled in (India). The female's bill can just be seen in the inner opening, which is the slit-entrance to the nest chamber through the mud wall built by the bird. *Phot. Christina Loke.*

b *Lower :* Mallee-fowl (or Lowan) *Leipoa ocellata*—pair at mound (Australia). As in other megapode species, the eggs are incubated by the heat engendered inside the mound. In this photograph the male, which usually does all the work on the mound, is testing the temperature of the egg-chamber ; the female stands on the top of the mound, waiting to lay another egg. *Phot. R. P. Cooper*

(See articles NEST ; HORNBILL ; MEGAPODE)

occurred before and has been seen since, so the reactions of the animal populations can be judged with some assurance.

If one of these kinds was, therefore, by accident attracted to the temporary shelter of the trees, then quite considerable benefits might have been achieved. There would be some greater amount of safety from enemies and the trees would, on the other hand, yield to them a new source of food, mainly of insects. The teeth in the Pseudosuchians are undoubtedly those of carnivores, but the animals were small, and they were reptiles, and therefore the quantity of food that must have been consumed daily cannot be calculated on mammalian levels ; it would be much less than that required for mammalian insectivores of the present day.

Adaptation to an insect diet would therefore seem, in the circumstances of less competition, to have given them adequate food ; but this diet would be less demanding on the jaws. To catch and eat insects, even of large size, would need less teeth and less heavily developed muscles than the animals already possessed. This would lead progressively, and no doubt slowly, to a reduction in the number of the teeth, to a consequent shortening of the jaw muscles, and all these are among the changes that we can see have already taken place in *Archaeopteryx*.

Living in trees, however, imposes other demands and so makes for other secondary changes. Compared with the ground, the branches move and trunks may sway, so emphasis is placed on firmness

---

Plate 34 · Nesting Sites

Examples of tree nesting, cliff nesting, ground nesting, and aquatic nesting.

a *Upper left :* Kittiwakes *Larus tridactylus* at their nests on precipitous coastal cliffs (Scotland). A chick is visible in the upper nest.
        Phot. A. Landsborough Thomson (1912).

b *Upper right :* Martial Eagles *Polemaetus bellicosus* at their nest in a tall tree (Southern Rhodesia). The nest is a bulky affair of sticks. The photograph shows a pair, male on right, with a youngster between.   *Phot. Peter Steyn.*

c *Lower left :* Spur-winged Plover *Vanellus spinosus* at nest-scrape in sandy soil (Greece). The usual four eggs, cryptically coloured, are visible.
        Phot. Ilse Makatsch.

d *Lower right :* Black-necked Grebe *Podiceps nigricollis* on its floating nest of gathered vegetation etc. (Denmark).   *Phot. C. C. Doncaster.*

(See articles NEST ; GULL ; HAWK ; PLOVER (1) ; GREBE.)

---

of grasp, which means a gradual adaptation of hands and feet to meet the new situation. To gauge movement and to judge the distances involved in catching prey and, perhaps, in moving or jumping from branch to branch, needs great precision of perception. Tree-living animals thus show in due course an evolution of association between hand and eye that means an increase in the visual sense and an enlargement in the brain receptor areas that deal with vision and with locomotion. And this again is precisely what is seen in the skull of *Archaeopteryx* as compared with that of *Euparkeria*. Looking again at the illustration it can be seen that the eye of the bird is about one-quarter larger in diameter than that of the reptile.

It can be assumed that in these circumstances the use of the eye was greater than the use of the sense of smell, with the result once more that the olfactory region of the snout decreases. This too can be seen and results in the reduction of the upper part of the reptilian snout and in the concave upper surface of the *Archaeopteryx* bill, so that in that bird the height of the hinder part of the skull is almost three times that of the snout at the level of the front of the pre-orbital foramen. In the reptile the same forward region of the snout is about two-thirds that of the hinder measurement.

These important facts, although apparently demonstrable and logical, give by no means the whole story. It is a far cry from the reptile on the tree-branch to the bird with wings. How the wings arose is a matter of conjecture but one, none the less, on which there is some evidence in other groups, including the evolution of the primates. From this it is clear that the continued necessity of use of the limbs for balance in the trees and for movement tends to develop the arms into powerful and muscular aids, and the legs as slim and efficient organs. When the reptile was well established in the trees, it must have found it attractive, and perhaps necessary for its safety, to jump from branch to branch. In living reptiles and mammals this is often aided by lines of scales or folds of skin lying along the body and controlled in tension by the limbs. Similarly it may be thought that the arboreal reptile would extend its arms as it jumped, and that there would be in time a selective advantage in the possession of some longer scales along the hinder edge of the fore limbs, along the body, and along one side of the hind limbs.

Now, the reptile had scales, but at least one of the Pseudosuchians had a feather pattern almost stamped on the surface of its scales. Chemically we know that scales and feathers are similar, but how does a scale become a feather ? To that question there is no answer unless we put forward the theory that, after some long experience in the trees, the ancient reptile, like its distant relatives the pterodactyls and the more distant descendants the modern birds, may have become warm-blooded (see HEAT REGULATION). There are good reasons why this should be so. Increased activity, with a higher respiration rate for longer periods of time than would have been necessary on the ground, may have started the process ; and while this of itself would not have changed scale to feather, the incubation of eggs by warmer-blooded reptiles might have caused the necessary genetic change that would be of enormous selection value to the creature.

Thus the origin of a bird such as *Archaeopteryx*, which was not a fully developed flyer, from a Pseudosuchian reptile can logically be deduced. As yet there are no fossil remains of this progenitor ; nor is it clear at what precise geological time the change took place, whether in the late Permian or in the Trias, although more probably it was in the latter period. As can be seen in the article on FOSSIL BIRDS, *Archaeopteryx* is a milestone on a very dark road, with blankness for millions of years before and after it. One day, however, the evidence will be found. **W.E.S.**

Heilmann, G. 1926. The Origin of Birds. London.
Swinton, W. E. 1960. The origin of birds. *In* Marshall, A. J. (ed.). Biology and Comparative Physiology of Birds vol. 1. New York and London.
(See also under ARCHAEOPTERYX ; FOSSIL BIRDS.)

ORIOLE (1): substantive name of most species of Oriolidae (Passeriformes, suborder Oscines) ; in the plural, and in an Old World context, general term for the family. This is a remarkably homogeneous group of about 28 species, typically tropical, and extending from the extremities of Africa (not in Madagascar, unless *Tylas* be included) across Asia, the Philippines, and Malaysia to New Guinea and Australia (not New Zealand), but with one species, the well-known Golden Oriole *Oriolus oriolus*, ranging right across the southern Palaearctic Region as well as into India. Speciation has been most active in the eastern quarter of the family's range, where there are so many islands.

As a whole the orioles, which are placed in the systematic list between the drongos (Dicruridae) and the crows (Corvidae), do not have striking peculiarities. They are robust birds ranging in size from about that of a Starling *Sturnus vulgaris* to that of a Jay *Garrulus glandarius*, with strongly decurved bills. The wings are long and pointed ; the tails, consisting of twelve feathers, are slightly shorter. All the species are exclusively arboreal, feeding on insects and fruit, and most of them inhabit evergreen forest.

The Golden Oriole, 5 closely related African

Black Oriole *Oriolus hosii*, of Borneo. *C.E.T.K.*

species, and others of the Oriental Region, have their plumage patterned brilliant yellow and black. One species, *O. chlorocephalus*, limited to a few montane forests in eastern Africa, shows the unique combination of clear yellow and rich olive-green. The two Australian species are much duller, greenish, and streaky. Several Malaysian species are predominantly black, with patches of rich crimson ; and *O. hosii* of Borneo is completely black except for chestnut under tail coverts. As a rule, those orioles that have yellow pigment in the plumage have bills coloured a peculiar dull red, while those with crimson in the plumage have the bills horn-coloured or bluish. Only 4 species of the Oriolidae, in the area Timor–New Guinea–Australia, are currently separated from the genus *Oriolus* ; these constitute the genus *Sphecotheres*, distinguished mainly by bare skin round the eye and an exceptionally short bill. Throughout the family the females are, with very few exceptions, duller or more streaked—or both—than the males.

The orioles provide some typical examples of evolution in small islands. *O. crassirostris* of São Tomé in the Gulf of Guinea has lost most of the brilliant yellow so prominent in the African species from which it must have been derived, and it has an abnormally short and rounded wing. In the Moluccas, *O. bouroensis* and its relatives have lost both black and lipochrome to such an extent that they have become dull brownish birds (see MIMICRY).

Certain features of the voice are exceedingly widespread in the family, namely on the one hand peculiarly sweet, fluting and liquid songs and calls—the French name 'loriot' pronounced with guttural 'r' is good onomatapoeia—and on the other hand a peculiarly harsh growling or bleating note.

The nest is generally a deep and closely woven structure in a fork high above the ground, beard lichen being a favourite material where it is available ; but the nests of *Sphecotheres* differ in being exceptionally flimsy. The eggs are handsome, with rich dark blotches on a buff or nearly white ground.

Those species that do not inhabit evergreen forest are migratory in various degrees, above all the Golden Oriole of the Palaearctic, for it winters exclusively south of the Sahara. It is well known for its predilection for figs as it passes through the Mediterranean basin—compare the common name of ' figbird ' for the Australian *Sphecotheres* spp.

Very little detailed study has been made of the orioles, which for the most part are shy and difficult to observe, but of the European bird it is known that care of the eggs and young is shared by both parents. The nests and eggs of several species remain to be described.

See Plate 17 (colour).   R.E.M.

Greenway, J. C., Jr. 1962. Family Oriolidae. *In* Mayr, E. & Greenway, J. C., Jr. (eds.). Check-list of Birds of the World vol. 15. Cambridge, Mass.

ORIOLE (2): substantive name of *Icterus* spp. ; in the plural form ' American orioles ', general term for the family Icteridae (Passeriformes, suborder Oscines). This New World assemblage of nine-primaried song-birds is derived from emberizine stock and forms a remarkably heterogeneous family that includes such diverse natural groups as the oropendolas, caciques, grackles, American blackbirds, true American orioles or troupials, cowbirds, and meadowlarks.

General Characters. The 87 species differ considerably in size (6½–21 inches long), but all have conical bills that may be variable in proportions although never much longer than the head. The bill is unnotched and usually pointed ; rictal bristles are usually lacking, otherwise obsolescent. In some of the larger forms, notably oropendolas and caciques, the culmen is expanded or swollen basally to form a conspicuous frontal shield or casque. The plumage may be wholly black, the predominant family colour, but in many species the basic colour is conspicuously patterned with various shades of brown, red, or yellow. Streaking is relatively uncommon, often limited to the female, and found chiefly in savanna or marsh dwellers such as meadowlarks *Sturnella* spp., the Bobolink *Dolichonyx oryzivorus*, certain blackbirds *Agelaius* spp., and military starlings or ' marsh-birds ' (*Pezites*, *Leistes*). Sexual dimorphism in colour is the rule, the most pronounced examples being among the northern migratory species ; the Bobolink, which has the

longest migration of any, also undergoes drastic seasonal changes of plumage. Sexual dimorphism may also be expressed in size, the males of oropendolas, caciques, and various grackles being conspicuously larger than the females.

Troupial *Icterus icterus*, of South America (New World oriole family). *C.E.T.K.*

Distribution. American orioles are best represented in the tropics, especially at lower altitudes, but several genera are confined to temperate regions, and one species, the Rusty Blackbird *Euphagus carolinus*, ranges to within the Arctic Circle. Most of the species that breed in higher latitudes, whether of the north or the south, perform seasonal migrations ; the most noteworthy is that of the Bobolink, which nests in Canada and the northern United States but winters in South America as far as northern Argentina. The tropical species are non-migratory, but after the breeding season may have local movements of greater or lesser extent, their temporary presence or absence in a given area being dictated principally by the availability of suitable food. As a group, the Icteridae are highly adaptable, and virtually every type of habitat in the New World suitable for land birds is occupied by several or many forms. Humid tropical forests are inhabited by the greatest variety of species ; some are essentially terrestrial, or at least feed on the ground, and others seldom leave the forest crown. Temperate forests, prairie grasslands, fresh-water and salt-water marshes, and deserts also support orioles of varying degrees of specialisation.

Feeding Habits. The remarkable adaptability of the Icteridae—exceeded by few avian families—is perhaps best shown by the diversity of their habits, social organisation, and nest construction. Their food includes both plant and animal matter, the relative percentages varying with the species and to some extent with the season. Most nearly omnivorous are the grackles, some of which prey on small vertebrates in addition to consuming quantities of insects, seeds, and fruit ; in at least one genus, *Quiscalus*, specialised jaw musculature and a slight keel within the upper mandible aid in the opening of nuts. The various cowbirds (*Molothrus, Tangavius, Scaphidura*) feed mainly on insects and seeds found on or near the ground, and also commonly pluck ticks from the backs of cattle. Most arboreal icterids, such as oropendolas, caciques, and typical orioles or troupials *Icterus* spp., are essentially fruit-eaters and nectar-sippers, but may supplement this diet with insects and other animal life. Blackbirds, grackles, and cowbirds customarily forage on the ground, as do meadowlarks and the Bobolink, and some (*Dives, Cassidix, Scaphidura* ('*Psomocolax*')) use their bills for turning over stones in their search for food.

Voice. Orioles have marked vocal abilities, and some, such as oropendolas, have repertoires that include a variety of calls ranging from harsh to gurgling, liquid, and flute-like notes. Among tropical species especially, the females' song may be scarcely inferior to that of the male. Birds of drab as well as of brilliant plumage are numbered among the more gifted musicians, which include such outstanding songsters as the Yellow-rumped Cacique *Cacicus cela*, the Spot-breasted Oriole *Icterus pectoralis*, the Troupial *I. icterus*, and the Melodious Blackbird *Dives dives*. Flight-songs are exceptional, but the Bobolink and Military Starling, of North America and South America respectively, commonly sing while engaged in courtship flight.

Social Organisation and Breeding. Diversity of social organisation is one of the most notable characteristics of the American orioles. Some species are conspicuously gregarious at all seasons and others solitary in habits. Many nest in colonies and others spend the breeding season as isolated pairs. Winter flocking is common although not universal. The prevalence of polygamy is marked, especially among the colonial-nesting oropendolas, caciques, and grackles ; but many genera (*Amblycercus, Dives, Icterus, Sturnella, Dolichonyx*) are normally monogamous and others, such as the cowbirds, promiscuous. The practice of polygamy may be either habitual or occasional, the determining factor with some species being the sex-ratio in the colony at a given time. Imbalance of sexes may also occasionally result in polyandry, a relationship that has been noted in the normally promiscuous cowbirds (see POLYGAMY ; POLYANDRY).

Nest parasitism is the rule with the cowbirds, the majority preparing no nest of their own but instead habitually dropping their eggs in the nests of other birds destined to become foster-parents (see PARASITISM). The sole exception is the monogamous Bay-winged Cowbird *Molothrus badius* of South America, which pairs for the breeding season and either appropriates the occupied or abandoned nest of another species or, occasionally, builds a nest of its own. Nest parasitism may be either highly selective or essentially an action of random opportunism ; examples of the former are the Screaming Cowbird *Molothrus rufoaxillaris*, which apparently victimises only the Bay-winged Cowbird, and the Giant Cowbird *Scaphidura oryzivorus*, which limits its attention to the colonial-nesting oropendolas and caciques. (See Plate 46a (phot.).)

Among the parasitic cowbirds there is scant evidence of species selectivity, but birds of the same or of smaller size are most frequently victimised. However, in a recent study it was found that the Brownheaded Cowbird *M. ater* of North America often selects its intended victim in advance and may furtively watch the nest building over a period of days. The cowbird delays depositing its egg until at least one host-egg has been laid, but if a nest contains several host-eggs all but one may be removed by the interloper. Usually the cowbird eggs hatch before those of the host, but the legitimate young are often fledged successfully unless unable to compete for food while at a critical age.

The nests of icterids are among the most diversified of any avian family, and all manner of sites are utilised. Essentially terrestrial species, such as the Bobolink and the meadowlarks, make relatively simple nests on the ground in grassy fields where they are well concealed by vegetation and, in the case of the meadowlarks, further camouflaged by a hood of grass stems. Many grackles and blackbirds prefer to nest in shrubs or thickets ; their bulky nests of interwoven twigs usually have cuplike centres plastered with mud and lined with rootlets or plant fibres. The marsh-dwelling blackbirds (*Agelaius, Xanthocephalus*, etc.) customarily attach their compact, open-cupped nests to reeds or cat-tails one to several feet above water, where they are safe from most predators. Some orioles suspend their woven sack-like nests beneath broad leaves, and the nests of others are hung conspicuously from the topmost branches of towering forest trees. Largest and most spectacular of all are the beautifully woven pensile nests of the polygamous fruit-eaters, such as oropendolas and caciques ; a single colony may include one hundred or more dangling nests that measure up to 6 feet in length (*Gymnostinops*) and are among the most memorable sights of tropical America.

Among orioles virtually all family responsibilities

are assumed by the female alone. After mating, the male's principal role is usually guardian of the nest site, but in some species he assists in feeding the young. Generally the nest is made exclusively by the female; but nest building is a joint undertaking with Melodious Blackbirds, and the male Bay-winged Cowbird is largely responsible for the nest when one is made. Although successive broods may be raised in the same nest—a rarity—icterids seldom use the nest of a previous year, even the most elaborate structures generally being abandoned after a single season.

The eggs of the Icteridae are almost white, or various shades of green or blue, and usually spotted, blotched, or scrawled with black, brown, or reddish. A clutch of 2–3 eggs is characteristic of tropical species, but orioles of temperate latitudes normally lay 4–6 eggs, and occasionally as many as 8. Incubation is performed exclusively by the female, the periods ranging from 11 to 14 days. The nestlings are apparently brooded only by the female, and in the majority of species she alone cares for the young. Nestling periods vary from a minimum of about 9 days for the Brown-headed Cowbird *Molothrus ater* to as much as 37 days for the larger oropendolas. E.R.B.

Bent, A. C. 1958. Life History of North American Blackbirds, Orioles, Tanagers, and Allies. U.S. Natl. Mus. Bull. 211.
Hellmayr, C. E. 1937. Catalogue of Birds of the Americas and the Adjacent Islands. Fieldiana 13: pt. 10, Icteridae.
Orians, G. H. 1961. The ecology of blackbird (*Agelaius*) social systems. Ecol. Monog. 31: 285–312.
Skutch, A. F. 1954. Life histories of Central American birds. Pt. 1. Pacific Coast Avifauna no. 31. Berkeley, Cal.
Selander, R. K. & Giller, D. R. 1961. Analysis of sympatry of Great-tailed and Boat-tailed Grackles. Condor 63: 29–86.

ORIOLIDAE: a family of the Passeriformes, suborder Oscines (see ORIOLE (1)).

ORNAMENTATION, BIRDS IN HUMAN: mainly in respect of their plumage. There are few peoples in the world who never use birds for ornamentation, and very many who once used them freely even if they no longer do so. Although wild birds' plumes are out of favour for European ladies, a man's hatband in Britain or Bavaria may still sport a flash of blue Jay *Garrulus glandarius* ('vermin') or Mallard *Anas platyrhynchos* ('game'). In the less clothed and hotter countries of the world, feathers often play a considerable role in daily—and especially in ritual—dress. In parts of central New Guinea it is not always easy to tell whether the object approaching you along the trail is a taxidermic

gala or a human in flames! On the whole, wearing feathers is nowadays more masculine than feminine; and in many cases it links with persistent warlikeness or aggression (the speed of flight, power of strike, and so on) rather than with placidity and the admiration of those peaceful virtues that are more readily expressed in flowers. Generally, advancing techniques in weaving and dyeing, with imported manufactured cloth, beads, and jewellery, have further tended to reduce the natural use of birds in modern times, and nearly to vanishing point even in some remote cultures.

North America. Eagle and hawk (Accipitridae) provide the characteristic, flowing headdresses of the Red Indians, known to all—some curiously like hornbill capes from Indonesia (see below). Nowadays, these are mostly donned for the benefit of photographers or distinguished visitors.

South America. Macaw and other parrots (Psittacidae) are favoured among the many and varied Central and South American jungle groups who love feather ornamentation, primarily in headdresses. The wild Jivaros, best known head-shrinkers on the eastern slopes of the Andes, make great shock-up feather hats in white, blue, scarlet, and lemon. To the east the Carajas, on the Araguaya River in Brazil, prefer black, dark blue, and white, impressively set in 'sunburst' effect by placing each feather within a tube; they also make 'florals' with feathers stuck in the ears.

Oceania and the Pacific basin. This is the centre of diversity in the contemporary use of birds for ornamentation. In Australia feathers are used less extensively than paints and dyes, although feathers of cockatoo (Kakatoeinae) and emu *Dromaius* sp. are favoured in the hair of some groups (e.g. the Tiwi of Melville Island). A special feature in some central Australian coroberee dances are performers covered with painted-on small feathers and down, representing emu, hawk (*Accipiter*, etc.), or other 'totemic' characters. Totemism is, of course, widely associated with bird ornamentation.

In Polynesia the more limited bird fauna of the islands has tended to specialised uses there; flowers are more widely favoured, with one outstanding exception—the superb feather cloaks of Hawaii, of which only a few perfect specimens now remain (in the Bernice Bishop Museum there, the British Museum, and a few others). These beautifully colour-blended garments, worn by the magically great when Cook found the Friendly Islands, were intricately composed from the breast feathers of parrakeets (Psittacidae), tropicbirds (Phaethontidae), honeyeaters (Meliphagidae), doves (Columbidae), and others.

In Melanesia the most elaborate usage is in feather money, notably that made from tiny black and scarlet feathers of a honeyeater *Myzomela* sp. in the Banks and other islands between the Solomons and the New Hebrides ; in parts of Espiritu Santo Island a form of this is worn as head-fillet by the very highest grades in the male secret society (based on sacrifice of intersex pigs).

New Guinea is the nearest to a 'living fossil' of one-time bird ornamentation on a wide scale. In the lately discovered stone-age heart behind Mt. Hagen and the Wahgi valley, many even still wear magnificent headdresses of plumes from birds-of-paradise (Paradisaeidae) and cockatoo, mixed with shells and native dyes. Lemon, pink, scarlet, violet, black, orange, and white may all merge in a superb melange, imaginative and wildly dynamic. Some of the finest effects came by the arrangement of shimmering blue breast feathers ; and from the glorious golden tail-spread of the Greater Bird-of-paradise *Paradisaea apoda*, whose ecstasies of courtship virility were first described by Alfred Russel Wallace on the Aru Islands (see frontispiece of his *The Malay Archipelago*, 1872).

Papuan overland trade in plumes was big business long before a white man appeared—and remains so. For instance, some hill peoples put a premium value on the bare primary shafts of various cassowaries *Casuarius* spp., as nose septum and other head ornament. Young birds may be carried and walked for weeks from the coast up into the mountains, to be reared as pets ; but the tame adult can be dangerous.

Asia. Over much of the Asian mainland, bird ornamentation has long been on the wane. In China 'feather jewellery', dating back to prehistoric times, persists in traditional form only on operatic hats, hairpins, and buckles. An effect rather like Brazilian 'butterfly wing' jewellery is achieved by setting in silver the scintillating blue body feathers of the wide-ranging White-collared Kingfisher *Halcyon chloris*. Among the primitive hill tribes south and east of the Himalaya only the Konyaks nowadays make any extensive use of feathers—those of hornbills (Bucerotidae) ; the remote and colourful Kachins and Karens rarely wear any kind of bird ornament.

On the islands of the Indonesian Archipelago, however, bird usages continue on a larger scale. Black and white, rather than colour, prevail. The pied wing and tail feathers of the big Rhinoceros Hornbill *Buceros rhinoceros* are most esteemed, especially by the Dayaks of Borneo, who make fine dancing-cloaks from 60–70 sewn together on a leopard skin. The immensely elongated (3 feet)

central tail feathers of the even larger Helmeted Hornbill *Rhinoplax vigil* top off this ensemble as headdress, while the bill of the bird can be used as cap, belt, or ear ornament (see also IVORY, HORNBILL). The handsome spectacled feathers of the Argus Pheasant *Argusianus argus grayi* and several eagles are also worn (almost exclusively by men) in Sumatra, Celebes, and Borneo, replaced in Java and among the relic of Malayan aboriginal negritos by peacock *Pavo* spp. and junglefowl *Gallus* spp.

Africa. With a plethora of potential ornaments provided by various large mammals (lion's manes, zebra and giraffe skins, eland and rhino horns, etc.) and flowers, the avian role is relatively weak in much of Africa. Within a moderate range of feather usage, outstanding are the upswept headdresses of Ostrich *Struthio camelus* plumes worn by the once warrior Masai and Zulu, taller than any British guardsman's bearskin. In 1937 Meinertzhagen wrote of *Turacus hartlaubi* in Kenya : 'In the old days—I speak of thirty-five years ago, when I lived in the Kikuyu country—the crimson feathers of this Plantain-eater were much prized by the Kikuyu. It was a custom among them that young ladies were compelled to wear such a feather in their hair once a year, and that whilst wearing it they were forced to comply with the wishes of the first young man they met.'

General. Although little specific research has been done on the subject, it seems that some cultures have a positive, others a negative attitude to birds, depending partly on tradition, partly on the total ecology of the environment. It is a striking fact that in many areas where birds are treated with high respect (see OMENS, BIRDS AS) and even reverence, they are also most used for personal ornamentation. But this usage may vary from individual choice in secular costume (e.g. some South American Indians) to the restricted use of hornbill feather coats in Borneo or the long obsolete Hawaiian coloured cloaks.

In some areas, brilliant colours are the first concern, while in others size and power are often prime considerations, even if the feathers are plain—as with eagles (large Accipitridae), owls (Strigiformes), geese *Anser* spp., and hornbills. In many tropical countries colour usage finds a readier outlet in bright flowers. Feathers, naturally enough, predominate over all other parts of the bird in favour. But birds with powerful quills, queer beaks, or harsh calls may acquire special and sometimes strange local esteem.

Bird bone is in fairly common use for nose septa in Melanesia and central Africa. In the late Stone Age much was made of bone in Polynesia. At the

Niah caves in Sarawak the hollow limb bones of hornbills and pheasants (Phasianidae) were cut and polished as beads, which were later (A.D. 800 onwards) copied in glass by mainland traders of the T'ang period ; these ceramic copies still survive on the necks of Kelabit hill tribesmen, who continue to call them 'manik tolang' (bone beads).

Replicas of birds occur widely, the finest being the gold brooches of the Transcaucasian Bronze Age and the pre-Columbian Inca-Aztec civilisations of Central America. Largest things of the kind are the bird masks of the now defunct secret societies among the Kwakiutl Indians of British Columbia. Similar themes occur in recent American Indian totem-poles and—at the other (and often unclear) end of the time-space scale—in pre-dynastic Egyptian tomb art, on the plumed bird-dancers of the splendid bronze drums found in Indo-China and the Shan States, and in the avian petroglyphs of Pacific Easter Island and Indian Mahenjo Daro. How much these and other parallels are due to separate and convergent acts of thought in art, how much to the diffusion of cultural traits remains a matter for scholarly—but often heated—argument. See also ART, BIRDS IN ; HERALDIC BIRDS.

Many representations of birds as ornamentation and on jewellery, in art, on postage stamps, and as symbols, are either traditional carry-overs from periods when direct use of feathers was routine ; or they are borrowings from earlier and replaced cultures—as with the national symbol of the United States of America, the Bald Eagle *Haliaetus leucocephalus* ; or the Hindu 'Garuda' (see FABULOUS BIRDS), symbol lately adopted by the now Mohammedan Republic of Indonesia.

The above information has been compiled from hundreds of books and papers, mainly of travel or ethnology. No one study covers a wide field ; those mentioned below are of special value.

T.H.

Simpson, Colin. 1954. Adam in Plumes. London. (New Guinea.)
Smythies, B. E. 1960. The Birds of Borneo. Edinburgh.
Weyer, E. 1959. Primitive Peoples Today. London.

ORNIS: Greek word (plural 'ornithes') for bird, used scientifically (in the singular)—but seldom nowadays—in the sense of AVIFAUNA.

ORNITHIC: pertaining to birds.

ORNITHICHNITE: geological term for a bird's footprint preserved in stone.

ORNITHOGAEA: name for a zoogeographical region (not one of the classical divisions) considered to include New Zealand and Polynesia. Reasons are given elsewhere for treating New Zealand as a subregion of the Australasian Region, and for excluding oceanic islands from any such scheme (see AUSTRALASIAN REGION ; DISTRIBUTION, GEOGRAPHICAL)

ORNITHOLITE: geological term for the fossilised remains of a bird (see FOSSIL BIRDS).

ORNITHOLOGY: the scientific study of birds ; the branch of zoology concerned with the Class Aves (see ANIMAL KINGDOM ; AVES).

Aspects of Ornithological Study. Research into the problems of bird-life may be considered under five main heads, but there is no sharp separation of the various aspects. First, there is the general zoological study of the form and function of the bird as a type of animal, and of different kinds of birds comparatively, using the methods of such branches of science as anatomy, physiology, and embryology. These specialised researches add to ornithological knowledge, and are often fundamental for its purposes, even although the particular investigators may not be ornithologists in the sense of being comprehensively concerned with birds.

Secondly, there is systematics, which is based largely on morphology, uses the methods of taxonomy, and includes avian palaeontology. It leads on to the study of evolution and genetics.

Thirdly, there is the study of distribution and ecology. This is concerned with birds in relation to their environment, animate and inanimate ; and its purview includes food, migration, and population dynamics. The animate environment consists of all the organisms with which particular birds have interrelations, not excepting parasites.

Fourthly, there is ethology, dealing with the habits of different kinds of birds and including the psychological approach to behaviour.

Fifthly, there is what might be termed 'applied ornithology', which has as its subject matter the special relation of birds with the human race, including the economic importance of birds and questions of conservation and of domestication.

Cross-references to articles relating to the abovementioned topics will be found in the similarly arranged List of Major Articles on General Subjects at the beginning of the volume. It is amusing to be reminded (Sibley 1953) that no longer ago than 1901 the eminent American ornithologist Ridgway asserted that anatomy and systematics constituted 'scientific' ornithology—life histories and habits were 'popular'!

Contributions to General Biology. The contributions of ornithology to general biological knowledge have been immense, and along several lines ornithologists have taken a leading part—sometimes the greatest part of all. This is aside from the fact that much work by embryologists, geneticists, and physiologists has been done on birds ; and that in some instances a purely ornithological approach has aided in such studies—notably the discovery of the effect of light on the reproductive cycle of animals.

It was in respect of the finches of the Galápagos Islands that Charles Darwin, in 1845, gave his first public indication of the views that eventually changed not only the outlook of biology but the whole trend of human thought : and in the great work in which he published his developed thesis, fourteen years later, the first chapter deals largely with the varieties of the domesticated pigeon. In more recent times, ornithological systematists have played a leading part in advancing the understanding of evolutionary processes and of the manner in which new species originate ; very relevant to this is the fact that birds are probably better known taxonomically than any other class of animals.

The classical work of P. L. Sclater, in 1858, on the geographical distribution of birds opened up this subject for the whole of zoology, and the zoogeographical regions into which he divided the world were largely adopted by A. R. Wallace, eighteen years later, for animals in general. The problems of migration have not been more intensively studied in respect of any other class of animals ; and students of birds share with students of fishes the main credit for having developed the method of marking individual wild animals as a means of studying their movements and life histories. Ornithologists have also been pioneers in studying the factors that regulate animal populations.

In the analysis of animal behaviour the contribution of ornithologists has also been outstanding, from such early work as that of Whitman on instinct and of Heinroth on imprinting, to a great range of more modern studies of such subjects as vocalisation, courtship, displacement activities, and learning ability. Many other lines of observation of living birds, both ecological and ethological, have played their part in the advance of general biological knowledge.

Outside the field of biology, mention may be made of the information on aerodynamics that has been derived from studying the flight of birds, stemming from the classical work of Marey in 1890.

(For cross-references, again see list of Major Articles on General Subjects at the beginning of the volume.)

Impact of Other Sciences. While ornithology has made great contributions to biology, it has also derived much from other branches of science and must take account of knowledge in contiguous fields. Ornithologists benefit by adopting methods and testing principles that have emerged from cognate work on other classes of animals. Comparisons, as for example between the migratory movements of birds and those of fishes, are likewise often illuminating. Moreover, the circumstances of the ornithologist's problems require him to consider the interrelations of birds with other organisms and therefore to have some understanding of the latter, whether their role is that of predators, competitors, parasites, or prey.

It is only by what may be called the interplay of the disciplines that the full value can be extracted from the rich phenomena that birds present. The ornithologist cannot interpret his systematic data without regard to ecological and genetic factors. He cannot understand behaviour without some knowledge of physiology and psychology. He must be observational, as always in the past, but his methods must be quantitative as well as qualitative ; and appeal must be made to experiment where such can be applied.

History and Organisation. The history of ornithology is outside the scope of the present work. For a comprehensive review there is Stresemann's book on the subject. There is also Newton's masterly summary, up to the last decade of the nineteenth century, constituting the long Introduction to his famous *Dictionary of Birds*. A general conspectus of recent developments is provided by the published proceedings of the International Ornithological Congresses that have been held at regular intervals during the intervening period.

As regards organisation, the scientific background is provided, on the one hand, by the departments of zoology and allied subjects in the universities of the world. Occasionally there are separate departments of ornithology, or attached institutes such as the Edward Grey Institute of Field Ornithology at the University of Oxford. On the other hand, and especially with regard to morphological and systematic work, the basis is in the great museums of natural history (see MUSEUM). Expeditions for collecting and observational study are, from time to time, sent to various parts of the world by institutions of the types just mentioned or by scientific societies. Field work in developed countries is, by its nature, more diffuse and to a large extent the province of the non-professional ornithologist ; but some of it is highly organised, or is centred on bird observatories and ringing schemes (see BIRD-WATCHING ; OBSERVATORY ; RINGING).

The whole endeavour of ornithology is knit together by societies. There are numerous societies specially devoted to birds, ranging from national to purely local bodies, and from those that are strictly scientific in their outlook to those that have a less technical appeal or are concerned primarily with questions of bird protection. There are also important national societies dealing with zoology, as a general subject or in respect of particular aspects of animal life (e.g. ecology, behaviour), and many local societies concerned with natural history as a whole ; these to a greater or less extent take birds within their purview.

Most scientific societies publish periodical journals, and it is mainly in the pages of these that additions to knowledge are published. Of the many journals devoted entirely to ornithology, notable examples are the *Journal für Ornithologie* (Deutsche Ornithologen Gesellschaft), *Ibis* (British Ornithologists' Union), *Auk* (American Ornithologists' Union), *L'Oiseau et la Revue Française d'Ornithologie* (Societé Ornithologique de France), *Ardea* (Nederlandsche Ornithologische Vereeniging), *Dansk Ornithologisk Forenings Tidsskrift* (D.O.F.), *Aquila* (Institutus Ornithologicus Hungaricus), *Condor* (Cooper Ornithological Society, California), *Emu* (Royal Australasian Ornithologists' Union), *Tori* (Ornithological Society, Japan), and *Hornero* (Ornithological Society, La Plata, Argentina)—with the long established *British Birds* exceptional in not being the organ of a society or institute. A guide to the contents of journals, as well as to other publications, is provided annually by the *Zoological Record* (see under BIBLIOGRAPHY). Standard abbreviations of the titles of journals, to be used in citing references, are given in the *World List of Scientific Periodicals*.

International organisation is dealt with in a separate article (see CONGRESSES, INTERNATIONAL).

A.L.T.

Mayr, E. 1963. The role of ornithological research in biology (Presidential Address). Proc. XIII Internat. Orn. Congr., Ithaca, N.Y., 1962 : 27–38.
Mayr, E. & Schüz, E. (eds.). 1949. Ornithologie als biologische Wissenschaft. 28 Beiträge als Festschrift zum 60. Geburtstag von Erwin Stresemann. Heidelberg.
Moreau, R. E. (ed.). 1959. Ibis 101 (1), (3–4). (Centenary Number, and reports of Centenary Meeting.)
Newton, A. 1896. A Dictionary of Birds. London. (Especially the Introduction.)
Sibley, C. G. 1953. Ornithology. In A Century of Progress in the Natural Sciences 1853–1953. San Francisco.
Stresemann, E. 1951. Die Entwicklung der Ornithologie von Aristoteles bis zur Gegenwart. Berlin.
Thomson, A. Landsborough. 1955. The place of ornithology in biological science (Presidential Address). Acta XI Congr. Internat. Orn., Basel 1954 : 47–58. (References to literature on instances mentioned above.)

ORNITHOMANCY: divination from observations of the flight of birds—the words ' augury ' and ' auspice ' both owe their origin to this superstitious practice, being derived from the Latin ' avis ' (see OMENS, BIRD AS).

ORNITHOPHILOUS: botanical term applied to plants fertilised through the intermediacy of birds (see POLLINATORS AND DISTRIBUTORS).

ORNITHOSCOPY: same as ORNITHOMANCY

ORNITHOSIS: term (plural ' ornithoses') applied to diseases identical with, or closely related to, psittacosis (occurring in birds not necessarily of psittacine species)—see PSITTACOSIS.

OROPENDOLA: substantive name of species in five tropical genera (*Zarhynchus*, etc.) of Icteridae (see ORIOLE (2)).

ORTHOCOELOUS: see INTESTINE

ORTHONYCHINAE : see RAIL-BABBLER

ORTOLAN; name, alternatively ' Ortolan Bunting ', of *Emberiza hortulana* (for subfamily see BUNTING) ; the gastronomic application of the name is wider than its specific one (see GASTRONOMIC AND MEDICAL USES).

OSCINES: see under PASSERIFORMES

OSPREY: *Pandion haliaetus*, in America often called ' Fish-hawk ' (see HAWK). Also a plumage trade misnomer for egrets (Ardeidae). See Plates 9a, 48a (phot.).

OSSIFICATION: see SKELETON ; and DEVELOPMENT, EMBRYONIC ; DEVELOPMENT, POSTEMBRYONIC

OSSIFRAGE: archaic name for the Lämmergeier *Gypaetus barbatus* (see VULTURE (1) ; also BIBLE, BIRDS OF THE).

OSTEOLOGY: the study of bones (see SKELETON).

OSTRICH: name of *Struthio camelus*, sole species of the Struthionidae (Struthioniformes) ; in the plural (ostriches), general term for the family and order ; for ' American Ostrich ' see RHEA. As Newton wrote : ' There must be few persons in any civilized country unacquainted with the appearance of this, the largest of living birds.' An adult male will stand nearly 8 feet in height (4 feet 6 inches from the back) and weigh up to 345 pounds (South Africa). The body plumage of the male Ostrich is black, the wing quills and tail are white and plumelike, the head, two-thirds of the neck, and the legs bare of feathers. The naked skin of the face and neck varies in colour in the several forms ; very prominent are the thick black eyelashes. The legs are thick and exceptionally powerful. The family is distinguished from all others by the presence of only two toes ; the larger, corresponding to the middle anterior toe in other birds, has a stout nail, but in the smaller outer toe the nail is wanting. Females differ in having the body plumage mainly brown with pale edgings to the feathers ; wings and tail are like the body in colour but there is more down, of a dirty grey-brown shade on the neck, than in the male.

Before about 1920 the 5 kinds of Ostrich then known were given specific rank, but modern opinion has reduced them to subspecies (the nominate race described from ' North Africa '—an area where the Ostrich is now extinct). The most northerly representative is the Syrian race *S. c. syriacus*, formerly found in the desert country of Syria and Arabia but extinct since 1941 ; it is reported to have been fairly common up till 1914 in the desert areas which it inhabited. The North African race *S. c. camelus*, although greatly reduced in numbers and habitat, occurs south of the Atlas Mountains, from the Upper Senegal and Niger country to the Sudan and central Abyssinia. The most westerly representatives, *S. c. spatzi*, was described in 1926 from the Rio de Oro on the basis of the comparatively small size of the egg and the structure of its shell, and it seems very doubtful whether this name should be recognised—or even whether an Ostrich still inhabits that little investigated area. Best known of the family is the Masai race *S. c. massaicus*, which is found in eastern Kenya south of the Tana River, ranging to Tanganyika ; north of the Tana in eastern Kenya the Somali race *S. c. molybdophanes* takes its place, ranging to Somalia and southern Abyssinia. Lastly, the Southern Ostrich *S. c. australis* is distributed on the open and savanna veld south of the Zambesi and Cunene rivers and not beyond. This is the bird which has been farmed so successfully for its plumes in South Africa—in the Little Karoo area of Cape Province—and was later crossed with birds imported from the north of Africa ; the market for ostrich feathers later became much restricted and the crossing experiments were then discontinued (see DOMESTICATION). As a result of introduction under domestication, a small feral population exists in one or two localities in South Australia.

Ostriches inhabit the sandy wastes and deserts as well as—in East Africa—districts studded with low bushes and thorn trees. In such an environment they associate with herds of zebras, antelopes, and giraffes. Usually they are met with in parties of 5 or 6, but travellers in desolate areas may encounter single birds. Troops of 40 to 50 birds will occasionally assemble together, more especially in the great game country.

The Masai Ostrich, in particular, lives in a very different environment from that formerly inhabited by the Syrian representative. In the African bush it is given to displays of remarkable agility, to the accompaniment of much wing flapping, twisting, and swerving at great speed ; a frightened bird has been seen to catch up with and shoot ahead of a hartebeest going at full gallop. Ostriches have to contend with other dangers besides man ; lions in particular prey upon the young birds. Their eggs are also preyed upon by man and beast, especially by jackals. The birds have exceptional eyesight ; ever vigilant, they can seldom be approached on foot closer than 100 yards in open country.

The known roving habits of the Ostrich are no doubt prompted by the prevalence or scarcity of some favourite food, as they are incapable of living in completely arid country where vegetable food of some kind cannot be secured. The myth that they can thrive in absolute desert country has long since been exploded, although they are believed to obtain considerable moisture from certain succulent plants which occur in such wastes. Ostriches feed mainly on vegetable matter such as flowering shrubs, parasitic creepers, ground-creeping gourds, and fallen wild figs. They are also said to capture small tortoises and lizards, and so varied is their diet that they have been described as omnivorous. Much grit is also swallowed to aid digestion, and it is said that the recent movements of a bird can sometimes be ascertained by examination of the quartz-pebbles and stones which dissection shows the stomach to contain.

The advent of precision rifles and fast-moving cars has driven the Ostrich from many haunts where it was formerly comparatively safe. Man alone has been responsible for its extermination in many districts, and as regards the Syrian-Arabian race this has occurred before its life history was even imperfectly known and its habits had been studied ; nothing had in fact been recorded of its nidification in the Empty Quarter or in the Syrian wastes. In olden days this form roamed over the whole Syrian desert, right up to the banks of the Euphrates ; then for a long period its range was purely Arabian, until its doom was sealed. The Masai Ostrich and the Somali Ostrich are not as yet in imminent danger, and from them we have learned much of what is known of the life history of the species.

Ostriches are polygamous, each male being accompanied by several hens ; 3 is a usual number, but as many as 5 hens to one cock are recorded. **The hens** belonging to one cock deposit their eggs in a common nest, the latter a shallow excavation in sandy soil. In the North African Ostrich 15–20 eggs are reported to have formed the complement ; in South Africa as many as 30 eggs may be laid in the same pit ; while in the case of the Masai race 50–60 eggs in a nest have been recorded—the product perhaps of 5 hens. The male bird undertakes a great part of the incubation, brooding during the night but relieved by the hens for at least part of the daylight hours ; this rule is not absolute, as in South Africa the hens appear to have a longer spell by day. Incubation lasts from 5 to 6 weeks.

A recent study of wild Ostriches in South West Africa (Sauer & Sauer) has given us a further picture of the breeding habits of the form found there. A typical family party consists of a cock and 3 hens, all sharing the duties of the nest. Each hen may lay up to 6–8 eggs, and the combined laying may extend over 18 days. Towards the end of incubation, eggs nearly ready are rolled into hollows on the periphery of the nest, a procedure which helps to synchronise hatching. Adults of both sexes perform a ' broken-wing display ' when danger threatens. At the age of one month the chicks are capable of running at a speed of 35 miles per hour.

Ostrich eggs, which show considerable diversity in measurement, in pitting, and in gloss, are creamy white and nearly spherical, rather longer than broad (about 150×125 mm.). Early in the breeding season the cock has been seen to display by squatting on the ground, rocking from side to side and expanding his white wing plumes ; the blood-red gape is believed to act as a threat signal. During the excitement of display the skin of the front of the legs and the neck momentarily ' blush ' a fiery red.

See Plate 30 (colour).   D.A.B.

Sauer, F. & Sauer, E. 1959. Polygamie beim süd-afrikanischen Strauss (Struthio camelus australis). Bonn. Zool. Beitr. 10 : 266–285. (English summary.)

OTIDES ; OTIDIDAE : see under GRUIFORMES ; and BUSTARD. (The spelling ' Otidae ' is patently erroneous.)

OTOLITH : see HEARING AND BALANCE

OU : *Psittirostra psittacea* (for family see HONEY-CREEPER (2)).

OUZEL : substantive name, also spelt ' ousel ', of the Ring Ouzel *Turdus torquatus*, but formerly applied to the Blackbird *T. merula* (cf. German ' Amsel ')—see THRUSH. ' Water-ouzel ' is a popular name in Britain for *Cinclus cinclus* (see DIPPER).

OVARY : female gonad, in birds usually developed only on the left side (see REPRODUCTIVE SYSTEM ; also ENDOCRINE SYSTEM).

OVENBIRD (1) : substantive name of typical species of Furnariidae (Passeriformes, suborder Tyranni) ; in the plural, serves as a general term for the family but applies particularly to the nominate subfamily. Other general terms used for included groups are ' spinetail ' and ' treerunner ', but many English substantive names have been invented for various genera. The family is purely Neotropical ; and it comprises about 221 species, in 58 genera.

In a short review it is hardly possible to do justice to a group which is probably more diverse than any other avian family. Peters did not recognise any subfamilies, but other systematists have done so and the grouping may be usefully introduced here. The Furnariinae, besides true ovenbirds of the genus *Furnarius*, include a variety of divergent genera such as the miners (*Geobates, Geositta*), the plainrunners (*Coryphistera, Clibanornis*), the earthcreepers (*Upucerthia*), the Tococo (*Chilia*), and shaketails (*Cinclodes*). Next and equally important are the Synallaxinae or spinetails, which are rather less variable and tend to be characterised by peculiar tail structure and the building of relatively enormous enclosed nests, for the latter reason sometimes being called castle-builders. The third large and diverse subfamily, the Philydorinae, includes treerunners (*Pygarrhichas*), treehunters (*Thripadectes*), *Heliobletus contaminatus*, Hookbill (*Ancistrops*), Pointed-tail (*Berlepschia*), cachalotes (*Pseudoseisura*), Recurved-bill (*Megaxenops*), and several other important genera inter alia without English or other common names—*Philydor, Automolus* (sometimes termed ' foliage-gleaner '), *Pseudocolaptes, Xenops*, etc. The remaining two subfamilies are much smaller, the Margarornithinae consisting of only 3 genera—*Margarornis, Premnornis* (treerunners), and *Premnoplex* (Barbtail)—and the Sclerurinae of 2 genera—*Sclerurus* (leafscrapers) and *Lochmias* (Stream-creeper).

Characters. If one says that for the most part the family consists of small brown birds, that is as much as can be said by way of generalisation. The largest members are about 9 inches in total length, e.g. cachalotes, species of *Pseudocolaptes*, and *Cinclodes palliatus*. The colour of nearly all members of the Furnariinae is exceedingly dull, being shades of brown, sometimes tending to rufous or chestnut or with rufous parts, usually paler or even white below, and sometimes with white in the wing. The miners, treecreepers, and shaketails, which are all grey-brown or dark brown birds, perhaps paler and somewhat mottled below or with white in the wing (*Cinclodes*), reach the acme of drabness. The true Ovenbird *Furnarius leucopus* ('El Hornero' of the South Americans) differs in being essentially bright chestnut above and white below. The spinetails tend to be less drab and uniformly coloured, being mostly variegated on the upper parts with brown, chestnut, and almost black, and sometimes with dark streaking on the throat and breast (otherwise usually almost white). Some members even have some bright colour, e.g. the White-cheeked Spinetail *Schoeniophylax phryganophila* with a bright yellow chin, and *Asthenes* spp. with a touch of reddish chestnut on the throat. The Margarornithinae generally resemble the Dendrocolaptidae (see WOODCREEPER) in plumage, with some prominent light or buff streaking on the head or under parts, and are altogether darker plumaged than the previous groups. Species of *Margarornis* are rufous above and dark olive below, heavily marked with pear-shaped drops of light buff. Similarly, the Sclerurinae are generally dark coloured and may be scalloped with white below. Many of the Philydorinae resemble woodcreepers, again, with their characteristic streaking on head and under parts, e.g. *Berlepschia rikeri* and *Pseudocolaptes* spp., while the genus *Philydor* has bright orange under parts.

The wing is as variable as other features of the family, from soft, short, and rounded, to long and somewhat pointed. The tail may be normal, or rather short as in *Furnarius* and *Geositta*, but is remarkably diverse among the spinetails. In that subfamily there is a tendency for it to be graduated or forked, long and attenuated, with the feather barbs breaking down and the webs becoming degenerate so that the naked quills project. For instance, *Leptasthenura* spp. have long tails with tapering rectrices, and *Synallaxis* spp. have graduated tails with the ends of the rectrices frayed and broken down so that the shafts project. Most remarkable of all is Des Mur's Spinetail *Sylviorthorhynchus desmursii*, with a tail two or three times as long as the rest of the bird, of very thin feathers with poorly developed webs. On the other hand, 'softtails'— *Metopothrix aurantiacus*, *Thripophaga*, and *Drioctistes* spp.—have normally developed rectrices, but with the shafts not at all strong, while the rectrices of *Berlepschia* (Pointed-tail) are sharply tapered. Those forms which resemble dendrocolaptids (*Pseudocolaptes*, treerunners, treehunters, *Xenops*, etc.) are distinguished from members of that family by not having the shafts of the rectrices stiffened.

A very few species are crested, such as the Plainrunner *Coryphistera alaudina* and the Brown Cachalote *Pseudoseisura lophotes*. The bill is mostly rather short, straight and pointed, and is normally wide; but many variations occur, the bill being long and decurved in *Upucerthia*, short and slightly curved in *Geositta*, moderate in both respects in *Furnarius*, long and straight in *Sclerurus*, laterally compressed in *Xenoctistes*, and short, wedge-shaped with upturned mandible in *Xenops*. The legs and feet are usually medium to short, but are strongly developed in terrestrial forms such as the true ovenbirds and cachalotes.

Like all other characters, the voice varies considerably. Generally, the spinetails and many other genera have short, harsh, rattling and jarring calls; but miners have clear ringing, reiterated cries, likened to the laughing of a child; the Ovenbird *Furnarius leucopus* has a sequence of clear, resonant notes produced as a duet or harmonious singing; the Black-faced Spinetail gives wooden-sounding raps and creaks; Hudson's Spinetail *Asthenes hudsoni* has a plaintive four-note song audible for 1000 yards or more; and the cachalotes are especially noisy with jay-like screams (Brown Cachalote) or a piercing chorus (White-throated Cachalote *P. gutturalis*).

Ecology. Most genera and species inhabit thickly wooded areas or those with plenty of good cover, and this applies particularly to those within the tropics (where the majority of the family live); but even so there are differences in habitat and behaviour. The foliage-gleaners (*Anabacerthia*, *Automolus*) are birds of the canopy and forest trees, where they hunt through the leaves like warblers (Sylviinae). *Heliobletus contaminatus* has the habits of a treecreeper (Certhiidae) or woodcreeper (Dendrocolaptidae), as have the treerunners. The leafscrapers inhabit the densest undergrowth, are great skulkers, and have the habit of rooting through leaves and tossing them in the air in their search for food. The Sharp-tailed Streamcreeper *Lochmias nematura* is equally unobtrusive, and it shows such a preference for sewage effluent that the Brazilians have aptly named it 'president of filth'. More widely distributed birds such as the true ovenbirds and many spinetails are inhabitants of less densely wooded areas; the former, being largely terrestrial, prefer fairly open country yet with plenty of trees, while spinetails characteristically skulk unobtrusively in thickets or low cover even in treeless lands.

In the southern part of its range, and to a limited extent in the Andean highlands as far north as Colombia, the family shows the greatest measure of adaptive radiation. In the open pampa of Argentina and the mountainous fjord areas of Chile, different genera and species have invaded every possible habitat. The miners and earthcreepers are entirely terrestrial and typical of both barren mountainous country and the flat pampa. The Patagonian Earthcreeper *Upucerthia dumetaria* is even unwilling to fly, preferring to escape by running and thus looking like a small curlew *Numenius* sp. The Brown Cachalote is also largely terrestrial and tends to run off behind trees and other obstacles rather than fly when disturbed. Species of *Cinclodes* occupy the niche of dippers (Cinclidae) and are always found near water, from mountain torrents in the high Andes down to sea level ; they are even known to feed off-shore on the floating masses of giant kelp, being thus the only passerines to have even partially conquered a marine habitat. The White-throated Treerunner *Pygarrhichas albogularis* of Chile and Argentina fills the niche of a nuthatch (Sittidae) or even a woodpecker (Picidae). The Black-faced Spinetail *Phleocryptes melanops* is a bird of the marshes, as is the Curved-billed Reedrunner *Limnornis curvirostris*. *Aphrastura* and *Leptasthenura* are arboreal genera. For the most part, members of the family are active yet unobtrusive birds, even in open country, keeping well to cover, constantly creeping about in bushes, reeds, or thick grass, and even running off like mice rather than flying ; and they show a great tendency to remain in pairs. The Greater Thorn-bird *Phacellodomus ruber* in Argentina is exceptional in being not at all restless and never making an effort to hide.

Most species are insectivorous, but *Cinclodes* spp. also take small crustacea and aquatic animals, as would be expected, while some miners and the Tococo feed on seeds and vegetable matter.

Breeding. The breeding habits are known mostly from species inhabiting the open lands of the southern parts of South America, but even within these limits the diversity is astonishingly great. The only constant feature is that all lay white eggs—except the Black-faced Spinetail, which lays bright blue eggs, and a few others which lay slightly bluish or off-white eggs. Clutch size is usually 3–5, but as many as 9 eggs are mentioned for the White-throated Spinetail *Synallaxis albescens*, and tropical species probably tend to have smaller average clutches. Terrestrial forms such as miners and earthcreepers nest in holes in the ground, either natural cavities or tunnels dug by the birds themselves, e.g. the Common Miner *Geositta cunicularia* nesting in the burrows of the vizcacha on the Argentinian pampa. *Cinclodes* spp. nest in rock cavities or dig their own holes. Leafscrapers and the Streamcreeper also nest in holes or burrows in banks, and the leafscrapers have an odd habit of flying out of the hole and clinging to a tree-trunk when flushed from the nest. *Aphrastura* and *Lep-*

tasthenura nest either in holes in trees, behind bark, or in the abandoned nests of such birds as *Asthenes* spp.

In contrast, the true ovenbirds build very substantial, domed mud-ovens on the branches of trees well above the ground. The spinetails in general build vast nests, remarkable for such small birds. The Firewood-gatherer *Anumbius annumbi* (a bird about 8½ inches long) makes its big structures of large twigs, even in tall trees to which it may have difficulty in carrying up the material. The White-throated Cachalote perhaps makes the largest nest of the family, an enclosed structure with a cavity big enough for an eagle or vulture, and strong enough for a man to stand upon without damaging it ; the Brown Cachalote also makes a nest the size of a barrel. The Black-faced Spinetail makes a perfectly tiled nest, domed and impervious to the wet, with entrance near the top, out of grasses and leaves daubed together with mud and probably saliva. Species of *Phacellodomus* place their castles at the ends of branches that are at first several feet from the ground, but as the structure grows the boughs bend down and the nest may eventually rest on the ground. Hudson's Spinetail makes domed nests on the ground under the thickest cover, such as the giant cardoon thistles. On the other hand, the Striped-crowned Spinetail *Cranioleuca pyrrhophia* and the Wren-like Spinetail *Spartonoica maluroides* make open cup-shaped nests, which is quite exceptional for the Synallaxinae.

Owing to the impossibility of observing most of the nests of Furnariinae and Synallaxinae without destruction or excessive disturbance (the nests of these two subfamilies are much better known than those of the rest of the family), breeding details are virtually unknown in spite of the fact that these huge nests are such a conspicuous feature of the countryside in the open parts of South America. The incubation and nestling periods are very superficially known, for only about 6 species, being 15 to 20 days and 13 to 18 days respectively. The abandoned castles of the spinetails and the ovens of El Hornero are often used by other birds such as cowbirds (Icteridae genera), swallows (Hirundinidae), wrens (Troglodytidae), and parrots (Psittacidae) ; sometimes the owners are even expropriated after building their nest.

Distribution. The family, like the Formicariidae (see ANTBIRD), ranges from the montane and lowland forests of southern and central Mexico through Central to South America ; likewise it reaches Trinidad and Tobago, but is not found in the Antilles. In the south its range is greater than that of the antbirds, being over the whole of the continent to Cape Horn and Tierra del Fuego, as well as to the Falkland Islands. As has been said, many specialised forms have developed in the open, barren lands of the extreme south, and the monospecific genus *Chilia* is confined to Chile, where it inhabits semi-arid country. In Argentina a few species, such as the Black-faced Shaketail *Cinclodes fuscus* and perhaps the Patagonian Earthcreeper, are said to be migratory. As with the antbirds, no comprehensive account of the family has ever been written, and the majority of species are known only by their appearance.

See Plate 32 (colour).   S.M.

Skutch, A. F. 1952. Life history of the Chestnut-tailed Automolus. Condor 54 : 93–100.

OVENBIRD (2): *Seiurus aurocapillus* (see WARBLER (2)).

OVERFLOW ACTIVITY: consummatory acts apparently in excess of the normal reaction to the particular stimulus.

OVIDUCT: see REPRODUCTIVE SYSTEM ; and LAYING

OVIPARITY: the characteristic of laying eggs in which the embryos develop outside the maternal body ; universal in birds, but see under VIVIPARITY ; see also EGG ; LAYING ; and DEVELOPMENT, EMBRYONIC.

OVIPOSITION: see LAYING

OVULATION: see REPRODUCTIVE SYSTEM ; also LAYING

OVUM: the female germ-cell (plural ' ova ')—see DEVELOPMENT, EMBRYONIC ; EGG ; GENETICS ; RE-PRODUCTIVE SYSTEM.

OWL: substantive name of all species of Strigidae and Tytonidae (Strigiformes) ; in the plural, general term for the order. These two families of world-wide distribution are sometimes treated as sub-families (under Strigidae) but at all events constitute a single order. Owls are the nocturnal counter-parts of the diurnal birds-of-prey (Falconiformes), but not all of them hunt exclusively by night. As raptorial birds they show a convergent development with the Falconiformes, from which they differ among other things in not having a crop and in possessing long caeca with club-shaped ends (vestigial in diurnal birds-of-prey). Their nearest phylo-genetic relationship is probably with the nightjars (Caprimulgiformes).

General Characteristics. Owls are soft-plumed, short-tailed, big-headed birds with large eyes directed forwards and surrounded by a facial disc. The bill is hooked, usually short and not conspicuously

strong, directed downwards and partly hidden by the feathers of the facial disc, which meet between the eyes. As in the diurnal birds-of-prey, the nostrils are placed in a soft cere at the base of the bill. The outer toe is reversible but is usually directed sideways ; the claws are sharp and strongly hooked. The colour of the plumage is very varied, but tends towards patterns that make the birds less conspicuous by day. In many species, markedly different colour phases have been reported (see POLYMORPHISM) ; but males and females usually have similar plumage, the Snowy Owl *Nyctea scandiaca* being an exception. Females are usually slightly larger and heavier than males, particularly in the Strigidae. The flight is silent in most species, and buoyant (see FLIGHT). The voice varies con-siderably, from melodious hooting and whistling (in some species following a chromatic scale) to shrill hissing, screeching, and barking. Under con-ditions presumed to be of fear or aggression, owls of both families frequently produce loud bill-snapping or clicking sounds.

In size, owls range from little bigger than a Sparrow *Passer domesticus* (pygmy owls *Glaucidium* spp. ; Elf Owl *Micrathene whitneyi*) to almost that of an eagle *Aquila* sp. (eagle owls *Bubo* spp.). In relation to the mainly nocturnal habits the eyes are large, not round, but slightly elongated, and with a notably thickened cornea which acts as an additional lens (see VISION). Owls can see perfectly well in daylight ; in absolute darkness they cannot see. As the number of light-sensitive elements (mostly rods) in the retina is exceedingly high, particularly in definitely nocturnal species such as the Tawny Owl *Strix aluco*, these species sometimes appear to be blinded by very strong sunlight. Of at least the less nocturnal species, such as the Little Owl *Athene noctua*, it has been shown that they are capable of colour vision. In comparison with other birds, which unlike owls can move the eyes independently of each other, owls have limited powers of stereo-scopic vision. The auditory powers are well devel-oped and are aided by a wide outer ear tube and, in some species, by the presence of large conchae, which, surrounded by the feathers of the facial disc, can be erected at will. In several species a striking asym-metry in the shape and relative position of the external part of the ear, including the bones surrounding the tympanic region and the operculum, has been described. This asymmetry is thought to be of value in locating sound sources not in the horizontal plane (see HEARING AND BALANCE). As the opercula or conchae are situated anteriorly to the orifices, they may also help in receiving sounds coming from behind. Ear-tufts (' horns ') which suggest outer ears have nothing to do with the auditory organ ; they occur only in some Strigidae. The head is very freely movable, which helps to compensate for the small angle of vision and also in locating the origin of sounds heard ; in the Long-eared Owl *Asio otus* the head has been reported to be capable of turning through at least 270°.

Habits. The majority of the species have arboreal habits, although some species live among rocks, in dry grasslands, in swamps, and in cactus deserts (Elf Owl). Long-legged terrestrial species are known both in the Tytonidae (Cape and Australian Grass Owls, *Tyto capensis* and *T. longimembris*) and in the Strigidae (Burrowing Owl *Speotyto cunicularia*). Owls are mainly sedentary ; regular migrations are known in respect of only a few species, among which are the Scops Owl *Otus scops* and the Oriental Hawk Owl *Ninox scutulata*, and also the Short-eared Owl *Asio flammeus*. Irruptions probably resulting from the simultaneous effects of food scarcity and over-population have been recorded in the case of the Snowy Owl and in that of Tengmalm's Owl *Aegolius funereus* (see IRRUPTION). Owls seem to feed exclusively on animals, which may range from insects, earthworms, crabs, and fish, to reptiles, birds, and small and medium-sized mammals up to the size of a roedeer. Small ground-living rodents (voles, mice, rats) form the principal food. Semi-aquatic fish-eating owls occur in Africa (*Scotopelia* spp.) and in southern Asia (*Ketupa* spp.—considered to be closely related to the eagle owls). Owls usually hide away by day in holes, or in dark places in thick foliage taking advantage mainly of their highly protective plumage coloration. Most species hunt by night ; others are known to be active at dusk or in full daylight. In northern latitudes the Snowy Owl and the Hawk-owl *Surnia ulula* hunt during the light nights of the Arctic summer and in winter during the short hours of daylight. Some species seem to enjoy sun-bathing (Little Owl, Burrowing Owl). The prey is generally swallowed whole, indigestible matter such as fur, feathers, bone, and chitin being regurgitated some hours after the meal in the form of large pellets (see PELLET).

Breeding. Few owls adhere strictly to breeding seasons ; several species, including the Barn Owl *Tyto alba* and the Short-eared Owl *Asio flammeus*, breed occasionally in winter when food conditions happen to be favourable. With minor exceptions, owls make hardly any nests themselves ; instead, they use other birds' nests—such as those of crows (Corvidae) and birds-of-prey—and holes in trees or rocks and a great variety of other suitable places, including human habitations. The eggs are chalky-white and roundish, the number varying from 1–14.

Clutch size is dependent on the food supply available, the differences from one season to the other being most notable in species which feed on rodents subjected to cyclic population fluctuations (see POPULATION DYNAMICS). Hence, in years of abundance the Snowy Owl may have clutches of 10–14 eggs, and in years of food scarcity it may have clutches of 2–4, or not breed at all. Incubation starts with the first egg laid, resulting in marked differences in the size of the young in the nest ; the youngest and smallest chicks thus often fall victim to their older brothers and sisters, particularly in years of food scarcity. Usually only the female incubates, but both sexes care for the young. The incubation period is long, being 32–34 days in the Barn Owl, 27–28 in the Long-eared Owl, and 34–36 in the Eagle Owl *Bubo bubo*.

Unlike the birds-of-prey, the young hatch with ears and eyes closed. They are nidicolous, with a plumage of white down, followed by a downy (Tytonidae) or semi-downy (Strigidae) second plumage (mesoptilae), which in its turn is followed by true feathers appearing on the same feather papillae. Owls have the reputation of reaching a great age, but records of their longevity are still inadequate. The life expectation of Barn Owls in Switzerland has been found to be surprisingly short, being at the average 16 months ; only a few individual birds are known to have reached the age of 9 years. One Tawny Owl in captivity lived for 22 years and an Eagle Owl for 68.

Tytonidae. The Tytonidae or barn owls differ only in minor osteological details from the Strigidae or typical owls. Barn owls have proportionately smaller eyes and are easily recognisable by the heart-shaped facial disc and the long slender legs. The family comprises about 10 species, all belonging to the single genus *Tyto*, among which is the almost world-wide ranging species of Barn Owl *Tyto alba*, with at least 32 recognisable geographical forms. The largest number of species (5) is found in Australia. They are mostly strictly nocturnal. Sometimes the small genus *Phodilus* (Bay Owl *P. badius* of tropical Asia and a rare congener in Africa) is included in this family.

Strigidae. This family contains more than 120 species, distributed over about 25 genera, of variable size, coloration, and habits. The facial disc is circular and the legs are usually rather strong and in most cases thickly feathered. Members of this family occur in every part of the world.

Thirteen species of owl are known from Europe, 10 of which are on the British list. Commonest of these in Britain is probably the Tawny Owl *Strix aluco*, which is a strong, truly nocturnal species, with an extremely varied diet ; it breeds in holes. It belongs to a widely distributed thick-headed genus (absent from Australia) without ear tufts and with large, dark eyes. The Ural Owl *S. uralensis*, the North American Barred Owl *S. varia*, and the South Asiatic Brown Wood Owl *S. leptogrammica* are other members of this genus. The much smaller Little Owl *Athene noctua* has no ear tufts either ; it is less strictly nocturnal and has light yellowish eyes. It has a mainly Palaearctic distribution. The Burrowing Owl from the steppe and desert regions of America is probably its present closest relative.

Throughout the zone of boreal coniferous forests of Europe, Asia, and North America quite a number of other species are found ; some of them are restricted to this zone, such as the Hawk Owl *Surnia ulula* (with an exceptionally long tail), the fluffy-feathered Tengmalm's Owl *Aegolius funereus* (known in North America as the Boreal Owl), and the Pygmy Owl *Glaucidium passerinum*. The last has a number of closely related forms in tropical America and Africa. The 'horned' species, although certainly not forming a natural group, resemble one another to some degree ; their actual relationship is a difficult but promising subject for further research. The eagle owls *Bubo* and *Huhua* spp. are the largest of this group and truly impressive in their appearance, strength, and deep hooting calls. The Eagle Owl *Bubo bubo* of Europe and Asia, ranging from the cold northern forests to the hot southern deserts, has allied species in America (Great Horned Owl *B. virginianus*) and in Africa (Cape Eagle Owl *B. capensis* and Spotted Eagle Owl *B. africanus*). To the north of them, in Arctic tundra regions, the Snowy Owl *Nyctea scandiaca* takes over the place of the eagle owls, being of a comparable size and strength but lacking the ear tufts.

The genus *Asio* contains the medium-sized ' eared ' owls, such as the Long-eared Owl *A. otus*, distributed throughout the forest regions of the Northern Hemisphere, and the Short-eared Owl *A. flammeus*, having a still wider distribution and inhabiting boggy and marshy places. Various other species inhabit Africa (e.g. the Marsh Owl *A. capensis*) and America. The smallest among the ' eared ' owls are the numerous representatives of the world-wide group of the scops owls, only one of them occurring in Europe (*Otus scops*) but 9 being listed from Central America and 6 from tropical south-eastern Asia. The Screech Owl *O. asio* of North America, well known by its easily imitated call, also belongs to this genus.

Apart from the Eagle Owl and the Great Horned Owl, which are extinct in the regions densely populated by man, only one species of owl seems to be at present in direct danger of extermination, namely the Laughing Owl *Sceloglaux albifacies* of New Zealand, which has already vanished from North Island but still survives in limited numbers in the Southern Alps of South Island.

See Plates 16d (phot.), 20 (colour).   K.H.V.

Watson, A. 1957. The behaviour, breeding, and food-ecology of the Snowy Owl *Nyctea scandiaca*. Ibis 99 : 419–462.

OWLET : term for a nestling OWL.

OWLET-FROGMOUTH : substantive name of the species of Aegothelidae (Caprimulgiformes, suborder Caprimulgi) ; in the plural, general term, alternatively ' owlet-nightjars ', for the family. The group is related to the frogmouths (Podargidae) and consists of a single genus of small arboreal nightjars (in the ordinal sense) almost restricted to the Papuo-Australian area. One species has penetrated to the Moluccas and another is found in New Caledonia. New Guinea is inhabited by 5 species, of which *Aegotheles cristata* occurs widely in Australia. Plumage characters are similar to those of the frogmouths and true nightjars (Caprimulgidae). The frogmouth-like bill is shorter and weaker than in *Podargus* or *Batrachostomus*, and it is largely obscured by the forehead feathering. Stiff and partly erectile filoplumes occur on the forehead and lores, with a few softer recurved filoplumes on the chin. The bird sits with an upright, owl-like stance. The body length is 8–9 inches.

Aegotheles has the same arboreal habits as *Podargus*, and it lives in forested and semi-open country ; but it does not adopt the rigid ' broken branch ' stance, when alarmed, which is characteristic of *Podargus*. The feeding habits appear to be intermediate between those of the frogmouths and the

---

Plate 35 · Single and Compound Nests

a *Upper :* Pied Fantailed Flycatcher *Rhipidura javanica* on nest, with partly grown young (Malaysia). A beautiful example of the single nest that is the general rule among birds (even among colonial breeders, although these may have their nests close together). The sexes in this species are similar.   *Phot. Loke Wan Tho.*

b *Lower :* Compound nest of the Sociable Weaver *Philetairus socius* in a tree (South Africa).
                    Phot. G. J. Broekhuysen.

(See articles NEST ; FLYCATCHER (1) ; SPARROW (1))

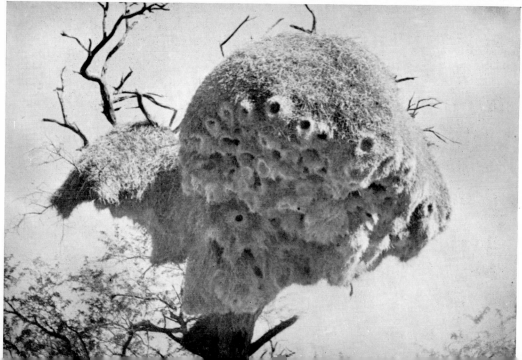

true nightjars. Aerial hawking for flying insects has been described, but most hunting is done from the ground, the bird sometimes rising to take flying insects ; most of the stomach contents analysed suggest that the bird feeds predominantly on terrestrial prey. The calls include a loud hissing note and a churring call.

Nesting takes place in hollow trees or occasionally in tunnels in banks. No actual nest may be constructed, or the eggs may be laid on a mat of dry leaves or mammal fur. The colour of the shell is white, as in *Podargus*, and the clutch is 3 or 4. The fledgling is covered with dense white down. The birds are readily flushed from their roosting or nesting hollows by tapping likely limbs or tree trunks.

Structurally, *Aegotheles* resembles *Podargus* but with several differences. The features in which it resembles *Podargus*, but which are not shared with true nightjars, include the desmognathous palate and the bronchial syrinx ; the sternum has two foramina on each side instead of being double-notched. However, it possesses the two carotids normal in the order and an oil gland, and it lacks the powder-down tufts found in *Podargus*. It is unique in the order in not having caeca.   D.L.S.

OXPECKER : substantive name of the two species constituting the subfamily Buphaginae of the Sturnidae (see STARLING) ; in the plural, general term for the subfamily. They are also called ' tick-birds '. These two species, forming a single genus confined to Africa, are notable for special adaptations to their peculiar habits. They obtain the whole of their food from the hides of the great African mammals, and latterly also of domestic stock, which they frequent in parties. Their most obvious adaptations to this way of life are their laterally flattened beaks, their extraordinarily sharp curved claws, and their stiff, rather long, tails, which are used like those of woodpeckers (Picidae) as a support when the bird perches on a vertical surface. The Yellow-billed Oxpecker *Buphagus africanus*, which actually has the terminal half of the bill red, and the Red-billed Oxpecker *B. erythrorhynchus*, which has the whole bill red, are otherwise much alike—both around 9 inches long, with brown plumage devoid of pattern, although *B. africanus* has a rump paler than the rest of the upper parts ; the sexes are similar, and the bill colouring is fully developed only in adults.

The Yellow-billed Oxpecker has much the larger geographical range of the two, from Senegal to Ethiopia and Natal ; the slightly smaller Red-billed Oxpecker is purely eastern, from Ethiopia southwards. The two species overlap considerably, and where they do it is not at all clear that they are ecologically segregated. Both species visit a wide variety of game animals, from rhinoceros, buffalo, giraffe, and various antelopes to warthogs, and also most kinds of domestic stock. Oxpeckers of the two species have actually been recorded on the same beast. Only elephants seem not to tolerate them.

More than a dozen oxpeckers can be seen on a single cow or zebra, and undoubtedly their main sustenance is derived from the ticks they pick off the animals' hides. It appears that it is not so much the tissue of the ticks themselves that provides the birds' main food as the blood with which they are engorged. The ticks are removed partly by normal pecking and nibbling, but generally by a scissoring movement, with the flattened bill laid sideways on the hide. The tick diet is supplemented by scurf, by flies, especially the blood-sucking *Stomoxys*, and to a considerable extent by scar-tissue, blood, and exudate taken by the oxpecker direct from wounds on the living animal. One result is that a sore once formed on a beast in oxpecker country may take a very long time to heal, and may even be enlarged. The consequence is that divided views have been held about oxpeckers. Some people, both European and African, welcome the bird's attentions to their stock—Fulani cattlemen in West Africa and Nandi in Kenya have been known to put out milk for them—as tending to clear them of external parasites that are often vectors of disease ; others object to the amount of damage they may do to the hides ; and others again point to the possibility that oxpeckers may themselves transmit blood parasites mechanically. However, under modern conditions in Africa, which involve the regular use of cattle dips, the numbers of oxpeckers frequenting cattle country has been greatly reduced. A special inquiry in Kenya has shown that the birds do not simply divert their attention to beasts' tissue when the parasites vanish, but themselves tend to disappear from the locality.

Plate 36 · Nest Building

One passerine and one other example, with nests of very different materials in different situations.

a *Upper :* Red-rumped Swallow *Cecropis daurica* carrying lining material into its mud nest (Portugal).   *Phot. M. D. England.*

b *Lower :* Squacco Herons *Ardeola ralloides* rebuilding their nest of sticks in a tree (Hungary).   *Phot. Zoltán Tildy.*

(See articles NEST BUILDING ; SWALLOW ; HERON)

On any animal an oxpecker can, thanks to its needle-sharp claws, scamper rapidly in any direction—up and down a leg, under the belly, all over the host's face. As a rule the host shows an astonishing indifference, even when birds are nibbling at its sores. From a herd of cattle a party can hardly be driven away ; each bird rapidly slides round to the blind side of its host, and, if further pursued, merely transfers to a neighbouring beast. They are almost unpleasant to watch, reminding one of blowflies attracted to carrion. On wild animals oxpeckers are altogether more wary, leaving their beast and flying round with their raucous hissing notes as soon as a human being comes anywhere near. It does seem that in this way they can be of direct value to their temporary host, especially a rhinoceros, in warning of the approach of danger.

Display and copulation take place on the back of a host, which also provides a warm place on which to lie outstretched, and hair to line the nest. The latter consists of a pad of grass in some hole in a rock, tree, or building. The 4 or 5 eggs are nearly white, as a rule heavily marked or spotted with shades of purplish brown.

See Plate 30 (colour). R.E.M.

Moreau, R. E. 1933. The food of the Red-billed Oxpecker *Buphagus erythrorhynchus*. Bull. Entom. Res. 24 : 325–335.
Someren, V. D. van. 1951. The Red-billed Oxpecker and its relation to stock in Kenya. E. Afr. Agric. J. 17 : 1–11. (Good photographs.)

OXYRUNCINAE: see SHARPBILL ; and under FLYCATCHER (2)

OXYURINI: see DUCK

OYSTERCATCHER: substantive name of all the species of Haematopodidae (Charadriiformes, suborder Charadrii) ; in the plural, general term for this small cosmopolitan family. Oystercatchers, sometimes called 'sea-pies', are large waders (16–21 inches long) with either black-and-white or wholly black plumage. The powerful bill is characteristic—being long, stout, laterally compressed, and bright orange-red. The rather thick legs are reddish ; and each foot has 3 toes, slightly webbed. The tail is short ; the wings are long and pointed. There are some slight seasonal and sexual differences ; and the juveniles are more dark brown than black and have less brightly coloured bills and legs.

On the ground the birds normally walk but can run swiftly. They can swim well on occasion. The flight is rapid and direct, with rather shallow wing-beats. Oystercatchers are noisy and restless birds, often by night as well as by day, the characteristic call being a loud clear 'klee-eep, klee-eep'.

The food consists chiefly of molluscs, crustaceans, annelid worms, and insects, varying with the particular habitat (rocky or sandy shores, estuaries, river gravels, moorland, farmland). The bill is specially adapted for opening the shells of bivalve molluscs but is also used for probing in mud or sand.

Oystercatchers are mainly birds of the seashore, and outside the breeding season they gather in flocks, sometimes of many thousands. Flocks of immature birds persist throughout the year, especially in certain favoured areas, for instance, in the British Isles, the northern coasts of the Irish Sea. It has been shown that the birds (at least of the European species) do not breed until three years old.

Oystercatcher *Haematopus ostralegus*. C.E.T.K.

As described for the species present in Europe, there is an elaborate 'piping' ceremony in which three or more birds run about with 'shoulders hunched' and bills held pointing to the ground, while they utter together a rapid high-pitched trill. This behaviour is probably concerned with the separation of breeding pairs from the flock ; both sexes take part and either may initiate it—and, apparently, immature birds do not pipe. As Makkink says, this ceremony is 'a mechanism which first enables the sexes to arrange themselves into pairs, and subsequently creates opportunities for the formed pairs to take up a position' against their fellows. Although this performance usually takes place on the ground, it sometimes occurs when the birds are in flight.

The nest is a mere scrape in the ground, which is often decorated—rather than lined—with white shells, bones, stones, and other objects. The 2–4 eggs (usually 3 in the European species) are yellowish buff, heavily marked with dark brown or black. One clutch is laid and both sexes take part in incubation. The cryptic coloration of the eggs is highly effective, and the old birds avoid betraying the position ; distraction displays (' injury feigning ') occur, and also ' false brooding ' at spots where no eggs lie. Incubation, in the European species, normally lasts for 26 or 27 days. The chicks run as soon as their cryptic down is dry ; they are, however, at first fed by their parents ; they take about five weeks to fledge.

The family has no representatives breeding in very high latitudes or in tropical Africa or southern Asia. Otherwise, the distribution includes the coasts of most of both Old and New Worlds, and also certain inland areas to be mentioned below. Populations in higher latitudes tend to be migratory.

There is only a single genus, and the numerous forms comprised in it are grouped by different authors in from 4 to 6 or 7 species. The taxonomic position is complicated by the existence of melanistic populations, by some regarded as consisting of black mutants and by others as constituting distinct species. The Oystercatcher *Haematopus ostralegus* in various subspecific forms, some pied and some black, breeds from Arctic Europe to the coasts of the Aegean, Black, and Caspian Seas ; on the Canary Islands and the coasts of temperate South Africa ; and in Australasia from New Guinea to Tasmania and New Zealand. Further, the race *H. o. longipes* breeds mainly about inland waters from Kiev eastwards through southern and eastern Russia and Siberia to the Cis-Altai steppes. The British race *H. o. occidentalis* has bred inland in Scotland for centuries

and has recently begun to spread along the river valleys in the north of England. The form *H. o. unicolor* (*H. ' finschi '* of some authors) breeds far inland along the courses of the snow rivers of South Island, New Zealand. All these inland breeding birds apparently winter on the coasts.

Certain of the New World forms are treated by some as races of *H. ostralegus*. By others they are assigned to separate species, such as the Black Oystercatcher *H. bachmani* of western North America and the more widely distributed American Oystercatcher *H. palliatus* subspp.

Other species which have been recognised are the Sooty Oystercatcher *H. fuliginosus* of the coasts of Australia and two which both inhabit the coasts of southern South America and the Falkland Islands ; of these last, *H. ater* is a black form while *H. leucopodus* is pied but with a black chest and under wing coverts, yellow (not crimson) eyelids, and other peculiarities of plumage. E.J.M.B.

Buxton, E. J. M. 1939. The breeding of the Oystercatcher. Brit. Birds 33 : 184–193.

Dircksen, R. 1932. Die Biologie des Austernfischers, der Brandseeschwalbe und der Küstenseeschwalbe nach Beobachtungen und Untersuchungen auf Norderoog. J. Orn. 80 : 427–521.

Huxley, J. S. & Montague, F. A. 1925. Studies on the courtship and sexual life of birds. V. The Oystercatcher (*Haematopus ostralegus* L.). Ibis (12 ser.) 1 : 868–897.

Makkink, G. F. 1942. Contribution to knowledge of the behaviour of the Oyster-catcher (*Haematopus ostralegus* L.). Ardea 31 : 23–74.

Stresemann, E. 1927. Die schwarzen Austernfischer (*Haematopus*). (Mutationstudien xxvi). Orn. Mber. 35 : 71–77.

Webster, J. D. 1941. The breeding of the Black Oystercatcher. Wilson Bull. 53 : 141–156.

P

PACHYCEPHALINAE: see MUSCICAPIDAE ; and THICKHEAD

PACINIAN CORPUSCLES: tactile nerve-endings in the dermis (see SKIN ; TOUCH).

PADDY: alternative name (plural ' paddies ') for *Chionis* spp. (see SHEATHBILL).

PADDY-BIRD: otherwise the Indian Pond Heron *Ardeola grayii* (see HERON).

PAINTED SNIPE: substantive name (sometimes colloquially ' painter ') for the two species of Rostratulidae (Charadriiformes, suborder Charadrii) ; in the plural, general term for the family. This is a remarkable tropical and subtropical group occurring in Africa, Asia, Australia, and South America. An anatomical character is that the sternum has two notches on the posterior border, as in the Jacanidae and Gruidae ; any resemblance to snipe *Gallinago* spp. is superficial. There are two genera, *Rostratula* and *Nycticryphes*, both monotypic.

In the Old World Painted Snipe *Rostratula benghalensis* the long bill, although shorter than in most snipe, is strongly decurved terminally and has a deep narrow groove, in which the nostril lies, extending more than half-way along each side of the maxilla. Distinctive also is the placing of the eyes for stereoscopic vision. There is no interwebbing of the toes. The tail, of 14–16 feathers, is short, stiff, and rounded. The sexes differ markedly in size and colour, the females—which are dominant in sex matters—being the larger and more brightly plumaged. The female is rich bronzy-green above, darkly vermiculated and with a buff V in the centre of the back ; a black breast-band separates the rich chestnut sides of the head and neck from the white under parts. The duller male is brownish, with white under parts, and the back is widely barred black with two buff streaks. Diagnostic in both sexes are the white or buff ' spectacle marks ' around the eye, and the conspicuous yellowish spots—also in the juveniles—on the silver-grey flight feathers and tail. There is no seasonal change. The nestling is striped.

The American Painted Snipe *Nycticryphes semicollaris* is smaller and is confined to South America. It differs, also, in some structural characters. The bill is more curved at the tip, and much expanded terminally on both the maxilla and the mandible, and pitted at the distal end ; there is a slight web between the middle and outer toes ; and the tail is wedge-shaped, with the median rectrices tapered and soft at the tip. The plumage of the sexes is similar, but brighter in the larger female. Above, it is almost black, without spectacle marks and with a central and two lateral stripes of buffish colour on the head ; there are two buff streaks on the back, and on the coverts there are conspicuous oval spots of white. There is a white patch on the sides of the lower neck and the under parts also are white. In Argentina the bird is called ' sleepy-head '.

Insects, especially orthoptera, small molluscs, worms, and vegetable matter form the food of these species. Painted snipe are unobtrusive skulkers and rarely seen in the open. Their flight is sluggish, and when flushed they fly off noiselessly and with legs hanging down. They run with lowered heads, and stand with the head down and bob the body. Naturally silent, both sexes utter a soft purring croak, which has been described as a deep mellow call ; there is also a whistling note. When the female is displaying she hisses and ' growls ' ; her voice is the more powerful as she has a long convoluted trachea, an organ which in the male is short and straight. Breeding takes place during the rains when food is plentiful. The female *Rostratula benghalensis*—there are two races, the nominate in Africa and Asia, and the other, *R. b. australis*, in Australia—has a spectacular courtship display, which is also a threat posture. The wings are spread and brought forward to beyond the tip of the bill and the tail is expanded, so that the bright spots show up

American Painted Snipe *Nycticryphes semicollaris*, of South America. *C.E.T.K.*

impressively. The females are territorially conscious and fight for the males. Pairs are rarely seen together, as pairing is temporary. Only males have been found incubating and rearing the chicks, and in Asia the typical race seems to be polyandrous. In domestic duties, as in coloration, the usual sex relationship is reversed. Brooding birds sit tight and creep away before rising. The nest is a pad of soft grass or other vegetation and is built by the male. It is usually well concealed in damp cover, the grass tips being pulled down over it. Four eggs are normal, but not infrequently the set is 5 or 6. They are pointed ovals or ovate, hard-shelled, glossy, and handsome. The ground colour is creamy or yellowish, profusely marked with bold black blotches, sometimes with lines and speckling, on underlying ashy and purplish tints. Eggs of the race *R. b. australis* are highly polished. The chicks are precocious and run freely soon after hatching.

In *N. semicollaris* it is the female that incubates. The eggs are two in number, white, and more evenly mottled with black ; but some are so densely blotched as to appear wholly black, and others look like black eggs flecked with white. The cry of this species is a plaintive whistle.

Painted snipe are found from sea level to about 7000 feet (East Africa) in marshy areas with adjacent drier conditions. Occurring singly, in pairs, or in small parties, they are nomadic and indulge in local movements, but it has not been established whether they are truly migratory.   C.R.S.P.

PAIR : collective noun for, inter alia, two birds of opposite sexes, ordinarily used of adults (normally of the same species) believed to be mated together.

PAIR FORMATION : establishment of a special relation between two birds of opposite sex. Practically every type of relationship between the sexes occurs among birds. Some species, e.g. ' lek birds ', have merely a temporary pair bond, the sexes meeting only for copulation (see LEK DISPLAY). More usually there is a lasting relationship, which may endure for days, weeks, or even years, and which may be monogamous, polygamous, or polyandrous (see POLYGAMY ; POLYANDRY). Monogamous relationships are most frequent, and it is with that type that this article is primarily concerned. Such relationships are of course normally heterosexual ; although homosexual pairing is common in captive birds, it is rare in the wild.

Pair formation implies that a number of social responses, potentially elicitable by any member of the species, become more or less limited to one individual ; at the same time other responses (e.g. aggressive ones) become inhibited towards the partner. When paired, the mates often tend to keep together for much of the time, and may show a special type of searching behaviour if they lose contact.

Pair formation depends on an exchange of signals between potential mates over a period of time. These may be visual (e.g. colours or structures, often exhibited by courtship displays—see DISPLAY), or auditory (e.g. song—see SINGING). Since hybrids are usually at a selective disadvantage compared to their parental types, it is important that pairing should be intraspecific (see HYBRID). For this reason the signals usually differ markedly between closely related species living in the same area (see ISOLATING MECHANISM). Specific differences in courtship postures are shown in every comparative study, and the relevant plumage patterns usually differ between species more than the displays themselves. Sympatric closely related species also often differ markedly in song (e.g. Willow Warbler *Phylloscopus trochilus* and Chiffchaff *P. collybita*). The study of hybrids shows that such interspecific differences are usually polygenic, and are thus likely to be of adaptive value. That this value lies in the prevention of hybridisation is suggested by the following types of evidence.

1. Divergence is most marked in those characters important in pair formation. Thus amongst carduleine finches, where there may be an interval of some weeks between pair formation and copulation, the

early courtship displays differ between species more than do those immediately preceding copulation (see COPULATION).

2. Divergence is often greatest where hybridisation is most likely, for instance in the overlap zone of potentially sympatric species.

3. Species characteristics often tend to disappear on oceanic islands, where no closely related species are present.

4. Divergence is more marked in males than in females. This is in harmony with Dobzhansky's view that since gamete loss is more serious for females than for males, it is primarily female preference that will be selected for ; but the fact is also explicable in other ways, such as the maintenance of female uniformity by selection for cryptic coloration.

Mayr has shown that hybrids are more common in genera in which copulation is not preceded by an 'engagement' period (e.g. Paradisaeidae ; some Tetraonidae), although hybrids do of course occur in groups that form lasting pair bonds. On the whole, however, hybrids are extraordinarily rare in nature, even among species that hybridise readily in captivity when conspecific mates are not available (see HYBRID).

Pair formation has been most studied in territorial song-birds (see TERRITORY). Where territorial establishment precedes pair formation and this occurs some time before copulation (e.g. Robin Erithacus rubecula, Snow Bunting Plectrophenax nivalis, Chaffinch Fringilla coelebs), the female is usually first attracted by the song or appearance of the male. The male normally responds aggressively to all intruders on his territory. If the intruder is a male, he flees or fights back. If it is a female not yet ready to pair, she flees. If, however, it is a female in condition, she usually stays around, often showing a 'submissive' posture, and the male's attacks gradually cease. The male then gradually ceases to be aggressive and begins to show courtship behaviour. The range of variations on this theme is of course enormous. For instance, the process may take anything from minutes to days ; the stimuli to which each sex responds may be primarily structural, behavioural, or both ; and the male's aggressiveness may cease almost at once or persist right up to copulation. Where pair formation precedes territorial establishment, it may start with the male's behaving aggressively to other members of the flock, although the process is fundamentally similar. Usually the increasing tendency of the male to behave sexually as the season advances is associated with a reduction in his aggressiveness towards his partner, who may then become domin-ant. Outside territorial song-birds, the diversity of behaviour is even greater. For instance, in some crows (Corvidae) and ducks (Anatidae) pair formation seems to involve a social ceremony. In most cases that have been studied in detail (e.g. Larinae), however, there seems to be a similar interplay between tendencies to attack, to flee from, and to behave sexually (or socially) towards the mate. The term sexually is, of course, to be interpreted rather widely, since in the early stages the consummatory situation is proximity to the mate rather than copulation, and the relation between male and female is little different from that between flock companions. It will be clear that the dominance relations during pair formation may be very complex ; indeed many species pass through a phase in which the female attacks the male during courtship, but the male attacks her at other times, so that a distinction can be made between sexual and social dominance. Although pair formation is usually associated with changes in dominance, it is very difficult to make useful generalisations about the role that dominance plays (see DOMINANCE (2)).

Because of the diversity of the processes of pair formation, it is impossible to classify species into a limited number of types. Lorenz attempted a classification that depends primarily on whether the displays of the sexes are similar or different, on whether one or both sexes show 'releasers', and on whether males respond initially to other members of the species by aggression or courtship. Although his classification has been criticised by Tinbergen, Lack, and others, and it is clear that his categories do not represent inclusive groups, they are useful as types.   R.A.H.

Armstrong, E. A. 1947. Bird Display and Behaviour. London.

Hinde, R. A. 1959. Behaviour and speciation in birds and lower vertebrates. Biol. Rev. 34 : 85–128.

Lack, D. 1939. The behaviour of the Robin. I and II. Proc. Zool. Soc. Lond. A, 109 : 169–178.

Lack, D. 1940. Pair formation in birds. Condor 42 : 269–286.

Lorenz, K. 1935. Der Kumpan in der Umwelt des Vogels. J. Orn. 83 : 137–213, 289–413 (and, 1937, The companion in the bird's world. Auk 54 : 245–273).

Mayr, E. 1942. Systematics and the Origin of Species. New York.

Tinbergen, N. 1948. Social releasers and the experimental method required for their study. Wilson Bull. 60 : 6–52.

Tinbergen, N. 1952. Derived activities : their causation, biological significance, origin and emancipation during evolution. Quart. Rev. Biol. 27 : 1–32.

Tinbergen, N. 1953. Social Behaviour in Animals. London.

Tinbergen, N. 1959. Comparative studies of the behaviour of gulls (Laridae) : a progress report. Behav. 15 : 1–70.

PALAEARCTIC REGION: 'Palearctic Region' (in American usage) or 'Palaearctis', the zoo-geographical region (see DISTRIBUTION, GEOGRAPHICAL) comprising the whole of Europe, Africa north of the Sahara, and Asia north of the Himalaya. Some seventy years ago the concept of a 'Holarctic Region' was introduced, reducing the Palaearctic and Nearctic (North America) to the rank of sub-regions of this ; but, despite substantial similarities in their more northern parts, these are now generally recognised as being sufficiently distinct to be treated as Regions in accordance with the classical terminology.

Effects of Glaciation. The Palaearctic Region is so-called because it includes that part of the Old World which lay under arctic conditions during the Quaternary Glaciation which terminated some 10 000 years ago after persisting for many thousands of years. But although it was subjected to arctic conditions, only a small area was actually covered by an ice-cap involving the complete extermination of life. The latter area included the whole of north-west Europe south to the British Islands, Holland, the Baltic, northern Europe north of 50° N. lat., south to the Black Sea and Caspian, and north-east to the Taimyr Peninsula. (See also GEOLOGICAL FACTORS.)

There were minor ice-caps in the Atlas, Pyrenees, Alps, Himalaya, and mountains of north-east Asia. There is no evidence that glaciation extended to Japan, but it was continued over the greater part of North America except parts of Alaska. But even in glaciated regions small pockets of unglaciated land persisted as it does today in Greenland : Ireland was probably much like Greenland is today.

Far the greater part of the Palaearctic Region was ice-free, with a tendency to a warmer climate in east and south-east. Birds, the most mobile type of animal, were forced east, south-east, and south, and this has its counterpart in the general return expansion westwards, north-westwards, and northwards continuing even today. During the last hundred years more than 28 species have extended their range westwards and north-westwards, following the retreat of the ice-cap, the most spectacular extensions being that of the Fieldfare *Turdus pilaris* to Greenland and the Collared Dove *Streptopelia decaocto* to Britain. There are 51 species of birds breeding regularly in Britain that do not do so regularly in Ireland ; the Magpie *Pica pica* reached Ireland only in 1676, the Stock Dove *Columba oenas* as recently as 1875, and the Black-necked Grebe *Podiceps nigricollis* in 1906.

Either glaciation or other influences also transformed many continuous distributions into discontinuous distributions. Today we find the Blue Magpie *Cyanopica cyanus* in south-west Spain and again in east China ; the Firecrest *Regulus ignicapillus* in Europe and Formosa, the Twite *Acanthis flavirostris* in north-west Europe and again in the Caucasus. Also it was almost certainly the effect of glaciation that drove the Magpie *Pica pica* into Yemen, and some European species into tropical Africa, where they left isolated populations when conditions in Europe allowed them to spread once more into the northern areas where the bulk of their numbers are now found.

Features and Boundaries. The main physical features of the Palaearctic Region are an almost continuous chain of mountains from the Pyrenees, Alps, Carpathians, Caucasus, Elburz, to the Himalaya, and an almost continuous belt of desert from Morocco to Sinai, Arabia, north Persia, Tibet, and Gobi. These features have exercised a profound influence on bird-life and its distribution.

The boundaries of the Palaearctic Region are clearly defined in the west, north, and east by the Atlantic, Arctic, and Pacific Oceans, separating it from the Nearctic. But in the south, where there is no ocean barrier between it and either the Ethiopian or the Oriental Region, there is no clearly defined boundary.

Greenland, although geographically part of the Nearctic Region, is, on the evidence of plants, insects, and birds, part of the Palaearctic, probably in consequence of some unknown distribution of ice in the post-glacial period. Only 8 Nearctic species have established themselves in Greenland, whilst 3 species (the Harlequin Duck *Histrionicus histrionicus*, Barrow's Goldeneye *Bucephala islandica*, and the Great Northern Diver *Gavia immer*) have reached Iceland.

The Atlantic has been an efficient barrier to avian dispersal. It is remarkable that no purely Palaearctic passerine species has reached North America within the memory of man, whilst but a single non-passerine —the Cattle Egret *Ardeola ibis*—has established itself in the New World by crossing the Atlantic. And despite the hundreds of American birds blown across the Atlantic or assisted by ships every year, not one single species of these has yet established itself in Europe.

In southern Europe the Mediterranean has been a less efficient barrier to dispersal than the Sahara, a desert constituting a more precise limit than a narrow sea. The northern and central Sahara are predominantly Palaearctic ; but at both ends we find Ethiopian species seeping up—some along the coast of Morocco and spreading east to Tunis and even to Spain, e.g. the Buttonquail (or Andalusian Hemipode) *Turnix sylvatica* and the Marsh Owl *Asio helvola*, and several up the Nile Valley and into

Egypt. The Canary Islands, Madeira, and the Azores are definitely Palaearctic.

Sinai is pure Palaearctic. In Arabia many Palaearctic forms reach to Yemen and Aden, some Ethiopian forms north to the Jordan Valley and Syria, and a few Oriental forms across southern Arabia as far as Yemen. In south-west Asia there are two remarkable cases of interrupted distribution, both Oriental kingfishers—*Halcyon smyrnensis* reaching Smyrna in Asia Minor and *H. chloris* reaching the southern Red Sea, the latter's nearest relative being 2000 miles distant in India.

The Persian Gulf and Persia are predominantly Palaearctic with slight Ethiopian and Oriental elements ; but farther east we find a more exact boundary between the Palaearctic and the Oriental Regions in the mountains of northern Beluchistan, the Afghan-Pakistan frontier, and then east along the higher levels of the Himalaya and into China about Szechwan and Hupeh, where there is a large transition zone. North of the Hwang-ho is definitely Palaearctic, as well as Korea and the whole of Japan.

In Kamchatka we find a close relationship with northern Alaskan birds ; several Nearctic species have spread to eastern Siberia, but only a few true Palaearctic species have spread to Alaska.

Subdivisions. Bird-life in the Palaearctic Region is by no means uniform ; there is scarcely a species in Korea that breeds in the British Isles ; nor is there any uniformity among birds from Scandinavia and the eastern Himalaya. It may therefore be useful to suggest 7 zones of bird-life in the Palaearctic Region.

1. An Arctic Zone of mainly circumpolar species, some of them extending south to the Alpine levels of European and Asiatic mountains, but absent from the Himalaya, Caucasus, and Tien Shan. The Ptarmigan *Lagopus mutus*, Snow Bunting *Plectrophenax nivalis*, and Lapland Bunting *Calcarius lapponicus* are typical of this zone.

2. A Siberian Zone characterised by boreal and coniferous forest and occupying a continuous area from eastern Siberia into Scandinavia, with a gradual reduction of species to northern Mongolia and Scandinavia, and again with isolated species in the Alps and Pyrenees, such as the Capercailzie *Tetrao urogallus*. The Siberian Jay *Perisoreus infaustus* and the Hawk Owl *Surnia ulula* are typical of this zone.

3. The Western European Zone of deciduous forest, narrowing to the southern Urals. A few birds typical of this zone extend to Scandinavia, south-west Siberia, and even Baikal. The forests of North Africa, Caucasus, and Turkestan contain others, such as the jays *Garrulus* spp., most of the

tits *Parus* spp., nuthatches *Sitta* spp., treecreepers *Certhia* spp., and some of the thrushes *Turdus* spp.

4. The Mediterranean Zone typified by xerophilus shrubs, steppe, and semi-desert, and extending through most of southern Europe, North Africa, and south-west Asia to Persia and Afghanistan, with a few elements extending north to southern England, Germany, Hungary, and the steppes of southern Russia. The Courser *Cursorius cursor*, bustards *Otis* and *Chlamydotis* spp., many larks *Calandrella* and *Melanocorypha* spp., and warblers *Sylvia* spp. are typical.

5. The Mongolian Zone including Mongolia, the arid parts of Turkestan, Persia, Syria, Asia Minor, Sinai, and northern Arabia, partially extending into the northern Sahara and Lybian deserts. Typical of this zone are the ground jays *Podoces* spp., the Marbled Teal *Anas angustirostris*, the Egyptian Nightjar *Caprimulgus aegyptius*, the rock partridges *Ammoperdix* spp., several wheatears *Oenanthe* spp., and the rock nuthatches *Sitta* spp. In the south-west of this zone there are many infiltrations from the Ethiopian Region, such as the Ostrich *Struthio camelus* in North Arabia until quite recently, and various species in Egypt.

6. The Tibetan Zone including the high Himalaya and extending sporadically to all high mountains of the Palaearctic Region and even to North America. There is no other continental area of the size of Tibet with such a distinct fauna, although we also find many types of European bird-life recurring. Typical are *Grandala coelicolor*, many rose finches *Carpodacus* spp., the Snow Partridge *Lerwa lerwa*, the snow-cocks *Tetraogallus* spp., the Blood Pheasant *Ithaginis cruentus*, and the Ibisbill *Ibidorhyncha struthersii*.

7. The Chinese Zone typified by the broad-leaved forests of south-east Asia prevailing in Japan and China and extending in the Himalayas as far as Kashmir, with a few elements in Afghanistan and one in the Caucasus. A few elements extend to Amurland, Trans-Baikal, and the Altai. Typical of this zone are the laughing thrushes *Garrulax* and *Pomatorhinus* spp., and pheasants of the genera *Pucrasia*, *Syrmaticus*, *Chrysolophus*, etc.

Characteristic Forms. If we omit infiltrations from other regions, the Palaearctic is more easily characterised by what it has not than by what it has ; this applies particularly to its western half. If we take the buntings *Emberiza*, we find 7 species in western Europe and 17 in eastern Asia. We have 4 flycatchers (Muscicapinae) in Europe and 14 in Palaearctic Asia. On the other hand, of the 15 species of warblers *Sylvia* breeding in Europe and western Asia, not one occurs east of the Yenesei or in Japan.

A comparison between the two extremes of the Palaearctic Region shows that 188 species breed regularly in Japan and 184 in the British Islands.

There are 116 passerine genera in the Palaearctic Region, taking genera in their widest sense. Of these, 25 occur also in the Nearctic, 32 in the Ethiopian, and 40 in the Oriental Regions. There are 213 non-passerine genera in the Palaearctic. Of these, 89 occur also in the Nearctic, 79 in the Ethiopian, and 84 in the Oriental Regions.

500 passerine species occur in the Palaearctic Region. Of these, 16 occur also in the Nearctic, 30 in the Ethiopian, and 101 in the Oriental Regions. 443 non-passerine species occur in the Palaearctic Region. Of these, 102 occur also in the Nearctic, 112 in the Ethiopian, and 105 in the Oriental Regions.

The Palaearctic Region has 65 genera peculiar to it, and of these 27 are passerine and 38 non-passerine.

A few groups require especial mention. Among the kingfishers (Alcedinidae) there are 88 species in the world, of which only 2 are Palaearctic and 2 Nearctic. Among the nightjars *Caprimulgus* there are 39 species in the world, 6 of which occur in the Palaearctic and 2 in the Nearctic Regions. Among the larks (Alaudidae) only one species occurs in the Nearctic, 18 in the Palaearctic, and 52 in the Ethiopian Region.

In the wagtails and pipits (Motacillidae) there are 5 species of wagtail *Motacilla* in both the Palaearctic and the Ethiopian Regions, and only one (a recent arrival) in the Nearctic. There are 10 species of pipits *Anthus* in the Palaearctic, 19 in the Ethiopian Region, and only 2 in the Nearctic. In the accentors (Prunellidae) there are 9 species in the Palaearctic and none in either the Nearctic or the Ethiopian Regions.

The Raven *Corvus corax* and the Horned (Shore) Lark *Eremophila alpestris* are truly 'holarctic': both encompass the globe in its Northern Hemisphere, both extend from the Arctic to the tropics, and both breed from 18 000 feet above sea level to below sea level.

For characteristic birds (Holarctic) see Plate 29 (colour). R.M.

Origin of the European Avifauna. Europe is only a relatively small western peninsula of the Eurasian land-mass and therefore a relatively small part of the Palaearctic Region. It is almost equal in size to the whole of China (including Manchuria), viz. roughly 3 820 000 square miles (9 950 000 square kilometres). Yet the number of bird species recorded from Europe is only about half of that known at present from China, 566 against 1099.

Nevertheless, the faunal composition of Europe is complicated. The composition of this fauna can be considered from the point of view of regional zoogeography in two ways, geographical and faunal. The geographical method is part of the classical zoogeography of Philip Lutley Sclater and Alfred Russel Wallace of the second half of the nineteenth century : it is a static method, that tries to define the boundaries of zoogeographical regions, districts, provinces, and so on (see DISTRIBUTION, GEOGRAPHICAL). The faunal method is dynamic : it tries to detect and to describe the far-reaching intergradation of separate faunas. This method, developed by such authors as Stegmann (1938) and Voous (1960), starts from the conception that there are distinct faunas but no distinct zoogeographical regions. The composition of the avifauna of Europe from this point of view will be discussed below. In the faunal analysis use is made of the concept of so-called 'faunal types'. A faunal type is a specific part of a regional fauna with a characteristic and well defined geographical and ecological historical background.

The Palaearctic Region of static regional zoogeography, of which Europe is a small part, is the Old World portion of the Holarctic Region. This latter comprises the whole of the non-tropical parts of the Northern Hemisphere. In the avifauna of Europe no less than 381 out of 419 known breeding species are of a so-called Holarctic faunal type (91 per cent). This means that each of these species has taken part in, or has been influenced by, the geographical and climatological history of Europe, Asia, and North America at least during the Pleistocene and part of the Tertiary periods ; furthermore, that the ecological characteristics of the geographical distribution of that species have been acquired during that history. The principal events of the history of the Northern Hemisphere have been discussed in an ornithological context by Moreau (1954, 1955) and can be summarised as follows : (*a*) A series of alternating expansions and contractions of glacial and arctic conditions and corresponding shifts of all ecological zones (ice ages). (*b*) The diminution and restriction of warm and subtropical forest areas and their attendant forest fauna, during the ice ages, into small and isolated geographical areas, notably in countries surrounding the Mediterranean Sea, in the South Caspian region, in parts of Manchuria, China, and Japan, and in restricted areas in western and south-eastern North America. (*c*) Periodic changes of sea level causing, among other things, the alternation of the presence of land connections and sea straits in many parts of the Northern Hemisphere. Any species of bird that has been subject to this history and has

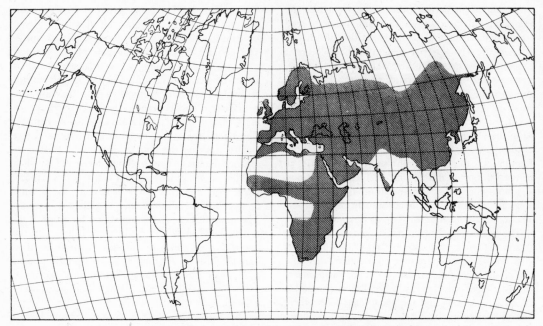

FIG 1. Breeding distribution of Kestrel *Falco tinnunculus* : Old World faunal type.

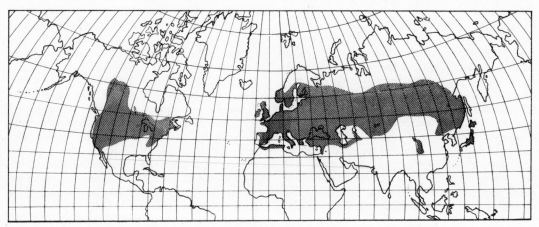

FIG 2. Breeding distribution of Longeared Owl *Asio otus* : Holarctic faunal type.

taken part in the vicissitudes of the Northern Hemisphere may be called a Holarctic faunal type, which means that it is a genuine element of the Holarctic fauna. (See also GEOLOGICAL FACTORS.)

Species of the Holarctic faunal type at present have geographical ranges differing enormously in size and location. The Mallard *Anas platyrhynchos* and the Long-eared Owl *Asio otus* (Fig. 2) with their wide Northern Hemisphere distribution are Holarctic faunal types equally with the White Stork *Ciconia ciconia* and Lesser Spotted Woodpecker

Dendrocopos minor (Fig. 3) of the Old World. The Robin *Erithacus rubecula* (Fig. 4), with its European distribution, the strictly Mediterranean Sardinian Warbler *Sylvia melanocephala*, and the Dartford Warbler *Sylvia undata* (Fig. 5) are also Holarctic faunal types. This means that for a faunal analysis the concept of Holarctic faunal type has to be subdivided. The necessary subdivisions include a 'Holarctic faunal type sensu stricto' (range: Old and New World parts of Holarctic Region), a 'Palaearctic faunal type' (range: Palaearctic part

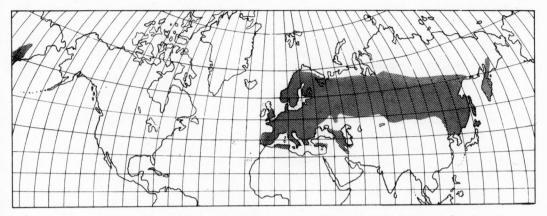

FIG 3. Breeding distribution of Lesser Spotted Woodpecker *Dendrocopos minor* : Palaearctic faunal type.

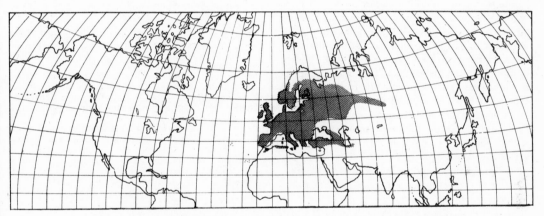

FIG 4. Breeding distribution of Robin *Erithacus rubecula* : European faunal type.

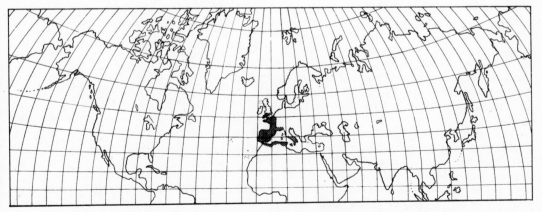

FIG 5. Breeding distribution of Dartford Warbler *Sylvia undata* : Mediterranean faunal type.

of Holarctic Region), 'European faunal type' (range: European part of Palaearctic Region), a 'Mediterranean faunal type' (Mediterranean part of European area). Several still finer subdivisions have been proposed, each with their own characteristic fauna and ecological geographical history.

In the *Atlas of European Birds* (Voous 1960) the following subdivisions of Holarctic faunal types have been proposed, the number of species being added in parentheses: Arctic (42), Holarctic sensu stricto (42), Siberian-Canadian (6), Siberian (21), Chinese-Manchurian (1), Palaearctic (104), European (28), European-Turkestanian (24), Turkestanian-Mediterranean (16), Sarmatic (9), Turkestanian (9), Palaeoxeric (7), Palaeo-xeromontane (4), Palaeomontane (9), Tibetan (1), Mongolian-Tibetan (3), Old World (18; e.g. *Falco tinnunculus*, Fig. 1).

In the Holarctic fauna a prominent aspect of the process of geographical species formation is the isolation of Old World (Palaearctic) versus New World (Nearctic) populations. Thus, apart from 5 North Atlantic faunal types (including *Larus marinus* and *Alca torda*), there are 81 (19 per cent) species of European birds that are still equally widely distributed in the Nearctic and the Palaearctic parts of the range. These represent the Holarctic faunal type sensu lato. In contrast there are at least 274 other species (65 per cent) which have clearly received their specific characters through geographical isolation in the Old World. These constitute the Palaearctic faunal type sensu lato. Finally, in the European avifauna 3 species are listed as of Nearctic faunal type (*Gavia immer*, *Bucephala islandica*, *Larus argentatus*) and one is listed as of Arctic type of Nearctic origin (*Larus glaucoides*). This means that these species are considered to be North American in geographical origin and that they have only recently extended their ranges into Europe.

The European avifauna also includes 4 species of Ethiopian and 14 of Indian-African faunal type. These are considered to have received their ecological determination, and to have had their speciation history, outside the Holarctic Region. They are members of other faunal groups, as indicated by their names; at least some of the Old World faunal types seem to have had their main geographical history not in the Holarctic range but in Africa or tropical Asia instead.

A last and almost negligible proportion of the European avifauna consists of Antarctic faunal type (1, *Catharacta skua*), Cosmopolitan faunal type (14, e.g. *Falco peregrinus*, *Gallinula chloropus*), and species that cannot at present be satisfactorily included in any of the recognised faunal types (5, e.g. *Sula bassana*, *Phoenicopterus ruber*).

The dynamic aspect of the geographical analysis of a local fauna by means of faunal types may be illustrated by the analysis of the regular breeding birds of Britain. These include the following faunal types, with the number of species in parentheses: Palaearctic (61), Holarctic sensu stricto (32), European (20), European-Turkestanian (19), Arctic (14), Cosmopolitan (9), Old World (7), North Atlantic (5), Turkestanian-Mediterranean (4), Mediterranean (3), Palaeomontane (3), Palaeo-xeromontane (1), Sarmatic (1), Tibetan (1), Nearctic (1), Indian-African (1), Antarctic (1), unknown (2). The foregoing terms are all defined in the *Atlas of European Birds* and some of the less obvious in this work (see PALAEOMONTANE; PALAEO-XEROMONTANE; SARMATIC; also PALAEOXERIC). K.H.V.

Faunistic works

Bannerman, D. A. 1953–63. Birds of the British Isles. 12 vols. Edinburgh & London.
Dementiev, G. P., Gladkov, N. A. et al. 1951–54. Ptitsy Sovietskoyo Soiuza. [Birds of the Soviet Union.] 6 vols. Moscow.
Etchécopar, R. D. & Hüe, F. 1963. Les Oiseaux du Nord de l'Afrique de la Mer Rouge au Canaries. Paris.
Hartert, E. 1910–22. Die Vögel der paläarktischen Fauna. 3 vols. Berlin.
Meinertzhagen, R. 1930. Nicoll's Birds of Egypt. 2 vols. London.
Meinertzhagen, R. 1954. Birds of Arabia. Edinburgh.
Niethammer, G. 1937–42. Handbuch der deutschen Vogelkunde. 3 vols. Leipzig.
Peterson, R., Mountfort, G., & Hollom, P. A. D. 1954. A Field Guide to the Birds of Britain and Western Europe. London.
Vaurie, C. 1959. Birds of the Palearctic Fauna vol. 1 (Passeriformes). London.
Witherby, H. F., Jourdain, F. C. R., Ticehurst, N. F., & Tucker, B. W. 1938–41. The Handbook of British Birds. 5 vols. London.
And many others, mainly of more local scope.

Zoogeographical references

Stegmann, B. 1938. Grundzüge der ornithogeographischen Gliederung des paläarktischen Gebietes. Inst. Zool. Ac. Sci. U.R.S.S. Nouv. éd. 19. Faune de l'U.R.S.S. Oiseaux I (2).
Moreau, R. E. 1954. The main vicissitudes of the European avifauna since the Pliocene. Ibis 96: 411–431.
Moreau, R. E. 1955. Ecological changes in the Palaearctic Region since the Pliocene. Proc. Zool. Soc. Lond. 125: 253–295.
Voous, K. H. 1960. Atlas of European Birds. Edinburgh & London. (Atlas van de Europese Vogels. Amsterdam, 1960.)

PALAEOGNATHAE: a formerly recognised superorder (see under CLASS).

PALAEOGNATHOUS: also 'palaeognathine' (Pycraft)—see PALATE; SKELETON.

PALAEOMONTANE: belonging to the fauna of the alpine or snow (nival) zones of the high mountains of the Palaearctic Region.

PALAEONTOLOGY: the study of fossilised remains of animals and plants (see ARCHAEOPTERYX ; FOSSIL BIRDS ; ORIGIN OF BIRDS).

PALAEOSPECIES: a species existing at an earlier level of geological time, possibly ancestral to one or more species of the present day but distinct from any of them ; the ordinary criteria of a species are purely contemporary (see SPECIES ; also CHRONOCLINE ; FOSSIL BIRDS).

PALAEOTROPICAL: inclusive term used by Sclater for his three southern zoogeographical regions in the Old World, contrasted with the Palaearctic Region (and on the other hand with the Neotropical) ; more generally, a term implying wide distribution in the tropical parts of the Old World (see DISTRIBUTION, GEOGRAPHICAL).

PALAEOXERIC: belonging to the fauna of the steppes and deserts of the southern Palaearctic Region.

PALAEO-XEROMONTANE: belonging to the fauna of the arid slopes of the low mountains of the southern Palaearctic Region.

PALAEOZOOLOGY: the part of palaeontology that is concerned with forms ascribed to the Animal Kingdom.

PALATABILITY OF BIRDS AND EGGS: regarded both from the subjective human standpoint and, so far as possible, from that of the observed preferences of other animals. The inverse relation that is commonly found between palatability on the one hand and vulnerability and conspicuous coloration on the other is particularly considered.

Palatability of the Flesh. It is well known that the flesh of birds differs widely in palatability. Some enjoy a high reputation in this respect, e.g. Quail *Coturnix coturnix*, Partridge *Perdix perdix*, Red Grouse *Lagopus scoticus*, Golden Plover *Pluvialis apricarius*, Woodcock *Scolopax rusticola*, Snipe *Gallinago gallinago*, Teal *Anas crecca*, Canvasback *Aythya vallisneria*, Corncrake *Crex crex*, Bittern *Botaurus stellaris*, and Skylark *Alauda arvensis*. Others are unfit for the table, e.g. Kelp Goose *Chloephaga hybrida*, Smew *Mergus albellus*, Shelduck *Tadorna tadorna*, Oystercatcher *Ostralegus haematopus*, Egyptian Plover *Pluvianus aegyptius*, Hoatzin *Opisthocomus hoazin*, and various hornbills (Bucerotidae), kingfishers (Alcedinidae), and drongos (Dicruridae). (See also GASTRONOMIC AND MEDICAL USES ; UTILISATION BY MAN.)

Attempts to assess relative palatability more exactly by experiments with meat-eating animals, and by observations of tasting panels, have extended knowledge to include a wide range of species not normally eaten by man, and have shown that among relatively vulnerable species, cryptic coloration, whether in the female alone or in both sexes, is generally associated with edibility, and conspicuous coloration with distastefulness. For example, in a series of experiments in which hornets were used in Egypt as assessors of the acceptability of the flesh of 38 species, the two rated as most acceptable (Wryneck *Jynx torquilla* and Crested Lark *Galerida cristata*) are also the two most cryptic in appearance ; and those of lowest edibility (White-rumped Black Chat *Oenanthe leucopyga*, Mourning Chat *O. lugens*, Hooded Chat *O. monacha*, Pied Kingfisher *Ceryle rudis*, Masked Shrike *Lanius nubicus*, and Hoopoe *Upupa epops*) are all conspicuous and include the only three species in the series examined having exclusively black-and-white coloration. On available evidence other and quite unrelated tasters, such as cat and man, show generally similar preferences and aversions. Nauseousness is a common but not invariable attribute of conspicuous birds, for many highly conspicuous species are nevertheless relatively palatable, e.g. various albatrosses (Diomedeidae), storks (Ciconiidae), egrets *Egretta* spp., swans *Cygnus* spp., cranes (Gruidae), gulls (Larinae), and macaws and cockatoos (Psittacidae) ; but such birds have no need of a nauseous deterrent, being otherwise protected—by large size, fighting strength, social habits, or ability to escape.

Tests recently carried out by members of a tasting panel in Northern Rhodesia (Department of Game and Tsetse Control) confirm the above general conclusions. Samples of flesh were assessed on a scale from 9·0 (excellent) to 2·0 (inedible). Of 191 species examined, the 19 rated higher than 7·0 include 15 cryptic species, and in 10 of these the female or both sexes are highly cryptic (Quail *Coturnix coturnix*, the Kaffir (or African Water) Rail *Rallus caerulescens*, Corncrake *Crex crex*, African Crake *Crecopsis egregia*, Water Dikkop *Burhinus vermiculatus*, Senegal Bustard *Eupodotis senegalensis*, Black-bellied Bustard *Lissotis melanogaster*, Double-banded Sandgrouse *Pterocles bicinctus*, Yellow-throated Sandgrouse *P. gutturalis*, and Fiery-necked Nightjar *Caprimulgus pectoralis fervidus*. In contrast, of 14 species with plumage that is black, white, or a combination of both, only the White-breasted Cormorant *Phalacrocorax carbo lugubris* (7·0) was rated as palatable, and Little Egret *Egretta garzetta* (6·3), and Openbill Stork *Anastomus lamel-*

ligerus (6·0) as moderate. Nine of the remainder are relatively or markedly distasteful, notably Pied Crow *Corvus albus* (4·9), White-winged Black Tit *Parus leuconotus* (4·8), Black (or Sooty) Chat *Myrmecocichla nigra* (4·5), Whiteheaded Black Chat *Thamnolaea arnotti* (4·5), Pied Kingfisher *Ceryle rudis* (4·1), Southern Black Tit *Parus niger* (4·1), and Black Cuckoo *Cuculus cafer* (3·0). The relation between visibility and distastefulness is also seen within the limits of restricted groups, for example : among 6 crakes examined, the only conspicuous species (Black Crake *Limnocorax flavirostra*) has the lowest edible rating (5·1) ; of 6 chats, the 3 most conspicuous are also the 3 most distasteful (all 4·5) ; the same relationship is found in 5 plovers, of which two (Blacksmith Plover *Vanellus* ('Hoplopterus') *armatus*, 5·1 ; and Long-toed Water Plover *Vanellus* ('Hemiparra') *crassirostris*, 4·8) are both relatively conspicuous and distasteful.

Colour Conflict. The inverse relation between acceptability of the flesh and visibility of the plumage is of special interest in connection with the concept of 'colour conflict'. It has been shown elsewhere (see COLORATION, ADAPTIVE) that concealing (cryptic) and revealing (phaneric) characters subserve many and diverse functions of adaptive value in the struggle for survival. Yet for optical-psychological reasons the two types of coloration, although both advantageous, are generally antagonistic and tend to be mutually exclusive.

The conflicting needs of effacement and of advertisement are reconciled in various ways. (*a*) Conspicuous characters, in birds of which the coloration is predominantly cryptic, may be revealed at special times by the momentary display of bright ornaments normally hidden (as in deflection displays, social recognition marks exposed only in flight, and the buccal feeding releasers of nidicoles, etc.). (*b*) Again, in many species, cryptic coloration is confined to the more valuable or vulnerable individuals, e.g. females in sexually dimorphic species where the males are conspicuous, e.g. many Anseriformes, Galliformes, and some territorial Passeriformes ; and nidicolous young, where adults of both sexes are conspicuous, e.g. oystercatchers (Haematopodidae), some plovers (Charadriidae), gulls (Larinae), and terns (Sterninae). (*c*) Relatively non-vulnerable species otherwise protected have no need for concealment ; for them the road to conspicuousness lies open and has generally been taken by both sexes, e.g. cassowaries (Casuariidae), gannets (Sulidae), pelicans (Pelecanidae), flamingos (Phoenicopteridae), some birds-of-prey (Falconiformes), cranes (Gruidae), swans *Cygnus* spp., many gulls (Larinae), and parrots (Psittacidae). Such birds are not protected by

distastefulness. (*d*) In many small and otherwise vulnerable birds the advantages of concealment have over-ridden those of visual advertisement, and cryptic coloration is developed in both sexes, e.g. in partridges *Perdix* spp. etc., francolins *Francolinus* spp., quails *Coturnix* spp., coursers *Cursorius* spp., stone-curlews (Burhinidae), nightjars (Caprimulgidae), pipits *Anthus* spp., larks (Alaudidae), warblers (Sylviinae). The palatability of such birds tends to render cryptic coloration of paramount importance. (*e*) Another line of evolution has led in the opposite direction, towards conspicuousness in both sexes, e.g. various plovers (Charadriidae), auks (Alcidae), turacos (Musophagidae), hoopoe *Upupa epops*, wood-hoopoes (Phoeniculidae), kingfishers (Alcedinidae), barbets (Capitonidae), shrikes (Laniidae), drongos (Dicruridae), starlings (Sturnidae), chats *Oenanthe* spp. etc., and tits (Paridae). But this trend has been possible only for relatively defenceless species when it is associated with the counter-deterrent of repugnant taste. The advertising coloration of such birds is (in part) warning (proaposematic) in function.

Palatability of Eggs. Experiments with egg-eating mammals of several orders (cat, ferret, mongoose, hedgehog, rat), and observations by members of a tasting panel (Low Temperature Station, Cambridge) afford results parallel in many respects to those considered above. Edibility and coloration are related to various factors that influence the availability of eggs to predators. Thus, eggs laid by larger birds, or in colonies, or in sites difficult of access, are in general more palatable than those laid by smaller birds, or by solitary nesters, or in accessible sites. Among otherwise vulnerable species, many eggs in the higher edibility grades are protected by cryptic coloration or are covered by a close-sitting cryptic parent, e.g. in many ducks (Anatidae), game-birds (Galliformes), bustards (Otididae), rails (Rallidae), waders (Charadrii), sand-grouse (Pteroclididae). On the contrary, conspicuousness of the shell is often associated with a repugnant taste.

In a series of 212 species examined, the shells of the most ill-flavoured eggs were commonly either immaculate white or white with reddish spots : Red-faced Mousebird *Colius indicus* (3·5), Green Woodpecker *Picus viridis* (3·5), Verreaux's Eagle Owl *Bubo lacteus* (3·3), House Wren *Troglodytes aedon* (3·2), Wren *T. troglodytes* (2·7), Speckled Mousebird *Colius striatus* (2·5), Black Tit *Parus leucomelas* (2·0). Among eggs of low-grade edibility, the most widespread distasteful property is bitterness, which is highly developed in the flavour-pattern of Columbiformes, Cuculiformes, Strigiformes, Coliiformes, Coraciiformes, Piciformes, and Passeriformes.   H.B.C.

Cott, H. B. 1946. The edibility of birds. Proc. Zool. Soc. Lond. 116 : 371–524.
Cott, H. B. 1954. The palatability of the eggs of birds. Proc. Zool. Soc. Lond. 124 : 335–463.

PALATE: forming a partition between the nasal cavities and the mouth and composed of both non-bony tissue and bone. In birds it seldom forms a complete shelf of tissue as it does in mammals, as there is often a cleft in the midline that leads backwards into the internal nares, and upwards into the nasal cavities on each side of the nasal septum (see NARIS). Folds of tissue at the sides of the internal nares (which may have a common opening) and the aperture for the Eustachian tubes (which lies farther back) are homologous, broadly speaking, with the soft palate of mammals. Salivary glands, arranged in paired groups, are usually present around the internal narial and Eustachian openings.

Bony Palate. The bony palate (Fig.) is made up of the same elements as are found in reptiles, except that the ectopterygoid or transpalatine is absent. Anteriorly are the premaxillae, which have shelf-like palatal processes fused in the midline at the front of the bill. Farther back these processes may be separated from each other by a cleft. There is often a large vacuity between them and the palatal processes of the maxillae, or maxillopalatines, which may or may not be fused or closely approximated in the midline.

The vomers, or prevomers, are usually fused into a single bone in the adult. On either side of these, and often separated from them by a gap on each side, are the palatines ; behind these again are the pterygoids, attached posteriorly to the quadrate.

The internal nares lie between the palatines and the vomers, and usually behind the maxillopalatines ; but in kiwis *Apteryx* spp., where the palate is exceptionally complete, the anterior parts of the palatines and vomers approximate in front of the internal nares.

Deeply placed in the midline of the palate is the rostrum of the parasphenoid ; posteriorly this bone widens out and is fused with the lower surface of the basiphenoid. The common opening of the Eustachian tubes can be seen at the base of the rostrum (Fig., B).

In many birds the pterygoids articulate with the parasphenoid and palatines by means of movable joints and the palatines are attached in front to the premaxillae. Movements of the lower end of the quadrate (kinesis) are transmitted through the pterygoids and palatines to the bill, which is thus raised or lowered (see SKELETON).

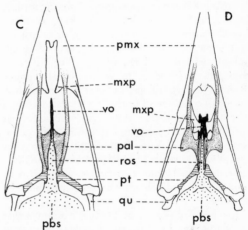

Palate bones, seen from below, in **A**, *Rhea* (dromae-ognathous) ; **B**, duck *Anas* (desmognathous) ; **C**, fowl *Gallus* (schizognathous) ; **D**, crow *Corvus* (aegitho-gnathous). In **A** the contact between pterygoid and vomer is on the dorsal surface of the palate.

A. d'A. Bellairs.

bp basipterygoid process **eu** opening of Eustachian tubes **f** facet for pterygoid on rostrum **mxp** maxillo-palatine **pal** palatine **pbs** parasphenoid and basi-sphenoid fused **pmx** premaxilla **pt** pterygoid **ros** rostrum of parasphenoid **qu** quadrate **vo** vomer

Taxonomic Significance. Since T. H. Huxley's work (1867), the structure of the bony palate has been used as a basis for classifying birds into major groups. The following types of palate have been distinguished.

1. Palaeognathous or dromaeognathous, found in 'ratite' birds and tinamous (Fig., A). Vomers large and imperfectly fused, in contact posteriorly with pterygoids, and separating pterygoids and palatines from parasphenoid rostrum. Well-developed basi-pterygoid processes for articulation with pterygoids set well back on parasphenoid, as in lizards.

2. Neognathous, characteristic of carinate birds. Vomers often small and completely fused. Pterygoids and palatines usually in contact with parasphenoid rostrum, and articulating with each other at a movable joint. Palatines usually attached in front to premaxillae. Typical basipterygoid processes usually absent, but often replaced by facets on rostrum farther forwards (Fig., B).

Neognathous palates have been further subdivided as follows. (i) Desmognathous (Fig., B), as in Anseriformes, Pelecaniformes, Psittaciformes, most Falconiformes, Strigiformes, and some other groups. Vomers small and tapering or absent. Maxillopalatines broad and meeting each other or the vomers in the midline. (ii) Schizognathous (Fig., C), as in Columbiformes, Galliformes, Sphenisciformes, Laridae, and others. Vomers tapering in front. Maxillopalatines not meeting each other or vomers in midline, so that there is an extensive longitudinal cleft in the bony palate. The palate of woodpeckers (Picidae), to which Pycraft applied the term ' saurognathous ' to cover the (erroneously supposed) condition of paired and separated vomers is not distinguishable from the schizognathous condition (de Beer 1937). (iii) Aegithognathous (Fig., D), as in Passeriformes and a few other groups such as swifts (Apodidae). Maxillopalatines separated, fused vomers truncated and broad in front, and forked behind, embracing parasphenoid rostrum.

Recent work (e.g. by McDowell) has shown that the distinction between the palaeognathous and neognathous types of palate can no longer be upheld. Important differences in palatal structure are to be found among the various 'ratite' forms and no single definition of the palaeognathous condition can be framed. These differences suggest that the ' ratites ' are not a natural group, and some of them are related to adaptive modification such as loss of cranial kinesis.

It is impossible to distinguish sharply between a palaeognathous and neognathous condition ; and, as de Beer has pointed out, some neognathous forms show palaeognathous features during embryonic development. For example, in some neognaths the pterygoid in the embryo makes contact with the vomer as in adult palaeognaths, but later the front end of the former bone becomes detached from the rest as the ' hemipterygoid ' and fuses with the palatine. Consequently the separation of the pterygoid from the vomer by the palatine, thought to be characteristic of neognaths, is in some cases illusory.

From this and other considerations (such as the probable presence of a neognathous palate of schizo-

gnathous type in the earliest fossil bird, *Archaeopteryx*) it would seem that the existing ' ratites ' are specialised rather than primitive in nature. They do show, however, many evidences of the persistence of embryonic characters into adult life (neoteny) in the structure of the palate and other parts of the body (see RATITES, PHYLOGENY OF THE).

The various subdivisions of the neognathous condition also merge into one another, and while palatal characters may be of value as a guide to the systematics of the smaller groups, they do not in themselves provide a reliable basis for major classification.   A.d'A.B.

de Beer, G. 1937. Development of the Vertebrate Skull. London and New York. (See p. 445.)
de Beer, G. 1956. The evolution of ratites. Bull. Brit. Mus. (Nat. Hist.), Zool. 4 : 57–70.
McDowell, S. 1948. The bony palate of birds. Part I. The Palaeognathae. Auk 65 : 520–549.

PALATINE: a paired bone of the skull (see SKELETON).

PALILA: *Psittirostra bailleui* of the Hawaiian Islands (for family see HONEYCREEPER (2)).

PALLIUM: the mantle (see TOPOGRAPHY).

PALMAR: pertaining to the ventral surface of the manus, or sometimes of the whole wing.

PALMATE: having three toes connected by webs (see LEG).

PALMCHAT: *Dulus dominicus*, sole member of the Dulidae (Passeriformes, suborder Oscines). It is confined to Hispaniola, West Indies. Some investigators place it in the same family as the waxwings (Bombycillinae) and their presumed relatives the silky flycatchers (Ptilogonatinae)—see BOMBYCILLIDAE ; others prefer classification as a separate family, principally because of the ' communal ' nests but also because of the harsher plumage, which lacks the silky quality and blended coloration of waxwings.

The total length is about 7 inches. The sexes are alike—greyish-olive (or brownish in worn plumage) above, and longitudinally striped with dark brown on a white base below. The head is darker than the back, the feathers having dark shafts ; the rump is dark green. The tail is relatively long, the wings short and rounded, and the tenth primary rather long and thin, when compared with waxwings. Likewise the bill is stronger, more curved and compressed, and the nostril is exposed. The juvenile differs in having the throat and foreneck almost entirely dark brown, with only faintly paler edges, and a buffish rump.

The species is locally abundant throughout the island of Hispaniola (comprising Haiti and the Dominican Republic) except in rain-forest and at higher altitudes. On nearby Gonave Island the birds are slightly more local in distribution.

New nests are built, or old ones repaired or added to, during the spring months (March–June). These are usually large bulging structures—sometimes 3 feet in diameter—of sticks and twigs, woven all about the smooth trunks of Royal Palms (*Roystonea*) and the bases of their fronds ; when the fronds die, the nests fall. Pines are also used, but to a lesser extent, and nests built in them are smaller—used by one or two pairs.

Likening such nests to a block of flats is perhaps more apt than the word ' communal '. Pairs occupy their own compartments, to which they alone have access by passages from the outside. Each nest is lined with fine grass and shredded bark, and here the eggs are laid. Nests with central chambers and passages have been described. About 4 eggs are to be found in a clutch ; they are white, heavily spotted and blotched with dark purplish grey or with a ring of this colour at the large end.

Berries (perhaps especially those of palms), as well as flowers of *Cordia* and other plants, are known to be staple foods. The birds are sociable and gregarious, even drawing together on the tree-limbs when roosting. No song has been recorded, but rather a noisy chattering in chorus as well as a variety of more or less pleasing notes.   J.C.G., Jr.

Greenway, J. C., Jr. 1960. Family Dulidae. *In* Mayr, E. & Greenway, J. C., Jr. (eds.). Check-list of Birds of the World vol. 9. Cambridge, Mass.
Wetmore, A. & Swales, B. H. 1931. The birds of Haiti and the Dominican Republic. U.S. Natl. Mus. Bull. 155 : 345–352.

PAMPA : an environment of prairie type characteristic of southern South America (see PRAIRIE).

PAMPRODACTYL : having all four toes directed forwards or (the first being movable) capable of being so directed (see LEG).

PANCREAS : an unpaired organ lying within the loop of the duodenum (see ALIMENTARY SYSTEM). In addition to secreting digestive juices into the duodenum, it secretes insulin internally, i.e. into the blood-stream (see ENDOCRINE SYSTEM ; NUTRITION).

PANDIONINAE : or ' Pandionidae ' if accorded familial rank (see under HAWK).

PANGAMY : indiscriminate mating (see under POLYGAMY ; also LEK DISPLAY ; POLYANDRY).

PANIC : in a special sense, a sudden wave of alarm

that—often for no reason apparent to the observer —spreads very quickly through a part or the whole of a colony of gulls or terns , the birds rising from their nests and flying seawards (if coastal), but that usually subsides very soon ; also called a ' dread '.

PANTROPICAL : of widespread distribution in the tropical parts of the world (see DISTRIBUTION, GEOGRAPHICAL).

PAPILLA, FEATHER : see FEATHER

PARADISAEIDAE : a family of the Passeriformes, suborder Oscines (see BIRD-OF-PARADISE).

PARADISE BIRD : see BIRD-OF-PARADISE

PARADISE-CROW : substantive name of *Lycocorax pyrrhopterus* (see BIRD-OF-PARADISE).

PARADOXORNITHINAE : see MUSCICAPIDAE ; and PARROTBILL

PARAKEET : substantive name (sometimes ' parrakeet ') of some small species of Psittacidae, usually with long pointed tails (see PARROT).

PARALECTOTYPE : see TYPE-SPECIMEN

PÁRAMO : term applied to an altitudinal zone in the Andes, just above the limit of trees.

PARASEMATIC : see under SEMATIC

PARASITE : an organism that lives at the expense, so to speak, of another species and commonly in or upon it, without reciprocal advantage to the host— and indeed often with disadvantage. Birds have many parasites (see ECTOPARASITE ; ENDOPARASITE ; also DISEASE). No bird is itself wholly parasitic. A few, however, are parasitic in respect of parental care (see PARASITISM) ; others are in a sense parasitic, as distinct from predatory, in their feeding habits (see PIRACY). True parasitism, in which the advantage is all on one side, is to be distinguished from associations that tend to be either neutral or mutually beneficial ; thus, in ' commensalism ' two species of organisms share the same food, while ' symbiosis ' denotes a more intimate partnership (see NESTING ASSOCIATION).

PARASITISM : the appropriation by one organism of a share in the resources of another. As a rule it exists between a more highly organised host and a less highly organised parasite ; thus birds support many ' lower ' parasites (see ECTOPARASITE ; ENDOPARASITE), but are rarely parasites themselves. There are birds, such as the skuas (Stercorariidae), which pirate the food catches of other species (see

PIRACY) ; and those in many groups which appropriate the nests of others, but it needs a stretch of the imagination to include these under true parasitism (see NEST ; NESTING ASSOCIATION ; NEST-SITE SELECTION).

On the other hand, nest parasitism, with which this article is mainly concerned, is a kind which birds and hymenopterous insects have made peculiarly their own. In this type, eggs are laid in the nest of another species, which then tends and rears the parasite's young. It is variously called ' brood parasitism ' (German ' Brutparasitismus '), ' breeding parasitism ', or ' social parasitism ' (by the entomologists), but it seems preferable to use the simpler term ' nest parasitism '. Among birds the Cuckoo *Cuculus canorus* (and related species) is the exemplar, and the bees, wasps, and ants which foist their brood upon the care of others are called cuckoo-bees, and so on. Nest parasitism has thus been evolved in the two groups of animals which have attained the greatest elaboration of instinctive behaviour.

Incidence. Nest parasitism exhibits the most notable and fascinating adaptations to enable the family cares of one species to be taken over by another. Altogether 5 or 6 families of birds are now known to have parasitic members. In the Anatidae there is only one example, the Blackheaded Duck *Heteronetta atricapilla* of South America, which lays in the nests of other ducks ; this is probably a recent and almost accidental change of habit. The family of weavers (Ploceidae) has one species known to be parasitic, the Parasitic Weaver *Anomalospiza imberbis* (see WEAVER) ; and among the weaver-finches (Estrildidae), the handful of species sometimes assigned to the subfamily Viduinae are probably all parasitic (see WEAVER-FINCH ; WHYDAH (1)).

The remaining 3 families, however, have specialised in parasitism much more thoroughly. In the Icteridae, most of one of the 5 subfamilies (Agelainae) are parasitic, forming a group known as the cowbirds, the species of which show an interesting gradation in the elaboration of parasitic habits (see ORIOLE (2)). These are the most important parasites in the New World, and the Common Cowbird *Molothrus ater* is an extremely successful species.

Among the cuckoos (Cuculidae) the whole of one subfamily (Cuculinae), and some species in a second subfamily (Neomorphinae), are parasitic ; the remaining 4 subfamilies have normal breeding habits (see CUCKOO). It is well known that specialisations connected with parasitism have reached a high standard among cuckoos, and the habit is probably a very old one.

Lastly there are the honeyguides (Indicatoridae),

most of the members of which are now known to be parasitic (see HONEYGUIDE). Further information will probably reveal that the remainder are parasitic also, and this may be the only bird family totally dedicated to the habit.

Adaptations. It is instructive to compare the structures and habits that have been evolved in these groups for the furtherance of their parasitic success. First, there are certain general conditions which restrict the spread of the habit. A parasite obviously cannot use host species which feed on entirely different food or are unable to bring enough. It is not worth while to parasitise scarce species, or those with nests hard to find or enter. Again, there must be a rough equivalence between the incubation and fledging periods of parasite and host. On account of these restrictions the two partners tend to be fairly closely related systematically except when the parasite is a cuckoo. Thus, the Viduinae parasitise other species of Estrildidae, and *Anomalospiza imberbis* parasitises other species of Ploceidae and also warblers (Sylviinae). The cowbirds parasitise either other cowbird species or other passerines, and the honeyguides predominantly the closely related woodpeckers (Picidae) and barbets (Capitonidae). This last is particularly significant, because woodpeckers, barbets, and honeyguides have a much longer fledging period than most small birds. The cuckoos, which make use almost entirely of small passerines, are the furthest sundered systematically from their hosts ; in this group alone, adaptation has reduced the size of the parasite's egg and the length of the incubation period.

The crux of the parasite's problem is to get its egg into the fosterer's nest in such a way that it will be accepted and incubated and the chick reared and fed. In the first place, therefore, nests have to be found just at the right stage, i.e. during or just before the host's laying. Where the nests are abundant and conspicuous, as with the crow hosts (Corvidae) of the eastern cuckoo species, the koels *Eudynamys* spp., the matter is easy ; but both in the typical cuckoos (Chance) and in the cowbird (Hann) there is a period of intensive searching and watching by the hen before each egg is laid.

Again, the egg must be laid quickly to avoid outraging the host to the point of desertion. The cowbird sneaks to the host's nest at first light when the parents are often absent, especially before the clutch is complete, but the Cuckoo *Cuculus canorus* most frequently lays in the middle of the afternoon and for a short time will have the parents mobbing it in a highly excited state. The hawk-like appearance of many cuckoos may elicit reactions on the hosts' part in defence of themselves rather than of their nests ; also, the evolution of egg mimicry in colour and pattern probably minimises retaliation by desertion or ejection. In the honeyguides there may be a struggle lasting a day or more before the male can lure the hosts away so that the female can get into the nest hole ; but, from the very fact that the hosts' nests are in holes and the colour of all the eggs is white, there is probably little danger of ejection.

Egg Mimicry. This is one of the most surprising adaptations in the evolution of nest parasitism. The cuckoos are the only group which has evolved a satisfactory matching of complex colours and patterns. They copy an extremely wide range of egg types and, when the standard reaches its highest point, it is difficult to distinguish the eggs of the cuckoo from those of the host. Any doubt on this point can be resolved by a glance at the colour plates given by Stuart Baker.

The standard of mimicry varies, of course, between different species of cuckoos and between cuckoos of the same species. Sometimes there is a glaring contrast, e.g. between the eggs of the Cuckoo *Cuculus canorus* and those of one of its common fosterers in Great Britain, the Dunnock *Prunella modularis* ; often there is only a rough approximation. But in most parts of the Old World there is now sufficient information to show that mimicry of a high fidelity exists. This information is most complete for the areas of India studied by Stuart Baker and for Europe (various authorities summarised by Southern) ; but enough is now known about the situation in Africa (Friedmann, Moreau) and a little about Australia (Barrett, Chisholm), which shows that, wherever there are cuckoos, mimicry of the hosts' eggs can become established.

Chance and others have shown that a single hen cuckoo remains attached throughout her life to one species of host, presumably that in the nest of which she was herself reared. This means that cuckoo species are subdivided into host-specific clans (or 'gentes', as Newton called them). Cuckoos of different clans can coexist in the same area, each being attached to a different host species. How the efficiency of mimicry in each clan is maintained, if there is crossing between males and females of different clans, is discussed later.

Adaptations of Young. Next for review are the adaptations to ensure that the parasite's chick shall be fed and reared, and these are as remarkable as egg mimicry. A parasite is either roughly equivalent in size to its host or larger. If about the same size, then the foster-parents will be able to collect enough food to rear both the changeling and their own chicks, and it frequently happens that

more than one parasite's egg is laid in the host's nest. But some of the cuckoos which parasitise small passerines are much larger than the hosts ; here the remarkable instinct of the young cuckoo to throw out its nest-mates redresses the balance, so that the whole of the food supply is devoted to the single chick. It follows that it is rare, except when host and parasite are similar in size, for more than one cuckoo egg to be laid in each nest.

It is puzzling to find a similar adaptation in young honeyguides, which possess transient hooks on each mandible with which they attack and wound and sometimes eject their nest-mates ; the available information has been summarised and discussed by Friedmann. Now, honeyguides are rarely larger than their hosts and are sometimes smaller, so that it seems unnecessary for this somewhat bizarre adaptation to have been evolved.

Young cowbirds never attempt to eject their nest-mates, although some may fail to survive in the competition for food. In cuckoos, such as the Great Crested Cuckoo *Clamator glandarius*, which in some regions foist their eggs upon crows, there is similarly no ejection of nest-mates, but there is a tendency for the upper juvenile plumage of the young cuckoo to mimic that of the nest-mates (Jourdain).

This last adaptation has arisen independently among the weaver-finches (Estrildidae) and, indeed, has been carried to a much greater degree of complexity. The young of each host species carry distinctive colours and markings on their palates, which presumably serve to release the feeding behaviour of the parents. Chicks of the parasitic whydahs (Viduinae) mimic these markings with notable accuracy. Information on the details of this mimicry is not yet as full as for the parasitic cuckoos and cowbirds, but the known facts have been discussed by Neunzig and by Hoesch.

Comparisons. To sum up, it can surely be said that, of the six groups, the cuckoos have shown the greatest resource with their reduction in size of egg and in length of incubation period, with their egg mimicry involving the subdivision of species into host-specific clans, and with their instinctive equipment to rid the nest of competitors. The honeyguides probably come next with their complex apparatus for attacking their nest-mates ; it is not yet known whether they are host-specific, but it seems certain that they are more restricted in the hosts they can use than the cuckoos. The cowbirds are remarkable in that only one species has attained true distinction as a parasite, but without evolving any of the complicated adaptations of the previously mentioned groups ; their eggs contrast with those of their hosts and they will lay in the nests of any locally abundant species, but yet they flourish. The whydahs have been even less adventurous (although knowledge is least about them) and have confined themselves to near relatives, thus avoiding detailed adaptations except in the one outstanding instance of the palatal markings.

Evolutionary Aspects. There are several fascinating evolutionary problems posed by nest parasitism. One concerns the selective situation arising from the wide range of discriminatory powers exercised by the host. Experimental work on species which normally foster young cuckoos has shown that some of them usually reject unlike eggs and others usually accept them, but most vary individually. Thus, there must be a double process of selection—to raise the standard of egg mimicry and to sharpen the host's discrimination. It has been argued that the logical outcome will be the perfection of the cuckoo's egg and, therefore, the extermination of the host ; this might happen regionally, but the result would be equally unfortunate for the cuckoos, and selection pressure both ways would be slackened.

One striking fact about cuckoo mimicry is the great preponderance of 'misfit' eggs in some regions. Southern has argued elsewhere that the highest standard of mimicry appears in habitats that are homogeneous over wide stretches of country, or which provide other methods of isolating birds of different clans. In western Europe, where intensive cultivation has long ago broken up the original habitats into a mosaic, the standard of egg mimicry in *Cuculus canorus* is very poor.

Indeed, in these regions matching is actually worse than if the cuckoos all laid one generalised type of egg. Capek (1896) cites 8 individual Cuckoos of which he followed the histories, all parasitising the Redstart *Phoenicurus phoenicurus*. Six of them laid eggs which matched well the pale-blue eggs of the host ; of the other 2, one always laid a chocolate-grey egg clouded with brown, the other a greenish-brown type, and nothing could have contrasted more sharply with the hosts' eggs.

These observations of Capek show that a Cuckoo may be permanently attached to the 'wrong' host, presumably because of crossing between the Cuckoo clans. This makes it even clearer that some form of isolation between the clans is necessary for a high standard of mimicry to be achieved ; so Cuckoo clans seem to fall somewhere between polymorphic phases and biological races.

Another problem is how the phenomenon of nest parasitism arose and whether it had the same mode of origin in the different groups. Friedmann has considered this question and has pointed out that the parasitic habit is usually accompanied by a decrease in territorial and courtship behaviour. In the cowbirds one can see a graded series from *Molothrus badius*, which steals another bird's nest but incubates its own clutch, through *M. rufoaxillaris*, which lays in the nests of *M. badius*, up to *M. ater* which parasitises a whole range of passerine species. Similarly, among the non-parasitic cuckoos many are poor nest-builders and may lay their eggs at odd intervals and sometimes in the nests of other species. Thus in each group the evolution of parasitism has been accompanied by some failure in the timing and emphasis of the different phases of breeding behaviour.

Finally, why have the two most successful groups, the cuckoos and the cowbirds, remained so radically different in the matter of host specificity ? The cuckoos, by their specialisations of egg mimicry and host attachment, have almost certain sacrificed some of the plasticity which the cowbirds have retained. In regions where eggs are well mimicked, individual cuckoos are probably either very successful or very unsuccessful ; thus there may be considerable regional oscillations in numbers of cuckoos and hosts, whereas cowbirds may maintain more stable populations.

Two small pieces of evidence may be offered. Schiermann gives the following figures on the decline from year to year of a cuckoo-parasitised population of the Reed Warbler *Acrocephalus scirpaceus*, together with the increase per cent in victimisation : 14 nests (29 per cent parasitised), 15 (40 per cent), 12 (50 per cent), 11 (73 per cent), 9 (67 per cent), 9 (67 per cent), and 8 (88 per cent). Clearly a successful Cuckoo may undo itself and find it has left little in its territory to parasitise. On the other hand, Common Cowbirds not only patronise a wide range of host species, instead of one, but their chicks are reared at the expense of only one of the host's chicks. Nice has shown that the survival of Cowbird chicks in nests of the Song Sparrow *Melospiza melodia* is about the same as that of the host's chicks (32 per cent compared with 36 per cent), so that a Song Sparrow population could carry a fairly heavy load of Cowbirds without fluctuating too much. However, these points may be misleading and it would be well to wait for more complete population figures to illuminate the matter.

The phenomenon of nest parasitism in birds has exercised a fascination on naturalists for many years and has stimulated some notable pieces of field observation ; one need cite only the work of Chance

(1922) among many others. The continuation of this tradition should bring many more interesting facts to light.

See Plate 46a (Cowbird—phot.).   H.N.S.

Baker, E. C. S. 1942. Cuckoo Problems. London.

Barrett, C. L. 1905. Cuckoo notes. Emu 5 : 20–23.

Barrett, C. L. 1906. The origin and development of the parasitical habits in Cuculidae. Emu 6 : 55–60.

Capek, V. 1896. Beiträge zur Fortpflanzungsgeschichte des Kuckucks. Orn. Jahrb. 7 : 41–72, 102–117, 146–157, 165–183.

Chance, E. 1922. The Cuckoo's Secret. London.

Chisholm, A. H. 1933. The cuckoo problem in Australia. Auk 50 : 385–395.

Friedmann, H. 1930. Social parasitism in birds. Smithson. Rep. 1929 : 363–382.

Friedmann, H. 1948. The Parasitic Cuckoos of Africa. Washington, D.C.

Friedmann, H. 1955. The Honey-guides. Bull. U.S. Natl. Mus. 208.

Friedmann, H. 1956. Further data on African parasitic cuckoos. Proc. U.S. Natl. Mus. 106 : 377–408.

Friedmann, H. 1960. The parasitic weaverbirds. Bull. U.S. Natl. Mus. 223 : 1–196.

Hann, H. W. 1941. The cowbird at the nest. Wilson Bull. 53 : 209–221.

Haverschmidt, F. 1955. Beobachtungen an Tapera naevia und ihren Wirtsvögeln. J. Orn. 96 : 337–343.

Hoesch, W. 1939. Kritische Betrachtungen zum Problem des Brutparasitismus bei den afrikanischen Viduinen. Beitr. Fortpfl. Vög. 15 : 200–214.

Jourdain, F. C. R. 1925. A study on parasitism in the cuckoos. Proc. Zool. Soc. Lond. 1925 : 639–667.

Lack, D. Cuckoo hosts in England. Bird Study 10 : 185–201.

Moreau, R. E. 1949. Special review : Friedmann on African Cuckoos. Ibis 91 : 529–537.

Neunzig, R. 1929. Zum Brutparasitismus der Viduinen. J. Orn. 77 : 1–21.

Nice, M. M. 1937. Studies in the life history of the Song Sparrow I. Trans. Linn. Soc. N.Y. 4 : 1–248.

Schiermann, G. 1926. Beitrag zur Schädigung der Wirtsvögel durch Cuculus canorus. Beitr. Fortpfl. Vög. 2 : 28–30.

Southern, H. N. 1954. Mimicry in cuckoos' eggs. In Huxley, J. S., Hardy, A. C. & Ford, E. B. (eds.). Evolution as a Process. London.

PARASPHENOID: a paired bone of the skull (see SKELETON ; and PALATE).

PARASYMPATHETIC: see NERVOUS SYSTEM

PARATHORMONE: see ENDOCRINE SYSTEM

PARATHYROID GLAND: see ENDOCRINE SYSTEM

PARATREPSIS: term for DISTRACTION DISPLAY

PARATROPIC ACTIVITIES: same as DISPLACEMENT ACTIVITIES.

PARATYPE: see TYPE-SPECIMEN

PARDALOTE: substantive name, alternatively ' diamond-bird ', of Pardalotus spp. (see FLOWERPECKER).

PARENTAL CARE: the protection, feeding, and general care of young by one or both of the parents from the time of hatching to independence. But FEEDING OF YOUNG is the subject of a separate article, and for care of eggs see INCUBATION ; see also DEVELOPMENT, POSTEMBRYONIC ; PARASITISM.

Hatching. Occasionally a male or female bird may bring food for yet unhatched young and even go through the motions of offering it.   When this is done by the incubating bird the stimulus probably comes from sounds or movements, or both, made by the chick within the egg.   These also inhibit the turning of eggs when they are pipped.

Normally the chick escapes from the egg by its own efforts, but in this and other forms of early parental behaviour the reactions of individuals may vary according to the circumstances.   The parent may merely lean attentively over the pipped egg, pick gently at the shell or flick away tiny fragments (Greenshank Tringa nebularia).   More than this is unusual.   Cranes Megalornis grus assist by breaking bits of the shell, and the female Water Rail Rallus aquaticus may enlarge the opening.   A Stone Curlew Burhinus oedicnemus has been observed to lift the tops off two eggs, and an Ostrich Struthio camelus will crack a shell with its breastbone and pull the chick out with its bill.   Passerines, when picking up half an eggshell, may ' empty out ' the chick.

Eggshell Disposal. Although in a few groups, mainly large ground-nesting species such as the geese and ducks (Anatidae) and game-birds (Galliformes), the parents leave the eggshells in the nest, the majority of birds remove or eat them.   Most species which abandon the shells have comparatively large families of precocious young which hatch within a fairly short time-span, and to leave them unguarded while removing shells would expose them to danger.   Many waders (Charadrii) remove the eggshells, sometimes to a considerable distance.   Even species such as the Ringed Plover Charadrius hiaticula, in which the eggshells are inconspicuous and the young active soon after hatching, do this.   A Spotted Sandpiper Tringa macularia has been known to eat the shells, but in this group such behaviour is exceptional.   Young American Flamingos Phoenicopterus ruber ruber eat fragments of shell.

In general, passerines more frequently carry away than eat the larger portions of shell.   Small fragments may be trodden into the nest.   Fine-billed insectivorous birds, such as the Sylviinae, usually carry off the shells ; species with stouter bills may eat at least some fragments, but individuals vary and occasionally the same individual may deal differently with separate fragments.   In some species, mostly large and nesting high in trees or close to water (Heron *Ardea cinerea*, Bittern *Botaurus stellaris*, Little Bittern *Ixobrychus minutus*), the shells are dropped over the edge of the nest ; but usually birds carry them far enough away to avoid their betraying the nest's whereabouts to a potential predator. The Goshawk *Accipiter gentilis* leaves the eggshells in the nest, but the Honey Buzzard *Pernis apivorus* often puts one half into the other before carrying them away. Eggshell disposal has practical value in preventing the chicks from injuring themselves on the sharp edges.

Nest Sanitation. Disposal of the faeces (see DROPPINGS) by the parents, either by removing or swallowing, is mainly confined to the Passeriformes and the orders nearest to them. There are exceptions such as the Ruddy Ground Dove *Columbigallina talpacoti*, which eats the faeces. Removal of faeces is associated with the construction of a nest of fine materials or nesting in a cavity, so these forms of behaviour must have evolved pari passu with the physiological adaptation involving encapsuled faeces and the procedures for disposing of them. Nests composed of, or lined with, fine materials could readily become unhygienic if sanitation were neglected, so selection has apparently operated in favour of birds which do not foul their nests. Normally, during the first few days, the faeces are swallowed by one of the parents, usually the female, who is most attentive then ; later they are carried away, although swallowing may continue to some extent. In some species, towards the end of the nestling period, the chicks may deposit sacs on the rim of the nest or, if the nest is roofed, they are usually extruded at the entrance. In some species of hummingbirds (Trochilidae) the female at first casts out the droppings but later the nestlings eject the faeces over the rim. When the nestlings are naked, swallowing the sacs reduces the numbers of journeys made by the parents and the amount of time during which the young are not being brooded. The procedure may depend on circumstances : thus in the Turdinae, when the nestlings are fairly well grown, if two of them extrude faeces while the parent is at the nest one sac may be swallowed and the other carried away. In many species the sac is taken from the chick which has just been fed. At roofed nests this obviates confusion, the chicks in turn replacing each other at the entrance. At an open nest the parent waits while the chick squats and raises the cloaca ; the chick may be stimulated by prodding or tugging its down (Yellow Wagtail *Motacilla flava*). Rarely, sacs may be laid on the rim of the nest and carried off when the brooding bird leaves (Chough *Pyrrhocorax pyrrhocorax*). Towards the end of the nestling period the rim of nests of some passerines such as the Gold-

finch *Carduelis carduelis* and Crossbill *Loxia curvirostra* may become badly soiled : this may be correlated with the comparatively infrequent visits of the parents to the nest. The chicks of most nidicolous non-passerines squirt the faeces over the edge of the nest, or from the entrance if the nest is in a cavity, as is the case with hornbills (Bucerotidae), although the passage in burrow-style nests may become foul (Kingfisher *Alcedo atthis*).

In regard to nest sanitation some species seem imperfectly adapted. The excrement of nestlings of *Guira guira*, belonging to a subfamily of cuckoos (Crotophaginae), is not encapsuled, and the nest becomes filthy ; the behaviour of this tropical American species has exceptional characteristics, several females laying in a common nest. Changes in nest sanitation are apt to lag behind changes in nesting behaviour. The nesting place of the Swift *Apus apus* becomes dirty, but the niches in buildings commonly used hold excrement more readily than the cliff crevices which were the bird's ancestral nesting niches. Guano serves to enlarge the nesting ledges used by the Black Noddy *Anous tenuirostris* and to bind together the nest material.

When the nest is so situated that the chicks can move out and return without unduly increasing their vulnerability they may defecate outside it (Montagu's Harrier *Circus pygargus*). Young Nightjars *Caprimulgus europaeus* deposit the droppings some distance from their squatting place. If there is a stream within 100 yards the female Lyrebird *Menura novaehollandiae* carries the faeces and deliberately submerges it ; otherwise she digs a hole and buries it. The Dipper *Cinclus cinclus* picks up sacs which fail to fall into the stream and washes them off its bill in the water. Other passerines will flutter after, and try to catch, sacs which accidentally fall. Some woodpeckers (Picidae) hammer the sides of the nesting cavity and carry out the faeces covered in powdered wood dust. The removal of excrement probably has value in reducing the danger of the nest being discovered by predators, but the winter roosts of Wrens *Troglodytes troglodytes* and treecreepers *Certhia familiaris* and *C. brachydactyla* are identifiable by the clotted white excreta outside, and there is no evidence that this increases vulnerability.

Nest Probing and Nest Cleaning. Many species, varying from the White Stork *Ciconia ciconia* to small passerines, probe the nest floor. Tits (Paridae), for example, plunge head downwards among the nestlings, making vigorous movements. This procedure serves to keep the nest clean and tidy. Probably parasites and foreign matter are removed and swallowed, and the lining smoothed. Species with nidicolous young remove small objects, such as leaves, which fall on the young, and they may carry off small dead nestlings. Raptors take away picked carcasses and bones and bring branches with green leaves which sometimes form a soft pad over the main structure.

Brooding Rhythm. When the young of nidicolous species emerge from the egg the number of parental sorties per day increases, usually rather abruptly, and as the chicks grow there is a progressive reduction in the amount of time spent brooding them. For example, the Wren reduces brooding by 6–8 per cent per day. In passerines the cessation of brooding during the day and the effective functioning of the chicks' temperature control tend to coincide. Thus, rearing the chicks involves a progressive compromise between time spent warming the young and seeking food for them. See FEEDING OF YOUNG.

Protection from Weather. Nestlings are shaded from the sun or rain when necessary, the parent's wings and tail being spread over the nest. Birds with nidifugous young may also shelter them from sun or heavy rain.

Protection from Predators. Many birds utter warning cries which cause the chicks, in or out of the nest, to squat motionless or, if they have left the nest, to disperse to cover. The brooding Wryneck *Jynx torquilla* vocally simulates a hissing snake when an intruder is at the nest entrance, but incubating tits (Paridae) of several species achieve the same effect by rapidly flipping their wings. The parents may adopt menacing postures or offer physical violence with bill, wings, or feet, flutter near the predator, or behave in such a way as to deflect it by their utterances, movements, or adornments (see DISTRACTION DISPLAY). Where birds nest in colonies, or a number of species react together, a predator may be mobbed (see FLOCKING). Birds with nidifugous chicks will entice them away from danger with calls and appropriate movements. They may shelter them under their bodies or wings (Willow Ptarmigan *Lagopus lagopus*), and some species will carry them away in their mandibles (Water, King, and Clapper Rails *Rallus aquaticus*, *R. elegans*, *R. longirostris*) or between their thighs (Woodcock *Scolopax rusticola*, American Woodcock *Philohela minor*). Young grebes (Podicipitidae) and cygnets of the Mute Swan *Cygnus olor* ride on the parent's back (see also CARRYING).

Watering, etc. A few birds, such as the White Stork *Ciconia ciconia* and Cormorant *Phalacrocorax carbo*, bring fluid or water which they pour into the gapes of the nestlings. Male Sandgrouse (Pteroclididae) have been said to soak their breast feathers and allow the young to suck them, but this has been questioned ; the Kea *Nestor notabilis* is reputed to bathe frequently and thus to maintain humidity in the nesting cavity. The feathers given to young grebes probably lodge in the gizzard and assist the assimilation of food. Some passerines may bring grit to the nestlings (see GRIT). A Golden Eagle *Aquila chrysaetos* may preen the downy eaglets.

Guiding from Nest ; Leading to Roost. Nidicolous young usually leave the nest on their own initiative, although the excited movements of the parents with food may sometimes have a stimulatory effect. Nidifugous chicks have a strong inborn tendency to follow a parent as soon as they are sufficiently active (see IMPRINTING). In some species (Bittern *Botaurus stellaris*, Marsh Harrier *Circus aeruginosus*, Short-eared Owl *Asio flammeus*) the young may take cover in the surrounding vegetation, especially if disturbed, so that the vacation of the nest is a gradual process. One or other or both parents may lead newly fledged young to a roost, as in the Wren *Troglodytes troglodytes* and some woodpeckers (Picidae). Young Little Grebes *Podiceps ruficollis* may spend the night on the parent's back as she sits on the nest ; Ringed Plover chicks rest on the shingle beneath the squatting parent. Among ducks (Eider *Somateria mollissima*, Redbreasted Merganser *Mergus serrator*, Shelduck *Tadorna tadorna*) and some other birds, the female may take charge of young other than her own.

Roles of Male and Female. There are wide variations in the extent to which, in different species, one or other of the parents tends the young. It is sometimes possible if one parent disappears for the other to rear the chicks (White Stork, Wren). Many factors are involved, particularly the nature of the pair bond (see POLYGAMY ; POLYANDRY). In some waders (Charadrii, e.g. Whimbrel *Numenius phaeopus*) the female abandons the unfledged downy chicks to the male's care. In general, and especially in passerines, even if the male does not incubate he helps to feed the newly hatched young. The performance of duties may depend on which parent is present. Thus the female commonly removes the eggshells and the male removes faeces if he happens to be at the nest when they are extruded.

In general, female birds show distraction behaviour more readily and vehemently than males (see DISTRACTION DISPLAY). Even in groups, such as the tyrant-flycatchers (Tyrannidae), in which the male assists comparatively little, he will shade the nestlings from the sun. In some species (Snow Bunting *Plectrophenax nivalis*) each parent undertakes the care of some of the chicks after they have left the nest. In strongly territorial birds adults may become intolerant of their own young if they have not departed before the inception of a later nesting cycle, but there are species (Southern House Wren *Troglodytes musculus*, Swallow *Hirundo rustica*, Moorhen *Gallinula chloropus*) in which the young feed chicks of a later brood. Parent birds are sometimes assisted in tending the young by another individual of the same species (Long-tailed Tit *Aegithalos caudatus*), and occasionally nestlings are fed by a bird of another species as well as by the parents.

Learning. Chicks may learn to a minor extent from the example of the parents or other birds. They may be stimulated to peck by observing the action of a parent, and some song-birds learn their songs to greater or lesser extent by hearing adults ; but birds do not, in the ordinary sense of the word, teach their young (see BEHAVIOUR, DEVELOPMENT of ; LEARNING ; SINGING).

See Plates 38ab, 39ab, 40ab, 45ab, 46ab (phot.).

E.A.A.

Eisner, E. 1960. The relationship of hormones to the reproductive behaviour of birds, referring particularly to parental behaviour : a review. Anim. Behav. 8 : 155–179.

Kendeigh, S. C. 1952. Parental Care and its Evolution among Birds. Illinois Biol. Monog. 22 (1–3) : 1–356.

PARIDAE: a family of the Passeriformes, suborder Oscines (see TIT).

PARIETAL: a paired bone of the skull (see SKELETON).

PARROT: substantive name of many species of Psittacidae, sole family of the Psittaciformes ; in the plural, general term for the family and order. The name ' parakeet ' (or ' parrakeet ') is usually restricted to small species with long pointed tails ; various other names are mentioned below.

Almost no other large group of birds is more sharply set apart from all others than the parrots, which form an exclusive order by themselves. All of them, in common, show striking characteristics and a very high degree of specialisation. In spite of wide variation in size, ranging from 4 to 40 inches in total length, they are all similar in appearance and structure. The bill is always short, stout, and strongly hooked, with a bulging cere (sometimes feathered) at its base. The upper mandible is articulated and not firmly joined to the skull, allowing some movement. The short neck and compact body give a bulky appearance to these birds, which have strong yet rather rounded wings, so that, although most species can fly very fast over short distances, their powers of sustained flight are generally poor. Indeed, some species, such as the

Australian Ground Parrot *Pezoporus wallicus*, have almost lost the power of flight. The tail is variable in length, sometimes short as in lories and lorikeets, sometimes very long as in parakeets and macaws. The tarsi are short ; the toes zygodactyl and covered with tiny granular scales. The plumage, sparse and hard, is brightly coloured in most species. The most common coloration is green, but many species are gaudily multi-coloured, with red, yellow, and blue areas. The sexes are alike in colour, with some remarkable exceptions. Most parrots, strictly arboreal, are very capable climbers owing to the structure of their feet. They also use the hooked bill, as a third foot, to pull themselves forward among branches or along tree trunks. Parrots are typically birds of forested areas ; but some of them, especially the Australian parakeets, live mainly on the ground, feeding there but climbing and perching freely in trees and also nesting therein.

The diet of the parrots is mainly vegetarian, although some of them occasionally eat insects. The heavy bill and thick fleshy tongue allow them to feed even on nuts with hard thick woody shells such as those of the Oil Palm, which they break very easily while holding the nut in one foot. They are very fond of fruits and berries of every kind, and some species are nectar-feeders. They all thus tend to be attracted to farms and orchards, where they may cause damage.

Parrots nest in holes, mostly in trees and rarely in rocks or in sand banks. Termite nests are also usurped by some species. Most parrots bring no nest material to the cavity ; the eggs are merely laid on wood chips, although some species, such as the lovebirds *Agapornis* spp. and hanging parrots *Loriculus* spp., collect grass and other fibres, which they carry to the nest in the bill or (in *Agapornis*) among the rump feathers. An exception, the Green Parakeet *Myiopsitta monachus* of Argentina, breeds in large colonies and builds huge communal nests in trees, each pair having its own separate chamber. The almost flightless Australian Ground Parrot nests on the ground in tufts of grass, as did the now extinct Night Parrot *Geopsittacus occidentalis* (also almost flightless) of the same continent.

The eggs are relatively small, generally 2–5 in number but sometimes up to 8, and are always pure white. After incubation, averaging three weeks, the young are hatched naked and helpless ; they are fed by the parents by regurgitation of partially digested vegetable crop-contents.

Parrots, usually very gregarious and of high psychological development, are the noisiest of all birds. Their voices tend to be harsh, screaming, and definitely disagreeable. In captivity, several species can be taught to imitate human words with amazing fidelity (see MIMICRY, VOCAL).

The distribution of parrots covers the whole inter-tropical zone of the world, from which they have spread to subtropical and even to cold parts of the Southern Hemisphere (Patagonia, Tasmania) and even of the Northern Hemisphere, especially in the New World. The main centres of dispersion are South America (Amazon basin) and Australasia. Most of them are sedentary, but they show a certain nomadism governed by seasonal ripening of fruits and the flowering of blossoms, especially in arid parts of their habitat (Australia).

The highly specialised characters of parrots make relationships with other groups very hypothetical. In spite of some superficial similarity to the owls (Strigiformes), they are also related to the turacos (Musophagidae) and cuckoos (Cuculidae). All these links, however, are indistinct and suggest a very ancient origin. Some Tertiary fossils, from the Miocene of France and of North America, are already distinctly parrots. The family comprises about 82 genera and 316 species. Except for a few extreme types, the whole group is structurally similar ; in fact, divisions into subfamilies are artificial, although convenient.

Nestorinae. The two parrots of the genus *Nestor*, the Kea *N. notabilis*, and the Kaka *N. meri-dionalis* (with two subspecies), are native to New Zealand and adjacent islands and have dull olive-brown plumage and rather long compressed bills, the least curved among all parrots. They have been charged with killing sheep, by tearing away the wool to peck the fat and flesh ; the sheep-killing habit and carnivorous diet are recently acquired tendencies of these primarily vegetarian birds.

Strigopinae. Another parrot native to New Zealand is the Kakapo (or Owl Parrot) *Strigops habroptilus*, which is wholly nocturnal in habits and even looks somewhat like an owl owing to the way in which the head feathers radiate like a facial disk and to its rather soft plumage. This bird remains hidden by day among the roots of trees, where it also nests. It does not fly, but runs on the ground or climbs about in trees, aiding its progress by using its wings.

Loriinae. The lories and lorikeets, of wide dis-tribution through Papua, Australia, and Polynesia, are extremely bright in colour and rather small in size. They all have relatively small bills, and the tongue has a brush-like tip. As in the honeyeaters (Meliphagidae), this structure permits the lories to gather pollen and nectar within the flowers rich in honey, especially those of the lofty gum (eucalyptus) trees. They are also fond of fruits and buds. Most of the lories are gregarious. The large species such as the Rainbow Lorikeet *Trichoglossus haematodus* have long pointed tails, whereas the smaller species of *Chalcopsitta* and related genera have rather short rounded tails. They probably play a major part in the pollination of trees on the flowers of which they feed (see POLLINATORS AND DISTRIBUTORS).

Micropsittinae. The pygmy parrots *Micropsitta* spp., native to New Guinea and adjacent islands, are often considered a subfamily; they are the smallest of all the parrots, as they do not exceed 4 inches in length. The tail is short and square, with stiff feather-shafts extending back beyond the vanes. They show well defined sexual dimorphism, the male being duller. They live in dense forests, and they feed not only on fruits but even on fungi and on arboreal termites that they pry from the nests with the bill.

Kakatoeinae. The cockatoos form a small group restricted to Papua, Australia, and adjacent islands. The most conspicuous external character-istic of these large parrots is the long erectile crest. Several species are mainly white, except for a few red or yellow marks. The Black Cockatoo *Probos-ciger aterrimus* and the raven cockatoos *Calypto-rhynchus* spp. have dark slaty or almost black plumage. The powerful bill of these birds, often compressed and sharply tipped, is used as a crushing and extract-ing tool to open hard nuts, especially those of the palm trees on which these birds commonly feed.

Psittacinae. The typical parrots (including para-keets, parrotlets, macaws, amazons, lovebirds, bud-gerigars, and rosellas) are distributed over a vast area of the tropical and subtropical regions of the entire world. The ranges of some species extend even into temperate and cold regions, notably the Andean parakeets *Bolborhynchus* spp., which live at heights of up to 12 000 feet ; but most species live in warm forested areas. The most spectacular American parrots are the macaws *Ara* and *Anodorhynchus* spp., ranging from Mexico to Paraguay. These long-tailed brightly coloured birds are the largest Psit-tacidae in the world, averaging 40 inches in length. The amazons *Amazona* spp., medium-sized parrots with rather short tails, have a mainly green plumage, marked by brilliant red, yellow, or blue areas, especially on the ventral surface.

The best-known African species is the Grey Parrot *Psittacus erithacus*, the distribution of which embraces all tropical Africa. Feeding on all kinds of seeds and fruits, it is very fond of nuts of the Oil Palm (*Elaeis*), which it thus helps to disseminate over the African forests. The lovebirds *Agapornis* spp. include several distinct species, none of them exceed-ing 6½ inches in length ; the name comes from the affection which seems to link the pairs together.

Another well-known African species is the Ring-necked Parakeet *Psittacula krameri*, also distributed over the warmer parts of south-eastern Asia (along with other well-defined species which are confined to that continent). The Eclectus Parrot *Lorius roratus*, distributed from eastern Indonesia to North Queensland and the Solomons, shows one of the most striking examples of sexual dimorphism to be found among birds ; both sexes are brightly coloured, but whereas the male is green, the female is red and blue. The bat-parrots *Loriculus* spp., distributed from the Himalaya to Papua, are the strangest of the smaller species, owing to their peculiar habit of hanging like bats from branches by their feet, head down.

Australia is inhabited by a wide variety of colourful species of parakeets or rosellas *Platycercus* spp. and allies, often kept in captivity. The commonest of all, the Budgerigar *Melopsittacus undulatus*, swarms by millions in the most arid parts of the continent ; in captivity it has given rise by selective breeding to a vast number of colour variations, white, yellow, grey, violet, or blue, in sharp contrast with the green wild bird.

Since remotest antiquity, parrots have been captured on a very large scale for use as cage or aviary birds (see AVICULTURE ; CAGE BIRDS). This, and the fact that many species may be injurious to agriculture and are therefore persecuted, have threatened the survival of many species. Several indeed are already extinct, especially on small islands such as the Mascarenes and Antilles (see EXTINCT BIRDS). The most notable extinct species is the Carolina Parakeet *Conuropsis carolinensis*, the only parrot of temperate North America, formerly very abundant in the Gulf and Middle United States but completely wiped out in the twentieth century.

See Plates 5 and 17 (colour), 13c (phot.).

J.D. (2)

PARROTBILL (1) : substantive name of most of the species of the subfamily Paradoxornithinae of the Muscicapidae (Passeriformes, suborder Oscines) ; in the plural, general term for the subfamily (sometimes called ' suthoras '). By some authors the group is considered to be a mere tribe of the Timaliinae (see BABBLER) ; others have placed it elsewhere as a subfamily of the tits (Paridae). They are small to medium-sized, in appearance somewhat tit-like, but with one exception distinguished from all other oscine birds by the peculiarly formed (usually yellowish) bill, which is shorter than the head, very much compressed, and with strikingly convex outlines : the culmen is strongly curved for its entire length, the gonys terminally ascends abruptly, and both the maxillary and mandibular

Great Parrotbill *Conostoma oemodium*. C.E.T.K.

tomia are more or less distinctly sinuated. Their body plumage is soft and copious, and the small nostrils are wholly concealed by setose, antrorse, latero-frontal plumules ; the feet, toes, and claws are robust. The sexes are alike in plumage, and the young differ little from the adult.

All species are gregarious, some restlessly foraging through the lower trees, others through tall grasses or bamboos, in bands of up to 50 individuals, carrying on a continuous, low, conversational bleating and twittering. Their coloration ranges from almost uniform greys and browns in the larger forms to complicated patterns of black, white, red-brown, buff, orange-rufous, or vinaceous-pink in the smaller ones. The 53 named forms currently recognised can be combined into 19 or 20 species ; most of them are restricted to the Oriental Region (but not entering the Malayan Subregion), although a few wide-ranging species overflow into the Palaearctic Region, and one aberrant species, the Reedling *Panurus biarmicus*, is wholly Palaearctic and occurs as far west as Britain.

Their food consists mainly of insects, supplemented by the seeds of grasses and, in the case of the larger species, by berries. Many of the Oriental forms are rare and little known in life ; those of which the breeding is known agree in constructing compact, deep, cup-shaped nests of grass and bamboo leaves, bound together with cobwebs, at no great height from the ground. There are 2–4 eggs, unspotted blue, or clay-coloured and irregularly marked with such hues as reddish-brown, lavender, and greenish-grey.

Although numerous generic names have been

proposed for the parrotbills on the basis of shape of bill, only 3 genera are currently accepted, of which 2 are monotypic. The giant of the group, almost a foot long, is *Conostoma oemodium* of the Himalaya and south-western China, a grey-brown bird with heavy but almost normally formed bill. Another large, plain-coloured species, *Paradoxornis* ('*Cholornis*') *paradoxus* of south-western China, deserves special mention for having the outer toe abortive, it being reduced to a short clawless stump adherent to the middle toe. Despite this anomaly, it is barely distinguishable in coloration from a sibling species, *P. unicolor*, of the same general region and the eastern Himalaya. The numerous forms earlier placed under the generic name '*Suthora*', only 3–4 inches long, are more strikingly patterned and more plastic ; *P. nipalensis*, with 12 subspecies, ranges from Nepal to Formosa and southwards into the Indo-Chinese countries. One of this group, the Vinous-throated Parrotbill *P. webbianus*, with vinaceous-pink throat and breast, is widely distributed in China and north-eastward to Ussuriland ; it has, in contrast to its relatives, become a familiar garden bird in such cities as Shanghai. On the other hand, the Reedbed Parrotbill *P. heudei*, a very distinct intermediate-sized species, is wholly restricted to reedbeds bordering a fifty-mile reach of the Yangtze River in the Chinese province of Kiangsu.

Despite its very differently shaped bill, this last is very similar in colour and pattern, and in its way of life, to the Reedling (or Bearded Tit) *Panurus biarmicus*, sole representative of the third genus. It is beautifully dressed in tones of cinnamon-buff, grey, and vinaceous rose, with conspicuous, erectile black moustachial stripes. It ranges in areas of reedbeds from the Broads of Norfolk and Suffolk eastward into Manchuria. From the typical parrotbills it differs in a number of particulars, such as having a much more conventionally formed bill, having the sexes different (with the young resembling the female), and laying a clutch of from 5 to 7 eggs in a less firmly woven nest. H.G.D.

PARROTBILL (2) : term sometimes applied, in the plural, to the Psittirostriinae (see HONEYCREEPER (2)).

PARROT-FINCH : substantive name of *Erythrura* spp. (see WEAVER-FINCH).

PARROTLET : substantive name of *Forpus* spp. (for family see PARROT).

PARTIAL MIGRANT : see MIGRATION

PARTRIDGE : substantive name of species of

Phasianidae in several genera (*Perdix, Ammoperdix, Alectoris*, etc.) ; also the tree partridges *Arborophila* spp. etc., the Snow Partridge *Lerwa lerwa*, and the bamboo partridges *Bambusicola* spp. etc. (see under PHEASANT).

PARULIDAE : a family of the Passeriformes, suborder Oscines (see WARBLER (2)).

PASSAGE MIGRANT : term, alternatively 'transient', applied to birds from the viewpoint of an observer in an area that they pass through on migration without remaining throughout either the summer or the winter ; 'bird of passage' is sometimes used as an equivalent but is applied poetically to any migrant (see MIGRATION). For 'passage hawk' see FALCONRY.

PASSERES : used both as an ordinal name synonymous with 'Passeriformes' and (less commonly) as a subordinal name synonymous with 'Oscines' (see below). It was the name used by Linnaeus for his sixth order of birds.

PASSERIFORMES : the great order, alternatively 'Passeres', that includes more than half of all the species of birds and more than a third of the recognised families. It comprises the following suborders and families, the latter dealt with separately as (in part) shown :

Eurylaimi :
    Eurylaimidae   see BROADBILL
Tyranni :
  Superfamily Furnarioidea
    Dendrocolaptidae   see WOODCREEPER
    Furnariidae   see OVENBIRD (1)
    Formicariidae   see ANTBIRD
    Conopophagidae   see ANTPIPIT
    Rhinocryptidae   see TAPACULO
  Superfamily Tyrannoidea
    Pittidae   see PITTA
    Philepittidae   see ASITY
    Xenicidae   see WREN (3)
    Tyrannidae   see FLYCATCHER (2) ;
                           SHARPBILL
    Pipridae   see MANAKIN
    Cotingidae   see COTINGA
    Phytotomidae   see PLANTCUTTER
Menurae :
    Menuridae   see LYREBIRD
    Atrichornithidae   see SCRUB-BIRD
Oscines :
    Some 40 families (see Table of Classification in List of Major Articles on Bird Groups at beginning of volume).

The first 3 suborders are often referred to collectively as the 'suboscine Passeriformes'. The name 'Clamatores' is used alternatively for the Tyranni (but earlier had a wider connotation). The monotypic subfamily Oxyruncinae (Sharpbill) of the Tyrannidae is sometimes given independent familial status ; the Xenicidae (New Zealand wrens) are sometimes called 'Acanthisittidae', e.g. by Wetmore.

The order can also be divided in accordance with the number and arrangement of the syringeal muscles (see SYRINX). In the terminology most lately used, the Tyranni or Clamatores (with which the Eurylaimi agree in the particular respect, although otherwise peculiar), are called 'Mesomyodi', and are subdivided into 'Tracheophonae' (=superfamily Furnarioidea) and 'Haploophonae' (=Tyrannoidea) ; the Menurae and the Oscines together constitute the 'Acromyodi'. There have been other variants of this scheme.

The Passeriformes, as an order, are often referred to as the 'perching birds', and the Oscines as the 'song-birds', and from the point of view of European ornithology these two common names are in practice synonymous, the Oscines being the only suborder represented in the Palaearctic Region.

General Characters. Perching and singing are functions reflected in the structure of members of the order. The foot is characteristic. There are always 4 toes, joined at the same level ; the hallux is directed backwards and is not reversible. This form of foot is well adapted to perching by the method of gripping a slender branch or, in the case of small species, a twig, reed, or grass-stem ; it is equally suited to perching on an artificial substitute such as a wire. The muscles and flexor tendons involved in the action are so arranged that any tendency for the bird to fall back tightens the grip. The toes are never webbed, even in the very few forms that have acquired aquatic habits (Cinclidae, and *Cinclodes* spp. in the Furnariidae). The syrinx is tracheal in a few (Tracheophonae—see above) ; otherwise it is in the common tracheo-bronchial position, but with various arrangements of its muscles as already mentioned. The quality of song varies greatly, even among the Oscines, but the order certainly includes the best musicians—and the most accomplished vocal mimics (see SINGING ; and MIMICRY, VOCAL).

Among other morphological characters, the wing is eutaxic and has either 9 or 10 distinct primaries. The tail most usually has 12 rectrices. The spermatozoa have a distinctive form, not found in other birds.

The form of bill shows various adaptations to the kind of food—the generalised type of soft bill for a mixed animal and vegetable diet, the hard conical bill for seeds, the short bill with wide gape specialised for the capture of small insects, the thin decurved bill for nectar feeding, or the stout hooked bill for larger prey. In body size, the members of the order range from very small to the moderate dimensions attained in the larger crows (Corvidae) and the lyrebirds (Menuridae). In feathering they range from inconspicuous drab hues and lack of adornment to brilliant colours and ornamental plumes.

Mode of Life. The Passeriformes are land birds. Some particularly frequent the vicinity of fresh water, and a very few find their food in it ; some live near, or visit, the seashore ; but the open sea figures in the lives of any of them only as a dangerous area to be crossed on migration. Many of them, especially insectivorous species breeding in high latitudes, are migratory in the highest degree ; others perform shorter journeys, while others again are sedentary. Within the general limitation mentioned, widely varying habitats are exploited ; these include even desert and montane areas in which there may be little or no vegetation providing perches. Many passerine birds have been notably successful in adapting themselves to environments largely man-made, inhabiting cultivated or otherwise tended land, roosting or nesting on buildings, and making use of 'unnatural' food.

Breeding habits show a wide range of difference in nesting sites, in the form of nests, in the number and characters of eggs, and so on. The young are nidicolous, being hatched blind, naked, and helpless. In general, parental care—by both sexes—is well developed ; a few species, however, are parasitic in this respect (see PARASITISM).

Distribution. The order is cosmopolitan, unrepresented only in polar latitudes and on the most forbidding islands. Indeed, its members predominate in the avifaunas of all but a few highly specialised types of environment. The same remarks would be true of the suborder Oscines by itself, but that one must except the Neotropical Region. In the latter it is the Tyranni that play the greater role ; and 9 of its 12 families are restricted to the New World. Of its other families, the Pittidae have a fairly wide distribution in the tropics of the Old World, the Philepittidae are restricted to Madagascar, and the Xenicidae are peculiar to New Zealand. As regards the other 2 suboscine suborders, the Eurylaimi are an Afro-Asian group, and the 2 families of the Menurae are wholly Australian.

Some families of the Oscines are almost cosmopolitan, or are widespread in either the Old World or the New. Others have more limited distributions, sometimes restricted to a single main zoogeographical region or, in a few instances, to some smaller area such as Madagascar, New Zealand, the West Indies, or Hawaii.

Familial Taxonomy of the Oscines. This is a subject of the greatest difficulty, and the field of speculation need be no more than indicated here. Speculative it largely is, because the degree of general resemblance is so high, and the effect of convergence on adaptive characters so great, that trustworthy evidence of relationships between groups is hard to find. As Mayr has pointed out, with the exception of the Alaudidae (absence of pessulus) and the Hirundinidae (closed bronchial rings) none of the families can be defined unequivocally by anatomical characters—there is always a hint that these may be functional and not phyletic.

Many of the families are nevertheless reasonably distinctive—or at least appear to be so—and their validity as taxa has not been seriously challenged. Others are very unsatisfactory, and their boundaries are obscured by the existence of aberrant forms that may be included or excluded as a matter of opinion. Thus, the Turdinae, Sylviinae, and Muscicapinae in the Palaearctic Region have been considered to be so distinct as clearly to warrant the status of separate families ; but on a world basis the distinction breaks down. These groups, with others, are therefore now usually treated as subfamilies of the Muscicapidae, with the reservation that their respective limits still inevitably remain indistinct at this less important level ; that it is 'inconvenient' to have such a large assembly of species in a single family is not a valid objection (see MUSCICAPIDAE). Another area of special doubt includes the Fringillidae and the families nearly related, or at least somewhat similar, thereto (see FRINGILLIDAE ; EMBERIZIDAE). There are, in addition, instances where it is merely a matter of opinion, on degrees of difference, whether a few apparently nearly related groups should be treated as separate families or as subfamilies of one (see, for example, BOMBYCILLIDAE) ; such points are of minor importance.

Where it is difficult even to delimit many of the families, it is still more difficult to arrange them all in larger groups. Mayr & Amadon (1951) suggested a division into 9 main groups (after setting aside the Alaudidae and Hirundinidae) as a possibly natural arrangement ; they carefully refrained, however, from using any nomenclature implying that their tentative groups could rank as valid taxa (say, superfamilies). More usually, the bulk of the song-bird families (again excluding the larks and swallows) is divided into three major assemblages :

(1) Old World insect-eaters and relatives ; (2) New World insect-eaters and finches ; and (3) crows (Corvidae), birds-of-paradise (Paradisaeidae), and associated families. The remaining more peculiar and isolated families, as well as the Old World nectar-eaters, are then placed rather irregularly within this broad framework (see Mayr & Greenway 1956).

Whether or not any groups of families be expressly designated, it is necessary for practical purposes to arrange the families of the suborder in some sequence. Customarily, such a sequence purports to lead from the most primitive to the most specialised, or (chiefly in the past) vice versa. The same lack of real evidence, however, makes this equally in vain ; the essential facts are just not known, and may perhaps never be ascertainable. In any event, even were it possible to construct an adequate concept of phyletic relationships, this could not be expressed in a linear sequence such as, for instance, the arrangement of any check-list or other systematic work requires (see ARRANGEMENT). The most that a sequence can do is to keep together, here and there, a few families that are probably closely related ; but it equally brings into juxtaposition other families between which no such near relationship can be supposed to exist.

Current views tend to favour a sequence that is traditional, and thus in some ways convenient. There may be reason for believing that the sequence is to some slight extent a 'natural' one, and that it at least serves to keep a few probably related families together—especially those that might perhaps equally well be brought under a single head as subfamilies, and are indeed so treated by some authors. It should nevertheless be recognised and made abundantly clear that the device is for the most part merely a convention. Such a sequence was agreed upon by a committee appointed by the XI International Ornithological Congress (Basel, 1954), and it was published by Mayr & Greenway (1956). As this is being followed by the successors of Peters in the *Check-list of Birds of the World* it could with much convenience—and considering that all deviations represent merely personal opinions based on inconclusive evidence—be generally accepted as a standard that is as satisfactory as any that can be devised in the light of current knowledge. It is used in the present work (see Table of Classification in the List of Major Articles on Bird Groups at the beginning of the volume).

Families based on the fossil type-genera *Palaeospiza* and *Palaeoscinis* are also placed in the suborder Oscines—respectively near the Alaudidae and (provisional placing) the Pycnonotidae.   A.L.T.

Amadon, D. 1957. Remarks on the classification of the perching birds. Proc. Zool. Soc. Calcutta, Mookerjee Mem. Vol. : 259–268.

Beecher, W. 1953. A phylogeny of the Oscines. Auk 70 : 270–333.

Delacour, J. & Vaurie, C. 1957. A classification of the Oscines (Aves). Los Angeles County Mus. Contrib. Sci. no. 16 : 1–6.

Mayr, E. 1958. The sequence of the songbird families. Condor 60 : 194–195.

Mayr, E. & Amadon, D. 1951. A classification of recent birds. Amer. Mus. Novit. no. 1496 : 1–42.

Mayr, E. & Greenway, J. C., Jr. 1956. Sequence of the passerine families (Aves). Breviora (Mus. Comp. Zool.) 58 : 1–11.

Storer, R. W. 1959. The arrangement of songbird families. Condor 61 : 152–153.

Storer, R. W. 1960. The classification of birds. In Marshall, A. J. (ed.). Biology and Comparative Physiology of Birds vol. 1. New York and London.

Tordoff, H. B. 1954. A systematic study of the avian family Fringillidae based on the structure of the skull. Misc. Publ. Mus. Zool. Univ. Michigan no. 81 : 1–42.

Tordoff, H. B. 1954. Relationships in the New World nine-primaried Oscines. Auk 71 : 273–284.

Wetmore, A. 1957. The classification of the oscine Passeriformes. Condor 59 : 207–209.

Wetmore, A. 1960. A classification for the birds of the world. Smithsonian Misc. Coll. 139 (11) : 1–37. (And earlier versions, 1930 and 1951.)

PASSERINAE: see SPARROW (1)

PASSERINE: appertaining to the order Passeriformes ; commonly used substantively for species belonging to that order, members of all others being collectively called ' non-passerines ' (see PASSERIFORMES). The form of the word would also admit of its being applied in a restricted sense with reference to the subfamily Passerinae, but to obviate confusion this is better avoided.

PASTOR: substantive name of the Rosy Pastor (or Rose-coloured Starling) *Sturnus roseus* (see STARLING).

PATAGIUM: see METAPATAGIUM ; PROPATAGIUM ; WING

PATELLA: the ' knee-cap ', not present in all birds (see SKELETON ; and LEG).

PATHOLOGY: the science of abnormal structure and function in living organisms ; includes the study of disorders due to the presence of infective microorganisms or metazoan parasites (see DISEASE ; ECTOPARASITE ; ENDOPARASITE).

PATRISTIC: term sometimes applied in taxonomy to resemblances between forms due to common ancestry, as distinct from resemblances due to convergent adaptation (see CONVERGENCE).

PAURAQUE: substantive name of *Siphonorhis* spp. (for family see NIGHTJAR).

PEACOCK: see below

PEAFOWL: substantive name of *Pavo* spp. and also of *Afropavo congensis* (and there are also ' peacock pheasants ' *Polyplectron* spp.)—see PHEASANT. ' Peacock ' and ' peahen ' are special names for male and female, but the former may also be used irrespective of sex.

PEALEA PHENOMENON: the occurrence of ' spotting or streaking as variations from the normal plumage pattern ' in some species of storm-petrels (Hydrobatidae). Specimens showing this and at one time ascribed to a supposed form ' *Pealea lineata* ' were later found to belong to three otherwise well known species.

Murphy, R. C. & Snyder, J. P. 1952. The ' Pealea ' phenomenon and other notes on storm petrels. Amer. Mus. Novit. no. 1596 : 1–16.

PECKING: see BEHAVIOUR, DEVELOPMENT OF

PECK-ORDER: see DOMINANCE (2)

PECTEN: a structure on the retina of the avian eye (see VISION).

PECTINATE: provided with a serrated (comblike) edge, as on the inner aspect of the claw on the middle toe of some species and on the sides of the toes in certain Tetraonidae (see LEG).

PECTORAL: pertaining to the breast (see TOPOGRAPHY) ; for pectoral girdle see SKELETON.

PEDIONOMIDAE: see under GRUIFORMES ; and PLAINS-WANDERER

PEDIUNKER: name for *Adamastor cinereus* (see PETREL).

PEEWIT: see PEWIT

PELAGIC HABITAT: see OCEANIC BIRDS

PELECANI; PELECANIDAE: see below

PELECANIFORMES: an order, alternatively ' Steganopodes ', comprising the following suborders and families, the latter treated separately as shown :

Phaethontes :	
Phaethontidae	see TROPICBIRD
Pelecani :	
Superfamily Pelecanoidea	
Pelecanidae	see PELICAN
Superfamily Suloidea	
Sulidae	see GANNET
Phalacrocoracidae	see CORMORANT
Anhingidae	see DARTER

Fregatae :

Fregatidae see FRIGATEBIRD

Some authorities include the darters in the Phalacrocoracidae.

The order is one of mainly fish-eating birds of substantial size, characterised by having all 4 toes connected by a web (totipalmate), the hallux being turned forward and connected with the second digit. Except in the families first and last named above, the 8th and 9th of the 17-20 cervical vertebrae are so shaped that they articulate at an angle with those in front and behind.

The order is cosmopolitan in distribution, but some of the families are restricted to low latitudes. The birds are all necessarily associated with water, but whereas some are wholly marine, others frequent inland waters as well or mainly. The methods of catching fish are diverse. The call notes tend to be guttural. Except in the tropicbirds, the eggs are unspotted and have a chalky outer layer. Nesting is commonly in colonies, sometimes of enormous size and among the most spectacular phenomena of bird life.

Families (involving two additional suborders) based on the following fossil type-genera are also included in this order : suborder Odontopteryges—*Odontopteryx*, *Pseudontornis* ; suborder Pelecani, superfamily Pelecanoidea—*Cyphornis* ; suborder Pelecani, superfamily Suloidea—*Pelagornis*, *Elopteryx* ; suborder Cladornithes—*Cladornis*. See FOSSIL BIRDS.

PELECANOIDEA: see above

PELECANOIDIDAE: see under PROCELLARIFORMES ; and DIVING PETREL

PELICAN: substantive name of all species of Pelecanidae (Pelecaniformes, suborder Pelecani) ; in the plural, general term for the family. The latter comprises 6-8 species (depending on taxonomic opinion) in a single genus, widely distributed in tropical and some temperate parts of the world. Pelicans are among the largest birds (50-72 inches long) and are adapted to an aquatic life. The characteristic feature is the very large bill ; this is long, straight, and flattened from above downwards, the upper mandible with a medium ridge ending in a hook (and in some species having a relatively small upward projecting flap or ' horn ' in the breeding season). From the lower mandible is suspended a large distensible pouch, well adapted to engulfing fish. The legs are short and thick, the feet strong and totipalmate. The tail is short and the wings are very large.

In the majority of species the adult plumage is mainly white, in some suffused with pink in the breeding season, but the primaries are black or at least dark. Some species have crests, and in some there is bright coloration—yellow, orange, red—on the bill, gular pouch, and bare part of the face. In some the dull colour of the legs gives place to bright reddish hues in the breeding season. The sexes are alike ; immature birds are mainly brownish and do not acquire full plumage for several years.

$\frac{1}{14}$

White Pelican *Pelecanus onocrotalus.* K.S.

The Old World species are found chiefly on inland waters, but also on estuaries and coastal lagoons, while one of the New World species is definitely maritime. Pelicans feed principally on fish, but crustaceans are also taken. The birds are highly gregarious, and when fishing they may sweep the shallows in line with flapping wings ; or a compact party may swim quietly about, buoyantly and with bills depressed, dipping their heads under water in unison. In one species, as will be noted later, the method of fishing is quite different. Although rising from the water is laborious, the eventual flight—with head retracted—is strong ; on occasion the birds soar at a great height. They regularly fly in formation ; the sight of a flock gliding down like a squadron of flying-boats is spectacular. Pelicans are in the main silent birds, although croaking sounds are sometimes uttered and the nestlings may chatter noisily ; the young of the Brown Pelican *Pelecanus occidentalis* are described as having a piercing scream as a food call.

Breeding is colonial. The nesting site varies more in accordance with locality than with species. Sometimes the birds nest in trees, building large unlined structures of dry sticks. Elsewhere they nest on the ground—on small islands, on hillsides, or in swamps—and may use reeds, mud, or other materials. The 1–4 eggs, the number depending partly on species, are tinted pale blue with a chalky coating. The nidicolous young are naked on hatching but acquire a covering of down ; the bill is at first small, but it quickly develops. When the nests are on the ground, the young move about the colony for some time before they are able to fly. Both parents care for the young, which after the first two days thrust their bills into the adult's gullet ; fish is not brought in the pouch. For ' pelican in piety ', see HERALDIC BIRDS.

Pelicans are absent from high latitudes, from most of Europe and from northern Asia, from north-west Africa, from eastern temperate South America, and from New Zealand and the islands of the Pacific Ocean ; with these exceptions the family is widely represented. Two species are found in the New World, the rest in the Old World. The ranges of the species tend to be highly discontinuous, but in suitable areas the numbers may be very great. Non-breeding birds remain abundant throughout the year in some areas where no nesting colonies exist.

The large, silvery white Dalmatian Pelican *Pelecanus crispus* (very pale grey below) has still a footing in the extreme south-east of Europe, and ranges eastwards from there into central Asia ; it visits Egypt and northern India in winter. Characterised by a warm suffusion of pink on head and breast in the breeding season, the White (or Rosy or Spotted-billed) Pelican has two forms, *P. onocrotalus onocrotalus* and *P. o. roseus*, which are sometimes treated as separate species. The former is now rare in south-eastern Europe but is found in northern India and parts of Africa ; the latter is distributed in eastern Asia (visiting Indonesia and the Philippines in winter), on the White Nile, and in South Africa. The Pink-backed Pelican *P. rufescens* is a smaller bird, with more dark on the wings and in the breeding season with a pink tinge on the back. It is the common species of Africa and widely distributed on that continent south of 16° N. lat., and also in southern Arabia and in Madagascar. Its nesting colonies are usually but not invariably in trees, often in baobabs and often mixed with nests of the Marabou *Leptoptilos crumeniferus* (see STORK) and other species. The colonies are sometimes within the walls of African towns such as Sokoto and Kano (Northern Nigeria). The Grey Pelican *P. philippensis* is a somewhat similar representative of the genus in south-eastern Asia. Two races of the Australian Pelican *P. conspicillatus* inhabit the

Australo-Papuan area, and this species has occurred accidentally in New Zealand.

The New World has two species. The White (or Rough-billed) Pelican *P. erythrorhynchos* breeds from western Canada (as far north as Great Slave Lake) to southern Texas. Part of its migration (during which flocks will fly over deserts and even mountain tops) takes a diagonal course to the Gulf of Mexico and Florida ; some birds reach Central America. More widely distributed is the Brown Pelican *P. occidentalis*, the subspecies of which breed in the southern United States and the Antilles on the Atlantic side, and from British Columbia to the Galápagos and Chile on the Pacific side. It is the smallest member of the family and distinguished by its dark plumage. It is a sea bird, and notwithstanding the very different type of bill it catches fish by plunging from the wing, often from a considerable height and with a resounding splash, after the manner of gannets (Sulidae). It is described as doing this with the head retracted as in ordinary flight, so that the main impact is on the fore part of the body. The large Chilean race *P. o. thagus* is an important producer of guano (see GUANO).

The relationship of the different species has not yet been closely worked out, and one cannot rely upon the subgenera that have been proposed.

A.L.T.

PELLET : an agglomeration of the undigested portions of a bird's food that, instead of being evacuated with other waste material, is regurgitated and ejected via the mouth; sometimes referred to as a ' casting '. The contents of the pellets often give valuable clues to the food of the birds producing them, and they are therefore of assistance to ornithologists investigating the feeding habits of birds and changes of diet consequent upon seasonal conditions.

Pellets are best known in respect of birds-of-prey, but the further investigation goes the clearer it becomes that birds of very widely differing species regularly eject pellets ; among the apparently less likely groups are the honeyeaters (Meliphagidae) and flowerpeckers (Dicaeidae). There are records of more than 60 different species among British birds alone that cast up pellets. Singularly little work has been done on this subject, and further research would probably reveal many more species of pellet-producing birds. There also seems to be a lack of information as to how the pellet is formed within the bird's digestive system, but it is worthy of note that the habit of casting up pellets is found among birds with true crops as well as among those without them (see ALIMENTARY SYSTEM).

Generally speaking, the pellet is composed of hard materials such as bones, claws, beaks, insect wing-cases and so on, surrounded by softer substances such as fur, feather, and vegetable matter. Sometimes the pellet may be entirely composed of such things as corn husks (Rook *Corvus frugilegus*), sand (Dipper *Cinclus cinclus*), or the hard shells of certain seeds (Robin *Erithacus rubecula*).

At times, birds that cannot find sufficient binding or protective substances in their normal food to form a solid pellet will pick up materials quite unconnected with the food taken. The writer has found pellets of the Heron *Ardea cinerea* that contained small mammal bones or crayfish claws surrounded by paper or cellophane wrapping. On one occasion a tame Little Owl *Athene noctua* produced a pellet of hard insect parts well protected by numerous rubber bands that the bird found in a shed in which it was temporarily housed. Pellets are of interest to entomologists also, since they frequently become the repositories for eggs laid by insects of many kinds.

With regard to the collection of pellets and their preservation for reference, it is as well to bear in mind that pellets cast up by birds such as the Robin or various warblers (Sylviinae) will be found with ease only if the bird is actually seen making the characteristic 'retching' movements after which the pellet is brought up ; an immediate search near the spot in question will usually result in the discovery of the pellet. In the case of larger birds—e.g. birds-of-prey (Falconiformes), owls (Strigiformes), Rooks—regular visits to roosts, nesting sites, or preening points will provide excellent collecting opportunities.

The dissection of pellets is best carried out by soaking the pellet in a dish of warm water and then separating the contents with needles or forceps so that, with the aid of a good pocket lens or low-power microscope, it will be possible to identify most of the items disclosed. The preservation of complete pellets for future reference is difficult, since the pellets of some birds, such as the Kingfisher *Alcedo atthis* for instance, are so fragile that they disintegrate easily ; while the furry or feathery pellets of birds-of-prey, crows (Corvidae), and herons (Ardeidae) are often attacked by mites, or the pellets may eventually be destroyed by the larvae of small moths and beetles. Glass tubes of varying sizes or plastic pill boxes are good for storage purposes ; but it is advisable to place in each receptacle some strong insecticide. If it is wished to retain the dissected contents of pellets, the best method is to mount the items on stiff cardboard and keep them in a plastic bag containing a supply of insecticide.

Many pellets are almost impossible to identify without additional information. Those found at known nesting sites or roosts are of course obvious ; but, as pellets of a given bird frequently vary much in size and shape, only a careful assessment of all other details available—plus dissection—will result in precise identification.

There have been a few physiological studies of the formation of pellets in the upper alimentary tract, recently including the use of radiography in the case of a captive Great Horned Owl *Bubo virginianus*.

M.K.

PELLORNEINI: see BABBLER

PELVIC GIRDLE: see SKELETON

PEN: special term for a female SWAN.

PENGUIN: substantive name of all species of Spheniscidae (sole family of the Sphenisciformes) ; in the plural, general term for the family and order. (The name was apparently first applied to the Great Auk *Pinguinus impennis*, but in English is now entirely obsolete in that sense.)

General Characteristics. Penguins are flightless sea birds of the Southern Hemisphere and are better adapted for their aquatic life than any other family. Unlike most other birds, they have feathers uniformly and densely covering the entire surface of the body, with no apteria. The wings are reduced to strong narrow flippers, covered with small scale-like feathers, and do not fold ; the bones in them are flattened and expanded. The tail is short and made up of stiff narrow feathers. The bill ranges from long and rather slender, more or less decurved, to short and stout. The feet and tarsi are short, the legs set far back on the body ; the three front toes are joined by a web, and the small hind toe is closely united to the tarsus. Although the order has been placed apart by Wetmore in a superorder of its own ('Impennes'—see under CLASS), most authorities now consider it to be more nearly related to the Procellariiformes than to any other group (see PETREL).

With their flippers penguins propel themselves through the water, often at great speed, using the feet and tail for steering. 'Porpoising' is the usual swimming movement of many of the species and is used by no other birds ; the bird swims for several yards under water, then surfaces to breathe while rising as much as a foot into the air, and vanishes below a few feet ahead. Penguins can travel at ten knots or more in this fashion ; they can also leap several feet clear of the water to effect

Heads of representatives of the six genera of the Spheniscidae.
a Little Blue Penguin *Eudyptula minor* ; **b** Emperor Penguin
Aptenodytes forsteri ; **c** Galápagos Penguin *Spheniscus mendi-
culus* ; **d** Macaroni Penguin *Eudyptes chrysolophus* ; **e**
Adélie Penguin *Pygoscelis adeliae* ; **f** Yellow-eyed Penguin
Megadyptes antipodes. All ¼ nat. size. *M.Y.*

a landing on a steep ice-foot (see also SWIMMING
AND DIVING). The usual carriage on land is upright ;
some species run with agility, but others can only
hop or waddle. Some, when on snow, can increase
their speed by flopping on their bellies and ' tobog-
ganing ', propelling themselves in this position
with flippers and legs. Adélie Penguins *Pygoscelis
adeliae* can outrun a man in soft snow.

Penguins range in standing height approximately
from 1 to 4 feet (16–48 inches in extended length).
The plumage pattern is generally similar in all
species—white breast, black or bluish back—and the
sexes are alike. The chief specific differences in
plumage are to be seen on the head and neck.
Some have loose crests of long feathers on the sides
of the crown. The chicks are covered with dense
dark down ; and there is commonly a distinctive
juvenile plumage.

The habitat of penguins is the sea and its coasts,
although the breeding localities may be some distance from open water, especially when the shore
is fringed with pack-ice. They feed on fish, cuttle-
fish, and crustaceans. The species are all highly
gregarious. The voice is loud and harsh, different
species showing a variety of croaking, braying, or
(in *Aptenodytes*) loud trumpeting notes.

The breeding colonies, or ' rookeries ', are often
very large ; in some species they may contain as
many as a million birds. Some penguins lay their

eggs in caves or burrows, others in the open. The
nest may be lined with stones, or, in the more
temperate habitats, with grass or twigs. Instead of
maintaining nesting territories, the two large penguins *Aptenodytes* spp. carry the single egg, and later
the chick, while small enough, pressed against the
tarsi and covered by a pouch-like fold of the abdominal skin. They can thus shuffle for short distances
while incubating or brooding. In all other penguin
species there are 2 (occasionally 3) eggs.

Penguins are monogamous and long-lived, often
maintaining the pair bond for life. During incubation, some species are capable of fasting for longer
periods than are any other birds. Indeed these
fasts are necessary for overcoming the environmental
peculiarities of the Antarctic as they affect flightless
birds dependent on the sea for food. Thus, the
male Adélie Penguin fasts for 6 weeks, losing 40 per
cent of its body weight (reducing from 6.5 to 3.5 kg.) ;
the larger Emperor Penguin *Aptenodytes forsteri*,
incubating during the Antarctic winter, fasts for as
long as 3 months. The chicks remain in the nest
at first and are fed by regurgitation until they can
go to the sea after attaining adult size. ' Crèches '
are usually formed by the half-grown chicks of those
species that nest in the open. Among these groups,
which may number up to 200 or more individuals,
the parents recognise their own offspring and feed
them only.

The family is peculiar to the Southern Hemisphere
and fills much the same niche as do the Alcidae in
the Northern (see AUK). It probably originated in
the Antarctic or sub-antarctic, as fossils found there
go back to the early Tertiary period. Penguins are
not, however, confined to that area, although some

of the species are. Their breeding distribution as a family follows the cold sea currents northwards to New Zealand, the coasts of Australia (one species), South Africa (one species), and the west coast of South America (two species) as far as, in one case, the Galápagos Islands ; for details see below. Some species, when not breeding, migrate for long distances over the open sea. Penguins thus have a very wide latitudinal range, from 77° S. lat. (Adélie and Emperor Penguins) to the Equator (Galápagos Penguin *Spheniscus mendiculus*). The greatest variety of species is found in New Zealand waters, the greatest numbers of individuals along the coast of Antarctica and on the Antarctic and sub-antarctic islands.

See Plates 10a, 25, 38b (phot.).   W.J.L.S.

Genera and Species. The Spheniscidae are divisible into 6 genera comprising in all 17-18 species, of which some have distinguishable geographical races. This total excludes fossil forms, of which a number are known. It may be noted that some of the English adjectival names, e.g. ' Jackass ' and ' Macaroni ', are not very firmly attached to particular species.

Aptenodytes. This is an Antarctic genus, comprising the 2 largest species of penguin ; the bill is long, rather slender, and distinctly decurved ; patches of orange-yellow at the sides of the neck are conspicuous. The Emperor Penguin *A. forsteri* is 4 feet in length ; it breeds only on the Antarctic continent, doing so colonially during the rigorous winter of that area. The King Penguin *A. patagonica* is 3 feet long but otherwise rather similar in appearance ; its breeding places are on islands in Antarctic seas: South Georgia, Kerguelen, Macquarie, and others. For breeding habits of both species see below.

Pygoscelis. This is another Antarctic genus, and the species are of medium size (about 2 feet long) and, with the exception of the Adélie, have rather long bills. The Adélie Penguin *P. adeliae* is widely distributed round the coasts of Antarctica and also breeds on the South Orkneys and South Shetlands ; it is an exceedingly numerous species, and some of its rookeries are of immense size (see further below). The Gentoo Penguin *P. papua* also has a circumpolar distribution, breeding on the Antarctic Peninsula (Graham Land), Falkland Islands, Kerguelen, Macquarie, South Georgia, and various Antarctic islands. The Chinstrap (or Ringed) Penguin *P. antarctica* is most abundant in the Antarctic Peninsula, South Orkneys, South Shetlands, and South Sandwich Islands, but appears to be spreading to become a circumpolar species.

Eudyptes. This is a genus of which most of the species are found in the New Zealand area, some exclusively. They are birds of medium size with rather stout bills and with yellow superciliary crests on the sides of the head. The Fiordland Crested Penguin *E. pachyrhynchus* is restricted to New Zealand ; and the Erect-crested Penguin *E. sclateri* breeds on the Auckland Islands. The Rockhopper (or Victoria) Penguin *E. crestatus* (' chrysocome ') likewise breeds in New Zealand, but also on Tristan da Cunha, Gough Island, the Falkland Islands, and various islands of the Antarctic. The nominate race of the Macaroni Penguin *E. chrysolophus* is found on sub-antarctic islands from South Georgia to Kerguelen ; the Macquarie Island race *E. c. schlegeli*, known as the Royal Penguin (see further below), has sometimes been accorded specific rank. The Snares Island Penguin *E. robustus*, of restricted distribution, was formerly not recognised as specifically distinct.

Megadyptes. The sole species is of medium size and has a rather long bill ; the yellow superciliary bands unite behind. The Yellow-eyed (or Yellow-crowned) Penguin *M. antipodes* breeds only in New Zealand (Otago Peninsula and Stewart Island) and neighbouring islands (see further below).

Eudyptula. This is a genus of small penguins confined to the Australasian Region. They have no crests ; the bill is of moderate length and slightly hooked ; and the plumage of the upper parts is blue. The Little (or Little Blue, or Fairy) Penguin *E. minor* breeds in New Zealand and Australia, being the only species of penguin that is at all common on the coasts of Australia (see further below). The White-flippered Penguin *E. albosignata* is restricted to the South Island of New Zealand.

Spheniscus. The species are from medium to small in size ; one is African, and the rest are South American. The Jackass (or Blackfooted) Penguin *S. demersus* breeds on islands off the west coast of South Africa. The Peruvian (or Humboldt) Penguin *S. humboldti* breeds from Valparaiso in Chile northward along the coast of Peru. Both these species are important producers of guano in their respective areas (see GUANO). The Magellanic Penguin *S. magellanicus* breeds from Tierra del Fuego to Chile and on the Falkland Islands. The small Galápagos Penguin *S. mendiculus* is restricted to the archipelago of that name and is the only species of penguin to reach the Equator (see further below).

The Spheniscidae as a family are unique in so many respects, and the members are so inaccessible to observation by most ornithologists, that it has been thought useful to add to the general article a ' symposium ' on the breeding biology of representatives of the several genera (Editor).

Breeding Biology of Aptenodytes. The Emperor Penguin *Aptenodytes forsteri* and the King Penguin *A. patagonica* are distinguished from all other members of the family by their size and colouring. Emperors, weighing between 50 and 100 lb. and standing 3 feet high, are the world's largest and heaviest sea birds. Kings are slighter in build, but with weights of 30–40 lb. are over twice as heavy as any of the smaller penguins. Both species are ornate, with brilliant golden auricular patches and vivid pink or purple-blue mandibular plates. The two species share the common problem of rearing large chicks in environments where climate is harsh and food scarce for 8 or 9 months of the year. Both tend their chicks in winter, to ensure that they reach independence during the short summer season of abundant food, but in detail their breeding cycles are entirely different. King Penguins, breeding on islands at the fringe of the Antarctic Ocean and throughout the sub-antarctic in ice-free areas where winters are oceanic and comparatively mild, lay in spring and summer and keep their chicks on the colonies until the following spring. Emperors, breeding only in the far south on the shores of the Antarctic continent, lay in autumn soon after the sea-ice forms, and so rear their chicks during the coldest and darkest months of winter.

King Penguins. These birds incubate for about 54 days, both parents taking part in incubation and in raising the single chick. Growth is rapid, and by late autumn the season's earliest chicks (those hatching from eggs laid in November) are almost as large as their parents. Those hatched later from eggs laid in January or February may be only three-quarters grown by early winter, and remain at this size until the following spring. April and May mark the beginning of the colder weather and food shortage. Laying and incubation cease, and for the rest of the winter the chicks are fed only at intervals of 2–3 weeks. Their weights fall steadily; the smallest succumb early in winter and only those with adequate reserves of fat are able to survive the lean months. By October and November the largest chicks have lost half their autumn weights. The spring proliferation of the plankton brings food animals (fish and squid) to the surface waters in November, and the parents are once again able to provide abundant food. The chicks fatten, lose their brown down, and leave the colonies in juvenile plumage from December onward. The parents also moult and may lay again in January or February. Those that lost their chick in autumn and winter have then laid again and hatched new young; thus in summer two seasons' chicks are present in the colonies simultaneously, and two 'waves' of laying, in November–December and in January–February, are seen among the breeding adults. Successful early breeders of one season become late breeders in the next; they cannot raise three chicks in consecutive seasons but may breed successfully twice in three years.

Emperor Penguins. These face harsher winter conditions. Only the males incubate, huddling tightly together to conserve heat and each holding the single egg on its feet for some 64 days. The females spend this time at sea, which may be ice-covered for 50 or 100 miles between colony and open water. Later the ice-edge usually breaks back, and colonies are generally found at points where an early break-up may be expected. The chicks hatch in July and August, and are fed by the males from a crop secretion on hatching. The females return and take over care of the chicks for 2–3 weeks while the males resort to the sea. The chicks grow slowly at first, but growth is more rapid when both parents bring food after the fifth or sixth week. By December and January the chicks lose their grey down; although not of full size they leave their parents and fend for themselves, continuing to grow during their juvenile year. In January the parents begin their own moult and by March and April are ready to breed again. B.S.

Breeding Biology of Pygoscelis. The breeding habits of the Adélie Penguin *Pygoscelis adeliae*, taken here as representing the genus, were studied by the writer at two rookeries, in the Antarctic Peninsula and South Orkneys respectively (Sladen 1958). The birds return to the rookery in September and October from their winter quarters in the open pack-ice possibly 200 miles or more away, lastly travelling for up to 60 miles over rough sea-ice still unbroken so early in the season. They then occupy nest sites, finding the former spot even if it be under a foot or more of snow. On the whole, individual birds are very faithful to their old sites and also retain the same mates. One member of a pair may 'keep company' with a different bird of the opposite sex until its true mate arrives.

Age and breeding experience are important in determining the behaviour of individuals. The population of the rookery comprises: (1) Experienced (established) breeders, probably 4–5 years old or over. (2) Inexperienced (unestablished) breeders, which have first to establish themselves and pair off; they often arrive later, taking up territories on the periphery of the colony or in vacant spaces; they are the cause of most of the fighting that goes on; their courtship behaviour is more prolonged, and their breeding efficiency is lower, with a higher egg and chick mortality. (3) Non-breeders ('wanderers') in adult plumage (2–3 years old); they may build poor nests or temporarily occupy sites, and some of those dissected showed undeveloped gonads. (4) Yearling non-breeders in immature plumage (white throats); these usually remain in the pack-ice, which is nearer as the season advances, but occasionally come into the rookery and even do some half-hearted nest building. (5) In due course, the new chicks.

Various displays are associated with pair formation and other elements in the breeding behaviour. There are mutual displays between members of a pair before an egg is laid and during nest relief, and later, between parents and nestlings. The Adélie Penguin is the most aggressive member of its genus, and its actions include those of threatening, attacking, fighting, and pecking.

The sexes share in building the heap of stones that constitutes the nest. There is much stealing of stones from nest to nest, and it may be that this serves a useful purpose in distributing stones through the colony towards its centre, reducing the need for long treks by some individuals. The normal clutch is 2, the eggs being laid at an interval of 2–4 days. The incubation period is 33–38 days, averaging 35 days.

Both parents necessarily fast during the period of occupation for 2½–3½ weeks. When the eggs have been laid the female leaves for the sea to feed, and the male continues to fast for 2–2½ weeks more while he incubates the eggs. He is then relieved by the female, and in his turn goes off to feed while she begins her second fast. The male returns to resume incubation and fasting a few days before the eggs hatch. The male's first fast may therefore be as long as one of up to 6 weeks, exclusive of those days spent on the journey. The female's first fast is shorter, one of 23 days being the longest recorded. The male, as noted above, loses some 40 per cent of his body weight in the process. The female starts the season lighter and loses weight more rapidly although for a shorter time. It will be seen that each bird has a second but shorter fast before the end of the incubation period. If eggs or chicks are lost, the parents break off the routine and go to sea to feed; they usually return and reoccupy their nest sites for a further period of fasting, the 'reoccupation period', but no more eggs are laid.

When the young are hatched, there is at first a 'guard' period during which one parent remains at the nest while the other visits the sea to collect food. When about 4 weeks old the young are left alone and congregate in groups or crèches of 100 or more, providing some defence against predation by the Skua *Catharacta skua* subspp. The crèches have no adult 'guardians', although unsuccessful breeders and non-breeders have sometimes been mistakenly thought to be fulfilling this role. It has also been determined that the parents feed only their own offspring. When the young are in their eighth week the crèches disperse and the well-grown chicks lie near their old nests. In the ninth week most of the young assemble along the coast and then depart to sea independently of the adults.

Taylor has recently published an account of the breeding of this species at Cape Royds, Ross Island. This rookery is more than 16 degrees farther south than that in the South Orkneys, and the breeding season begins later. The fasting periods of incubating birds are rather shorter, and the development of the chicks is more rapid; the existence of a plentiful and readily available food supply is probably the chief factor. At a small minority of the observed nests, the female took the first turn at incubation. If the first egg was lost, more often than not a third was laid. The initial fine down of the nestlings is described as ranging in colour from 'dark sooty' to 'pale silver', with intermediate shades; by the age of 10 days this has been replaced by the almost woolly second down plumage, of a uniform sooty colour.

W.J.L.S.

Breeding Biology of Megadyptes. The Yellow-eyed Penguin *Megadyptes antipodes*, sole member of the genus, was studied by the writer on the Otago Peninsula for eighteen consecutive seasons (August 1936 to March 1954). As a breeding bird it is confined to the south-eastern end of New Zealand, including the Auckland and Campbell Islands. It does not breed in dense colonies, as do, for example, the crested penguins *Eudyptes* spp. also characteristic of New Zealand, but has its nests scattered about the breeding area. The latter is naturally in heavy forest or thick scrubby vegetation, which may reach almost to the water's edge—a habitat in strong contrast to that of the Antarctic penguins. The species is sedentary.

Breeding period. For 701 clutches over 18 seasons the mean laying date was September 23·7 ($\pm$5·4 days, range 11 September to 11 October). Two evenly sized white eggs are laid, except that some of the two-year-olds produce only one egg. The incubation period for 200 second eggs was 43·5 days ($\pm$2·2, range 40 to 51). Eighty-five chicks were ashore for the mean time of 106·2 days ($\pm$4·9, range 97 to 118 days). Both parents feed the chicks, and there is no starvation period. As a rule, non-breeders and unsuccessful breeders begin their moult first, followed by the breeding birds after their chicks have left for the sea ; 93 per cent of all types of birds moult in February and March. The moult lasts 3½ weeks, during which time 40 per cent of the initial body weight is lost.

Fertility. Something around 50 per cent of these penguins breed as two-year-olds (i.e. beginning at an age of about 22 months), and practically all the rest as three-year-olds. Age does not influence laying dates, as young females may be late or early layers. Age affects the width of the eggs, the maximum being reached between the 7th and 13th year, after which the width appears to diminish. Age also affects fertility of the eggs : 32 per cent of eggs fully incubated by two-year-olds hatched ; this figure gradually increased to 92 per cent, attained by six-year-olds and maintained to the 13th year ; from the 14th to the 19th year fertility fell to 77 per cent. The birds are not fully mature (full fertility, full egg size, etc.) until their 4th and 5th year, even although they acquire their adult plumage around 14 months of age.

Population. In the ten-year period 1939–48, the penguin community was composed of 62 per cent breeders, 6 per cent unmated previous breeders, 18 per cent birds between their 2nd and 8th year that had not yet bred for the first time, 12 per cent yearlings, and 2 per cent that were not assessed. The survival rates for males at least 4 years old was 86·3 per cent, and for females 84·7 per cent ; this gives an average expectation of further life of 6·8 years for males and 6·0 for females. After 18 years, 5 (3 females and 2 males) were still in residence out of the original 36 breeders ; 6 eggs were laid by the females and 5 hatched. These birds were at least 19 years old, and no sign was observed of senile birds. In fact all females, once of breeding age, bred ; but owing to an unfavourable sex ratio this was not so with the males.

Pair bond. Of 577 annual matings in which the complete pair bond could be assessed, 27 per cent lasted 1 season, 61 per cent lasted from 2 to 6 seasons, and 12 per cent from 7 to 13 seasons. From 515 mated pairs, the 'divorce rate' was 14 per cent.

L.E.R.

Breeding Biology of Eudyptes. The Royal Penguin *Eudyptes chrysolophus schlegeli* is the light-faced Macquarie Island form of the Macaroni Penguin, of which the nominate race is widespread. Breeding is similar to that of *E. c. chrysolophus*, and details given here are based on 10 000 young and 2000 adult Royal Penguins flipper-banded during 1956–62. Fully two million breeding adults form vast colonies on beaches and in valleys at Macquarie Island (in about 54° S. lat., southward of the Tasman Sea). The largest has over half a million birds, 6 others have over 100 000, 13 over 10 000, 6 over 1000, and about 10 are smaller. There are about 600 000 immature birds at the breeding places ; and fully 100 000 young fledge annually. The sex ratio remains equal.

The annual cycle shows high seasonal regularity and synchrony, with constancy of return of adults to former nest sites and immatures to their natal colony. After winter at sea, the males return first. The pair stand on the site for about 10 days, and then eggs are laid on bare ground or pebbles throughout October, with a pronounced peak on 20th to the 22nd of the month. Two eggs are laid, at an interval of 4 days, and both are fertile ; but the first is smaller and is rejected in favour of the second, being incubated only if the second is lost. Incubation takes 35 days ; the male may remain up to the 10th day, sharing incubation, and then departs until the 17th day ; the female may now remain until the 23rd day, and then departs, returning a week before hatching. The male guards the chick for 2–3 weeks ; then small crèches form for about 4 weeks before moult and departure to sea in late January.

Onset of maturity is delayed, and age groups up to 7 years old show considerable overlap in level of breeding activity. Each successive age group comes ashore earlier, stays longer, and increases nest-site occupation and association with partners. A few precocious five-year-olds lay, but some individuals are not mature at 7 years old. Breeding success of younger birds is low, and the overall fledging success is about 40 per cent. R.C. (2)

Breeding Biology of Eudyptula. The Little (or Fairy or Little Blue) Penguin *Eudyptula minor* is the smallest of the penguins, and uncrested ; the sexes of the adults can be distinguished in the field by the heavier bills of the males. It is found on the coasts and islands of southern Australia from Perth to Brisbane, around Tasmania, on both main islands of New Zealand, and at the Chatham Islands. The other form, the White-flippered Penguin *E. albosignata* of Banks Peninsula, New Zealand, may be only subspecifically distinct. Ringing results suggest that the adult birds are sedentary, with the immatures showing some dispersal from their natal islands. Breeding birds return repeatedly to the same nesting places and to their previous mates. Activities on land take place after dark ; the birds nest either in burrows dug by themselves or by petrels (Procellariidae spp.), or in crevices among rocks or tree-trunks, and the sites may be near the sea or several hundred feet above it. The display repertoire is restricted to threat with hissing and lunges of the bills, copulation preceded by flipper-patting of the prostrate female by the male, forward trumpeting with flippers dangling, and vertical trumpeting with flippers waved up and down in time with the brayings. Breeding occurs during the austral spring and summer, the season being rather prolonged. The normal clutch is 1 or 2 eggs, occasionally 3. Re-laying sometimes occurs after the loss of a clutch. Incubation is by both sexes, and nest reliefs take place after dark accompanied by loud mutual trumpetings. The total incubation period is 33–40 days. The chicks are guarded for 10–20 days by the parents in turn and are fed nightly by the relieving bird, which then takes charge for the next day. In the 'post-guard' stage the parents come in separately and the chicks are still fed almost nightly. The total fledging period is 53–60 days. After about 4 weeks' fattening at sea, the adults return either to their nest sites or to other retreats and fast, while moulting, for 14–18 days. Thereafter the adult penguins may reoccupy their nests irregularly at night during the winter months, cleaning them out in preparation for the next breeding season.   J.W.

Breeding Biology of Spheniscus. Published information on the Galápagos Penguin *Spheniscus mendiculus*, taken here as representing the genus, is so meagre that it may be useful to summarise such personal observations as it was possible to make during a recent stay in the islands (1960–62). From the accounts, it seems likely that the species was formerly more widely distributed in the archipelago ; now it appears to breed only on Albemarle (including inshore islets) and Narborough, although Charles is visited occasionally. The entire range is thus restricted to approximately one and a half degrees of latitude mainly south of the Equator. It is doubtful whether the total population much exceeds 500 breeding pairs.

The species is a cool-season breeder ; there is a span of at least 3 months, in the period May–July, during which laying regularly occurs. Clutch size is usually 2. A sheltered piece of coastline seems to be required ; and the nesting site varies to some extent with the geological character of the shore. The eggs are laid in holes in the rock, e.g. in the face of a lava flow, often a metre or less above high water—but sometimes a few metres. The sitting bird is sometimes in plain view but is more often deeper in the rock or effectively concealed by neighbouring boulders or slabs ; in one instance it was on a ledge merely protected by an overhang.

Several pairs breed in close proximity, when possible, and usually with Flightless Cormorants *Nannopterum harrisi*, Boobies *Sula nebouxi*, or Noddies *Anous stolidus* as their only breeding neighbours. On the water they associate with various other species having similar food requirements (*Sula* spp., *Puffinus lherminieri*, etc.). Their predators seem to be mainly in the sea, where the birds always appear to be nervous—in contrast with their tameness on land. They were found to be noisy, uttering their melancholy cry, in June and July ; but they were rather silent in February.   R.L.

Bagshawe, T. W. 1938. Notes on the habits of the Gentoo and Ringed or Antarctic Penguins. Trans. Zool. Soc. Lond. 24 : 185–306.

Kinsky, F. C. 1960. The yearly cycle of the Northern Blue Penguin *Eudyptula minor novaehollandiae* in the Wellington Harbour area. Records Dominion Mus. 3 : 145–218.

Oliver, W. R. B. 1953. The crested penguins of New Zealand. Emu 53 : 185–188.

Prévost, J. 1955. Observations écologiques sur le Manchot empereur *Aptenodytes forsteri*. Acta Congr. Internat. Orn., Basel 1954 : 248–251.

Prévost, J. 1961. Écologie du Manchot empereur *Aptenodytes forsteri* Gray. Publ. Expéd. Polaires Françaises no. 222.

Richdale, L. E. 1951. Sexual Behaviour in Penguins. Laurence, Kan.

Richdale, L. E. 1957. A Population Study of Penguins. Oxford.

Roberts, B. 1940. The breeding behaviour of penguins, with special reference to *Pygoscelis papua* (Forster). Brit. Graham Land Exped. 1934–1937 Sci. Rep. 1 : 195–254.

Sapin-Jaloustre, J. 1952. Découverte et déscription de la rookerie de Manchots empereurs de Pointe-Géologie. Oiseau 22 : 143–184, 225–260.

Sapin-Jaloustre, J. 1960. Écologie du Manchot Adélie. Publ. Expéd. Polaires Françaises no. 208.

Simpson, G. G. 1946. Fossil penguins. Bull. Amer. Mus. Nat. Hist. 87 : 9–99.

Sladen, W. J. L. 1958. The pygoscelid penguins. I—Methods of study. II—The Adélie Penguin. Falkland Is. Depend. Surv. Sci. Rep. 17 : 1–97.

Sladen, W. J. L. 1955. Some aspects of the behaviour of Adélie and Chinstrap Penguins. Acta XI Congr. Internat. Orn., Basel 1954 : 241–247.

Stonehouse, B. 1953. The Emperor Penguin, *Aptenodytes forsteri* Gray. I—Breeding behaviour and development. Falkland Is. Depend. Surv. Sci. Rep. 6 : 1–33.

Stonehouse, B. 1960. The King Penguin *Aptenodytes patagonica* of South Georgia. I—Breeding behaviour and development. Falkland Is. Depend. Surv. Sci. Rep. 23 : 1–81.

Stonehouse, B. 1963. Observations on Adélie Penguins (*Pygoscelis adeliae*) at Cape Royds, Antarctica. Proc. XIII Internat. Orn. Congr., Ithaca, N.Y., 1962 : 766–779.

Taylor, R. H. 1962. The Adélie Penguin *Pygoscelis adeliae* at Cape Royds. Ibis 104 : 176–204.

Warham, J. 1958. The nesting of the Little Penguin *Eudyptula minor*. Ibis 100 : 605–616.

Warham, J. 1963. The Rockhopper Penguin, *Eudyptes chrysocome*, at Macquarie Island. Auk 80 : 229–256.

PENIS: male copulatory organ, present in a few kinds of birds (see REPRODUCTIVE SYSTEM).

PENNA: alternatively ' pennaceous feather ', one in which the barbs form a coherent vane (see PLUMAGE ; and compare PLUMA).

PEPOAZA: substantive name of *Xolmis* spp. (see FLYCATCHER (2)).

PEPPER-SHRIKE: substantive name of the two species of the subfamily Cyclarhinae of the Vireonidae (Passeriformes, suborder Oscines) ; in the plural, general term for the subfamily. This is a Neotropical group usually placed among (as here) or close to the vireos. Pepper-shrikes are heavily built birds, 6–7 inches long, with large heads and powerful bills strongly hooked at the tip. The wings are short and the flight is weak ; the plumage is loose in texture. The better-known species, the Rufous-browed Pepper-shrike *Cyclarhis gujanensis*, has a wide range from southern Mexico south to Uruguay ; the other, *C. nigrirostris*, is confined to Colombia and Ecuador.

The Rufous-browed Pepper-shrike is greenish above, with a red-brown streak through the eye, grey crown, and yellow breast. It is a bird of open woodland, cultivation, and second growth ; it lives in pairs and is sedentary. The food consists mainly of insects and other invertebrates, which the birds search for among the foliage of the middle levels and tops of trees. Pepper-shrikes hold down large prey with the foot and pull it to pieces with the bill, which is also well adapted for tearing open cocoons adhering to leaves and bark. The commonest call is a melodious but monotonous phrase of set pattern, like that of an Old World oriole (Oriolidae) ; this is uttered repeatedly from leafy cover where the bird itself is often difficult to see. The alarm calls are loud and extremely harsh.

The nest is a semi-pendent hammock slung, like that of a vireo, from a fork of a tree or tall bush. The eggs, 2 or 3 in number, are pale cream or pinkish, spotted and blotched with brown. The part played by male and female in incubation is uncertain, but both sexes feed the young.

D.W.S.

PERCHING: loosely, the act of standing (sometimes sitting) on some more or less elevated object, especially one providing only exiguous space ; more particularly, doing this while gripping the perch with the feet. The Passeriformes are sometimes referred to as the ' perching birds ' because their toes, and the flexor tendons actuating these, are notably adapted to gripping a small branch or similar object, e.g. taut wire (see LEG). Many other birds, however, are well able to perch, although lacking the particular specialisation of foot structure. Others again can only stand on an object flatfooted, as they do on the ground, and have therefore limited powers of perching ; some, of course, make no use of any kind of narrow perch, if indeed they stand in elevated positions at all. A few birds, e.g. nightjars (Caprimulgidae), commonly perch along the axis of a branch instead of transversely. Distinct from perching is clinging to the roughnesses of a vertical or overhanging surface ; to this action some birds are particularly adapted, e.g. swifts (Apodidae)—which are unable to perch in the ordinary sense—woodpeckers (Picidae) and nuthatches (Sittidae) among others. The bat parrots *Loriculus* spp. have the habit of hanging head downwards, by their feet, from branches. See also under LOCOMOTION.

PERCHING BIRDS: see above ; and PASSERIFORMES

PERDIZ: name used in Latin America for *Rynchotus* spp. (see TINAMOU).

PEREGRINE: *Falco peregrinus* (see FALCON).

PERICARDIUM: see HEART

PERICOELOUS: see INTESTINE

PERIODICALS, ORNITHOLOGICAL: see under ORNITHOLOGY

PERIODICITY: see PHOTOPERIODISM ; RHYTHM ; TIME MEASUREMENT

PERIOSTEUM: see SKELETON

PERIOTIC: a paired bone of the skull (see SKELETON).

PERISTALSIS: see ALIMENTARY SYSTEM

PERITONEUM: membranous lining of the abdominal cavity and reflected over the outer surfaces of organs lying therein.

PERNINAE: see HAWK

PERVIOUS: as applied to nostrils, see NARIS.

PESSULUS: see SYRINX

PESTICIDES: see TOXIC CHEMICALS

PESTS, BIRDS AS: see CONTROL ; QUELEA CONTROL ; SCARING.

PETREL: whole or part of the substantive name of many species in three of the four families of the Procellariiformes (Tubinares) ; in the plural, a general term—together with the more modern 'tubenoses'—for the order. The order comprises the 4 families Diomedeidae (albatrosses), Procellariidae (typical petrels and shearwaters), Hydrobatidae (storm-petrels), and Pelecanoididae (diving petrels) ; some authors treat the Hydrobatidae as a subfamily of the Procellariidae. This article deals with the order in general and with the Procellariidae and Hydrobatidae more particularly ; the other two families are treated separately elsewhere, as indicated below. For more general aspects of marine ornithology see OCEANIC BIRDS and ANTARCTIC.

$\frac{1}{3}$

Leach's Petrel *Oceanodroma leucorrhoa*, of northern Atlantic and Pacific Oceans. *C.E.T.K.*

General Characters of the Order. The Procellariiformes are a large, highly distinct group of sea birds characterised by the possession of a peculiar musky smell (which may or may not be derived from oil secreted or excreted in the stomach—see under ALBATROSS), by their thick plumage, webbed feet, and deeply grooved, markedly hooked bill with prolonged tubular nostrils. The function of the distinctive nostrils is not completely clear, but it may be related either to the excretion of excess salt by the nasal gland (see EXCRETION, EXTRARENAL), or to the great development of the whole olfactory apparatus in this order (see SMELL), which is so marked that it seems likely that the birds must locate either their feeding area, food, each other, or the breeding stations by smell.

The tubenoses appear to be a very ancient group,

most probably originally of southern origin, although several modern genera are already present in northern deposits dating back to the Miocene ; they are possibly most closely related to another southern order, the penguins (Sphenisciformes), these two orders between them showing the greatest development of adaptation for a marine environment now found among birds. There are, according to different authors, between 12 and 24 genera and 80 to 100 species distributed throughout the oceans ; one family, the Pelecanoididae, and about half the genera and species are still restricted to the Southern Hemisphere, with progressively fewer species in the North Pacific, North Atlantic, Indian Ocean, and Mediterranean. They all have very similar life histories adapted to the relatively stable, secure, uniform marine environment, with a long period of immaturity, a long breeding cycle and low reproductive rate, and a long expectation of life ; but they show great variation in other characters adapted for the exploitation of different aspects of the environment and the avoidance of interspecific reactions, including their size, structure, and markings, the pattern of their distribution and migrations, and the timing of the breeding seasons and moult.

They are all totally marine, feeding alone or in groups dispersed over the open ocean according to the distribution of their food, more birds and flocks tending to occur in the richer feeding areas which are usually found in areas of upwelling with a rich plankton along the lee shores of the continents and the convergences between water masses at sea. Their actual food usually consists of the larger zooplankton, fish, cephalopods, and fish or whale offal where it is available ; different groups specialise on different foods caught under different conditions at different distances from the shore, while each group has usually broken up into a number of sibling species characteristic of the different circumpolar climatic zones of surface water in different oceans. They all normally come ashore only to breed, often on small remote islands, sometimes on mainland headlands, cliffs, or mountain slopes. They are very helpless on land, most species being weak and inoffensive and walking only with difficulty, with the result that many forms have become seriously reduced in numbers with the spread of introduced predators such as rats, cats, and mongooses to their island breeding sites in recent years ; these greatly need protection.

Young birds spend the first years of their life entirely at sea, often apparently congregating in special 'nurseries' where there is a good food supply away from the breeding area, and then come to land for increasing periods late in the season to prospect nest sites, burrow, and display for several more seasons before starting to breed successfully ; the smallest storm-petrels probably breed first when 2 or 3 years old, larger species when from 5 to 10 years old. Once they have started to breed they normally breed annually or, in the case of the largest species, biennially ; they lay a single large white egg with a coarse shell which may have fine spots but never well developed markings. Two eggs have been recorded, but this is extremely unusual and perhaps often the work of two females. Large nests are built by the southern albatrosses, poor ones by most other species and only where material is easily available at the site. They all have complex social vocal displays at the breeding station, the largest species nesting in the open and displaying at the nest by day, the smaller ones breeding in dense herbage, crevices, or burrows and displaying in the air over the breeding ground and in the nest at night. At their breeding stations, different species utter a variety of screaming, croaking, wailing, or cooing noises—often with weird effect at night. At sea they are usually shy, quiet, and undemonstrative except when quarrelling over food. Some follow ships for refuse or the marine organisms churned up in the wake, and some avoid them ; all avoid land, but may be blown ashore in large ' wrecks ' after prolonged gales.

In some sedentary species the birds may visit the nest at intervals throughout the year. Otherwise the adults start to visit the breeding station to prospect, burrow, and display weeks or months before laying. Serventy has shown that, in the case of the Short-tailed Shearwater *Puffinus tenuirostris* at least, the parents then both go off for a ' honeymoon ' of several days before laying, the female returning to lay and the male to take the first shift on the nest. Both parents then incubate in turn for shifts of several days, the unoccupied bird sometimes but not always visiting the nest between change-overs. The egg is so large that the female has a distended cloaca for several days after laying (the only clue to sexing many species in life) ; the egg rarely, if ever, seems to be replaced if lost, the birds then gradually abandoning the breeding station and going into a premature moult. The incubation period is long, nearly 6 weeks in the smallest storm-petrels, 2 months or more in larger species, and the chick is hatched blind but covered in long thick down. It is brooded by one parent for several days and then visited only at increasing intervals to be fed, the frequency of feeding varying greatly with the weather at sea and possibly also the experience of the parents. It is fed by regurgitation, and if fed well becomes very fat, much heavier than the

parents at one stage although the weight falls again during the growth of the feathers and is near normal when the bird fledges. The fledging period is very long, some 2 months in the storm-petrels, 3 to 5 in larger species, 9 or 10 in the 2 largest albatrosses.

It has been suggested in the past that the parents abandon the young before they fledge, but more careful investigation has shown that, in some species at least, they are fed irregularly right up to the normal fledging time and that the parents may revisit the nest after they have left ; but weakly and backward young, possibly the offspring of dead or incompetent (immature or senile) birds, may be abandoned in the nest, especially in migratory species. The young exercise themselves by flapping in front of the nest for several days before fledging, and then probably normally fly directly from the nest, especially if it is situated inland, although weakly young may swim out to sea if they can reach the water. Strong young fly well on fledging and probably never see the nest or their parents again ; some immediately set out on long migrations, which in the case of transequatorial migrants must include a period of starvation while they cross the tropics. Ringed birds have been recovered in the opposite hemisphere within a few weeks of fledging.

Marked variations in appearance with age and sex are found in the albatrosses and Giant Petrel. Young birds may show more prominent pale feather edges above in some other species, especially the Hydrobatidae, and at first have soft, undeveloped bills, whereas senile birds tend to have more rugged bills, scaly legs, worn or missing claws, and poor plumage. Some southern storm-petrels are said to have only one coat of down, most other species two. The juvenile plumage is moulted at sea during the breeding season when the bird is a year old, often in the winter quarters or a ' nursery ' away from the breeding area, and apparently thereafter at the end of each breeding cycle. Some of the larger species start a slow body-moult in the terminal stages of the breeding cycle ; otherwise the moult is completed afterwards, in the case of migrants often very rapidly in some good feeding area in the winter quarters. The power of flight may be impaired where the moult is very rapid, as in some shearwaters and storm-petrels, but there is no definite evidence that it is ever lost entirely. Males are sometimes but not always larger than females in most groups, but may be smaller in the Hydrobatidae ; marked variations in sexual dimorphism may be found even among races of the same species (Wynne-Edwards).

Great variations in size, structure, and markings are found throughout the group. The albatrosses are among the largest and the storm-petrels the smallest sea birds, while within several of the larger groups closely related species of different sizes and habits have evolved in the same area. In some cases, such as the prions and gadfly petrels, these are all very similar in structure ; in others, such as the fulmars and shearwaters, they show marked variation in structure adapted for different types of flight or methods of feeding. Many species show a simple counter-shaded colour-pattern, dark above and light below, sometimes with contrasting markings on the head, wing coverts, tail coverts, or flight feathers ; but pale, mottled, or uniformly dark variations are common even among closely related species, many species being markedly polymorphic and most showing some trace of polymorphism. The species nesting in high latitudes tend to be white all over, or grey or pale brown above and white below, with yellow, pink, green, or blue and black soft parts ; those breeding in warmer climates tend to be dark brown or black above with less or no white below and red and black or entirely black soft parts ; some groups of closely related species or races show much geographical variation in conformity with this trend.

Many groups show characteristic recognition marks, including brightly coloured bills and complex wing markings in the larger species which display by day, white faces in some shearwaters and many gadfly petrels, and white rumps in many storm-petrels which display by night. Closely related species which breed together often show contrasting markings or occur in different colour phases, and races of the same species may show marked differences in their appearance which can sometimes be related to the distribution of related species with which they might come into conflict at the breeding stations. In general, representative species often tend to be smaller and representative races of species larger in lower latitudes, but there is much local variation. Some well-defined larger species have very closely related smaller ' shadow species ' breeding in the same area at another season, as in the case of the Manx and Little Shearwaters *Puffinus puffinus* and *P. assimilis*, and the Capped and Bonin Petrels *Pterodroma hasitata* and *P. hypoleuca*.

Most species seem to be closely restricted to distinct circumpolar zones of surface water at sea, some being more or less sedentary or dispersing at random within the appropriate zone outside the breeding season, others performing more or less complex migrations between good feeding areas in the same zone of surface water or different zones in the same or opposite hemispheres. The movements of related species often have a complementary pattern in different zones of surface water. Some of the migrants appear to perform circular movements either round the world in the circumpolar belts of winds in high latitudes of the Southern Hemisphere, or around the anticyclones stationary in the middle latitudes of other oceans so that they enjoy following winds throughout their migrations ; the Short-tailed Shearwater *Puffinus tenuirostris* seems to perform a figure-of-eight migration between breeding stations around the Bass Strait (between Victoria and Tasmania) and a moulting place around the Aleutians in the Pacific (Serventy), and a number of other species may perform similar movements in this and other oceans (Kuroda). In general, the species occurring in high latitudes in either hemisphere seem to be either relatively sedentary or to move into lower latitudes in winter ; the additional species occurring in middle latitudes may be sedentary, or they may move into the tropics or the middle latitudes of the opposite hemisphere in winter; and the tropics are occupied by resident species and at different seasons by wintering populations from both hemispheres. Most species breed in the highest latitudes of their range in the summer of that hemisphere, but some in the lowest latitudes in winter, possibly either because there are no suitable breeding places in higher latitudes or because there are too many related species competing for food or nest sites there ; in any event, where closely related species are found breeding at the same station they are commonly found to have different breeding seasons (Kuroda).

Albatrosses. For the Diomedeidae see ALBATROSS.

Typical Petrels and Shearwaters. The family Procellariidae includes the main body of medium and large-sized petrels (11–36 inches long), totalling some 6 to 12 genera and over 50 species. They can be divided into 4 main groups. Of these, the fulmars include 6 very distinct medium-sized to large, heavily built, short-tailed species characteristic of high latitudes, 4 monotypic genera being restricted to the Southern Hemisphere while *Fulmarus* itself has closely related species in both hemispheres. The Giant Fulmar *Macronectes giganteus* and Northern Fulmar *Fulmarus glacialis* are polymorphic and may be dark or pale ; the Cape Pigeon *Daption capensis* and Antarctic Petrel *Thalassoica antarctica* are chequered brown and white ; the Northern and Southern Fulmars are normally grey and white ; and the small Snow Petrel *Pagodroma nivea*, found only around ice in the south, is pure white. All have broad bills with distensile gular pouches, all except the Southern Fulmar *F. glacialoides* some sort of filtering plates or lamellae in the bill. Most of them probably fed mainly on plankton in the past, but they take readily to scavenging and several species have spread greatly following the development of commercial fishing. All have a mixed gliding and flapping flight, and swim freely but dive little. They nest in the open or in shallow niches, visiting the nest by day. They have developed oil-spitting as a form of defence against predators.

The prions *Pachyptila* spp. are a group of some 12 very closely related species and subspecies of small petrel adapted to feed directly upon the smaller zooplankton in the surface water by straining the water through lamellae fringing the bill. They are all very similar in size and appearance, blue-grey above and white below with dark ear coverts, dark ' W ' markings on the back, and dark tips to the tail feathers, and differ mainly in the size and development of the bill and its lamellae. The different forms seem to replace each other ecologically in different zones of surface water of the southern ocean, feeding in dense flocks in the high plankton areas along the marine convergences at sea and breeding in large warrens on the sub-antarctic islands (Voous ; Fleming).

The gadfly petrels *Bulweria* and *Pterodroma* spp. are a group of some 24 very similar, very closely related medium-sized petrels with short, stout, heavily grooved and hooked black bills, occurring in different zones of surface water in the centre of the oceans. The larger forms are relatively heavily built, with long wings and short round tails, and exhibit a very fast, swooping flight in great arcs over the water ; the smaller ones are more lightly built, with shorter wings and larger wedge-shaped tails, and have a more mobile soaring, dipping flight. They show much variation in their coloration, many species being polymorphic, but in general the pale forms are dark above with white faces, wing markings, and under parts, the rest uniformly dark. A few of the largest species nest on open ground in the Pacific ; the rest do so in burrows, often in mountain slopes far inland. Little is known about their biology, but they apparently feed mainly on cephalopods caught at night, and have a very long breeding cycle ; they disperse at sea outside the breeding season, some carrying out transequatorial migrations in the Pacific (Falla ; Murphy & Pennoyer).

The shearwaters are another large group of some 15 species distributed throughout the oceans. They are usually either dark above and white below or uniformly dark, and can be divided into two main groups with different flight and feeding adaptations. The genera or subgenera *Procellaria*, *Thyellodroma*, and *Calonectris* have developed as aerial forms with long wings, long wedge-shaped tails, and long legs, and are adapted for soaring flight and feeding from the surface in the middle of the oceans. The genera or subgenera *Adamastor* and *Puffinus* have developed as aquatic forms with shorter wings, tails, and legs, and with flattened tarsi, and are adapted for the capture of fish by diving in offshore waters. One species nests in the open in the central Pacific ; the rest do so in burrows, usually in very large colonies near the shore on offshore islands but sometimes in hills inland. Most species have very complex migrations between well defined feeding areas in the same or opposite hemispheres.

Storm-petrels. The family Hydrobatidae includes some 2 to 8 genera and over 20 species of small petrels ($5\frac{1}{2}$–10 inches long) adapted to catch individual zooplankton from the water surface. They are all more or less dark above, with paler wing coverts and tail coverts, and vary in colour below ; and all breed more or less socially in crevices or burrows, usually on offshore islets, the species breeding in the higher latitudes of opposite hemispheres replacing each other as winter visitors to the tropics at different seasons. They may be divided into two main groups characteristic of opposite hemispheres with a wide overlap in their range in the tropics.

The southern species include some 7 more or less highly differentiated forms characterised by the possession of rounded wings, square tails, long tarsi, and short toes ; they are adapted for a distinctive mode of progression, ' walking' along the water with spread wings, picking organisms from the surface as they go. They occur in two colour phases, dark above and dark or· light below, all species being polymorphic in some degree. The most distinctive species is Wilson's Storm-petrel *Oceanites oceanicus*, which breeds all round Antarctica and winters throughout the tropics, also visiting northern waters (Roberts ; Murphy & Snyder).

The northern group includes another 12 or more closely related species which may originally have been derived from the most migratory of the southern forms, *O. oceanicus*, since they all resemble it rather closely in appearance, occurring only in the dark phase with more or less white wing coverts and tail coverts ; but they now show a progressive development of very different flight and feeding habits, with long wings, forked tails, short tarsi, and long toes, being adapted for swooping and skimming over the water like terns (Sterninae). The main development of the group has occurred in the Pacific, where a swarm of species of different sizes and colours exploit the rich food supply in the areas of upwelling off California, Japan, and Peru ; but three forms also occur in the Atlantic, one of them, the British Storm-petrel *Hydrobates pelagicus*, breeding only in the eastern North Atlantic and the Mediterranean (Austin).

See Plates 16b (phot.) and 29 (colour).

Diving Petrels. For the Pelecanoididae see DIVING PETREL.   W.R.P.B.

Alexander, W. B. 1954, 1955. Birds of the Ocean : a Handbook for Voyagers. 2nd ed. New York and London.

Allan, R. C. 1962. The Madeiran Storm Petrel *Oceanodroma castro*. Ibis 103b : 274-295. (B.O.U. Centenary Expedition to Ascension.)

Austin, O. L. 1952. Notes on some petrels of the North Pacific. Bull. Mus. Comp. Zool., Harvard. 107 : 391-407.

Bourne, W. R. P. 1963. A review of oceanic studies of the biology of seabirds. Proc. XIII Internat. Orn. Congr., Ithaca, N.Y., 1962 : 831-854.

Falla, R. A. 1942. Review of the smaller forms of *Pterodroma* and *Cookilaria*. Emu 42 : 111-118.

Fisher, J. 1952. The Fulmar. London.

Fisher, J. & Lockley, R. M. 1954. Sea-Birds. London.

Fleming, C. A. 1941. The phylogeny of the prions. Emu 41 : 135-152.

Fleming, C. A. et al. 1953. Checklist of New Zealand Birds. Wellington.

Godman, F. du C. 1907-10. A Monograph of the Petrels. London.

Jones, F. Wood. 1937. The olfactory organ of the Tubinares. Emu 36 : 281-286 ; 37 : 10-13, 128-131.

Kuroda, N. 1954. On the Classification and Phylogeny of the Order Tubinares, particularly the Shearwaters (*Puffinus*). Tokyo.

Kuroda, N. 1957. A brief note on the pelagic migration of the Tubinares. Misc. Rep. Yamashina's Inst. Orn. 11.

Kuroda, N. 1960. Notes on the breeding season in the Tubinares (Aves). Jap. J. Zool. 12 : 449-464.

Lockley, R. M. 1942. Shearwaters. London.

Loomis, L. M. 1918. A review of the albatrosses, petrels and diving petrels. Proc. Calif. Acad. Sci. (4) 2 : 1-187.

Mathews, G. M. 1934. A check-list of the order Procellariiformes. Novit. Zool. 39 : 151-206.

Mathews, G. M. 1948. Systematic notes on petrels. Bull. Brit. Orn. Cl. 68 : 155-170.

Mathews, G. M. & Hallstrom, E. J. L. 1943. Notes on the Order Procellariiformes. Canberra.

Murphy, R. C. 1936. Oceanic Birds of South America. 2 vols. New York.

Murphy, R. C. & Pennoyer, J. M. 1952. Larger petrels of the genus *Pterodroma*. Amer. Mus. Novit. no. 1596 : 1-17.

Palmer, R. S. (ed.) 1962. Handbook of North American Birds vol. 1. New Haven and London.

Richdale, L. E. 1963. The biology of the Sooty Shearwater *Puffinus griseus*. Proc. Zool. Soc. Lond. 141 : 1-117.

Roberts, B. 1940. The life cycle of Wilson's Petrel, *Oceanites oceanicus* (Kühl). Brit. Graham Land Exped. 1934-37. Sci. Rep. 1 : 141-194.

Serventy, D. L., Serventy, V. N., & Warham, J. (in press). A Handbook to Australian Sea-birds.

Verheyen, R. 1951. Note sur la classification des Procellariiformes (Tubinares). Bull. Inst. Sci. Nat. Belg. 34 : 1-35.

Voous, K. H. 1949. The morphological, anatomical, and distributional relationship of the Arctic and Antarctic fulmars. Ardea 37 : 113-122.

Warham, J. 1962. The biology of the Giant Petrel *Macronectes giganteus*. Auk : 79 139-160.

Wynne-Edwards, V. C. 1952. Geographical variation in the bill of the Fulmar (*Fulmarus glacialis*). Scot. Nat. 64 : 84-101.

See also references under ALBATROSS ; DIVING PETREL ; PEALEA PHENOMENON.

PEWEE : substantive name (in some cases 'wood-pewee') of *Contopus* ('*Myiochanes*') spp. (see FLYCATCHER (2)).

PEWIT : common alternative name (from the call, and variously spelt) in Britain for the Lapwing *Vanellus vanellus* (see PLOVER (1)) ; formerly used also for the Blackheaded Gull *Larus ridibundus*.

PH : written *p*H, a symbol followed by a value that is a logarithmic expression of the hydrogen ion concentration of a solution, and thus an index of its reaction. The *p*H of a neutral solution is 7 ; above 7 alkalinity increases, below 7 acidity increases.

PHAENICOPHAEINAE : see CUCKOO

PHAETHONTES ; PHAETHONTIDAE : see under PELECANIFORMES ; and TROPICBIRD

PHAINOPEPLA : generic name used as common name of *P. nitens* (see SILKY FLYCATCHER).

PHAINOPTILA : generic name often used as common name of *P. melanoxantha* (see SILKY FLYCATCHER).

PHALACROCORACIDAE : see under PELECANIFORMES ; and CORMORANT

PHALANX : a bony element (plural 'phalanges') of a digit (see SKELETON ; and LEG ; WING).

PHALAROPE : substantive name (invented by Brisson in 1760) of the three species of Phalaropodidae (Charadriiformes, suborder Charadrii) ; in the plural, general term for the family. This is a group of small, graceful, sandpiper-like, swimming birds breeding in northern (mainly high) latitudes. They have dense duck-like plumage on their under parts, which provides a raft of trapped air on which they float as lightly as corks ; their toes are slightly webbed at the base, and beyond that expanded and broadly fringed by a row of conjoined flattened scales along the sides ; the tarsus is laterally compressed. Two of the 3 species are not only aquatic, but completely oceanic and capable of dispensing with fresh water indefinitely (see SWIMMING AND DIVING). Another characteristic of phalaropes is the reversal of the normal sexual relationships, the female being larger than the male and in nuptial plumage more richly coloured ; she takes the lead in dispersion and courtship.

The family has probably long been distinct. Not only are the aquatic adaptations deep-seated, but the 3 species are so different from one another that most systematists put them into 3 genera. They are, respectively, the Grey (or Red) Phalarope *Phalaropus fulicarius*, the Red-necked (or Northern) Phalarope *Lobipes lobatus*, and Wilson's Phalarope *Steganopus tricolor* ; the English names within brackets represent American usage—the first mentioned species is 'grey' as a migrant but 'red' on its breeding grounds. In size they differ little, and roughly resemble a Sanderling *Crocethia alba*. Wilson's Phalarope is slightly the largest ; it has very long legs and a very long, needle-like bill ; and its toes are evenly fringed, whereas those of the other two species are lobed or scalloped at each joint. The Grey Phalarope is more stocky and has a short bill, unusually broad for a wader. The Red-necked Phalarope is the smallest and most delicate, with a bill as fine but not nearly as long as that of Wilson's.

All have beautiful nuptial plumages, generally acquired late in spring and lost early by the majority of individuals ; bay or maroon reds are variously contrasted with white, black, light grey, and buff, producing in the females patterns as colourful as any to be found in the Charadrii. The males are similar but much more subdued in colour, and when motionless on the nest very difficult to detect.

The Grey and Red-necked Phalaropes are northern circumpolar breeders, the former chiefly in the arctic life zone and the latter in the sub-arctic or boreal, but there is extensive overlapping. In the brief northern summer they are usually found not very far inland, or on islands, almost always living beside shallow freshwater ponds or lakes. Although they feed partly on land, they swim very freely. They share with Wilson's Phalarope the characteristic habit of spinning round and round on the surface (or ' pirouetting '), while they pick up small insect larvae or crustacea from the water : the stirring action of their feet is supposed to stimulate their minute prey to move and thus become visible. They also sometimes ' up-end ' like ducks (Anatidae), but they cannot submerge. In the non-breeding season they live on the open tropical ocean remote from land, feeding on plankton. The Red-necked Phalarope breeds very sparingly in the British Isles (Ireland, Outer Hebrides, Orkney, and Shetland) ; the Grey Phalarope is an uncommon migrant there.

Wilson's Phalarope, in contrast, is confined in summer to the austral life zone of Canada and the United States, from the prairie provinces and southern Ontario south to Kansas and California. It appears at all times to be essentially a freshwater, inland bird, and winters in the tropics and South America : it feeds more on land than the others. It is a very rare vagrant in Britain.

Phalaropes tend to be sociable breeders, nesting in diffuse colonies, in some places of enormous extent. In south-west Baffin Island and Southampton Island, in the Canadian Arctic, the Grey Phalarope is among the commonest summer birds, and the same is locally true of the Red-necked Phalarope on the west shore of Hudson Bay. The females are the first to arrive—not until June in the high Arctic—competing among themselves and displaying in small parties. They do, however, defend individual territories, and they court or solicit the attention of single males ; authorities differ as to whether or not they are habitually polyandrous. The nest and 4 eggs (rarely 3) are typically limicoline. Incubation is apparently done exclusively by the male, but the female commonly remains at hand and may (at least in the Grey Phalarope) share in tending the chicks.

A proportion of the females nevertheless leave the nesting grounds very early, only a few weeks after arriving, and in the Grey and Red-necked species form close-knit flocks that congregate at sea, chiefly in coastal or off-shore waters, and quickly lose their nuptial plumage. These gatherings build up from late July onwards, and by the time the males and young have adopted a similar way of life (late August and early September) the numbers present between Baffin Bay and the Straits of Belle Isle, for instance, are enormous.

Like the equally small storm-petrels (Hydrobatidae), phalaropes are too light (ca. 50–60g.) to remain water-borne in strong gales, and tend to be driven to leeward. The migrations of the Grey and Red-necked species are normally wholly pelagic, the former being rather seldom seen anywhere by land observers except on its breeding grounds ; but after especially prolonged gales in spring or autumn large numbers of migrants may occasionally pile up inshore on either side of the Atlantic and elsewhere, and coastal stragglers may accidentally appear almost anywhere in the world. In Newfoundland they are called ' gale-birds '.

All 3 species are long-distance migrants. Wilson's Phalarope is apparently chiefly confined in winter to South America, but the 2 pelagic species have a number of widely separated wintering grounds, characteristically located well out to sea off the western shores of the continents, where upwelling waters rich in nutrients support an abundant plankton. The best-known areas are off West Africa between 5° and 20° N., off Angola and South Africa from, say, 20° to 35° S., and off South America from the Galápagos and Peru to Chile ; numerous other sea birds are concentrated in these same regions. The Red-necked Phalarope is the more strictly tropical and is less frequent in south temperate latitudes than the Grey ; it is especially abundant off Peru between about 4° and 12° S. lat., and is the species most commonly recorded in the tropical south-west Pacific region ; in the Indian Ocean it is particularly abundant in Arabian waters. Phalaropes remain in their wintering quarters from September or October to April. In winter plumage they are not easy to distinguish specifically when seen from a moving ship.

See Plate 29 (colour). V.C.W.-E.

Bent, A. C. 1927. Life Histories of North American shore-birds. Order Limicolae (Part 1). U.S. Natl. Mus. Bull. 142. (See pp. 1–37.)

Bruijns, W. F. J. M. & M. F. M. 1957. Waarnemingen van de Grauwe Franjepoot *Phalaropus lobatus* (L.), in de Indische Oceaan. Ardea 45 : 72–84. (Wintering.)

Manniche, A. V. L. 1910. Nordøstgrønlands fugle : biologische undersøgelser. Medd. Grønl. 45—reprinted Dansk Orn. Foren. Tids. 5 : 1–114. (Breeding biology of Grey Phalarope.)

Meinertzhagen, R. 1925. The distribution of the phalaropes. Ibis (12) 1 : 325–344.

Murphy, R. C. 1936. Oceanic Birds of South America. 2 vols. New York. (See vol. 2, pp. 993–999—wintering.)

Nelson, E. W. 1877. A contribution to the biology of Wilson's Phalarope. Bull. Nuttall Orn. Cl. 2 : 38–43.

Stanford, W. P. 1953. Winter distribution of the Grey Phalarope *Phalaropus fulicarius*. Ibis 95 : 483–491.

Sutton, G. M. 1932. The birds of Southampton Island, Hudson Bay. Mem. Carnegie Mus. 12 (pt. 2, sect. 2) : 1–275. (See pp. 150–156—breeding biology of Grey Phalarope.)

Tinbergen, N. 1935. Field observations of East Greenland birds. I. The behaviour of the Red-necked Phalarope (*Phalaropus lobatus* (L.)) in spring. Ardea 24 : 1–42.

PHALAROPODIDAE: see under CHARADRIIFORMES ; and PHALAROPE

PHANERIC: term applied to coloration or other characters that are the opposite of cryptic in that their purpose is to be conspicuous (see COLORATION, ADAPTIVE ; also SEMATIC).

PHARYNX: the cavity of the throat, behind the buccal cavity and leading to the oesophagus and trachea respectively (adjective 'pharyngeal ').

PHASE: equivalent of MORPH (see also POLYMORPHISM).

PHASIANIDAE: see under GALLIFORMES ; the family comprises birds known as pheasants, partridges, quails, francolins, junglefowl, snowcocks, spurfowl, and peafowl, and by various special names (see under PHEASANT ; also DOMESTICATION).

PHASIANOIDEA: see under GALLIFORMES

PHEASANT: substantive name of many species of Phasianidae (Galliformes, suborder Galli) ; used without qualification in Britain for *Phasianus colchicus* ; in the plural, serves as a general term for the family. In the pheasants, called by that name, the males have bright colours or elaborate markings ; the duller species, mostly a great deal smaller and with shorter tails, are given names such as ' partridges ', ' quail ', ' francolin ', ' snowcocks ', and so on, but are not differentiated by any important characteristics, there being in fact a gradual transition between them.

The family is one of terrestrial birds which as a rule feed and nest on the ground but in the majority of cases roost on trees at night. They are heavy birds ; their wings are short and rounded, curved and fitting closely to the body, making them capable of a powerful, fast flight, but—except in some migratory quails—one that cannot be sustained for long (see FLIGHT). The legs are strong, with 4 toes (the hallux inserted somewhat higher than the others) armed with heavy claws, and adapted to scratching ; the tarsus often shows a spur, or even 2 or more. The bill is short and thick, the upper mandible overhanging the lower, and is an excellent digging tool well adapted to unearth roots, bulbs, grubs, and worms which complete the main diet of seeds, berries, and leaves. The proportion of animal proteins consumed varies with species, and also with season. The chicks of all species are raised mostly on insects and other invertebrates.

The tail varies from short to very long, with long coverts. The plumage is ample and soft ; the sexes are alike in some species, different in others. The smaller and plainer species are generally monogamous, pairs being formed and maintained all the year round ; the female alone incubates, but the male helps in rearing the brood. Their calls and displays are relatively simple. The larger and more ornate, however, are polygamous as a rule. The brilliantly clad cock emits loud and very special calls, screams, or whistles, and he displays elaborately in a territory which he defends against competitors. He thus attracts females ready to breed, who wander away after mating and alone incubate the eggs and care for the chicks. Most of the pheasants have a compressed, arched tail, and therefore their display is normally lateral. But those with more or less flat tails (*Argusianus, Pucrasia, Tragopan, Lophophorus, Pavo, Polyplectron* spp., etc.) have in addition a frontal display of great splendour which includes the spreading of tail and wings. Each genus has a highly specialised display and voice.

The nest is very simple, usually placed on the ground and protected by a bush, or situated at the foot of a tree ; a few species, however, build on forks of trees or in old nests of other birds. The chicks are born fully covered with down and they leave the nest soon after hatching ; some have well-developed wing feathers and are soon able to fly and to roost up at night with the mother. The eggs are either plain (white, buff, olive-green) or spotted, and they vary in number from 2 (*Argus*, *Polyplectron* spp.) to 15.

Pheasants, partridges, and quails are of great importance to man as game-birds. The most useful domestic bird, the common fowl, derives from a pheasant, the Red Junglefowl *Gallus gallus*. Other species have long been kept and reared in complete or semi-captivity, but they have not yet changed in size or characteristics, although mutations have occurred, such as the ' Black-shouldered Peafowl ', the ' Melanistic Pheasant ', and the ' Dark-throated and the Yellow Golden Pheasants '.

The family is a predominantly Old World one and, apart from artificial introductions, is represented in the New World only by the American quails, which constitute a subfamily (Odontophorinae) or tribe—the remainder, including the true quails, being then grouped as Phasianinae. In all, about 165 species are recognised. The larger birds popularly known as pheasants are found in Asia, notably Malaysia, only one reaching Europe and another being a native of the Congo ; but the family in general is represented throughout the world with the exception of a number of small oceanic islands and the polar regions. The members are sedentary, moving only in search of food, the only exceptions being the Old World quails nesting in Europe and northern Asia ; these last accomplish long migrations, an astonishing feat for such heavy round-winged little birds.

American Quail. These differ from the Old World members of the family in having a stronger bill, the tip and edges of which are sharp and more or less serrated, and by important anatomical features as shown by recent studies. Otherwise they resemble the quails and partridges of the Old World and have similar habits. There are some 36 species. They are, as a rule, brightly and elaborately marked with brown, buff, yellow, reddish, grey, black, and white. The tail varies from very short to moderately long. The tarsi carry no spurs. The head is often crested, and the sexes are different. They are found in the temperate and warm parts of North, Central, and South America, from the northern

United States (one reaches southern Ontario in Canada) to Peru, Bolivia, Paraguay, and southern Brazil. They are particularly numerous and well represented in the southern United States, Mexico, and Central America. Some live in forests, others in woody or bushy plains and deserts. Quite a number are adapted to life at a high altitude, although they never transcend the limit of trees.

The best known of the American quails is the Bobwhite *Colinus virginianus*, one of the most popular game-birds. of the eastern and middle United States and found, in many subspecific forms, from southern Canada to the border of Guatemala. It lives on fairly open plains and on plateaux. The head is not crested, but the feathers of the crown are elongated and erectile ; the tail is short. Allied species live in Yucatan, Central America, northern Colombia, and Venezuela ; some are tufted on the head.

Truly crested quails of this group, with a well developed topknot of various shapes and length and with beautifully marked plumage, are found in western North America from the Rocky Mountains to the Pacific Ocean, as far north as Washington State and south to western Mexico. One of the most beautiful is the Mountain Quail *Oreortyx picta* living at high latitudes in the western States, south to Baja California. The well known California Valley Quail *Lophortyx californica* has a similar range, but at low elevation, being replaced in the desert by the closely allied Gambell's Quail *L. gambelli*, while a more distinct species *L. douglasii* is found in north-western Mexico. The related Blue Quail *Callipepla squamata* inhabits southern Colorado, Texas, Arizona, and northern Mexico. The Banded Quail *Philortyx fasciata* is found in south-western Mexico. The curious Montezuma Quail *Cyrtonyx montezumae*, round and tailless with a black-and-white head, is

---

Plate 37 · Colonial Nesting

a *Upper :* Greater Flamingos *Phoenicopterus ruber* with eggs and young (South Africa). The colonies are often of vast size, with the nests close together. The nest is typically a low cone of mud, with a hollow at the top for the single egg. Incidentally, this was the first breeding colony ever recorded in South Africa.   *Phot. G. J. Broekhuysen.*

b *Lower :* Gannets *Sula bassana* on the island of Grassholm (Wales). The photograph shows only part of the colony but conveys a good idea of the dispersion. Each nest is a heap of, principally, seaweed ; and there is usually a single egg.
                                                 Phot. Eric Hosking.

(See articles NEST ; FLAMINGO ; GANNET)

most beautifully marked ; it lives on mountains, and the genus (2 species) ranges from Arizona and New Mexico to Nicaragua. *Dactylortyx, Rhynchortyx,* and *Dendrortyx* are genera (the first 2 monotypic) of little-known birds, fairly large, which live in the mountain forests of southern Mexico, Central America, Colombia, and Ecuador. The birds of the large genus *Odontophorus* (15 species), with very strong bill and legs, are big partridge-like inhabitants of forests from Costa Rica to southern Brazil, Paraguay, Bolivia, and Peru ; they are the only Phasianidae widespread in South America.

Old World Quails. Quite distinct from the group just dealt with, these belong to the genus *Coturnix* (including the birds sometimes placed in *Excalfactoria* and *Synoicus*). They are small, rounded, apparently tailless, with weak bill and legs. The migratory Quail *C. coturnix* of Eurasia is well known. It has more brightly coloured sedentary representatives in Africa (*C. africana, C. delagorguei*), India (*C. coromandelica*), and Australia (*C. pectoralis*) ; the New Zealand form (*C. novaezelandiae*) has become extinct there. The very small but beautiful Indo-Australasian species *C. chinensis* and its African counterpart *C. adamsoni* are closely related, as also are the larger and duller Swamp Quails *C. ypsilophorus* subspp. of Australia, New Guinea, and the Lesser Sunda Islands. The rare Mountain Quail (*Anurophasis*) of New Guinea and the pretty *Margaroperdix* of Madagascar are but glorified *Coturnix*.

Partridges. Those which we call by this name are birds with larger bills, stronger legs, and longer tails. There are many genera and species of them throughout Europe, Asia, and Africa. The Stone Partridge *Ptilopachus petrosus* is a curious little bird found in the rocky parts of West and East Africa. It is brown, with very short legs and a long tail shaped as in the domestic hen. The so-called ' bush quails' of India (*Perdicula*) are dwarf partridges living hidden in the grass, scrub, and bush. The very rare *Ophrysia* is also rather quail-like, but it has not been found for a long time in

its north-western Himalayan home and it may have become extinct ; it has lanceolate feathers, like *Ithaginis*, and it is very little known. See-see partridges *Ammoperdix* spp. are elegantly marked, sandy-coloured desert birds ; the 2 species inhabit the dry parts of Transcaspia, Persia, Afghanistan, and north-western India (*A. griseogularis*), Palestine, Egypt, and Arabia (*A. heyi*).

The Grey Partridge (or just ' Partridge ') *Perdix perdix* is the famous game-bird of the cultivated plains of Europe and the Caspian area, replaced in Turkestan, Mongolia, Amurland, and northern China by the closely allied *P. barbata*, and in central Asia and the Himalaya, at high altitudes, by *P. hodgsoniae*. These are all ground birds which never perch, have no spurs, and thrive on cultivated lands. The red-legged partridges *Alectoris* spp., on the contrary, roost on trees and bushes at night, living in more wooded country, some on rocky, high mountains. The Chukar *A. graeca* is found from the Alps eastwards to Manchuria. The typical Red-legged Partridge *A. rufa* is found from southern France to the Canary Islands. Its near ally *A. barbara* inhabits North Africa, and the giant species *A. melanocephala* Arabia. They all have strong red bills and feet, and blunt spurs in the males.

Snowcocks *Tetraogallus* spp., as large as big pheasants, live at high altitudes in Central Asia, the Caucasus, Asia Minor, the Himalaya, north-western China, and Mongolia, and are locally known as ' ramchukar' (5 species). The 2 species of *Tetraophasis* are also large, but darker and more pheasant-like ; they inhabit the mountains of eastern Tibet and western China. The Snow Partridge *Lerwa lerwa*, in a monotypic genus, is found high up from Afghanistan to Sikkim and western China.

Very different are the tree partridges *Arborophila* spp. (including ' *Tropicoperdix* '), a large and beautiful genus inhabiting, at low, moderate, and high altitudes, the forests from eastern India to southern China and Malaysia (16 species). They have short bills and tails, rather long spurless legs, soft and beautifully marked plumage. Next to be mentioned are 5 monotypic genera. The Black Wood Partridge *Melanoperdix nigra* of Malaya, Sumatra, and Borneo is black in the male, brown in the female. The Crimson-headed Partridge *Haematortyx*, a rare bird from northern Borneo, is chestnut and crimson. The beautiful Roulroul *Rollulus roulroul* from Malaysia, blue, green, and red, with crimson crest, is the most specialised and showy of the wood partridges. The Ferruginous Wood Partridge *Caloperdix oculea*, a handsome chestnut, black, and white bird, and the large Long-billed Partridge *Rhizothera longirostris*, both Malaysian, have short spurs and somehow link

---

Plate 38 · Parental Care

Two stages in the parental care of the Emperor Penguin *Aptenodytes forsteri*, breeding colonially in the polar winter (Antarctica).

a *Upper :* the single egg being incubated as it rests on the parent's tarsi.   *Phot. J. Prévost.*

b *Lower :* a crèche of partly grown chicks.
                                                 Phot. J. Prévost.

(See articles INCUBATION ; PARENTAL CARE ; PENGUIN)

the previously mentioned partridges to the great group of the francolins.

The francolins comprise 5 Asian species (one extending to the eastern Mediterranean countries) and some 36 African species of the genus *Francolinus* (including ' *Pternistis* '). They make first-class game-birds, as most of them live in fairly open country and are of large size. They have rather coarse, large bills and legs, with one or several spurs. Many are dull and brownish, but others have pretty black, white, or chestnut markings.

The bamboo partridges *Bambusicola* spp. have spurred tarsi and a fairly long tail ; they are a little more pheasant-like in shape. There are 3 species, in the mountains of China, Assam, Burma, and Indo-China. The eastern Chinese birds have been successfully introduced into Japan. The spurfowl *Galloperdix* spp. are purely Indian birds which resemble in shape small pheasants, particularly the peacock-pheasants. The cocks have 3, sometimes 4, spurs, the hens 1 or 2 ; their legs are long, as are the slender bill and the tail ; there is a large bare patch of skin around the eyes. The sexes are different. There are 2 species in India and 1 in Ceylon.

Pheasants. The large and beautiful birds commonly called ' pheasants ' are represented by 49 species, some with many subspecies, belonging to 16 well defined genera. The first 4 genera to be mentioned are rather partridge-like, with relatively short tails, and they live on the high mountains of Asia. The Blood Pheasant *Ithaginis cruentus* is rather small and resembles a partridge in shape. The males have lanceolate feathers coloured in shades of grey, pale green, and crimson, with black and white markings ; they have several sharp spurs to their red legs. The females are dark brown. There is but one species, with 13 well marked subspecies, living at high altitudes in the Himalayas and on the mountains of western and northern China.

The tragopans *Tragopan* spp. also have a comparatively short, round, and compressed tail and a short bill. Their legs are pink in the males and brown in the females. The cocks are elaborately spotted and mottled with white and have much red, buff, or grey on the plumage. The head is not crested, but the feathers of the crown are long ; the face and throat are naked, the skin brightly coloured in blue, yellow, or orange ; there are two erectile fleshy blue horns on the head, and a fold of skin under the bill which can be spread into a huge bib in display ; it then looks like a brilliantly coloured and patterned piece of silk. The females are brown, spotted, and marked with darker and lighter tones. These wonderful birds live in the wet forests of high mountains along the Himalaya, in Assam, Burma, Tonkin, and China, and are exceptional in this family in that they build bulky nests in trees. There are 5 distinct species.

The Koklas *Pucrasia macrolopha* frequents similar but drier mountains. There is but one species in the genus, with 10 well marked subspecies in the western Himalaya and in China ; there is a gap, hard to explain, in their distribution, as none are found between western Nepal and Yunnan. The cocks have a long, double crest and a pointed but not very long tail. Their feathers are lanceolate. The head and neck are mostly greenish, black, and white, the rest of the plumage lined and pencilled brown, yellowish buff, grey, and chestnut. The females are brown, streaked with buff and black.

The monals *Lophophorus* spp. are large, thick-set, with a fairly short, square tail. The males are magnificently coloured with metallic green, blue, purple, and coppery red above, velvety black below. The females are brown and streaked. There are 3 different species, the common *L. impejanus* along the Himalaya and 2 rarer ones in northern Assam, Burma, Tibet, and Yunnan, and in Szechuan.

The junglefowls *Gallus* spp. constitute a very special genus of game-birds. They are rather small ; the tail is arched and compressed in the cock, and his head is adorned with a fleshy comb and lappets. There are 4 species ; one of them, the Red Junglefowl *Gallus gallus*, is the ancestor of domestic poultry (see DOMESTICATION). The male is black and red, the female russet and brown. It is found at low and moderate elevations along the Himalaya, in north-eastern India, Burma, southern China, Indochina, Hainan, Malaya, Sumatra, and Java ; and from domestication it has become feral on numerous islands, including the Philippines. The other species occur in western and southern India, Ceylon, Java, and the lesser East Indies.

The gallopheasants *Lophura* spp. include 10 species, some with many subspecies, known as ' kalijs ', ' silver pheasants ', and ' firebacks ', found from the Himalaya to China and Malaysia. All have an arched compressed tail, velvety wattles on the face (usually red, sometimes blue), and, with one exception, crimson legs. The cocks vary from black to blue, purple or white above, variously streaked and marked, and are black below ; almost all are crested. These birds live in forests at low and moderate altitudes.

The eared pheasants *Crossoptilon* spp. are denizens of the high slopes and valleys of Tibet and of western and northern China. They are the only pheasants, strictly so-called, in which the sexes are alike, the male differing from the female in having a spur on the leg. These large birds have a plumage hair-like in texture, velvety wattles on the face like those of the gallopheasants ; the tail is large and compressed, with broad, decomposed feathers ; two tufts of long white feathers decorate the sides of the head. Of the 3 existing species, one inhabits Tibet and adjoining countries, another Kansu and Kokonor, a third (perhaps now nearly extinct) Shansi and Chihli.

The Cheer *Catreus wallichi*, of the Himalaya, somehow links the eared pheasants to the long-tailed pheasants and the true game pheasants, which last it resembles in shape and in its long, narrow, pointed tail. The head is crested. The cock's colours are not bright—grey elegantly spotted and mottled with black, passing to rusty buff on the wings and rump ; the tail is broadly barred. The female is not very different, but a good deal browner and duller.

The long-tailed pheasants *Syrmaticus* spp. inhabit the hills, mountains, and plateaux of northern Burma and Siam, China, Formosa, and Japan. They have very long barred tails and red face-wattles, but no crests. They vary in colour from yellow and coppery red to dark blue, with black, grey, and white bars and markings. The females are brown, eleborately marked with black and buff, each of the 5 species having a special pattern. They live in woods and forests.

The typical pheasants *Phasianus* spp. are well known. There are two species : the Green Pheasant *P. versicolor* in Japan and the ordinary game Pheasant *P. colchicus* found naturally in all suitable parts of central Asia from the Caucasus to the China Sea and Formosa. They live in open and often cultivated country, unlike practically all other pheasants. There are 31 well marked subspecies of *P. colchicus*. Those of the western areas of the range are a rather uniform dark coppery red and have no white ring on the neck, while the Far Eastern ones have con-trasting colours on the mantle, flanks, rump, and tail, and wear a broad white collar ; but there are all sorts of intermediate forms linking them. Sev-eral forms have been imported and established in the game preserves of European, American, and other countries ; these feral populations are generally a mixture of several subspecies, which accounts for the ring-necked character of most of the birds now found in Britain (see NATURALISED BIRDS).

The ruffed pheasants *Chrysolophus* spp. comprise two magnificent small, well-known species, the Golden Pheasant *C. pictus* and Lady Amherst's Pheasant *C. amherstiae*, from the mountains of central and western China. The head of the cocks is crested and the nape and hind neck are covered with a large ruff of broad feathers ; the brightest colours—red, yellow, blue, green, and white— adorn their plumage.

The peacock pheasants *Polyplectron* spp. form a very distinct genus of small pheasants with long tails and a grey or brown plumage marked with metallic green and purple ocellae on the mantle, wings, and tail. The legs of the male have 2 spurs, sometimes more. The head is crested, and the tail is broad and flat in all but one species. They live in deep, tropical forests from eastern India to Borneo and Palawan. The hen lays only 2 eggs in a clutch.

The Crested Argus *Rheinartia ocellata* occurs in the mountains of central Annam and central Malaya. A large bird, brown-speckled and spotted with buff and black, it has a thick occipital crest. The cock's tail is enormous ; the central feathers, 6 inches wide and reaching over 5 feet in length, show a beautiful and complicated pattern of chestnut and almost white spots and ocellae on a grey background. These very secretive birds haunt the damp, high jungle and are almost impossible to see. The female lays 2 eggs in a clutch. The Great Argus *Argusianus argus* is related to the Crested Argus and to the peacock pheasants. Its head and neck are mostly naked and blue. The 2 central tail feathers are very long, dark grey and brown, spotted with white. The brown body is spotted and marked with chest-nut, yellow, and black ; but the most extraordinary part of the plumage is the wing—the primaries, normal in shape, show an incredibly fine pattern of spots and lines, grey, blue, chestnut, and buff ; the secondaries are huge and broad at the tip, adorned with large, shaded, non-metallic ocellae ; the ter-tiaries are large, but coloured like the mantle. The female lacks the long tail and specialised wings. Unlike the Crested Argus, the Great Argus lives at relatively low levels, up to 4000 feet above sea level, in the dry and rocky forests of Malaya, Sumatra, and Borneo. The display of the cock is wonder-ful ; the wings are held open and flattened vertically and the head hidden behind so that the bird looks like a huge, beautifully painted fan. The female lays 2 eggs.

The peafowl *Pavo* spp. are well known ; male and female are commonly referred to as 'peacock' and 'peahen', but the former term may also be used irrespective of sex. There are two species—the Blue Peafowl *P. cristatus* and the Green Peafowl *P. muticus*, the former in India and Ceylon, the latter in Burma, Siam, Indochina, Malaya, and Java. The Blue (or Indian) Peafowl has been kept and reared in captivity for over 2000 years ; although no signs of domestication such as changes in shape or size have ever occurred, 2 or 3 mutations (white, pied, black-shouldered) have developed. These large birds are remarkable, in the males, for their huge tails, the upper coverts of which are greatly elongated, partly decomposed, and tipped with large blue and green ocellae. These coverts can be erected and spread in the bird's famous display. The species lives at low altitudes, in forest or well-wooded country; the females lay 4–8 eggs.

The Congo Peacock *Afropavo congensis* was described in 1936—a sensational discovery, as no other large pheasant had so far been found in Africa. It lives in deep forests where it is difficult to detect. The cock is blue and green, with a fairly short, broad tail, a curious double crest of white and black, and a bare patch of red skin showing on the foreneck. The female is chestnut and coppery green. This beautiful bird is very rare. Clutches of 3–4 eggs are laid.

See Plate 5 (colour). J.D.

Beebe, W. 1918–22. A Monograph of the Pheasants. 4 vols. London.
Delacour, J. 1951. The Pheasants of the World. London and New York.
Hall, B. P. 1963. The francolins, a study in speciation. Bull. Brit. Mus. (Nat. Hist.), Zool. 10 : 105–204.
Toschi, A. 1959. La Quaglia ; Vita—Allevamento—Caccia. Bologna.

PHEASANT, CROW-: see CROW-PHEASANT ; and under CUCKOO

PHENETIC: term applied in taxonomy to a grouping or arrangement based on observable resemblances that may or may not also be evidence of phyletic relationship.

PHENOLOGY: literally the study of visible appearances, and thus used in respect of seasonally recurring events in animate nature, such as—in the ornithological field—first arrival of a migratory species, first laying of a species, last singing of a species, and the relation of these with meteorological data.

PHENON: term sometimes used for a SIBLING SPECIES.

PHENOTYPE: the group in which an individual falls by reason of its appearance, which is the result of interaction between external factors and the GENOTYPE ; see also GENETICS.

PHILEPITTIDAE: see under PASSERIFORMES ; and ASITY

PHILYDORINAE: see OVENBIRD (1)

PHOEBE: substantive name of *Sayornis* spp. (see FLYCATCHER (2)).

PHOENICOPTERI ; PHOENICOPTER-IDAE: see under CICONIIFORMES ; and FLAMINGO

PHOENICULIDAE: see CORACIIFORMES ; and WOOD-HOOPOE

PHOENIX: see FABULOUS BIRDS

PHORESY: transport of one species of organism by another that is not parasitic upon it ; the term is applied particularly to insects, e.g. Mallophaga carried by louse-flies on a bird (see ECTOPARASITE).

PHORORHACI: see under GRUIFORMES ; and FOSSIL BIRDS

PHOTOGRAPHY: as applied to birds—a comparatively young aspect of ornithology. Although its pioneers were active in the 1890s, it was in fact only during the first decade of the present century, and especially after the First World War, that its impact became important and its practice widespread, until today the camera may be regarded, in varying degrees and with different purposes, as the tool of all ornithologists. At one extreme, its object may be purely scientific ; at the other, merely recreational—a field sport as it were, with the bird taking second place to the artistic effectiveness of the result.

Whilst it is for its scientific value as an aid to ornithology that the camera appeals to the serious student, it is of wide importance in more general directions. Fundamentally, the ornithologist is a collector, as are all naturalists. The museums and private collections are the foundation stone of the science. But as these grew more and more complete, interest turned to the living bird, and with the advent of conservation, as we know it today, aimless collecting fell into disrepute. Here it was that the camera came into its timely own, for with it the instincts of the collector could be satisfied without the need to take life.

Again, if today the public is much more ' bird-minded ' than even twenty years ago, photography, more than scientific awareness, is one of the main causes. Ornithology, once the hobby of the few, was the interest of those to whom leisure and opportunity gave access. Today it is shared, with vastly differing degrees of seriousness, by all the many who subscribe to societies and clubs that serve birds and their observers (see BIRD-WATCHING).

Illustration. In this minor revolution of our age the bird photographer has played a decisive part. Without illustration it was of little avail to write about, or appeal for, an unknown bird with some strange name. The photograph has added reality and substance to the written word ; and the ease with which it can be reproduced has made it available to the public press. Its rise has been at the expense of, or at least has coincided with the decline of, the coloured Plate, and none would for a moment fail to regret that fact. The age, however, of the stately coloured Plate was the age of patronage, and with its passing the photograph filled a vital gap. Moreover, the skill of the painter was confined to the gifted few ; the ability to take a photograph, albeit with different degrees of perfection, was open to all capable of mastering its fundamental technique. Thus those who visit distant places are able, either by illustrated books or lectures, to convey visually to the layman their experiences, the countryside, and its birds. This has been the case especially with the moving film, and the influence of bird photography on the public has reached a new peak with its adoption by television. In short, photography in all its guises—monochrome, colour, and cinematography—has gained for birds a very wide audience, not necessarily knowledgeable, but sympathetic and interested ; and it is largely from this pool that has sprung modern ' ornithomania ' and the general acceptance of the concept of conservation.

Scientific Applications. In the scientific field, the camera stands supreme in recording bird behaviour, e.g. displays and the like. However vivid the written word, it can never compete with the visual record, with the possibility of frame-by-frame analysis. Electronic flash has enabled the student of avian aerodynamics to see in detail wing positions too fast for the human eye to register. Its ability to stop all movement has assisted in the exact identification of insect food brought by birds to their young.

Photography can also give valuable aid in the enumeration of birds, e.g. sea birds breeding densely on a cliff-face, or flocks of birds such as Anatidae in the open photographed from the air (see CENSUS ; COUNT). Mention may also be made of the photography of radar screens showing birds flying overhead (see RADAR).

In systematic work, even monochrome photographs of a series of skins are often useful to illustrate an author's point. Clearly, if colour photography is truly perfected, the taxonomist will be able to use transparencies instead of original skins (where these are not easily available) to work on racial differences in plumage ; a beginning has already been made.

Trends. Heralded at its advent with acclaim, bird photography has with its increasing popularity come under the fire of criticism. Today pictures of outstanding merit and technical excellence have become the rule, so that the serious ornithologist tends to be scornful of the man who uses a camera but too often, in his eyes, fails to make any biological contribution along with the photograph. Moreover, photography at the nest, which has for long been the chief focusing point, does entail disturbance. The fact that correct technique and due care of approach can minimise this danger to a negligible degree was satisfactory so long as bird photographers were few in number and therefore of little importance. But today many have adopted the pursuit as a field sport, and with numbers the element of possible disturbance becomes of more significance, particularly in sanctuaries and major bird haunts to which they desire access. Education and the promulgation of the correct principles of hide work have had a salutary effect. There is, too, a marked tendency today to react from the rather stereotyped bird-at-nest portrait to bird-in-habitat : waders on the tide, carrion-eaters at bait, birds in flight, and so on ; likewise to illustrate activities rather than to make portraits.

Equipment. Bird photography has been very conservative in its equipment—the large camera, large lens, and large film or plate. Of late its technique has been greatly changed by the 35 mm. camera, which has removed much of its drudgery and simplified a number of technical problems by its versatility, although often at some expense of quality. The introduction of colour has added new glamour and appeal, while the 16 mm. cine camera has put the possibility of making films into the layman's hands. Electronic flash has removed the problem of dark, uneven, and impossible lighting, and not only made night into day, but caught birds in actions too fast for the eye to record. These developments have given bird photography new life, new purpose, and fresh fields to conquer.

G.K.Y.

Cott, H. B. 1956. Zoological Photography in Practice. London.

Hosking, E. & Newberry, C. 1944. The Art of Bird Photography. London.

Hosking, E. & Newberry, C. 1961. Bird Photography as a Hobby. London.

Kinne, R. 1962. The Complete Book of Nature Photography (introduction by R. T. Peterson). New York.

Warham, J. 1956. The Technique of Photographing Birds. London.

Yeates, G. K. 1945. Bird Photography. London.

Yeates, G. K. & Robertson, A. W. P. R. 1955. Photography and the Bird. London.

PHOTOPERIODISM: the regulation of cyclical changes in physiology and behaviour (e.g. breeding, migration) by light acting as an external stimulus (see MIGRATION ; also RHYTHM). Variations in length of day are an especially constant factor in the environment at any one latitude ; they were therefore theoretically attractive as possible causative factors of notably regular seasonal events in animate nature. The work of Rowan (1925 et seq.), and of those who came after him, has shown—first for birds, later for other animals—that light can be an effective stimulus in some cases, whether absolute or relative (increasing, decreasing) length of day has importance. The circumstances are various, and the relations with other factors are complicated. The subject has recently been reviewed in summary form by Marshall.

Rowan, W. 1925. Relation of light to bird migration and developmental changes. Nature 115 : 494–495. (The starting point of an extensive literature.)
Marshall, A. J. 1961. Breeding seasons and migration. *In* Marshall, A. J. (ed.). Biology and Comparative Physiology of Birds vol. 2. New York and London.

PHYLETIC: used in the same sense as ' phylogenetic ' (see PHYLOGENY).

PHYLOGENY: sometimes written ' phylogenesis ', the evolutionary history of a taxon—contrasted with ' ontogeny ', the development of an individual within its own life-span ; both ' phylogenetic ' and ' phyletic ' are used as adjectives.

PHYLUM: a taxonomic category higher than class (see ANIMAL KINGDOM).

PHYSIOLOGY: the science of bodily function. The use of chemical and physical methods for this study involves the disciplines of biochemistry and biophysics ; or the subject may be divided, according to the particular function studied, into such specialities as neurology and endocrinology. The physiology of birds is dealt with in this work under the names of the various systems of the body, and under other special heads, e.g. HEAT REGULATION ; METABOLISM ; NUTRITION ; SENSES.

PHYTOTOMIDAE: see under PASSERIFORMES ; and PLANTCUTTER

PIAPIAC: *Ptilostomus afer* (see CROW (1)).

PICAE: the second order of Linnaeus.

PICARIAE: formerly used as the name of an order, placed next to the Passeres, which included a motley assemblage of groups now placed in the Piciformes, Apodiformes, Caprimulgiformes, Coraciiformes, and Cuculiformes (and by Stresemann in a still greater number of orders), and originally also the birds now placed in the Psittaciformes.

PICATHARTINI: see BABBLER

PICI; PICIDAE: see below

PICIFORMES: an order, alternatively ' Pici ', comprising the following suborders and families, the latter dealt with separately as shown :

Galbulae :	
Superfamily Galbuloidea	
Galbulidae	see JACAMAR
Bucconidae	see PUFFBIRD
Superfamily Capitonoidea	
Capitonidae	see BARBET
Superfamily Ramphastoidea	
Indicatoridae	see HONEYGUIDE
Ramphastidae	see TOUCAN
Pici :	
Picidae	see WOODPECKER

The Galbulae are here divided into 3 superfamilies comprising in all 5 families ; but some authors prefer to place all but the first 2 families in the suborder Pici. The Picidae are divisible into 3 subfamilies—Picinae (typical woodpeckers), Picumninae (piculets), and Jynginae (wrynecks).

The relationship of the families is indicated by certain anatomical characters common to all. These include a zygodactyl foot, with a distinctive arrangement of the flexor tendons ; also, except in the Galbulidae, absence of down plumage at any age in most species. A specialised form of bill is characteristic of each family.

The members of the order are predominantly arboreal birds, nearly all inhabiting forests or more sparsely wooded country ; they are able to perch on trees, but some feed wholly or partly on the ground. The toucans and barbets are largely vegetarian in their diet, while the others live mainly on animal food, especially insects ; the honeyguides are unique, among birds, in using wax (from honeycombs etc.) as food. They are all hole-nesters, either using natural cavities or excavating in wood, termitaries, or soil ; but at least some of the Indicatoridae are parasitic in their breeding habits. The eggs are unspotted white, and the young are at first blind, helpless, and usually naked.

The order has an almost cosmopolitan distribution, although unrepresented in the Malagasy and Australasian Regions as well as in very high latitudes and remote islands. This is so, however, only by reason of the wide range of the Picidae. The other families are purely tropical, and of them only the Capitonidae are found in both Old and

New Worlds ; the Indicatoridae are Afro-Asian, and the remaining 3 are purely Neotropical.

PICULET: substantive name of Picumninae spp. (see WOODPECKER).

PICUMNINAE: see WOODPECKER

PIE: see MAGPIE ; TREE-PIE

PIEDTAIL: substantive name of *Phlogophilus* spp. (for family see HUMMINGBIRD).

PIGEON: substantive name, with ' dove ' as a frequent alternative, of the species of Columbidae (Columbiformes, suborder Columbae) ; in the plural, general term for the family. In popular speech ' dove ' is used for the smaller and ' pigeon ' for the larger forms, but this usage is not invariable ; thus, the Stock Dove *Columba oenas* is a typical pigeon in every way. The family is almost cosmopolitan, being absent only from the Arctic, subarctic, Antarctic, and sub-antarctic areas and some oceanic islands.

Pigeons vary in size from the Diamond Dove *Geopelia cuneata*, no bigger than a Skylark *Alauda arvensis*, to the crowned pigeons *Goura* spp., which are nearly as large as hen Turkeys *Meleagris gallopavo*. They have soft, dense plumage and plump, compact bodies with rather small heads. The wings may be short or long ; the tail square-ended, rounded, or pointed, and of variable length. The bill is usually rather small, hard at the tip but soft at the base, with a naked cere. The legs are usually short, but are rather long in some of the terrestrial species. In most species the female is slightly duller than the male ; in some the sexes are alike, but in others the male differs strikingly in colour from the female.

Most species are at least partly arboreal, but a few are terrestrial or cliff-dwelling. Most are strong flyers and some are highly migratory (see FLIGHT). Most of the species of which the social behaviour is known are more or less gregarious when not breeding, some gathering into large flocks. Some species often, or usually, breed colonially ; and in some which do not do this large numbers of individuals may congregate at good feeding places even in the breeding season.

Seeds, fruits, berries, buds, and other vegetable substances are the main foods of pigeons, but many species also take small snails or other invertebrate animals. Most pigeons have strong, muscular gizzards and long, narrow intestines, but in some of the fruit-eating species the stomach is soft and the gut short and wide ; these latter birds digest only the pulp of the fruits they feed on, voiding the stones intact. Pigeons drink by immersing the bill and sucking, a habit shared with the Pteroclididae and also with the Turnicidae (see SANDGROUSE ; and BUTTONQUAIL).

All species of which the behaviour is known build a slight but often strongly interwoven nest of twigs, roots, or stems and lay 1 or (in most species) 2 white, or at least pale, unmarked eggs ; from these hatch helpless nestlings clad sparsely in coarse yellow down. The young insert their bills into the parent's mouth and are fed by regurgitation. They grow rapidly ; some of the smaller species can fly before they are 2 weeks old. The female alone builds, the male bringing her materials. Both sexes share in incubation and care of the young. Both produce ' pigeon milk ', a nutritious, curdlike substance formed by the proliferation and sloughing off of the cells of the lining epithelium of the crop (see MILK, PIGEON) ; for the first few days this constitutes the sole food of the young.

Typically, pigeons utter cooing, crooning, or booming calls and inflate their necks when so doing. Some utter whistling, harsh, or cackling cries in lieu of, or additionally to, ' cooing '. Some often or usually punctuate their display flights with loud wing-clapping. Rather similar but less deliberate and more rattling or clattering wing-claps may be made by pigeons suddenly taking wing when alarmed.

The family has been divided into numerous genera, of which the present writer recognises 43 ; 12 of these are monotypic. The subfamily Columbinae includes not only all the more typical pigeons and doves but also the various superficially partridge-like forms such as the quail-doves *Geotrygon* spp. of Central and South America, the Pheasant Pigeon *Otidiphaps nobilis* of New Guinea, the many rather small South American doves, and the Australian bronzewings (see later). Most members of this subfamily are primarily seed-eaters ; they differ much in colour, but are mostly clad in soft shades of brown, grey, or vinous in various combinations. Often they have iridescent, white, or black areas on the neck, wings, or tail that are exhibited in display or when the bird takes wing.

The subfamily Treroninae consists of a possibly polyphyletic assemblage of arboreal, fruit-eating species. Among them are the green pigeons *Treron* spp. of the Ethiopian and Oriental Regions. These are primarily soft green in colour, often with beautiful yellow, orange, or mauve markings and brilliantly coloured eyes and ceres. Unlike other fruit pigeons, they have hard muscular gizzards and digest the seeds of the wild figs on which they largely feed. The often brilliantly coloured fruit doves of the genus *Ptilinopus* and the larger imperial pigeons *Ducula* spp. differ from each other in size and in the more diverse colours found in the smaller species ; they are widespread in the Indo-Malayan and Pacific areas, a few species reaching India proper and Australia. Closely related to them are the Top-knot Pigeon *Lopholaimus antarcticus* of Australia, the New Zealand Pigeon *Hemiphaga novaeseelandiae*, and the blue fruit pigeons *Alectroenas* spp. of the islands of the Indian Ocean. The affinities of the brown fruit pigeons *Phapitreron* spp. of the Philippines are uncertain.

The subfamily Gourinae consists of the 3 closely related crowned pigeons *Goura* spp. of New Guinea. They have large laterally flattened crests of lacy-looking disconnected or spatulate-tipped feathers.

The subfamily Didunculinae comprises only one species, the Tooth-billed Pigeon *Didunculus strigirostris* of Samoa.

Only a few of the more noteworthy of the 255 species of pigeons can be mentioned individually here. The Rock Pigeon *Columba livia*, a native of Europe, western Asia, India, and North Africa, is the ancestor of the many breeds of domestic pigeons and of their feral descendants now common in towns throughout most of the world (see DOMESTICATION ; HOMING PIGEON). The wild form is bluish-grey with black wing-bars and an iridescent neck ; it roosts and breeds in caves and on sheltered cliff-ledges and feeds on the ground in open country.

The long-tailed Passenger Pigeon *Ectopistes migratorius* of eastern North America was remarkable for its extreme gregariousness, nesting and migrating in enormous flocks. Unfortunately this made it very vulnerable to human predation and it was exterminated some sixty years ago, after a long period of relentless exploitation by man (see EXTINCT BIRDS). A closely related, but smaller and less colourful species, the Mourning Dove *Zenaida macroura* is still common, ranging from Alaska to Panama.

The African form of the Collared Dove *Streptopelia decaocto roseogrisea* is the ancestor of the domesticated Barbary Dove or Blonde Ringdove and its white variety the so-called 'Java Dove'. An Asiatic form of this species, *Streptopelia d. decaocto*, has recently spread across Europe in a remarkable manner and now breeds as far west as Holland and eastern parts of Britain.

The little Namaqua (or Masked) Dove *Oena capensis* of Africa and Madagascar frequents open country and is of nomadic habits. It has a very long, graduated tail and shows marked sexual dimorphism, the male having a black face and breast, bordered with light grey, while these areas

are light drab in the female. Its nearest relatives are the wood or scrubland doves of the genus *Turtur*, all of which are short-tailed and only one of which is sexually dimorphic.

The chubby, pinkish-brown and grey Ground Dove *Columbina passerina*, although slightly larger than a Diamond Dove, looks smaller because of its short tail. It is a common town and garden bird in parts of Central and South America and the West Indies. The Flame Dove *Ptilinopus victor* of Fiji is unique in colour and shows an unusual type of sexual dimorphism ; the male is vivid orange with an olive-yellow head, and the female is dark green but with the head the same colour as her mate's—see Plate 6 (colour).

The Australian bronzewing pigeons of the genera *Phaps, Histriophaps, Geophaps, Lophophaps, Ocyphaps,* and *Petrophassa* are good examples of adaptive radiation. Although they have diverged greatly in the course of their speciation and adaptation to different biotopes, their colour patterns and behaviour still show their close phylogenetic affinities. They include the only 2 genera of pigeons, *Ocyphaps* and *Lophophaps*, which have pointed crests like that of a Lapwing *Vanellus vanellus*.

See Plates 6 and 17 (colour), 28a and 45b (phot.).

D.G.

Cain, A. J. 1954. Subdivisions of the genus *Ptilinopus*. Bull. Brit. Mus. (Nat. Hist.), Zool. 2 : no. 8.

Goodwin, D. 1956a. Observations on the voice and displays of certain pigeons. Avicult. Mag. 62 : 17–33, 62–70.

Goodwin, D. 1956b. The significance of some behaviour patterns of pigeons. Bird Study 3 : 25–37.

Goodwin, D. 1959. Taxonomy of the genus *Columba*. Bull. Brit. Mus. (Nat. Hist.), Zool. 6 : no. 1.

Heinroth, O. & K. 1948. Verhaltensweisen der Felsentaube (Hausetaube) *Columba livia livia*. LZ. Tierpsychol. 6 : 153–201.

Husain, K. Z. 1958. Subdivisions and zoogeography of the genus *Treron* (*green* fruit-pigeons). Ibis 100 : 334–348.

Skutch, A. K. 1959. Life history of the Blue Ground Dove. Condor 61 : 65–74.

Stresemann, E. & Nowak, E. 1958. Die Ausbreitung der Türkentaube in Asien und Europa. J. Orn. 99 : 243–296.

Whitman, C. O. 1919. The Behaviour of Pigeons. Vol. 3 of the posthumous works of C. O. Whitman, published by the Carnegie Institute, Washington, U.S.A.

PIGEON, CAPE: sailors' name for the Pintado Petrel *Daption capensis* (see PETREL).

PIGMENT: see COLOUR ; EGGS, NATURAL HISTORY OF ; PLUMAGE

PIGMENTS, VISUAL: see VISION

PIHA: substantive name of *Lipaugus* spp. and allies (for family see COTINGA).

PILEUM: the whole top of the head, from forehead to occiput inclusively (see TOPOGRAPHY).

PILOT-BIRD: *Pycnoptilus floccosus* (see WREN (2)).

PINEAL BODY: see NERVOUS SYSTEM

PINFEATHER: a growing feather still in its sheath (see FEATHER ; MOULT).

PINION: poetical word for a wing ; sometimes applied to the part of the wing comprising the primary feathers, or even to a single one of these.

PINIONING: rendering a captive bird permanently incapable of flight by cutting one wing at the carpal joint and so removing the basis from which the primary feathers grow (compare CLIPPING). This procedure makes it possible to keep waterfowl and reasonably large ground-birds in the open ; it is the lopsidedness, more than the reduction in wing area, that is effective.

PINKFOOT: colloquial short name (plural ' pinkfeet ') for the Pinkfooted Goose *Anser fabalis brachyrhynchus* (see under DUCK).

PINTAIL: substantive name of certain *Anas* spp. ; used without qualification for *A. acuta* (see DUCK).

PIPIT: substantive name of species of *Anthus* and related genera (see under WAGTAIL).

PIPRIDAE: see under PASSERIFORMES ; and MANAKIN

PIQUERO: name for *Sula nebouxii* (see GANNET).

PIRACY: one bird robbing another of the food which the latter has obtained. This is frequent among most birds but has developed as a regular habit only in a few. Starlings *Sturnus vulgaris* sometimes rob Blackbirds *Turdus merula* of worms ; Blackbirds will rob Song Thrushes *T. philomelos* of snails; shrikes (Laniidae) will rob wheatears *Oenanthe* spp. and even rollers *Coracias* spp. of beetles. The Fulmar *Fulmarus glacialis* frequently robs gulls (Larinae) larger than itself ; and all the raptors are inveterate pirates, especially some of the eagles, such as the Tawny Eagle *Aquila rapax*. A remarkable case of treble piracy is recorded by Corbett, who saw a Sparrowhawk *Accipiter nisus* catch a bush chat *Saxicola* sp. in the Himalaya ; a Merlin *Falco columbarius* chased and robbed the Sparrowhawk, a Honey-buzzard *Pernis apivorus* chased and robbed the Merlin, and a Peregrine *Falco peregrinus* robbed the Honey-buzzard ! Piracy has developed into a regular habit in the African Fish Eagle *Haliaetus vocifer*, its particular victim being the Osprey *Pandion haliaetus* ; but it will also rob herons (Ardeidae), pelicans (Pelecanidae), and kites (Milvinae) of their food—one of these eagles, in attempting to rob a Goliath Heron *Ardea goliath*, became impaled on the latter's bill. Although an expert fisherman itself, this eagle will ' wait on ' a fishing Osprey and attack the moment a fish is caught, compelling the Osprey to drop the fish and then recovering the prey before it reaches the water.

The Frigatebirds (Fregatidae) are inveterate pirates and have a larger wing area for body weight than any other bird. Gannets (Sulidae) are their favourite victims, being pursued until food is disgorged and can be caught in the air. Any hesitation on the gannet's part is followed by contact attack ; the same gannet has been seen to be attacked on three consecutive occasions, the pirate remaining close whilst the gannet fished and the latter getting no peace until the frigatebird's appetite was satisfied. They will also attack gulls, pelicans, cormorants (Phalacrocoracidae), and tropicbirds (Phaethontidae), using the same technique to force them to disgorge.

The skuas (Stercorariidae) are pirates by preference, although capable of securing their own food. The Great Skua *Catharacta skua*, in addition to harrying gulls and terns (Sterninae), has been known to attack herons and gannets, forcing them to disgorge by striking with the powerful bill and attempting to drown them by a paddling action of the feet. During the breeding season these skuas will intercept gannets bringing food for their young, fly up behind the victim, and, holding the tip of its wing, tilt the bird into the sea and compel it to disgorge, using both feet and bill.

The Arctic Skua *Stercorarius parasiticus* is a constant pirate of terns, colliding with them and buffeting them, using the wings but neither bill nor feet ; victory is commonly psychological, the tern dropping its fish before the aggressor strikes. This skua will also attack some of the auks (Alcidae) when they are surfacing with food, but evasion by diving is invariably successful.

Although all gulls will chase their own kind when in possession of food, piracy has not become a regular habit. A unique case of piracy has been recorded, the victim being an adult Shag *Phalacrocorax aristotelis* feeding its chick ; as fast as food was regurgitated by the Shag, a Herring Gull *Larus argentatus* interposed its bill right into the Shag's mouth and secured what was intended for the chick —no resentment was shown by the Shag.

See also AUTOLYCISM. R.M.

Meinertzhagen, R. 1959. Pirates and Predators. The Piratical and Predatory Habits of Birds. Edinburgh and London.

PITTA: substantive name of the species of Pittidae (Passeriformes, suborder Tyranni) ; in the plural, general term for the family. The word is of Telegu origin and has been adopted as both the scientific and the English name. The family is a very homogeneous group of brightly coloured birds found in the Old World tropics, from Africa to the Solomon Islands.

Superficially the majority of the species look like plump short-tailed thrushes (Turdinae), and indeed the names 'ground-thrushes', 'ant-thrushes', and 'jewel-thrushes' have been bestowed upon them. Anatomically they are distinguished by the peculiar attachment of the intrinsic muscles of the syrinx and by the formation of the tarsus. The wing has 10 primaries, the outermost always long ; there are 12 rectrices, generally noticeably short.

There are 23 species, all usually placed in the genus *Pitta*. The main centre of distribution of the group is Indo-Malaya, where some 15-20 species occur and have many racial forms. Three species extend to Australia and 2 are found in Africa. They include some of the most brightly and diversely coloured birds in the world, but their shape, appearance, and habits are remarkably constant. One species (often treated as generically distinct) has long tufts or aigrettes at the side of the nape, while all have erectile crown feathers that are elevated when the bird is excited. In some species the male and female are very distinct, but in others they are practically indistinguishable. In size they vary from that of one of the larger larks (Alaudidae) to that of a Partridge *Perdix perdix*.

Pittas are ground birds of forest, jungle, or tropical scrub. They usually feed among dead leaves and litter or in low forest growth and progress at speed with long fast hops. For most of the year they are found singly or in pairs. They are mainly insectivorous. Some species are sedentary ; others are definitely migratory, and there are instances of their being attracted to lights at night. As a family they are retiring birds, not easily seen, and they would be frequently overlooked but for their characteristic calls. All the known calls of pittas have some similarity, being either a trilling rolling sound or a short series of distinct whistles.

The nests are large, rough, oval, or oven-shaped structures with the entrance low down on one side. They are made of leaves, roots, tendrils, and the like, with a finer lining, and they are usually placed on stumps, on fallen trees, at the base of bushes or among the roots of trees, frequently on the ground itself. The eggs are hard and glossy, 4-5 or more in Indo-Malaya, 3-4 in Australia, 2-3 in Africa. They are very constant for the family, being white or cream in ground colour with reddish or purplish spots or speckles and lilac or grey undermarkings.

To take an example, the African Pitta *Pitta angolensis* breeds from central Tanganyika southwards to the Transvaal, but in the non-breeding season it reaches as far north as Uganda. It is 7 inches long, and in adults of both sexes the mantle is green, the rump cobalt blue, the wings spotted with blue, the throat pale pink, the chest fawn, the belly and under tail coverts crimson ; and there is a broad black stripe through the eye from forehead to nape, with a broad buff stripe between it and the black crown. It bobs, and flirts its tail, like a Dipper *Cinclus cinclus* ; and it has a fighting attitude in which it crouches, with feathers puffed out, wings spread, and bill pointed upwards. It is one of the species which has been observed to perform repeated short looping flights from its perch on a bough.

See Plate 6 (colour).   C.W.M.-P.

Elliott, D. G. 1863. A Monograph of the Pittidae or Family of Ant Thrushes. New York. (2nd ed. 1893-95, London.) (Coloured Plates.)
Peters, J. L. 1951. Check-list of Birds of the World vol. 7. Cambridge, Mass.

PITTA, ANT-: see ANTPITTA ; and ANTBIRD

PITTIDAE: see under PASSERIFORMES ; and PITTA

PITUITARY GLAND: see ENDOCRINE SYSTEM ; NERVOUS SYSTEM

PITYRIASINAE: see BRISTLEHEAD ; and SHRIKE

PLAGIOCOELOUS: see INTESTINE

PLAINRUNNER: substantive name of *Coryphistera alaudina* and *Clibanornis dendrocolaptoides* (see OVENBIRD (1)).

PLAINS-WANDERER: alternatively ' Collared Hemipode ', *Pedionomus torquatus*, sole member of the Pedionomidae (Gruiformes, suborder Turnices). It is a small bird like a buttonquail *Turnix* sp. and inhabits the open grasslands and plains of southeastern Australia, where it apparently keeps to open areas and avoids the scrubby sections and stubble that are favoured by most buttonquail species. *Pedionomus* is placed apart from the buttonquails (Turnicidae) on account of the persistent hind toe, the pyriform instead of oval eggs, and the persistence of paired carotid arteries ; but many consider separation as a subfamily (Pedionominae) sufficient. Although superficially like a buttonquail, the Plains-wanderer typically does not exhibit the crouching posture but stands erect like a bustard (Otididae) ; an interesting photograph published by Purnell shows clearly the bird's habit of standing ' elevated on its toes ' so as to achieve a wide view of the surroundings.

The bill is slender and of medium length. The wings are short and rounded, the tail is very short, and the whole body is compact. The plumage shows a cryptic pattern of reddish-brown, buff, and black, paler below ; there is a ' collar ' of black spots on a white ground. Sexual dimorphism is marked, the female having a chestnut-coloured breast. The male incubates the eggs and raises the young. The length of the female is given as 5 inches, that of the male about 4 inches.

Plains-wanderers, although partly migratory, are usually loth to fly, preferring to run or ' freeze ', and have on occasions been caught by hand. They have a whirring flight like that of a buttonquail. Such stomach analyses as have been carried out disclose the presence of insects, seeds, vegetable matter, and sand. The nest is a slight depression in the ground, and 4 eggs make up the clutch ; they are pale yellowish or greenish, spotted with grey and olive. The breeding season is described as being from September to January. The breeding range is from Duaringa, Queensland,. in the north, to western New South Wales, Lake Frome (one or two records) and south-eastern South Australia. Most recent records are from Victoria.

D'Ombrain has reviewed certain aspects of the scanty knowledge of the habits of the species, speculating about the reason for its increasing rarity in modern times ; these remarks apply as much today as they did in 1926, it being recorded equally rarely now. Alteration of habitat due to sheep, rabbits, and fires, and the introduction of the fox and feral cat, have undoubtedly contributed to the numerical reduction of the species.

See Plate 31 (colour).   A.K.

D'Ombrain, E. A. 1926. The vanishing Plains-wanderer *Pedionomus torquatus*. Emu 26 : 59–63 (map).
Purnell, H. A. 1915. The Plains-wanderer in captivity. Emu 15 : 141–143 (photograph).

PLANTAIN-EATER : substantive name (unfortunately misleading) of some species cf Musophagidae (see TURACO).

PLANTAR : pertaining to the posterior surface of the tarsus (equivalent to the sole).

PLANTCUTTER : substantive name of the three species of Phytotomidae (Passeriformes, suborder Tyranni) ; in the plural, general term for the family. Plantcutters are purely South American. They are about the size of a Hawfinch *Coccothraustes coccothraustes*, and are heavily built finch-like birds with short wings and rather long-tails, and with the feathers of the crown pileated to form a slight crest. The plumage on the upper parts is plumbeous and brown, and in the male streaked with black ; the throat, breast, and under parts in the female are light buff and dull ochre, with dark streaks, these colours being replaced in the male by bright rufous and brick-red tints. The legs are short and the feet large in comparison ; the bill is stout, short, conical, and finely serrated ; the eyes are bright amber yellow in both sexes. There is a single genus.

Chilean Plantcutter *Phytotoma rara.*   C.E.T.K.

The bill is admirably suited for plucking buds, tender leaves, shoots, and fruit, these being the staple articles of diet. The bird being provided with such an instrument of destruction, it is easy to understand why fruit-growers and agriculturists regard the ' rara ' as one of their worst enemies. Nevertheless, in despite of efforts to destroy both birds and nests, the species show no sign of decreasing in numbers.

The Chilean Plantcutter *Phytotoma rara* is confined to central and southern Chile, and to a strip of Argentina from the province of Neuquen to northern Chubut. In Chile it is present all the year round but shows migratory movements with the change of the seasons. It frequents orchards, gardens, and open scrub country, and in the spring pairs may be found in the wooded mountain valleys of the Andean foothills up to a height of 6500 feet. The birds are nowhere plentiful, except in orchards and gardens, and, although they do not flock in winter, small groups of half a dozen or more may be seen. In the spring the male makes his presence known by an oft-repeated unmusical rasping trill, and soon his bright rufous breast may be seen on the topmost branch of a nearby bush or tree. If undisturbed, the bird will remain motionless for several minutes except for an occasional slight movement of the head, and when he finally decides to change his look-out he will take off with a sluggish flight and alight again close by.

Nesting starts in October and continues into December. The nest is a flat untidy structure of twigs with a shallow saucer-like cup lined with slender twigs and pliable rootlets ; it is placed in the fork of horizontal branches near the top of a small fruit tree or shrub, or, in the open country, in high bushes or thorns. The eggs vary in number from 2 to 4 ; the ground colour is greenish-blue, sparsely dotted with dark brown or black with a tendency to zone at the larger pole.

The Red-breasted Plantcutter *P. rutila* is resident in Central Argentina, Uruguay, the Paraguayien Chaco, and in Bolivia from La Paz to Tarija. It is very similar in appearance to the Chilean species, except that the rufous of the forehead, throat, breast, and under parts is brighter in the male, while in the female the under parts are light buff with dark striations. This bird is common on the prairies of Patagonia where the stony reaches are interspersed with bush vegetation, shrubs and thorns, or other small trees. In these drab surroundings, inhabited mostly by dull-plumaged birds, the bright breast of the male Plantcutter provides a welcome splash of colour. Nesting habits and eggs are similar to those of the other species.

The third member of the family, the Peruvian Plantcutter *P. raimondii*, is found only in the coastal regions of north-western Peru in the departments of Tumbez and La Libertad. It differs very little in general appearance from *P. rutila* and *P. rara*. The upper parts are greyish cinereous, the front of the crown is rufous, and the under tail coverts are bright cinnamon red ; the wings are almost black, with two white cross bands ; the tail is likewise almost black, the lateral rectrices tipped with white. As in the other 2 species, the female's plumage is much more subdued in colouring, the under parts being tinted with pale yellow ochre.

J.D.G.

PLANT LIFE : considered as part of the environment, see VEGETATION ; also POLLINATORS AND DISTRIBUTORS.

PLASMA : see BLOOD

PLATALEINAE : see SPOONBILL

PLAUTINI : see AUK

PLAY : a form of activity much less apparent in birds than in many mammals, but nevertheless occurring—and not exclusively in the young. Playful behaviour in young animals can commonly be identified as, so to speak, a 'rehearsal' of adult activities ; so it forms part of the learning process, whereby innate capabilities are educated for full performance (see LEARNING ; and FIXED ACTION PATTERN). Thus, nestling birds will often, in the absence of other motivation, engage in sparring matches with each other ; or, in the case of raptors, will make hunting movements towards inedible objects ; or will manipulate potential nest material. Young Christmas Island Frigatebirds *Fregata minor minor*, already on the wing, have been seen to swoop at, pick up, and then drop, leaves and other objects floating on the surface of the sea.

Seemingly playful actions of adult birds, of which a few examples are known, cannot be so readily explained. Rooks *Corvus frugilegus* will commonly indulge in tumbling aerobatics ; and Ravens *C. corax* have been described as, in addition, carrying up twigs or pieces of heather, which they drop and then catch again in the air. Various aquatic birds, e.g. Eider *Somateria mollissima* and Black Guillemot *Cepphus grylle*, have been seen to disport themselves in swift currents in a way that appears to serve no useful purpose, and that to the human mind suggests merely 'having fun'. Similarly, Adélie Penguins *Pygoscelis adeliae* have been described as riding in vociferous parties on small icefloes in a tide race, only to swim back to the starting point and begin again.

However amusing some of the antics may appear to the human eye, one has to be careful to exclude from consideration, in this regard, all forms of display that serve social, sexual, or self-preserving ends (see DISPLAY ; RITUALISATION). Nevertheless, one is tempted to think that some of the performances of bowerbirds (Ptilonorhynchidae) may go beyond such needs (see BOWERBIRD).

PLENARY POWERS : of the International Commission, see NOMENCLATURE.

PLOCEIDAE : a family of the Passeriformes, suborder Oscines (see WEAVER ; also SPARROW (I)).

PLOVER (1): substantive name of the majority of species of the Charadriidae (Charadriiformes, suborder Charadrii) ; in the plural, general term for the family. The other substantive name widely used in the group is 'lapwing', but not all the species that are generically lapwings are in practice so called. A few members of the family have particular names, and one of these, 'dotterel', is sometimes transferred (especially in Australia and New Zealand) as a substantive name of other species.

The plovers are birds of from small to medium size (6–15½ inches long), compactly built and thick-necked ; they inhabit bare or thinly covered ground, often near water ; they run swiftly and fly strongly. The bill is usually straight, fairly stout, and of moderate length—not showing numerous specialised forms such as are found in the Scolopacidae (see SANDPIPER). The wings are long, the tail is short to medium, the legs are of various lengths, and with or without a vestigial hallux. The plumage differs from that commonly found in the Scolopacidae in that it shows bold colour patterns (in brown, olive, grey, black, and white), but it is nevertheless cryptic owing to the disruptive effect. Common features are a white post-nuchal band, a dark thoracic band or area, and a dark terminal or subterminal band on the tail. The downy chicks of most species have the white band on the nape, and also a dark cap. A few species show pronounced seasonal change ; the sexes are alike or nearly so, and the juvenile plumage is also not strikingly different.

Outside the breeding season, plovers tend to be highly gregarious. Some species utter melodious whistles, but in others the cries are shrill. The food is mainly animal, consisting of small invertebrates, but partly vegetable. The birds are often active by night as well as by day. The nest is a mere scrape in the ground, with little or no lining. The 2–5 eggs (in many species very consistently 4) are buff or grey heavily marked with black. The chicks are downy and nidifugous. As a rule, both parents incubate the eggs and care for the young. Distraction displays ('injury-feigning'), when the nest or young are threatened, are common.

There are 56 species of plovers, with a few others doubtfully belonging to the group. The family is cosmopolitan in its distribution, but whereas the Scolopacidae are predominantly native to the Northern Hemisphere, the Charadriidae are to a large extent tropical. As with the other family, the species breeding in higher latitudes are migratory, some of them performing remarkable journeys.

The internal classification of the group here followed is that of the most recent critical revision (Bock 1958). This amalgamates many genera, these having been multiplied to such a degree that the majority of them were monotypic. Much of that taxonomy was based on characters of very doubtful validity—notably the shape of the skull, which is in fact particularly affected by the size of the nasal glands, this in turn depending on adaptation to a fresh-water or saline environment (see EXCRETION, EXTRARENAL). There remains some doubt about the inclusion of a few forms ; *Phegornis* is retained here as an aberrant plover but might be placed in the Scolopacidae ; the turnstones (Arenariinae) may possibly belong here but are dealt with under the Scolopacidae (see SANDPIPER) ; and *Peltohyas* is dealt with under the Glareolidae (see COURSER).

The species included here can be broadly divided into the lapwings and the true plovers. Bock recognises 24 species of lapwings in a single genus, *Vanellus*, as against 26 species in 19 genera of Peters, and therefore finds no occasion for retaining a subfamily Vanellinae. He recognises 26 species of true plovers in 5 genera (as against 29 in 13 of Peters). These figures do not include the doubtfully charadriid forms mentioned above.

Lapwings. Although the general appearance of the several species of *Vanellus* is diverse, certain elements in the plumage pattern are common to all or most ; the tail is always white basally and usually has a broad black band distally, while the wing always has black primaries and usually a broad white stripe. Characters frequent among the lapwings, but not found in other plovers, are a crest, facial wattles, and wing-spurs ; the last correlate with the aggressive nature of the birds, and in species which have no actual spur on the carpal joint a bony knob is present beneath the skin. Africa has the largest number of species and seems to have been the centre of distribution. North America has no lapwings, apart from the occasional occurrence of vagrant individuals or flocks of the European bird ; South America has 3 species, probably descended from birds crossing directly from Africa. New Zealand had none, even as regular visitors, until its successful invasion by an Australian form (*V. miles novaehollandiae*) within the last thirty years.

The English name was originally given to the Lapwing *Vanellus vanellus* and refers to the rather slow wing-beat ; the bird is also popularly known in Britain as Pewit, from its cry, and Green Plover. It is a crested species native to middle Palaearctic latitudes, and performing migrations mainly within the region (but reaching northern India). Its ecology, behaviour, and movements have been the subject of intensive study. The Sociable Plover

Vanellus ('*Chettusia*') *gregarius* has a circumscribed inland breeding range on both sides of the Ural Mountains. The handsome Spur-winged Plover Vanellus ('*Hoplopterus*') *spinosus* is found in south-eastern Europe, the Middle East, Egypt, and tropical Africa (mostly north of the Equator) ; farther south it is replaced by the Blacksmith Plover *V. armatus*, with much white in the plumage. Among the other African species are the Wattled Plover *V. senegallus*, the Crowned Lapwing *V. coronatus* (with a black cap surrounded by a white ring and that in turn by black), and the Long-toed Lapwing *V. crassirostris.*

Of the smaller number of species in the Oriental Region, the Red-wattled Lapwing *V. indicus* and the Yellow-wattled Lapwing *V. malabaricus* are well-known birds in India. Australia has the Banded Plover Vanellus ('*Zonifer*') *tricolor* and two sub-species of the Masked Plover *V. miles.* Of the 3 South American species, the Southern Lapwing *V. chilensis* is widely distributed.

Golden Plovers. The four species of *Pluvialis* are exceptional in their plumage pattern ; the white nuchal band is not present even in the downy chick, and the colour of the back is 'spangled' instead of uniform. The under parts are largely black in the breeding season in the 3 northern species. They are relatively larger birds than those in the next group.

The Golden Plover *P. apricaria* (northern and southern races) breeds in northern Europe and the extreme north-west of Asia, reaching the Mediterranean countries and northern India on migration ; the southern race is present throughout the year in Britain. The closely related American Golden Plover *P. dominica* (Atlantic and Pacific races) is native to high latitudes in North America and eastern Siberia. Its migrations extend as far as Australia and Argentina and are notable for the long sea-crossings which some of the journeys involve—from Nova Scotia to northern South America, and from Alaska to Hawaii. The Grey Plover Pluvialis ('*Squatarola*') *squatarola*—called Black-bellied Plover in America—has a Holarctic breeding distribution in very high latitudes, and migrations extending as far as Chile, Cape Province, and Australia. The so-called New Zealand Dotterel *P. obscurus* has reddish-brown under parts in the breeding season ; it is restricted to New Zealand, and one may suppose it to be descended from migrant ancestors of the northern species remaining in the south to breed.

Sand Plovers. This is sometimes used as a convenient general term for the species here regarded as constituting the genus *Charadrius*, although Bock applies it in a more restricted sense. They are mostly rather small plovers, but some are of medium size. In general the plumage is brown or grey above and white below except for some expression of a pattern of darker markings that is characteristic of the genus—a dark band across the breast, a black forehead, and a black line from bill to eye. The complete pattern is found in some species, but at the other extreme there are a few showing only traces of it. Sometimes the breast-band is double.

Ringed Plover *Charadrius hiaticula*, of Holarctic distribution. *C.E.T.K.*

Bock recognises 24 species and divides them into (a) a typical group ; (b) sand plovers in the narrow sense ; (c) mountain or plains plovers ; (d) a number of aberrant forms. The genus is cosmopolitan in its distribution. Many of the species are migratory in some degree and several perform long journeys, e.g. from eastern Siberia to Australia. Some species inhabit sandy or pebbly seashores throughout the year, often nesting only a short distance above the tide-line ; others frequent open ground near inland waters or marshes ; a few prefer drier habitats, sometimes at a considerable altitude.

The familiar Ringed Plover *Charadrius hiaticula* of Europe, a littoral species, has the breast and head pattern particularly well developed ; with it, the Semipalmated Plover *C. semipalmatus* of North America is often considered to be conspecific. The Kentish (or Snowy) Plover *C. alexandrinus* is a small and pale species with only an interrupted breast-band ; it is practically cosmopolitan, in different subspecific forms, a fact which makes the name given to it in Britain (where it is now practically extinct) seem somewhat parochial. The Killdeer *C. vociferus*, which is larger than those just mentioned, has two breast-bands ; it is a bird of inland pastures and breeds from Canada to Peru. Another species with two black bands (leaving three white areas) is the Three-banded Plover *C. tricollaris* of tropical Africa and Madagascar. In the Banded Dotterel *C. bicinctus*, which breeds in New Zealand and visits Australia, there is an upper black band and a lower chestnut one. The Great Sand Plover (or Large Sand Dotterel) *C. leschenaultii* has no black on the chest, but a broad band of pale rufous in the male only ; it is one of the mountain species and a notable migrant, breeding in Central Asia and reaching South Africa, Australia, and the Solomon Islands. The Mountain Plover *C. montanus* inhabits semi-arid plains in the southern area of the Rocky Mountains and does not frequent the vicinity of water at any season. The Caspian Plover *C. asiasticus* (including *C. veredus* as conspecific), breeding in the eastern Palaearctic and reaching South Africa and Australia on migration, seems to be very closely related to the Winter Plover *C. modestus*, breeding in Patagonia and the Falkland Islands and wintering as far north as Uruguay ; they were nevertheless formerly placed in separate genera (' *Eupoda* ' and ' *Zonibyx* ').

Other Genera. The Wrybill Plover *Anarhynchus frontalis* of New Zealand, breeding in South Island and migrating to North Island, is unique among birds in having a laterally deflected bill, the distal quarter being turned to the right ; with this it probes for insects, under stones on beaches. The Dotterel *Eudromias morinellus* is native to the extreme north of Europe and of western Siberia and to mountain ranges somewhat farther south (Scotland, Tirol, etc.) ; it winters in the Mediterranean area and south-western Asia. Its congener *E. ruficollis* breeds on high ground in the very south of South America, migrating northwards towards the Equator. Also in that area, confined to Tierra del Fuego, is *Pluvianellus socialis*. The little-known *Phegornis mitchellii*, which may not be a plover, likewise also belongs to southern South America ; it is a rather solitary, silent, and tame bird, found on the rocky borders of mountain streams. There are no other species in the genera mentioned in this paragraph.

See Plate 8 (colour), 15, 34c, 39b (phot.), and 43 (egg). A.L.T.

Bock, W. J. 1958. A generic review of the plover, (Charadriinae, Aves). Bull. Mus. Comp. Zool., Harvard 118 : 27–97.

Drury, W. H. 1961. The breeding biology of shore-birds on Bylot Island, Northwest Territories, Canada. Auk 78 : 176–219.

Larsen, S. 1957. The suborder Charadrii in Arctic and Boreal areas during the Tertiary and Pleistocene. A zoogeographic study. Acta Vertebratica 1 : 1–84.

Laven, B. 1941. Beobachtungen über Balz und Brut beim Kiebitz (*Vanellus vanellus* (L.)). J. Orn., Erg. Band 3 : 1–66.

Laven, H. 1940. Beiträge zur Biologie des Sandregen-pfeifers (*Charadrius hiaticula* (L.)). J. Orn. 88 : 183–287.

Rinkel, C. L. 1940. Waarnemingen over het gedrag van de Kievit *Vanellus vanellus* (L.) gedurende de broodtijd. Ardea 29 : 108–147.

Sibson, R. B. 1943. Observations on the distribution of the Wrybill in North Island, New Zealand. Emu 43 : 49–62.

Simmons, K. E. L. 1953. Some aspects of the aggressive behaviour of three closely related plovers (*Charadrius*). Ibis 95 : 115–127.

Simmons, K. E. L. 1955. The nature of the predator-reactions of waders towards humans ; with special reference to the role of the aggressive, escape and brooding drives. Behav. 8 : 130–173.

Spencer, K. G. 1953. The Lapwing in Britain. London.

PLOVER (2) : used as substantive name of certain species not included in the Charadriidae (above)— Egyptian Plover *Pluvianus aegyptius* (see COURSER) ; Norfolk Plover (or Stone-curlew) *Burhinus oedicnemus* and Stone Plover *Esacus magnirostris* (see THICKKNEE) ; Upland Plover (or Bartram's Sandpiper) *Bartramia longicauda* (see SANDPIPER) ; Crab-plover *Dromas ardeola* (see CRAB-PLOVER) ; and, not even in the Charadriiformes, Quail-plover *Ortyxelos meiffrenii* (see BUTTONQUAIL).

PLOVERCREST: *Stephanoxis delalandei* (for family see HUMMINGBIRD) ; see Plate 44a.

PLOVER, QUAIL-: see BUTTONQUAIL

PLUMA: alternatively ' plumose feather ', one in which the barbs are free instead of forming a coherent vane (see PLUMAGE ; and compare PENNA).

PLUMAGE: also called ' ptilosis ', the aggregate of which the feather is the unit, and the outstanding character distinguishing the Class Aves from all others (see FEATHER). While the general nature of plumage is constant for all birds, differences in its characteristics are found between one species and another, and to a minor extent between populations of a species (whether sharply separable into races or not) ; and certain broad differences are common to particular taxonomic groups of species. Further, there are differences related to age, sex, and season. There is also individual variation, strongly marked in some species ; and occasional abnormalities occur (see PLUMAGE, ABNORMAL AND ABERRANT ; PLUMAGE VARIATION). The plumage of the individual bird is periodically renewed (see MOULT).

Functions. The plumage constitutes a mechanical and thermal protective covering for the body. Parts of it are essential components of the organs of flight—the wings, and to a lesser extent the tail (see FLIGHT). In addition, the plumage helps to stream-line the body, reducing friction during movement on the ground, in the air, and—in the aquatic environment of many species—on or below the surface of the water. For all these it combines high efficiency with minimal weight. Apart from its permanent role in the thermal regulation of the body (see HEAT REGULATION), the plumage has a special one during incubation in that the feathers and associated brood patches of bare skin are important in maintaining the eggs at optimum temperature (see INCUBATION).

The plumage is also the most important element in the external appearance of the bird. As such, the differences which it shows play a great part in determining recognition of other members of the same species. In some, also, the plumage is mainly responsible for a cryptic, mimetic, or aggressive appearance of the bird (see COLORATION, ADAPTIVE). In very many it includes the principal manifestations of the secondary sexual characters, and parts of the plumage are often specially adapted for use in display (see DISPLAY). Apart from providing visual stimuli, feathers—sometimes specially modified—play a part in the production of auditory signals (see INSTRU-MENTAL SOUNDS). In all these relations to behaviour the plumage is important for the perpetuation of the species.

Natal Plumage. The plumage of the chick on hatching is downy. But in many species this is sparse, providing virtually no covering, and in some it is entirely absent ; in others it is thick, soft, and beautiful—and in these instances often of cryptic coloration (see YOUNG BIRD). An exception to the general rule is found in the megapodes (Megapodi-idae), in which a much degenerated type of natal plumage is shed in ovo so that the chicks hatch out in their first definitive plumage.

The downy natal plumage is termed ' neossoptile '. By contrast, the plumages that follow are (with certain exceptions) of fully developed feathers and are termed ' teleoptile ' ; it is these latter that impart to the bird its familiar contour. Swifts of the genus *Cypseloides*, although hatched naked, develop a covering of ' down ' consisting of the plumaceous semiplume portion of the first teleoptile plumage (Collins 1963).

Distribution on Skin. Outwardly, most birds appear to be uniformly covered with contour feathers, except for the whole or part of the bill and legs and for the eyes. In some, however, areas of naked skin are visible—especially near the base of the bill, round the eyes, on the crown, or on the neck. In some carrion-feeders such as the Old and New World vultures (Aegypiinae ; Cathartidae) and the Marabou Stork *Leptoptilus crumeniferus*, the whole head and neck are largely naked ; and a similar condition is found in the Ostrich *Struthio camelus* and among the cassowaries (Cassuariidae).

This evenly distributed covering is, however, usually only apparent. In most species the feathers, other than down, grow only from definite tracts

(pterylae) of skin and the intervening areas (apteria) are bare. Exceptions are the penguins (Spheniscidae), the orders of ' ratite ' birds, and the toucans (Ramphastidae), in which apteria are almost completely absent. This absence of apteria is, in the penguins and ' ratites ', associated with a very simple construction of the feathers, these being loose (plumose) and lacking in barbules.

More commonly there is a definite distribution of feather tracts, and the different patterns of this—the bird's pterylosis or pterylography—have been used as taxonomic characters. Thus, the spinal tract extends from neck to tail but varies in width ; in some birds it is particularly broad, or even bifurcated, between the shoulders ; and in some it is interrupted, or bifurcated lower down. The corresponding ventral tract always has a median apterium and is sometimes double throughout ; a branch on each side may be present in the pectoral region. The cervical tract is continuous in some birds but has more often apteria on the sides of the neck, and sometimes on the back or front of it. Other tracts are the alar (wing feathers), caudal (tail feathers), humeral (shoulder feathers), femoral or lumbar (oblique band on outer aspect of thigh), crural (leg feathers), capital (head feathers—in a few forms with a definite occipital apterium), and uropygeal (feathers associated with the oil gland).

Component Units. The plumage of an adult bird comprises feathers of several different types (for details of structure and development see FEATHER) :

1. *Contour feathers* (pennae and plumae—or ' pennaceous ' and ' plumose ' pennae) constituting the ordinarily visible plumage. They include the primary and secondary remiges of the wings and the rectrices of the tail, the coverts that—above and below—cover the bases of the remiges and rectrices

---

Plate 39 · Parental Care

Two examples of brooding young—one a small passerine species, an arboreal nester with nidicolous young ; the other a small plover species, a ground nester with nidifugous young.

a *Upper* : Spotted Flycatchers *Muscicapa striata* at their nest in a garden (England). The photograph shows the male (on left) just after he has fed the female, which is brooding small young.
Phot. J. B. & S. Bottomley.

b *Lower* : Banded Dotterel *Charadrius bicinctus*—male covering recently hatched chicks (New Zealand). *Phot. M. F. Soper.*

(See articles PARENTAL CARE ; NEST ; YOUNG BIRD ; FLYCATCHER (I) ; PLOVER (I))

and also cover the ear orifices, and feathers on other parts of the body (see TOPOGRAPHY). Contour feathers are ' plumose ' when the barbs are free and ' pennaceous ' when the barbs are bound into a coherent vane by their barbules. The actual number of contour feathers varies, but a total of 4915 in Brewer's Blackbird *Euphagus cyanocephalus* and one of 3235 in a Bobolink *Dolichonyx oryzivorus* have been counted. Passerine birds in general seem to range between 1500 and 3000, but few counts have been recorded.

2. *Down feathers* (plumulae), forming an undercoat in many species—usually hidden from view (in adult birds), but sometimes partly visible as at the root of the neck in vultures, where the contour feathers have become suppressed as an adaptation to the method of feeding. The down plumage of chicks (neossoptiles) has already been mentioned.

3. *Intermediate feathers* (semiplumae), showing a combination of the characters of pennae and plumulae and usually bearing a well-developed aftershaft.

4. *Filoplumes*, hair-like feathers usually quite lacking in vanes or possessing them in very feebly developed form. They can be seen typically in a domestic fowl that has been plucked. Although filoplumes are normally associated with and concealed by the contour feathers they may be visible in some species, e.g. Chaffinch *Fringilla coelebs*, and in some of the thrushes (Turdinae) and warblers (Sylviinae) at the nape. They are, when associated with contour feathers, regarded as degenerate rather than primitive feathers. In a different category, however, appear to be those specialised filoplumes found on the heads and necks and thigh patches of some cormorants (Phalacrocoracidae) as part of the secondary sexual characterisation. Filoplumes are seen very strikingly on the nape and back of the Hairy-backed Bulbul *Hypsipetes criniger*.

5. *Vibrissae*, specialised feathers that are essentially stiff and bristle-like. Such structures are credited with a tactile function, and this would certainly seem likely in the case of the rictal bristles of the Muscicapinae and Caprimulgidae, which may serve an important function in facilitating the catching of insects in flight (see TOUCH). Vibrissae would therefore represent a specialised evolutionary structure subserving function, as distinct from a degenerate functionless structure as in the case of filoplumes. Close to vibrissae are the bristles found in some birds as eyelashes (see EYELASH) ; there is a complete gradation between such structures and the pennaceous feather.

6. *Powder down*, consisting of soft and friable downy material giving off minute particles of a dusty substance used by the birds in cleaning the feathers generally. It is found only in certain groups of birds, such as herons (Ardeidae), toucans (Ramphastidae), parrots (Psittacidae), and bowerbirds (Ptilonorhynchidae). When present, powder down occurs in patches ; in the herons there is one placed centrally in the pectoral region and one above and behind each thigh.

(A more elaborate terminology, purporting to indicate the sequence of feathers, was proposed by Ewart. The nestling down feathers are classed as prepennae, preplumulae, and prefiloplumae according to whether they will be succeeded in the adult by pennae (contour feathers), plumulae (adult down feathers), or filoplumae. When there are two sets of prepennae, as in penguins (Spheniscidae) and ducks (Anatidae), they are distinguished as protoptiles and mesoptiles. Further, the plumose pennae (the plumae of others) are called metaptiles and the pennaceous pennae are called teleoptiles, the latter being a more restricted use of the term than that already mentioned.)

Diastataxis. This is an apparent absence of the fifth secondary remex in some groups of birds—also called ' aquintocubitalism '. In diastataxic wings every pair of major coverts except the fifth embraces a remex, and this effect is believed to be due to torsion of the feather papillae during embryonic life. Where the effect does not occur the condition is known as eutaxis.

The following are diastataxic : Gaviidae, Podicipitidae, Procellariiformes, Pelecaniformes (except *Nannopterum*), Ardeidae, Phoenicopteridae, Anhimidae, Accipitridae, Gruidae, Heliornithidae, Eurypygidae, Charadriiformes (except *Philohela*), Pteroclididae, Psittacidae, Strigidae, Caprimulgiformes, and Coraciidae.

Eutaxic forms include : Struthionidae, Galliformes (except Megapodiidae), Rhynochetidae, Cariamidae, Psophiidae, Cuculiformes, Meropidae, Momotidae, Todidae, Coliidae, Trogonidae, Piciformes, and Passeriformes.

Plate 40 · Parental Care

a *Upper :* Purple Heron *Ardea purpurea* sheltering its nestlings from the hot sunshine (Camargue, France).   *Phot. G. K. Yeates.*

b *Lower :* Jay *Garrulus glandarius*—female, with crest erected and abdominal feathers fluffed, about to brood her nestlings (Sweden). She had been feeding the young birds just before the photograph was taken.   *Phot. P. O. Swanberg.*

(See articles PARENTAL CARE ; HERON ; CROW (1))

Adaptive Differences. Some degree of specialised adaptation can be recognised in practically all the feathering of a bird. Most important of all is the modification of wing feathers to serve the vital function of flight, to which they are most perfectly suited. Minor examples are the beautifully graded and shaped feathers of the facial disc and 'ears' of many owls (Strigiformes) and the curious rosette of feathers surrounding the uropygeal gland (see OIL GLAND).

During the course of evolution, notable differences of plumage quality have become established between different taxonomic groups. Contrast, for example, the scale-like feathers of penguins (Spheniscidae)—a character already discernible in embryonic life—and the soft, abundant feathering of owls, in which flight as near silent as possible is essential to the birds' mode of predation. Take again the water-resistant property of the feathering of the Anatidae and other aquatic birds, which may be due to a chemical rather than a structural adaptation. However, there is a recent view that failure of water-repellant action results from a disarrangement of barbules from excessive rubbing as well as from food smearing (to which small ducklings and other downy young are very vulnerable).

Sexual Dimorphism. Most species show some degree of sexual dimorphism, and in many this is well marked. The males usually have the brighter plumage (see under MOULT), but for a few species— e.g. phalaropes (Phalaropodidae)—the reverse is true. The plumage of female birds, when less brightly coloured, tends to be cryptic in pattern. A different type of sexual dimorphism is shown by the Red-sided Eclectus Parrot *Lorius roratus* of the south-western Pacific ; the male is predominantly green while the female is bright red above and blackish below in striking contrast, so that the sexes may be said to be equally bright but in quite different ways. (The same species shows sexual dimorphism in the colour of the bill—pale flesh-colour in the male and very dark slate in the female.) Some males of certain species, notably the Pied Flycatcher *Ficedula hypoleuca*, have an intermediate plumage— by some authors termed a 'retarded' plumage—in which they breed, the usual sexual dimorphism being suppressed : such individuals breed in a brown plumage rather similar to that of the females.

Immature Plumage. Where sexual dimorphism occurs, the juveniles of both sexes, i.e. those with their first covering of definitive feathers, usually quite closely resemble the adult females. There are exceptions to this rule, for in the Koel *Eudynamys orientalis* and the Somali Chestnut-wing Starling *Onychognathus blythii* the immature birds of both

sexes resemble the male, the young females later assuming the adult dress of their sex. In some species, e.g. the Gannet *Sula bassana*, where the adults show no broad differences between the sexes, the immature plumage is totally different. In others the immature plumage resembles that of the adults but is nevertheless distinguishable, e.g. in the Kingfisher *Alcedo atthis*, where the young have similar colouring but lack the brilliance of the adults.

Yet another pattern, in which the young have a distinctive dress, is exemplified by the Great Spotted Woodpecker *Dendrocopos major* ; the immature birds of both sexes have the top of the head red, but after moulting from the juvenile plumage they acquire the distinctive sexual dimorphism of the parents, i.e. the black crown in both and the red nuchal band that distinguishes the male. This may be an instance of ontogeny repeating phylogeny, and the inference may be drawn that an ancestral form had at one time the red crown both in adults and in the young, and that present sexual dimorphism represents a later specialisation. The possible intermediate stage in the phylogenetic development of the sexual dimorphism is reflected in the Lesser Spotted Woodpecker *D. minor*, where the adult males have the crown red and the juvenile males have the fore part of the crown brownish-white with the feathers darkly tipped and the feathers of the back of the crown with the distal half red, while the females have only a few red-tipped feathers at the back of the crown. In the Green Woodpecker *Picus viridis* the red crown has persisted in both sexes in the adult, although indeed it is also present in immatures ; this character has in fact become intensified in the adults, and the sexual dimorphism is expressed by a red moustache in the male and a black one in the female, and it should be noted that sexual dimorphism is also found in the immatures.

Spotting and longitudinal striation in adult plumages may be regarded as a persistence of a primitive state. Spotted and striped plumages are found in the young of many species that lack such characters in their adult dress, e.g. stripes in the grebes (Podicipitidae) and cassowaries (Casuariidae).

In many species a nuptial plumage is assumed by both sexes, but it may be different in the two, e.g. as in the Scarlet Tanager *Piranga olivacea*. The cryptic plumage of many immature birds can be related to their lack of environmental experience and consequently greater vulnerability to predators.

The acquisition of fully adult plumage may take a number of years, e.g. gannets (Sulidae) and certain gulls (Larinae), possibly as many as five in some species ; more commonly the adult dress is acquired towards the end of the first year of life (see MOULT).

Seasonal Changes. Striking seasonal changes favouring cryptic function occur in such species as the Ptarmigan *Lagopus mutus*, which has the winter plumage almost entirely pure white. In others the reason for the seasonal change is not so apparent ; for example, among the Charadriidae, the white under parts of the winter plumage become black in the breeding season in the Dunlin *Calidris alpina*, the Golden Plover *Pluvialis apricaria*, and the Grey Plover *P. squatarola*, and become red in the Knot *Calidris canutus*, the Curlew-sandpiper *C. testacea*, and the Bartailed Godwit *Limosa lapponica*.

Striking nuptial plumages and accessories are assumed by both sexes in the grebes (Podicipitidae), the divers (Gaviidae), and the herons (Ardeidae)—the head and mantle plumes of the last-named forming most impressive additions to the breeding dress. Recently, Curry-Lindahl and Marshall & Williams have brought forward evidence that the nuptial plumage in the Yellow Wagtail *Motacilla flava* is induced by a genetically stabilised internal rhythm and that there is no correlation between the full assumption of breeding dress and gonad size : individuals have been taken in January assuming summer plumage with resting gonads, while definite enlargement of the latter does not commence until March.

There is a character in the plumage of some birds that does not depend on any structural change but on the infiltration of the feathers with chemical substances derived from the natural food of the species, and thus absent if the source is not available (as may occur in captivity). There is, for example, the pink suffusion of the plumage in certain birds that live on small aquatic animals, e.g. the flamingos (Phoenicopteridae) and the Goosander *Mergus merganser* ; a similar condition appears to occur in some species of shearwaters (Puffininae).

Associated Behaviour. Some species make use of their own or other down and feathers as nesting material. The habit of plucking their own breast down to use as a nest lining is well developed among ducks (Anatidae). In the bowerbirds (Ptilonorhynchidae), any available bright feathers are among the objects used for decorative purposes in the surroundings of the nest (see BOWERBIRD).

There is also the physiological value of ingested feathers. Among the Falconiformes and Strigiformes feathers are taken in the course of ingesting avian prey and facilitate pellet formation (see PELLET). In grebes (Podicipitidae) the feathers are apparently plucked from the bird's own body surface, but subserve the same purpose.

Preening, 'anting', dusting, sunbathing, and flirting with smoke and fire form part of the behaviour of a bird towards its own plumage (see FEATHER MAINTENANCE). 'Allopreening' is a social response in some species, while mutual preening by a pair occurs in the normal relations between the sexes. An apparent perversion of unknown cause is the feather picking indulged in by domestic fowls and by game-birds (Galliformes) in captivity.

See Plates 5, 6, 7, 8, 17, 18, 19, 20, 42, and 44 (colour). J.M.H.

Coues, E. 1890. Handbook of Field and General Ornithology. London.
Ewart, J. Cossar. 1921. The nestling plumage of the Mallard, with observations on the composition, origin and history of feathers. Proc. Zool. Soc. Lond. 1921 : 609–642.
Mayaud, N. 1950. Téguments et Phanères. *In* Grassé, P. P. (ed.). 1950. Traité de Zoologie vol. 15. Oiseaux. Paris.
Pycraft, W. P. 1910. A History of Birds. London.
Schüz. E. 1927. Beitrag zur Kenntnis der Puderbildung bei den Vögeln. J. Orn. 75 : 86–224.
Stresemann, E. 1927–34. *In* Kükenthal, W. & Krumbach, T. (eds.). Handbuch der Zoologie vol. 7, pt. 2. Aves. Berlin and Leipzig.

PLUMAGE, ABNORMAL AND ABERRANT :

two categories between which there is probably no sharp line of division, although some cases are clearly abnormal, depending upon disorders or diseases, and others aberrant in the genetic sense. Instances can be grouped to some extent according to the underlying causes, as follows.

Heterochroisms. This group probably comprises both phenologically and genetically determined cases and includes such well-known examples as :

(*a*) *Albinism*, which condition may be total—the true albino where pigment is completely absent even from the soft parts and irides—and in this form can be reckoned as a pathological state of genetic origin. The partial or pied state may be patchy, forming a mosaic, or may be symmetrical ; but individuals so affected are usually robust and this condition may well be of a different nature.

(*b*) *Leucism* (paleness) is closely allied to albinism and results from varying degrees of dilution of normal pigmentation. It is best seen in those species that are normally black iridescents, e.g. the Starling *Sturnus vulgaris*, and it is often possible to grade the cases from a rufous leucism to a pale ginger, and then on to silver-grey and to an almost or even absolutely total albino. It has recently been suggested (Rollin) that pied and leucistic states in the Blackbird *Turdus merula* and the Song Thrush *T. philomelos* can be induced experimentally by giving artificially prepared foods, and corrected by reversion to normal diet ; it is suggested that the condition occurs in wild birds in urban areas, where the availability of substitutes for natural foods is highest, as well as in experimental subjects.

(c) *Melanism*, not to be regarded as the opposite of albinism, is due to an excess of the dark pigment eumelanin, many cases being genetically determined. Phenotypical melanism is well known, and it has been recorded in the Bullfinch *Pyrrhula pyrrhula* as a result of the birds being fed on hemp. Many species have a naturally occurring melanic form, e.g. Montagu's Harrier *Circus pygargus*, Eleanora's Falcon *Falco eleanorae*, the Booted Eagle *Hieraaetus pennatus*, the Schach Shrike *Lanius schach*, the Snipe *Gallinago gallinago* (the so-called ' Sabine's Snipe '), the Woodcock *Scolopax rusticola*, and the Pheasant *Phasianus colchicus* (the melanistic mutant var. ' *tenebrosus* '), to mention but a few (see POLYMORPHISM). An instance of pathological melanism is mentioned later.

(d) *Erythrism* (reddishness) occurs not infrequently as an abnormal colour variant in some species, e.g. the Common Partridge *Perdix perdix* (var. ' *montana* '), the Red-legged Partridge *Alectoris rufa*, and the Quail *Coturnix coturnix* ; but it is to be particularly noted that a rufous phase is within the normal polymorphism of some species, especially in the Strigidae, e.g. the Tawny Owl *Strix aluco*, in which it is the predominant colour variant in British populations. Another example is the so-called ' hepatic ' phase of some adult female Cuckoos *Cuculus canorus*, while in the immatures of that species there is both a grey and a brownish type.

(e) *Xanthochroism*, the occurrence of yellow colour variants, is less usual, although the ' lutino ' varieties of some of the Psittacidae are well known, e.g. *Aratinga* spp. and the familiar Budgerigar *Melopsittacus undulatus*, as well as the very numerous varieties of the Canary *Serinus canaria*. That such phases can be found in wild as distinct from aviary birds is established by an instance of excessive pigmentation in the Yellow Wagtail *Motacilla flava*. Some such cases are genetically and others phenotypically determined.

Effects of Endocrine Imbalance. Certain abnormalities and aberrations depend on physiological factors, including those determining the development of the secondary sexual characters. The most important of these factors is clearly the influence of the endocrine glands (see ENDOCRINE SYSTEM) ; any imbalance of this system, whether produced by pathological changes or by direct experimentation, produces the most profound plumage changes. The influence of the thyroid secretion on plumage colour, and in causing pattern accentuation, darken-

ing, and bleaching, is noted elsewhere (see under MOULT). The normal endocrine balance is largely determined by a proper functioning of the pituitary gland. Our knowledge of the establishment of secondary sexual characters has resulted from direct experimentation, but some remarkable instances of spontaneous disturbance of endocrine function have nevertheless been recorded. Evidence has been brought forward that, for example, the assumption of cock-feathering in hen Pheasants *Phasianus colchicus* is not invariably due to atrophy of the ovaries in old or diseased individuals, but may in fact result from a phasic imbalance of endocrine function. Nor is male plumage always determined by hormonal control ; in the well-known case of the House Sparrow *Passer domesticus*, the male plumage is genetically determined and the only secondary sexual character under endocrine influence after early embryonic life is the colour of the bill. Castrated male House Sparrows acquire normal male plumage except for the bill, the normal black bill of the nuptial dress appearing only when the bird is given injections of male hormone ; the response is so sensitive that the bill can be partly or completely turned black according to the dose of hormone administered. In most birds, once past the stage of immaturity when a neutral or female-like dress is worn, the influence of the sex hormones takes over and the normal sexual dimorphism becomes established.

Morejohn & Genelly, working on the Pheasant *Phasianus colchicus* by hormonal implants, have demonstrated that plumage differentation of both sexes is dependent upon genetic as well as hormonal factors, and that autosomal as well as sex chromosomes are involved.

The importance of the function of the testis in the male and the ovary in the female is revealed by experimental ablation. If the male is castrated a neutral type of plumage results, closely resembling that of the female. If the female is subjected to the removal of the ovary, which in the vast majority of birds is a single organ situated in the left side of the abdominal cavity, a right-sided gonad develops ; this on histological examination is a mixed gland (ovotestis), and the individual develops a male-like plumage. The longer this persists, i.e. the older the bird becomes, the more nearly does the plumage approximate to that of the male (including the increase in the size of the comb, wattles, and spurs in the domestic fowl).

As a rare event a hen has been recorded as laying eggs while carrying the plumage of the cock (see REPRODUCTIVE SYSTEM). This phenomenon has also been recorded in the Redstart *Phoenicurus phoenicurus* in the wild state, and the occurrence of cock-feathered hens of the Rock Bunting *Emberiza cia cia* is to be noted.

An anomalous condition is found in certain breeds of domestic fowl (Hamburgs, Campines, and Seabrights) in which the cocks are normally hen-feathered. Two types of males occur, one closely resembling the hen and the other having a male type of plumage. Castration of the former results in the assumption of the latter's type of plumage, so the hen-feathering in such cases is conditioned by testicular function. The essential point about breeds with hen-feathered cocks is that their plumage appears to be hypersensitive to female hormone, and the testes of hen-feathered cocks have been shown to contain luteal cells such as are found in the ovary. Further evidence is afforded by skin-grafting. If a skin-graft from a hen Leghorn is grafted to a cock of the same breed, cock-feathering results ; whereas if a hen Campine's skin is grafted on to the same host, the feathering is normal hen-feathering, for it is acknowledged that female sex hormone is elaborated by the male even if its influence in most males is subsidiary. Thus the males of hen-feathered male breeds have a lower threshold to female sex hormone. A similar explanation is advanced to account for the 'eclipse' plumage in ducks when testicular influence is waning at the end of the reproductive season (see MOULT). It has recently been established that the condition of hen-feathered cocks in pure-bred individuals of the above-mentioned breeds of domestic fowl is determined by a single dominant gene. Castration leads to the assumption of cock plumage, although the comb and wattles (under hormonal control) fail to develop fully.

The above is only a brief account, and intensive experimentation involving the injection of developing embryos with sex hormone is being undertaken that will undoubtedly clarify many issues at present obscure.

The only other organs having a significant influence on plumage in certain circumstances are the adrenal glands. As has already been stated, in failure of testicular and ovarian influence the adrenals can contribute to the production of maleness, and testicular strands have been recognised in sections of the adrenals of Pheasants *Phasianus colchicus* in cases of ovarian atrophy.

Recently, melanism in the Wood Pigeon *Columba palumbus* has been noted in birds affected with tubercular disease involving the adrenal glands, which causes an increase in pigmentation notably reminiscent of the pigmentation of Addison's disease in human beings. Associated with this pathological melanism there are structural (atrophic) feather changes, loss of gloss and excessive wear, the latter somewhat similar to that seen in missed moult.

Aberrant Feather Structure. What would appear to be a genetic state is to be seen in the so-called 'hairy albescents'. This is a condition of albinism linked with a looseness of the plumage, the feathers lacking the normal interlocking mechanism of barbicels. It has been recorded in the Moorhen *Gallinula chloropus* and the Jay *Garrulus glandarius*. An analogous condition in poultry and pigeons and even in the Canary, although not necessarily associated with albinism, has resulted from selective breeding and has been referred to variously as 'silky' and 'frizzled'. In both the Guillemot *Uria aalge* and the Black Guillemot *Cephus grylle* there occurs occasionally what has been called a 'needle-tailed' variety in which the shafts of the rectrices project beyond the atrophic feathering of the vanes, the condition also affecting the flight feathers ; the causation is obscure.

There is a condition that would appear to be genetic in origin, in which all the remiges and rectrices are fragile. When the bird is grown and ready to fly, these break off close to their insertions, rendering the birds flightless, the rachis of the feathers being apparently unable to support flight stresses. It has so far been recorded in the European Jay *Garrulus glandarius rufitergum* and the Asiatic subspecies *G. g. atricapillus*. In non-passerine species, up to date, it has been met with only in the Sheld-duck *Tadorna tadorna*. Another genetically determined abnormality is that of complete absence of feathers, the avian counterpart of hairlessness in mammals.

Gynandromorphism. This condition (found also in insects) is believed to be caused by a chromosomal accident. Gynandromorphic individuals have one half of the body male and the other female, on either side of the mid-line.

The suggestion was made in 1932 (Lillie & Juhn) and confirmed in 1934 (Huxley & Bond) that bilateral (gynandromorphic) distribution of sex characters in birds depends upon chromosomal aberration affecting the growth rate of the two sides lengthwise. In the rectrices each feather is thus affected in so far as each half of the feather is concerned ; not only is the pattern of the feather gynandromorphic but, as there is a size difference, there is a distortion of the feathers resulting from one half being longer than the other. This can be explained only on the basis that the halves of each feather differ in their response to female sex hormone.

Gynandromorphism has been recorded in the Bullfinch *Pyrrhula pyrrhula*, Chaffinch *Fringilla coelebs*, Siskin *Carduelis spinus*, Gouldian Finch *Poephila gouldiae*, Green Honeycreeper *Chlorophanes spiza*, Flicker *Colaptes mexicanus*, and the Pheasant *Phasianus colchicus*. The condition has also been produced experimentally.

Effects of Irradiation. There is evidence to support the suggestion that normal plumage sequences can be affected by irradiation. Williams was the first to indicate this when he observed northern species arriving in Kenya in winter in nuptial plumage. Immediately thereafter the present writer exhibited an Icelandic Redshank *Tringa totanus robusta* that had been shot on 9 November 1955 and was in freshly moulted summer plumage. A further example of the same species was collected on 24 December 1955 again in precocious summer dress ; a degree of abnormal enlargement of the ovary and oviduct was noted on dissection, and radio-active contamination of the part-skeleton was also detected (Harrison, J. M. & J. G.). In explanation it has been suggested that in all probability the primary effect of such an accident is to depress cellular activity, and that later, out of the proper season, by what is termed a ' rebound phenomenon ' the nuptial plumage is assumed.

The problem has been investigated experimentally on the Black-faced Dioch *Quelea quelea*. The nuptial dress of the males of this African species includes a black facial mask and a golden crown and breast. Some feathers of the black facial mask were plucked and a few days allowed for the follicles to reorganise, after which the birds were subjected to whole-body exposures of 15 MEV X-rays, administered at doses of 50, 200, 400, 800, and 1000 röntgens respectively. The irradiated birds were compared with controls. Doses below 1000 r. produced no visible effects, but of the three survivors of the 1000 r. dosage the feathers of the black facial mask regenerated as unpigmented feathers, except for the tips which had developed during the four days prior to the irradiation.

Females exposed to the 50 r., 200 r., and 400 r. dosage regenerated feathers of the mask area that showed a black intermediate band of melanin deposition, thus exhibiting an anomaly of a secondary sexual character. It is stressed that birds irradiated with 800 r. and 1000 r. regenerated normal hen-feathering, and that all the irradiated subjects subsequently underwent a normal post-nuptial moult into eclipse plumage. The melanin deposition in females' feathers may, it is thought, be due to pituitary stimulation resulting from the lower dosage. This condition was noted as only temporary, and the birds subsequently underwent normal moult cycles.

J.M.H.

Harrison, J. M. 1932. A series of nineteen pheasants (*Phasianus colchicus* L.) presenting anomalous sexual characters in association with changes in the ovaries. Proc. Zool. Soc. Lond. 1932 : 192–203.

Harrison, J. M. & Harrison, J. G. 1956. Abnormal seasonal assumption of spring plumage in the Redshank (*Tringa totanus* L.) in association with possible radioactive contamination. Bull. Brit. Orn. Cl. 76 : 60–61.

Harrison, J. M. 1960. The flightless Jay—what is the explanation ? Bull. Brit. Orn. Cl. 80 : 162–164.

Lillie, F. R. & Juhn, M. 1932. Physiology of feathers. I. Growth-rate and pattern in the individual feather. Physiol. Zool. 5 : 124–184.

Lofts, B., Marshall, A. J., & Rotblat, J. 1960. Effects of whole-body irradiation on the breeding plumage of the weaver-finch *Quelea quelea*. Nature 187: 615–616.

Huxley, J. S. & Bond, C. J. 1934. A case of gynandromorphic plumage in a Pheasant re-examined in the light of Lillie's hypothesis of hormone threshold. J. Genetics 29 : 51–59.

Rollin, N. 1959. White plumage in Blackbirds. Bull. Brit. Orn. Cl. 79 : 92–96.

Williams, J. G. 1955. Birds from Siberia in summer plumage. The Times, 10 Dec. 1955.

And general references under PLUMAGE.

PLUMAGE VARIATION : term for the purposes of this article restricted to variation that (*a*) is outside the ordinary range of difference between individual members of the population concerned, (*b*) is not abnormal or aberrant in the sense of the preceding article, and (*c*) appears to have phylogenetic significance as an atavistic manifestation. Such variation is in the pattern rather than in the colour of the plumage, but there are exceptions. The study of the subject received a great stimulus from the classical experiments of Darwin in back-breeding fancy varieties of domestic pigeon to the similitude of the original stock, the Rock Dove *Columba livia*. Since then, in addition to further experimentation, there have been many observations of apparently atavistic variations occurring among wild birds ; the following instances are grouped according to whether or not the influence of interspecific hybridisation can be excluded (see also HYBRID). For a different phenomenon, here excluded by (*a*) of the opening definition above, see POLYMORPHISM.

Interspecific Hybridisation Not Involved. It is to be supposed that, by some fortuitous and rare recombination of the genes (see GENETICS), a character may be brought out that had been manifest in the species in the past but had long since ceased to be so. Or the character may be one that is still shown by other races of the species but had been lost in the particular race or population to which the variant individual belongs ; and what is true at subspecific level may apply also at specific level. So one finds, in cases where no question of hybridisation arises, individuals presenting characters showing a close resemblance—not perfect, but nevertheless very striking—to those of distant forms that are subspecifically or even specifically distinct. It may be postulated, with probability, that such variations are more likely to occur among sedentary populations, where conditions favour in-breeding.

To some variation it is difficult, in the present state of knowledge, to assign any certain phylogenetic significance. One may mention the striking and handsome mutation of *Phasianus colchicus* known as the 'Bohemian Pheasant'. There is also the occasional occurrence of barring and mottling in members of the crow family (Corvidae). Many individuals of the Jay *Garrulus glandarius* show some faint and obscure blue barring on the longer feathers of the posterior part of the crown ; this suggests that at one time the crown itself may have had the handsome blue, black, and white barring found on the wing coverts and alula, which would account for the apparent translocation of this pattern as a rare mutation. Wing-barring in the Rook *Corvus frugilegus*, the Carrion Crow *C. corone*, and the Jackdaw *C. monedula* may well have an evolutionary significance, and this is further strongly suggested by the occurrence of the same distinctive variation in three so closely related species.

Consider firstly some instances of homologous characters occurring occasionally in certain species where no question of interspecific hybridisation arises. This phenomenon had been recognised by earlier systematists, e.g. Hartert remarks that individuals of the nominate race of the Magpie *Pica pica pica* in populations in the British Isles and Germany have been obtained with rumps as white as are found in the north-eastern race *P. p. bactriana* or, again in the same countries, as black as are characteristically found in the Iberian race *P. p. melanotos*. (Such sporadic instances must of course be taken into account when assessing the true incidence of supposed immigrant individuals into any area or country.) The manifestations may be very transient and be recognisable only in immature individuals ; instances of this are afforded by a percentage of juveniles of the Jay showing in outline, and sometimes by a general duskiness, the black cap of the southern and south-eastern *G. g. atricapillus-cervicalis* complex.

Further instances are found in the occurrence in immature Great Spotted Woodpeckers *Dendrocopos major anglicus* of the facial pattern of the Syrian Woodpecker *D. syriacus*, showing an absence of the vertical dusky line dividing the whitish colour of the check and neck, or of the confluent white outer vanes of the primaries as in *D. m. leucopterus* of Turkestan. Again in the Picidae may be mentioned the appearance of the red spot in the crop region in populations of the Great Spotted Woodpecker in Britain, Switzerland, and elsewhere, a normal character in North African and Iberian populations of this species (Harrison).

In the Passeriformes similar cases are evident in the British race of the Robin *Erithacus rubecula melophilus*, where a variant has been described in which the breast pattern approximates closely to that found in the Japanese Robin *Luscinia akahige* ; and in the British race of the Bullfinch *Pyrrhula pyrrhula pileata* ('nesa'), where individuals in which the pattern of the undersides resembles that of the eastern *P. p. griseiventris* are on record ; other instances could be cited. In the Accipitridae, colour phases of the nominate race of the Buzzard *Buteo buteo buteo* resembling the Rough-legged Buzzard *B. lagopus* occur, while examples of the former species with the feathered tarsi of the latter have been recorded. A recurring character in the gulls of the genus *Larus*, an oblong white patch in the region of the carpal joint, has been noted in individuals of Heermann's Gull *L. heermanni*, the Herring Gull *L. argentatus*, and the British race of the Lesser Black-backed Gull *L. fuscus graellsii*, indicating the extremely close affinity of these three forms.

Interesting as these cases are as pointers to affinities, it is amongst the Anatidae that some of the most remarkable examples are to be found, and that characters recur—with and without the agency of interspecific hybridisation—of a kind suggesting that they are archaic and ancestral. It would seem indeed that the Anatidae as a family are a reservoir of genes bearing primitive characters.

It is best to consider first the phenomenon as exhibited by pure species where no question of hybridisation (in the strict sense) arises. One such character is the white neck ring—a constant character in the drake Mallard *Anas platyrhynchos* and one which, it should be noted, can occur in the duck of that species. This character, with which can perhaps be included the white triangular marking seen in some species anteriorly at the root of the neck, occurs on occasions in the Gadwall *A. strepera* both in immature and adult drakes, in the Shoveler *A. clypeata*, in the Wigeon *A. penelope*, in the Yellow-billed Teal *A. flavirostris*, and in the European race of the Teal *A. crecca crecca*, although in the last two it is at best vestigial and incomplete ; it also occurs in some Pintail *A. acuta* drakes in eclipse plumage. In the same category may be mentioned the white chin-spot, a character that has been seen in both surface-feeding and diving ducks. A condition of generalised spotting of the undersides is also regarded as a primitive plumage state, and the fact that very many species of birds have spotted immature plumage may provide further evidence that plumage sequences reflect the early primitive plumage patterns.

A pale loral spot is a character shared by many species both in surface-feeding and diving ducks. Particular importance attaches to the fact that although it is mostly carried as a constant by the female in some species, e.g. the Baikal Teal *Anas formosa*, it occurs in others as a less constant but recurring feature and is also found in the drakes in the juvenile and eclipse plumages ; as instances one may cite again the Baikal Teal and also the Garganey *A. querquedula*. If one may regard the immature, female, and eclipse plumages as primitive, then a loral spot is in all probability also to be regarded as an archaic character. The accentuation of the nuchal tuft that is occasionally very pronounced in drakes of *A. crecca crecca*, and the slight downward curvature of the white-margined scapulars, are characteristics clearly indicative of the affinity of this species with the Falcated Teal *A. falcata*, while the latter species also shows some affinities with the Gadwall *A. strepera*. Of much significance are cases of facial bridling seen in some drakes of the European race of the Teal *A. c. crecca* when in first winter plumage, the condition occurring spontaneously without any influence of hybridisation. The affinity of the Tufted Duck *Aythya fuligula* and the Scaup *A. marila* is confirmed by the occasional appearance of a white face-mask in the former species.

A recent close study of the plumage sequences in the Shoveler *A. clypeata* has disclosed the recurrence of at least five homologous characters in the transition drakes, viz. (1) a crescentic whitish marking running upwards in front of the eyes, (2) a white neck-ring, (3) the presence of overt or concealed spotting of the breast, (4) crescent-shaped markings on the breast, relating them closely to the Australasian Shoveler *A. rhynchotis* and to other species in the group of 'blue-winged duck', and (5) a white chin-spot of varying size, in some individuals small and in others well developed. A faint crescentic marking on the face occurs also in drakes in eclipse plumage.

Influence of Interspecific Hybridisation. It is, however, under the influence of interspecific hybridisation that the most important and striking instances have occurred (see also HYBRID). It is well known that the progeny of an interspecific cross can take one of several forms ; it may be more or less intermediate between the parent species,

inclining more to one or the other according to which species was the male parent and also to some extent upon the sex of the hybrid, or it may resemble neither parent and, most importantly, may show characters quite foreign to the morphology of either parent species but resembling those of another species altogether. In considering such cases not only are the morphological characters of great interest but stance, gait, habits, courtship behaviour, and voice should also be taken into account ; all these points can help to demonstrate phylogeny and establish affinities. Unfortunately, in the past, aberrant individuals and hybrids have been summarily dismissed, and their great value in the study of evolution has thus been lost. Misidentification of a hybrid and its erection as a new species, as was done in the case of the so-called 'Bimaculated Duck' as '*Anas glocitans*', or equally erroneous identifications (as in the case of this particular specimen as a Baikal Teal *A. formosa*) by some of the early authors, further confused systematics and obscured the value of the phenomenon in phylogenetic research.

Recent study of two interspecific crosses of known parentage illustrates the importance of such cases, for both exhibit a striking and common morphological similarity, not only with each other but also with the 'Bimaculated Duck' and above all with the drake Baikal Teal in full plumage. The first of these is the progeny of a drake European Teal *A. c. crecca* and a duck Shoveler *A. clypeata*, in which appeared the striking facial bridling that is the most characteristic feature of the drake Baikal Teal *A. formosa* when in full plumage. The second cross resulted from the mating of a drake Wigeon *A. penelope* and a duck Shoveler *A. clypeata*, and this again shows the characteristic bridling of *A. formosa* drakes (already mentioned as also occasionally recurring in drakes of the European Teal without the influence of hybridisation). The last-named cross also exhibited other characters believed to be derived from the ancestry of *A. formosa*. It should be particularly noted that another drake from the same clutch of the Wigeon × Northern Shoveler cross presented not bridling but bimaculation ; on this evidence one can postulate that bridling and bimaculation represent degrees of the same atavistic character.

Bimaculation has been recorded in the following hybrids in addition to the two above-mentioned crosses in which it took the bridled form : in a presumed *A. c. crecca* × *A. acuta* hybrid and in a presumed *A. c. crecca* × *A. platyrhynchos* hybrid (the 'Bimaculated Duck'), in neither of which was the parentage exactly known ; and in *A. p. platyrhynchos* × *A. superciliosa superciliosa* hybrids. A summary of some of these recurring homologous characters in the Anatidae is contained in a recent paper by J. M. & J. G. Harrison.

In the phenomena described above is a field of research of fascinating and absorbing interest, and in such hybrid and other material lie the clues to the clarification of many problems of evolution and affinity. They are instances of Darwinian atavism in the true sense. J.M.H.

Bonhote, J. L. 1905. Some notes on the hybridisation of ducks. Proc. IV Int. Orn. Congr., London 1904 : 235–264.

Harrison, J. M. 1951. Some phylogenetic trends in *Garrulus glandarius* L., and *Dendrocopos major* (L.). Proc. X Int. Orn. Congr., Uppsala 1950 : 167–172.

Harrison, J. M. & J. G. 1963. A Gadwall with a white neck ring and a review of plumage variants in wildfowl. Bull. Brit. Orn. Cl. 83 : 100–108.

Morejohn, G. V. & Genelly, R. E. 1961. Plumage differentiation of normal and sex-anomalous Ring-necked Pheasants in response to sympathetic hormone implants. Condor 63 : 101–110.

PLUMELETEER : substantive name of *Chalybura* spp. (for family see HUMMINGBIRD).

PLUMULA : a down feather (see PLUMAGE). Natal or nestling down plumage, when present, is called ' neossoptile '.

PLUNGING : see SWIMMING AND DIVING

PNEUMATISATION OF BONE : a condition, in birds, in which many bones are hollow and contain air-sacs lined with epithelium. This has been evolved as an adaptation for flight. The cranial air-sacs are developed as extensions from the nasal and auditory capsules, those of the post-cranial skeleton from the bronchial system. See RESPIRATORY SYSTEM; SKELETON.

Development of Skull Pneumatisation. Pneumatised bone in the skull is opaque, the bony trabeculae between the inner and outer layers giving it a dotted appearance. The spongy (diploic) bone is translucent. The development and comparative anatomy of skull pneumatisation is therefore more easily studied in the skull than it is in the rest of the skeleton.

The embryology of skull pneumatisation has been studied by de Beer and by Bremer ; the process begins about the ninth day of incubation. Completion may take as long as two years after hatching. Both Nero and Harrison have studied the method of pneumatisation. This varies as between genera, but in closely related species in which the process reaches completion the bones pneumatise by the same method ; this may provide evidence of phylogenetic relationship.

Development of Post-cranial Pneumatisation.

The post-cranial skeleton is pneumatised by extensions from the air-sac system : the cervical vertebrae from the cervical air-sacs, the upper limb from the clavicular air-sacs, the lower limb from the abdominal air-sacs. Bremer has studied the penetration of the air-sac into the head of the humerus, which occurs at the site of an exit of a vein. The bone at this point undergoes degeneration, the appearance being like *osteitis cystica fibrosa* in humans, and Bremer suggests that this may be due to oestrogens liberated into the circulation as the residual yolk-sac retracts into the intestine on hatching ; this stimulates the parathyroids, the hormone of which causes the bony changes. The air-sac then ramifies until it comes to fill the whole of the shaft cavity, leaving only residual bony trabeculae.

Extent of Skull Pneumatisation. Both Verheyen and Harrison have studied the comparative anatomy of skull pneumatisation. Many species fail to develop complete pneumatisation, and Harrison has attempted to classify these on a functional basis. In birds which dive from the surface of the water, particularly the Anatidae, skull pneumatisation is diminished, the diminution varying directly with the efficiency of the species as a diver (see SWIMMING AND DIVING). Thus, closely related species show differing degrees of pneumatisation : the Brown Pelican *Pelecanus occidentalis*, which seldom goes much below the surface, has an almost totally pneumatised skull, whereas in other families of the Pelecaniformes (e.g. Phalacrocoracidae) air is limited to the mastoid and nasal regions. Similarly, the South Georgian Diving Petrel *Pelecanoides georgicus* has far less air than non-diving petrels (Procellariidae).

Pneumatisation is also diminished in species that plunge into the water from the air, such as terns *Sterna* spp. and the Kingfisher *Alcedo atthis*. The Gannet *Sula bassana*, with a heavily reinforced and streamlined skull, is only partially pneumatised, but the nasal area is pneumatised in spite of the absence of nostrils.

' Hammering ' species, such as the woodpeckers (Picidae), possess large airless areas in the parieto-frontal bones ; the Nuthatch *Sitta europaea*, a species that does not hammer so vigorously, has more pneumatisation.

Others showing diminished pneumatisation can be loosely classified as ' swift fliers ' and include such species as the gallinaceous birds (Galliformes) which accelerate rapidly, sandgrouse (Pteroclididae), most of the limicoline birds (Charadrii), and the swifts *Apus apus* and *A. affinis*. An exception among the Charadrii is the slow-flying Jack Snipe *Lymnocryptes minimus*, which develops complete pneumatisation.

The two goldeneyes *Bucephala clangula* and *B. islandica* are quite different from all other species examined in that the adults of these duck species possess large air sinuses, often covering most of the dome of the skull.

Extent of Post-cranial Pneumatisation. There is far less data on the extent of post-cranial pneumatisation. Bellairs & Jenkin, in their review of the whole subject, state that it is minimal in many small birds, including the swifts (Apodidae), and also in some aquatic birds such as penguins (Spheniscidae) and gulls (Larinae). They note that in the cormorants *Phalacrocorax* spp. only the humerus is pneumatised, whereas in the Gannet many bones are pneumatised. Extensive pneumatisation is found in large flying birds, such as the albatrosses (Diomedeidae), and the eagles *Aquila* spp. The hornbills (Bucerotidae) are poor fliers but are among the most highly pneumatised of birds. Many of the 'ratites' are also moderately well pneumatised, but in the kiwis *Apteryx* spp. the only pneumatisation is in parts of the skull.

Function of Pneumatisation. The air-sacs in the post-cranial skeleton represent the end point of the respiratory system, and they have therefore a function in this respect which is probably only a minor one in that the amount of tidal air in the skeletal air systems is small. The main function of pneumatisation is probably associated with flight, and the relative absence of pneumatisation with diving (when the buoyancy produced by the air might be a considerable disadvantage to a bird when submerged). Pneumatisation saves weight, which would be of advantage particularly to large flying species, and these are in general more highly pneumatised than smaller ones. See FLIGHT.

Headley pointed out as long ago as 1895 that the girth of a pneumatised bone is relatively greater in relation to its length than the corresponding bone in a species without pneumatisation. This results in a greater resistance to bending stresses, and further strength is provided by the bony trabeculae acting as internal struts. Also, the greater circumference of the bone provides a larger surface area for muscle attachments.

However, as Bellairs & Jenkin have pointed out, there are probably other factors to be discovered, such as the exact function in respiration and temperature control. The partial absence of skull pneumatisation in woodpeckers suggests that this type of skull may be relatively heavier and therefore a more effective hammer. The remarkable sinuses of the two goldeneyes may act as a reservoir for air, to be used when diving, but in this case their total absence in such deep-diving species as the Longtailed

Duck *Clangula hyemalis* is difficult to explain. Certainly, this is a rich field for further research into functional anatomy. J.G.H.

Bellairs, A. d'A. & Jenkin, C. R. 1960. The skeleton of birds. *In* Marshall, A. J. (ed.). Biology and Comparative Physiology of Birds vol. 1. New York and London. (See pp. 289–293.)

Bremer, J. L. 1940. The pneumatisation of the head of the common fowl. Morphol. 67 : 143–167.

Bremer, J. L. 1940. The pneumatisation of the humerus of the common fowl and the associated activity of theelin. Anat. Rec. 77 : 197–211.

de Beer, G. 1937. The Development of the Vertebrate Skull. London and New York.

Harrison, J. G. 1957. A review of skull pneumatisation. Bull. Brit. Orn. Cl. 77 : 70–77.

Harrison, J. G. 1958. Skull pneumaticity in wildfowl in relation to their mode of life. Wildfowl Trust Ninth Ann. Rep. : 193–196.

Harrison, J. G. 1960–61. A comparative study of the method of skull pneumatisation in certain birds. Bull. Brit. Orn. Cl. 80 : 167–172 ; 81 : 12–17.

Nero, R. W. 1951. Pattern and rate of cranial 'ossification' in the House Sparrow. Wilson Bull. 63 : 84–88.

Verheyen, R. 1953. Contribution à l'étude de la structure pneumatique du crâne chez les oiseaux. Bull. Inst. Roy. Natl. Belgique. 29 : 1–24.

POCHARD: substantive name of some *Aythya* spp. and of *Netta* spp. ; used without qualification in Britain for *A. ferina* ; in the plural, general term for the tribe Aythyini (see DUCK).

PODARGIDAE: see under CAPRIMULGIFORMES ; and FROGMOUTH

PODICIPEDES ; PODICIPEDIFORMES: see below (next two entries).

PODICIPITIDAE: see below. The spelling of the familial name ' Podicipitidae ', as here given (out of no less than six that have been used), is at present governed by a Direction of the International Commission on Zoological Nomenclature, but etymological reasons why the Commission might reconsider this in favour of ' Podicipedidae ' have been advanced (Thomson, A. I. 1960, 1961. Ibis 102 : 333 ; 103A : 296. Wetmore, A. 1960. Smiths. Misc. Coll. 139 (11) : 5–60 ; Mountfort, G. & Thomson, A. L. 1963. Bull. Zool. Nomencl. 20 (2) : 159–160). For another point of nomenclature see COLYMBIDAE.

PODICIPITIFORMES: order, alternatively ' Podicipites ', comprising only the cosmopolitan family Podicipitidae (see GREBE). As ordinal names are not regulated by the International Code, one is free to spell the root either consistently with the familial name (see preceding entry) or, in accordance with another view of the etymology, ' Podicipediformes ' (alternatively ' Podicipedes ').

PODOTHECA: the horny covering of the un-feathered parts of the legs and feet (see LEG).

POETRY, BIRDS IN: an inspiration, and also a convenient item of stock-in-trade, to innumerable poets and versifiers. Only omniscience could say whether this general statement is true of all periods and all languages, but certainly it applies to a very wide range of poetry. The Psalmist (although bird references are not frequent in the Psalms) longed to have 'Wings like a dove, for then would I fly away and be at rest ' (see also BIBLE, BIRDS OF THE). Homer and Anacreon had noticed the phenomenon of bird migration. Catullus mourned the death of Lesbia's sparrow. In the fourteenth century Song Thrush, Skylark, owls, and many other birds flit through the poems of the great Welshman Dafydd ap Gwilym, who wrote also of the dawn chorus ; while his English contemporary, Geoffrey Chaucer, sang of the rebirth of bird-song in the spring, besides writing in the lines

> And other egles of a lower kinde,
> Of which that clerkes well devysen conne
> (The Parliament of Fowls)

what the late Harold Massingham called ' apparently the first literary recognition of the ornithologist—and the last ! '

That quotation from Chaucer may serve to emphasise the fact that, of all the immense number of British poets who have written about birds since Chaucer and Dafydd ap Gwilym, very few indeed have looked at them factually and objectively, as an ornithologist does. Most poets have used birds in a rather general way as local colour, or to supply a simile or vivid illustration based on some particularly striking quality in the bird ; or as a basis for some pure bit of fancy, or perhaps for the associations of some classical story or fable (e.g. that the swan sings before it dies, or, even more notably, the story of Philomel and Itylus) ; or even for some familiar jocularity suggested by its name or habits, or both, as in Shakespeare's refrain :

> Cuckoo, Cuckoo—O word of fear,
> Unpleasing to a married ear !
> (Love's Labour's Lost)

You can find all these poetical uses of birds in Shakespeare (see SHAKESPEARE'S BIRDS). He took birds, as so many of the great poets have done, as part of the world of which the intelligent man is conscious and appreciative, part of the background against which the good life is lived—especially

> In the spring time, the only pretty ring time,
> When birds do sing, hey ding a ding,
> Sweet lovers love the Spring.
> (As You Like It)

The birds here are background music, as they are in Goronwy Owen's somewhat Horatian eighteenth-century picture of the poet sitting reading in the shade of his garden, while above his head in the boughs the birds sing (*Awdl y Gofuned*). It is a literary convention of bird-song, undescribed and unparticularised, as an accompaniment to a happy life, that probably exists in most languages.

There are, naturally, poets who did particularise. William Cowper, for example, in his ' *Winter Walk at Noon* ' (*The Task*, Book VI) has a passage about the Robin flitting among trees after a night of snow and singing his sub-song, that could scarcely be bettered as a piece of observation :

> No noise is here, or none that hinders thought.
> The redbreast warbles still, but is content
> With slender notes, and more than half suppress'd :
> Pleased with his solitude, and flitting light
> From spray to spray, where'er he rests he shakes
> From many a twig the pendant drops of ice,
> That tinkle in the wither'd leaves below.

There is, again, an admirably observed passage in Andrew Marvell, describing the Green Woodpecker :

> He walks still upright from the root,
> Measuring the timber with his foot.
> (Upon Appleton House)

But such pieces of direct observation with the naturalist's eye are not very common in poetry, and many of them are but flashes of a moment. One such is Browning's

> That's the wise thrush ; he sings each song twice over,
> (Home Thoughts, from Abroad)

an almost diagnostic line, for the Song Thrush does repeat his notes, often twice—but just as often thrice, as Tennyson knew when in ' *The Throstle* ' he made his bird say :

> Summer is coming, Summer is coming,
> I know it, I know it, I know it !

There is a similar imitative quality in parts of Gerard Manley Hopkins's unfinished poem *The Woodlark*. But perhaps rather more successful, as imitations, are two attempts to suggest the song of the Nightingale. One is by the Elizabethan, Richard Barnfield :

> Fie, fie, fie, now would she cry,
> Teru, teru, by and by.   (Philomel)

The other is from George Meredith :

> In this shrill hush of quietude,
> The ear conceived a severing cry.
> Almost it let the sound elude,
> When chuckles three, a warble shy,
> From hazels of the garden came.
> (Night Frost in May)

Yet it must be confessed that there is very little natural history in the greatest poetry inspired by the Nightingale, in Keats's 'Ode', or Swinburne's 'Itylus' or his magical passage in 'Atalanta in Calydon':

> And the brown bright nightingale amorous
> Is half assuaged for Itylus,
> For the Thracian ships and the foreign faces,
> The tongueless vigil, and all the pain.

Haunting and eloquent verse, but hardly significant as ornithology—much as Shelley's 'To a Skylark' tells us a great deal about human thought and emotion but little about the bird, save as a symbol of man's aspirations. Indeed it becomes evident, as one thinks of poems about birds, that the very great majority of poets do use birds merely as a form of symbolism, seizing upon certain aspects of their behaviour and fitting to them a human significance which seldom has any relevance to what we can conceive to be the bird's own emotions. Seldom—but not perhaps quite always, for when Michael Bruce wrote in 'To the Cuckoo':

> Sweet bird ! thy bower is ever green,
>   Thy sky is ever clear,
> Thou hast no sorrow in thy song,
>   No winter in thy year !

may he not have been expressing something which, in some degree, corresponds to the Cuckoo's motive—or whatever you like to call it—for migration ?

One frequently recurring theme is that of the bird in captivity. Often—at least from the time of Catullus onwards—such poems have been in the form of laments upon the death of a pet, usually a child's or a woman's pet. An example is Cowper's 'On the Death of Mrs Throckmorton's Bullfinch', and another, perhaps the most charming type of this kind in English, is Samuel Rogers's 'Epitaph on a Robin Redbreast'. A variation is the caged bird seen as an insult to the natural spirit of freedom, and in many instances as an image of enslaved humanity, sentiments expressed most crisply in Blake's

> A Robin Red breast in a Cage
> Puts all Heaven in a Rage ;
>   (Auguries of Innocence) ;

with the utmost depth of popular banality in ' She's only a bird in a gilded cage ' ; and with nobility and much ironic force in Christopher Smart's 'Ode on an Eagle confined in a College Court', which begins :

> Imperial bird, who wont to soar
> High o'er the rolling cloud,

and ends :

> Thou type of wit and sense confin'd
> Cramp'd by the oppressors of the mind,
>   Who study downward on the ground ;
> Type of the fall of Greece and Rome ;
> While more than mathematic gloom
>   Envelops all around !

The poet seldom troubles to discover what a particular sound or action may mean to the bird itself ; rather he observes, or takes out of the stock of poetic tradition, some quality held to be characteristic of a species, and uses that bird at the appropriate moment to suggest that quality. Thus owls suggest wisdom (presumably by the look on their faces), or eery haunting (the hoot), or nocturnal terror (the screech) ; the Nightingale mourning ; the Raven grim foreboding ; the Jackdaw mischief (and is there a more delightful bird poem than Barham's ' The Jackdaw of Rheims ' ?) ; the Lark joy that lifts man's soul far above the things of the earth ; the Turtle Dove fidelity in love ; the Robin friendliness ; the Swallow the coming and going of summer ; and so on—all ideas with a strong human relevance.

Rather more rarely a poet will take some bird and build a whole fancy round what he has noticed about it ; and this type of poem can combine both the naturalist's practical observation and the poet's illuminated imagination. A beautiful example of this form of lyric is the recent Welsh poet Robert Williams Parry's ' Y Gylfinir ' (The Curlew), in which he hears, in the various phases of the cry of the Curlew, the whistling of an unseen shepherd and the barking of his dogs driving the flock of clouds across the pastures of heaven.

Wordsworth, Tennyson, Thomas Hardy, John Clare, W. H. Davies (all countrymen, it may be noticed)—these are only some of the poets who have made much use of birds in their poetry ; and the list could be extended immensely without straying beyond the English language. The subject, in fact, is so vast that it can be touched only in the slightest fashion here. Naturally enough, several anthologies of bird poetry (sometimes with prose passages also included) have appeared. Those of which the present writer knows are : P. Robinson, *The Poet's Birds* (1883) ; Noel Paton, *The Birds and the Bards* (1894) ; H. J. Massingham, *Poems about Birds* (1922) ; Mary Priestley, *A Book of Birds* (1937) ; Christian Chapin, *The Bird-Lovers' Book of Verse* (1937) ; and G. Hilditch, *In Praise of Birds* (1954). Eric Parker's *World of Birds* (1941) contains a good chapter on ' Bird Song in Poetry '.   † I.A.W.

POIKILOTHERMAL: opposite of HOMOIO-THERMAL (see HEAT REGULATION).

POINTED-TAIL: substantive name of *Berlepschia rikeri* (see OVENBIRD (1)).

POISONING: see TOXIC CHEMICALS

POISONING, LEAD: see DISEASE ; and under GRIT

POLIOPTILINAE: see MUSCICAPIDAE ; and GNATCATCHER

POLLEX: the thumb, first digit of the fore-limb (see SKELETON ; WING).

POLLINATORS AND DISTRIBUTORS: agents—avian in this context—in the pollination and distribution of plants.

Pollination. The principal pollinating agents of flowering plants are wind and insects, followed in decreasing importance by birds, bats, and water. Pollination by birds is rare in the temperate regions of the Northern Hemisphere, but frequent in the tropics and common in parts of Africa and Australia. In Africa the sunbirds (Nectariniidae), sugarbirds *Promerops* spp. (Meliphagidae), white-eyes (Zosteropidae), and bulbuls (Pycnonotidae) provide most of the avian pollinators, although occasional members of such groups as the weavers (Ploceidae), orioles (Oriolidae), shrikes (Laniidae), warblers (Sylviinae), and mousebirds (Coliidae) have been observed taking nectar. The hummingbirds (Trochilidae) in the Neotropical Region are the most widely known of avian pollinators and the most highly adapted for life as nectar-feeders by their curved bills, brush-tipped tongues, and hovering flight ; only 3 species penetrate far into North America. The New World honeycreepers (Coerebinae) also have habits of this kind. About 80 species of birds are known in Australia as nectar-feeders ; these belong to the honeyeaters (Meliphagidae), and to the parrots (Psittacidae).

Many of the plants visited by birds for nectar are not specially adapted for avian visitors and can be, and frequently are, pollinated by insects of various kinds. *Eucalyptus* flowers are visited by members of the Australian families mentioned as well as by numerous Diptera and Hymenoptera, including the imported honey-bee. Similarly, some parrots have no special adaptations for nectar or pollen feeding. Adaptation is apparent in the curved slender bills and the tongues of those families in which the nectar-feeding habit is constant, and correlated adaptations are found among the more specialised plants on which they feed. Rock reports that the bills of the Hawaiian honeycreepers (Drepanididae) match the curvature of the corolla tubes of the *Clermontia* spp. (Lobeliaceae) which they visit.

Slender corolla tubes are frequent among plants regularly pollinated by birds ; such are the *Aloe*, *Kniphofia*, and *Erica* spp. visited by sunbirds and the sugarbirds in South Africa, and numerous *Epacridaceae* and the Kangaroo Paws *Anigozanthos* visited by honeyeaters in Australia. Flowers arranged in brush-like inflorescences constitute another group favoured by birds in Australia ; these include a number of Myrtaceae—*Callistemon, Melaleuca, Beaufortia*—and *Banksia* in the Proteaceae. The brush-like appearance is due mainly to the stamens in the Myrtaceae, but in *Banksia* the protruding structures are the styles, which are so tough and wiry in consistency that they withstand the attentions of such large visitors as the Red Wattle-bird *Anthochaera-carunculata*.

Some plants, in addition to providing nectar, have developed special perches for their avian visitors. Rigid bracts, which at first enclose the flowers, serve this purpose in *Ravenala* and *Strelitzia* pollinated by sunbirds. In South America, several species of *Puya* (Bromeliaceae) are visited by the icterid *Notiospar curaeus*, which perches upon the sterile ends of the inflorescence branches. One species, *Puya venusta*, lacks these bird perches and is visited only by hummingbirds. Although insects may visit these plants, observation has shown that birds are the effective pollinators.

Avian pollinators are attracted to flowers mainly by the nectar, which is secreted freely in bird-adapted species. The sugar concentration of the nectar, about 5 per cent, is relatively low, compared with that of flowers worked by the honey-bee, which is rarely attracted by concentrations lower than 15 per cent. Birds may take insects in or on the flowers that they visit for nectar. The habit of nectar-feeding appears to have evolved in insectivorous groups by a transfer of attention to the food supply afforded by the flowers in the form of nectar and insects found therein. The early stages in this process can be observed in the warblers (Sylviinae), which are predominantly insectivorous, although some species, such as the Garden Warbler *Sylvia borin* and the Willow Warbler *Phylloscopus trochilus*, occasionally sip nectar.

Colour is an important factor in the attraction of both flowers and fruits for birds. Red or crimson, followed by orange and yellow, are the most favoured colours. The remaining colours of flowers are placed in the order blue, violet, white, and cream by Werth, and for fruits black, white, blue, brown-purple, and rose-pink by Ridley ; this order depends partly on the frequency of black pigmentation in fruits and its rarity in flowers, although shininess in the fruits enhances their attraction.

Colour contrast may be as important as the colour itself. Red and yellow occur against a background of green in both flowers and fruits ; other frequent contrasts are blue and yellow, white and scarlet, and more rarely black and yellow or black and scarlet. Such colour contrasts parallel those of bird plumage.

Seed Dispersal. Plant seeds and fruits provide a very wide range of food attractive to birds. Ridley details 68 families of frugivorous birds that play some part in seed dispersal. The effectiveness of birds as dispersal agents varies greatly, as does the distance the seeds are carried. The smaller birds such as finches (Fringillidae) and tits (Paridae) may scatter seeds only a few feet from the parent plant, or the small proportion of those ingested that pass through the gut unharmed may be voided some miles away. Larger birds are more effective in long-distance transport, especially ducks (Anatidae) and pigeons (Columbidae), which migrate far and rapidly. Seeds of numerous aquatic and waterside plants have been recovered from duck, including *Sparganium*, *Potamogeton*, and many Cyperaceae. The seeds often germinate more freely after passage through a bird ; Guppy obtained 60 per cent germination of *P. natans* seed recovered from ducks, compared with 1 per cent germination in untreated seed. Duck must frequently carry *Lemna* and other water plants and floating seeds to adjacent waters when flushed, the plants being held on their legs and bodies for some time by surface tension or mucilage.

The effectiveness of birds in seed dispersal depends on the length of time the seeds are retained before being disgorged or voided and on the proportion remaining undamaged. Seeds disgorged within a few minutes, as are those of *Taxus* by the Mistle Thrush *Turdus viscivorus*, are quite unharmed. Yew seeds are thus deposited, generally on grass, some distance from the parent tree where they have a good chance of survival. Euphonias *Tangara* spp. (Thraupinae) are important distributors of Loranthaceae seeds in the New World. Fruit pigeons of the genus *Ducula* are greedy feeders on the berries and drupes of tropical Lauraceae, Sapotaceae, and other families. Seeds as large as the nutmeg *Myristica fragrans* are regularly dispersed and may be retained long enough for transport from one island of an archipelago to another. The failure of the Dutch attempt in the eighteenth century to maintain a monopoly of the nutmeg trade on Amboina is attributed to *Ducula concinna*. Columbidae in general are some of the most important of avian plant distributors ; a proportion of the smaller seeds frequently passes through unharmed, and

many seeds of all sizes must be dispersed when pigeons fall prey to raptorial birds.

The thrushes (Turdinae) and crows (Corvidae) disperse immense numbers of seeds in viable condition. In North America, Barrow estimated that over 778 million seeds were deposited on the ground in a roost of Common Crows *Corvus brachyrhynchus* covering 15 acres near Washington. The bulk of the seeds were of sumachs *Rhus* spp., disgorged after the flesh of the drupes had been consumed, but there was also a proportion of the stones of *Juniperus*, *Cornus*, and *Nyssa* ; many others deposited away from the roosts would have had a better chance of survival. Single acorns hidden by Jays *Garrulus glandarius* some distance from the parent oak are more likely to reproduce the tree than the many taken by pigeons and mice underneath its branches. In a like manner the thrushes are important in plant dispersal as much because they deposit seeds far and wide as because of the variety of species taken.

The relationship between granivorous and frugivorous birds and plants has resulted in fewer mutual specialisations than nectar feeding. The bills of the finches (Fringillidae) are well adapted for crushing the shells of seeds, and the powerful bills of some parrots can break open the stout woody seeds of *Canarium* or the iron-hard cones of *Banksia*. The food reserves of seeds, although much eaten by birds, cannot be regarded as primarily adaptations for bird dispersal. Fleshy seed-coats, blue in *Peliosanthes*, black in *Sterculia* spp., and orange in *Iris foetidissima*, are often modifications for bird dispersal, as are the coloured fleshy arils of many large or medium-sized seeds such as *Myristica*, *Taxus*, and *Euonymus*. Drupes, berries, and other fleshy fruits, and also false fruits such as pomes, are adaptations for animal dispersal in general, birds playing a large part in the process. The same may be said of the hairs, barbs, and hooks of many dry seeds and fruits that attach themselves equally to feather or fur. Mucilaginous seed-coats as in *Plantago* and many Cruciferae, and adhesive hairs on fruits of *Peperomia* and *Boerhaavia*, are also of general value as dispersal mechanisms. The extremely tenacious secretion of *Pisonia brunnoniana* sometimes captures small birds such as white-eyes *Zosterops* spp. and introduced House Sparrows *Passer domesticus* in New Zealand, but the fruits have probably been dispersed through the Pacific by herons, boobies, and frigatebirds, attached to their feathers.   R.M.(2)

Ash, J. S., Jones, P. H., & Melville, R. 1961. The contamination of birds with pollen and other substances. Brit. Birds 54 : 93–100.
Ridley, H. N. 1930. The Dispersal of Plants throughout the World. Ashford, Kent.

POLYANDRY: in birds, best considered in the strict sense of the sexual relationship between a female and two or more males such that incubating and tending the young are left to the males. Association with the males may be contemporaneous or successive. The attendance of two males at a nest does not necessarily connote polyandry. Affiliations between a female and two or more males that do not amount to multiple pairing sometimes occur and may be loosely called 'polyandrous'. Mated or unmated females that copulate exceptionally with more than one male, as some Pied Flycatchers *Ficedula hypoleuca* do, should not be considered polyandrous, any more than males that copulate with more than one female should necessarily be considered to be polygamous. As associations between a female and two or more males may vary from very brief liaisons to bonds of some duration, and in some species the males concerned may copulate with more than one female, it is sometimes difficult to distinguish between polyandry, polygamy, and transient multiple pairing (see POLYGAMY; LEK DISPLAY).

Polyandry is rare among birds and few detailed field studies of polyandrous species have been made, so that reliable information is scanty. After the male Rhea *Rhea americana* has made a number of nesting scrapes he calls the females, which go about in troops, and copulates with them, and when 4 or 5 eggs have been laid he begins to sit; the females consort with, and lay eggs in the nests of, several males. Bonaparte's Tinamou *Nothocercus bonapartei* copulates with several females after a modified form of lek display (see LEK DISPLAY); he incubates the eggs, which are laid in a common nest, and if females visit successive males the procedure in this species would resemble that of the Rhea. The female Variegated Tinamou *Crypturellus variegatus* courts the male and lays a single egg in a hollow on the forest floor; the male incubates and cares for the chick, which is well developed on hatching, and he may soon begin sitting on another egg, and later on yet another. The Little Buttonquail *Turnix sylvatica* also lays successive clutches, which the males incubate. In this and other species of *Turnix* the female calls the male by uttering a booming note. The female Pheasant-tailed Jacana *Hydrophasianus chirurgus* lays 7–10 clutches of four eggs in each year; a male may rear two broods in a season. He calls the female for copulation, but it is she who defends the territory. Apparently the female Painted Snipe *Rostratula benghalensis* retains the territory from year to year, vigorously courting the males which enter it, and after laying she abandons incubation and the care of the young to

the male and courts another; the second clutch may be completed before the first is hatched. (This procedure may not be invariable, for a female has been shot from the eggs.) In most polyandrous species males are believed to outnumber the females.

Occasional polyandry may be found to some extent in species about which our information is meagre. It has been recorded in the Dotterel *Eudromias morinellus* and suspected in the Red-necked Phalarope *Lobipes lobatus*; incubation is the responsibility of the male Phalarope and is mainly undertaken by the male Dotterel. The Cuckoo *Cuculus canorus* is said to be polyandrous but it is also suspected of being polygamous (see PARASITISM). Occasional polyandrous associations apparently occur among Starlings *Sturnus vulgaris*, a species in which males greatly outnumber females, and also among Ovenbirds *Seiurus aurocapillus* and some other species.

As regards correlated adaptations, polyandry is mainly characteristic of species with nidifugous young. It is not adaptive in species with chicks that need to be tended in the nest, except perhaps in some parasitic species. It occurs in groups in which the males of nearly related species undertake more than the usual share of domestic responsibilities, such as much of the incubation. In polyandrous species the female tends to be more brightly coloured and larger than the male, and may defend territory and take the initiative in courtship. The nesting season tends to be prolonged. Polyandry is thus not to be considered as an aberration but as a form of pair bond closely integrated with structure, behaviour, and environmental conditions. It emancipates the female from the hazards inseparable from incubating and tending the young, and enables her, during the laying season, to continue to devote more time to feeding herself so that, other things being equal, she can lay more clutches than if she concerned herself with incubation and guarding the chicks. This may be a significant factor in the evolution of polyandry.

E.A.A.

Beebe, W. 1925. The Variegated Tinamou, *Crypturus variegatus variegatus*. Zoologica, N.Y. 6 : 195–227.
Cairns, J. 1940. Birds of Penang and Province Wellesley. Malayan Nature J. 1 : 29–34, etc. (Painted Snipe at p. 32.)
Hoesch, W. 1959. Zur Biologie des südafrikanischen Laufhühnchens *Turnix sylvatica lepurana*. J. Orn. 100 : 341–349.
Hoffman, H. 1949. Über die Brutpflege des polyandrischen Wasserfasans *Hydrophasianus chirurgus* (Scop.). Zool. Jb. (Syst.) 78 : 368–403.
Lowe, V. T. 1963. Observations on the Painted Snipe. Emu 62 : 221–237.
Molnar, B. 1950. The Cuckoo in the Hungarian Plain. Aquila 51–54 : 100–112.
Nethersole-Thompson, D. 1951. The Greenshank. London.

Schäfer, E. 1954. Zur Biologie des Steisshuhnes *Nothocercus bonapartei*. J. Orn. 59 : 219–232.

Steinbacher, G. 1951. Nandus beim Brutgeschaft. Natur und Volk 81 : 212–217.

Whistler, H. 1949. Popular Handbook of Indian Birds, 4th ed. London.

POLYBOROIDINAE: see HAWK

POLYGAMY: in the strict sense, the establishment of a pair bond between a male and more than one female ('polygyny') or between a female and more than one male ('polyandry'). As polyandry among birds is rare (see POLYANDRY), and polygamy carries the sense of a ritualised bond (see RITUALISATION), it is preferable to use the more familiar term 'polygamy' rather than 'polygyny' for mating between a male and more than one female, except when confusion might arise. When a distinction has to be made in regard to the number of mates the familiar cognate term 'bigamy' may be employed. The term 'polyandry' is less satisfactory, as in human society it is applicable when there is a sustained bond between a female and more than one male but among birds in such relationship the bond may be brief. When a bond of this kind is not sustained the relationship may be confused with promiscuity. This latter term should, however, be restricted to types of irregular sexual relationship outside the normal pair bond, as when birds not in full sexual condition early in the breeding season copulate with individuals with which they do not form a pair bond (Oystercatcher *Haematopus ostralegus*), or when ardent males of monogamous species sometimes have forced copulations with females (Mallard *Anas platyrhynchos*, Buller's Albatross *Diomedea bulleri*). See also PAIR FORMATION.

None of these terms adequately describes the sexual relationships of certain species. When the female Wagler's Oropendola *Zarhynchus wagleri* (Icteridae) has completed her pensile nest she associates with a male for a few days. He then proceeds to court another female and gives no help with rearing the broods. In the Yellowheaded Blackbird *Xanthocephalus xanthocephalus*, the Boat-tailed Grackle *Cassidix mexicanus*, and some hummingbirds (Trochilidae), the relationship between male and female may involve scarcely more than a flight towards one another, or together, followed by coition. However, there is some evidence that in the Boat-tailed Grackle true polygamy may occur. Several male Blackthroated (or Greater) Honeyguides *Indicator indicator* may make use of a call-post visited by females ; copulation takes place without courtship display, and the female promptly flies away. Such relationships are best defined as forms of 'transient multiple pairing'.

Two types of polygamy among birds have been distinguished—'simultaneous' (better called 'contemporaneous'), in which the male copulates within a brief period with more than one female with which he is in pair-bond relationship (Corn Bunting *Emberiza calandra*) ; and 'successive', in which the male initiates successive broods with different females (Penduline Tit *Remiz pendulinus*, Crimson-crowned Bishop *Euplectes hordeaceus*, Baya *Ploceus philippinus*). This classification should not be pressed too closely, as contemporaneous and successive polygamy may, and often do, occur in the same species (Wren *Troglodytes troglodytes*). In many species polygamy may be facultative, i.e. successful breeding may occur in either a monogamous or a polygamous relationship.

Polygamy and Territory. In relation to nesting territory (see TERRITORY), two main types of polygamy may be distinguished : that in which there is more than one breeding female in the male's territory (Wren, Penduline Tit), and the rarer situation when the females breed in separate territories belonging to the male (Pied Flycatcher *Ficedula hypoleuca* ; also recorded once in the Whitethroat *Sylvia communis*). A form of polygamy in which several females associate with a male in his territory until, after fertilisation, they find nesting sites and lay (Pheasant *Phasianus colchicus* when preserved as game) may be called 'harem polygamy'. Likewise, a cock Ostrich *Struthio camelus* has a harem of several (commonly three) hens, laying in the same nest. This form merges into types of lek behaviour (see LEK DISPLAY) in which the females associate with a male or males at a display ground or arena, but in most such species the birds are not polygamous in the sense defined, as the association between individuals is brief. Polygamy occurs in such strongly territorial species as the Wren, and also in less territorial species such as some weavers (Ploceidae), but as forms of sex relationship in the latter case approximate to transient multiple pairing the association with nesting territorialism becomes reduced. Polygamy or transient multiple pairing obtains in a number of social-nesting species (some Ploceidae ; Red-winged and Tricoloured Blackbirds *Agelaius phoeniceus* and *A. tricolor*), and also in some species of particularly homogeneous habitats, such as reed-beds (Long-billed Marsh Wren *Cistothorus palustris*, Bittern *Botaurus stellaris*, some harriers *Circus* spp.).

Relationship between Mates of Polygamous Males. Where a male's two mates nest contemporaneously in his territory they are often intolerant of one another, but occasionally, in species in which polygamy is exceptional, the two females sit on nests close together (Mute Swan *Cygnus olor*) or even incubate side by side (Red-backed Shrike *Lanius collurio*). The two mates of a Robin *Erithacus rubecula* held territories from which each expelled the other when she intruded.

Predisposing Circumstances. The conditions in which occasional polygamy occurs clarify the factors that may have operated to render it frequent or usual in other species. These include a recrudescence of male ardour when the female has become unwilling or unable to copulate (Snow Bunting *Plectrophenax nivalis*) ; the frequent straying of females into a male's territory (Lapwing *Vanellus vanellus*) or chance association between a mated male and another female ; the destruction of the nest of a monogamous male (Brewer's Blackbird *Euphagus cyanocephalus*) or contact between a widowed female and a mated male (White-crowned Sparrow *Zonotrichia leucophrys*) ; a female building outside the male's territory ; a male pairing with a female and then with another when he moves his territory (Sedge Warbler *Acrocephalus schoenobaenus*) ; a male forming a pair bond with females with which he had formed a sexual bond in the previous year (Starling *Sturnus vulgaris*) ; when cramped habitats are dominated by a single male (Great Reed Warbler *A. arundinaceus*) ; when a male's domestic responsi-bilities are reduced (Starling) ; when pairing first takes place with an early arrival and again after other females appear (White-collared Flycatcher *Ficedula albicollis*) ; and when mature females are in excess of males. In normally polygamous species polygamy is, of course, an adaptation, not an aberration.

Polygamy and the Sex Ratio. In some populations of polygamous birds the mature females outnumber the males (Crimson-crowned Bishop, Wagler's Oropendola). This is true of the Pied Flycatcher, in populations of which only from 3 per cent (Germany) to 7 per cent (southern Finland) are polygamous ; but in other species, in which there is no evidence of an unbalanced sex ratio, polygamy may occur (Wren) and sexual selection may operate through females preferring the most vigorous males, as shown by song, quality and size of territory, nest building, and display activity. It is unusual for a polygamous Pied Flycatcher to be less than two years old ; one-year-old birds may be less attrac-tive to the females. The excess of females and prevalence of polygamy vary in Brewer's Black-bird from year to year. The Pheasant, as a natural-ised species, is monogamous in New Zealand but maintains itself satisfactorily in Canada (Pelee Island) with a ratio of one cock to 7–10 hens. Flexibility in regard to the pair bond varies considerably in different species and may, on occasion, have impor-

tance in enabling a population or species to survive.

Correlated Adaptations. Many species in which polygamy occurs regularly or frequently show correlated adaptations, such as, in passerines, a covered or cavity nest (Penduline Tit, various species of wren and weaver, Pied Flycatcher) or a prolonged song period (Corn Bunting, Wren). An enclosed nest conserves heat and provides protection when the eggs or young are left unattended. A long song season enables successive females to locate the male in his territory (see SINGING). A series of nests for females to occupy may be built by the male (some wrens and weavers, Penduline Tit, Crimson-crowned Bishop), but in some other species with multiple mating the female builds (some icterids and birds exhibiting lek behaviour). The adaptability of some polygamous birds is shown in that the female sometimes helps with, or undertakes, the building of the nest in species in which this is normally a male responsibility (Wren) (see NEST BUILDING). Bigamous male Hen Harriers *Circus cyaneus* and Montagu's Harriers *C. pygargus*, House Wrens *Troglodytes aedon*, Wrens *T. troglodytes*, Black Redstarts *Phoenicurus ochrurus*, Chaffinches *Fringilla coelebs*, and Sedge Warblers *Acrocephalus schoeno-baenus* will co-operate to feed both of two con-temporaneous broods, but cock Pied Flycatchers and Bobolinks *Dolichonyx oryzivorus* usually feed only one of such broods. The amount of assistance given by the males varies greatly according to species and even according to circumstances. In polygamous birds (but not normally those in which harem polygamy prevails) the male may help in emergencies or even take complete charge if his mate disappears or is killed (Wren). This seldom or never occurs in birds with transient multiple pairing.

When they assist in no other way, males may act as sentinels or guards (Boat-tailed Grackle). Wrens tend to be monogamous in relatively bleak, insular areas (indicating a relationship between the character of the pair bond and availability of food—see WREN), but comparisons between polygamous or multiple-pairing species and monogamous species in the Troglodytidae and Icteridae do not reveal significant differences in clutch size in those species in which the male assists with feeding the young, compared with those in which he does not. Where comparisons can be made within a species there are indications that the young are fed less frequently at the nests of polyga-mous males and that the death rate of the nestlings is higher (Brewer's Blackbird).　　　E.A.A.

Armstrong, E. A. 1955. The Wren. London.
Bent, A. C. 1958. Life Histories of North American Blackbirds, Orioles, Tanagers and their Allies. U.S. Natl. Mus. Bull. 211.

Drury, W. H. 1962. Breeding activities, especially nest building, of the Yellowtail (*Ostinops decumanus*) in Trinidad, W. I. Zoologica (N.Y.) 47 : 39–58.

Groebbels, F. 1937. Der Vogel vol. 2. Berlin.

Haartman, L. von. 1951. Successive polygamy. Behav. 3 : 256–274.

Kendeigh, S. C. 1952. Parental Care and its Evolution in Birds. Illinois.

Nethersole-Thompson, D. 1952. The Greenshank. London.

Ryves, H. H. & Ryves, B. H. 1934. The breeding-habits of the Corn Bunting as observed in North Cornwall. Brit. Birds 28 : 2–26, 154–164.

Williams, L. 1952. Breeding behaviour of the Brewer Blackbird. Condor 54 : 3–47.

POLYGYNY: term sometimes used for a liaison or pair bond between a male and more than one female ; the term ' polygamy ' is more appropriate when a ritualised pair bond is established (Armstrong).

POLYMORPHISM: term denoting the co-existence in a single interbreeding population of two (dimorphism) or more readily distinguishable and genetically determined forms—called ' morphs ' (' phases ' in older terminology)—all in numbers too great to be due merely to recurrent mutation. Familiar avian examples are the egg polymorphism of the various cuckoos (Cuculidae), the white and blue plumage dimorphism of the Reef Heron *Egretta sacra*, and the numerous cases described as ' mutations ' by Stresemann. For an extensive list of avian polymorphisms, and for references to original sources, see Huxley (1955b).

As R. A. Fisher has stressed, the existence of a permanent polymorphism implies a selective balance between the two morphs, both enjoying some selective advantage but also suffering some disadvantage. Whenever the genetic basis for this balance has been investigated, it proves to be secured by some form of heterosis in which the heterozygote between the alleles concerned has an advantage over both homozygotes (see GENETICS). Sometimes, indeed, one homozygote is lethal (or sublethal), or closely linked with a lethal. However, the genetic mechanism of avian polymorphisms has been little studied. Their main interest to ornithologists is ecological and taxonomic. In many cases, polymorphism provides a type of intraspecific variation that adapts the species to extremes of a wide range of environmental conditions, or acts as an insurance against exceptionally unfavourable seasons. An example of the latter is the Swift *Apus apus* ; in the latitude of Oxford, three-egg broods yield a higher absolute number of fledged young in good seasons, but two-egg broods have the advantage in exceptionally bad seasons (Lack). Such meristic polymorphisms in clutch size would repay

further study and might indicate how sharp dimorphism passes over into wide variability. The dimorphism in behaviour between migrant and resident individuals in a single population of many species constitutes a similar insurance mechanism.

Since the degree of relative advantage will differ in different conditions, we often find so-called ' ratio-clines ', in which the proportion of the two morphs changes geographically (as obviously occurs in regard to the frequency of resident and migrant individuals). A classical example is the Guillemot *Uria aalge*, where the frequency of the bridled morph ' ringvia ' increases with latitude and apparently with humidity, from below 0·5 per cent to over 50 per cent (Southern) ; curiously enough, the ' ringvia ' mutant does not exist in the Pacific subspecies. The plotting of ratio-clines will give indication of the selective forces operating on these sensitive balance mechanisms, and periodic repetition of such censuses may indicate changes in climatic or other conditions.

Among other avian ratio-clines may be mentioned that of the female Black Grouse *Lyrurus tetrix*, where a yellow morph is absent at both ends of the species' wide range, but reaches a frequency of over 50 per cent in south-western Siberia ; in the Great Blue Heron *Ardea herodias* the study of a ratio-cline of increasing frequency of whites from Yucatan eastwards, has permitted us to conclude that the Great White Heron *A. occidentalis* of the Florida Keys is not a distinct species, but a monomorphic white population of a dimorphic species in which isolation has permitted subspecific differentiation (Mayr).

The extreme of polymorphism is found in the male Ruff *Philomachus pugnax*. It appears to be a case of synergic polymorphism : the stimulating effect of male display on the females is presumably enhanced by the variety of plumages displayed.

An almost equally extreme case is that of shrikes of the genus *Chlorophoneus* (Moreau & Southern). Here, however, there is no relation with male display, and the polymorphism occurs in both sexes. In *C. multicolor* (with *C. nigrifrons* probably conspecific) there are 5 morphs, affecting the colour of the under parts—black, crimson, pale red, yellow and buff. Up to 3 morphs may coexist in one area. The morphs differ in their distribution—yellow almost universal ; black with a discontinuous and extremely restricted occurrence ; crimson restricted to West Africa ; pale red, central and southern, sometimes occurring alone ; and buff, eastern and central. Though well-marked clines occur in size and some plumage characters, there is no correlation between geography and morph distribution. Clearly the subject needs careful research to establish the selective value of the different morphs, as has been done for the equally striking genetic polymorphism of the land snail *Cepaea* (Cain & Currey).

The polymorphic egg mimicry of some parasitic cuckoos (Cuculidae) is a special case (see PARASITISM). It appears originally to have been half-way to geographical polymorphism, the different mimetic egg-types being laid by the females of distinct gentes ; these represent a form of ecological race, each adapted to one main type of fosterer characteristic of a particular large habitat area. Owing to intercrossing there are always some misfits, and the number of these non-adaptive intermediate types has increased with the breaking down of the distinctiveness of the habitats due to human interference.

The Cuckoo *Cuculus canorus* seems to be prone to morphic variation, since it also shows a plumage dimorphism (red and grey) in females only. Cases of non-mimetic morphic variation in egg colour, as in some shrikes (Laniidae) and pipits *Anthus* spp., deserve further investigation.

In other groups, many cases of cryptomorphisms, i.e. polymorphisms which are not detectable by simple inspection, prove to be common. Examples are the chromosegmental (inversion) polymorphisms of the fruit-fly *Drosophila* and the blood groups and sensory threshold polymorphisms of man. These have been scarcely investigated in birds and would certainly repay study.

Some whole genera or groups of closely allied genera show similar polymorphisms in several species. Thus in herons (Ardeidae), in addition to *Ardea herodias* and *Egretta sacra* (where in some cases the all-white populations appear to be due to the 'founder principle', only white morphs having succeeded in reaching the islands concerned), we have the Reddish Egret *Hydranassa rufescens* and the Little Egret *Egretta garzetta*. The latter species is monomorphic white in its European subspecies, but dimorphic or polymorphic with dark morphs in other areas. In such cases sex recognition cannot depend on colour or pattern, as in e.g. ducks (Anatidae), and must be based only on posture. On the other hand sex stimulation by male display may in some circumstances demand constancy of visual appearance, which may explain why only the females of Black Grouse are dimorphic. This appears definitely to be the case in some butterfly polymorphisms (Ford).

When we survey the class Aves as a whole, we find marked differences between different groups in their proneness to visible polymorphism. Thus it is frequent in Procellariidae, Strigiformes, Accipitridae, Falconidae, and Cuculiformes, but absent in Caprimulgiformes, Trogoniformes, Gruiformes ;

or rare, as in Anseriformes (two striking cases) and Piciformes. So far, no reason can be assigned for these differences.

In conclusion, it is important to distinguish true polymorphism from polymorphic variability due to recombination after hybridisation. The latter is not genetically stabilised or selectively balanced ; it will tend to settle down into a unimodal type if extensive hybridisation has occurred, e.g. in *Junco* spp. (see HYBRIDISATION, ZONE OF SECONDARY). If hybridisation is rare, of course only sporadic recombinants will be found, as in the American wood-warblers of the genus *Vermivora* (Bateson), and probably in the so-called 'mutants' of the *Motacilla flava* group of wagtails.

See Plate 20 (colour). J.S.H.

Bateson, W. 1913. Problems of Genetics. New Haven, Conn.
Cain, A. J. & Currey, J. D. 1963. Area effects in *Cepaea*. Phil. Trans. Roy. Soc. (B) 246 : 1–81.
Ford, E. B. 1945. Polymorphism. Biol. Rev. 20 : 73–88.
Huxley, J. S. 1955a. Morphism and Evolution. Heredity 9 : 1–52.
Huxley, J. S. 1955b. Morphism in birds. Acta XI Internat. Congr. Orn., Basel 1954 : 309–328.
Mayr, E. 1956. Is the Great White Heron a good species ? Auk 73 : 71–77.
Moreau, R. E. & Southern, H. N. 1958. Geographical variation and polymorphism in *Chlorophoneus* shrikes. Proc. Zool. Soc. Lond. 130 : 301–328.
Stresemann, E. 1926. Übersicht über die 'Mutationsstudien' I-XXIV. J. Orn. 74 : 377–385.
Southern, H. N. 1951. Change in status of the bridled guillemot, etc. Proc. Zool. Soc. Lond. 121 : 657–671.

POLYMYODIAN: see SYRINX

POLYPHASY: 'the existence of any sharply marked variations of a species occurring within the same habitat' (Ford 1939)—see POLYMORPHISM.

POLYPHYLETIC: of more than one evolutionary ancestry ; applied to an assemblage of species, and contrasted with MONOPHYLETIC.

POLYTOPIC: found in different places—applied to a form that has widely separated populations.

POLYTYPIC: term applied to a taxon that has more than one unit in the immediately subordinate category, e.g. a genus comprising two or more species, or a species divisible into subspecies—contrasted with MONOTYPIC.

POMATORHININI: see BABBLER

POORWILL: *Phalaenoptilus nuttallii* (see NIGHTJAR ; also WHIP-POOR-WILL).

POPULATION DYNAMICS: the factors

governing the numbers of individuals constituting the population of a given species in a particular habitat. See also CENSUS ; COUNT ; ECOLOGY ; LIFE, EXPECTATION OF ; NUMBERS.

Natural stability. The basic problem in population dynamics is to determine how the comparative stability of bird populations is brought about. When a bird is introduced to a new region and prospers there (e.g. the Starling *Sturnus vulgaris* in North America), there is at first a tremendous increase, but eventually the numbers tend to level off and subsequent fluctuations are much smaller. The initial rapid increase shows what a natural population can do when unchecked, and the subsequent comparative stability shows that powerful checks are normally in operation. In nearly all species of birds, fluctuations in numbers are irregular, but a few northern raptors and gallinaceous species are cyclic, with a period of about four or ten years.

Reproductive Rate. It was formerly supposed that stability in numbers was achieved because the reproductive rate of an animal is adjusted to its mortality rate. This attractive idea is, however, misconceived and there is no evidence in its favour. Instead, the reproductive rate of each species is probably the highest of which the bird is capable under the conditions in which it lives. This means that it raises as many broods as can be fitted into the times of year when food is sufficiently abundant for raising young, and lays that number of eggs which will, on average, give rise to the greatest number of survivors per brood. In passerine and other nidicolous birds, the limit to clutch size is ultimately determined by the greater mortality in large broods due to shortage of food ; the mortality rises so steeply in abnormally large broods that they produce fewer young per brood than do broods of average size, as has been shown in swifts (Apodidae), Starling, and Great Tit *Parus major.* In raptors, crows (Corvidae), and herons (Ardeidae), the eggs hatch asynchronously, so that the last nestlings to hatch are smaller than their siblings, and one or more of them quickly dies if there is a shortage of food, although all may be raised successfully when food is plentiful.

While the ultimate factor determining the average clutch of each species is presumed to be natural selection working on hereditary variations, many species show adaptive modifications in their clutch size to particular conditions—laying larger clutches at some than at other seasons of the year, in some than in other habitats, in some years than in others, and so on. Some of these variations have been correlated with the amount of food available later

for the young in the broods concerned, but the proximate physiological factors that might be involved are not known. At least in one species, the Great Tit, both the mean clutch and the proportion of second broods are smaller at high than low population densities, but the differences concerned are much too small to be the cause of population stability. The factors affecting clutch size in nidifugous species have not been studied.

Mortality Rate. Mortality in birds is extremely high. Thus, in passerine birds with open nests rather under one-half, and in hole-nesters about two-thirds, of the eggs laid give rise to flying young ; and there is a further mortality of unknown extent, but perhaps large, before the flying young become independent of their parents. Similarly in nidifugous species, only about one-quarter of the eggs laid produce fledged young. Moreover, in all birds so far studied, mortality is much higher in the juveniles than in the adults. As a result, only between 8 and 18 per cent of the eggs laid give rise to adult birds (although this is, of course, a much higher proportion than in fishes or invertebrates). The annual death rate is also high among adult birds, ranging from 40–60 per cent in various passerines, ducks, and gallinaceous birds, and 30–40 per cent in various wading birds and gulls, to 20 per cent in swifts, and 10 per cent in the Yellow-eyed Penguin *Megadyptes antipodes*. In various ducks and gallinaceous birds the mortality rate is higher among females than males, and by inference this also holds in many other birds in which males are rather more numerous than females in the population. The adult death rate in those species so far studied is constant with respect to age, up to an age when extremely few individuals are left alive ; and because the rate is so high, most wild birds live only a small fraction of their potential life span (see LONGEVITY).

Mortality Factors. Since variations in the reproductive rate are much too small to produce the stability of bird populations, numbers are presumably held in check by mortality factors, which must be density-dependent, i.e. they must increase in severity when numbers are high and decrease in severity when numbers are low. Some causes of mortality, e.g. bad weather experienced on migration, operate independently of population density, so cannot be critical in regulating numbers. The three most likely causes of density-dependent mortality are disease, predation, and food shortage, while emigration might be a secondary factor mitigating the influence of food shortage.

While many bird parasites have been described, together with their pathological effects, extremely little is yet known as to the occurrence of diseases in wild populations, and there are as yet no cases in which disease, as such, has been established as the normal factor controlling numbers. The most suggestive instance was *Trichostrongylus* (see ENDO-PARASITE) in the Red Grouse *Lagopus scoticus*, but this work should be repeated, as the possible modifying effects of starvation and other factors are uncertain. There have also been extremely few detailed studies of predation on birds (see PREDATION). It is known that predatory birds and mammals remove many young gallinaceous chicks and, at least at times, many adults ; and it is also known that the European Sparrowhawk *Accipiter nisus* may remove a significant proportion of certain small passerine species, but knowledge is insufficient to allow a definite statement as to whether or not the predators provide an effective limit to numbers in these cases.

There is likewise no direct evidence that food shortage is normally limiting bird numbers, but there is strong presumptive evidence of its wide importance in that (i) birds tend to be more abundant where their food is more abundant, (ii) it is extremely uncommon to find two species with similar food requirements in the same area except where the food in question is known to be temporarily superabundant, which implies that there is normally competition for food, and (iii) there is much fighting, usually involving threat display, for food among various sorts of birds in winter. The apparent scarcity of starving birds does not necessarily mean that food shortage is unimportant as a limiting factor, since probably only the few individuals lowest in the dominance hierarchy will be starving at any one time, and there is always the chance that these will be removed by predators very quickly. In a few cases, notably the raptors that prey on cyclic lemmings and voles, and the seed-eating or fruit-eating irruptive species of the taiga (e.g. Nutcracker *Nucifraga caryocatactes*, Waxwing *Bombycilla garrulus*) there is much stronger evidence that shortage of food limits numbers (see also IRRUPTION).

Any possible effects of food shortage on numbers are greatly influenced by movements, both on a large scale, such as seasonal migration and irregular irruptions (see MIGRATION), and on a small scale, such as the dispersion characteristic of both territorial and colonial species in the breeding season ; the existence of such movements makes the possible impact of food shortage on numbers far harder to assess. Further, it is possible that disease, predation, and food shortage interact, disease and starvation increasing the liability to predation, predation reducing the proportion of diseased prey in the population and allowing a more effective use of food and other resources. The whole subject is still in its infancy.

The idea that animal numbers are regulated by density dependent factors, advocated especially by A. J. Nicholson and accepted here, has been challenged by Andrewartha & Birch and also on different grounds by Wynne-Edwards. Hence the views expressed here should be regarded as controversial.   D.L.

Lack, D. 1954. The Natural Regulation of Animal Numbers. Oxford.
Andrewartha, H. G. & Birch, L. C. 1954. The Distribution and Abundance of Animals. Chicago.
Farner, D. S. 1955. Birdbanding in the study of population dynamics. *In* Wolfson, A. (ed.). Recent Studies in Avian Biology. Urbana, Ill.
Richdale, L. E. 1957. A Population Study of Penguins. Oxford.
Gibb, J. A. 1961. Bird populations. *In* Marshall, A. J. (ed.). Biology and Comparative Physiology of Birds vol. 2. New York and London.
Wynne-Edwards, V. C. 1962. Animal Dispersion in relation to Social Behaviour. Edinburgh and London.

POPULATION SYSTEMATICS: see SYS-TEMATICS

PORPHYRIN PIGMENTS: see COLOUR

PORTAL: term applied, especially, to a system of veins draining the abdominal portion of the alimentary tract and associated organs to the liver, but also to some other systems similarly leading into glandular organs (see VASCULAR SYSTEM).

POSTURE: see SHAPE AND POSTURE ; and in relation to preening etc., comfort-movements, and sleep, see FEATHER MAINTENANCE.

POTOO: substantive name of the species of Nyctibiidae (Caprimulgiformes, suborder Caprimulgi) ; in the plural, general term, alternatively 'tree-nighthawks', for the family. 'Potoo' is the creole name for one of the species ; it was apparently used for the first time in ornithology by Gosse in *Birds of Jamaica* (1847), and it is certainly onomatopoeic.

The Nyctibiidae are confined to tropical Middle and South America. They are rather long-winged and long-tailed birds with a soft cryptic coloration of grey, white, buffish-brown, and almost black. The sexes are alike. The nestlings are white with narrow dark shafts (*N. griseus*) or white barred all over with brown (*N. grandis*). The bill is small, and terminally decurved with a projecting 'tooth' on the maxillary tomium. There is a huge mouth, of which the inside is flesh-coloured. The legs are very short. The eyes are very large ; *N. griseus*

has a bright yellow iris, *N. grandis* a dark
brown one, but both species reflect bright orange
at night.

The life of the potoos is but imperfectly known,
and most of our information concerns *N. griseus* and
N. grandis. These two species inhabit light forests
but also cultivated land, e.g. coffee and citrus
plantations. They are strictly nocturnal, solitary,
and arboreal, spending the day sitting crosswise in
an upright attitude on a branch of a tree. Head
scratching is done indirectly (over the wing). The
day roost is often used for a long time at a stretch.
The birds become active at night, especially on
bright moonlight nights, catching flying insects.
This they do in flight from an elevated perch, after
the fashion of flycatchers (Muscicapinae), returning
with their prey to the observation point. The
recorded food of *N. griseus* consists of insects of
several orders (Hemiptera, Orthoptera, Coleoptera,
Isoptera), that of *G. grandis* of various Coleoptera.
The flight of the birds is silent. *N. grandis* has a
rich vocabulary : ' oorrr, ooorrooo ', also a barking
' wow '.

Nesting is only known in respect of *N. griseus*,
N. grandis, and probably *N. aethereus*. The single
egg is laid in a small crevice (so that it cannot slip
and fall down) on a tree-stump, sometimes quite
near the ground but occasionally at a great height.
The bird incubates by sitting in an upright attitude
on the egg. When it feels unobserved and is at
ease, it incubates with the head withdrawn and the
bill pointed forwards, the plumage fluffy and relaxed,
the bill closed and the eyes partly open ; on feeling
observed and becoming alarmed, the whole bird
stiffens and lengthens slowly upwards, the bill
pointing straight into the air and partly open, the
eyes partly closed. It can be closely approached and
even handled, but then the bird threatens by opening
its large eyes, fluffing out its plumage and spreading
its tail, snapping its bill and widely opening its huge
mouth.

The eggs are oval and white, without much gloss,
and are sparsely marked with rather small lilac and
brown spots (*N. griseus* and *N. grandis*). Eggs of
N. griseus from Trinidad measured 41·5×32 mm.,
from Brazil 36·2×29 mm., from Surinam 35·9
×26·1 mm. ; an egg of *N. grandis* from Brazil
measured 52·1×38·3 mm. Eggs of *N. griseus* were
found in Trinidad in April and August, in Surinam
in April, and in Brazil in November and December.
An egg of *N. grandis* was found in Brazil in July and
a nestling in Surinam in June. Incubation is said to
be by both sexes, but the incubation period, the
care of the nestlings, and the fledging period are not
yet known.

$\frac{1}{4}$

Potoo *Nyctibius aethereus*. *C.E.T.K.*

There is only one genus, *Nyctibius*, with 5 species.
The Great Potoo *N. grandis* is the largest (19½ inches
in length, wing 14–15½ inches) ; it is found from
the Panama Canal Zone to Peru, the Matto Grosso,
São Paulo, and Rio de Janeiro. *N. aethereus* is
known from western Colombia, eastern Ecuador,
eastern Peru, Amazonian and south-eastern Brazil,
and British Guiana. The Common (or Grey)
Potoo *N. griseus* has the widest distribution—from
southern Mexico, Guatemala, Honduras, Nicaragua,
and Panama southwards to Peru, Brazil, the Argentine Chaco, Paraguay, and Rio Grande do Sul, and
also on the islands of Jamaica, Hispaniola, Gonave,

and Trinidad. *N. leucopterus* is found in western Colombia, eastern Ecuador, and the coastal region of eastern Brazil. *N. bracteatus* is the smallest species (wing 6½ inches) ; it inhabits Amazonian Colombia, Ecuador, Peru, and British Guiana.

F.H. (3)

Haverschmidt, F. 1948. Observations on *Nyctibius grandis* in Surinam. Auk 65 : 30–32.
Muir, A. & Butler, A. L. 1925. The nesting of *Nyctibius griseus* (Gmel.) in Trinidad. Ibis (12) 1 : 654–659 (6 photographs).
Sick, H. 1953. The voice of the Grand Potoo. Wilson Bull. 65 : 203.

POTOYUNCO: a name for *Pelecanoides garnotii* (see DIVING PETREL).

POULT: a domestic chicken ; sometimes applied to other species.

POULTRY: collective term for birds of domesticated species (as distinct from 'game') used for the table (see DOMESTICATION).

POWDER DOWN: disintegrating feather material occurring in definite patches in some species (see PLUMAGE).

PRAIRIE: treeless grassy plain, especially (and originally) in North America.

PRAIRIE CHICKEN: substantive name of *Tympanuchus* spp. (see GROUSE).

PRATINCOLE: substantive name of all the species of the Glareolinae, a subfamily of the Glareolidae (Charadriiformes, suborder Charadrii) ; used without qualification for *Glareola pratincola* ; in the plural, general term for the subfamily. The pratincoles, a widely distributed Old World group, are closely related to the Cursoriinae in the same family (see COURSER), but are mostly smaller, of different habits, and gregarious. They are 7–9 inches long, including the outer tail feathers—about the size of a Starling *Sturnus vulgaris* or smaller. The wings are long and pointed and the legs short, the bill is small and the tail forked. Their swift and graceful flight, resembling that of swallows (Hirundinidae), and the ease with which they run plover-like, have earned them the popular name of ' swallow-plovers '. The sexes are alike. The plumage generally is dull brown ; the rump is white and the tail is white, tipped broadly or subterminally with black. The black bill, broad and red at the base, tapers to a sharp decurved point. A wide gape assists the capture of insects on the wing. The legs are red or brownish and the feet small. The hind toe is well developed and a web connects the middle and outer toes ; the claw of the middle toe is long and pectinated (pectination absent in *Stiltia*).

Insects, taken mainly in the air, constitute the principal food. In Africa, pratincoles are called ' locust-birds ' from their habit of following and feeding on the invading locust swarms. Like the coursers, they become very active in the evening twilight, when they start feeding and the flocks zig-zag to and fro with high-pitched screaming. Otherwise, except when breeding and sometimes during rain or when alarmed, they are not noisy. The riverine species, when feeding, often skim the surface of the water. Flocks may wheel high in the air. The various calls include an attractive trilling at breeding time and a shrill but not unpleasant twittering alarm.

Pratincole *Glareola pratincola*.   C.E.T.K.

Pratincoles breed in scattered colonies varying from a few pairs to hundreds of birds. Most species nest on the ground, some on sandbanks, and a few on rocks. No nest is made ; the eggs are laid in a shallow hollow, hoof-mark, or unlined scrape, sometimes (*Galachrysia nuchalis*) on bare rock. An Asian species has been known to lay its eggs in the shelter of a tamarisk tuft. Nests as a rule are exposed to conditions of intense heat. Some species at nesting time indulge in a spectacular distraction display. The eggs, 2 or 3 in number—in an Indian locality the normal set is 4—are ovate or broad ovals, pointed at one end, and smooth-surfaced without gloss, and rather fragile. They closely resemble their background, whether black soil, sand, or rock, and are difficult to detect. Their colour is a neutral tint of olive, yellow, or brown, boldly blotched (often obscuring the ground colour), speckled or finely and irregularly marked with black or brown or ash colour. The brooding bird sits tight, but once disturbed the parents fly noisily to and fro over the nesting ground. A parent, with an outstretched wing, will protect its young or eggs from the midday heat. Both sexes incubate.

Breeding takes place after the rains or flood season. Colonies on river sandbanks may suffer a series of disasters from late floods, when as many as three layings can be lost. Suitable nesting grounds —except permanent rock sites—are dependent on local conditions and vary from year to year. When hatched the young are downy and precocious and can run about immediately; their mottled coloration is cryptic.

The subfamily ranges from Europe to Africa, Asia, and Australia, but is not represented in America. The two main genera are *Glareola*, of the open plains and mostly migratory, and the smaller, resident *Galachrysia* (not separated by all authors), of which some indulge in local movements. There is also the monotypic Australian Pratincole *Stiltia isabella*, which in certain respects is a courser, for it has long legs and the claw of its middle toe is not pectinated; yet its very long pointed wings and short decurved bill are typical of the pratincoles, besides which it is gregarious, a migrant, and not a ground species.

The 3 species of *Glareola* have a wing-spread of nearly 2 feet: the Pratincole *G. pratincola* (with several races, some resident); the Black-winged Pratincole *G. nordmanni*, distinguished from *G. pratincola* (of which it may be a colour phase) by having black instead of chestnut beneath the wings; and the Madagascar Pratincole *G. ocularis* (native to that island, but migrating to eastern Africa). *G. pratincola* is found from southern Europe to Africa, Asia, and Australia (on migration); and *G. nordmanni* in south-east Europe and south-west Asia, migrating to Africa.

Galachrysia is represented by 3 species with relatively short wings, all associated with water. The Collared Pratincole *G. nuchalis* (a few races), is an African resident, with characteristic pale collar, and frequents rocks in perennial rivers and inland waters. The Grey Pratincole *G. cinerea* of West Africa and the Little Indian Pratincole *G. lactea* of south-east Asia are both pallid species associated with large rivers and nesting on sand-banks. In *Galachrysia* the tail is shorter than in *Glareola*, and more square and less forked. Characteristics of *Glareola* spp. include craning and raising their heads like coursers when suspicious; raising the outstretched wings perpendicularly above the back butterfly-wise on alighting; and settling in a close pack, all facing in the same direction, and remaining motionless and inconspicuous. C.R.S.P.

PRE-ADAPTATION: see under ADAPTATION

PRECIPITATION: see CLIMATOLOGY; METEOROLOGY

PRECOCIAL: active immediately after hatching (see YOUNG BIRD).

PRECOCIOUS FLIGHT: see FLIGHT, PRECOCIOUS

PREDATION: the killing of members of one species by members of another species for food (see FEEDING HABITS); the term is almost entirely confined to the discussion of the effects of the activities of predators upon the populations of the prey species (see also POPULATION DYNAMICS). A predation study demands a means of ascertaining the numbers in which a species is present in a given area, and the numbers killed within that locality by a known predator. The population may be measured directly or by some such sampling method as the LINCOLN INDEX; the second parameter requires that some visible and measurable traces of the slaughter remain—feathers, bones, skulls, elytra or wings of insects, or even rifled dwelling places—as in the cases of the larvae of the beetles of the genus *Pissodes* or of the moth *Ernarmonia conicolana*, whereof the ravaged and the uninvaded over-wintering chambers can be distinguished.

In Holland, remnants at nests and plucking places were used to show that about half the deaths of all House Sparrows *Passer domesticus* in the area were in the clutches of Sparrowhawks *Accipiter nisus*. During a vole plague on the Scottish border, pellets and stores at nesting sites showed that Short-eared Owls *Asio flammeus* were making inroads upon the rodent population at a rate of not more than 0·05 per cent per diem, and that the owls were not, in fact, in any way checking the plague. During an outbreak of *Archips fumiferana* in the spruce forests of Ontario, Kendeigh calculated that, at most, bird predation destroyed 5 per cent of the larvae. There is one classic case of the effects of bird predation being immediately visible: during an outbreak of defoliating insects in Prussia in 1905, the woods of the Baron von Berlepsch, where the nesting of birds had been encouraged, were said to stand out 'among the surrounding woods like a green oasis'.

The incidence of bird predation may vary greatly from year to year in one locality, or within a single season between places very close together. In samples of marked snails *Cepaea nemoralis* released in Wytham Great Wood in Berkshire, England, some 5 per cent were taken by Song Thrushes *Turdus philomelos* in a six-week period in 1951. In samples of marked *Helix aspersa* released within an area of 100 yards radius in Suffolk in 1958 the incidence of thrush predation upon the different samples, in a twelve-week period, varied from 36 to 4 per cent.

The effects of predation are not always adverse to the population level of the victim species. It has been demonstrated mathematically that if the principal cause of death in a species be the attacks of a pathogenic organism, and that if a predator tends to take weak or sickly specimens, the final result of predation will be to increase the population of the prey species.

The effects of predation are not, of course, limited to alterations in the population levels of the prey species. Predation pressure is the effective agent in the evolution of cryptic adaptations of form and behaviour, as has recently been so clearly demonstrated in the relationship between Song Thrushes and the polymorphic snail *C. nemoralis*—see COLORATION, ADAPTIVE ; NATURAL SELECTION.

P.H.T.H.

Lack, D. 1954. The Natural Regulation of Animal Numbers. Oxford.
Nicholson, A. J. 1933. The balance of animal populations. J. Anim. Ecol. 2 : 131–178.
Rudebeck, G. 1950–51. The choice of prey and modes of hunting of predatory birds with special reference to their selection effect. Oikos 2 : 65–88 ; 3 : 200–231.
Sheppard, P. M. 1951. Fluctuations in the selective value of certain phenotypes in the polymorphic land snail Cepaea nemoralis (L.). Heredity 5 : 125–134.
Tinbergen, L. 1946. Der Sperwer al Roofijand van Zangvogels. Ardea 34 : 1–213.

PREENING: see FEATHER MAINTENANCE

PREFILOPLUMA: obsolete term (see PLUMAGE).

PREFRONTAL: a paired bone of the skull (see SKELETON).

PREMAXILLA: the main bone, on each side, of the upper jaw (see SKELETON).

PREPENNA: obsolete term (see PLUMAGE).

PREPLUMULA: obsolete term (see PLUMAGE).

PRESSURE, ATMOSPHERIC: see CLIMATOLOGY ; METEOROLOGY

PRIMARY: or 'primary feather', any one of the flight feathers borne on the manus (carpometacarpus and digital phalanges)—contrasted with the 'secondaries', borne on the forearm (see PLUMAGE ; WING). The primaries are best numbered from the carpal joint outwards, but as the opposite practice is followed by some authors it is always desirable to say which is being used (cf. Ashmole et al. 1961). In most non-passerine species there are—not counting a remicle, if present (see REMICLE)—10 primaries in normal individuals, but in grebes (Podicipitidae) except the flightless *Centropelma*, storks (Ciconiidae), and flamingos (Phoenicopteridae) there are 11 ; in most passerine birds either there are only 9 primaries or the 10th (outermost) is much reduced (Stresemann 1963).

Ashmole, N. P., Dorward, D. F., & Stonehouse, B. 1961. Numbering of primaries. Ibis 103a : 297–298.
Stresemann, E. 1963. Variations in the number of primaries. Condor 65 : 444–459.

PRIMITIVE STREAK: see DEVELOPMENT, EMBRYONIC

PRINIA: generic name commonly used as English substantive name of *Prinia* spp., alternatively 'longtail' (see WARBLER (1)). See Plate 43 (egg).

PRION: substantive name of *Pachyptila* spp. (see PETREL).

PRIONOPINAE: see SHRIKE

PRIORITY, LAW OF: see NOMENCLATURE

PROAPOSEMATIC: see under APOSEMATIC

PRO-AVIS: see ORIGIN OF BIRDS

PROCELLARIIDAE: see below

PROCELLARIIFORMES: alternatively 'Tubinares', an order comprising the petrels (in the widest sense) or 'tubenoses'. For general characteristics of the order, and for the families Procellariidae (typical petrels and shearwaters) and Hydrobatidae (storm-petrels), see PETREL. As regards the other two families, for the Diomedeidae see ALBATROSS, and for the Pelecanoididae see DIVING PETREL.

PROCRYPTIC: see under CRYPTIC

PROEPISEMATIC: see under EPISEMATIC

PROGESTERONE: see ENDOCRINE SYSTEM

PROJECTION: see MAPPING

PROLACTIN: see ENDOCRINE SYSTEM ; also FEEDING OF YOUNG ; MILK, PIGEON

PROOTIC: a paired bone of the skull (see SKELETON).

PROPATAGIUM: a membranous fold of skin along the anterior margin of the wing from shoulder to carpal joint (see MUSCULATURE ; WING).

PROPRIOCEPTIVE: see SENSES

PROTECTION: the legal protection of wild birds against excessive human predation or cruelty, as distinct from more positive measures of conservation aimed at preserving or improving the habitat (see CONSERVATION ; NESTBOX ; OIL POLLUTION ; TOXIC CHEMICALS). The problem for each country is one of enacting suitable legislation and providing for its effective enforcement. Further, the subject has an important international aspect, having regard to the natural mobility of birds (see MIGRATION) and also to the existence of trade in birds (live or dead), their plumage, and their eggs (see UTILISATION BY MAN).

Underlying Concepts. In Great Britain the legal protection of birds primarily emanated from the concept that 'quarry' is the possession and right of the owner or occupier of land. Thus in the Middle Ages, birds such as the Heron *Ardea cinerea* were protected as the quarry for falconry, a royal sport (see FALCONRY). The development of game preservation and the need for further protection of owner's rights was reflected in the Game (Scotland) Act 1772, followed later by the Night Poaching Act 1828 ; and these Acts laid down which birds were legally recognised as 'game'— and consequently regarded as property. A close time for the species enumerated in the Act of 1828 was laid down in the Game Act 1831, and the Acts in the series which followed were principally aimed at safeguarding the rights of owners and occupiers, affecting the scope given for the killing or taking of game, or helping to make the pursuit of game more difficult. These provisions continue in force to the present day, although some excisions from the list were made in 1954 (SEE GAME-BIRDS), and there is thus a legal distinction between game-birds and all other wild birds, the latter not being regarded as private property.

The narrowness of the British definition of game is not easily understood in other countries, where all birds normally shot for food are regarded as game and therefore have special legal protection. In some European countries, even such birds as thrushes *Turdus* spp. are included in this category for legal purposes. Further, in many other countries, the principle that birds are the property of the owner or occupier of land does not apply.

The first indication in Great Britain of some feeling of public responsibility towards wild birds, in general, was the Act for the Preservation of Sea-birds 1869. Next, the Wild Birds Protection Act 1880—the principal Act for three-quarters of a century—was a great step forward, establishing a definitely close season for all wild birds ; but the privilege of owners and occupiers of land was still respected, since, except for a list of certain species, they were exempt from the application of the close season. The feeling of local ownership was also maintained by the fact that the close-time and other provisions of the Act could be varied by Order, for any species in any county. This led to the issue of long lists according varying protection from county to county, which resulted in extreme difficulty in enforcing the law and in great confusion. This system persisted in all legislation on the subject until the whole of this was replaced by the greatly simplified Wild Birds Protection Act 1954, under which Orders having purely local effect (except for the establishment of bird sanctuaries) are very sparingly made.

At the end of the nineteenth century the humanitarian attitude towards birds was pre-eminent ; and in 1889 the Royal Society for the Protection of Birds was founded, by a group of women, with the object of preventing the cruelty and enormous destruction involved in taking birds-of-paradise (Paradisaeidae), egrets *Egretta* spp., and other birds for millinery purposes. This primary object was not, however, achieved until the passing of the Importation of Plumage (Prohibition) Act 1921. A similar campaign in the United States attained success more quickly, and the importation of plumage was prohibited in 1913 ; two years later a similar measure came into effect in Canada.

International Action. A great increase in knowledge of migratory movements led to an appreciation of the fact that birds could not be regarded as the property of one country alone. The first international convention between two countries was the Migratory Bird Treaty signed in 1916, which provided for reciprocal legislation for the protection of migratory birds, between the United States and Canada ; this was extended in 1937 to include Mexico.

In Europe the international aspect of bird protection was first raised at Vienna in 1868, when a meeting of German agriculturists and foresters put forward a resolution to procure international agreements for the protection of birds and other animals useful to agriculture and forestry. Although up to the end of the century various efforts were made to bring this proposal into effect, it was not till 1902 that an International Convention for the Protection of Birds useful to Agriculture was signed in Paris. This Convention accorded protection to certain birds enumerated as useful and also to their nests, eggs, and young, while other species were pronounced harmful and exempted from protection. Various methods of taking and killing birds were prohibited, and also the sale of protected birds during the close season.

During the first two decades of the twentieth century, with the increase in field observations, better knowledge of the role of birds in the national economy, and the experience of the dire results of commercial exploitation of certain species, an entirely new concept of bird protection was evolving. There was also the awakening to the fact that international protection of birds is essential ; and in 1922 the International Council (then Committee) for Bird Preservation (Conseil International pour la Préservation des Oiseaux)—the first international organisation concerned with the preservation of wildlife—was founded by Dr T. Gilbert Pearson of the United States.

In 1925, Professor Einar Lönnberg of Sweden drew attention to the urgent need for international co-operation for the protection of the Anatidae, pointing out that the Scandinavian countries bred the birds and the countries farther south shot them. His efforts led to active co-operation between European countries in investigation of the status of this group of birds, to the passing of the Wild Birds (Ducks and Geese) Protection Act 1939 in the United Kingdom and of similar protective measures in other European countries, and to the establishment of the International Wildfowl Research Bureau.

In 1935, at a meeting of the International Committee for Bird Preservation held in Brussels, the representatives of the Finnish, Norwegian, and Swedish Governments presented a draft Convention for the international protection of birds ; but it was agreed that an entirely new convention was not practicable and that the proposals should be incorporated in a revision of the Paris Convention of 1902. The amendments presented a complete change round from the system of listing birds as useful or harmful and adopted the principle of protection for all birds, with exceptions in the interests of agriculture, science, education, and so on. This system of legislation had been adopted in the Netherlands in 1914 and in Prussia in 1929. The prevention of the destruction of birds en masse was an outstanding point in the new proposals, and the trade in protected species and their eggs was also dealt with. The provisions of the convention were deliberately framed to make it possible for countries to adjust their particular requirements, but it took twelve years for the requisite number of countries to ratify and accept the Convention, which is restricted to Europe, in order to bring it into force in 1963. The adherents so far are Belgium, Iceland, Luxembourg, Netherlands, Spain, Sweden, and Switzerland. At the moment of writing, the United Kingdom has not adhered as its law is at variance in at least one substantial respect with the principles of the Convention.

Present Position in Great Britain. In many countries, legislation concerning the protection of birds is the responsibility of the Government department concerned with agriculture ; but in Great Britain, where the bird protection Acts are administered by the police, the Home Office (for England and Wales) and the Scottish Office are responsible. The respective Secretaries of State for the Home Department and for Scotland accordingly appoint advisory committees composed of independent members with specialised knowledge of the different aspects of bird protection legislation. By 1939 there were no less than sixteen complete Acts for the Protection of Birds in operation in Great Britain, and references to birds were included in several more ; the law was difficult to understand, troublesome to enforce, and in some respects much too rigid. The Act of 1954 includes many of the provisions of earlier Acts, but it is based on the modern principle of according protection to all birds, their nests, and their eggs. Exceptions are made in respect of certain species scheduled because they are considered to be injurious, or to be proper objects of sport (outside a defined close season). The law is much more flexible than formerly, as the Secretaries of State are empowered to make Orders varying the schedules, with either general or local effect ; and as there is also provision for the grant of licences for scientific, educational, agricultural, and certain other purposes, including falconry. In addition, there is provision for the control of sale and import.

P.B.-S.

United States of America. Wild birds and other wild animals are considered to be within the public domain, regardless of the ownership of the land on which they may be found. Under the federal governmental system, protection of birds is divided between the Federal (national) government and the fifty state governments. The Federal government legislates in this field when the matter is deemed by Congress to be of national, international, or interstate concern. The Federal government has made treaties with Canada (1916) and Mexico (1937) for the protection of most migratory birds occurring in the United States. Implementing these treaties Federal laws protect all included species, and their killing or possession is prohibited or carefully regulated by the U.S. Fish and Wildlife Service (a bureau of the Department of the Interior). Certain migratory birds that are considered to be game—most Anatidae, some Rallidae, and a few

Charadrii and Columbidae—may be hunted for sport (but not commercially), subject to licence and annual regulations by the Fish and Wildlife Service. At present, hunting of game-birds is restricted to autumn and early winter, and of shorebirds (Charadrii), only two species—the American Woodcock *Philohela minor* and the Common Snipe *Gallinago gallinago*—may be killed for sport. The sale of birds so taken is prohibited. Killing, taking, or possession, alive or dead, of other birds included in the treaties, and taking or possession of their eggs, are totally prohibited, except for licensed scientific collecting or in special situations. Federal laws also protect certain birds not included in the migratory bird treaties, i.e. the Bald (or American) Eagle *Haliaetus leucocephalus*, and the Golden Eagle *Aquila chrysaetos* ; and likewise birds on Federal domains, including national parks, forests, and preserves, and in areas not within state jurisdiction. Federal laws likewise prohibit interstate or foreign commerce (export or import) in wild birds' feathers or bird skins (except in very restricted situations). Similarly, importation of living birds from abroad is prohibited if they belong to species native to the United States or if their exportation violates the laws of the country of origin. In addition, the various states have laws protecting all or most birds not covered by the Federal laws, and regulating the hunting of certain non-migrating game, such as the Turkey *Meleagris gallopavo*, grouse (Tetraonidae), and quail (Odontophorinae). There are both Federal and state game wardens. The states have their own bureaus (often called Department of Conservation or Department of Fish and Game) charged with enforcing state regulations as to hunting and bird protection.

As a result of the Federal and state laws and regulations, in combination, it is fair to say that in the United States commercial traffic in native birds is prohibited and that almost all native birds are protected. The exceptions are some birds-of-prey, certain fish-eating species, and certain Icteridae that, gathering in great flocks, may sometimes be injurious to agriculture. In various states, however, all or most of these species are also protected, and their destruction permitted only when they are actually found to be endangering property. The modern legislative tendency is to adopt laws granting protection to all native birds, with special provision for control in case of injurious activity.

These laws are the result of a widespread and growing public sentiment in the United States favourable to birds. Those most interested are organised in a variety of national and local conservation societies and bird clubs. Probably the organisa-tions that have been most influential in obtaining the enactment of laws for the protection of birds have been the National Audubon Society (formerly National Association of Audubon Societies) and the many affiliated state and local Audubon societies.

E.E.

The subject is treated above from an international point of view, but with more particular reference to the situation in the two principal English-speaking countries. In a work more specially concerned with protection, details might well have been given of the legislation, often admirable, in many other lands. (Editor.)

International Council for Bird Preservation. 1963. IX Bulletin. London. (A recent assessment of world-wide scope, based largely on the proceedings of the XIII I.C.B.P. Conference, New York City, 1962.)

PROTEINS AS TAXONOMIC CHARACTERS :

because the structure of protein molecules is genetically determined, and apparently phylogenetically conservative, they have been found to provide taxonomically valuable information. Several methods that provide an index to protein structure have been utilised (see Sibley 1962).

Serology. If a foreign protein is injected into an animal the ' immune reaction ' of the host produces antibodies, themselves proteins, which combine with the invading substances and inactivate it. The antibodies thus formed are specific for the foreign protein, the antigen. This reaction may be carried out in a test tube and the amount of the resulting precipitate, formed when antibodies and antigen come together, is used as the basis for determining the degree of relationship between two animals, as follows. A source of protein, usually blood serum, from species A is injected into a rabbit, a chicken, or some other animal. This animal responds by producing antibodies against the serum proteins of species A. If the serum of such rabbit or chicken is now tested against serum from species A, a large amount of precipitate will be formed and the amount of reaction is taken as a 100 per cent response ; this can be quantitatively measured with suitable instruments. If the anti-A serum is now tested against species B, C, etc., the amount of precipitate formed, compared with the 100 per cent reaction of anti-A with A, provides a means for comparisons among a group of species. There are many complications and difficulties, but this is the essential nature of this method (see Boyden 1953).

Electrophoresis. This is an electro-chemical method for the fractionation of mixtures of charged particles, applied in avian taxonomy to the characterisation of the egg-white proteins. In ' paper electrophoresis' a sample of fresh egg-white is applied to a strip of filter paper saturated with a suitable buffer (e.g. barbital buffer, pH 8·6) and a constant direct current is applied for a standard period. The operation is carried out in a special apparatus under controlled conditions. The different proteins move through the filter paper at different speeds depending upon their net charge, size, shape, and so on. These properties result primarily from the sequence of amino acids in the protein chain ; and, since this sequence is genetically determined, the electrophoretic behaviour of the different proteins provides an index to the genetic information that determined it. The proteins in the paper strip are dyed, and the strip may then be scanned with a photoelectric densitometer that produces a pen-drawn curve indicating the positions and amounts of the proteins present. Comparisons among these electrophoretic ' profiles' provide information on genetic, and hence taxonomic, relationships. Starch gel, cellulose acetate, and other supporting media may be used as well as filter paper.

A review of related work and the results of a study of some 360 species of non-passerines have been published (Sibley 1960). In most instances the egg-white protein evidence agrees with that from anatomy ; but it has been possible to determine relationships among orders and families which were uncertain, and to reveal previously undetected instances of convergence.

Haemoglobin Crystal Patterns. If washed erythrocytes (see BLOOD) are allowed to dry on a glass slide, under certain conditions, a pattern of crystallisation is produced which reflects the structure of the protein (globin) part of the haemoglobin molecule. Reichert & Brown showed that degrees of phylogenetic relationship were indicated by the patterns produced. However, this method does not seem to be of great value in systematics.

Erythrocyte Haemolysis. Because the rate of haemolysis (i.e. dissolution) of red blood-cells in various solvents is a function of the structure of the protein molecules composing the cell wall, the time required for haemolysis reflects some of the properties of these proteins. Johnston & Hochman studied three species of birds and found evidence of degrees of relationship.

Paper Chromatography. If proteins are hydrolysed into their constituent amino acids, as is customary when analyses by paper chromatography are carried out, the sequence is destroyed and hence the genetic information is destroyed. This method is therefore not recommended for taxonomic work.

C.G.S.

Boyden, A. 1953. Fifteen years of systematic serology. Systematic Zool. 2 : 19–30.
Johnston, R. F. & Hochman, B. 1953. Erythrocyte permeability and bird relationships. Condor 55 : 154–155.
Reichert, E. T. & Brown, A. P. The differentiation and specificity of corresponding proteins and other vital substances in relation to biological classification and organic evolution : the crystallography of haemoglobins. Carnegie Inst. Wash. Publ. no. 116.
Sibley, C. G. 1960. The electrophoretic patterns of avian egg-white proteins as taxonomic characters. Ibis 102 : 215–284.
Sibley, C. G. 1962. The comparative morphology of proteins as data for classification. Systematic Zool. 11 : 108–118.

PROTEIN METABOLISM: see METABOLISM ; NUTRITION

PROTOPTILE: term applied to the first of two nestling down plumages, in cases where there is such a sequence, the second then being called ' mesoptile ' (see PLUMAGE).

PROTOZOA: see ENDOPARASITE

PROVENTRICULUS: see ALIMENTARY SYSTEM ; also, for stomach oil, under ALBATROSS.

PROXIMAL: nearest to the centre of the body or to the point of attachment (e.g. of a limb) ; opposite of DISTAL.

PROXIMATE: applied to factors, in a system of causation, that immediately precede the effect ; contrasted with ULTIMATE.

PRUNELLIDAE: a family of the Passeriformes, suborder Oscines (see ACCENTOR).

PSALTRIPARINAE: subfamily recognised by some authors (see TIT).

PSEUDAPOSEMATIC: see under APOSEMATIC

PSEUDEPISEMATIC: see under EPISEMATIC

PSEUDOCHELIDONINAE: see SWALLOW

PSEUDOSCHIZORHINAL: see NARIS

PSEUDOSUCHIA: see under ARCHAEOPTERYX ; ORIGIN OF BIRDS

PSILOPAEDIC: with little or no down when hatched (see YOUNG BIRD).

PSITTACIDAE: see below

PSITTACIFORMES: order comprising only the family Psittacidae (see PARROT).

PSITTACOSIS: a virus disease, on occasion communicable to man, originally described as affecting parrots (Psittacidae) and allied birds but now known to affect widely different species (e.g. the Fulmar *Fulmarus glacialis*), as the result of infection by an identical or closely related virus, and therefore sometimes called 'ornithosis' (see DISEASE).

PSITTIROSTRIINAE: see HONEYCREEPER (2)

PSOPHIAE; PSOPHIIDAE: see under GRUI-FORMES ; and TRUMPETER

PSYCHOLOGY: the scientific study of mental processes ; in respect of birds necessarily the study of the manifestations constituting BEHAVIOUR.

PTARMIGAN: substantive name of *Lagopus* spp. other than *L. scoticus* and sometimes *L. lagopus* ; used without qualification in Britain for *L. mutus*, elsewhere known as the Rock Ptarmigan ; in the plural (sometimes unchanged), serves as a general term for the genus (see GROUSE). See Plates 8 and 29 (colour).

PTEROCLETES; PTEROCLIDIDAE: see under COLUMBIFORMES ; and SANDGROUSE. 'Ptero-cletes' (P. L. Sclater 1880) is the usual spelling of the subordinal (or ordinal) name, but Newton pointed out that it was based on a grammatical misconception ; he preferred 'Pteroclides' (Sundevall 1836) as a more possible, although not certainly correct, plural of Pterocles. The familial name is some-times spelt 'Pteroclidae' or 'Pterocletidae'.

PTERODACTYL: see WINGS, COMPARATIVE ANATOMY OF

PTERYGOID: a paired bone of the skull (see SKELETON ; and PALATE).

PTERYLA: a feather-bearing area of skin (compare APTERIUM ; see PLUMAGE).

PTERYLOGRAPHY: delineation of the distribution of feathers on the skin, or the distribution (pterylosis) itself (see PLUMAGE).

PTERYLOSIS: the distribution of feathers on the skin (see PLUMAGE).

PTILOGONATINAE: see BOMBYCILLIDAE ; and SILKY FLYCATCHER

PTILOGONYS: generic name often used as substantive name of *Ptilogonys* spp. (see SILKY FLY-CATCHER).

PTILONORHYNCHIDAE: a family of the Passeriformes, suborder Oscines (see BOWERBIRD).

PTILOPAEDIC: clad in down when hatched (see YOUNG BIRD).

PTILOPODY: the condition of having feathers on the tarsus and toes (Danforth 1919).

PTILOSIS: synonym of PLUMAGE.

PUAIOHI: *Phaeornis palmeri* of the Hawaiian Islands (for subfamily see THRUSH).

PUBIS: a paired bone (plural 'pubes') of the pelvic girdle, partly fused with the other elements (see SKELETON).

PUFF-BACK: substantive name of *Dryoscopus* spp. (see SHRIKE). There are also 'puff-back fly-catchers' *Batis* spp. (see FLYCATCHER (1)).

PUFFBIRD: substantive name of some species of Bucconidae (Piciformes, suborder Galbulae) ; in the plural, general term for the family. This consists of 10 genera and about 30 species of small or medium-sized birds (5½–10½ inches long) confined to continental tropical America. The puffbirds are closely related to the jacamars (Galbulidae). Their large heads, abundant, lax, dull-coloured plumage, and short tails make them appear stout and 'puffy', whence their name. The bill, of short or medium length and often notably stout, is decurved or hooked at the tip. The feet are zygodactylous, with two toes directed backwards. The family is best represented in the Amazon valley and Colombia, and it is largely confined to the warm lowlands.

One of the largest and most widespread members of the family is the White-necked Puffbird *Noth-archus macrorhynchus*, which ranges from southern Mexico to Amazonia. This handsome bird is about 9½ inches in length. Both sexes are largely black on the dorsal surface ; the forehead, nuchal collar, sides of the head, and under parts are white, with a broad black band across the breast. The thick tapering bill is black.

Slightly smaller is the White-whiskered Softwing *Malacoptila panamensis*, which is found from southern Mexico to western Ecuador. The male is clad largely in chestnut-brown and cinnamon, with the posterior under parts pale buff or nearly white. Both above and below the female is more olive and greyish. Both sexes are liberally spotted and streaked with tawny and buff on the upper parts and streaked with brown and dusky on the breast and sides. Both sexes wear the long, slender, slightly curved, white, malar tufts which are indicated by their name. Their large eyes are dull red.

Both the White-necked Puffbird and the White-whiskered Softwing are found singly or in pairs, or sometimes in family groups of three or four, but never in flocks. The bird rests motionless for long periods on a more or less exposed lookout perch, apparently lethargic but actually keeping a sharp watch for suitable food. By means of a surprisingly sudden dart, it snatches a caterpillar, winged insect, spider, or small lizard from a neighbouring bough, or sometimes it drops down to seize it among low herbage ; then it carries the prey back to a perch to devour at leisure.

White-whiskered Puffbird *Malacoptila panamensis.*
C.E.T.K.

A very different type of puffbird is the Swallow-wing *Chelidoptera tenebrosa,* widespread in South America. This is a stout, large-headed bird about 6 inches in length ; its long wings when folded reach almost to the end of its short tail. Both sexes are largely black or almost black, with a patch of white on the lower back and rump. The abdomen is rufous-chestnut, paling to white on the under tail coverts. The voyager along the Amazon and its great tributaries often sees these graceful little birds perching in pairs on the topmost naked twigs of tall riverside trees, whence they make long, spectacular darts to snatch insects from the air, much in the fashion of some of the bigger American fly-catchers (Tyrannidae).

Because of their very plain attire, puffbirds of the genus *Monasa* are called 'nunbirds'. The Black-fronted Nunbird *M. nigrifrons* of the Amazon valley is about 7 inches long. In both sexes, the upper plumage, wings, and tail are dull black and the ventral surface is dark grey. The bill, which tapers from a broad base to a sharp point, is bright orange —whence the name 'pico de lacre' ('sealing-wax bill') sometimes applied to birds of this genus. More gregarious than other puffbirds, nunbirds travel in small flocks.

The Grey-cheeked Nunlet *Nonnula frontalis* repre-sents a genus of small puffbirds, about $5\frac{1}{2}$ inches in length. Both sexes are plain brown above and ochraceous or tawny below. This species inhabits the lowlands of eastern Panama and Colombia and little is known of its habits.

Puffbirds are habitually silent, and the notes which they sparingly utter are low and weak. The loudest utterance of the White-whiskered Softwing is a high, thin whistle or 'peep'. The Swallow-wing has a weak, appealing whistle ; and the Black-fronted Nunbird utters soft, musical murmurs. As they call, puffbirds often twitch their tails from side to side.

The breeding habits of puffbirds are poorly known, but two types of nests have been discovered : cavities that they carve in the hard, black arboreal nests of termites, and burrows in the ground. In the Black-breasted Puffbird *Notharchus pectoralis* the male and female take turns at digging into a termitary. In the side of the large roughly globular structure they make with their bills a narrow horizontal tunnel, which at its inner end expands into a neatly rounded chamber on the hard floor of which the eggs rest, no soft lining being provided for them.

Burrows of the White-whiskered Softwing have been found in gently, or at times steeply, sloping ground in the forest. From a round opening in the leaf-strewn ground, the tunnel descends with a slight inclination for about 20 inches. At the lower end it widens into a chamber that is lined on the bottom and sides with brown dead leaves. Around the opening of the burrow, which is flush with the ground, the birds arrange twigs, petioles, and the like, to form a low collar through which they enter and leave and which makes the aperture less conspicuous. This feature is far more strongly developed in the Black Nunbird *Monasa nigra* of Venezuela, which above the entrance to its descending burrow in level ground raises a large pile of coarse dead sticks ; the birds reach their burrow by means of a rounded tunnel that runs along the surface of the ground beneath the heap of sticks. The Swallow-wing, however, places no sticks or other material around the entrance to its burrow, which may be in a bank or in level ground. Like the tunnels of other puffbirds, those of the Swallow-wing are inclined downwards and straight ; but they are longer than those of other species—up to 80 inches in length. The eggs rest on a slight lining of dry grass.

Puffbirds lay 2–3 white, glossy eggs that resemble the eggs of woodpeckers (Picidae). These are incubated by both parents, at least in the Black-breasted Puffbird and the White-whiskered Softwing. The latter incubates according to a simple but unusual schedule; the male sits continuously from the early afternoon to the following dawn; the female takes one long session of five hours or more in the forenoon; and the eggs are unattended for half an hour or more between these sessions. Black-breasted Puffbirds take shorter sessions, entering and leaving the nest a number of times in a day. The incubation period is unknown.

Newly hatched puffbirds are blind and perfectly naked, without natal down. In the White-whiskered Softwing, the only species for which details of parental care are known, the male parent does all the brooding and the duller female nearly all the feeding, an arrangement that may have some slight protective value. When only a day or two old, the blind nestlings move up the tunnel to take food from their mother at the burrow's mouth. After the father ceases to brood by night, the nestlings—now with open eyes and becoming feathered—at nightfall somehow raise up the fragmented leaves from the bottom of the chamber to form a screen between themselves and the entrance tunnel. They leave the burrow at the age of 20–21 days, when they are well feathered and have 'whiskers' like their parents.   A.F.S.

Haverschmidt, F. 1950. Notes on the Swallow-wing, *Chelidoptera tenebrosa*, in Surinam. Condor 52: 74–77.
Peters, J. L. 1948. Check-List of Birds of the World vol. 6. Cambridge, Mass.
Sclater, P. L. 1882. A Monograph of the Jacamars and Puff-birds, or Families Galbulidae and Bucconidae. London.
Skutch, A. F. 1948. Life history notes on puff-birds. Wilson Bull. 60: 81–97.
Skutch, A. F. 1958. Life history of the White-whiskered Softwing *Malacoptila panamensis*. Ibis 100: 209–231.

PUFFIN: substantive name of *Fratercula* spp., *Cerorhinca*, and *Lunda* (see AUK); used without qualifica-tion, in Britain, for the sole Atlantic species, *F. arctica*. See Plate 29 (colour).

PUFFINOSIS: name given to a disease of the Manx Shearwater *Puffinus puffinus*, probably allied to psittacosis and sometimes causing heavy mortality among the young birds (see PSITTACOSIS).

PUFFLEG: substantive name of *Eriocnemis* spp. (for family see HUMMINGBIRD).

PULLET: an immature female domestic fowl (which may lay infertile eggs).

PULLUS: see under YOUNG BIRD

PULMONARY ARCH: see VASCULAR SYSTEM

PUPIL: the opening in the iris of the eye (see VISION).

PURPLETAIL: *Metallura williami* (for family see HUMMINGBIRD).

PYCNONOTIDAE: a family of the Passeriformes, suborder Oscines (see BULBUL).

PYGOPODES: formerly used as the name of an order which embraced the present Gaviiformes and Podicipitiformes (or Podicipediformes) and originally also the Alcae.

PYGOSTYLE: the fused caudal portion of the vertebral column (see SKELETON).

PYLORIC ORIFICE: the exit of the gizzard into the duodenum (see ALIMENTARY SYSTEM).

PYRRHULOXIA: generic name used as common name of *P. sinuata* (see CARDINAL-GROSBEAK).

PYRRHULOXIINAE: see EMBERIZIDAE; and CARDINAL-GROSBEAK

Q

QUADRATE: a paired bone of the skull (see SKELETON).

QUADRATOJUGAL: a paired bone of the skull (see SKELETON).

QUAIL: substantive name of species in two distinct groups of Phasianidae, the American quails of the subfamily Odontophorinae and the Old World quails *Coturnix* spp. etc. (the so-called 'bush-quails' of India are in fact dwarf partridges)—see PHEASANT. The arrival of migratory parties, still a familiar event in Mediterranean countries, is described in the Book of Numbers, 11, 31: 'And there went forth a wind from the Lord, and brought quails from the sea, and let them fall by the camp, as it were a day's journey on this side, and as it were a day's journey on the other side, round about the camp, and as it were two cubits high upon the face of the earth.'

QUAIL, BUSTARD- or BUTTON-: see BUTTONQUAIL

QUAIL-DOVE: substantive name of *Geotrygon* spp. (see PIGEON).

QUAIL-FINCH: *Ortygospiza atricollis* (see WEAVER-FINCH).

QUAIL-THRUSH: alternatively 'ground-thrush', substantive name of *Cinclosoma* spp. (see RAIL-BABBLER).

QUELEA CONTROL: action to counter the depredations caused throughout much of Africa by the extraordinarily numerous Red-billed (or Black-faced or Sudan) Dioch *Quelea quelea* (see WEAVER). This small bird (less than 5 inches long and weighing just over ½ oz.) has been known from its earliest recorded history as a menace to crops of small grain. Large-scale efforts at control, coupled with research, began in Sudan 1946, and by 1953 had become necessary in other territories. In spite of immense slaughter the plague continues.

The species is completely colonial in habit and often found in concentrations of over a million birds—in flight sometimes mistaken for locusts. It usually nests in thick thorn bushes and trees in uninhabited country, a colony covering from a few acres up to 4 square miles ($13\frac{1}{2} \times 3\frac{1}{2}$ miles recorded from Sudan), with up to 400 or more nests in each bush. Breeding takes place towards the end of the rains, when the seeds of annual grasses are in the milky stage for feeding the young (although for the first few days these are fed mostly with insects). The main habitat is in areas south of the Sahara with less than 30 inches of rain annually, the range extending to South Africa and from coast to coast (3 races recognised). Ringing has proved that migration of up to 900 miles occurs, that most of Kenya's trouble comes from birds bred in Tanganyika, and that South Africa receives invasion from Bechuanaland and Southern Rhodesia.

Examples of damage to grain crops: central Tanganyika (1890)—famine caused and millet cultivation replaced by sorgum; Kenya (1952)—loss of wheat estimated at 100 000 bags, worth £250 000; Northern Transvaal (1953)—European areas alone lost sorgum valued at £500 000, native crops completely failed, many farmers abandoned sorgum cultivation; Senegal (1954)—24 acres of rice eaten in 14 days, and damage so great that many farmers abandoned millet for sorgum; Sudan—whole village crops destroyed, causing many farmers to stop growing sorgum, their basic food crop. Although cage tests show that a bird requires 8 grams of food per day, it has been calculated that a wild bird may destroy the equivalent of 2 oz. of mature wheat—just pecking at the germ when the grain is green, and nearer harvest time knocking on the ground as much as it eats; thus a million birds could destroy 60 tons a day.

Examples of other damage: in the dry season leaves may be stripped from trees and branches several inches thick broken down by weight; in

Sudan *Acacia arabica* plantations of 50 acres have been flattened by roosting birds, costing £10 per acre for reseeding and losing about 15 years' increment of timber ; in East Africa vegetable gardens have been stripped.

Possible reasons for the success of the species are its rigid colonialism, giving protection ; the high mobility of the birds, enabling them to breed successfully hundreds of miles from an original attempt ; and outstanding persistence in breeding. As regards the last, if the young are destroyed when out of the nest but still being fed, the parents will try again ; females will even lay eggs after their postnuptial moult has started ; young birds hatched in March and April in Tanganyika can breed 9 months later, and possibly 200 miles to the north in southern Kenya following normal migration. The predation by raptors, storks (Ciconiidae), crocodiles, snakes, and others has no appreciable effect. The biggest ordinary predator is probably man, catching adults and collecting nestlings for food. No natural control is known, except that many birds get knocked into the mud by their fellows when drinking at drying up water-holes.

Present-day increase may be attributed to the development of marginal land to meet the food requirements of a rising human population, and to more water-holes and dams, with over-stocking of cattle. Continuing food supply from crops maturing later than natural grasses, and continuing water from water-holes, obviate the need for migrating to areas with limited food supplies near permanent rivers and lakes, a factor that may earlier have naturally limited the numbers. Farming changes in South Africa since 1950 mean that the birds need no longer migrate north to the tropical savannas and bushveld to breed, as they were believed to do ten or twenty years ago. On overstocked land the grasses are eaten before they have seeded, which makes the birds a menace to crops earlier in the season.

The present method of control is by dusk or dawn aerial spraying with a strong contact poison at roosts and nesting sites. Destroying nests by cutting down or by burning with flame-throwers allows the adults to breed again. Roosts may also be destroyed by explosives. So far, ' the balance of nature ' seems unlikely to be upset any more than it is by the artificial destruction of locusts.

Numbers in vast flocks are difficult to estimate, but in Tanganyika in 1956 some 40 000 000 nestlings were destroyed and later over a million birds in roosts near the wheat lands ; in 1957 over 32 000 000 nestlings were destroyed and 5 400 000 adults at 16 roosts, plus a further 5 000 000 which had moved to Kenya and were destroyed at 28 roosts there. In French West Africa in 1956, despite 124 000 000 nestlings being destroyed, further roost destruction had to be done. Of 100 000 000 birds invading South Africa between January and March 1957, about 75 per cent were destroyed. These figures demonstrate the extent of the menace and the need for developing successful methods of control.

H.J. de S.D.

QUEO: *Rhodinocichla rosea* (for subfamily see TANAGER).

QUETZAL: *Pharomachrus mocino*, also called Resplendent Trogon (see TROGON).

QUILL: the calamus of a feather, or the calamus and rachis together ; more loosely used for the feather itself, especially a remex or rectrix (see FEATHER).

QUINTOCUBITALISM: or ' eutaxis ' (see PLUMAGE ; WING).

R

RACE: used synonymously with SUBSPECIES. The term 'race' is preferred by many, as indicating the geographical basis of subspecific differentiation and perhaps suggesting a more flexible concept. On the other hand, 'subspecies' is the official term in the International Code of Zoological Nomenclature (1961)—see NOMENCLATURE.

RACHIS: sometimes 'rhachis', the distal portion of the shaft of a feather, bearing the vane (see FEATHER).

RACING PIGEON: see HOMING PIGEON

RACKET; RACQUET: a terminal broadening of the vane of a feather, characteristic of (especially) certain of the rectrices in some species; the subterminal portion of the rachis of such a feather may be devoid of barbs or carry a relatively narrow vane.

RACKETTAIL: substantive name of *Discosura longicauda* and *Ocreatus underwoodii* (see HUMMING-BIRD); and of *Tanysiptera* spp. (see KINGFISHER).

RADAR: of interest to ornithologists since radar echoes were first identified as coming from birds in the spring of 1940, and commonly in the following year when 10 cm. equipment was introduced in Britain. At this stage and throughout the Second World War only large birds were detected by radar and no information of ornithological value resulted. After the war, with an increase in the power of the sets, bird echoes (popularly known as 'angels') became at times an operational nuisance, but their identity was not recognised until Sutter, using the airport radar at Zürich (Switzerland) appreciated that all big displays were due to migratory birds, mainly passerines. With a further increase in the power of military sets, birds could be detected to more than 60 miles, and a new tool was thus provided for the study of migration (see MIGRATION).

Radar gives for the first time a measure of the volume of migration by day and night, all birds being detected except those flying extremely low or those in the immediate neighbourhood of rain-clouds. While identification of species is not possible by direct means, much can be inferred. The direction and the speed of migratory birds can also be recorded, and, with a different type of equipment, so can their height.

The chief advances in the study of migration made up to the end of 1959 with the help of radar are (1) a survey of the volume and directions of migration throughout the year in particular places; (2) a study of the variations in the volume of migration at particular seasons with respect to weather; (3) a study of the directions taken by migrants over the sea out of sight of land in relation to the direction of the wind, and also of their directions over the land; (4) a survey of the heights at which migration can take place. Since radar equipments are extremely expensive, both to make and to run, ornithologists can normally use only those already in use for other purposes, notably at airports, where they are of lower power, or at military stations, where they are of higher power but are governed by conditions of security.

D.L.

Sutter, E. 1957. Radar als Hilfsmittel der Vogel-zugforschung. Orn. Beob. 54 : 70–96.

Sutter, E. 1957. Radar-Beobachtungen über den Verlauf des nächtlichen Vogelzuges. Rev. Suisse Zool. 64 : 294–303.

Harper, W. G. 1958. Detection of bird migration by centimetric radar—a cause of radar 'angels'. Proc. Roy. Soc. B. 149 : 484–502.

Tedd, J. G. & Lack, D. 1958. The detection of bird migration by high-power radar. Proc. Roy. Soc. B. 149 : 503–510.

Eastwood, E., Isted, G. A. & Rider, G. C. 1960. Radar 'ring angels' and the roosting movements of starlings. Nature 186 : 112–114.

Lack, D. 1959. Migration across the North Sea studied by radar. Part 1. Survey through the year. Ibis 101 : 209–234.

Lack, D. 1959. Watching migration by radar. Brit. Birds 52 : 258–267.

Lack, D. 1960. Migration across the North Sea studied by radar. Part 2. The spring departure 1956–59. Ibis 102 : 26–57.

Lack, D. 1962. Migration across the southern North Sea studied by radar. Part 3. Movements in June and July. Ibis 104 : 74–85.

RADIALE: one of the proximal carpal bones (see SKELETON ; WING).

RADIATION (1): in the evolutionary sense, divergence of forms of common ancestry, with increasing dissimilarity as a result of differences in adaptation—the antithesis of convergence (see ADAPTATION ; CONVERGENCE ; EVOLUTION ; NATURAL SELECTION ; SPECIATION). See Plate 41 (colour).

RADIATION (2): in the distributional sense, geographical spread of a species or group of related species from the area in which the particular species or the ancestral species of the group (e.g. family) was originally evolved as a separate entity (see DISTRIBUTION, GEOGRAPHICAL ; RANGE EXPANSION ; SPECIATION).

RADIATION (3): in the physical sense, with only incidental application in ornithology, emission of ionising rays—to which birds or other organisms may become exposed (see PLUMAGE, ABNORMAL AND ABERRANT).

RADIUS: a bone of the forelimb (see SKELETON ; WING) ; also a barbule in the vane of a feather (see FEATHER).

RAIL: substantive name of many species of Rallidae (Gruiformes, suborder Grues) ; in the plural, general term for the family. The rails constitute a homogeneous and cosmopolitan family. They are ground dwellers, often aquatic, well adapted to live in dense vegetation. They are small to medium-sized birds with the body laterally compressed, with moderate to long legs and toes, short rounded wings, and a short and soft tail. The bill varies from long and curved to short and conical. The plumage is of loose texture and the flight feathers are moulted simultaneously. Rails walk with bobbing head and flirting tail. They are mainly water and swamp birds (see SWIMMING AND DIVING), although some forms prefer dry plains. Some of them are good flyers covering long distances during migration ; but in others, living on oceanic islands, the power of flight has been reduced, and in these cases the introduction of rats or other predators can at once endanger the existence of the species.

The diet is varied—mainly animal, but some species prefer vegetable food. The robbing of eggs and young of other birds is known. The majority of the species have secretive habits and many are nocturnal, so that our knowledge of the life of many forms is still scanty. At dusk or during the night rails make themselves conspicuous by their specific loud calls and squawks. As a rule they do not nest colonially, and in general the nests are well concealed. The number of eggs is variable, mostly 6–12 ; the ground colour varies from near white to ochreous or brownish buff, often with reddish, greyish-brown, or black specks, spots, or blotches. The eggs are incubated by both sexes. The nestlings are covered with black or dark brown down ; they mostly leave the nest soon after hatching and are cared for by both parents, sometimes also by young of an earlier brood. The sexes often differ in size, the males being larger, but rarely differ in coloration. The plumage varies from nearly black or greenish-blue (but even deep purple) to olive-brown, buffish, or chestnut, sometimes with dark streaks and with white bars or spots.

Rails are found in all continents, but are lacking in the Arctic and Antarctic regions. More than 130 species are known, of which 7 are now extinct and 5 are listed as probably extinct. The species are spread over about 45 genera, of which most are monotypic ; several of these monotypic genera are restricted to particular islands or island groups. The typical genus includes the Water Rail *Rallus aquaticus*, the only member of this genus with a Palaearctic distribution ; it is distinguished by a long red bill. It occurs from Great Britain and Iceland, discontinuously, to eastern Asia ; migrants often fall victims to striking against lighthouses and power-lines. North American representatives are the larger Clapper Rail *R. longirostris*, inhabiting salt marshes, and the somewhat smaller King Rail *R. elegans*, preferring fresh-water marshes ; in this latter habitat is also found the much smaller and warmly brown-tinged Virginia Rail *R. limicola*. Widely spread over the southern part of Africa is the Cape Rail *R. caerulescens*, very similar to the Water Rail but with uniform dark brown upper parts. In south-eastern Asia, from southern China and India to the Philippines and Celebes, the Blue-breasted Banded Rail *R. striatus* is found ; in India this species, with its rufous crown and hind neck and its dark brown upper parts barred with white, is one of the most familiar water birds. Rather similar, but smaller and with the back black-streaked olive-brown, is the Slate-breasted (or Lewin) Water Rail *R. pectoralis*, occurring in Australia, Flores, and the mountains of New Guinea. In the same area and distributed also over the lesser Sunda Islands, Celebes, and Philippines, is the beautiful Banded Rail *R. philippensis*, characterised by a rufous pectoral band and a grey eye-stripe. More restricted in distribution is the Barred Rail *R. torquatus*, inhabiting the Philippines,

Celebes, and New Guinea. The head is blackish with a broad white line under the eye. Of the 10 other species included in this genus, there are 3 in South America and one in Madagascar, while the other 6 are or were inhabitants of small islands ; of these last, one species still survives on Guam, but the others, known from Tahiti, Wake Island, the Auckland Islands, and the Chatham Islands (2) are believed to be extinct.

Of the 2 known species of island woodrails *Tricholimnas* spp., the one formerly occurring on New Caledonia is extinct, but a small population of the other is still found on Lord Howe Island ; these forms are more forest than swamp birds. Another peculiar form is the still common Inaccessible Island Rail *Atlantisia rogersi*, a very small, flightless, dark rail with degenerate hairlike plumage ; it lives in the tussock grass which covers the island, and the nest usually contains 2–3 eggs. Representatives of the banded crakes *Rallina* spp. are distributed from India to northern Australia. All have warm rufous heads and breasts, the abdomen more or less clearly banded black and white ; they are shy and retiring birds, living in marshes or along streams in dense forest. In New Guinea, in the mountain forests covered with dense undergrowth, live the 4 species of the related genus *Rallicula*, in which the sexes differ in plumage ; the males have the upper parts plainly coloured, the females have these parts darker with pale spots or stripes.

Of the woodrails *Aramides* spp. of Middle and South America 8 species are known. They are large rails with stout bills, generally olive-brown upper parts, grey breast, and black hind parts ; when flushed they take wing reluctantly. The wekas *Gallirallus* spp. are restricted to New Zealand and are now usually considered as belonging to 2 species. They occur from sea level to well up in the mountains in different habitats. They are brownish in colour and the wings are rudimentary. Not unlike in general appearance, but with a more conical bill and red legs, is the Nkulengu Rail *Himantornis haematopus*, living in the forests of West and central Africa. Here also occurs the Grey-throated Rail *Canirallus oculeus*, with chestnut neck and breast, olive upper parts and white spots on the almost black wing feathers.

The Corncrake (or Landrail) *Crex crex* is distributed over most of Europe and well into central Asia ; its favourite habitat is grassland. In winter it migrates into Africa.

One of the larger genera is *Porzana*, with a world-wide distribution and comprising more than a dozen species. Of these the Spotted Crake *P. porzana*, the Little Crake *P. parva*, and Baillon's Crake

P. pusilla, are European birds which also range over part of middle Asia. Baillon's Crake has a peculiar discontinuous distribution, being also known from the southern part of Africa and from Australia and New Zealand. A widespread North American species is the Sora (or Sora Rail) *P. carolina*, in winter reaching northern South America and accidentally occurring in Great Britain. Ranging from the Philippines to Australia, New Zealand, and many Pacific islands is the Spotless Crake *P. tabuensis*, a dark leaden-grey species with dark brown upper parts. Other species occur in South and Central America (3), in eastern and south-eastern Asia (3), in Australia (1), and in Madagascar (1)—the last by some authors included in the genus *Amaurornis*. In some species there is a slight difference in plumage between the sexes.

In Africa the Black Rail *Limnocorax flavirostra*, with a yellow bill, is one of the commonest species. Restricted to America are the three species of *Laterallus* ; of these the only one known in North America is the American Black Rail *L. jamaicensis*, a small bird with white spots and streaks on the upper parts, frequenting grassy inland swamps and brackish coastal marshes. Diminutive in size are the pigmy rails *Sarothrura* spp. ; the 9 species are exclusively African in distribution, show a well-marked sexual dimorphism, and are exceedingly secretive in habits. The Grey-bellied Crake *Poliolimnas cinereus* ranges widely from the Malay Peninsula eastward to the Fiji and Samoa Islands. Four species of *Amaurornis* are distributed from India to the Solomon Islands ; except for the White-breasted Waterhen *A. phoenicurus*, they are dull grey and olive-brown.

The large Watercock *Gallicrex cinerea* has a reddish frontal shield projecting backwards in a horn ; it is found over a wide area from southern to eastern Asia, and migrants reach the Greater Sunda Islands. The Moorhen (or Waterhen or, in America, Common Gallinule) *Gallinula chloropus* is distributed over much of the world, being found in all continents except Australia and having colonised many oceanic islands. In Australia, New Guinea, and eastern Indonesia it is replaced by the nearly related Dusky Moorhen *G. tenebrosa*. In Africa occurs the small Lesser Moorhen *G. angulata*. The moorhen of Tristan da Cunha, *Gallinula* (' *Porphyriornis* ') *nesiotis nesiotis*, was hardly able to fly and is now extinct ; but another subspecies, *G. n. comeri*, is still not uncommon on Gough Island.

A large species is the Purple Gallinule or Swamp-hen *Porphyrio porphyrio*, with a discontinuous distribution from southern Europe through southern Asia to Australia, New Zealand, and islands in the

Pacific, and also occurring in Africa and Madagascar. It is azure or greenish-blue below, brown or almost black above, and has a stout and conical bill ; all populations are now generally considered as belonging to the one species. Nearly related is the flightless Takahe *Notornis mantelli* from New Zealand, thought to have become extinct but rediscovered in recent years in some inaccessible valleys in the Murchison Mountains on South Island. The American Purple Gallinule *Porphyrula martinica* is much smaller and more slender and has the legs bright yellow (not red as in *Porphyrio porphyrio*) ; it ranges from the southern United States to South America. Other species of this genus live in Africa (1) and South America (1). See Plate 17 (colour).

The Coot *Fulica atra* has lobed toes and a white frontal shield and is found over the greater part of Europe, Asia, and Australia, as is the American representative *F. americana* over the greater part of the Americas. Of the remaining 8 species, one is African and all others are Central and South American in distribution. Of these the Giant Coot *F. gigantea* and the Horned Coot *F. cornuta* breed in the high mountain lakes of the Andes ; the latter species has the remarkable habit of using stones for building its nest. The coots are commonly separated from the rest of the Rallidae in a subfamily Fulicinae.

† G.C.A.J.

Baldwin, P. H. 1947. The life history of the Laysan Rail. Condor 49 : 14–21.
Kornowski, G. 1957. Beiträge zur Ethologie des Blässhuhns (*Fulica atra* L.). J. Orn. 98 : 318–355.
Steinbacher, G. 1939. Zur Brutbiologie des grünfüssigen Teichhuhns (*Gallinula chloropus* L.). J. Orn. 87 : 115–135.
Walkinshaw, L. H. 1940. Summer life of the Sora Rail. Auk 57 : 153–168.
Williams, G. R. 1960. The Takahe (*Notornis mantelli* Owen 1848) : a general survey. Trans. Roy. Soc. N.Z. 88 : 235–238 (and colour plate).

RAIL-BABBLER : substantive name of some species of the subfamily Cinclosomatinae of the Muscicapidae (Passeriformes, suborder Oscines) ; in the plural, general term for the subfamily. The latter is provisionally recognised as a grouping for a small number of genera and species of insectivorous birds, found in the Australo-Papuan area, of which the affinities are rather puzzling ; only one of them extends to Malaysia. They do not seem to be closely related to one another, and they may even belong to entirely different groups. They have often been placed among the Timaliinae (see BABBLER), but the writer considers that they are too different and that they deserve subfamilial status, at least until they are better known. They usually have a small head, a thin neck, a light bill, long

tarsi, a broad tail, long and thick feathering on the back and rump. They live on or close to the ground, in forest or bush.

The scrub-robins *Drymodes* spp. are probably closer to the Turdinae (see THRUSH). The songlarks *Cincloramphus* spp. are more puzzling, and have alternatively been referred to the Malurinae (see WREN (2)) ; the females look very much like pipits *Anthus* spp., while the males, considerably larger, are tinged with grey and sooty black.

The two Australian whipbirds *Psophodes* spp. and the Papuan *Androphobus*, dark olive-green above, recall timaliine birds by their shape and ways, as also does, up to a point, the crested, brown Wedge-bill *Sphenostoma cristatum*. The 4 Australian quail-thrushes or ground-thrushes *Cinclosoma* spp. resemble certain *Turdus* spp. in shape, in habits, and in the pattern of plumage of adults and young, the latter being spotted. However, they also suggest the typical rail-babblers *Eupetes* spp., one of which—the Rail-Babbler *E. macrocerus*—lives in Malaysia ; but the young of these birds are not spotted, while the adults are brightly coloured in blue, chestnut, and reddish. They have curiously long, thin necks.

There are also 2 aberrant Papuan genera, usually placed in the present group—the logrunners *Orthonyx* spp., with relatively huge legs and feet, and with the plumage brown, red, black, and white ; and the peculiar *Melampitta* spp., black and short-tailed. Each of these 2 genera includes one large and one small species, otherwise similar. Finally, the Papuan species *Ifrita kowaldi* looks like any of the bush babblers, but the male has a bright blue crown, an unknown feature among the timaliine birds, so that it is better left provisionally with the rail-babblers.

(The subfamily has also been named Orthony-chinae.)   J.D.

RAIL, BENSCH'S : misnomer for the Monias *Monias benschi* (see MESITE).

RAIN-BIRD : name variously applied in different parts of the world (usually because the birds, when particularly noisy, are supposed to predict rain), e.g. to the Green Woodpecker *Picus viridis* in Britain (see WOODPECKER), the Grey Currawong *Strepera versicolor* in Australia (see MAGPIE (2)), the White-browed Coucal *Centropus superciliosus* in parts of Africa and other members of the Cuculidae in the New World and Australia (see CUCKOO), and Peale's Petrel *Pterodroma inexpectata* in New Zealand (see PETREL) ; also ' rain-goose ' to the Red-throated Diver *Gavia stellata* in Orkney (see DIVER), and ' rain-quail ' (because abundant in some parts in the rainy season) to *Coturnix coromandelica* in India (see under PHEASANT).

RAINBOW: *Coeligena iris* (see HUMMINGBIRD).

RAINBOW-BIRD: Australian name, alternatively Rainbow Bee-eater, of *Merops ornatus* (see BEE-EATER).

RAIN-FOREST: a tropical environment characteristic of areas where there is both high temperature and heavy rainfall, the latter spread throughout the year ; seasonal heavy rains (monsoon) produce a different result. In most parts of the world the true rain-forest has little undergrowth and consists mainly of trees rising unbranched for 100–150 feet and then spreading to form part of a ' canopy ' that is continuous for great distances, broken only—except temporarily for accidental reasons—by vertical rock faces and the courses of large streams. At ground level there is the avifauna of the forest floor, while the canopy has its own population of fruit-eating and insect-eating birds ; the intermediate zone provides little in the way of avian habitat.

RALLI; RALLIDAE: see under GRUIFORMES ; and RAIL

RALLOIDEA: see under GRUIFORMES

RAMI, MANDIBULAR: (plural of ' ramus '), the two halves of the lower mandible, separated by soft tissue near the base but uniting distally in the gonys (see BILL).

RAMPHASTIDAE: see under PICIFORMES ; and TOUCAN

RAMPHASTOIDEA: see under PICIFORMES

RAMUS: a barb of a feather (see FEATHER) ; also in the sense shown under RAMI, MANDIBULAR.

RANGE EXPANSION: a process tending to enlarge, in particular, the breeding area of a species (see DISTRIBUTION, GEOGRAPHICAL) ; it may be gradual or abrupt. The common occurrence of such expansion (geographical radiation) in the past can be inferred from the present wide ranges of many species, on the presumption that each of these has spread from a more limited area in which speciation took place. This point has all the more validity where a species has begun to fragment into geographical races, showing that some factor or factors have interrupted the even gene flow that kept the original population homogeneous. There are instances, too, where a species or subspecific form is obviously outside the usual geographical context of the group to which it belongs. Apart from all such theoretical considerations, range expansion has visibly occurred, in various species and to a substantial extent, within the period of detailed ornithological recording.

The present distribution of many species is indeed very wide—a few species are even cosmopolitan or nearly so. Very often, too, they show subspecific differentiation (see SUBSPECIES). Of species that seem to be out of context, so to speak, a few examples may be mentioned. The larks (Alaudidae) are essentially an Old World family, but the Shore (or Horned) Lark *Eremophila alpestris* has, uniquely, a circumpolar distribution (extending southwards into the tropics in both hemispheres). The converse is true of the New World family of wrens (Troglodytidae), with its single Holarctic species, the Wren (or Winter Wren) *Troglodytes troglodytes*. Again, the Arctic Warbler *Phylloscopus borealis* is mainly a Palaearctic species of an essentially Old World group, but it is represented by the race *P.b. kennicotti* in Alaska. And, conversely, two species of the New World wood warblers (Parulidae) have gained a footing in eastern Siberia.

As regards the causative factors of gradual range expansion, one may make two assumptions. First, range expansion implies a population pressure in the area already inhabited ; theoretically, this could be due either to increase in absolute numbers or to a deterioration in environmental conditions. Secondly, it implies that the new area invaded provides suitable conditions ; and that if this situation did not previously obtain, the conditions must have in some way improved, in respect of the requirements of the species concerned.

This kind of gradual spread has been exemplified in northern Europe by a northward shift, during the last few decades, in the northern breeding limit of various species. This general phenomenon is clearly related to climatic amelioration during the same period. It has been accompanied by the establishment in Iceland of several species not formerly breeding there, and also the establishment of the Fieldfare *Turdus pilaris* in Greenland following an invasion in 1937.

While expansion involving long sea-crossings must necessarily be abrupt, although invasions can be multiple, the spread of a species over a continental area may, on occasion, also be quite rapid. A most remarkable instance, difficult to explain, is that of the recent spread of the Collared Dove *Streptopelia decaocto* from southeastern Europe northwestwards as far as the British Isles. This contrasts, among specific phenomena, with the slow northward spread of the Black Redstart *Phoenicurus ochruros* over Germany and neighbouring countries during 150 years or more, including a small-scale colonisation of southern England from 1923 onwards.

Certain irregular irruptions, especially those occurring in spring, may lead to breeding in new areas, although not usually to permanent establishment therein (see IRRUPTION). On the other hand, some overseas invasions—possibly accidental in origin— may result in successful colonisation simply because suitable conditions were already present in the new area, inaccessible until the ocean barrier was passed. A case in point is that of the Cattle Egret *Ardeola ibis*, widespread in Africa and southern Asia, and found also in southern Europe. It reached South America early in the present century, and from about 1930 it has extended its range in the New World explosively, both to the north and to the south. About the same time it started to increase markedly in Australia, although possibly only from stock that had been artificially introduced.

One particularly clear-cut example of an abrupt expansion may be mentioned. The Australian race of the Masked Lapwing *Vanellus miles novaehollandiae* was known in New Zealand only as a straggler until 1932. In that year stragglers remained to breed ; and twenty years later the New Zealand population was estimated at 200 birds.

Range expansion of an artificially introduced species may be rapid for the same reason as some- times operates after an accidental traverse of an ocean barrier—suitable conditions may already exist in an area formerly inaccessible, and the newcomer may happen to be more viable therein than the potential competitors already established (see NATURALISED BIRDS). Secondary range expansion may occur not only within but also from the area of naturalisation. Thus the Starling *Sturnus vulgaris* of Europe, widely naturalised in America, Australia, New Zealand, and elsewhere, has by some means been able to colonise places as remote as Macquarie Island in the Southern Ocean.

The circumstances of range expansion among sea birds are obviously somewhat different, in that their often wide non-breeding ranges may include many potential new breeding localities, capable of being utilised if population pressure demands. This has been remarkably exemplified by the Fulmar *Fulmarus glacialis* in the British Isles, where until 1878 it bred only on St Kilda, although there in enormous numbers. Since then it has spread in a spectacular manner to many other islands, and also to numerous suitable localities on the mainland coasts, some of the new colonies being themselves of great size.

A.L.T.

Fisher, J. 1952. The Fulmar. London.
Fisher, J. 1953. The Collared Turtle Dove in Europe. Brit. Birds 46 : 153–181.
Gudmundsson, F. 1951. The effects of recent climatic changes on the bird life of Iceland. Proc. X Internat. Orn. Congr., Uppsala 1950 : 502–514.

Stresemann, E. & Nowak, E. 1958. Die Ausbreitung der Türkentaube in Asien und Europa. J. Orn. 99 : 243–296.

RANK : see STATISTICAL SIGNIFICANCE

RAPHIDAE : see under COLUMBIFORMES ; and DODO

RAPTOR : term used in much the same senses as BIRD-OF-PREY.

RASSENKREIS : term introduced by Rensch in 1929 for what would today be regarded as a polytypic species (or sometimes a clearly separable group of subspecies within such a species), restricting the term 'species' to those that are monotypic (see SPECIES ; SUBSPECIES). At a higher taxonomic level he used the term 'Artenkreis' (see SUPERSPECIES).

RATIO-CLINE : a geographically continuous change in the ratio in which different morphs are present within a species that is dimorphic or poly- morphic in appearance or behaviour (see POLY- MORPHISM).

RATITAE : see below

RATITE : having a flat, raft-like sternum, i.e. without a keel ; the converse of 'carinate' (see SKELETON). The structure is especially characteristic of the orders of flightless running birds, mainly of large size, formerly grouped together as the 'Ratitae' and still loosely referred to collectively as the 'ratites' although close relationship is now doubted (see RATITES, PHYLOGENY OF THE). A more or less ratite condition of the sternum is also found in some flightless species in other orders (see FLIGHTLESSNESS).

The living or geologically recent ratites comprise the following orders and families, the latter dealt with separately as shown.

Struthioniformes :
   Struthionidae (Africa, and formerly parts of Asia ; 1 species)—see OSTRICH
Rheiformes :
   Rheidae (South America ; 2 species)—see RHEA
Casuariiformes :
   Casuariidae (New Guinea and Australia ; 3 species)—see CASSOWARY
   Dromaiidae (Australia ; 1 extant species)—see EMU
Dinornithiformes :
   Dinornithidae and Anomalopterygidae (New Zealand ; all extinct)—see MOA
Apterygiformes :
   Apterygidae (New Zealand ; 3 species)—see KIWI
Aepyornithiformes :
   Aepyornithidae (Madagascar ; all extinct)—see ELEPHANT-BIRD.

In addition, a family based on the fossil genus *Eleutherornis* is referred to the Struthioniformes, and one based on *Dromornis* to the Casuariiformes (see FOSSIL BIRDS). Further, the Tinamiformes (Tinamidae) of the Neotropical Region, although flying and carinate, are considered to be closely related to the ' ratites ' (see TINAMOU).

RATITES, PHYLOGENY OF THE: The evolutionary origin and relationship of the orders of ' ratite ' birds (see above) ; a subject of considerable controversy. The ' ratites ' have been defined as flightless birds that lack a keel on the breast-bone, feathers with stiff vanes, and oil glands ; and that have reduced wings and a bony palate of the type called dromaeognathous (Huxley) or palaeognathine (Pycraft). Owen recognised that they had lost the power of flight, and the view that they are degenerate descendants from flying birds is accepted by all leading ornithologists. Huxley's definition of the dromaeognathous type of palate, and his opinion that it was the most primitive type of palate found in birds, have nevertheless led some persons to the view that the ratites were a primitive group descended from ancestors that had never evolved the power of flight, and therefore that ratites were more primitive than flying birds (carinates).

Descent from Flying Ancestors. There are many ways in which it can be shown that the latter view is untenable, the first being a comparison between the structure of *Archaeopteryx* and carinates (see ARCHAEOPTERYX). *Archaeopteryx* had feathers of a structure exactly identical with that in living carinates ; furthermore, these feathers were arranged on the wing as in carinates, differentiated into remiges and contour feathers, the remiges further differentiated into primaries borne on the wrist and hand and secondaries borne on the forearm. The wing formed an air-resistant surface. The similarity in these respects between *Archaeopteryx* and carinates is so perfect that without any doubt *Archaeopteryx* was on the line of ancestry of carinates.

But *Archaeopteryx* was incapable of active flight, an assertion that follows inescapably from the following anatomical facts. First, there was no keel (carina) on the breast-bone (sternum) such as that to which the powerful pectoral muscles of carinates are attached, and the structure of the humerus shows that the pectoral muscles in *Archaeopteryx* were indeed feebly developed. Secondly, the carpal and metacarpal bones in the wrist and hand were mostly separate from each other, and not fused to form the strong carpometacarpus that serves as a firm base for the attachment of the primary remiges in carinates. Thirdly, the tail in

Archaeopteryx was as long as the rest of the body and contained a skeleton of 20 elongated vertebrae extending to its tip, each bearing a pair of rectrices and thus providing an organ capable of imparting aerodynamic stability in gliding but utterly unsuitable for the rapid movements of pitching, yawing, and banking that active flight involves. Lastly, the cerebellum in the brain of *Archaeopteryx* was simple in structure and small, as in terrestrial reptiles such as a lizard ; it was thus in no condition to perform the rapid adjustments and co-ordinations of muscular action required in flying birds, moving in three dimensions of space, in response to the nervous impulses received from the organs of dynamic and static balance in the semicircular canals of the ears, which are stimulated by alterations in speed and direction of motion in flight. It is therefore quite certain that *Archaeopteryx* was incapable of active flight, and that it glided from higher to lower branches of trees and to the ground, from which it climbed up the trunks of trees again by means of the claws at the ends of the digits of its wings. At the same time, it is equally clear that the descendants of *Archaeopteryx* had comparatively little evolutionary change to undergo before they became true flying birds, because *Archaeopteryx* already possessed the wing.

All the important differences in structure between *Archaeopteryx* and carinates are adaptations to active flight. The carina on the sternum serves for the attachment of enlarged and powerful pectoral muscles ; the carpal and metacarpal bones are fused to form the carpometacarpus ; the first digit of the hand bears a few feathers forming the ' bastard wing ', and the space between this and the true wing forms a slot serving for the passage of air and maintenance of a slip-stream that prevents stalling in flight. The skeleton of the tail is shortened into the pygostyle bone over which the rectrices are arranged transversely, enabling the bird to brake and perform aerobatic flight movements. Finally, the cerebellum is enormously developed.

Turning to ratites, if these birds were really primitive and had evolved from ancestral forms that were terrestrial and had neither glided nor flown, it would be necessary to conclude that they were nearer to the original reptilian ancestors than was *Archaeopteryx*, with the further consequences that *Archaeopteryx* could not have been on the direct line of ancestry of modern birds at all, and that its feathers and their arrangement on the wing must have been evolved independently of the same structures in carinates. In view of the similarities in these respects between *Archaeopteryx* and carinates, such a view is untenable ; and it is also unnecessary, for it is directly contradicted by the fact that ratites themselves show three of the essential structural features that distinguish carinates from *Archaeopteryx* and are adaptations to flight. Ratites have the carpometacarpus resembling the same structure in carinates even in small details, such as the points of fusion of the various elements composing it, the curvatures of the 2nd and 3rd metacarpal bones, and the expansion of the basal joint of the 3rd wing digit. In the rheas (Rheidae) there are traces of the differentiation between primary and secondary remiges, and the feathers on the 1st digit form a bastard wing. In the tail, which is short, the number of vertebrae is reduced ; and in the Ostrich *Struthio camelus* there is a pygostyle. In the brain, the cerebellum is large and similar to that of carinates in its structure (Starck). These features cannot have been evolved independently in ratites and carinates ; and as they are adaptations to flight, their presence in ratites is conclusive proof that ratites were evolved from carinates.

Neotenous Characters. *Feathers.* There remain to be considered the features that led to the view that ratites were primitive. In ratites the barbules on the barbs of the feathers are degenerate, with the result that the barbs are not held together to form a stiff air-resistant vane. Instead, the feathers are plumose as in ' ostrich feathers ' and the nestling down that ratites preserve throughout life. In carinates the down feathers are the fluffed-out tips of the rudiments of adult feathers, and these down feathers are particularly well developed in those birds that are nidifugous and have a chick stage. Before the young carinates reach the flying stage, the down feathers are largely discarded and adult feathers, with stiff air-resistant vanes, take their place. The ratites are permanent chicks, as it were, and as they have lost the power of flight, because they have become too large and heavy and their wings are too small, they do not develop air-resistant feathers. This retention in the adult of an ancestral infantile character is not primitive at all, but an example of neoteny, a widespread phenomenon in the Animal Kingdom, being nothing more than an arrest of differentiation during development, leading to a type of specialisation often associated with giant size.

Skull Sutures. Next, the sutures between the bones of the skull are persistent in adult ratites. In carinates the bones of the skull are of course separate in the embryo, but they soon become fused with one another during development and give rise to a strong and solid skull, capable of protecting the soft tissues of the brain from the mechanical stresses consequent on active flight (see SKELETON). Having

lost the power of flight, and also having evolved to large size, ratites have retained this ancestral juvenile character of persistent sutures, providing another example of neoteny.

Palate. Lastly, there is the structure of the bony palate of the skull. The essential feature of the dromaeognathus or palaeognathine palate of ratites is that the pterygoid bones extend forwards and come into firm contact with the prevomers, while the palatine bones lie farther to the side. In the palates of adult carinates the pterygoid bones do not make contact with the prevomers but are separated from them by the palatine bones, with which the pterygoids articulate by a movable joint. By means of this joint, when the quadrate bone moves forward as the mouth opens and the lower jaw drops, the pterygoid is also moved forward and presses the palatine forward ; this raises the whole of the fore part of the skull, including of course the upper jaw, with the result that the gape of the mouth is still further enlarged. This ability to raise the upper jaw on a sort of hinge in the skull, a condition known as ' kinetic ', is primitive ; it was well developed in the reptiles and probably present in *Archaeopteryx*. By contrast, the palate of the ratites is relatively immovable, so that they have lost the power of raising the upper jaw ; this is a secondary and degenerate character, and it is now known how and why the loss occurred.

In early stages of development, carinate birds have a palate like that of ratites, but at a later stage the foremost tip of the pterygoid bone becomes detached from the hinder part and attached to the palatine. At the place where the detachment of the foremost portion of the pterygoid occurred, the joint is formed, and this joint is therefore strictly inside the original pterygoid bone ; it is only because the foremost part of the latter becomes attached to the palatine that the adult skull gives the appearance that the joint lies between the pterygoid and palatine bones.

The important point to notice is that carinates, during their development, pass through a stage equivalent to that at which the development of ratites is arrested. This discovery would, in the past, probably have been hailed as a case of recapitulation ; but as this would imply that ratites were primitive, and that carinates with all their adaptations to flight in working order were evolved from ratites (in which these adaptations are present but degenerate because the birds have without any doubt lost the power of flight), this case provides a striking example of the fallaciousness of the theory of recapitulation. It is therefore necessary to reverse the views previously held as to what were the primitive conditions of the palate in birds, and to conclude that the dromaeognathous or palaeognathine type is secondary and that the other types of so-called neognathous palates found in carinates, and probably in *Archaeopteryx*, are primitive. As for the ratites, there is no great difficulty in regarding their palates as secondary and neotenous, because they also show neoteny in their feathers and their skull-bone sutures. The reason for the neoteny and arrested development of the palate in ratites is probably that these birds have evolved to large sizes and that their mouths open sufficiently wide without the necessity for an additional hinge to raise the upper jaw.

Further Evidence. There is independent and confirmatory evidence of the secondary nature of the ratites' type of palate, and of the fact that they have lost the power of flight. This rests on the simple fact that the dromaeognathous type of palate is found not only in ratites but also in the tinamous (Tinamidae), and these are carinates, and flying birds. If the ratites were descended from ancestors that never flew and the dromaeognathous palate was primitive, it would be necessary to conclude that tinamous had evolved with ratites, and had developed their power of flight and all the structures concerned with it (carina, air-resistant feathers, etc.), in which they so closely resemble carinates, separately from and independently from carinates. Such a view would be utterly unacceptable. On the contrary, the condition in tinamous shows the manner in which the palate of ratites was evolved from that of carinates when the necessity for raising the upper jaw no longer existed.

A small point of geographical distribution leads to the same conclusion regarding the loss of the power of flight by ratites. As *Archaeopteryx* lived in Europe in Jurassic times, and New Zealand has had no land connection with any other part of the world since that period, the ancestors of moas (Dinornithiformes) and kiwis (Apterygiformes), can have reached New Zealand only by having flown there. A similar argument can probably be applied to the Aepyornithiformes of Madagascar.

A comparison between the different ratites shows that they can be regarded only as a series of degenerate forms ; for while the wings of Ostrich, rheas, Emu *Dromaius novaehollandiae*, and cassowaries (Casuariidae), although reduced in size are still substantial and can sometimes be used as sails to run before the wind (as Darwin observed), the wing in kiwis is very small and useless, and in moas and elephant-birds (Aepyornithiformes) there is scarcely any wing at all. The series can be read in only one direction.

Embryology has revealed an important piece of evidence in the development of the Emu which, at early stages, shows an opposition between the 1st digit of the foot and the other digits, as in embryo carinates. In *Archaeopteryx*, as in all carinates, the 1st foot digit is opposed to the others, and this is an adaptation that enables the birds to grasp twigs with their feet ; it is the evidence that *Archaeopteryx* lived in trees. Ratites live on the ground and are cursorial ; their feet, which have 3 or 2 digits, show no opposition between digits, and the 1st digit is reduced or lost in the adult. The embryonic opposed 1st digit in the Emu is therefore evidence that it had ancestors that lived in trees, as H. Lutz pointed out.

On all counts, therefore, ratites can only have evolved from flying birds that, if alive today, would be classified among carinates.

Monophyletic Origin or Convergence ? There remains the problem whether ratites represent a natural group of related birds that have evolved together, or whether they are an odd assemblage of forms that have independently followed parallel lines of evolution consequent on the loss of power of flight. Comparative anatomy provides little help in this problem, because the structure of ratites is too uniform to allow lines of subdivision in the group to be recognised with any degree of probability.

While Stresemann and Mayr & Amadon are inclined to ascribe independent origins and convergent similarities to the different kinds of ratites, Bock, on the strength of detailed points of similarity in the skull, finds it difficult to believe that these could have evolved independently, particularly as the different ratites have differing food habits. Further differences in ethology between different ratites have been pointed out by Meise, including habitat, social organisation, diurnal or nocturnal habits, mating season, egg size, clutch size, and incubation period. On the other hand, similarities such as high speed of running, the habit of taking stones into the stomach, delayed sexual maturity, structure of the nest, early nidifugous habit, and self-feeding by the young without the help of the parents, taken in conjunction with the structural similarities, lead him to conclude that the ratites are a monophyletic natural group. Nevertheless, he admits that some ethological similarities such as the method of fighting with the feet, the major responsibility of the male in brooding and care of the young, and the slow growth of the young, are probably consequences of loss of power of flight ; and it is not clear why this explanation does not apply to some of the other similarities between ratites noted by him.

Of other methods of estimating relationships, blood-precipitin tests have not been applied systematically to different ratites, although it has been shown that emus are perhaps distantly related to gallinaceous birds. Studies on the structure and chemical composition of the eggshells have led Tyler & Simkiss to think that the emus and cassowaries fall into one group distinct from others, and possibly kiwis and tinamous into another group. Electrophoretic properties of egg-white proteins studied by Sibley lead to the conclusion that the Ostrich is probably related to cassowaries and emus, but that the relations of these to the rheas are uncertain. On the other hand, parasitology in the hands of Theresa Clay has shown that the Ostrich of Africa and the rheas of South America are both infested by a genus of bird-louse, *Struthiolipeurus*, that is found on no other birds.

Finally, there are some problems of the geographical distribution of ratites. All except the Ostrich occur either on old islands such as New Zealand or Madagascar, or on continents such as Australia and South America where the danger from predators to birds that cannot fly is not great. But Africa, the chief habitat of the Ostrich, is a predator-ridden area ; so the question arises whether it was there that the Ostrich became flightless. Mayr has suggested the possibility that, if the Ostrich and rheas are closely related, they may both have become flightless in South America, whence the Ostrich might have migrated in late Tertiary times through North America to the Old World, where fossil ostrich species are widespread. Perhaps it may be significant that the Ostrich consorts in troops with herds of zebras and large antelopes, the Rhea with herds of deer, and Darwin's Rhea with guanacos. If the Ostrich did originate in South America it would be expected that fossil ostriches would be found in North America, but so far they have not.

North America has, however, provided fossils of flightless birds that throw indirect light on the problem of ratites. From basal Eocene strata of Wyoming and New Mexico, about 70 million years old, have come fossils of a giant flightless bird *Diatryma*, while contemporary strata in western Europe have provided similar forms such as *Gastrornis* ; but these show more similarities with geese than with ostriches, and are tens of millions of years too old to be connected with ostriches. Miocene beds of South America have revealed fossils of another giant flightless bird, *Phororhacos*, probably related to the seriemas (Cariamidae). The recently extinct Dodo *Raphus cucullatus* of Mauritius and Solitaire *Pezophaps solitaria* of Rod-

riguez were closely related to the pigeons (Columbidae), although that view has recently been challenged—in favour of rallid affinities. *Notornis*, still living in New Zealand, is a rail (Rallidae)—for other examples see FLIGHTLESSNESS. All these are reminders that loss of flight has occurred repeatedly during the evolution of birds ; and ratites are only a few among many examples of this phenomenon.

Disregarding the evidence given above, Blotzheim has concluded from the comparative anatomy and development of the sternum and limb-girdles in Ostrich, Rhea, and Emu that there is no convincing argument for the descent of reptiles from flying birds. He returns to the view (held by Nopcsa, Lowe, Holmgren) that flight originated in cursorial ancestors, which was demolished by Tucker. There is no alternative to the arboreal pro-avis theory.

The question whether ratites are more closely related to one another than to other groups of birds is still uncertain. It depends for its solution largely on the discovery of fossil forms in regions of the world intermediate between the areas where they are or have been found ; unfortunately, the habits of life of ratites as flightless, terrestrial birds are very unfavourable for fossilisation. G. de B.

References to most of the literature earlier than 1956 will be found in the fourth publication cited below.

Blotzheim, U. Glutz von. 1958. Zur Morphologie und Ontogenese von Schultergürtel, Sternum und Becken von *Struthio*, *Rhea* und *Dromiceius*. Ein Beitrag zur Phylogenese der Ratiten. Rev. Suisse Zool. 65 : 609–772.

Bock, W. J. 1963. Relationships of the Ratites based upon their skull morphology. Proc. XIII Internat. Orn. Congr., Ithaca, N.Y., 1962 : 39-54.

Clay, T. 1957. The Mallophaga of birds. First Symposium on Host Specificity among Parasites of Vertebrates, Neuchâtel : 120-155.

de Beer, G. 1956. The evolution of Ratites. Bull. Brit. Mus. (Nat. Hist.), Zool. Ser. 4 : 57–76.

de Villiers, C. G. S. 1946. The relations of the vomer and palatoquadrate bar to the cranial rostrum in the Tinamou. Ann. Univ. Stellenbosch 24 : 21–39.

Frank, G. H. 1954. The development of the chondrocranium of the Ostrich. Ann. Univ. Stellenbosch 30 : 179–248.

Holmgren, N. 1955. Studies on the phylogeny of birds. Acta Zool. 36 : 243–328.

Lang, C. 1956. Das Cranium der Ratiten mit besonderer Berücksichtigung von *Struthio camelus*. Z. wiss. Zool. 159 : 165–224.

Mayr, E. 1957. First Symposium on Host Specificity among Parasites of Vertebrates, Neuchâtel : 156.

Mayr, E. & Amadon, D. 1951. A classification of recent birds. Amer. Mus. Novit. no. 1496 : 1–42.

Meise, W. 1963. Verhalten der straussartigen Vögel und Monophylie der Ratitae. Proc. XIII Internat. Orn. Congr., Ithaca, N.Y., 1962 : 115-125.

Sibley, C. G. 1960. The electrophoretic patterns of avian egg-white proteins as taxonomic characters. Ibis 102 : 215–284.

Starck, D. 1955. Die endokraniale Morphologie der Ratiten. Morph. Jahrb. 96 : 14–72.

Tucker, B. W. 1938. Functional evolutionary morphology : the origin of birds. *In* de Beer, G. R. (ed.). Essays on Aspects of Evolutionary Biology. Oxford.

Tyler, C. & Simkiss, K. 1959. A study of the egg shells of ratite birds. Proc. Zool. Soc. Lond. 133 : 201–242.

RAVEN: substantive name of some large species of Corvidae ; used without qualification, in Britain, for *Corvus corax* (see CROW (1)).

RAZORBILL: name—in American usage ' Razor-billed Auk '—of *Alca torda* (see AUK).

REALM: see under DISTRIBUTION, GEOGRAPHICAL

RECAPITULATION: see BEHAVIOUR, DEVELOPMENT OF

RECENT BIRDS: those forms that either exist at the present day or at least survived into geologically recent times.

RECESSIVE: see GENETICS

RECOGNITION: a term that was originally applied to human behaviour but requires a new definition when applied to animal behaviour. The prefix ' re ' implies a learning process which allows the subject to identify an object as something that it has met before, and to distinguish it from other things. It has nevertheless been shown (Hinde) that a Canary *Serinus canaria* will ' recognise ' nest material as something to build a nest with (its behaviour shows that it identifies it and distinguishes it from other objects) when it has never before seen such material. Similarly, we speak of ' sex recognition ', ' species recognition ', and so on, when responses are confined to certain classes of objects, irrespective of the way in which this specificity of the response developed—whether it is ' innate ' or has to be acquired. ' Recognition ' is therefore usually taken to mean identification and distinction of an object or a class of objects among the multitude of external things that an animal is likely to encounter. It is not an absolute achievement ; the range of objects identified and grouped together may vary from very wide (sex recognition) to very narrow (individual recognition) ; it never is so wide that it comprises all things ; it probably never is so narrow as to be just one unique thing—even the best human observer may find it difficult to distinguish between identical twins. The width of the range is adapted in such a way as to make ' errors ' in the natural situation sufficiently rare to avoid frequent miscarriages. ' Recognition ', therefore, is an expression referring to what could be called the ' degree of specific releasability ' of a response, and it has to be studied by an analysis of the stimulus situation evoking the response. This response is not (as often in human beings) a verbal one, but it has to be a recognisable movement.

In this sense, birds can be said to recognise a very great number of things. The range is usually wide in responses to food ; a Song Thrush *Turdus philomelos* recognises red berries as a class (and perhaps distinguishes between several kinds), and also snails and earthworms. The range is extremely narrow in all cases of individual recognition. There is a graded series between these two extremes.

Recognition is often achieved in a series of steps, viz. when the response is really a chain of separate reactions, each elicited by different stimuli provided by the same object. Thus the first response of a female Red-necked Phalarope *Lobipes lobatus* to a prospective mate is often misdirected ; she may approach birds of several other species (Purple Sandpiper *Calidris maritima* ; Lapland Bunting *Calcarius lapponicus* ; Ringed Plover *Charadrius hiaticula*). After this initial approach, however, the next response is shown only to Red-necked Phalaropes, while the other birds are ignored. Yet this second response is still the same to males and females and only the third step shows sex recognition, for it is then that females are chased and males are accepted. This seems to be a very general method of achieving specificity of response in spite of the relatively unspecific nature of each stimulus situation (see SIGN STIMULUS).

In many examples recognition is not dependent on previous conditioning ; the female Canary's recognition of nest material has already been mentioned ; similarly, a young Herring Gull *Larus argentatus* responds ' innately ' to the adults' alarm calls. But song-birds refusing to eat wasps or their mimics have had to learn to recognise them as obnoxious, and a goose *Anser* sp. learns to recognise its fellow geese, first as representatives of a species, and later as individuals (see LEARNING ; BEHAVIOUR, DEVELOPMENT OF). In symbiotic relationships in the widest sense (including intra-specific as well as inter-specific relationships), recognition has been enhanced by specialisations both on the sensory side (responsiveness to special stimuli) and on the effector side (by the development of unambiguous releasers (see RELEASER)) ; a striking example of the latter is the specificity of song, and of signals that keep a flock of birds together. Highly specific releaser-response relationships seem to have been developed in connection with reproductive isolation between sympatric species (see SPECIATION ; also ISOLATING MECHANISM ; and COLORATION, ADAPTIVE).

N.T.

RECORDING: ultra-quiet song (see SINGING) ; also, of course, the human activity of mechanically registering and reproducing bird or other sounds (see SOUND RECORDING).

RECTRIX: a main tail feather ; the rectrices indeed virtually constitute the tail (see PLUMAGE ; TAIL).

RECTUM: the large intestine (see ALIMENTARY SYSTEM).

RECURVED-BILL: *Megaxenops parnaguae* ; sometimes applied also to *Xenops* spp. (see OVEN-BIRD (1)).

RECURVIROSTRIDAE: see under CHARADRI-IFORMES. The family comprises the avocets and stilts—see under AVOCET.

REDBILL: name in South Africa for *Anas erythrorhyncha*, otherwise Red-billed Pintail (see DUCK).

REDBREAST: alternative name of the Robin *Erithacus rubecula* (see THRUSH).

REDHEAD: *Aythya americana* (see DUCK).

REDIRECTION: the direction of a behaviour response at other than the normal object. As a rule, animal behaviour is directed at certain parts of, or objects in, the environment—food-pecking is directed at food, attack is directed at a rival, and so on—and this is made possible by steering (as distinct from merely releasing or inhibiting) mechanisms ; but in certain circumstances a response is directed at an object other than that normally drawing the response. Such responses to abnormal objects can be classed in two categories. On the one hand, when an animal is very hungry it may peck at inedible or inadequate objects not normally aimed at ; a sexually deprived animal may copulate with substitute partners sometimes very unlike the normal partner ; and a broody bird may sit on objects very dissimilar to eggs. These responses have in common that they are directed at a substitute object in the absence of the adequate object, and that the adequate object is preferred as soon as it is present. On the other hand, when a man scolds his subordinate when he has himself been rebuked by his superior, or kicks a chair in anger although the fellow human who aroused his anger is there, we speak of a redirected attack ; and such redirected attacks are common in birds. They occur when an individual is provoked to attack another individual, but cannot do so because it is either afraid of its attacker or is inhibited in some other way, for instance by personal

' love ' for its sex partner. A redirected attack may be aimed at a third bird happening to be near, or it may be as extreme as table-banging by an angry human ; thus a male Herring Gull *Larus argentatus* regularly pecks violently into the ground when facing a rival near the territory's boundary. It seems likely that such redirected attacks have also contributed to the ' raw material ' from which signal movements have evolved (see DISPLACEMENT ACTIV-ITY ; RELEASER). They are often followed by dis-placement activities, and can probably determine which particular displacement activity will be shown by providing stimuli that facilitate one particular movement. N.T.

REDPOLL: substantive name of two *Acanthis* spp. ; used without qualification, in Britain, for *A. flammea* (see FINCH).

REDSHANK: substantive name of *Tringa totanus*, for which it is used in Britain without qualification, and one congener (see SANDPIPER).

REDSTART (1): substantive name of *Phoenicurus* spp. ; used without qualification, in Britain, for *P. phoenicurus* (see THRUSH).

REDSTART (2): substantive name, in North America, of species of *Setophaga* and *Myioborus* (see WARBLER (2)).

REDTHROAT: *Pyrrholaemus brunneus* (see WREN (2)).

REDUCTION-DIVISION: meiosis (see CELL ; GENETICS).

REDWING: *Turdus iliacus* (see THRUSH) ; in North America sometimes applied to the Redwinged Blackbird *Agelaius phoeniceus* (see ORIOLE (2)) ; in Africa applied to *Francolinus levaillanti* (see PHEASANT).

REEDLING: *Panurus biarmicus* (see under PARROT-BILL).

REEDRUNNER: *Limnornis curvirostris* (see OVEN-BIRD (1)).

REEVE: see RUFF

REFLEX: ' an innate relatively simple and stereo-typed response involving the central nervous system and occurring very shortly after the stimulus which evokes it ; it specifically involves a part only of the organism, though the whole may be affected, and is usually a response to localised sensory stimuli ' (Thorpe 1951)—see FIXED ACTION PATTERN ; LEARNING.

REFUGE: see CONSERVATION

REGENT-BIRD: Regent Bowerbird *Sericulus chrysocephalus* (see BOWERBIRD).

REGION, ZOOGEOGRAPHICAL: or faunal region, see DISTRIBUTION, GEOGRAPHICAL.

REGULIDAE: a family recognised by some authors, but here merged in the subfamily Sylviinae of the Muscicapidae (see WARBLER (1)).

REINFORCEMENT: see LEARNING

REJUNGENT SPECIES: see RING-SPECIES.

RELEASER: term originally given a precise and unambiguous definition by Lorenz in 1935 but since applied in two very different senses. In the original sense, a releaser is not a stimulus, but a type of effector device (in the widest sense—either a structure, or a movement, or a scent, or a call) with a very specific function, namely that of providing stimuli which release (or inhibit) a response or a set of responses in another animal of the same species. The concept became necessary when it was pointed out that there are structures, movements, sounds, and so on which can be shown to provide such stimuli, for which no other function can be found, and which are obviously well suited to the broadcasting of stimuli. Thus, the red colour of the breast feathers of a Robin *Erithacus rubecula*, the brightly coloured wing specula of ducks (Anatidae), the red patch on the lower mandible of a Herring Gull *Larus argentatus*, the nest-showing ceremonies of various male birds (Wren *Troglodytes troglodytes* ; Kestrel *Falco tinnunculus* ; Blackheaded Gull *Larus ridibundus* ; Redstart *Phoenicurus phoenicurus* ; Pied Flycatcher *Ficedula hypoleuca*), the head-tossing movements of female gulls (Larinae), the song of male song-birds, alarm calls, and many more, all provide stimuli releasing or directing more or less specific responses in fellow members of the species, and are therefore called releasers. The ' rodent-run ' and other distraction displays of waders (Charadrii) and other birds lure predators away from the brood (see DISTRACTION DISPLAY) ; these activities, like the hissing of the Great Tit *Parus major* and Wryneck *Jynx torquilla*, aposematic coloration, and the luring flight of honeyguides (Indicatoridae), subserve interspecific communication ; the term releaser can of course be applied to them as well.

While the word is not important, provided that it is used consistently, the distinction between the two concepts (releaser and stimulus) is essential. The difference between the concept of releaser and that of sign stimulus, to which the word ' releaser ' is often applied, is to be found in the adaptedness of the releaser as a signalling device (see SIGN STIMULUS).

A pike, snapping at a piece of shiny metal dragged through the water, is responding to a sign stimulus normally provided by its prey. Yet the silvery shine of, for example, a roach has certainly not developed as a means to enable the roach to be captured by a pike ; if anything, the pike has helped to exert selection pressure against such conspicuousness. The red spot on the bill of the Herring Gull, on the contrary, must have been favoured by selection pressure, since it helps in eliciting the chick's begging, which in turn stimulates its parent to feed it ; and song, by attracting females, facilitates pair formation and as such is favoured by selection. The argument is particularly convincing in those cases where releasers have developed in spite of the dangers to which they expose their bearers in other contexts, especially when they make them more vulnerable to attack by predators.

Thus the term ' releaser ' is intended to characterise a category of effector by its exclusive or main function, just as the term ' wing ' is used to name any organ which provides lift and propulsion in flight, even although a wing may also be used as, for instance, a weapon in fighting.

Many releasers, such as alarm calls, have been shown literally to release a response. Others, such as the head-flagging in gulls and other ' appeasement gestures ' stop a response (see DISPLAY) ; others again, such as the song of male song-birds, release and also direct the movements of other birds (in this case, repulsion of males and attraction of females). For this reason, the term ' signalling device ' is perhaps preferable. The latter example also shows that one feature may have more than one function. The second function need not be that of signalling, and its demands may even conflict with those of the releaser function ; the most obvious examples of such conflicting demands are procryptic birds that have at the same time conspicuously coloured structures ; such species have reached a compromise by concealing the bright colours so long as they are not actually needed.

Comparative studies sometimes enable one to make a guess at the origin of releasers, and it is probable that they are secondary specialisations of organs and movements primarily adapted to other functions, selection pressure having favoured simplicity, conspicuousness, and unambiguity ; and this seems in accord with the known properties of the sensory functions through which they exert their effect (see SIGN STIMULUS). Evolution being a slow and gradual process involving a very large number of extremely small steps, it is evident that the distinction between organs which are obvious, highly specialised releasers (such as the wings of a male Argus Pheasant *Argusianus argus*) and those that are not yet, or no longer, or not exclusively releasers cannot be sharp. This is of course true of every category of organ.

The function of an alleged releaser is often suggested by observations but can be experimentally tested in experiments with dummies.   N.T.

Lorenz, K. 1935. Der Kumpan in der Umwelt des Vogels. J. Orn. 83 : 137–213, 289–413.

RELICT: term applied to isolated (sometimes discontinuous) populations that appear to represent a former much wider distribution.

REMEX: a main flight feather ; the remiges are classed as primary and secondary (see PLUMAGE ; PRIMARY ; WING).

REMICLE: term properly restricted to a small feather found on the wing in some species, attached to the second phalanx of digit II. Most authors have considered it to be a vestigial primary remex,

but Stresemann believes it to have been a covert to the terminal claw possessed by ancestral forms (see under PRIMARY).

REMIGES : plural of REMEX.

REMIZINAE : see TIT

RENAL FUNCTION : see EXCRETORY SYSTEM

REPRODUCTIVE ISOLATION : a situation in which intrinsic factors wholly or largely prevent interbreeding between closely related species, or populations of a species (see ISOLATING MECHANISM ; SPECIATION). It is to be distinguished from geographical or ecological isolation, where extrinsic circumstances prevent contact between populations that might otherwise be fully capable of interbreeding.

REPRODUCTIVE RATE : see POPULATION DYNAMICS

REPRODUCTIVE SYSTEM : in birds, as in the majority of vertebrates, this consists essentially of a

---

Plate 41 · Evolutionary Radiation (Kingfisher Family)
by D. M. REID-HENRY

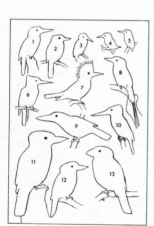

ca. $\frac{3}{10}$ nat. size

The purpose is to illustrate the evolution of diverse forms of clearly common descent. The kingfishers (Alcedinidae) have been chosen partly because of their well marked plumage patterns, and partly because they constitute a distinctive and geographically widespread family. Diversity in size of body and in form of bill, as well as in plumage pattern, is exhibited. One species (sometimes the sole species) of each of 13 out of the 15 genera is shown (the male, in the few cases where there is sexual dimorphism). The information in parentheses after each name relates to the genus (number of included species ; general distribution) See articles KINGFISHER ; SPECIATION.

1 White-breasted Kingfisher *Halcyon smyrnensis* (39 spp.—Africa, Asia, Australia, Polynesia, New Zealand)

2 Banded Kingfisher *Lacedo pulchinella* (monotypic genus—southeastern Asia)

3 Kingfisher *Alcedo atthis* (9 spp.—Europe, Africa, Asia)

4 Forest Kingfisher *Ceyx erithacus* (10 spp.—southern Asia, Australia, Polynesia)

5 Pigmy Kingfisher *Ispidina picta* (2 spp.—Africa, Madagascar)

6 Pied Kingfisher *Ceryle rudis* (monotypic genus—Africa, southern Asia)

7 Belted Kingfisher *Megaceryle alcyon* (4 spp.—N. and S. America, Africa, Asia)

8 Caroline Racket-tail *Tanysiptera carolinae* (6 spp.—Australia, New Guinea)

9 Stork-billed Kingfisher *Pelargopsis capensis* (monotypic genus—southern Asia)

10 Amazon Kingfisher *Chloroceryle amazona* (4 spp.—southern N. America, S. America)

11 Kookaburra *Dacelo novaeguineae* (4 spp.—Australia and New Guinea)

12 Hook-billed Kingfisher *Melidora macrorrhina* (monotypic genus—New Guinea)

13 Earthworm-eating Kingfisher *Clytoceyx rex* (monotypic genus—New Guinea)

Not represented :
Dwarf Kingfisher *Myioceyx lecontei* (monotypic genus—Africa)
Blue-eared Kingfisher *Cittura cyanotis* (monotypic genus—Celebes)

D.M.H.

C.E. Talbot Kelly.

pair of gonads in which the gametes (reproductive cells) are produced, and a pair of ducts through which the gametes reach the exterior. In birds the gonads of both sexes lie permanently in the abdomen, attached to its dorsal wall near the anterior end of the kidneys. They change greatly in size according to the season of the year, and at their maximum during the breeding season they are many times larger than when they are involuted.

Development. The primordial germ-cells are differentiated early in the development of the embryo and are aggregated at the site of the future gonad, which they invest as the germinal epithelium. They sink below the surface, into the stroma (connective tissue), surrounded by a layer of epithelial cells that give rise to the lining epithelium of the follicle in the ovary or of the seminiferous tubules in the testis. During early development, also, two pairs of ducts—the Müllerian and Wolffian ducts, which are derived from the primitive kidney-ducts —run from gonad to urinogenital sinus. In the female the Müllerian ducts become the oviducts but the Wolffian ducts remain vestigial ; in the male the Wolffian ducts become the vasa deferentia but the Müllerian ducts remain vestigial. See also DEVELOPMENT, EMBRYONIC.

Female Organs. *Ovary.* In nearly all birds the female gonad (ovary) and its duct (oviduct) of the left side alone are functional ; the development of those on the right is arrested, and they may degenerate. The functional ovary resembles a minute bunch of grapes ; it is enveloped by a fold of peritoneum, which with its contained blood vessels and connective tissue forms the stalk (mesovarium) that attaches the ovary to the dorsal wall of the abdomen. The stroma consists of a mass of connective tissue and blood vessels supporting the follicles. Each of the follicles at first consists of a sac lined by a single layer of cells containing the germ-cell or ovum. As the follicle grows, its lining is differentiated into several layers of cells of different kinds.

Ovum. Before the ovum is released from the follicle a large quantity of yolk is added to it and serves as nutritive material in later stages of the development of the chick. The yolk is derived from the follicle cells and reaches so large a size that the protoplasmic ovum, the living part of the egg cell, is pushed to one side of the surface where, after further change, it appears as the blastodisc of the complete egg. During the process of maturation the nucleus of the ovum undergoes meiosis but only one of the resulting nuclei survives, the others being rejected as the polar bodies. The accumulation of yolk greatly increases the size of the follicle and its contents so that it protrudes from the surface of the ovary, to which it is connected by a constricted stalk or pedicle. The tissues, or theca, enclosing the follicle form a very thin layer when the growth of the ovum is complete. The cluster of pedunculated follicles in various stages of maturity in the active ovary produce the characteristic 'bunch of grapes' appearance to the naked eye. When the ovum, popularly the 'yolk', is ripe it is extruded

---

Plate 42 · Geographical Variation by C. E. TALBOT KELLY

Upper part ca. ½ nat. size ;
lower part ca. 4/15 nat. size

Two polytypic species are used as examples. A few representative subspecies or races of each are shown, chosen from a larger number to illustrate the extremes of geographical variation within the species. In the upper example, the variations are closely related to the colour of the ground in the area inhabited by the form. See articles SUBSPECIES ; and COLORATION, ADAPTIVE ; CROW (I) ; LARK.

DESERT LARK *Ammomanes deserti*

1   *A. d. kollmanspergeri* (Darfur, Sudan—in red sandstone country)

2   *A. d. azizi* (eastern central Arabia—in chalky hills)

3   *A. d. annae* (Jordan—in black lava desert)

4   *A. d. phoesuloidenic* (Pakistan and north-western India)

JAY *Garrulus glandarius*

5   *G. g. cervicalis* (Algeria and Tunisia)

6   *G. g. glandarius* (north-western continental Europe)

7   *G. g. japonicus* (Japan)

8   *G. g. brandti* (Siberia)

9   *G. g. leucotis* (Burma to Indo-China)

10   *G. g. bispecularis* (central Himalayas)

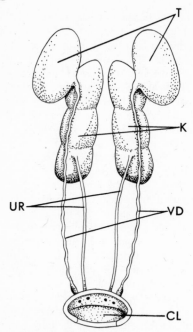

FIG 1. Diagram of the reproductive and excretory systems of a male bird (viewed ventrally)

T testis   **VD** vas deferens   **K** kidney   **UR** ureter
CL cloaca

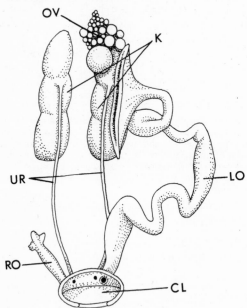

FIG 2. Diagram of the reproductive and excretory organs of a female bird (viewed ventrally)

OV ovary (left only)   **LO** left oviduct (functional)
RO rudimentary right oviduct   **K** kidney   **UR** ureter
CL cloaca

from the follicle. A thin part of the theca, the stigma, ruptures and the ovum is liberated into the abdominal cavity surrounded by a very thin skin, the vitelline membrane, secreted by the follicular epithelium.

Corpus luteum. When the ovum leaves the follicle the theca collapses, and the cells of the follicular epithelium increase in size to form a transient body, the corpus luteum, occupying the position of the former follicle. During the maturation of the follicle the cells of its epithelium produce oestrogenic hormone, but after the dehiscence of the follicle they become luteinised and produce another hormone, progesterone, the action of which is less understood in birds than in mammals. In the domestic fowl, and in most wild birds in which it has been examined, the luteal tissue does not fill the collapsed follicle ; the corpus luteum quickly regresses and is replaced by scar tissue which soon disappears. But in some of the petrels (Procellariiformes) the corpus luteum is a spherical body, filled with luteal cells, which closely resembles the corpus luteum of mammals, and apparently has a much longer life than that in most birds. All the developing ova in a bird's ovary do not reach maturity ; many of them undergo degeneration (atresia) before they are ripe. Some burst into the stroma of the ovary and others break down within the follicle. In both types of atresia the ovum dies and is resorbed with the yolk material. The follicular epithelium generally becomes luteinised and forms an atretic corpus luteum that usually persists for only a short time but may sometimes survive for some months. Before the occurrence of atretic corpora lutea was recognised it was suggested that the numbers of corpora lutea or their remnants corresponded with the total number of eggs laid by a bird during its life ; calculations of the age of the birds, based upon counts of these bodies, are now known to be erroneous.

Oviduct. On leaving the ovary the ovum enters the oviduct, a tube attached to the body wall by dorsal and ventral ligaments or double folds of peritoneum between which the blood vessels supplying and draining the organ ramify. The oviduct is covered externally by the peritoneum and its wall contains two muscular layers, one consisting of longitudinal and the other of circular fibres. It is lined by mucous membrane, which is thrown into longitudinal ridges and is covered with glandular and ciliated epithelium. The degree of development of the muscular layers, of the mucous membrane, and of the ridges differs in the different parts of the oviduct. The egg is fertilised in the upper part of the oviduct before the albumen is added to the yolk, and cell division starts before the egg is laid. The inner end of the oviduct opens into the abdominal cavity, and the outer into the cloaca. Although, technically, the ovum is shed from the ovary into the body cavity it does not normally lie free within it. The expanded membranous lips of the inner end of the oviduct surround the follicle so that when it bursts the ovum is in effect immediately received into the duct. The expanded part (infundibulum) is funnel-shaped and flattened from side to side ; it rapidly converges to form a short, thin-walled neck in which the mucous membrane is thrown into low folds. The next part of the oviduct, the convoluted glandular portion or albumen-secreting region (magnum), forms nearly half of the total length of the organ and is much convoluted when it is in the active state. It has muscular walls lined with a highly glandular mucous membrane that is thrown into prominent ridges, some of which follow a slightly spiral course. During the passage of the ovum through this part of the oviduct the glands secrete the successive layers of albumen around it—the chalaziferous, the inner liquid, the middle dense, and the outer liquid (see EGG). The spiral ridges of the mucous membrane cause the ovum to rotate as it passes down, so that the chalazae acquire their characteristic spiral twist.

The distal end of the convoluted glandular part of the oviduct is abruptly demarcated from the narrow and shorter isthmus that follows. The walls of the isthmus are more muscular than those of the preceding part, the mucous membrane is thinner and less glandular and its ridges are lower. The isthmus secretes the two shell-membranes, consisting of felted protein fibres cemented together with albuminous material. At each end of the egg the mucin fibres of the dense albumen layer interlace with the inner shell-membrane to form the albumen ligament ; elsewhere the smooth lining of the inner shell-membrane is in contact with the outer liquid layer of albumen. The surface of the outer shell-membrane is rough and provides a key to bind it to the shell (see EGGSHELL). The inner and outer shell-membranes are everywhere in contact until the complete egg is laid ; when the egg cools on leaving the body of the bird its contents contract and air is drawn in through the pores of the shell. The outer shell-membrane then separates from the inner shell-membrane at the blunt pole, so that the air cell is formed.

The isthmus merges gradually into the next part of the oviduct, the wider and greatly distensible uterus, where the shell and pigment are added to make the finished egg. The uterus is about equal in length to the narrow isthmus but is considerably greater in diameter. Its walls are thick and muscular, and the glandular mucous membrane is well developed although thinner than that in the albumen secreting portion. The cells of the mucous membrane in the uterus secrete the calcium salts that, reinforced with protein fibres, make up the shell (see also NUTRITION). In coloured eggs the ground colour is deposited during the later stages of shell formation, and the superficial markings after the shell is complete. The terminal part of the uterus adds a thin cuticle of transparent protein material and, in some species, a comparatively soft and friable chalky coating. The uterus is divided from the terminal part of the oviduct, the vagina, by a strong sphincter muscle ; it is at this point that the egg may be rotated on its long axis. Normally the egg travels down the oviduct with its pointed end first, but, in the domestic fowl at least, up to 30 per cent of eggs do not enter the vagina immediately on reaching the distal end of the uterus. The sphincter apparently does not relax, and the contraction of the uterine musculature forces the egg onwards so that it causes part of the uterus to bulge out as a pocket projecting caudal to the vaginal sphincter. Further muscular contraction rotates the egg end over end so that the blunt pole lies in apposition to the sphincter, which then relaxes and admits the egg to the vagina with its blunt end first. It is not known whether a similar longitudinal rotation occurs in other birds.

The vagina is short and has very muscular walls ; its mucous membrane contains glands the secretion of which probably serves as a lubricant, for it adds nothing to the egg. Its junction with the cloaca dorsal to the rectum is guarded by another sphincter. There is some evidence that in the domestic fowl the egg barely comes into contact with the walls of the vagina, because at the moment of laying the uterus is prolapsed through the vagina and cloaca so that the egg is in effect deposited directly from the uterus. See also EGG ; LAYING.

Seasonal changes. The whole of the reproductive tract, from the ovary to the external sphincter of the vagina, undergoes great seasonal variations in size and weight. In the breeding season the ovary may weigh as much as 15 times its weight during the inactive season, and the oviduct similarly may be 4 times as long and weigh over 15 times as much. During the inactive season the oviduct and ovary are usually very inconspicuous structures in the abdominal cavity, and in small species of birds they may be difficult to recognise without strong magnification ; in contrast they are conspicuous and unmistakable to the naked eye when active.

Persistence of right ovary. An exception to the

rule that only the left ovary of birds becomes functional is shown by the Falconiformes, in various species of which both ovaries may persist although the right oviduct remains vestigial. The right ovary is generally most highly developed (in addition to the left) in the Accipitrinae ; it is present but progressively smaller in the Falconidae and Cathartidae. There is one known instance, in a Goshawk *Accipiter gentilis*, where ovulation occurred from both ovaries ; but all the eggs passed down the left oviduct, which alone was functional.

Changes of sex. If the functional left ovary of a bird is removed or destroyed by disease the rudimentary right ovary may increase in size and become a functional gonad. It does not, however, become an ovary but a testis—so that the bird changes its sex. At the same time the functional oviduct on the left side and the rudimentary one on the right decrease in size, and the rudimentary Wolffian ducts of both sides increase ; that on the right side makes contact with the testis and becomes a functional sperm duct or vas deferens. Old hens in which the left ovary has been destroyed by pathological changes may thus turn into cocks, put on male plumage, crow, and become fathers of chicks. These changes are presumably caused by the withdrawal of the female hormone (see ENDO-CRINE SYSTEM) ; it is conceivable that administration of suitable quantities of female hormone immediately following removal of the left ovary might result in the development of the right gonad into a functional ovary.

Male Organs. *Testis.* In male birds the gonads (testes) of both sides are functional, as are the ducts through which their products are discharged ; the left testis, however, is frequently larger than the right. The testis is generally ovoid or globular in shape, and is covered by a reflection of the peritoneum forming the ligament of the testis at its place of attachment to the dorsal wall of the abdomen. Under the peritoneal covering the testis is invested by the tunica albuginea, a tough fibrous coat from which supporting trabeculae extend into the substance of the testis and divide it into lobes. The seminiferous part of the testis consists of a vast number of tubes, blind at their origins, which pursue a tortuous path to join the epididymis. The tubes are lined with an epithelium consisting mainly of spermatogonia and supporting Sertoli cells. When the testis becomes active the spermatogonia divide to produce primary spermatocytes which by further division produce secondary spermatocytes. The spermatocytes in their final division undergo meiosis to produce spermatids in each of which the number of chromosomes is half of that in the nuclei

of the somatic cells. The spermatids are transformed into spermatozoa by a process of development during which they are nourished by the Sertoli cells. See also GENETICS.

Epididymis and vas deferens. The mature spermatozoa are released into the lumina of the spermatic tubules and travel down them into a number of highly convoluted tubules that are packed closely together and form the epididymis, a compact body applied to the median side of the testis. The tubules of the epididymis join to form a single duct, the vas deferens, leading from the epididymis to the urodaeum of the cloaca. The vasa deferentia are slightly expanded immediately before they open into the urodaeum on small papillae lateral to the openings of the ureters. The vasa deferentia follow a slightly sinuous course over the ventral surfaces of the kidneys and the dorsal wall of the abdomen ; during the breeding season they increase in length and the sinuosities are consequently emphasised and in some species form a mass of convolutions that produces a bulging of the cloacal walls. There are no accessory glands such as prostate or vesiculae seminales, nor is the epithelium of the vasa deferentia glandular.

Leydig cells. The closely packed seminiferous tubules of the testes are individually surrounded by a thin layer of connective tissue, and specialised interstitial (Leydig) cells are lodged in the interstices between the tubules. The Leydig cells undergo cyclic changes in their lipoid metabolism and produce the male hormone that controls both the cyclic alterations in the activity of the testes and their ducts, and the waxing and waning of sexual behaviour (see ENDOCRINE SYSTEM).

Seasonal changes. In the breeding season the testes increase enormously in size ; in small passerine birds they are hardly recognisable to the naked eye when they are involuted, but when they are in full activity they may be half an inch or more in diameter. At the end of the breeding season the testes undergo an equally rapid diminution in size, during which the cells of the seminiferous tubules degenerate and striking changes occur in the Leydig cells.

Copulation. The erectile papillae in the urodaeum on which the vasa deferentia open are small and inconspicuous in most birds. (Nevertheless, the technique of ' sexing ' newly hatched domestic chicks introduced by the Japanese depends upon recognising the minute papillae in the cloaca when it is artificially everted for inspection.) In copulation, the cloaca of both sexes is everted so that the papillae are brought into contact with the orifice of the oviduct for the transference of the sperm. In some birds part of the cloaca is modified to form a penis ; this occurs in the curassows (Cracidae), the tinamous (Tinamidae), the Anseriformes, and the 'ratite' birds (for a penis-like organ in *Bubalornis albirostris*, see WEAVER). In the anseriform birds the penis is a vascularised evertible sac protruded by the action of a muscle and retracted by an elastic ligament which gives it a spiral form. The sperm passes from the cloacal papillae at its base into a spiral groove that conveys it to the apex. In the 'ratite' birds the penis lies in a recess in the anterior wall of the cloaca ; it consists of two fibrous bodies between which lies the seminal groove bounded by erectile tissue ; a ligament gives it a twisted shape, and it is protruded and retracted by muscles. In the females of the birds of these groups, the counterpart of the penis is the comparatively small clitoris, most conspicuous in the 'ratite' birds. See also COPULATION.   L.H.M.

Marshall, A. J. 1961. Reproductive system. *In* Marshall, A. J. (ed.). Biology and Comparative Physiology of Birds vol. 2. New York and London.
Marshall, F. H. A. (ed. Parkes, A. S.). 1952. Physiology of Reproduction vol. 1, pts. 1 and 2. London.
Romanoff, A. L. & Romanoff, A. J. 1949. The Avian Egg. New York and London.

REPTILIAN ANCESTRY: see ORIGIN OF BIRDS

RESERVE, NATURE: see CONSERVATION

RESIDENT: remaining throughout the year in the area under reference, the term being applied to a species, subspecies, population, or individual bird as the context requires ; in another usage the term means breeding in the area, a distinction being then drawn between 'permanent resident' and 'summer resident' (='summer visitor')—see MIGRATION.

RESONANCE: setting up vibrations that increase the volume of a sound (see SINGING ; SYRINX ; also INSTRUMENTAL SOUNDS).

RESPIRATORY SYSTEM: highly specialised in birds for the dual purpose of aeration of the lungs and thermoregulation. In many respects the avian respiratory system is unique in the Animal Kingdom and deserves greater attention in text-books and more study by morphologists and physiologists than it has been given so far. The system consists of air-passages and lungs and the air-sacs connected with them ; not included in this definition are certain air receptacles, such as the gular pouch of frigatebirds (Fregatidae) and bustards (Otididae), which are inflated in certain aspects of display (see INTEGUMENTARY STRUCTURES). See also DEVELOPMENT, EMBRYONIC.

Air-passages. The air-passages begin in the external nares, paired openings situated in the upper mandible—usually in the basal section, except in the kiwis *Apteryx* spp. where they are located near the tip (see BILL ; NARIS). In some groups, e.g. pigeons (Columbidae), the external nares are situated in the soft cere at the base of the bill. In the Procellariiformes (Tubinares) they are in forwardly directed tubes formed from separate elements of the rhamphotheca. They are variously shaped in different groups and sometimes protected by a movable operculum or by bristles that are modified frontal feathers. Exceptionally the external nares are occluded (impervious) as in the gannets (Sulidae) and adult cormorants (Phalacrocoracidae), or partially blocked as in the pelicans (Pelecanidae), when respiration is oral by means of special modifications of the structures at the angle of the mouth (Macdonald 1960).

The external nares communicate with the nasal cavities, which are sometimes divided by a bony septum ; the latter may be perforate or imperforate. The nasal cavities open into the mouth through the internal or posterior nares. The air-passage from mouth to lungs begins at the glottis, a single slit-like opening controlled by muscles and situated at the base of the tongue. The glottis opens into the larynx, a modification of the anterior end of the trachea, which has no vocal chords as in mammals. Respiratory sounds are produced in the syrinx, sometimes referred to as posterior larynx, a feature peculiar to birds and usually located at the end of the trachea where it bifurcates into the primary bronchi (see SYRINX) ; or it may be elsewhere in the posterior section of the trachea or even in the primary bronchi, a part in each, as in the Oilbird *Steatornis caripensis* and the anis *Crotophaga* spp. See also TRACHEA.

Lungs. The lungs are small. In the Mallard *Anas platyrhynchos* they are about 2 per cent of the body volume, compared with 5 per cent in man, whereas the air-sacs are 20 per cent (Zeuthen 1942). The lungs are situated dorso-anteriorly in the body cavity. They lie in close contact with the vertebral column and vertebral ribs, the latter often being deeply inserted in them. They are contained ventrally by a partly muscular pulmonary diaphragm. There is no diaphragm homologous with that present in mammals.

The two branches into which the trachea divides form the main stem of each lung ; they are the primary bronchi. The distal portion of each primary bronchus branches into a compact mass of bronchi, of decreasing bore, to form the main body of the lung. This section of the primary bronchus is often named mesobronchus, although the name was originally given (Huxley 1882) to the part distal to the vestibulum. The vestibulum is the wider medial section of the mesobronchus; it is not always clearly distinguishable. Secondary bronchi arise from the mesobronchus; certain groups of similar size and function are recognised, the two most important being the ventrobronchi and dorso-bronchi (or ectobronchi and entobronchi). The ventrobronchi arise proximally from the meso-bronchus and form the main part of the ventral aspect of the lung. The dorsobronchi arise distally and form the dorsal aspect. These two sets of secondary bronchi, together with their offshoots, the parabronchi, make up a large part of the lung; in the domestic fowl they amount to from two-thirds to three-quarters of the volume (King 1956).

Other secondary bronchi of smaller bore are classified as laterobronchi; sometimes they are divided into laterobronchi and dorsolaterobronchi, the latter especially functioning as parabronchi, although they arise from the mesobronchus. Recurrent bronchi are secondary connections of certain air-sacs with the lungs; they do not occur in the cervical sac of the domestic fowl, for example, or in the abdominal sac of cassowaries *Casuarius* spp. (Schulze 1909).

The main parts of the avian respiratory system as shown (*left*) in a text-book diagram of the system in a pigeon *Columba livia* and (*right*) in a drawing of an actual cast obtained by filling the system of a Mallard *Anas platyrhynchos* with synthetic resin. *Drawn by G. S. Cowles from a preparation in the British Museum (Natural History).*

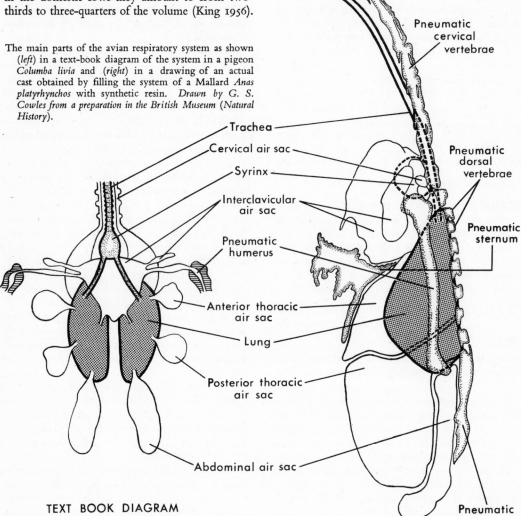

Trachea

Cervical air sac

Syrinx

Interclavicular air sac

Pneumatic humerus

Anterior thoracic air sac

Lung

Posterior thoracic air sac

Abdominal air sac

Pneumatic cervical vertebrae

Pneumatic dorsal vertebrae

Pneumatic sternum

Pneumatic pelvis

TEXT BOOK DIAGRAM

ANAS PLATYRHYNCHOS

They originate as diverticula from the air-sacs and are homologous with parabronchi, being tertiary branches of inflated secondary bronchi. They anastomose mainly with other parabronchi at the lung surface.

The secondary bronchi branch into numerous tertiary bronchi, or parabronchi, tubes of fairly uniform small bore but varying in diameter from one species to another. An important feature of the avian lung is that the parabronchi anastomose ; in the fully adult lung there are no blind-ending bronchi corresponding with the alveoli of the mammalian lung. The parabronchi fuse to form closed circuits, the most important circuits being those formed by the fusion of the parabronchi belonging to the ventrobronchi and dorsobronchi. The offshoots of the laterobronchi also form continuous air-passages by fusing with each other and with other parabronchi and recurrent bronchi. The parabronchi carry a dense mass of fine air capillaries which anastomose with one another and sometimes with those of adjacent parabronchi, especially in birds of vigorous flight (Fischer 1905). This network of fine air-passages is interwoven with a similar mesh of blood capillaries to provide the facilities for gaseous exchange which is the principal function of the respiratory system.

Air-sacs. The fact that air-sacs are part of the respiratory system was established by William Harvey in 1651. Air-sacs are sections of bronchi expanded into thin-walled reservoirs. They are formed from secondary bronchi, except that the abdominal sac is an extension of the terminus of the primary bronchus. Like the bronchi, the sacs have few muscle fibres and a very limited blood supply and are in consequence largely passive. Air-sacs ramify throughout the body cavity, sending diverticula between viscera and muscles, the latter especially in the region of the humeral and femoral joints, entering various bones in many species (see PNEUMATISATION OF BONE), and even occasionally extending into the subcutaneous areas of the skin. Although pneumatised bones retain their connections with air-sacs and lungs there is evidence that they are not ventilated (Zeuthen 1942), at least in the resting condition ; it follows, therefore, that a bird with a constricted trachea would not be able to breathe adequately through a broken humerus, as is popularly suggested, a conclusion that one could in any event suspect in certain species from the small size of the foramen through which the sac enters. One pair of sacs fuses completely at an early stage of development to form a single sac, and there is some evidence of fusion between other pairs. The pattern of lungs and air-sacs is basically similar in the species so far examined—relatively few in number—but there are indications of phylogenetic similarities and adaptive modifications. The five sacs, in anterior-posterior sequence are, cervical, interclavicular, thoracic, anterior abdominal, posterior abdominal (Cowles unpub.).

The source of each sac is known in a number of species and seems fairly constant ; there is evidence of some slight variation in the interclavicular. The first three, cervical, interclavicular, and thoracic, originate in the anterior part of the lung, while the anterior and posterior abdominal originate posteriorly. They have been described as anterior group of sacs and posterior group of sacs (Hazelhoff 1943). The functional significance of this grouping has been discussed but is not clearly understood.

The cervical sac has its origin a short distance along the first ventrobronchus. It is usually described as paired, although fusion has been found in the domestic fowl (Brandes 1924). The sac is sometimes said to be small and unimportant (Zeuthen), but modern injection techniques reveal that it can have extensive ramifications. It is associated particularly with the anterior section of the vertebral column, and diverticula may extend along the cervical vertebrae as far as the axis, but apparently not into the skull, and posteriorly along the thoracic vertebrae. The diverticula consist mainly of a complex network of extravertebral canals ramifying along the vertebrae and in some species forming an intravertebral system, entering each vertebra through foramina which are sometimes extremely narrow.

The interclavicular sac has a number of unusual features. It is connected with both the 1st and 3rd ventrobronchus in the domestic fowl, the origins being in close proximity to those of both the cervical and thoracic sacs (Locy & Larsell 1916). In the kiwis the interclavicular has separate connections with the 1st and 2nd ventrobronchi, the thoracic being connected with the 3rd ventrobronchus (Huxley 1882). The sacs from each lung fuse early in development—by the first day after hatching in the domestic fowl (Locy & Larsell)—so that in adults there is found to be only one interclavicular sac, although the separate connections with each lung remain. This sac has a number of diverticula, some being inserted between muscles in the pectoral region and others penetrating various bones. In one species or another they enter coracoid, scapula, clavicle, sternum, ribs, and humerus, and sometimes other bones of the forelimb. The thoracic sac shares a common origin with the interclavicular in some species, both being connected with the third ventrobronchus by a short interclavicular canal (Locy & Larsell). It is usually a simple sac lacking in diverticula.

The anterior abdominal sac, the first of the two posterior sacs, is also simple in form. It is a terminal extension of one of the larger laterobronchi—the 3rd in the domestic fowl (Locy & Larsell)—which branches from the mesobronchus directly opposite the dorsobronchi. The abdominal sac is an extension of the terminus of the mesobronchus. It is mainly simple in form, but in some species it gives rise to a number of diverticula inserted between muscles and tendons in the vicinity of the coxal joint, and sometimes also pneumatises pelvic bones and caudal vertebrae, including the pygostyle. It also pneumatises the femur, and occasionally other leg bones, in a number of species.

Aeration. The primary function of the respiratory system is to aerate the lungs, achieving gaseous exchange in the interlocking networks of air and blood capillaries. There is little or no expansion and contraction in the bronchi, at least in any way comparable with such movements in the mammalian lung. Changes in volume are confined to the air-sacs, and air is forced or drawn through the bronchial circuits. How air movements are brought about and the direction in which it flows are not fully understood. It is certain at least that the air-sacs play an important part although they are not capable of independent movement. Their volumes are controlled by the action of muscles external to them. One important movement is the compression of the thoraco-abdominal cavity by the sternum, which is hinged with the vertebral column through the coracoids and ribs. Another is the compression of the thorax by the action of the wings in flight: the rhythm of the wing-beats in the pigeon is found to be synchronised with the phases of breathing (Tomlinson & McKinnon 1957).

That the method of aeration of the lungs in birds is different from what it is in mammals is evident from their great structural differences, and in spite of the external appearance of rhythmic breathing and movements of thorax and abdomen. An important point, established by Brandes (1924), is that air circulates from one secondary bronchus to another by way of the anastomosing parabronchi. There are earlier comments, for example Huxley (1882) and Locy & Larsell (1916), relating to air circulating through the sacs, entering by way of the main bronchial connections and leaving by way of the recurrent bronchi. In the main bronchial circuits the deposition of carbon from inspired and injected soot-laden air (Dotterweich 1930) showed the direction of flow to be from dorsobronchi to

parabronchi and ventrobronchi, the 'd-p-v' system of Hazelhoff (1943) ; it will be remembered that access to the dorsobronchi is posterior to that of the ventrobronchi in the mesobronchus. At the same time there were heavy depositions in the posterior sacs. This evidence is supported by the analysis of the air in various sacs ; in the domestic fowl at rest, ventilation is highest in the posterior sacs (Zeuthen) ; the rate of penetration of pure oxygen in a given time is slowest in the anterior sacs (Vos 1935) ; the percentage of carbon dioxide in normal breathing is much higher in the anterior sacs (Zeuthen).

A continuous flow of air in one direction in the bronchial circuits, with a system of valves or sphincters operating between the phases of breathing, was postulated by Brandes (1924) and by Bethe (1925). Assuming the presence of valves, one view is that air is drawn directly into the posterior sacs at inspiration and then forced through the d-p-v system at expiration (Vos). Another view is that a continuous flow is maintained by air being sucked through the circuits by the anterior sacs at inspiration and forced through them by the posterior sacs at expiration (Dotterweich). This startling conclusion of continuous flow in one direction through the parabronchi in both phases of breathing—or continuous aeration of the lungs—was demonstrated by Hazelhoff (1943) in the lungs of a dead bird when he filled the respiratory system with a formalin solution containing chalk in suspension. When the ebb and flow of respiration was simulated he observed that the chalk particles moved in one direction only in the dorsobronchi. Vos (1935) believed that only one valve was required and that it was situated in the mesobronchus between the ventrobronchi and the dorsobronchi.

The presence of valves or sphincters in the bronchi has never been demonstrated morphologically. It is argued by some that they are not necessary and that aeration of the lungs is possible on aerodynamic principles. Dotterweich, a supporter of the valve theory (1930, 1933), later changed to this view (1936). Contrary to his earlier continuous-aeration theory, he concluded that without valves air flowed in the d-p-v system at inspiration but mainly by-passed it at expiration. A strong case for valveless lungs with continuous air-flow was made by Hazelhoff (1943). He believed that all the sacs expanded and contracted in unison and that the architecture of the lungs is such that fresh air keeps moving continuously in one direction in the bronchial circuits. Both Dotterweich and Hazelhoff stressed the importance of various structures, such as the curvature of the mesobronchus, the presence of a vestibulum, the positions and angles at which secondary bronchi open off the mesobronchus, and so on ; and both demonstrated their theories by means of models in which glass tubes represented certain main bronchi and rubber bulbs certain air-sacs. One relevant and revealing calculation is that the total area of the parabronchial bores is at least ten times as much as that of the mesobronchus, so that air under pressure would follow the least resistant, although longer, route (Zeuthen). Zeuthen also tried to show that differential resistance might be obtained by the action of the plain muscle fibres in the parabronchi being used to vary bore area. A logical evolution of that action, one imagines, would be for restriction to be concentrated at certain critical points, thus giving rise to sphincters of which the presence is still disputed. These differences of opinion are reflected in the inconsistencies in current text-books and emphasise the need for further study.

    Thermoregulation. The secondary function of the respiratory system is temperature regulation. It has long been known, by Soum (1896) and Victorow (1909) for example, that cooling by sweat glands, as in mammals, is replaced by respiratory cooling (see HEAT REGULATION). Visual evidence of this is found in the ' panting ', or shallow or superficial respiration, of resting birds exposed to hot sun. The metabolic heat generated by flight muscles in action must be very great and the presence of numerous diverticula, mainly from the interclavicular sac, inserted between muscles in the pectoral region and even in the sternum at their very origins, suggests that they function mainly as cooling radiators. The subject is summarised by Zeuthen, who estimated that the ventilation of the respiratory system in a flying bird may be as much as three times as much as is necessary for the aeration of the lungs. He also pointed out that the needs for thermoregulation being different from those of aeration there is likely to be some automatic method of controlling the amount of air supplied to the parabronchi, such as the use of the parabronchial plain muscle fibres to vary air-flow resistance by altering bore size.   J.D.M.

Brandes, G. 1924. Beobachtungen und Reflexionen über die Atmung der Vögel. Pflüg. Arch. ges. Physiol. 203 : 492–511.

Dotterweich, H. 1930. Die Bahnhofstauben und die Frage nach den Weg der Atemluft in der Vögellunge. Zool. Anz. Leipzig 90 : 259–262.

Dotterweich, H. 1936. Die Atmung der Vögel. Z. vergl. Physiol. 23 : 744–770.

Hazelhoff, E. H. 1943. Vergelijkende physiologie-bouw en functie van de vogellong. Vers. Afd. Natuurk. ned. Akad. Wet. Amsterdam 53 : 391–400. (English summary ; also translation in Poultry Sci. 1951, 30 : 3–10.)

King, A. S. 1956. Structure and function of the respiratory pathways of Gallus domesticus. Vet. Record 68 : 544–547.

Locy, W. A. & Larsell, O. 1916. Embryology of the bird's lung. Am. J. Anat. 19 : 447–504 ; 20 : 1–44.

Macdonald, J. D. 1960. Secondary external nares of the Gannet. Proc. Zool. Soc. Lond. 135 : 357–363.

Tomlinson, J. T. & McKinnon, R. S. 1957. Pigeon wing-beat synchronised with breathing. Condor 59 : 401.

Vos, H. J. 1935. Über den Weg der Atemluft der Entenlung. Z. vergl. Physiol. 21 : 552–578.

Zeuthen, E. 1942. The ventilation of the respiratory tract in birds. K. Danske Vidensk. Skr. 17 : 1–51.

RESTLESSNESS, PRE-MIGRATORY : see MIGRATION

RETICULATE : term applied to a podotheca consisting of small scales, the divisions between which form a fine network (see LEG).

RETINA : part of the eye (see VISION).

RETROMIGRATION : term proposed by Lack & Williamson (1959) for a migratory movement in a direction almost opposite to normal, as a result of diversion by a ' leading line ' (see MIGRATION).

RHACHIS : see RACHIS

RHAMPHOTHECA : the horny covering of the bill, the upper and lower parts of it being sometimes separately designated rhinotheca and gnathotheca (see BILL).

RHEA : substantive name of the two species of Rheidae (Rheiformes) ; in the plural, general term for the family and order. The group is restricted to the campo region of South America, where the birds are called ' Ema ' or ' Nhandu ' (Nandu). They are large running ' ratites ', showing a general resemblance to the Ostrich *Struthio camelus* of Africa. The Common Rhea (or Common Nandu) *Rhea americana*, to which the following account primarily refers, stands about 5 feet high and weighs 44–55 lbs. (20–25 kg.) or more. The normal coloration is not conspicuous, but white individuals are not uncommon. The sexes are similar, but the males are slightly taller.

    Each foot has three well-formed toes, and the birds are fine runners. When alarmed they run with their necks stretched almost horizontally, and they can double at right angles to their course. At the same time they lift one of their wings, with a sail-like or ballooning effect. When there is enough cover they crouch down to conceal themselves. Although the wings are bigger in proportion than those of other ' ratites ', they are useless for flying ; they cover the upper part of the rump like a cloak when they are at rest. Unlike those of the Ostrich, the feathers have little commercial value ; they are used in South America as dusters. Rectrices are absent. Rheas love to bathe and they are good swimmers. They feed on tender leaves, roots, seeds, and the like, also eating many insects, especially grasshoppers, and small vertebrates.

The birds live in flocks ; except in the breeding periods these groups consist of 20–30 individuals, at times considerably more. Occasionally they mix with herds of the Bush Deer *Dorcelaphus bezoarticus*, both species keeping a sharp look-out. In regions where they are not hunted they also mix with grazing cattle. Old cock-birds are solitary.

At the beginning of the breeding period the older males chase away the young ones and fight with their rivals by twisting their necks together, biting, and kicking. The cock displays in front of 3–8 females : he runs to and fro, stands in front of them, pulls his neck in, jerks his wings and then spreads them away from his body so that the feathers flutter in the breeze. He frequently then lets out a kind of low roar which sounds more like the voice of some wild beast than of a bird. At the same time he stretches his neck straight upwards, the inflated oesophagus serving as a sounding board. The Rhea also produces other sounds ; the syrinx is better developed than in the Ostrich.

The victorious cock-bird stays in a certain territory, if possible near a swamp or river. Generally the species prefers country with taller vegetation to pure grasslands. At a dry spot protected by bushes the cock prepares a shallow hollow in the ground by ripping away the grass with his bill ; frequently he uses an already existing depression and often works at a number of spots. Finally, he lines the hollow with some dry vegetable matter. Some of the nests are surrounded by an open zone partly prepared by the birds themselves by biting off the grass ; this zone occasionally serves to protect the nest against campo fires.

The cock-bird then leads the hens to the nest, showing his strikingly light-coloured rump. Frequently the hens had already started laying, dropping their eggs in various spots ; but now they concentrate on the definite nest. It may happen that 6 hens, one after another, each lay an egg in the nest and then leave together. Even females that belong to a different flock will join in and, consequently, the clutch may increase rapidly. Each female lays an egg every 2 or 3 days up to a total of 11–18. Otherwise they do not bother with the nest.

After there are a certain number of eggs in the nest the cock begins to incubate. From then on he defends the nest by stretching out his neck and moving it in a snake-like fashion accompanied by hissing and snapping. Females who want to lay more eggs in the nest must do so while the male is absent. More eggs are also laid in the vicinity ; the male rolls into the nest, with his bill, those eggs nearest it. Depending on circumstances, the clutch is complete with from 13 to 20–30 eggs ; but clutches with more than twice that number of eggs have been found (e.g. 80). The number of eggs which go to waste is even larger. The measurements of the eggs vary considerably, the average is about 132×90 mm. ; the weight of an egg is about 600 grams.

Common Rhea *Rhea americana.*
M.Y.

$\frac{1}{16}$

After an incubation of 35–40 days by the male alone, the young hatch, one shortly after the other. They are grey with dark stripes. The young soon leave the nest, led by the cock. They keep contact with each other by long-drawn plaintive whistles. Even so they get lost at times, especially when they lag too far behind after cowering low at the sign of danger. The strays will join another flock, if possible, and this results in considerable age variations within flocks. The development of the young is rapid ; after 5 months they are already as big as the adult birds. Sexual maturity, however, is not reached for 2 years.

The species with which we have been dealing, *Rhea americana*, is found from north-eastern Brazil to central Argentina ; in the male the base of the neck is black ; the newly laid eggs are golden yellow, but this quickly fades to an off-white colour.

The other species, in a closely related genus, is Darwin's Rhea *Pterocnemia pennata*, occurring from Patagonia to the high plateaux of the Andes in southern Peru. It is somewhat smaller ; the plumage shows white spots on a brownish background ; the eggs are green.   H.S.

Darwin, C. 1845. The Voyage of H.M.S. 'Beagle' (abbreviated title). London.
Hudson, W. H. 1920. Birds of La Plata vol. 2. London and New York.
Krieg, H. 1940. Als Zoologe in Steppen und Wäldern Patagoniens. München.

RHEAE ; RHEIDAE : see below

RHEIFORMES : an order, alternatively ' Rheae ', of ' ratite ' birds comprising only the family Rheidae of South America (see RHEA ; also RATITES, PHYLOGENY OF THE).

RHINOCRYPTIDAE : see under PASSERIFORMES ; and TAPACULO

RHINOTHECA : term sometimes applied to the part of the rhamphotheca covering the upper mandible (see BILL).

RHIPIDURINAE : see under MUSCICAPIDAE

RHOMBOID SINUS : a structure in the avian spinal cord (see NERVOUS SYSTEM).

RHYNOCHETI ; RHYNOCHETIDAE : see under GRUIFORMES ; and KAGU

RHYTHM : regular periodicity in function or behaviour that may be to some extent independent of external stimuli. Apart from purely intrinsic physiological rhythms, notably the heart-beat, the most important periodicities in the life of birds are, respectively, quotidian (' circadian ') and annual ; both physiology and habits are obviously related to the succession of day and night and to the cycle of the seasons. In some shore-feeding species the ebb and flow of the tides may have more significance than the alternation of light and darkness (and in some marine organisms it has been shown that a tidal rhythm may become autonomous) ; the phases of the moon, also, may affect the habits of noctural species in a periodical manner.

The daily periodicity in habits is obviously adapted to the incidence of daylight and is probably started and regulated by external stimuli (although the induced rhythm may be maintained under conditions artificially kept constant). The beginning and ending of activity are closely related to the intensity of light, as determined not only by the time of sunrise or sunset but also by the amount of cloud-cover, as many carefully timed observations have shown (see also ROOSTING). Further evidence is to be found in the behaviour of birds subject to artificial changes in lighting (or, simply, when put in the dark), or on the occurrence of a total eclipse of the sun, or in the perpetual summer day of high latitudes (again see ROOSTING). On the other hand, experimental evidence of the possession of a ' clock ' faculty, enabling the bird to allow for time of day in using the sun for orientation, seems to argue the existence of some sort of intrinsic registration of time interval, presumably by the nervous system (see TIME MEASUREMENT ; and NAVIGATION ; SENSES).

In the case of the annual cycle, the grounds for postulating an intrinsic rhythm, in at least some instances, is even stronger. The bird's year consists of an alternation between a breeding season and a non-reproductive phase, often with a migration before and after the former and always with a moult or moults interpolated at points of relative inactivity (see BREEDING SEASON ; MIGRATION ; MOULT). The timing of this cycle is adapted to ' ultimate ' factors of seasonal change, and is probably governed by ' proximate ' stimuli also arising from the environment but differing in nature according to circumstances (see PHOTOPERIODISM). In some instances, however, suitable extrinsic stimuli for return migration do not obviously exist (see MIGRATION) ; in such cases it seems likely that there is an inherent rhythm linked at one point in the year with environmental factors and otherwise operating as the result of the mere effluxion of time (probably following a refractory period—see Burger 1942). More concrete is the fact that some (but not all) species, when artificially transported from the Southern to the Northern Hemisphere, do not readily adapt their breeding times to the reversal of the climatic seasons. There is also one species, among other but less clear-cut examples, in which the natural breeding cycle is known to occupy a little over nine months, a periodicity not recognisable in the environment (see BREEDING SEASON).   A.L.T.

Baker, J. R. & Ranson, R. M. 1938. The breeding seasons of Southern Hemisphere birds in the Northern Hemisphere. Proc. Zool. Soc. Lond. (A) 108 : 101–141.
Burger, J. W. 1942. A review of experimental investigations of seasonal reproduction in birds. Wilson Bull. 61 : 211–230.
Thomson, A. L. 1951. Reproduction, migration and moult : factors controlling the annual cycle in birds. Proc. X Internat. Orn. Congr., Uppsala 1950 : 241–244.

RIB : see SKELETON

RICHMONDENINAE : see EMBERIZIDAE ; and CARDINAL-GROSBEAK

RICTAL: pertaining to the gape ; often applied to bristles in that area.

RIDING: young on parents' backs, see CARRYING.

RIFLE-BIRD: substantive name of species of *Ptiloris* and *Craspedophora* (see BIRD-OF-PARADISE).

RIFLEMAN: *Acanthisitta chloris* (see under WREN (3)).

RINGDOVE: name (also 'Ring-dove', 'Ring Dove') applied to the so-called *Streptopelia 'risoria'*, a domesticated variety of one of the subspecies of *S. decaocto* ; liable to confusion with 'Ring Dove' (etc.) used as an alternative name for the Wood Pigeon *Columba palumbus* (see PIGEON).

RINGING: the marking of birds to permit their subsequent recognition as individuals or as members of a limited group. Three techniques may be recognised : split-ring marking, colour ringing, and close ringing. In current British usage the term 'bird-ringing' is applied mainly to the first two ; and in North America and Australasia the term 'banding' is preferred to 'ringing'. The use of wing-clips may be regarded as a variant of split-ring marking.

Split Rings and Wing-clips. The rings are bands of metal that are fixed round one or other tarsus (or, occasionally, tibia) of the bird. They range in size from an inside diameter of 1·8 mm. to one of over 30 mm., and are usually made of aluminium or an alloy of aluminium. Small rings are commonly prepared in the shape of a 'C', which is closed to form a circle round the leg ; larger rings are often secured on the leg by having the two ends brought together and bent over to form a clip. Certain marking schemes also make use of wing-clips ; these resemble small safety-pins, the pin being passed through the patagium and secured in the cap, upon which is marked the inscription. Wing-clips are used chiefly for marking young Anatidae, which are very difficult to catch by the time that their legs have grown sufficiently to permit the use of ordinary rings ; their chief disadvantage is that they are inconspicuous when partly concealed by feathers, and hence they produce proportionately fewer recoveries than do rings. Each ring or clip carries an adequate postal address and a serial number. Usually both appear on the outside of the ring, but on the smallest sizes the address may be inside.

The rings may be fitted on nestlings, as soon as the legs and feet are sufficiently developed, or on fully grown birds caught specially for ringing (see TRAPPING). Details of species, race, age, sex (if ascertainable), date, and locality are recorded for each ring used, and the bird is released or returned to the nest. The ringing data are entered on schedules, which are sent to the headquarters of the scheme for reference should the bird be reported subsequently.

Objects. Ringing on these lines is undertaken to provide precise data on the life histories of individual birds. Two broad categories of study may be recognised, migration and vital statistics ; the more spectacular nature of migration studies attracted attention from the outset (see MIGRATION), whereas the use of ringing for population studies and similar investigations began much later and new methods of interpretation are still being developed.

Results. As ringing is based on the accumulation of individual case histories, it is generally more precise than other migration study techniques. Its limitations arise from the small proportion of birds recovered and the fact that the geographical distribution of these recoveries may not be fully representative. Its effectiveness in determining the summer and winter distribution of migratory species tends to bear close relationship to the density of the human populations in the areas concerned, their literacy, and their hunting traditions. Thus, for the Anatidae wintering in Britain, with a breeding range extending northwards and eastwards across Europe, the recovery rate may exceed 20 per cent for some species, and is generally over 10 per cent. In contrast, small passerines wintering in Africa may show a recovery rate of less than 0·5 per cent. Common British garden birds have over-all recovery rates in the range 1–4 per cent, although the figure for a particular species may vary appreciably between rural and suburban areas.

For species with low recovery rates there are generally insufficient records to permit detailed analysis of summer or winter distribution. Recoveries providing data about migration are more numerous and may be used to determine such features as the direction and sometimes the speed of migration, time of arrival of passage migrants in given areas, and so on. Only ringing can provide quantitative data for the study of partial migration and abmigration, and the presence of ringed birds in 'wrecks' and other weather movements is often a valuable guide to the origin of the populations involved. Locally, ringing has proved effective as a means of studying the gathering area for communal roosts and the feeding ranges of colonial nesters.

In the study of population dynamics, ringing data have been used to establish the age at which breeding

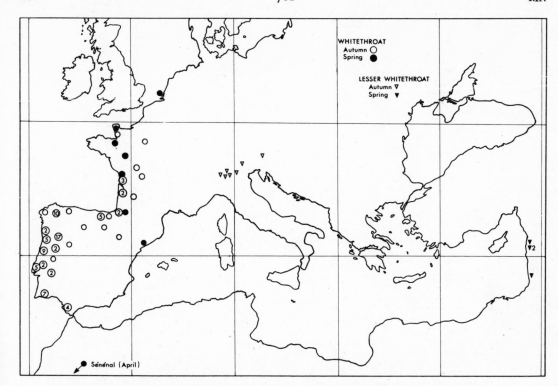

FIG 1. Foreign recoveries of Whitethroats *Sylvia communis* and Lesser Whitethroats *S. curruca* ringed as nest-lings in the British Isles. These records show a marked difference in directions of migration between two closely related species of summer visitors. The autumn records for the Whitethroat fall between 13 August and 24 November (but also include two winter records, December and January, from the Iberian Peninsula); the spring records between 15 March and 11 June. Those for the Lesser Whitethroat fall between 2 September and 17 October, and between 22 March and 23 April. *P. Davis, British Trust for Ornithology.*

begins; age structures of populations: annual, seasonal, and regional variations in mortality; common causes of death; and the like. The value of such data depends on the recoveries reported being representative of what happens to all birds; this may be almost impossible to prove, but allowance can be made for recognised sources of bias, and recovery data are generally regarded as valid (see POPULATION DYNAMICS). Longevity studies have been handicapped by the weakness of aluminium rings, but only duraluminium and monel have been used extensively as alternatives (see LONGEVITY).

History. Although there had been earlier sporadic attempts and a few schemes (in Great Britain from 1890) of limited scope, the first person to undertake systematic large-scale ringing was Christian Mortensen of Viborg (Denmark), who commenced his experiments in 1899. Germany was quick to take up the study (1903) and the pioneer 'Vogelwarte' at Rossitten, on the Baltic, did much to establish the value of ringing. The practice soon gathered impetus: Hungary (1908), Great Britain (1909),

Yugoslavia (1910), Holland (1911), Sweden (1911), Denmark (1914), and Norway (1914) all had effective schemes before the 1914–18 war. Between the two World Wars there was a rapid growth in the number of ringing schemes, especially in Europe, at least fifteen being established between 1918 and 1930, and a further eight by 1939. In North America the start was later, for although an American Bird Banding Association was founded in 1909 (and Jack Miner was marking wildfowl before 1914 with rings carrying Biblical quotations instead of serial numbers!), the two main centres, at Washington and Ottawa, were not established until 1920 and 1922 respectively; but the growth of activities was rapid and the scale of ringing soon outpaced work of individual European centres. Outside Europe and North America, ringing has been on a small scale, and generally of recent development, as is shown by the following dates of commencement: Japan (1924), Egypt (1937), Union of South Africa (1948), Belgian Congo (1954), Tasmania (1947), New Zealand (1947),

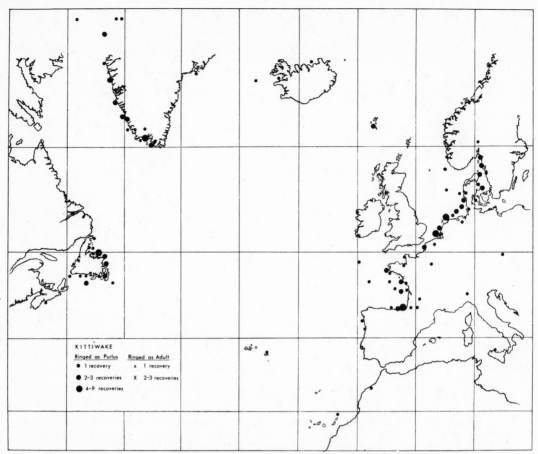

FIG 2. Foreign recoveries of Kittiwakes *Larus tridactylus* ringed at breeding places (especially the Farne Islands,
Northumberland) in the British Isles, chiefly as nestlings. The records are evidence of a wide dispersal of
native British birds in northern latitudes, with a large transoceanic element. This species of gull breeds on
both sides of the Atlantic Ocean. *British Trust for Ornithology.*

Australia (1953). Marking has also been done in the
Antarctic (British Antarctic Survey) and from time
to time on oceanic islands such as Ascension (B.O.U.
Centenary Expedition).

In Britain, H. F. Witherby in London and A.
Landsborough Thomson in Aberdeen both started
comprehensive schemes in 1909. The latter scheme
came to an end during the First World War, but
the former developed steadily under the guidance of
its founder until 1937, when responsibility for the
organisation was handed over to the British Trust
for Ornithology, and a special Bird-Ringing Committee was appointed to control activities, with
headquarters at the British Museum (Natural
History). Although the scheme was for many
years financially self-supporting, a stage was reached
when it could no longer be administered on a
voluntary basis, and from 1954 the Nature Conservancy has given financial support for a whole-

time Ringing Officer and other staff (now housed
at Tring, Hertfordshire). See also OBSERVATORY,
BIRD.

In North America the main ringing effort has
been directed towards birds of economic importance, and the high annual intake of recoveries has
necessitated the use of data processing machines
and electronic computers to facilitate analysis.
Sophisticated capture-recapture techniques have
been evolved for use in population studies, while
in the field of passerine migration corporate studies
are undertaken annually under the code name
'Operation Recovery'.

Colour Ringing. Colour rings are commonly
made of celluloid, other materials used being
anodised aluminium and plastics. They are supplied in a wide range of colours, and their purpose
is to permit recognition in the field. Two systems
are in common use : separate colour coding, one or

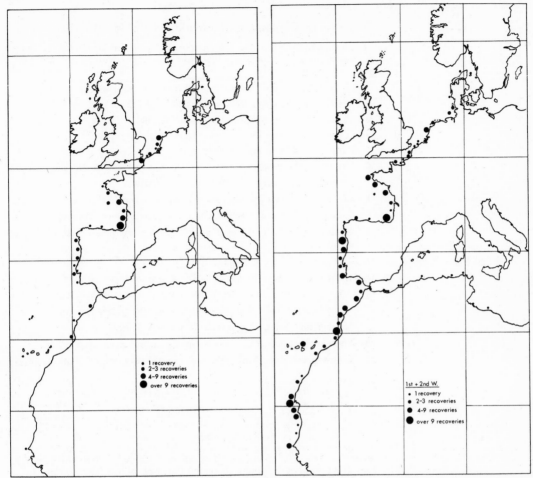

FIG 3. Foreign recoveries from November to February of Gannets *Sula bassana* ringed as nestlings in the British Isles : **a** recoveries in the 1st and 2nd winters of life (37 additional recoveries in home waters, not shown) ; **b** recoveries in the 3rd and later winters (26 additional in home waters). Comparison of the two maps shows that the southward movement along the Atlantic seaboard is more pronounced in young than in older birds. *British Trust for Ornithology.*

more rings being used on one or both legs to render a bird recognisable at a glance as a particular individual ; and mass-marking, the same colour being allocated to a group of birds, e.g. a brood, a colony, or those ringed in a particular period. This second method, which does not permit individual recognition, is used to study such aspects as local dispersal of juveniles and the return of wintering birds to the same area in successive winters. Despite the limitations that only the informed can interpret observations of colour-ringed birds and that the colours tend to fade with age, the technique is indispensable when recognition in the field is important.

Close Ringing. This technique differs from the others in that the rings are not split but are true rings. Their use is confined to nestlings, which are marked while the foot is still small enough to permit the rings to be slipped on ; once the foot is fully grown the ring cannot be removed. Close rings are of little value to ornithologists, but aviculturists and pigeon-fanciers use them extensively to establish individual identity and ownership ; and in British law a correctly fitted close ring is taken as evidence that the bird was bred in captivity.

See Plates 25 and 48a (phot.).   R.S.

Mortensen, H. C. C. 1899–1922 (Dansk Orn. Foren. Tidsskr. etc.). *Reprinted in* Jespersen, P. & Taning, A. V. (eds.) 1950. Studies in Bird Migration, being the collected papers of H. Chr. C. Mortensen. Copenhagen. (The pioneer project in scientific bird-ringing.)

Thomson, A. L. 1911. The possibilities of bird-marking,

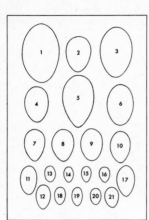

⅕ more than natural size

Plate 43 · Egg Coloration and Marking by A. M. HUGHES

The purpose of this plate is to illustrate the greatest variety of coloration, uniform or marked, in a wide range of eggs from all over the world. See article EGGS, NATURAL HISTORY OF.

1 Ingouf's Tinamotis *Tinamotis ingoufi* (southern Argentine)
2 Bronze-wing Courser *Rhinoptilus chalcopterus* (Africa)
3 Chilean Tinamou *Nothoprocta perdicaria* (Chile)
4 Lesser Bird-of-paradise *Paradisaea minor* (New Guinea)
5 Cape Crow *Corvus capensis* (Africa)
6 Cameroon Bareheaded Rockfowl *Picathartes oreas* (West Africa)
7 Three-banded Plover *Charadrius tricollaris* (Africa)
8 African Jaçana or Lilytrotter *Actophilornis africanus* (Africa)
9 Variegated Bittern *Ixobrychus involucris* (southern South America)
10 White-throated Laughing Thrush *Garrulax albogularis* (Himalayas and western China)
11, 12 Brown Babbler *Turdoides plebeja* (Equatorial Africa)
13, 14, 15, 16 Tawny-flanked Prinia *Prinia subflava affinis* (southern Africa)
17 Grayish Saltator *Saltator coerulescens* (Central and South America)
18 Marsh Grass-warbler *Cisticola galactotes galactotes* (southern Africa)
19 Another subspecies, *C. g. nyansae* (Equatorial Africa)
20 Another subspecies, *C. g. haematocephala* (coastal East Africa)
21 Yellow-green Vireo *Vireo virescens flavoviridis* (Central and South America)

The six immaculate eggs include examples having such a highly glossed surface as to appear varnished (1, 3, 10), some that are less glossy (11 and 12), and one with a dull surface (9). The egg of the Cape Crow (5) shows specific erythrism in a family of which the other members normally lay greenish eggs, and also a common form of spotting. In general, the range of marking is so wide that some distinctive types—especially of girdling—have had to be omitted.

The most striking egg is that of the Lilytrotter (8), with its highly polished surface and medley of extraordinary, dense scribbling. The bird-of-paradise egg (4) is typical of the unique marking of the eggs of that family—most distinctive, broad, elongate streaks. The Saltator (17) provides an example of girdling by well-spread, irregular, fine hair-lines around the top. The vireo (21) demonstrates sparse, discrete spotting. The courser (2) has a remarkably handsome egg (especially when fresh, before blowing) that typifies the common combination of bold, almost black surface markings and greyish underlying markings. The *Picathartes* egg (6), similarly, exemplifies a common type of light brown or yellow-brown surface markings on underlying greys. The plover's egg (7), besides showing distinct zonal bands, also typifies fine dark streaks and spots on underlying greys.

The three races of *Cisticola galactotes* illustrate geographical variation within a species. The eggs of the nominate *C. g. galactotes* (18) are uniform terra-cotta ; those of *C. g. haematocephala* (20) are marbled with shades of rufous ; those of *C. g. nyansae* (19) are usually quite distinct with white ground, finely and darkly speckled—but in the neighbourhood of Nairobi, in Kenya, all three varieties of egg are known from the local representatives of *C. g. nyansae*.

The four examples of eggs of *Prinia subflava affinis* (13, 14, 15, 16) demonstrate variation within a single subspecies in one locality ; although showing a wide divergence in ground colour (those figured show white, light blue, pale rufous, and pale olive-green grounds, respectively), these eggs indicate a similar pattern of somewhat marbled marking, with a wreath of fine irregular hair-lines superimposed around the top of the broad end. In Nigeria, the immaculate eggs of *Turdoides plebeja* (11, 12) likewise reveal remarkable divergence of coloration within the nominate race—from hedgesparrow blue to turquoise blue, grey-blue, grey, mauve, or lilac (a pink and a grey one are figured) ; two mauve eggs and a pink one have been found in the same set.   C.R.S.P.

Ann Hughes
1961

with special reference to the Aberdeen University Bird-Migration Inquiry. Proc. Roy. Phys. Soc. Edinb. 18 : 204–218. (An early assessment.)

Schüz, E. & Weigold, H. 1931. Atlas des Vogelzugs nach den Beringungergebnissen bei palaearktischen Vögeln. Berlin.

Rydzewski, W. 1951. A historical review of bird marking. Dansk Orn. Foren. Tidsskr. 45 : 61–95.

Lockley, R. M. & Russell, R. 1953. Ringing Birds. London.

Spencer, R. 1959. The progress and prospects of bird ringing. Ibis 101 : 416–424. (A recent assessment.)

Numerous contributions on the objects, development, and technique of ringing will be found especially in the journals *Bird Banding* (U.S.A.) and *The Ring* (ed. W. Rydzewski, Warsaw). Results of the various national schemes are published in the ornithological journals of the different countries, notably in *British Birds* (London) and *Die Vogelwarte* (Stuttgart), the latter also providing a guide to the current literature on an international basis.

RING-SPECIES:

term (for which Meinertzhagen has alternatively suggested 'rejungent species') expressing the concept that a species may divide into a graded series of geographical forms and that extreme members of the series may later come into direct contact, through range expansion, and then prove to be so different from each other as to behave as separate species ; this occurs in that fraction of the total range in which both forms are found, whereas elsewhere (the long way round the ring, so to speak) they remain connected by intermediate forms. In such a case, when the extreme forms are recognised as separate species, the allocation of intermediates as subspecies of one or the other becomes somewhat arbitrary. Examples are to be found in *Parus major/minor, Lanius schach/tephronotus, Pycnono-*

Plate 44 · Colour Photography

a *Upper :* Hummingbird in Flight (1⅔ times natural size)—Delalande's Plovercrest *Stephanoxis delalandei.* A male of this Brazilian species is shown flying *back* from a feeding point. The picture not only portrays the species and illustrates the remarkable flight, but also exemplifies the possibilities of high-speed colour photography.
Photograph by Crawford H. Greenewalt ; courtesy of National Geographic Magazine, copyright American Museum of Natural History.

b *Lower :* Cryptic Coloration—Rednecked Nightjar *Caprimulgus ruficollis.* This picture, taken in Spain, is of a bird difficult to see on its nest on the ground among fallen twigs and the like. As well as portraying the species and illustrating the biological point, the picture shows the value of colour photography in accurately recording the appearance of a bird in its natural setting.

Phot. Eric Hosking.

(See articles FLIGHT ; HUMMINGBIRD ; COLORATION, ADAPTIVE ; NIGHTJAR)

tus barbatus/tricolor/capensis, Acrocephalus arundinaceus/stentoreus, Apus apus/pallidus, Merops superciliosus/philippinus, and *Larus argentatus/fuscus.* See ISOLATING MECHANISM ; SPECIATION ; SPECIES ; SUBSPECIES.

RITUALISATION:

the evolutionary process tending to stereotype patterns of display performance (see DISPLAY). Signal movements comprise intraspecifically directed courtship and social displays, and interspecific displays directed against predators. Such behaviour patterns have certain features in common. The form of the movements is closely correlated with the morphological structures that they serve to exhibit : and the movements in most cases have proved, on investigation, to be inborn. The co-ordination is rigidly determined, and a given display is highly stereotyped. Comparative studies have suggested that these specialised movements have been evolved from more ancient behaviour patterns ; for example, locomotory movements and actions concerned with heat regulation, care of the body surface, and the like have been postulated to underlie the present forms taken by particular displays. The displays have consequently been termed ' derived ', and the evolutionary process by which they have arisen is known as ' ritualisation '. Although these phenomena have been studied in a wider range of animal groups, bird behaviour provides very satisfactory material for the study of the evolution of social signals.

Intraspecific displays present two distinct evolutionary problems ; one concerns the evolution of the motor patterns and causal organisation of the displays themselves, while the other concerns the evolution of the special patterns of responsiveness in the reacting individuals. Almost nothing is known about the latter problem, and so far attention has been largely concentrated on the former. The causal problems presented by the evolution of ritualised motor patterns may be considered under two headings : First, in terms of the changes taking place in the motor co-ordination of the ancestral acts ; and, secondly, in terms of the changes in motivation which have in most cases accompanied them.

Co-ordination changes have been classified by a number of authors ; they include changes in the intensity or strength of the motor patterns, increase or decrease in the speed of performance, the omission of components, and changes in component sequence and their detailed co-ordination. Often, components are differentially exaggerated. Lastly, one of the most important and frequently encountered changes is the tendency for a simple motor act to be rhythmically repeated. These trends have been described as leading to the production of acts of 'typical intensity'. Acts so characterised are highly stereotyped, and tend to occur at the same strength irrespective of the strength of the eliciting stimulus ; they are, therefore, on the way to being all-or-none responses. Sexual displays of this type have been described from many avian groups ; estrildid weavers (Estrildidae), finches (Fringillidae), buntings (Emberizidae), and gulls (Larinae) have been the subject of particularly intensive comparative study by ethologists, and the first of these groups provides numerous excellent examples of the association of stereotyped acts performed at typical intensity, with highly specialised and often bizarre morphological patterns to the exhibition of which the movements are perfectly adapted.

Perhaps the majority of displays have been evolved from locomotory and comfort movements (see FEATHER MAINTENANCE). For example, they may be derived from the intention movements of flight, or from preening movements, which are often ancestrally performed as 'displacement activities' in approach/avoidance conflicts arising in sexual contexts (see DISPLACEMENT ACTIVITY). It follows, therefore, that the ritualised displays of a given species are commonly found to co-exist with the behaviour patterns from which they were originally evolved. This fact has necessitated the development of a further concept, that of 'emancipation'. As originally used, this term simply characterised the change in neural mechanism that must be supposed to underlie the change in form of a ritualised movement. There may, possibly, be instances in which the change in form of a movement has been accomplished by, for example, an alteration in the position of a muscle attachment, but in most cases emancipation as originally used had much the same meaning as 'ritualisation'. However it has more recently come by usage to have a more specialised connotation.

Where a display and the movement ancestral to it co-exist in a single species, certain factors must be present to prevent the simultaneous release of both patterns. Control of the gross context of a ritualised pattern may be achieved by the acquisition of differential specificity to hormonal priming ; sexual and parental displays are specifically affected by hormones, and may require particular and even delicately balanced endocrine states for their appearance (see ENDOCRINE SYSTEM). But the motor patterns of an ancestral act and its derivative are not necessarily mechanically incompatible, and there are, therefore, systems preventing their simultaneous performance. The prevention of such potential interference between the ancestral and the derived patterns appears

to be achieved by the operation of two sets of factors : on the perceptual side, there is the acquisition of different releasing systems governing the old and new activities, and, most probably in addition, the evolution of inhibitory relationships between the systems of neural activity underlying the two acts. Thus, several criteria are available that allow some assessment to be made of the degree of separation of the causal systems mediating the two acts, and 'emancipation' can be regarded as that evolutionary process responsible for those aspects of the causal separation of a ritualised act from its ancestral pattern that are distinct from mere differences in the form and co-ordination of the motor patterns. It is a weakness of studies on the ritualised displays of birds that to date most of the evidence bearing on the problem of emancipation has been derived from the contexts in which displays occur. There is an urgent need for more precise experimental investigations in this field.

Comparative studies have investigated the role of the environment in providing selection pressures influencing the course of the evolution of displays. The view has been expressed that sexual displays in particular are subject only to intraspecifically mediated selection pressures and are, therefore, largely independent of the environment. Were this strictly true, these displays would occupy a unique position in avian taxonomy, for the possibility of environmentally induced convergence would be ruled out. Recent evidence suggests that this extreme view may need to be modified ; cases have been described in which displays appear to have suffered some modification in response to particular features of the normal habitat, to predation or its absence. There is also much to indicate that social signals may be selected for maximum interspecific divergence when two or more closely related species occupy the same habitat. Relationships of this type may prove to be more widespread than has been realised.

While the majority of studies of ritualisation have been concerned with rather simple instances in which the components of the displays are fairly easily detected, the final products of ritualisation can be extremely complex. Obvious examples are the elaborate ceremonies of the bowerbirds (Ptilonorhynchidae), courtships such as that of the Cock-of-the-rock *Rupicola* sp., and the grotesque communal displays of certain Neotropical manakins (Pipridae). Direct analysis of these examples is often difficult, but even the most complicated displays would seem to be explicable in terms of the general concepts that have been drawn from simpler cases of ritualisation. A.D.B.

ROA: former Maori name for a bird that may have been *Apteryx haasti*, as some authorities have concluded, or possibly a late surviving species of Dinornithiformes (see MOA).

ROADRUNNER: substantive name of *Geococcyx* spp. (see CUCKOO).

ROATELO: in the plural ('roatelos'), alternative general term for the Mesitornithidae (see MESITE).

ROBIN: commonest name in Britain today for *Erithacus rubecula*, the more formal alternative 'Redbreast' having become an almost pedantic usage. From this original source, the name has been transplanted to other parts of the English-speaking world and attached to local species actually or supposedly resembling the prototype, in being redbreasted or in other ways. Thus, in North America it is applied to the familiar *Turdus migratorius*, a larger but also redbreasted bird; and the Indian Robin *Saxicoloides fulicata* is a chat with chestnut under parts. It has also been used by ornithologists in fabricating English names for foreign species of Turdinae, either as a simple substantive name or in compounds such as 'magpie-robin', 'scrub-robin', 'bush-robin', and 'robin-chat' (see under THRUSH; also CHAT; SCRUB-ROBIN). See Plate 22c (phot.).

Outside the Turdinae, 'robin' is the substantive name used in the Australasian Region for various Muscicapinae, some of them with red breasts, e.g. *Petroica* spp. in Australia and *Miro* spp. in New Zealand (see FLYCATCHER (1)); and in Australia for certain Pachycephalinae, e.g. *Eopsaltria* spp. (see THICKHEAD). And it is an avicultural name ('Pekin Robin') for *Leiothrix lutea* (see BABBLER).

Further, 'robin' is misapplied in some quite unrelated groups, e.g. as a popular misnomer for the Jamaican Tody *Todus todus*, a small, dumpy, redbreasted bird (see TODY).

ROC: see FABULOUS BIRDS

ROCKFOWL: substantive name of *Picathartes* spp. (see BABBLER). See Plates 30 (colour) and 43 (egg).

RODENT RUN: see DISTRACTION DISPLAY

ROLLER: substantive name of the species of the subfamily Coraciinae of the Coraciidae (Coraciiformes, suborder Coracii); in the plural, general term for the family—for the other subfamily, the Brachypteraciinae (by some given separate familial rank), see GROUND-ROLLER; and for the monotypic family Leptosomatidae see CUCKOO-ROLLER. The typical rollers (Coraciinae) constitute an Old World group of stoutly built birds of 9½–13 inches in length (not counting the tail streamers present in

some). The head is large, the neck short, the bill strong, wide, somewhat decurved, and slightly hooked. The legs are short, the feet strong and syndactyl. The wings are strong, and the tail is also long—square, slightly notched or deeply forked at the end. The plumage of most species shows a pattern of bright colours, various shades of green, blue, and chestnut being the most usual; there is little or no difference between the sexes.

Rollers get their name from their habit of somersaulting and rolling in the air during display flights. They are at all times strong on the wing, and wonderfully acrobatic on occasion, such as when attacking a passing bird-of-prey. The migratory species travel by day, usually in small parties. Otherwise they are solitary as a rule, and spend long periods conspicuously perched (with a rather upright stance) on branches, posts, or wires, swooping down from time to time on some insect or other small animal detected on the ground—and when on the ground they hop. Small birds are sometimes taken. Some species catch insects on the wing, and the birds may congregate at bush-fires. Fruits are sometimes eaten. The birds tend to be noisy, uttering loud and harsh cries; and they are often aggressive and quarrelsome.

Rollers nest in holes in trees, banks, or rocks, adding little or no lining, and sometimes in the old nests of other species. The 3–6 eggs are white. The nidicolous young are naked when hatched and are cared for by both parents. As in some related families, the feathers of the nestlings remain closely encased in their waxy sheaths until the birds are almost ready to leave the nest; the first plumage is a duller version of that of the adults.

The subfamily is a small one and restricted to the tropical and milder temperate parts of the Old World; Africa has the largest number of species. There are in all 11–12 species, divided between the genera *Coracias* and *Eurystomus*. The European Roller *C. garrulus* (an uncommon vagrant to the British Isles) breeds in southern and eastern Europe, western Asia, and North Africa, and migrates mainly to tropical and southern Africa. Much of the plumage shows a blending of azure and greenish blue, but the back is tawny and there is purple on rump and wings; when it flies, a beautiful purple-blue band across the flight feathers is revealed. The Abyssinian Roller *C. abyssinica* has a similar plumage pattern but the colours are even brighter, and the tail, instead of being square, has the outermost pair of feathers greatly elongated, extending more than 6 inches beyond the next pair.

The Blue-bellied Roller *C. cyanogaster* of West Africa is a markedly stout bird of similar size but with a less deeply forked tail ; its plumage pattern is quite different, but none the less striking : the head, nape, and breast are pinkish-fawn, the back is almost black, the belly deep blue, the wings are dark blue with a lighter patch, and the tail is greenish-blue. There are 3 other African species, including the Racquet-tailed Roller *C. spatulata*, in which the elongated outermost tail feathers have broad racquet-shaped ends ; but the genus is not represented in Madagascar. The Indian Roller (or ' Blue Jay ') *C. benghalensis*, with 3 races, is distributed through southern Asia from eastern Arabia to Cambodia ; and *C. temminckii* is restricted to the Celebes and neighbouring islands.

The broad-billed rollers of the genus *Eurystomus* are rather smaller birds. They do not roll or tumble, but make long swooping flights ; they feed on the wing. Half-a-dozen races of the Broad-billed Roller *E. glaucurus* inhabit tropical Africa (*E. g. afer* of West Africa treated by some as a separate species). The yellow bill is broad and triangular, the gape very wide. The plumage is cinnamon-brown above and lilac below, with ultra-marine flight feathers, and a mainly lighter blue tail. The nominate race breeds in Madagascar, from which it migrates north-westwards as far as the eastern Congo. The Blue-throated Roller *E. gularis*, with a more restricted range in tropical Africa, is rather similar. The remaining species, the Broad-mouthed Dollarbird *E. orientalis*, is so-called because of a wing speculum resembling a silver coin ; it is represented by numerous races from northern India to Manchuria and as far east as the Solomon Islands. The Australian race *E. o. pacificus* breeds in the northern and eastern parts of the continent and migrates to New Guinea and neighbouring islands.

See Plate 17 (colour). A.L.T.

Dresser, H. E. 1893. A Monograph of the Coraciidae, or Family of the Rollers. Farnborough, Kent.
Peters, J. L. 1945. Check-list of Birds of the World vol. 5. Cambridge, Mass.

ROLLER CANARY: see CAGE BIRD

ROOK: *Corvus frugilegus* (see CROW (1)).

ROOKERY: primarily a nesting colony of Rooks *Corvus frugilegus* ; but applied to colonies of some other birds, including penguins (Spheniscidae).

ROOSTING: term covering the sleeping of birds, but imprecise in that it includes resting behaviour when the bird is not actually asleep ; on the other hand, it is not generally used for the occasional ' catnaps ' of a few minutes that many birds take during an otherwise active period. The whole

subject of roosting has never been reviewed, although numerous observations on the habits of particular species are scattered through the literature. Most papers devoted specifically to roosting are concerned with timing, of which those of Franz, Kluijver, and Dunnett & Hinde may be mentioned. Most of the information on sleeping postures is due to Heinroth (see section on comfort movements under FEATHER MAINTENANCE).

Times. The time of day when birds roost is adapted to the time of their other business, especially the time when they must feed, and hence is usually at night. Species that feed at night roost during the day. Waders (Charadrii) and wildfowl (Anatidae) on the seacoast may also be seen asleep during the day, because it is the state of the tide that often determines when their food is available, and, as they find their food largely by touch, they can feed when it is dark.

Diurnal birds do not all become active at the same time in the morning, and some of the differences between species can be related to special habits. The larger raptors (Falconiformes) do not take wing until the sun is strong enough to produce the thermals necessary for soaring. Swifts (Apodidae), bee-eaters (Meropidae), and at least one American flycatcher (Tyrannidae)—all of them feeders on flying insects—become active relatively late as compared with small birds for which food is available earlier in the morning.

Birds roost for a shorter time in summer than in winter. But even in the continuous daylight of the Arctic summer they take time for sleeping ; some species do this at a particular time of day, usually around or a little before midnight, others sporadically throughout the twenty-four hours. As the times of sunrise and sunset change during the year, the times of awakening and roosting change accordingly ; the awakening is almost always at a lower light intensity than the roosting. Some authors have claimed that there is a light intensity for awakening (' Weckhelligkeit ') characteristic for each species, but the term does not seem very useful since prolonged studies have mostly shown gradual changes during the season, and these are even more marked in the times of going to roost. This seasonal trend is most obvious in high latitudes, e.g. Lapland, where in the middle of winter passerines awaken and retire when there is far less light than there is in summer when they respectively leave and go to their roosts. This must be because they cannot otherwise get enough food in the short winter day. In temperate latitudes there is the same tendency to delay the time of roosting as the days shorten in winter and this is probably also connected with the need to feed, since Great Tits *Parus major* provided with unlimited food roost earlier than their less fortunate fellows. On the other hand, as the days lengthen again in spring, birds in temperate latitudes tend to awaken earlier relatively to the sun, rather than later as the Lapland birds do. This trend, which in the Great Tit at least is not the result of hunger, is probably due to the onset of the breeding season and over-rides the other seasonal trend.

Superimposed on the gradual seasonal changes are day-to-day deviations due in part to the weather, especially when this affects light intensity. But it is not light alone that determines the waking-sleeping cycle, since some species kept under artificially constant conditions maintain a rhythm similar to that under natural conditions, at least for a few days.

General Behaviour. Roosting behaviour varies from species to species, and to some extent within a species. Birds with territories usually roost there during the breeding season, although this does not always apply to colonial sea birds such as the terns (Sterninae). Outside the breeding season, birds that spend their days in flocks generally roost communally, e.g. Rooks *Corvus frugilegus*, Starlings *Sturnus vulgaris*, finches (Fringillidae), hirundines, pigeons (Columbidae), many waders (Charadrii), and even raptors such as *Falco amurensis*. Some relatively unsociable species, such as Pied Wagtails *Motacilla alba*, occasionally assemble to roost in great numbers.

In the late summer, Starlings often occupy small communal roosts near their feeding places, but when winter sets in abandon them for a larger roost; the latter may collect birds from a considerable distance, even as far as 30 miles away. Some roosts are used winter after winter for years, and one is known to have been occupied for at least 135 years. The numbers present at a large roost are difficult to estimate, but sometimes there must be at least hundreds of thousands of Starlings. The roosts of the now extinct Passenger Pigeon *Ectopistes migratorius* of America must have been even more impressive, judging from the surviving accounts; the Red-billed Dioch *Quelea quelea*, a grain-eating weaver and the scourge of large parts of Africa, collects at night in millions (see QUELEA CONTROL). Before retiring for the night many of these communal roosters indulge in spectacular aerobatics. At a large roost the droppings sometimes damage the vegetation and occasionally branches are broken with the sheer weight of perching birds.

Many birds roost in cover of some kind, either in reeds, thickets, or taller trees—even on buildings. Larks (Alaudidae), partridges *Perdix* spp., and waders roost in the open, while waterfowl and gulls (Larinae) often choose an island or move to open water. Other species, whether solitary or social, have more special requirements. Many hole-nesting birds roost also in holes—woodpeckers (Picidae), tits (Paridae), House Sparrows *Passer domesticus*—sometimes using the same place night after night and defending it against other would-be users. The holes are mostly pre-existing ones, often old nest holes, but woodpeckers occasionally chisel themselves special roosting chambers. Old nests are also used by more open-nesting birds at times, especially at the end of the season by the family that was reared there. (See also NEST-SITE SELECTION.) Tree-creepers *Certhia familiaris* roost in the deeply creviced bark of the Wellingtonia (*Sequoia*). Wrens (Troglodytidae) roost in holes or nests, sometimes in parties, and some of the American species build special roosting nests (as the Bananaquit *Coereba flaveola* is also reported to do). In winter several species of grouse (Tetraonidae) tunnel out roosts beneath the snow; the Ruffed Grouse *Bonasa umbellus* begins his by plunging from flight into the snow. It has now been definitely established that Swifts *Apus apus* can pass the night on the wing, although they use more conventional sites; the remarkable diversity in the roosting habits of species of swifts has been fully discussed by Lack.

Requirements. Roosting implies two special requirements. First, the roost must provide protection from predators at a time when the bird is drowsy and unresponsive to danger. Holes presumably provide security from enemies; wildfowl roosting in the open are safer from surprise by predators; quail *Coturnix* spp., in addition, roost in a circle, each bird facing outwards to give all-round observation; pheasants *Phasianus* etc. sleeping on a branch are out of reach of a fox, which would find them if they stayed on the ground where they spend the day. In a communal roost the alarm call of the most alert individual presumably warns its companions of danger. The ability of Swifts to pass the night on the wing is also thought to be an adaptation to the difficulty of finding a safe roost away from their nest places.

The second requirement is that to maintain their body-temperature birds must burn their reserve food supply, which they cannot replenish till the morning. This is particularly serious in cold climates for small birds, which have a large surface/volume ratio and therefore lose heat relatively fast (see HEAT REGULATION). To reduce heat loss, many roosting birds fluff their feathers, which improves the insulating properties of the plumage. Those using holes and other more or less confined spaces have the advantage that the air surrounding them is warmed by the heat they lose. Great Tits often roost among brambles in the summer but occupy holes when it becomes colder. Another way of reducing heat loss at night or during longer spells of cold weather is for a group of birds to huddle together; this device is used by Long-tailed Tits *Aegithalos caudatus*, Treecreepers, wrens, swifts, the African colies (*Colius* spp.), the Australian wood-swallows (*Artamus* spp.), the Emperor Penguin *Aptenodytes forsteri*, and others.

The tiny hummingbirds (Trochilidae) sometimes roost in enclosed spaces such as caves, but they also have the remarkable ability, for birds, of becoming cold-blooded. At night their body temperature may fall as much as 40° F. and they become torpid. In this state they lose less heat because there is a smaller temperature drop between the body and the surrounding air, and as a result they can live in areas where they could not otherwise survive the long cool nights (see TORPIDITY).

Posture. In the familiar sleeping posture of birds the head is not put under the wing, as is commonly said, but rests on the back with the bill inserted beneath the scapular feathers or, as in the penguins (Spheniscidae), which have not distinct scapulars, hooked behind the wing. But even species that normally roost in this way do not always do so, and sometimes sleep with the bill forward, the head being hunched up between the shoulders. While birds of many different families sometimes sleep with the bill on the back, others never do so; pigeons, storks (Ciconiidae), and grebes (Podicipitidae), for instance, always sleep with the bill forward. In other ways too, different groups of birds differ in the details of their sleeping postures. Woodpeckers and treecreepers roost clinging vertically, and the *Loriculus* parrots hang upside down like bats.

Many species roost on some kind of perch. They are able to do so because of a special locking device that automatically curls up the toes as the tarsal joint is flexed. The more the leg muscles relax, the tighter the toes grip the perch. In addition there are specially roughened areas on some of the tendons and their enveloping sheaths, which improve the effect by preventing the tendons slipping.

J.M.C.

Dunnett, G. E. & Hinde, R. A. 1953. The winter roosting and awakening behaviour of captive great tits. Brit. J. Anim. Behav. 1 : 91–95.

Franz, J. 1949. Jahres- und Tagesrhythmus einiger Vögel in Nordfinnland. Z. Tierpsychol. 6 : 309–329.

Kluijver, H. N. 1950. Daily routines of the great tit *Parus m. major* (L.). Ardea 38 : 99–135.

Lack, D. 1956. Swifts in a Tower. London.

ROSELLA: substantive name (sometimes ' roselle ') of *Platycercus* spp. (see PARROT).

ROSTRATULIDAE: see PAINTED SNIPE

ROSTRUM : the bill or beak (see BILL); adjective, ' rostral '.

ROSY-BILL: *Netta peposaca* (see DUCK).

ROSYTHROAT: *Heliodoxa rubinoides cervinigularis* (for family see HUMMINGBIRD).

ROULROUL: *Rollulus roulroul* (see under PHEASANT).

ROUTE: see MIGRATION

RUBY: *Clytolaema rubricauda* (for family see HUMMINGBIRD).

RUBY-CHEEK: name, alternatively ' Ruby-cheeked Sunbird ', of *Anthreptes singalensis* (see SUNBIRD).

RUBYTHROAT: substantive name of some *Luscinia* spp. (for subfamily see THRUSH).

RUFF: name of *Philomachus pugnax* as a species; also a term particularly for the male, the female then being termed ' reeve ' (see SANDPIPER). See Plates 20 (colour) and 24b (phot.).

RUKH: see FABULOUS BIRDS

RULES: statements formulating what appear to be regularities in natural phenomena, e.g. in the correlation of morphological variation with geographical, climatic, or other factors—e.g. ALLEN'S RULE ; BERGMANN'S RULE ; GLOGER'S RULE.

RUMP: see TOPOGRAPHY

RUNNING: see LOCOMOTION ; LEG

RYNCHOPIDAE: see under CHARADRIIFORMES ; and SKIMMER

S

SABREWING: substantive name of *Campylopterus* (including '*Pampa*') spp. (for family see HUMMINGBIRD).

SACRAL: pertaining to the part of the vertebral column between the lumbar and caudal portions (see SKELETON).

SADDLEBACK: *Creadion* ('*Philesturnus*') *carunculatus* (see WATTLEBIRD (2)).

SADDLEBILL: sometimes used alone as the name of the Saddle-billed Stork *Ephippiorhynchus senegalensis* (see STORK).

SAGE-BRUSH: an environment, consisting of shrubs growing in moderate density, characteristic of parts of North America.

SAGITTAL: in the median longitudinal plane of the body, e.g. a section from head to tail in the mid-line; the 'sagittal suture' is the junction of the parietal bones of the skull.

SAGITTARII; SAGITTARIIDAE: see under FALCONIFORMES; and SECRETARY-BIRD

SAKABULA: *Euplectes progne* (see WEAVER).

SAKER: *Falco cherrug* (see FALCON).

SALIVARY GLANDS: see ALIMENTARY SYSTEM; PALATE; TONGUE

SALTATOR: generic name used as substantive name of *Saltator* spp. (see CARDINAL-GROSBEAK). See Plate 43 (egg).

SALT GLAND: alternatively 'lateral nasal gland' (see EXCRETION, EXTRARENAL; NARIS).

SAMPLING: see STATISTICAL SIGNIFICANCE

SANCTUARY: see CONSERVATION

SANDERLING: *Crocethia alba* (see SANDPIPER); see Plate 11a (phot.).

SANDGROUSE: substantive name of the species of Pteroclididae (Columbiformes, suborder Pterocletes); in the plural (unchanged), general term for the family. This mainly Afro-Asian group has affinities with the pigeons (Columbidae), although there is a case for separate ordinal rank; any resemblance to grouse (Tetraonidae) or other gallinaceous birds is superficial.

Of the size of small pigeons, all the species are terrestrial. Their general coloration is that of the soil on which they live, with much spotting and barring; the females are less brightly coloured than the males. Those species inhabiting open desert tend to be paler above than those spending daylight in the shade of bushes. The plumage is close and thick, with a sun-resisting underdown, and the skin is very tough. The central tail feathers are often elongated. The wing has 11 primaries and is aquintocubital; the primaries are very long, a fact relevant to the long daily flights to water undertaken by most species. Sandgrouse cannot run, their progression on the ground being a rapid walk or waddle; the legs are short and in some species the toes are partially webbed.

The group includes only 2 genera, *Syrrhaptes* and *Pterocles*, the former having the tarsus feathered back and front to the base of the toes, the latter having the tarsus feathered in front only. Other proposed genera based on whether the birds drink by night or by day, or on the length of the central tail feathers, cannot be accepted.

The 2 species of *Syrrhaptes*, Pallas's Sandgrouse *S. paradoxus* and the Tibetan Sandgrouse *S. tibetanus*, live in desert or semi-desert countries at high altitudes or in lowland steppe in central Asia. The Tibetan form is almost sedentary, but Pallas's Sandgrouse has undergone eruptive migrations in, especially, 1863, 1872, 1876, 1888, and 1908, to as far west as the British Isles and with one eastward eruption to the neighbourhood of Peking (see

IRRUPTION). British immigrants remained and bred, and they might even have established themselves if man had not interfered.

The genus *Pterocles*, with 13 or 14 species in all, ranges throughout Africa except in forest areas, with *P. personatus* confined to Madagascar. The Imperial Sandgrouse *P. orientalis* has also races in southern Russia, the Canary Islands, and Asia Minor, while the Large Pin-tailed Sandgrouse *P. alchata* has one in southern France. Several of the species are represented in south-eastern and central Asia, while 3 of them have resident races in India—the Small Pin-tailed Sandgrouse *P. exustus*, the Coroneted Sandgrouse *P. coronatus*, and Lichtenstein's Sandgrouse *P. indicus*, the last extending almost throughout the peninsula.

The nest of all sandgrouse is but a scratching on the ground, rarely lined with a little grass. The eggs, equally rounded at both ends and double-spotted, are usually 3, rarely 2 or 4 ; incubation is by both sexes, the male (also having brood-patches) incubating by night. The young are covered with down and leave the nest soon after birth. Both parents feed and water the young by regurgitation.

The food of adults consists entirely of hard seeds of various plants, that of bush-loving species being mainly seeds of *Acacia* and leguminous plants. Much hard grit is taken, sometimes one-third in weight of stomach content.

The drinking habit of sandgrouse is almost unique. Generally speaking, the birds of open desert water soon after dawn, the bush species soon after sundown. The birds are very conservative about their watering places and are not easily driven from them even when other water is available ; vast numbers sometimes congregate at favourite places. In Bikanir (north-western India) their numbers (4 species) have been estimated at hundreds of thousands ; in Iraq, near Baghdad on the Euphrates, about 80 000 birds

have been seen watering in November. Man has taken advantage of this habit ; in north-western India as many as 1000 birds have been killed in one morning by blocking alternative watering places, but the shooting of birds tortured by thirst can scarcely be regarded as sport. Nor is man alone in taking advantage of the habit, as avian predators take their toll at drinking places.

The morning drinkers go straight to the water's edge and drink ; having satisfied themselves, they are off at once, back to the desert. Sandgrouse will occasionally drink hovering over water ; in Kenya a case occurred of crocociles snapping them when drinking. The dusk-drinking species are more cautious when drinking, settling a little distance from water and slowly waddling to the brink. This is very necessary, as predatory birds and mammals are often in attendance. Occasionally these dusk-drinking species water again well before sun-up.

The birds drink like pigeons, placing the bill in the water and continuously swallowing without raising the head ; as many as 44 gulps have been counted. The water passes into the crop, which can hold one ounce of liquid and when fully distended $1\frac{1}{4}$ ounces with overflow to the gullet and mouth, the latter occurring when water has to be carried to young in the desert. It has been suggested that water is also carried to young in the abdominal feathers, but that is not so.

Distances covered from the desert home to water are considerable. The greatest distance ascertained is 38 miles, entailing a flight of 76 miles there and back at a rate of a little over 40 miles an hour ; a brooding pair would therefore be absent from their nursery for just under two hours. The *Syrrhaptes* species, however, live far from water and in some cases *S. tibetanus* does not fly to water at all, being content with little puddles on moorland or even drops from a melting snow-field.   R.M.

Marchant, S. 1961. Observations on the breeding of the sandgrouse *Pterocles alchata* and *senegallus*. Bull. Brit. Orn. Cl. 81 : 134–141.

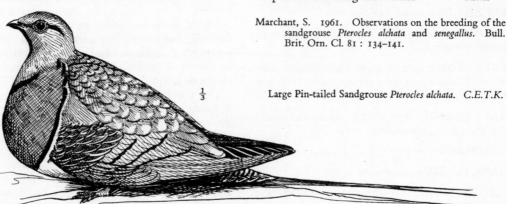

$\frac{1}{3}$ Large Pin-tailed Sandgrouse *Pterocles alchata*. *C.E.T.K.*

SANDPIPER : substantive name of many members of the Scolopacidae (Charadriiformes, suborder Charadrii) ; in the plural, and usually in some such combination as ' snipe and sandpipers ', serves as a general term for the family—there is in fact no single English word accurately covering the whole, but sandpipers constitute the largest element. Many other substantive names are used for particular species or small groups within the family, as will be noted below. For references to the various related families see under CHARADRIIFORMES.

The Scolopacidae are a family of ground-dwelling wading birds ranging in size from small to moderately large (5-24 inches long, of which some inches may be bill). They have long wings and the tail is short to medium. The legs are often long, with the tibiae partly bare and with rather long front toes (hallux short—entirely absent in one species). The neck may be rather long, and the slender bill is often long and sometimes very long (straight, decurved, or recurved). The plumage is cryptic, that of the upper parts commonly a mottled pattern of browns and greys ; the under parts are often pale, with or without streaks or spots. The sexes are as a rule more or less alike, but there is often a seasonal change affecting both ; when this is so, the winter dress tends to be paler, and sometimes the breeding plumage has black or warm chestnut on the under parts.

Most members of the family frequent open country and the vicinity of water. Outside the breeding season many of them become birds of the seashore and then tend to be gregarious, often in flocks of mixed species. They are nearly all strong on the wing, and many species have the habit of flying in close formation, rising, wheeling, and settling with astonishing unanimity. Some species remain birds of marsh or even woodland throughout the year. The diet is mainly animal, small invertebrates forming the greater part ; the food may be picked off the ground, sometimes even caught on the wing, but is to a large extent found by probing in mud or sand, either exposed or in shallow water. Many species are at least crepuscular as well as diurnal in their activities. There is a great variety of calls. Some are harsh but others are melodious piping, sometimes trilling, sounds ; many calls of two or three syllables are very distinctive, and some of the louder cries seem particularly suited to the wild places in which the birds are found. In one group there is a notable development of non-vocal sounds.

There are many elaborate courtship flights and other displays ; some of the sounds, both vocal and instrumental, are particularly associated with the breeding season. The nest is usually on the ground, sometimes concealed in the herbage and in other cases quite in the open ; the actual nest is often a mere scrape, with a greater or lesser amount of grasses or the like as lining. A few species use abandoned arboreal nests of other birds and are then seen perching on the trees ; one species uses burrows made by other birds. The eggs are usually 4 in number, very consistently, but in some species 2 or 3. They are cryptically coloured, with heavy darker markings on a buff or olive ground. The downy young are alert from the time of hatching, ready to follow the parent or to crouch immobile on alarm. The roles of the sexes in parental duties are various.

The members of the family are mostly natives of the Northern Hemisphere, and the majority breed in high latitudes ; some are circumpolar in distribution. There is a marked contrast in this respect with the allied family Charadriidae, in which the great majority of species are tropical (see PLOVER (1)). Most of the Scolopacidae are highly migratory and in this way are widely spread over the world as non-breeding birds. The tendency is for the Arctic and subarctic breeding species to perform long transequatorial migrations, while those breeding in more temperate latitudes make shorter journeys and may indeed winter within the limits of the summer range. The feeding habits of the birds are such as to make them highly vulnerable to freezing of the ground and shallow water.

The bases for taxonomic subdivision of the family are uncertain, but it is customary to recognise four subfamilies : Tringinae (curlews and ' tringine ' sandpipers) ; Scolopacinae (woodcock and snipe— these two words commonly unchanged in the plural) ; Calidritinae—the ' Eroliinae ' of some authors (godwits, dowitchers, ' calidritine ' sandpipers, etc.) ; and Arenariinae (turnstones), although this last group is often placed in the Charadriidae in the absence of objective evidence on which to base a firm decision. It was formerly usual to place the godwits in the first group and the dowitchers in the second. In all, there are about 70 species, assigned to about 24 genera.

Curlews and Tringine Sandpipers. Curlews *Numenius* spp. are the giants of the family. The characteristic cry and the long decurved bill are other marks. Of the 8 species, the Eskimo Curlew *N. borealis* is perhaps now extinct. The Curlew *N. arquata* is the large Palaearctic form, the Long-billed Curlew *N. americanus* its Nearctic counterpart. The smaller Whimbrel *N. phaeopus* is Holarctic (its American race being sometimes called ' Hudsonian Curlew ') ; it breeds only in high latitudes and is a notable migrant to the shores of all the southern continents. The Pygmy Curlew *N. minutus* of Siberia, migrating to Australia, is markedly smaller than the Whimbrel.

The genus *Tringa* includes 9 species of sandpipers, of which several breed in temperate latitudes ; none is very small, and they run as large as the Greenshank *T. nebularia* (12 inches) of the Palaearctic and the Greater Yellowlegs *T. melanoleuca* (13–15 inches) of the Nearctic Region. The Redshank *T. totanus* is the familiar representative in temperate Europe, but the Greenshank breeds sparingly in Scotland as well as farther north ; it is a common visitor on the shores and swamps of Africa, usually in ones and twos rather than flocks. The members of the genus are in fact less gregarious than the calidritine sandpipers. Loud piping calls, distinctive of the species, are characteristic. The Green Sandpiper *T. ochropus*, breeding in Scandinavia and eastwards, is an example of a species that lays its eggs in old arboreal nests of other birds such as thrushes *Turdus* spp., or occasionally on other ready-made sites in trees.

Not far removed from the foregoing are the Common Sandpiper *Actitis hypoleucos*, native to middle latitudes of the Palaearctic Region, and the Spotted Sandpiper *A. macularia* of North America. They are by some thought to be conspecific ; both frequent the banks of rivers and lakes in the breeding season and have a marked ' bobbing ' or ' teetering ' action (even in the first half-hour of life !) ; they are numerous but mostly solitary visitors to the southern continents, and in Africa the Common Sandpiper is often to be seen on the back of a wallowing hippopotamus. In a monotypic genus, the Terek Sandpiper *Xenus cinereus*, breeding from Finland eastwards and wintering on the coast of East Africa, has an upturned bill.

Two American species in monotypic genera are the Upland (or Bartram's) Sandpiper *Bartramia longicauda*, sometimes miscalled ' Upland Plover ', and the large Willet *Catoptrophorus semipalmatus*, a native of middle latitudes. Among the few other forms are the Polynesian Tattler *Heteroscelus incanus*, breeding in Alaska and migrating through the Pacific to Hawaii and Polynesia, occasionally as far as New Zealand ; the Wandering Tattler (or Greyrumped Sandpiper) *H. brevipes* breeds in eastern Siberia and visits Australia. Two or three species found on Cook's voyages had an uncharacteristic and limited distribution in Polynesia—the Whitewinged Sandpiper *Prosobonia leucoptera* of Tahiti and the Sharp-billed Sandpiper *Aechmorhynchus cancellatus* (known only from a unique specimen no longer extant) are now extinct ; the possibly conspecific Peale's Sandpiper *A. parvirostris* may still

survive on remote atolls of the Paumotu group.

Woodcock and Snipe. The members of the subfamily Scolopacinae have the bill very long and quite straight. The distal part of this probing instrument is very flexible and the tips of the mandibles can be opened below ground to grasp any prey located. Emphasising this length of bill, the eye is set far back and the head has a characteristic shape ; in *Scolopax* the external opening of the ear is beneath instead of behind the orbit. The legs are not particularly long, the body is rather compact, and the neck is short. The cryptic plumage tends to include dark and rufous elements.

These birds are apt to sit very closely, even when not nesting, and may be almost trodden upon before they reveal themselves by going off with a quick dodging flight. Woodcock frequent woodland country, especially if the trees are not too dense and the ground is rather damp ; snipe are birds of open marshland. Such haunts are preferred throughout the year, and the seashore is not frequented at any season. Gregariousness does not usually extend beyond the formation of small parties (' wisps ' of snipe), or of larger flocks on migration, and some of the species are always solitary. Several species emit loud non-vocal sounds, a subject discussed elsewhere (see INSTRUMENTAL SOUNDS).

For the most part, woodcock and snipe breed in temperate rather than high latitudes, and some of them are not migratory in any great degree. The Woodcock *Scolopax rusticola* is widely distributed in the Palaearctic Region and has resident races at high altitudes in Indonesia and New Guinea ; forms found in the Celebes and the Moluccas have been accorded specific rank. It is notable for its courtship flight, known as ' roding ' in Britain, and for its ability— long disputed but now well authenticated—to transport its young in the air (see CARRYING). The American Woodcock *Philohela minor*, in a monotypic genus, is a smaller bird.

Snipe of the genus *Gallinago* (' *Capella* ') are found breeding over much of the world but are only visitors on migration to southern Asia and to Australia. The Common Snipe *G. gallinago* is particularly widespread, being not only Holarctic but with representatives in Africa and South America that are probably conspecific. The North American form *G. g. delicata* is often known as Wilson's Snipe ; and as a migrant in India the nominate race is called the Fantail Snipe to distinguish it from the Pintail Snipe *G. stenura* coming from Siberia (and having the remarkable number of 26 rectrices). The Great Snipe *G. media* has a more limited range, breeding in central longitudes of the Palaearctic Region. The small Jack Snipe *Lymnocryptes minima*, also Palaearctic, is placed apart in a monotypic genus.

In another monotypic genus, the various races of *Coenocorypha aucklandica* inhabit subsidiary islands of the New Zealand group and are given English names to correspond, e.g. Chatham Island Snipe for *C. a. pusilla*. This species has the habit, unique in the family, of nesting in burrows excavated in the ground by other birds ; it seems to fly little and to be to a considerable extent nocturnal. The 3 *Chubbia* spp. are purely South American.

Godwits, Dowitchers, Calidritine Sandpipers, and Ruff. The godwits are among the larger members of the family and have long legs and long bills that are either straight or slightly upturned. There is 1 genus with 4 species, 2 Palaearctic and 2 Nearctic. The Black-tailed Godwit *Limosa limosa* breeds in temperate Europe and Asia and migrates to Africa and Australia. The Hudsonian Godwit *L. haemastica* migrates from North America to South America.

Rather smaller are the 2 species of dowitchers inhabiting subarctic and Arctic North America, migrating far to the south. The Short-billed Dowitcher *Limnodromus griseus* has a straight bill (the term 'short' is purely relative) like that of a snipe—hence the inaccurate name 'Red-breasted Snipe' used by some authors, referring to a feature of the summer plumage. The breeding habits are remarkable, in that the female alone incubates the eggs and the male alone cares for the nidifugous young. The third species is a larger bird of doubtful affinities found in Siberia, the Semipalmated Dowitcher (or Snipe-billed Godwit) *L. semipalmatus*, sometimes placed in a genus of its own ('*Pseudoscolopax*').

The true sandpipers of this group, with bills of only moderate length, are the many species of *Calidris*, of which a number are assigned by some authors to other genera ('*Erolia*', '*Ereuntes*'). Most of them are small, some very small. They all breed in high northern latitudes and perform long migrations ; some are circumpolar in their breeding distribution and therefore widespread as migrants. When not breeding, they are shore birds and highly gregarious. They have piping or twittering calls, usually not at all loud—in contrast with the ringing tones of *Tringa* spp. ; they are known collectively on the American coast as 'peeps'. The smaller species are called 'stints' by British ornithologists. The Knot *C. canutus* is relatively large, about 10 inches long, whereas the Least Sandpiper (or American Stint) *C. minutilla* measures only half that ; others fall between these extremes. The Dunlin *C. alpina* is exceptional in breeding as far south as northern Britain and the southern Baltic.

The Purple Sandpiper *C. maritima* is a visitor to rocky rather than sandy or muddy shores ; it is easily approached and has the legs coloured deep yellow.

More easily separable, in monotypic genera, are the Spoon-billed Sandpiper *Eurynorhynchus pygmeus* of north-eastern Asia, the Broad-billed Sandpiper *Limicola falcinellus* of high Palaearctic latitudes, and the Stilt Sandpiper *Micropalama himantopus* and Buff-breasted Sandpiper *Tryngites subruficollis* of Arctic America ; specialised bill structures distinguish the first and second, long legs the third. Better known is the Sanderling *Crocethia alba*, the only sandpiper lacking a hind toe. It has a Holarctic breeding range in very high latitudes and is a migratory visitor to the coasts of all continents (although relatively scarce in the western Pacific area). It frequents open sandy shores rather than estuarine mudflats, usually in small compact flocks of which the members run about very busily collecting their minute prey at the water's edge and often permit close approach. The winter plumage is pale, the bill and legs are black, and the general appearance is rather dumpy ; in breeding plumage the head and breast are light chestnut.

There remains a species that is unique in several respects, the Ruff *Philomachus pugnax* ; 'reeve' is a particular term for the female, but the appellation of the male serves as the name of the species. The general appearance is more that of a tringine sandpiper, but the male is noticeably larger (11½ inches long) than the female and in breeding plumage has a large erectile ruff and eartufts showing marked polymorphism in coloration. This ornamentation is associated with 'tournaments' in special areas or 'hills' in the breeding area (see LEK DISPLAY) ; this in turn involves promiscuity rather than polygamy and a consequent absence of paternal behaviour. The species breeds from northwestern France eastwards to Siberia and migrates as far as Cape Province and Ceylon ; in Africa it is a visitor to the swamps and lakes of the interior rather than to the sea-coasts.

Turnstones. As already mentioned, it is uncertain whether the Arenariinae should be placed in this family or in the Charadriidae. There are 3 species, of which the Ruddy Turnstone *Arenaria interpres* (with 2 subspecies) is the most widely known ; the substantive name needs no qualification in Europe, where no other species occurs. It has a circumpolar breeding distribution, mainly in Arctic latitudes but in Europe extending as far south as the Baltic Sea ; as a migrant it reaches the extremities of the southern continents and New Zealand. It is a compact, short-legged, short-billed shore bird 9 inches long ; the breeding plumage is rufous above and light below, with a black chest-band and mask-like facial pattern, but in winter the upper parts are darker. Using its bill, and sometimes also pushing with its body, it overturns stones and other objects on the beach in its diligent search for the small marine organisms on which it feeds. As a migratory visitor it is usually seen on rocky or stony shores in small and easily approached parties. The Black Turnstone *A. melanocephala* breeds only in Alaska. The Surfbird *Aphriza virgata* also breeds only in Alaska, but inland in the high mountains; for the rest of the year it frequents rocky coasts, south to the Strait of Magellan.

See Plates 20 and 29 (colour), 11a, 24b, and 48b (phot.). A.L.T.

Bergman, G. 1946. Der Steinwalzer, *Arenaria i. interpres* (L.), in seiner Beziehung zur Umwelt. Acta Zool. Fennica 47 : 1–151.
Nethersole-Thompson, D. 1951. The Greenshank. London.
Nørrevang, A. 1959. The migration patterns of some waders in Europe, based on the ringing results. Vid. Medd. Dansk Nat. Foren. 121 : 181–222.
Pettingill, O. S. 1936. The American Woodcock, *Philohela minor* (Gmelin). Mem. Boston Soc. Nat. Hist. 9 : 169–391.
Pitelka, F. A. 1948. The problematical relationships of the Asiatic shorebird *Limnodromus semipalmatus*. Condor 50 : 259–269.
For wider references see under PLOVER (1).

SANITATION, NEST: see PARENTAL CARE

SAPPHIRE: substantive name of *Chlorestes notatus* and many *Hylocharis* spp. (for family see HUMMINGBIRD).

SAPPHIREWING: *Pterophanes cyanopterus* (for family see HUMMINGBIRD).

SAPPHIRONIA: substantive name (some authors) of *Lepidopyga* spp. (for family see HUMMINGBIRD).

SAPSUCKER: substantive name of *Sphyrapicus* spp. (see WOODPECKER).

SARMATIC: derived from the coastal fauna of the brackish or salt inland 'Sarmatic Sea' of late Tertiary and Pleistocene times, an extension of the eastern Mediterranean (see GEOLOGICAL FACTORS; PALAEARCTIC REGION).

SATPURA HYPOTHESIS: see ORIENTAL REGION

SAUROGNATHOUS: see PALATE

SAUROPSIDA: term embracing reptiles and birds (see ANIMAL KINGDOM).

SAURORNITHES: name formerly used for a

sub-class equivalent to the Archaeornithes (see under CLASS).

SAVANNA: also written 'savannah', a type of open country found in semi-arid regions or in those with a long dry season; term originally applied in South America but now used widely as a habitat description. For example, in Africa immediately south of the Saharan desert there is a belt of 'thorn-scrub savanna', characterised by a sparse vegetation of spiny bushes and tufted grass; south of that, where there is a substantial rainfall during part of the year, is a belt of 'grass-woodland savanna', park-like country characterised by patches of woodland and isolated trees in a general area of abundant long grass withering in the dry season.

SAWBILL: general term for the mergansers *Mergus* spp. (see DUCK); also, substantive name of *Ramphodon* spp. (for family see HUMMINGBIRD).

SCANSORIAL: pertaining to the act of climbing, especially on tree-trunks (see LEG; LOCOMOTION).

SCAPULA: a paired bone ('shoulder blade') of the pectoral girdle (see SKELETON).

SCAPULARS: (plural) the feathers above the shoulder (see TOPOGRAPHY).

SCAPUS: term sometimes applied to the whole stem of a feather, i.e. calamus and rachis combined (see FEATHER).

SCARING: any stimulus that promotes in a bird the tendency to flee or conceal itself may be referred to as a scaring stimulus; in this article, however, the intra-specific social signals, which function in the spacing out of the members of a species population (e.g. in competition for territories, for breeding partners, or for food) will be excluded, although the fleeing responses shown in a social context may often be similar to those shown to extra-specific scaring stimuli.

Responses. In its typical complete form the response to a scaring stimulus is flight away from the source of the stimulus or, in the case of some species adapted for concealment, crouching and 'freezing' in appropriate surroundings. Fleeing is often preceded by other sorts of responses, and sometimes a scaring stimulus will produce only the fleeing precursors. These are typically a sleeking of the feathers, opening of the eyes to their fullest extent, perhaps lengthening of the neck, and perhaps a call characteristic for the situation. Calls and visual features of the pre-fleeing and fleeing behaviour may function as signals alerting other members of the same or other species in the vicinity to the presence of the scaring stimulus, and there may be specialisation in this direction. In some species there are displays directed at the source of the scaring stimulus, e.g. the distraction displays (see Simmons 1952, 1955).

In some species scaring produces close formation flying ; the compact flocks may make silent, sweeping, twisting manoeuvres close to the ground or water, e.g. the ' dreads ' of terns (Sterninae) and the ' panic flights ' of gulls (Larinae). Sometimes attacking behaviour is mixed with fleeing as the response to potential predators, e.g. mobbing.

Stimuli. In nature the most usual stimuli releasing fleeing and the other scaring responses are potential predators, e.g. birds-of-prey, weasels, snakes, man. The placing of stuffed specimens or models of predators in the vicinity of the birds will also usually produce scaring. Changes in the characteristics of places with which birds have become familiar, such as the vicinity of the nest, will also cause fear ; for instance, it is the experience of people who feed birds from a garden table that if the table is painted a new colour, or altered in some other conspicuous fashion, visits to the table immediately decline in frequency, returning to their former level only after the birds have become habituated to the new features.

Auditory stimuli can also effect scaring. Sudden loud noises such as the reports of rifles or artillery, sirens, and so on, can put birds to flight or cause them to crouch. The social signals signifying danger can be visual but are probably more often auditory ; many species have warning calls which are uttered when a scaring stimulus is perceived, or distress calls that are made when a bird is seized by a predator (see Frings et al. 1955). These warning or distress calls are often species-specific, i.e. do not have a warning or scaring effect when broadcast to birds of other species. However, if birds of two or more species move together in mixed flocks for parts of their life cycles, the birds of each of these species may learn to respond to the calls of the others (e.g. Frings & Frings 1958).

Economic Application. There are circumstances in which man finds himself in competition with birds for ' Lebensraum ' or for the goods of the world. Thus, birds can be economic pests in fields, orchards, gardens, and vineyards ; birds can infest cities, where the noise and dirt they create are a nuisance ; birds can constitute a hazard to aircraft. The traditional method used to remove birds from places where they are not wanted is scaring by means of some sort of scarecrow ; a model of a man, or some other sort of predator, or some shape with supposed scaring potential, is placed in the area to be cleared of birds. The usual history of such a treatment is an initial effectiveness, in keeping birds away, which declines quite rapidly as the birds learn that the stimulus is not the signal of any real danger. A similar result follows the use of reports and other loud noises that have little biological significance for the birds. It appears that only if such noises are regularly accompanied or followed by killing or pursuing of the birds will these signals sustain their scaring effect. It is known that reinforcing visual or auditory stimuli with experience of genuine danger can make them into more or less permanent scaring signals for the birds treated to such a programme (e.g. Kramer & von St Paul 1951).

The latest and perhaps most promising attempts to use auditory signals to disperse birds have been the broadcasts of the recorded alarm or distress calls of the birds. Recordings are made of the relevant calls of the birds to be dispersed and these recordings are played to the birds through loud-speakers. On initial presentations this treatment has proved very effective, but there is evidence that after a certain number of repetitions the birds become habituated to this type of stimulus also. Efforts are being made to eliminate or reduce the waning of effect by improving the quality of the recording and reproduction of the calls and the presentation schedules. It is possible that augmenting certain characteristics of the calls, such as the high-frequency portions of the sound spectra and the intensity of output, may increase their effectiveness. If habituation cannot be sufficiently eliminated, a programme of calls reinforced with killing or the coincident presentation of persistently noxious stimuli may provide the most satisfactory bird-dispersal technique.

C.G.B.

Frings, H., Frings, M., Cox, B., & Peissener, L. 1955. Recorded calls of Herring Gulls (*Larus argentatus*) as repellents and attractants. Science 121 : 340–341.

Frings, H. & Frings, M. 1959. The language of crows. Scientific American 201 : 119–133.

Kramer, G. & St Paul, U. von. 1951. Über angeborenes und erworbenes Feinderkennen beim Gimpel *Pyrrhula pyrrhula* L. Behav. 3 : 243–255.

Simmons, K. E. L. 1952. The nature of the predator-reactions of breeding birds. Behav. 4 : 161–171.

Simmons, K. E. L. 1955. The nature of the predator-reactions of waders towards humans ; with special reference to the role of the aggressive, escape and brooding drives. Behav. 8 : 130–173.

SCAUP: substantive name of some *Aythya* spp. ; used without qualification in Britain for *A. marila* (see DUCK).

SCHIZOGNATHOUS: see PALATE

SCHIZORHINAL: see NARIS

SCIMITAR-BILL: substantive name of *Rhinopomastus* spp. (see WOOD-HOOPOE).

SCISSOR-BILL: alternative substantive name of species of Rynchopidae (see SKIMMER).

SCLEROTIC: see SKELETON ; VISION

SCLERURINAE: see OVENBIRD (1)

SCOLOPACIDAE: see under CHARADRIIFORMES. The family includes species known as ' woodcock ', ' snipe ', ' sandpipers ', ' curlews ', and ' godwits ', and by various special names (see under SANDPIPER).

SCOPIDAE: see under CICONIIFORMES ; and HAMMERHEAD

SCOPOIDEA: see under CICONIIFORMES

SCOTER: substantive name of *Melanitta* spp. (see DUCK).

SCRATCHING: for head scratching see FEATHER MAINTENANCE ; for scratching the ground see FEEDING HABITS.

SCREAMER: substantive name of the 3 species of Anhimidae (Anseriformes, suborder Anhimae) ; in the plural, general term for the family. The latter is of wide distribution in tropical and sub-tropical South America. All have the body size of large geese, but are longer legged, with much longer and spreading toes webbed only slightly at the base, and with the hind toe on the same level as the 3 in front. Two curved, sharp-pointed spurs on the forward edge of the wing, the anterior pair from 1 to 2 inches long, are formidable weapons. An unusual anatomical feature is found in the extensive development of small air-cells between the skin and the body ; the extent of this exceeds that in pelicans (Pelecanidae) and boobies (Sulidae), as it reaches to the toes.

The Crested Screamer *Chauna torquata*, which ranges from eastern Bolivia, Paraguay, and southern Brazil to central Argentina, is the one most familiarly known, and is also the one that has been most persecuted by hunters. It is grey in plumage, with a blackish ruff around the neck and a short nuchal crest. It is found in marshy areas and around ponds, and in the open pampas it often walks about among cattle or sheep. The common name ' Chajá ' is taken from the double-noted trumpeting call, a sonorous sound that carries for more than a mile ; this is pleasing when first heard, but soon becomes an annoyance through prolonged repetition. The bird produces another sound, an internal rattling

rumble, audible only near by, that resembles the noise produced by rubbing a dried, distended bladder ; apparently this is made through distension of the air-cells over the body. The nest is an untidy heap of sticks, reeds, and weeds, built in marshy localities, elevated a foot or so above the shallow water in which it stands. The 4–6 eggs with slightly granular shells are white, tinged with buff or pale green. Both male and female incubate. The newly hatched young, clad in pale yellowish down, suggest goslings in appearance as they follow their parents. The birds range in pairs, sometimes in small flocks, and often perch in trees. Although they rise rather heavily, the flight is strong, and they often soar in circles, high in air, like vultures (Cathartidae).

Crested Screamer *Chauna torquata*. C.E.T.K.

The closely related Black-necked Screamer *Chauna chaviaria* of northern Colombia and western Venezuela is much darker, but with whiter cheeks and a longer crest. The Horned Screamer *Anhima cornuta* of tropical America, distributed from Colombia (rarely in western Ecuador) and Venezuela (formerly in Trinidad) to eastern Bolivia and south-central Brazil, is somewhat larger than the other species— the size of a turkey *Meleagris gallopavo* ; it is mainly black, with white in the feathers of the crown, in the wings, and on the abdomen. A slender, stiff, hornlike process that may be 4 inches long curves forward from the forehead. This appears to be cartilaginous and is supported firmly from a low boss of bone. The bird is found in wet savannas and along the wooded banks of sluggish streams, where it feeds on the ground and perches regularly in trees. It is mainly vegetarian like the other two, but also eats insects. Two white eggs are laid in a nest built in marshy ground.   A. W.

SCRUB-BIRD: substantive name of the 2 species of Atrichornithidae (Passeriformes, suborder Menurae) ; in the plural, general term for the family. This singular and probably primitive passerine family, comprising a single genus, is restricted to the mainland of Australia. The systematic position of the group has been under discussion at intervals during many years but is still uncertain. Newton assessed earlier opinions in 1896, and advanced the view that *Atrichornis* and *Menura* (see LYREBIRD) should be placed together, but in distinct families ; and latterly Mayr & Amadon, while conceding that scrub-birds and lyrebirds are very dissimilar in appearance, have postulated that, as the two groups share a number of anatomical peculiarities, they are ' probably nearer to each other than either is to any other group '.

The first species to be discovered, the Western Scrub-bird *Atrichornis clamosus*, was taken by John Gilbert in the southwest of Western Australia in 1842. A fleet-footed bird of the ground, with an extraordinarily powerful voice, it was found to be 8 inches in length and to have plumage mottled brown and black above and lighter below, with white on the throat and abdomen. Because of the ' great peculiarity ' of the species in completely lacking bristles at the base of the mandibles, John Gould in 1844 gave it the generic name *Atrichia*, but as this was found to be preoccupied it was replaced by *Atrichornis*. As an English name, Gould first used ' Noisy Brush-bird ', on the basis of Gilbert's information, and later ' Noisy Scrub-bird '. Aborigines, according to Gilbert, knew it as ' Jee-mul-uk '. Newton protested against the name ' Scrub-bird ' as lacking in distinctiveness, but it has remained in use for want of anything better.

For many years after Gilbert's period, very few reports of the Western Scrub-bird were made, and no specimen was taken after 1889. In all, only 20 specimens of the species had been collected, these being held in museums of Australia, London, and the United States ; all were regarded as males until, in 1942, it was learned that an example of the female was contained in the Gould collection at Philadelphia. Fears that the species had become extinct arose during recent years, and, partly because of this feeling, a substantial memorial commemorating both Gilbert and the bird was erected in 1949, by ornithologists

and historians, near the site of the original discovery. Late in 1961, however, a single male of *A. clamosus* was discovered among sandhill scrub 20 miles east of Albany, and in the next year several other examples were heard in the area ; these discoveries caused widespread interest, and the government of Western Australia immediately placed the species under strict protection. Subsequent developments included the photographing of a male bird—called into fleeting view by the playing of a tape-record of its own voice—and the finding in January 1963 of the first authenticated nest ; this structure, unoccupied but apparently fresh, was placed in thick grass 8 inches above ground, was globular and loosely built of dry leaves, and had for lining a suggestion of the dried wood-pulp which had earlier been found to characterise the nest of the Scrub-bird of eastern Australia.

The second species, the Rufous Scrub-bird *A. rufescens*, was discovered in the north-east of New South Wales, some 2500 miles from the locality of *A. clamosus*, in 1865, and was described by E. P. Ramsay. It was found to be 6½ inches in length and to have a colour pattern similar to, but more rufous than, that of the western species. Other features early remarked, and regarded as generic, were a peculiar formation of the sternum, strong development of the syringeal muscles, and, above all, the rudimentary clavicles. Like its immediate relative, the Rufous Scrub-bird became revealed as an insectivorous ground-dweller, a poor flier but very fleet of foot, and the possessor of remarkable vocal ability—the expressions including a loud ' chip-chip ', various other powerful and melodious calls, with a high degree of ventriloquism and frequent imitations of the voices of other birds. These characteristics, combined with elusiveness in a dense habitat, have given rise to the terms ' mystery-bird ' and ' mouse-bird '. The female of the species, being restricted to faint notes, is even more elusive and has rarely been collected.

Breeding of the Rufous Scrub-bird occurs in spring and early summer (September–December). The nest, built in a tuft of rank grass or among débris on the forest floor, is round and bulky, with a side-entrance. It is composed of twigs, dead leaves, scraps of fern, and dried grasses, and is lined with wood-pulp ; this last, being plastered and smoothed in a damp condition, dries into something suggesting light cardboard—perhaps the most curious lining of any Australian bird's nest. About a month is required to complete a nest, mainly because of the need to await the drying of the interior. The 2 eggs are pale pinkish with markings of purplish and reddish brown.

Although much of the original habitat of the Rufous Scrub-bird has been cleared, the species persists, sparsely as a rule, in certain coastal rain-forests from the middle of New South Wales to south-eastern Queensland—a broken distribution of about 300 miles. Clearly, this remnant of birds is the eastern outpost of a genus that once extended right across the continent ; the intermediate links were lost, no doubt, in the period of intense aridity that developed some 8000 years ago, following the Pleistocene ice age, and latterly the western end of the chain has fallen away, in part through the impact of settlement but mainly because of the bird's specialised nature.

See Plate 31 (colour). A.H.C.

Chisholm, A. H. 1951. The story of the scrub-birds. Emu 51 : 89–112, 285–297.
Webster, H. O. 1962. Rediscovery of the Noisy Scrub-bird, *Atrichornis clamosus*. West Aust. Nat. 8 : 57–59.
Webster, H. O. 1963. Discovery of the nest of the Noisy Scrub-bird. West Aust. Nat. 9 : 1–3.
Whittell, H. M. 1943. The Noisy Scrub-bird. Emu 42 : 217–234.

SCRUBFOWL: name sometimes applied to *Megapodius* spp. (see MEGAPODE).

SCRUB-ROBIN: substantive name of *Drymodes* spp. (see THRUSH ; and RAIL-BABBLER) ; also used for *Erythropygia* (or ' *Cercotrichas* ') spp., alternatively ' bush-robins ' or (in one case) ' Rufous Warbler ' (see WARBLER (1) ; and THRUSH).

SCRUB-WREN: substantive name of *Sericornis* spp. (see WREN (2)).

SCUTELLATE: term applied to a podotheca consisting of rather large and often overlapping scales (see LEG).

SCYTHEBILL: substantive name (formerly ' sicklebill ') of *Campylorhynchus* spp. (see WOOD-CREEPER).

SEA-GULL: term not used by ornithologists but common in ordinary speech for *Larus* spp., irrespective of whether the species are marine or not (see GULL).

SEASONAL CHANGE: occurring in birds in respect of physiological condition and behaviour, and very often also of external appearance and location (either or both). The cycle of a bird's life is usually an annual one, linked with the recurring seasons—whether these be summer or winter, or wet season and dry (see CLIMATOLOGY ; METEOROLOGY). The alternation in physiology and habits is, in adults, between reproductive and non-reproductive periods (see BREEDING SEASON). It may involve a greater or lesser degree of geographical displacement (see MIGRATION ; and IRRUPTION). The physiological changes include the seasonal replacement of feathers and other integumentary structures (see MOULT). This may or may not involve marked change in external appearance, as when there is a distinctive breeding plumage in one or both sexes (see PLUMAGE ; and Plates 7, 8, and 19 (colour)).

SEA-SWALLOW: popular name for TERN.

SECONDARY: or ' secondary feather ', any one of the flight feathers borne on the forearm (ulna), as contrasted with the ' primaries ' borne on the manus (see PRIMARY ; also PLUMAGE ; WING) ; they are sometimes called ' cubitals '. The secondaries are customarily numbered inwards from the carpal joint.

SECRETARY-BIRD: *Sagittarius serpentarius*, the sole extant species of the Sagittariidae (Falconiformes —sometimes placed in the suborder Falcones, but by Stresemann, in his recent revision, in a separate suborder, Sagittarii). The family is represented today in no other part of the world but Africa, although fossil remains have been found in France. Relationship to the Falconiformes is now generally accepted, although the Secretary-bird's appearance suggests a long-legged bustard (Otididae) or a crane (Gruidae) rather than a bird-of-prey. A full-grown male stands about 3 feet 2 inches in height and spans 7 feet from wing-tip to wing-tip. Bill and face are decidedly hawk-like, the former strongly hooked. Part of the face is bare. A remarkable crest of elongated feathers protrudes from the occiput, suggesting the bird's common name in all languages. The legs are very long, feathered to the inter-tarsal joint, and provided with extremely powerful but short toes ; a well-developed basal web joins the 3 front toes, while the hind toe is very small. Very striking is the tail of 12 feathers, the outer ones graduated and the central pair elongated to protrude 8–10 inches beyond the next pair. The plumage is black and grey—the flight feathers and thighs black, the body grey. The bird's habitat is open, short-grass country, thinly bushed or interspersed with areas of thicker bush. In Kenya it is not uncommon on the grasslands and open plains, and in the bushveld of South Africa it roams only in the more or less open stretches or in grasslands over which patches of trees are scattered.

The Secretary-bird spends most of its life on the ground, walking with long measured strides. No other large bird is so graceful in its movements when landing on the ground or when taking flight. Its range in Africa is bounded by the type of environment which it prefers ; in the Sudan, park-like country, where stretches of grass prairies alternate with thorn-bush and scattered groves, is typical terrain upon which to find it. In that type of country it is thinly distributed from the Gambia to Eritrea and Abyssinia, ranging south on the west coast to Nigeria and in the east from Kenya and Uganda to Cape Province. From one to three birds may usually be seen, for it is not a gregarious species unless a bush fire has attracted many to one spot.

Of great economic value, it preys on all creeping things. In the stomach of a single bird have been found rats, an adder, chameleon, frogs, locusts, a quail, a tortoise, and the remains of small animals ; insects form part of its diet, including white ants and wasps. It wages incessant war on snakes, which it kills by using its feet as sledge-hammers, striking forwards and pounding its victim to death. When attacking poisonous snakes it protects its body with outstretched wings from their bites. Although it is becoming uncommon over much of its range, protection is generally given to it as its value to mankind is universally recognised despite some damage to game-birds.

The nest is a large structure of sticks and turf, often lined with green twigs and leaves, grass, and occasionally some feathers. It is usually placed on the summit of a flat-topped tree or bush at 8–20 feet from the ground, but sometimes a highly placed site is chosen. The same structure is used year after year. Eggs are normally 2, rarely 3, white with a rough texture and on occasions streaked with reddish-brown. The young do not leave the nest until able to fly.

In the mating season the males are pugnacious ; and there is a spiral courtship flight. The Secretary-bird is usually mute, but 'deep raucous groans' (L. H. Brown) are uttered in display or alarm, or by young when food is brought to them.

See Plate 30 (colour). D.A.B.

Brown, L. H. 1952, 1955. Ibis 94 : 592–595 ; 97 : 43–48—for full reference, and others relating to the Falconiformes generally, see under HAWK.

SECRETION, INTERNAL : see ENDOCRINE SYSTEM

SEDENTARY : commonly used in the special sense of 'non-migratory' (compare RESIDENT).

SEED-CRACKER : substantive name of *Pirenestes* spp. (see WEAVER-FINCH).

SEED DISPERSAL : by birds—see POLLINATORS AND DISTRIBUTORS.

SEEDEATER : substantive name of species of *Sporophila* and allied genera in the New World, and of *Serinus* spp. in southern Africa (for family see FINCH).

SEED-FINCH : substantive name of certain small seed-eating species, particularly in the Neotropical genus *Oryzoborus*, also called 'rice grosbeaks' (for family see FINCH).

SEED-SNIPE : substantive name of the four species of Thinocoridae (Charadriiformes, suborder Charadrii) ; in the plural (often unchanged), general term for the family. This is a purely South American group. The name derives from the fact that they are seed-eating birds with the rapid zig-zag flight of a Snipe *Gallinago gallinago*, but there is no near relationship to the Scolopacidae. Seed-snipe are plump ground-feeding birds varying in size from that of a Partridge *Perdix perdix* to that of a small plover *Charadrius* sp. Their plumage is partridge-like, with a speckled pattern of brown and buff on the upper parts, the throat and breast being white to greyish with, in two species, a black 'necktie' effect. The wings are long and pointed ; the tail is short and rounded ; the legs are short, with small feet ; the bill is strong and conical.

The habitat of the 4 species ranges from the snow-line in the Andes to sandy and barren stretches on the sea-coast. Their plumage is so drab and inconspicuous, and blends so perfectly with the surroundings, that their presence is usually realised only when they spring up and fly off with a rapid zig-zag flight to alight again some distance away. When forced to leave the ground they utter a sharp rasping alarm cry similar to that of a Snipe. They are essentially seed-eaters, their diet consisting almost entirely of seeds, tender shoots, and leaves, mixed occasionally with minute particles of gravel. Some species are partially migratory, moving north in autumn, while for the high-altitude species the first heavy fall of snow seems to be a signal to descend to the more temperate foot-hills and central valleys.

All seed-snipe are ground-nesters. The eggs, almost invariably 4 to the clutch, are markedly conical in shape, and, with the exception of one species, have a polished surface tinted pale stone or buff and speckled with faint lilac and dark chocolate or nearly black markings.

In Gay's Seed-snipe *Attagis gayi* the upper parts and wings are grey, with arrow-like black markings : the throat, breast, and under parts are pale rufous, with black transverse markings on the upper breast. The plumage of the female is similar, but the coloration is less pronounced. The species inhabits the so-called 'Puna' Zone or 'Páramo' (11 000 to nearly 18 000 feet) of Ecuador, Peru, southwestern Bolivia, Argentina, and Chile south to the Magellan Strait, frequenting mountain pastures and swamps up to the edge of the melting snow and migrating in winter to lower altitudes. Although feeding in swamps and grassy tracts, it almost invariably nests on the adjacent barren and stony hillsides, where the eggs harmonise so perfectly with their surroundings as to be all but invisible.

The White-bellied Seed-snipe *A. malouinus* is similar in plumage to *A. gayi*, but is larger and has the upper parts more rufous and the throat much paler ash, blending into white on the under parts. It inhabits the extreme southern regions of Argentina and Chile, including the island of Tierra del Fuego, the Cape Horn area, and also the Falkland Islands. Little is known of this species, living as it does in such desolate and lonely places far from human habitation ; but it is on record that it feeds almost entirely on seeds. The first authentic nest was found near Puerto Williams, Isla Navarino (south of Beagle Channel), at an elevation of 1900 feet, on 28 January 1959, by the Royal Society Expedition to southern Chile. The eggs show a perfect adaptation to dark-coloured earth interspersed with mosses and lichens and squat heather-like clumps. On a dark olive-green background, they are profusely spotted and blotched with dark brown and black, and were found heavily incubated and half-buried in nesting material of moss, lichens, and twiglets of heather on top of a small tussock. It is significant that the ground colour of these eggs is in sharp contrast to the light buff colour characteristic of all the other species of the family. The same thing occurs in the case of the Magellan Oyster-catcher *Haematopus leucopodus*.

D'Orbigny's Seed-snipe *Thinocorus orbignyianus* is freely distributed through the 'Puna' zone of Peru, Bolivia, Argentina, and Chile, and ranges as far south as Tierra del Fuego and Staten Island. Appreciably smaller than Gay's Seed-snipe, it has very similar plumage harmonising perfectly with the arid and stony regions which the birds frequent. During the night hours, when the temperature usually drops below freezing point, they utter at short intervals an eerie but melodious cry which may be rendered as ' poo-koo, poo-koo, poo-koo ', the name by which they are known to the indigenous inhabitants. Nesting habits and eggs are similar to those of Gay's Seed-snipe.

The Pigmy Seed-snipe *T. rumicivorus* is resident on the arid coasts of south-western Ecuador, Peru, and Chile, and also occurs inland in certain parts of Bolivia, Paraguay, Argentina, and Chile. In these two latter countries its range extends right down to Tierra del Fuego and the Falkland Islands. The smallest member of the family, this species is also drab in plumage and has the characteristic collar or black ' necktie ' effect in the male. The birds are found among sand-dunes and arid stretches near the coast and on dry inland plains, where they may be observed in small flocks even in the nesting season. Their plumage blends with the surroundings to an extraordinary degree, and they are prone to remain motionless and invisible until the very last moment before rising up hurriedly and taking off in zig-zag flight just above ground level. The eggs, conical in shape, are creamy white, finely spotted with dark coffee-coloured and nearly black markings. They are laid on sandy ground and are often half-buried by the sitting bird before it leaves the nest. Nesting and incubation dates vary according to latitude, commencing as early as August and continuing into December.

See Plate 32 (colour).   J.D.G.

SEGMENTATION : see DEVELOPMENT, EMBRYONIC

SELECTION : see NATURAL SELECTION ; and under SPECIATION

SEMATIC : serving as a signal, e.g. of warning or attraction. This adjective is the base of such terms —applied particularly to coloration—as ' aposematic' (protective) and ' episematic ' (aiding recognition), and of compounds thereof (see under APOSEMATIC ; EPISEMATIC) ; also GAMOSEMATIC (see), ' allosematic' (adventitiously derived from association with other organisms—see NESTING ASSOCIATION), and 'parasematic' (deflecting attention from one part of the body to another, e.g. from more to less vulnerable parts). Not all such terms as these have application in ornithology. See, in general, COLORATION, ADAPTIVE.

SEMICIRCULAR CANALS : in the ear (see HEARING AND BALANCE).

SEMIPLUMA : an intermediate type of feather combining characters of pennae and down (see PLUMAGE).

SEMI-SPECIES : a term of convenience (Mayr 1942) for geographically isolated forms, with obviously near relatives elsewhere, that may be either species (members of a superspecies) or subspecies, there being no way of applying the objective test (see SPECIES).

SENESCENCE : see under LONGEVITY

SENMURV : see FABULOUS BIRDS

SENSES: in this plural form, the functions subserving perception. The senses involved when what is perceived is external to the body are known as 'exteroceptive' ; when it is internal, as 'proprioceptive' (sometimes termed 'interoceptive' and subdivided into 'proprioceptive' and 'visceroceptive'). The exteroceptive group corresponds with the popular concept of 'the five senses'— sight (visual function), hearing (auditory), smell (olfactory), taste (gustatory), and touch (tactile). It is necessary to make only the reservation that so-called 'touch' should be regarded as a complex of senses, probably accepting (as in man) such varied stimuli as superficial contact, deep pressure, vibrations, painful trauma, and contiguous heat or cold.

Vision and hearing depend on the reception of waves of light and of sound respectively ; and in each case the function is performed by highly specialised sense-organs, the eyes and the ears. Olfaction and taste are chemoreceptor senses, appreciating certain chemical characteristics of external matter presented in fine particles or in solution ; the sense-organs are simpler and more diffuse, but localised within the nasal or buccal cavity. The senses grouped under 'touch' respond to contact with objects or effects, as already noted ; the senseorgans are mainly nerve-endings widely distributed in the skin and underlying tissues, but there are also some more complex corpuscles. The special senses of birds thus conform with the general pattern found among vertebrate animals, and much of our knowledge is really deduction from analogy with the much more intensively studied senses of man ; critical experiments are extremely difficult to devise, especially in the inevitable absence of subjective data. Each of these senses is dealt with separately at length (see HEARING AND BALANCE ; SMELL ; TASTE ; TOUCH ; VISION).

The proprioceptive sense of balance (equilibration) is included in the same article as hearing, because its sense-organ is likewise in the ear (see HEARING AND BALANCE). This sense discerns the position of the head in relation to the horizontal and vertical planes, and also any acceleration (positive or negative) to which it is subjected ; it is thus important for the posture-orientation of the body, at rest or in motion (i.e. static or dynamic equilibrium). Other proprioceptive senses may be presumed to exist, but can be only vaguely assigned to particular sites. Thus, there must be a sense, or complex of senses (neuromuscular, neurotendinous), making the bird

aware of the state or position of parts of its own body, e.g. the tensed muscle or the outstretched limb—and so, too, of movements performed (kinaesthetic sense).

Further, one can postulate on theoretical grounds the existence of certain other 'senses' although these cannot, in the present state of knowledge, be definitely assigned to any particular sensory apparatus. One of these is a 'sense of time', because the perception of movement implies the faculty of arranging impressions in a time sequence —even of extrapolating into the immediate future. Over longer periods the appreciation of time may be regarded as a sense of interval, for which the reference standard is the solar day ; or, alternatively, the reference standard may be regarded as inherent and associated in some way with the rate of living of the animal organism, independently of external stimuli (Pumphrey). Whatever the explanation may be, there is good evidence for the existence in birds and other animals of some sort of 'internal clock' (see also NAVIGATION ; RHYTHM ; TIME MEASUREMENT).

Similarly, a 'sense of direction' may be regarded as either the expression of a kind of 'dead reckoning' for which the starting point is a particular orientation in a known topography, or as being based on some kind of 'internal compass needle' (Pumphrey). That some sort of compass sense is located in the semicircular canals of the ear is not impossible, although there are objections to the particular hypothesis propounded by Ising (see HEARING AND BALANCE ; NAVIGATION). On the other hand, the popular idea of a mysterious 'sense of direction' that could by itself explain the phenomena of bird migration, over unknown and trackless areas of vast extent, will not bear analysis ; a clock and a compass are first essentials, but not in themselves sufficient without the equivalent of a map. Finally, there is no evidence—in spite of much theorising and some experimentation—that any compass sense that may exist is related to terrestrial magnetism, or that birds have any means of appreciating the latter and its variations from place to place.

In considering the role of the various senses, allowance must be made for co-ordination between them, and for integration of their perceptions. Thus, eye and ear may work together in localising a distant object ; and there is some evidence for a visual aid to the semicircular canals in giving the bird a horizontal plane of reference (see under VISION). Sight and touch—or touch and awareness of one's own muscular movements—may similarly co-operate in appreciating the form of an object in contact. The functions of taste and smell have obvious affinities with each other.   A.L.T.

Portmann, A. 1961. Sensory organs : skin, taste, and olfaction. *In* Marshall, A. J. (ed.). Biology and Comparative Physiology of Birds vol. 2. New York and London.
Pumphrey, R. J. 1948. The sensory organs of birds. Ibis 90 : 171–199.
And works cited under the separate senses.

SERAL COMMUNITY: a biotic community that is of a transitory nature, in the sense that it will ultimately be replaced owing to changes in the environment (e.g. through growth of forests)—compare CLIMAX COMMUNITY.

SERE: ecological term for the whole series of plant changes in an environment leading from a bare area of land or water to a climax of maximum development ; the adjective 'seral' applies to transitional phases of this process (see above).

SERIEMA: substantive name of the two species of Cariamidae (Gruiformes, suborder Cariamae) ; in the plural, general term for the family. The birds are found in drier areas in south central South America. Seriemas are allied to cranes (Gruidae) and rails (Rallidae), and are placed in the same order. They show resemblance in form to small cranes, as they have long necks, long slender legs, and elongated muscular bodies. The head has a bushy crest, the tail is long, and the wings are rounded.

The common name is derived from the Tupi word 'çariama', rendered in Latin as *Cariama* by Marcgrave in his account published in 1648, copied by Willughby in his *Ornithologia* of 1676, and so given in many subsequent accounts. Seriema, a modification of the original American Indian word used in Brazil, is preferred and is now replacing the other form in current ornithological writings. Both species of the family are omnivorous in feeding, and are among those birds that regularly eat smaller snakes of any kind. The common supposition that seriemas have an immunity to the venom of the poisonous species is not true, since it has been found experimentally that birds of both species were killed by injections of attenuated amounts of a crotaline snake poison.

The Crested Seriema *Cariama cristata*, which ranges from central and eastern Brazil south through Paraguay to north-western Argentina and to Uruguay, is the best known, from its wide distribution and from the fact that the young are readily domesticated and are often taken and reared among fowls, where they serve efficiently as guardians to give warning of predators. The Crested Seriema, which stands about 30 inches tall, is greyish in colour with fine darker vermiculations throughout ; the wings and tail are broadly banded with black and white. It lives in areas of open scrub mixed with grasslands, where it moves about on foot and runs rapidly to escape any enemy. Its loud calls often indicate its presence when the bird itself is not seen. The nest, rather compactly made of sticks, is recorded from a few feet to 10 feet above the ground. The eggs, which regularly number 2, are faintly pink when fresh but fade to dull white, sparingly marked with lines or small blotches of brown that appear dark grey or dull purple where overlaid by deposits of shell. The young, covered with dark down when hatched, remain in the nest under the care of the parents until well grown.

Burmeister's Seriema *Chunga burmeisteri*, found only in north-western Argentina from Jujuy to Córdoba and the western Chaco of Paraguay, is somewhat larger, with a longer and heavier bushy crest. It is darker coloured and is heavily streaked on the under surface. It lives in areas of rather open, thorny woodland, where it ranges the ground like the other species. As they are hunted for game, they are wary, so that except for occasional distant glimpses of birds running swiftly through cover their presence is known mainly through their high-pitched yelping calls. The nest (located low in trees) and the 2 eggs are similar to those of the other species but with heavier markings.

Numerous fossil species related to the modern Cariamidae have been described from middle Tertiary beds of Argentina, and a closely related fossil family, the Bathornithidae, with 4 species described in the genus *Bathornis*, was common during Oligocene time in the great plains area of North America.
                                                         A.W.

SERIN: substantive name of most *Serinus* spp. ; used without qualification, in Britain, for *S. serinus* (see FINCH).

SEROLOGICAL CHARACTERS: those expressing differences between species in respect of the chemical nature of the proteins in, particularly, the blood serum—as shown by precipitation reactions and other tests. These proteins (also referred to as 'antigens' or 'serum globulins') represent an important part of the animal constitution and are conservative hereditary traits ; they are thus of potential value as supplementary taxonomic criteria ; and the same applies to the albumens of egg-white (see PROTEINS AS TAXONOMIC CHARACTERS ; TAXONOMY).

SERPENT EAGLE: same as HARRIER EAGLE (and see HAWK).

SERTOLI CELLS: see REPRODUCTIVE SYSTEM

SERUM: see BLOOD ; SEROLOGICAL CHARACTERS

SESAMOID: term applied to small, isolated pieces of bone or cartilage formed in tendons or ligaments.

SET: in respect of eggs, has the same meaning as CLUTCH (see also EGGS, NATURAL HISTORY OF).

SETOSE: carrying bristle-like feathers.

SEVEN SISTERS: name applied collectively to parties of the Jungle Babbler *Turdoides somervillei* in India, from the habit of associating in small bands, often of about seven birds, at all times of year (see BABBLER). Whistler points out that there is a vernacular (but masculine) equivalent, ' sathbhai ', in which the numeral is used in an approximate sense. Related species have similar habits and may sometimes have the term applied to them.

SEX, CHANGE OF: see REPRODUCTIVE SYSTEM

SEX, DETERMINATION OF: see GENETICS

SEXES, ROLE OF THE: see under POLYANDRY ; POLYGAMY ; also COPULATION ; COURTSHIP FEEDING ; DISPLAY ; INCUBATION ; LEK DISPLAY ; NEST BUILDING ; NEST SITE SELECTION ; PAIR FORMATION ; PARENTAL CARE ; and generally in articles on bird groups

SEXING OF CHICKS: see REPRODUCTIVE SYSTEM

SEXUAL CHARACTERS: those differentiating male and female. Primary sexual characters are the testis and ovary ; accessory sexual characters are other parts of the REPRODUCTIVE SYSTEM ; secondary sexual characters are those, apart from the foregoing, in which the sexes differ—in birds, notably in plumage and voice, sometimes also in size (see below).

SEXUAL DIMORPHISM: the existence of differences in appearance between male and female members of a species (or subspecies), age and season being equal ; for dimorphism not related to sex see POLYMORPHISM. The characters peculiar to one sex or the other that determine the difference in appearance are known as ' secondary (or accessory) sexual characters '.

   Structural Dimorphism. The difference in appearance between the sexes is seldom structural. An exception is the Huia *Heteralocha acutirostris* of New Zealand, a species now presumed to be extinct, in which the shape of the bill shows a strong sexual

FIG 1. Outlines showing male (upper) much larger than female in the Capercaillie *Tetrao urogallus* (Palaearctic). About $\frac{1}{12}$ nat. size. *M.Y.*

FIG. 2. Outlines showing female (right) much larger than male in the Sparrowhawk *Accipiter nisus* (Palaearctic). About $\frac{1}{4}$ nat. size. *M.Y.*

dimorphism ; in the male the bill is stout, arched, and shorter than the tarsus, while in the female it is slender, strongly curved, and longer than the tarsus. Other differences that might be regarded as structural lie mainly in the presence or special shape of particular feathers, or of other outgrowths of the integument, in one sex ; these are mainly associated with an ornamental function, e.g. special plumes (but see below) or excrescences on the bill. In the Peafowl *Pavo cristatus* there are 20 rectrices in the male, 18 in the female.

Size Dimorphism. In many species there is a difference in size between male and female, sometimes slight and perhaps only on an average ; the male is then usually the larger—but there are exceptions, as also in brightness of plumage (see below). Sometimes the difference is very substantial and readily apparent. Thus, the male Capercaillie *Tetrao urogallus* is a much larger bird than the female. In many of the birds-of-prey (Falconiformes) the female is markedly larger, and the sexes may even hunt different quarry.

Plumage Dimorphism. This is usually a matter of colour and pattern, although there may also be differences, as already mentioned, in decorative plumes of special shape or in integumentary structures of an ornamental nature. The differences may not be very large—just a greater brightness in colour, or a more definite pattern, in one sex. Or the differences may be so great that the two plumages are strongly contrasted. Commonly it is the male bird that has the bright colours or carries special plumes, the female often being inconspicuous. In a minority of species the position is reversed, and this tends to be associated with a dominant role in the female and sometimes with polyandry (see POLY-ANDRY) ; examples are the phalaropes (Phalaropo-didae), painted snipe (Rostratulidae), and button-quails (Turnicidae). However, in the New Zealand Shelduck *Tadorna variegata*, and to a lesser extent in the South African Shelduck *T. cana*, the female has the brighter plumage but the male is the larger and dominates the pair.

Occasionally both sexes are bright or strongly patterned, but quite different. Thus, in the Eclectus Parrot *Lorius roratus* the male is predominantly green, the female largely bright red (Plate 5). In the Leaden Flycatcher *Myiagra rubecula* the male has a distinctive pattern but no bright colouring, while the female has a red breast (Plate 6). In the Upland Goose *Chloephaga picta*, to cite one more example, the male is a handsome, mainly black-and-white bird, with a white head and neck and black legs ; the female is a brownish bird with a cinnamon head and neck and yellow legs.

FIG 3. Heads of male (upper) and female (lower) Black-casqued Hornbill *Ceratogymna atrata*, showing difference in form of bill. *M.Y.*

Relation to Seasonal Change. The sexual dimorphism may be permanent, neither sex showing any pronounced seasonal change (Plates 5 and 6). Examples can be found among the pheasants (Phasianidae), and also among the ducks (Anatidae) apart from a short period of ' eclipse ' plumage in the male (see PLUMAGE).

Or the bright plumage of the male may be a special breeding dress, and the sexes may be more or less alike in winter (Plate 7). An example is the Scarlet Tanager *Piranga olivacea*, in which the breeding male is predominantly bright red, and the female and winter male are greenish birds. In the Rock Thrush *Monticola saxatilis* the sexes remain somewhat different in winter, but not to nearly the same degree as when the male is in breeding plumage, with his blue head, white patch on back, and orange under parts.

Relation to Age. Where the adult male has a bright plumage, immature birds of both sexes tend to resemble the duller adult female ; but even in relatively dull immature plumages sexual dimorphism may be quite apparent, e.g. in the Blackbird *Turdus merula*. There are instances, however, in which immature birds of both sexes resemble the adult male, as in the Paradise (or New Zealand) Shelduck *Tadorna variegata*, where the male is a mainly dark bird with a greenish-black head and neck, and the female is a mainly rich chestnut bird with a pure white head and neck. Mention may also be made of cases where a bright plumage feature in the immature birds of both sexes may not persist into adult life in either ; the crimson crown of the Great Spotted Woodpecker *Dendrocopos major* is an example, the adult male having only a narrow band of that colour on the nape and the adult female no red anywhere on the head.

Absence of Plumage Dimorphism. In many species the sexes are similar in plumage and cannot be distinguished in the field, unless by behaviour. One thinks at once of such groups as the penguins (Spheniscidae), herons (Ardeidae), gulls (Laridae), tits (Paridae), crows (Corvidae), and many others. The species without sexual dimorphism include birds in which the plumage is of sober hue, and others in which it is brightly coloured either in the breeding season or throughout the year (Plate 17). Bright plumage alike in both sexes is found in most of the Coraciiformes, and in many parrots (Psittacidae) and pigeons (Columbidae) ; other examples include the Wallcreeper *Tichodroma muraria* and the Goldfinch *Carduelis carduelis*.

Evolutionary Factors. Sibley has ascribed the evolution of sexual dimorphism partly to inter-specific and partly to intraspecific sources of selec-tion. In the first place, there is selection against hybridisation between closely related species ; ' The reinforcement of isolating mechanisms in animals which utilize visual signal characters in pair forma-tion results in the enhancement of visible structures and associated behaviour patterns.' As it is usually the females that instinctively ' choose ' mates of their own species, it is the species-specific signal characters of the males that are important as releasers of the choice mechanism. So, where hybridisation occurs in groups of closely related species, but is selected against, the males tend to develop ' exaggerated ' signal characters. It is significant that in some insular populations, segregated from any closely interacting species, the males may lose their signal characters ; there being no other similar species present, the females cannot make a mistake in choice of mate and the selective effects of hybridisation are removed.

Secondly, there is intraspecific competition for mates, specially important in polygamous species (see POLYGAMY). Since only the secondary sexual characters of the males (in most groups) are con-cerned, the result of this ' sexual selection ' is an increase in sexual dimorphism.

Taxonomic Implications. Sibley has also remarked on the excessive number of monotypic genera that have been set up in groups showing a high development of sexual dimorphism ; ' Too

much weight has been given to the differences between the males of the species and too little to the similarity of the females, while the evidence of hybridisation (where such occurs) has been ignored.' One result of this taxonomic splitting is to give certain hybrids a purely artificial ' intergeneric ' status. The tendency now is to reunite monotypic genera formerly based on male differences (see GENUS).

See Plates 5, 6, and 7 (colour).   A.L.T.

Amadon, D. 1959. The significance of sexual differences in size among birds. Proc. Amer. Phil. Soc. 103 : 531–536.
Sibley, C. G. 1957. The evolutionary and taxonomic significance of sexual dimorphism and hybridisation in birds. Condor 59 : 166–191.
Witschi, E. 1961. Sex and secondary sexual characters. *In* Marshall, A. J. (ed.). Biology and Comparative Physiology of Birds vol. 2. New York and London.

SEXUAL SELECTION : see under SPECIATION

SHAG : substantive name almost interchangeable with ' cormorant ' for *Phalacrocorax* spp. ; but in the British Isles, each name standing alone, Shag means *P. aristotelis* and Cormorant means *P. carbo* (see CORMORANT).

SHAKESPEARE'S BIRDS : over sixty species mentioned in the works of William Shakespeare (see also POETRY, BIRDS IN). If frequency of refer-ences may be regarded as a sign of personal pre-dilection, England's—and the world's—greatest poet was without doubt a bird-lover. He shows more than a poetic knowledge. All natural phenomena awakened Shakespeare's deep interest, but his delight in wild-life, especially in birds, is unmistakable ; no other class of animals appealed to him so much. (On a smaller scale perhaps, only John Webster among Elizabethan playwrights appears to have been equally interested in the animal world ; in *The White Devil* alone two dozen different species of birds have been counted.) Although poets in general have been accused of ignorance of bird behaviour, Shakespeare stands out as an exception for his accuracy in bird-lore. He was of course no ornithologist, nor can he be esteemed an expert naturalist ; but as a country-born poet he had ample opportunity of watching living things in his most impressionable years. Nor was nature very far away when later he resided in the capital, with the countryside still close to the city gates. His know-ledge of various methods of bird-catching makes one suspect that, like other boys, he was addicted to bird's-nesting and fowling in his young days ; he was also well acquainted with the technicalities of hunting and of hawking. But although he mentions the cruel Elizabethan sport of cock and quail fighting, suffering animals—captive and injured birds among them—moved his compassionate heart. Popular beliefs and miscellaneous information gathered from books (Elizabethan zoology was based mainly on Pliny), tempered with genuine first-hand observation of birds' habits, combined to form a considerable body of fanciful ornithology which served the poet's purpose as a prolific source of evocative imagery.

In Shakespearian imagery, nature and animals come first, and among the latter birds play the leading part. Almost any bird may be used with two functions, natural and symbolic. All kinds of birds from the ' princely ' eagle to the ' diminutive ' wren, and from the table poultry to the mythical phoenix, are liable to be treated as symbols or else to serve as embodiment of certain qualities which are metaphorically related to men. These twin aspects are perhaps nowhere so well exemplified as in the references to the owl family. Its ' clamorous ' members can be recognised by their respective cries, variously qualified as ' hooting ', ' screaming ', ' shrieking ', or ' screeching '. To a detached student of natural history the brown owl's hoot comes as a pleasant sound, ' a merry note ', especially noticeable in long winter nights (Love's Labour Lost, v. ii. 906). The epithets are invariably suggestive : the silent, seemingly effortless flight of the soft-feathered owl is termed ' lazy ' (3 Henry VI, II. i. 130). The mobbing of owls by small birds in daytime in retaliation for their nocturnal raids (Macbeth, IV. ii. 11) is hinted at by the poet (3 Henry VI, v. iv. 56). However, the naturalist's accurate observation gives way to unscientific superstitions as soon as an atmosphere of fear and foreboding is called for ; in traditional belief the owl—the ' bird of night ', the ' obscure bird '—is a bird of ill omen, the ' fatal bellman ' (Macbeth, II. ii. 3). An owlet's wing forms an ingredient of the bubbling cauldron of Macbeth's witches. The ' nightly ' owl is coupled with the ' fatal ' raven (Titus Andronicus, II. iii. 97) or with the wolf (King Lear, II. iv. 213). Bearers of bad news are called owls (Richard III, IV. iv. 209), but since the bird is Athena's favourite the name is also jestingly applied to a dullard or a wiseacre (Love's Labour Lost, IV. 1. 132).

Shakespeare had a keen eye for telling detail. Throughout his work there are scattered sharply imaged bird similes and metaphors : the eagle shaking the moisture from its wings after a bath or flapping them eagerly over its food are probably snapshots from some aviary. Proud impetuous Coriolanus is aptly compared to an eagle fluttering a dove-cot or again to the kindred osprey who takes a fish ' by sovereignty of nature ' (Coriolanus, IV. vii. 34), and Antony to a ' doting mallard ' in the mating season (Antony and Cleopatra, III. x. 21). There are striking proofs of bird-watching, such as the delicate miniature portrait of the dabchick, ' a dive-dapper peering through a wave ' (Venus and Adonis) ; the vivid description of a flock of ' russet-pated choughs ', i.e. grey-headed jackdaws (russet= ash-coloured), ' rising and cawing at the gun's report ' (A Midsummer Night's Dream, III. ii. 21) ; the famous panorama of the cliffs of Dover with the ' crows and choughs ' which far below ' show scarce so gross as beetles ' (King Lear, IV. vi. 13) ; the colony of ' this guest of summer, the temple-haunting martlet ' nesting about the towers of Macbeth's castle at Inverness, where ' no jutty frieze, buttress, nor coign of vantage, but this bird hath made his pendant bed and procreant cradle ' (Macbeth, I. vi. 4 ; 7)—all these seem to be based on personal observation. (The ' martlet ' is usually identified with the swift, and in the passage just quoted the fact that the birds were flying in the dusk—the scene is by torchlight—lends some support ; on the other hand the nesting habits suggest the house martin as the species intended in this instance.) The manoeuvres of the wily pewit leading potential enemies from its nest were common property ; but the picture of Beatrice who ' like a lapwing runs close by the ground ' (Much Ado about Nothing, III. i. 24) is Shakespearian realism at its best.

His sympathies generally follow the current pattern. The ' plain-song ' cuckoo is a ' hateful ' bird, a selfish greedy changeling hatched in a hedge-sparrow's nest, or a ' bad ' wandering voice believed to be ' unpleasing to a married ear ' (Love's Labour Lost, v. ii. 908) because of the irregular habits of the female (cf. cuckold). The greatest favourites with poets are fine songsters such as robin-redbreast or ruddock, who in addition is praised for his ' charitable bill ' (Cymbeline, IV. ii. 224) covering the dead with flowers and leaves. For Shakespeare, the sensitive lover of nature and music, it is not the aesthetic value of the plumage that matters so much as the ' nimble ' movement of the birds on the wing and their songs.

The joy of spring ' under the greenwood tree ' is unthinkable without the warbling of the ' sweet bird's throat'. Wintry leafless boughs are to him ' bare ruined choirs where late the sweet birds sang ' (Sonnet, LXII. 4). The poet's two chief musicians, the lark and the nightingale, are forever linked in the lyrical debate (' aube ') of the parting lovers at dawn (Romeo and Juliet) ; the ' herald of the morn ' and ' ploughman's clock ' singing ' at heaven's gate ' his ecstatic 'tirra lirra' is opposed—not quite accurately—to the romantic 'night bird' who elsewhere assumes the tragic name of Philomel echoing the ancient tale of Tereus.

Shakespeare the naturalist and folk-lorist was equally well equipped with the picturesque legends and fables of medieval bestiaries and classical mythology. Accordingly the 'royal' eagle is introduced as 'Jove's bird', doves are sacred to Venus, and the swan's dying song, as well as the fabulous halcyon and the Biblical sparrow, are the subjects of repeated allusion. All sorts of birds are put to symbolic uses, their traditional attributes making of them emblems of particular qualities, virtues, or vices : the falcon of towering aspiration, the domestic hen of motherliness, the peacock of pride, the turtle dove of chaste and constant love, the turkey cock of foolish vanity, the pelican of parental self-sacrifice, the squalid vulture and greedy cormorant of voracity, the kite of rapacity—examples could be multiplied. Properties, real or fictitious, ascribed to birds ('eagle-sighted', 'pigeon-livered', etc.) explain why some bird names are used as terms of reproach and as nicknames : woodcock implies stupidity, paraquito or parrot stands for chatterbox, and jay, as well as quail and guinea-hen, is associated with loose females ; but it is doubtful whether the abusive 'loon' and 'gull' are derived from bird names. 'Cock' is used as a swear-word, but other names of domestic birds serve as terms of endearment : chick, chuck, dove, duck. The juxtaposition of a bird-of-prey with such terms is intensely pathetic : 'What, all my pretty chickens and their dam at one fell swoop' (Macbeth, IV. iii. 218). Some bird names lend themselves to puns and quibbles, e.g. fowl/foul, buzzard/buzz.

Shakespeare's vocabulary has preserved some earlier stages of meaning. Thus 'fowl', the common Teutonic word for bird (cf. Dutch and German 'vogel', Danish 'fugl', etc.) is still occasionally used in the original general sense. 'Bird', formed by metathesis from O.E. 'bridd' and found only in English, originally meant the young and was used by Shakespeare in that sense : 'As that ungentle gull, the cuckoo's bird '(1 Henry IV, v. i. 60) ; 'gull' meant an unfledged nestling. Some early or dialect names are encountered : 'ouzel' stands for blackbird and 'chewet' for 'chough' (i.e. jackdaw), and both are used metaphorically about chatterers.

Some obscurities await elucidation by ornithologists. Are the enigmatic 'scamels' (Tempest II. ii. 162) seamews or staniels (i.e. kestrels) or, perhaps, some sort of woodcock ? What is a 'pajock' (Hamlet, III. ii. 295) ? Is 'handsaw' (Hamlet, II.

ii. 375) to be interpreted as a dialect form of hern-shaw (i.e. heron) ? The 'temple-haunting barlet', emended to 'martlet' (heraldic ; also 'merlot'), has already been mentioned. What, however, is a 'night-crow' (3 Henry VI, v. vi. 45) ? What is the exact meaning of 'redbreast teacher' (1 Henry IV, IV. iii. 261) ? Do 'estridges'—baited or bated (1 Henry IV, IV. i. 98)—denote ostriches or unhooded goshawks (compare 'gentle estringer', All's Well that Ends Well, v. i. 7, keeper of goshawks, a court official—sometimes explained as 'a gentle stranger' and replaced by 'a gentleman') ? And why does Silence call his daughter disparagingly 'a black ouzel' (2 Henry IV, III. ii. 9) ? Is it a play on the complimentary 'fairest' ? Gentlemen preferred blondes in the days of Queen Elizabeth I.

To summarise : nearly all the major orders of birds are represented in Shakespeare's work ; and in the whole Shakespearian canon, which includes an allegorical bird poem (The Phoenix and Turtle), there is not a single play or poem that does not contain some bird allusions. One may conclude this glimpse of a vast subject with the remark that poets have often been compared with singing birds, and that Shakespeare was referred to by Milton as 'warbling his native wood notes wild'. To an envious fellow-dramatist, however, the versatile young poet was only 'an upstart crow beautified with our feathers'. But Ben Jonson, in a posthumous prophetic tribute to his friend's future greatness, coined the famous phrase 'sweet swan of Avon'; the metaphor seems peculiarly appropriate to the immortal nestling of Britain, an island described by Imogen (Cymbeline, III. iv. 142) as 'in a great pool a swan's nest '. O.V.

Armstrong, E. A. 1946. Shakespeare's Imagination : a study of the psychology of association and inspiration. London. (Revised edition published in U.S.A. 1963.)
Geikie, A. 1916. The Birds of Shakespeare. Glasgow.
Harting, J. E. 1917. The Ornithology of Shakespeare critically examined, explained, and illustrated. London.
Knight, G. W. 1932. The Shakespearian Tempest. Oxford.
Onions, C. T. 1916. Animals. In Shakespeare's England vol. 1. Oxford.
Spurgeon, C. F. E. 1935. Shakespeare's Imagery and what it tells us. Cambridge.

SHAKETAIL: substantive name of Cinclodes spp. (see OVENBIRD (1)). See Plate 32 (colour).

SHAMA: substantive name of some Copsychus spp. (for subfamily see THRUSH).

SHANK: a popular term for the whole or some part of the leg, lacking definition (see LEG). In such bird names as 'redshank' it clearly refers to the visible part of the leg, and especially to the so-called tarsus (which is in fact the foot, and thus not equivalent to any part of the human leg that would be thus termed).

SHAPE AND POSTURE: the general form of the body and the pose in which the latter is held (see also SIZE). Both are broadly determined by the adaptive specialisation for flight characterising birds as a class, not excepting the minority that have secondarily lost the power of aerial locomotion or use it relatively little (see AVES). Likewise, difference in shape and posture between one kind of bird and another are—within the limits imposed by the general pattern—related to their respective modes of life. In short, birds are beautifully streamlined for flight, an effect perfected by the plumage covering the actual body ; and the modification of the fore-limbs as wings entails a bipedal stance and a large dependence on the head for 'manual' operations.

There is of course a range of difference, in body shape, between the extremes of elongation and 'dumpiness' ('chunkiness')—although the latter appearance is sometimes due mainly to fluffed-out plumage. More noticeable in its effect on general contour is the relative length of neck, a character in which there are notable differences. Sometimes the head may be particularly large, or the size or shape of the bill may make it a noticeable feature (see BILL). Relative length of tail is also a factor (see TAIL) ; and relative length of leg has much to do with the appear-ance of a bird (see LEG). There is an obvious cor-relation between length of neck and length of leg. When the bird is in the air, the apparent shape depends to a large extent on the relative length of wing and the manner of flight (see FLIGHT ; WING) ; but neck and tail are again contributory, and some-times also the legs.

When the bird is perching, or when it is standing or proceeding on the ground, the body may be car-ried almost horizontally—with the neck turning towards the vertical—but more commonly there is a greater or lesser degree of upward tilt forwards. In extreme cases the carriage may be practically upright, notably in swimming birds that have the legs placed far back, e.g. penguins (Spheniscidae). In some instances, e.g. among auks (Alcidae) and storks (Ciconiidae), the birds may stand, regularly or occasionally, with the tarsus—and not just the toes—applied to the ground.

When standing at rest, a bird may retract its neck ; or, asleep, the head may be turned round so that the bill is hidden among the feathers on the back (*not* 'under its wing'). Many birds also habitually stand on one leg, with the other retracted. Cor-morants (Phalacrocoracidae) commonly stand with the wings half extended, as if to dry in the breeze ; frigatebirds (Fregatidae) extend their long wings in such a way that the tips point forwards and the under sides face upwards. Many birds sometimes rest in a sitting position, with the legs folded beneath the body, and this is of course the normal posture for incubation. For concealment in the presence of danger, some birds crouch with neck extended along the ground ; various special postures are adopted for the purposes of different kinds of display (see DISPLAY).

Some birds habitually perch, while others do not— or even cannot—in the strict sense of the term (see PERCHING). The attitudes of birds that cling to vertical surfaces may be characteristic, e.g. wood-peckers (Picidae) and treecreepers (Certhiidae). Some birds are adept at hanging upside down from a perch, e.g. tits (Paridae), *Machaeropterus* spp. (Pipridae), and bat parrots *Loriculus* spp.

In the air, posture is largely governed by the act of flying (see FLIGHT). A long neck is in some instances retracted during flight, as in herons (Ardeidae), and in others is extended forwards, as in storks (Ciconiidae) and cranes (Gruidae). The flying bird usually retracts its legs, but some species with long legs trail them behind, e.g. herons and storks. For posture on and in the water see SWIM-MING AND DIVING ; for progression on the ground, or other solid surfaces, see LOCOMOTION.

SHARPBILL: *Oxyruncus cristatus*, constituting the monotypic subfamily Oxyruncinae of the Tyran-nidae (Passeriformes, suborder Tyranni)—see FLY-CATCHER (2) ; by some authors placed in a family of its own (Oxyruncidae). Without debating the taxonomic question, it is convenient to give this aberrant bird separate mention. It is a purely Neotropical species, inhabiting the humid forests from Costa Rica southwards, through the eastern parts of tropical South America, to Paraguay. It is a small bird, 6½–7 inches long, with a low crest along the middle of the crown and a straight, acuminate bill of moderate length ; the wings and tail are rather long, and the legs are short, with strong toes. The plumage is predominantly olive-green above, with very dark brown on wings, tail, and crown, and with some small bright red feathers in the crest ; the under parts are pale yellowish, boldly spotted and barred with dark brown. The sexes are similar. Little has been recorded of its habits ; it is said to be a strong flier, to be rather solitary, and to live on fruit. The breeding has not been described, and the eggs are unknown.

The name 'Sharpbill' has also been applied to *Heliobletus contaminatus* in the Furnariidae—see OVEN-BIRD (1).

SHARPTAIL: abbreviated name of the Sharp-tailed Grouse *Pedioecetes phasianellus* (see GROUSE).

SHEARTAIL: substantive name of *Doricha* spp. and *Thaumastura cora* (for family see HUMMING-BIRD).

SHEARWATER: substantive name of certain species of Procellariidae, in the genera *Puffinus*, *Procellaria*, etc. ; in the plural, a general term for these (see PETREL). The name is sometimes locally misapplied to other sea birds, e.g. *Rynchops* spp. (see SKIMMER). See Plate 16b (phot.).

SHEATHBILL: substantive name of the 2 species of Chionididae (Charadriiformes, suborder Charadrii) ; in the plural, general term for the family. They are small white shore-birds (14–17 inches in length) which, in spite of a strong superficial resemblance to domestic pigeons, are anomalous members of the order Charadriiformes. Sheathbills, also known as 'paddies', are the only birds with unwebbed feet which penetrate to the shores of the Antarctic continent. They are found in abundance on oceanic islands in the sub-antarctic sectors of the Atlantic and Indian Oceans, ranging in the Atlantic from the Falkland Islands and Tierra del Fuego to the Palmer Archipelago, off Graham Land, Antarctica.

The name is derived from the rough, horny sheath which covers the base of the short, stout bill. The plumage is entirely white. The eyes are pink-rimmed as though inflamed ; the cheeks are wattled with hard, yellowish papillae, and the blue-grey legs are unusually stout for so small a bird. Although sheathbills have been seen in flight several hundred miles from land, they spend much of their time on the ground, trotting busily along the shore in search of food and showing reluctance to fly even when pursued. The wings are small, with sharp carpal 'spurs' which the birds use in fighting. Between breeding seasons they live in small flocks, quarrelling frequently among themselves and feeding com-munally. They are inquisitive and enterprising, associating readily with men at whaling stations and expedition bases.

Sheathbills feed on shore animals of the intertidal zone ; they consume large quantities of *Ulva* and other algae, presumably for the animals which live among these, and dig with their bills in crevices between the rocks. Stranded plankton, faeces of seals and penguins (Spheniscidae), carcasses, and offal of every kind are also taken. On penguin colonies

they scavenge for eggs and fallen or ailing chicks, darting between the brooding parents to pick up scraps of spilled food ; some make a regular practice of fluttering or pecking at parents which are engaged in feeding their chicks, causing both to drop their food on the ground. Although constantly in danger from darting beaks, they are usually quick enough to escape without harm.

$\frac{1}{3}$

Sheathbill *Chionis alba.* C.E.T.K.

The nests are built in crevices and under boulders, often on a rocky headland overlooking a penguin colony. Although continuing to feed gregariously, sheathbills usually nest in isolated pairs ; the nests are well hidden and the birds approach them indirectly. Two, occasionally three, large eggs are laid, usually of pale brown flecked heavily with grey or black. Incubation, in which both parents participate, takes 28 days. The chicks are covered with grey down, changing directly into white adult plumage. Very few reliable observations have been made on the nesting habits of this family, but reports suggest that only one chick is reared from the clutch. With the approach of winter sheath-bills tend to migrate northward from the southern end of their range, but the populations of the sub-antarctic islands are probably sedentary throughout the year.

The sheathbills of the south-western Atlantic Ocean, with yellow or flesh-coloured bills, constitute the species *Chionis alba*. Those of the Crozets, Marion, Prince Edward, and Kerguelen Islands are black-billed and slightly smaller ; although previ-ously listed as a separate genus ('*Chionarchus*'), they are now generally referred to the species *Chionis minor*. Subspecific rank has been suggested for the various island populations.   B.S.

SHELDGEESE: general term for some larger species of Tadornini (Anatidae) (see under DUCK).

SHELDUCK: substantive name of *Tadorna* spp. ; used without qualification in Britain for *T. tadorna*, and sometimes written ' sheld-duck ' or ' sheldrake ' (see DUCK).

SHELL: see EGGSHELL

SHELL-GLAND: or ' uterus ', part of the oviduct (see LAYING ; REPRODUCTIVE SYSTEM).

SHIELD, FRONTAL: a hard, featherless plate extending from the base of the upper mandible backwards over the forehead, as in coots *Fulica* spp. and others (compare CASQUE).

SHIKRA: *Accipiter badius* (see HAWK).

SHOEBILL: name, alternatively ' Shoe-billed Stork ' or ' Whale-headed Stork ', of *Balaeniceps rex*, sole member of the Balaenicipitidae, a family of disputed affinities. It has usually been placed in the order Ciconiiformes, sometimes in the suborder Ardeae, sometimes in the suborder Ciconiae—even in the Ciconiidae (see STORK) instead of in a separate family—and sometimes (as in the classification followed in this work) in a suborder of its own. Recent osteological evidence has been adduced (Cottam) in favour of an earlier view placing it among the Pelecaniformes. Wetmore (1960) holds that it has affinities both with Ciconiae and Ardeae, and that the resemblance of the skull to that of Pelecaniformes is due to convergence.

The Shoebill is a large bird, standing 3½ feet high or more, with slaty plumage and long black legs. The most obvious character is the large head, on a not very long neck, with a slight untidy crest on the nape and an enormous bulging bill, particoloured and carrying a hook on the upper mandible. It is a bird of swamps and water margins, often standing on ' islands ' of floating vegetation. In such situations it remains motionless, bill on breast, waiting for fish or other aquatic prey to come within reach. It has been suggested that the bill may also be used for digging lungfish—a known food of the species—out of the muddy bottom. It is partly nocturnal in its habits and is considered to be of a rather sluggish disposition ; but it can fly strongly—and soar—on its broad wings, with neck drawn in and bill resting on the breast (as in Pelecanidae). It is not a gregarious bird ; and it is

rather silent, although a shrill cry, a laughing note and a stork-like clattering of the bill have been described. The nest is placed on the ground, and in this 1 or 2 white chalky eggs are laid. The young are downy and nidicolous.

The species has a limited range in eastern tropical Africa, mainly in the southern Sudan, northern Uganda, and some eastern parts of the Congo. The ' sudd ' region of the White Nile and the swampy borders of Uganda lakes are typical habitats.

See Plate 30 (colour).   A.L.T.

Benson, C. W. 1961. The breeding of the Whale-headed Stork in Northern Rhodesia. Northern Rhodesia J. 4 : 557–560.
Cottam, P. A. 1957. The Pelecaniform characters of the skeleton of the Shoe-bill Stork, *Balaeniceps rex*. Bull. Brit. Mus. (Nat. Hist.), Zoology 5 : No. 3, 1–72.

SHOEMAKER: name applied to the White-chinned Petrel *Procellaria aequinoctialis*, also called ' Cape Hen ' in South Africa (see PETREL).

SHOOTING: see under UTILISATION BY MAN

SHORE-BIRD: term used in North America in the same sense as ' wader ' is in the British Isles (see WADER).

SHORELARK: *Eremophila alpestris*, the ' Horned Lark ' in American usage (see LARK).

SHORTWING: substantive name of *Brachypteryx* spp. (see THRUSH).

SHOULDER: see under MUSCULATURE; SKELETON; WING

SHOVELER: substantive name of some *Anas* spp. ; used without qualification in Britain for *A. clypeata* (see DUCK).

SHRIKE: substantive name (or part of compound name) of most species of Laniidae (Passeriformes, suborder Oscines) ; in the plural, general term for the family. This widespread but mainly Old World family comprises 4 subfamilies : Laniinae, true shrikes ; Malaconotinae, bush-shrikes ; Prionopinae, helmet-shrikes (or wood-shrikes) ; and Pityriasinae, including only the Bornean Bristlehead. That the bush-shrikes are related to the true shrikes is not wholly certain ; the helmet-shrikes are treated by some authors as a separate family on account of some morphological and biological differences ; and the inclusion of the aberrant Bristlehead in the Laniidae may be regarded as merely provisional. Rand (1960) recognises 74 species of Laniidae : 25 in the Laniinae, 39 in the Malaconotinae, 9 in the Prionopinae, and 1 in the Pityriasinae. The first subfamily includes the only 2 representatives of the Laniidae in the New World ; the second and third are restricted to Africa (not Madagascar).

General Characters. The Laniidae are characterised by a strong, or moderately strong, hooked bill often with a distinct ' tooth ' on the upper mandible and a corresponding notch on the lower. Rictal bristles are well developed ; the external nares are round or oval. The legs and feet are strong ; the claws, which are used in grasping prey, are sharp ; the tarsus is scutellated in front and lamellated, semi-lamellated, or even scutellated behind. The wing has 10 primaries. The tail, with 12 rectrices, is rounded or graduated ; it is of various lengths—short in *Nilaus*, very long in *Urolestes*.

The plumage shows much variety in colour and also in texture. In some species of *Lanius*, *Laniarius*, and *Dryoscopus*, a black-and-white pattern predominates ; occasionally black is the sole colour, as in some boubou *Laniarius* spp. In contrast, species of *Chlorophoneus*, *Telophorus*, and *Malaconotus* often show vivid colours, among which green, yellow, and red predominate. In several genera the plumage of the lower back and rump is soft and downy ; this character is exceptionally well developed in *Dryoscopus* spp., called ' puff-backs ' for that reason. The plumage of immature birds of many species shows dark vermiculation or barring, a character which in some species persists in the adults of one or both sexes. There is a single moult, in autumn.

Habits. Shrikes are bold and aggressive birds, essentially carnivorous. Some species catch only insects ; others add small reptiles, birds, and mammals. Many species have the habit of impaling their prey on thorns, dry stalks, or barbs of wire fencing, or of hanging it from the fork of a branch ; this is presumably to enable them to dispatch it more easily, but perhaps also to create a reserve store when the chase has been particularly successful. This provision of a ' larder ' is responsible for the English popular name ' butcher bird '.

The majority of shrikes do not live in the interior of woods and forests but keep to their verges, or even to ground with only scattered trees and bushes ; perched on a high branch or a telegraph wire, from which it has a good view, the bird swoops on prey which it has detected on the ground or darts, in the manner of flycatchers (Muscicapinae), at insects in flight and then returns to its observation post. Others, such as *Telophorus* and *Malaconotus* spp.,

hunt among the big trees, or in the undergrowth of the densest thickets. Still others, such as *Tchagra* and *Rhodophoneus* spp., often hunt on the ground, running under the bushes like rats, recalling the movements of the Dunnock *Prunella modularis*. Several true shrikes, especially the Great Grey (or Northern) Shrike *Lanius excubitor* and the Lesser Grey Shrike *L. minor*, hover after the manner of some birds-of-prey (Falconiformes). The flight of many shrikes recalls that of the Waxwing *Bombycilla garrulus* or the Mistle Thrush *Turdus viscivorus*. On leaving a vantage point they often fly close to the ground and finally reach the new perch by an almost vertical ' zoom '.

Although the ordinary cries are apt to be harsh and discordant—hence the name (cognate with ' shriek ')—shrikes are good or moderate songsters. Certain *Laniarius* spp. have very pleasing fluty songs that have justly earned them the name of ' bell shrikes '. Many members of the family are most excellent mimics, mingling the songs of other species with their own.

Breeding. All shrikes appear to be monogamous. The nest is always rather large, in the form of a cup of greater or less depth, and constructed of twigs, grasses, moss, flowers, wool, and hair. It is sometimes very compact, as in the Lesser Grey Shrike and the Woodchat *L. senator*, but more often very loose—even ' transparent ', as in the Black-crowned Tchagra *Tchagra senegala*. It is placed in a bush or tree, but the height from the ground varies greatly. The 2–8 oval eggs vary in colour from pale pink, or pale brownish or greenish, to bright green ; they are slightly glossy and irregularly marked with brown, olivaceous brown, or reddish brown.

True Shrikes. The subfamily Laniinae is just represented in North America and is widely distributed in Europe, Africa (not Madagascar), and Asia —and as far as New Guinea, but not Australia or New Zealand. Its members are placed in the genera *Lanius*, *Corvinella*, and *Urolestes*, of which the third is merged in the second by Rand and others. The *Lanius* species show in the highest degree the characters described for the family—the bill is particularly robust, with the ' tooth ' and notch strongly marked ; the external nares, oval and not operculated, are partly covered by short vibrissae ; the rictal bristles are well developed ; the tarsus is rather strong, scutellated in front and lamellated behind.

The Great Grey Shrike *L. excubitor* is a Holarctic species, divisible into numerous races. It is $9\frac{1}{2}$ inches long, and in both sexes the French-grey upper parts contrast with the black eye-streak and mainly black (marked with white) wings and tail ; it is distributed over much of Europe (but only a winter visitor to the British Isles), temperate Asia, and North America, in which last it is known as the Northern Shrike and has a close relation in the Loggerhead Shrike *L. ludovicianus*. (These are the only 2 New World shrikes, and the latter is the sole species found nowhere else.) In the much smaller Red-backed Shrike *L. collurio*, the male has a grey head with a black eye-streak, warm reddish upper parts and pale under parts washed with pink, while the female has the head and back rusty brown with darker markings and the under parts pale with fine dusky bars ; it is a summer visitor to much of Europe (including southern England and southern Scandinavia) and temperate Asia, wintering in Africa and southern Asia. The Red-tailed (or Brown) Shrike *L. cristatus* of Asia is probably a close relative. The Woodchat (or Woodchat Shrike) *L. senator* is more of a Mediterranean species, wintering in tropical Africa ; it has a contrasting black-and-white plumage with warm red on crown and nape. The Lesser Grey Shrike *L. minor* is a summer visitor to southern Europe and central Asia ; it resembles a smaller edition of *L. excubitor*, but has a black forehead and, in the breeding season, a rosy tinge on the under parts. Various forms of the Rufous-backed Shrike *L. schach* are found in the Oriental Region and as far as New Guinea ; the Burmese Shrike *L. collurioides* is an inhabitant of India, Burma, Siam, and Indo-China.

Among the many African species mention may be made of the Grey-backed Fiscal *L. excubitorius*, which shares with the Long-tailed Fiscal *L. cabanisi* (also African) and the Bay-backed Shrike *L. vittatus* (of India) the habit—unusual in the group—of going about in parties of 4–12 individuals and of indulging in a variety of fantastic ' dances ' accompanied by discordant cries. On the other hand, the Fiscal (or Fiscal Shrike) *L. collaris*, widely represented in Africa, is to be seen singly or in pairs ; it is a species easily recognisable by its strongly contrasted black-and-white plumage.

Likewise in Africa one finds the monotypic genera *Corvinella* and *Urolestes* (if the second be recognised as separate). The Long-tailed (or Yellow-billed) Shrike *C. corvina* has the sides of the tarsus completely lamellated and has a stright culmen ; it is a noisy, gregarious, and mainly arboreal species. In the Magpie Shrike *U. melanoleucus*, with its contrasted black-and-white plumage, the tarsus is laterally semi-lamellated and the bill is very short, with a very convex culmen and the ' tooth ' and notch strongly marked ; the frontal feathers have a peculiar structure and project forwards so that they almost entirely conceal the nostrils ; the lanceolated feathers of the crown and neck form a small crest ;

and the strongly graduated tail is made up of narrow feathers of which the median ones are almost twice as long as the wing.

Bush-shrikes. The wholly African subfamily Malaconotinae is much less homogeneous than the true shrikes and comprises 7–9 genera. In comparison, they are birds of medium size. In some the bill is strong (e.g. *Malaconotus*), in some moderately strong (e.g. *Tchagra*), and in others relatively weak (e.g. *Telophorus*) ; it is hooked, with a ' tooth ' and corresponding notch, as in *Lanius* but less markedly. The feathers on the rump are soft and elongated. These are general characters, in addition to which each genus has its peculiarities.

In *Laniarius* the plumage is sometimes entirely black, as in the Sooty Boubous *L. poensis* and *L. leucorhynchus* ; sometimes black-and-white, occasionally tinted rusty or rosy below, as in the Bell Shrike *L. ferrugineus* ; and sometimes with bright colours on the under parts, as in the gonoleks *L. atroflavus*, *L. barbarus*, *L. atrococcineus*. Of these, *L. barbarus* is better known as the Barbary Shrike, a familiar bird in West Africa with a distinctive ' whip-lash ' call ; in both sexes the crown is yellow, the rest of the upper parts black, and the under parts bright vermilion. In all members of the genus the feathers of the rump are soft and disintegrated, generally of the same colour as the mantle but with pale markings in the form of ' droplets '. Some species have harmonious and musical voices, and often the male and female sing in duet (see DUETTING). The birds are often difficult to observe because they keep to the thickest foliage, for example the Mufumbiro Gonolek *L. mufumbiri*, living in the great beds of papyrus between Mount Elgon and Kivu ; but, on the other hand, the South African Gonolek *L. atrococcineus* can frequently be seen hunting on the ground, although its plumage is so striking that one would expect it to seek concealment.

As already mentioned, the puff-backs *Dryoscopus* spp. are especially remarkable in respect of the formation of the feathers of the rump, which the bird is able to arrange like a powder-puff and even, in certain species, to erect almost completely. One species is described, in this condition, as looking as if it carried a white chrysanthemum on its rump. These feathers are white or grey, contrasting strongly in colour with the mantle, and differing in tint between the sexes ; they carry no markings. On account of the peculiar shape of its bill, Sabine's Puff-back *D. sabini* is by some authors placed in a genus of its own (' *Chaunonotus* ').

The most handsome of the bush-shrikes are undoubtedly to be found in the genera *Chlorophoneus* and *Telophorus* (united by Rand and others, under the latter name) ; their plumage presents a harmonious pattern of fine colours, but unfortunately, like most bush-shrikes, they are difficult to observe. The Black-fronted Bush-shrike *C. nigrifrons* and the Many-coloured Bush-shrike *C. multicolor* have, in each case, several phases ; it indeed seems not unreasonable to suspect that all the phases of both may represent a single highly polymorphic species (see POLYMORPHISM). Doherty's Bush-shrike *T. dohertyi* inhabits the heights in Kenya on either side of the Rift Valley, being found also in south-western Uganda and in adjacent parts of Kivu ; the Bokmakierie *T. zeylonus* is well known in South Africa.

In the genus *Malaconotus* the bill is very strong and markedly hooked ; the wings are equal to the tail in length. The various species are as much at home in woodland savanna as in denser woods. The Gladiator *M. blanchoti* of West Africa is a giant among the shrikes, measuring 11 inches in length, and is a fierce-looking bird with its huge bill. It is most conspicuously coloured, with grey head, white band in front of the eye, bright green back, and bright yellow under parts ; the very local Cameroon Mountain Gladiator *M. gladiator* is a vivid relative.

The tchagras *Tchagra* spp. are especially characterised by a rather strong bill, well hooked and 'toothed', by the rust colour on the wings, and by a very characteristic pattern on the crown and on the rectrices ; the plumage of the young never shows vermiculation. The hunting habits of these birds have already been indicated. The genus is represented throughout the greater part of Africa— even in North Africa, by the Black-crowned Tchagra *T. senegala*, a very elusive bird of which the presence is often betrayed only by its magnificent song. The Little Blackcap Tchagra *T. minuta*, peculiar in having an entirely black crown, has a range extending across Africa from Kenya to Angola, where it delights in the long grass of the swampy zone ; its nest differs from those of its congeners in being carefully constructed and compact, the outside often ornamented with fragments of snake-skin.

The species of *Rhodophoneus* somewhat resemble the tchagras in structure and in behaviour ; Rand and others include them in that genus. Like the tchagras, they hunt under low bushes, often running on the ground and always being careful not to show themselves in the open. On the other hand, they differ in exhibiting a marked sexual dimorphism.

The monotypic genus *Nilaus* is in some respects intermediate between the Malaconotinae and the Prionopinae, showing certain characters of both groups. The external nares are oval and operculated ; the wings are pointed and the tail much rounded. The plumage of the young shows transverse barring. The Brubru *N. afer* is a small bird represented by different subspecific forms throughout almost the whole of Africa, from Eritrea to the Cape ; it is a bird of the savannas and even of the semi-arid zone. Its characteristic call consists of two notes ; when this is uttered by the male, the female responds by 'echoing' it in a lower tone. The breeding habits and the eggs are little known.

Another monotypic genus, *Lanioturdus*, is sometimes placed in the Laniidae. The bill of the White-tailed Shrike *L. torquatus*, of south-western Africa, is scarcely hooked or 'toothed ; the nostrils are elliptical and operculated ; the wings are relatively pointed ; and the tarsus is very strong and very long. These characters make the bird's taxonomic position doubtful.

Helmet-shrikes. The members of the African subfamily Prionopinae (treated as a separate family by some authors) are especially remarkable for their sociability. At all seasons they are to be found in parties of 5-20 individuals ; several pairs nest side by side, and a number of birds often combine to build a nest or even to feed the young. In conformity with appearances, they are strictly insectivorous. Morphologically, they are characterised by having the tarsus scutellated anteriorly and laterally (as in *Nilaus*).

The two species of *Eurocephalus*, one in East Africa (north to Abyssinia) and one in South Africa, are especially remarkable for their flight, resembling that of a large butterfly ; and for their small and very compact nests, described as resembling flat cheeses stuck on the branches.

In both *Prionops* and *Sigmodus* (combined by Rand and others under the former name) there are brilliantly coloured caruncles beside the eye ; the feathers of the head, however, show considerable difference. In *Prionops* the frontal feathers are stiff and project forwards almost to conceal the nostrils ; in some of the species these curve inwards to form a tuft of disintegrating feathers, while those of the crown constitute a crest (or 'helmet') that differs in length and shape with the species. In *Sigmodus* these characters are less well developed ; and, in addition, the nostrils are elliptical instead of oval. In both genera the plumage is very firm even on the back and rump, in contrast to the condition in most members of the preceding subfamily.

Races of the Plumed Helmet-shrike *Prionops plumata* are widely distributed in Africa. It is amusing to watch parties of these birds on the hunt ; very often, as if parachuted from the higher branches, they fall to the lower ones or to the ground and there perform various evolutions among themselves ; if they perceive the observer they depart with one accord. The Grey-crested Helmet-shrike *P. poliolopha* is a close but somewhat rare relative, with a limited range in Kenya and Tanganyika.

With richly coloured eyes, caruncles, bill, and feet, the Red-billed Shrike *Sigmodus caniceps* and Retz's Red-billed Shrike *S. retzii* are very handsome birds found over much of Africa. The Chestnut-fronted Shrike *S. scopifrons* occurs only in East Africa, from north of Mount Kenya to the extreme east of Southern Rhodesia ; its blue caruncles contrast strikingly with the red bill.

Bristlehead. The monotypic subfamily Pityriasi-nae is very doubtfully placed among the shrikes, despite the character of its bill. The sole species, the Bornean Bristlehead *Pityriasis gymnocephala*, is restricted to Borneo. It is about 10 inches long and has mostly sombre plumage, relieved by scarlet on the head and throat ; the head is partly naked and warty, and the feathers on the rest of the head and throat are modified in the form of stiff bristles. This species has also been called ' Bald-headed Wood Shrike '.

See Plate 20 (colour).   G.G.O.

Miller, A. H. 1931. Systematic revision and natural history of the American shrikes (*Lanius*). Univ. Calif. Publ. Zool. 38 (2) : 11–242.

Moreau, R. E. & Southern, H. N. 1958. Geographical variation and polymorphism in *Chlorophoneus* shrikes. Proc. Zool. Soc. Lond. 130 : 301–328 (and colour plate).

Olivier, G. G. 1944. Monographie des Pies-Grièches du genre *Lanius*. Rouen.

Rand, A. L. 1960. Family Laniidae. *In* Mayr, E. & Greenway, J. C., Jr. (eds.). Check-list of Birds of the World vol 9 : 309–365.

Scheurs, T. 1936. *Lanius collurio* L. and *Lanius senator* L. Ein Beitrag zur Biologie zweier Würgerarten. J. Orn. 84 : 442–470.

Stresemann, E. 1927. Wanderungen der Rotschwanz-Würger (Formenkreis *Lanius cristatus*). J. Orn. 75 : 68–85.

SHRIKE, ANT-: see ANTSHRIKE ; and ANTBIRD

SHRIKE-BABBLER: substantive name of *Pteruthius* spp. (see BABBLER).

SHRIKE, BUSH-: see BUSH-SHRIKE ; and SHRIKE. Also used as substantive name in some genera of Formicariidae (see ANTBIRD).

SHRIKE, CATTERPILLAR-: see CUCKOO-SHRIKE

SHRIKE, CROW-: see CROW-SHRIKE ; and MAGPIE (2)

SHRIKE, CUCKOO-: see CUCKOO-SHRIKE

SHRIKE, FLYCATCHER-: see CUCKOO-SHRIKE

SHRIKE, HELMET-: see SHRIKE

SHRIKE, PEPPER-: see PEPPER-SHRIKE

SHRIKE, SONG-: see SONG-SHRIKE ; and MAGPIE (2)

SHRIKE, SWALLOW-: see WOOD-SWALLOW

SHRIKE-THRUSH: substantive name of *Colluricincla* spp. (see THICKHEAD).

SHRIKE-TIT: substantive name, in Australia, of *Falcunculus* spp. (see THICKHEAD).

SHRIKE, VANGA: see VANGA

SHRIKE-VIREO: substantive name of species of the subfamily Vireolaniinae of the Vireonidae (Passeriformes, suborder Oscines) ; in the plural, general term for the subfamily. The shrike-vireos constitute a small group of arboreal song-birds confined to the forested region of continental tropical America. The 2 genera and 3 or 4 species are by some systematists placed in a separate family, Vireolaniidae, but are now more usually included, as here, in the Vireonidae. The shrike-vireos differ from the typical vireos in having a heavier bill, which is hooked at the tip (see VIREO ; also PEPPER-SHRIKE).

The Chestnut-sided Shrike-vireo *Vireolanius melitophrys*—the only member of its genus—is a stout, long-tailed bird nearly 7 inches in length. Its upper plumage is plain olive-green, with the hindneck and top of the head slate-grey, bordered on each side by a broad yellow superciliary stripe below which is a black band from the lores to the ear coverts. The ventral plumage is white, with prominent black malar stripes and a chestnut band crossing the breast and continuing along the sides and flanks. This rare and little-known bird is found, chiefly in the oak forests, from southern Mexico to Guatemala, and from about 4000 to 10 000 feet above sea level. It forages, often in pairs, amid the foliage of trees, where it moves slowly and deliberately, peering from side to side, sometimes hanging upside down to pluck a morsel from the foliage. It holds larger insects beneath a foot while it tears them apart with its strong bill. Among its notes are a low, nasal rattle and a peculiar, long-drawn, high-pitched, far-carrying, whistled screech. No information on the nesting of any species of shrike-vireo appears to be available.

The 2 or 3 species of *Smaragdolanius* (formerly

called ' greenlets ') range through the heavier forests at low altitudes, from Mexico to Bolivia. The Green Shrike-vireo *S. pulchellus* is slightly over 5 inches in length. Its upper plumage is bright parrot-green with (in the northernmost race) the top of the head largely cerulean blue. The throat is yellow and the remaining under parts are light yellowish-green. This bird lives high up in the great trees of the Central American lowland forests, where it advertises its presence by its loud, clear, tirelessly repeated whistles ; these are grouped in trios, as though the bird counted rapidly ' one-two-three '. Seldom seen, it remains a bird of mystery.

A.F.S.

SIBIA : substantive name of *Heterophasia* spp. and *Crocias albonotatus* (see BABBLER).

SIBLING SPECIES : two or more closely related species that are morphologically very similar but are reproductively isolated (i.e. able to inhabit the same area without interbreeding) ; sometimes called ' cryptic species '.

SICKLEBILL : sole or substantive name used for various species possessing the form of bill suggesting it ; these belong to several widely separated families. Thus, it is the name of *Falculea palliata* (see VANGA) and of *Hemignathus procerus* (see HONEYCREEPER (2)), the latter alternatively called ' Akialoa '. Again, it is the substantive name of *Drepanornis* spp. and *Epimachus* spp. (see BIRD-OF-PARADISE), and also of *Eutoxeres* spp. (see HUMMINGBIRD). Further, it has been used (but ' scythebill ' is now preferred) as the substantive name of *Campylorhynchus* spp. (see WOODCREEPER) ; and it is sometimes applied, in Australia, to the White Ibis *Threskiornis molucca* (see IBIS).

SICKLES : term (plural) sometimes applied to elongated central tail feathers, found in certain species (see TAIL).

SIEGE : see ASSEMBLY, NOUN OF

SIGHT : see VISION

SIGNAL : see DISPLAY ; RELEASER

SIGNIFICANCE : see STATISTICAL SIGNIFICANCE

SIGN STIMULUS : term coined by E. S. Russell to indicate those parts of the available environmental information to which an animal responds at any given moment, particularly when these are strikingly limited. One sees the first indications of this restriction to a few stimuli in observations of astonishing errors, such as a Herring Gull *Larus argentatus* chick

pecking at a cherry in the way in which it does at its parent's red bill-tip ; or waders (Charadrii) panicking when another wader descends in a wildly swooping flight, thus showing roughly the same type of movement as a striking Peregrine *Falco peregrinus* ; or aggressive or sexual responses to animals only remotely similar to the adequate objects. Such ' errors ' are in curious contrast to other evidence demonstrating the wonderful acuteness of a bird's perceptive abilities, and this apparent paradox has led to experiments in which the potentialities of the sense organs were compared with the actual stimulus situations releasing particular responses. In birds, the majority of papers on this subject deal with visible stimuli. The potentialities of the eyes are studied with as great a variety of methods as possible : by studying conditioned responses of the intact animal, by observing pupillary reactions, by electrophysiological recordings in or behind the retina, and so on. There is now much evidence to show that the visual acuity of birds is high, that they can recognise forms well, and that their discrimination of intensity and colour is of the highest order (see VISION). Observations on geese (*Anser* spp.), gulls (Larinae), crows (Corvidae), and other birds have shown that they can distinguish between individuals of their own species much better than even a highly trained human observer.

Actual stimulus situations releasing a particular response have been studied by means of tests with dummies. In these, precise imitation of the natural object normally releasing the response (the standard dummy) is offered in alternation with dummies lacking one or more characteristic, and the intensity or frequency of the response to these various dummies is compared. If there is no or little difference of effect between the standard dummy and one of the incomplete dummies, the character lacking in the latter can be of no or little importance as a stimulus ; if the difference is striking, this is indicative of a sign stimulus. There are indications that the difference between a sign stimulus and a non-effective aspect of the environment is often one of degree only. In this way it was found, for instance, that the red patch on an adult Herring Gull's lower mandible is effective in releasing the chick's begging response, whereas the yellow of the rest of the bill is no more effective than any other colour, and this is expressed by saying that the red patch provides a sign stimulus. Further tests showed that it acts by its colour as well as by its contrast with the rest of the bill. Similarly, dummy tests with Song Thrush *Turdus philomelos* nestlings revealed that one of the sign stimuli is provided by the parent's head, which acts through being a protuberance of the outline of the body—above the body and with a certain size in relation to that of the body.

Precise investigations of this type, in which the potentialities of the sense organs involved and the actual stimulus situations are systematically explored and compared, are still very much needed, but there seems to be little doubt that many responses are released (and others inhibited) by very simple stimulus situations.

The fact that not all available information is 'used' or admitted for eliciting the response is posing an interesting physiological problem : where and how is the information refused passage ? Lorenz pointed out that the restriction of a response to very few aspects of the total situation seems to be typical of 'innate' (i.e. non-conditioned) behaviour, and that conditioning usually leads to a fuller use of all details of the situation (unless special manipulations of the experimenter subsequently reduces the numbers of details used). Thus the conditioned responses to individual birds, or fear responses to (often amazingly slight) changes in the usual environment, are strikingly different from responses that occur prior to conditioning. This suggestion has not been followed up experimentally to any extent.

Sign stimuli often have to be described in 'configurational' terms, which means that they evoke complicated processes of reception that cannot, at the present stage of analysis, be measured on one linear scale. Thus, many responses can be elicited only by a special type of movement, or by a special shape, or by a certain degree of contrast between two colours. In such cases it has been possible to design 'supernormal' stimuli, exaggerating the quality of the natural object to which the animal responds. For instance, the speckling of eggs can be exaggerated in models until they are preferred to normal eggs.

Accurate experimental studies of actual stimulus situations are still greatly needed.   N.T.

Lorenz, K. 1935. Der Kumpan in der Umwelt des Vogels. J. Orn. 83 : 127-213, 289-413.
Russell, E. S. 1943. Perceptual and sensory signs in instinctive behaviour. Proc. Linn. Soc. Lond. 154 : 195-216.
Tinbergen, N. 1951. The Study of Instinct. Oxford.

SILKY FLYCATCHER : substantive name sometimes used for species of the subfamily Ptilogonatinae of the Bombycillidae (Passeriformes, suborder Oscines) ; in the plural, accepted general term for the subfamily (for related forms see under BOMBYCILLIDAE). This New World group (possibly of polyphyletic origin) is by some treated as a separate family. To a large extent the generic names, especially *Phainopepla*, are used as common names of the four species, the birds being too little

known to have names in ordinary speech. As presently arranged, the subfamily includes 3 genera —*Phainoptila*, *Phainopepla*, and *Ptilogonys*, the first two being monotypic and the third having two species.

Phainopepla *Phainopepla nitens*. *C.E.T.K.*

The English term for the group refers to a soft, shiny quality of the plumage. Other characteristics possessed in common are the relatively short wings, long tail, and short tarsi. The bill is short and rather broad, resembling that of the waxwings (Bombycillinae). Both *Phainopepla nitens* and *Ptilogonys* spp. have broad white markings on the underside of wings and tail. *Phainoptila melanoxantha* has not, nor is silky quality of the plumage so apparent. Furthermore, the feet and legs are somewhat stouter and stronger, the wings are slightly longer relative to the tail-length, and the bill is longer and more compressed. Such differences have led to doubt that *Phainoptila* should be classified here ; but they appear to be of degree, not of kind.

The total length is about $7\frac{1}{2}$ inches, except for the Longtailed Silky Flycatcher *Ptilogonys caudatus*, which has a slightly longer tail. The plumage of the *Ptilogonys* spp. is generally pale grey (brownish in the female) with bright yellow vent and flanks. The pattern of the Black-and-yellow Silky Flycatcher *Phainoptila melanoxantha* is similar, but the male has the head and back purplish black and the back of the female is dark green. The Phainopepla is plainly coloured, the male being solid purplish black and the female dark grey. The young are of solid colours, never streaked or spotted.

Nests of the Phainopepla and of *Ptilogonys* spp.

are similar. In both genera it is a rather shallow, loosely constructed (not woven) nest placed in a fork of a limb, or on the limb itself, 10–50 feet above the ground. Eggs of the Phainopepla are pale grey, profusely spotted brown and black. Eggs of *Phainoptila melanoxantha* have been described as having the marking denser and forming a ring around the larger end. Both male and female of the Phainopepla incubate and care for the young.

The family is distributed throughout Mexico (*Ptilogonys*), north to Texas, Nevada to central California (*Phainopepla*), and south to Costa Rica and Panama (*Phainoptila*). All 3 genera are arboreal. The Phainopepla and the *Ptilogonys* spp. catch insects on the wing and are said to feed also on berries. Virtually nothing is known of the habits of *Phainoptila*.   J.C.G., Jr.

Crouch, J. E. 1943. Distribution and habitat relationship of Phainopepla. Auk 60 : 319–333.
Newman, R. J. 1950. A nest of the Mexican Ptilogonys. Condor 52 : 157–158.
Rand, A. L. & Rand, R. M. 1943. Breeding notes on Phainopepla. Auk 60 : 333–341.

SILVERBILL: substantive name of some *Lonchura* spp. (see WEAVER-FINCH) ; also alternative name of the Spectacled Tyrant *Lichenops perspicillata* (see FLYCATCHER (2)).

SILVER-BIRD: *Empidornis semipartitus* (for subfamily see FLYCATCHER (1)).

SILVER-EYE: name used for some species of Zosteropidae (see WHITE-EYE).

SIMURG: see FABULOUS BIRDS

SINGING: used here as a convenient term within which to include the varied vocal utterances of a wide diversity of birds, particularly that large division of the Passeriformes known as the Oscines or ' songbirds '. The Oscines were originally separated from the rest of the Passeriformes primarily on the basis of the number and the complexity of attachment of the syringeal muscles (see SYRINX) ; and a group—the Sub-oscines (in one sense of that term)—was distinguished from the Oscines by having, among other morphological characters, only 2 or at most 3 pairs of such muscles. The remaining passerine birds have their vocal muscles inserted in such a manner as to give the impression that the syrinx can hardly be very effective as a song-producing mechanism (see under PASSERIFORMES). Although this differentiation into Oscines and others is in some respects a convenient way of making a broad division in the vast collection of birds known as Passeriformes, it does not really help very much in defining the term ' song ' either acoustically or functionally. It is not, in fact, possible to draw a hard and fast line between the sounds that constitute call-notes and those comprised in the term ' song '. Many examples of ' song ' can be found that appear to be little more than a succession of call-notes (e.g. Charadriidae). In general, however, it can be said that call-notes are mostly monosyllabic or disyllabic and practically never consist of more than 4 or 5 notes. When call-notes are uttered in a longer series, then it is without any clear organisation of the sequence into bursts of definite length, and the series continues without interruption as long as the external circumstances and the state of the bird dictate. What is usually understood by the term song is a series of notes, generally of more than one type, uttered in succession and so related as to form a recognisable sequence or pattern in time. Thus the song as a whole displays characteristic complexities of rhythm and modulation not discernible to anything like the same extent in what are usually regarded as call-notes.

When we consider the function and acoustic characteristics of bird utterances, the definition of song becomes slightly easier ; but we still encounter many difficulties. Everyone who has seriously studied the songs and call-notes of birds from any angle, scientific or otherwise, has come to the conclusion that bird sounds are a means of expression of internal states and not merely accidental concomitants of them. The question of course is : expression of what, and to whom ? Unless we assume that the bird is using song merely as an emotional release without relation to any other individual, we have to take it for granted that song and call-notes are directed towards other individuals and are adapted for that purpose—are, in fact, a form of language. The idea that bird-song is often an expression of irresponsible joy or similar emotion is certainly not without some scientific justification and can, in fact, be supported by arguments which are far from negligible. It may indeed be true that songs of birds can be regarded as the first step towards true artistic creation and expression ; and if so it follows that birds were probably the evolutionary pioneers in the development of ' art ', certainly preceding by immense stretches of time the development of artistic activities by the human stock. Amongst present-day song-birds it has been shown, for instance, that individuals of the Blackbird *Turdus merula* and Sprosser Nightingale *Luscinia luscinia*, and probably many other species, do produce new songs by spontaneous recombination of phrases that they have used before, some of which are inherited, others probably learned. But, however this may be, we can be certain that the vocal mechanism of birds has not been evolved solely for the purpose of *self*-expression : in other words, bird vocalisations clearly constitute language of a kind.

Obviously, if language is to be found anywhere in the Animal Kingdom it must be among social species, since unless there is a listener whose behaviour is influenced by hearing the utterance the whole idea of language is nonsense. There are, of course, many forms of communication used in the Animal Kingdom—mammals and insects communicate largely by the use of specific scents, but this is almost completely unknown in birds, with their poorly developed olfactory organs (see SMELL). Many groups of animals have also developed a system of communication by movements and gestures. This is a device that has, of course, been carried to a high degree of perfection in birds, as is obvious when we consider their elaborate displays and the very complex and beautiful specialisations of plumage and other structures which have been evolved in this connection (see DISPLAY). But, however convenient scent language and gesture language may be in certain circumstances, it is quite clear that a language of sounds has very great advantages over other methods of communication. Sound signals carry far and fast, they readily by-pass obstacles and 'go round corners', so that they are far better for distant communication than is gesture. Then there is the wide spectrum of frequency and intensity available for use ; and, finally, sounds are extremely economical to produce—and, since they vanish as quickly as they are produced, the language can consist of a series of closely articulated utterances following one another in extremely quick succession. So it is obvious why a language, if it is to achieve its full potentialities, must be a language of sounds. The language of sounds has also been brought to a high degree of development by a few groups of insects (e.g. Orthoptera) and by some mammals. But, if we exclude human language from consideration, there is no doubt that birds are pre-eminent in the degree to which they have developed the technique of vocal communication.

Song and Call-notes. If, then, we consider the song production of birds as language, it is obvious that we still are without a satisfactory mode of distinction between call-notes and song, although clearly bird language is in the main something very different from human speech. Song is primarily under the control of the sex hormones and is in general concerned with the reproductive cycle (see ENDOCRINE SYSTEM). It is of great functional importance in the establishment and defence of ter-

ritory, often serving as a substitute for physical combat (see TERRITORY). Probably it is also intimately concerned with the maintenance of the pair bond and the mutual adjustment of the sexual cycle of the two members of the pair during its earlier phases. It is thus a form of sexual display. Call-notes, on the other hand, are concerned with the co-ordination of the behaviour of other members of the species (the young, and the flock and family companions) in situations that are not primarily sexual but rather concerned with maintenance activities—feeding, flocking, migration, and response to predators.

Most of the language of birds depends upon an innate ability to produce the required sounds and an equally innate ability to make the proper response. Thus there is no doubt that in a great many birds, even although the hearer shows by its behaviour that information has been received (e.g. a Chaffinch *Fringilla coelebs* when taking cover from a hawk on hearing the 'seeet' alarm call), the response we observe may be largely or entirely controlled by inborn mechanisms, and this response does not imply that the recipient makes any conscious assessment of the 'meaning' of the call—although this may of course occur as well. In general, call-notes do seem to be genetically determined and the response to them relatively automatic. The function of call-notes is thus chiefly to ensure quick and appropriate action in other members of the species —mate, or flock companions—that hear the sound. There are two situations in which it is likely to be extremely urgent for the hearer to make an immediate and appropriate response to the sound, namely where the sound is giving warning of some immediate danger, or where it is necessary to get a flock, group, or family of birds together during their communal search for food or communal migration. The call-notes of feeding flocks of tits (Paridae) or migrating flocks of waders (Charadrii) are good examples of this second category.

Relation to Vocal Organs. The attempt to relate the type and quality of sound produced to the structure of the vocal organs has met with very little success (see SYRINX). On the one hand we have the very restricted vocabulary, comprising only a few notes, possessed by many of the 'lower' families of birds such as the Gaviidae, Podicipitidae, some of the Galliformes, and some of the Laridae. On the other hand we come to the extreme development of bird vocalisations in groups such as the Muscicapidae—including Turdinae (thrushes and nightingales), Sylviinae (warblers)—and the Mimidae (mockingbirds). Moreover, there is the astonishing mimicry of the human voice that can be achieved by a well-trained parrot or Budgerigar *Melopsittacus undulatus,* or by the best mimics amongst the Sturnidae (starlings and mynahs). See further under MIMICRY, VOCAL.

The early bird anatomists, of course, noted the structure of the syrinx and its related elaborations of the trachea forming what appear to be complex resonating chambers. It is, however, far from clear how, even in the less highly evolved groups of birds, these supposed resonating chambers actually affect the voice production of the bird. As Pycraft pointed out, although the cassowaries (Casuariidae) have perhaps the simplest form of syrinx, yet they can give vent to a considerable variety of sounds, including a noise that has been described as a deep roar. The emus (Dromaiidae), which are equipped with an elaborate inflatable sac associated with the trachea, do not seem to be able to do much, if any, better than the cassowaries in regard to the variety or volume of sounds which they can produce. Again, among the ducks (Anatidae) a great many structural modifications of the vocal apparatus have been described, but in no case does any clear correlation seem possible between the tracheal structure and the type or variety of sounds produced. Moreover, as Pycraft said, if some of these structures in ducks are for modulating the voice, then it is curious —to say the least—that in many ducks the female, which has no resonator, has the louder voice, and that duck species with precisely similar resonators have entirely different calls. To some extent passerine birds provide a similar puzzle, at least in so far that the possession of an elaborate syringeal organ does not necessarily imply elaborate vocalisations. Nevertheless, the groups containing the best songsters are certainly those in which the syrinx has the most complex musculature.

One of the most striking features that have emerged from the study of bird vocalisation is the evidence that there is in some birds a double or multiple sound-producing mechanism. From spectrographic studies of songs of a variety of birds including the Gouldian Finch *Poephila gouldiae,* the Brown Thrasher *Toxostoma rufum,* the Wood Thrush *Hylocichla mustelina,* and the Reed Warbler *Acrocephalus scirpaceus* (Fig. 1), it is clear that a double or multiple sound-producing mechanism must be operating. There may be overlapping of notes, with one note beginning before the preceding note ends, and in one case with *Hylocichla mustelina* there is a moment in the song when four separate notes, having no simple harmonic relation to one another, are apparently uttered simultaneously. It thus appears that there must be, in some birds at least, more than one vibratory mechanism at work at the same time.

FIG 1. Sequence of notes from the song of the Reed Warbler *Acrocephalus scirpaceus* providing evidence for two vocal mechanisms. Note that in notes nos 6, 8, 10, 12 and 14 in this series (and particularly in nos 10 and 12, at about 1·4 and 1·7 seconds respectively) two entirely different sounds are being simultaneously produced. The lower occurs at about 3 kc. and has a slightly falling pitch; the higher at 3·5 kc. rising sharply to 4 kc. Note that, particularly in nos 10 and 12, the first harmonics of these two sounds can be clearly seen.

N.B. In all figures, unless otherwise stated :
Vertical scale : Frequency in kilocycles per second
Horizontal scale : Time in seconds

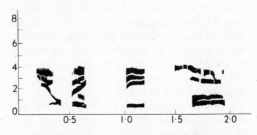

FIG 2. The sentence 'You make me laugh' spoken by a human voice. Note that the three resonance bars representing the three main formants of the vowels are not horizontal and parallel but sweep down and up, to some extent independently, giving a characteristic pattern for each vowel. This indicates that there are resonating chambers under independent control in the vocal apparatus.

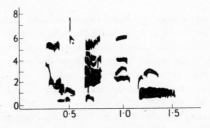

FIG 3. The sentence 'You make me laugh' spoken by an Indian Hill Mynah *Eulabes religiosa.* Compare with Fig 2. Note that although the bird voice is not as clear as the human, it shows evidence of a functionally similar vowel producing mechanism.

The techniques that have so far been applied to the study of avian vocal organs are not such as to give us the necessary information to decide exactly how these multiple sounds, these ' vocal gymnastics ', are produced. It is almost certain that the ability to produce similar complex sounds is found in the Sturnidae, and it is expected that when further study of bird-song is undertaken by modern methods many more will come to light.

Not only must there be in some birds more than one vibratory apparatus, but it is quite clear that there are also two or more separately adjustable resonating structures present in some species. The production of vowels in human speech depends on there being separately controllable resonating cavities ; in man these are primarily the throat, mouth, and nose. The sound spectrograms of vowels (Fig. 2) show that each vowel is characterised by having resonances from these various cavities with a particular pitch relation to one another. Many talking birds, such as parrots and Budgerigars, when trained to imitate human speech do not, in fact, produce genuine vowels. More often than not they may give the hearer the impression of a vowel by an appropriate change in the fundamental pitch of the note they are producing, and since our ear is expecting a particular vowel, we very easily imagine it to be there. This, however, is not the whole story in such expert bird talkers as the mynahs. The Indian Hill Mynah Eulabes religiosa can produce at least four perfectly genuine vowels showing, on spectrographic analysis (Fig. 3), that the bird has almost as complete control of three resonating cavities as has the human being (Thorpe 1958). The anatomical basis for this is not yet fully understood. The voice production of such birds raises an interesting problem as to the function of vocal mimicry in parrots and others that are ready to imitate sounds very different from those normally produced by the species in the wild. It is a puzzling fact that there seems to be no record of a wild parrot imitating.

Some species produce ' call-notes ' and auditory displays in flight by striking the wings together or by allowing the air stream to vibrate a pair of tail feathers (as in the Snipe Gallinago gallinago) after the manner of a bull-roarer, without the intervention of the vocal apparatus at all (see INSTRU- MENTAL SOUNDS). Conversely, the rapid vocal chattering of the Oilbird Steatornis caripensis and some of the swifts of the genus Collocalia, which are cave dwellers, is not primarily for communication but is used for echo-location of obstacles, when flying in the dark, on the same principles as are the supersonic cries of bats. But as far as is known the bird echo-location sounds lie primarily within the human auditory range, never completely outside it as in bats (see ECHO-LOCATION).

Szöke (1962) states that in the more primitive birds which do not have any song proper the vocal organs are acting like a simple wind instrument, so that the tonal system consists solely of notes from the series of physical overtones such as can be obtained by overblowing a simple pipe. The more highly evolved birds, particularly the Oscines, can produce other musical intervals by modifying the physical or acoustic overtone system of the vocal apparatus through nervous control from the brain.

Thus bird song is not only a physical process in the windpipe but a neuro-physiological process in the brain. The more highly developed types of bird vocalisation are in some respects more like human song than the playing of, for example, a harmonic flute. The richness of musical invention displayed in the song of, for example, the Wood Lark Lullula arborea far exceeds the complexity of primitive vocal folk music. One specimen sang 103 different melodic lines in 5 minutes at a speed of 68 to 80 notes per second. Szöke finds evidence that a good Blackbird Turdus merula singing slowly, with clear phrasing, can be induced to adopt for his song the key of a pipe playing a major triad or even a major third ; and by progressively blowing a series of pitch pipes to him the bird can be led to sing in all the keys (through the ' cycle of fifths ').

Szöke points out that the vocal apparatus of man, unlike that of the bird, is not forced by its construction to the step-wise production of notes of the harmonic series, yet men sing in defined, restricted musical systems. In so far, then, as man uses intervals from the natural series of overtones, these must have been learned from the environment, since the vocal apparatus does not produce the series naturally. The author suggests that man learned to sing in this way by listening to birds, for of course bird song was highly developed on the earth by the time of man's first appearance. It is therefore unnecessary to suppose that man derived knowledge of the harmonic intervals from the inorganic material world, since bird song was all around and always audible. Thus man may have developed a musical signal system by imitating the birds. This gradually developed to be a component of the total art of primitive society, and later to a differentiated musical art.

Relation to Hearing Organs. We cannot fully understand the nature of bird vocalisation unless we have some knowledge about the mode of action of the hearing organs of birds (see HEARING AND BALANCE). This in fact does not raise such great difficulties as might have been anticipated, since all the evidence goes to show that the avian ear works on very much the same principles as the mammalian ear ; that is to say, it is a frequency analyser very well adapted for pitch discrimination. This is in strong contrast to the hearing organs of insects, which are highly sensitive to amplitude modulation (to which the human ear is relatively insensitive) and almost completely insensitive to pitch differences as such. If, therefore, we consider the hearing organs of birds as essentially similar to our own we shall not go very far wrong. Thus it appears that the hearing organs of birds as a whole are not markedly more sensitive than are those of humans to higher frequency ranges. Many birds do, however, appear to have a finer time perception than do human beings. That is to say, they can distinguish as separate a series of notes that to our ears would merge into a uniform sound. This conclusion about the mode of action of the avian ear has another important implication for the study of bird-sounds. Birds, like ourselves, have three practical ways of detecting the direction from which a sound is coming. These are phase difference, sound-shadow, and time difference. Discrimination on the basis of the perception of phase difference is most useful at low frequencies, i.e. something below one kilocycle per second ; this limitation is in all probability an expression of the refractory period of the auditory nerve. Phase difference will not, therefore, provide clues of much use to small birds, since the voices of most of them are mainly above this frequency. Sound-shadow (i.e. the intensity difference between the sound received by the two ears) is appreciable only when the width of the head is greater than the wavelength of the sound.   Now, if a sound is ' designed ' to give warning of the approach of danger, in particular the approach of a predator, it is not necessary for it to be readily localised. In other words, the sound should be such as to lead the hearer to take cover but need not, and indeed should not, be itself easily localised. It follows, then, that a predator alarm call will be more efficient if it has something of a ventriloquial quality. On the other hand, calls designed to keep the members of a flock together, or to enable parent to find young and vice versa, will require to be exactly the opposite. They will therefore need to contain frequent repetitions of notes of wide frequency range which will give plenty of items by which the hearer can appreciate the differences in time of arrival of the sound at the two ears. Consequently we expect to find, as indeed we do find, that alarm calls of small birds that are in a position to take

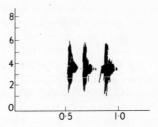

FIG 4. ' Chink ' alarm call of Chaffinch *Fringilla coelebs*. Note big frequency range, brief duration, abrupt beginning and ending, and repetition—all features tending to make location easy.

FIG 5. ' Seeet ' alarm call of Chaffinch.   Note small frequency range, long duration, gradual beginning and ending, and lack of repetition—all features opposite of those shown by the ' Chink ' call (Fig 4) and tending to make location difficult.

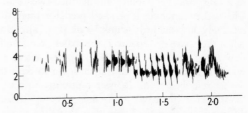

FIG 6. Full song of Chaffinch. Can be roughly represented by the syllables ' Chip, chip, chip, chip ; tell, tell, tell, tell ; cherry-erry-erry ; tissy-chee-wee-oo.' Note that the song contains rapidly repeated notes with big frequency range, having abrupt beginnings and endings.

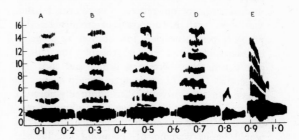

FIG 7. Phrase from song of Nightingale *Luscinia megarhynchos* consisting of a succession of 4 rich sweet-sounding notes (**a–d**) followed by a relatively harsh ' tu-wip ' (**e**). Note that **a–d** have a strong full fundamental at about 1 kc. with a series of 6 harmonics superimposed, nos 2, 4 and 6 being relatively strong and the others weaker. The harsh note **e** lacks this structure.

immediate cover are single and without any well-defined beginning and ending—they grow and decay gradually (Fig. 5). Other alarm calls and, of course, the songs of most birds, since these too are of primarily territorial function (that is to say, they are designed to give good clues for location), will contain repetitions of notes that start and stop sharply and have a wide frequency range (Fig. 4), i.e. of wide and indefinite pitch, to give plenty of clues for a hearer to establish direction.

Functions of Call-notes. A bird's alarm call then, in contrast to its song, is a brief sound with a relatively simple acoustic structure. Its main function, in the case of small birds, is to sound a warning of the presence of a dangerous enemy such as a hawk or an owl. If the bird-of-prey is perched conspicuously in a tree, the small birds will often make themselves conspicuous also by behaviour known as 'mobbing'; they will set up a chorus of cries that, so to speak, points out the predator to all and sundry. If the bird-of-prey is in flight, on the other hand, the small birds dash to the nearest cover and utter their warning cries from there. Now, the calls are very different in the two cases. Chaffinches mobbing a perched predator utter the relatively low-pitched 'chink' call (Fig. 4). But when they have fled to cover, the males give a high thin note, the 'seeet' call (Fig. 5), the effect of which is to cause other Chaffinches also to dash to the nearest shelter and to peer cautiously upward, 'looking for' the hawk in the sky. The significant difference between the two calls is that the 'chink' note is easy to locate whereas the 'seeet' is extremely difficult to place. The low frequencies of the 'chink' sound are of a wave-length such as may allow the two ears of a hawk (or a man) to detect phase differences, and the repeated click-like pulses are well adapted to giving clues for perception of sound-shadow and time differences. On the other hand, the 'seeet' call is composed of frequencies that probably permit no clues for location by phase or intensity difference; and it probably also fails to give a time clue, because it begins and ends imperceptibly, instead of coming as a sharp click. So it seems that the 'seeet' call is admirably adjusted to avoid giving positional clues to any kind of predators. Yet it is just as effective as any other sound would be in warning neighbouring Chaffinches, and indeed is appreciated by other species also.

Functions of Song. The full song of the male Chaffinch (Fig. 6) performs the function of keeping other males from its territory and of attracting unmated females. As sound spectrograms show, the Chaffinch song is sufficiently complex not only to identify the species but also to allow wide individual variation, so that individual birds are recognisable (even by human beings) by their personal 'signature tunes'.

Study Techniques. The foregoing remarks have drawn attention to the great influence that recent advances in technique have had in facilitating the study of singing. Chief of these is the sound spectrograph, which, as the accompanying Figures show, provides an analysis, giving frequency against time (together with fairly accurate information about relative amplitude or 'loudness'), of the sound signals presented to it. When used for the study of bird-song it thus provides (see Figs. 4–6) a kind of picture of the song, and serves as a form of notation as well as a method of precise measurement. Moreover, it enables one to compare, side by side, the sounds produced by different individuals or different species. The song, or call-note, is thus transformed into a precise visual pattern enabling comparison to a degree of accuracy never before obtainable. Looking at Figures 7 and 8, we see that while many of the notes may have high-frequency components that are above the sound spectrograph scale used in the previous illustrations, they are of lesser intensity (amplitude) than the lower components; and this confirms the previous conclusion that, in most bird-songs at least, by far the greater part of the sound produced is well within the auditory range of the human ear at its best. It will be seen that the sounds produced by birds are often of exceedingly short duration, and it is not unusual to find song phrases in which there may be 45 notes per second, each note separated by an interval of only 0·01 seconds. Notes with such short duration are not likely to sound to us as having any very definite 'pitch' although, as has been suggested above, the bird ear is perhaps better equipped in this respect and can distinguish the fundamental frequency in a very brief sound as the

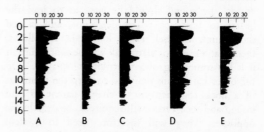

FIG 8. Amplitude section of notes **a–e** of Fig 7. Vertical scale: frequency in kilocycles per second. Horizontal scale: amplitude in decibels. Note clear evidence of the alternately strong and weak harmonics of notes **a–d** and the entirely different acoustic structure of note **e**.

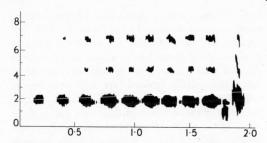

FIG 9. Full phrase of 10 notes of Nightingale's song from which Figs 7 and 8 were taken. The same essential features can be seen as in Fig 7 but frequencies above that of the second harmonic are cut out.

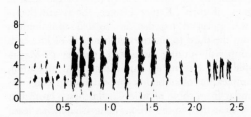

FIG 10. Series of harsh notes from song of Reed Warbler *Acrocephalus scirpaceus*. Note more or less random spread of energy over a very big frequency range.

main pitch more easily than we can. To our ears the steepness of the slope of onset of the notes probably does more to determine its tonal quality than does the frequency distribution of the sound energy in the various components. Sounds that glide steeply from one pitch to another are very characteristic of bird vocalisation (see middle notes in Fig. 6), and almost entirely lacking in human speech.

When we look at some other examples, however, we see notes of a very different kind. In Figures 7–9 the notes marked A, B, C, etc., are of much longer duration and show on the sound spectrograph not as long vertical streaks but as more or less rounded marks, each note being represented by several such marks one above the other. It will be seen that in Figures 7 and 9 the lowest of the marks is the most intense, indicating that the fundamental frequency is the loudest, that the marks above represent the harmonics of the fundamental, and that these harmonics tend to be alternately strong and weak. Such a distribution of energy implies a note of rich sweet sound, entirely different from that produced by such warblers as, for instance, *Acrocephalus scirpaceus* (Fig. 10).

See also SOUND RECORDING.

Specific Recognition. The study of acoustic structures as revealed by the sound spectrograms of

a wide range of bird songs supports very strongly the conclusion arrived at from the study of their natural history, that the main function of true song is that of a territorial proclamation. When the male song-bird has appropriated a territory, he at once establishes boundaries, usually by singing from one or several conspicuous song-posts within the area, and this song serves as a specific recognition mark informing other males of the fact that here is a male in possession of a territory, ready to dispute his possession with all comers. Since in many species the hearers respond appropriately, there is little doubt that competitive singing at the time of establishment of territory and subsequently is a sort of substitute for fighting, and probably has an important function in preventing the development of actual physical combat. If the song of a bird is to serve as a reliable specific recognition mark, it follows that it is likely that the ability to produce it will be inherited, so as to ensure that at any rate the main features of it remain constant from generation to generation and over a whole range of the species. One would expect, therefore, that many songs would resemble call-notes in being innately determined and thus produceable, when the appropriate time comes, without a period of learning and 'practice' (in the human sense) being necessary. The development of the 'Roller Canary' by aviculturists has provided us with a most convincing piece of evidence for this. The 'Roller Canary' has been produced by artificial selection for certain characteristics of the voice. If we compare the sound spectrograms of the song of a wild Canary *Serinus canaria canaria* with that of the domesticated forms such as the 'Border Canary', which has been bred for shape and colour, we find that the resemblance is very close indeed, almost the only significant difference being that the wild bird has a series of harsh phrases in the middle part of the song which have been eliminated in the case of the 'Border'. The song of the 'Roller', however, is clearly different in pitch, in time pattern, and in tonal quality, although in spite of these differences one can recognise a number of the elements constituting the original song-type in its newer version. There are, indeed, many birds in which the song is a reliable specific and generic character, much too constant to warrant the conclusion that it is acquired afresh in its entirety in each generation as the result of the imitative powers of the young bird.

Where the song shows such good specific characters the resemblance usually concerns the length of the song, the duration of the song burst, and the temporal pattern constituted by the notes. When we find generic resemblances, on the other hand, the common feature is more generally the quality of the voice, and it is more often than not an expression of similarity in the structure of the vocal organs—although it may also indicate precise mechanisms in controlling modulation in frequency and in time. As Marler has pointed out, there are many groups of birds in which songs, while providing extremely good specific differences, are almost useless in defining higher categories. This is understandable, for if a song is a factor in reproductive isolation, the songs are likely to be highly divergent between two closely allied sympatric species. In such cases there will have been intense selection for specific distinctiveness ; but, conversely, similarity between the songs within a genus would confer no evolutionary advantages at all ; in fact it is much more likely to be actually dysgenic.

Lack & Southern were the first to draw attention to the possibility that differences in song between the populations of the same species in, respectively, the crowded avifauna of continental Europe and in the smaller and more sparse avifauna of the Atlantic islands such as Tenerife might be explained by the reduction in selection pressure for specific distinctiveness in the latter environment. This seems to be borne out by more recent investigations. Thus the Blue Tit *Parus caeruleus*, which throughout most of its European range has to co-exist with 4 or 5 other members of the genus, in Britain at least has a fairly stereotyped song that provides a good specific character ; but on Tenerife, where it is the only tit species, it has a confusing variety of utterances. It is as if, with specific distinctiveness no longer required, individual distinctiveness has became valuable or at least allowable. Marler & Boatman found a rather similar situation in respect of the Goldcrest *Regulus regulus* in the Azores.

With the Chaffinch *Fringilla coelebs* (perhaps because in continental Europe it competes with no nearly related form, yet has on the whole a dense population), individual and local variation is advantageous provided that it does not go beyond certain bounds ; hence its songs are both specifically (but not subspecifically) and individually recognisable. The island subspecies, however, seem to exist at a lower population density. As a result, the island Chaffinches seem no longer to require the learned elaboration that is such a feature of European Chaffinches ; their songs seem accordingly to have reverted, by the reduction or restriction of learning ability, in the direction of the simpler form that is nearer to the innate basis of the specific song.

Innate and Imitative Components. The song of the Chaffinch has been studied more intensively than that of any other bird, and the results throw

light on the general significance of the song of passerines. Birds caught as juveniles in their first autumn and isolated until the following summer produce nearly normal songs almost as elaborate as those of wild Chaffinches. If such birds, instead of being individually isolated, are kept together in groups in such a manner that they can hear only the songs of the members of their own group, these birds (as a result of counter-singing) copy one another and so come to produce a fairly uniform community pattern. Close matching of the final phrase of the song is particularly evident.

Birds hand-reared in auditory isolation from early nestling life, produce extremely simple songs representing the inborn component of the specific song. If such ' Kaspar Hauser ' birds are themselves grouped together in isolated communities from the third to the thirteenth month of life, each group will—during the period February to May—build up, by mutual stimulation and imitation, complex but often highly abnormal songs quite dissimilar from those of wild Chaffinches. From this it is clear that, in the wild, young Chaffinches learn some features of the song from their male parents or from other adults during the first few weeks of life. But most of the finer detail of the song is learnt by the young bird when, in its first breeding season, it first comes to sing in competition with neighbouring territory-holders. There is little doubt that this is the way in which local song-dialects are built up and perpetuated. Full Chaffinch song is thus an integration of inborn and learned song-patterns, the former constituting the basis for the latter.

Subsong. This can often be distinguished from full song by being quieter ; by having song-bursts of longer duration ; and by having the fundamental frequency of the individual notes lower. This gives the impression that the subsong is generally of lower overall pitch ; subsong, as at present tentatively defined, is also characterised by having a quite different temporal pattern or structure as compared with full song (Thorpe & Pilcher).

The subsong of the Chaffinch shows all these distinguishing features, and seems also to have no communicatory function. It is characteristic of the early spring of first-year birds, and also of low but increasing production of sex hormones in birds of all ages. It provides in some degree the raw material out of which, by practice and by elimination of unwanted extremes of frequency, the full song is ' crystallised '.

Innate call-notes are used to some extent as components of the subsong and full song, but are more evident in the full songs of Kaspar Hauser birds than they are in the full song of normal birds. This is presumably an expression of the reduced auditory experience of the hand-reared isolated birds.

Imitative Learning. Chaffinches are not 'imitative' birds, in that they do not normally copy anything but sounds of Chaffinch origin. Once a Chaffinch has heard Chaffinch song as a young bird in the wild, it appears to have learnt enough about it to refuse to copy any sound pattern that departs far from the normal, i.e. it will learn only the fine individual variations of other Chaffinches. So, in the wild, Chaffinches practically never, in their full songs, imitate anything but other Chaffinches. Kaspar Hauser birds will learn songs of far greater abnormality provided the tonal quality is not too different from that of Chaffinch song. Voices as 'abnormal' as that of a Canary may be learned by hand-reared birds, and very occasionally by wild birds, but when this happens the alien notes are kept as components of the non-communicative subsong only; the full song is not contaminated with them. If the tonal quality is sufficiently close to that of the Chaffinch, as with the song of the Tree Pipit *Anthus trivialis*, and as with artificial songs constructed from genuine Chaffinch notes and played by tape-recorder to hand-reared birds (Thorpe 1958), these will be learned at least to some extent, and the learned pattern will become part of the bird's full song.

The counter-singing that occurs between birds in adjacent territories is an important factor in stimulating and restricting the imitative abilities of birds such as the Chaffinch. As a result of this process an individual Chaffinch may acquire several different songs from several different Chaffinch neighbours. When a Chaffinch has acquired more than one song-type, each song outburst consists of a sequence of one song-type followed by a sequence of another. When such songs are played back to a Chaffinch we find that those songs it uses most frequently itself are the most effective in evoking song. A Chaffinch in the wild will thus tend to reply with that song of its own repertoire most nearly resembling the song of its rival.

With the more 'imitative' finches, such as the Bullfinch *Pyrrhula pyrrhula* (for centuries the favourite pupil species for training by means of the bird flageolet in the competitive bird-song training schools of central Europe), Hawfinch *Coccothraustes coccothraustes*, and to some extent Greenfinch *Carduelis chloris*, the song, while functional in co-ordinating the breeding cycle and behaviour of the mated pair, is of less importance as a territorial proclamation. Thus in some respects it resembles the subsong rather than the full song of the Chaffinch, and similarly contamination with alien notes can be

tolerated to an extent that might be highly disadvantageous in a strongly territorial song.

In contrast, the buntings (Emberizinae) as a whole have highly territorial songs. Some of the species (e.g. Reed Bunting *Emberiza schoeniclus* and Corn Bunting *E. calandra*) have songs that are markedly stereotyped and completely innate. The song of the Yellowhammer *E. citrinella* appears to consist of an integration of innate and learned components, but with much less flexibility than in the Chaffinch.

Apart from a very few and partial exceptions, Chaffinches can learn song-patterns only during the first thirteen months of life, and towards the end of this time there is a peak period of learning activity of a few weeks during which a young Chaffinch may, in extreme cases, learn—as a result of singing in a territory—as many as six different songs. This special period of high learning ability is brought to an abrupt close by internal factors. This restriction of learning ability to a particular type of object, and to a sharply defined sensitive period, recalls the phenomenon of 'imprinting' (see IMPRINTING).

Individual Recognition. There is little doubt that learning to recognise the individual vocalisations of other members of the species, particularly between parent and young, can have very important consequences in the rearing of the young and in the maintenance of a family bond. This seems to apply to some gulls (Larinae), e.g. Kittiwake *Larus* ('*Rissa*') *tridactylus*, probably to some terns (Sterninae), and certainly to some penguins (Spheniscidae) and flamingos (Phoenicopteridae). Thus, the adult King Penguin *Aptenodytes patagonica* murmurs to its young for long periods during the weeks after hatching. The vocalisations of each individual have, apparently, a characteristic rhythm, and as a result of hearing them for a long period at close quarters, the chick comes to learn and recognise this. At a later stage in development, the young assemble in crèches containing many hundreds if not thousands of chicks. The parents, returning from the sea with food, call out persistently from the edge of the milling mass of young, with the result that the young bird belonging to the particular parent comes out to be fed.

It must not be thought that territorial proclamation is by any means the only important function of full song. There are many examples of song that are 'full' in the sense of being of the same general pattern as the territorial song although uttered quietly, hurriedly, or with slightly abnormal emphasis. Song used at the time of mating is often quiet, as if held back under great emotional tension, sometimes giving the impression of being 'congested'. Songs may be given in a subdued form as part of courtship display, e.g. in the Wren *Troglodytes troglodytes* (Armstrong 1951, 1963), and they may be used, in the same species, in connection with nest invitation, with going to roost, and with co-ordinating the movements of a family of young. There is little doubt that songs have a language function in all these circumstances, but in every case the details remain to be fully investigated.

The individual characteristics of songs that are, nevertheless, clearly recognisable as belonging to a given species, have already been mentioned with respect to the Chaffinch. The same phenomenon is found in a great many other birds. By no means all these individual differences are the result of learning by imitation from other members of the species. Even where, as seems probable in the Nightingale *Luscinia megarhynchos* and in some of the North American buntings (e.g. Henslow's Sparrow *Passerherbulus henslowi* and the Song Sparrow *Melospiza melodia*), the main elements of the song are innate, distinguishable differences can be produced by slight consistent variation in the duration of different notes, the duration of phrases (i.e. the spacing of the notes), and variations in relative pitch during the course of the song. Absolute pitch changes seem less important. Even within the restriction imposed by an entirely 'innate' song, therefore, there is a good deal of room for individual characteristics to develop. Where the song is long and the number of innate phrases great, then there will be still further possibilities for individual variation in that the phrases themselves can be re-arranged, and differences have been noted based on the frequency with which particular phrases are interposed. This seems to be the situation in general in the Turdinae (*Turdus*, *Hylocichla*, etc.), although it is probably true that in these genera a certain number of genuinely new phrases may be worked out and become incorporated in the full song. Even where, as in the Mistle Thrush *Turdus viscivorus*, the song strikes the casual listener as monotonous and showing very little difference from one individual to the next, one finds on closer inspection that there is, in fact, much more variation than one would have thought ; but this variation occurs particularly in the first few notes of each phrase, the final notes being relatively stereotyped. The ordinary listener subconsciously pays much more attention to the final notes and so gets a false impression of monotony.

Motivation. In passerine birds, and probably in others too, there is no doubt that the song production is mainly under the control of the annual cycle of sex hormone production (see ENDOCRINE SYSTEM). The psychological as well as the physio-logical motivation of songs, however, also requires much more study. The inclusion of aggressive call-notes in the full songs of birds suggests that these notes have a fundamental psychological connotation of aggression, which may function both when they are used individually and when they are components of a longer sequence. The acoustic characteristics of warning and alarm calls have already been mentioned. A closer study of the distribution of sounds of this type in the minor subdivisions of the true song may be expected to throw light on the functions of the latter. The study of songs of the same individual birds from season to season (e.g. Chaffinch, Blackbird) shows that the 'vocal memory' of birds is extremely good, and even a completely deaf Kaspar Hauser Blackbird is able to produce its melodies in successive years with complete fidelity as to pitch and rhythm ; it is quite clear, therefore, that although birds can change the pitch and rhythm of their songs with motivation and experience, they are also able to maintain these with extraordinary precision over long periods : they have, in other words, 'absolute pitch '—although when we use this phrase in connection with bird vocalisation we must remember that few bird notes are as clearly defined in pitch as are the notes of a musical instrument. Rather, as in the Blackbird for instance, what seems to us as a pure note of fairly constant pitch is found on analysis to fluctuate rapidly, but with small amplitude, around a mean. The evidence from the study of bird vocalisations gives very strong reasons for believing that birds hear their songs very much as we do ; in other words, that their auditory apparatus is functioning as a frequency analyser. It seems, too, that the hearing range of the bird is in general very similar to that of human beings. The presence of strong supersonic components in bird notes appears to be unusual and probably biologically unimportant (Thorpe & Griffin 1962).

Female Singing. Song from female birds is exceptional, particularly where there is striking sexual dimorphism. Studies with ringed birds have, however, shown that it is not, in some species, as rare as was formerly supposed. Thus female Song Sparrows *Melospiza melodia* occasionally sing early in the season before nest building begins, and there are about twenty other species in which elaborate songs have been heard from both sexes—families represented include the Cinclidae, Icteridae, Mimidae, and Rhinocryptidae. In some species, for instance the Robin *Erithacus rubecula*, both sexes hold territories at least temporarily in the autumn, and song from the female then seems to be more usual. Skutch records that the female Orange-billed Sparrow *Arremon aurantiirostris* actually sings while incubating. In Europe the female Wren *Troglodytes troglodytes* has a quiet but fully articulate whisper song, the function of which is equally obscure but does seem to be in some way related to care of the young. However, these exceptions only serve to emphasise the rarity of full territorial songs by female birds in species with a normal breeding organisation. Where, however, the female takes the initiative in courtship, as in the phalaropes (Phalaropodidae), buttonquails (Turnicidae), tinamous (Tinamidae), and others, the female sex may have elaborate vocalisations, even although the male has none ; but in any species that has marked division of labour in the process of territory holding, nesting, and rearing young, song from both sexes would probably be of no benefit and might in fact cause great confusion and consequent disorganisation of the breeding cycle. Some examples of female song in species that do not usually show it can probably be explained on the basis of hormonal imbalance, that is, some pathological upset of the normal delicate balance between male and female sex hormones (see ENDOCRINE SYSTEM). It is well known that female sex hormone inhibits the development of the male-type syrinx, and there are some examples on record of female Canaries *Serinus canaria* injected with a male sex hormone developing song indistinguishable from that of normal males. Female Chaffinches can also be made to produce a brief and elementary song by the same method. Beyond this there is little but conjecture.

Duetting and Antiphonal Singing. Particularly interesting cases of female song are those in which it occurs in duetting ; that is, when two members of a pair sing simultaneously as part of the courtship display or to maintain the pair bond. This has been described for several species amongst the oven-birds (Furnariidae), and also for motmots (Momotidae). In a number of the South American tyrant-flycatchers (Tyrannidae), Central American wrens (Troglodytidae), African shrikes *Laniarius* spp., barbets (Capitonidae), and grass warblers *Cisticola* spp., to mention only a few, a very special type of duetting known as antiphonal singing occurs. In this type, two members of a pair may alternate with extraordinarily accurate timing, often singing different phrases, so that unless one is actually watching it may be impossible to tell that the song is not coming from one bird.

In the Blackheaded Gonolek *Laniarius erythrogaster* the duet is extremely simple. The first bird, presumably the male, makes a 'yoick'-like sound which is followed immediately by a tearing hiss-like

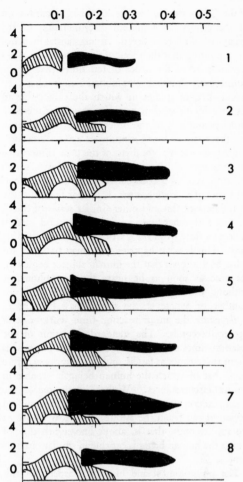

FIG 11. Diagrammatic sound spectrograms of eight consecutive duet patterns of a pair of *Laniarius erythrogaster* at Old Entebbe, Uganda, 6 March 1962. The note of bird A is shown cross-hatched ; that of bird B is black. All higher harmonics and overtones are omitted. Vertical scales : frequency in kc/sec ; horizontal scale time (secs).
W. H. Thorpe

sound from the second bird (Fig. 11). In a variety of birds that have been studied (including three species of *Laniarius*, two of *Cisticola*, and one *Trachyphonus*) the timing of the singing is normally so perfect that no one would suppose that two birds were involved unless he sees them or happens to come between them and hear the sound coming from two directions. In the particular case of *L. erythrogaster* it appears that the individual peculiarity of the duet is expressed not in peculiarity of pattern (for the bird apparently lacks the ability to vary this) but in a very precise, and exactly maintained, time interval between the contributions of the two sexes. The precision of this timing at once raises questions of the auditory reaction-time as, in part, an expression of the powers of temporal discrimination of the avian ear. (There is already circumstantial evidence for supposing that the speed of response of the avian ear must be of the order of ten times that of the human ear.) In the case of human beings it has been found that, in studies in which the subject has to respond by pressing a key, the reaction-time to a visual stimulus is of the order of 200 milliseconds, and that to an auditory stimulus of 150 milliseconds. If the response is a vocalisation the time is increased to circa 450 milliseconds. Figure 11 shows sound spectrographs of a consecutive series of eight duets by a pair of *L. erythrogaster*. It is clear from a study of the data of this and other similar series of duets, of this and other species, that the second bird is taking its time from the start of the note of the first bird. This is what happens to human beings ; for it has been shown that the human subject begins his response as soon as he hears the first phoneme, without waiting for completion of the letter or number or whatever the signal may be. In *L. erythrogaster* the mean reaction-time works out at 135 milliseconds. The standard deviation of the reaction-times is 12·6 milliseconds. This response is about three times as fast as, and much more accurate than, that of which the human being is capable in similar circumstances. With *Cisticola chubbi* the mean reaction-time is much longer, but the standard deviation can reach the astonishingly low figure of 2·9 milliseconds, that is, about one-eighth that of which the human being is capable in similar circumstances.

The physiological and biological aspects of this complex duetting are uncertain ; but it may be that the habit arose as a method of mutual recognition and communication between the two members of a pair in species living in very dense tropical scrub vegetation.

See Plate 22c (phot.).   W.H.T.

Armstrong, E. A. 1951. The Wren, London.
Armstrong, E. A. 1963. A Study of Bird Song. London.
Lack, D. & Southern, H. N. 1949. Birds on Tenerife. Ibis 91 : 607–626.
Marler, P. 1952. Variations in the song of the Chaffinch, *Fringilla coelebs*. Ibis 94 : 458–472.
Marler, P. 1955. Characteristics of some animal calls. Nature 176 : 1–6.
Marler, P. 1956. The voice of the Chaffinch and its function as language. Ibis 98 : 231–261.
Marler, P. 1956. Behaviour of the Chaffinch, *Fringilla coelebs*. Behav. Suppl. 5.
Marler, P. 1957. Specific distinctiveness in the communication signals of birds. Behav. 11 : 13–39.
Marler, P. & Boatman, D. J. 1951. Observations on the birds of Pico, Azores. Ibis 93 : 90–99.
Messmer, E. 1956. Die Entwicklung der Lautäusserungen einiger Verhaltensweisen der Amsel. Z. Tierpsychol. 13 : 341–441.
Pycraft, W. P. 1910. A History of Birds. London.
Rüppell, W. 1933. Physiologie und Akustik der Vogelstimme. J. Orn. 81 : 433–542.
Szöke, P. 1962. Zur Entstehung und Entwicklungsgeschichte der Musik. Studia Musicologica 2 : 33–85.
Thorpe, W. H. 1955. Comments on 'The Bird Fancyer's Delight' together with notes on imitation in the sub-song of the Chaffinch. Ibis 97 : 247–251.
Thorpe, W. H. 1958. The learning of song patterns by birds, with especial reference to the song of the Chaffinch, *Fringilla coelebs*. Ibis 100 : 535–570.
Thorpe, W. H. 1959. Talking birds and the mode of action of the vocal apparatus of birds. Proc. Zool. Soc. Lond. 132 : 441–455.
Thorpe, W. H. 1961. Bird Song : the biology of vocal communication and expression in birds. Cambridge.
Thorpe, W. H. 1963. Learning and Instinct in Animals. 2nd ed. London.
Thorpe, W. H. 1963. Antiphonal singing in birds as evidence for avian auditory reaction time. Nature 197 : 774–776.
Thorpe, W. H. & Griffin, D. R. 1962. Ultrasonic frequencies in bird song. Ibis 104 : 220–227.
Thorpe, W. H. & Griffin, D. R. 1962. The lack of ultrasonic components in the flight noise of owls compared with other birds. Ibis 104 : 256–257.
Thorpe, W. H. & Lade, B. I. 1961. The songs of some families of the Passeriformes. I. Introduction : the analysis of bird songs and their expression in graphic notation. II. The songs of the buntings (Emberizidae). Ibis 103a : 231–245, 246–259.
Thorpe, W. H. & Pilcher, P. M. 1958. The nature and characteristics of sub-song. British Birds 51 : 509–513.

SINUATED : term applied to a feather of which one edge appears as if cut away along a wavy line—not abruptly as when the vane is EMARGINATED.

SINUS VENOSUS : see HEART

SIRKEER : *Taccocua leschenaultii* (see CUCKOO).

SIRYSTES : generic name used as common name of *Sirystes sibilator* (for family see FLYCATCHER (2)).

SISKIN : substantive name of some *Carduelis* (or 'Spinus') spp. ; used without qualification, in Britain, for *C. spinus* ; applied in the West Indies to *Loximitris dominicensis* (see FINCH).

SITE-ATTACHMENT : see TERRITORY

SITELLA : discarded generic name used as English substantive name for *Neositta* spp. (see NUTHATCH).

SITTIDAE : a family of the Passeriformes, suborder Oscines, here treated as including the Neosittidae and Hyposittidae (doubtful affinities) of some authors (see NUTHATCH).

SIVA : substantive name of some *Minla* spp. (see BABBLER).

SIZE: in respect of a bird's body, usually expressed in terms of total length, from tip of bill to end of tail—with neck extended and bill in line (see MEASUREMENT). This is a useful way of determining variations in size within a species, or differences in size between species of similar proportions. Otherwise it gives only a rough indication, because it is affected by differences in shape (see SHAPE AND POSTURE), and particularly by length of bill, neck, and tail. Like considerations apply to the other measurements usually recorded, e.g. length of culmen, length of tarsus, length of wing from carpal joint to tip of longest primary (see BILL ; LEG ; WING). Height of crown above the ground may be a useful indication in the case of birds with upright stance or long legs, but it is obviously so dependent on attitude that it can scarcely rank as a measurement. Weight has the advantage of indicating general size independently of proportions ; but it is enormously variable even in the individual at different times, and in any event can be ascertained only in the captive living bird or the fresh specimen (see WEIGHT).

Range of Size: Although there are no birds comparable in size with the largest mammals, the range is nevertheless substantial. The largest known bird is the flightless Giant Moa *Dinornis maximus*, which became extinct in geologically recent times ; ostrich-like in build, but probably not holding its neck erect, it stood nearly 10 feet (3 m.) high (see MOA). About as large was another recently extinct 'ratite', *Aepyornis titan* (see ELEPHANT-BIRD). Other running birds known from fossils, *Diatryma* of the Eocene and *Phororhacos* of the Miocene, probably stood about 7 feet and 5 feet respectively (see FOSSIL BIRDS). Some of the penguins (Spheniscidae) known from fossils were much larger than the big Emperor Penguin *Aptenodytes forsteri* of today ; the height of *Pachydyptes* of the Miocene is estimated at 5 feet 4 inches. *Hesperornis*, the giant diver of the Cretaceous, was more than 6 feet long from the tip of its bill to the end of its short tail.

The largest living bird is the Ostrich *Struthio camelus*, of which some specimens may be 6 feet (1·83 m.) in length, stand 8 feet (2·44 m.) high, and turn the scale at 300 lb. (136 kgm.) ; and some of the other 'ratite' birds are also very large (see CASSOWARY ; EMU ; OSTRICH ; RHEA). The Emperor Penguin attains nearly 4 feet (1·22 m.) in height and may weigh up to 94 lb. (42·5 kgm.).

All the very large birds mentioned above are, or were, flightless species adapted either to running or to swimming. *Teratornis incredibilis*, a quaternary bird believed to be related to the New World vultures (Cathartidae), is credited by Howard with a wing span of 16–17 feet, which would make it the largest known flying bird ; it is necessary to observe, however, that this bird has been described from a fossil consisting of a single carpal bone (cuneiform), and that the calculation of size is theoretical in the highest degree. Other extinct flying birds, known from more extensive fossil remains, are not notably large.

Among flying birds of today, the Trumpeter Swan *Cygnus cygnus buccinator* (maximum weight, in males, 38 lb. (17 kgm.)) and the American White Pelican *Pelecanus erythrorhynchos* both range up to 6 feet (1·83 m.) in length, with wing-spans of up to about 10 feet (3 m.), but have very different bodily proportions. The greatest wing-span is probably that of a considerably lighter bird, the Wandering Albatross *Diomedea exulans*—a recorded maximum of 11·5 feet (3·5 m.) ; reports of wing-spans of over 10 feet in the Andean Condor *Vultur gryphus* are regarded as unreliable.

At the other extreme, the smallest of the hummingbirds (Trochilidae) are only $2\frac{1}{2}$ inches (63 mm.) long, including a relatively long bill, and may weigh less than 3 grams, or about $\frac{1}{10}$th of an ounce (see HUMMINGBIRD).

Sex Differences. There is some sexual dimorphism in size, but this is often so slight as to be unnoticeable (see SEXUAL DIMORPHISM). Commonly the males are slightly larger, although this may be only on average. In some instances the males are substantially larger—as in the Capercaillie *Tetrao urogallus*, to name an example in which the average linear measurements are in the ratio of about 4 : 3. Less frequently the female is the larger, as commonly and sometimes conspicuously occurs among birds-of-prey (Falconiformes) ; in the Peregrine *Falco peregrinus* average linear measurements are in the ratio of about 6 : 7.

Age Differences. Young birds at hatching are of course very much smaller than adults ; in the domestic fowl the chick's weight is 3 per cent of the adult's. On the other hand, full size is attained by birds at an early age, usually by the time that the young are fully fledged—a matter of a very few weeks in the case of small passerines (see GROWTH ; YOUNG BIRD). Notably among petrels (Procellariiformes), the nestling may at one stage be somewhat heavier than one of its parents, having stored subcutaneous and internal fat. Size in birds is determinate, and there is no further increase with age after the initial period of growth.

Individual Differences. There are individual variations in dimensions among members of any population of a species. Average, maximum, and minimum figures may be quoted, separately for each sex ; the validity of the mean figure depends on the measurement of an adequate sample (see STATISTICAL SIGNIFICANCE), and the greater the number of individuals measured the more closely will the observed maximum and minimum approximate to the absolute limits (standard deviation therefore a desirable datum).

Geographical Differences. In the case of a species divisible into geographical races (see SUB-SPECIES), the distinguishing differences may be as much in size as in other characters ; but this may be apparent only when mean values are compared, as the ranges of size may overlap.

Warm-blooded animals, including birds, tend to be larger in the cooler parts of the breeding range of the species (' Bergmann's Rule '). Warm-blooded animals also tend to show reduction in the size of projecting parts of the body in the colder parts of the range (' Allen's Rule ') ; but this is not notably exemplified by birds (in which ' projecting parts ' are mainly feathers, devoid of circulation), although there are some instances relating to length of bill, e.g. in the Pine Grosbeak *Pinicola enucleator*.

As between species of similar shape, surface area will vary as the square of the linear dimensions, and volume (weight) as the cube. This means that if one species is twice as long as another its surface area will be four times as great, and its weight eight times ; thus its weight will be doubled per unit of surface area. This last consideration is all-important for flying birds (see FLIGHT). The proportionately greater weight can be carried, in anything like equivalent flight performance, only by anatomical and physiological adaptations to yield proportionately greater power, or by changes in shape, particularly in the wing, that will provide a proportionately greater surface area. There are, however, theoretical limits to improvement of design, so to speak, in either of these respects ; and there must also be a limit to what can be conceded in the way of diminished performance, consistently with remaining airborne at all. It is accordingly not surprising that, as has been seen above, there are no truly gigantic flying birds, or indeed flying animals—and probably never have been.

General Considerations. Some mechanical principles of anatomy, involved in the relative dimensions of different parts of the body, are discussed elsewhere (see AVES ; FLIGHT ; GROWTH ; SHAPE AND POSTURE). Here the question is rather that of the biological significance of ' bigness '—or, indeed, of ' smallness '.

It is obvious that large size is advantageous in conferring some degree of immunity from enemies. Among birds, this is sometimes attained at the cost of losing the power of flight ; but powers of running or swimming may be highly developed instead, as in most of the ' ratite ' orders and in the penguins respectively (although not all of the latter are very large). Some birds have become relatively large, and have lost the power of flight without greatly developing any other form of locomotion ; thus the Dodo *Raphus cucullatus* and its kin fell easy victims when predators larger than the indigenous mammals invaded the islands that they inhabited (see DODO).

Another advantage of some degree of largeness is that it tends towards conservation of energy, because the surface/weight ratio decreases as size increases and thus a smaller proportion of body heat is lost in a given time. This may be an important factor in cold climates (see TEMPERATURE REGULATION ; TORPIDITY).

Size is to some extent related to feeding habits (see also ECOLOGY). Thus a predator must, in general, be larger than its prey. Many large raptorial and piscatorial species have thus been evolved ; the majority of the largest flying birds indeed fall in this category. Species that eat numerous small insects, seeds, and so on may themselves be quite small, depending for safety on quickness of movement or on concealment. The smallest birds are found among the nectar-feeders.

A point of some interest is that closely related species may differ little from each other except in size ; and that sometimes a smaller and larger one may inhabit the same area—seeming to indicate that each size has some particular advantage obviating total competition (see ECOLOGY). The Greater Yellowlegs *Tringa melanoleuca* and the Lesser Yellowlegs *T. flavipes* present a case in point. Other good examples are to be found among the woodpeckers (Picidae). Thus, in the Palaearctic Region, the Great Spotted Woodpecker *Dendrocopos major* and the Middle Spotted Woodpecker *D. medius* are closely similar in plumage, slightly different in size, and sympatric over a wide area ; the Lesser Spotted

---

Plate 45 · Feeding the Young

a *Upper :* Short-toed Eagles *Circaetus gallicus*—pair and nestling (Spain). When the photograph was taken, the male (on left) had just given the female a water snake, which she is holding preparatory to feeding the young bird.   *Phot. Eric Hosking.*

b *Lower :* Peaceful Dove *Geopelia placida* feeding nestlings ' in tandem ' by regurgitation (Western Australia).   *Phot. John Warham.*

(See articles FEEDING YOUNG ; HAWK ; PIGEON ; MILK, PIGEON)

Woodpecker *D. minor* shows a rather different plumage pattern of the same general type, is much smaller, and has a range in the main coincident with that of *D. major*. In the Nearctic Region the same genus includes the Downy Woodpecker *D. pubescens* and the Hairy Woodpecker *D. villosus*, the former appearing like a small edition of the latter and having a similar distribution.   A.L.T.

SKEIN: see ASSEMBLY, NOUN OF

SKELETON: the internal bony and cartilaginous framework of the body, forming a protective investment for vital organs such as the brain and the heart, giving sufficient rigidity to support posture, and providing a jointed structure to which muscles are attached so that it plays an essential part in locomotion and other kinds of movement. The main divisions, considered separately below, are the skull, the vertebral column and ribs, the sternum, the pectoral girdle and the bones of the forelimbs (wings), and the pelvic girdle and the bones of the hindlimbs (legs).

Nature and Development. As in most other vertebrates, the skeleton consists of cartilage and bone ; the former is tough and springy, the latter hard and comparatively rigid. Both tissues are composed of a matrix or ground-substance secreted by cells that remain within it, occupying small spaces. The hardness of bone is due to the fact that its matrix is impregnated with calcium phosphate and calcium carbonate salts. Bone is well supplied by blood-vessels ; cartilage, when mature, contains few if any blood-vessels although in early life it may be nourished by a system of vascular channels. Further details of the minute structure of bone are given in many text-books, but it should be noted that these are almost invariably based on mammalian studies ; conditions in birds are not well known and

Plate 46 · Parasitism ; Nest Sanitation

a *Upper :* Brown-headed Cowbird *Molothrus ater*, 11 days old, being fed by one of its foster-parents, a Black-throated Green Warbler *Dendroica virens* (Pennsylvania, U.S.A.). The species belong to the families Icteridae and Parulidae, respectively. *Phot. Donald S. Hentzelman, from National Audubon Society, U.S.A.*

b *Lower :* Jungle Babbler *Turdoides somervillei*— parent removing faecal sac from the nestling's cloaca, after stimulating the latter to produce ejection (India).   *Phot. Christina Loke.*

(See articles PARASITISM ; ORIOLE (2) ; WARBLER (2) ; PARENTAL CARE ; BABBLER)

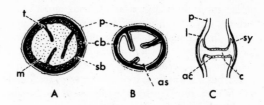

FIG I. A, B. Transverse sections through mid-shaft of femur (A) not pneumatised, and humerus (B) pneumatised, of fowl *Gallus*. The thickness of the bone wall, and the relative thickness of the compact and spongy bone, varies in different specimens, especially in the femur.   *Partly based on data from A. S. King.* C. Diagram showing structure of synovial joint.

ac articular cartilage **as** air sac **c** cavity of joint **cb** compact bone   **l** ligament of joint capsule **m** marrow **p** periosteum **sb** spongy bone **sy** synovial membrane **t** bone trabecula

do not necessarily resemble those in mammals in all particulars.

Most bones have quite a complicated organisation (Fig. 1). Around the outside is a tough fibrous membrane known as the periosteum. Inside this is a layer of dense compact bone, and inside this again is a layer of spongy bone that is often hollowed out so that there is a central cavity. This contains the marrow tissue (in which blood corpuscles are formed—see BLOOD) and fat, in varying proportions. In birds the cavities of some of the bones are invaded by outgrowths from the air-sacs (pneumatisation— see below ; also PNEUMATISATION OF BONE ; RES-PIRATORY SYSTEM) ; the bone-wall is then reduced to a thin shell and much of the marrow disappears.

Cartilage is predominantly a tissue of the embryo, the greater part of the skeleton being first laid down as a cartilaginous framework and later converted into bone by a process of ossification. The majority of bones thus ossify in cartilage, and are called cartilage bones. Some, however, ossify directly without going through a cartilaginous stage, and these are known as membrane bones ; except for the clavicle, they are confined to the skull, where they make up the roof, parts of the side walls, and most of the jaws and palate. A certain amount of cartilage remains in the adult skeleton ; for ex-ample, there are thin sheets of it (articular cartilages) over the ends of many bones where they form joints. See also DEVELOPMENT, EMBRYONIC.

Bones begin to appear quite early in embryonic life, but many of them do not become completely ossified until maturity. The ossification of a car-tilage bone, such as a limb bone, begins in the middle of the shaft, the ends remaining cartilaginous for a time. The bone grows longer as the result of the proliferation of cartilage near the ends, and as new cartilage is formed it is progressively converted into bone. In mammals secondary centres of ossification (bony epiphyses) develop in the outlying parts of the bone in addition to the primary centre in the shaft ; but in birds these secondary centres are found only in a few places such as the tibiotarsus and certain other limb-bones.

In addition to growing in length, a bone also grows in thickness owing to the deposition of new material beneath the periosteum. As the whole structure increases in size it has to undergo a process of remodelling in order to retain its overall shape, bone tissue being added in some places and removed in others. In this sense, living bone is a remarkably plastic material, retaining its capacity for structural modification even after it has reached maturity. This is shown by its power of repair after a fracture.

The joints between bones differ a good deal in their structure and mobility. The arrangement of a typical freely movable joint is shown in Figure 1C. It will be seen that the joint cavity is enclosed by a synovial membrane which does not, however, cover the articular cartilage (except in the embryo), and that it is strengthened by ligaments which help to keep the bones together and to limit their movement. Some joints have no synovial cavity, while in others, such as the sutures between the membrane bones of the skull, there is no articular cartilage, the ends of the bones being united by fibrous tissue ; such joints have very little movement.

Factors Influencing Form and Structure of Bones. It is well known that the shape of bones and joints and their internal structure are adapted to the functions which they perform and the strains to which they are subjected in life. Much attention has been devoted to the problem of how far this is the result of hereditary factors and how far the result of use during embryonic or later life ; and some of the crucial experiments have been performed on chick embryos. It has been found that a femur of relatively normal shape will develop in isolated fragments of limb-bud removed from the embryo and grown in some form of tissue culture, despite the absence of muscles and the possibility of movement. In cultures of limb-bud material the skeleton will differentiate into the elements of the thigh and leg, and joint rudiments will appear at the appropriate places. On the other hand, the finer details of the normal skeleton are not perfectly reproduced. The rudimentary joints tend to fuse, although they can be made to develop more normally if the bones are artificially moved.

It seems from these and other experiments that the major features of the skeleton's architecture are determined by heredity ; but many of the finer details that appear later in the embryo, or after hatching, depend for their proper development on environmental factors such as movement and mechanical stress. Skeletal structure is also affected by the nature of the diet, and by the action of chemical substances (hormones) secreted into the bloodstream by certain ductless glands such as the pituitary, parathyroids, and sex glands (see ENDOCRINE SYSTEM). Adequate supplies of calcium and of vitamins such as A and D are necessary for normal ossification and growth, and (as in mammals) ' rickets ' and other types of deficiency disease will occur in their absence (see DISEASE).

Changes in the composition of the adult skeleton are induced by activity of the sex and other glands in relation to such activities as moulting and egglaying. It has been found that, in pigeons, additional bone tissue is laid down in the marrow spaces of limb bones before the eggs are laid, and that this is subsequently destroyed, the calcium so liberated being used in the formation of the eggshell. A similar phenomenon may be artificially induced in male or immature female birds by the administration of suitable hormone preparations.

Anomalies. Inherited skeletal abnormalities of many types occur in birds and have been very thoroughly studied in the fowl. Among the most important are the conditions known as ' rumplessness ', in which the caudal and sacral regions of the skeleton are defective ; the ' creeper ' condition in which the legs are very short and bent owing to abnormalities in the development and ossification of cartilage ; various abnormalities of the jaws and bill ; and polydactyly (the presence of extra digits, on the hand or on the foot). Some of these inherited anomalies can be simulated experimentally by injecting the eggs with various substances such as insulin, by altering the temperature during incubation, or by various other methods.

Evolutionary History. The skeleton of birds most closely resembles that of reptiles, especially of the members of the reptilian subclass Archosauria (e.g. dinosaurs, pterosaurs, crocodiles). Birds were derived from primitive members of this group, and so also were the extinct flying reptiles or pterosaurs, the skeleton of which shows some adaptive similarities with that of birds (see ORIGIN OF BIRDS).

Except for the Jurassic bird *Archaeopteryx*, which possessed a remarkable combination of reptilian and avian features (see ARCHAEOPTERYX), the range of osteological differences seen among the different types of birds is comparatively slight, such differences being mainly ones of detail. The skeletons of the flightless ' ratite ' birds do differ, however,

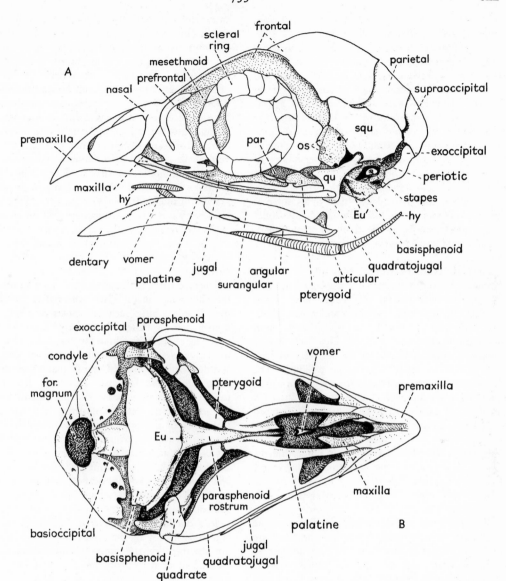

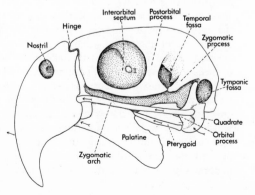

FIG 2. Side view (**A**), and ventral view (**B**) of 2–3 day old chick skull. In **A** much of the interorbital septum is still unossified. The hyoid apparatus (**hy**) is shown in line shading. Eu, Eu', anterior and posterior opening of Eustachian tube. *After Jollie* 1957, *J. Morph.* *v :* 100, *with modification.*

Bones shown by abbreviations in **A.** **os** orbitosphenoid and laterosphenoid **par** parasphenoid rostrum **qu** quadrate **squ** squamosal

FIG 3. Skull of Cockatoo *Cacatua* sp. showing mechanism of kinesis. Arrows indicate directions in which bones move.

II foramen for optic nerve.

from those of flying, carinate birds in certain obvious respects, such as the absence of the sternal keel. Some authorities have regarded these peculiarities as truly primitive, but recent work suggests (*a*) that the 'ratites' are descended from flying birds and have secondarily lost the power of flight and certain skeletal adaptations, such as the sternal keel, associated with it ; (*b*) that some of the allegedly primitive characters of the 'ratites', such as the structure of the palate, are not in fact primitive but are the result of the process known as neoteny—the persistence of embryonic characters into adult life ; and (*c*) that the 'ratites' may not form a single natural group, but include the descendants of several different groups of flying birds that have acquired similar osteological features as the result of evolutionary parallelism (de Beer 1956) (see RATITES, PHYLOGENY OF THE.)

Special Avian Features. Most of the striking features of a bird's skeleton are associated with its two independent and specialised methods of locomotion, flying with the forelimbs and walking with the hind ones (see AVES). In typical birds, both limb girdles are stoutly built, since each has to support the whole weight of the body alone when the bird is respectively flying or walking. The shoulder (pectoral) girdle and sternum form a unit that is firmly (although not immovably) attached to the ribs, and the pelvic girdle is rigidly fastened to a long segment of the backbone. The skeleton of the forelimb is highly modified ; the arm, forearm, and hand all play a part in supporting the wing—in contrast to the condition in pterosaurs and bats, where a long finger or fingers form the principal support of a membranous wing (see WINGS, COMPARATIVE ANATOMY OF).

The hindlimb is also specialised. Some of the metatarsals, which really belong to the foot, are fused and lengthened so that the leg appears to contain an extra segment, as also in certain dinosaurs and running mammals. The vertebral column, except for the neck region, is comparatively immobile and many of the vertebrae are fused. As in pterosaurs, the skeleton of many birds is lightened by extensive pneumatisation.

Skull. The general positions of most of the skull bones (almost all of them paired, occurring on each side) are shown in Figures 2 and 3, and only a few are named in the text. On the whole they are similar to those of reptiles, although certain reptilian bones such as the post-orbital and transpalatine are absent and the temporal region is much modified. Here it is possible only to touch on certain points of special importance.

The skull is light, with a compact rounded brain-case, which (unlike that of reptiles) is filled quite tightly by the brain. It is pierced by various foramina which transmit cranial nerves and other structures. Except in 'ratite' birds, many of the cranial sutures close early in life, so that identification of the various bones in the adult may be difficult.

Orbits and Nares. The orbits are usually very large, and, except in a few forms such as parrots (Psittacidae—Fig. 3), are not completely ringed by bone. They are separated from each other by a vertical plate known as the interorbital septum or mesethmoid bone ; this may be deficient in places, the holes being filled in life by cartilage or membrane. In the kiwis *Apteryx* spp., which have (for birds) very small eyes, this septum is absent, and the orbits are separated by the very large nasal cavities ; this is a specialised condition associated with the great development of the organs of smell (see SMELL).

The external nostrils are set back near the base of the bill, except in the kiwis where they are at its tip. In some birds such as gannets *Sula* spp. the nostrils become closed by the growth of the surrounding bones (see RESPIRATORY SYSTEM). The nasal cavities, which are lined by mucous membrane, and the cartilaginous nasal capsule that invests them, are situated inside the bones of the bill. Each nasal cavity opens in front at the external nostril and on the palate at the internal nostril ; it is separated from that of the opposite side by a cartilaginous septum. Turbinal cartilages project into each nasal cavity from its outer wall, increasing the area of mucous membrane. In some birds the nasal capsule and septum are poorly ossified, and this fragile region of the skull is seldom well preserved in museum specimens.

Jaws and Palate. The skeleton of the upper bill is formed mainly by the premaxillae, which in life are sheathed by the horny rhamphotheca. The attachment of the bill to the skull roof behind is quite flexible, so that, as in many reptiles, the upper jaw is able to move slightly in relation to the brain-case, increasing the gape ; this condition is known as kinesis. The mechanism depends on the fact that the upper end of the quadrate is movably attached to the side of the skull, while its lower end is attached to the zygomatic arch and to the strut formed by the pterygoid and palatine bones ; these are in turn attached at the front to the bill. Forward or backward movements of the lower end of the quadrate are therefore transmitted to the bill, which will be raised or lowered accordingly. The protactor quadrati muscle, which runs from the skull base to the orbital process of the quadrate, is important in swinging the quadrate forwards.

The mobility of the upper jaw is especially marked in parrots (Fig. 3), where there is a well developed hinge between the bill and skull. It is, on the other hand, very slight or absent in the 'ratites', and in a few other birds such as the Hawfinch *Coccothraustes coccothraustes*, which requires a rigid bill to crack the hard kernels of the fruits on which it feeds.

The palate bones are usually rather slender and do not form a complete shelf between the nose and mouth as they do in mammals. Their arrangement has been widely used as a basis for classifying birds into major groups, and in particular, for separating the 'ratites' (with a 'palaeognathous' type of palate) from the carinate ('neognathous') birds. Recent work has shown, however, that this distinction is an artificial one, and that some neognathous birds show palaeognathous features during early development. The subdivision of the neognathous palate into various types may be of value as a guide to the classification in the lower taxonomic categories (see PALATE).

The lower jaw, on each side, is usually made up of six bones, the front one being the dentary and the back one the articular. As in amphibians and reptiles, the jaw joint is situated between the quadrate and the articular. The two halves of the lower jaw are fused at the symphysis. In the nightjars (Caprimulgidae spp.) there is a kind of joint half-way along the lower jaw on each side, enabling the mouth to be opened very widely.

Except for *Archaeopteryx* and possibly the Cretaceous sea bird *Hesperornis*, teeth are unknown in birds, although the edges of the bill are sometimes serrated. Some workers, however, have claimed to identify rudimentary tooth-germs in bird embryos. The 'egg-tooth' of birds is, of course, not a true tooth but a horny caruncle at the tip of the upper bill which disappears soon after hatching (see EGG-TOOTH).

Ossicles. As in amphibians and reptiles, there is only a single bone, the stapes or columella auris, for conducting sound vibrations from the ear-drum to the inner ear. The extra 2 mammalian ear ossicles, the incus and malleus, are represented by the quadrate and articular respectively. The outer part of the stapes (the extrastapes), which is in contact with the ear-drum, remains cartilaginous. In certain owls (Strigiformes) the bony ear region is asymmetrical on the two sides of the head, a condition perhaps associated with their acute hearing (see HEARING AND BALANCE).

The tongue (or hyoid) skeleton is made up of a complicated series of bony or cartilaginous rods. In woodpeckers (Picidae) the hyoid horns, which

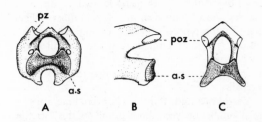

FIG 4. Neck vertebra of bird : **a** from in front, **c** from behind ; **b** shows hind part of vertebra from the side.

a.s articular surface **pz, poz** pre- and post-zygapophyses

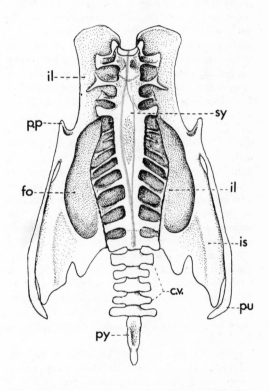

FIG 5. Pelvis and synsacrum of fowl, seen from below.

cv caudal vertebrae **fo** fossa for part of kidney **il** ilium **is** ischium **pp** pectineal process **pu** pubis **py** pygostyle **sy** synsacrum

give attachment to the muscles working the protrusible tongue, are extremely long, curving round the back of the skull and in some species entering the external nostril and passing inside the bill to its tip (see also TONGUE ; WOODPECKER).

The sclerotic coat of the eye is cartilaginous, and the front of the eyeball is reinforced by a series of small overlapping bony plates known as the scleral ossicles ; usually these are 10–18 in number. They assist in the process of visual accommodation (see VISION). In some birds there is also a small horse-shoe-shaped bone (os opticus) in the sclera, surrounding the optic nerve as it enters the back of the eyeball.

Vertebrae and Ribs. The vertebrae vary in total number between about 40 and 60, this variation being due mainly to differences in the length of the neck. The joint surfaces of the bodies of the neck vertebrae (Fig. 4) are characteristically saddle-shaped (heterocoelous), the front surface being concave in the transverse plane and convex in the vertical, while at the back these outlines are reversed. This arrangement allows great mobility. The first 2 vertebrae (atlas and axis) differ in structure from the rest ; in the hornbills (Bucerotidae) they are fused into a single bone. Some of the neck vertebrae are highly modified in the darters (Anhingidae), where the neck is permanently kinked but can be partly straightened suddenly to impale fishes on the bill. The rib-bearing thoracic vertebrae have little movement and some of them may be fused. The ribs articulate with the vertebrae by two heads and are divided into dorsal (vertebral) and ventral (sternal) segments which are jointed together (Fig. 6). The sternal segments are bony, unlike the corresponding costal cartilages of mammals ; possibly their ossification, although it occurs in ' ratites ', is an adaptation to the stresses of flight. Most of the ribs have uncinate processes, each bound by ligaments to the rib behind, which help to strengthen the chest.

A number of posterior thoracic, lumbar, sacral, and anterior caudal vertebrae are fused together to form a structure known as the synsacrum (Fig. 5). This is anchylosed, or at least very firmly attached, to the pelvic girdle, so that the weight of the body when borne by the legs is widely distributed along the backbone.

Behind the synsacrum are a number of movable tail vertebrae and then a structure composed of several fused elements known as the pygostyle. This bone carries the tail feathers, and its movements are important in flight. It is generally absent in the ' ratites ', but its presence in the Ostrich *Struthio camelus* is one of the features suggesting that the ancestors of this bird were able to fly (de Beer 1956).

Sternum. The sternum or breast-bone has a well developed keel (carina) in modern flying birds (' carinates '), which gives attachment to the strong pectoral muscles and greatly strengthens the whole bone. Its posterior end varies in shape, having one or two notches on each side in many species (Fig. 6). In swans *Cygnus* spp. and some cranes (Gruidae) it is hollowed out in front to contain folds of the trachea. There is no sternal keel in ' ratites ', the sternum being flat (' raft-like ') or slightly bossed.

Pectoral Girdle and Wings. The pectoral girdle (Fig. 6) consists, on each side, of the scapula, coracoid, and clavicle. The scapula is very long and firmly attached to the ribs by ligaments ; the coracoid runs down from the front of the scapula to the sternum. The glenoid cavity, with which the head of the humerus articulates, is situated at the junction between scapula and coracoid. It is shallow, allowing the limb free mobility. Each clavicle articulates with the front of the coracoid and scapula in such a way that a hole, the foramen triosseum, is enclosed between the 3 bones. The tendon of the pectoralis secundus muscle passes through this hole and, curving backwards, is attached to the head of the humerus ; this muscle gives the wing its powerful upstroke (see FLIGHT).

The 2 clavicles are fused together in the mid-line forming the furcula (' wishbone ' or ' merry-thought '). The angle of the furcula is generally widest in birds with strong flight, the bone acting as a curved strut to brace the wings apart. It is said that a bird cannot fly if one side of the furcula is broken. There are, however, a few flying birds in which the clavicles are much reduced (e.g. some parrots). Reduction or loss of the clavicles is also seen among certain ground-living birds ; these include the ' ratites ', in which the two bones do not even approach one another in the mid-line. In ' ratites ' the forelimb as a whole is reduced, especially in the kiwis and the giant extinct moas (Dinornithidae) ; in the latter the skeleton of the arm and hand seem to have been entirely absent.

The head of the humerus is expanded and has crests for muscle attachment. Its outer end articulates with the radius and ulna. The latter is the stouter of the 2 forearm bones and often has a row of quill-knobs along it for the attachment of the secondary wing feathers. Attempts have been made to correlate the relative lengths of the various wing bones with the strength or method (e.g. flapping or soaring) of flight, but no simple conclusions have been reached.

The carpal bones of the wrist are reduced in the adult to two (radial and ulnar complexes), though others occur in the embryo and later either disappear or fuse with each other or with the metacarpals (to form a ' carpometacarpus '). Only three of the fingers are present, probably the 2nd, 3rd, and 4th digits of the series. Each of these is represented by a metacarpal and one or more phalanges. Metacarpal II is fused with the base of III, and III and IV are partly fused. The 2nd digit has some power of independent movement, and carries the bastard wing (alula). In a few birds, notably the nestling Hoatzin *Opisthocomus hoazin*, one or more of the digits are clawed and are used for scrambling about the nest. See also WING.

Pelvic Girdle and Hindlimbs. As in other vertebrates, the pelvic girdle is formed, on each side, by the ilium, ischium, and pubis, which become partly fused together. The pubis has a most unusual position, seen elsewhere only in some dinosaurs; it lies parallel with and beneath the ischium (Figs. 5, 6). Except in the Ostrich, the pubic bones do not meet to form a symphysis enclosing the pelvic outlet; this may be correlated with the size and hardness of the bird's egg. The acetabulum, into which the head of the femur fits, lies at the junction of the three pelvic bones and is perforated. Behind it there is usually a large ischiadic foramen.

The proximal end of the femur has a prominent

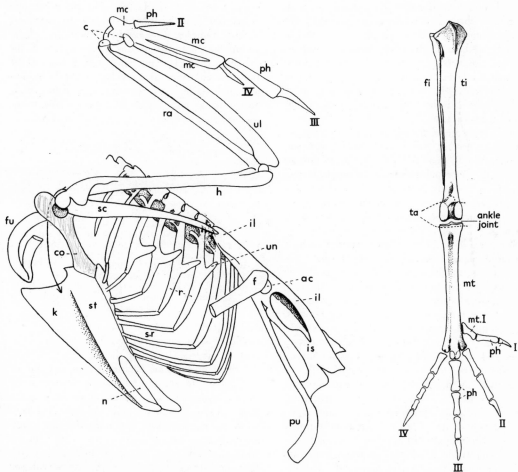

FIG 6. Skeleton of trunk of goose *Anser* sp. *After Kingsley, Comparative Anatomy of Vertebrates*, 1917.

ac acetabulum **c** carpals **co** coracoid **f** femur **fu** furculum **h** humerus **il** ilium **is** ischium **k** sternal keel **mc** metacarpals **n** sternal notch **ph** phalanges **pu** pubis **r** ribs **ra** radius **sc** scapula **sr** sternal ribs **st** sternum **ul** ulna **un** uncinate process **II, III, IV,** digits. Curved arrow shows direction of pull of pectoralis secundus muscle.

FIG 7. Right leg and foot of fowl, seen from in front.

fi fibula **mt.I** first metatarsal **mt** fused metatarsals **ph** phalanges **ta** tarsal contribution to tibiotarsus above and tarsometatarsus below shown between the interrupted lines. **ti** tibia. **I-IV,** digits.

process (trochanter) to which muscles are attached. A knob on the trochanter abuts against a facet on the ilium, and this prevents the body falling inwards when the bird is balanced on one leg. A knee-cap or patella is present in many species.

The condyles of the femur articulate with the tibia and fibula at the knee. The tibia, the inner of these bones, is much the larger. In most birds the fibula ends as a thin splint about two-thirds of the way down the tibia (Fig. 7), though in a few, e.g. penguins (Spheniscidae), it may reach the ankle (intertarsal joint).

A bird's 'ankle' is very differently constructed from that of a mammal such as man. In most vertebrates there is a series of small bones, the tarsals, arranged in two rows between the bones of the leg and those of the foot. In birds, however, some of the tarsals of the inner row have disappeared while others have fused with the lower end of the tibia. The bone so-called in the previous paragraph should therefore, strictly speaking, be termed the tibiotarsus.

Similarly, some of the bones of the outer tarsal row have become fused with the metatarsus. Consequently the 'ankle' joint is really situated between the inner and outer rows of tarsals, instead of between the inner tarsals and the leg bones as in man. These observations are based mainly on the study of embryos and cannot be verified from adult skeletons.

Most birds have four toes, each represented by a metatarsal element and a number of phalanges. The 5th toe is absent except as a freak. The metatarsals of the 2nd, 3rd, and 4th toes are very long and fused with each other, as well as having some of the tarsals fused with their upper ends. The result is a single bone known as the tarsometatarsus ; its compound nature is apparent at its lower end, where it divides into 3 pulley-shaped processes or trochleae each corresponding with one metatarsal (Fig. 7). In penguins the metatarsals are less closely fused than in other birds : this is no longer regarded as a primitive feature, since it has been shown that the fusion was often more complete in fossil than in living forms.

The 2nd, 3rd, and 4th toes each articulate with the appropriate metatarsal pulley and generally point forwards. They contain 3, 4, and 5 phalanges respectively, the end one being clawed. In many birds there is also another toe, the first (hallux), which is short and points backwards. Its metatarsal is small and attached to the back or side of the tarsometatarsus ; it contains at most only 2 phalanges. Since it is opposed to the other toes it may act as an important aid in perching. It tends to be reduced

in birds that do not perch and may be elevated some distance above the other toes. In 'ratites' it is absent. The Ostrich is peculiar in having only 2 toes in all, probably the 3rd and 4th. Special modifications of the toes in various birds are described elsewhere (see LEG).

Pneumatisation. Some of the bones in birds contain extensions from the nose and middle ear (in the case of the skull bones) or from the air-sacs that originate from the lungs (see RESPIRATORY SYSTEM). During the process of pneumatisation, which begins in the late embryo and is not completed until some time after hatching, these extensions grow into the bones. The holes through which they enter may be seen in the dry skeleton ; in the humerus, for example, there is a large pneumatic foramen on the inner aspect of the proximal end. The number of bones that become pneumatised varies greatly in different birds, but accurate data on the precise extent of pneumaticity are available for only a few species (see PNEUMATISATION OF BONE).   A.d'A.B.

A general account of the skeleton, with extensive references to the literature, is given by the first three of the following :

Stresemann, E. 1927–34. Aves. In Kükenthal, W. & Krumbach, T. (eds.). Handbuch der Zoologie vol. 7 pt. 2. Berlin and Leipzig.
Portmann, A. 1950. In Grassé, P-P. (ed.). Traité de Zoologie vol. 15. Paris.
Bellairs, A. d'A. & Jenkin, C. R. 1960. The skeleton of birds. In Marshall, A. J. (ed.). Biology and Comparative Physiology of Birds vol. 1. New York and London.
de Beer, G. 1956. The evolution of ratites. Bull. Brit. Mus. (Nat. Hist.), Zool. 4 : 57–70.
Waddington, C. H. 1952. The Epigenetics of Birds. Cambridge. (For review of work in experimental biology and skeletal abnormalities.)

SKIMMER : substantive name, alternatively ' scissor-bill ', of the species of Rynchopidae (Charadriiformes, suborder Lari) ; in the plural, general term for the family. This is a remarkable group of birds of inland and coastal waters, mainly in the tropics, consisting of 3 species in the sole genus *Rynchops* and allied to the gulls and terns (Laridae), which in many respects they resemble ; the group is sometimes classified as a subfamily or tribe of the Laridae. Although they are considerably larger than the average tern, their total length—with the exception of a South American race—is less than 18 inches.

Skimmers cannot be mistaken. The narrow, elongated wings reach far beyond the short, forked tail, the outer primary being the longest. The sexes are alike in coloration, but in size the females are the smaller. The general plumage pattern is blackish-brown above and white below, the face and forehead also being white. The Indian Skimmer *Rynchops albicollis* has a white collar, which too the Black Skimmer *R. nigra* of America and the African Skimmer *R. flavirostris* have in the off-season. The juvenile plumage is duller. The bill is vermilion basally in adults of all species, black distally in *R. nigra* and yellow distally in others. In immaturity the bill is almost black, with a pink (*R. nigra*) or yellow base.

Indian Skimmer *Rynchops albicollis*. *C.E.T.K.*

The grotesque deep bill, which is unique, has the upper mandible markedly shorter than the lower. The whole bill is much compressed laterally and can be opened very widely ; the lower mandible is knife-like and flexible, its sides closely marked with minute oblique ridges. A groove beneath the distal end of the upper mandible accommodates the very sharp tomia when the bill is closed. When the bird is newly hatched the bill has the two mandibles of equal length and can be used to pick up food ; but once the young bird begins to feather the typical bill quickly develops. In flight the bill is held at rather a downward angle. When the eye is viewed externally, the pupil is a vertical slit like that of a cat, unique among birds (Wetmore).

The small, slightly webbed feet and short legs— the tarsus is longer than the middle toe and claw— are vermilion, and the claws nearly black. The webs have concave or incised edges, but a skimmer rarely attempts to swim. The flight, made with steady measured wing-beats, is powerful and rather fast, resembling that of a large tern. The downward sweep of the wing-tips carries them well below the body.

Skimmers feed on small fish and other aquatic life taken from just below the surface of the water ;

the method of feeding is unique, for, with the bill open, the lower mandible ploughs the water. Typically, as the upper mandible closes on the prey, the head moves downwards and backwards (Zusi). The bird flies at some height above the water and repeatedly glides down to skim along the surface, for some yards at a stretch. A few birds may be skimming at any time of the day, but feeding mostly takes place in the twilight and also at night. Calm, shallow water is preferred ; when rivers are in flood the birds living on them disappear, and local movements are dependent on water conditions. They are sociable birds, and where plentiful may be found in large flocks of hundreds and even thousands.

When not nesting they rest on isolated sandbanks by day and sometimes, in South America, on open grassland ; a flock at rest squats in a close pack, heads all pointing in one direction. At eventide a flock may indulge in aerial evolutions. The cry of the African species is a strident, oft-repeated, shrill ' kek-kek-kek ', which becomes a whistle when prolonged into a tern-like trill. That of the American species has been compared to a dog's bark, while Stuart-Baker described that of the Indian as a ' shrill, chattering scream '.

For tropical populations, nesting coincides with the low water conditions of the dry season, if any. Breeding colonies vary in size, the known maximum (in Virginia) being about 4000 pairs, but mostly not more than 100 pairs. Skimmers do not nest in close colonies, although there may be many nests—often in groups—scattered over a fairly small area. They do not associate much with other species, but in India nesting colonies of the Little Indian Pratincole *Galachrysia lactea* and the River Tern *Sterna aurantia* have been found on the same sandbank as the skimmers ; and in Africa the White-headed Plover *Vanellus* (' *Xiphidiopterus* ') *albiceps* and the Grey Pratincole *G. cinerea* may nest close to them ; and in North America the Common Tern *Sterna hirundo*, the Little (or Least) Tern *S. albifrons*, the Piping Plover *Charadrius melodus*, and the American Oyster-catcher *Haematopus palliatus* do likewise. On a breeding ground the adults are not so demonstrative as are most of the terns. At other times skimmers may be very wary and difficult to approach. The brooding bird—the male assists in incubation—is conspicuous, and in the prevailing conditions of excessive heat sits tight. The nest is a hollow scooped out of the bare sand. A series of grooves radiating from the nest shows where the brooding bird rests its bill.

The set is 4, 3, or 2 eggs ; in one part of India and in South America 4 is normal. The eggs are broad ovals, smooth and slightly glossy. The colour is light stone or buff, resembling the background, but in America some are pale shades of blue and greenish-blue; they are spotted or blotched all over with black on similar underlying purplish and ashy markings. The chicks leave the nest as soon as they are hatched, and can swim well. When they crouch, their cryptic plumage of sandy buff and brown above, with white below, makes them also invisible.

Widely distributed, the Black Skimmer *R. nigra* (3 races), the African Skimmer *R. flavirostris* (it is only partly yellow-billed), and the Indian Skimmer *R. albicollis* are found respectively in temperate and tropical America, in Africa (it no longer occurs in the Nile valley in Egypt), and in India, Burma, and Indo-China. In Asia, Africa, and South America skimmers are restricted to rivers and lakes where there are extensive sand-banks, but also occur in some coastal areas; in North America they are exclusively coastal species.

C.R.S.P.

Moynihan, M. 1959. A revision of the family Laridae (Aves). Amer. Mus. Novit. no. 1928 : 1–42.
Murphy, R. C. 1936. Oceanic Birds of South America vol. 2. New York.
Wetmore, A. 1919. A note on the eye of the Black Skimmer (*Rynchops nigra*). Proc. Biol. Soc. Washington 32 : 195.
Zusi, R. 1962. Structural adaptations of the head and neck in the Black Skimmer, *Rynchops nigra* L. Publ. Nuttall Orn. Cl. no. 3 : 1–101.

SKIN: the protective and containing integument of the body, consisting of an underlying dermis and an overlying epidermis. The dermis is relatively thick and highly organised, being supplied with muscles, blood vessels, and nerves. The thinner and simpler epidermis consists of layers of cells, renewed by proliferation from the basal (Malpighian) layer as the outer layers die and become horny (keratinised). The epidermis of birds is notable for the special external structures to which it gives rise and by which it is almost wholly covered—especially the feathers, but also the horny sheathing of the bill, legs, and feet, with the claws on these last (see FEATHER; and BILL; LEG). Correlated with the presence of this covering is the almost complete absence of skin glands; the exceptions are a few small glands within the external auditory meatus and the oil gland on the rump (see OIL GLAND). The skin of birds thus does not perform the function of sweating, which has an important physiological role in mammals, and does not produce a sebaceous secretion for lubrication of its surface or outgrowth; nor can it play a great part in heat transmission (see HEAT REGULATION). The skin is, however, supplied with tactile nerve-endings or 'Pacinian corpuscles' (see TOUCH). Its blood vessels give the skin, at least in some instances, the capacity of exhibiting transient colour changes (flushing), visible on bare patches or even through the horny covering of bill and legs (see HERON; OSTRICH). In some birds there are such appendages as spurs, wattles, combs, lappets, sacs, or pouches (see INTEGUMENTARY STRUCTURES). For care of the body surface generally see under FEATHER MAINTENANCE.

'Skin' is also the term applied to the usual unmounted study specimen of a bird (see MUSEUM).

SKUA: substantive name, especially in British usage, of all members of the Stercorariidae (Charadriiformes, suborder Lari); in the plural, general term for the family. Usage in North America and elsewhere prefers the name 'jaeger' (German word meaning 'hunter') and restricts 'skua' to *Catharacta*. The family contains only 2 genera, *Catharacta* (not recognised as separate by all authors) and *Stercorarius*; the former has one boreal representative, the Great Skua *C. skua skua* (called 'Bonxie' in Shetland) and other forms in the far south; the latter has 3 species, all northern and on the British list: the Arctic Skua (or Parasitic Jaeger) *S. parasiticus*, the Pomatorhine Skua (or Pomarine Jaeger) *S. pomarinus*, and the Long-tailed Skua (or Long-tailed Jaeger) *S. longicaudus*. The skuas are related to the gulls and are by some treated as a subfamily of the Laridae. They are roughly similar to gulls in size, but have dark plumage. They are widely known for their habit of chasing other sea birds in flight until they disgorge food (see PIRACY). Like gulls, they are chiefly associated with the sea but may breed far inland.

The plumage is generally dark brown, at least above. In *Catharacta* it is much the same above and below, and speckled; in *Stercorarius* speckling is pronounced only in juveniles. The sexes are alike. In *Catharacta* the contiguous white bases of the primaries form conspicuous wing patches in flight; these are often displayed also by standing birds holding their wings stretched vertically upwards back to back, a habit not found in *Stercorarius*. In the latter the adult plumage varies between a light phase, with the under parts and collar creamy or almost white and the head conspicuously dark-capped, and a dark phase with the whole plumage almost uniformly dark; the primary shafts and bases are always white, but less prominent than in *Catharacta*. In *Stercorarius* the 2 central rectrices are much elongated—pointed and fluttering in *S. longicauda* but twisted through 90° and appearing clubbed in *S. pomarinus*. The bill is gull-like, unusually soft in its basal half, where a pair of separate thin plates overlie the nostril area, but hard and rather strongly hooked towards the tip. The feet are gull-like also, but with more strongly curved claws ; the basal part of the toes and webs are pallid in juvenile Arctic Skuas but become wholly dark by maturity.

Great Skuas (*Catharacta*) are roughly the size of Herring Gulls *Larus argentatus*, but heavier, and they flap their wings much faster ; they are surprisingly quick and agile when chasing victims, and usually swoop to catch disgorged food before it reaches the water. Over land they frequently soar. In temperament they are bullying and aggressive, and stoop fiercely and repeatedly at anyone venturing into their nesting territories. When not breeding they are entirely independent of land and can remain indefinitely at sea without shelter or fresh water. At sea they are solitary, and take pelagic food from the surface in flight ; they often follow ships, usually some distance astern. On breeding grounds they are highly raptorial, killing adult and young sea birds and small mammals, and eating eggs (and also carrion), but much food is obtained at all times by harrying other sea birds. They never use their feet to hold prey.

The distribution of the Great Skuas is notable for being bipolar. The northern Great Skua is confined to the Atlantic, and nests in a restricted area comprising northern Scotland (Shetland, Orkney, Caithness, and Lewis), the Faeroes, and Iceland. Non-breeders may appear anywhere in the Atlantic between the Arctic Circle and Tropic of Cancer. In the Southern Hemisphere Great Skuas are circumpolar, with 4–6 races (or perhaps species) in Chile, the coasts of Antarctica, and many islands in the Southern Ocean north to New Zealand. In winter these birds spread into lower latitudes and some cross the Equator into the temperate North Pacific. No southern forms have so far been recognised in the North Atlantic. They nest socially, with nests widely-spaced on the ground, often near bird-cliffs or penguin rookeries. Two eggs are normal (occasional clutches of 3 perhaps due to 2 hens) ; in South Georgia only one chick generally survives, but in Europe both are usually reared.

Of the 3 *Stercorarius* species, the Pomatorhine is the largest and the Long-tailed the smallest. They are northern circumpolar breeders, frequenting similar habitats to *Catharacta* and not differing much in breeding habits. The Arctic Skua *S. parasiticus* uses a ' distraction display ' as well as dive-bombing intruders near the nest. It nests in Scotland, but the others are wholly tundra-nesters. The ranges of all 3 overlap widely, but *S. longicaudus* generally

extends farthest north. All 3, but especially *S. pomarinus*, are influenced in abundance by local fluctuations in numbers of lemmings, which often form their staple food ashore. Along coasts they habitually mob kittiwakes *Larus* (' *Rissa* ') spp. and terns (Sterninae) to make them disgorge. The terror they instil is largely psychological, their bills being hardly lethal weapons. They are vocal chiefly at their breeding places, and make high-pitched cat-calls or harsh deeper notes. *S. parasiticus* begins to breed (on Fair Isle) at between 3 and 6 years of age (most at 4).

An interesting feature of *Stercorarius* is the possession of light and dark phases, with intermediates (see POLYMORPHISM). The dark phase is very rare in *S. longicaudus* and possibly does not occur in adult plumage ; in the other 2 species the proportions of light and dark birds vary much from area to area, and even from colony to colony. In Shetland less than one-fifth of the Arctic Skuas are light, but elsewhere the proportion is higher, up to almost 100 per cent in Spitzbergen and arctic Canada.

Stercorarius spp. are all long-distance migrants. Most individuals reach the tropics in winter and some travel far beyond ; they are common for instance in eastern Australian waters. Migration is partly coastwise, partly oceanic, the Long-tailed Skua being the most pelagic. The Pomatorhine Skua has a well-marked winter concentration off the coast of West Africa between 25° and 8° N., and non-breeders occur there in summer also.

See Plate 20 (colour).   V.C.W.-E.

Murphy, R. C. 1936. The skuas and jaegers. *In* Oceanic Birds of South America. New York.

Pitelka, F. A., Tomich, P. Q. & Treichel, G. W. 1955. Breeding behaviour of jaegers and owls near Barrow, Alaska. Condor 57 : 3–18.

Southern, H. N. 1943. The two phases of *Stercorarius parasiticus*. Ibis 85 : 443–485.

Southern, H. N. 1944. Dimorphism in *Stercorarius pomarinus*. Ibis 86 : 1–16.

Stonehouse, B. 1956. The brown skua *Catharacta skua lönnbergi* (Mathews) of South Georgia. Falkland Is. Depend. Surv. Sci. Rep. 14 : 1–25.

Williamson, K. 1959. Changes of mating within a colony of Arctic Skuas. Bird Study 6 : 51–60.

Wynne-Edwards, V. C. 1935. On the habits and distribution of birds on the North Atlantic. Proc. Boston Soc. Nat. Hist. 40 : 233–346.

Young, E. C. 1963. The breeding of the South Polar Skua *Catharacta maccormicki*. Ibis 105 : 203–233.

SKULL : see SKELETON

SKYLARK : *Alauda arvensis* (see LARK).

SLEEPING : see under ROOSTING ; also, in respect of postures, FEATHER MAINTENANCE.

SMELL: a sense for which the receptive surface is the sensory lining of the nasal passages. The olfactory organs of birds are well developed and are situated in the paired nasal cavities that open by the nostrils (external nares) at the base of the bill (see NARIS ; SKELETON). The nasal cavities are separated by a median partition, the nasal septum, and they also communicate posteriorly with the roof of the mouth by paired openings, the internal or posterior nares (or choanae). The walls of the cavities are enlarged by the formation of folds (the nasal conchae) in such a way that each is subdivided into three chambers. The surface area in many species is further increased by the coiling of the conchae, or by the development of longitudinal furrows as in the Ostrich *Struthio camelus*.

The first two chambers appear to serve respiratory functions only and are of particular importance in warm-blooded animals, since they act as an air-conditioning apparatus (see RESPIRATORY SYSTEM). The lining epithelium has a rich blood supply and the removal of dust particles from the inhalant air-stream is effected here, probably with the aid of the secretions of the nasal glands, which open into the first chamber. These glands are relatively small in terrestrial species, but they are especially well developed in marine birds and are believed to play a part in the elimination of excess of salt (see EXCRETION, EXTRARENAL).

Only the third (dorsal) chamber is lined by olfactory epithelium similar in histological appearance to that found in mammals. Thus, the olfactory receptors are pigmented and are long, narrow, columnar cells, each of which has one or more thin olfactory hairs passing to the surface of the olfactory area. These sensory cells are surrounded by columnar supporting cells. Information gathered by the olfactory receptors is carried to the brain by the olfactory nerve, non-medullated fibres of which form a plexus in the olfactory mucosa. This third, or 'olfactory', chamber is particularly well developed in the nocturnal kiwis *Apteryx* spp., whilst in such birds as emus (Dromaiidae), geese *Anser* spp., shearwaters and other petrels (Procellariiformes) the olfactory lobe of the brain is well developed (see NERVOUS SYSTEM). Recently, Bang has drawn attention to the very large and heavily innervated nasal organs of the Turkey Vulture *Cathartes aura*, the Oilbird *Steatornis caripensis*, and the albatrosses *Diomedea immutabilis* and *D. nigripes*. She suggests that the morphological and behaviourial evidence (the latter for long familiar in the case of albatrosses and other petrels) indicates a well-developed olfactory sense in these species (see also OILBIRD).

However, although birds apparently possess adequate olfactory organs, it seems possible that in some species the sense of smell is poorly developed and plays little part in their lives ; a great deal of conflicting evidence has been accumulated. Observations and simple experiments in America as early as 1826 suggested that vultures (Cathartidae) do not find carrion by a sense of smell. Hill concluded that domestic turkeys were unable to detect a variety of odours, since he could not affect their choice of food by the addition of such substances as oil of lavender, camphor, and chloroform to one of two piles of grain. Even the fumes of prussic acid did not drive the bird from the pile of food that it happened to choose first, although it was almost poisoned.

Strong placed domesticated ringdoves *Streptopelia* 'risoria' in a labyrinth in which the birds could go to one of four separate chambers, three being empty whilst the fourth contained food together with the odour under test. He attempted to train the birds to enter the chamber containing the food, and decided that their behaviour was, in certain cases, affected by olfactory stimulation, although his results seem far from conclusive. Observations have suggested that kiwis, which feed on earth-worms, find their prey by means of their sense of smell ; their vision is thought to be poor, whilst the olfactory organs are relatively well developed and the nostrils are situated at the end of the bill. Nevertheless, convincing evidence from critical experiments is still lacking.

Walter has obtained entirely negative results in a series of careful investigations with pigeons, using the technique of conditioned reflexes. During the experiments, the bird's respiratory rate was recorded, whilst it was subjected to two different stimuli presented simultaneously. A pain stimulus was applied to the wing with a needle, and at the same time a bell was rung. The pain stimulus alone will evoke an acceleration in the respiratory rate, this being termed an unconditioned response. However, when the combined acoustic and pain stimuli had been repeated a number of times, it was found that the sound of the bell alone would cause accelerated respiration in the bird. This is an example of a conditioned response, and Walter found that—as in many other animals—a variety of visual and acoustic stimuli, which the bird can detect, could be used to obtain similar results. However, it proved impossible to produce such an increase in the rate of respiration when one of a number of scents was used as the conditioning stimulus, combined as before with a pain stimulus. Similarly, no conditioned movement of the legs was established with pigeons and domestic ducks when a range of odours was again used, each in turn during a series of experiments, as conditioning stimuli together with electric shocks (the unconditioned stimulus). The experiments suggest that the birds' sensory receptors were not capable of detecting any of the odours tested.

In man, stimulation of the olfactory nerve endings causes alterations in the records of electrical activity in the brain. During some of the experiments with pigeons described above, two needles inserted into the bird's brain were used as the electrodes, and records of the fluctuation in electrical activity were made. The results suggested that the electro-encephalogram so obtained was unaffected by the odours administered.

Siskins *Carduelis spinus* and parakeets (Psittacidae) were used in a series of training experiments, in which the birds were allowed to eat from the feeding trays provided with an odorant, whilst they were forbidden to take their food from trays that contained food alone and were offered simultaneously. Again, it proved impossible to train the birds by olfactory stimulation to make the correct choice. On the other hand it has been shown that the Bobwhite Quail *Colinus virginianus virginianus* can be trained to associate the odour of coumarin with food, although it was a difficult animal to train to respond to such an olfactory stimulus and coumarin unexpectedly proved to be repellent to this species. The caged Bobwhite also learned to discriminate between two feeders, apparently the same to man, and the investigators concluded that their olfactory sense was probably involved. The nature of the differentiating odour was not determined, but it was suggested that it was a species odour transferred to the feeders when the birds touched them. Such experiments indicate a relatively well developed sense of smell.

Recently, two independent series of conditioning experiments in America have again been used to test olfactory sensitivity in pigeons, and have produced conflicting results. In one, the pigeons were trained to move from one part of their cage to another by using light and odour (a cheap penetrating perfume) paired together as a conditioned stimulus, with electric shocks acting as the unconditioned stimulus. The pigeons were then unable to learn to use the odour alone, and it was concluded that they did not detect this scent. Another worker, however, trained two pigeons to peck at the correct key when appropriately stimulated (under carefully controlled conditions) with an odour (iso-octane). It thus seems that further experiments with other species, and using a wider variety of olfactory stimuli, are necessary before we may reach any definite conclusions about the sense of smell in birds.

For smell in its other meaning see ODOUR.

C.J.D.

Bang, B. G. 1960. Anatomical evidence for olfactory function in some species of birds. Nature 188 : 547–549.

Calvin, A. D., Williams, C. M. & Westmoreland, N. 1957. Olfactory sensitivity in the domestic pigeon. Amer. J. Physiol. 188 : 255–256.

Frings, H. & Boyd, W. A. 1952. Evidence for olfactory discrimination by the Bobwhite Quail. Amer. Midl. Nat. 48 : 181–184.

Hamrum, C. L. 1953. Experiments on the senses of taste and smell in the Bob-white Quail *Colinus virginianus virginianus*. Amer. Midl. Nat. 49 : 872–877.

Hill, A. 1905. Can birds smell? Nature 71 : 318–319.

Jones, F. Wood. 1937. The olfactory organ of the Tubinares. Emu 36 : 281–286 ; 37 : 10–13, 128–131.

Michelson, W. J. 1959. Procedure for studying olfactory discrimination in pigeons. Science 130 : 630.

Strong, R. M. 1911. On the olfactory organs and the sense of smell in birds. J. Morph. 22 : 619–661.

Walter, W. G. 1943. Some experiments on the sense of smell in birds. Arch. Néerland. Physiol. 27 : 1–72.

SMEW: *Mergus albellus* (see DUCK)

SMOKE-BATHING: see under FEATHER MAINTENANCE

SNAKE-BIRD: alternative substantive name of species of Anhingidae (see DARTER) ; also a popular name in Britain for the Wryneck *Jynx torquilla* (see WOODPECKER).

SNIPE: substantive name (commonly unchanged in the plural) of species of *Gallinago* (' *Capella* ') and allied genera, and also sometimes misapplied to the dowitchers *Limnodromus* spp. (see under SANDPIPER ; for other families see PAINTED SNIPE and SEED-SNIPE).

SNOWCAP: *Microchera albocoronata* (for family see HUMMINGBIRD).

SNOWCOCK: substantive name of *Tetraogallus* spp. (see PHEASANT).

SOARING: see FLIGHT

SOCIAL ORGANISATION: see AGGRESSION ; DISPLAY ; DOMINANCE (2) ; FLOCKING ; RECOGNITION ; SINGING ; TERRITORY ; also CROW (1) ; PENGUIN

SOCIETIES, ORNITHOLOGICAL: see under ORNITHOLOGY

SOFT PARTS: for definition of term see under TOPOGRAPHY ; for care of, see under FEATHER MAINTENANCE.

SOFTTAIL: substantive name of *Xenerpestes* spp., *Thripophaga* spp., and allies (see OVENBIRD (1)).

SOFTWING: substantive name of *Malacoptila* spp. (see PUFFBIRD).

SOIL: see GEOLOGICAL FACTORS

SOLAN GOOSE: former alternative name (misnomer) for *Sula bassana* (see GANNET).

SOLITAIRE: substantive name of 2 species of the extinct family Raphidae (see under DODO) ; and, in North America, of *Myadestes* spp. (see THRUSH).

SOMATERIINI: see DUCK

SOMITE: see DEVELOPMENT, EMBRYONIC

SONG: see SINGING

SONG-BIRDS: term often used for the suborder Oscines (see PASSERIFORMES).

SONGLARK: substantive name of *Cinclorhamphus* spp. (see WREN (2) ; also RAIL-BABBLER).

SONG-SHRIKE: sometimes used, in the plural, as a general term for the Cracticidae (see MAGPIE (2)).

SORA: name, alternatively ' Sora Rail ', of *Porzana carolina* (see RAIL).

SOUND RECORDING: one of the more recently evolved methods of collecting data about birds. The succession is, in essence : field observations and sketches, collecting of specimens, still photography, filming, and then sound recording.

History. The earliest bird recording known still to exist in that of a captive Common Shama *Copsychus malabaricus* made in Germany in 1889 by Ludwig Koch. The earliest reference in ornithological literature to the reproduction of a bird sound is in the account of the 16th Congress of the American Ornithologists' Union in 1898, which mentions a ' graphophone demonstration of a Brown Thrasher's song '. The first recordings of *wild* birds made anywhere are almost certainly those of Cherry Kearton, who in England in 1900 captured on wax cylinders a few Song Thrush *Turdus philomelos* notes and the song of the Nightingale *Luscinia megarhynchos*. The first recordings of wild birds in Africa and America were made in 1929, and in Australia in about 1931.

At least one utterance has been recorded (up to the middle of 1962) from over a quarter of the species in the world—a surprisingly high total. The approximate figure is 2300 ; of these, about 1200 are available on commercially issued gramophone records and the rest are in the libraries of broadcasting organisations, research institutes, universities, and private individuals.

A world discography of published gramophone records of bird sound gives 170 references to discs, or sets of discs, published between 1908 and 1962 (see Table below). The earliest records were of caged birds, and these were followed by many selections of the commoner wild species. The first faunistic treatment was ' Witherby's Sound-Guide to British Birds ' by North & Simms, published in 1958 (195 species) ; this was closely followed by Kellogg & Allen with their ' Field Guide to Bird Songs of Eastern and Central North America ' (305 species), and by Kellogg's western Nearctic album (515 species).

With two remarkable records from Borror & Gunn the ' quantitative ' phase of bird-sound publication is entered : ' Warblers ' (1958) gives songs by 150 individuals of 38 species of Parulidae, and ' Finches ' (1960) songs of 226 individuals of 43 species of Fringillidae.

Libraries of Bird Sound Recordings. The number of such libraries, large and small, in the world is probably under 100. Easily the most comprehensive is that in Cornell University's Laboratory of Ornithology, with over 1500 species, mostly from the Nearctic and Neotropical Regions. In the European part of the Palaearctic Region, the British Broadcasting Corporation's collection has rather over 240 species, and that of the Swedish Broadcasting Corporation about 250 ; the only sizeable library of Mediterranean species is that of Jean-Claude Roché. In the eastern Palaearctic, the only significant collections known are in Japan, where for example T. Kabaya has 280 species. No more than fragmentary work has been done in the Oriental Region. The only large African library is that of Myles North in Nairobi, with about 220 species. In the Australasian Region rather over 100 species have been recorded : in Australia itself by P. Bruce and others, and in New Zealand by K. & J. Bigwood. Altogether, public or private libraries are known to exist in about 30 countries.

Recordings of Sound Production by Bird Species

Region of recording	Available on discs	Total recorded
Palaearctic	351	380
Nearctic	ca. 540	ca. 600
Australasian	78	ca. 110
Neotropical	ca. 151	ca. 870
Ethiopian	ca. 80	ca. 300
Oriental	—	ca. 10
Antarctic	—	ca. 30
	ca. 1200	ca. 2300

The Table shows the zoogeographical region of origin of the recordings available on gramophone records and the totals to be found in libraries (as at mid-1962).

Technique. The earliest recordings were made on wax cylinders, later superseded by wax discs. These in turn were followed by magnetic wire (very occasionally), optical sound film (much used by Cornell University), acetate discs, and finally—most important of all the modern developments—magnetic tape, which was first used for bird-sound recording by Palmér in Sweden in 1946. The parabolic reflector, which acts like a great mechanical ear, enables the recordist to work at distances from the singing bird up to 40 times as great as would be necessary with an open microphone. (Dynamic microphones are now the most widely used type.) The parabolic reflector was first tried by the Cornell workers in 1932 and is now regarded as an indispensable tool. Brand & Kellogg of Cornell were also the first workers to transmit the sounds of a bird by short-wave radio for the purpose of recording them ; this was in Canada in 1936. Later, this method was used by Weismann in Denmark in 1947, by Palmér in Sweden in the same year, and by Simms in England in 1954.

In addition to the use of the reflector and short-wave transmitter, field techniques include hiding the microphone near known singing places or the nest, and playing back in the field to territorial and other species recordings of advertising sounds in order to stimulate a reply and lure the birds within range of the microphone.

Purposes. The ultimate scientific aim must be to record the full vocabulary, vocal and instrumental, of every species, with all the major individual, seasonal, and geographical variations. The uses of these recordings are many and varied. They are employed for purposes of identification, and in studies on bird behaviour, ontogeny, learning ability, heredity, and taxonomy. For the use of the sound spectrograph in the technical analysis of bird vocalisations, see SINGING.

The Puerto Rican Whip-poor-will *Caprimulgus noctitherus*, thought for over 40 years to be extinct, was rediscovered in 1961 by means of a sound recording of its voice. The recordings also have utilitarian applications, as for example in scaring gulls *Larus* spp. from airfields and Starlings *Sturnus vulgaris* from orchards and buildings (see SCARING).

For the production of sound by birds, see SINGING ; and INSTRUMENTAL SOUNDS.   J.H.R.B.

Boswall, J. 1961. A World Catalogue of Gramophone Records of Bird Voice. Bio-Acoustics Bull. 1 (2) : 1–12.

Boswall, J. 1963. Amendments and Additions to a World Catalogue of Gramophone Records of Bird Voice. Bio-Acoustics Bull. 1(3) : 25–29.
Boswall, J. (in press) A discography and species index of Palaearctic bird sound recordings.
Kellogg, P. P. 1961. Sound recording as an aid to bird study. Atlantic Nat. April-June : 85–92.
Koch, L. 1955. Memoirs of a Bird Man. London.
Lanyon, W. E. et al. 1960. Animal Sounds and Communication. (Amer. Inst. Biol. Sci.) Washington, D.C.
North, M. E. W. 1956. Tape recording for the field ornithologist. *In* Hutson, H.P.W. (ed.). The Ornithologists' Guide. (B.O.U.) London.
Purves, F. 1962. Bird Song Recording. London.
Simms, E. 1957. Voices of the Wild. London.
Simms, E. & Wade, G. F. 1953. Recent advances in the recording of bird songs. Brit. Birds 46 : 200–210.

SOUNDS : see INSTRUMENTAL SOUNDS ; SINGING ; and ECHO-LOCATION ; HEARING AND BALANCE ; MIMICRY, VOCAL

SOUND SPECTROGRAPH : see SINGING

SPADEBILL : substantive name of *Platyrinchus* spp., also called 'flatbills' (see FLYCATCHER (2) ; and FLATBILL).

SPARROW (1) : substantive name of most species of Passerinae (Ploceidae) ; in the plural, general term for the subfamily. The Passerinae were formerly treated as finches (Fringillidae) but are now placed in the Ploceidae (see WEAVER (1)). The subfamily is here treated, in accordance with current views, as including the sparrow-weavers and scaly weavers of Africa. On this basis, it comprises 8 genera, although some authors further subdivide it. Five of these contain only 10 species in all and are confined to Africa. The remaining 3 genera, *Passer* (true sparrows), *Petronia* (rock-sparrows), and *Montifringilla* (snow-finches), are distributed widely over the Ethiopian, Palaearctic, and Oriental Regions, with recent deliberate introductions spreading 2 species of *Passer* over many parts of the New World and Australasia.

General Characteristics. The species are all small (4–7 inches long, with one exception) and—except for the white on the snow-finches—have plumage mainly of brown and grey hues, but sometimes with black and in a few species with bright yellow. They are thick-billed, mainly seed-eating birds, feeding particularly on the ground and nesting in a variety of situations but most frequently in holes in rocks, banks, or buildings, although sometimes in trees. In the African genera and in *Passer* the nests are typically bulky, lined with feathers and usually domed ; in the other 2 genera the nest may be reduced to a mere pad of grass, although again lined with feathers. The clutch size is 3–7. The main feature distinguishing the sparrows from the rest of the weavers is that the first primary is much reduced ; in this and a number of other characteristics they resemble the finches, although whether this is evidence of a true relationship or merely of convergence is not yet agreed. *Montifringilla* and *Passer* share the characteristic that the bill of the male changes from horn-coloured to black during the breeding season.

As a general rule, the species in the 3 main genera of the Passerinae are not markedly migratory ; sedentary behaviour is very striking in the House Sparrow, the majority of individuals spending their lives within a compass of a few miles. In many cases the same nest site is used from year to year ; and in all species, including the sexually dimorphic members of *Passer*, both sexes take part in nest building and care of the young.

Desert Sparrow *Passer simplex saharae*, of northern Africa. *C.E.T.K.*

Distribution. The species of *Montifringilla* are mountain birds occurring from the Pyrenees eastwards across the Palaearctic to the Pamirs, Himalaya, and Mongolia ; 1 species only, the Snow Finch *M. nivalis*, occurs in Europe (as well as in Asia) ; the other 6 in the genus are confined to Asia. The habitat of the rock-sparrows ranges from light, open wooded or scrub country to arid bush and even, in the case of the nominate species, to rocky, mountainous country similar to that occupied by the snow-finches ; there are 5 species, all occurring in Africa, 3 extending to Asia and one, the Rock Sparrow *P. petronia*, to Europe as well. There are 15 species in the genus *Passer* ; 5 of these are found only in Africa ; one, the Desert Sparrow *P. simplex*, is found in desert regions in Africa and Asia ; the Golden Sparrow *P. luteus* is predominantly African but extends into Arabia ; the remainder are found in the Palaearctic and Oriental Regions, the House Sparrow *P. domesticus* and Tree Sparrow *P. montanus*

being very widely distributed, the Spanish Sparrow *P. hispaniolensis* being mainly western but extending to India, 3 being found only in the Far East, and the remaining 2 (Dead Sea Sparrow *P. moabiticus* and Sind Jungle Sparrow *P. pyrrhonotus*) having extremely restricted distributions in Asia. In comparatively recent times (since 1850) the range of 2 of the above species has been extended by introductions into other parts of the world. The House Sparrow has been extremely successful in this and is now probably the most widespread species of land bird, being found in all major settled areas with the exception of China and Japan ; the Tree Sparrow has been less successful but is established in the U.S.A., Australia, and parts of the East Indies. The birds of the wholly African genera, comprising the sparrow-weavers and the scaly weavers, are of rather local distribution and mainly found in arid habitats, ranging from dry bush to full desert.

True Sparrows. Most species of *Passer* are sexually dimorphic, with the male having typically a black stripe from the bill to the eye and a black throat and chin patch ; in the Tree Sparrow this pattern occurs in both sexes. One characteristic of this genus, more pronounced among the black-throated group, is the tendency to associate with man ; at least 8 of the species regularly nest in the eaves of inhabited buildings. This trait is so marked in the House Sparrow that it can be fairly described as a commensal of man and is to be found breeding away from man only in exceptional circumstances. The Tree Sparrow fills the same role in the eastern parts of its range, where the House Sparrow is lacking, but it becomes more of a country bird where the 2 species occur together. The extent of this adaptation in the House Sparrow is quite remarkable, as not only is this bird to be found living in the heart of extensive built-up areas but it is even found inside large buildings and stores, and it is possible that some individuals may spend their whole lives under cover.

Plate 47 · Fledged Young

a *Upper :* New Guinea Wood-swallow *Artamus maximus*—parent flying past young clamouring to be fed (New Guinea). Family Artamidae.
Phot. Loke Wan Tho.

b *Lower :* Red-tailed Tropicbird *Phaethon rubricaudus*—juvenile (foreground) with adult (Pelsart Island, Indian Ocean). Family Phaethontidae.
Phot. John Warham.

(See articles YOUNG BIRD ; WOOD-SWALLOW ; TROPICBIRD)

The true sparrows are largely seed-eaters with a marked preference for cereals, although House Sparrows living in the more built-up surroundings exist mainly on such 'unnatural' foods as bread and household scraps; the young nestlings are fed at first principally on insects, but they are regularly given bread and some young birds born in highly urbanised districts appear to be reared on nothing else. Despite their close association with man, sparrows are extremely wary birds; they are not easily tamed and do not readily settle down and breed in captivity.

Many of the sparrows are gregarious and breed in colonies, although the nests are discrete and not communal structures such as are found with some other weavers. The Spanish Sparrow is the most social; colonies of several hundred nests of this species have been found in a few bushes or trees. In the other species the breeding colonies are not so large, but there is still a tendency for large foraging flocks and extensive communal roosts to be formed.

The House Sparrow and Spanish Sparrow bear an interesting relationship to each other. In Europe and Asia, where the two species occur together they behave as good species, ecologically separated from each other, the House Sparrow living in the towns and villages, the Spanish Sparrow in the surrounding countryside with a preference for moister conditions; in Morocco the same situation obtains, but in eastern Algeria and in Tunisia the species interbreed, producing a complete range of intermediates. The Italian Sparrow *P. domesticus italiae*, a well-marked subspecies of the House Sparrow occurring in Italy and Crete, appears to be a stabilised intermediate; and stable populations very similar in appearance are found at the isolated southern Algerian oases.

Snow-finches. The species of *Montifringilla* are among the highest-living birds, nesting from 6000 to 15 000 feet; they are slightly larger than the members of the other genera. The sexes are alike, and all species have much white on wings and tail. The nest is most commonly situated in the hole of a burrowing animal, although it is also found in crevices, walls, and even in the eaves of mountain huts. The birds keep almost entirely on the ground and are gregarious in winter, forming small parties or even flocks of several hundred birds, which may descend to lower altitudes although they do not leave the mountains.

Rock-sparrows. The species of *Petronia* are dull-plumaged birds, mainly brown and grey except for a yellow patch on the throat; the sexes are alike. The African species and the one that extends to India are birds more of trees than of rocks (probably more appropriately named 'bush-sparrows'), nesting in holes in trees and spending much time feeding on insects in trees; but some are found in more open country, where they feed on the ground. The remaining 2 species (particularly the Rock Sparrow *P. petronia* of the southern Palaearctic) are more truly 'rock' sparrows, frequenting barren country and nesting in holes in walls and in the ground. All species tend to be gregarious outside the breeding season, but much less so than the members of the other genera. D.S.-S.

Sparrow-weavers. The members of the purely African genera are all notably gregarious. The sparrow-weavers comprise 4 species of *Plocepasser*, one of *Histurgops*, 2 of *Pseudonigrita*, and one of *Philetarius*. They are all birds of brown plumage and, with one exception, about 5-6 inches long. They inhabit dry parts of Africa and build rough-looking covered nests, with grass-stalks so disposed round the entrance as to impede a predator. In the most widespread species, the Black-billed (or Stripe-breasted or White-browed) Sparrow-weaver *Plocepasser mahali*, which ranges from Abyssinia to the northern part of Cape Province, it has been shown that several nests may be built by the same pair and some used for roosting. The Rufous-tailed Weaver *Histurgops ruficauda* is some 9 inches long, exceptionally large for the subfamily, and is confined to part of northern Tanganyika. The Grey-headed Social Weaver *Pseudonigrita arnaudi* and the Black-headed Social Weaver *P. nigrita*, both of north-eastern Africa, build stout and prickly nests of strong grass-stems, in closely packed bunches in thorn trees. The nests often have two entrances; and they are

---

Plate 48 · Flown Young; Flocking

a *Upper*: Ospreys *Pandion haliaetus*—young birds not long out of the nest (North America); it will be seen that they have been ringed. This hawk species has an almost cosmopolitan distribution. See also Plate 9a.
Phot. Allan D. Cruickshank, from National Audubon Society, U.S.A.

b *Lower*: Knots *Calidris canutus*—part of a flock of about 5000 resting on migration and waiting for the ebb tide to expose feeding grounds (England). This sandpiper species has a circumpolar breeding range in high northern latitudes and is a migrant visitor elsewhere. *Phot. Eric Hosking.*

(See articles YOUNG BIRD; RINGING; HAWK; FLOCKING; MIGRATION; SANDPIPER) sometimes found on twigs that are alive with aggressive ants.

The Social Weaver *Philetarius socius* of south-western Africa constructs a communal nest, which is a most extraordinary achievement. Apparently the birds build successive individual nests in contact in a big acacia. As with other species of this group of weavers, the grasses and small twigs of which the nests are composed are not interwoven but are rather roughly put together ; the unique feature is that all the occupants, both males and females, work at all seasons of the year to build and repair a communal roof over the colony—a 'fairly definite thatching arrangement, causing the rain to run off and not soak through' (Friedmann 1930). One colonial dwelling described by the same author had been about 30 feet by 20 feet at the base and 5 feet high, and it contained about 95 nests. The life of one such structure may exceed 20 years. Apparently the birds are monogamous.

Scaly Weavers. There are 2 species of *Sporopipes*. The Speckle-fronted Weaver *S. frontalis* inhabits the dry belt south of the Sahara, and the Scaly-fronted Weaver *S. squamifrons* south-western Africa. They are seed-eaters of dry country, nesting colonially in thorn trees or under eaves (*S. squamifrons*) and associated a good deal with man. The eggs are greyish or greenish, very thickly clouded.

See Plate 35b (phot.). R.E.M.

Friedmann, H. 1930. The Social Weaver Bird of South Africa. Nat. Hist. (N.Y.) 30 : 205–212.
Summers-Smith, D. 1963. The House Sparrow. London.

SPARROW (2): substantive name used in America for many species of Emberizinae found there (see BUNTING).

SPARROW (3): name applied or misapplied to some other birds than those comprised in the two groups dealt with above, e.g. the Hedgesparrow (or Dunnock) *Prunella modularis* in the family Prunellidae (see ACCENTOR), and the Java Sparrow *Padda oryzivora* and other species of Estrildidae (see WEAVER-FINCH ; and CAGE BIRD).

SPARROW-WEAVER: see SPARROW (1)

SPATULETAIL: *Loddigesia mirabilis* (see HUMMINGBIRD).

SPECIATION: the process whereby new species are evolved (see EVOLUTION ; SPECIES). They can arise in two slightly different ways, namely by the complete transformation of one species into another (anagenesis) or by the breaking up of one species

into two or more (cladogenesis). The first is a simple product of evolutionary change, but the second involves an increase in the number of species existing at any one time and is therefore of special importance.

Darwin was especially concerned to show that species could arise from mere varieties and then proceed to diverge still further until they had to be put into separate genera, families, or higher groups. Divergence was his principal interest, and he regarded the species as only one stage in divergence, with no particular properties of its own. He did not discuss how a species could break up into several different ones, and it has been said with much truth that in the *Origin of Species* there is nothing about the origin of species—i.e. speciation. The study of speciation is in great part post-Darwinian.

Several methods of speciation are now known, but the only one that applies to wholly bisexually reproducing animals, such as birds, is geographical speciation. It is easy enough to see how a favourable variation can spread through a species, but less easy at first sight to see how different variations can spread through different parts of a species population, and how the parts can come to differ so much that they no longer interbreed. In the early part of this century much emphasis was laid on preferential mating, whereby individuals would tend to mate far more often with others of the same variety. This would have the effect of splitting up a population of individuals living in the same area into little subsidiary populations, which, although mingling with one another spatially, would function as separate breeding populations and so be able to evolve separately. Although there is no reason to deny that preferential mating ever occurs, there is very little evidence that such ' sexual selection ' is of importance in breaking up a species.

The evidence that geographical barriers are of importance, however, is extremely strong. Very few species are so confined to one small area in the breeding season that all the individuals meet each other, and that the chances that any one will mate with any other of the opposite sex are the same, so that mating will be at random. Even when a species has a rather extended breeding range, so that individuals from one end of it are more likely to mate with others from the same end or near by, there may be enough movement of individuals for a new variety occurring at one end to spread throughout the range in a few generations. Far more often, the breeding range of a species is broken up into a number of separate areas, with very little flow of individuals from one to the next. Then, if different selective forces are acting in the different ranges, the populations can come to differ, since there will not be continual mixing and swamping of local peculiarities, and may differ so much as to achieve specific status. Then, if they should overcome the barrier and meet each other, they will not merely fuse into a hybrid swarm and lose their identity. In general, the different parts of the earth's surface do differ, in climate, physiography, flora, and fauna, and it is more likely than not that populations isolated from one another will come to differ.

Birds have been especially valuable in working out the theory of geographical speciation (see Mayr 1942). It was early realised, especially in Germany, that many species show marked geographical races (eventually given formal recognition as subspecies) and that the boundaries of these often coincide with geographical barriers which the birds are unlikely to cross frequently in the breeding season. For example, the Great Tits *Parus major* of most of Britain, separated from those of continental Europe by the Channel, are noticeably darker and duller than the nearby continental ones and have less heavy bills. The various species of geospizine finches in the Galápagos, and also the giant tortoises, have recognisably different populations on the different islands of the group, a fact which startled Darwin. On some of the more ancient and widespread archipelagos, the forms may differ so much from island to island that it is very doubtful whether they should be called subspecies of the same species, or different species. Exactly the same can be seen on isolated 'islands' of high mountain forest surrounded by lowland savanna or forest in Africa. The barriers depend on the habits of the species ; large stretches of ocean may be open highways to one species, while even small ones may be a barrier not to be passed by others (see DISTRIBUTION, GEOGRAPHICAL). Such barriers can be described equally well as ecological or geographical, but their essential feature from the point of view of speciation is that in conjunction with the habits of the birds they cause a spatial separation in the breeding period, thus splitting up the species into separate breeding populations. It is important to take actual habits into account. Mayr has pointed out that in the central Solomons there are white-eyes *Zosterops* spp., on a group of islands, that differ from each other quite remarkably ; yet the distances between the islands are so small that the birds could easily cover them in a few minutes. Their considerable differences from island to island show, however, that they very seldom do. Other land birds might find such small straits no barrier at all, and be unable to speciate on these same islands. Similarly, the distinctness of the St Kilda Wren *Troglodytes troglodytes hirtensis* suggests that wrens very seldom cross to that island.

The causes of geographical variation are very diverse. Often the climatic 'rules' are exemplified, so that a population on a rainy island is markedly larger in body size and more intense in coloration, while one on a dry island is smaller in body size and much paler. Habits may vary also, in relation to what other species are present. In the Solomons, where there are two species of *Zosterops* on an island, one takes the mist-forest, the other the lowland forest ; but where there is only one, it is found all over the island. In Germany, where two species of nightingale *Luscinia megarhynchos* and *L. luscinia* overlap, one keeps to drier woods and the other to wetter, although each may be widespread outside the zone of overlap. The Island Thrush *Turdus poliocephalus* is a bird of the montane forest in many islands of the South Pacific, but it occurs also on the hot and exposed raised atoll Rennell Island, which has a reduced and peculiar avifauna. A difference in the average size of insect or other food taken may occur from island to island in correlation with differences of bill and body size. Races in more extreme climates, which must migrate, may have more pointed wings than sedentary ones of the same species. Lastly, many forms living far from their nearest relatives on remote islands, with very poor avifaunas, have very simplified and often dull plumage patterns.

When two populations have diverged morphologically but remain geographically separate, it is not possible to decide with any certainty whether they are 'good' species, or only subspecies. Instances are known of very similar species that overlap widely and never interbreed, e.g. the Willow Warbler *Phylloscopus trochilus* and Chiffchaff *P. collybita* ; and of quite different forms that produce hybrid swarms where they meet, with total loss of identity in the hybrid zone, e.g. the Red-shafted Flicker *Colaptes cafer* and Yellow-shafted Flicker *C. auratus* of North America.

When, however, a barrier is removed, so that two populations actually meet in the wild, a definite conclusion may be reached. Either (i) the two populations fuse together into a single hybrid swarm ; or (ii) there may be only a limited zone of hybridisation ; or (iii) they may remain distinct as breeding populations. In the first case, they cannot really be regarded as separate species. In the second, the process of speciation has advanced considerably further. Dobzhansky has pointed out that if there is only a limited degree of hybridisation, and the hybrids are definitely inferior (in the wild) to either parental form, there will be selection against promiscuous mating between the forms, to the same amount as the inferiority of the hybrids. Those individuals that mate with their own kind will leave more, or more viable, progeny than those that mated with the other kind. Selection can then act to improve the discrimination of the two forms and reduce sharply, and eventually eliminate, hybridisation between them. This has been verified experimentally in fruitflies (*Drosophila*). When this happens, the two forms (now thoroughly 'good' species) have evolved specific 'isolating mechanisms' against each other.

Many complex courtships and highly specific plumage patterns have been evolved as isolating mechanisms. Now, it is obvious that two populations evolving in complete isolation from one another (on two distant islands, say) cannot build up a *specific* isolating mechanism against each other. In course of time, they may come to differ so much that when eventually they meet either they never try to mate together, or the eggs are infertile, or the hybrids are sterile, as a result of accumulated genetical difference. But a specific isolating mechanism can be built up only when two forms come into contact without swamping one another, but with the production of some inferior hybrids. This explains why in the Golden Whistler *Pachycephala pectoralis* an extension of range of one subspecies has produced complete hybrid swarms where it comes into contact with very different but formerly wholly isolated forms; yet in New Guinea two closely similar forms overlap widely and behave as good species. Presumably, when New Guinea was divided up into several islands in the past, these two evolved on adjacent islands and then came near enough to each other over a broad front for numerous stragglers to invade each other's areas over a considerable period, so that specific isolating mechanisms could be built up.

A particularly interesting example is that of the Carrion Crow *Corvus corone* and Hooded Crow *C. cornix*, which have different areas for their breeding ranges, and behave as good species except that, the ranges being contiguous, there is a narrow hybrid zone running the whole length of the common boundary. These two forms, like many other pairs of animals in Europe, were presumably eastern and western populations of an original single species which were separated during the Ice Age. With the amelioration of the climate their ranges have extended until they now meet. Although hybridisation still takes place, the zone is narrow, and apparently fairly stable. This must mean that

the hybrids are at a disadvantage to both parent forms on their own ground, since otherwise they would have spread far more widely. It is possible that, if the hybrids are at a great disadvantage (a point not established), the hybrid zone is maintained by continual recruitment out of the rest of the two ranges; and that there is thus a constant inflow of birds from elsewhere, and no chance to build up an experienced local population that can develop a proper isolating mechanism. Such a situation as this, although of the greatest interest to the evolutionist, is very awkward for the taxonomist, since the two forms could be called separate species because the hybrids must be inferior, or only subspecies because hybrids are constantly produced.

An equally interesting situation occurs when populations, although fairly continuous, are spread out over so extended a range that the ends can come to differ, even specifically, although still connected by annectant populations. In this case, mere distance is the isolating mechanism. If the two end populations come to overlap, they may behave as good species, even though connected in a roundabout way. Several such 'ring-species' (see also RING-SPECIES) have been described in birds; the Great Tit is a good example, in which populations of *Parus major* very like those of Europe stretch across to the upper Amur Valley and there overlap, without interbreeding with, the Lesser Great Tit *P. major minor*. The latter is, however, connected by way of Chinese populations with the '*cinereus*' group of races in India, which itself connects, through a hybrid zone in Persia, with the Great Tits of Europe and the Near East.

A consideration of speciation, therefore, brings out the fact that the species (at least in bisexually reproducing forms such as birds) does differ from mere varieties in one most important particular; it is a separate line of evolution, not contributing genetically in any important degree to any other species but consisting of an array of geographically definable populations that either do actually interbreed freely or are judged able to do so should they ever meet in the wild. The process of speciation is gradual, and intermediate situations difficult to classify have been found; in particular, it may be difficult to decide whether two geographically isolated and rather distinct but nevertheless related populations should be considered as two subspecies of the same species, or as two species in a single 'superspecies', an array of geographically representative forms of which some are too different to be put into the same species. But at any one locality, there is rarely any difficulty in determining what are the separate species, genetically and evolutionarily distinct and each with its characteristic ecological role.   A.J.C.

Cain, A. J. 1954. Animal Species and their Evolution. London (Hutchinson University Library).
Dobzhansky, T. 1951. Genetics and the Origin of Species (3rd ed.). New York.
Mayr, E. 1942. Systematics and the Origin of Species. New York.

SPECIES: in simple terms, a 'kind' of bird (or other organism) ; more precisely, 'species are groups of actually or potentially interbreeding populations which are reproductively isolated from other such groups' (Mayr). The word (unchanged in plural) connotes both a taxonomic category in general or a particular example or examples of that category.

Unlike other taxonomic categories, the species is not merely a human concept but represents a natural reality. It is unique in being definable, as a category, in wholly objective terms. That particular cases cannot always be fitted to the definition, owing to lack of information, does not affect the principle. (The idea that sympatric forms that do not interbreed must be distinct species dates back to Cuvier, 1798.)

A species may be considered as a stock that is irrevocably committed to its own peculiar line of evolution—irrevocably, because it has lost the potentiality of recombining with other species of common ancestral origin ; and peculiar, in the proper sense of that word, without precluding the possibility that the line of evolution may in future divide or is even already tending to do so (see SPECIATION).

A species may be represented by a single population or a virtually homogeneous group of populations—it is then 'monotypic'. Or it may be represented by a series of populations showing considerable geographical variation over a wide and perhaps discontinuous total range—it is then 'polytypic'. In the latter case, there may be geographical 'races' sufficiently distinct to be regarded as subspecies (see SUBSPECIES) ; or there may be instead, or sometimes in addition, a more or less continuous geographical gradation of characters (see CLINE). Or there may be sympatric and interbreeding 'phases' or 'morphs', showing much greater differences than the ordinary level of individual variation within a population (see POLYMORPHISM). This is apart from the occurrence of occasional abnormalities (see PLUMAGE, ABNORMAL AND ABERRANT), and also, of course, from varieties or 'breeds' produced by artificial selection (see DOMESTICATION).

Difficulty in applying the objective definition of the species category may arise when one has to try to distinguish between (*a*) a number of closely similar allopatric species that are evidently geographical representatives of a common ancestral stock (see SUPERSPECIES), and (*b*) a polytypic species comprising a number of geographical subspecies. In some instances, indeed, the distinction may be very finely balanced in nature, because the process of speciation leads almost imperceptibly from the second of these situations to the first. In other instances the difficulty is the subjective one of inability to put the question of reproductive isolation to the test ; the potentiality to recombine may conceivably persist without there being any opportunity for it to become explicit—there may be geographical or ecological barriers, without any physiological isolation having been irrevocably established (see ISOLATING MECHANISM). The occurrence of casual hybridisation, and a fortiori of hybridisation in captivity, is no criterion ; nor is fertility of the hybrids. Even regular interbreeding in a boundary area is not conclusive ; the very fact that the intermediates remain localised suggests that they are at a disadvantage under natural selection, and therefore that the parent forms have reached or passed the point of no return in their separate lines of evolution (see HYBRIDISATION, ZONE OF SECONDARY).

The case for specific separation is clearest when the forms are sympatric without merging. The case for specific identity is clearest when the forms are connected by continuous clinal gradation. The case is marginal when the forms are allopatric but show regular hybridisation in a boundary zone. The case is simply open to doubt when closely similar forms are allopatric and have no opportunity to show whether they would regularly interbreed, and possibly merge completely, under suitable conditions. Where doubts cannot be resolved, an arbitrary decision may have to be taken provisionally as a taxonomic expedient, but in the knowledge (all too rarely expressed) that it may not correspond with the biological reality.

At a higher taxonomic level, species are grouped in genera (sometimes divided into subgenera) in accordance with subjective ideas of their relationship (see GENUS) ; a species believed to be without near relatives may be placed in a genus by itself. The scientific name of a species is a 'binomen', of which the first word is the name of the genus and the second (meaningless if dissociated) is known as the 'specific name' (see NOMENCLATURE ; TYPE-LOCALITY ; TYPE-SPECIMEN ; also, for the types of genera, TYPE-SPECIES). It may be remarked that the requirements of nomenclature tend towards a typological concept of species that might be highly misleading if pressed further.

The term 'biospecies' denotes a species defined in accordance with the biological concept of species on which this article is based. The term 'morphospecies' denotes one distinguished on morphological grounds alone—sometimes, as already implied, the only practical method available. Bock has used the term 'biogeographical species' to comprise entities that are either (a) superspecies or (b) species not included in any superspecies. See also RING-SPECIES; SEMI-SPECIES; SIBLING SPECIES.

The term 'synchronous' is applied to species existing at the same level of geological time; and it will be obvious that the considerations discussed here refer to the present. When a species is regarded in the time dimension it takes on the character of an evolutionary stream ('chronocline'), which has in the past branched from other streams and which in the future may or may not subdivide. A species existing at an earlier period of geological time is sometimes termed a 'palaeospecies'.

The final reservation should be made that the species concept seemingly appropriate to birds may not be wholly valid throughout animate nature.

A.L.T.

Mayr, E. (ed.). 1957. The Species Problem. (A symposium.) Publ. no. 50, Amer. Assoc. Adv. Sci. Washington, D.C.
Mayr, E. 1963. Animal Species and Evolution. Cambridge, Mass., and London.

SPECIES-GROUP (1): with reference to the ranks of taxa, term embracing the categories species and subspecies (see NOMENCLATURE).

SPECIES-GROUP (2): in taxonomy, a group of closely related species, less definite than a subgenus and not constituting a formal taxon for purposes of nomenclature. See also SUPERSPECIES.

SPECIFIC: in taxonomic terminology, appertaining to a species, e.g. 'specific name' (see TAXON); more generally (in one of the everyday senses), characteristically peculiar to some mentioned category. The two meanings are combined in the expression 'species-specific', i.e. specific (in the second sense) for a species.

SPECIFIC ACTION POTENTIAL: 'the state of the animal responsible for its readiness to perform the behaviour patterns of one instinct in preference to all other behaviour patterns; this specific readiness diminishes or disappears when the consummatory act of the charged instinct has been performed' (Thorpe 1951).

SPECKLE-BELLY: a name in North America for the Whitefronted Goose *Anser albifrons* (see under DUCK).

SPECTACLE-BIRD: name used for some species of Zosteropidae (see WHITE-EYE).

SPECTROGRAPH, SOUND: see SINGING

SPECULUM: a patch of distinctive colour on the wing, in some plumage patterns, especially the metallic patch seen in dabbling ducks (see DUCK; WING).

SPERMATOZOON: (plural 'spermatozoa') or 'sperm', a male germ-cell (see REPRODUCTIVE SYSTEM; and GENETICS). Also called 'spermatozoid' in the free-swimming stage, e.g. when in the female reproductive tract after copulation and before union with an ovum.

McFarlane, R. W. 1963. The taxonomic significance of avian sperm. Proc. XIII Internat. Orn. Congr., Ithaca, N.Y., 1962 : 91–102.

SPHENISCI; SPHENISCIDAE: see below

SPHENISCIFORMES: an order, alternatively 'Sphenisci', comprising only the family Spheniscidae (see PENGUIN); the group is placed by Wetmore in a superorder, Impennes, of its own (see under CLASS). They are marine birds, with wings modified as flippers, and restricted to the Southern Hemisphere.

SPIDER-HUNTER: substantive name of *Arachnothera* spp. (see SUNBIRD).

SPINAL CORD: see NERVOUS SYSTEM

SPINEBILL: substantive name of *Acanthorhynchus* spp. (see HONEYEATER).

SPINETAIL: substantive name of Synallaxinae spp. (see OVENBIRD (1)); also sometimes used (Africa) as an abbreviation of 'spine-tailed swift', substantive name of species in more than one genus (see SWIFT).

SPINIFEX-BIRD: *Eremiornis carteri* (see under WREN (2)).

SPOONBILL: substantive name of the species of Plataleinae, a subfamily of the Threskiornithidae (Cicioniiformes, suborder Ciconiae); used without qualification for the European species; in the plural, general term for the subfamily. The spoonbills have some of the same general characteristics as the other subfamily, the Threskiornithinae (see IBIS). They have, however, the distinctive feature

—unique in this degree—of a bill that is long, flattened in the horizontal plane, and broadened to a thin spatulate tip. They are large birds, up to 30 inches or more in length, with long legs. Except in one species, the plumage is almost entirely white.

The subfamily has a cosmopolitan distribution, mainly in tropical and subtropical countries. Spoonbills are essentially inhabitants of the vicinity of fresh water, living on aquatic crustaceans, molluscs, insects, and small fish. They feed while wading in the shallows, the bill being held almost vertical and partly open while it is moved rapidly from side to side in the water. They are gregarious, and some species also associate with others of similar habits. They fly slowly, with outstretched necks, and can both glide and soar. They perch freely on trees ; and they occasionally swim. They are rather silent birds.

Breeding is in colonies, and sometimes mixed with other species. The nest is commonly a platform of sticks in a tree or bush, but it may be among reeds or even on the ground. The eggs, usually 4, are ovoid and dull white with scanty brown markings. The downy young are nidicolous ; the bill is at first short but soon acquires the specialised shape.

There are 5 species in the Old World, all of them white ; 4 of them are closely similar and replace each other geographically, so that some authors have regarded them as conspecific. The Spoonbill *Platalea leucorodia* breeds in the Netherlands (whence presumably the occasional visitors to the British Isles), southern Spain, south-eastern Europe, through much of southern Asia, and in northern Africa. In the higher latitudes it is a summer visitor ; ringing results show that the Netherlands birds travel by the Atlantic seaboard, sometimes as far as Mauretania and the Azores, and that those bred in Hungary go in southerly directions to North Africa and sometimes beyond. The plumage is pure white, except that in the breeding season there is a buff tinge at the base of the neck and in the long crest then depending from the back of the head ; the bill and legs are black. The African Spoonbill *P. alba*, found through Africa south of the Sahara and in Madagascar, differs in having bare red skin on the face, some red in the upper mandible, and bright pink legs. The Lesser Spoonbill *P. minor* is found in the Far East, and 2 species inhabit Australia—the Royal (or Black-billed) Spoonbill *P. regia* and the Yellow-billed (or Yellow-legged) Spoonbill *Platalea* ('*Platibis*') *flavipes*, the former occasionally wandering to New Zealand.

The sole New World species, generically separated, is the Roseate Spoonbill *Ajaia ajaja*. Its adult plumage is tinged with pink, deepening to red on the scapulars ; the legs are also pink, but the bill is yellow. It breeds in the extreme southern part of the United States, and thence southwards through much of South America. The habits are similar to those of the Old World species.

See Plates 3a, 11c (phot.). A.L.T.

Brouwer, G. A. 1964. Some data on the status of the Spoonbill, *Platalea leucorodia* L., in Europe, especially in the Netherlands. Zool. Meded. 39 : 481–521.

SPORT, BIRDS IN : a subject not, in general, covered by this work ; but see FALCONRY ; GAMEBIRDS ; UTILISATION BY MAN ; WILDFOWL).

SPOTBILL : *Anas poecilorhyncha* (see DUCK).

SPRAYS, AGRICULTURAL : see TOXIC CHEMICALS

SPREO : sometimes used as substantive name of African glossy starlings of the genus *Spreo* (see STARLING).

SPRIG : a name in North America for the Pintail *Anas acuta*, a drake of the species being known to some American sportsmen as a 'buck sprig' (see DUCK).

SPRING : see ASSEMBLY, NOUN OF

SPROSSER : German name often used as English (in preference to the fabricated 'Thrush Nightingale') for *Luscinia luscinia* (for subfamily see THRUSH).

SPUR : see INTEGUMENTARY STRUCTURES ; LEG ; WING

SPURFOWL : substantive name of *Galloperdix* spp., and in Africa of *Pternistis* spp. (see PHEASANT).

SQUAB : an unfledged nestling, particularly of pigeons (Columbidae).

SQUACCO : or Squacco Heron, *Ardeola ralloides* (see HERON ; and Plate 36b (phot.)).

SQUAMOSAL : a paired bone of the skull (see SKELETON).

SQUAW, OLD : the American name of the Longtailed Duck *Clangula hyemalis* (see DUCK).

SQUEAKER : popular alternative name for *Strepera versicolor* (see under MAGPIE (2)).

STAGEMAKER : alternative name of *Scenopoeetes dentirostris* (see BOWERBIRD).

STANDARD DEVIATION : see STATISTICAL SIGNIFICANCE

STANDARD DIRECTION: see MIGRATION

STANDARDWING: substantive name of *Semi-optera wallacei* (see BIRD-OF-PARADISE).

STAPES: the ear ossicle (see HEARING AND BALANCE ; SKELETON).

STARFRONTLET: substantive name of some *Coeligena* spp. (see HUMMINGBIRD).

STARLING: substantive name of many species of Sturnidae (Passeriformes, suborder Oscines) ; used without qualification (Britain) for the Common Palaearctic species ; in the plural, general term for the family. The name has also been used for other birds similar in appearance to starlings or once believed to be allied to them, such as some members of the Icteridae, e.g. the Military Starling (or Red-breasted Blackbird) *Leistes militaris* (see ORIOLE (2)). By origin, it belongs to the well known *Sturnus vulgaris*, which ranges across Europe and the Middle East to as far into Asia as parts of Mongolia ; this same species has in modern times been unwisely introduced into other parts of the world—for example, into the United States of America, where it is now found in enormous numbers. The family comprises approximately 110 species, in 25 genera, all belonging in the natural course to the Old World.

General Characteristics. Starlings are of medium or rather large size (7–17 inches in length). Usually chunky, they have strong legs and bill. Many of them are more or less black in colour, but often with iridescent plumage. In some this iridescence is highly developed ; these are called glossy starlings (several genera), and are often very beautiful. Other species have lappets, wattles, or bristly feathers on the head and are quite ugly. Typical starlings are at home both on the ground, where they trot about actively and rapidly, and also in trees ; but many of the tropical species are purely arboreal. The flight is rapid and direct, and some species perform striking mass evolutions ; many are migratory. They are omnivorous and in some places are a serious pest to cultivated small fruit. None has a really accomplished song, but many utter a variety of pleasing whistles. Some, notably the so-called Talking Mynah *Gracula religiosa* of India and the East Indies, can learn to talk (see MIMICRY, VOCAL).

Habits. Several of the starlings, including the Common Starling and the Indian Mynah *Acridotheres tristis*, must be classed among the rather unpleasant creatures, like the House Sparrow *Passer domesticus*, which have established a more or less commensal or semi-domesticated relationship with man. The Common Starling, in the countries where it has been introduced, is not only at times an agricultural pest but also a serious competitor of valuable and attractive native birds such as, in North America, the bluebirds *Sialia* spp. ; yet at times it eats quantities of such pests as larvae of the Japanese beetle. The Indian Mynah, its tropical counterpart, has been widely introduced ; it now swarms in such areas as Hawaii, where it too has become an obnoxious pest.

Superb Glossy Starling *Spreo superbus*. C.E.T.K.

Some species of starling nest in colonies, and many others are social during the non-breeding season. Some, especially the species associated with man or with agriculture, gather into truly immense flocks in winter, and these may aggregate thousands or even hundreds of thousands of birds.

Breeding. Most species of starling nest in hollows in trees. Secondarily, quite a few of them have come to nest in crannies around buildings, in bird-houses, under the tiles of roofs, and so forth. A few, such as the Bank Mynah *Acridotheres ginginianus*, dig nesting burrows in vertical river banks. Others, instead of seeking a ready-made hollow in which to nest, build a rough globular nest with a side entrance and a nesting chamber within ; a few, such as the Indian Mynah, do either. The eggs, 4–5 in number, may be pale greenish, sometimes spotted with brown. The female incubates, but both sexes care for the young. In the Common Starling, 2 broods are not infrequently reared in a season. The young are brown and lack the metallic iridescence of the older birds, but moult into the adult plumage when they are only 2 or 3 months old. One species, the Long-tailed Starling *Aplonis metallica* of New Guinea, nests in colonies and makes long hanging nests like those of weavers (Ploceidae) and oropendolas *Gymnostinops* spp. Indeed, some regard starlings as being related to the Ploceidae, but they have something in common also with other primarily Old World, medium-sized, and rather coarsely built song-birds, such as the orioles (Oriolidae), the drongos (Dicruridae), and even the crows (Corvidae).

Distribution and Examples. The starlings are entirely Old World and primarily tropical, although several reach Europe, China, and Japan. The group is well represented in Africa, but the greatest diversity occurs in the East Indies and India. The family barely reaches Australia, where but a single species is known. One genus, *Aplonis*, is widely spread in Polynesia, and had reached even Tahiti although now extinct there.

Many of the African starlings are among the more beautiful members of the family. The Superb Spreo (or Superb Glossy Starling) *Spreo superbus* of East Africa, and the brilliantly metallic green and purple Emerald Starling *Lamprotornis iris* of West Africa, may be mentioned. The related Long-tailed Glossy Starling *L. caudatus* of northern tropical Africa has a flowing purple and blue tail that may attain 14 inches in length in male birds.

An interesting Ethiopian species is the Wattled Starling *Creatophora cinerea*. Immense flocks of this species search for concentrations of migratory locusts. When a vast flight of locusts lays eggs in an area where favourable rains have produced grass, the Wattled Starlings also nest ; and later they feed their young on the flightless immature ' hoppers '. In such circumstances, each little tree in an area may carry several nests of the Wattled Starling. In the breeding season it has a bald head, from which hang rather long wattles. In the non-breeding season, the wattles disappear and the head becomes feathered —a phenomenon that has even become of interest to biologists seeking the hormonal basis for human baldness.

The 2 African tick-birds or oxpeckers of the genus *Buphagus* are aberrant but seem to belong to this family and can be assigned to a subfamily of their own (Buphaginae). They spend most of their time on large game animals and livestock, hitching their way about in search of ticks. Quick to take alarm and fly away with harsh cries, they inadvertently warn the large mammals of the approach of hunters. Further details of their specialised habits are given in a separate article (see OXPECKER ; and Plate 30 (colour)). Two species of starlings which inhabited small islands near Madagascar, of which the best known was *Fregilupus varius*, became extinct a century or more ago, as did also 2 Polynesian species likewise restricted to small islands.

Another interesting species is the Rosy Pastor *Sturnus roseus*. The head and wings are glossy black with a purple sheen, and the body is pale pink. This species of the Middle East occasionally becomes very abundant and may then enter eastern Europe in large numbers. Some remain to nest, but after a few years it again becomes uncommon or absent in Europe. It is a valuable enemy of locusts.

The Crested Starling *Basilornis galeatus* of Sula Island, east of Celebes, is perhaps the most beautiful member of the family. Bluish-black, but with white patches on the sides of the face and at the shoulders, bordered with orange-yellow, it has a big erect medial crest composed of lacy feathers extending the full length of the head. Yet other species rather closely related to it, such as Dumont's Mynah *Mino dumontii* of New Guinea, lack the crest and have the head partly covered with bristly feathers, thus producing an altogether unattractive appearance.

The aberrant Celebesian Starling *Scissirostrum dubium* is unique in the family in having a strong bill, almost like that found in woodpeckers (Picidae), which it uses to excavate a nesting hole in dead wood, supporting itself with its tail, also after the manner of a woodpecker ; it feeds, however, on soft fruit.

D.A.

Amadon, D. 1943. The genera of starlings and their relationships. Amer. Mus. Novit. no. 1247 : 1–16.
Amadon, D. 1956. Remarks on starlings, Family Sturnidae. Amer. Mus. Novit. no. 1803 : 1–41.
Amadon, D. 1962. Family Sturnidae. *In* Mayr, E. & Greenway, J. C., Jr. (eds.). Check-list of Birds of the World vol. 15. Cambridge, Mass.

STARTHROAT : substantive name of *Heliomaster* spp. (for family see HUMMINGBIRD).

STATISTICAL SIGNIFICANCE : term covering a question which the biologist must frequently ask himself, or expect to be asked, when a set of numerical data reveal some pattern and it is essential to decide whether this represents a genuine phenomenon or just a coincidence. Suppose a sample of 3 skins from Faizabad in Afghanistan all have thicker-than-average bills and shorter-than-average wings, is it a new race ? Would a larger sample from the same place reveal the difference to be a consistent one, or is it just an accident of sampling ?

Of course, this particular question could be answered only by obtaining another sample from the same place in Afghanistan ; any ' decision ' that one makes in the meantime is sheer guesswork. A ' test of statistical significance ' is a technique that enables one to make such a guess objectively, and to have some measure of control over the proportion of one's guesses that will turn out to be correct in the long run.

Null Hypothesis. One simply asks, ' Assuming the " null hypothesis " that this is not a new race, how big a coincidence would my sample be ? ' The ' statistical significance ' is the calculated improbability of this presumed coincidence. If one has decided arbitrarily, in advance, how improbable a coincidence one will tolerate before declaring that a null hypothesis is unreasonable, then the decision in any particular case follows automatically. The most lenient ' critical level of significance ' usually tolerated is a presumed coincidence of 1 in 20, or ·05. Using this criterion, one must expect to make a wrong decision (naming a new ' race ' when the specimens do not actually represent a new race) once in about every 20 cases, simply because that is how often, in the long run, a coincidence of ·05 will occur. By insisting on a more stringent level of significance, say ·01, one can expect to make fewer errors of that first kind, but one will pay a price for this by making more ' mistakes ' of a second kind (failing to name a new race that would in fact be valid). In other words, one will create fewer synonyms, but one will name fewer valid races as well (see also SUBSPECIES).

Sign Test. In the present hypothetical example, if the 3 Afghanistan skins really are from the described race, then the probability (P) that all 3 of them would have shorter wings than the ' true median ' (mid-ranking individual of the whole race) is the same as the probability of flipping a coin and getting 3 tails in a row, viz. $\frac{1}{2} \times \frac{1}{2} \times \frac{1}{2} = \frac{1}{8} = ·125$. One must add to this the probability of getting 3 heads in a row, because one would have been unprepared to say before seeing the skins whether they were likely to have shorter or longer wings than usual. (This is called applying a ' two-tailed test ' of significance ; if one did have a priori reasons for expecting shorter wings, then one could use a ' one-tailed test '.) The presumed coincidence is therefore $\frac{1}{8} + \frac{1}{8} = \frac{1}{4} = ·25$, so one would say : ' The difference is not statistically significant, P > ·05.' The skins may indeed represent a new race, but the sample is not large enough to rule out the possibility of a coincidence. One must therefore suspend judgment, pending a larger sample.

Power of a Test. Alternatively, one might decide to apply a more powerful statistical test, i.e. a test that can detect smaller differences, or detect differences in a smaller sample, by making use of more information. The test applied above, called the ' sign test ', is very easy to use but takes no notice of the amount by which the present sample deviates from the average wing length. Suppose published records indicate that, out of 9 museum skins that have been measured, the total ' range of variation ' in wing length is from 10·3 to 11·7 cm., but all 3 Afghanistan skins are less than 10 cm. One therefore knows that if one could lay out all 12 skins on a table, ranked in order of size, the 3 Afghanistan skins would all be together at one end. Now, the total number of possible ways of arranging 12 skins in a line is $1 \times 2 \times 3 \times 4 \times 5 \times 6 \times 7 \times 8 \times 9 \times 10 \times 11 \times 12$, called ' twelve factorial ', written 12 !, and amounting to 479 001 600. Under the null hypothesis, each of these arrangements was equally probable. There are only 3 ! ways of arranging 3 skins in a row, and for each of these there would be 9 ! ways in which the other skins could be arranged. Therefore, only 3 ! × 9 ! out of the 12 ! arrangements, or 1 in every 220 ($2 \times 3/10 \times 11 \times 12$, after cancelling), would have all the Afghanistan skins at one end. Add the same number for the other end, and one has a coincidence of 2/220, or less than 1 in 100. One would therefore say : ' The difference is statistically significant, P < ·01.' In ordinary language, this statement implies the following : ' If these 3 skins do not really represent a new race, then a coincidence has occurred in my sample which I would expect less than 1 time in 100. I don't believe that such coincidences can go on happening indefinitely. Therefore, I will take the more reasonable view that this is a new race and give it a name. I know that about 1 in every 100 of such decisions will turn out to be invalid, but this is a risk that I must run if I am to make any decisions at all.'

If the difference had been less extreme than this— say, the skins had ranked 1, 3, 5—then the job of writing down all the possibilities soon becomes prohibitive. Most statistical methods are ingenious approximations which enable one to get the answer without doing all the work, but the principle remains the same.

Weighting Factors. Of course, a difference that is ' statistically significant ' is not necessarily ' biologically significant '. Many local populations will show consistent differences in metric characters, but that does not of itself make all of them different races. In the present example, the trained taxonomist would certainly take into account also the consistency of the difference in bill thickness before making his decision. In this connection, there exists a valuable statistical tool, called the ' discriminant function ', which enables one to find the best possible set of weighting factors for a series of different metric characters in order to discriminate between 2 races.

Random Sampling. No statistical test is valid if the sample is not 'random'. In the above example, the bird being a rare species, the collector might have shot 4 specimens and kept the largest for himself. Needless to say, this 'bias' would make the statistical manipulations quite meaningless. One of the most difficult problems facing the investigator who wishes to use statistical methods of inference is how to obtain a sample that is sufficiently close to random for statistical methods to apply. It is far more important to give careful consideration to this aspect than it is to try to obtain a very large sample. In practice, one's data are nearly always biased in one way or another, but sometimes the bias can safely be ignored. Hickey (*A Guide to Bird Watching*, p. 25) has emphasised how birds 'tend' to migrate most abundantly at week-ends! This would be a very serious bias if one were trying to determine peak periods of activity, but would probably not matter if one were studying migration routes. In the latter case, one would obviously be more concerned about randomising the locations of the observers than about randomising the times of observation.

A 'random sample' is one in which, at the moment of sampling, every individual has an equal probability of being selected and the selection of one particular individual cannot in any way influence the probability that any other particular individual is chosen. For example, if one studies the food intake of 127 young birds in 20 randomly selected nests, one's sample size is 20, not 127. The 127 birds could not qualify as a random selection from all the nestlings in the area, because those in the same nest are not independent. One's unit of analysis must therefore be the nest, rather than the nestling. If one chooses to census ground-nesting birds by dragging a rope in a transect across a field, then one has measured the density along that transect, but one has not randomly sampled the density of the whole field. In order to do this, one would need to map the area, divide it into small subareas, give each a number, draw these numbers at random, and find the nests in those subareas that were chosen. Again, it may be biologically sound to draw conclusions about the courtship of Rooks in all of England from a study of Rooks in Berkshire, but this has nothing to do with statistics. Statistically, one's conclusions apply only to Berkshire, and even then only if the particular Rooks studied were a random sample of all Rooks living in Berkshire at the time.

Ranks. 'Ranks' are a form of data that make it possible to study relationships between factors that one can perceive in the field but cannot readily measure. As a purely hypothetical example, suppose that one suspects that for a given bird species in a given area, the breeding territories tend to be smaller where there is more cover. Now, cover is very difficult to measure precisely, but it is usually not hard to say whether one area has more, or less, cover than another. Suppose, then, that one selects 8 areas at random out of 20 accessible areas of suitable habitat, without any previous knowledge of territory size in these areas. One then visits each area, and by revisiting and careful cross-checking, decides by eye which area has the least cover, which the most, and what is the order in between. Designating the areas A, B, ..., H, suppose one finds the following ranking :

Area : A B C D E F G H
Rank of relative cover : 6 2 3 1 8 5 7 4,

where D has the least cover and E the most. One then maps breeding territories in these areas, measures territory size, and ranks these in the same way :

Area : A B C D E F G H
Rank of territory size : 3 6 8 7 1 2 5 4

In general, it can be seen from the ranks that areas having the most cover tend to have the smallest territories, but the relationship is not perfect. A measure of the strength of this relationship is provided by the 'rank correlation coefficient'. This statistic, designated 'tau', has been fully treated in a very readable treatise by Kendall (1955). It varies between -1, indicating a perfect inverse correlation, and $+1$, a perfect direct correlation. In the example above, $\tau = -\cdot73$, indicating a strong inverse association.

The sample size is only 8, however, and one would naturally be anxious to test the statistical significance. As before, we state the null hypothesis that no correlation exists, and consider the $8! = 40\,320$ equally probable ways in which the 8 territory sizes could have been ranked, for any given ranking of cover. If we were to calculate all 40 320 correlation coefficients, we would find that only 1250 of them were on the negative side of $-\cdot73$. The correlation is therefore statistically significant, with $P = 1250/40\,320 = \cdot031$. Note that a one-tail test is used here, because the investigator had a priori reasons for expecting a negative correlation.

Of course a correlation, no matter how significant statistically, does not imply causation. The birds might be maintaining smaller territories because greater cover makes a territory more difficult to defend, or for some other reason, but it might just as well be that some third factor is causing them both. Greater rain and fog in certain areas, for example, might support a greater density of the particular plant species responsible for the cover, and might also directly inhibit the territory-defending activities of the birds.

Multiple Correlation. These intricate relationships can often be disentangled by measuring some of the other variables as well, and using the more elaborate statistical techniques of 'multiple correlation' and 'partial correlation'. When dealing with measurements rather than with ranks, it all too frequently happens that, when one variable is plotted against another, a complex 'curvilinear regression' appears to be the best fit. In such cases, the most fruitful method of attack may be to employ special graphical methods. An excellent treatise on these, requiring no more background than elementary algebra, is given by Ezekiel.

A Priori Hypothesis. Having once 'scanned the data' for relationships, testing their statistical significance becomes a very hazardous operation. One must take great care not to be wise after the fact. Since there are a great many different kinds of relationships which one might be able to perceive in a set of figures, some are bound to show up from time to time by chance alone. One cannot simply take the precaution of applying a two-tail test here, because one has 'tails' sticking out in all directions, so to speak. Only by deciding a priori which particular relationships are expected can one test their statistical significance. In other words, statistics cannot simultaneously be used as an instrument of discovery and as a means of judging the strength of a presumed coincidence. If an unexpected relationship turns up and is 'statistically significant', then this relationship is deserving of further study, but the question of whether it is real or coincidental can be decided only by further data.

Frequencies. Apart from ranks, one's data are usually either measurements or 'frequencies'. Failure to understand this distinction can cause endless confusion. Frequencies always involve repeated independent events, each of which must fall into one of various mutually exclusive categories—like drawing beads of different colours from an urn. For example, the building of a nest might be the event, and the possible outcomes (categories) might be fledging at least one young, total loss of a full clutch of eggs or young, or desertion before a full clutch has been laid. In a sample of nests, the numbers of nests falling into the respective categories would form a set of frequencies. If one had such data from different areas, one could test for differences in breeding success between the areas by means of a 'contingency table', using the statistic

known as 'chi-square'. (Chi-square must not be used, however, for data that are not frequencies ; see Cochran for a good discussion of the use and misuse of chi-square tests.)

The number of times a given measurement occurs in a sample can also be regarded as a frequency. That is, the categories need not be qualitatively different things ; they can be step-wise categories of a quantitative measure. Suppose one has data for the body weights of a sample of migrating birds killed at a lighthouse. Say the range was from 22·9 to 34·7 grams for one species. One's categories, or 'classes' of measurements might then be 22·5–23·4, 23·5–24·4, 24·5–25·4, ..., etc., ..., to 34·5–35·4. These are mutually exclusive, and they cover all the possibilities. If one arranges the classes in order on the horizontal axis and for each of them erects a vertical bar, proportional to the number of birds falling into that class, a 'histogram' is produced, illustrating the 'sample frequency distribution'. This will often be a symmetrical bell-shaped figure, approximating the theoretical 'normal distribution', but it may be highly 'skewed' (asymmetrical), or perhaps even 'bimodal' (having two peaks). The point along the horizontal axis that would divide the histogram into equal areas is the 'sample median' ; the point of balance of the diagram is the 'sample mean' (the arithmetical average, usually designated $\bar{x}$, called 'x-bar').

Very often the ornithologist will have no particular hypothesis in mind, but simply wish to report how much the birds weighed and how variable they were. When the data are too lengthy to be reported in full, and it is not feasible to present a histogram, the variability of the observations is best reported by giving the 'sample variance' (designated s^2) or its square-root, the 'sample standard deviation' (s), or the 'coefficient of variation' ($s/\bar{x}$, expressed as a percentage). If desired, one can avoid the trouble of calculating s^2 by reporting instead : the number of observations (n), the sum of all n measurements (Σx), and the sum of squares of all n measurements (Σx^2). Anyone trained in statistics will be able to calculate both $\bar{x}$ and s^2 from these 3 figures.

Confidence Limits. If one could measure not a sample but the total population—e.g. if one could measure the body weight just before migration of all existing individuals of a given species—one could then construct a (huge) histogram showing the 'true mean' (m) and the 'true variance' ('sigma-square', σ^2). The usual problem confronting the investigator is to make some reasonable guess from his sample estimates, $\bar{x}$ and s^2, about what the true mean must be. A precise way of stating such a guess is to give 'confidence limits' for the mean, such as, for example,

$$\text{Probability } [26\cdot7 < m < 29\cdot9] \geqslant \cdot95$$

What this says is : 'The observed mean and the variability in relation to size of sample were such that I believe the true mean must lie between 26·7 and 29·9. Furthermore, the statistical rules that I have used to arrive at these limits assure me that, in the long run, at least 95 per cent of such statements as this will be correct.'

The statistical theory that makes such statements possible is complicated, but can be explained briefly as follows. Imagine taking many repeated samples of size n from a very large population of birds. Suppose one recorded only the mean of each sample, until one had a very large series. One could then construct a new histogram of sample means. Now, a fundamental theorem in statistics states that the shape of this new histogram of means will be very nearly normal (the more so the larger the sample), and therefore symmetrical, no matter what the shape of the histogram representing the total population! Furthermore, the variance of this new distribution of means will be very much smaller, in fact only one n-th part of the true variance of the original distribution. The sample estimate of this new variance is therefore s^2/n, and its square root is called the 'standard error of the mean'. (The 'probable error', calculated as ·6745 times the standard error, was once widely used but is now going out of fashion.) A frequently used convention is to state the sample mean 'plus or minus' one standard error, e.g. $28\cdot3 \pm 0\cdot8$. Such statements can be converted into 95 per cent confidence limits, like the one given earlier, simply by doubling the standard error and adding and subtracting this amount from the sample mean. This is true because it is a property of the normal distribution of sample means (for samples of 30 or more) that 95 per cent of all the sample means will fall within 2 standard errors from the true mean. Therefore, if one habitually makes the assertion that the true mean lies within 2 standard errors of the sample mean which one happened to get, one can expect to be correct on 95 per cent of the occasions. (For samples of fewer than 30, one must use a factor of slightly more than 2, which can be found in tables of 'Student's t-distribution'.)

Confidence limits for a percentage can also be calculated. Here the data are frequencies, the theory derives from the 'binomial distribution', and the limits depend only on the numbers of independent observations falling into each category. Hence, it is possible to tabulate, once and for all,

the confidence limits associated with any given proper fraction. For example, if a random sample of birds contains 8 males and 22 females, one can read confidence limits for p, the true proportion of males, directly from the tables :

$$\text{Probability } [\cdot123 < p < \cdot459] \geqslant \cdot95$$

These figures are available in an excellent collection of statistical tables by Hald.

Size of Sample. If one is taking a sample to test some hypothesis, it is essential to decide in advance how many individuals will comprise the sample, or when sampling will be stopped. For instance, suppose one has made a guess—or perhaps a wager—that migrating flocks of a certain species contain more males than females. Even if the true sex ratio were 50 : 50, one could easily 'prove' that the ratio was 60 : 40, simply by continuing to observe and record individuals until the accumulated sample happened to have a 60 : 40 ratio, and then stopping the sampling. By handy reference to Hald's tables, one could make sure not to stop sampling, however, until the result would be 'statistically significant'. Sooner or later, random deviations would produce just the sample for which one was waiting. There is a kernel of truth in the epigram : 'Figures cannot lie, but liars can figure!' Unhappily, it has not been fashionable to state in scientific papers how one decided on the size of one's sample, or how many hypotheses one tested before finding a 'significant difference'.

The problem of fixing the sample size is particularly acute in ornithology, where one may be unable to predict how large a sample one is going to get, or the sampling may require a great deal of effort (tempting one to stop short of the original plan if the 'results look pretty good'), or one may not wish to sacrifice any more birds for the cause of science than is really necessary. There exist special statistical methods, known as 'sequential analysis', which help to get round this problem in cases where one is attempting to decide between two clear-cut alternatives, e.g. 'The sex ratio is 50 : 50' versus 'The sex ratio deviates from this by at least as much as 60 : 40'. Under this scheme, one makes a decision after each addition to the sample whether to accept one or the other hypothesis or to go on sampling. Sequential analysis, properly applied, can save much time, but investigators who use this method ought to get advice from a competent statistician before they begin.

Conclusion. It is sound advice in general to consult a statistician before beginning a quantitative piece of research, but the biologist must be careful to treat the statistican fairly. The biological problems involved are likely to seem as abstruse to the statistician as the statistics do to the biologist. Only by making sure that the mathematician has a full understanding of the biological principles involved can one expect to get sensible advice.

(The writer of the article acknowledges helpful criticisms by R. MacArthur, R. E. Moreau, and H. N. Southern.)   M.L.

Cochran, W. G. 1954. Some methods for strengthening the common chi-square tests. Biometrics 10 : 417–451.
Ezekiel, M. 1930. Methods of Correlation Analysis. New York.
Goulden, C. H. 1952. Methods of Statistical Analysis. New York. (An excellent text-book for beginners.)
Hald, A. 1952. Statistical Tables and Formulas. New York.
Kendall, M. G. 1955. Rank Correlation Methods. London.
Kendall, M. G. & Stewart, A. 1958 et seq. Advanced Theory of Statistics. 3 vols. London. (The standard reference work for statisticians ; third volume of revised edition still in preparation.)
Moroney, M. J. 1956. Facts from Figures. London. (An inexpensive Penguin Book easy to understand, but should be read selectively.)

STEAMING: term applied to the mode of progression of steamer ducks *Tachyeres* spp. (see DUCK ; FLIGHTLESSNESS).

STEATORNITHES ; STEATORNITHIDAE: see under CAPRIMULGIFORMES ; and OILBIRD

STEGANOPODES: see PELECANIFORMES

STENOECIOUS: occupying a narrow range of the habitats available in an area, i.e. showing 'narrow habitat tolerance'—contrasted with EURYOECIOUS.

STEPPE: treeless uncultivated plain, usually as found in Central Asia.

STERCORARIIDAE: see under CHARADRIIFORMES ; and SKUA

STERNINAE: see TERN

STERNUM: the breast-bone (see SKELETON ; and CARINATE ; RATITE).

STEROID: see ENDOCRINE SYSTEM

STIFFTAIL: substantive name of the White-headed Stifftail *Oxyura leucocephala* ; in the plural, general term for the Oxyurini (see DUCK).

STILT: substantive name of some species of Recurvirostridae (see under AVOCET ; and Plate 14a (phot.)).

STIMULUS: see RELEASER ; SIGN STIMULUS ; also SENSES

STINT: substantive name (in British rather than American usage) of certain small sandpipers assigned to the genus *Calidris* or to 'Erolia' (see SANDPIPER).

STOMACH: a mammalian organ of which the equivalent in birds is the proventriculus and ventriculus (gizzard) considered together (see ALIMENTARY SYSTEM).

STONECHAT: substantive name of some *Saxicola* spp. ; used without qualification, in Britain, for *S. torquata* (see CHAT ; THRUSH).

STONE-CURLEW: usual or alternative substantive name for species of Burhinidae ; applied without qualification, in Britain, to *Burhinus oedicnemus* (see THICKKNEE).

STOOPING: term used of a bird-of-prey descending steeply on its quarry from a greater height in the air (see FALCONRY) or of any bird making a real or threatening attack in like manner ('dive-bombing').

STORING OF FOOD: see FEEDING HABITS

STORK: substantive name of most members of the Ciconiidae (Ciconiiformes, suborder Ciconiae) ; in the plural, general term for the family. The other substantive name used is 'wood-ibis', for members of the subfamily Mycteriinae, while a few of the Ciconiinae have special names that commonly stand alone. For uses of 'stork' outside the family see succeeding entries.

Storks, in the familial sense, are birds of from large to very large size (30–60 inches in length, and from under 2 feet to over 4 feet in standing height) ; they have very long legs and long, stout, pointed bills (straight, decurved, or recurved). They are quite heavily built birds, with long necks, long and broad wings, and short tails. The plumage often shows a bold pattern of black and white, the flight feathers being nearly always of the former colour. In some species the face, and in others the whole head and upper neck, are practically bare of feathers ; in one genus there is a well developed gular pouch, and in another there are small lappets at the base of the lower mandible. In the adults of some species the bill and legs are bright red. The sexes are alike in appearance.

Storks are strong on the wing, most species flying with neck extended and legs trailing behind ; many are capable of feats of soaring, and some perform long migrations. Most of them are gregarious and nearly all are wholly diurnal in habits. They live mainly on animal food : large insects (e.g. grass-hoppers, locusts), land or fresh-water molluscs, amphibians, fish ; the members of one genus are mainly carrion-eaters. Although long legs—and slight webbing at the base of the toes—suggest wading, many of the species find most of their food on open plains and fields, or only partly in marshy spots and ditches. Most storks are practically voiceless and capable of no more than low grunts and hisses, but some have melodious notes of a quiet kind. The chief sound uttered, although not by all species, is a noisy clattering of the mandibles. Various display activities, including dancing movements, have been described ; in the White Stork *Ciconia ciconia*, e.g., there is a characteristic greeting ceremony between mates at the nest, both birds bending the neck right back until the head rests on the top of the body.

Most species of storks nest in trees, often at a great height, as well as perching on them at other times. Cliffs are sometimes used, and the White Stork has come to prefer buildings (or special nesting platforms put up for its benefit). When the availability of sites permits, nesting tends to be colonial and the numbers together may be large. The nest is in most cases a large platform of sticks. The 3–6 eggs are white or nearly so, and the young do not acquire the first of 2 successive down plumages until after hatching. Both parents take part in building the nest, incubating the eggs, and caring for the young.

The family is predominantly an Old World one, and mainly tropical ; the 2 species breeding in the Palaearctic Region are summer visitors there, and the only representative in the Nearctic Region has no more than a subtropical range within it. Only one species has a distribution extending to Australia, and none reaches New Zealand. Africa and southern Asia thus have the majority of the species. There are in all 17 species (some with subspecific forms) in 11 genera.

Palaearctic Storks. The stork of popular knowledge and fable is the White Stork *Ciconia ciconia*, to which some reference has already been made. It is a large bird, standing nearly 3 feet high, with white plumage except for the black flight feathers ; in the adult the bill and legs are red. As a summer visitor it is distributed from the Netherlands eastwards through Germany to Russia, and south-eastwards to Asia Minor ; it also breeds in the Iberian Peninsula (but not in Italy) and in north-western Africa. Other races, discontinuously distributed, are found in central and eastern temperate Asia. In Britain, apart from an ancient record of breeding on one occasion in Scotland, the White

Stork has never been more than a vagrant, and as such it is now rarer—doubtless because of decreasing population on the Continent. In spite of the protection afforded to the species both by law and by popular esteem, its numbers in northern Europe have indeed markedly diminished in the present century, and the White Stork is no longer the ubiquitous bird that it was in Denmark or the Netherlands, for instance, nor a breeding species in southern Sweden or in Switzerland. Among possible reasons, overhead wires cause many casualties, and mortality in Africa from feeding on poisoned swarms of locusts is sometimes heavy. It seems probable, however, that deep biological causes are at work, as it is noticed that in some years the birds arrive late and breeding results are poor.

There is an extensive scientific literature on this species, so readily observed in its close association with man. It has, among other things, been ringed on a large scale, and much has thereby been learnt about its migrations. From most of the European breeding area the birds go south-eastwards to the Levant and southwards along the Rift Valley, many reaching the eastern part of South Africa. From the extreme western part of the breeding area the birds fly south-westwards to the Iberian Peninsula and, with the birds native there, southwards into West Africa ; their subsequent movements are not yet fully determined. Some immature birds—for breeding does not usually begin before the age of 4 or 5 years—remain in Africa instead of performing a return migration ; a few birds even breed in South Africa, but this is not known to be more than sporadic.

The Black Stork *C. nigra* is a bird of almost the same size as its congener, also with red bill and legs, but having the plumage dark except on the belly. It is a summer visitor in eastern Europe (from northern Germany) and across temperate Asia ; it breeds in the Iberian Peninsula also, and in an area in South Africa which seems to have been colonised by migrants in the present century. Its breeding habits present a contrast to those of the White Stork, as it shuns the haunts of man and nests in tall trees near marshy clearings in deep forest. It is not nearly as numerous as the White Stork, and its population likewise is decreasing—although in this case the destruction of its habitat may be sufficient explanation.

Palaeotropical Storks. Four species in monotypic genera may first be mentioned, beginning with 2 which are purely African. Abdim's (or the White-bellied) Stork *Sphenorynchus abdimii* stands a little over 2 feet high and has a mainly dark plumage ; it is highly gregarious at all times. It breeds in the rainy season in the most northerly zone of the African tropics, and thence migrates across the Equator as far as South Africa. The Saddlebill (or Saddle-billed Stork, or sometimes Jabiru) *Ephippiorhynchus senegalensis* is a handsome black-and-white bird standing more than 4 feet high and looking notably long in the leg ; the heavy bill is red, with a black band round the middle and a yellow patch at the base of the upper mandible. The species is widely distributed over tropical Africa, but seldom seen in numbers ; its feeding habits resemble those of a heron *Ardea* sp.

The Woolly-necked (or White-necked or Bishop) Stork *Dissoura episcopus* is found (with racial differences) both in Africa and in southern Asia, eastward to Borneo. It is a small species with mainly dark plumage. The Black-necked Stork *Xenorhynchus asiaticus* is a large and mainly dark eastern species, distributed from India to Australia, with a slightly upturned bill. It is mainly aquatic in its feeding habits and is not gregarious.

The Openbill (or Open-billed Stork) *Anastomus lamelligerus* of tropical Africa and Madagascar is less than 2 feet high and has dark plumage. Its most remarkable character is the shape of the bill, which is such that when the mandibles are opposed a wide gap is left between their respective distal portions except where the tips meet—probably an adaptation to holding large and slippery water-snails. This species is more aquatic than some of the others, and it sometimes feeds by night. The same English name is used for *A. oscitans*, the congener in southern Asia.

Finally, under this heading, there is the Afro-Asian genus *Leptoptilos*, consisting of very large carrion-eating storks with the head and neck naked except for scattered downy or hairlike feathers. The African representative is the Marabou (or Marabou Stork) *L. crumeniferus*, standing 4 feet high and with a wing-span which may attain $8\frac{1}{2}$ feet. The bill is heavy, but straight and pointed ; on the front of the neck there is a long distensible pouch of almost naked pink skin. There is a large development of white fluffy under tail coverts (' marabou down ') in the breeding season. The birds gather at carrion after the manner of vultures (Aegypiinae), and often in company with them. They are also scavengers of refuse, and will eat any small animals that they can catch. The Adjutant (or Adjutant-bird or Adjutant Stork) *L. dubius* is closely similar, and the Lesser Adjutant *L. javanicus* is smaller ; both are distributed from India to Borneo.

Neotropical Storks. Two species of typical storks are found in the New World, both confined to the tropics. From the Guianas to Argentina,

and common in the latter, there is the Maguari Stork *Euxenura galeata*. It is of medium size, for the family, with white-and-black plumage and red feet. It finds its food both in water and on dry ground, as do many of the Old World species. Rather more widely distributed, from southern Mexico to Argentina, is the Jabiru *Jabiru mycteria*, clearly the rightful owner of that Brazilian common name. It is one of the larger species of stork and has mainly white plumage ; but the head and upper neck are naked, the skin being dark blue or black with some red. The bill is particularly heavy and slightly upturned at the tip. The species is not very gregarious but is sometimes seen in flocks.

Wood Ibises. The subfamily Mycteriinae consists of 1 monotypic genus in the New World and 1 genus of 3 species in the tropics of the Old World. These birds are characterised by markedly decurved bills, which doubtless accounts for the name ; but they are storks and have nothing to do with the Threskiornithidae (see IBIS). The Wood Ibis (or Wood Stork) *Mycteria americana* is distributed from South Carolina to Argentina and is also found in the Greater Antilles. It is a large bird, white with black wing areas and tail; the skin of the head and upper neck is bare and black. The birds nest colonially in trees and sometimes hunt the shallows in flocks.

The Wood Ibis *Ibis ibis* of Africa is a bird about the size of the White Stork and not wholly dissimilar in colouring—but the tail is black, the bill orange, and the legs are pink. Together with the shape of the bill, the most striking diagnostic character is the bare red face. The Wood Ibis is said to be largely a fish-eater ; and it nests colonially in trees, often in villages or towns. It is widespread in the tropical parts of the continent. The Painted Stork (or, sometimes, Pelican-ibis) *I. leucocephalus* of southern Asia is similar, but with an orange-yellow face and a dark band across the breast. The Southern Painted Stork *I. cinereus* is also found in southern Asia.

See Plate 28c (phot.). A.L.T.

Bernis, F. 1959. La migración de las cigüeñas españoles y de las obras cigüeñas 'occidentales'. Ardeola 5 : 1–77.
Bouet, G. 1951. La Vie des Cicognes. Paris.
Haverschmidt, F. 1949. The Life of the White Stork. Leiden.
Siewert, H. 1932. Erlebnisse mit dem schwarzen und weissen Storch. Berlin.
Schüz, E. 1960. Die Verteilung des Weissstorchs im südafrikanischen Ruheziel. Vogelwarte 20 : 205–221.
Schüz, E. & Szijj, J. 1960. Vorläufiger Bericht über die Internationalen Bestandsaufnahme des Weissstorchs 1958. Vogelwarte 20 : 253–257.

STORK, HAMMER-HEADED: see HAMMER-HEAD

STORK, SHOE-BILLED or WHALE-HEADED: see SHOEBILL

STORM-PETREL: substantive name of species of Hydrobatidae (Procellariiformes) ; in the plural, general term for the family (see PETREL).

STREAMCREEPER: *Lochmias nematura* (see OVENBIRD (1)).

STRIGES; STRIGIDAE: see below

STRIGIFORMES: an order, alternatively ' Striges ', comprising the families Strigidae (typical owls) and Tytonidae (barn owls), regarded by some merely as subfamilies of the Strigidae (see OWL). A family based on the fossil type-genus *Protostrix* is also placed in this order.

STRIGOPINAE: see PARROT

STUMP-TAIL: in the plural, alternative general term for the crombecs *Sylvietta* spp. (SEE WARBLER (1)).

STURNIDAE: a family of the Passeriformes, suborder Oscines (see STARLING).

STRUTHIONES; STRUTHIONIDAE: see below

STRUTHIONIFORMES: an order, alternatively ' Struthiones ', of ' ratite ' birds comprising the monotypic family Struthionidae of Africa and until lately of south-western Asia (see OSTRICH ; also RATITES, PHYLOGENY OF THE). A family based on the fossil type-genus *Eleutherornis* is also placed in this order.

STRUTHIOUS: resembling the Ostrich *Struthio camelus* ; often used as a general term for all the true ' ratite ' birds, although begging the question of their relationship (see RATITES, PHYLOGENY OF THE).

STRUTTING GROUND: special term in North America for the social display ground of the Sage Grouse *Centrocercus urophasianus* (see GROUSE ; LEK DISPLAY).

STYMPHALIAN BIRDS: see FABULOUS BIRDS

SUBCLASS: see under CLASS ; TAXON

SUBFAMILY: see under FAMILY ; NOMENCLATURE ; TAXON

SUBGENUS: see under GENUS ; NOMENCLATURE ; TAXON

SUBMERGENCE: see SWIMMING AND DIVING

SUBORDER: see under ORDER ; TAXON

SUBOSCINE: term often applied collectively to the suborders of the Passeriformes other than the Oscines (see PASSERIFORMES).

SUBSONG: see SINGING

SUBSPECIES: a population of which the members can be morphologically distinguished, if sometimes only on average, from the members of other populations of the species to which all belong ; the term ' race ', or ' geographical race ', is used synonymously and is in some ways a truer representation of the concept. In Mayr's words, subspecies are ' geographically defined aggregates of local populations which differ taxonomically from other such subdivisions of a species '.

Subspecies are designated trinominally, a third term being added to the specific binomen ; the subspecific form corresponding with the original description of the species is treated as the ' nominate subspecies ', the third term of the trinomen being a repetition of the second. An early notion that the nominate subspecies was ' the species '—other races representing, as it were, departures from the orthodox—was based on a misconception ; the original choice of a particular population as the basis of the specific name was of course purely fortuitous. The nominate subspecies has in reality no greater importance than others, and it is ' typical ' only in a nomenclatural sense.

Ornithology passed through a phase, earlier in the present century, when there was a tendency—not yet completely defunct—to treat the subspecies as the natural unit, losing sight of the fact that species is the only taxon that can be defined in objective terms (see SPECIES). As Mayr has said : ' Four features of geographic variation make it difficult to delimit a subspecies objectively : (1) The tendency of different characters to show independent trends of geographic variation ; (2) the independent re-occurrence of similar or taxonomically indistinguishable populations in widely separated areas (" polytopic subspecies ") ; (3) the occurrence of micro-geographic races within formally recognised subspecies ; and (4) the arbitrariness of the degree of distinction selected by different authors as justifying subspecific separation of slightly differentiated local populations.'

The subspecies is therefore ' merely a practical device for the taxonomist ', and many that have been described have since proved to be no more than samples arbitrarily taken from a population continuum showing clinal variation (see CLINE). Attempts have been made by taxonomists to give an appearance of objectivity to such subspecies by applying an arbitrary rule that 75 per cent (some say 50 per cent) of specimens must be identifiable. On the other hand, a geographically isolated population, whether or not it has been recognised as subspecifically distinct (or as including more than one subspecies), may be an incipient species and thus of potential importance as an evolutionary unit (see SPECIATION ; also RING-SPECIES).

See Plate 42 (colour).

Mayr, E. 1959. Trends in avian systematics. Ibis 101 : 293–302.

SUBSTANTIVE NAME: see NAME, SUBSTANTIVE

SUGARBIRD (1): substantive name of the two species of *Promerops*, a genus of the Meliphagidae (Passeriformes, suborder Oscines). This genus is remarkable for its wide geographical separation, in South Africa, from the remainder of this otherwise mainly Australasian family (see HONEYEATER). The relationship has indeed been doubted on distributional grounds, and in any event the isolated position of the genus justifies a separate account here. The two species are the Cape Sugarbird *P. cafer*, common in the south and south-west of Cape Province, and the Natal Sugarbird *P. gurneyi*, which replaces it in the Eastern Province, Natal, eastern and north-eastern Transvaal, and as far north as Southern Rhodesia. The following account is based mainly on studies of *P. cafer*.

Sugarbirds are readily distinguished by their some-what large size, general dull brownish colour, long decurved bill, and long slender tail ; the last is often considerably longer in the male than in the female and can attain a length of 12 inches. The call is a creaking and clanging song with occasional ' chicks ' interjected. The birds are restricted to the neighbourhood of *Protea* vegetation, although in the non-breeding season (southern summer) they may travel some distance in search of food. In Southern Rhodesia they are found only on some mountain slopes where *Protea* species grow.

In the breeding season, sugarbirds are territorial. In south-western Cape Province the season lasts from February until August, with a peak in April–June when certain *Protea* species are in flower. The Sugarbird is double-brooded, and male and female remain paired for the whole of the breeding season. The cup-shaped nest is most commonly placed some 3–5 feet above the ground. Only the female builds, applying a very simple method of collecting and depositing small dead twigs and then pressing and moulding them with her body into the required shape. The lining always consists of a thick layer of *Protea* fluff as a basis, with wiry rush-grasses above. The usual clutch is 2, and the eggs vary from light

buff to reddish-brown, covered with blotches of dark purple or fine brown spots and lines. Only the female incubates, and the eggs hatch on the seventeenth day after incubation began.

Flight of *Promerops cafer* (male) over *Protea* vegetation (South Africa). *G. J. Broekhuysen.*

The young are at first sparsely covered with long, thin, grey down. The female frequently covers them during the day, as well as by night, for the first 6 days. Both parents feed the young, but the female does the bigger share ; some honey is brought, but chiefly insects and spiders. Faeces are removed to a particular bush at the boundary of the territory. The young leave the nest after 18–20 days, but receive parental attention for about 3 weeks more. The attitude of the parents to the young then becomes aggressive ; but it sometimes happens that the female has started to incubate the second clutch while the young of the first brood are still dependent.   G.J.B.

Broekhuysen, G. J. 1959. The biology of the Cape Sugarbird *Promerops cafer* (L.). Ostrich supp. no. 3.

SUGARBIRD (2): used, especially by avicul-turists, as substantive name of species of Coerebinae in such genera as *Coereba, Dacnis, Chlorophanes*, and *Cyanerpes* (see HONEYCREEPER (1)).

SULIDAE: see under PELECANIFORMES ; and GANNET

SULOIDEA: see under PELECANIFORMES

SULTANA: alternative name of gallinules *Porphyrio* spp. (see RAIL).

SUMMER VISITOR: see VISITOR

SUNANGEL: substantive name of *Heliangelus* spp. (see HUMMINGBIRD).

SUNBEAM: substantive name of *Aglaeactis* spp. (for family see HUMMINGBIRD).

SUNBIRD: substantive name of most species of Nectariniidae (Passeriformes, suborder Oscines) ; in the plural, general term for the family. A few species are called ' spider-hunters '. For well over a hundred years the name sunbird has been applied to this family of brightly plumaged little birds, widespread in the warmer parts of the Old World. The characters of the family have been well described by several authorities, and it was the subject of a sumptuous monograph by Shelley in 1876–80. The African species were revised by Sclater in 1930 and the whole family by Delacour in 1944. The last-named made revolutionary changes, reducing the number of full species to 106 and the genera to 5— *Arachnothera, Aethopyga, Neodrepanis* (now referred to the Philepittidae), *Anthreptes*, and *Nectarinia* ; the 66 species which are, on this basis, placed in *Nectarinia* (with 5 sub-genera) include most of those previously assigned to *Cinnyris*. This system is not followed in the present article, but it is necessary to mention it as differences in nomenclature are involved.

The largest concentration of sunbird forms is in Africa and its islands, but numerous representatives of the family occur widely in India, Ceylon, Burma, Malaya, the East Indies, and Australia. Palestine has its own sunbird, related to African forms ; Arabia has representatives of 4 species ; and one of the Indian species is found even in Baluchistan.

The family is one of small to very small birds (from $3\frac{3}{4}$ inches long, upwards), with long, thin, curved bills that in most genera show varying degrees of serration. The nostrils are oval, placed in a groove and covered with an operculum ; the tongue is tubular in its anterior two-thirds and split near the end ; rictal bristles are wanting. The tarsus is strong and scutellate ; the toes are short and stout, with sharp nails. The rounded wing has 10 primaries. The tail is square, rounded, or graduated ; in the males of some species the 2 central feathers are narrow and lengthened. The plumage is generally bright, metallic, and sometimes velvety, in the males, but usually dull in females and lacking all metallic lustre. In several less specialised forms of *Nectarinia* and *Anthreptes*, metallic colours are absent or much reduced, and the sexes are alike or differ only slightly ; on the other hand, some females in these genera have partially metallic plumage, either similar to that of the males or a little less elaborate. Those grouped in *Anthreptes* have shorter and less curved bills than *Cinnyris* or *Nectarinia*. The males of certain species of Nectariniidae have a dull off-season plumage which replaces their brilliant dress after the breeding season. Males of many species, and females of some, possess bright pectoral tufts of lengthened fluffy feathers, erectile during display and varying in colour from yellow to red.

Sunbirds have sharp, metallic voices, but some sing fairly well. They are active and sprightly in manner. They are not truly sociable, although birds of several species may gather in flowering trees. Some *Anthreptes* spp. have been observed in foraging parties, where birds of several kinds band together to search for insects, passing through the bush in company and driving the insects before them. Male sunbirds are extremely pugnacious in the breeding season.

All types of country are inhabited by sunbirds— primeval and second-growth forest, clearings, gallery forests, parklands, and dry bush. Some are familiar garden-dwellers, others are restricted to high mountains. In general, and particularly in Africa, the very brilliant species are found in the more open situations, while the duller members are inhabitants of shady and heavy forest. Some species spend much of their lives in the treetops, others keep close to the ground. All sunbirds build a covered or oval nest which is suspended from a bough or leaf of a tree, less often from a bush. It is usually an elaborate structure, into which cobwebs are sometimes woven, and it is often provided with a porch-like projection above the lateral entrance. In many nests the outside has a ragged appearance, and in some a tail of loose building material is suspended. It may be lined with soft white down or some similar substance. The eggs are normally 2 in number, more rarely 3 ; they are spotted or blotched, or streaked longitudinally, on a ground which is usually white or pale bluish-white. The apparently close association between sunbirds and aculeate Hymenoptera has been noted in several species of *Cinnyris* and *Chalcomitra* in the breeding season (see NESTING ASSOCIATION).

Sunbirds feed on insects and upon nectar, extracting the nectar both on the wing after the manner of the hummingbirds (Trochilidae) and from a perch, more often by the latter method. The constant search for flowering shrubs and trees causes the sunbirds, especially the long-billed species, to move about locally in quest of their food, and— without any very obvious migration—some species definitely move from one area to another.

The Pigmy Long-tailed Sunbird *Hedydipna platura* is a case in point. This common inhabitant of the Sudanese arid belt arrives from the north in the Uelle district of the Congo in December and remains but $3\frac{1}{2}$ months, during which time it rears a brood. During the latter part of its stay the bushes and trees of the savanna put forth a wealth of blossom, but it may be remarked that this bird is less dependent on flowers than many of the long-billed species. A race of the Palestine Sunbird *Cinnyris oseus* arrives in Uelle in the second week of October, but disappears again after February ; where they go has not been discovered. These are only 2 instances from Africa of very definite movements, and examples could no doubt be multiplied.

The largest species in the Ethiopian Region is the Great Sunbird *Dreptes thomensis*, restricted to the island of São Tomé, males measuring 8½ inches from bill to tail-tip and appearing almost black in plumage with steel-blue metallic edges to the feathers ; its tail is strongly graduated, and it has a definite song. Some of the smallest sunbirds are found in the genera *Cinnyris* and *Anthreptes*, measuring little over 3 inches in length. The medium-sized but very beautiful *C. superbus* is often quoted as the most gorgeous of the whole family ; it is a second-growth forest species, of which the male has a blue-green crown, golden-green upper parts and coverts, purple or blue metallic throat, and deep crimson under parts set off by the black wings and tail. Running it closely for beauty is the Splendid Sunbird *C. coccinigaster*, with purple head, green back, and steel-blue reflections—a bird of the savanna belt and of the grasslands. Deep in the primary forest lives Johanna's Sunbird *C. johannae*, a large sunbird as bright in plumage as the Superb Sunbird but much less often seen. One other African form deserves particular mention, the montane Scarlet-tufted Malachite Sunbird *Nectarinia johnstoni*, a large green and blue sunbird with red pectoral tufts and greatly elongated middle tail feathers measuring 6·5 inches in length. It has races on all the highest mountains of East Africa, differing but slightly from one another ; *N. j. dartmouthi* was discovered at 12 000–14 000 feet on Mount Ruwenzori, close to the limit of vegetation, by the expedition of 1905 sent out by the British Museum, and like many of its family its lack of fear of man was astonishing, one bird perching on the gun-barrel of a distinguished member of the expedition! Another very beautiful highland species is the Golden-winged Sunbird *Nectarinia reichenowi*, living in mountainous areas of East Africa between 4800 and 11 200 feet ; in the normal breeding season adult males have the whole head, foreneck, and back glossy bronze or copper colour, but in the off-season these parts are mainly clothed in dull black, with scattered metallic feathers on the lower foreneck and back. In Kenya, birds in this extraordinary non-breeding plumage, of which it provides a striking example, may be seen from February till

June ; the species lives in bush or cultivated land and loves to feed on patches of *Leonotis*, and at the highest point of its vertical range it has been seen above the bamboos.

Geographically between the African and Asiatic sunbirds is *Cyanomitra dussumieri*, restricted to the Seychelles Islands. Interesting sunbirds inhabit the Comoro Islands as well as Assumption and Aldabra.

Although Africa is the continent where sunbirds are seen in the greatest profusion, the family is well represented in southern Asia. In India the best-known species are the Purple Sunbird *Cinnyris asiatica*, which ranges from Persia to Cochin-China and is found up to 7500 feet, and the Purple-rumped Sunbird *C. zeylonica*, restricted to India and Ceylon ; each makes a lovely nest, a hanging purse with the entrance on one side near the top and surmounted by a little portico. Another brilliant form, the Small Sunbird *C. minima*, is the smallest representative of the family in India ; the male has a green cap, deep crimson breast and upper parts, lilac rump, and a purple throat. In India we meet the genus *Aethopyga*, of which the Yellow-backed Sunbird *A. siparaja* is so striking an example ; the male is scarlet, with yellow rump, an olive-grey abdomen, and a long pointed tail, while the female is short-tailed and of nondescript colour ; one race is a summer visitor to the Himalaya up to 7000 feet. In striking contrast are 2 other Himalayan species, the Nepal Sunbird *A. nepalensis*, with the whole head and hind neck metallic green and the lower parts yellow flecked with red, and the Black-breasted Sunbird *A. saturata*, a black-looking bird with violet and blue metallic feathers. Burma is rich in sunbirds of the genera *Aethopyga*, *Nectarinia*, and *Anthreptes*.

In the Malay Archipelago over 25 species of sunbirds have been recorded, of which the Scarlet Sunbird *Aethopyga mystacalis*—scarlet in colour including the tail, with yellow lower back and metallic violet rump—and the crimson Ruby-cheeked Sunbird *Anthreptes singalensis* with its brilliant metallic green back with rust-coloured and yellow under parts, are both well known. In Malaya too we find the closely allied spider-hunters *Arachnothera* spp., which are included in the Nectariniidae but are duller and larger birds than the examples hitherto mentioned. There are 7 species of spider-hunters in Malaya alone.

The family is represented in Australasia by 13 species, of which the widespread Yellow-bellied Sunbird *Cyanomitra jugularis*, with a maroon band across the chest of the male, a metallic purple throat, and yellow under parts, is one of the best-known, ranging from Burma to New Guinea and northern

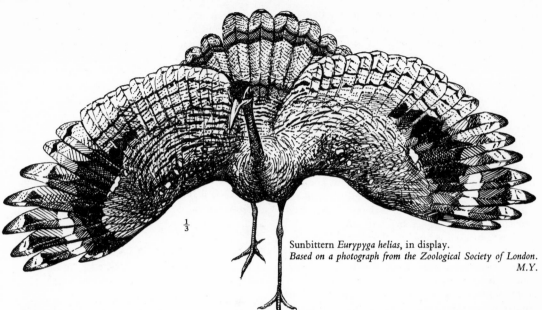

Sunbittern *Eurypyga helias*, in display.
Based on a photograph from the Zoological Society of London.
M.Y.

Australia. At least 3 species—Macklot's Sunbird *Chalcostetha chalcostetha*, Van Hasselt's Sunbird *Leptocoma brasiliana*, and the Black Sunbird *L. sericea*—represent the family in the Far East, one or other occurring in Borneo, the Philippines, the Celebes, the Moluccas, New Guinea, and the Bismarck Archipelago.   D.A.B.

Sclater, W. L. 1930. Systema Avium Aethiopicarum Pt. 2.
Shelley, G. E. 1876–80. A Monograph of the Nectariniidae or Family of Sunbirds. London. (Many plates in colour.)
Delacour, J. 1944. A revision of the family Nectariniidae (Sunbirds). Zoologica (New York) 29 : 17–38.

SUNBIRD, FALSE: name sometimes applied to *Neodrepanis* spp. (see under ASITY).

SUNBITTERN: *Eurypyga helias*, sole member of the family Eurypygidae (Gruiformes, suborder Eurypygae). It is found in the forested regions of America from southern Mexico to Bolivia and central Brazil and is represented by 3 currently recognised races. About 18 inches in length, this graceful, stout-bodied, long-necked, long-legged, largely ambulatory bird is most intricately barred, spotted, and mottled. The sexes are alike. The head is almost black, with a narrow white superciliary stripe and a broader white stripe along the lower edge of the cheeks. The neck, shoulders, and breast are brown. The throat, abdomen, and under tail coverts are white and pale buff. The remaining plumage is largely grey and olive in general tone, with prominent black bars and white spots ; and the long tail is crossed by two broad black bands.

Only when the Sunbittern spreads its wings does it reveal its brightest colour, a large round shield of deep orange-chestnut set in the midst of an area of pale orange-buff in the middle of each wing, like a sun darkly glowing in a sunset-tinted sky. The upper mandible of the long straight bill is largely black and the lower is orange. The eyes are deep red, and the long naked legs are bright orange.

Singly or in pairs, Sunbitterns forage along watercourses that traverse the forests, up to an altitude of 3000 feet or more above sea level. With slow, sedate steps, they walk along the muddy shores of sluggish streams and over the exposed rocks in rushing mountain torrents, where they fly across the deeper pools but wade through shallow water. They also frequent swampy areas in woodland. Their food, which consists largely of insects, small crustacea, minnows, and the like, is caught beneath shallow water or gathered from exposed mud and rocks. Generally silent, the Sunbittern is reported to utter a soft, long-drawn whistle or plaintive piping.

From the nature of their habitat, it seems that Sunbitterns must pass most of their lives in the shade, but they are said to seek sunny openings in the forest, where they sometimes display. Widely spreading their wings with the richly coloured upper surface tilted forward, they fan out the raised tail to fill the gap between them, thereby forming a semicircle of plumage in the midst of which the head stands.

Although there are reports of Sunbitterns breeding on the ground, usually the nest is built in a tree or bush. A nest beside a Costa Rican mountain stream was precariously saddled upon a 2-inch branch about 20 feet above the ground. The dark, roughly globular structure, about 12 inches in diameter, was composed of decaying leaves and stems, some green moss, and apparently also mud. In the top of the bulky mass was a shallow depression lined with green leaves, on which 2 eggs rested. This appears to be the usual number. The nearly oval eggs are buffish or clay-coloured with darker spots and blotches. The most complete account of the nesting of this bird is that of a pair which bred in the gardens of the Zoological Society of London almost a century ago. Both sexes built the nest of vegetable materials and mud, and they alternately incubated an egg which hatched after 27 days. The newly hatched young was thickly covered with short down and resembled the chicks of plovers (Charadriidae) and snipe (Scolopacidae). Fed by both parents with food carried in the bill, it remained in the nest until, at the age of 21 days, its wing feathers had expanded and it could fly to the ground. It is remarkable that, although the young Sunbittern resembled a precocial chick, it was attended like an altricial nestling ; but it is not known whether the behaviour of this captive pair was typical.

A.F.S.

Bartlett, A. D. 1866. Notes on the breeding of several species of birds in the Society's Gardens during the year 1865. Proc. Zool. Soc. London, 1866 : 76–79. (Colour plate of chick.)

Riggs, C. D. 1948. The family Eurypygidae : a review. Wilson Bull. 60 : 75–80 and Pl. 2.

Skutch, A. F. 1947. A nest of the Sun-bittern in Costa Rica. Wilson Bull. 59 : 38.

SUNGEM: *Heliactin cornuta* (for family see HUMMINGBIRD).

SUNGREBE: see FINFOOT

SUNNING: see FEATHER MAINTENANCE

SUPERCILIARY: term applied to a marking, in some plumage patterns, above the eye.

SUPERFAMILY: see under FAMILY ; NOMEN-CLATURE ; TAXON

SUPERORDER: see under CLASS ; TAXON

SUPERSPECIES: a grouping of species, of lesser rank than a subgenus and having no nomenclatural status ; the term was introduced by Mayr (1931) and defined as a ' monophyletic group of very closely related and largely or entirely allopatric species '. It is implied that the included species are geographical representatives of a common stock, but have at least probably attained true reproductive isolation and are not merely subspecies of a single polytypic species. ' Artenkreis ' is a partly equivalent term. A ' species-group ' (in one sense of the term) differs in that the included species may be less closely related and often sympatric (see SPECIES-GROUP (2)).

SUPRAOCCIPITAL: a paired bone of the skull (see SKELETON).

SUPRASPECIFIC: general term applied to taxa higher than the species (see TAXON).

SURANGULAR: a paired bone of the lower jaw (see SKELETON).

SURFBIRD: *Aphriza virgata* (see SANDPIPER).

SUTHORA: former generic name sometimes used, in the plural, as a general term for the Paradoxornithidae (see PARROTBILL).

SWALLOW: substantive name of most species of Hirundinidae (Passeriformes, suborder Oscines) ; in the plural, general term for the family. The only other substantive name used is ' martin ' ; the distinction has little significance, and there is an instance in which, on different sides of the Atlantic Ocean, both names are applied to the same species (*Riparia riparia*, see later).

Taxonomy. The swallows have been described as, taxonomically, the best-defined family in the Oscines ; they have the anatomical peculiarity of more or less complete bronchial rings, as compared with half rings with a membrane across the inner face as in other families of the Oscines. They are also among the birds popularly best known. Only in respect of the African River Martin *Pseudochelidon eurystomina* can the propriety of its inclusion be questioned ; this bird, differing inter alia in its bronchial rings, is usually segregated in a subfamily of its own, Pseudochelidoninae (the rest being Hirundininae), and even so with the reservation that it may not belong to the family at all. Of the true swallows, Peters recognised 19 genera and 78 species, many of the latter polytypic. This classification is followed here ; but the tendency nowadays is to reduce the number of genera.

Distribution. The distribution of the group is cosmopolitan, only the highest latitudes and some oceanic islands being without swallows ; New Zealand has none, apart from occasional vagrant individuals of an Australian species, and Madagascar appears to have only 2 breeding species despite the particularly abundant representation of the family on the African continent.

Characters. Swallows are rather small birds, ranging from 3¾ to 9 inches long (a good deal depending on the proportion of the tail). They have short necks, slender bodies, and long pointed wings ; the tail is of moderate length but often extended by elongated outer rectrices, and it is commonly forked in greater or less degree. The legs are short, and the feet are weak although armed with strong claws. The bill is short, flattened, and triangular ; and the gape is very wide.

The plumage, especially on the upper parts, tends to be dark—black, brown, green, or blue, often with a metallic lustre. The rump and the under parts are often white, buff, or chestnut, and a few species are strongly streaked. There are often white spots on the rectrices, noticeable when the tail is spread. The tarsi and even the toes are feathered in some species. There are 9 primaries, of which the outermost is greatly reduced, and these may be over double the length of the longest secondaries. A few species are ' rough-winged ', i.e. with serrated edges to the outermost primaries, and this character is present in 2 otherwise not very similar genera— *Stelgidopteryx* and *Psalidoprocne*, New World and African respectively. The sexes are alike, or nearly so, in most species. There is one moult in the year, post-nuptially.

General Habits. With their long wings, swallows are strong and rapid fliers, showing great agility in the air. They are wholly insectivorous, and catch their prey on the wing, flying with wide gape. They can perch on twigs, wires, reeds, or the like, or cling to their nests or the surroundings of these, but their walk is little more than a feeble shuffle. Indeed, they alight on the ground very little except to collect mud, where that material is used for nest building. The notes are mainly squeaks or twitters, although sometimes more musical ; some species even have a slight song. They are gregarious birds, sometimes very markedly so, and the flocks roosting together before autumn migration may be of immense size. Migration is clearly a necessity for aerial insect-eaters in temperate climates, and some of the journeys performed are of great length.

Breeding Habits. Swallows are to a greater or less extent colonial in their breeding habits. As will be noted further below, the nest may be a hollow of some sort or a structure made with mud. When there is a nest of the latter kind, the female may do most of the building while the male brings the material. The 3–7 eggs are white, sometimes speckled and sometimes plain. The young are nidicolous and indeed tend to stay rather long in the nest (sometimes more than 3 weeks) ; there is a

little down on the upper parts at hatching. Both parents care for the young, although the female tends to take the major part in incubating the eggs. In some species, 2 or sometimes 3 broods are reared in a season, even in temperate areas where the birds are only summer visitors ; but there may be only one brood in the brief season at the latitudinal limit of range (Lind).

Mayr & Bond have pointed out that, with the high degree of structural uniformity in the Hirundininae, differences in nesting habits may provide the best basis for the attempt at a natural grouping of the included genera. The most primitive habit is probably the use of a natural hollow in a tree, bank, cave, or building, or a burrow made by another species, without the use of any mud in such construction as there may be. Next comes the use of tunnels excavated by the birds themselves, with the addition of no more than lining material in the terminal chamber. The most specialised habit is that of building nests of mud, collected in tiny pellets from soft ground. Such nests may be placed in holes, including holes in trees, or on a ledge or rafter ; or they may be applied to the vertical face of a cliff or building. Further, the mud nests may be open cups, or completely enclosed except for either a simple opening or a funnel-like entrance giving the shape of a retort to the whole construction.

Another point of evolutionary interest is the extent to which some species have become dependent on man-made structures for their nesting sites. Although some species use either the natural or the artificial site, according to circumstances, others practically never use anything except a building. However nearly equivalent the new site may be to the original natural one, the definite preference for it does involve a change in adaptation. It is only within the last few centuries that suitable buildings can have existed over great parts of the present range of species now normally using them.

Cosmopolitan Genera. Three genera—*Hirundo* (13 species), *Petrochelidon* (10), and *Riparia* (4)—have something approaching a world-wide distribution ; in the first and third instances, the New World representation consists of a single form that is only subspecifically distinct from one inhabiting the Old World. The Swallow *Hirundo rustica*, known in America as the Barn Swallow, is a summer visitor practically throughout the Palaearctic and Nearctic Regions, except in the highest latitudes, and performs migrations extending as far as South Africa, Ceylon, northern Australia, and northern Argentina. In the American form *H. r. erythrogaster* the under parts are pinkish or cinnamon-buff ;

and males are more brightly coloured than females.) Of the remaining species, 10 are purely African, and 1 other is found in Africa and southern Asia ; *H. tahitica* is widely distributed in the western Pacific area, one of its races, *H. t. neoxena*, being known to Australians as the Welcome Swallow. In this genus the nest is an open cup made of mud, variously sited in different species.

A retort-shaped nest of mud, usually attached to a rock face, is typical of *Petrochelidon*, a genus not far removed from the last named. The Cliff Swallow *P. pyrrhonota* breeds from Alaska to Mexico and migrates as far as northern Argentina. There are 2 other American species, 4 African, 1 Asian, and 2 Australian, the last including the Tree Martin *P. nigricans*.

The Sand Martin *Riparia riparia*, known in America as the Bank Swallow, has a Holarctic breeding distribution. Of its congeners, 2 are purely African and the other ranges from Africa and Madagascar to southern Asia. These birds have the plumage pale brown on the upper parts ; and they excavate nesting tunnels, often some feet in length, in steep banks or sometimes even in almost level ground.

Old World Genera. In addition to its representatives of the cosmopolitan genera, the Old World has 7 genera of its own. The House Martin *Delichon urbica* has a Palaearctic range, and its 2 congeners are found in southern Asia. These birds are feathered to the toes and have much white and no chestnut in their plumage. They build domed nests of mud, with simple openings, against walls or rock-faces. *Ptyonoprogne* includes the Crag Martin *P. rupestris* of the southern portion of the Palaearctic Region, and 3 other species in Africa and southern Asia. These are birds with dull brown plumage, and build open cups of mud against rock-faces. The Red-rumped Swallow *Cecropis daurica* has a southern European, southern Asian, and middle African distribution. Of its congeners, 1 is in south-eastern Asia and the other 4 are in Africa. These birds have more reddish colour in the plumage than *Hirundo* spp., which they otherwise resemble a good deal ; the large Mosque Swallow *C. senegalensis*, for instance, has the whole of its under parts bright chestnut. The members of the genus build retort-shaped nests of mud on walls or rock-faces.

The rough-winged swallows *Psalidoprocne* spp. are purely African ; they nest in natural holes or on ledges. White has recently proposed to reduce the 12 species to 5 ; the square-tailed *P. nitens* is sympatric with fork-tailed forms, and the latter are considered as constituting a superspecies with 4

species and some races. Another African species is the Grey-rumped Swallow *Pseudhirundo griseopyga*, in a monotypic genus ; it is unique among swallows in nesting in burrows made by small rodents, and as it does this on flat ground breeding is necessarily in the dry season. The Mascarene Martin *Phedina borbonica* of the Malagasy Region has one congener on the African continent. The remaining Old World genus is monotypic, the Black-and-white Swallow *Cheramoeca leucosternum* being an inhabitant of parts of Australia.

New World Genera. There are 9 genera peculiar to the Americas, and not all need be named here. All of them nest in holes of some kind, not excavated by themselves and not having mud as a material. The Tree Swallow *Tachycineta bicolor* breeds from Alaska southwards and has 5 congeners, 3 purely South American. The Rough-winged Swallow *Stelgidopteryx ruficollis*, in a monotypic genus, has various subspecific forms ranging from southern Canada southwards. The Purple Martin *Progne subis*, also distributed from southern Canada southwards, is a large species, with the plumage of the male dark below as well as above ; its four congeners are in the Neotropical Region. The genus *Atticora* has two Neotropical species. The Golden Swallow *Kalochelidon euchrysea*, in a monotypic genus, is restricted to the islands of Jamaica and Hispaniola ; its plumage is shining bronze-green above, white below. In South America, *Notiochelidon cyanoleuca* nests in abandoned holes of the Minera *Geositta cunicularia* (Furnariidae).

River Martin. The African River Martin *Pseudochelidon eurystomina*, sole member of its genus and of the subfamily Pseudochelidoninae, is known only from a limited area in the Congo. Doubts about its taxonomic position have already been mentioned. It is a relatively large and stoutly built bird ; the whole of its plumage is almost black, with a purple or green gloss ; the bill and irides are scarlet. It breeds in colonies of great size, the birds tunnelling in almost level sand exposed by the river in the dry season. It lays 3 white eggs. The general habits appear to resemble those of true swallows.

See Plate 36a (phot.).   A.L.T.

Allen, R. W. & Nice, M. M. 1952. A study of the breeding biology of the Purple Martin (*Progne subis*). Amer. Midl. Nat. 47 : 606–665.

Lind, E. A. 1960. Zur Ethologie und Ökologie der Mehlschwalbe, *Delichon u. urbica* (L.). Ann. Zool. Soc. Vanamo 21 (2) : 1–122.

Lowe, P. R. 1938. Some anatomical notes on the genus *Pseudochelidon* Hartlaub with reference to its taxonomic position. Ibis (14) 2 : 429–437.

Mayr, E. & Bond, J. 1943. Notes on the generic classification of the swallows. Ibis 85 : 334–341.

Moreau, R. E. 1940. Numerical data on African birds' behaviour at the nest—II. *Psalidoprocne holomelaena massaica* Neum., the Rough-wing Bank-Martin. Ibis (14) 4 : 234–248.

Peters, J. L. 1960. Family Hirundinidae. *In* Mayr, E. & Greenway, J. C. (eds.). Check-list of Birds of the World vol. 9. Cambridge, Mass.

Skutch, A. F. 1960. Life Histories of Central American Birds Pt. II. (Pacific Coast Avifauna no. 34.) Los Angeles.

White, C. M. N. 1961. The African rough-winged swallows. Bull. Brit. Orn. Cl. 81 : 29–33.

SWALLOW-SHRIKE : see WOOD-SWALLOW

SWALLOWTAIL : *Eupetomena macroura* (for family see HUMMINGBIRD).

SWALLOW-TANAGER : *Tersina viridis*, sole member of the subfamily Tersininae, in the classification here followed placed in the Emberizidae (Passeriformes, suborder Oscines) but sometimes given independent familial rank. The Swallow-tanager, a bird about 6 inches long, bears some resemblance to the tanagers (Thraupinae) but—in addition to having a very peculiar palate—differs in being longer-winged and short-legged, as well as in having a wide flattened bill slightly hooked at the tip ; in its nesting habits, also, it stands apart from the tanagers. The male is mainly a brilliant turquoise blue, with a black face and throat, and black bars on the flanks ; the female is green above and yellowish below with green barring. The Swallow-tanager is found in northern parts of South America up to Panama, and in Trinidad. The birds are migratory, at least in parts of the range ; they breed in the mountains, where they prefer wooded country with clearings, and spend the non-breeding season in the humid lowlands.

The Swallow-tanager is both an insect-eater and a fruit-eater. Insects are captured on the wing, a method of feeding which gives the bird its name ; fruit is taken from a perched position. The method of eating fruit is peculiar : the bird holds the whole fruit in the widely opened bill and turns it about until all the pulp is scraped off. The seed is not swallowed, as it is by many frugivorous birds, but is dropped after the flesh has been eaten off it. Relatively large masses of fruit are swallowed and held in a distensible throat-sack.

The Swallow-tanager's calls are varied but unmusical : the song of the male is poorly developed. During the breeding season territories are held. The nest is built at the end of a horizontal burrow in a bank or in an artificial hole in a wall or similar structure. Holes in earth banks, the natural site, may be excavated by the birds themselves or taken over from other species. The nest is a cup-shaped structure made of a variety of materials such as

rootlets, grasses, and vegetable fibres. The eggs, usually 3 in number, are glossy white. Incubation is by the female alone ; but the male takes a part, smaller than that of the female, in feeding the young. Outside the breeding season Swallow-tanagers are highly social, forming flocks that—unlike those of most other tropical passerine birds—never associate with other species. D.W.S.

SWALLOW-WING : *Chelidoptera tenebrosa* (see PUFFBIRD).

SWALLOW, WOOD- : see WOOD-SWALLOW

SWAMP : a semi-aquatic habitat of which the chief types are (*a*) fresh-water swamp or marsh, (*b*) mangrove swamp, and (*c*) boggy tundra (see MANGROVE SWAMP ; TUNDRA).

SWAMPHEN : substantive name used in Australia for *Porphyrio* spp. (see RAIL).

SWAN : substantive name of *Coscoroba coscoroba* and *Cygnus* spp., all in the tribe Anserini (with the ' true geese ') of the subfamily Anserinae of the Anatidae (see under DUCK). ' Swan ' is of common gender, but ' cob ' and ' pen ' are sometimes used as special terms for male and female swans and ' cygnet ' for the young.

SWIFT : substantive name (varied to ' swiftlet ' in some cases) for the species of Apodidae and Hemiprocnidae (Apodiformes, suborder Apodi) ; in the plural, general term for the suborder. The swifts form a very well defined group of birds with purely superficial resemblances to swallows (Hirundinidae). Swifts are usually united in one order (Apodiformes) with the hummingbirds (Trochilidae), although this is doubtfully correct. Both swifts and hummingbirds have an extremely short, thick humerus, a short ulna with short secondary feathers, and a long carpus with 10 primaries ; the wing is narrow, with a shallow camber, adapted for high-speed flight. However, while swifts have long wings and are primarily adapted to sailing through the air, hummingbirds have relatively much shorter wings and are specially adapted for hovering ; further, in breeding and feeding habits, in coloration, and in form of bill, the two groups are extremely different. Swifts are usually regarded as constituting a suborder, of which the Hemiprocnidae (crested swifts) include only 1 genus of 3 species, and the Apodidae (true swifts) include all the rest.

Apodidae. The true swifts are the most aerial of all birds, feeding entirely in the air and in many cases collecting their nesting material there, copulating in the air (although also at the nest), drinking and bathing from the air by descending to water, and regularly spending the night on the wing (see FLIGHT). All are predominantly sooty or brown in colour, with some patches of white or pale grey. They do not normally settle on the ground or vegetation, although some of them roost on vertical cliffs or more rarely on trees. The legs are extremely short, the strong claws being adapted for clinging. Swifts can take off from flat ground, although with difficulty. In copulating in the air and in regularly spending the night on the wing, swifts are apparently unique ; while in northern regions they may travel hundreds of miles to avoid depressions, returning after these have passed.

Alpine Swift (African race) *Apus melba africanus.* C.E.T.K.

All swifts glue their nest-material together with saliva produced by unusually large salivary glands. Clutch size varies from one in *Cypseloides* to 4–6 in *Aeronautes* and some *Chaetura* spp. The incubation period is rather long for the size of bird, being 19–20 days in *Apus*. The nestling period is also long, and is unusually variable (from 5 to 8 weeks, depending on the weather) in *A. apus*.

The Apodidae include two subfamilies—the Chaeturinae, in which the tail feathers have spiny tips that help the bird to cling to a vertical surface ; and the Apodinae, which have no such spiny tips but instead have the hind toe pointing forward to assist in gripping. In all, there are some 65 species in 8 genera, spread throughout Eurasia, Africa, and America, but none breed in Australasia except in the extreme north. Nearly all the species are tropical, but a few breed in northern parts of Europe, Asia, and America, all of them migrating to the tropics for the winter.

Chaeturinae. The genus *Chaetura* includes some 17 species in Asia, Africa, and America, the best-known of which is the Chimney Swift *C. pelagica*

of eastern North America ; under natural conditions nearly all nest inside hollow trees, but several now use chimneys, the bracket-shaped nest of twigs being attached to the vertical inner surface. *Collocalia* includes some 20 small species of cave swiftlets in south-east Asia and the islands of the Pacific and Indian Oceans, many of them being extremely hard to distinguish from each other ; some of them nest inside dark caves, finding their way by echo-location (see ECHO-LOCATION) ; and they have a bracket-shaped nest of vegetable material and much saliva, a few species using only saliva (see EDIBLE NESTS). *Cypseloides* includes 9 species in tropical America, 1 of which extends to Alaska ; the mossy nest is placed on a rock-ledge close to water, sometimes under a waterfall.

Apodinae. The genus *Apus* comprises 10 Old World species, most of them in Africa, and includes the Common Swift (or 'Swift' unqualified in Britain) *A. apus*. They usually nest in holes in cliffs or buildings, one species in burrows in sand, and several in old nests of hirundines. *Cypsiurus* consists of one small African and Asiatic species, the Palm Swift *C. parvus*, with a long forked tail ; it builds a small open nest on the inner side of a palm leaf, the egg being glued to the nest with saliva, and the bird brooding vertically. Of the other 3 small genera, all in the New World, *Aeronautes* nests in holes in cliffs ; *Panyptila*, with a long tail-fork, builds a hanging sleeve some 2 feet long under a branch or rock, with a nest chamber near the top and entrance at the bottom ; while *Tachornis* places a bag-shaped nest in palm foliage.

The Common Swift has several adaptations for an unusually variable food supply, since air-borne insects are plentiful in warm, dry, and calm weather but very scarce in cold, windy, and wet weather. The interval between the eggs, normally 2 days, is lengthened to 3 days if food is short. The parents normally relieve each other in turn on the eggs, but if food is short they leave the eggs unbrooded, these being unusually resistant to cooling. The young can likewise be left unbrooded, and can also withstand several days of starvation by utilising their fat reserves and retarding their rate of development. Further, feathered young can, if starved, lose their temperature control and become temporarily poikilothermic, while the adults can clump together in a semi-torpid condition, although for how long is not known (see TORPIDITY).

Hemiprocnidae. The Crested Swifts *Hemiprocne* spp. in this small separate family are found in south-eastern Asia and the western Pacific, from India to the Solomon Islands. They do not show such extreme specialisation for an aerial habit as the true swifts, are capable of greater manoeuvre, perch freely on trees, and have patches of bright colour. The tiny cup-shaped nest is just large enough to hold the single egg ; it is attached to the side of a lateral branch of a tree, the branch taking the weight of the brooding bird.   D.L.

Lack, D. 1956. Swifts in a Tower. London. (Gives all important references to that date.)
Lack, D. 1956. A review of the genera and nesting habits of swifts. Auk 73 : 1–32.
Medway, Lord. 1962. The swiftlets (*Collocalia*) of the Niah Cave, Sarawak. Part I. Breeding biology. Ibis 104 : 45–66.

SWIFTLET: see above

SWIMMING AND DIVING: terms that cover the methods of aquatic locomotion, broadly comprising : (*a*) swimming on the surface ; (*b*) diving from the surface and swimming under water ; (*c*) plunging into the water from a height. At least 390 species, in 9 orders, habitually swim, while many others can do so. About two-fifths of the regular swimmers seek their food by diving, the remainder normally feeding on the surface, or up-ending in shallow water, or plunging from the air. The surface-feeders show comparatively minor adaptations to this mode of life, the most obvious being in the position and proportions of the hind limbs and in the webbed feet or lobes on the toes to increase their effective area (see LEG). Diving and plunging birds show more extensive modifications in structure and physiology. Effective diving requires the specific gravity of the bird, normally much less, to approach that of water, so that as little as possible of the available energy is used simply to remain submerged. Diving birds have less pneumatic skeletons than swimmers ; this increases their specific gravity, although it more probably arises from the necessary strengthening of their motor apparatus (see PNEUMATISATION OF BONE). The techniques of changing specific gravity prior to diving are two. First, a reduction of volume is achieved by exhalation ; the air-sacs of diving birds are large, and expulsion of air from them does effect a substantial reduction in body size, although quantitative data do not seem to be available (see RESPIRATORY SYSTEM). Second, many diving birds are able to reduce buoyancy by compressing their body plumage and so forcing out most of the air normally trapped within it.

Some birds, most notably the divers (Gaviidae) and the Long-tailed Duck *Clangula hyemalis*, can descend to over 200 feet and remain submerged for 3 minutes or more ; and they can stay alive for as much as 15 minutes when forcibly held under. Several physiological adaptations make this possible.

While under water the main source of oxygen is not air in the respiratory system but oxyhaemoglobin and oxymyoglobin stored in the muscles. Diving birds have a high tolerance for carbon dioxide, the accumulation of which actually promotes the liberation of oxygen from oxyhaemoglobin. They can obtain energy from the anaerobic breakdown of glycogen as well as by the usual aerobic means. In addition, the regulation of the circulation is so modified that in diving the flow of blood to the muscles and perhaps to other organs can be greatly reduced, the supply being reserved mainly for the central nervous system.

The great variety in the details of adaptations for swimming and diving can be indicated by a brief review of the families including habitual swimmers. The penguins (Spheniscidae) are the supreme exemplars of diving birds. Their wings are built for flight under water, not in the air ; these lack normal quill feathers and are reduced in size to short, relatively inflexible flippers with extraordinarily flattened wing bones and muscles. The leading edge of the wing is depressed on the downstroke, as it is in normal flying birds, so that the water is pushed backwards by the concave under-surface of the wing. In swimming the wing is usually raised only a little above the horizontal plane on the upstroke, a departure from the technique of aerial flight. Penguins spend relatively little time on the surface, where they float very low in the water. Their density is high because the body feathers are reduced to very small size, affording no lodgment for air ; the important insulating function of normal plumage is taken over by thickening of the skin and particularly by subcutaneous fat. Penguins feed mainly pelagically, rather than close to the bottom, and dive neither deeply nor for very long periods.

Many other diving birds feed on or close to the bottom. For this reason, depth of water is the principal factor determining the duration of their dives. Dewar showed that in less than 6 fathoms (36 feet) of water the relation of time to depth is approximately 20 seconds for the first fathom and 10 additional seconds for every fathom thereafter ; this rule seems to hold for most diving birds that have been studied. The interval between dives seems also to be determined in part by the depth of water, although it increases more rapidly in deep diving than in shallow water, as would be expected on physiological grounds. Each species of diving bird has its favourite depth of water and a definable bathymetric range. For eye adaptations to diving see VISION.

The divers or loons (Gaviidae) are among the

most efficient swimmers and excel in both duration and depth of diving, although their normal limits (up to $1\frac{1}{2}$ minutes and 35 feet) are much less than the extreme performances noted above. They are elongated in form—the sternum is particularly long and convex—with the feet set very far back, the tibial part of the leg being bound to the body. The front toes are fully webbed. The feet alone are used for propulsion and steering underwater. The grebes (Podicipitidae) superficially much resemble the divers, although the structure of their limbs and their pelvic and pectoral girdles differ greatly ; they have all 4 toes palmately webbed or lobed.

The petrels (Procellariiformes) all float high on the water and can swim easily, but they do so infrequently except for the small group of diving petrels (Pelecanoididae). The last, although unmistakably Procellariiformes, show remarkable resemblances to the auks (Alcidae) and occupy a corresponding niche in the Southern Hemisphere. These petrels are short-winged, with a whirring flight in the air, diving from the wing into the sea, continuing to ' fly ' under water and often emerging flying. They make little use of their feet.

Tropicbirds (Phaethontidae) feed by plunging into the sea from heights of 50 feet or more, but are comparatively poor swimmers and divers. The young seem unable to dive. Brown Pelicans *Pelecanus occidentalis* feed by plunging from the wing, but most Pelecanidae feed by dipping their long bills and necks while floating high on the surface. Their legs are short and stout, not laterally compressed as in most swimming birds ; the feet are large, and webbed between all 4 toes.

Gannets and boobies (Sulidae) feed by plunging, sometimes from over 100 feet. As they are large birds, their momentum on striking the surface is considerable, and they show special adaptations to prevent damage on impact, notably strengthening of the skull and a remarkable system of subcutaneous air-sacs which are thought to be primarily shock-absorbing. They sometimes pursue fish under water, and may use wings as well as feet in swimming. Cormorants (Phalacrocoracidae) use feet more than wings. They ride low in the water and dive from the surface, for periods often of more than a minute and to depths of about 30 feet. Unlike that of most aquatic birds, the plumage of cormorants readily becomes sodden. The long, stiff tail is used as a rudder : in most other diving birds the tail seems to be unimportant. Darters (Anhingidae), like cormorants, ride low in the water, and often only the head and neck remain visible ; underwater they swim with the wings slightly expanded. Like cormorants, too, they become sodden.

Screamers (Anhimidae), although they frequent the waterside, only occasionally swim. All ducks, geese, and swans (Anatidae) swim, and possibly all can also dive, although only about two-fifths of the 145 species habitually do so. The most accomplished divers are the sea-ducks (Mergini), eiders (Somateriini), and stifftails (Oxyurini). The Long-tailed Duck (or Oldsquaw) vies with the Great Northern Diver *Gavia immer* as a deep-diving bird, apparently feeding down to 27 fathoms in the Great Lakes of America. Most of the diving ducks make little use of their wings under water, although adult eiders usually dive with them partly opened, flicking them to accelerate their descent. Likewise, the White-winged (or Velvet) Scoter *Melanitta fusca* may adopt a peculiar posture in which the wing-tips are kept crossed over the tail but the carpal joints are lifted and the alula extended ; in this position the wings may serve as rudders, at least on the return to the surface. Steamer ducks *Tachyeres* spp. use their wings partially extended while under water. Occasional divers such as the Mallard *Anas platyrhynchos* and swans *Cygnus* spp. have their wings nearly fully extended under water. The most able swimmers in the family are the ducks of fast-running waters, particularly the torrent ducks *Merganetta* spp. of South America.

Nearly all the rails (Rallidae) swim well, although only the gallinules (*Gallinula* spp., *Porphyrio* spp., etc.) and coots (Fulicinae) are primarily aquatic. The gallinules are swimmers, with the long toes typical of the family increased in swimming efficiency by narrow strips of skin extended laterally. They rarely dive when feeding but may do so if disturbed, when they sometimes flap the wings slowly in swimming under water. The coots, which have lobed toes, are habitual divers ; they do not use their wings while submerged. The diving of coots is less efficient than that of other bottom-feeders ; in a given depth of water the duration of their dives is much less, food plants being brought to the surface rather than eaten at the bottom.

The 3 species of finfoot (Heliornithidae) are good swimmers with broadly-lobed toes. They swim very low in the water. Their ability as divers is in dispute. The jacanas (Jacanidae), normally using their extraordinarily long toes to walk on floating plants, are like the Moorhen *Gallinula chloropus* in their ability to swim and to dive in escaping danger.

Among the Charadriiformes, the phalaropes (Phalaropodidae) are the only family of waders that are specialised for swimming. They have lobed, semipalmate toes, a flattened tarsus, and dense body plumage. They feed afloat, sitting high on the water, commonly moving rapidly in very small circles. Avocets and stilts (Recurvirostridae) and the Crab-plover *Dromas ardeola* also swim well, and more frequently than other waders. The Black-winged Stilt *Himantopus himantopus* can dive well.

Skuas (Stercorariidae), gulls (Larinae), and terns (Sterninae) resemble each other in their equipment for swimming—short, or rather short, legs and stout fully-webbed feet. The gulls swim very much more than the others. Many terns plunge for food but do not go deep or travel far under water.

The 22 species of auks (Alcidae) are able and highly specialised divers, using their wings for underwater propulsion at relatively high speeds. Except *Cepphus*, they tend to feed pelagically rather than at the bottom. Their wings are short, with very short inner secondaries and axillaries—a less extreme version of the penguin flipper, still useful for aerial flight. The feet are little used for propulsion under water. Auks retain dense body plumage, which is less obviously compressed prior to diving than is that of, for example, grebes.

The remaining orders contain only 2 families of aquatic habit. In the Coraciiformes, the 87 species of kingfishers (Alcedinidae) include a number of fish-eaters that feed by plunging either from a perch or while hovering over water. The anatomically more primitive members of the family are non-aquatic woodland birds, feeding by pouncing on insects and other prey on the ground or by pursuing them in the air. The techniques and structure of the fish-eaters show only very minor adaptations, for the prey is taken at or close to the surface and prolonged immersion does not occur. Unlike most other plunging birds, they do not regularly swim ; this is true also of the fish-eaters among the birds-of-prey (Falconiformes) and owls (Strigiformes).

Among the Passeriformes the members of the small family of dippers (Cinclidae) are aquatic. They swim well, often under water, and are able to walk on the bottoms of swift-flowing streams. Their adaptations to aquatic life are very dense plumage and an unusually obvious nictitating membrane, which is presumably of value in protecting the eye under water. The mechanism of their underwater walking has been the subject of much controversy (see DIPPER). Some approach to similar habits is found in such relatively little-known birds as *Enicurus* spp. (Turdinae) and in *Cinclodes* spp. (Furnariidae) (see THRUSH ; OVENBIRD (1)). Otherwise no members of the order are aquatic, although some frequent the vicinity of water and some tyrant-flycatchers (*Pitangus* spp. and *Lessonia rufa*) regularly take food from its surface.

See Plate 12a (phot.). H.J.B.

Dewar, J. M. 1924. The Bird as a Diver. London.
Schorger, A. W. 1947. The deep diving of the Loon and Old-squaw and its mechanism. Wilson Bull. 59 : 151–159.
Storer, R. W. 1960. Evolution in the diving birds. Proc. XII Internat. Orn. Congr., Helsinki 1958 : 694–707.

SYLPH: substantive name of *Aglaiocercus* spp. (see HUMMINGBIRD).

SYLVIINAE: see MUSCICAPIDAE ; and WARBLER (1)

SYMBIOSIS: see under PARASITE ; also NESTING ASSOCIATION

SYMPATHETIC NERVES: see NERVOUS SYSTEM

SYMPATRIC: term used of related taxonomic forms, e.g. species, found in the same geographical area—contrasted with ALLOPATRIC.

SYMPHYSIS: union or junction of two bones (see SKELETON).

SYNALLAXINAE: see OVENBIRD (1)

SYNANTHROPIC: see under EUSYANTHROPIC

SYNAPOSEMATIC: see under APOSEMATIC

SYNCHRONIC: existing at the same level of geological time—contrasted with ALLOCHRONIC.

SYNDACTYL: having two toes (III and IV) coalescent for part of their length (see LEG).

SYNECOLOGY: term for the ecology of communities—contrasted with AUTECOLOGY ; see also ECOLOGY.

SYNONYM: see NOMENCLATURE

SYNOVIAL CAVITY: see SKELETON

SYNSACRUM: the long fused portion of the vertebral column to which the pelvic girdle is firmly attached (see SKELETON).

SYNTHLIBORAMPHINI: see AUK

SYNTYPE: see TYPE-SPECIMEN

SYRINX: the organ of voice or song (plural ' syringes '). It differs from the mammalian larynx in both situation and structure ; the larynx, although present in birds, lacks vocal cords and has little or no share in voice production. Situated at or near the bifurcation of the windpipe (trachea) into its 2 bronchi, the syrinx comprises, in its typical form, a resonating chamber (tympanum) associated with elastic vibrating membranes derived from the intervening connective tissue between the cartilages, the whole under the control of specialised muscles capable of altering the tension and position of the membranes. According to site, syringes are classifiable as tracheal, bronchial, or tracheo-bronchial—the last being the commonest. See also RESPIRATORY SYSTEM.

Tracheo-bronchial Syringes. Here the lowest rings of the trachea coalesce and ossify to form the tympanum, which is movably connected with the neighbouring bronchial rings. The latter are incomplete, their medial ends being connected by membrane (membrana tympaniformis medialis) whilst on the lateral surface occur a variable number of smaller membranes between the bronchial half-rings or between the first ring and the 2 hindmost tracheal rings. At the angle between the bronchi the 2 medial tympaniform membranes unite and are produced into the air-passage as a semilunar fold. Across the base of the trachea a cartilaginous or bony bar (pessulus) runs dorso-ventrally separating the medial tympaniform membranes of the two sides. It is attached in front to the last tracheal ring and behind to the penultimate or antepenultimate rings. If no pessulus is formed, the right and left membranes are connected by an elastic band, the bronchidesmus, the position of which is subject to variation ; both structures may, however, coexist.

Muscles acting upon the syrinx include both intrinsic and extrinsic bundles. The former have migrated from the hyoid and larynx, carrying with them their nerve supply from the hypoglossal. Extrinsic fibres constitute the tracheo-clavicular and sterno-tracheal slips. Intrinsic muscles are often numerous (1–9 pairs) and complex, and are variable from avian group to group. They arise above and insert variously on the lateral or middle portions of the bronchial half-rings (Mesomyodi), or to the ends of those rings where they become replaced by the medial tympaniform membrane (Acromyodi). The former arrangement is by far the commoner and is regarded as the more primitive, the latter being restricted, with few exceptions, to the Oscines or so-called 'song-birds' (see PASSERIFORMES). There are, however, other variants where the muscles insert on the dorsal (anacromyodian), ventral (catacromyodian), or both ends (diacromyodian) of the bronchial half-rings. Distinction has been made between forms with few (oligomyodian) or many (polymyodian) intrinsic syringeal muscles, but this

distinction is not now considered taxonomically reliable even when applied solely to passerines.

Myologically, 7 types of syringeal structure may be recognised.

1. Trachea and syrinx devoid of intrinsic muscles, e.g. in 'ratites' except *Rhea*, storks (Ciconiidae), vultures (Aegypiinae), and most Pelecaniformes.
2. A single pair of muscles inserted on distal end of trachea, e.g. in anserines, doves (Columbidae), and most gallinaceous birds (Galliformes) including the Hoatzin *Opisthocomus hoazin*.
3. A single muscle pair arising from trachea and inserting on one or more bronchial half-rings, e.g. in *Rhea*, penguins (Spheniscidae), grebes (Podicipitidae), petrels (Procellariiformes), auks (Alcidae), gulls (Laridae), and many others.
4. Two pairs of short tracheo-bronchial bundles, e.g. in *Falco*, some hummingbirds (Trochilidae), and some lower passerines.
5. Three muscle pairs present, e.g. in parrots (Psittacidae) and lyrebirds (Menuridae).
6. Four or more muscle pairs, e.g. in *Grallina*, *Prosthemadera*.
7. Five to 9 pairs of muscles. Only in the Oscines does this complexity occur. In the Corvidae, where 7 pairs are present, they are arranged as follows :

(a) m. tracheo-bronchialis ventralis (from trachea to anterior ventral end of second half-ring).

(b) m. tracheo-bronchialis obliquus—inserting on ventral end of third half-ring.

(c, d) mm. tracheo-bronchialis longus et brevis to the dorsal end of second half-ring and the medial tympaniform membrane.

(e) m. bronchialis (or syringeus) ventralis to ventral end of second half-ring deep to (a).

(f) m. syringeus ventro-lateralis inserting on membrane between second and third half-rings deep to (b).

(g) m. syringeus dorsalis to the dorsal end of the second half-ring.

Tracheal Syringes. In forms with a purely tracheal syrinx the hindmost part of the windpipe has purely membranous walls, the last 6 rings being extremely thin or deficient. Both medial and tympaniform membranes are present also. Muscles —usually a single pair—are laterally placed. Birds with this arrangement are termed Tracheophonae or Clamatores and are loud-voiced, vocalisation being accompanied by swelling of the throat (see PASSERIFORMES). The arrangement is confined to certain families of tropical birds—the antpipits (Conopophagidae), tapaculos (Rhinocryptidae), antbirds (Formicariidae), and woodcreepers (Dendrocolaptidae).

Bronchial Syringes. In a purely bronchial syrinx the trachea has typically no sound-producing structures, these being confined to the bronchi, which exhibit expanded lateral tympaniform membranes between 2 or more successive half-rings ; a medial membrane may also be present; e.g. in the Oilbird *Steatornis caripensis*, nightjars *Caprimulgus* spp. and cuckoos (Cuculidae) ; some members of these groups, however, display intermediate conditions between a bronchial and a tracheo-bronchial type of syrinx.

Physiology. The physiology of the syrinx has recently been studied by Thorpe, who has concluded that among song-birds 2 or more vibrators may be in action at any one time, and that these may include, in addition to the tympaniform membranes and the semi-lunar membrane, structures in the larynx. See also SINGING.   W.C.O.H.

Thorpe, W. H. 1959. Talking birds and the mode of action of the vocal apparatus of birds. Proc. Zool. Soc. Lond. 132 : 441-455.

SYSTEMATICS : the aspect of biological work dealing with the systematic description of the forms of life, and also with their orderly arrangement (see CLASSIFICATION). The latter is the special concern of taxonomy, but as it permeates the whole that term is often used synonymously with systematics (see TAXONOMY). The handmaid of systematics is nomenclature (see NOMENCLATURE).

Systematic work is a basic necessity for other kinds of ornithological endeavour, as it defines the subjects of study. It is itself grounded largely on morphology and geographical data, as the museum specimen is of necessity the main material in the descriptive or analytical phase, as well as being the permanent record. In the taxonomic or synthetic phase, however, ornithological systematists—although primarily using morphological criteria—have increasingly drawn upon the data of field studies to assist in elucidating problems of phylo-

genetic relationships ; various laboratory tests are also being increasingly invoked (see PROTEINS AS TAXONOMIC CHARACTERS). What has been called ' the new systematics' goes further, into a third phase in which the aim is to investigate the factors influencing the evolution of the different forms. The systematic biologist of today has thus to take account of ecological, ethological, physiological, and genetic data bearing on the problems that the results of earlier faunistic and morphological labours suggest (see TAXONOMY).

In ornithology, systematic work in the old Linnean tradition has been pursued with notable assiduity. So much so that it has been claimed that birds are better known taxonomically than any other class of animals. This places a heavy responsibility on the ornithological systematist to make the fullest use of the opportunity for making still further contributions to general biological knowledge. To do this he must abjure conservatism in his concepts of taxonomy, the limitations of the typological approach, and the pedantry of regarding nomenclature as more than a means to an end. It has been well said by Stresemann that ' whoever wants to hold firm rules should give up taxonomy. Nature is too disorderly for such a man.'

The present tendency is, indeed, towards a much more fluid concept of ' population systematics '. In this study, as Mayr has pointed out, cognisance must be taken of three major phenomena : (1) the geographical isolate, possibly an incipient species (see SPECIATION) ; (2) the population continuum, subject to clinal variation (see CLINE) ; (3) the zone of secondary intergradation, due to isolates re-establishing contact (see HYBRIDISATION, ZONE OF SECONDARY). An isolate may or may not have been formally recognised as a subspecies, or it may comprise more than one ; a continuum, likewise, may or may not include forms that have been accorded subspecific rank (see SUBSPECIES).

See references under TAXONOMY.

T

TACTILE SENSE: see TOUCH

TADORNINI: see DUCK

TAIGA: coniferous forest-land, typical of vast areas of the North Temperate Zone, lying south of the TUNDRA.

TAIL: in recent birds, an appendage of feathers protruding more or less backwards from the rump, but absent or much reduced in some ; *Archaeopteryx* had the reptilian character of a bony tail prolonging the vertebral column, and from this the feathers sprang laterally. The main tail feathers are the rectrices, but upper and lower tail coverts (greater and lesser of both) conceal the bases of these and the gaps between their calami.

Number of Rectrices. The tail quills are referred to by numbers, counting outwards from the right and left members of the central pair. Most commonly there are 12 rectrices in all, i.e. 1–6 on each side. A very few small passerines have only 6 altogether, e.g. emu-wrens *Stipiturus* spp. (Malurinae), or 8, e.g. the Long-tailed Apalis *Apalis moreaui* (Sylviinae) ; a few other birds have 8, e.g. *Crotophaga* spp., some rails (Rallidae), and some grebes (Podicipitidae) ; some birds have 10, e.g. most hummingbirds (Trochilidae), swifts (Apodidae), toucans (Ramphastidae), and cuckoos (Cuculidae) other than *Crotophaga*. Numbers in excess of 12 are more frequent, e.g. 14 in guinea-fowl (Numididae), 16 in grouse of the genus *Lagopus*, 18 in the Pheasant *Phasianus colchicus* and the female Peafowl *Pavo cristatus*, 20 in the male Peafowl, 24 in the American White Pelican *Pelecanus erythrorhynchos*, 26 in the Pintailed Snipe *Gallinago stenura*, and 32 in the White-tailed Wattled Pheasant *Lobiophasis bulweri*. As can be seen from the examples quoted, the number is not always constant within a family ; it even differs by as much as from 14 to 26 among snipe *Gallinago* spp., and the Mountain Yellow Flycatcher *Chloropeta similis* of

Africa (Muscicapinae) has 12, whereas its congeners have 10. The number of greater upper tail coverts may be the same as the number of rectrices, or more (especially in aquatic birds), or less (notably in passerines) ; this may be true also of the greater under tail coverts, but information is relatively scanty.

Shape. Kiwis (Apterygidae), cassowaries (Casuariidae), emus (Dromaiidae), and rheas (Rheidae) are practically tailless, no special tail feathers being recognisably differentiated from the general plumage covering the hinder parts ; the Ostrich *Struthio camelus* is an exception among the 'ratite' birds in having something of a tail. In grebes (Podicipitidae) the quills are rudimentary ; and in many aquatic birds the tail is very short, e.g. in divers (Gaviidae) and in penguins (Spheniscidae).

Tails may be rather short and stumpy, of moderate or substantial length, or greatly elongated. Very long tails are found, for instance in the tropicbirds (Phaethontidae), in many true pheasants (Phasianidae), in certain parrots (Psittacidae), in the mouse-

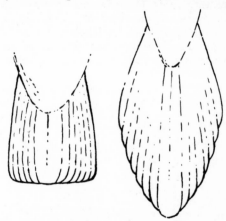

FIG 1 (a) Dipper *Cinclus cinclus*—square-ended.
(b) Tawny-flanked Prinia *Prinia subflava*—graduated
(Not same scale) *M.Y.*

birds (Coliidae), and in species of various passerine families—e.g. in tyrant flycatchers of the genus *Muscivora* in the New World, and in the Paradise Flycatcher *Terpsiphone paradisi* and the Paradise Whydah *Vidua paradisaea* in the Old World. (The Japanese have a breed of domestic fowl with a 'train' of enormous length, in which the feathers grow continuously without moult.) Elaborate tails are often much more highly developed in the male of a species.

The end of the tail, depending on the relative lengths of the paired rectrices, may be square or rounded, forked or wedge-shaped—examples are too well known to need citation. Very long tails are sometimes due to elongation of the central pair of rectrices, whether the others be graduated or of uniform length. In some fork-tailed species, however, it is the outer rectrices that are very long.

Various modifications occur in the shape of separate rectrices. Sometimes the distal part of the rachis carries no web but projects as a spine, e.g. in the spine-tails of the family Furnariidae and in the spine-tailed swifts (Chaeturinae). Some other birds are 'racket-tailed', notably the motmots (Momotidae) ; here the terminal part of the shaft in the 2 central rectrices carries a web on both sides, but there is a sub-terminal part that is bare, thus isolating the 'racket' (or 'raquet') from the main web. In the male Loddiges' Raquet-tail *Loddigesia mirabilis*, a hummingbird, it is the outer pair that carry raquets at the end of long wire-like shafts that cross over. Sometimes certain rectrices may be twisted in the vertical plane, e.g. the somewhat elongated central tail feathers of the Pomatorhine Skua (or Pomarine Jaeger) *Stercorarius pomarinus*. In some birds-of-paradise (Paradisaeidae) the central tail feathers are elongated in wire-like or narrow ribbon-like form, often much twisted or curled.

Ornamental tail plumes are by no means always modified rectrices. In the male Peacock *Pavo cristatus*, for instance, the gorgeous feathers of the train are greater upper tail coverts. The ornamental plumes of the male Ostrich *Struthio camelus* have probably this same homology. In some species, the birds at rest may appear to have ornamental tail feathers but these in fact belong to the wings, as can be seen when the latter are unfolded. This is exemplified in the cranes (Gruidae) ; thus in *Grus grus* one of the most noticeable characters is what appears to be a large and loosely feathered tail, but the plumes are actually elongated secondary wing feathers. In the Pennant-winged Nightjar *Semeiphorus vexillarius* it is an enormously elongated primary on each side that, in the breeding male, extends beyond the tail when the bird is at rest.

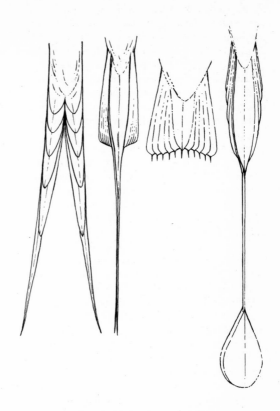

FIG 2 (a) Arctic Tern *Sterna paradisaea*—strongly forked (outer rectrices elongated)
 (b) White-throated Bee-eater *Merops albicollis*—elongated central rectrices
 (c) Chimney Swift *Chaetura pelagica*—needle-tailed
 (d) Turquoise-browed Motmot *Eumomota superciliosa*—racket-tailed
 (Not same scale) M.Y.

Movements. Muscles in the rump enable the tail to be raised, depressed, moved from side to side, or spread. In flight the tail forms part of the surface on which the air presses, and it can give some assistance to the wings in steering and braking (see FLIGHT). The tail tends to be broad in soaring species and short in rapid flyers. The tail, when of some length, may also be used in helping to balance a perched bird.

In several different groups of birds that either climb or cling to vertical surfaces, such as tree-trunks or walls, the tail is used as a prop ; and the rectrices tend to be stiffened in adaptation to this habit. Examples are the woodpeckers (Picidae), spine-tailed swifts (Chaeturinae), woodcreepers (Dendrocolaptidae), treecreepers (Certhiidae), and oxpeckers (Buphaginae).

The tail in some birds is normally cocked up, as

for instance in the Wren *Troglodytes troglodytes*, the Grey Gallito *Rhinocrypta lanceolata*, and the Rufous Scrub-bird *Atrichornis rufescens*, to name a varied assortment. Among the stiff-tailed ducks (Oxyurini), e.g. in the North American Ruddy Duck *Oxyura jamaicensis*, the tail of the swimming bird may be either cocked up or extended horizontally. Other birds momentarily cock up the tail, e.g. on alighting —the familiar characteristic movement of the Blackbird *Turdus merula*. Many birds also raise the tail to a greater or less extent in the act of defaecation. The female's tail is usually, and that of the male sometimes, deflected laterally during copulation.

In many different kinds of birds there is a repeated or continual wagging, shaking, or flirting of the tail. These movements are often associated with bobbing or twitching of the whole body ; indeed, the tail is in some instances not moved separately at all but merely serves to accentuate the movement of the body. The continual up and down movement of the tail in wagtails *Motacilla* spp. is familiar, and is performed while the bird is otherwise still. In the forest wagtails *Dendronanthus* spp. the tail has been described as being wagged from side to side ; but here it is in fact the whole body that is continually swung, through a horizontal arc, on motionless legs. The function of such movements is not understood, but it has been remarked that the tendency seems to be especially common among birds that have their usual habitats in the neighbourhood of running water. Apart from the wagtails, one thinks at once of the ' teetering ' of sandpipers of the genus *Actitis*, the similar movements of waterthrushes *Seiurus* spp. (Parulidae), and the bobbing of dippers *Cinclus* spp. ; and those furnariids of aquatic habits, *Cinclodes* spp., are not called ' shaketails ' without reason. Yet examples among birds not particularly associated with water are not lacking ; for instance, the African Pitta *Pitta angolensis*, a bird of thickets and dense woodland, constantly bobs its body and flirts its tail like a dipper.

If the tail is of any considerable size, whether it have ornamental plumes or not, it commonly plays a large part in display postures, particularly those of males in courtship performances ; it is often erected, sometimes depressed, and generally spread fanwise in addition (see DISPLAY). It may also be quivered by females or young in solicitation or begging postures.

For sounds made by the tail, e.g. the drumming of snipe *Gallinago* spp., see under INSTRUMENTAL SOUNDS. A.L.T.

TAILOR-BIRD : substantive name of *Orthotomus* spp. (see WARBLER (1)).

TAKAHE : *Notornis mantelli* (see RAIL).

TALKING BIRDS : see under MIMICRY, VOCAL

TALON : a claw (toe), especially of a bird-of-prey and mainly used in the plural.

TAMENESS : toleration by birds of the close presence of human beings, in some instances amounting to a positive tendency to seek such presence. A substantial degree of tameness is characteristic of certain species, and this is presumably genetic. Tameness may also be acquired by individuals or communities of a species in favourable circumstances ; again, however, there seems to be a genetic element, in that some species become tame much more readily than others.

An innate lack of fear of man may be shown by birds inhabiting remote islands or other relatively inaccessible places. The tameness of birds on the Galápagos Islands has been remarked by visitors from Charles Darwin onwards. In the case of large species breeding in such places, e.g. boobies (Sulidae) and penguins (Spheniscidae), a reaction to predators of any kind, if these do not normally intrude on the nesting grounds, may be absent from the birds' psychological make-up.

On the other hand, the many species of birds that have become adapted to using houses and gardens, finding their nesting sites and feeding opportunities in the vicinity of man, show various degrees of toleration of the presence of the human beings who also live there. Similarly, the birds will follow the gardener or agricultural worker to take the foodprey that he incidentally disturbs or uncovers— much in the way that the Cattle Egret *Ardeola ibis*, for instance, accompanies grazing mammals, domesticated or wild. So also there may be a great attendance of gulls *Larus* spp. at a fishing harbour ; and so on. It is clear that there is an advantage in the association with man ; and where the latter is friendly in his attitude towards the birds, tameness may become normal behaviour.

Special interest attaches, however, to the differences between species in their natural tameness or capacity to acquire tameness. In Britain, where the Robin *Erithacus rubecula* is mainly a garden bird, the species is outstanding in its capacity for familiarity with man ; as has been said, it is never the Dunnock *Prunella modularis* that perches on the gardener's spade. In truly wild habitats in northern Europe, the amazing tameness of the Rednecked Phalarope *Lobipes lobatus* and the Purple Sandpiper *Calidris maritima* contrast with the extreme wariness of some other species of ' waders ' (Charadrii) breeding on the same ground. Found from the Sahara to India, the House Bunting *Emberiza striolata* is a remarkably tame bird, feeding inside houses.

There are also some interesting geographical differences in this respect within a single species, and these are not easily explicable. Thus the Robin, already mentioned as being so tame in Britain, is a shy woodland bird over much of Continental Europe, including countries in which it is subject to no persecution. Likewise, the Moorhen *Gallinula chloropus* readily becomes accustomed to man in the populous areas of Britain and some other parts of western Europe, but is elsewhere a notably timid bird. In North America, the Florida race of the Scrub Jay *Aphelocoma coerulescens* is described as bold and confiding, and the Great Basin race as furtive and shy.

As regards tameness acquired by individuals, it was pointed out by Edward Grey (Viscount Grey of Fallodon) that birds became tame in relation to places rather than persons ; he instanced the behaviour of the same individual ducks *Anas* spp. towards the same people at different points on his lake. The present writer has had eight Speckle-fronted (or Scaly-fronted) Weavers *Sporopipes frontalis* come unhesitatingly on his hand, outstretched with crumbs, on the verandah of a house in Tanganyika that he had never visited before but where the hostess regularly fed the birds.

It is better to discount as exceptional those cases in which a human being has taken more than usual pains to win the confidence of a wild bird or birds, thus establishing something like a personal relationship (cf. L. Howard). Sometimes there may even be an abnormal factor in that the bird has become conditioned to accept a certain person as a substitute mate or parent (see IMPRINTING). One has also to allow for possible differences in temperament between individual birds of the same species (see INDIVIDUAL VARIATION). Residual tameness on the part of a bird that has been released from captivity is also outside the general picture considered here.

Further, it is necessary to distinguish boldness from tameness—the urge to continue sitting on eggs, or to remain with the young, or to seize prey, is for the time being stronger than the urge to flee. That there may be little real toleration in such cases is shown by the fact that in some species the passive role can give place to an attack on the human intruder ; also by the fact that an incubating bird may desert its nest permanently if its capacity for sitting tight is strained to breaking point.

Of the acquisition of tameness by a local population of a species, habituated to human presence in places where no hostile action towards birds ever

occurs, there can be no better example than the Wood Pigeon *Columba palumbus*—so wild and wary in the ccuntryside, so extremely tame in the public parks of London. It was noticed that during the Second World War, when steps to keep down these birds were taken, the degree of tameness became much less ; but it has since become re-established.

There·are some interesting points about the tameness or otherwise of young birds, including those reared in captivity. Interpretation is difficult, however, in the absence of controlled experiments. For the question of habituation see under LEARNING.

Wild birds, like various other animals, show little fear of vehicles, and can often be approached much more easily in a motor car than on foot. The shape of the vehicle apparently evokes no predator response.

A.L.T.

Grey of Fallodon, Viscount. 1927. The Charm of Birds. London.

Howard, L. 1956. Living with Birds. London.

Huxley, J. S. 1947. Notes on the problem of geographical differences in the tameness of birds. Ibis 89 : 539–552. (Followed by notes by various authors, 1948–49. Ibis 90 : 312–315 ; 91 : 108–110, 356–358, 528.)

Lack, D. 1946. The Life of the Robin. 2nd ed. London.

Leopold, A. S. 1944. The nature of heritable wildness in turkeys. Condor 46 : 133–197.

TANAGER : substantive name of species of Thraupinae (=Tanagrinae) and, in the plural, general term for the group—here treated as a subfamily of the Emberizidae (Passeriformes, suborder Oscines), but in the past usually given separate familial rank. The name comes from ' tangará ' in the language of the Tupi Indians of Brazil. The tanagers are 9-primaried song-birds, confined to the Western Hemisphere and very largely to its tropical portion. Systematists now tend to include in this subfamily certain genera of honeycreepers (Coerebinae), but for the time being it is convenient to keep separate these small birds with bills and tongues highly modified for drawing nectar from flowers (see HONEYCREEPER (1)). The so-called Thrushtanager *Rhodinocichla rosea*, a ground-feeder, seems to be uncertainly included among the tanagers. With these exclusions, the family contains 200 species.

General Characteristics. The tanagers, ranging in size from under 4 to over 8 inches in length, contribute more than any other family to the brilliant colour displayed by tropical American birds ; although hummingbirds (Trochilidae) are more numerous in species and individuals, they are smaller and their bright metallic colours can be appreciated only under special conditions. For variety of colours and diversity of patterns, the small tanagers of the genus *Tangara* are outstanding even in this highly endowed family. One of the most gorgeous of these is the Red-rumped Paradise Tanager *T. chilensis*, the ' Siete colores' of the South Americans. This 5-inch bird has the head golden-green ; the upper plumage is largely black, with a bright red rump ; the chin and throat are light purple, and the remaining under plumage is chiefly turquoise blue. The sexes are alike, as seems to be true throughout this brilliant genus, in which adults wear the same bright colours at all seasons.

The genus *Tanagra* (name not to be confused with ' *Tangara* ') likewise contains a number of small and colourful species, the ' euphonias '. Less varied in coloration than the aforementioned group, the males are mostly black glossed with violet, blue, or green on the upper parts and sometimes also on the throat ; the forehead and more or less of the crown, and the under parts, are chiefly bright yellow. Female euphonias are usually greenish and yellowish, far duller than the males. *Ramphocelus* is a genus of larger and stouter tanagers, of which the males, but not the females, are brilliantly attired. In the Scarlet-rumped Tanager *R. passerinii* of Central America, the male is everywhere velvety black except for the vivid rump, but the female is clad in shades of brown and olive. In the widespread Blue Tanager *Thraupis episcopus* both sexes have blue-grey body plumage with bright sky-blue wings and tail, and in some races there is a large white patch on each wing.

In the Summer Tanager *Piranga rubra* of the southern United States, the male is all red and the female is yellowish. In the Scarlet Tanager *P. olivacea*, which breeds in the United States and Canada, the male is brilliant scarlet with black wings and tail. It is of interest that the most migratory species in a generally non-migratory family is the only one known to undergo pronounced seasonal changes in coloration ; in the months of the northern winter, which the species spends in South America, the males are clad in green and yellow, much like the females. In the Western Tanager *P. ludoviciana*, which breeds on the Pacific side of temperate North America and migrates to Central America in the winter, the annual changes of the males are far less pronounced. See Plate 7 (colour).

Among the less usual types of coloration in this extremely varied family may be mentioned the Magpie Tanager *Cissopis leveriana*, widely distributed in South America, in which both sexes are largely white, with the whole head, upper back, and breast blue-black. The wings and the long, graduated tail of this large tanager are black and white. In the Golden-green Tanager *Chlorochrysa calliparaea* of the eastern foothills of the Ecuadorian Andes, both sexes are largely brilliant metallic green, with a bright orange spot on the crown, a metallic orange patch on the rump, and a black gorget bordered with orange. In the bush-tanagers of the genus *Chlorospingus*, the prevailing colour is olive-green, sometimes with white or nearly black marks on the head. These plain little tanagers are found chiefly in the high mountains, where also a few brilliant species occur ; but the family is best represented at low and middle altitudes.

Voice. The tanagers as a whole are poorly endowed with song, and this is especially true of the most brilliant genus, *Tangara*, some of the members of which are quite devoid of melody. A few species in other genera have pleasing songs, among them the Scarlet Tanager, Grey-headed Tanager *Eucometis penicillata*, and the ant-tanagers of the genus *Habia*, which sing most persistently at dawn ; but no member of the family seems to be a first-class musician. The poorly developed voice in many tanagers appears to be correlated with weak territorial defence or absence of territoriality.

Habits. Relatively few tanagers dwell in the dark depths of heavy forest. Many wander through the upper levels of the forest, and like other treetop birds they may forage and even nest in the scattered trees of neighbouring clearings and plantations. Many tanagers inhabit low, bushy growth, but no undoubted member of the family is known to forage over the ground. Tanagers as a whole are largely frugivorous, but probably all of them vary their diet with insects, which are sometimes captured on the wing—especially by the Summer Tanager. This species also frequently tears open nests of small wasps to extract larvae and pupae. Grey-headed Tanagers follow army ants in company with ant-birds (Formicariidae), woodcreepers (Dendrocolaptidae), and many other small forest dwellers, capturing the insects and spiders driven from concealment by the hunting ants, rather than the ants themselves. The euphonias feed largely on the fruits of mistletoes (Loranthaceae), the seeds of which pass through the alimentary tract enclosed in a viscid envelope that attaches them to trees, so that these birds are probably the chief disseminators of the parasites (see POLLINATORS AND DISTRIBUTORS). Tanagers are readily attracted to feeding trays where bananas are provided, and over the years 10 kinds have visited a single tray in southern Costa Rica.

Tanagers roost in trees and bushes, never in holes so far as is known. Mated individuals rest a few feet or yards from their partners rather than in contact with them. At times a number of pairs gather to roost in an attractive tree. In a number of species the birds remain mated throughout the year, but others travel in flocks in which pairs are not evident. In those that are constantly mated, the male sometimes gives food to his partner, especially as the breeding season approaches. Nuptial feeding has been observed in species of *Tangara*, *Thraupis*, *Eucometis*, *Piranga*, *Tanagra*, and *Chlorophonia*.

Breeding. Most tanagers build open cup-shaped nests, high in trees, in low bushes, very rarely on the ground ; no species is known to build habitually on the ground. Euphonias and chlorophonias are exceptional in constructing covered nests with an opening in the side, sometimes placing them in a cranny in a post or tree, or even in a tunnel in the ground. The Palm Tanager *Thraupis palmarum* builds its cup-shaped nest in a hole in a tree or other cranny. The Blue Tanager *Thraupis episcopus* sometimes wrests a nest from a smaller bird and hatches its eggs and feeds its young along with those of the dispossessed builder. The nest is constructed by both sexes in numerous species of *Tangara*, *Thraupis*, *Eucometis*, *Tanagra*, and *Chlorophonia* ; by the female alone in *Ramphocelus* and *Piranga*.

Tanagers' eggs may be bright blue, blue-green, blue-grey, grey, cream, or white, and they are nearly always spotted, blotched, or scrawled with brown, lilac, or black. They seem usually to be laid early in the morning, before or soon after sunrise. The set usually consists of 2 eggs. Larger sets, up to 4 or 5, are laid by the euphonias and chlorophonias, and by the migratory species of *Piranga* that breed outside the tropics. The eggs are incubated by the female alone ; through the day she takes a number of short sessions, usually lasting from 20 to 30 minutes and rarely exceeding an hour, and keeps her nest covered from 60 to 80 per cent of the daytime. Although there is no well authenticated instance of incubation by a male tanager, he is usually attentive to his mate, sometimes bringing her food while she sits, or else, as in *Ramphocelus*, presenting it to the eggs while she is absent, seeming thereby to anticipate the hatching of the nestlings. Recorded incubation periods range from 12 to 14 days, rarely longer.

The nestlings are hatched with tightly closed eyes and sparse, loose down. The interior of the mouth is red. Brooded by the female only, they are fed by both parents ; the chief exceptions to this rule are certain nests of the Scarlet-rumped Tanager, in which species females are more numerous than males with the result that some of them form irregular attachments and rear their young without a mate's help. In the Golden-masked Tanager

Tangara larvata, young of the first brood, still in immature plumage, may help to feed a later brood of the same season ; and in this and several related species (e.g. the Plain-coloured Tanager *T. inornata* and the Speckled Tanager *T. chrysophrys*) 3 or 4 individuals in full adult plumage sometimes attend 1 or 2 nestlings. Food is brought to the nest in the parent's bill or mouth, except in the euphonias and chlorophonias, which regurgitate to the nestlings. Droppings are swallowed or carried off in the bill, and the nest is kept clean. The nestling period varies in an interesting manner according to the character and site of the nest. It is shortest (10–13 days) in species that build low, open nests, including *Ramphocelus* and *Eucometis* ; in the higher, open nests of *Tangara* and *Thraupis* it is longer (14–20 days) ; and in the covered, often high, nests of *Tanagra* and *Chlorophonia* it is longest (17–24 days). Tanagers scarcely ever give a distraction display when their nest or young are, or appear to be, in danger, but this has been witnessed in the ant-tanagers *Habia* spp. by Willis. Euphonias and chlorophonias may take more than a year to acquire adult plumage and the males sometimes breed in transitional attire.

See also FINCH, PLUSHCAPPED. A.F.S.

Bent, A. C. 1958. Life histories of North American blackbirds, orioles, tanagers and allies. U.S. Natl. Mus. Bull. 211.
Moynihan, M. 1962. Display patterns of tropical American ' nine-primaried ' song-birds. Auk 79 : 310–344, 655–686. (Bush-tanagers.)
Skutch, A. F. 1954. Life histories of Central American birds. (Pacific Coast Avifauna 31.) Berkeley, Cal.
Willis, E. 1961. A study of nesting ant-tanagers in British Honduras. Condor 63 : 479–503.

TANAGER, SWALLOW: see SWALLOW-TANAGER

TANAGRINAE: same as Thraupinae (see TANAGER).

TAPACULO: substantive name of some species of Rhinocryptidae (Passeriformes, suborder Tyranni) ; in the plural, general term for the family. This group of less than 30 species is considered to be related to the antbirds (Formicariidae). They are ground-dwelling birds of South and Central America, from about the size of a wren *Troglodytes* sp. to that of a thrush *Turdus* sp. One of the special morphological characteristics of the tapaculos is a large movable flap (operculum) which covers the nostril completely and gave rise to the name currently used for the family (previously called Pteroptochidae). Another structural characteristic is that the back edge of the sternum (metasternum) has 4 notches.

The legs are long, indicating that locomotion is almost solely by them. Some species have strikingly large and strong feet that serve well for scratching on the ground. They move more by running than by hopping. They fly very little ; their wings are short and rounded. Many species (*Scytalopus*) have a short tail, others have a strikingly long one (*Merulaxis, Psilorhampus*). The tail is always soft and therefore not very helpful to steering in flight. One of the special characteristics of the tapaculos is that they cock up their tails when they get excited, which is particularly impressive with the long-tailed species ; in this respect they resemble the wrens (Troglodytidae), to which they have other similarities. It is this characteristic that has given them the name 'tapaculo', from the Spanish.

The tapaculos are usually dark, some species (certain *Scytalopus* spp.) being almost uniformly black ; these birds spend their life hidden in dark thickets. Other species (*Teledromas fuscus*), which live in the dry bush pampas, have a light colouring like that of larks (Alaudidae), in keeping with the light-coloured surroundings in which they live. In this they resemble certain ovenbirds (Furnariidae), with which they share this landscape. Males and females are often coloured alike (e.g. *Liosceles thoracicus*), but sometimes not (e.g. *Merulaxis ater*).

It is as easy to hear the tapaculos as it is difficult to see them. Their song consists of more or less continuous monotonous calls. These are rather rough, as with *Scytalopus* spp., or melodious (e.g. *Pteroptochos* spp.) ; certain species produce a strikingly pure scale, going up or down (*Merulaxis ater*). The females also sing. Frequently the voice, like that of a ventriloquist, is hard to localise. They have sharp monosyllabic call-notes for attracting and warning.

The food consists mostly of insects, including larvae, and spiders ; in some cases stomach contents have been found to include fibres and seeds.

The tapaculos build their nests on the ground, sometimes in burrows which they dig (e.g. *Scelorchilus* spp.), or in hollow trees (*Pteroptochos* spp.). There are some species (*Eugralla paradoxa*) that build a ball-shaped nest, with a side opening, in thickets about 3 feet from the ground. For building material, the birds use grass, twigs, and so on. The 2–4 eggs are relatively large and uniformly white, although they get quite dirty at times and then appear to be spotted. Both parents share in incubation and raising the young.

There are 12 genera with 27 species from Costa Rica to Patagonia. Half of the genera are monotypic. Chile, with 8 species, has particularly many tapaculos. On the western coast of South America they occur from sea level to an altitude of 13 000 feet.

The Huet-huet *Pteroptochos tarnii* has the upper parts and foreneck very dark brown ; crown, rump, and belly dark rust-coloured, partly with black bars. It is about 9 inches long and lives like a rail (Rallidae) in the heavy underbrush of the forests of Chile and western Argentina, where it is well known because of its loud call ; it sounds like ' wed-wed-wed ', hence Huet-huet. They have other striking calls also. The nest is in a burrow as much as 20 inches deep, or in a hollow tree-trunk as much as several metres above the ground. Egg measurements are 37×29 mm.

The Grey Gallito *Rhinocrypta lanceolata* has a crested head, rust-coloured with white shaft-stripes ; the upper parts are greyish olive, the under parts grey, the middle of the belly is white, and the flanks are chestnut. The length is about 8 inches. It is a common inhabitant of some dry grassy and bush-covered plains of Argentina, where it runs about rapidly with crest erect and tail cocked above the back, resembling a tiny domestic fowl (hence its name). It has a chirping or calling voice and builds a large covered nest in thorny thickets.

The male of the White-breasted Babbler *Scytalopus indigoticus* is coloured like a Dipper *Cinclus cinclus*, but is much smaller (length about 4 inches). The female is more dully coloured. The birds live completely hidden in the thickest brush of south-eastern Brazil, where they move about like mice without making a sound. The song resembles that of the antshrikes *Thamnophilus* spp., consisting of a series of scratchy syllables, gradually gaining in speed (see ANTBIRD). The nest is built on the ground.

Other common names used include Barrancolino for *Teledromas fuscus* and 'turco' for *Pteroptochus* spp.
See Plate 32 (colour). H.S.

Goodall, J. D., Johnson, A. W. & Philippi, R. A. 1946. Las Aves de Chile vol. 1. Buenos Aires.
Hudson, W. H. 1920. Birds of La Plata vol. 1. London and New York.
Sick, H. 1960. Zur Systematik und Biologie der Bürzelstelzer (Rhinocryptidae), speziell Brasiliens. J. Orn. 101 : 141–174.

TARGET ORGAN: see ENDOCRINE SYSTEM

TARSAL: name of the bones of the ' ankle ' (intertarsal joint), the proximal row in birds being fused in the tibiotarsus and the distal row in the tarsometatarsus (see SKELETON ; and LEG).

TARSOMETATARSUS: the bone of the part of the leg commonly spoken of as the ' tarsus ', in birds formed by a fusion of tarsal and metatarsal elements (see SKELETON ; and LEG).

TARSUS: see above

TASTE: a sense of which the degree of development in birds can be judged partly on anatomical and partly on experimental evidence. The sensory receptors in the tongue are termed ' taste buds' and consist of ovoid clusters of cells lying in cavities in the stratified epithelium (see TONGUE). They resemble mammalian taste buds in appearance, having fusiform gustatory cells that are surrounded by a sheath of supporting cells.

The majority of the taste buds of birds (in species investigated) are confined to the soft area at the base of the tongue, the anterior part being hard and horny, and in the palatine region. The striking feature is the small number of buds : in the domestic pigeon, a maximum of 59 and an average of 37 ; in day-old chicks of the domestic fowl the number of taste buds averaged 8, and in the 3-month-old cockerel there were 24. This is in contrast with the estimated numbers in mammals, there being about 9000 buds in man and 17 000 in the rabbit. ' Tastes ', as we refer to them in everyday life, are not the result of simple chemical stimulation alone, but are modified by tactile, thermal, and olfactory sensations, each detected by separate receptor systems. However, the small number of taste buds present in birds has led to the suggestion that their sense of taste is rudimentary.

When a taste bud is stimulated by chemicals, nervous impulses are generated which, in birds, are mainly transmitted to the brain by the ninth cranial nerve, the glossopharyngeal (see NERVOUS SYSTEM). The lingual and laryngo-lingual branches of the glosso-pharyngeal nerve subdivide progressively beneath the epithelium of the tongue, finally forming a plexus of very fine nerve fibres. These enter the taste buds and become closely applied to the gustatory cells. In this way the brain receives ' messages' and information from the taste buds. The passage of these nervous impulses along the nerve can be detected, amplified, and finally displayed on the screen of a cathode ray oscilloscope, by the use of suitable electronic techniques. By these methods it is possible to investigate the nature and concentration of chemical solutions that the bird is able to appreciate, as indicated by the nervous impulses generated when the tongue is rinsed with any particular solution. In such experiments positive responses were obtained following the application to the tongues of chickens of distilled water, salt. glycerine, quinine or acetic acid solutions. Sucrose and saccharine solutions, however, produced no response. Similar results have been recorded in pigeons, except that no responses were observed with quinine, while 50 per cent of the birds responded positively to saccharine.

The preference or aversion shown by birds for a variety of chemicals has been investigated by adding these in known concentrations to their drinking water, under carefully controlled conditions. In some experiments the birds were offered a choice between the test solution and water, whereas in others, following fluid deprivation overnight, they were given the test solution alone for a given period each day. In both cases a measure of the preference or rejection was determined from the volume of solution drunk, when this was compared with the water intake. The results obtained by studying pigeons and domestic fowls indicated that they have an apparently well developed sense of taste, and they showed a marked rejection for a surprising variety of substances. Thus fowls showed a strong preference for a two parts per thousand solution of butter-type flavour, whereas they rejected a solution of cocillana flavour at the same concentrations. They will discriminate between different sugars, and whilst they fail to perceive—or are indifferent to—dextrose and sucrose, they reject xylose. Following these results it has been suggested that sweetness, as we recognise it, is of no significance to the fowl, and that possibly discrimination is based upon absolute specificity for the sugar concerned.

The response varies with the concentration of the solution offered. To man acids taste sour ; pigeons rejected dilute acids, but this aversion decreased progressively with reduced concentration. Thus, acetic acid was accepted as readily as water only at concentrations of less than 0·016N. An equally high sensitivity was found with hydrochloric acid, and the pigeons similarly showed an aversion to solutions of bitter substances, such as quinine, whereas common salt (sodium chloride) and other ' salty' substances in dilute solution are apparently ' preferred ', rejection becoming marked only at higher concentrations. This response to salt solutions is generally similar to results obtained during studies on mammals, using the same experimental techniques. Thus, in both rats and pigeons, increasing rejection of sodium chloride is shown in solutions above a concentration of about one per cent.

In these preference experiments, considerable variation between individual birds was found, and in some details the results do not agree with the electrophysiological experiments. However, all the evidence strongly suggests that the species investigated possess a well developed sense of taste and are able to detect at least some substances that taste salt, sour, and bitter. Further, pigeons demonstrated a surprising sensitivity to certain substances, rejecting solutions that were tasteless to man. It seems possible, however, that the sense of taste plays little part when the bird selects its food. Following a series of tests in Germany, Engelmann concludes that hens base their preferences for certain cereals primarily on shape and only secondarily on colour, whilst he found that taste had little or no effect. Experiments in which the grain was soaked in flavouring solutions similarly suggested that tactile stimulation will predominate over even a strong taste stimulation. Thus, compared with the results obtained by coating the grain with talc or water-glass and so altering the tactile sensation, the effect of adding flavourings remained small. It would be unwise to generalise from these results, since the hen is a domestic species. Although no equally comprehensive tests have been performed using wild birds, observations do suggest that taste may not be an important factor in the selection of their food (see also FOOD SELECTION).

Investigations in Great Britain, the United States, and Germany on the sense of taste in birds have been of interest in the search for repellents that might be sprayed on crops and so reduce damage by birds. Nevertheless, more fundamental research on the physiology of taste, and on bird behaviour in this regard, will be needed before such remedies can be found.   C.J.D.

Duncan, C. J. 1960. Preference tests and the sense of taste in the feral pigeon (*Columbia livia* var. Gmelin). Anim. Behav. 8 : 54–60.

Duncan, C. J. 1962. Salt preference of birds and mammals. Physiol. Zoöl. 35 : 120–132.

Duncan, C. J. 1963. The response of the feral pigeon when offered the active ingredients of commercial repellants in solution. Ann. Appl. Biol. 51 : 127–134.

Engelmann, C. 1940. Versuche über die 'Beliebtheit' einiger Getreidearten beim Huhn. Z. Vergl. Physiol. 27 : 525–544.

Engelmann, C. 1943. Über die Geschmackssinn des Huhnes. VIII. Der Einfluss zusätzlichen Geschmacks auf die Annahmehäufigkeit fester Futterstoffe durch Zwerghühner. Z. Tierpsychol. 5 : 552–574.

Halpern, B. P. 1962. Gustatory nerve impulses in the chicken. Amer. J. Physiol. 203 : 541–544.

Kare, M. R., Black, R. & Allison, E. G. 1957. The sense of taste in the fowl. Poult. Sci. 36 : 129–138.

Kitchell, R. L., Ström, L. & Zotterman, Y. 1959. Electrophysiological studies of thermal and taste reception in chickens and pigeons. Acta Physiol. Scand. 46 : 133–151.

Lindenmaier, P. & Kare, M. R. 1959. The taste endorgans of the chicken. Poult. Sci. 38 : 545–550.

Moore, C. A. & Elliot, R. 1946. Numerical and regional distribution of taste buds on the tongue of the bird. J. Comp. Neurol. 84 : 119–131.

TATTLER: substantive name of *Heteroscelus* spp. (see SANDPIPER).

TAUTONYMY: the application of one and the same name to a genus and to an included species (see NOMENCLATURE ; TYPE-SPECIES ; and compare NOMINATE).

TAXA: plural of TAXON.

TAXIS: movement directly towards or away from a source of stimulation ; or 'locomotory behaviour involving a steering reaction' (compare KINESIS (2) ; and see FIXED ACTION PATTERN).

TAXON: general term (plural 'taxa') for any category used in classification, or any particular example of such a category (see CLASSIFICATION ; NOMENCLATURE). The fundamental taxon is the species, which represents a real biological entity ; this category can be defined generally in objective terms (see SPECIES), even although there is sometimes practical difficulty in applying the definition. All other taxa are either subdivisions of the species or groupings of species— concepts that cannot be defined except in terms involving subjective judgments. Occasionally a subspecies may represent an objective reality, e.g. a distinctive form constituting an isolated population (possibly a species in the making—see SPECIATION) ; but the category in general cannot be defined in such terms. All supraspecific categories are theoretical, representing human ideas of degrees of evolutionary relationship among different species ; that these ideas can sometimes be held with substantial confidence does not alter the principle.

The categories used by Linnaeus were 'classis', 'ordo', 'genus', 'species', and 'varietas'. Of these, class and species remain much as they were ; order and genus are in practice applied more narrowly, and instances are thus more numerous ; while varietas was rather a different concept from the subspecies or geographical race of modern taxonomists. Between order and genus the family has been added, and this taxon has acquired particular importance.

The primary taxa are thus now class, order, family, genus, species, and subspecies. The convention is that every species must be placed in a genus, family, order, and class, even if it be unique at any or all of these levels. A species may or may not be divisible into subspecific forms, i.e. it may be monotypic or polytypic.

Between these primary levels, when it is considered that relationships can be expressed in a more elaborate hierarchical system, secondary categories may be interpolated at will. Thus one may have subclass and superorder, suborder and superfamily, subfamily and tribe, subgenus and superspecies.

These are, however, used only as required ; it would be pedantic to name, say, a subfamily that would be the only one in its family.

The International Code of Zoological Nomenclature does not deal with any taxa higher than the superfamily (owing to a lack of general agreement) ; and it does not recognise, for nomenclatural purposes, any categories below the genus except subgenus, species, and subspecies. Only generic and specific names have operative significance in the nomenclature of species, with subspecific names in addition where subspecies are recognised and it is desired to refer to one separately by using a trinomen (see NOMENCLATURE).

For separate categories see CLASS ; FAMILY ; GENUS ; ORDER ; SPECIES ; SUBSPECIES ; also SUPERSPECIES.

TAXONOMY : orderly arrangement—the science of classification ; the term is often used synonymously with 'systematics', of which study taxonomy, with nomenclature as its tool, certainly forms a large part (see CLASSIFICATION ; NOMENCLATURE ; SYSTEMATICS). The three phases of systematic work, defined in the article thereon, have been called 'alpha, beta, and gamma taxonomy'.

Discrimination. The taxonomist's first problem is one of discrimination ; he must separate and define the forms under study, and then determine the status of each. At this stage he is concerned primarily with the question of species ; he has to assign the available material to particular species, and determine the distinctness of each of these in accordance with the objective definition of that category (see SPECIES). Sometimes this may be done on morphological grounds alone, where differences are substantial and clear-cut. Very often it will be possible only with the aid of adequate data on distribution and reproductive isolation. Where such data are lacking, the decision may have to be empirical—and therefore provisional. Even if there is apparent reproductive isolation, there may be no evidence as to whether it is purely geographical (with potentiality of full interbreeding) or constitutional (see SPECIATION).

Secondarily he is concerned with differences between and within populations of a species. There may be a number of allopatric forms sufficiently distinct to be regarded as subspecies (see SUBSPECIES) ; or a continuous geographical grading of characters (see CLINE) ; or a collection of sympatric 'morphs' or phases (see POLYMORPHISM) ; or, again, no more than the individual variation that is never absent. In all this, of course, account has to be taken of differences that are related solely to sex, age, or season.

Phylogeny. The taxonomist's second problem is that of classification, based on his estimate of probable phyletic relationships. For this purpose he requires different criteria ; whereas for discrimination it is both convenient and proper to use readily visible characters, provided that they are not too variable, it now becomes necessary to consider what characters are fundamental rather than superficial. This question becomes increasingly important the higher the taxonomic category that is being considered—what shared characters can be regarded as primitive and so probably derived from a common ancestor ? Here one must remember that a character is not necessarily primitive merely because it appears to be simple.

Much earlier work on these lines went astray through lack of appreciation of the effects of adaptive convergence ; it is now realised that this may produce most striking similarities between species that are only distantly related (see CONVERGENCE). Sometimes the adaptation to a similar mode of life may lead to resemblance in a whole 'constellation of characters', which if reckoned separately might appear to establish a very strong case for relationship. There is the further point that some differences between species, without being fundamental, may not be directly (or at least obviously) adaptive ; they may be by-products of the gene pattern, linked constitutionally with characters having adaptive value for natural selection (see GENETICS ; NATURAL SELECTION).

Taxonomic Characters. Towards the solution of these problems, the taxonomist has an increasing variety of criteria. General characters of external morphology remain predominant, as they are the most readily described and the most convenient to preserve for record in the museum specimen. In dealing with the more distant relationships, involving the higher taxonomic categories, greater recourse will be had to internal anatomy, and here osteological characters are particularly convenient. Research may, however, have to extend as far as cytological and embryological characters, or invoke laboratory tests for physiological differences such as in the chemical composition of the tissues (see PROTEINS AS TAXONOMIC CHARACTERS).

The trend, however, is not all towards the laboratory. Increasing taxonomic use is made of characters of the living bird observed in the field. Knowledge of geographical range is in any event essential. Among the ecological factors, parasites may be particularly helpful, in that their own phylogeny may be parallel to that of their hosts (see ECTOPARASITE). In the ethological sphere, behaviour related to sex (song, display) is of special importance owing to the part that it plays in the crucial matter of reproductive isolation.

Friedmann, H. 1955. Recent advances in classification and their biological significance. *In* Wolfson, A. (ed.). Recent Studies in Avian Biology. Urbana, Ill.

Mayr, E., Linsley, E. G. & Usinger, R. L. 1953. Methods and Principles of Systematic Zoology. New York.

Miller, A. H. 1955. Concepts and problems of avian systematics in relation to evolutionary processes. *In* Wolfson, A. (ed.). Recent Studies in Avian Biology. Urbana, Ill.

van Tyne, J. 1952. Principles and practices in collecting and taxonomic work. Auk 59 : 27–53.

TCHAGRA: substantive name of *Tchagra* spp. (see SHRIKE).

TEAL: substantive name (unchanged in plural) of various small species of duck, properly of some in the genus *Anas* (used without qualification in Britain for *A. crecca*) but also applied to others (see DUCK).

TECTRIX: (plural ‘ tectrices ’) a covert, i.e. one of the feathers fulfilling the function of upper or lower wing coverts or tail coverts (see PLUMAGE ; TAIL ; WING).

TEETH: (plural of ‘ tooth ’), not found in recent birds, even as embryonic rudiments. Teeth of reptilian type were, however, characteristic of earlier forms (see ARCHAEOPTERYX ; FOSSIL BIRDS). In the modern bird the place of teeth is taken by the cutting edges (tomia) of the horny mandibles ; and in some groups there are also ridges or papillae, which may even be partly calcified (see BILL). For another structure, in no sense truly dental, see EGG-TOOTH.

TELEOPTILE: term applied to plumages subsequent to (and especially that immediately following) the ‘ neossoptile ’ or natal down plumage, if any (see PLUMAGE).

TELOGYROUS: see INTESTINE

TEMPERATURE, ATMOSPHERIC: see CLIMATOLOGY; METEOROLOGY

TEMPERATURE, BODY: see HEAT REGULATION ; TORPIDITY ; also DEVELOPMENT, POST-EMBRYONIC ; INCUBATION ; MEGAPODE

TEMPLE: see TOPOGRAPHY

TENDON: see under MUSCULATURE

TERGAL: pertaining to the back.

TERN: substantive name of most species of the subfamily Sterninae of the Laridae (Charadriiformes, suborder Lari) ; in the plural, general term for the subfamily. By some authors the group is treated as a tribe of the Larinae (see GULL) ; these authors include Moynihan, whose revision is followed here as regards generic and subgeneric taxonomy. The other substantive name used is ‘ noddy ’, for one genus.

The terns are in many ways like the gulls, but on the average the species are smaller ; they are also more slender birds, with long wings and often with forked, sometimes deeply forked, tails—hence the popular name ‘ sea-swallows ’. Many of the species have white plumage with grey backs and wings, and with dark crowns at least in the breeding season ; the sexes are alike. The bill is tapering and pointed, except in one species, and often directed downwards in flight. The feet are webbed, with the hallux vestigial, although most of the species seldom swim. In some species the bill and legs are bright red in the adult, in others yellow or dark, or the bill may be parti-coloured ; but there is some seasonal change in these colours, as well as in the extent of the black cap that is often present.

Fish and other marine animals form the food of most species, and the characteristic method of catching prey is to plunge from a height ; those that frequent marshes feed on large insects, caught on the wing or in the water. The calls are harsh, but a species may have a considerable vocabulary ; sometimes there is a rapid succession of short notes, sometimes a long drawn-out cry. Aerial displays and courtship feeding are often notable features of their behaviour, which has been described very fully for some species.

Terns are markedly gregarious and often breed in colonies of vast size. Most of the species nest on the ground, often on sand or shingle in the open but in some species more or less under cover of rocks or vegetation. Sometimes the nest is an unlined scrape, but in other instances either a little or a substantial amount of grass-stems or like material may be used. The marsh terns build floating nests of water weeds. A few members of the subfamily lay their eggs on cliff-ledges, bushes, or trees. The eggs are commonly 2–3 in number, but in some species only one ; they tend to be grey to brown in colour, with both dark brown and pale ashy blotches, and there is considerable individual variation. The young are alert and downy when hatched, and as a rule with cryptic coloration ; they remain in the nest at first, but when this is on the ground they soon start wandering in its vicinity. The parents are bold in making threatening dives at human or other intruders in the nesting area, sometimes actually striking. The sexes share parental care.

Terns have a world-wide distribution, but the largest number of species is found in the Pacific Ocean. Most are found on the coasts, and to a lesser extent the rivers and marshes, of the warmer countries ; but some breed in more northern latitudes and are migratory in high degree, while 4 species breed in the Antarctic Ocean. Moynihan recognises only 3 genera : *Sterna* (black-capped terns), *Anous* (noddies), and *Larosterna* (monotypic).

Black Noddy *Anous tenuirostris*. M.Y.

Black-capped Terns. The genus *Sterna* includes the majority of the species, 30 or more distinguishable, and can be divided loosely into half a dozen groups. The typical black-capped species are the most numerous. Examples are the Common Tern *Sterna hirundo*, with a Holarctic breeding distribution ; the Arctic Tern *S. paradisaea*, with a circumpolar breeding range up to 82° N. and migrations extending to the coasts of Antarctica ; and the Antarctic Tern *S. vittata* (see ANTARCTIC). Of darker plumage than these is the Sooty Tern *S. fuscata* ; the unceasing noise of its vast colonies on such islands as Ascension has earned it the local name of 'Wideawake' ; and in that locality the species is of great biological interest in showing a breeding cycle of about 9½ months (see BREEDING SEASON). The Blackbellied Tern *S. melanogaster* is a smaller bird inhabiting inland waters in southern Asia.

The small group of little terns is exemplified by the widely distributed Little (or Least) Tern *S. albifrons*. Then there is a group of several species, of medium to large size, characterised by a small crest on the nape. Of these crested terns, the Caspian Tern *Sterna* ('*Hydroprogne*') *caspia* is the largest of all terns and relatively heavy in flight ; it breeds locally in Europe, Asia, Africa, and North America, with another race in Australia and New Zealand. The not quite so large Royal Tern *Sterna* ('*Thalasseus*') *maxima* breeds on both sides of America and in West Africa (Mauretania ; Gambia). Other members of this group (all formerly assigned to '*Thalasseus*') include the Swift (or Crested) Tern *S. bergii* common in the Indian Ocean and Australian waters, the well known Sandwich Tern *S. sandvicensis* of the North Atlantic (migrating to and even round the Cape of Good Hope), and the Elegant Tern *S. elegans* of Baja California and Trinidad.

The group of marsh terns includes the Black Tern *Sterna* ('*Chlidonias*') *nigra*, darker than any of the above ; it has a Holarctic range in middle temperate latitudes and breeds in small colonies on fresh-water marshes, swampy grasslands, or reed-fringed shores of lakes or slowly flowing rivers. There are 2 other species, confined to the Old World.

Two species stand rather apart from the rest, and from each other although they both have heavy bills. These are the widely distributed Gull-billed Tern *Sterna* ('*Gelochelidon*') *nilotica* and the Large-billed Tern *Sterna* ('*Phaetusa*') *simplex* of tropical South American waters ; the former feeds from the surface of the water and also on land.

Noddies. There are 5 of these, all birds of tropical seas. Of the 2 dusky species, the widely distributed Common Noddy *Anous stolidus* is an example ; it nests on bushes or even low trees, where these are available, and elsewhere places its untidy nest of twigs or seaweed on the ground or lays its single egg on bare rock. Of the 2 intermediate species, the small Grey Noddy *Anous* ('*Procelsterna*') *albivittus* of the South Pacific is an example. The fifth species is the small White Noddy (or Fairy Tern) *Anous* ('*Gygis*') *albus* of tropical seas ; it commonly lays its single egg on the branch of a tree, but sometimes on a minute rock-ledge, the chick being able to hang on, even head downwards, by its claws.

Inca Tern. To a monotypic genus is assigned the Inca Tern *Larosterna inca* of the Humboldt Current, on the west coast of South America. It is a beautiful, slenderly built bird, with slate-coloured plumage, crimson bill and legs, yellow gape wattles, and a whisker-like ornamental white plume near each eye. It nests in burrows, an unusual habit among terns.

See Plates 3c and 28b (phot.).   A.L.T.

Ashmole, N. P. 1962. The Black Noddy *Anous tenuirostris* on Ascension Island. Part I. General Biology. Ibis 103b : 235–273. (B.O.U. Centenary Expedition.)
Ashmole, N. P. 1963. The biology of the Wideawake or Sooty Tern *Sterna fuscata* on Ascension Island. Ibis 103b : 297–364. (B.O.U. Centenary Expedition.)

Baggerman, B., Baerends, G. P., Heikens, H. S. & Mook, J. H. 1956. Observations on the behaviour of the Black Tern, *Chlidonias n. niger* (L.), in the breeding area. Ardea 44 : 1–71.

Cullen, J. M. 1960. Aerial displays of the Arctic Tern and other species. Ardea 48 : 1–37.

Cullen, J. M. & Ashmole, N. P. 1963. The Black Noddy *Anous tenuirostris* on Ascension Island. Part 2. Behaviour. Ibis 103b : 423–446. (B.O.U. Centenary Expedition.)

Dorward, D. F. 1963. The Fairy Tern *Gygis alba* on Ascension Island. Ibis 103b : 365–378. (B.O.U. Centenary Expedition.)

Dorward, D. F. & Ashmole, N. P. 1963. Notes on the biology of the Brown Noddy *Anous stolidus* on Ascension Island. Ibis 103b : 447–457. (B.O.U. Centenary Expedition.)

Hawksley, O. 1957. Ecology of a breeding population of Arctic Terns. Bird-banding 28 : 57–92.

Junge, G. C. A. & Voous, K. H. 1955. The distribution and the relationship of *Sterna eurygnatha* Saunders. Ardea 43 : 226–247.

Kullenberg, B. 1947. Über Verbreitung und Wanderungen von vier Sterna-Arten. Ark. Zool. 38 : 1–80.

Moynihan, M. 1959. A revision of the family Laridae (Aves). Amer. Mus. Novit. no. 1928 : 1–42.

Müller, H. 1959. Die Zugverhältnisse der europäischen Brandseeschwalben (*Sterna sandvicensis*) nach Beringungsergebnissen. Vogelwarte 20 : 91–115.

Palmer, R. S. 1941. A behaviour study of the Common Tern *Sterna hirundo hirundo* L. Proc. Boston Soc. Nat. Hist. 42 : 1–119.

Thomson, A. L. 1943. The migration of the Sandwich Tern. Results of British ringing. Brit. Birds 37 : 62–69.

TERNLET: name sometimes applied to the smaller noddies *Anous* spp. (see TERN).

TERRITORY: term indicating phenomena that were not really studied until Howard in 1920 called attention to their widespread occurrence and their importance ; the simplest definition of a territory, workable and commonly accepted, is ' a defended area ', the word ' defended ' being used in an objective sense stripped of subjective meaning. Such an area can be reserved by an individual, a pair, or a group. In this sense, territory occurs not only in birds, but in many other animals as well— vertebrates and invertebrates. The variety of territories is enormous ; they may be large or small ; the owners may be males, females, pairs, families, or large groups ; they may be defended in the breeding season only, or in part of it, or in the non-breeding season, or even the whole year round. There are many aspects which are typical of species, but within each species there is of course a great range of variability. See also under POLYGAMY.

Two problems have especially occupied ornithologists : First, what function does the territorial system serve ? Second, how is it organised, or how is it caused ?

Functions. The functions of territories are certainly as varied as their appearance. But the generalisation applicable to all territories seems to be that they result in dispersion, that is, that population units (individuals, pairs, or groups) of territorial species are more widely spaced out than they would be if they had no territorial system. Evidence for this has been obtained by artificially lowering the density in a given area (by repeatedly catching or killing territory owners) and observing the subsequent influx of new inhabitants. In such experiments the number of new settlers was much larger than ever observed in undisturbed areas of similar carrying capacity ; the data concern a variety of song-birds inhabiting spruce-fir forest in North America, and dragonflies in Britain. These results confirm circumstantial evidence of various kinds pointing to the same conclusion. Birds thus possess a dispersion mechanism, and the presence of territory owners in some way prevents a large number of potential settlers from establishing themselves in a given area. This means that the effect is density-limiting. See also AGGRESSION.

The effect of territory, however, is more than mere spacing out ; it also involves site-attachment. The two phenomena of spacing out and site-attachment are really quite distinct and either can occur without the other. For instance, roosting birds often show site-attachment without being spaced out ; in fact even the opposite may happen, roosting birds of some species huddling together as closely as they can. Conversely, spacing out can occur without attachment to a geographical location ; many instances of food-fighting in birds, and the defence by stags of a herd of hinds, fall into this category. However, the joint occurrence of the two effects is more common in birds, mainly because birds lay eggs—which cannot move about.

The functions of site-attachment alone seem to be manifold. They all have to do with the fact that acquired knowledge of the detailed topography of the home area is of considerable survival value. This is particularly true in respect of escape from predators, which is undoubtedly more efficient when hiding places and the best way to them are known from experience. Many birds also acquire a detailed knowledge of feeding sites, water holes, roosting sites, and (in the breeding season) of the nest ; in these cases such knowledge seems not only to be of advantage, but, particularly in birds that travel over long distances between feeding areas and the nest, to be indispensable. The advantages of topographical knowledge may well be much more varied than we know at present. For instance, field observations suggest that many birds know the particular places where updraughts occur, and perhaps even how they change with changing wind ;

parent birds feeding fledged young often remember the exact locality of each of the young ; nest-building birds learn quickly where required material such as feathers can be found ; and so on. In all such cases the increased efficiency that comes with topographical knowledge is very impressive. All this, however, is inferred from circumstantial evidence, and experimental work on these problems is still required.

The functions of spacing out have been the subject of much discussion and speculation. It at least seems certain that they may differ from one species to another, and even for different types of territories defended by one and the same species at different times (such as the winter territories and the breeding territories of Robins *Erithacus rubecula*) ; they may even be different for one type of territory under different conditions, depending on the limiting factors likely to become critical at the moment.

The main function of spacing out in birds with specialised nest-site demands, such as hole-breeders or cliff-breeders, is without doubt the reservation of a nest site for one family ; little imagination is needed to realise the disastrous consequences of more than one pair of Starlings *Sturnus vulgaris* sharing a nest hole suited to accommodate one family, or more than one pair of Kittiwakes *Larus* (' *Rissa* ') *tridactylus* trying to nest on one of the very narrow ledges typical of this species. The reservation of sufficient food, for the individual, the family, or the group, is probably one of the commonest functions of spacing out. It seems obvious in the case of food-fighting such as has been reported of several species. It is less obvious and is perhaps less important with breeding territories of small passerines, and in fact the available evidence is not decisive. In checking this hypothesis it should be borne in mind that the survival value might become clear only in critical circumstances, which might not occur every season. Spacing out during the pairing period might prevent interference with mating. In ground-breeding birds, with broods vulnerable to predation, spacing out often seems a corollary of procryptic coloration, and the behaviour of predators suggests that this may be very important. It has also been suggested that spacing out may reduce the risk of spread of diseases. It must be stressed that different species probably have developed spacing out for very different reasons, and that the few examples given here might well be considerably expanded as more species become better known.

Causation. Turning now to the way territorialism is organised, it seems that three behaviour systems are involved : selection of, and conditioning to, a suitable locality ; the tendency to attack other individuals that intrude into the chosen locality ; and the tendency to flee from other individuals when they are met in potential nesting areas outside the chosen locality. These three tendencies often appear roughly at the same time, although hostilities may precede site selection, particularly in migrants in spring (see NEST SITE SELECTION).

The selection of a suitable locality is a response to stimulus situations roughly typical of the species. To what extent this habitat selection is innate, and to what extent determined by early conditioning, is largely unknown ; there are indications that both factors are involved. So much is certain, that the stimulus situation is often complex ; it may contain the general features of the landscape such as flatness in the Horned Lark *Eremophila alpestris*, or steepness of a cliff as in Kittiwakes, or a hole of suitable dimensions and other properties. It may contain such specific features as a singing perch, or the presence of fellow-members of the same (or even other) species as in colonial birds ; the presence of a colony of terns or gulls (Laridae) seems to attract some ducks (Anatidae). Once a territory has been used, conditioning to it may make the bird return there in successive years, even although it may gradually become less suitable ; an instance of this is provided by Herring Gulls *Larus argentatus* that persist in nesting on territories in sand dunes after the latter have been planted with pines, so that they end up by nesting in a twelve-foot plantation (as happened in a colony in Holland).

The attack and escape tendencies give rise to a multitude of behaviour patterns that in their entirety effect spacing out. Attack on intruders drives many of them off ; escape from territory owners prevents individuals that are still searching for suitable localities from wasting their time in risky battles, forcing them to continue their search elsewhere. The staking out of boundaries (sharp or vague) between adjacent territories, and the repulsion of would-be settlers, are effected by a variety of so-called threat postures and sounds, of which one is usually adapted to long-distance repulsion and is therefore loud and at the same time specific, so that it repels conspecific rivals mainly. Such loud and specific sounds are called song (see SINGING). They are in many species accentuated by visual advertising, often through the performance of spectacular flights (Skylark *Alauda arvensis*, Wood Pigeon *Columba palumbus*, Snipe *Gallinago gallinago*, and others) (see DISPLAY). The timing of the onset of hostile behaviour is, like that of other reproductive activities, under hormonal control (see ENDOCRINE SYSTEM) ; it is also influenced by the stimuli releasing habitat selection.

Other Dispersion Systems. The problem of the functions of territory can be more clearly seen when animals other than birds are studied as well. It then becomes obvious that territorialism is one of many types of spacing out systems, and as such is a highly efficient one. Since spacing out promotes the utilisation of empty habitats and tends to prevent overcrowding, with its resultant depletion of vital resources and other dangers, it is not astonishing that dispersion mechanisms are so widespread in nature. Perhaps the simplest method is passive dispersal by the medium, which is found in many plant seeds, and in 'dispersal stages' of many marine invertebrates. Plant seeds depend entirely on luck ; they either develop or die where they land. Even within this simple dispersion system, however, many highly refined adaptations have evolved, such as floating devices, or burrs, or features that make fruits attractive to birds which disperse the seeds with their faeces (see POLLINATORS AND DISTRIBUTORS). Many marine larvae go one step further : they can reject or accept a site and accordingly either float on or settle. This is again improved upon by many higher forms, such as many insects, which can not only repeat trial and error numerous times, but can also respond from a distance to a suitable habitat. A further improvement is found in those forms that can react specifically, with either avoidance or repulsion or both, to competitors. This is done in a variety of ways. It seems that the attack-escape system is one of the highest forms if not the highest of all. Not only are attack and escape geared to sensory mechanisms of high selectiveness, which largely prevent needless responses to non-competitors, but in addition a great number of highly adapted signals have evolved that reduce the actual amount of combat—disadvantageous because it exposes the combatants to attack by predators and also requires much more energy than posturing.

Thus, territory seems to be the outcome of an extremely well adapted and very complicated system of behaviour patterns and structures with the overall function of spacing out and thus lessening local competition as well as forcing the animals to exploit the biosphere to its limits. The reason why the precise function can be so different is that there are so many different disadvantages of crowding ; which of these is most critical depends on species, season, and varying circumstances. We are only just beginning to understand in vague outline what the survival value of territorialism is and how the system is organised ; and it is obvious that much more research is needed.

N.T.

Howard, H. Eliot. 1920. Territory in Bird Life. London.
Moore, N. H. 1957. Territory in dragonflies and birds. Bird Study 4 : 125–130.
Symposium 1956. Series of articles on territory in birds by various authors. Ibis 98 : 340–530.
Tinbergen, N. 1957. The functions of territory. Bird Study 4 : 14–27.

TERSININAE: see EMBERIZIDAE ; and SWALLOW-TANAGER

TERTIARY: or 'tertial', a term preferably treated as obsolete ; at one time applied to the few innermost secondary remiges, especially in cases where these are differentiated in shape and colour from the other flight feathers borne on the ulna. The term has also been applied to feathers borne on the humerus in cases where they are developed to function as additional remiges instead of merely as coverts. See PLUMAGE ; WING.

TESTIS: plural 'testes', the male gonad on each side (see REPRODUCTIVE SYSTEM ; also ENDOCRINE SYSTEM).

TESTOSTERONE: see ENDOCRINE SYSTEM ; and AGGRESSION

TETRAONIDAE: see under GALLIFORMES ; and GROUSE

TETRAPOD: a technical term literally equivalent to the ordinary word 'quadruped' but used in a special sense to embrace all the classes of four-limbed, essentially terrestrial, vertebrate animals—thus including birds.

THALAMI: parts of the forebrain (see NERVOUS SYSTEM).

THECA: a sheath-like covering, as in such particular instances as PODOTHECA, RHAMPHOTHECA, and RHINOTHECA.

THERMOREGULATION: see HEAT REGULATION ; RESPIRATORY SYSTEM ; TORPIDITY

THICKHEAD: substantive name, alternatively 'whistler', of species of the subfamily Pachycephalinae of the Muscicapidae (Passeriformes, suborder Oscines)–or Pachycephalini if, as is possible, they should be included in the Muscicapinae) ; in the plural, general term for the subfamily or tribe. In Australia, various other substantive names such as 'thrush', 'shrike-thrush', 'tit-shrike', 'robin', and 'bell-bird' are current for various included species. The thickheads are restricted to the Australo-Papuan area, the Great Sundas and the Malay Peninsula, the Philippines, and some oceanic islands.

These flycatchers have robust bodies from the size of a sparrow *Passer* sp. to that of a jay *Garrulus* sp., thick heads, and imposing, not much flattened bills rather like those of shrikes (Laniidae). The plumage is dominated by yellow and green, in addition to rufous and black. Most of the thickheads are not sexually dimorphic ; the juvenile plumage is spotted or like that of the female. Wattles at the base of the bill (*Eulacestoma nigripectus*, New Guinea) or naked areas of skin at the throat (*Pachycephala nudigala*, Sumbawa and Flores) are exceptional adornments. Conspicuous crests are shown by the Crested Bell-bird *Oreoica gutturalis* of Australia, *Pitohui cristatus* (New Guinea), and the Eastern Shrike-tit *Falcunculus frontatus* (New Holland).

Golden Whistler *Pachycephala pectoralis macrorhynchus*. C.E.T.K.

The true thickheads are represented by the big genus *Pachycephala*, and further by *Eopsaltria*, *Pitohui*, *Myiolestes*, *Colluricincla*, *Pachycare*, *Hylocitrea*, and *Coracornis*. In contrast to them, *Rhagologus*, *Eulacestoma*, and *Falcunculus* possess a highly ridged and narrow bill *without* rictal bristles, probably an adaptation for feeding on berries.

The chief foods are insects, rarely berries of some kind. The Whistling Shrike-thrush *Colluricincla rectirostris* (Tasmania and neighbouring islands), even peels the bark from trees in search of insect larvae. The calls are melodious and loud, the females of some species answering their males in duets ; this feature led to the vernacular name ' whistlers '. The open or protected nest is crudely constructed of bark, grass-stems, rootlets, and spiders' webs. The female alone (White-breasted Whistler *Pachycephala lanioides*, northern Australia) or both sexes (Golden Whistler *P. pectoralis*, Australia and oceanic

islands) take part in building it. The Crested Bellbird adorns the rim of its nest with caterpillars that have been paralysed by squeezing. The 2–4 eggs are white, pink, or brownish ; they are incubated by the female (*Eopsaltria georgiana* of south-west Australia, and *Pachycephala lanioides*) or by both partners (*P. pectoralis*, Rufous Whistler *P. rufiventris*, Australia and oceanic islands). Both sexes care for the young and go through some form of distraction display as soon as an enemy approaches on the ground (*Eopsaltria georgiana*, Gilbert Whistler *Pachycephala inornata*, Buff-breasted Whistler *P. rufogularis*, all of Australia).   E.C.

THICKKNEE: substantive name commonly used for some species of Burhinidae (Charadriiformes, suborder Charadrii) ; in the plural, general term for the family. Other names (with alternative usages for some species) are ' stone-curlew ', ' stone-plover ', ' dikkop ' (of Afrikaans origin), ' wilaroo ' (Australia), and ' goggle-eye '. The names are derived from characteristics of the appearance, voice, or habitat of the unmistakable, odd-looking members of this group ; it is unfortunate that those in most general use are all misnomers !

The family is widely distributed in the Old World, with 2 species in the Neotropical Region. There are 3 genera—*Burhinus* (some of which certain authorities place in a separate genus ' *Oedicnemus* '), *Esacus*, and *Orthorhamphus*, the last 2 being monotypic. Although thickknees are plover-like (charadriiform) birds, in certain respects they superficially resemble bustards (Otididae). The species range from 14 to 20 inches in length, those in *Burhinus* being about the size of a Lapwing *Vanellus vanellus* and the others larger. The black-tipped yellow or greenish bill is short, straight, and stout in *Burhinus* ; in *Orthorhamphus* it is longer than the head, massive and swollen ; in *Esacus* it is similarly long and massive, but compressed and slightly upturned. The nostrils are long pervious slits. The large broad head and abnormally big yellow eye (*Orthorhamphus* has also a yellow orbital ring of bare skin) tend to produce a grotesque effect. The huge eyes, like those of owls (Strigiformes) and nightjars (Caprimulgidae), are related to the nocturnal activities of the birds, and the iris is remarkably contractile. The long legs are yellow and greenish ; the tarsus is reticulated all round, and there is a conspicuous thickening at the inter-tarsal joint (popularly mistaken for the knee). There is no hind toe ; the others are webbed at the base, and the middle one has the inner side of its nail dilated. The wing is long and pointed in some species, short and rounded in others. There are 12 slightly graduated tail feathers.

The sexes are alike, the female being slightly smaller, and there is no marked seasonal change in plumage. The latter is generally tawny, sandy-brown, or greyish-brown, striated or (as in *B. capensis*) spotted with darker markings. The chin and throat are white ; there are dark or pale alar bars—sometimes both ; and the under tail coverts are cinnamon-buff. In *Esacus, Orthorhamphus, B. bistriatus,* and *B. superciliaris* the upper parts are more or less uniform and there is little streaking on the breast ; also, these have a dark superciliary stripe, which others lack, although all species have a pale eye-stripe. The juvenile plumage resembles that of the adults but is usually paler. The coloration of birds of all ages is cryptic and blends remarkably well with the surroundings ; this is particularly true of that of the downy chick, which in all species is a mixture of light mottling and darker stripes.

Thickknees feed on insects—especially Orthoptera and beetles—worms, molluscs, crustaceans (mainly *Orthorhamphus* and *Esacus*), small amphibians, lizards, tiny rodents, seeds, and other vegetable matter. Feeding takes place principally at night. Their flight, low over the ground, is silent and deceptive ; although appearing slow and flapping, it is really, like that of bustards, quite swift, with rapid wing-beats and the legs outstretched. The birds are reluctant to take to the wing and never fly far ; they 'taxi' to take off, and when landing open the wings wide before finally closing them. When they run the head is lowered and the neck retracted, in a furtive posture. Thickknees can run fast, but prefer to patter like plovers in short spurts. They crouch to avoid detection and to rest, squatting on the tarsus ; also, at all ages they—and especially the brooding bird and chicks—will flatten on the ground with outstretched head and neck.

Generally, thickknees are exceedingly wary, resting motionless by day in the shelter of a bush or similar cover. But they can be absurdly tame ; *B. senegalensis* is a shy bird in Uganda but nests on house roofs in Egypt. Similarly, *B. bistriatus* is typically shy, but if caught young and kept as a domestic pet it becomes utterly fearless, to function as a noisy 'watch-dog' at night. Most species are unobtrusive and silent by day, but *B. oedicnemus* has a diurnal, strident alarm cry. At night the thickknees become really noisy ; and although some cries have been described as piping, cackling, or a croak, the general pattern is rather an eerie, mournful cadence. Calling is heard mostly during the breeding season and especially in moonlight. The males display at mating time.

No nest is made, and the 2 eggs, harmonising well with their surroundings and large for the size of the bird, are laid on the ground in an unlined scrape sometimes decorated with pebbles, shells, tiny pieces of wood, bits of straw, and the like. *Orthorhamphus* lays only one large egg. The eggs are broad to long ovals, creamy to light shades of brown, spotted, streaked, and boldly blotched—often in heavy concentrations—with sepia and blackish on underlying greys. Erythristic eggs of *B. senegalensis*, a beautiful salmon-pink, have been found. The eggs of *B. vermiculatus* are sometimes laid on dried elephant, hippotamus, or buffalo droppings. The brooding bird sits upright and is inconspicuous ; both sexes incubate, and the incubation patches are not central but in lateral positions. The incubation period is 25–27 days. The chicks leave the nest on the day they are hatched and are very active. All thickknees shun the company of other species. They mostly occur singly or in pairs, but out of the breeding season may be found in small parties, while the migrant *B. oedicnemus* has been observed in flocks of up to one hundred individuals. Where there are crocodiles, *B. vermiculatus* nests on the crocodile breeding grounds amidst these huge creatures—so far an unexplained association (see CROCODILE-BIRD).

The genus *Burhinus* is represented by seven species. The Stone-curlew *B. oedicnemus* (sometimes called 'Norfolk Plover') is found in the south-east of England and eastwards and southwards in suitable parts of continental Europe, North Africa, south-western and central Asia, India, and Ceylon ; it is only a summer visitor to the more northern parts of its breeding range, but its migrations are not precisely known. The Water Dikkop *B. vermiculatus* of Africa is a bird of the shore line ; the Senegal Thickknee *B. senegalensis* has an association with water ; the Cape Thickknee *B. capensis* frequents dry scrub and stony flats ; the Double-striped Thickknee *B. bistriatus* of Central and South America has its haunts in the grassy savannas ; the South American Thickknee *B. superciliaris*, found in Peru and Ecuador, favours sandy deserts with scattered bush ; and the Australian Stone-curlew *B. magnirostris* is found both in sparse woodland and in open country.

The habitat of the Great Stone-curlew (or Reef Thickknee) *Esacus recurvirostris* is along the sandy river beds and the coastline of India. The Beach Curlew *Orthorhamphus magnirostris*, found from the Andaman Islands to the Solomon Islands and Australia, is exclusively a bird of the seashore. Apart from *B. oedicnemus*, the species are mainly sedentary, although some, e.g. *B. senegalensis*, show local movements.

See Plate 22a (phot.).   C.R.S.P.

Meinertzhagen, A. C. 1924. A review of the genus *Burhinus*. Ibis (11) 6 : 329–356.

THIGH: see LEG ; SKELETON

THINOCORI ; THINOCORIDAE: see under CHARADRIIFORMES ; and SEED-SNIPE

THINOCOROIDEA: see under CHARADRIIFORMES

THORACIC: pertaining to the thorax, or the region of the thorax.

THORAX: the 'chest', being the part of the body between the neck and the abdomen, and containing the heart and lungs (see HEART ; RESPIRATORY SYSTEM).

THORNBILL: substantive name, alternately 'thornbill-warbler', of species in some genera (especially *Acanthiza*) of Malurinae (see WREN (2)) ; also used as substantive name of *Chalcostigma* spp., *Opisthoprora euryptera*, and *Ramphomicron* spp. (for family see HUMMINGBIRD).

THORNBIRD: substantive name of *Phacellodomus* spp. (see OVENBIRD (1)).

THORNTAIL: substantive name of *Popelairia* spp. (for family see HUMMINGBIRD).

THRASHER: substantive name of species in several genera (*Toxostoma*, *Oreoscoptes*, etc.) of Mimidae (see MOCKINGBIRD).

THRAUPINAE: see EMBERIZIDAE ; and TANAGER

THREAT: see AGGRESSION

THRESKIORNITHIDAE: see under CICONIIFORMES. There are two subfamilies, Threskiornithinae (see IBIS), and Plataleinae (see SPOONBILL).

THRESKIORNITHOIDEA: see under CICONIIFORMES

THROAT: see RESPIRATORY SYSTEM ; TOPOGRAPHY

THROSTLE: archaic or poetic form of 'thrush' —cf. German 'Drossel' (see THRUSH).

THRUSH: substantive name of some typical species of the subfamily Turdinae of the Muscicapidae (Passeriformes, suborder Oscines) ; in the plural, general term for the subfamily. Many of the smaller species are known as 'chats', and others have special names. This widely cosmopolitan group has in the past often been given separate familial rank (see MUSCICAPIDAE). The name also appears in the compound 'water-thrush' for *Seiurus* spp. (see WARBLER (2)), and as substantive name (some-

times 'shrike-thrush') of *Colluricincla* spp. (see THICKHEAD)—and see following entries.

General Characteristics. Thrushes in general are slender-billed song-birds of medium size with 10 primaries and with a booted tarsus in most cases, the feet being acutiplantar and well developed. The tail is square, rounded, or occasionally emarginate, and contains 12 (or, in one case, 14, in another, 10) rectrices. Rictal bristles are present. In nearly all cases the young have a spotted first plumage. The moult is a single, annual prebasic moult in the autumn. A complete spring moult is lacking ; such moult as occurs at that time is by abrasion or by casting the points of the feathers. Partial body moult, or prealternate moult, occurs in some wheatears *Oenanthe* spp. and 'chats', in one of the rockthrushes *Monticola* spp., and in White's Thrush *Zoothera dauma*. In colour thrushes range from brown to grey, to russet, to blue, or green. The syrinx is tracheo-bronchial. The tongue is nontubular, with an extensive blade-like reedy tip. Feet are generally strong, without syndactyly, except in the Wren-thrush *Zeledonia coronata* (which has sometimes been placed in a family of its own).

Breeding. The eggs are pale, usually speckled, and range from 3 to 6, occasionally more, in a nest well built of grasses, moss, or lichen, or kindred materials ; this may be in a bush or tree, or in a hole, or in a house, or barn. In some species, nests are made in crevices among rocks, near waterfalls, or among strong grass or heather on islands in a stream.

The female is usually responsible for nest building, incubation, and brooding. Both sexes feed the young. Feeding of the female by the male is infrequent. Incubation ranges from 13 to 14 days ; the nestling period is 12–15 days, sometimes reduced in the Arctic in association with longer periods of daylight. A feeding rate of 20 times per hour has been reported in the American Robin *Turdus migratorius*.

Habitat. Thrushes are largely terrestrial, although many are highly arboreal ; some occur primarily on open grassland or near watercourses. Species are frugivorous or insectivorous ; many eat worms or snails. Some thrushes are found in arid desert, some in the tundra zone, and others may occur in dense equatorial rain-forest. Many species are found in farmland, gardens, on lawns, or in forest clearings, sometimes on rocky outcrops.

Distribution. The subfamily has a world-wide distribution except for the Antarctic and New Zealand (Song Thrush *Turdus philomelos* and Blackbird *T. merula* introduced in the latter). Its approximately 300 species have been divided into several subgroups, of which the simplest arrangement comprises 2—the chat-like thrushes and the true thrushes. The greatest number and complexity of forms occurs in the Old World, and it is perhaps possible to assert that the thrushes appear to have a Palaearctic centre of dispersal. Africa has also been an important evolutionary centre, particularly of the chat-like forms. From Eurasia there appear to have been several invasions into the New World, as well as into the Australasian Region and Polynesia. Remote isolated islands such as Hawaii and Tristan da Cunha have evolved distinctive species of thrushes.

Chat-like Thrushes. The chat-thrushes are small, with more slender legs, more varied nesting habits and plumage, and weaker song than the true thrushes. Many are highly specialised for tropical habitats. The group is highly diverse and presents the impression of containing more evolutionary end-lines and relict species. The exceptional cases of characters unusual for the subfamily (e.g. unspotted young, scutellate tarsus, prominent bristles) tend to occur among the chat-like thrushes. Some genera approach the subfamily of the warblers (Sylviinae), others the flycatchers (Muscicapinae). The most primitive chat-thrushes appear to be the dense-jungle-inhabiting, non-migratory, short-winged species, of which there are 2 genera—the shortwings *Brachypteryx*, found in India and south-eastern Asia through the Sunda Islands and Philippines to the Celebes, and *Zeledonia*, a monotypic New World relict genus with 10 tail feathers, found only in Central America (Costa Rica and western Panama). Another primitive genus comprises the scrub-robins *Drymodes* spp. of Australia and New Guinea. From such rather warbler-like birds, including *Erythropygia* of Africa (see also WARBLER (1)), have perhaps come the complex of Old World robins, *Erithacus* spp. and their relatives, a large group of which centre in the forest robins of Africa. Some authors separate these species of simply coloured, rather inconspicuous little birds into several genera—the nightingales, for example, in *Luscinia*. Others prefer to lump many of the genera together.

This group of robins and nightingales ranges from the taiga zone of northern Eurasia south to the Cape of Good Hope in Africa and to south-eastern Asia, the birds tending to prefer damp forest or forest edges or parks and gardens. Offshoots of this group are the robin-chats or forest robins of Africa *Cossypha* spp. and *Alethe* spp., the magpie-robins (or ' shamas ') *Copsychus* spp., bluish to black singers of southeastern Asia ; and the redstarts *Phoenicurus* spp., mainly rock-inhabiting birds, widely distributed in the Palaearctic Region. The colourful

North American bluebirds *Sialia* spp. are birds of open country and are perhaps not far removed from the solitaires *Myadestes* spp., magnificent singers of jungle and forest in western North America, the West Indies, and the New World tropics. A subgroup sometimes treated as a separate family are the forktails *Enicurus* spp., black-and-white birds of south-eastern Asia.

Next there are the open country or desert chats such as *Cercomela* spp., dull coloured and found primarily in Africa, and *Saxicola* spp., tending to be black-and-white, sometimes with brown ; the latter include the Stonechat *S. torquata* and Whinchat *S. rubetra* of Eurasia. Near them come the redstarts, already mentioned, and the wheatears *Oenanthe* spp., found in deserts, tundra, and meadows of Eurasia, Africa, and India. They have their rock-living relatives in Africa, the sooty chats ('ant-chats') *Myrmecocichla* spp., and the Indian Robin *Saxicoloides fulicata*.

True Thrushes. The true thrushes centre round the genus *Turdus*, the familiar one of the Blackbird, Song Thrush, and American Robin, already mentioned, and also of the Ring Ouzel *T. torquatus*, Redwing *T. iliacus* (' *musicus*'), and Fieldfare *T. pilaris*. This central genus, distributed more widely than any other of the subfamily, has perhaps 63 species, many of them migratory. Round it we may group the rock-thrushes *Monticola* spp., chat-like birds of open country tending to bright blues and browns, of Africa and Eurasia ; the ' Whistling Schoolboy ' or Whistling Thrush *Myiophoneus caeruleus*, a plaintive and beautiful dark blue song-bird, found in south-eastern Asia. The *Zoothera* thrushes, with rounded wings and non-migratory, have white bases to the primaries and underwing and are found in the Old World tropics, with offshoots such as White's Thrush (or Golden Mountain Thrush) *Z. dauma*, the isolated Varied Thrush *Z. naevia* of western America, and the Aztec Thrush *Z. pinicola*. Near these are the forest thrushes of the West Indies *Cichlherminia* spp. and the Tristan Thrush *Nesocichla* ; and finally the New World nightingale-like thrushes *Catharus* spp. (including the Hermit Thrush *C. guttata* and Veery *C. fuscescens*) and the North American Wood Thrush *Hylocichla mustelina*.

See Plates 7 (colour) and 22c (phot.). S.D.R.

Lack, D. 1943 ; 1946 (rev. ed.). The Life of the Robin. London.
Buxton, J. 1950. The Redstart. London.
Ripley, S. 1952. The Thrushes. Postilla (Yale Univ.). No. 13. (A taxonomic study.)
Skutch, A. F. 1960. Life histories of Central American Birds. Pt. II. (Pacific Coast Avifauna no. 34.) Los Angeles.
Snow, D. W. 1958. A Study of Blackbirds. London.

THRUSH, ANT-: see ANT-THRUSH ; and ANT-BIRD

THRUSH-BABBLER: *Ptyrticus turdinus* (see BABBLER).

THRUSH, GROUND-; THRUSH, JEWEL-: names sometimes applied to Pittidae (see PITTA) ; the former is also used instead of QUAIL-THRUSH.

THRUSH, JAY-: substantive name of some laughing thrushes *Garrulax* spp. (see BABBLER).

THRUSH, LAUGHING: in the plural, general term for *Garrulax* spp. and also *Liocichla* spp. (see BABBLER). See Plate 43 (egg).

THRUSH, QUAIL-: see QUAIL-THRUSH ; and RAIL-BABBLER

THRUSH-TANAGER: *Rhodinocichla rosea* (see TANAGER).

THRUSH, WATER: see WATERTHRUSH

THYMUS: a small glandular body of obscure function lying near the bronchi ; as in mammals, it is best developed in the young and later diminishes.

THYROID GLAND; THYROXIN: see ENDOCRINE SYSTEM ; also MOULT

TIBIA: see below

TIBIOTARSUS: a bone of the leg, in birds formed by the fusion of the tibia and the proximal tarsals ; often loosely called the 'tibia' (see SKELETON ; and LEG).

TICK-BIRD: see OXPECKER; STARLING

TICKS: see ECTOPARASITE

TIERCEL: special term for a male falcon, the latter word being used both generally and for the female only (see FALCON ; FALCONRY).

TIGRIORNITHINI: see HERON

TIMALIINAE: see MUSCICAPIDAE ; and BABBLER

TIME MEASUREMENT: the perception and quantitative assessment of the passage of time. All rhythmic movement involves the measurement of, and reaction to, short time intervals. In flight, particularly in flocks, or in the presence of obstacles, or when landing, a precise estimation of speed and hence of time interval is required. Birds can also be trained to make responses at selected intervals which may be very short (as in rhythmical pecking) or longer (a matter of minutes). While such interval measurement is probably neural in basis, the nature of the mechanism involved is by no means clear. It may be analogous to a stop-watch, restarted at the beginning of each phase of activity, or it may be more truly clock-like and based on continuously repeated rhythms of short periodicity.

An important class of rhythms with longer periods are the circadian rhythms, so-called because the periods are about but seldom, if ever, exactly 24 hours in length. They are thus related to (but not necessarily governed by) the daily flux of events that derive from the earth's rotation. Features in the lives of birds that have a circadian rhythm include body temperature changes, general activity and that associated with migration (' Zugunruhe '), ovulation and incubation, feeding of self and young, and compass orientation. Observations have been made in the field but more and more in automatically registering devices. A distinction may be drawn between behaviour that commences, or peaks, at 24-hour intervals, and behaviour that changes according to the actual time of day. An example of the latter is the changing angle that is taken up relative to the sun's position by birds moving in one given direction at different times of day.

There has been much controversy concerning the extent to which circadian rhythms are dependent on external stimuli. Much of the most penetrating experimentation has been done with animals other than birds, so the conclusions that follow may not be generally applicable. It appears that the circadian mechanisms themselves are innate, but that exposure to one 24-hour cycle of events, or even to briefer and non-rhythmic stimuli, are essential to start them into action. Once initiated, many circadian rhythms show remarkable persistence for days, weeks, even months, in conditions apparently constant as regards light, temperature, pressure, external disturbance, and so on. Some rhythms are less persistent and all show some tendency to slide out of exact phase with external events. This argues that all-pervading influences such as changes (due to the earth's rotation) in gravitation, magnetism, or cosmic rays are not acting as time checks to keep the rhythms synchronised. Indeed, experiments have now been done at the South Pole in which circadian rhythms continued in constant conditions in which the earth's rotation was effectively neutralised.

Under natural conditions external stimuli serve as time checks. The light/dark sequence of day and night is one of the most widespread of such regulatory factors. The clock mechanism governing sun-compass orientation in birds appears to be readily changed to fit a new light/dark rhythm (see NAVIGATION). Birds kept in an artificial regime 6 hours out of phase with the normal, for only 4 days, will orientate at right angles to the direction they would have taken up before treatment. A week of treatment 12 hours out of phase results in a complete reversal of direction around sunrise/sunset when the physiological 'day' overlaps with the real day. Releases during the birds' physiological 'night' produce results suggesting that the orientation mechanism is 'unwinding', i.e. if the angle made to the sun position decreases during the course of the day it increases after sunset to regain the original value at sunrise. On the other hand, birds in high latitudes, actually experiencing the midnight sun in the north, continue to alter the angle on through the full 360°. Compass orientation at night appears to use the alignment of the star patterns without the need for any time measurement.

Any form of true navigation (as against simple compass orientation) that involves an appreciation of displacement in longitude must, by definition, involve measurement of the difference between local time at release and the local time at home. This necessitates a 'chronometer' that is much less easily forced into a new phase than the sun-compass clocks just considered. The evidence for the presence of such mechanisms in birds is not yet convincing. But there has been a clear demonstration of both readily changeable and rigid time-keeping mechanisms in bees after very large translocation in longitude. Certainly there is plenty of evidence of more than one 'clock' in the same animal, and that these may have reinforcing, interacting, or even conflicting rhythms. In cockroaches the site of the clock governing locomotor activity has been narrowed down to certain neurosecretory cells below the sub-oesophageal ganglion.

The natural rhythm with the next longest period is the lunar one of about 30 days. A number of bird activities, particularly feeding patterns, change in accord with the moon phase and the associated tidal fluctuations, but there is at present no evidence of endogenous lunar or tidal rhythms in these animals, as have been demonstrated in a number of marine invertebrates. It would seem probable that such synchronisation in birds results from perception of and reaction to the changes as they occur. Similar arguments can be used in connection with the annual cycles of reproduction and the associated migrations. In some cases breeding is wholly opportunist, triggered off by, for instance, the onset of a rainy period. In most cases, however, a definite rhythm is obvious, and much experimental work has demonstrated that changes in day-length are the external stimuli bringing about gonadal and behavioural changes. Here again, of course, time

measurement enters into the picture, and the changes are often very small, a matter of minutes a day.

The demonstrable dependence of many annual breeding cycles on external stimuli does not exclude the possibility of underlying endogenous rhythms of this sort of length. Thus the Sooty Tern *Sterna fuscata* on tropical Ascension Island has a breeding cycle of ca. 9½ months, which does not equate with annual changes. Again, many Palaearctic birds winter near the Equator, where changes in day-length would seem too minute to be detected and to initiate the return migration. Most remarkable of all is the case of the trans-equatorial migrant the Short-tailed Shearwater *Puffinus tenuirostris*, which returns each year with astonishing regularity to its breeding islands in South Australia, and obviously in a highly synchronised reproductive state since egg laying in the colonies extends over only 12 days. Yet birds taken captive after breeding and held on a steady light/dark regime of 12 : 12 hours passed through very much the same gonad and moult cycles as the free birds that experience a wide range of day-lengths in the course of their migrations to and from the Aleutian Islands off Alaska. There were suggestions that internal events were beginning to slide out of phase with the environment and that some time check at least once a year is required.

To summarise; there is good evidence of endogenous rhythms with a wide range of periods. Probably all require some external stimulus to start the mechanism going, but there is much variation in the number of time checks required from the environment to keep in step with it. Similarly, some rhythms are more easily forced into a new phase by external influences than are others.

See also RHYTHM.   G.V.T.M.

Cold Spring Harbour Symposium on 'Biological Clocks'. 1960. New York. (Fifty papers, but see especially those of J. Aschoff, J. Harker, M. Renner, K. Hoffmann, K. Schmidt-Koenig, H. O. Schwassmann, A. J. Marshall.)
Harker, J. E. 1958. Diurnal rhythms in the animal kingdom. Biol. Rev. 33 : 1–52.
Matthews, G. V. T. 1963. The astronomical bases of 'nonsense' orientation. Proc. XIII Internat. Orn. Congr., Ithaca, N.Y., 1962 : 415-429.

TINAMIDAE: see below

TINAMIFORMES: an order, alternatively 'Crypturi', comprising only the Neotropical family Tinamidae (see TINAMOU). They are generally placed, in taxonomic sequences, next to the 'ratite' orders.

TINAMOTIS: generic name used as substantive name of *Tinamotis* spp. (for family see below).

TINAMOU: substantive name of the species of Tinamidae (Tinamiformes) ; in the plural, general term for the family. In the Neotropical Region, to which the family is restricted, the birds are known variously as 'perdiz' (*Rhynchotus*), 'codorna' (*Nothura*), 'inhambu' (*Crypturellus*), 'macuco' (*Tinamus*), and so on. Some of these names owe their origin to a superficial resemblance between these ground-dwelling birds and the Galliformes ; in proportion and carriage some tinamous do indeed resemble guineafowl (Numididae). The similarity, however, rests not on phylogenetic relationship but on parallel development. Anatomically and biologically the tinamous are more closely related to the rheas (Rheidae), although the sternum is carinate.

The species of tinamou range in size from that of a Quail *Coturnix coturnix* to that of a male Black Grouse *Lyrurus tetrix*. Male and female tinamous look much alike, but the females are slightly bigger and have more pronounced colouring. The bill is thin and slightly curved, the head is small, and the neck is thin. The rear part of the body seems to be high, owing to the enormous development of rump feathers ; these often hide the very short and soft tail. The thick, heavy-looking legs are built for running ; there are 3 short front toes, the hallux being either elevated or absent. Although tinamous are adapted for ground dwelling, running soon tires them ; when chased they are apt to stumble and fall. The wings are short and rounded, with stiff, curved primaries. The flight is clumsy, and accompanied by a rumbling or whistling noise ; they fly with the neck curved, and the head may be held slightly erect (*Nothura*). When frightened and flushed, tinamous frequently collide with branches, tree-trunks, and other obstacles and may injure themselves fatally. It is strange that they fly so poorly, seeing that their flight muscles are as well developed as those of birds which fly very well ; on the other hand, the heart and lungs are exceptionally small.

Tinamous succeed best in escaping the attention of their enemies by standing motionless, with the head stretched high, or by stealing away while cleverly using all available cover. They like to crouch, and rise only when one is almost upon them. Species living in open terrain sometimes hide in holes in the ground. All these modes of escape are very effective, as required, and contribute to the continued existence of a group which, in South America, is represented by a considerable number of species and individuals.

The coloration of the plumage is highly protective—brown, grey, or sand-coloured, depending on the environment, frequently with dark spots and bands. There is commonly a considerable quantity of powder down. The tinamous love to take a bath either in dust (*Eudromia*, certain of the *Crypturellus* spp.) or in water (*Tinamus*). With the exception of *Tinamus*, which uses trees, they sleep on the ground. Their voice consists of a loud, melodious, usually polysyllabic whistle. In the breeding season they call often, some of them nocturnally as well as by day. They may be attracted by imitating their calls.

Solitary life is the rule. With some species family groups or larger coveys are formed towards the end of the breeding period (*Eudromia*). The food is largely of vegetable origin, such as seeds and fruit, supplemented by insects and other small animals. The gape is wide enough to swallow, occasionally, even mice (*Rhynchotus*). Tinamous have a crop and large caeca. Certain species appear more inclined towards animal food (*Nothoprocta*), as are the young of some other species (e.g. *Crypturellus tataupa*). Some dig for roots, e.g. of *Codoma*.

The eggs are relatively large for the size of the bird, and beautifully coloured ; they are indeed among the most handsome birds' eggs known. They are always unicoloured and heavily glazed as if polished. Colours include light chocolate, almost black, purple, dark bluish green, light yellowish green, and grey ; the colour changes rapidly when exposed to light. The number of eggs in a clutch varies from 1 to 12 or more. The larger clutches are probably always the result of the efforts of more than one female. A flat, hollowed-out indentation in the ground serves as nest, and is protected by a bush, tufts of grass, or the base of a tree. The nest is poorly lined with dry matter, rarely well cushioned. Brooding is apparently done by the cock only ; on the male of *Nothoprocta* an incubation patch has been noted. The cock may concentrate on brooding to such an extent that, on occasion, he allows himself to be picked up by hand. Sometimes (e.g. *Crypturellus tataupa*) the cock feigns lameness in order to distract the disturber from the nest. Some species cover the eggs with leaves (*Tinamus*) or feathers (*Nothoprocta*) when they leave the nest. For figures of eggs (*Tinamotis* and *Nothoprocta*) see Plate 43 (colour).

Polygamy appears to predominate. One or more females lay eggs in one nest. Sometimes the hen lays eggs also in other nests guarded by different males. Thus, all combinations of polygamy (=polyandry and polygyny) may exist. These conditions vary between species or even within species. Some tinamous live in pairs (*Nothoprocta*). Species have different sex ratios ; preponderance of males has been noted more frequently, such as 4 : 1 with *Crypturellus variegatus*, but in other species such as *Nothoprocta ornata* the ratio is 1 : 1.

Incubation is short—in *Eudromia* 19 days, in *Crypturellus tataupa* and *Tinamus solitarius* 20 days. Led by the cock, the young leave the nest on their first or second day. The cock defends them, even against human beings. The young run very well and are guided by hearing ; when danger threatens they crouch low and the colour of their down feathers blends with the ground so that they become almost invisible. While certain species (*Tinamus*) have a well defined breeding period, others (some *Crypturellus* spp.) breed throughout the year.

Reproduction in captivity is frequently successful, even in Europe. Nevertheless, domestication has not succeeded, and the attempted introduction of the Argentine Tinamou *Rhynchotus rufescens*, e.g. into England, was a failure. All tinamous are in demand on account of their tender although oddly transparent meat.

There are 9 genera and about 50 species from southern Mexico to Patagonia. The Variegated Tinamou *Crypturellus variegatus* has the neck and chest uniform rust colour, and the upper parts rusty yellow with closely bunched black bands ; it is about 12 inches long. It is fairly common but lives a solitary existence in dense woods. It is timid, like other tinamous, and gives itself away only by its loud fluty voice. In courtship the female is the active party ; she runs back and forth, calls frequently and, when approaching the male, takes little mincing steps ; at the same time the wings are dropped and the tail and rump feathers become erect, thus suddenly forming a beautifully patterned fan which is displayed. The female lays one egg in any one nest, and the males do all the brooding. In this manner the male may be induced to incubate 3 eggs in succession ; at times the female lays the next egg while the male is still attending a three-quarters-grown chick. The female also lays in nests of neighbouring males. Their eggs have a purple vinaceous colour. The range is from the Guianas to Brazil.

Bonaparte's Tinamou *Nothocercus bonapartei* has the upper parts chocolate-brown with light spots and the under parts rust coloured. The cock is the more active in courtship ; he calls persistently from a chosen spot until up to 3 hens have collected, and these are chased by the cock in narrow circles and loops. The hens lay their eggs in a single nest, 3 females producing 9 dark green eggs, which are incubated by the cock only. The species is found in the mountain forests of Venezuela and Colombia.

The Ornate Tinamou *Nothoprocta ornata* is grouse-like in appearance and has erectile feathers on the crown. It inhabits bunch-grass-covered, treeless plateaux of the Andes. It lives in pairs, the females defending the territory. In courtship the male raises the rump and displays the bright crissum ; the female reacts by first dashing away and then crouching in front of the male inviting copulation. The nest is well cushioned. The female lays 4–9 eggs of violet-chocolate colour, which are incubated by the male only. It is found from southern Peru to Bolivia.

The Martineta Tinamou *Eudromia elegans* is earth-coloured and adorned with a long slender crest which the bird when excited carries directed forwards. The bird is about $14\frac{1}{2}$ inches long. It lives on open tablelands in coveys of from half a dozen to 20 or 30 birds, or even 100 adults. During the breeding period, the coveys disperse and the calls of the birds can be heard all around. A clutch, probably produced by more than one female, consists of 12–16 deep green eggs. The species is found in southern Argentina.

See Plates 32 (colour) and 43 (egg).   H.S.

Beebe, W. 1927. The Variegated Tinamou, *Crypturellus v. variegatus* (Gmelin). Zoologica (N.Y.) 6 : 195–227.

Liebermann, J. 1936. Monografia de las Tinamiformes Argentinas. Buenos Aires.

Pearson, A. K. & Pearson, O. P. 1955. Natural history and breeding behaviour of the Tinamou *Nothoprocta ornata*. Auk 72 : 113–127.

Schäfer, E. 1954. Zur Biologie des Steisshuhns *Nothocercus bonapartei*. J. Orn. 95 : 219–232.

Wetmore, A. 1926. Observations on the birds of Argentine, Paraguay, Uruguay and Chile. U.S. Natl. Mus. Bull. 133.

TINKER-BIRD : substantive name of *Pogoniulus* spp. (see BARBET).

TIPPET : name earlier given to a woman's cape made of the under feathers of grebes (Podicipitidae), but used ornithologically for the elongated facial feathers of typical grebes *Podiceps* spp., as distinct from other types of head-ornamentation in this group, e.g. ' facial disc ' (well defined area of short feathers on the face) and ' auricular fan ' (elongated feathers on side of head behind eye)—see under GREBE.

TISSUE : a more or less homogeneous aggregation of cells (see CELL). Tissues form the structural basis of the organs and parts of the body. They are of four main kinds, each of which is divisible into various specialised types. (1) Epithelium occurs as a very thin covering layer, e.g. the external layer (epidermis) of the skin, or the lining of the alimentary canal (see SKIN). (2) Connective tissue has supporting and binding functions, and there may be an intercellular matrix (secreted by the cells) ; it occurs in many diverse forms, e.g. fibrous tissue, fatty tissue, cartilage, bone (see SKELETON). (3) Muscular tissue (see MUSCULATURE). (4) Nervous tissue (see NERVOUS SYSTEM).

TIT: substantive name, abbreviated from 'tit-mouse', of most species of Paridae (Passeriformes, suborder Oscines) ; in the plural, general term for the family. The name is strictly applicable only to them ; although various unrelated but superficially similar birds are commonly called 'tits', or have names of which 'tit' forms a part, e.g. 'Bearded Tit', 'Shrike-tit', 'Wren-tit'—in other cases 'tit' is a prefix with diminutive effect (see succeeding entries) ; it is also used as a substantive name for some Australasian flycatchers such as the Yellow-breasted Tit *Petroica macrocephala* of New Zealand and the Tree Tit *Mayrornis brevirostris* of New Guinea (see FLYCATCHER (1)).

General Characters. Tits are small, active, woodland birds with stout, roughly conical bills ; as in the crows (Corvidae), the nostril is concealed by bristles. They feed mainly on insects and other small invertebrates, some species also largely on seeds. The plumage is typically olive, brown, grey, or greenish above and white, yellow, or buff below. Many species have a striking black-and-white head-pattern and a few have crests. The wing and tail feathers are often tipped with yellow or white.

The family is widely distributed, but is not represented in South America, Madagascar, or Australasia. Although commonly considered as a single family, the tits are probably not monophyletic. They fall into 3 distinct subfamilies, the typical tits (Parinae), the long-tailed tits (Aegithalinae), and the penduline tits (Remizinae), by some authors treated as separate families. The first of these may possibly be closer to the nuthatches (Sittidae) than to the other 2 subfamilies. The bushtits *Psaltriparus* spp. of North America are sometimes treated as a separate subfamily and sometimes united with the Aegithalinae.

Parinae. The typical tits comprise about 43 species distributed throughout North America (including parts of Mexico), Europe, much of Asia (including parts of south-east Asia), and Africa, wherever there is suitable woodland. Some of the northern populations are migratory ; others winter in very cold regions and are among the hardiest of small birds. They are well able to deal with hard food, such as hard-shelled nuts, holding it down with the foot and hammering it to extract the contents. Several species, especially the northern ones, store food in the autumn, hiding it under bark or in crevices and using it in the following winter.

The nest, a comparatively large mass of moss or other soft material, typically with a hair lining, is placed in a hole in a tree or, less usually, in the ground. A few species, including the Willow Tit *Parus montanus*, excavate their own holes in rotten tree-trunks. The eggs, which are white with small brown spots, are very variable in number : in the northern species the clutch is very large, up to 15 or 16 eggs, while tropical species lay much smaller clutches, as few as 3 or 4 eggs. Some species on leaving the nest cover the incomplete clutch with the nest-lining. The female incubates the eggs, and both parents feed the young.

The Parinae include such well-known species as the Great Tit *Parus major* and Blue Tit *P. caeruleus*, which are among the most thoroughly studied of all birds ; in North America some *Parus* spp. are called 'chickadees', the best known being the Blackcapped Chickadee *P. atricapillus* (formerly regarded as conspecific with the Willow Tit). There are also some not very well known, mainly tropical, species : among them are the relatively very large Sultan Tit *Melanochlora sultanea* of eastern Asia, a black bird with a bright yellow crest ; the local *Parus superciliosus* and *P. davidi* of the mountains along the eastern border of Tibet, unusual in having the under parts uniformly rufous ; the very local *P. fringillinus* of central Africa, lacking the contrasting head-markings found in all the other species ; and the Mexican Chickadee *P. sclateri* from the mountains of Central America. There are also 2 Asiatic species of very atypical appearance—*Sylviparus modestus*, which resembles a warbler (Sylviinae) and may be primitive, and *Cephalopyrus flammiceps*, which has a flame-coloured forehead and should perhaps not be included in the family at all.

Aegithalinae. The longtailed tits comprise 6, or if the bushtits *Psaltriparus* spp. (above) of North America are included, 8 species. The best known is the Longtailed Tit *Aegithalos caudatus*, with a very wide distribution in Europe and Asia. The 4 other species of *Aegithalos* have much more limited ranges, in the Himalayan area and China. The remaining Old World species, *Psaltria exilis*, is found only in Java. The tiny Common Bushtit *Psaltriparus minimus* is found from British Columbia south to Baja California ; its congener south to Guatemala. Longtailed tits build elaborate domed nests with a side entrance, lined with large numbers of feathers and covered on the outside with lichens.

Remizinae. The penduline tits differ from the other tits in having the bill finely pointed at the tip. They are mostly very small birds, inhabiting semi-open country with trees and bushes rather than true woodland. The single Palaearctic species, *Remiz pendulinus*, has a wide range from Europe to China, but is very local, occurring in several markedly different geographical forms that were earlier regarded as separate species ; unlike other tits, it prefers habitats near water and locally breeds in reed-beds. The 6 African members, *Anthoscopus* spp., divide up between them most of Africa south of the Sahara. The single New World species, the Verdin *Auriparus flaviceps*, occurs in semi-desert areas of western North America (including Mexico). Penduline tits build a very finely felted globular nest, with a tubular side entrance which closes up when the bird has passed through it. In the African species the texture of the nest is so tough and durable that old nests are used by the local people as purses. The Verdin's nest is similar but less elaborately made.

See also HYBRIDISATION, ZONE OF SECONDARY ; SPECIATION.

See Plate 22b (phot.)   D.W.S.

Betts, M. M. 1955. The food of titmice in oak woodland. J. Anim. Ecol. 24 : 282–323.

Gibb, J. A. 1950. The breeding biology of the Great and Blue Titmice. Ibis 92 : 507–539.

Gibb, J. A. 1960. Populations of tits and Goldcrests and their food supply in pine plantations. Ibis 102 : 163–208.

Hartley, P. H. T. 1953. An ecological study of the feeding habits of the English titmice. J. Anim. Ecol. 22 : 261–288.

Hinde, R. A. 1952. The behaviour of the Great Tit (*Parus major*) and some other related species. Behav. Suppl. 2. Leiden.

Kluijver, H. N. 1951. The population ecology of the Great Tit, *Parus m. major* L. Ardea 39 : 1–135.

Lack, D. 1958. A quantitative breeding study of British tits. Ardea 46 : 91–124.

Snow, D. W. 1954. The habitats of Eurasian tits (*Parus* spp.). Ibis 96 : 565–585.

Snow, D. W. 1954. Trends in geographical variation in palaearctic members of the genus *Parus*. Evolution 8 : 19–28.

Snow, D. W. 1955. Geographical variation of the Coal Tit, *Parus ater* L. Ardea 43 : 195–225.

Vaurie, C. & Snow, D. 1957. Systematic notes on Palaearctic birds. No. 27 Paridae : the genera *Parus* and *Sylviparus*. Amer. Mus. Novitat. no. 1852 : 1–43.

TIT-BABBLER : in the plural, a general term for the Timaliini (see BABBLER) ; also an alternative name for TIT-WARBLER.

TIT, BEARDED : see REEDLING ; and PARROTBILL

TIT-FLYCATCHER : name applied to *Parisoma* spp. (for subfamily see FLYCATCHER (1)).

TITLARK : popular name applied in Britain to *Anthus* spp., particularly the Meadow Pipit *A. pratensis* (see under WAGTAIL).

TITMOUSE : name now usually abbreviated to 'tit' (see TIT) ; still used to some extent, but more often as a group term ('titmice') than as a substantive name of species.

TIT-SHRIKE : alternative name of *Calicalicus madagascariensis* (see VANGA) ; see also SHRIKE-TIT.

TIT-WARBLER : substantive name, sometimes 'tit-babbler', of *Leptopoecile* spp. (see WARBLER (1)).

TIT-WEAVER : *Pholidornis rushiae* (for family see WEAVER-FINCH).

TIT, WREN- : see WREN-TIT

TITYRA : generic name used as substantive name of *Tityra* spp. and allies (see COTINGA).

TOBOGANNING : in respect of penguins (Spheniscidae), see LOCOMOTION.

TOCOCO : *Chilia melanura* (see OVENBIRD (1)).

TODI ; TODIDAE : see CORACIIFORMES ; and TODY

TODOIDEA : see under CORACIIFORMES

TODY : substantive name of the 5 species of Todidae (Coraciiformes, suborder Alcedines) ; in the plural ('todies'), general term for the family. Todies are confined to the West Indies and form a compact group in the order Coraciiformes, where they appear to be allied to the motmots (Momotidae) of tropical America, and more remotely to the kingfishers (Alcedinidae). In general appearance these small birds ($3\frac{1}{2}$–4 inches in length, with relatively long, broad bills) are closely similar regardless of locality, as all 5 are clear green above, with bright red throats. Cuba, Jamaica, Hispaniola, and Puerto Rico each has a representative of one closely related group, these being distinguished from each other by differences in the colour of the sides and breast. They appear to comprise a 'superspecies' that in modern terms might be considered as one entity with 4 geographical forms, although in addition to the obvious colour distinctions, each has its own peculiarity of voice. The fifth species, the Narrow-billed Tody *Todus angustirostris*, is separated at a glance by its narrow bill ; it is found in Hispaniola and mainly in humid mountain forests, although encountered at times in the lower elevations inhabited by the Broad-billed Tody *T. subulatus* of the island ; its chattering call is quite distinct from the notes of the others.

The 4 lowland species inhabit humid or relatively dry forest indifferently, their principal requirement being a reasonable amount of shade. They rest

Broad-billed Tody *Todus subulatus.*
Natural size. *C.E.T.K.*

quietly on twigs amid leaves, usually near the ground, with the bill at an angle of 45°, and because of their tiny size are easily overlooked. Their main food of small insects, seized with an audible snap of the bill, is taken on the wing ; they also eat minute young lizards. Their flight is often accompanied by a loud whirring sound, made apparently by the attenuated outer primary ; this is under control of the bird, is made by both sexes, and is heard most often in the mating season. For a nest, todies, like motmots, use their bills to dig a tunnel from a few inches to 2 feet long in the face of a bank. As the bird is tiny, the opening may be only $1\frac{1}{4}$ inches in diameter, but at the end the nest chamber is enlarged to 3 by 5 inches in area and is usually about 3 inches high. The eggs number 2–3, sometimes 4, and are large for so small a bird. They are plain white, and as they are laid on the earthen nest-floor, with no protective cover, they soon become heavily stained, particularly where the soil is the common reddish clay of the tropics. The throat of the nestling is plain pale grey, but a rapid moult soon changes this to the normal red. The Jamaican Tody *T. todus* is locally sometimes called ' robin redbreast '.

A.W.

TODY-FLYCATCHER, TODY-TYRANT: alternative substantive names of *Todirostrum* spp. (see FLYCATCHER (2)).

TOE: see under LEG ; SKELETON

TOMIUM: the cutting edge of a mandible ; the upper and lower mandibular tomia on either side meet, in the closed position, in a line known as the commissure (see BILL).

TONGUE: a mobile, muscular organ situated in the floor of the mouth. It is covered with epithelium, which may be thick and horny, particularly towards the tip. Its general shape tends to conform to that of the bill (see BILL). The muscles are attached to the paired hyoid bones and together provide for the organ's mobility (see MUSCULATURE ; SKELETON). The tongue in birds is highly variable in size, form, and function. This applies particularly to the horny epithelium ; its tendency to fray at the tip has been increased by selection to produce complex structures. The varied papillae and serrations are also developments of this layer.

While it is possible to describe many adaptations according to function, particularly feeding habits, there are many contradictions. Thus, the penguins (Spheniscidae) have long, pointed tongues, the upper surface being covered with conical papillae pointing backwards to hold and direct slippery fish towards the oesophagus, whereas the auks (Alcidae), divers (Gaviidae), and grebes (Podicipitidae) have similarly sized and shaped tongues that are quite smooth. Other fish-eating birds, notably the Pelecaniformes and certain kingfishers (Alcedinidae), that swallow their food whole, possess only rudimentary tongues ; so do the spoonbills and ibises (Threskiornithidae) and the storks (Ciconiidae), all of which feed on small animals. Any attempts to classify types of tongue are therefore bound to be unsatisfactory, and it is more helpful to consider the various functions of the organ.

Functions of the Tongue. Although the tongue can be seen to move when a bird is singing, it does not in fact play any part in the production of the song (see SINGING). The actual functions can be grouped as follows :

1. *Collecting food.* Included here are those few species that use the tongue instead of the bill for the collection of food, by protruding it rather as a questing probe. Selection has produced the most remarkable adaptations among these species.

Insectivorous species of woodpecker (Picidae), notably those of the genus *Colaptes* and the Green Woodpecker *Picus viridis*, possess exceptionally long round tongues, associated with greatly elongated hyoids, so that the tongue can be thrust out ; the highly developed salivary glands cover it with a sticky secretion. The surface of the tongue is roughened with hair-like papillae, and a few back-ward pointing barbs near the tip. This results in increasing the thickness of the salivary coating in which the insects become stuck. The Wryneck *Jynx torquilla* is similar, the tongue being nearly two-thirds the length of the bird's body (excluding the tail feathers).

Other tree woodpeckers have shorter tongues in which the terminal barbs are more developed and are of use in extracting larvae from their crevices. The sap-sucking woodpeckers have still shorter tongues, the tips of which are covered with fine hair-like processes, which draw up sap by capillary traction.

The same brush-like tip is seen in the lories (Loriinae), while the tongues of sunbirds (Nectariniidae) and hummingbirds (Trochilidae) are long and bifid, folded over in the form of two tubes, the ends of which are greatly frayed and feather-like. The tongue is worked in and out of flowers at great speed, nectar and contained insects being forced into the tubes. The resemblance of this tongue to that of the nectar-sucking bee has been remarked upon. The brush-tongue characteristic of the Meliphagidae is notably different from that found in most other families of birds with like habits (see HONEYEATER), but a similar structure is found in the Zosteropidae and the Loriinae (see WHITE-EYE ; PARROT).

2. *Eating*. In general, those species with relatively thick, fleshy tongues, closely conforming to the inner margin of the lower mandible, use the tongue as an eating organ, but without protruding it to take in food. The flattened tongues of the grazing geese *Anser* etc. spp. bear serrations along the edge, corresponding with those of the lower mandible, and serve to fix and break the vegetation. Dabbling ducks *Anas* spp., with a more varied diet, have on the tongue a series of serrations and papillae that serve additionally as a sieve, this condition reaching maximal development in the Shoveler *Anas clypeata* and allied species. The slender backward-pointing barbs of the tongues of saw-billed ducks *Mergus* spp. assist in holding and swallowing slippery prey, as in the case of the penguins.

In the flamingos (Phoenicopteridae) the tongue fills the whole cavity of the lower mandible and is capable of moving only backwards and forwards. It bears many soft papillae and has closely serrated edges, being used to sift food from soft mud (see FLAMINGO).

Seed-eating species tend to have thick, fleshy tongues, that of the crossbills *Loxia* spp. playing an important part in extracting fir seeds from the cone. The tongue is used in these species in discarding unwanted husks.

3. *Swallowing*. There are a number of adaptations in the tongue that facilitate swallowing. In those species that swallow their food whole, as has already been mentioned, the tongue is unnecessary and rudimentary. Many other tongues possess the backward-pointing, spiny papillae to direct the food towards the oesophagus, the papillae becoming more numerous around the glottis, guarding it from any obstruction.

The raised edges of the tongues of some seed-eating species give such tongues a scoop-like form in which the seeds are directed towards the oesophagus. The bifid tongues of the owls (Strigiformes), larks (Alaudidae), and swifts (Apodidae) are probably concerned with swallowing.

4. *Taste and touch*. The sense of taste seems to be poorly developed in birds, with the possible exception of the parrots (Psittacacidae), the thick, fleshy tongues of which possess more taste-buds than any other species. In birds, however, many of these are situated elsewhere in the mouth (see TASTE). Tactile end-organs are much more widespread and the tongue is definitely an organ of touch, as would be expected (see TOUCH). The tongue has possibly a temperature-perceiving function in Megapodiidae (see MEGAPODE).

5. *Nest building*. In the swiftlets *Collocalia* spp. the mucinous salivary secretion used to build their nests is deposited by the tongue (see EDIBLE NEST).

There remain many tongues in which it is not possible to correlate function with form, e.g. the long, thin horny tongues of the toucans (Ramphastidae).

Tongue and Mouth Markings. A widespread characteristic of the mouths of nestling birds is that they are brightly coloured, often with a variable number of contrasting spots on the tongue and soft palate. These are considered to be directive marks or targets, revealed by the gaping response on the arrival of the parent with food. A more primitive arrangement is seen in the enlarged, light-coloured margins of the gape, as in the nestlings of thrushes (Turdinae) and many other passerines. Nestlings of some birds, e.g. the parrot-finches *Erythura* spp., possess semi-luminous blue warts on the sides of the mandible, again to direct the parents in placing food. See also COLORATION, ADAPTIVE ; DEVELOPMENT, POSTEMBRYONIC.

It has also been suggested that the bright mouth-colouring in adult birds may serve as threat and warning coloration, the gaping response being induced as a last resort when the bird is attacked and cornered. It is also a factor in display, revealed particularly by certain sea birds, notably the auks (Alcidae). J.G.H.

Swynnerton, C. F. M. 1916. On the coloration of the mouths and eggs of birds—1. The mouth of birds. Ibis (10) 4 : 264–294.
And general text-books.

TOOLS, USE OF: a most unusual form of behaviour among birds, in the sense of actually wielding some external object as an implement. The only fully authenticated instance is that of one of the Geospizinae of the Galápagos Islands, *Camarhynchus pallidus*, which has the habit of using a spine or small twig, held in the bill, as a probe in search of insect prey (see DARWIN'S FINCHES). The performance has been well recorded by cinematography (Sielmann) ; the tool is used most deliberately to bring the prey to the surface of the crevice, and is then temporarily laid aside while the bill is brought directly into play. A borderline case is that of the male Satin Bowerbird *Ptilonorhynchus violaceus*, which colours the inside of its bowers by applying masticated fruit-pulp or other material with its bill ; but the analogy is with paint rather than paint-brush. The use of static objects (stones, branches) as 'anvils' against which to break hard items of food (molluscs, nuts) or batter live prey clearly falls in another category.

TOOTH: see (plural) TEETH ; also EGG-TOOTH

TOOTHBILL : *Androdon aequatorialis* (for family see HUMMINGBIRD).

TOPAZ: substantive name of *Topaza* spp. (for family see HUMMINGBIRD).

TOPOGRAPHY: as applied to a bird, the detailed description of its superficial features ; this involves the use of terms for the different parts or areas, but few of these need much explanation. Some of the terms refer to what are normally plumage areas, although exposed patches of skin occur in some species and psilopaedic young are at first more or less naked. The boundaries of these areas are mostly incapable of close definition, except where they are named from particular groups of feathers. Other terms refer to what are somewhat absurdly known collectively as the 'soft parts'— the principal items being in fact rather hard ! They are the bill, the legs and feet, the surface of the eyes, and special structures present in some cases ; these are dealt with in separate articles (see BILL ; LEG ; IRIS COLORATION ; INTEGUMENTARY STRUCTURES). So also are certain of the plumage areas (see WING ; TAIL ; also PLUMAGE). There remain the plumage areas (as they usually are) of the head, neck, and body.

Head and Neck. From the base of the bill backwards the areas are named as follows, any

special adjectives referring to them being also given.
Dorsally : forehead (adj. frontal) ; crown ; occiput (back of head, adj. occipital) ; nape (upper hindneck, adj. nuchal) ; hindneck (lower). The forehead, crown, and occiput (the whole top of the head) are sometimes collectively called the pileum.

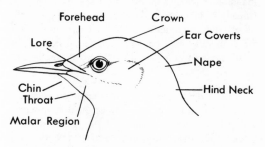

Topographical terms designating superficial areas of a bird's head (see also BILL). *M.Y.*

Laterally (the terms are more commonly used in the plural, the two sides being similar) : lore (between the upper mandible and the eye, adj. loral) ; ear coverts or auriculars (behind eye) ; side of neck (the adjective malar, although literally relating to cheeks, is applied in ornithology to the part below the base of the lower mandible).
Ventrally : chin (mentum) ; throat (upper foreneck, adj. gular) ; foreneck (lower) or jugulum.
The whole side of the head may be referred to as the cheek and its upper part is sometimes called the temple. Other terms derive from particular colour patterns. Thus there may be a hood, or a cap, or a collar ; or there may be a moustachial streak (running back from the base of the bill), or a superciliary stripe (above the eye), or an orbital ring (round the eye) either of distinctively coloured feathers or of bare horny skin. A band of colour on the throat (or on the upper breast) may be called a gorget. Elongated feathers may constitute a crest on the top or back of the head or hackles on the hindneck.
Body. Between the neck and the tail the areas, excluding the limbs, are
Dorsally : interscapular region (upper back) ; back ; lower back and rump (uropygium).
Laterally (on each side) : the scapular feathers (on the shoulder), the axillaries (beneath the wing) ; flank.
Ventrally : breast (sometimes chest, adj. pectoral) ; belly (abdomen) ; crissum (circumcloacal).
The need for naming different areas of the upper or under parts depends largely on the requirements for describing a particular colour pattern. When

the back, scapulars, and wing coverts together present an area of distinctive colour, this may be called a mantle (pallium).

Openings. The openings in the body surface are the anterior nares (sometimes impervious) in the upper mandible ; the mouth (adj. buccal), of which the gape (adj. rictal) is between the bases of the mandibles ; the auditory meatus on each side (usually hidden by feathers) ; the openings of the oil gland (sometimes absent) above the root of the tail ; and the vent (anus), the external end of the cloaca (see NARIS ; TONGUE ; HEARING AND BALANCE ; OIL GLAND ; ALIMENTARY SYSTEM).

TOPOTYPE: term sometimes applied to a specimen, not forming part of the original type-series, collected at the type-locality of the species or subspecies concerned (see TYPE-SPECIMEN ; and TYPE-LOCALITY).

TOQ TOQ: *Foudia sechellarum* (for family see WEAVER).

TORPIDITY: a state of inactivity and lowered body temperature enabling a bird to conserve energy during a period of fasting ; known to occur in certain families, and in one recorded instance amounting to hibernation (see HIBERNATION ; METABOLISM ; also HEAT REGULATION). In the eighteenth century it was widely believed that in winter Swallows *Hirundo rustica* became torpid and passed the winter in hollow trees and other crevices, or even ' conglobated ' into a mass of birds clinging together buried in the mud at the bottom of ponds. When the true whereabouts of Swallows during the European winter became known, the hibernation theory was discarded as a myth. It was so discredited that when evidence pointing to the possibility of hibernation in birds began to accumulate little attention was aroused.

Hanna studied the White-throated Swift *Aeronautes saxatilis* (' *melanoleucus* ') for some years at its nesting place in the cliffs in Slover Mountain, San Bernardino County, California. During an extremely cold wave, in January 1913, eight birds were taken out of a crevice where they, with many others, were roosting ' in a dazed or numb state '. He concluded that it seemed possible that these birds may have an intermittent hibernation period because, although they did not appear for many days in the coldest weather, yet he found that they were plentiful in the rocks in a dormant state. Although Hanna's observations showed that torpidity occurs in some birds, they attracted little attention.

Chaplin, in 1933, recalled that in the nineteenth century Gould had noted torpidity in hummingbirds (Trochilidae), and reported that he had himself found *Chrysolampis mosquitus* and *Eupetomena macroura* torpid at ambient temperatures of 63–70° F (ca. 17–21° C). The birds sat on their perches with the head drawn down on to the shoulders, and ' showed to all appearances no spark of life ; they could be moved about and laid on the table like as many dried skins '. Chaplin also observed that torpidity was not due to cold, as the birds were aroused when disturbed at lowered ambient temperatures and were often active at 56° F (13·3° C) ; torpidity occurred in one bird for periods of 17, 15, and 20 hours within 4 days. He suggested from his experience that the allied swifts (Apodidae), nightjars (Caprimulgidae), and even the colies (Coliidae) might have a similar power of torpidity. Six years later Huxley, Webb, & Best, apparently in ignorance of the literature, published similar although less precise observations. In 1947 McAtee reviewed the literature on torpidity in birds and could find few records, beyond those just mentioned, in which reliable witnesses reported first-hand observations. He wrote just too soon to include the remarkable discovery by Jaeger of a bird that undoubtedly hibernates. Nuttall's Poorwill *Phalaenoptilus nuttallii* is an insectivorous summer migrant to parts of the southern United States of America, whence it departs at the onset of winter to parts unknown. At the end of December 1946 Jaeger came across one of these birds hibernating in a rock crevice of a deep canyon among the Chuckawalla Mountains of the Colorado Desert in California. The bird was sitting inert, with its respiration and heart rate reduced to so low a level that they could not be detected with the apparatus available in the field ; its temperature was more than 40° F (ca. 22° C) below that normal for its active state. A ring was placed on its leg, and Jaeger was later able to report that in four successive winters the bird was found hibernating in the same niche of refuge. It is strange that since then only one other bird of this species has been found hibernating in the wild. Marshall, however, has observed hibernation in captive Poorwills and the allied Trilling Nighthawk *Chordeiles acutipennis*.

Bartholomew, Howell, & Cade have been able to show that a fat deposit weighing 10 grams would sustain a torpid Poorwill for 100 days. In these birds, torpor and a reduced body temperature are a means for energy conservation for survival during long periods of fasting. On the other hand, in hummingbirds and bats, the only homoeothermic animals known to have a daily cycle of torpor, it is (as Bartholomew and his colleagues point out) associated with small body size and high metabolic rates during daily activity. Nestlings of the Swift *Apus apus* become torpid when weather conditions are such that their parents cannot obtain the supply of insects necessary for feeding them (Koskimies ; Lack & Lack). They can withstand many days of fasting that would be fatal to the nestlings of most birds, and while they are unfed their body weight falls steadily as first the fat deposits and then the tissues are drawn upon to maintain the basal metabolism ; recovery sometimes occurs when as much as 50 per cent of the weight has been lost. The temperature of the adult Swift is 105–106° F (ca. 41° C) ; that of the feathered young ranges from 99° F to 102° F (37–39° C) but rises to 105° F shortly before they leave the nest. After several days of starvation, the temperature of the unfeathered nestling, however, falls at night nearly to that of the air, sometimes as low as 70° F (21° C), but rises to normal during the day. The nestlings are thus homoeothermic by day but poikilothermic by night.

In the hummingbirds, on the other hand, the incubating bird does not become torpid at night, and it thus maintains the temperature of the eggs or nestlings. The insulation of the nest helps in this, and the young do not become torpid at night before they leave the nest. Pearson points out the considerable saving in calories per 24 hours in a hummingbird if it becomes torpid instead of going to sleep at night, and the comparatively small expenditure of time and energy needed for warming up in the morning. In larger birds the saving in calories is comparatively small, and the time and energy needed for warming up are comparatively much greater.

It is interesting to note that the birds known to become torpid belong to the families Caprimulgidae, Trochilidae, and Apodidae, which on other grounds have long been closely associated systematically.

See also HUMMINGBIRD (second article).

L.H.M.

Bartholomew, G. A., Howell, T. R. & Cade, T. J. 1957. Torpidity in the White-throated Swift, Anna Hummingbird and Poor-will. Condor 59 : 145–155.
Chaplin, A. 1933. Of fable and fact. Avicult. Mag. (4) 11 : 209–210.
Chaplin, A. 1933. Torpidity in the Trochilidae. Avicult. Mag. (4) 11 : 231–232.
Chaplin, A. 1933. Humming-birds. Avicult. Mag. (4) 11 : 431–434.
Hanna, E. C. 1917. Further notes on the Whitethroated Swifts of Slover Mountain. Condor 19 : 1–8.
Huxley, J. S., Webb, C. S. & Best, A. T. 1939. Temporary poikilothermy in birds. Nature, Lond. 143 : 683–684.
Jaeger, E. C. 1948. Does the Poor-will ' hibernate ' ? Condor 50 : 45.
Jaeger, E. C. 1949. Further observations on the hibernation of the Poor-will. Condor 51 : 105–109.
Kosskimies, J. 1948. On temperature regulation and metabolism in the Swift, *Micropus a. apus* during fasting. Experientia 4 : 274–282.
Lack, D. & Lack, E. 1951. The breeding biology of the Swift *Apus apus*. Ibis 93 : 501–546.
McAtee, W. L. 1947. Torpidity in birds. Amer. Midl. Nat. 38 : 191–206.
Marshall, J. T. 1955. Hibernation in captive goat-suckers. Condor 57 : 129–134.
Matthews, L. H. 1961. Hibernation in mammals and birds. Brit. Med. Bull. 17 : 9–13.
Pearson, O. P. 1960. Torpidity in birds. Bull. Mus. Comp. Zool. Harvard 124 : 93–103.

TORRESIAN: see AUSTRALASIAN REGION

TOTIPALMATE: having all 4 toes connected by webs (see LEG).

TOUCAN: substantive name of species of Ramphastidae (Piciformes, suborder Galbulae) ; in the plural, general term for the family. The name comes from ' tucano ' in the language of the Tupi Indians of Brazil. The family consists of 5 genera and about 37 species of middle-sized or large birds (12–24 inches long) confined to the tropical parts of the American continents. Wholly arboreal, they occur only in wooded regions, chiefly at low and middle altitudes. The outstanding feature of these ungraceful birds is the bill, which in all species is enormously enlarged, while in some it exceeds the body in length and almost equals it in bulk ; the nostrils are at the extreme base. Nearly always it is coloured with several bright and contrasting hues. Although in some species it appears almost too heavy for the bird to support, lightness combined with strength is obtained by a network of bony fibres ramifying through the space within the horny outer shell. In size this bill compares with that of the hornbills (Bucerotidae) of the Old World tropics, but it always lacks the dorsal outgrowth or casque of the latter ; the two families are not closely related. The toucan's tongue is also remarkable ; it is a long, narrow, horizontally flattened, thin lamina that may attain a length of 6 inches in the largest species, and its distal part is on both sides obliquely notched by indentations that become progressively deeper toward the apex, where it has a bristly aspect. The wings are short and rounded ; the tail tends to be long ; the legs are strong and the feet zygodactylous.

The largest toucans belong to the genus *Ramphastos*, which includes species up to about 2 feet in length. The Rainbow-billed (or Keel-billed) Toucan *R. sulfuratus* ranges through the forests from southern Mexico to northern South America. As is the case in most toucans, the sexes are alike in coloration, but the males are on the average larger than the females. About 18–20 inches in length, this stout bird is largely black, slightly glossed with green on the upper parts, and washed with maroon on the hindneck. The upper tail coverts are white. The cheeks, throat, and foreneck are bright yellow, and the under tail coverts are bright poppy-red. The coloration of the great, swollen bill varies considerably with individuals, and, with the exception of violet, all the colours of the rainbow occur. The tints blend rainbow-wise into each other, and the basal margin of the bill is deep black. Other members of this genus have fewer but more strongly contrasting colours on their bills.

The genus *Pteroglossus* consists of long-tailed, middle-sized or small toucans usually called araçaris. The Collared Araçari *P. torquatus* is a slender bird, about 16 inches in length, which is found in wooded country at the lower altitudes from southern Mexico to Colombia and Venezuela. In both sexes, the upper plumage is generally almost black, glossed with green on the back, with a bright red rump and upper tail coverts. The throat and foreneck are black ; the more posterior under plumage is largely yellow, with a band of black and red across the upper part of the abdomen. The bill, less vividly coloured than in certain other araçaris, is off-white, grey, and black. The cutting edge of the upper mandible has widely spaced tooth-like projections. The bright yellow eyes are surrounded by red bare skin. In this genus is sometimes placed the curious Curl-crested Toucan *P. beauharnaisii* of the upper Amazon valley ; the feathers of its head consist largely of the broadly expanded horny shaft ; those on the pileum are curled forward and resemble shavings of glossy black horn.

The toucanets of the genus *Aulacorhynchus* are largely green in plumage and live at higher altitudes than other members of the family, reaching about 10 000 feet in the Andes and in the highlands of Middle America. The Blue-throated Toucanet *A. caeruleogularis*, confined to the mountains of Costa Rica and western Panama, is about 11 inches in length. In both sexes the green plumage which covers most of the body lacks metallic brilliance. The cheeks, chin, and throat are dark blue, and the under tail coverts are chestnut. The bill is yellow, white, red, and black, with yellow predominating. Toucanets perform ' vertical migrations ', but other members of the family seem not to migrate.

Toucans are sociable birds, often found in small flocks of a few to more than a dozen individuals, yet they are almost devoid of group impulses. When they travel, one flies away and then another follows, and so they straggle on, one by one, until the whole flock has moved. The larger species fly with alternate flapping and gliding, tracing an undulatory course ; but the flight of some of the smaller kinds is swift and direct. Toucans bathe in the water that collects in hollows in the crotches of trees or in the upper side of horizontal limbs, often high above the ground. They evince curiosity, and in remote forests they may look down with interest at the activities of a botanical collector or other human intruder. They are frolicsome birds, jumping about and sometimes playfully striking their bills together in a sort of fencing, or grasping each other's bills and pushing. Sometimes they preen each other's plumage with the tips of their great bills. In the Rainbow-billed Toucan and the Fiery-billed Araçari *Pteroglossus frantzii*, one individual has been seen to feed another, doubtless its mate.

Toucans eat many berries and other small fruits, and they vary their diet with such insects, spiders, and the like as they can catch, including fluttering termites on evenings when the air is full of the winged sexual brood. Seizing the food in the tip of its great bill, the toucan tosses its head upward to throw the piece back into its throat. Large items are first torn with the bill while held against the perch with a foot. The toucan that Humboldt and Bonpland carried on their historic canoe voyage up the Orinoco liked to fish in the river. Species of *Ramphastos*, *Pteroglossus*, *Aulacorhynchus*, and doubtless other genera, devour the eggs and nestlings of small birds.

It is in connection with the toucans' feeding habits that their peculiar bills must be considered. The long bill enables these heavy, clumsy birds to reach fruits that grow at the slender tips of branches, while they themselves perch farther inward where they find more adequate support. But to give a longer reach, the bill need be neither thick nor brightly coloured. The size and vividness of toucans' bills probably serve them well when they make predatory visits to the nests of other birds ; they are so intimidating that even small hawks (Accipitridae) and the boldest of the American flycatchers (Tyrannidae) fear to attack a toucan perching beside their nest. But when the pirates are flying and cannot turn their heads to defend their backs, the outraged parents sometimes buffet them. The vivid bill may also enter into courtship, although little is known about toucans' nuptial displays. It has been suggested that the long bill may also help the incubating or brooding toucan to repel enemies from the doorway of its hole, but most toucans hurry forth from their nests at the first hint of danger.

Toucans are poorly endowed vocally. Their monotonous calls have been compared to the croaking of frogs, the mewing of gulls (Larinae), and the yelping of puppies. Rattling notes are sometimes given. The araçaris utter high, sharp notes, surprisingly weak for such large birds. The 'dios te de, te de, te de' of the Chestnut-mandibled Toucan *Ramphastos swainsonii* is, however, not unmelodious as the birds float down from distant tree-tops; these birds sing much at nightfall.

Araçaris roost throughout the year in the old holes of woodpeckers (Picidae) or other cavities, usually high in trees. Each flock seems to have a number of such lodgings; if their suspicions are aroused as they approach one of these, they may retire into another. Five or 6 adults may sleep in the same hole, folding their tails over their backs to save space in crowded quarters. In captivity, *Ramphastos* spp. roost with the bill laid among the plumage of the back and the tail folded forward over the bill, so that they become featureless balls of feathers; it is not known where they sleep in the wild.

Toucans nest in trees, in hollows resulting from decay or, in the smaller species, in the holes of woodpeckers (Picidae), of which they may dispossess the makers. They may remove rotten wood from a hole or enlarge the doorway if the surrounding wood is soft, but they do no real carving. Toucans' nests are often at a great height, but exceptionally, for lack of a high hole, they choose one near the ground. Each clutch consists of 2–4 white, broadly ovate eggs. The Rainbow-billed Toucan brings a few green leaves into its hole and may carry them away after they wither. Otherwise, toucans take no lining into their nests; but the many large seeds that they regurgitate while they sit soon form a pebbly bed beneath the eggs. Incubation is performed by both parents, who are surprisingly restless for such large birds. They seldom sit for more than an hour at a stretch, and often the eggs are left exposed for from a few minutes to nearly an hour while both attendants go off to forage. Even if, as in the araçaris, both parents had slept in the nest hole before laying began, only one stays with the eggs at night; but it is not known whether this is the male, as in woodpeckers and certain puff-birds (Bucconidae) and cuckoos (Cuculidae), or the female, as in most kinds of birds. At a nest of the Blue-throated Toucanet the incubation period was 16 days, but that of the larger species is unknown.

Toucans are hatched perfectly naked, with no trace of down. Their eyes are tightly closed, and the lower mandible is both longer and broader than the upper one. Their heels are equipped with prominent thickened pads, from which project a number of strong tubercles, arranged in a peripheral ring in species of *Ramphastos*. These heel-pads, along with the abdomen, bear the nestling's weight; their function appears to be to prevent abrasion of the heel joint by the rough floor of the nest. The nestling's uropygium is extraordinarily long and prominent and is often held with a strong upward tilt. The young toucans develop with extreme slowness; they are 3 weeks old or more before their eyes begin to open, and at this age they are still largely naked.

Both parents brood and feed the nestlings, nourishing them largely with fruits, insects (especially while they are younger), and occasionally a lizard, small snake, or the nestling of some other bird. Much of the food is carried to the nest in the throat or crop, but usually a final item is held prominently in the bill and given to a nestling before the remainder of the load is brought forth. Waste material is removed from the nest in the parent's bill. In the case of the Blue-throated Toucanet, a single parent sleeps with the nestlings until a few days before their departure, but in the araçaris both parents pass the night with them. In Panama, 6 Collared Araçaris roosted in a very high hole that was afterwards used for breeding; only one parent slept in it while incubation was in progress, but after the eggs hatched 5 adults roosted in the nest hole each night; and all 5 of them fed the nestlings, of which there were at least 3. The nestling period of this species is 43–46 days, and that of the Blue-throated Toucanet is 43 days. Fledgling araçaris return to sleep in the nest hole with their parents, but apparently this is not true of toucanets. In the highlands, toucanets rear 2 broods in a season, but the larger toucans of the lowlands apparently attempt to produce only a single brood.

See Plate 32 (colour).   A.F.S.

Beebe, W., Hartley, G. I. & Howes, P. G. 1917. Tropical Wild life in British Guiana vol. 1. New York.

Gould, J. 1834 (2nd ed. 1854 with suppl., 1852–55). A Monograph of the Ramphastidae, or Family of Toucans. London.

Peters, J. L. 1948. Check-list of Birds of the World vol. 6. Cambridge, Mass.

Skutch, A. F. 1944. Life history of the Blue-throated Toucanet. Wilson Bull. 56 : 133–151.

Skutch, A. F. 1958. Roosting and nesting of araçari toucans. Condor 60 : 201–219.

Van Tyne, J. 1929. The life history of the toucan *Ramphastos brevicarinatus*. Univ. Mich. Mus. Zool. Misc. Publ. no. 19 : 1–43.

TOUCANET: substantive name of *Aulacorhynchus* spp. (see TOUCAN).

TOUCH: a sense of which the characteristics in birds are little known apart from what can be deduced from field observations, from analogy with man, and from such histological evidence as there is. In man, the skin is sensitive to a number of ' sensations ', such as warmth, cold, touch (light pressure), deep pressure, and pain, although to be complete the list should be greatly amplified (see also SENSES). However, some authors think of the skin as having three systems of sensitivity, concerned respectively with pressure reception, with change of temperature, and with pain.

Little is known of the histology and physiology of the cutaneous receptors in birds. Portmann describes a number of free nerve-endings in the epidermis, and these are especially common in the areas of skin that are devoid of feathers (see SKIN). Their function is unknown, but he suggests that they may be pain or temperature receptors.

Encapsulated nerve-endings lying in the dermis have been described, and of these Herbst's corpuscles and Grandry's corpuscles appear to be found only in birds. Both are probably concerned with the reception of tactile stimuli. Herbst's corpuscles are about 150μ long and are composed of a central mass of cells surrounded by several concentric layers of connective tissue, giving a general appearance like that of an onion. They are ovoid in shape, and the sensory nerve fibre enters at one pole and terminates in the central mass of cells. The corpuscles of Herbst are comparable with the mammalian Pacinian corpuscles and are particularly numerous in the tip of the tongue of woodpeckers (Picidae).

In several species of birds a row of Herbst's corpuscles is found between the tibia and fibula bones of the leg, and experimental work with Bullfinches Pyrrhula pyrrhula suggests that these are responsible for the detection of vibrations. Resting birds are remarkably sensitive to the shaking of their perch, and their sensitivity to vibration is considerably better than that of man.

Grandry's corpuscles are also ovoid structures, each being formed of two sensory cells between which a sensory nerve fibre ramifies and terminates. In the bill of ducks (Anatidae) Herbst's corpuscles were found to predominate at the tip, whilst Grandry's corpuscles were numerous at the base ; Krogis concluded that such a topographic independence indicated that the two receptors have different physiological functions. Herbst's corpuscles are found in the bills of many birds, being well developed at the tip of the bill in swallows (Hirundinidae) and woodpeckers (Picidae). The tactile sense of the bill in waders (e.g. Scolopacidae) is thought to be of importance, since the horny covering is thin and the bill is richly innervated.

It has been suggested that the rictal bristles possessed by many birds may have a sensory function, but supporting evidence seems to be lacking. The tongue is a tactile as well as a gustatory organ (see TONGUE).   C.J.D.

Krogis, A. 1931. On the topography of Herbst's and Grandry's corpuscles in the adult and embryonic duck-bill. Acta Zool., Stockh. 12 : 241-263.
Schildmacher, H. 1931. Untersuchungen über die Funktion der Herbstschen Körperchen. J. Orn. 79 : 374-415.
Schwartzkopf, J. 1955. Schallsinnesorgane, ihre Funktion und biologische Bedeutung bei Vögeln. Acta XI Congr. Internat. Orn., Basel 1954 : 189-208.

TOURACO: see TURACO

TOWHEE: substantive name of species of *Pipilo* and *Chlorura* (see BUNTING ; also HYBRIDISATION, ZONE OF SECONDARY).

TOXIC CHEMICALS: considered here as a hazard to bird-life. Chemicals have been used in agriculture and horticulture to combat insect and other pests for many years, but it was not until the rise of the new synthetic pesticides after 1945 that their effects on wildlife became important. The synthetic pesticides fall into two main groups—the organo-phosphorus compounds, such as parathion and malathion, and the chlorinated hydrocarbons, including DDT (the first and best known), aldrin, dieldrin, and others. The organo-phosphorus compounds are allied to the nerve gases and act by destroying enzymes ; they are highly toxic to both invertebrates and vertebrates (they are a popular method of human suicide in some countries), but although their immediate effects may be deadly they decompose fairly rapidly into harmless compounds. The chlorinated hydrocarbons are, on the contrary, highly persistent and accumulate, especially in the fatty tissues, in the body ; moreover, they pass from one animal in the food chain to another, often becoming more concentrated in the process. Thus, at Clear Lake, California, the chlorinated hydrocarbon DDD was applied at a maximum concentration of one-fiftieth parts per million (p.p.m.) in order to clear gnats. After Western Grebes *Aechmophorus occidentalis* on the lake began to die and the population fell from more than 1000 pairs to about 30, with no young reared, analyses revealed that the plankton organisms in the lake had about 5 p.p.m. of DDD, the plant-eating fishes from 40 to 300 p.p.m., and the fatty tissues of the grebes 1600 p.p.m. Some of the older inorganic pesticides are also a potential danger ; they include arsenic, now withdrawn in Britain after human casualties, and mercury, still widely used as a fungicidal seed-dressing.

The effects of toxic chemicals on bird-life may be both direct and indirect. The direct effects include the deaths of birds which have fed on treated insects or crops, and also reduced fertility from sub-lethal amounts of poison. The indirect effects are caused by changes in the environment, from reductions in the numbers and variety of insects, weed plants, or other foods, to changes in the soil organisms, which have as yet been relatively little studied but could ultimately have the most far-reaching effects on all forms of life.

Although long denied, the killing of birds by toxic chemicals has now been proved by field observation, by chemical analyses of corpses, and by experiment. A few examples must suffice. In Great Britain, corpses of 89 species, including game-birds (Galliformes), water birds (Podicipitidae, Ardeidae, Anatidae), pigeons (Columbidae), nocturnal and diurnal predators (Strigiformes, Falconiformes), and thrushes (Turdinae), tits (Paridae), finches (Fringillidae), and other passerines, as well as some waders (Charadrii) and swallows (Hirundinidae), have been reported in incidents between 1960 and 1962 involving toxic seed-dressings or sprays ; and, of these, 57 species have so far been shown on analysis to contain residues of chlorinated hydrocarbons or mercury. (Fuller details can be found in the reports from 1960 onwards of the Joint Committee of the British Trust for Ornithology and the Royal Society for the Protection of Birds on Toxic Chemicals, latterly in collaboration with the Game Research Association.)

In Sweden, analysis has shown toxic residues, including mercury and both organo-phosphorus and chlorinated hydrocarbon compounds, in at least 25 species. In Holland, 55 different species were reported killed by parathion in 1960, involving some 27 000 individual birds. In the United States of America, where pesticides have been used far more widely and on a much larger scale than in Europe, details of many incidents involving a wide range of species will be found in Rachel Carson's excellent summary *Silent Spring* (1962).

Although it is unlikely that any species of bird is immune to the effects, these effects vary according to the use of a pesticide and the resistance of the species concerned. Thus, in Britain, until the voluntary ban on the use of the more toxic forms in 1962, seed-dressings caused most bird deaths, especially among grain feeders such as game-birds and pigeons ; but more recently sprays have increased in importance, affecting a rather different range of species. In the United States, on the other hand, the spraying of forests and marshes on a very large scale has led to the widespread pollution of water supplies and the death of fish and of fish-eating birds. Much work remains to be done to determine specific resistance, but its existence is suggested by the fact that the scale of deaths of certain species does not always appear to be closely correlated with the numbers at risk ; and it has been demonstrated experimentally in some species. Thus, for feral pigeons *Columba livia* the LD50 (dose lethal for 50 per cent) has been calculated at 67 p.p.m. for dieldrin and 55 p.p.m. for aldrin, whereas as little as 5·8 p.p.m. of dieldrin and 3·3 p.p.m. of aldrin were found to be lethal to Bobwhite Quail *Colinus virginianus*. Individual resistance has also been shown to vary, although to a smaller extent.

The sub-lethal effects of toxic chemicals were demonstrated experimentally for American quail (Odontophorinae) and Pheasants *Phasianus colchicus* when it was found that doses of chlorinated hydrocarbons fed to the birds reduced fertility by lowering egg production, and by reducing egg fertility and the survival of young. Since then these effects have been increasingly noted in wild birds. The spraying of elm trees with DDT in Michigan, besides causing the death of many species, led to reduced fertility in Robins *Turdus migratorius* ; analyses showed large concentrations of DDT in the testes and ovaries of breeding birds. A sharp fall in fertility in the Bald Eagle *Haliaetus leucocephalus*, in Florida and elsewhere, was noted following the application of DDT to salt-marshes to control mosquitoes, and DDT residues have recently been found both in adult birds and in infertile eggs. In Britain reduced hatching success was reported in Pheasants in areas where toxic seed-dressings had been used on a large scale, and residues have been found in addled eggs. The recent catastrophic decline in the British population of the Peregrine *Falco peregrinus* has been accompanied by a marked reduction in fertility ; both are correlated, geographically and in time, with the increasing use of synthetic pesticides, and an addled egg from a Perthshire eyrie has been found to contain residues of four such chemicals.

Both direct mortality and the sub-lethal effects of pesticides on reproduction might affect bird populations. Serious reductions in the numbers of birds have been found in limited areas, for example in some sixty communities in the American Midwest after the DDT spraying of elms, and in Canadian forest areas following the use of DDT to control spruce budworm outbreaks. Changes over wider areas are harder to establish because of our ignorance of the total numbers of many species of birds, due both to the inherent difficulties and to the relative neglect of census work (see CENSUS). It is now clear, however, that some birds-of-prey are facing a serious decline in numbers in Britain. This has been shown conclusively in the case of the Peregrine, where a national census showed that by 1962 about half the pre-1939 population of some 650 breeding pairs had gone, and that only just over a quarter of the remainder bred successfully. Field observations suggest that the Kestrel *Falco tinnunculus* and Sparrow-hawk *Accipiter nisus* have been similarly affected. In all three species the declines coincided with the increased use of chlorinated hydrocarbons and were most marked in those areas where these chemicals were most used. The decline in birds-of-prey is not confined to Britain (the serious decrease in Bald Eagle numbers in U.S.A. is well documented), and this appears to be another example of animals at the end of a food chain concentrating the persistent pesticides. Sub-lethal effects on reproduction, which have now been proved in a number of species, may be more serious in the long run than limited mortality. Field observations suggest that some of the smaller and more numerous bird species in Britain may also have recently declined in numbers, but exact evidence on this must await the results of the census of common species recently inaugurated by the British Trust for Ornithology.

Some of the more obvious effects of toxic chemicals on bird life are now becoming apparent, but the more subtle and long-term consequences require much more investigation. There is a growing recognition of the need for extended research in many fields, especially ecological, and for restricting to the essential minimum the use of the more deadly and persistent chemicals.   S.C.

Cramp, Stanley. 1963. Toxic Chemicals and Birds of Prey. Brit. Birds 56 : 124–139.

De Witt, J. B. 1955. Effects of chlorinated hydrocarbon insecticides on quail and pheasants. J. Agric. and Food Chem. 3 : 672–676.

Hunt, E. G. & Bischoff, A. I. 1960. Inimical effects on wildlife of periodic DDD applications to Clear Lake. Calif. Fish and Game 46 : 91–106.

Ratcliffe, D. A. 1963. The status of the Peregrine in Great Britain. Bird Study 10 : 56–90.

Rudd, R. L. & Genelly, R. E. 1956. Pesticides : their use and toxicity in relation to wildlife. Calif. Dept Fish and Game, Game Bull. 7 : 1–209.

TRACHEA : the windpipe, an air passage leading from an opening (glottis) at the back of the mouth, running down the neck (ventrally to the oesophagus), and dividing into the two bronchi leading to the lungs (see RESPIRATORY SYSTEM). The anterior part, surrounded by the cricoid and other cartilages, is known as the larynx but is without vocal cords. At the posterior end and commonly also involving the bronchi (but wholly tracheal in some species, and wholly bronchial in some others) is the syrinx, an organ peculiar to birds (see SYRINX). The whole tube is reinforced by cartilaginous or bony rings, and dilatations or enlargements are found in some species, notably among ducks (Anatidae). In certain species, either in the males only or in both sexes, the tube is elongated by being coiled ; different versions of this character are found in a wide diversity of birds, but its presence may not be constant even within a genus. In some swans *Cygnus* spp. and cranes (Gruidae), the bone of the sternal carina is extensively excavated to accommodate the tracheal loops.

TRACHEOPHONAE : see under PASSERIFORMES ; SYRINX

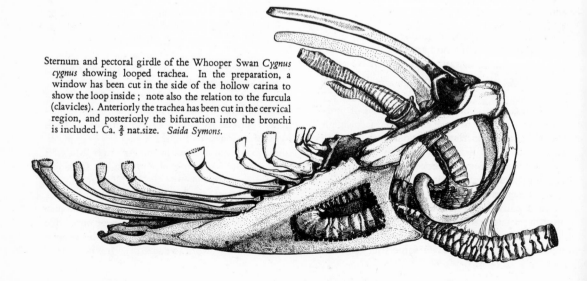

Sternum and pectoral girdle of the Whooper Swan *Cygnus cygnus* showing looped trachea. In the preparation, a window has been cut in the side of the hollow carina to show the loop inside ; note also the relation to the furcula (clavicles). Anteriorly the trachea has been cut in the cervical region, and posteriorly the bifurcation into the bronchi is included. Ca. ⅖ nat.size. *Saida Symons.*

TRACK: the path of a flying bird relative to the earth's surface ; the resultant (allowing for speeds) of the bird's heading and the local wind (see MIGRATION).

TRACKS: the footmarks left by birds in soft ground (mud, sand, etc.) or snow. These vary with the shape of foot, length of leg, and method of terrestrial locomotion of the various species (see LOCOMOTION).

Urner, C. A. 1943. *In* Hickey, J. J. Guide to Bird Watching. London, New York, and Toronto. (Chapter on bird tracks.)

TRAGOPAN: substantive name of *Tragopan* spp. (see PHEASANT).

TRAIN: term sometimes applied to a long tail, e.g. of a Peacock *Pavo cristatus*, or by falconers to the tail of a bird-of-prey (see TAIL).

TRAINBEARER: substantive name of *Lesbia* spp. (see HUMMINGBIRD) ; also of several *Pharomachrus* spp. (see TROGON).

TRANSECT: see CENSUS ; STATISTICAL SIGNIFICANCE

TRANSFERENCE ACTIVITY: term introduced by Armstrong (1952) for what has since been called 'redirection activity' (see REDIRECTION).

TRANSIENT: perhaps the most precise term for a species or subspecies (on occasion applicable to individual birds) that appears on migration in the area under reference but neither breeds nor overwinters there ; also 'passage migrant' (see MIGRATION).

TRANSIENT MULTIPLE PAIRING: see under POLYGAMY

TRANSILIENT: term (Stresemann 1961) for a mode of moulting the primary feathers, proceeding by forward or backward leaps across one or more adjoining quills (see MOULT).

TRANSPORTATION: see CARRYING ; PARENTAL CARE ; POLLINATORS AND DISTRIBUTORS

TRAPPING: in respect of wild birds, permitted in the United Kingdom only for marking or under licence for study purposes (except certain pest species by authorised persons) ; but no methods that might cause suffering are countenanced (e.g. bird-lime, stupefying baits, tethered decoys), and a special permit is required for using lights for catching birds at night. The position naturally varies from country to country, and in some the trapping of

birds for food or caging is practised on a large scale.

Various types of traps are used for ringing purposes. At one extreme there is the large Heligoland trap set up at bird observatories—a long permanent wire-netting cage, up to 12 feet high at the mouth and 20 yards wide between wings (Fig. 1), narrowing and beset by baffles as it gives access beyond a swing-to door to a 'lock-up', and finally to a windowed catching-box whence birds are removed through a sleeve : migrants on Heligoland sixty years ago were driven into such traps from low cover in the catching area ahead, or were attracted by water or bait provided. At the other extreme are the small Potter and Chardonneret traps used in suburban gardens, operating automatically on the tripped-door principle.

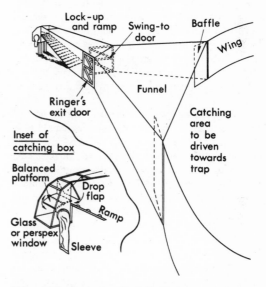

FIG 1. Heligoland trap. *E. A. R. Ennion.*

Intermediate types include miniature 'Minigolands' ; aviary-sized crow-traps, where ingress is by wide-mouthed funnel from above and a tame crow used as 'bait' ; garden house-traps, entered either through a drop-door worked by trip or pull-stick or through little tunnels at ground level ; duck-traps, straddling the water margin, with adjustable slit entrances let in on three sides, employed with excellent results for both ducks (Anatidae) and waders (Charadrii) on reservoirs, e.g. Abberton ; floating duck-traps moored on endless cable and sparrow-traps, both constructed on lobster-pot principles ; and a variety of smaller automatic wire-netting traps with maze or creep-in funnel entrances, baited for finches (Fringillidae) etc., or set with low lead-in 'fences' between them on shores or sewage-beds for pipits and waders—these have proved most successful on tideless rotting seaweed beds infested with shore-fly larvae in Scandinavia. For removal from these larger traps a catching-box (like the Heligoland's) is built-in, or a landing-net is used ; in the smaller types a flap opens to let the bird pass through a corresponding opening into an independent carrying-box.

Provided that these wire-netting traps are watched conscientiously and approached quietly, especially when taking birds out, no harm should result : a slight casualty rate, one in 500 or 600 perhaps, is nevertheless inevitable. Numbers taken must depend, obviously, on the number of birds available in the area at the time ; with plenty about, a skilfully driven, well sited Heligoland trap will sometimes take 20 or more at one drive—the most in the writer's experience was 77 Greenfinches *Carduelis chloris* at once—but catches of 2 or 3 birds are more normal. Other types normally take less, although up to 20 small waders or finches would not be exceptional for a 'battery' of, say, 6 figure-of-eight-type maze traps at the right time and place.

Small oval, circular or rectilinear spring-nets of soft netting strung on stout wire frames, baited (e.g. with mealworms) and set like breakback mousetraps, will catch individual wheatears, shrikes, etc., and—with care in expert hands—ground-nesting birds. Drop-nets of various patterns and dimensions worked by pull-cord and smaller drop-cages sprung automatically by trip-line or trigger also make useful individual traps. There are many other devices : the Fleyg, a long-handled outsize butterfly-Y-net, is wielded by experts to intercept flying Fulmars *Fulmarus glacialis* and Puffins *Fratercula arctica* ; wire crooks adjusted to their leg diameters are used to take Puffins, Kittiwakes *Larus tridactylus*, etc., on the rock ; 'stopped' snares to take Shags *Phalacrocorax aristotelis* and Gannets *Sula bassana* on their nests. The use of fine leg-snares pegged out for gulls (Larinae) or waders (Charadrii) is not to be recommended—they may cause damage and are too easily mislaid.

The large double clap-nets used formerly by birdcatchers relied for their high efficiency on the tethered decoy (now illegal in Britain) : a smaller simplified version, of net area up to about 20×8 feet (but often less) and thrown by a single pole, has been developed with some success, notably for taking waders on the tide-line (Fig. 2). A far larger double net, rocket-propelled and remotely operated (by electric device), has been perfected by the Wildfowl Trust for catching geese *Anser* spp. etc., up to 400

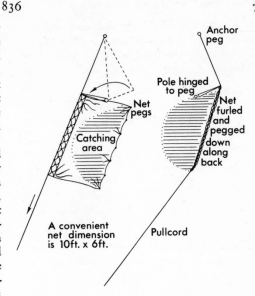

FIG 2. Single pole clap-net. *E. A. R. Ennion.*

having been netted in a single throw : the coralling of flightless geese in Iceland has proved even more exciting and rewarding, considered as a single effort ; but such ventures involve major organisation and expense.

Since 1956, when the Japanese mist-nets became available, this technique has come into ever expanding use. Against suitable backgrounds in reasonably calm conditions, the nets stretched upright between supporting poles are almost invisible even in full daylight ; the birds, on flying in, pocket themselves over taut nylon strings threaded through the fine loose mesh of the net's panels—usually 3, giving a total area of 20×9 feet per net ; but various modifications, e.g. 'single-deckers', triple nets, wider mesh, are available. Extraction, and indeed the whole technique, require special experience and care. As with the smaller clap-nets, their simplicity, adaptability, and relative cheapness, and above all mobility, confer great advantages over the older and fixed types of trap ; they materially increase the numbers and variety of birds caught. 'Bat-fowling' with tall folding nets clapped together to take birds as they fly out when disturbed from their nests at night, or dropping nets over groundroosting birds dazzled by strong light are other useful techniques, particularly at communal roosts of finches, gulls or Starlings *Sturnus vulgaris* ; and mist-nets, used with especial caution, are also exceptionally profitable at dusk.   E.A.R.E.

Hollom, P. A. D. & Brownlow, H. G. 1955. Trapping Methods for Bird Ringers. B.T.O. Field Guide no. 1 (revised). Oxford.

Ennion, E. A. R. 1959. The House on the Shore. London. (Chapters 5 and 6.)

Low, S. H. 1957. Banding with mist nets. Bird-Banding 28 : 115-128. Also 1958 as : Ringing with Mist Nets. B.T.O. Field Guide no. 4. Oxford.

TREAD : verb used, with the male as subject and the female as object, to signify the act of copulation in birds (see COPULATION).

TREDUICKER : Afrikaans name, sometimes used as if English, for *Phalacrocorax capensis* (see CORMORANT).

TREECREEPER (1) : substantive name ('creeper' in American usage) of the species of Certhiidae (Passeriformes, suborder Oscines) ; in Britain commonly used without qualification for the sole native species ; in the plural, general term for the family (see also under CREEPER and next entry below). Treecreepers are small, brownish birds, streaked above and almost white below, with slender decurved bills, long curved claws, and stiff pointed tails. They share with the Sittidae (nuthatches, spotted creepers, and wallcreepers) the habit of climbing about on trees and, more occasionally, rocks, creeping up vertical surfaces and along the undersides of branches ; they will also move head downwards, but much more rarely than nuthatches. Unlike the Sittidae, they share with the woodpeckers (Picidae) the habit of using their stiff tails as supports pressed against the bark. They have short, rounded wings and their flight is undulating, rather weak and usually for short distances. They are almost exclusively insectivorous, although they occasionally take tiny seeds, and their method of feeding is to work in a series of jerks up one tree and then fly diagonally down to the base of the next to climb that in a similar manner. All are therefore essentially birds of deciduous and coniferous forests or well-timbered parkland. Their nests are typically placed behind loose bark or ivy stems or in deep cracks or crevices, but also occasionally in nest-boxes, wall crevices, or accumulations of dead leaves and twigs. The nests themselves are untidy structures of twigs, roots, grasses, and mosses with a neat cup lined with feathers and bits of bark. The eggs are commonly 5-7 in number, while as few as 3 and as many as 9 have been recorded ; they are white marked with red-brown, varying between species from a zone of fine spots at the large end to a fairly even distribution of spots and blotches.

The family is confined to the Northern Hemisphere. The 5 species are largely non-migratory, although birds nesting in high mountain regions tend to move to lower levels in winter. All but one have restricted ranges in the Old World. The fifth, on

Treecreeper (or Brown Creeper) *Certhia familiaris.*
C.E.T.K.

the other hand, is circumglobal between extremes of 70° and 15° N lat. This last, *Certhia familiaris,* is the only one occurring in the British Isles (where it is called simply ' Treecreeper ') and in North America (where it is known as ' Brown Creeper '). There is considerable geographical variation within this species, and a dozen or more races are recognised in a series of clines. In different parts of its range it occurs in various types of woodland at all levels, but over much of continental Europe to the south of Britain and Scandinavia it overlaps with the very similar Short-toed Treecreeper *C. brachydactyla,* which also extends to northwestern Africa (Morocco to Tunisia). In this area of overlap *C. brachydactyla* seems largely to have taken over the lowland, deciduous niche and *C. familiaris* is primarily a mountain species of dense conifer forest. The other three species are partly or exclusively Himalayan. They are the Himalayan Treecreeper *C. himalayana,* which has a rather longer bill and breeds from Turkestan and Afghanistan to western China and Burma, and the Brown-throated Treecreeper *C. discolor* and Stoliczka's Treecreeper *C. nipalensis,* which are both found up to about 12 000 feet in mountains from Nepal eastwards, *C. discolor* extending into the semi-tropical regions of Thailand and Indo-China.   I.J.F.-L.

TREECREEPER (2): substantive name of the species of Climacteridae (Passeriformes, suborder Oscines); in the plural form 'Australian tree-creepers', general term for the family. This small group of Australian birds illustrates in a very nice way how similarity of feeding habits can produce a striking likeness in appearance to the members of another family, in this case the Northern Hemisphere treecreepers (Certhiidae)—see above. The single genus *Climacteris* contains 3 species groups, with 6 morphological species, according to the latest reviser (Keast 1957), although 9 species are admitted in the current check-list of the Royal Australasian Ornithologists' Union. They inhabit all of the faunal sub-divisions recognised in Australia; and one species also extends into New Guinea, where a series of apparently relict subspecies occurs discontinuously in mountain-top forests.

Climacteris has in the past usually been placed in the family Certhiidae, but many ornithologists have had an unhappy feeling about this association. John Gould (1865) added a query against this family placing, and Alfred Newton (1896) expressed his doubt whether *Climacteris* really belonged here. J. A. Keast (1957) referred it to the family Sittidae. A suggestion has been made that it may even be a tree-climbing radiation of the Australian wrens or warblers (Maluridae), with affinities to the *Sericornis-Acanthiza* group of genera (see WREN (2)). Pending further investigations it is better to retain it as an independent family, Climacteridae, regarded as a descendant of one of the older passerine immi-grations into Australia, from the Old World tropics, which has secondarily differentiated so much that its origins and affinities are now obscure.

The Australian treecreepers are about 6 inches in total length and have a fairly uniform dorsal coloration (grey-brown to rufous and black), with a coloured wing-bar (off-white to rufous), a defined superciliary line, and strongly patterned ventral parts (longitudinal striations being the main element). The tail is rounded and the rectrices have none of the specialisations for tree-climbing such as charac-terise *Certhia*. There is a long, down-curved bill. The legs and toes are long, with the claws greatly developed and curved, particularly that of the hallux. The sexes are distinguishable, but the differences between them are slight.

The nest is made of grasses, plant down, soft bark, and animal fur and is always placed inside the hollow spout of a tree, often deep down, and sometimes in hollows of fallen logs. The clutch consists of 2–3 eggs (occasionally 1 or 4), which are white or of a pale flesh tint in ground colour and freely spotted with reddish-brown. Two broods may be raised in a season. Both parents care for the young and remove the faecal pellets from the nest.

The several species frequent timbered country, and range from wet mountain eucalypt forest to dry savanna and semi-arid mulga (*Acacia aneura*) country in the interior. The birds feed like *Certhia* by spiralling upwards around tree-trunks, and some species will search for insects on the ground among fallen tree-trunks and boughs. The call is a shrill high-pitched whistle. The birds are rather sedentary, and never form mixed flocks with other species as does *Certhia*.

To cite examples from each of the 3 species groups recognised by Keast, the Red-browed Tree-creeper *C. erythrops*, the Brown Treecreeper *C. picumnus*, and the White-throated Treecreeper *C. leucophaea* all occur in the eastern parts of Australia.

D.L.S.

Howe, F. E. 1921. The genus *Climacteris* (Tree-creepers). Emu 21 : 32–41. (A general account of the genus.)
Keast, J. A. 1957. Variation and speciation in the genus *Climacteris* Temminck (Aves : Sittidae). Austr. J. Zool. 5 : 474–495. (Latest taxonomic revision.)

TREEHUNTER: substantive name of *Thripa-dectes* spp. (see OVENBIRD (1)).

TREE-PIE: or written 'treepie', substantive name of *Dendrocitta* spp. (see CROW).

TREERUNNER: alternative substantive name of *Daphoenositta miranda*, and (alternative to 'sitella') of *Neositta* spp. (see NUTHATCH); also substantive name of *Margarornis* spp., *Premnornis guttuligera*, and *Pygarrhichas albogularis* (see OVENBIRD (1)).

TREMBLER: substantive name of *Cinclocerthia ruficauda* and *Ramphocinclus brachyurus* (see MOCKING-BIRD).

TRERONINAE: see PIGEON

TRIAL AND ERROR: see LEARNING

TRIBE: see under FAMILY; NOMENCLATURE; TAXON

TRILLER: substantive name of some species of Campephagidae (see CUCKOO-SHRIKE).

TRINGINAE: see SANDPIPER

TRINOMINAL SYSTEM: see NOMENCLATURE

TRIVIAL NAME: see NAME, TRIVIAL; NOMENCLATURE

TROCHANTER: a process on the head of the femur (see SKELETON).

TROCHILI; TROCHILIDAE: see APODI-
FORMES ; and HUMMINGBIRD

TROCHLEA: pulley-shaped process at the distal
end of each metatarsal element of the tarsometatarsus (see SKELETON).

TROGLODYTIDAE: a family of the Passeriformes, suborder Oscines (see WREN (1)).

TROGON: substantive name of most species of
Trogonidae (sole family of the Trogoniformes) ;
in the plural, general term for the family. Trogons
rank among the most beautiful birds. They are
surprisingly uniform in colour pattern and shape,
considering their distribution in three widely separated tropical regions. In all species adult males
have the breast and abdomen bright red, pink,
orange, or yellow, usually in strong contrast with
the colour of the chest and upper parts. The tail,
long and graduated, is normally carried closed, so
that it most often has a square-tipped appearance,
and from below often a specifically distinctive pattern of black and white. In the American and
African species, adult males have most of the upper
parts, and often the entire head and chest, brilliant
metallic green (sometimes with a golden or bronzy
gloss) or metallic blue or violet. The Asian species,
with one exception, lack metallic colour, but males
may have red or pink on the head, rump, chest, or
tail. Females are considerably duller, with metallic
colour reduced or absent ; but in many species
(including all American and African ones) they
have almost the same bright abdominal tints as the
males.

Trogons range in size from medium to large for
arboreal birds (length 9–13¼ inches). They have
rounded wings (10 primaries), exceeded in length by
the tail (12 rectrices). The bill is short, broad at
the base and with a curved culmen. The tarsus is
short ; the weak feet have 2 toes directed forward and 2 backwards. The toe arrangement
(and that of the deep plantar tendons) is unique,
for it is the first and *second* digits that are directed
backwards (see LEG).

The skin of trogons is delicate and easily torn ;
in museum specimens the feathers drop off readily
and the bright abdominal colours have a tendency
to fade. Anatomical characters fail to indicate close
relationship of the trogons to any other single bird
order. So far as modern birds go, the trogons are
evidently a rather ancient group. Fossil bones from
southern France, believed to date from the Upper
Eocene or the Oligocene, have been attributed to
the Trogonidae.

Trogons are primarily birds of forest, or woodland, but some occur in second growth, in clearings,
and in cultivated areas (such as coffee plantations)
where there is sufficient tree growth. They are
arboreal, usually perching on a horizontal branch or
a liana below the tree canopy. They sit erect, with
the tail hanging almost vertically below and sometimes with the neck rather hunched down. They
will perch in one spot for long periods. Generally
they seem solitary or are observed in pairs or small
family groups. But in some species a number of
males may gather during the courtship period, calling loudly within sight, or at least within sound, of
each other. Courtship and social behaviour have
been little studied in this group. Vocalisations,
although often resonant and rhythmic, are of structurally simple character. The more elaborate (probably functioning as ' song '), recorded for most
members of the American and African species, may
be described as a series of hollow whistles, hoots,
caws, coos, or ' cows ' varying, according to species,
in pitch, loudness, timbre, rhythm, time, and number
of notes. Some of these species also have chirring
calls. Several species raise and lower the tail slowly
when calling, and apparently also when appre-
hensive. Guttural and squeaky notes have been
reported for some species ; in many species the
female utters notes very similar to those of the
male.

Insects and other arthropods form the main food,
although berries and small fruits provide a substantial part of the diet in a number of American
species. The Quetzal (or Resplendent Trogon)
Pharomachrus mocino, for example, is reported as
being particularly fond of *Ocotea* fruit (related to
the avocado), which it swallows whole, regurgitating
the ' pit '. It also takes insects, small arboreal frogs,
lizards, and snails. The characteristic trogon method
of feeding is aerial ; the bird darts out and flutters
vertically in the air before a leaf or twig and picks
off the insect or fruit. Some insects are captured
in flight.

While trogons are in the zoogeographical sense
birds of the Neotropical, Ethiopian, and Oriental
Regions, they are not confined to the warm lowlands. Many species are restricted to the cool
montane zones (some extend to about 10 000 feet),
and a few range beyond the Tropics of Cancer and
Capricorn. Thus the Coppery-tailed Trogon, now
regarded as a race of the Elegant Trogon *Trogon
elegans* of Middle America, breeds north to southern
Arizona, and the Narina Trogon *Apaloderma narina*
of tropical Africa breeds as far south as Cape
Province.

Trogons nest in cavities, usually of a tree or
decayed stub ; some species excavate nest-holes in

occupied arboreal nests of termites or wasps. Both sexes participate in nest building, in incubating the eggs, and in brooding and feeding the young. The clutch is usually 2 or 3, sometimes 4 ; eggs are immaculate white, cream, buff, brown, pale blue, or pale green. Incubation periods have been reported for only a few (American) species ; they have ranged between 17 and 19 days. The young are hatched naked and are altricial and nidicolous. Nestling plumages resemble those of the females, but usually show some spotting on the wings and lack bright abdominal colour.

From 35 to 40 species are recognised, depending on taxonomic judgment. Present ignorance as to details of behaviour and distribution of the South American forms, and the great similarity in appearance between some sympatric species, make decision as to species limits difficult. The group is best represented in tropical America, both as to number of species and apparently also as to individual abundance. In Middle and South America there are 2 widely distributed genera (*Trogon* and *Pharomachrus*) ; 1 monotypic genus (*Euptilotis*) is restricted to Mexico ; the West Indies have monotypic genera in Cuba and Hispaniola (*Priotelus* and *Temnotrogon*) ; the 3 African species are placed in 2 genera (*Apaloderma* and *Heterotrogon*) ; and in Asia the sole genus (*Harpactes*) includes 11 species, distributed from western India and Ceylon to south-eastern China, Indonesia, and the Philippines. The large genus *Trogon*, with 12 or more species, has been divided into 3 subgenera (*Trogon*, *Curucujus*, and *Trogonurus*). Of the various genera, the American *Pharomachrus* is the most distinctive, with upper tail coverts greatly elongated, so that 'train-bearer' has been used as the name for several members of the group. The train reaches its greatest development in the resplendent Quetzal *Pharomachrus mocino* of the mountain forests from southern Mexico to western Panama. In this famous species, sacred to the ancient Mayas and Aztecs, the long upper tail coverts extend in a graceful curve far beyond the tip of the tail, and a rounded crest tops its brilliant green, vermilion, and white plumage. Species with the most extensive ranges are : in America, the Violaceous Trogon *Trogon violaceus* (Mexico to the lower Amazon) and the Black-throated Trogon *T. rufus* (Honduras to north-eastern Argentina) ; in Africa, the Narina Trogon *Apaloderma narina* (Liberia to Eritrea and south to Cape Province) ; in Asia, the Red-headed Trogon *Harpactes erythrocephalus* (Nepal to central Fukien and south through the Indo-Malayan Peninsula to Sumatra).

See Plate 17 (colour). E.E. (2)

Chapin, J. P. 1939. Birds of the Belgian Congo. Pt. 2. Bull. Amer. Mus. Nat. Hist. 75 : 479–488. (Ranges and behaviour of African species.)

Gould, J. 1838 (2nd ed. 1875). Monograph of the Trogonidae, or Family of Trogons. London. (Colour plates.)

Peters, J. L. 1945. Check-list of Birds of the World vol. 5. Cambridge, Mass. (Taxonomy and ranges.)

Skutch, A. F. 1942. Life history of the Mexican Trogon. Auk 59 : 341–363.

Skutch, A. F. 1944. Life history of the Quetzal. Condor 46 : 213–235.

Skutch, A. F. 1959. Life history of the Black-throated Trogon. Wilson Bull. 71 : 5–18.

Stuart-Baker, E. C. 1934. The Nidification of Birds of the Indian Empire. 3. (Behaviour of Asiatic species.)

Zimmer, J. T. 1948. Studies of Peruvian birds. No. 53. The family Trogonidae. Amer. Mus. Novitat. no. 1380. (Taxonomy : new species.)

TROGONIDAE: see below

TROGONIFORMES: order comprising only the Trogonidae (see TROGON).

TROPICBIRD: substantive name of the species of Phaethontidae (Pelecaniformes, suborder Phaethontes) ; in the plural, general term for the family. There are three species in the sole genus *Phaethon*. Tropicbirds range over the warmer tropical and sub-tropical waters of the world, nesting mainly on oceanic and off-shore islands and wandering far from land between breeding seasons. They may be numerous about the breeding grounds, where groups of 6–12 birds are often seen together in noisy courtship flight. At sea they tend to be solitary or to fly silently in pairs, swooping low over the water and plunging for small fish and squid.

The long central tail feathers (which may exceed the length of the body) give tropicbirds an unmistakable outline in flight, and have prompted the vernacular names of 'marlin-spike', 'paille-en-cul', and 'paille-en-queue'. The name 'bo'sun bird', common among British travellers, may be derived also from the shrill, trilling call of the larger species, which strongly resembles the call of a boatswain's pipe. Tropicbirds are typically white, with a black bar across the eyes and solid black markings on some or all of the flight feathers. The plumage may, however, be flushed with delicate or rich roseate pink, and one subspecies, *P. lepturus fulvus*, is distinguished by plumage of a strong orange-pink. The bill, which is stout and slightly decurved, is usually of vivid crimson, coral-red, or yellow. First-year juveniles of all species lack the elongated central rectrices and are more or less heavily barred and speckled with black on head, back, wings, and tail. Barred plumage is also found in adults of the Red-billed Tropicbird *P. aethereus*.

The short legs are set far back and cannot support

the weight of the body on land. The webbed feet are used for paddling, for shuffling over the ground, and for digging a shallow nest-scrape. Normally tropicbirds nest high on steep cliffs, or in other places from which they can take off without walking or springing. The nests are found in cavities or under overhanging rocks, in sites which afford shade and can be defended against intruders.

Tropicbirds are gregarious in courtship, flying in excited groups along the cliff faces, swooping, circling, and calling in close formation. The tail-streamers are depressed and undulated during the aerial courtship display. Pairing may involve fighting over nest sites and partners ; the birds grip each other with their bills and, with feet and wings spread to gain purchase, strive to eject each other from the chosen site. Many bear scars and gashes about the head and neck. Coition occurs in the nest ; a single egg is laid, and is incubated by both parents in watches of 2–5 days. The eggs are oval, varying in shade between deep and pale purple-brown and generally becoming paler in the course of incubation as the surface pigment is rubbed off. Incubation lasts from 41 days in the smaller species to 44–45 days in the larger species.

Newly-hatched tropicbird chicks are covered with heavy grey or fawn down from half an inch to an inch in thickness. They are left alone at the nest shortly after hatching while both parents hunt for food. In localities where the laying season is spread over many months the small chicks are vulnerable to attack by adults of the same species in search of nest sites, and many are killed by intruders during their first week of growth. Juvenile plumage begins to appear about the tenth or twelfth day ; the chicks grow slowly and leave the nest as fully-fledged juveniles some 11–15 weeks after hatching.

Three species of tropicbird are at present distinguished. The Red-tailed Tropicbird *Phaethon rubricauda*, with several rather doubtful subspecies listed, is known from the south tropical Indian Ocean and the tropical Pacific ; largest of all the tropicbirds, this species may reach 18 inches in length (excluding the central tail feathers) with wing-span of 35–40 inches. The narrow vanes of the 2 central rectrices are red, and the plumage of the newly-moulted adults may be flushed with a pale roseate pink. The bill is generally orange-yellow or red. The Red-billed Tropicbird *P. aethereus*, slightly smaller (length about 14 inches), is distinguished by the barred adult plumage and coral-red bill. The species extends from Tower Island (Galápagos Islands) through the Caribbean Sea and tropical Atlantic Ocean, and into the Red Sea and northern Indian Ocean. The Indian Ocean and Gulf of Aden birds are slightly smaller than those of the Atlantic, and by some authorities are regarded as a separate species *P. indicus*.

The Yellow-billed (or White-tailed) Tropicbird *P. lepturus* ranges through the Caribbean Sea, Atlantic and Indian Oceans, and south-west Pacific Ocean. This is the smallest species of the genus (length about 12 inches). The adult plumage is generally clear white or tinted, but without barring ; among the birds of Ascension Island, some of which show salmon-pink tinting, there is evidence that males are more strongly coloured than females. In the subspecies *P. l. fulvus* of Christmas Island (Indian Ocean) both sexes are vividly coloured.

Detailed studies of *P. aethereus* and *P. lepturus*, with populations of ringed birds, have been made on Ascension Island. Individual Yellow-billed Tropicbirds were found to breed at intervals of approximately 9–10 months, with the breeding of the species as a whole spread throughout the year. In contrast, the Red-billed Tropicbirds were breeding approximately annually, the species showing a marked peak of laying between July and September and very little breeding activity between January and March. All species are believed to breed annually elsewhere in the world.

See Plate 47b (phot.). B.S.

Stonehouse, B. 1962. The tropic-birds (genus *Phaethon*) of Ascension Island. Ibis 103b : 124–161. (B.O.U. Centenary Expedition.)

TROPICOPOLITAN : same as PANTROPICAL

TROPISM : in the most general sense, a tendency (at the simplest level) to react in a certain way to a particular kind of stimulus—compare TAXIS.

TROUPIAL : *Icterus icterus* ; in the plural, sometimes used in place of ' oriole ' as a group name for the genus, or even the family (see ORIOLE (2)).

TRUMPETER : substantive name of the 3 species of Psophiidae (Gruiformes, suborder Grues) ; in the plural, general term for the family. The latter is purely Neotropical, and the name is given on account of the trumpeting call note. Trumpeters are of about the size of a domestic fowl, with a rather long neck and long legs, a small rounded head, and a stout and short, somewhat curved bill. The tail is short and the wings rounded. The plumage is largely velvety black with a purplish gloss on the lower foreneck. The sexes are alike. They have a somewhat humpbacked appearance especially when calling, so the common name in Surinam, ' Kammee kammee ' (=camel back), is well chosen.

Trumpeters are gregarious birds, living in flocks on the ground of the tropical rain-forests of South America. They can run fast ; they fly laboriously and but seldom ; they roost in trees. Their food is partly vegetable (fruits and berries) but consists also to a large extent of insects—Formicidae (Hymenoptera) and Tabanidae (Diptera) are recorded for the common species.

The ordinary call of *Psophia crepitans* when in a group is a long-drawn ' uh uh uh uh ooooooo ooooooo oooooooo ', the first ' uh 's in a quick tempo and then followed by two or three long-drawn ' ooooooo 's. When the bird is uttering this, the feathers on the back are somewhat raised and the bill is opened and shut a few times. The birds are easily lured (and shot) by imitating this note. A loud trumpeting call is given when they threaten other members of the flock ; and a soft ' wheet, wheet ' is also heard, the significance of which is not clear. Posturing is done with widely spread wings. The birds like bathing in shallow water, after which they sink down on the ground with widely spread wings to dry their feathers in the rays of the sun.

Very little is known about their life in the wild, and the remark by Newton that it is much to be wished that fuller accounts of them had appeared still holds good at the present day. Most of our knowledge comes from captive birds, which become very tame in a short time. Our information about the nesting of *Psophia crepitans* is still very scanty and even contradictory. Lloyd found in British Guiana a nest in a hole of a fork of a tree, and from Surinam there is a reliable report of a sitting bird in a large hole in a tree. The clutch may be rather large, as Lloyd found 7 eggs in a nest. The eggs are dirty white, with a rather rough shell ; in shape they resemble, in miniature, the eggs of the Ostrich *Struthio camelus*. An egg from Amazonia in the Nehrkorn collection measures 52×39 mm. ; the average dimensions of 4 laid in captivity were 58·5×47·55 mm., weight 76·5 grams (shell 7·6 grams). The incubation period is not known ; the female is said to incubate. The nestlings are, according to observations by Beebe in British Guiana, nidifugous and were found in April. Their downy plumage was very complex—blackish with elaborate cinnamon streaks.

There are 3 species, in a single genus. The Common Trumpeter *Psophia crepitans* is generally black with the tertials, scapular coverts, and the middle of the back grey ; a freshly collected male weighed 1019 grams (about 2¼ lb.) and a female 1060 grams. It is found in eastern and southern Venezuela, the Guianas, north-western and north-eastern Brazil, south-eastern Colombia, and eastern Ecuador. The Green-winged Trumpeter *P. viridis* is generally black, with glossy green wing coverts, olive-green scapulars and tertials, and a chocolate-brown back ; it occurs in northern Brazil. The White-winged Trumpeter *P. leucoptera* is generally black, with white scapular coverts and tertials and a black back ; it occurs in north-western Brazil and eastern Peru.

See Plate 32 (colour). F.H. (3)

TUBENOSES : general term for the Procellariiformes (Tubinares) (see PETREL).

TUBERCULOSIS : see DISEASE

TUBINARES : see PROCELLARIIFORMES

TUFTEDCHEEK : substantive name of *Pseudocolaptes* spp. (for family see OVENBIRD (1)).

TUI : *Prosthemadera novaeseelandiae* (see HONEY-EATER).

TUMOURS : see DISEASE

TUNDRA : frozen or half-frozen swamp with vegetation largely of mosses and lichens ; the main bird habitat in vast areas of the North Temperate Zone, lying between the region of ice and the TAIGA.

TURACO : substantive name of most species of Musophagidae (Cuculiformes, suborder Musophagi) ; in the plural, general term for the family. The word has also been spelt ' touraco ', and the names ' lourie ' (sometimes), ' go-away-bird ' (one genus), and ' plantain-eater ' (commonly) have likewise been used for some species. For the last (plantain =banana) there is no justification whatever in the birds' habits in the wild state. The species of this purely African group are, however, all fruit-eaters, and they are thoroughly arboreal, occuping the entire range of tree-habitats, from the driest thorn-bush to evergreen forest at all altitudes, and from the southern border of the Sahara to the Cape Province. They have rather long tails ; and most of them have short rounded wings, with poor flight.

As a family, the Musophagidae have been associated in the past with either the Galliformes or the Cuculiformes, and have also been exalted to a distinct order, the Musophagiformes (Musophagae of Stresemann). The affinities of their Mallophaga are all galliform, but superficially some of the turacos resemble certain non-parasitic cuckoos, especially the couas of Madagascar, and preliminary work on egg-white proteins (see PROTEINS AS TAXONOMIC CHARACTERS) clearly favours cuculiform affinities. The family consists of about 18 species (there is much difficulty in deciding the limits of those allied to the Knysna Lourie *Taraco corythaix*) ; the species may be grouped in 5 genera : *Corythaeola* (1 species), *Crinifer* (2), *Corythaixoides* (3), *Musophaga* (2), and *Turaco* (10). With the last, the genera ' *Proturacus* ', ' *Ruwenzorornis* ', and ' *Gallirex* ' have been synonymised.

Among these birds the Giant (or Great Blue) Turaco *Corythaeola cristata* is exceptional, the others are much of a size, with body about as big as that of a Wood Pigeon *Columba palumbus*. The *Musophaga* and *Taraco* spp. are brilliantly coloured, with glossy blue, violet, and green plumage, and in the wing, extending over most of the remiges, a lovely crimson. Except for the Violet Plantain-eater *Musophaga violacea*, in which the head feathers are like very short hair, all these birds have crests, glossy ' mops ' or constricted to the middle line of the head and tipped red or white. The Giant Turaco has green and blue plumage but no red. By contrast, the other species are dull-coloured, predominantly greys and browns, with vestigial green on the breasts of the Bare-faced Go-away-bird *Corythaixoides personata* and the Grey Go-away-bird *C. concolor*. Throughout the family the sexes are alike.

Bills are strong and decurved, often with a ' keel '. A peculiar feature of the family is the exceptional variability of both position and shape of the nostril ; it may be anything from circular to slit-shaped. In fact 2 species, the Red-crested Turaco *Taraco erythrolophus* and Bannerman's Turaco *T. bannermani*, which are so alike in plumage that they could not easily be told apart in the field, have respectively circular nostrils and slit nostrils. Another unusual feature is that in most species the feathers of the head and breast are largely deficient in barbules, so that they seem ' hairy '. Feet are also peculiar—semi-zygodactyl ; that is, the outer toe is most often at about a right angle to the main axis of the foot, but it can be moved farther back or directly forward. This adaptability no doubt contributes to the birds' notable agility in running and jumping about in trees.

An even more remarkable feature of the family, unique among birds, is the nature of the green and/or red coloration which is so striking in the species of *Taraco* and *Musophaga*. Whereas green is in most birds produced by a combination of melanin and yellow carotinoid, in these it is turacoverdin, a peculiar pigment the nature of which is not yet certain. Moreover, the glorious red found only in the remiges and head feathers, turacin, has received a good deal of chemical attention and has been shown to be a copper complex of uroporphyrin III, a pigment unique in the whole Animal Kingdom (see COLOUR). For over a century the statement has been repeated at intervals that this red pigment is washed out of the living bird by rain ; this is entirely untrue, but the fact is that the red is immediately dissolved by alkali. Turacoverdin exists in several species that are devoid of turacin, but the reverse does not hold good. The amount of the green pigment is correlated with the luxuriance of the vegetation in which the birds live, being most developed in the numerous species of evergreen forest, and least or not at all in the deciduous environments, especially thornbush. It may therefore be supposed to have some protective function.

All of the Musophagidae have ' got something '. The brightly coloured species are extremely lively, agile, and attractive, the *Corythaixoides* spp. are droll, and the *Crinifer* spp. grotesque. But many of these are difficult to observe in the wild state and their habits are not well known. Displays, which have never been formally described, appear to vary much within the family—in *Corythaixoides* one bird hovering over the other on a tree-top, and in at least a number of the other species, bowing, raising of the crest and flirting of the tail and wing (which shows the brilliant red patches). In all species the voice is harsh. Many utter a reiterated bark ; but the characteristic call of *Corythaixoides* spp. is a nasal ' gwaaa ', hence the name of ' go-away-bird '.

Throughout the family the nests are flat, flimsy structures of twigs, like those of pigeons (Columbidae), with 2 eggs that are white or tinted. Incubation and fledging periods have hardly ever been recorded, but seem to be about 18 and 28 days respectively. The young are born with thick down, and the wing-claw may be well developed ; they often move off the nest and clamber about their tree long before they can fly. A number of details of juvenile behaviour and development are given by Moreau (1938), and Van Someren has studied the Blue-crested Plantain-eater *Taraco hartlaubi*. Courtship feeding takes place ; the young are fed on regurgitated fruit-pulp, and while they are in the nest their faeces are swallowed by the parents.

Several species of turaco are widespread in Africa. For example, *Corythaeola cristata* ranges through the evergreen forests of all West Africa and the Congo to Uganda ; Ross's Turaco *Musophaga rossae* inhabits woodland in a belt round the Congo forest, from Angola to Uganda and Ubangi ; *Corythaixoides concolor* is characteristic of the dry savannas from the mouth of the River Congo to Bechuanaland and up the east coast to about Dar es Salaam. The genus

Tauraco includes species of very different geographical extension ; 2 are of special interest for their extreme restriction, *T. bannermani* to the Bamenda Highlands of the Cameroons and Prince Ruspoli's Turaco *T. ruspolii* to, apparently, a few square miles in Abyssinia.

See Plate 30 (colour).   R.E.M.

Moreau, R. E. 1938. A contribution to the biology of the Musophagiformes. Ibis (14) 2 : 639–671.
Moreau, R. E. 1958. Some aspects of the Musophagidae. Ibis 100 : 67–112, 238–270. (Especially ecological and geographical ranges, variation and classification.)
Van Someren, V. G. L. 1956. Blue-crested Plantain-eater. Fieldiana Zool. 38 : 164–174.

TURBINAL CARTILAGE: in each nasal cavity (see SKELETON).

TURCO: substantive name of *Pteroptochos* spp. (see TAPACULO).

TURDINAE: see MUSCICAPIDAE ; and THRUSH

TURDOIDINI: see BABBLER

TURKEY: substantive name of the 2 species of Meleagrididae (Galliformes, suborder Galli) ; in the plural, general term for the family. Turkeys are large gallinaceous birds and mainly terrestrial, confined to North America. Peculiar to the family is a slender, straight furcula. Of the 2 monotypic genera, *Meleagris* and *Agriocharis*, the former is by far the most numerous and widely distributed.

The plumage of the Turkey *Meleagris gallopavo*, especially the males, is dark with brilliant green, bronze, and copper metallic reflections ; the races with white or pale buff upper tail coverts are the most amenable to domestication. The male, and occasionally the female, has a long tuft of bristles on the upper breast. The rectrices are barred and mottled and have nearly square tips. The head and neck are bare except for a scattering of sparsely vaned feathers. There is a long fleshy frontal caruncle (distensible at will), tubercles on the neck and head, and a throat wattle ; the colours of these ornaments, according to mood, may be red, blue, or white. In spring and summer the head and neck are predominantly red. During display the tail is spread into a fan, the wings scrape on the ground, the head rests on the shoulders, and a puffing sound is emitted. The 'gobble' is characteristic of the male ; the female's usual note is 'quit', while the young make a piping sound. Unusually large (wild) males will weigh 22 lb., but the average for mature males is 17½ lb. ; the females weigh only half as much. They are strong fliers for a short distance, usually dropping to the ground within a quarter of a mile ; the longest recorded flight is one mile.

The male has a harem comprising several females, and these seek his attention rather than he theirs. The nest is built in a hollow in the ground, usually well concealed under vegetation. The female lays 8–15 eggs, the average being 11, which are lightly spotted with varying shades of brown. More than one female sometimes lays in the same nest. The incubation period is 28 days. The loss of young by September is approximately 50 per cent. Following the breeding season there is segregation of the sexes.

The Turkey usually drinks twice a day and is seldom found more than two miles from water. It will wade into the water to drink but does not bathe in it. Its food is very largely vegetable ; some succulent foods, but chiefly seeds, are taken, and preference is shown for mast, such as acorns, beechnuts, and pecans. A wide variety of insects is eaten, grasshoppers (Locustidae) being consumed in quantity. Minor animal foods are crustaceans, amphibians, and reptiles.

Seven races are now recognised. The Eastern Turkey *M. g. silvestris* is characterised by dark chestnut upper tail coverts and chestnut tips on the rectrices. It formerly occupied all of the eastern United States from southern Maine west through southern Ontario to south-central South Dakota, and south to eastern Texas. There have been numerous introductions in the northernmost states, but no indigenous stock remains except in Pennsylvania, West Virginia, Kentucky, and Missouri, and southward to the Gulf of Mexico. The Florida Turkey *M. g. osceola* occupies most of the peninsula of Florida ; it differs from the Eastern Turkey in being smaller, in the failure of most of the white bars on the primaries to reach the shaft, and in the absence of barring on the inner secondaries. The Rio Grande Turkey *M. g. intermedia* ranges from Tom Green, Shackelford, and Nueces Counties, Texas, south to north-western Coahuila, south-eastern San Luis Potosí, Nuevo León, and southern Tamaulipas ; the rump in this race is wholly glossy black and the upper tail coverts are buff to cinnamon. The South Mexican Turkey *M. g. gallopavo* is the race domesticated by the Mexican Indians and introduced into Europe (see DOMESTICATION). It ranged formerly from the lowlands of the state of Vera Cruz west through the Federal District of Mexico to western and southern Michoacan, but it has been exterminated except in the latter state. The feathers of the rump and upper tail coverts are tipped with buff and the rectrices with white and a tinge of buff. Moore's Turkey *M. g. onusta*, a form of questionable validity, is found on the western slope of the Sierra Madre Mountains from south-western Chihuahua, south-eastern Sonora, south to Jalisco ; the median rectrices are barred and not mottled or vermiculated as in *M. g. gallopavo*, and have white tips. Gould's Turkey *M. g. mexicana* occurs in the Sierra Madre Occidental from northern Chihuahua to southern Jalisco ; it is larger than *M. g. gallopavo* but similarly marked, having the lower back and rump with metallic reflections in place of very dark blue. Merriam's Turkey *M. g. merriami* was domesticated by the ancient Pueblos ; it occurs in scattered areas throughout New Mexico, eastern Arizona, and southern Colorado, and formerly to north-central Colorado, and it has the tips of the barred rectrices and upper tail coverts white or very pale buff.

The Ocellated Turkey *Agriocharis ocellata* is a diminishing species ranging formerly throughout the Yucatan Peninsula west to Tabasco, eastern Chiapas, and central Guatemala. It has been exterminated in northern Campeche and western Yucatan, and in the south has withdrawn to northern Guatemala and northern British Honduras. Some authorities would restore this species to the genus *Meleagris*. Osteologically the 2 turkeys are very similar ; but the Ocellated Turkey seems to have sufficient peculiar characteristics to deserve generic distinction. A large male will weigh 11 lb. and a large female about 6½ lb. In plumage it rivals the Peacock *Pavo cristatus*. The contour feathers are tipped with green and bronze, and the rounded, grey tail feathers with reddish bronze. The naked head and neck are bright blue, with scattered red and white tubercles. In addition to the long frontal caruncle, there is a prominent fleshy knob on the crown ; but a beard is absent. The display is very similar to that of *Meleagris*, but the gobble is decidedly different ; it has been rendered as 'ting-ting-co-on-cot-zitl-glung'. The nest is placed on the ground ; the number of eggs is about the same as for the Common Turkey, and in size and markings they are scarcely distinguishable. There is no segregation of the sexes following the breeding season. The Ocellated Turkey will take wing on the slightest threat of danger rather than trust to its legs as does the other species. The birds remain in the heavy jungle during summer and early autumn, then frequent the fields of maize to feed. The food consists of various fruits, seeds, succulent vegetation, and insects.

See also DOMESTICATION.   A.W.S.

TURKEY, BRUSH : see BRUSH-TURKEY ; MEGAPODE

TURKEY, WATER : popular misnomer (U.S.A.) for the Anhinga *Anhinga anhinga* (see DARTER).

TURNICES ; TURNICIDAE : see under GRUI-FORMES ; and BUTTONQUAIL. The Pedionomidae

are sometimes treated as a subfamily (see PLAINS-WANDERER).

TURNSTONE : substantive name of the 2 species of *Arenaria* ; used without qualification, in Britain, for *A. interpres* (see SANDPIPER).

TURUMTEE : name applied in India to *Falco chicquera* (see FALCON).

TWIN-SPOT : substantive name of some *Clyto-spiza* spp. and *Hypargos* spp. (see WEAVER-FINCH).

TWITE : *Acanthis flavirostris* (see FINCH).

TYPE : general term embracing TYPE-GENUS, TYPE-SPECIES, and TYPE-SPECIMEN ; used without quali-fication for any of these, in appropriate context, but especially the last mentioned—for the concept see NOMENCLATURE.

TYPE-GENUS : the nominal genus that is the type of a taxon in the family-group and that pro-vides the stem of the name of such taxon (or taxa of different ranks within the group). The mere naming of the higher taxa after the included genus selects the latter as the type. The names of the higher taxa are not affected by subsequent disuse of the generic name as such, whether by reason of the nominal genus being merged in another for taxo-nomic purposes or (after 1960) by rejection of the generic name as a junior synonym ; new names given to higher taxa before 1961 for the second reason are to be retained if they have meanwhile been generally accepted. The rejection of a generic name as a junior homonym invalidates names based upon it for family-group taxa. See FAMILY-GROUP ; NOMENCLATURE.

TYPE-LOCALITY : that from which a species or subspecies was described by the author of its name, or—failing that in the case of early names—one subsequently designated ; where applicable, that at which the type-specimen was collected. The type-locality of a nominate subspecies is that of the species. A type-locality may be changed if the original geographical attribution is definitely shown to have been erroneous ; and where a type-locality was too vaguely defined (e.g. only the country being named), a subsequent author may determine a 'restricted type-locality'. See NOMENCLATURE ; TYPE-SPECIMEN.

TYPE-SERIES : see TYPE-SPECIMEN

TYPE-SPECIES : the nominal species that is the type of a genus or a subgenus (or of both in the case of a nominate subgenus). The term 'genotype' (also 'generitype', 'generotype') is inadmissible as an equivalent, and has in fact quite a different meaning. The 'fixation' of a type-species is obligatory, and the author of a generic or subgeneric name proposed after 1930 must himself designate a type.

In the case of older generic names there may likewise be a 'type by original designation'; but failing this there may be a 'type by indication', and the latter may take various forms. If the author established the genus with a single nominal species, that species becomes the 'type by monotypy'; if he established it with an included species having its specific name or a subspecific name the same as the generic name, that species becomes the 'type by absolute tautonymy'; if he established it with only one of its species having in its synonymy a pre-1758 name (single word) identical with the generic name, that species becomes the 'type by Linnean tautonymy'. In the absence of original designation or indication, it is necessary to fix a 'type by subsequent designation'; any zoologist may do so, in accordance with rules contained in the International Code (see NOMENCLATURE).

It may be noted that a species with a tautonymous name is not necessarily the type of its genus. It may have been ineligible as a type by indication through not being expressly included in the nominal genus when that was established; or some other species might conceivably have been designated in preference.

TYPE-SPECIMEN: the single specimen that is the 'type' of a nominal species or subspecies, or of both in the case of a nominate subspecies (see NOMENCLATURE). If the specimen was expressly designated at the outset by the author of the name (the recommended course) it is a 'holotype'; if it was designated later, from an original 'type-series', it is a 'lectotype'; if it was designated later in special circumstances to replace a holotype or lectotype that, with all other members of any original type-series, had been lost or destroyed, it is a 'neotype'.

If there was an original type-series on which the author of the name based his description, all of them are 'syntypes' unless one has been expressly designated. If a holotype or lectotype has been designated, the remainder are 'paratypes' or 'paralectotypes' as the case may be. The term 'cotype' is no longer recognised.

As type-specimens are of particular and permanent value as standards of reference in nomenclature, they should be regarded as 'the property of science'. A special responsibility rests on museums for the custody and proper labelling of type-specimens.

A type-specimen, however, is no longer regarded as necessarily typical in any but a nomenclatural sense; it may in fact happen to be unrepresentative of the norm of the population from which it was drawn. The old type concept in biological thought has given way to a population concept, in which mean values and range of variation are what have real, as opposed to conventional, significance.

TYPICAL: apart from the ordinary meaning of the word, an adjective relating to TYPE; see also under NOMENCLATURE. Sometimes inappropriately used in the sense of NOMINATE.

TYPICAL INTENSITY: see DISPLACEMENT ACTIVITY

TYRANNIDAE: see under PASSERIFORMES; and FLYCATCHER (2)

TYRANNOIDEA: see under PASSERIFORMES

TYRANNULET: substantive name of small tyrant-flycatchers in *Camptostoma*, *Tyrannulus*, and other genera (see FLYCATCHER (2)).

TYRANT: substantive name (alone or in compounds such as 'ground-tyrant' and 'water-tyrant') of species in many genera of tyrant-flycatchers (Tyrannidae), many other members of the family having 'flycatcher' as substantive name (the two names being also to some extent interchangeable), and still others having various special names (see FLYCATCHER (2)).

TYRIANTAIL: substantive name of most *Metallura tyrianthina* subspp. (for family see HUMMINGBIRD).

TYSTIE: alternative substantive name of the guillemots of the genus *Cepphus* (see AUK).

TYTONIDAE: see under STRIGIFORMES; and OWL

U

ULNA: a bone of the forelimb (see SKELETON ; WING).

ULNARE: one of the proximal carpal bones (see SKELETON; WING).

ULTIMATE: applied to factors that are remotely causative but do not lead immediately to the effect—contrasted with PROXIMATE.

UMBILICAL CORD: connection between the embryo and transitory structures within the egg (see DEVELOPMENT, EMBRYONIC).

UMBILICUS: term applied to each of the two ('inferior' and 'superior') openings in the shaft of a feather (see FEATHER).

UMBRELLA-BIRD: substantive name of *Cephalopterus* spp. (see COTINGA).

UNCINATE PROCESS: a projection found on most of the ribs (see SKELETON).

UNGUAL: term applied adjectivally to the terminal phalanx of a digit, bearing the claw if any (see LEG ; WING).

UPUPAE ; UPUPIDAE: see CORACIIFORMES ; and HOOPOE

URATES: salts of URIC ACID.

URETER: see EXCRETORY SYSTEM

URIC ACID: see EXCRETORY SYSTEM ; METABOLISM

URINARY SYSTEM: see EXCRETORY SYSTEM

URINE: see DROPPINGS ; EXCRETORY SYSTEM

URODAEUM: see REPRODUCTIVE SYSTEM ; and EXCRETORY SYSTEM

UROPYGIUM: the rump (see TOPOGRAPHY) ; for uropygial gland see OIL GLAND.

UTERUS: part of the oviduct (see REPRODUCTIVE SYSTEM).

UTILISATION BY MAN: human exploitation of wild birds as one of the world's natural resources ; for other than wild birds see DOMESTICATION. Wild birds and their eggs have been taken for human food from the earliest times ; they still represent a main source of food for certain communities and a considerable supplementary source for many peoples. The modern shooting of birds for sport, a sophisticated development of hunting for the pot, has economic consequences of a special kind. Birds of wild species are kept in captivity for various purposes. Apart from food, the feathers of birds are put to various utilitarian and ornamental purposes ; and under some conditions accumulations of bird droppings (guano) provide a valuable supply of agricultural fertilisers. Some miscellaneous uses can also be mentioned.

Flesh. The flesh of probably the majority of avian species is in some degree palatable to man, and in many instances very palatable indeed (see GASTRONOMIC AND MEDICAL USES ; PALATABILITY OF BIRDS AND EGGS). Birds have accordingly been hunted from time immemorial for human food. Wild species are still killed in large numbers for this purpose in many parts of the world ; to cite a single instance, Serventy has recently estimated that about half a million of the Short-tailed Shearwater *Puffinus tenuirostris* of Australia are taken annually. In a country such as Britain, today, this is mainly restricted to those that are shot for sport, as discussed below, although in earlier times many small birds (e.g. Skylarks *Alauda arvensis*) were taken for the table. The same is true to a greater or less extent of many developed countries, but in others of these the slaughter of small passerines continues on a large scale. In primitive countries there may or may not be much use of birds for food, according to the habits of the people.

The taking of birds on a large scale necessarily depends upon these being concentrated under conditions in which their capture in numbers is practicable—where sporting interests are not involved, shooting is uneconomic. It therefore mainly occurs either where birds nest colonially in accessible places or where they form large flocks outside the breeding season, particularly on migration. Under the first head there are, notably, the seafowl colonies in various parts of the world, especially on islands, which may even suffice to provide the main food supply of the local inhabitants ; there are examples off the coasts of the British Isles, to look no farther. The adult birds may be netted as they fly low over the nesting area, or the young may be taken while still flightless ; and much of the catch may be preserved for future consumption.

Many species are highly gregarious at the time of migration ; and the birds are often particularly susceptible to capture when they make a landing, tired and hungry after a long flight. This situation is exploited, according to species and terrain, by various forms of netting and trapping. The Heligoland trap, which now plays an important part in the capture of migrants for scientific ringing, originated from a device used by fowlers for catching thrushes *Turdus* spp. and other birds (see TRAPPING). The netting of Quails *Coturnix coturnix* has for long been practised on a large scale in the Mediterranean countries and elsewhere, the birds being exported alive in small cages—nearly 2 million from Egypt alone in 1913, but the trade is nowadays more restricted (see PROTECTION). Special methods have been evolved for the capture of duck *Anas* spp. etc. (see DECOY). A means of catching small perching birds is provided by bird-lime smeared on twigs, and hosts of passerine migrants are taken annually in this way in countries where it is used (see LIME, BIRD-).

Eggs. The use of the eggs of wild birds for human food has been exhaustively reviewed by Cott. The birds chiefly exploited are large species and those nesting colonially ; in general, the eggs of such birds are both accessible and palatable. Some human communities, especially on islands, make great use of the enormous colonies of sea birds of various species. When these resources have been mismanaged, collection has tended to destroy the supply ; but when conservation of the resources is practised, the supply is maintained. In the latter circumstances the birds flourish, sometimes more so than if there were no economic motive for their protection ; and it may well be that systematic egging is desirable as a method of control of species that might become excessively numerous.

The species providing large supplies of eggs for human consumption are to be found especially in the orders Charadriiformes, Sphenisciformes, Procellariiformes, and Anseriformes. The only species probably yielding over 1 000 000 eggs annually is the Sooty Tern *Sterna fuscata* (tropical islands, e.g. Seychelles). Probably yielding over 100 000 are the Jackass Penguin *Spheniscus demersus* (South Africa), Short-tailed Shearwater *Puffinus tenuirostris* (Bass Strait, Australia), Moorhen *Gallinula chloropus* (Europe and Asia), Herring Gull *Larus argentatus* (North Atlantic and North Sea), Blackheaded Gull *L. ridibundus* (north-western Europe), Arctic Tern *Sterna paradisaea*, Common Noddy *Anous stolidus* (Seychelles, etc.), Guillemot (or Murre) *Uria aalge* (North Atlantic), Brünnich's Guillemot *U. lomvia* (Arctic), Lapwing *Vanellus vanellus* (northern Europe), and Junglefowl *Gallus gallus* (Asia). In the next group, probably yielding over 10 000 annually, come various ducks (Anatidae) and gallinaceous birds (Phasianidae), as well as further species of petrels (Procellariiformes) and penguins (Spheniscidae), and the Cattle Egret *Ardeola ibis* (Spain, China).

Sport. Modern firearms have made possible the development of shooting for sport, widely practised in different parts of the world. For this purpose, the prey must not only be palatable and sufficiently numerous but must also place demands on human skill. The species most highly prized are to be found chiefly among the pheasants and partridges (Phasianidae), grouse (Tetraonidae), guineafowl (Numididae), ducks and geese (Anatidae), plovers (Charadriidae), woodcock and snipe (Scolopacidae), sandgrouse (Pteroclididae), and pigeons (Columbidae). In many instances the birds are carefully preserved during the breeding season, both by the owners of land and by the law, and the seasons and amount of shooting may likewise be controlled (see PROTECTION) ; breeding of a few species (notably the Pheasant *Phasianus colchicus*) may even be assisted by artificial measures. The economic value of sporting rights, especially where there is strict private ownership of land, can thus be very substantial, the value of the killed birds as food being almost incidental. However, the economics and the techniques of shooting do not come within the scope of this work—but see under WILDFOWL. The indiscriminate shooting of all kinds of birds, often of species that provide neither sport nor valuable food, causes great destruction in many parts of the world and can scarcely be dignified as a form of utilisation.

Captivity. Wild birds of many kinds are kept in captivity for aesthetic, educational, and scientific purposes (see AVICULTURE ; CAGE BIRD). For a sporting use see FALCONRY. Analogous to the latter, but utilitarian, is the use of cormorants *Phalacrocorax* spp. by Oriental fishermen (see COR-

MORANT). There is also the use of frigatebirds *Fregata* spp. for carrying messages between islands in the Pacific Ocean (see FRIGATEBIRD).

Feathers. There have been many uses for feathers, but at the present day domesticated varieties of avian species provide the readiest source for most utilitarian purposes. Quills have been used as pens for writing, and for trimming the flight of arrows and of shuttlecocks. The softer feathers have been used in bulk for stuffing mattresses and the like. For filling quilts and quilted clothing, the down that various ducks pluck from their bodies to use as nest-lining is particularly suitable ; that of the Eider *Somateria mollissima*, in particular, has been systematically collected from the nests as an article of commerce. Small brightly coloured feathers are in demand for the manufacture of the artificial ' flies ' used by anglers.

The feathers of many wild birds, especially of species with decorative plumes or bright colours, have for long been used for human adornment, in the form of head-dresses, cloaks, tippets, and so on (see ORNAMENTATION, BIRDS IN HUMAN ; TIPPET). The demands of modern millinery gave rise to an appallingly destructive trade in plumage, but this is now much restricted (see PROTECTION).

Guano. See GUANO ; GUANO, CAVE.

Miscellaneous. See EDIBLE NESTS ; IVORY, HORN- BILL. Observations of birds in flight have assisted early human navigation (Hornell) ; and birds have been used in augury (see OMENS, BIRDS AS).

Cott, H. B. 1953–54. The exploitation of wild birds for their eggs. Ibis 95 : 409–449, 643–675 ; 96 : 129–149.
Hornell, J. 1946. The role of birds in early navigation. Antiquity 20 : 142–149.

V

VACUUM ACTIVITY: same as OVERFLOW ACTIVITY.

VAGINA: see REPRODUCTIVE SYSTEM

VAGRANT: a wanderer outside the normal migration range of the species or subspecies, so far as that can be judged.

VAGUS: the tenth cranial nerve on each side (see NERVOUS SYSTEM).

VALIDITY: for that of scientific names, see NOMENCLATURE.

VANE: alternatively 'vexillum', the more or less coherent series of barbs on each side of the rachis of a typical feather (see FEATHER).

VANGA: substantive name of most species of Vangidae (Passeriformes, suborder Oscines); in the plural, alternatively 'vanga-shrikes', general term for the family. 'Vanga' was originally the native name of the Hook-billed Vanga *Vanga curvirostris*, but by extension it is now applied to the group. The family, with 12 species, is restricted to Madagascar.

Vangas vary from 5 to 12 inches in length. In colour they are mostly boldly patterned in black and white or blue and white or with blacks, rufous browns, and greys. Sexual dimorphism may be present or absent. The bill is variable, but usually heavy and often with a pronounced hook at the tip; the perching feet are moderately strong; the wings are often rather long; and the tail is of moderate length. Some vangas rather resemble true shrikes (Laniinae) or bush-shrikes (Malaconotinae), and some recall wood-swallows (Artamidae). Their precise relationship to the great group of Old World insect-eating birds is not clear, but they are usually grouped near the shrikes (Laniidae). Presumably they represent an old colonisation of Madagascar that has radiated in the isolation there. This radiation is especially apparent in the bill shape, but we have no information as to specialised uses for these different bills.

They are all tree birds, feeding on insects and other small animals which they search out from the twigs and branches. The Hook-billed Vanga and the Helmetbird *Aerocharis prevostii* also take small tree frogs and lizards readily. Most species are strongly gregarious, feeding and moving in loose flocks of from 3 or 4 to several dozen individuals; and some are noisy, giving calls, whistles, or chattering notes. What little is known of the breeding habits indicates a cup-shaped nest of twigs built in a tree, and a clutch of 3 or 4 eggs which may be white or green, spotted with brown.

Helmetbird *Aerocharis prevostii*, of the Malagasy family Vangidae. *C.E.T.K.*

The Chabert Vanga *Leptopterus chabert* is black above, white below; the Blue Vanga *L. madagascarinus* is blue above, white below; the White-headed Vanga *L. viridis* has a white head, white under parts, and a black back; the Rufous Vanga *Schetba rufa* has a black head in the male, with rufous back and white under parts; and Bernier's Vanga *Oriolia bernieri* is all black in the male, mostly rufous in the female. The smallest species is the Red-tailed Vanga (or Tit Shrike) *Calicalicus madagas-*

cariensis, with a short bill and rufous, grey, and white plumage, the male with a black throat-patch. The black-and-white Hook-billed Vanga has a heavy, sharply hooked bill. The 3 species of *Xenopirostris* have the bill high and laterally compressed, and are black, grey, and white in colour, and along with *Oriolia* are the rarest and least-known vangas. The Sicklebill *Falculea palliata* was considered to be a starling (Sturnidae) for a long time ; it has a long, curved bill, head and under parts white, and back black. The Helmetbird *Aerocharis* ('*Euryceros*') *prevostii* has a long, much inflated bill and a black and rufous plumage ; it has been considered by some to represent a monotypic family.

(Dorst has suggested that *Tylas* and *Hypositta* should be placed in this family.)   A.L.R.

Delacour, J. 1932. Les oiseaux de la mission franco-anglo-américaine à Madagascar. Oiseau (n.s.) 2 : 1–96. (At pp. 71–76 ; taxonomy.)

Dorst, J. 1960. A propos des affinités systematiques de deux oiseaux malagaches : *Tylas eduardi et Hypositta corallirostris*. Oiseau 30 : 259–269.

Rand, A. L. 1936. The distribution and habits of Madagascar birds. Bull. Amer. Mus. Nat. Hist. 72 : 143–499. (At pp. 460–468 ; habits.)

Rand, A. L. 1960. Family Vangidae. *In* Mayr, E. & Greenway, J. C., Jr. (eds.). Check-list of Birds of the World vol. 9. Cambridge, Mass.

VANGIDAE: a family of the Passeriformes, suborder Oscines (see VANGA).

VANISHING BIRDS: species or subspecies threatened with extinction, as contrasted with those already irretrievably lost (see EXTINCT BIRDS). There are some who question whether it is really of great importance to spend large sums and great efforts in attempting to preserve every living species of bird throughout the world. It is arguable, no doubt, that too much effort is sometimes expended on the attempt to preserve some species which, owing to their present manner of life, seem foredoomed to early extinction ; and that it is futile to oppose human encroachment, whether in North America, India, or elsewhere, on traditional habitats of certain species, or to get excited because Eskimos or other peoples whose living is at all times precarious find it possible to slaughter more birds for food with modern firearms than they were able to do with more primitive weapons.

It may sometimes be possible, however, to modify human economies in a manner that will benefit birds, although when birds and man irrevocably clash it must be assumed that the birds will suffer most. On the other hand, so long as man has an eye for natural beauty, it is fair to presume that he would prefer not to see the avifauna of the world

reduced to starlings (Sturnidae), sparrows (Passerinae), gulls (Larinae), and crows (Corvidae). Something, therefore, should surely be attempted within reason to preserve the variety of wild bird-life in the world ; and when a particular species is obviously becoming very scarce, efforts should be made to discover the cause so that it can then be decided whether either local or world-wide efforts can usefully be taken to check the process. In the case of long-distance migrants, such as ducks (Anatidae), waders (Charadrii), or cranes (Gruidae), international action is likely to be needed ; for restricted insular forms, local action is more likely to be appropriate.

The first necessity is to establish the facts. With this in view, the International Technical Conference on the Protection of Nature, called together by UNESCO at Lake Success in 1949, prepared a preliminary list of birds that appeared to be on the danger list at that time. The following 13 species or races were named : Arabian Ostrich *Struthio camelus syriacus*, Hawaiian Goose (or Nene) *Branta sandvicensis*, Kagu *Rhynochetos jubatus* of New Caledonia, Pink-headed Duck *Rhodonessa caryophyllacea* of India, Australian Ground Parakeet *Pezoporus wallicus*, Laysan Teal *Anas laysanensis*, Marianas Mallard *Anas oustaleti*, Cuban Ivory-billed Woodpecker *Campephilus principali bairdii*, Bermuda Petrel *Pterodroma cahow*, Marianas Megapode *Megapodius laperouse*, California Condor *Gymnogyps californianus*, Eskimo Curlew *Numenius borealis*, and Whooping Crane *Grus americana*.

Such a list is not intended to be anything but preliminary ; if it challenges criticism from any quarter, on the ground of omissions, it has already achieved one of its purposes. In fact, subsequent inquiries have indicated that a number of island races are as near extinction as the Laysan Teal, Marianas Mallard, and Marianas Megapode ; and it may be questioned whether these very limited populations can be saved for more than a short time. Birds that are biologically specialised, such as megapodes, are perhaps more important to preserve than those that are closely allied to common existing species. If the Dodo *Raphus cucullatus* and the Great Auk *Pinguinus impennis* could have been saved, they would have been very well worth saving, as the study of their life histories might have thrown light on important evolutionary problems. From that point of view, the Passenger Pigeon *Ectopistes migratorius*, which was exterminated in North America in the nineteenth century, and the Eskimo Curlew, which is supposed to be very near extinction, perhaps matter less. Inquiries carried out since 1949 show that a number of other species or races are also becoming very scarce, and must be deliberately protected by man if they are to survive.

Beginning with the Old World, several northern Palaearctic species are becoming scarce. These include the Corncrake *Crex crex*, the Great Snipe *Gallinago media*, the Red-breasted Goose *Branta ruficollis*, and the Brent Goose *B. bernicla*. The last-named is still to be seen in hundreds during the winter in a few favoured localities, but it has decreased alarmingly in the past thirty years ; however, by changing its food habits, the North American race of the same species has made such an astonishing recovery that if man will give it a chance the species may do the same in Europe.

In southern Europe, the populations of Audouin's Gull *Larus audouinii*, Eleonora's Falcon *Falco eleonorae*, the Azure-winged Magpie *Cyanopica cyanus*, and the Corsican Nuthatch *Sitta whiteheadi* are among the forms with such very limited ranges that their future is precarious. Probably the case of the Corsican Nuthatch, an isolated form in Europe once thought to be conspecific with a common North American bird, is the most alarming.

The Great Bustard *Otis tarda* should also be mentioned. Indeed, it seems likely that all the larger bustards in the world are on the danger list, judging from recent reports of species in both India and Australia. Turning from Europe to Asia, it appears that the Arabian race of the Ostrich is now probably extinct. Several other Arabian species are known to be very scarce, possibly because of the encroachment of the desert during the past two thousand years or more.

In India and the adjacent countries, birds on the danger list include the Great Indian Bustard *Choriotis nigriceps*, the Pink-headed Duck (probably extinct), Jerdon's Courser *Rhinoptilus bitorquatus*, and the White-winged Wood Duck *Cairina scutulata*. Japan is trying to save from extinction the very small populations of the Japanese Crane *Grus japonensis* and the Japanese Ibis *Nipponia nippon*. A woodpecker of Japan, *Dryocopus richardsi*, is thought to be extinct.

In Ceylon, as indeed in other tropical islands of southern Asia and Indonesia, there are several jungle species that seem to be very scarce, although most are not as yet menaced by man's economic developments. Several hornbills (Bucerotidae) might thrive better if fashions in head-dress among the human inhabitants of the jungle were to change.

Several Australian parrots have decreased seriously, although other similar species maintain their numbers. One of the lyrebirds, *Menura superba*, was in danger a few years ago but is now reported to be holding its own. In the more restricted area of New Zealand, not unnaturally, several species have become scarce. The flightless Takahe *Notornis mantelli* was for some years thought to be extinct, but it has now been rediscovered and is being rigorously protected.

In North America, apart from the Ivory-billed Woodpecker *Campephilus principalis*, which is nearly extinct on the mainland although still surviving in Cuba, species that are very near extinction are the Whooping Crane and the California Condor ; but in both cases action for their preservation is at present keeping the numbers steady, the Whooping Crane showing a slight increase in the past few years. Several other large and conspicuous species have also become scarce.

In the two remaining continents, Africa and South America, the pressure of an increasing human population is broadly much less ; and for this very reason the situation of many species is comparatively obscure. The Congo Peacock *Afropavo congensis* is presumably rather scarce, but that does not mean that it is necessarily in any immediate danger of extinction.

When one turns to the islands of the Pacific, and indeed to other small remote islands or archipelagos, there are obviously many species that are extremely scarce ; and it is in these islands that the greatest mortality of species has occurred within this century. In a few cases, as with the Hawaiian Goose, it may be possible to revive the species in captivity and then restore it to special reserves or sanctuaries (see AVICULTURE) ; but in others it seems almost certain that increasing pressure of human populations and more intensive and extensive cultivation will be the end of a number of birds that are restricted to small islands and do not migrate.

There are striking and distinctive species of birds in various large islands that it is impossible to mention in a brief article, but New Guinea and Madagascar are two such islands that should at least be named. So long as large areas of tropical forest remain in their natural condition, most of the species should be able to hold their own. But in an age of aircraft, tractors, insecticides, bull-dozers, and other human inventions, there is hardly a bird in the world that can be sure of calling its home its own tomorrow.   H.G.A.

Greenway, J. C., Jr. 1958. The Extinct and Vanishing Birds of the World. New York.
Fisher, J. 1961. Bird species in danger of extinction. Internat. Zoo Yearb. 2 : 280–287.

VARIANCE: see STATISTICAL SIGNIFICANCE

VARIATION: SEE EVOLUTION ; GENETICS ; INDI-

VIDUAL VARIATION ; NATURAL SELECTION ; PLUMAGE VARIATION ; POLYMORPHISM ; SPECIATION ; SUBSPECIES

VARIATION, COEFFICIENT OF: see STATISTICAL SIGNIFICANCE

VARIETY: a variant form within a population that is in the main homogeneous ; used also for a breed under DOMESTICATION. 'Varietas' was the lowest of the taxonomic categories of Linnaeus, but the modern recognition of the polytypic nature of many species has rendered it obsolete in his sense ; see also under SPECIES ; SUBSPECIES ; and POLYMORPHISM.

VASCULAR SYSTEM: consisting essentially of three components : the arterial system, conveying blood at high pressure from the heart to all parts of the body ; the venous system, in continuity with the arterial system through a capillary network within the organs and tissues of the body, returning the blood to the heart ; and the lymphatic system. Arteries have thick, muscular walls ; veins have only a thin muscular coat ; and lymphatic vessels rarely have any muscle at all.

Arterial System. The pulmonary arch emerges from the right ventricle of the heart, its opening being guarded by 3 semi-lunar ('watch-pocket') valves, and quickly divides into right and left pulmonary arteries supplying their respective lungs (see HEART ; RESPIRATORY SYSTEM).

The carotico-aortic arch emerges from the left ventricle by way of a similarly valved opening and gives off branches that ultimately supply the whole body excluding the lungs. These arches represent the remains of 6 arterial arches that encircle the embryonic pharynx—the carotid arch being the 3rd, the systemic the 4th (right side only), and the pulmonary the 6th of this series (see Fig., inset A). See also DEVELOPMENT, EMBRYONIC.

The branching of the carotico-systemic arch is subject to much variation that is of considerable taxonomic significance (for details see papers by Glenny, especially 1955). Thus the common carotid arteries that pass up the neck to the head may be paired and symmetrical (most non-passerine birds—see main Figure) ; paired and sinistrally asymmetrical, i.e. left vessel most developed (e.g. Phoenicopteridae—see Fig., inset B) ; paired and dextrally asymmetrical (e.g. cockatoos, Kakatoeinae—see Fig., inset C) ; unpaired through fusion (e.g. Ardeidae—see Fig., inset D) ; the left vessel only may be present (e.g. Passeriformes—see Fig., inset E) ; or the right vessel only may be present (e.g. some Otididae, as *Eupodotis*—see Fig., inset F). Each of these divisions has subvarieties, while further subdivisions can be distinguished according to the presence or absence of the dorsal part of the left systemic arch and whether this is patent or ligamentous.

The main arteries—other than the common carotid arteries—leaving the carotico-systemic arch are the paired subclavian arteries, which immediately divide to give the brachial arteries to the wing and the pectoral arteries to the flight muscles of the breast. The systemic arch, as it then becomes, courses round the oesophagus on the right to the mid-dorsal line where it turns caudalwards and is known as the dorsal aorta. From this last arise the coeliac artery (to liver, spleen, proventriculus, gizzard, and duodenum) ; the anterior mesenteric artery (to most of the intestine) ; the paired renal arteries (to the kidneys, entering the anterior lobes) ; paired femoral arteries (anterior) and sciatic arteries (posterior) to the legs and also giving renal branches to the more posterior parts of the kidneys ; a pair of hypogastric arteries to the pelvis, and a single posterior mesenteric artery to the rectum. The aorta now becomes the caudal artery supplying the tail. The main artery to the leg is usually the sciatic artery, but this may be absent (e.g. Spheniscidae) ; the femoral and sciatic arteries, however, unite behind the knee to form the popliteal artery.

Venous System. The veins entering the heart are a pair of anterior venae cavae (precaval veins) bringing the blood from the head, neck, and wings ; a posterior vena cava (postcaval vein) draining the liver, kidneys, trunk, and hindlimbs, and the pulmonary vein from the lungs. Each anterior vena cava comprises a jugular vein (that on the right being the larger) from the head and neck, a brachial vein from the wing, and a pectoral vein from the flight muscles of the breast. The main veins from the hind limbs are the femoral veins which, after receiving small pelvic veins, pass dorsal to the kidneys and are joined by the renal portal veins and the renal veins. These vessels, from this point known as the external iliac veins, unite to form the posterior vena cava which courses forwards passing through the liver, receiving from it the hepatic veins, on its way to the heart.

The blood from the alimentary canal and pancreas is collected by various mesenteric veins that unite to form the hepatic portal vein which enters the liver and distributes blood to it. A vein, peculiar to birds, is associated with this system, viz. the coccygeomesenteric vein that joins the hepatic portal vein on the one hand with the two renal portal veins on the other : it receives the internal iliac veins from the pelvic roof and the hypogastric veins from the pelvic floor just after bifurcating to join the two renal portal veins. There is a valve within the external iliac vein just beyond its junction with the renal portal vein that ensures that the blood-flow from the coccygeo-mesenteric and renal portal veins shall always be towards the heart.

Lymphatic System. Although erythrocytes and larger protein molecules do not normally leave the blood vascular system, the more fluid portions (see BLOOD) readily do so and the resultant exudate, lymph, percolates between the tissues into a system of lymphatic capillaries which unite into lymphatic vessels. These vessels are valved to ensure that the lymph shall flow in one direction only, namely, towards the anterior venae cavae, which the main lymphatic trunks ultimately join. Lymph glands associated with these vessels are rare and are developed at all only in a few families of birds. A pair of 'lymph hearts' associated with this system are found in the sacral region in the embryos of all birds and persist through life in many : they reach their maximum development in the Ostrich *Struthio camelus*.   E.T.B.F.

Glenny, F. H. 1955. Modifications of pattern in the aortic arch system of birds and their phylogenetic significance. Proc. U.S. Natl. Mus. 104 : 525–621.

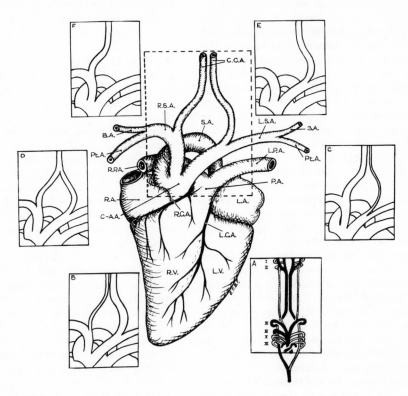

Ventral view of the heart of a bird (e.g. *Gallus*). Insets (corresponding to portion of main figure outlined by dotted rectangle) :

A. Diagram to show how the arterial arches of the adult bird correspond with those of the embryo. Vessels shown black persist throughout life, those with open lines disappear in embryonic life and the vessels shown dotted may persist as vestiges in the adult.

B. Condition of common carotid arteries found in e.g. *Phoenicopterus.*

C. Condition of common carotid arteries found in Kakatoeinae.

D. Condition of common carotid arteries found in e.g. *Ardea* and *Botaurus*.

E. Condition of common carotid arteries found in Passeriformes.

F. Condition of common carotid arteries found in *Eupodotis.*   *E. T. B. Francis*

B.A.—brachial artery (to wing)   C-A.A.—carotico-aortic arch   C.C.A.—common carotid arteries   L.A.—left atrium   L.C.A.—left coronary artery   L.P.A.—left pulmonary artery   L.S.A.—left subclavian artery   L.V.—left ventricle   P.A.—pulmonary arch   Pt.A.—pectoral artery   R.A.—right atrium   R.C.A.—right coronary artery   R.P.A.—right pulmonary artery   R.S.A.—right subclavian artery   R.V.—right ventricle   S.A.—systemic arch   I–VI—embryonic arterial arches

VAS DEFERENS: (plural 'vasa deferentia')—see REPRODUCTIVE SYSTEM.

VECTOR: an animal that is a carrier of parasites or infections to another species; sometimes the vector species is an intermediate host in which the parasite necessarily accomplishes a part of its life-cycle—and in that case is termed a 'biological vector', as contrasted with a 'mechanical' one (see DISEASE; ECTOPARASITE; ENDOPARASITE).

VEERY: *Catharus* ('*Hylocichla*') *fuscescens* (see THRUSH).

VEGETATION: considered here as an essential part of the environment in which most birds live (see ECOLOGY). For any species of bird to reside permanently in a locality the essential requirements are that the area provides an adequacy of food, shelter, and nesting sites. The nature, level, and fluctuations of food supply must basically depend on the productivity of the plant communities occupying the area. The plants themselves may be a direct source of supply or the starting points for a variety of food chains. The levels of food supply, either direct or indirect, will be highest during the periods of active plant growth and least at the end of periods when growth has been retarded or inhibited. Where climatic differences between seasons are well defined, then the sedentary bird population is likely to be delimited by the food available towards the end of the winter or dry season: in more favourable periods the greater productivity will support migrants as well. The nature of the plant communities will be in turn dependent on a combination of factors—climatic, edaphic, and physiographic.

The onset, cessation, and rate of growth of individual plant species will be linked on the one hand with solar radiation and temperature, and on the other with the availability of water and inorganic nutrients. The supply of inorganic nutrients will be governed by the nature of the site, the soil, and the climate (see CLIMATOLOGY). Last, soil formation and the type of vegetation are interrelated and both are linked with the climatic conditions (see GEOLOGICAL FACTORS).

Temperature and Growth. As a broad generalisation it can be concluded that for terrestrial plants in the temperate zones little or no growth takes place until the mean temperature reaches 40°–50° F (4·5°–10° C). There are, however, some species that are capable of growing slowly at lower temperatures. For example, in Great Britain the Scots Pine *Pinus sylvestris* makes a little growth over the winter months. At this point it is necessary to define growth as the net gain in weight of the whole plant. In this sense the first phase of activity of perennial plants in the spring is not growth, since shoot or leaf expansion is often dependent on the utilisation of food reserves in the shoot, root, or storage organs. Thus, at a time when the leaves of the Bluebell *Endymion non-scriptus* are first expanding the plants are losing weight. This ability to mobilise reserves for the formation of new shoots at a low temperature is of some significance where grasses are being eaten during the winter months.

Once the mean temperature exceeds the minimal and limiting value the growth rate rises sharply with temperature; and in temperate regions, although the evidence is still scanty, it would seem that (according to the species) growth usually starts between 45° and 55° F (7°–13° C) and is maximal around 70° F (21° C). In contrast, for truly tropical species active growth may not be initiated until considerably higher temperatures are attained, and the optimal temperatures are above 70° F (21° C).

Water Exchange. Recent research has demonstrated that, if the leaf canopy of herbaceous communities completely covers the ground, the water transpired by turgid plants is closely related to the amount of solar energy absorbed by the leaves. Even in regions of high insolation, in the tropics, the water demand is usually not likely to exceed 6–7 inches per month; while in the cool temperate zone, where the mean monthly temperature is below 50° F (10° C), the normal demand is less than 2 inches per month. Although much more information is required about forest communities, the present indications are that the same relationships hold.

The proportion of rain that penetrates the soil will be related to the intensity of the rain, the type of vegetation, the kind of soil, and the topographical features. Where the rain falls gently and there is a good cover of vegetation, run-off is negligible except on steep slopes. On the other hand, if the rate of precipitation is high, as in the tropics, the soil impermeable, and the vegetation sparse, the liability to run-off is greatly augmented and severe erosion may take place on slight slopes.

Where the rainfall penetrating the soil exceeds the amount of water transpired by the vegetation then the residue will be stored. Roughly one foot of soil can store the equivalent of 1–2 inches of rain. Thus, if the soils are deep and permeable and the root range extensive, the inimical effects of drought will be delayed for longer than under conditions where the root systems and soils are shallow. It should be added that on bare ground, and in the absence of deep and frequent cracks, the loss of soil water by evaporation is greatly reduced, and in arid areas the individuals of perennial species are rarely contiguous.

Soil Nutrients. The availability and supplies of inorganic nutrients will be controlled by biological, geological, and climatic factors. Soils are derived from the mineral particles and the vegetable and animal residues that they contain. The organic components are broken down by microorganisms to release nutrients, while further supplies arise from the decomposition of the mineral particles which, however, takes place at a much slower rate. The underlying material or exposed rocks can be disintegrated by purely physical means. The mineral particles can also undergo chemical decomposition through either the solvent action of water itself or the action of water in combination with the dissolved oxygen, carbon dioxide, alkalis, and organic acids. Some of these reactions can take place as much as 30 feet below ground, while others are confined to the surface layer where soil formation is proceeding. The net supplies of the major and minor essential elements will be dependent on the chemical composition of the mineral particles or parent material, the rates of decomposition, and the rate of removal from the zone exploited by the roots. Since the presence of water is an essential factor, and since decomposition is accelerated at high temperatures, the rate of decomposition is highest in the humid tropics. Percolating water, besides bringing about decomposition, also removes some of the products of decomposition ; in consequence, the greater the difference between the rainfall and the water lost by transpiration and evaporation, the more the downward leaching.

Save for the small quantities of ammonia and nitrate contained in rainwater, the nitrogen supplies in the soil are dependent upon the power of soil micro-flora to absorb atmospheric nitrogen and to incorporate it in their bodies. Under some conditions it is not the free living organisms in the soil that are important in nitrogen fixation but the symbiotic bacteria infecting the root hairs and causing nodule formation. At one time it was thought that only leguminous herbs and trees were capable of accumulating nitrogen in this way, but it is becoming increasingly evident that plants other than legumes can do this, e.g. the Alder *Alnus glutinosa*.

The inorganic nutrients taken up by the roots will be utilised for the growth of both the root and the shoot, and eventually the organic and inorganic components will largely be returned to the soil during or at the end of the life cycle. The plant residues of the shoot may in part remain on the soil surface since only the soluble products of decomposition will be washed into the soil, or the surface debris may be incorporated into the soil through the agency of earthworms, termites, and so on. Alternatively, especially where the root to shoot ratio is high, the major return may be by way of the roots. In any plant community all three processes will be operating ; in temperate regions the first is characteristic of coniferous forest, the second of deciduous or broad-leaved woodland, and the third of prairie or steppe.

Climatic Conditions. Where rainfall exceeds transpiration and evaporation for a high proportion of the year the vegetation is characterised by forest. In the temperate zone if the winters are severe and prolonged the dominant trees are coniferous, but as the winters shorten and the conditions become milder the conifers are replaced first by a mixture of coniferous and deciduous trees and then by wholly deciduous woodland. In parts of the tropics where dry periods are short or absent the forests are evergreen, but as the rainfall becomes more seasonal evergreens give way first to partially deciduous and then to wholly deciduous species. In the warm temperate zone the climatic inter-relationships are more complex ; under a combination of warm wet winters and rather dry summers evergreen species predominate.

Climatic conditions favouring forest formation will also favour leaching of nutrients from the surface layers of the soil ; but the presence of deep and extensive root systems leads to effective conservation of nutrients, since they are returned to the surface layers by way of debris from the shoots. Thus, in the wet tropics the very deep layers of leached and infertile soils associated with ancient peneplains may still bear luxuriant virgin forest, but if the trees are clear-felled and the balance of nutrient conservation disturbed there will be a shift in the nature of the vegetation to secondary forest or scrub.

In temperate regions where the seasonal dry periods are prolonged and the available water in the root zone becomes exhausted before the drought breaks, grasses predominate. Under the conditions where the severity of the drought is just too great to support trees, but there is sufficient rain at other times of the year to cause leaching, tall grasses are dominant. As conditions become drier and water rarely percolates below the root zone, the grasses become shorter, especially if grazing is severe.

Many regions of the tropics where the rainfall is markedly seasonal are characterised by a mosaic of grasses and scattered trees. In these savanna communities fires in the dry season may be frequent and fierce, and both the trees and perennial grasses must perforce be fire-resistant. In more arid regions the cover becomes sparser, ephemerals tend to replace perennials and the grasses may be interspersed or replaced by succulents or xerophilous shrubs. In very arid localities, the vegetation may be restricted to depressions where run-off water accumulates.

Physiography. Changes in topography may bring about marked variations in the types of vegetation. Other things being equal, in the Northern Hemisphere south slopes will be warmer and drier than north slopes. Again, as the angle of the slope increases the liability to erosion or downward creep of the whole soil is augmented. In mountainous regions factors like these may bring about abrupt shifts in vegetation. For example, from one side of a valley to another there may be a marked change in the elevation at which trees give way to shrubs and grassland. This replacement will be determined not only by the shortening of the growing season, and the environmental differences during active growth, but also by the conditions of winter. Low-growing plants covered with an insulating layer of snow will withstand the extremes of temperature better than the exposed trees. Again, trees will be more liable to suffer direct and indirect damage by high winds. These changes in vegetational pattern with altitude are paralleled by similar changes in latitude; as the winters become more severe and the length of the growing season shortens, shrubs or grasses replace trees, and under arctic conditions lichens may become an important component of the tundra.

Another factor connected with topography that may greatly affect the character of the vegetation is impeded drainage and the formation of a denser layer, or pan, some distance below the surface of the soil. If the drainage is impeded for long enough the pan may become so hard as to prevent root penetration. Where the land begins to fall away and there is lateral movement of the drainage water, the contained bases and soluble products of weathering not only enrich the soil but prevent pan formation. Thus, a plateau may consist of acid heathland, but the contiguous downward slopes may consist of deciduous forest with a neutral soil and an abundance of earthworms.

Similarly, the drainage waters finding their way into valleys will also be enriched; and if in the valley bottom there is occasional flooding, or the water table fluctuates seasonally, pan formation may again take place. If the valley bottoms or basins are themselves hot and arid, then as the water evaporates the salts are left behind in the surface layers and the content may eventually become so great that no plants can grow.

Under more humid conditions where the water table remains at or near the surface and bogs or swamps are formed, the movement of gases in the soil is restricted and the oxygen is removed by the roots and micro-organisms faster than it can enter. This deficit of oxygen produces major changes in the chemical form and availability of the essential nutrients. The balance of the micro-organisms is also altered and thereby the manner of the decomposition of organic matter. Since the rate of breakdown is slowed down, organic matter frequently accumulates; peat formation provides an example of this.

Productivity. There are as yet no precise criteria on which to evaluate what are the quantitative differences in gross productivity between different types of vegetation within and between broad climatic zones. Clearly, where the periods of active growth are very brief, as in the Arctic or very arid regions, productivity is lowest. At the other end of the scale, productivity will be highest in the humid tropics and sub-tropics where growth can continue throughout the year. Between these two ends of the scale, gross productivity will be determined first by the lengths of the periods when water supplies or temperature, or both, are high enough to permit active growth, and secondly by the density of the vegetation. The extent of the plant cover and the length of the period when the leaves will be actively assimilating will also be linked with the supply of inorganic nutrients. The limitations of nutrients will be least where the communities are either effective in obtaining or conserving nutrients or where supplies are being continuously replenished. In the first category come forests, in the second swamps if the incoming waters are rich in nutrients.   G.E.B.

VEINS: see HEART; VASCULAR SYSTEM

VELVETBREAST: *Lafresnaya lafresnayi* (for family see HUMMINGBIRD).

VENA CAVA: see HEART; VASCULAR SYSTEM

VENOUS SYSTEM: see HEART; VASCULAR SYSTEM

VENT: the CLOACA.

VENTRAL: pertaining to the abdominal aspect or, more generally, the lower surface of the body; opposite of DORSAL.

VENTRICLE: a hollow space within an organ, especially the heart or the forebrain (see HEART; NERVOUS SYSTEM).

VENTRICULUS: the gizzard (see ALIMENTARY SYSTEM).

VERDIN: *Auriparus flaviceps* (see TIT).

VERNACULAR NAME: see NAME, VERNACULAR

VERTEBRAL COLUMN: the backbone (see SKELETON).

VERTEBRATES: see ANIMAL KINGDOM

VESTIBULE: anatomically, a cavity leading into another ; used especially of the cavity of the ear-labyrinth (see HEARING AND BALANCE).

VEXILLUM: the vane of a feather (see FEATHER ; VANE).

VIBRISSA: a modified feather, like a bristle (see PLUMAGE).

VICE-COUNTY: a biogeographical subdivision of an administrative county, in Britain, used—primarily by botanists—as a unit area in distributional studies.

VIDUINAE: a subfamily recognised by some authors (see WHYDAH (1)).

VILLI: (plural of ' villus '), internal processes of the ileum and caeca (see ALIMENTARY SYSTEM).

VINCULUM: a fibrous band such as sometimes unites two or more tendons (see under MUSCULATURE).

VIOLETEAR: substantive name of *Colibri* spp. (for family see HUMMINGBIRD).

VIOLETTAIL: *Metallura tyrianthina smaragdinicollis* (for family see HUMMINGBIRD).

VIREO: substantive name of most species of the subfamily Vireoninae of the Vireonidae (Passeriformes, suborder Oscines) ; in the plural, general term for the subfamily. The members of this New World group were formerly known as ' greenlets ', but this name is now restricted to members of the Neotropical genus *Hylophilus*. For the other subfamilies see SHRIKE-VIREO ; PEPPER-SHRIKE.

Typical vireos are small (between 4–7 inches long) and plainly coloured birds, believed by some ornithologists to be most nearly related to wood-warblers (Parulidae) and by others to shrikes (Laniidae). They are usually olive-green or greyish (rarely more or less brown) above, near white to yellowish on under parts. The sexes are similar, and there are no seasonal plumage changes. Although many species have pale wing-bars, there is

never any streaking or spotting even in immature plumages. Some have conspicuously hooked bills.

Vireos are primarily birds of thickets or secondary growth, although a few species, notably the Red-eyed Vireo *Vireo olivaceus*, the Warbling Vireo *V. gilvus*, and the Yellow-throated Vireo *V. flavifrons*, habitually occur high in trees. The movements of vireos are more deliberate than those of wood-warblers. They often hang upside down in order to peer under leaves when searching for food, which consists mainly of insects although small fruit is also consumed ; they rarely forage on the ground. With the exception of the Warbling Vireos *V. gilvus* subspp., typical vireos are persistent but mediocre songsters. The song period of some North American forms extends to late summer, occasionally to early autumn.

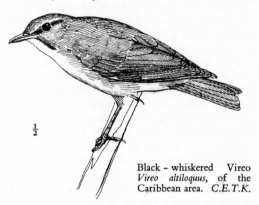

$\frac{1}{2}$

Black - whiskered Vireo *Vireo altiloquus*, of the Caribbean area. *C.E.T.K.*

Nests of vireos are situated in trees or bushes. These are well-built, pendent, cup-shaped structures, suspended between the forks of branches. The eggs are white, ranging from immaculate, as those of the Black-capped Vireo *V. atricapillus*, to heavily spotted, as those of the Thick-billed Vireo *V. crassirostris*. Eggs of most vireos, with those of the pepper-shrikes (Cyclarhinae), are characterised by sparse but distinct spotting. Clutch size is usually 3–4 in temperate regions, 2–3 in the tropics. Males of many species share the duties of incubation and often sing on the nest. Distraction display has never been recorded in this family.

Typical vireos, as well as the other Vireonidae, are confined to the New World, and the family is believed to be of tropical North American origin. The approximately 40 species included in the Vireoninae have been placed in 2–7 genera. There are clearly two main groups, the North American vireos proper and the Neotropical greenlets. The former is well represented in North America, Central America, and the West Indies, but there are only 2 resident species in continental South America ;

these are both members of the arboreal subgenus *Vireosylva* and are by many ornithologists considered to be conspecific with the North American Red-eyed Vireo and Warbling Vireo respectively. A large group of vireos that includes the familiar White-eyed Vireo *V. griseus*, of North America and Bermuda, is highly complex, and there is no uniformity of opinion about the number of species that should be recognised. The most aberrant forms in this assemblage, the Flat-billed Vireo *V. nanus* of Hispaniola, the Blue Mountain Vireo *V. osburni* of Jamaica, and the Slaty Vireo *V. brevipennis* of Mexico, are considered by many ornithologists to represent monotypic genera, viz. 'Lawrencia', 'Laletes', and 'Neochloe'. The last mentioned is noteworthy because of its unusual colour pattern—mostly slate-grey, with the pileum, hind neck, and much of the wings and tail bright olive-green, and the chin and centre of abdomen white.

The majority of North American vireos winter in Mexico and Central America : but northern Red-eyed Vireos pass over this region, migrating across the Gulf of Mexico to the Yucatan Peninsula and thence south to Upper Amazonia, where they mingle with resident South American races ; Central American forms, often considered to represent a distinct species (the 'Yellow-green Vireo *V. flavoviridis*'), also migrate to South America ; this is the only passerine native to Central America (excluding Mexico, north of the Isthmus of Tehuantepec) that is known to do so ; the closely related Black-whiskered Vireo *V. altiloquus* of the Caribbean islands and southern Florida is also migratory, although many individuals are resident on the more eastern Antilles.

The Neotropical greenlets of the genus *Hylophilus* comprise 15 species, and are a much more homogenous group than *Vireo*. All of the species inhabit South America, but only 3 reach Central America north of Panama ; 2 of these, the Tawny-crowned Greenlet *H. ochraceiceps* and the Grey-headed Greenlet *H. decurtatus*, range north to southern Mexico. Greenlets inhabit scrub and forest undergrowth and often associate with the flocks of birds of various families so often encountered in the South American jungle.

See Plate 43 (egg).   J.B. (3)

Skutch, A. F. 1960. Life Histories of Central American Birds. Pt. II. (Pacific Coast Avifauna no. 34.) Los Angeles.

VIREO, ANT-: see ANTVIREO ; and ANTBIRD

VIREOLANIINAE: see VIREONIDAE ; and SHRIKE-VIREO

VIREONIDAE: a family of the Passeriformes, suborder Oscines, treated here as comprising the Vireoninae—the true vireos, including greenlets (see VIREO) ; the Vireolaniinae (see SHRIKE-VIREO) ; and the Cyclarhinae (see PEPPER-SHRIKE). It may be doubted whether it is necessary to recognise 3 subfamilies, the second and third including only 1 genus apiece, but they have in the past been treated even as separate families, and the groups are given separate articles in this work.

VISIBILITY: see METEOROLOGY

VISION: a sense of the utmost importance to birds, almost all of which have extremely well developed and efficient eyes. Among very few exceptions are the nocturnal kiwis *Apteryx* spp., which have small short-sighted eyes. Most birds are dependent on their eyes for finding their food, for recognising their mates, and for avoiding their enemies ; and although blinded birds are able to fly if released in the air, they are incapable of alighting successfully and cannot be persuaded to take off.

Size and Movement of Eyes. The paramount importance of the visual sense is reflected in the relatively enormous eyes characteristic of birds ; some hawks (Accipitridae) and owls (Strigiformes), for instance, have eyes as large or larger than those of man. In some species the eyes are as big as the head can accommodate, the two bulbs almost touching one another with only a thin bony septum between them. This is not always obvious on superficial observation, since only the cornea, which is usually small in comparison with the rest of the eye, is externally visible between the lids. These large eyes are usually a tight fit in the orbit, and the extraocular muscles are, therefore, much reduced. In consequence there is little eye movement in any bird, such movement being mainly in the horizontal direction only. In nocturnal birds (e.g. owls, Fig. 2c) with tubular eyes there is no movement at all, and it is said that the eye fits so closely into the orbit that it cannot be moved even with a pair of pliers ! This general lack of eye movement is compensated by an extremely flexible neck ; in birds such as hawks and owls which have frontal eyes, and therefore a relatively small total visual field, the head can turn through well over 180°.

Nictitating Membrane. Like many other vertebrates, birds have a nictitating membrane or third lid which lies under the lids on the nasal side and can be drawn horizontally across the eye. In diurnal birds this is usually transparent and can be drawn across the cornea to clean or moisten it without shutting out the light. Many workers believe that the nictitating membrane covers the eye

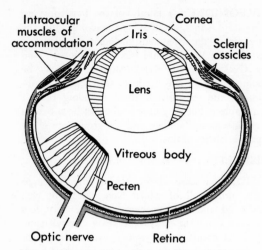

Intraocular muscles of accommodation

Cornea

Iris

Scleral ossicles

Lens

Vitreous body

Pecten

Optic nerve

Retina

FIG 1. Diagram of the avian eye. *After Duke-Elder*.

during most, if not all, of the time that a bird is in flight, so preventing air currents from drying the cornea. Some diving birds that use their eyes under water, e.g. diving ducks (Anatidae), divers (Gaviidae), auks (Alcidae), have a clear lens-like window in their nictitating membrane which is so highly refractive that it will bend light rays even under water ; this device helps to compensate for the loss of corneal refraction under these conditions.

General Structure of Eye. The basic structure of the avian eye follows the general pattern of all vertebrate eyes (Fig. 1). This consists roughly of an optical system made up of the cornea, lens, and vitreous body, which casts an inverted image of external objects on the light-sensitive retina—for connection with the brain, see under NERVOUS SYSTEM. Birds' eyes fall roughly into three groups, of which examples are shown in Figure 2. The first, from the Mute Swan *Cygnus olor*, is characteristic of most diurnal birds ; the second, from the Golden Eagle *Aquila chrysaetos*, is typical of diurnal birds with especially good vision ; and the third,

from the Eagle Owl *Bubo bubo*, is an eye adapted for useful nocturnal vision. See also DEVELOPMENT, POSTEMBRYONIC.

Retinal Pigments. The retina is light-sensitive because it possesses photo-sensitive pigments located in its visual receptors. Through these pigments light energy is transformed, in a way of which we know very little, into something capable of stimulating the fibres of the optic nerve so that a complicated pattern of nervous impulses is transmitted to the brain. Very little is known about these important pigments in birds. The red 'visual purple' which mediates night vision in many vertebrates has been extracted from the retinae of the domestic fowl and of the Tawny Owl *Strix aluco*. Several other owls, as well as the Kestrel *Falco tinnunculus*, Buzzard *Buteo buteo*, Kite *Milvus milvus*, and some ducks have deeply coloured red or purple retinae ; their pigments have never been studied in any detail. It is claimed that a second pigment can be extracted from the domestic fowl which may mediate day vision in this species. The retinae of many birds such as the Rock Dove *Columba livia*, the Starling *Sturnus vulgaris*, and, oddly enough, the nocturnal Nightjar *Caprimulgus europaeus*, appear quite colourless even when removed from freshly killed dark-adapted animals.

Pupil Reactions. The amount of light entering the eye depends on the reactions of the pupil. This is the aperture of the circular pigmented structure, the iris, situated over the anterior surface of the lens and giving the colour to the eye. The iris contains both radial and circular muscles which regulate the size of the pupil. In most vertebrates these are smooth muscles and are under involuntary nervous control dependent mainly on the level of illumination, but partly on the state of 'accommodation'. In birds both sets of muscles are striated and the pupil movements are strikingly rapid and extensive, especially as seen in wild birds in captivity. However, in spite of these very

a

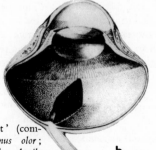

b

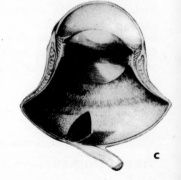

c

FIG 2. Three types of avian eye. **a** 'Flat' (commonest) type—in the Mute Swan *Cygnus olor* ; **b** 'Globose' type—in the Golden Eagle *Aquila chrysaetos* ; **c** 'Tubular' type—in the Eagle Owl *Bubo bubo. After Soemmering*.

marked changes, avian pupils do not seem to be as responsive to light as is the case with most vertebrates. This, together with the fact that the iris muscles are striated, has led some authorities to suggest that in birds the pupil is under voluntary control ; but there is no real evidence for this. The accommodation reflex that causes the pupil to constrict for near vision may be present, at least in some birds. The lack of a marked pupil response to light is probably associated with the mobility of the black epithelial pigment situated just behind the retina and moving forward in light adaptation to protect the highly sensitive receptor cells. (Such retinal pigment movements, often associated with a pupil relatively unresponsive to light, are also found in teleost fishes and some amphibia.) In general, the pupils of diving birds are more responsive to light ; vision in water of any depth requires a high light-sensitivity, and in many diving species the retina approaches the nocturnal type. Such a retina presumably needs extra protection in full daylight, especially over water. The pupil is relatively small in diurnal birds : this ensures that the light rays can enter the eye only through the centre of the lens, thereby cutting out the spherical aberration that would be produced by its less optically perfect edge. (For the unique shape of the pupil in *Rynchops* see SKIMMER.)

Pecten. One feature peculiar to the avian eye is the pecten. This is a pigmented, highly vascular structure, usually pleated but sometimes with vanes, attached to the optic nerve along its base and standing up in the posterior chamber of the eye supported by the highly viscous vitreous body. It is composed almost entirely of blood vessels supported by a light fibrous network derived from the optic nerve. It is smallest in nocturnal birds, larger in seed-eating species, larger still in insectivores, and largest of all in the diurnal predators such as hawks and eagles. The pecten, therefore, becomes bigger and more elaborate as the visual demands on species increase. There have been many theories as to its function, but it is most probably a device for providing nutrition and oxygen for the retina by means of its enormous vascular surface. A similar but much simpler structure is characteristic of reptiles ; neither birds nor reptiles have any blood vessels within the retinal tissue.

Retinal Structure. The bird's retina is unusually thick and well developed, with many complex nervous interconnections ; in this respect, at least in diurnal birds, it is superior even to the human retina. The actual visual receptors of birds, as of all vertebrates, are of two kinds, called rods and cones respectively. The former are generally

associated with good sensitivity to low illuminations, poor visual acuity, and imperfect or no colour vision. The nocturnal birds have a great preponderance of rods in their retinae. Cones are associated with good visual acuity and with colour vision, but usually with a low sensitivity—in other words, with poor dark adaptation. Diurnal birds have retinae in which larger or smaller areas contain only cones, according to their visual requirements.

Visual Acuity. Visual acuity (the ability to distinguish fine details) should not be confused with visual sensitivity, which is the ability to distinguish small quantities of light as such and is highly developed in all nocturnal species. The two faculties require rather differently constructed eyes and retinae, and it is rare for an eye to have both well developed. Visual acuity is a property first of the optical apparatus of the eye and secondly of the retinal structure. These can usefully be compared to the lens and the plate or film of a camera, the former determining the accuracy of the image and the ' grain ' of the latter the fidelity with which it can be reproduced. In birds the optical system is very well developed indeed ; those birds needing a high resolution at great distances (wing-feeding insectivorous forms, predators in general, and such birds as Corvidae) having eyes as large as possible and a somewhat flattened lens at a greater distance from the retina (Fig. 2b). This provides a larger image on the retina, while the highly curved cornea ensures that plenty of light shall enter the eye. At the same time, the retinal structure is specially well adapted for acute vision. All diurnal birds have a predominance of cones over the whole retina, and all have a central area from which rods are entirely absent. In addition, many have a small highly developed pit in the central retina known as a fovea. Foveae are not peculiar to birds ; they are not found in the lower mammals, appearing only in the primates and man, but they are a feature of such sharp-sighted animals as lizards and some teleost fishes. However, the avian fovea is the most highly developed of all, with the possible exception of the lizards. At the fovea the retina contains many extremely fine, tightly packed cones, each connected to its own fibre of the optic nerve. Such a structure is well designed for acute vision, since each cone can send an independent message to the brain, so making possible the appreciation of very fine detail within the retinal image. Some authorities think that the actual shape of the pit produces a slight magnification of the image in this region, thus further increasing visual acuity ; others believe that it aids in the perception of moving objects. Most birds have their eyes placed laterally in the

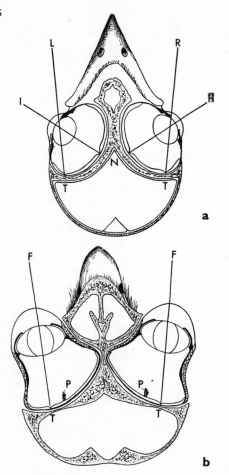

FIG 3. Bird foveae. **a** Two foveae of the White-bellied Swallow *Tachycineta bicolor* ; NI and NH visual axes of the central foveae used for binocular vision. **b** Single lateral foveae of the American Eagle Owl *Bubo virginianus*, used for binocular vision. *After Slonaker.*

head, and the central position of the fovea means that the most acute vision is usually to the sides. However, many birds—hawks, eagles, humming-birds (Trochilidae), bitterns (Botaurinae), and various passerine species including swallows (Hirundinidae) —that are especially well equipped visually, and particularly those that hunt on the wing and need a good distance judgment, have a second fovea placed in a posterior temporal position ; this can be used in conjunction with the other eye for binocular vision (Fig. 3). In this connection it is interesting that experiments on the Gannet *Sula bassana*, which has only one central fovea in each eye, have shown that its judgment of distance is apparently not very good. If fish are fastened to floating pieces of board a Gannet, diving at the bait, does not realise when to check its flight and may even transfix the

wood with its beak. Such an inability to judge distance exactly would be fatal to the stooping hawk with its prey on the hard ground and not in yielding water. Vultures (Aegypiinae), which certainly find their food by sight (they cannot find carrion if it is covered up) but can do so more or less at leisure, have no second fovea, in spite of their relationship to the hawks and eagles.

Some birds have, in addition to a central fovea, a ribbon-like central area running across the retina in a roughly horizontal direction. Recent examination of 5 species (Lapwing *Vanellus vanellus*, Oyster-catcher *Haematopus ostralegus*, Coot *Fulica atra*, Snipe *Gallinago gallinago*, and Herring Gull *Larus argentatus*) has shown that, although the position of the bill is very variable between these species, when the head is carried in its normal position during life this central retinal area, as well as one of the semi-circular canals in the ear labyrinth, is always horizontal. This finding immediately suggests a visual aid to giving the bird a plane of reference in relation to the horizon. Such a ribbon-like central area has never been found in forest inhabitants or in birds-of-prey, but mainly in birds of the open spaces. It has been suggested that it may be of importance in navigation.

A striking feature of the bird's retina is its profusion of coloured oil droplets. These are situated in the cones in such a position that the light rays must pass through them before being absorbed by the photo-sensitive pigments. These droplets are most often yellow, but they may also be red and orange and perhaps green ; blue ones have never been observed. In nocturnal birds they are much paler and often colourless. It has been thought that the coloured droplets were concerned with colour vision, but on the whole this seems rather unlikely, partly because the colour range is restricted and partly because at the fovea, the area of most distinct vision (and in man of the best colour vision), their colour is confined to yellow. Most diurnal vertebrates have some sort of intraocular yellow filter— either a yellow lens or some yellow pigmentation of the retina. Such filters are thought to be useful in cutting down blue rays, which can cause troublesome chromatic aberration. In addition, these small variously coloured filters in the bird may increase visual acuity by enhancing the contrast between different naturally occurring coloured objects.

Although it is certain from their habits that most diurnal predatory birds have a very high visual acuity indeed, it is difficult to get exact information, since experiments with wild birds are usually impossible. It has been estimated that hawks have a visual acuity eight times as high as that of man, although some workers consider this figure to be exaggerated. Training experiments have shown that pigeons (Columbidae) can attain an acuity a little better than the human, while the domestic gamecock, which has no fovea, has a visual acuity only one-tenth that of man.

Adaptations to Nocturnal Habit. The majority of birds are predominantly diurnal and become inactive at night. There are, however, great variations in the apparent ability of different species to see at low illuminations ; some roost much earlier in the evening than others which go on hunting well into the dusk. The retina of a bird active both by day and night, the Manx Shearwater *Puffinus puffinus*, has been compared with that of a purely diurnal petrel, the Fulmar *Fulmarus glacialis*, and has been found, not unexpectedly, to have an increased number of rods ; neither bird has any fovea. Even such diurnal birds as the pigeon and domestic fowl have powers of dark-adaptation as good as man, although the process is slow, taking nearly an hour to manifest itself in the pigeon as opposed to about ten minutes in man. In the Starling, Buzzard, and Kestrel the process is slower still, but when it is complete these birds appear to have very useful night vision.

The birds that have made the most successful visual adaptation to nocturnal living are, of course, the owls. In these the whole eye has become elongated (Fig. 2c) by the development of an enormously enlarged cornea and lens. By this means the amount of light entering the eye is increased so that a brighter image falls on the retina. Such an optical arrangement entails a relative decrease in the retinal image, but the great over-all size of the eye helps to minimise this disadvantage. In addition, the frontal position of the eyes, which provides better binocular vision than is usual in birds, not only gives a good perception of distance but probably also improves sensitivity by providing more visual information. (Frontal eyes are often present in nocturnal animals and in abyssal fishes.) Such owls as have been examined have a great predominance of rods in their retinae, and all have excellent powers of dark adaptation. Although some owls (e.g. Tawny Owl) are seldom seen during the day, others such as the Little Owl *Athene noctua* can hunt quite successfully in the light. Experiments with the Eagle Owl have shown that it can see, in full sunlight, diurnal predators invisible to a human observer. This species, although largely diurnal, and the Barn Owl *Tyto alba* both commonly hunt on the wing at night ; they both have silent flight and good hearing and may use this sense rather than vision. However, experiments made on captive

Eagle Owls as well as on the Scops Owl *Otus scops* have proved that these 2 species are undoubtedly able to find dead and therefore silent food in a light too dim for human vision, although both were found unable to do so in total darkness. It has been claimed that the Tawny Owl is sensitive to the infra-red wave lengths and thus finds its prey by recognising its warmth rather than its appearance ; attempts to confirm this finding, both on the same species and on the Long-eared Owl *Asio otus*, have proved unsuccessful.

Colour Vision. There can be no doubt that diurnal birds possess colour vision, although it is thought that most nocturnal ones do not—the Little Owl *Athene noctua* (less nocturnal than some) is an exception (Meyknecht). This is reflected in the gaudy mating displays of many diurnal species and the drab appearance and lack of colour adaptations in nocturnal birds. Actual experiments have mainly been done on such domesticated species as the fowl and pigeon. These have shown that the range of colours visible to them is about the same as in man, and that their ability to distinguish one hue from another is also similar. At one time it was thought that birds were blue-blind, but this was due to a misinterpretation of the experimental results. It was found that, when a spectrum was projected on scattered grain, hens would take all the food except that illuminated by the blue light. Later experiments, in which the birds were trained to take grain of different colours, revealed that this failure to peck at ' blue ' food was not due to its being invisible but to the fact that hens do not normally associate blue with edibility. With the exception of the Budgerigar *Melopsittacus undulatus*, such diurnal birds as have been tested (domestic fowl, pigeon, Kestrel, Mistle Thrush *Turdus viscivorus*), do show some decrease in sensitivity to blue, although they are by no means blind to this colour. This relative insensitivity is probably due to the profusion of yellow and orange droplets in their retinae ; nocturnal birds with very pale or colourless droplets do not show it. Although crucial experiments do not appear to have been made, all the evidence suggests that the fundamental colour mechanisms in birds are the same as in man ; their colour vision seems to be trichromatic, and they apparently experience the same contrast phenomena between complementary colours as human beings do. In diurnal, but not in nocturnal, birds there also appears to be an increased sensitivity to red.

Adaptation to Aquatic Habit. All fast-flying birds appear to need an efficient means of quickly altering the focus of the eye—in other words, good powers of accommodation—but for birds that have

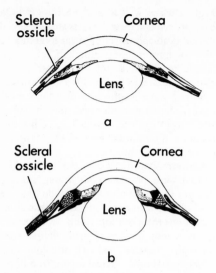

FIG 4. Accommodation in the Cormorant *Phalacroco-corax carbo*. **a** Unaccommodated; **b** Accommodated. Note the change in shape of the lens. *After von Hess.*

to see clearly both in air and under water this is particularly necessary. Accommodation in birds, as in man, is accomplished by altering the shape of the lens ; but whereas human accommodation is achieved by releasing the normal sideways pull on the lens so that it can take its natural shape, in birds the lens is actually squeezed into a more convex form (Fig. 4)—see also MUSCULATURE. Some birds (owls and hawks) also have an extra muscle which deforms the cornea. Birds' lenses are softer than human ones, and the intraocular muscles concerned with accommodation are more highly developed. In addition there is in the coat of the eye a bony ring of scleral ossicles to which these muscles are attached and which supports the globe, keeping it rigid against their pull. In the air a large part of the refractive power of the eye is produced by the highly curved cornea, and the effect of this is lost under water. The eye may be an efficient organ in the air and virtually useless under water, and this seems to be true of such plunging birds as terns (Sterninae) which spot their fish from above, dive blind, and often miss. Other eyes may be well adapted for under-water vision and poor instruments out of it. Penguins (Spheniscidae), for instance, can chase fish by sight but are badly short-sighted in air. But many birds—cormorants (Phalacrocoracidae), diving ducks, divers, and auks —have truly amphibious vision, and these possess tremendous powers of accommodation, so that the great increase in power of the lens makes up for the loss of the cornea as a refracting surface. Such

birds have very soft lenses indeed, enormously powerful accommodatory muscles, and very heavy scleral ossicles. Experiments on the Cormorant *Phalacrocorax carbo* indicate that its power of accommodation is from four to five times greater than that of the young human adult. This particular species does not have the specially adapted nictitating membrane already mentioned as characteristic of diving ducks, divers, and auks.

The Kingfisher *Alcedo atthis* is a bird that does not appear to accommodate under water, although it can see well in such conditions. This bird has two foveae, and it has been suggested that one is adapted for aerial and the other for aquatic vision.

Judgment of Distance, Binocular Vision, and Visual Fields. In man the most accurate method of judging distance and solidity is by means of stereoscopic vision. This appears to depend on the simultaneous appreciation of the slightly, but not too widely, dissimilar images from corresponding points of the two retinae. For this to be possible it is obviously essential to have binocular vision, i.e. the faculty of viewing an object with both eyes simultaneously and seeing one and not two images. There are, of course, a number of monocular clues that can be, and continually are, used for this purpose—such as size, overlapping contours, and parallax. Most birds have narrow heads and laterally placed eyes, and so they have only a small binocular field, from 6° in some parrots to 24° in pigeons. Such birds seem very dependent on monocular information. Domestic chicks, for instance, have difficulty in finding grain unless it is so illuminated as to produce shadows ; they also move their heads a great deal, peering at food to get different views of it before actually pecking. One-eyed chicks can learn to peck accurately.

Larger-headed predatory birds with more frontal eyes have a somewhat smaller total visual field than those with lateral eyes (250° as compared with 340°), but their binocular field is larger (about 50°). Owls have a much smaller total field of about 110° and binocular fields up to 70°. All these visual fields are, in practice, much increased by head movements, so that most birds have little difficulty in seeing all round themselves without turning the body. Some birds can do even better in the matter of seeing behind ; the American Woodcock *Philohela minor*, for instance, has its eyes set so far back in the head that its posterior binocular field is probably greater than its anterior one. Another curious modification occurs in the bitterns. These birds can turn their eyes so far ventrally that when they 'freeze' with the bill in the air they still have frontal binocular vision underneath it (see Pl. 23). K.T.

Duijm, M. 1958. On the position of a ribbon-like central area in the eyes of some birds. Arch. néerl. Zool. 13, suppl. 1 : 128–145.

Duke-Elder, W. S. 1958. System of Ophthalmology vol. I. The Eye in Evolution. London. (Chap. XIV. The eyes of birds. Chap. XVIII. The vision of vertebrates.)

Meyknecht, J. 1941. Farbensehen und Helligkeitsunterscheidung beim Steinkauz (*Athene noctua vidalii* A. E. Brehm). Ardea 30 : 129–174.

Pumphrey, R. J. 1961. Sensory organs : vision. *In* Marshall, A. J. (ed.). Biology and Comparative Physiology of Birds vol. 2. New York and London.

Rochon-Duvigneaud, A. 1943. Les yeux et la vision des vertébrés. Paris.

Walls, G. L. 1942. The Vertebrate Eye. Bull. 19. Cranbrook Inst. Sci., Michigan.

VISITOR: alternatively ' visitant ', meaning present in the area under reference only at certain times of year, the term being applied to a species, subspecies, population, or individual bird as the context requires. Thus, there are ' summer visitors ', ' winter visitors ', ' visitors on migration ' (=' transients '), and ' occasional visitors ' ; but these terms indicate merely local status and are meaningless except in relation to a stated area, a summer visitor in one place being necessarily a winter visitor somewhere else (see MIGRATION ; also VAGRANT).

VISORBEARER: substantive name of *Augastes* spp. (for family see HUMMINGBIRD).

VITAMIN REQUIREMENTS: see NUTRITION

VITELLUS: the egg-yolk (see EGG).

VITREOUS BODY: part of the eye (see VISION).

VIVIPARITY: the characteristic of giving birth to developed young, as contrasted with laying eggs in which the embryos develop outside the maternal body ; notably absent in birds, although it occurs in some fishes (cartilaginous and bony), amphibia, and reptiles, as well as being usual among mammals. The fact that oviparity is invariable among birds, as compared with the occurrence of exceptions in other classes of vertebrates, presents a biological point of some interest.

Matthews, L. H. 1955. The evolution of viviparity in vertebrates. Mem. Soc. Endocrin. 4 : 129–148.

Simkiss, K. 1962. Viviparity and avian reproduction. Ibis 104 : 216–219.

VOCALISATION: see SINGING

VOLANT: unusual word, meaning in the act of flying or capable of flight ; also a heraldic term for a bird flying or with wings stretched.

VOLTERRA-GAUSE PRINCIPLE: see ECOLOGY

VOMER: see PALATE; SKELETON

VULTURE (1): substantive name of most of the 14 species of 9 or 10 genera in the family Accipitridae (Falconiformes, suborder Falcones) ; in the plural form ' Old World vultures ', general term for the group—often treated as a separate subfamily (Aegypiinae) or even family, while some authors recognise a second subfamily (Gypaetinae) which is monotypic and contains only the Lämmergeier or Bearded Vulture *Gypaetus barbatus*. For the other members of the Accipitridae see HAWK. Superficially and in habits, the Old World vultures resemble the New World vultures (Cathartidae)—see VULTURE (2)—but on structural grounds that family is placed in a suborder of its own (Cathartae). Within the Accipitridae, the Old World vultures have their nearest allies in the fish eagles (*Haliaetus, Ichthyophaga*), the harrier-hawks (*Polyboroides*), and the serpent-eagles (*Circaetus, Spilornis*).

The Old World vultures are large birds, 5–9 feet in wing-span and $3\frac{1}{4}$–$15\frac{1}{2}$ lb. (1500–7000 grams) in weight. They are unlike most birds-of-prey in showing only slight size variation between the sexes, and the male may even be larger than the female. Most of them have sombre brown or black plumage, exceptions being the Egyptian Vulture *Neophron percnopterus*, the Palm-nut Vulture *Gypohierax angolensis*, and the Lämmergeier, while the griffons *Gyps* spp. are paler than the others. Except for the Lämmergeier and the Palm-nut Vulture, they are all characterised by having the whole or part of the head and neck bare except for a thin covering of down, and most have a distinct ruff of feathers at the base of the neck. Their bills are hooked and powerful, but their feet are weak and adapted for walking and running rather than for clutching. The wings are long and the birds can soar for long periods (see FLIGHT).

Old World vultures inhabit the warmer parts of Europe, the whole of Africa, and the drier parts of southern Asia, but they are not found in Malaysia or the Australasian Region. They are commonest in mountainous or open country, and are seldom found in forests or areas of high rainfall. Their range in places reaches altitudes of 20 000 feet or more above sea level ; but they are more characteristic of open plains and cultivated country from sea level to 6000 feet above, where carrion in the shape of dead game or domestic stock abounds. Four genera are widespread within the range of the group : *Gypaetus*, *Neophron* (in Africa chiefly in the north), *Gyps*, and (doubtfully regarded as a separate genus) *Pseudogyps* (not in Europe) ; *Sarcogyps* is restricted to southern Asia, and the others are wholly African.

With one exception they are carrion-feeders, consuming either the flesh or the skin and bone of carcasses. The exception is the Palm-nut Vulture, which feeds principally on the fruit pericarp of the Oil Palm *Elaeis guineensis* ; it also consumes dead fish and offal on the shore and can snatch small live fish from the surface of the water. Its feeding habits are thus quite different from those of any other members of the group, and it is likewise distinct from all but the Egyptian Vulture in its black-and-white plumage and from all but the Lämmergeier in having the neck fully feathered.

$\frac{1}{10}$

White-backed Vulture *Pseudogyps africanus*. C.E.T.K.

The Lämmergeier inhabits the mountainous regions of southern Europe, Asia, and Africa. Of very large size—8-9 feet in wing-span, 10-11½ lb. (4500-5200 grams) in weight—it is an uncommon species throughout its range. Its chief peculiarities are the loose texture of the body feathers, a beard of black bristly feathers projecting downwards on either side of the bill, and the habit (recorded of old and authenticated by recent observations) of dropping large bones from a height on rocks, splitting them in pieces so that the marrow can be extracted ; it also consumes carrion.

The remaining genera are likewise monotypic except *Gyps* (4 species of ' griffons ') and *Pseudogyps* (2 species). The members of these 2 genera and the Black Vulture *Aegypius monachus*, the Lappet-faced Vulture *Torgos tracheliotus*, the White-headed Vulture *Trigonoceps occipitalis*, and the King Vulture *Sarcogyps calvus* are all very large birds with wing-spans of 7-9 feet, the Black Vulture and the Lappet-

faced Vulture being the largest of all and among the largest of flying birds. All are carrion-feeders, congregating at a carcase in numbers. The griffons *Gyps* spp. and the 2 species of White-backed Vulture *Pseudogyps* spp. are highly gregarious at all times and at carcases are found in hundreds together. The others are less gregarious and show a tendency to seek small carcases in the open, although they will join with the more gregarious vultures and by virtue of superior size and strength will usually secure a meal in the face of greater numbers. The White-headed Vulture may possibly be able to kill its own prey on occasion.

The black-and-white Egyptian Vulture and the Hooded Vulture *Necrosyrtes monachus* are smaller species, with a wing-span of 5 feet and weighing 3-4 lb. (1500-2000 grams). The Egyptian Vulture has a very wide range in Europe, Asia, and Africa and is a common scavenger of offal in Eastern towns and villages ; in the northern parts of its range it is migratory. The Hooded Vulture performs much the same function in West and central Africa ; it is the only vulture that is at all common in forested regions, where it is able to pick up a living only because of the presence of human beings.

All vultures detect carrion by sight, and by the movements of other vultures and other carrion birds. Having detected a suspicious movement or seen the carcase, they plane down at great speed ; and if they arrive in good time they gorge so heavily that they can scarcely fly on being disturbed. They cannot easily break into large fresh carcases, but can often effect an entry through wounds or part-eaten portions of the kills of predators such as lions. Strangely enough, a carcase does not guarantee the presence of vultures but may lie for days in the open before being touched. A large mob of vultures will consume a dead cow in a short time, fresh birds continually arriving to replace those already sated.

They nest normally in trees, constructing huge stick nests lined with green leaves. The griffons, the Egyptian Vulture, and the Lämmergeier, however, breed principally or exclusively on crags. Of the tree-nesting species, the 2 White-backed Vultures *Pseudogyps africanus* and *P. bengalensis* are colonial, the others solitary. Normally only one egg is laid, white and variously marked—handsomely in the Egyptian Vulture and the Lämmergeier—with brown. Incubation and fledging periods are long, respectively 46-53 days and up to 120 days or more. The young and the sitting female are fed by the male with regurgitated carrion, and the female takes her share of feeding the young in the later stages of the fledging period.   L.H.B.

Fischer, W. 1963. Die Geier. Wittenberg-Lutherstadt.
Thomson, A. L. & Moreau, R. E. 1957. Feeding habits of the Palm-nut Vulture *Gypohierax*. Ibis 99 : 608–613.

For general works on the birds-of-prey see under HAWK.

VULTURE (2): substantive name of 4 of the species of Cathartidae (Falconiformes, suborder Cathartae) ; in the form ' New World vultures ', general term for the family. The substantive name used for the remaining 2 species is ' condor '.

$\frac{1}{15}$

Andean Condor *Vultur gryphus*. *C.E.T.K.*

These vultures and condors of the Americas are closely similar, in appearance and habits, to the Old World vultures (above) of the family Accipitridae, from which they are separable only anatomically. All except one species have generally black or dark brown plumage, some with ashy white in the primaries or secondaries or a ruff of ashy down round the neck ; the exception is the King Vulture *Sarcoramphus papa*, which has predominantly creamy white plumage with black in wings, rump, and tail. The head and neck are always naked, coloured yellow, orange or red in all species except the Black Vulture *Coragyps atratus*, in which they are dark greyish. The bill is hooked and rather slender, with a soft cere ; fleshy caruncles may be developed on the head, as in the male Andean Condor *Vultur gryphus* and in the King Vulture ; and the hind toe is very weak and poorly developed. Carrion and offal are the main diet, although the Turkey Vulture *Cathartes aura* (also called ' Turkey Buzzard ' and ' John Crow ' in the United States) is regarded as a pest on the Peruvian guano islands, taking eggs and young of sea birds. Some species appear to be able to inhabit more thickly wooded country than the Old World vultures, and apart from the condors range widely over all sorts of terrain. Nests are on crags or cliffs, in holes and gullies on the ground, in hollow stumps, in derelict buildings or simply on the ground under thick vegetation or at the foot of trees, with no material at all. Clutch size is mostly or always 2–3, the eggs of some species being immaculate dull white to light greenish grey, and of others light greenish handsomely spotted and blotched with reddish and purplish brown. Incubation, where known, is about 5 weeks and the nestling period 10–11 weeks.

The family ranges from southern Canada to Tierra del Fuego and the Falkland Islands and contains only 6 species. The Andean Condor is the most famous and largest, with wing-span of 9 feet 9 inches, and ranges along western South America from Venezuela and Colombia to Tierra del Fuego and Patagonia, being restricted to the Andes above 10 000 feet north of Peru but elsewhere occurring down to sea level. The California Condor *Gymnogyps californianus*, almost equally large, is at present (latest report 1953) reduced to about 60 individuals holding out in the mountains of California, though formerly it ranged into Mexico. The Turkey Vulture is the most widespread species—from Canada to Tierra del Fuego and the Falkland Islands, over all intervening lands : the very similar Yellow-headed Vulture *Cathartes burrovianus* is more restricted, occurring in the northern three-quarters of South America and in Middle America, while the Black Vulture (or ' Carrion Crow ', as it is called in the Antilles and Guiana) is only slightly less widespread than the Turkey Vulture. These 3 are all smaller birds, not greatly larger than a buzzard *Buteo* sp. Finally the King Vulture, intermediate in size between the condors and the other species, ranges from Mexico to Paraguay, Bolivia, and northern Argentina, but only as far south as Ecuador west of the Andes.   S.M.

Bent, A. C. 1937. Life histories of North American birds of prey. Part I. U.S. Natl. Mus. Bull. 167 : 1–409.
Kofoid, C. B. 1953. The Californian Condor. Natl. Audubon Soc. Res. Rep. no 1.

WADER: in the plural, general term commonly used in the British Isles for members of the suborder Charadrii of the Charadriiformes. ' Shore-birds ' has a similar meaning in North America, where ' waders ' tends to be applied to the Ciconiiformes.

WADING: see LOCOMOTION ; LEG

WAGTAIL: substantive name of species in one section of the Motacillidae (Passeriformes, suborder Oscines) ; in the form ' wagtails and pipits ', general term for the family (the subject of this article). The substantive names used in the other section are ' pipit ' and ' longclaw '. The members of the family are birds of medium or small size, usually with a long tail that is constantly in ' wagging ' motion—a habit particularly developed in the wagtails, and in them more noticeable because of their longer tails. (In the Forest Wagtail *Dendronanthus indicus* the tail appears to be wagged from side to side, not up and down—actually, the whole body is rotated through a horizontal arc, on stationary legs.) The bill is thin and slender. Most species, particularly the pipits, are not unlike larks (Alaudidae) in outward appearance, differing from that family inter alia in the structure of the horny covering of the tarsus ; no close relationship is believed to exist.

Habitat. These birds are mainly terrestrial in habits, walking or running on the ground like larks ; several species even do not commonly alight on shrubs or trees. The flight, however, is strong— often with exaggerated undulations in wagtails. Most of the species are inhabitants of grasslands and other types of open country ; others are found on swampy ground or on rocks beside water, or on the banks of brooks and rivers. They occur from the shores of the sea (for example, White Wagtail *Motacilla alba alba* and Rock Pipit *Anthus spinoletta petrosus*) upwards into the highest mountain ranges (for example Hodgson's Pipit *Anthus roseatus* to about 13 000 feet in the Himalaya and Kashmir, and the Bogotá Pipit *A. bogotensis* to at least 14 000 feet above sea level in the Andes of Ecuador).

Characters. All members of the family have strong feet and relatively long toes. In some species the hind claw is elongated and spur-like, but only rarely reaches a size comparable to that generally found in the larks, e.g. in Richard's Pipit *A. richardi* from central Asia. The longest toes are found in the longclaws *Macronyx* spp., inhabiting swampy grasslands in Africa. The Yellow-throated Longclaw *M. croceus*, a bird of the size of a Skylark *Alauda arvensis*, is stated to have a hind claw attaining nearly 2 inches, and a total length of foot of nearly 3½ inches.

Wagtails as a rule have a characteristic pied colour pattern of the plumage, in which grey, black, yellow, or green predominate. Pipits are generally plain brown, striped with dark above and below. The various species of pipit resemble each other closely, differing in minute morphological details ; in the general tone of their coloration they show a close correspondence with the colour of the soil and the ground vegetation in which they live. Among pipits, as among larks, fine examples of presumably cryptic coloration can be found, for instance in various African species, such as the Long-billed Pipit *A. similis*, the Sandy Plain-backed Pipit *A. vaalensis*, and Richard's Pipit. One species, the Yellow-breasted Pipit *A. chloris* from the highland grasslands of South Africa, has bright yellow under parts, like a Yellow Wagtail *Motacilla flava* ; and another African species, the Golden Pipit *Tmetothylacus tenellus*, is deep yellow all over, greatly differing from the majority of pipits and agreeing more in this respect with the wagtails.

Habits. All wagtails and pipits are mainly insectivorous, feeding on flies, mosquitoes, beetles, grasshoppers, and other insects living on or near the ground or among the grass ; also spiders and occasionally small molluscs or crustacea, small seeds, and other plant material. The call notes as well as the song are as a rule little varied, consisting of a series of repeated phrases. Some species of pipits exhibit song flights, similar to those of larks, but less extensive and less varied.

The members of the family usually make open, cup-shaped nests on the ground among grass and herbage, but some of the wagtails may nest in cavities in rocks, walls, and houses, under bridges, under the roofs of sheds, or in trees. The eggs are generally rather dark, with brownish, reddish, purplish, and greyish tinges, and finely speckled. Incubation is by the female, or by both sexes. The young are nidicolous and, when hatched, thickly covered with down on the upper parts. Both female and male feed the young.

Palaearctic wagtails and pipits are mainly migratory—particularly the yellow wagtails ; but sub-arctic and Arctic pipits also cover great distances and winter far south into the tropics, some reaching southern Africa and Australia. They have a complete moult in late summer and mostly an incomplete one in their winter quarters towards the end of the winter and in the early spring. In the pipits the sexes are alike in plumage, but in most of the wagtails males and females can usually be distinguished by plumage characters, even in winter dress.

Distribution. The Motacillidae comprise about 48 species, arranged in 4–6 genera. They are world-wide in distribution, but do not occur as breeding birds in New Guinea and Oceania. In the north they occur as far as Iceland, Greenland, and the coasts of the Arctic Ocean (absent from Spitsbergen) ; southwards they nest as far as Tierra del Fuego in southern South America, the island of South Georgia (where one species of pipit occurs, *Anthus antarcticus*), and New Zealand and adjacent sub-antarctic islands, including the Chatham and Campbell Islands.

Wagtails. Apart from the single species of *Dendronanthus*, already mentioned, the wagtails can be regarded as representatives of one genus, *Motacilla*, although several authors have placed the yellow wagtails in a separate genus, ' *Budytes* '. The genus contains only about 7 species (3 of which are found in Britain). They are mainly birds of the Old World, but they do not breed in Australia. A geographical race of the Yellow Wagtail, *M. f. tschutschensis*, nests in the tundra zone of western Alaska ; it is the only member of the genus to breed in the Western Hemisphere, having reached this region probably not before the end of the last glacial period in the Pleistocene.

As a species the Yellow Wagtail has a continuous Palaearctic range, inhabiting grasslands and open fields with low plants. It is remarkable for its high degree of geographical and individual variation in the colour and the colour pattern of the head. The British form of this species, *M. f. flavissima* (to

Grey Wagtail *Motacilla cinerea.* C.E.T.K.

which the name ' Yellow Wagtail ' particularly applies) has a mainly yellow or greenish-yellow head and a yellow stripe over the eye. The males of the continental populations of Europe have the crown of various shades of grey and the superciliary line white ; these birds are known as ' Blue-headed Wagtail ' *M. f. flava.* However, Yellow Wagtails with grey heads are also reported to have nested in Britain. A similar wide range of variation is known in numerous other places throughout the breeding range of the species. This variation has been regarded by some authors as the result of locally high frequencies of mutation. Other authors ascribe the enormous amount of local individual variation to the fact that stray individuals after having passed the winter in tropical regions are diverted from their normal homeward migration routes to the north by so-called migrational drift and consequently settle to breed in countries far remote from their own. Although evidence in favour of the first supposition is stronger than that for the latter, the problem of variation in this species is extremely complex and by no means clear. Together with a similar yellow-headed form from the South Russian and Kirghiz steppes, the British bird has been regarded by Williamson and some Russian authors as a separate species (*M. lutea*). However that may be, the ' Yellow Wagtail ' sensu stricto is one of the most striking examples of a geographical form of bird peculiar to Britain.

The Pied Wagtail *M. alba yarrellii*, the British form of the White Wagtail, is another such example. This species is less partial to grasslands than the Yellow Wagtail and often perches in trees. It is a regular attendant on human cultivation and frequently occurs in farmyards and around houses. It has a wide range in Europe, Asia, and Africa, showing a considerable amount of geographical variation in the black-and-white colour pattern of the plumage. The forms from India (*M. maderas-*

patensis) and Africa (*M. aguimp*) are sometimes regarded as separate species. The Cape Wagtail *M. capensis* from eastern and southern Africa is another close relative.

The Grey Wagtail *M. cinerea* occurs mainly near rivers and mountain streams. It has a Palaearctic range, but much more restricted than that of the previous species. It ascends to great heights in mountain regions, extending far beyond 6000 feet in the Alps and up to 11 500 feet in Kashmir. The Mountain Wagtail *M. clara* of Africa and the Madagascar Wagtail *M. flaviventris* are close relatives and have been regarded as Palaearctic colonists. The Yellow-headed Wagtail *M. citreola* (recorded once in Britain) has a central Palaearctic distribution. The Forest Wagtail *Dendronanthus indicus* lives in lightly wooded regions in Manchuria and Korea and regularly winters in the tropics of south and south-east Asia.

Pipits. Most pipits belong to the genus *Anthus*. They form a very homogenous group and occur in all continents. Thirteen species breed in the Palaearctic Region, 7 of them having occurred in Britain. In southern and eastern Africa at least 11 species occur ; and in the savannas, pampas, and upland grasslands of South America 6 species are generally recognised. Of the British pipits, the Meadow Pipit (or 'Titlark') *A. pratensis* has a European distribution ; in Arctic regions of Europe and Asia it is ecologically replaced by the Red-throated Pipit *A. cervinus*. Whereas the Meadow Pipit is one of the most abundant of the small passerine migrants throughout Britain, the Red-throated Pipit is a very rare transient through western Europe and winters mainly in tropical East Africa. The Meadow Pipit and the Tree Pipit *A. trivialis* form a pair of sibling species, resembling each other closely in outward appearance and breeding in the same area, although in slightly different habitats. The Tree Pipit often sings on tree-tops and starts its simple song flight from there.

The Rock Pipit *A. spinoletta* belongs to a complex group of populations inhabiting rocky seashores (Britain, Norway, Sweden, north coast of France) on the one hand, and high mountain valleys (where it is called Water Pipit) throughout the Palaearctic Region (up to 8200 feet in the Alps) on the other hand. In North America, and in the Kurile and Aleutian Islands in the North Pacific, these birds occur in both groups of habitats, reaching nearly 12 000 feet in the Rocky Mountains of New Mexico.

Other Palaearctic species are the Tawny Pipit *A. campestris*, mainly from arid or sandy regions, and the much larger Richard's Pipit *A. richardi*.

Recently various authors have lumped the latter species with pipits from Malaysia (*A. malayensis*), Australia (*A. australis*), and New Zealand (*A. novaeseelandiae*). According to this view Richard's Pipit, in its new sense and under the name *A. novaeseelandiae*, has a geographical range much larger than that of any other species of the genus except the circumglobal Water Pipit, and is present as a breeding bird from Russian Turkestan in the north to Cape Town, Tasmania, and New Zealand. The common pipit in North America is the Water Pipit mentioned above ; the only other species of pipit in North America is Sprague's Pipit *A. spraguei* from the grasslands of the western interior. The smallest species of the genus is the Short-tailed Pipit *A. brachyurus* from East Africa, with a total length of about 5 inches.

The remaining pipits, all African, have already been mentioned—the 8 species of longclaws *Macronyx*, and the Golden Pipit *Tmetothylacus tenellus* in a monotypic genus.   K.H.V.

Smith, S. G. 1950. The Yellow Wagtail. London.
Vaurie, C. H., White, C. M. N., Mayr, E. & Greenway, J. C., Jr. 1960. Family Motacillidae. *In* Mayr, E. & Greenway, J. C. (eds.). Check-list of Birds of the World vol. 9. Cambridge, Mass.

WAGTAIL, WILLY: misnomer applied to the ground-feeding *Rhipidura leucophrys* of the Australasian Region (see FLYCATCHER (1)).

WALDRAPP: alternative name of the Hermit Ibis *Geronticus eremita* (see IBIS).

WALKING: see LOCOMOTION ; LEG

WALLACE'S LINE: see ORIENTAL REGION ; also AUSTRALASIAN REGION

WALLCREEPER: *Tichodroma muraria* (see under NUTHATCH).

WARBLER (1): substantive name of most species of the subfamily Sylviinae of the Muscicapidae (Passeriformes, suborder Oscines) ; in the plural, general term for the subfamily. This group has in the past been more often treated as a separate family (see MUSCICAPIDAE). They are commonly known as Old World warblers (with 10 primaries), as opposed to New World warblers or wood-warblers (Parulidae) of the 9-primaried group (see WARBLER (2)). The Australian Malurinae, belonging to the same family as the Sylviinae, are also sometimes called 'warblers' (see WREN (2)). The systematic arrangement of the Old World warblers has led to much confusion and a considerable amount of disagreement among authors. Here the group is taken to include both the goldcrests and firecrests (or kinglets), sometimes referred to a separate family (Regulidae), and the New Zealand Fernbird of the genus *Bowdleria*.

General Characteristics. Generally, warblers are of small or very small size (from 3½ inches long), are plainly coloured, usually greenish, brownish, or pale greyish, although some tropical species have bright patterns ; and they have fine, narrowly pointed bills. They are mostly insectivorous and arboreal. In most species there is no difference in plumage between males and females ; the Blackcap *Sylvia atricapilla*, a few other members of that genus, and the several species of *Regulus* form notable exceptions, as in these the secondary sexual differences are conspicuous. Many species of warblers resemble each other closely, so that identification is sometimes a matter for experts, using as specific characters small structural differences, such as wing formulae or the presence and eventual extension of emarginations of the primaries. In not a few instances identification in the field is considerably facilitated by striking specific differences in the song, which is often melodious and varied, a fact from which the birds as a group derive their name. They differ from the flycatchers (Muscicapinae) and the thrushes (Turdinae) in having an unspotted juvenile plumage resembling the adult plumage. As a whole the warblers, together with the flycatchers, babblers (Timaliinae), and others, form a large assemblage of mainly Old World passerine birds which can be united within a large family, Muscicapidae.

Habits. Warblers inhabit trees, shrubs, low scrub, reeds, and sometimes even grass ; there they move among the foliage and thinner branches or the plant stems, generally in constant search of small insects and spiders, including the eggs and minute larvae of these. Some add berries and other small juicy fruits to their diets. They live mostly solitarily or in pairs, the males usually having striking territorial songs.

Breeding. The nest is commonly placed among thick foliage in trees and shrubs ; in other cases it is attached to vertical reed stems or placed on or near the ground. It is either open, cup-shaped, purse-shaped, or domed with a small entrance at the side. Some species build elaborate nests, placing neatly woven structures between reed or grass stems (reed-warblers *Acrocephalus* spp., grass-warblers *Cisticola* spp.), or inside the fold of a large hanging leaf of a tropical shrub or tree, the edges of the leaf being sewn together with plant fibre (tailor-birds *Orthotomus* spp.). The eggs are almost white, buffish, greenish, or pinkish, usually with fine spots ; they number from 3 to over 10, but in Britain the normal

number of warblers' eggs is 4–6. Incubation is by the female only (Willow Warbler *Phylloscopus trochilus*, Chiffchaff *P. collybita*), or by the female and the male (Reed Warbler *Acrocephalus scirpaceus*, Blackcap *Sylvia atricapilla*, Whitethroat *S. communis*) ; but the young, which are nidicolous, are generally fed and cared for by both sexes.

Blackcap *Sylvia atricapilla*.   C.E.T.K.

Migrations. In view of the mainly insect diet, the warblers living in cold and temperate regions are conspicuously migratory ; the species of *Regulus* form exceptions, but these birds are slightly aberrant in more than one respect. The majority of European warblers winter in tropical Africa. The spring migration of the Willow Warbler is one of the classic examples of that of an early spring migrant following closely the northward shift of the isotherm of somewhat less than 48° F (9° C) on a broad front throughout Europe. The migrations of the Willow Warblers of eastern Siberia to their wintering areas in East Africa and of the Arctic Warbler *Phylloscopus borealis* from its boreal breeding range to its wintering area in tropical south-eastern Asia, and vice versa, are renowned for their length. Arctic Warblers breeding in northern Scandinavia, Russia, or western Siberia must cover roughly 8000 miles twice a year, to and from Indonesia, the Philippines, and New Guinea. Apart from a complete post-nuptial moult, some species also have a more or less complete pre-nuptial moult. There is ample evidence that at least a few species postpone their post-nuptial moult until arrival in winterquarters (e.g. Garden Warbler *Sylvia borin*).

Distribution. The subfamily Sylviinae, in the present sense, comprises about 304 species. They are distributed throughout the Old World, to which they are virtually confined ; 39 species are known to breed in Europe, at least 150 in Africa (but only 49 of them south of the Cunene and Zambesi Rivers), 25 in south-eastern Asia (Malaya, Sumatra, Borneo, Java), and 21 in Australia. The British list (1952) contains 40 species, including 27 migrants and vagrants ; the recent list for China contains 82 species (1958). Two genera are also represented in the New World, the genus *Regulus* (2 species) and *Phylloscopus* (1 species). The latter case is extremely interesting, as it refers to an otherwise typically Palaearctic species, the Arctic Warbler *P. borealis*, which apparently not before post-glacial times has succeeded in crossing the Bering Strait from northeast Siberia far into Alaska, but still winters in the Old World tropics (Philippines, Moluccas).

In Europe the majority of the warbler species belong to the genera *Sylvia* (12 species), *Acrocephalus* (7 species), *Phylloscopus* (6 species), and *Hippolais* (5 species), all of them containing pairs of sibling species and causing great trouble in the delimitation and systematic arrangement of their forms. In western Europe the Willow Warbler and Chiffchaff (*Phylloscopus trochilus* and *P. collybita*), and the Marsh Warbler and Reed Warbler (*Acrocephalus palustris* and *A. scirpaceus*) form well-known pairs of sibling species that in the field are best identified by their songs and the habitats in which they are found. Of the genus *Phylloscopus* (leaf-warblers) no less than 30 species, occurring in Europe and Asia, were recognised by the able monographer of the group, C. B. Ticehurst, in 1938 ; but the genus *Cisticola* (grass-warblers), which found a no less eminent monographer in Rear-Admiral Hubert Lynes in 1930, comprises even more species (about 75) distributed throughout the warmer regions of the Old World.

Typical Warblers, etc. The genus *Sylvia* contains relatively large species such as the Blackcap *S. atricapilla* and the Orphean Warbler *S. hortensis*, but also small skulkers of arid scrub and Mediterranean vegetations. Some of them are among the finest avian songsters, such as the Blackcap and the Garden Warbler *S. borin* ; these, with the Whitethroat *S. communis*, are common birds of European woodlands and forest edges. In contrast to most other members of its group, the Blackcap has been repeatedly observed wintering in temperate regions of Europe. The Lesser Whitethroat *S. curruca* ranges less universally throughout Europe, but several of its geographical races have wide distributions in arid and desert-like parts of western central Asia. The Dartford Warbler *S. undata* is the northernmost of a group of Mediterranean warblers and occurs locally in England as a resident.

Other Mediterranean species such as the Sardinian Warbler *S. melanocephala* are non-migratory, but the Subalpine Warbler *S. cantillans* and the Spectacled Warbler *S. conspicillata* leave their Mediterranean breeding ranges in winter for northern tropical Africa. The small, pale Desert Warbler *S. nana* from North Africa and south-western Asia also belongs to this group.

No member of the genus *Hippolais* regularly nests in Britain, but the Icterine Warbler *H. icterina* and the Melodious Warbler *H. polyglotta* are widely distributed throughout central and southern Europe, the latter species being more particularly restricted to the south-western parts. They have a varied but somewhat harsh song and are well-known imitators of other birds' calls and a great variety of other noises. The species of this genus show uniform greyish, greenish, or yellowish colours, and they resemble each other strikingly in their morphological characters ; particularly in southwestern Asia, pairs of sibling species of this group are in need of comparative ecological and ethological studies.

The genus *Locustella* comprises several species known for their unobtrusive and skulking habit of moving through riverside scrub, reed beds, and other marsh vegetation, and also grass, corn, turnip fields, and other agricultural lands ; they are partially terrestrial in habits, have strong feet, and possess dull, brownish colours, in some species with heavy dark streaks on the upper parts. They show several variations on a pattern of long-sustained chirping song. Only one species, the Grasshopper Warbler *L. naevia*, nests in Britain, but Savi's Warbler *L. luscinioides* formerly did so in the reed beds of East Anglia and is still locally common in the Netherlands. Other members of the genus range widely throughout Europe and Asia ; some of them have been recorded as stragglers in Britain, but their main winter quarters are in southern Asia.

Reed Warblers, etc. The genus *Acrocephalus* contains many species that are widely distributed, being common in marshy habitats throughout the Old World. They are usually uniform brownish or even cinnamon in coloration, only a few of them showing dark streaks (Sedge Warbler *A. schoenobaenus* and Aquatic Warbler *A. paludicola*). Their song is harsh, sometimes monotonous, but that of the Marsh Warbler *A. palustris* is varied and not unlike that of the Melodious Warbler. The speciesgroup of the Great Reed Warbler *A. arundinaceus* has its members in dense and extensive reed beds in almost every part of Europe, Asia, and Australia. Like the smaller Reed Warbler *A. scirpaceus*, they make hanging nests attached to vertical reed stems.

The Sedge Warbler occurs in every kind of fresh-water marsh with low scrub and tall grasses in Europe and western Asia. Several other species occur in Europe, Asia, and Africa. In reed marshes in tropical Africa the genus is replaced by the very similar swamp-warblers *Calamocichla* spp. The same assemblage of genera also includes *Cettia* (including ' *Horeites* ') and *Bradypterus*, many species of which are known mainly from marshes and forest under-growth in sub-tropical and tropical parts of Asia and Africa. They have dull brownish or greyish colours, and soft, fluffy feathers, and are skulkers in the extreme. Several species have a loud, melodious song, by which they are fairly well known and easily identified, although they are very rarely seen. Only one species inhabits Europe, Cetti's Warbler *Cettia cetti*, occurring in marshes and riverside scrub in southern Europe, but it is particularly the Japanese Bush Warbler *Cettia diphone* (=' *Horeites cantans* ') that is famous for its melodious and varied song and in this connection plays a part in the country's folklore.

Leaf Warblers, etc. The genus *Phylloscopus* contains small birds of greenish and yellowish coloration and lively manners, living among the twigs and branches of bushes and tree-tops, even of tall coniferous trees. Apart from their song, which tends to be specifically highly distinct, they are difficult to identify, not only in the field but even in the hand. They are mainly Palaearctic and Oriental in their distribution ; quite a number of species occur in the Himalayan and Burmese mountain forests. The Willow Warbler *P. trochilus* is one of the commonest woodland and forest birds of temperate and northern Europe, extending far towards eastern Siberia in the lighter parts of the mainly coniferous forests (taiga) ; although feeding in bushes and the lower canopy of the tree-tops, it nests on the ground. The Chiffchaff *P. collybita*, has a monotonous disyllabic song different from the warbling song of the Willow Warbler ; and apart from nesting on the ground it is more a bird of the higher tree-tops. It has several geographical forms and close relatives in central Asia. The Wood Warbler *P. sibilatrix* is a typically European species. At least 7 other species of the genus are known as stragglers to Britain, most of them originating from remote Asiatic breeding ranges. Many members of this genus winter in tropical Asia and Africa, where they have been reported to sing as vividly as in their breeding ranges. The Greenish Warbler *P. trochi-loides* has come to notice through its remarkable westward spread from its Siberian breeding range, having recently settled as far west as Finland and north-eastern Germany. One species, *P. trivirgatus*, extends as far into the tropics as the mountain forests of Indonesia, New Guinea, and the Solomon Islands.

Tailor-birds, Wren-warblers, etc. In the tropics of Asia and Africa the genus *Phylloscopus* is mainly replaced by the genera *Seicercus* and *Abroscopus*, and in Africa further by *Apalis*, *Sylvietta*, and *Eremomela*. These birds are generally somewhat brighter in colour, some of them showing in addition distinct colour patterns with yellow, brown, rufous, and black. With their shorter and rounder wings and longer, often fan-shaped tails, they form the tran-sition towards the equally tropical tailor-birds *Orthotomus* spp. and wren-warblers *Prinia* spp. The remarkable nest-building habits of the tailor-birds have been referred to above. Several species of this genus are well known garden birds in tropical southern and south-eastern Asia. They have long, straight bills and long tails, the latter usually in nervous-seeming flicking movement, the whole bird being rather atypical for the subfamily. The members of the genus *Prinia* have shorter bills, and some show tendencies towards terrestrial life. They occur in tropical Asia and Africa, and their open, purse-shaped nests are ingeniously woven among twigs and plant stalks. Some wren-warblers resemble grass-warblers *Cisticola* spp. in habits, although not in colour pattern.

Grass Warblers. The systematics of the genus *Cisticola*—unobtrusive, usually dark-striped, small, brownish birds—was in a state of intriguing con-fusion until the publication of Lynes' admirable revision in 1930. The approximately 75 species of this widespread genus still provide a wealth of first-class biological problems relating to specific differ-ences and inter-specific relations and competition in habitat preference, food, feeding habits, nest build-ing, and song. The globular or bottle-shaped nests made of plant fibres, insect cotton, and cobwebs are wonders of perfection. The birds occur in dry scrub, swampy bush, grass fields, and reed beds throughout the Old World tropics and subtropics, but the majority of the species are found in Africa. Only 1 species occurs in the Mediterranean countries, and 2 in south-eastern Asia, but 29 are known from eastern Africa and 17 from Africa south of the Zambesi. The genus *Megalurus* (canegrass-warblers) is a group of large, almost babbler-like editions of the grass-warblers ; they are south Asiatic and Australian in distribution.

Ground Warblers and Fernbird. In the sub-family Sylviinae one at present also includes the few species of short-tailed, long-legged ground-warblers of the genus *Tesia* (including ' *Oligura* '), formerly placed either in the Troglodytidae or the Timaliinae. They live in the damp undergrowth of evergreen tropical forests of south-eastern Asia. The Fernbird *Bowdleria punctata* of New Zealand, which lives in reed-mace swamps and marshy scrub, is also placed in this subfamily.

Kinglets. The goldcrests and firecrests *Regulus* spp. are sometimes placed in a separate family (Regulidae) or at least subfamily, but are here treated as members of the Sylviinae ; they are certainly remote from the tits (Paridae), with which they had formerly been associated. They are nevertheless somewhat aberrant members of the group of warblers, mainly because of their loose, fluffy feathering and conspicuous colour pattern with fiery yellow, orange, or reddish colours on the crown. The globular nests made of moss and cobwebs and richly lined with feathers rival those of some grass-warblers in ingenuity and in some ways resemble the nests of the Long-tailed Tit *Aegithalos caudatus* and the Penduline Tit *Remiz pendulinus*. They are placed in tree-tops, suspended to the fine ends of branches of conifers and sometimes at great heights above the ground. These, Europe's smallest birds, are mainly inhabitants of coniferous forests, where they are in constant search of tiny insects and spiders, and the eggs of these, amongst the needles and twigs, and are often associated in mixed groups with tits of various species ; only the Firecrest nests also in deciduous woods. They have a very high-pitched song which consists of a series of short phrases in undulating sequence. Three species are found in the Old World, the commonest and most widespread being the Goldcrest *R. regulus*. The Firecrest *R. ignicapillus* is mainly European in distribution, whereas a third species *R. goodfellowi* is limited to the coniferous mountain forests of the island of Formosa ; but this form is treated by some authors as conspecific with the Firecrest. In North America this group is represented by the Golden-crowned Kinglet *R. sapatra*, which resembles the Old World Firecrest, and the Ruby-crowned Kinglet *R. calendula*, which differs from the other species by having a harsh, wren-like call-note.

Tit-warblers. The 2 species of central Asiatic and western Chinese tit-warblers (or tit-babblers) of the genus *Leptopoecile* (including ' *Lophobasileus* '), which resemble goldcrests in habits and fluffy feathering and in their multi-coloured plumages, are still more aberrant members of the subfamily Sylviinae. They inhabit mountain scrub and heathland and are most interesting birds, but relatively little is known about them.

Miscellaneous. The scrub-robins or bush-robins of the genus *Erythropygia* (or ' *Cercotrichas* ') form a transitional stage with the subfamily Turdinae because some members have an unspotted and others a more or less spotted juvenile plumage. They are relatively large for sylviines (although so are *Megalurus* spp.), and feed a good deal on the ground. In outward appearance (long, graduated tail and strong feet) and habits they resemble both the sylviine wren-warblers *Prinia* spp. and several of the turdine chats. They are now usually treated as turdine (see THRUSH).

Several other warblers, aberrant by reason of very long tails or bright coloration, are known from Africa and have been placed in separate genera. They include the long-tailed Cricket Warbler *Spiloptila clamans* and the little-known, red-headed Mrs Moreau's Warbler *Scepomycter winifredae* from the Uluguru Mountains of Tanganyika.

See Plate 43 (egg).   K.H.V.

Howard, H. E. 1907–15. The British Warblers. 2 vols. London.
Lynes, H. 1930. Review of the Genus Cisticola. Ibis suppl.
Ticehurst, C. B. 1938. A Systematic Review of the Genus Phylloscopus. London.

WARBLER (2): substantive name of most species of Parulidae (Passeriformes, suborder Oscines) ; in the plural, often in the form ' American warblers ' or ' wood-warblers ', general term for the family. The wood-warblers belong to the great complex of New World 9-primaried song-birds that includes such groups as the tanagers (Thraupinae), honey-creepers (Coerebinae), cardinal grosbeaks (Pyrrhuloxiinae), and troupials (Icteridae). Division of this complex into families is in some instances difficult, and various rearrangements at the familial and sub-familial level have been proposed in recent years (see EMBERIZIDAE).

The wood-warblers are small birds, the largest being little larger than a House Sparrow *Passer domesticus*. Many are brightly coloured, with yellow, orange, black, and white among the most frequent colours. A few species have blue or red plumage, while others are dull brown, olive, or grey. Sexual and seasonal dimorphism is frequent among northern species, but in many tropical wood-warblers the sexes are equally brightly coloured all the year round. Most species are insectivorous, but some add berries and other vegetable matter to their diet. Wood-warblers are widely distributed ecologically, inhabiting coniferous and deciduous woods, tropical rain-forests, swamps and marshes, open fields, shrubbery, and sparse desert vegetation.

Northern wood-warblers build their nests in a variety of sites—on the ground, in bushes and vines, or in trees. One species, the Prothonotary Warbler *Protonotaria citrea*, is a hole-nester, and members of the genus *Parula* nest in hanging bunches of Spanish 'moss', beard-lichen, or similar vegetation. Most tropical members of the family nest on the ground, or on ledges or banks. Eggs are usually white, more or less speckled with various colours; a few species lay immaculate white eggs. Clutches among tropical species usually range from 2 to 4, while northern wood-warblers lay 3–5 eggs, exceptionally 6.

The family ranges throughout the New World, from Alaska and northern Canada to southern South America. There are some 113 species, usually arranged in 26 genera (although many authorities agree that the family is somewhat oversplit generically). About half of the genera are predominantly North American or West Indian; the remainder are either primarily tropical or are widely distributed through both American continents. Most northern species are highly migratory, and frequently travel in mixed flocks. The great migratory 'waves' of wood-warblers are among the most impressive features of the bird-life of eastern North America.

The largest genus, with some 27 species, is *Dendroica*, a primarily North American group; 5 species are confined to the West Indies. One species, the Yellow Warbler *D. petechia*, is widely distributed in North and Middle America, the West Indies, and northern South America; predominantly bright yellow, the males of most races have chestnut streaks on the breast, and some have chestnut caps or heads. Among the North American species are the Myrtle Warbler *D. coronata* and its close (probably conspecific) relative Audubon's Warbler *D. auduboni* (which breeds south in the mountains to Guatemala). These are the most frugivorous members of the family, feeding extensively on berries in fall and winter. The Caerulean and Blackthroated Blue Warblers *D. cerulea* and *D. caerulescens*, also North American, are the only members of the family in which the males are conspicuously blue in colour. The large Kirtland's Warbler *D. kirtlandii* has one of the most restricted breeding ranges among non-insular birds; it nests only in an area of about 60 by 80 miles in central Michigan, and within this range only in dense stands of pines 3 to 18 feet tall.

Related to *Dendroica* are the 11 species of *Vermivora*, a genus of North and Middle America. Two species, the Blue-winged Warbler *V. pinus* and the Golden-winged Warbler *V. chrysoptera*, regularly hybridise where their breeding ranges overlap; 2 of the hybrid forms are so distinctive in appearance that they were originally named as species and are still known by the English names of 'Brewster's' and 'Lawrence's' Warblers. Few hybrid birds have been so thoroughly studied under field conditions, as the zone of hybridisation includes several of the major cities of the eastern United States.

Another large genus is *Basileuterus*, with about 22 species. This is primarily a tropical group, found from northern Mexico to northern Argentina. Most species of this genus are predominantly yellow, some with brown or grey in the plumage as well. Most have a sharply defined crown-patch or other conspicuous marks about the head. Typical of this group is the Golden-crowned Warbler *B. culicivorus*, the most widely distributed species of the genus. The Buff-rumped Warbler *B. fulvicauda*, another widespread species, is representative of a somewhat different group within the genus; these are dull-coloured birds with no striking markings, more terrestrial in habits than other *Basileuterus* spp.

One of the more specialised wood-warblers is the Black-and-white Warbler *Mniotilta varia* of North America. As its name suggests, its plumage pattern consists of longitudinal streaks of black and white. It has become adapted to a tree-climbing habit much like that of the treecreepers (Certhiidae), with corresponding development of toes and claws. Another monotypic North American genus is *Protonotaria*, mentioned earlier as the only hole-nesting wood-warbler; the single species, the Prothonotary Warbler *P. citrea*, is primarily an inhabitant of wooded swamps of the south-eastern United States, and is rich yellow with bluish-grey wings.

Several genera of wood-warblers have become adapted for the aerial capture of insects. As in the case of other families in which the fly-catching habit has developed, these genera are characterised by the possession of wide, flat bills and well-developed rictal bristles. Two genera, *Setophaga* and *Myioborus*, are known as 'redstarts', although they have little in common with the Old World birds of that name (*Phoenicurus* spp.). The North American Redstart *S. ruticilla* is a common and well-known species, breeding in the temperate portions of the United States and Canada, and wintering south to northern South America; the male is glossy black, with a white belly and patches of orange on tail, wings, and sides, while in the female the black and orange are replaced by grey and yellow. The Painted Redstart *S. picta* of Central America and the south-western United States, and the members of the tropical genus *Myioborus* (about 10 species), differ from the North American Redstart in having the sexes equally bright in colour.

Bright red colours are not common among the Parulidae, but are present in 3 species of Middle

America. The Redfaced Warbler *Cardellina rubri-frons* ranges north to the mountains of the south-western United States, whereas the Red Warbler *Ergaticus ruber* is exclusively Mexican and the Pink-headed Warbler *E. versicolor* is confined to Guatemala and adjacent Mexico. All 3 of these species are among those warblers adapted to the fly-catching habit. Another fly-catching group of wood-warblers is the genus *Wilsonia*, including 3 North American species that are predominantly yellow in colour but with various striking black markings on face or head.

The yellowthroats comprise a widespread group of closely related species of the genus *Geothlypis* (with the probably congeneric Ground-chat *Chamaethlypis poliocephala*). These are dwellers in marshes, wet meadows, and undergrowth, almost through the Americas. Most have greenish backs and yellow under parts, and males have a black facial mask of varying degrees of development. The largest of the wood-warblers is the Yellow-breasted Chat *Icteria virens*, which is a relatively heavy-bodied, stout-billed, long-tailed species that behaves and sounds more like a member of the mockingbird family (Mimidae) than a true wood-warbler; its position as a member of the Parulidae has indeed been questioned. It is a North American species, breeding south to the tableland of central Mexico.

The West Indies are the home of several some-what aberrant wood-warblers, including 4 endemic genera. Two of the latter are found only on single islands of the Lesser Antilles—the Whistling Warbler *Catharopeza bishopi* of St Vincent, and Semper's Warbler *Leucopeza semperi* of St Lucia; the former is nearly black, with white markings, and the latter, an exceedingly rare bird, is a nondescript grey.

Among the most terrestrial of a predominantly arboreal family are the 3 members of the North American genus *Seiurus*. Best known and most widely distributed is the Ovenbird *S. aurocapillus*. Like its namesakes of the unrelated Neotropical family Furnariidae, and like certain other terrestrial wood-warblers, the Ovenbird builds a dome-shaped nest, reminiscent of an old-fashioned outdoor oven, on the ground. It shares with the 2 species of waterthrushes *S. motacilla* and *S. noveboracensis* the habit of walking rather than hopping when on the ground. The waterthrushes, however, have a tail-bobbing motion much like that of a wagtail *Motacilla* sp. or a Common Sandpiper *Actitis hypoleucos*.

Several small genera, primarily North American in distribution, have not been otherwise mentioned above. These include 2 inconspicuous brown species, Swainson's Warbler *Limnothlypis swainsonii* and the Worm-eating Warbler *Helmitheros vermivora*; and

4 species of *Oporornis*, yellowish in colour, with either a grey hood or black facial mask. The Olive Warbler *Peucedramus taeniatus*, which extends from the south-western United States through Central America, has been thought to be related to *Dendroica*, but there is much anatomical and behavourial evidence to suggest that its affinities may be closer to the 'Old World insect-eaters' (Muscicapidae in the wide sense) than to the New World 9-primaried group.

In addition, there is a strong probability that some of the Coerebinae (Emberizidae) would be more appropriately placed in the Parulidae (see HONEY-CREEPER (1)).

See Plate 46a (phot.).   K.C.P.

Bent, A. C. 1953. Life Histories of North American wood warblers. U.S. Natl. Mus. Bull. 203.
Ficken, M. S. & Ficken, R. F. 1962. The comparative ethology of wood warblers: a review. Cornell Univ. Lab. Orn., Living Bird 1 : 103–122.
Griscom, L., Sprunt, A. et al. 1957. The Warblers of America. New York.
Skutch, A. F. 1954. Life Histories of Central American Birds. Pt. I. (Pacific Coast Avifauna no. 31.) Berkeley, Cal.

WARBLER (3): substantive name of species of Malurinae (see WREN (2)).

WARM-BLOODEDNESS: see HEAT REGULATION

WATERCOCK: *Gallicrex cinerea* (see RAIL).

WATERFOWL: vague term for aquatic (usually fresh-water) birds of wild species, especially of the Anatidae (see DUCK); in Britain applied more particularly to those kept for ornamental purposes, in some degree of captivity, on private lakes or artificial ponds (see AVICULTURE); in North America used in the sense (British) of WILDFOWL.

WATERHEN: alternative name (perhaps obsolescent) in Britain of the Moorhen *Gallinula chloropus*; also used as substantive name of *Amaurornis* spp. (see RAIL).

WATERING: see DRINKING; EXCRETION, EXTRARENAL; PARENTAL CARE

WATERTHRUSH: substantive name (now commonly written as one word) of 2 *Seiurus* spp. (see WARBLER (2)).

WATTLEBIRD (1): substantive name of *Anthochaera* spp. (see HONEYEATER). This Australian usage is of earlier date than the next below.

WATTLEBIRD (2): now used, in the plural, as a general term for the Callaeidae (Passeriformes, suborder Oscines), of which all the species have

different substantive names. The family is restricted
to New Zealand and comprises 3 monotypic genera
(1 extinct). The relationship of the Callaeidae to
other families is uncertain ; generally placed near
the starlings (Sturnidae), they may be closer to the
Apostlebird *Struthidea cinerea* (Grallinidae), according to W. B. Alexander, or to the bowerbirds
(Ptilonorhynchidae) and birds-of-paradise (Paradisaeidae), according to Amadon. They probably
arose by adaptive radiation in New Zealand from a
single immigrant stock.

Wattlebirds are medium-sized arboreal birds of
the primitive New Zealand forest. Their most
conspicuous common characters are the paired
fleshy wattles at the gape. They share certain
skeletal characteristics, and others such as extremely
rounded wings with very long first primaries,
reaching more than half-way to the wing tip ; long
tails, somewhat arched in profile and section, with
feather shafts projecting as small points ; powerful
legs and feet with long hind claws. The wattles
characteristic of the family (orange except in one
form) develop from the fold of skin at the angle
of the nestling's gape, remain small in juveniles, and
are largest in adult males ; their function is obscure.

Inhabitants of the forest interior, the birds generally live in pairs or family parties, often feeding
on the ground, progressing by long hops or bounds,
and gaining height by leaping from branch to
branch, using the wings for balancing but rarely for
sustained flight except when losing altitude. The
Saddleback *Creadion* ('*Philesturnus*') *carunculatus*
feeds mainly on insects from decaying wood, bark,
and forest floor, but also on fruits, and the diet of
the extinct Huia *Heteralocha* ('*Neomorpha*') *acutirostris*
was similar ; but the Kokako *Callaeas cinerea* feeds
mainly on young leaves and fruit. Food is occasionally grasped with a foot, parrot-fashion. Nests are
shallow, open, loosely built of rootlets, twigs,
leaves, and the like, lined with fern-scales, and
generally sheltered from above or placed in a hollow
or ledge up to 30 feet above ground level. The
2-3 (possibly 4) eggs are grey or brown, with
purplish-grey or brown blotches or spots, especially
at the larger end. Both sexes incubate (20-21 days),
and feed the young, the male sometimes passing
his contribution to the female ; nestling faeces are
removed (Saddleback) or eaten (Kokako).

The wattlebirds formerly inhabited forested parts
of New Zealand (main islands and closer outlying
islets) ; but the Huia (recorded only from the
southern part of North Island) is now extinct, and
the others are much localised. They persist only in
little-modified and fairly extensive remnants of the
original forest, apparently owing to their limited

adaptability to the ecological changes of the past
century, including the introduction of mammalian
predators.

The Huia was notable for the extreme sexual
differentiation of the bill (Fig. A, B). A pair sometimes co-operated in obtaining beetle larvae ('huhu')
and wingless orthoptera ('weta') from decayed
wood, their distinctive bills performing separate
functions (Buller) ; the male chiselled out grubs
while the female's long pliant bill probed borings in
resistant timber. The sexes were otherwise alike—
glossy black with a broad white band across the tip
of the tail. The Maori wore the prized tail feathers
in their hair as a mark of rank. Extinction has been
attributed to hunting during the later nineteenth
century (last record 1907).

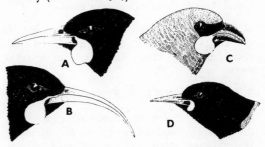

Types of bill in the New Zealand family Callaeidae. **A, B**
—Huia *Heteralocha acutirostris*, male and female, showing
sexual dimorphism of bill ; **C** Kokako *Callaeus cinerea* ;
D Saddleback *Creadion carunculatus*

The Saddleback (Maori 'tieke') is about the size
of a Starling *Sturnus vulgaris*, glossy black with a
'saddle' of chestnut. The 2 subspecies are distinguished chiefly by the immature plumages. In
the North Island race *C. c. rufusater*, now virtually
restricted to Hen Island, the young pass directly
into a plumage like that of adults, whereas the
South Island form *C. c. carunculatus*, now found only
on South Cape Islands (off Stewart Island), wears
uniform brown plumage until its second season and
was once thought to be a distinct species, the 'Jack-
bird' (*C.* '*cinerea*'). The song is a series of vigorous
call phrases of rather simple form.

The 2 races of the Kokako (formerly known as
'wattled-crows'), are bluish-grey birds of gentle
temperament, with velvety black lores. Their bills
are short, stout, and arched (Fig. C), and their diet
is dominantly vegetarian. The wattles are orange,
with bluish bases in the nominate subspecies (South
and Stewart Islands), and bright blue in the North
Island form *C. c. wilsoni*. The song, of mellow
bell-like notes and simple contemplative phrases,
earned the bushman's names of 'organbird' and
'true bellbird'. The South Island subspecies is

now very rare, but the North Island Kokako persists locally.   C.A.F.

Amadon, D. 1962. Family Callaeidae. *In* Mayr, E. & Greenway, J. C., Jr. (eds.). Check-list of Birds of the World vol. 15. Cambridge, Mass.
McKenzie, H. R. 1951. Breeding of Kokako. Notornis 4 : 70–76.
Stead, E. F. 1936. The New Zealand Saddlebacks. Ibis 13 (6) : 594–598 ; and Trans. Roy. Soc. N.Z. 66 : 185–187.
Stonor, C. R. 1942. Anatomical notes on the New Zealand Wattled Crow (*Callaeas*), with special reference to its powers of flight. Ibis (14) 6 : 1–18.
And text-books on New Zealand avifauna.

WATTLE-EYE: substantive name of *Platysteira* spp. and related forms (see FLYCATCHER (1)).

WAVEY: a name in North America for the Snow Goose *Anser coerulescens* (see under DUCK).

WAXBILL: substantive name of various *Estrilda* spp. etc. ; in the plural, general term for a tribe (Estrildini) of the family Estrildidae (see WEAVER-FINCH).

WAX, METABOLISM OF: see HONEYGUIDE

WAXWING: substantive name of the 3 species of the subfamily Bombycillinae of the Bombycillidae (Passeriformes, suborder Oscines) ; used without qualification, in Britain, for the only European species ; in the plural, general term for the subfamily (for related forms see under BOMBYCILLIDAE). There is only one genus, consisting of the (in American usage) Bohemian Waxwing *Bombycilla garrulus* of Holarctic distribution, the so-called Japanese Waxwing *B. japonica* native to eastern Siberia, and the Cedar Waxwing *B. cedrorum* of North America. From their breeding areas in the northern part of the North Temperate Zone, all species make irregular migrations in winter to central Europe (in some years to the British Isles), central China, Japan, and as far as Central America (see IRRUPTION).

The English name refers to the red, drop-shaped, and wax-like tips of the secondary flight feathers, which are prolongations of the shafts. The phenomenon can also be seen in the tail feathers, but to a much lesser degree. Many individuals of all species lack these ; the lack has not been explained. All 3 species are also quite similar in size and colour pattern. They are about 6½–7½ inches long, and have characteristically soft, silky plumage, relatively long wings, and slightly rounded tails. Their heads are crested, and the plumage is a soft, vinaceous brown, which shades into greyish-brown on the back and grey on the rump. From forehead to lores, and about the eye, the feathers are black ; at

the base of the lower mandible they are white. Primary and secondary flight feathers are black, marked with white, or yellow and white. All the birds are grey below, with black throats and brown, or reddish, under tail coverts. Tails are black, tipped with lemon-yellow or red. Bills are short, broad at the gape, slightly hooked and notched ; feet and legs are short and stout.

B. japonica and *B. cedrorum*, which may perhaps together be regarded as a superspecies, are somewhat paler and more ·greenish-grey below, and neither is marked with yellow on wing coverts and secondaries as is *B. garrulus*. *B. japonica* differs from the other 2 by its red-tipped tail feathers, and by having a bar of crimson across the upper wing coverts (the feathers here being quite normal).

The sexes are similar except that, as a rule, the black throats of females are duller, even tending to greyish ; many are somewhat less brightly coloured. Juveniles of *B. garrulus* are generally browner, less greyish, than adults and are faintly streaked below. Those of *B. japonica* and *B. cedrorum* are more obviously streaked, and juveniles of all species lack the black throat-patch. Nestlings are naked at first.

Nests are usually built in pines, but sometimes in deciduous trees. They are bulky and loosely constructed of twigs, with a lining of mosses and plant fibres, and a soft inner lining of grasses, feathers, and down. Both sexes take part in building, but the female is, as usual, the more zealous. Clutches of 3–7 eggs are laid, sometimes in late May but usually during June. The ground colour of these is pale, greyish (glaucous) blue, marked profusely with small, black dots and fine, irregular lines. The ground colour is said to be grey in some sets.

The birds seem to be without fear ; they have been described as ' tame ' and ' sluggish '. Their flight is strong and undulating. Nests are usually found singly or perhaps two in close proximity, but winter birds are (often, if not always) gregarious. They defend no territory other than the nest. Berries and small fruits are staple foods, although insects are captured in the air during the nesting season. A soft whistle, trill, and chatter have been recorded, but no true song.

See Plate 29 (colour).   J.C.G., Jr.

Arvey, M. D. 1951. Phylogeny of the waxwings and allied birds. Univ. Kansas Publ. Zool. 3 : 473–530.
Putnam, L. S. 1949. The life history of the Cedar Waxwing. Wilson Bull. 61 : 141–182.

WEATHER: see METEOROLOGY; also CLIMATOLOGY

WEATHER MOVEMENT: see MIGRATION

WEAVER: substantive name of many species of Ploceidae (Passeriformes, suborder Oscines) ; in the plural, sometimes in the form 'ploceid weavers', general term for the family. Current opinion excludes the 'weaver-finches' (waxbills, grass-finches, and mannikins—for some of which 'weaver' is used as a substantive name), placing them in a separate family, the Estrildidae (see WEAVER-FINCH). A distinctive diagnosis of the Ploceidae, an Old World and very largely African group, is difficult to provide. With few exceptions, they are strongly built birds varying in size from about the equivalent of a Goldfinch *Carduelis carduelis* to that of a Song Thrush *Turdus philomelos*, with strong short bill, 10 primaries (the outermost much reduced but not rotated to the upper surface) and 12 rectrices. Unlike the Estrildidae, the nestlings of the Ploceidae do not have patterned mouth-parts. All the members of the family build covered nests. They are not songsters ; with very few exceptions they merely chirp, buzz, or chatter.

The Ploceidae have usually been divided into the buffalo weavers (Bubalornithinae), sparrow-weavers (Plocepasserinae), sparrows (Passerinae), scaly weavers (Sporopipinae), and the 'true weavers' (Ploceinae) ; but the current tendency is to merge the Plocepasserinae and the Sporopipinae in the Passerinae, and in this enlarged sense that group forms the subject of a separate article (see SPARROW (1)). The other two groups are dealt with below.

Buffalo Weavers. The subfamily Bubalornith-inae includes 2 species, the Black Buffalo Weaver *Bubalornis albirostris* and the White-headed Buffalo Weaver *Dinemellia dinemelli*, both heavily built birds, about 10 inches long, which inhabit the drier parts of Africa. Neither has anything particular to do with buffalos. They are birds of mixed diet, which they seek on the ground in parties after the manner of starlings *Sturnus* spp. They build large untidy domed nests of thorny twigs, which are highly protective. The eggs of both species are typically almost white, heavily speckled and streaked, except that in the most north-easterly part of the Black Buffalo Weaver's range they are plain pale blue. At least this species is polygamous ; and also in this species a peculiar penis-like external organ has been described, but is said to be imperforate.

True Weavers. The subfamily Ploceinae con-sists of about 90 species, of which the English names are mainly fabricated and variable. Most of them have part of the plumage bright yellow or red. All are confined to Africa south of the Sahara, and neighbouring islands, except for 5 in India and Malaysia. Typically they build elaborate suspended nests that are beautifully woven of vegetable fibres, but within the subfamily there is a considerable range of techniques (cf. studies by Crook).

$\frac{1}{2}$

Red-crowned Bishop *Euplectes hordeaceus*, of tropical Africa. *C.E.T.K.*

The bill varies greatly in degree of heaviness, those species that are most insectivorous having as a rule the most slender bills. A good many species feed on both insects and seeds, rarely taken on the ground. They almost all fall readily into two groups : (A) the exclusively arboreal birds, nearly all with bright yellow or red in the plumage, that build elaborate suspended nests mostly with entrance tunnels ; (B) the diochs (*Quelea*), the fodis (*Foudia*), the whydahs (in one sense) and bishops (*Euplectes*). Of group B the males nearly all have brilliant colours or long tails, or both ; the nests are mostly not so specialised as those of group A. Out-side the two groups are 3 monotypic genera : the Black Swamp Weaver (or White-fronted Grosbeak) *Amblyospiza albifrons*, a clumsy bird with a very heavy bill, which weaves a marvellous globular nest of extremely fine fibres ; the so-called São Tomé Grosbeak *Neospiza concolor*, superficially rather similar, known only from two specimens collected in the 1880s in the island of São Tomé in the Gulf of Guinea ; and the Cuckoo Weaver *Anomalospiza imberbis*, a small yellow bird of which nothing is known except that it is parasitic on grass-warblers (*Cisticola* spp. and *Prinia* spp.)—the only one of the Ploceidae, as distinct from the Estrildidae, to have such habits (see PARASITISM).

Group A. There have been numerous conflicting attempts to arrange the 67 weavers of group A into a multiplicity of genera and subgenera. Pending much more critical information on life histories it seems best to retain them in only 2 genera: *Malimbus* (10 species), which are insectivorous birds with red in the plumage and mostly inhabiting evergreen forest, and *Ploceus* (57 species), mostly with brilliant yellow in the plumage and distributed in every kind of arboreal habitat. Many of the *Ploceus* species can be put together in informal species-groups, but some cannot. One of the clearest of such groups consists of the insectivorous species *P. insignis, P. preussi,* and *P. dorsomaculatus,* which resemble each other in colour pattern, slender bill, form of nest, and a habit of foraging on tree-trunks and branches after the manner of a Nuthatch *Sitta europea.*

A general character of the *Ploceus* and *Malimbus* species is the employment of nest-protective devices, usually two or more in combination and to a greater extent than in any other family of birds. Their nests are tough, with entrance generally on the underside or protected by a tunnel, or both; the tunnel may be as much as 2 feet long (see NEST). The nests are often built at the tips of twigs or palm fronds; and they are often sited over water or very close to the habitations of wasps, big birds, or human beings (see NESTING ASSOCIATION). It is perhaps because the egg colour is not subject to such rigid selection as usual that eggs of individual species of weaver are exceptionally variable. As an extreme case, the eggs of a single subspecies of one of the blackheaded weavers, *Ploceus melanocephalus capitalis,* have been recorded as white, pink, terracotta, and various shades of brown and green, with or without brown or purplish spotting.

Most of the *Ploceus* species inhabiting the drier country, but not the others, have strong sexual dimorphism, with the females permanently dull and streaky ('sparrowy') and the males assuming a similar dull plumage in the off-season. This arrangement generally goes with polygamy and the formation of big itinerant flocks in the off-season. A nesting colony of *Ploceus* sp. is an extraordinary scene of animation; often a tree-top is filled with nests slung on branches only a foot or so apart or on the tips of palm-fronds. Typical species are the widespread Village Weaver (as it is called in West Africa) *P. cucullatus* and the Golden Weaver *P. bojeri* of Kenya. The males build nest after nest, 'advertising' each to the females by hanging upside down at the entrances (in the bottom of the nest), flapping their wings and chattering.

The 5 Asiatic species of the Ploceidae, all of which can be placed in the genus *Ploceus,* are markedly similar to each other in plumage, with yellow and blackish coloration on the head and with large areas of the body dull or streaky. One, *P. hypoxanthus,* has an exceptionally thick bill. The species with the most extensive range is the Baya Weaver *P. philippinus,* distributed from Pakistan to Ceylon, Siam, Indo-China, and Sumatra (but not the Philippines—a good example of early naming under a misapprehension).

Group B. By contrast with the *Ploceus* and *Malimbus* species, the bishops, the whydahs, the diochs, and the fodis build globular nests; and except for the fodis (which are confined to the islands of the Indian Ocean) they place them in grass or herbage instead of in trees with special suspension. In general their nesting arrangements are much less protective than those of *Ploceus* and *Malimbus* spp., and this may account for the fact that their eggs, presumably under stronger selection, are speckled protectively and are far more uniform.

The bishop males in full plumage are glossy black, with much brilliant yellow or red, but with tails mostly about 50–70 per cent of the wing length. The whydahs (in one sense) have less brilliant colour and are longer-tailed; but there are transitional species and it seems best to retain them all in one genus, *Euplectes.* The biggest of the group, the Sakabula *E. progne,* has a wing of about $5\frac{1}{2}$ inches but a superb tail some 20 inches long, of abundant black feathers that ripple behind him as he flies.

The bishops and whydahs have the outermost primary more reduced than any others of the Ploceidae, to between 12 and 20 per cent of the wing-length. All have 'sparrowy' females very much alike, a similar off-season male plumage, and polygamous habits. Correlated with their polygamy and the fact that they are not arboreal nesters, territorialism is very highly developed in these birds. In grass on a flood-plain, or in herbage that is regenerating on cultivated land, several species may have their territories; for example, among the bishops in East Africa, the flaming red *E. nigroventris* and *E. hordeaceus,* along with the yellow *E. capensis* and the so-called Fan-tailed Whydah *E. axillaris.* One of these birds may have half-a-dozen or more females nesting in his territory, and he spends an agitated life patrolling his boundaries, with rump feathers puffed and aggressive sizzling calls. The displays of a number of species have been compared by Emlen (1957); that of Jackson's Whydah *E. jacksoni* is exceptional, for instead of 'floating' over a territorial area the male directs a 'dance' to a tuft of grass left in a beaten patch. (See WHYDAH (2)).

For the enormous abundance of the Red-billed Dioch *Quelea quelea* see QUELEA CONTROL.

                            R.E.M.

Bannerman, D. A. 1953. The Birds of West and Equatorial Africa vol. 2. London and Edinburgh.

Mackworth-Praed, C. W. & Grant, C. H. B. 1955. Birds of Eastern and North-eastern Africa vol. 2. London.

McLachlan, G. R. & Liversidge, R. 1957. Roberts' Birds of South Africa. Johannesburg.

These three books between them give coloured plates and details of nearly all African species.

Crook, J. H. 1960. Nest form and construction in certain West African weaver-birds. Ibis 102 : 1–25.

Crook, J. H. 1961. The fodies of the Seychelles Islands. Ibis 103a : 517–548.

Emlen, J. 1957. Display and mate selection in the whydahs and bishop birds. Ostrich 28 : 202–213.

Friedmann, H. 1950. The breeding habits of the weaver-birds. A study in the biology of behaviour patterns. Smithsonian Rep. 1949 : 293–316.

Moreau, R. E. 1960. Conspectus and classification of the Ploceine weavers. Ibis 102 : 298–321, 443–471.

Moreau, R. E. & Greenway, J. C., Jr. 1962. Family Ploceidae. In Mayr, E. & Greenway, J. C., Jr. (eds.). Check-list of Birds of the World vol. 15. Cambridge, Mass.

WEAVER-BIRD: synonymous with WEAVER, or with WEAVER and WEAVER-FINCH combined.

WEAVER-FINCH: in the plural, fabricated term—alternatively 'estrildid weavers'—for the Estrildidae (Passeriformes, suborder Oscines), including the waxbills, grassfinches, and mannikins (not to be confused with the manakins). In addition to various special substantive names, 'finch', 'sparrow', and 'weaver' are used for many. The members of the family are widespread in the warmer parts of the Old World from Africa to the Philippines, New Guinea, Australia, and the Pacific Islands east to Fiji and Samoa. According to Delacour there are 108 species in 15 genera. Many are well known in captivity (see CAGE BIRD).

They are mostly small to very small seed-eaters, and were formerly included in the same family (Ploceidae) as the weavers, with which they agree in being finch-like and in having the outermost primary merely reduced (not minute, nor rotated to the dorsal surface of the wing, as in the Fringillidae)—see WEAVER. However, they vary conspicuously from the weavers in most other characters, and have since been associated by different authors with other groups of 'finches' for various reasons, none of them very convincing. In view of their peculiarities, it seems best to follow Steiner and leave them as a separate family.

Many are very brightly coloured, but some of the mannikins are sombre brown, sometimes nearly black, with only barring or shaft-streaking. All degrees of sexual dimorphism are found. The juvenile plumage may be similar to that of the adult, but paler ; or it may be very dull, mostly grey. Only the Red Avadavat *Estrilda amandava* has a non-breeding plumage, and this is not sparrow-like (streaky brown) as in the weavers. The nest is an untidy bundle, never woven like a weaver's ; and it is firmly fixed among twigs, not suspended. The entrance is short and horizontal. The eggs are 4–6 and pure white (in weavers, 2–4 and coloured). The nestlings are remarkable for the decoration of their palates and tongues, which have conspicuous black spots, bands, or blotches, often on a white or bright yellow ground. The palate often has five black spots in a so-called domino pattern (many waxbills, some grassfinches) or two black horse-shoes (most mannikins). The edge of the gape usually has conspicuous white or black-and-white swellings, sometimes with large nodules that can reflect the light and are presumably conspicuous inside the dark cavity of the nest. The palate and tongue markings are conspicuously displayed when the nestling begs for food, which it does by a special crouching and waving of the head, the mouth being held wide open, very unlike the simple neck-stretched gape of most passerines. The whydahs or widow-birds (in one sense) *Vidua* spp. that parasitise species of weaver-finch in Africa have palate markings in their nestlings that closely mimic those of the host species. It is impossible to determine whether this close resemblance is due to convergence, being of obvious adaptive value to the parasite, or denotes close relationship (see WHYDAH (1)).

Both parents take part in incubation, which lasts on the average 21 days. The nest, at least after the first week of nestling life, is not kept clean by the parents. The nestlings defaecate on the walls of the

Striated Finch (or White-backed Munia)
Lonchura striata, of southern Asia. *C.E.T.K.*

nest, and the faeces rapidly dry and stick there, so that the nestlings are not fouled. Estrildids mature very quickly and may breed at the age of a few months, while ploceids take much longer.

Estrildids usually seem to form very stable pairs, which share in nest building, incubation, and care of the young. They seem often to be very social, perching in clumps and indulging in much mutual preening not confined to individuals of the same species, at least in aviaries.

There is considerable variety of courtship pattern in those estrildids that have been studied, but in all there is an absence of wing-quivering, common in other passerines ; and a marked peculiarity is the use of tail-quivering as a female solicitation display. The courtship dance of the male may consist almost entirely of stiff-legged leaps upwards, returning to the same spot each time, or rapid swings from side to side, or actions involving both these vertical and lateral motions. The ornamented areas of the plumage are usually erected and shown off. In many species the male may carry a long piece of grass in his bill while dancing, and in most there is some action of the bill (clappering, jerky opening and closing, sometimes tongue protrusion). The song may consist of high-pitched short phrases, rather melodious and clearly audible (some waxbills), or 'toy trumpet' notes (some grassfinches), or unmelodious clucks, faint whistles, and slurs in a definite pattern (many mannikins), sometimes inaudible only a couple of feet away.

There is not much agreement on the generic limits and detailed taxonomic arrangement of the weaver-finches, partly because of the great diversity of plumage pattern, sometimes even between birds very closely related in behaviour. Three tribes—the waxbills (Estrildini), grassfinches (Erythrurini), and mannikins (Amadini)—are recognised by Delacour and variously combined by others.

Waxbills. The Estrildini are almost entirely an African group except for 2 species of avadavat in India and the Orient and 1 form of problematical affinities, the Sydney Waxbill *Estrilda temporalis*, in eastern Australia. There is a considerable adaptive radiation in the African forms, there being many small seed-eaters (e.g. the Waxbill *Estrilda astrild* (introduced on St Helena), Lavender Finch *E. coerulescens*, Orange-breasted Waxbill *E. subflava*, and various congeners such as those to which the substantive names 'firefinch' and 'cordon-bleu' are commonly applied) ; large seed-eaters (e.g. the bluebills *Spermophaga* spp.) ; forms resembling the Hawfinch *Coccothraustes coccothraustes* (the seed-crackers *Pirenestes* spp.) ; arboreal insect-eaters (the negro-finches *Nigrita* spp.) ; and the little Flower-

pecker Finch *Parmoptila woodhousei* formerly put with the flowerpeckers (Dicaeidae). Chapin has summarised much of the field observations available.

Few of the species except the small waxbills of the genus *Estrilda* and some relatives (e.g. Melba Finch *Pytilia melba*) have been studied in captivity, and the diagnostic behaviour characters of this tribe given by Delacour seem to refer only to them. So far as is known, the palate markings are spots (reduced in a very few) ; the courtship includes carrying a straw in the mouth ; and there are usually reflective nodules on the gape. Most are rather brilliantly coloured.

The remaining genera, not particularly mentioned above, are the twin-spots *Clytospiza* and *Hypargos*, and the crimson-wings *Cryptospiza*.

Grassfinches. The Erythrurini also include well known cage birds, such as the Gouldian Finch *Poephila gouldiae*, Zebra Finch *P. castanotis*, Parson Finch *P. cincta*, and Diamond Sparrow *Zonaginthus guttatus*. What really holds this group together taxonomically is that they are predominantly Australasian, and certainly estrildids but (in Delacour's view) not mannikins. The characters given for the tribe amount to no more than their geographical distribution, harsher voices than in *Estrilda*, and great variation of palate markings from a typical domino pattern as in *Estrilda* through combinations of spots and horseshoes to as good a pair of horseshoes as is shown by any mannikin. In plumage they are extremely diverse, ranging from the brilliant crimson, black, white, and brown of the Painted Finch *Zonaginthus pictus*, or the iridescent green (unique in the estrildids) and reds or blues of the Gouldian Finch and the parrot-finches *Erythura* spp., to the dull browns and pale greys and purple of the Cherry Finch *Poephila modesta*. In consequence, in some revisions, nearly every species is put into a separate genus or subgenus. It is quite possible that most are really waxbills but that a few are modified mannikins.

Mannikins. The Amadini seem to be a much more homogeneous group. They are as a rule rather heavy-looking birds (as compared with *Estrilda*). Most are quietly coloured in browns and nearly black with bars or shaft-streaks, and some have large bold areas of black, white, and brown (e.g. the Tricolor Nun *Lonchura ferruginea malacca*). In the Cut-throat *Amadina fasciata* and Redheaded Finch *A. erythrocephala* there is brilliant red on the head. The largest is the well known Java Sparrow *Padda oryzivora*. Most are found in the hotter parts of the Orient, the Malay Archipelago, New Guinea, and northern Australia, but a few extend to India and Ceylon, and there are 3 groups in

Africa. These last are *Amadina* spp. mentioned above ; the Magpie Mannikin *Lonchura fringilloides*, the Black-breasted Mannikin *L. bicolor*, and the Bronzewing Mannikin *L. cucullata* ; and the two silverbills, of which the Common Silverbill *L. malabarica* extends to Arabia, Persia, and on to Ceylon. There is, lastly, the curious Bib Finch *L. nana* in Madagascar.

So far as is known, the palate markings are two horseshoes in all but *Amadina*, which has five large blotches with only narrow ridges of white between them. The silverbills are rather exceptional in their high-pitched voice. Several of the Oriental forms, such as the Spice Finch *Lonchura punctulata* and Striated Finch *L. striata*, are very common birds, sometimes pests of grain crops. The 'Bengalese Finch' is a very well known cage bird, excellent as a foster-parent for other seed-eaters, and known only in captivity ; Eisner has shown that it is a cultivated form of a subspecies of the Striated Finch.

Incertae sedis. As already mentioned, the why-dahs (in one sense) *Vidua* spp. of Africa are of doubtful affinities (see WHYDAH (1)).   A.J.C.

Boosey, E. J. 1956. Foreign Bird Keeping. London.
Chapin, J. P. 1954. Birds of the Belgian Congo. Part 4. Bull. Amer. Mus. Nat. Hist. 75B : 1–846.
Delacour, J. 1943. A revision of the subfamily Estrildinae of the family Ploceidae. Zoologica (New York) 28 : 69–86.
Eisner, E. 1957. The Bengalese Finch. Avic. Mag. 63 : 101–108.
Harrison, C. J. O. 1962. An ethological comparison of some waxbills (Estrildini), and its relevance to their taxonomy. Proc. Zool. Soc. Lond. 139 : 261–282.
Steiner, H. 1955. Das Brutverhalten der Prachtfinken Spermestidae, als Ausdruck ihres selbständigen Familiencharakters. Acta XI Congr. Internat. Orn., Basel 1954 : 350–355.
Wolters, H. E. 1957. Die Klassification der Webefinken (Estrildidae). Bonn. Zool. Beitr. 8 : 90–129.

WEB : a fleshy membrane between two toes (see LEG ; and SWIMMING AND DIVING) ; or the vane of a feather (see FEATHER ; VANE).

WEBER'S LINE : see ORIENTAL REGION

WEDGEBILL : name applied to several unrelated species : *Schistes geoffroyi* (for family see HUMMINGBIRD) ; *Glyphorynchus spirurus* (see WOODCREEPER) ; *Sphenostoma cristatum* (see RAIL-BABBLER).

WEEBILL : substantive name of *Smicrornis* spp. (see WREN (2)).

WEIGHT : partly a function of size, and in that sense dealt with elsewhere (see SIZE) ; partly an independent variable, and in that regard the main subject of this article. Many more detailed studies of bird weights are badly needed, however, and present knowledge is inadequate in various respects.

Bodily Proportions. The bones of flying birds are frequently hollow and thus weigh less than those of other animals of comparable size. Other parts of the body are relatively large, particularly the pectoral muscles, because of the great effort required in flying (see FLIGHT ; ENERGY REQUIREMENTS). Likewise, the heart may represent up to a fifth of the total body-weight, as in hummingbirds (Trochilidae), although it is more often about a tenth ; the large size of the heart may be partly due to the difficulty of heat maintenance in small animals, the heart being relatively larger in small birds than in large ones (see HEART ; HEAT REGULATION). The relative weights of the parts of the body differ as between young birds and adults ; in particular, the young of nidicolous species tend to have proportionately heavier heads and digestive systems as compared with those of full-grown birds (see DEVELOPMENT, POSTEMBRYONIC). The rate of increase in the weight of young birds varies considerably with the species ; passerines may attain full adult weight in about ten days from hatching (see GROWTH ; YOUNG BIRD).

Interspecific Differences. The range of weight in adults of existing species of birds is from about 2·55 grams (less than $\frac{1}{10}$ oz.) in the hummingbird *Klais guimeti* to 90–135 kg. (200–300 lb.) in the Ostriches *Struthio camelus* subspp. It is estimated that the largest of the extinct Aeypyornithidae probably weighed nearly 1000 lb. (see ELEPHANT-BIRD). The heaviest flying birds, e.g. swans *Cygnus* spp. and Andean Condor *Vultur gryphus*, have weights of about 10–12 kg. (22–26½ lb.), but Trumpeter Swans *C. c. buccinator* have been recorded up to 38 lb. and males of the larger species of bustards (Otididae) sometimes weigh 30 lb. (13·6 kg.) or even more— 37 lb. (16·8 kg.) once recorded for the Great Bustard *Otis tarda*. Among young birds, the lowest weight recorded for a nidifugous species is 1·78 grams for a newly hatched Andalusian Hemipode *Turnix sylvatica*—the chick of its relative the Lark-quail *Ortyxelos meiffreni* is presumably the smallest (Sutter & Cornaz—see BUTTONQUAIL).

Intraspecific Differences. Populations of the same species may differ considerably from each other in mean weight. Individuals in higher latitudes tend to be larger and heavier than those of more temperate range (Bergmann's Rule) ; for example, Kittiwakes *Larus tridactylus* from Britain weigh about 352 grams (12·4 oz.), while those from Arctic Russia weigh about 407 grams (14·35 oz.). There seems also to be a tendency for birds living at high altitudes to weigh more than those of the same species at lower levels.

Little seems to have been published about variations in weight within a population. In some species, however, there is marked sexual dimorphism in size and weight. Thus, for example, males are heavier than females in some game-birds (Galliformes) and passerines ; and females heavier than males in some birds-of-prey (Falconiformes). There may also be differences in weight between adults and full-grown young. In some species, particularly of sea birds, the young put on fat before leaving the nest, and this presumably helps them to survive the difficult post-fledging period ; in the Fulmar *Fulmarus glacialis*, for instance, the young bird may be as much as $1\frac{1}{4}$ times as heavy as an adult. However, before or shortly after leaving the nest, the birds lose this extra weight ; the juveniles of many passerine species weigh less in late summer than the adults.

Seasonal Variation. Of particular interest are those differences in weight that reflect the current condition of the bird and are unrelated to its size as conventionally measured. The weights of individuals vary considerably in the course of the year. In samples of two resident passerine species, the Silvereye *Zosterops lateralis* in New Zealand (Marples) and the Great Tit *Parus major* in Holland (Kluijver), the lowest weights in the year were, respectively, about 83 and 89 per cent of the highest. In general, birds tend to increase in weight before migration and before breeding. In the former case, the increase is due to the deposition of special migratory fat, and the amount laid down seems to be proportional to the distance that the bird has to travel in a single flight. In certain migrants that may make a non-stop journey of 1000 miles, as much as 100 per cent of the lean body-weight of the bird may be added as fat. Thus, a 20-gram bird may put on as much as 20 grams of migratory fat. (See also ENERGY REQUIREMENTS.)

The increase in weight before the breeding season is often especially marked in the female, being presumably largely due to increase in the size of the gonad, which regresses greatly in the non-breeding season. Some species, however, also put on fat before breeding, a notable example being the Emperor Penguin *Aptenodytes forsteri*. In this species the male incubates the egg continuously for about two months, and during the whole period ashore (including courtship) may drop from about 45 kg. to about 22 kg. in weight as a result of the enforced fast (see PENGUIN). Adults of most species seem to lose weight during the breeding season, presumably because of the strain of rearing young. The weight of young birds has already been mentioned.

·Increase in weight (presumably due to the deposition of fat) also occurs before the moult in some species. This is particularly marked among birds such as penguins (Spheniscidae), which may remain ashore (without feeding) for up to 5 weeks, and may then lose up to 50 per cent of their body-weight while moulting (Richdale).

In addition, birds of many species are heavier in winter than in summer, a layer of subcutaneous fat being laid down—presumably for insulation purposes and also as some reserve against hard times. Extra fat can also be laid down rapidly during cold spells in winter, if the food supply remains adequate ; but, of course, if the cold period is prolonged and food becomes scarce, the birds lose weight through starvation and may die. Some passerine species may be able to lose 50 per cent of their winter weight before death ensues. Diseased birds, at any season, may become wasted.

Daily Variations. In some of the smaller birds, daily fluctuations in weight are considerable, the birds losing weight overnight—10 per cent of body-weight in the House Sparrow *Passer domesticus*, and 14 per cent in the House Wren *Troglodytes aedon*. This is not due only to the emptying of the digestive tract, but to the utilisation (and replacement) of stored carbohydrates and fat in the tissues. The lost weight is put on next day, and the birds tend to be heaviest in the late afternoon. Fisher & Bartlett have found evidence of a similar cycle in the weight of the liver, in small samples of the Red-shouldered Blackbird *Agelaius phoeniceus* and the Starling *Sturnus vulgaris*. For ratio of food intake to body weight see NUTRITION.

Egg Production. The formation of eggs within the body must impose a considerable strain on the female, and presumably an increase in weight—followed by a decrease on laying. The weight of individual eggs may be as little as 1·5 per cent of the body-weight of the female, as in the Ostrich *Struthio camelus* ; or it may be as much as 20–25 per cent, as in some small petrels (Procellariiformes) and in kiwis *Apteryx* spp. (see EGGS, NATURAL HISTORY OF). The total clutch of some birds, e.g. ducks (Anatidae), game-birds (Galliformes), and tits (Paridae), may weigh as much as 100–150 per cent of the body-weight of the female—and be produced within two weeks.   **C.M.P.**

Fisher, H. I. & Bartlett, L. M. 1957. Diurnal cycles in liver weights in birds. Condor 59 : 364–372.

Kluijver, H. N. 1952. Notes on body-weight and time of breeding in the Great Tit *Parus major* L. Ardea 40 : 123–141.

Marples, B. J. 1945. *Zosterops lateralis* at Dunedin, New Zealand. Emu 44 : 277–278.

Richdale, L. E. 1951. Sexual Behaviour in Penguins. Laurence, Kansas.

Salt, G. W. 1963. Avian body weight, adaptation, and evolution in western North America. Proc. XIII Internat. Orn. Congr., Ithaca, N.Y., 1962 : 905–917.

WEKA: substantive name, alternatively 'weka rail', of *Gallirallus* spp. (see RAIL).

WHALE-BIRD: sailors' name for various species of petrel (Procellariidae) ; applied in the Antarctic to the Dove Prion *Pachyptila desolata*, and in Alaska to the Short-tailed Shearwater *Puffinus tenuirostris* (see PETREL).

WHAUP: popular name in Scotland for the Curlew *Numenius arquata* (see under SANDPIPER).

WHEATEAR: substantive name of various *Oenanthe* spp. ; used without qualification, in Britain, for *O. oenanthe*—the white rump of which is the origin of the name (see CHAT ; THRUSH).

WHIMBREL: *Numenius phaeopus*, a species of curlew (see under SANDPIPER).

WHINCHAT: substantive name of some *Saxicola* spp. ; used without qualification, in Britain, for *S. rubetra* (see CHAT ; THRUSH).

WHIPBIRD: substantive name of *Psophodes* spp. (see RAIL-BABBLER).

WHIP-POOR-WILL: *Caprimulgus vociferus* (see NIGHTJAR ; also POORWILL).

WHISTLER: alternative substantive name for species of Pachycephalinae (see THICKHEAD).

WHITE-EYE (1): substantive name of many species of Zosteropidae (Passeriformes, suborder Oscines) ; in the plural, general term for the family. Other names for species are 'silver-eye', 'spectacle-bird', and 'zosterops'.

General Characters. The white-eyes form a remarkably homogeneous Old World family of small birds of uncertain affinities. They have slightly decurved, sharply pointed bills (short in nearly all the species), brush tongues, rather rounded wings with only 9 primaries and, in nearly all species, the white ring round each eye from which they take their name. This ring is formed of minute silky-white feathers, and it varies much in width. In a few species it hardly shows ; at the other extreme, in certain of the African birds, it is enlarged to a big patch. Otherwise the plumage of the white-eyes is notably lacking in sharply defined pattern ; most of them have the upper parts more or less green or yellow-green, the under parts grey or yellow, clouded with melanin—giving green or brownish on the sides. Yellow pigment has been lost in a number of insular populations, the entire plumage of some of them being reduced to greys and browns. The sexes are always alike, and there are no seasonal changes in plumage.

Habits. White-eyes are birds of trees and bushes, hardly ever being seen on the ground, and individuals have a wide range of food—insects, nectar, and fruit. This last is obtained largely by piercing the skin of soft fruit with the sharp beak and then extracting the juice and pulp with the aid of the brush tongue, a habit which has caused the birds to be regarded with disfavour by fruit-growers. They are highly gregarious, keeping in touch all the time with soft, plaintive notes. Most species seem to have a definite song, some indeed a rich and far-carrying warble.

Indian White-eye *Zosterops palpebrosa*, of southern Asia. *C.E.T.K.*

The nests are remarkably alike throughout the family—a deep cup of mixed plant material slung in a slender fork. The eggs, white or pale bluish, usually number 2 or 3. Both parents sit, and hatching has been proved to take place in as little as $10\frac{1}{2}$ days—among the shortest periods known in birds. At the time they leave the nest the young of at least some species still have that part of the head where the eye-ring will appear completely naked. There has been little systematic observation of the white-eyes in life, except in two peripheral populations, *Zosterops lateralis* in New Zealand and *Z. virens* in the Cape Province of South Africa.

Distribution. The white-eyes extend over the whole of the Ethiopian, Oriental, and Australasian Regions. They are found in nearly every kind of country that carries trees, from sea level to the timber-line at about 10 000 feet above sea level, and from the acacias of south-western Africa to the mangroves of Australia and the richest evergreen forest (where they inhabit the edges, not the interior). They are essentially a tropical family, reaching their extremes of latitude in Japan and the neighbouring mainland, and at the Cape of Good Hope and on islands south of New Zealand. They have established themselves on remote tropical islands more widely than any other family of passerine birds, which is the more remarkable since they are so small, rather short-winged, and within the tropics apparently not long-distance migrants. This last, however, does not apply to two temperate-zone populations. *Z. erythropleura*, from beyond the north-eastern border of China, reaches Burma in winter, and Tasmanian birds representing a colour phase of *Z. lateralis* have recently been shown to reach New South Wales—with a sea-crossing of about 100 miles. No doubt the fact that the white-eyes constantly move about in close parties is important to their successful colonisation. A notable advance of theirs is historical. It seems to be established that birds of Tasmanian stock reached New Zealand, across the 1200 miles of the Tasman Sea, in the 1850s, since when they have flourished there exceedingly.

Species. There are about 85 species; but because so many of the populations are much alike, the systematics of the family have presented exceptional difficulties at the specific level, although there has been general agreement that most of them should be included in the genus *Zosterops*. The latest view is that there are 4 (highly polytypic) species of *Zosterops* in Africa, 9 others in the islands on both sides of Africa, and 49 in the rest of the range, from Pakistan eastwards. The genus *Zosterops*, within which the changes have been rung on few characters, provides striking examples of convergence—to the confusion of taxonomists. An extreme example is the great similarity of *Z. natalis* of Christmas Island in the Indian Ocean to *Z. griseovirescens* of Annobon in the Gulf of Guinea. The genus also contains many examples of the double invasion of islands, and even of triple invasion (Norfolk Island), typically with one species (presumably the earlier invader) differing much more than the other from the putative parent stock.

The continental species of *Zosterops* are particularly uniform, with much clinal variation. Especially in Africa they conform very frequently with Gloger's rule (melanin increasing with humidity) and consistently with Bergmann's rule (the cooler the climate the bigger the bird). Moreover, irrespective of temperature, the wing length increases with altitude. Perhaps the most widespread and characteristic species of white-eyes are in Africa *Z. senegalensis* and in the East *Z. palpebrosa*. The former extends from Senegal to Zululand, with great local variation in size, colour of plumage, and width of eye-ring. It has no comprehensive English name, since in its brighter forms it has been called the Yellow White-eye and in its darker the Green White-eye. *Z. palpebrosa*, known in Indian bird-books simply as 'the white-eye', ranges from eastern Afghanistan to Indo-China and Indonesia as far as Flores.

Insular birds are much more variable. Some, such as *Z. strenua* of Lord Howe Island, have become 'giants' without much change in their other features. *Z. modesta* of the Seychelles has lost its yellow pigment without ceasing to be in all other respects a typical white-eye. *Z. cinerea* of the Caroline Islands has lost both eye-ring and yellow. All sorts of combinations exist, of changes in size, in intensity of pigment, in shape of bill, and in eye-ring. Altogether there are 23 species that have been judged odd enough to be kept out of the genus *Zosterops*, and they are arranged in 11 small genera. The largest of them, *Lophozosterops*, with peculiar patterning on the head, includes 6 species in Indonesia. Of special interest is *Woodfordia*, consisting of 2 'giant' species with long bill, dull plumage, and no eye-ring, on Santa Cruz and Rennell Islands at the south-eastern end of the Solomons. *Chlorocharis emiliae* of Borneo has been called 'Blackeye'. The four birds found respectively on three islands (São Tomé, Principe, and Fernando Po) in the Gulf of Guinea and on the top of Cameroon Mountain comprise the genus *Speirops*; they are all extraordinarily large and devoid of any yellow at all, while three of them have more or less lost the white eye-ring characteristic of most members of the Zosteropidae. R.E.M.

Fleming, C. A. 1943. Notes on the life history of the Silver-eye based on colour-banding. Emu 42: 193–217. (*Z. lateralis* in New Zealand.)

Mees, G. F. 1957, 1961. A systematic review of the Indo-Australian Zosteropidae (Parts 1 and 2). Zool. Verh. Leiden 35: 1–204; 50: 1–168. (Gives detailed account of the *Zosterops* spp., but not of the other genera.)

Moreau, R. E. 1957. Variation in the western Zosteropidae. Bull. Brit. Mus. Nat. Hist., Zool. 4 (7): 311–433. (Reviews the white-eyes of Africa and the neighbouring islands.)

Skead, C. J. & Ranger, G. A. 1958. A contribution to the biology of the Cape Province white-eyes. Ibis 100: 319–333.

Stresemann, E. 1931. Die Zosteropiden der indo-australischen Region. Mitt. Zool. Mus. Berlin 17: 201–238. (The only comprehensive source for the characters of the species of the family from India eastwards.)

WHITE-EYE (2): substantive name of certain pochards *Aythya* spp. (see DUCK).

WHITEFACE: substantive name of *Aphelocephala* spp. (see WREN (2)).

WHITEFRONT: colloquial short name for the Whitefronted Goose *Anser albifrons* (see under DUCK).

WHITEHEAD: *Mohoua albicilla*, of New Zealand (for subfamily see FLYCATCHER (1)).

WHITETHROAT (1): substantive name of *Sylvia communis* and (Lesser) *S. curruca* (see WARBLER (1)).

WHITETHROAT (2): substantive name of *Leucippus* spp., *Leucochloris albicollis*, and *Talaphorus* spp. (for family see HUMMINGBIRD).

WHITETIP: substantive name of *Urosticte* spp. (for family see HUMMINGBIRD).

WHOOPER: name sometimes used alone for the Whooper Swan *Cygnus cygnus* (see under DUCK).

WHYDAH (1): substantive name, alternatively 'widow' or 'widow-bird', of some members of the genus *Vidua* (including 'Hypochera' and 'Steganura'); in the plural, preferably in the form 'viduine whydahs' (alternatively 'viduine weavers'), general term for the group—the name without qualification being also used in another sense, as shown under WHYDAH (2). A name for other species is 'combassou', alternatively 'indigo-bird' or 'indigo-lark'. This is a small and homogeneous group of African birds, mostly if not exclusively parasitic, in which the male in nuptial plumage is predominantly black, and frequently has the 4 central feathers of the tail greatly elongated.

Taxonomically, the viduine whydahs occupy an intermediate position between the Ploceidae (see WEAVER) on the one hand, and the Estrildidae (see WEAVER-FINCH) on the other. As in the case of the ploceid weavers, the females, immature males, and adult males outside the breeding season have a similar streaky sparrow-like plumage, and the male nuptial dress is not assumed until the second year. Similarities in plumage, and possibly also in display, suggest a link with certain members of the ploceid genus *Euplectes*.

In other characters, however, including their small size and bill shape, the whydahs are unlike ploceids, but similar to the estrildids; thus, their eggs are white, their nestlings hatch with conspicuous gape nodules and 'domino' palate markings, and there is a distinct grey-brown, non-streaky juvenile plumage. Delacour, however, views these three last characters merely as evolutionary adaptations to the fact that whydah eggs are typically laid and reared in estrildid nests; and he considers the viduines to be distinct from both the Estrildidae and the Ploceidae, although possibly slightly closer to the latter. Other authors, including Chapin, regard the viduines as estrildid derivatives, in the evolution of which as social parasites an initial resemblance to their potential hosts has been simply exaggerated.

Typically, the viduines are birds of the savannas and open plains, although some species also frequent villages and gardens. They are social birds and, particularly outside the breeding season, tend to move in flocks with various ploceid and estrildid species, including sometimes their specific host. They generally feed on the ground, and although they occasionally take insects they live principally on small seeds that they obtain by a characteristic scratching action of both feet.

Widely distributed over the whole of Africa south of the Sahara, there are in all, according to Delacour, 11 viduine species divided into 3 subgenera—*Hypochera*, *Vidua*, and *Steganura*—which most authors have listed as distinct genera.

Hypochera, perhaps the least specialised of the 3 groups, includes the combassous or indigo-finches and steel finches, birds characterised by the fact that, in the reproductive male, the plumage is predominantly dark with a metallic sheen, the tail square and shorter than the wings, and the bill red or white. Of the 6 species (*V. chalybeata*, *V. codringtoni*, *V. amauropteryx*, *V. nigeriae*, *V. camerunensis*, *V. funerea*), all very similar in appearance, the Senegal Combassou *V. chalybeata* and the Steel Finch *V. funerea* are the most common in Africa, and also the most familiar in Europe as cage birds.

Members of the *Vidua* group are distinguished by the equal elongation of the 4 central tail feathers to a length exceeding that of the wing. There are 4 species: the Resplendent Whydah (or Long-tailed Combassou) *V. hypocherina*, the Queen Whydah *V. regia*, Fischer's Whydah *V. fischeri*, and the Pin-tailed Whydah *V. macroura*; the last is a common species with a wide distribution in Africa.

The *Steganura* group includes only the Paradise Whydah *V. paradisaea*, another widely distributed bird, in which all 4 central tail feathers are longer than the wing, but the outer 2 are shorter than the central pair.

Of the viduines' reproductive behaviour very little is known. Breeding males are in some species (e.g. *V. paradisaea*) decidedly aggressive, and those of the Senegal Combassou fly about incessantly, perching at intervals in a conspicuous position to give their rather loud, metallic song. Polygamy has been claimed to occur, but this is by no means conclusively established. Courtship is reported as consisting of an erratic hovering flight executed immediately above the female's head.

That the viduine whydahs are all social parasites, laying their eggs in the nests of various African weaver-finches, has still to be proved beyond doubt ; but no viduine nest has ever been found in the wild. As Neunzig pointed out, the fact that the mouth-markings and juvenile plumage of each viduine species mimic to a quite remarkable degree those of a particular species of estrildid provides strong circumstantial evidence that each viduine is highly adapted as the specific parasite of a particular wax-bill. Their eggs, generally laid 2 or 3 to a nest, are distinguishable from those of the host only by their slightly larger size and more rounded form. It is said that the female may, at each laying, destroy one of the host's own clutch. Unlike other social parasites, however, viduine nestlings make no attempt to evict the host's own offspring, and their close association with their foster-family may continue for an appreciable time after fledging (see PARASITISM).

The host-parasite relationships suggested by indirect evidence or actually observed include the following : *V. funerea* and *Estrilda astrild* ; *V. hypocherina* and the Black-cheeked Waxbill *E. erythronotos* ; *V. regia* and the Violet-eared Waxbill *E. granatina* ; *V. fischeri* and the Purple-bellied Waxbill *E. ianthinogaster*. The supposition that the principal hosts of *V. macroura* are the Grey Waxbill *E. troglodytes* and *E. astrild* is supported by field observations, but this species is known to lay occasionally in the nests of species of several other genera, including *Euplectes* (' *Coliuspasser* '), *Spermestes*, and *Cisticola* (Sylviinae) ; and it is likely that a similar degree of latitude will eventually be found to occur in other viduine species. The principal host of the Senegal Combassou *V. chalybeata* in the wild is the Senegal Firefinch *Estrilda senegala*, and parasitising either this species or the Angolan Cordon-bleu *E. angolensis* it has occasionally bred successfully in captivity. It has, however, also been recorded that on one occasion a pair of captive Senegal Combassous built a nest and successfully hatched and reared young (Poulsen). Since in other respects the Senegal Combassou appears to be one of the least specialised of the viduine whydahs, this observation raises interesting possibilities regarding the evolution of parasitism in the group ; but in this, as in almost every aspect of viduine biology, no definite conclusion can be drawn without more detailed observation. See Plate 7 (colour).   M.F.H.

Boosey, E. J. 1956. Foreign Bird Keeping. London.

Chapin, J. 1954. Birds of the Belgian Congo. Part 4. Bull. Amer. Mus. Nat. Hist. 75B : 1–846.

Delacour, J. & Edmond-Blanc, F. 1934. Monographie des veuves. (Revision des genres *Euplectes* et *Vidua*). II. Les veuves combassous. Oiseau (n.s.) 4 : 52–110.

Friedmann, H. 1960. The parasitic weaver-birds. U.S. Natl. Mus. Bull. no. 223.

Neunzig, R. 1929. Zum Brutparasitismus der Viduinen. J. Orn. 77 : 1–21.

Poulsen, H. 1956. Breeding of the Senegal Combasou in captivity. Avic. Mag. 62 : 177–181.

White, C. M. N. 1963. The indigo birds. Bull. Brit. Orn. Cl. 83 : 83–88.

WHYDAH (2): substantive name, alternatively ' widow ' or ' widow-bird ', of some species of Ploceidae, placed by the writer of the article WEAVER here in *Euplectes* although formerly in ' *Coliuspasser* ' and ' *Drepanoplectes* ' (see WEAVER). Mackworth-Praed & Grant use ' widow-bird ' in this sense and ' whydah ' for viduines, but this distinction is not general and seems rather unlikely to resolve the confusion—the opposite convention has in fact been recently suggested and has perhaps better historical justification.

WIDEAWAKE: alternative name of the Sooty Tern *Sterna fuscata* (see TERN).

WIDGEON: obsolescent alternative spelling of WIGEON.

WIDOW: alternatively ' widow-bird ', same as ' whydah ' (see WHYDAH (1) ; WHYDAH (2)).

WIGEON: substantive name (usually unchanged in plural ; the spelling ' widgeon ' is practically obsolete) of certain *Anas* spp. ; used without qualification in Britain for *A. penelope* (see DUCK).

WILDFOWL: general term for quarry species of birds other than ' game-birds ' ; in the most common present usage in Britain it is confined to species of the family Anatidae (see DUCK ; also GAME-BIRDS) but sometimes extends to ' waders ' (Charadrii) and other edible birds associated with water. In North America ' waterfowl ' is more commonly used in this sense ; but in Britain ' waterfowl ' or ' ornamental waterfowl ' is used principally for live Anatidae when kept in captivity.

' Wildfowling ' is the practice or sport of taking wildfowl, and is conducted by a ' wildfowler ' ; in the past the terms embraced many forms of capture, often involving the use of nets, but it is now generally confined to the shooting of wild geese, wild ducks, and some species of waders, with shot-guns. ' Duck-hunting ' and ' duck-hunter ' are the equivalent terms in North America, where the sport is more strictly controlled by law than in most European

countries. In Europe, wildfowl are shot principally while 'flighting', either naturally at dawn
or dusk or under the moon, or when disturbed
from a resting place. In contrast, this method
(known there as 'pass shooting') is little used in
North America, where nearly all wildfowl are shot
when coming in to artificial models or 'decoy'
birds, made of wood ('blocks'), cardboard, rubber,
or plastic, the hunter being concealed near by in a
'blind'. Although such decoys are still relatively
unfashionable in Europe, the practice of 'feeding'
certain ponds regularly with grain to encourage a
'lead' of ducks is widespread and results in large
bags. In North America, where this is known as
'baiting', it is illegal. See also under DECOY.

An arduous old-time branch of the sport known
as 'punt-gunning' persists in Britain. In this a
large-bore 'punt gun' is mounted on a special
shallow-draught boat in which the wildfowler,
lying prone, stalks the birds—usually on the open
mudflats of an estuary. Punt-gunning is difficult,
sometimes dangerous, and demands great technical
skill for success. It is variously curtailed by law
in different European countries and altogether
prohibited in North America. Large-bore guns
mounted in fixed emplacements overlooking small
ponds are still used in France ('huttiers').

The sale of wildfowl for food is legally limited
to certain months of the year in most of Europe, the
period varying in different countries, but has long
been outlawed in North America.

The wariness of ducks and geese is such that wildfowling has been held to be one of the most exacting
and exciting of field sports. The subject has caught
the imagination of writers and painters, who have
portrayed the romance of the wild marshes and the
elusive quarry which frequents them.

See also COUNT.   P.S.

WILDNESS: see under TAMENESS

WILLETT: *Catoptrophorus semipalmatus* (see SAND-
PIPER).

WIND: see CLIMATOLOGY ; METEOROLOGY ; also
ANTARCTIC ; FLIGHT ; MIGRATION ; OCEANIC BIRDS

WINDPIPE: the TRACHEA.

WING: the paired forelimb of birds, specially
modified for flight. It was doubtless originally
5-fingered, although in *Archaeopteryx* it had already
acquired tridactyle form but with the wrist bones
as yet unfused (see ARCHAEOPTERYX).

The wing has become secondarily modified for
swimming in penguins (Spheniscidae), Simpson's
work proving that penguins were evolved from

flying ancestors and were freed from any restriction
on the ratio of body weight to wing and tail area
when they took to an aquatic life. Similarly, the
'ratite' orders of running birds are thought to be
derived from flying ancestors, as evidenced by the
fossil *Eleutherornis helveticus*, the wing becoming
secondarily reduced in these and other non-flying
species (see RATITES, PHYLOGENY OF THE).

Functions. The main function of the avian
forelimb is flight (see FLIGHT). It is also used solely
for swimming by penguins, as formerly by the
flightless Great Auk *Pinguinus impennis* (and earlier
by flightless auks of the fossil genus *Mancalla*).
Certain flying species also use their wings while
diving, notably the auks (Alcidae) of the Northern
Hemisphere and the diving petrels (Pelecanoididae)
of the Southern. In these, the feet are used merely
as rudders, but in such diving ducks as the scoters
Melanitta spp., eiders (Somateriini), and the Long-
tailed Duck *Clangula hyemalis*, both the wings and
the legs are used as paddles under water and the
wings are kept folded, but away from the body
with the alula held in hyperextension (see SWIMMING
AND DIVING).

All birds make use of their wings for balancing,
particularly when perched on a moving object in a
strong wind. During courtship and breeding, when
the males of many species become pugnacious
towards one another, the wings are frequently used
as weapons of combat, the bird in most cases seizing
the opponent with the bill and buffeting him with
the wings. Spur-winged Plovers *Vanellus* ('*Hoplopterus*') *spinosus* fight while in flight, turning and
striking with the wing, which, as it carries a spur,
is capable of inflicting mortal injury. Although
little is known about the use of wing-spurs in other
species, such as the Spur-winged Goose *Plectropterus
gambensis*, there seems to be little doubt that these
are also aggressive weapons.

Wings play an important part in the displays of
many species, and during these they are widely
spread and may be vibrated in front of the hen
bird, as in the Silver Pheasant *Lophura nycthemera*
and related species. Many of the birds are brightly
coloured, such as the birds-of-paradise (Paradisaeidae) and Sun-bittern *Eurypyga helias*, but the use
of the wings in courtship display is not confined to
colourful species and occurs in such sombre birds as
Savi's Warbler *Locustella luscinioides*, the Grasshopper Warbler *L. naevia*, and the Hedgesparrow
(or Dunnock) *Prunella modularis*. The wings are
also displayed in courtship flight by many waders
(Charadrii), the Roller *Coracias garrulus*, and the
Golden Oriole *Oriolus oriolus*, to mention but a few
examples.

As a further function, mention must be made of climbing, with special reference to the nestling Hoatzin *Opisthocomus hoazin* (see HOATZIN). This bird climbs around its nest and the nesting tree, using its feet and wings in true quadripedal fashion. The thumb and first fingers possess large claws, the manus is relatively large, and there is arrested development of the quill feathers of the thumb and fingers, thus enabling freer movement. The claws become absorbed in adult life and the manus assumes shorter proportions.

Structure. The wing consists of a light, variable vane for striking the air, the insertion of the wings being high up on the thorax, with the centre of gravity and the heavy internal organs well below the point of insertion.

The bones consist of the humerus, radius and ulna, and the bones of the hand or manus (see SKELETON). The latter are variable, owing to the loss of certain carpal bones and the fusion of others with the metacarpus. The radiale (or scapholunar) is present in all birds and the ulnare (or cuneiform) in many, exceptions being the emus and cassowaries (Casuariiformes) and the kiwis (Apterygidae). The 2nd and 3rd distal carpals are present in the young of most species, fusing in adult life with the metacarpal.

Digits lost in the evolution of the typical avian manus are (on the most widely accepted view) V, IV, and the distal part of III. The second digit forms the major part of the manus in penguins, emus, cassowaries, and kiwis. The function of the hand, in general, has become largely subordinated to the provision of a firm basis for the primary feathers. The three parts of the wing—upper ' arm ', forearm, and hand—can move only in one plane in relation to each other, a further adaptation towards stability.

The muscles present many problems in functional anatomy (see MUSCULATURE). Thus, the forearm and muscles of the manus are greatly reduced in kiwis, but in the Ostrich *Struthio camelus* there is little degeneration of musculature distal to the elbow. Lowe (1942) found that the only difference in the wings between the Flightless Cormorant *Nannopterum harrisi* (with almost no carina) and a flying cormorant *Phalacrocorax* sp. was in the general and relative proportions of wing to body ; the Falkland Flightless Steamer Duck *Tachyeres brachypterus* has larger wings than the Flying Steamer Duck *T. patachonicus*, which is probably to be accounted for by their use under water when swimming. Penguins lack the biceps brachii muscle, but specialisation of the pectoralis and tensor patagii longus takes over the function ; other distal muscles

of the wing are absent or reduced and the shoulder musculature is highly developed in response to the swiming action necessary.

The propatagium is a membranous fold of skin along the anterior margin of the wing, from shoulder to carpal joint ; it contains flexor muscles and tendons. The metapatagium is a similar fold between the body and the posterior margin of the upper wing (see MUSCULATURE).

Feathering. The feathers of the wing (see PLUMAGE) have a definite arrangement as follows : the flight feathers or remiges are developed in the wing membrane (ala membrana) and point backwards, each feather partly overlapping the next. They are divided into the metacarpo-digitals or primaries, attached to the manus, and the cubitals or secondaries, attached to the ulna. There are typically 11 primaries, 6 attached to the metacarpus and 5 to the phalanges, but the outermost primary is often rudimentary (' remicle ') or absent, while certain birds, notably the flamingos (Phoenicopteridae), grebes (Podicipitidae), and storks (Ciconiidae) have 7 primaries attached to the metacarpus and 12 in all. The 5th secondary remex (numbered inwards from the carpal joint) was formerly thought to be absent in some species, but the modern view of this ' diastataxy ' is that there is a gap between the 4th and 5th secondaries ; the condition occurs in owls (Strigiformes), grebes, geese *Anser* spp., and pigeons (Columbidae). (See also REMICLE.)

In *Archaeopteryx* there were 9 primaries, as in a number of modern birds. The Ostrich has as many as 16, and the cassowaries (Casuariidae) have as few as 2 or 3. The Masked Tityra *Tityra semifasciata* (Cotingidae) shows an interesting sexual dimorphism, in that the distal mid-digital remex is greatly reduced in the male. The primaries are best numbered outwards from the carpal joint, but as the opposite method is also practised it is necessary to specify which is being used (see PRIMARY).

The remainder of the wing is covered by three sets of wing coverts (tectrices) both on the upper surface and (constituting the ' lining ') on the under surfaces, the major, minor, and marginales, the last in several rows covering the leading edge of the wing. Each major tectrix is attached in relation to one of the remiges, the bases of which are thus covered ; the upper covert of the 1st metacarpal remex is generally rudimentary, as a requirement for folding the wing. The minor tectrices fill in the gap between the major and marginales feathers, overlapping the former and being overlapped by the latter. The shoulder region is covered by the humeral or tertiary feathers, and by the scapular feathers on the back and the axillaries underneath,

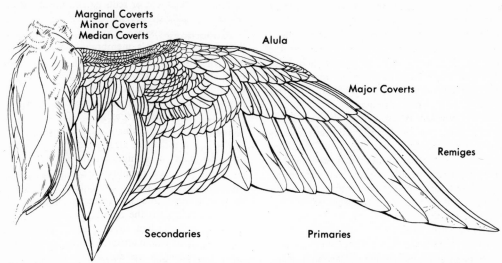

Marginal Coverts
Minor Coverts
Median Coverts

Alula

Major Coverts

Remiges

Secondaries   Primaries

FIG 1.   Right wing of a Mallard *Anas platyrhynchos* in extended position, showing the feathering of the upper surface.   The remiges (primary and secondary) are overlapped by the major coverts, and these in turn distally by the alula or ' bastard wing ' and proximally by (in succession from the leading edge) the marginal, minor and median coverts.   *From a preparation in the British Museum (Natural History).*   M.Y.

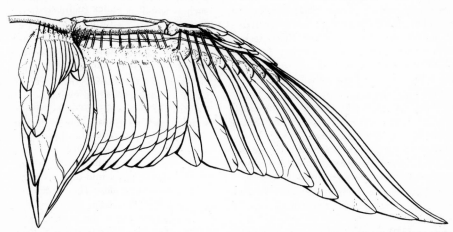

FIG 2.   Same as in Figure 1, with soft tissues and covert feathers (tectrices) removed to show the relation of the main flight feathers to the bones.   Distally, the 10 primary remiges are attached to the hand or manus (carpo-metacarpus and digital phalanges), which also bears the alula (on the pollex)—for detail see Figure 3.   Proximally to these, the secondary remiges are attached to the forearm (ulna), and the so-called ' tertiary ' feathers to the humerus.   An elastic tendon can be seen connecting the remiges near their bases.   *From a preparation in the British Museum (Natural History).*   M.Y.

FIG 3.   As in Figure 2, but left wing from below : detail of the manus area with the bones dissected apart.   CMC = carpometacarpus ; 1st D = first digit or pollex (fused 1st and 2nd phalanges) ; 2nd D = second digit (1st phalanx and fused 2nd and 3rd phalanges) ; 3rd D = third digit. Feathers as marked.   *From a preparation in the British Museum (Natural History).*   M.Y.

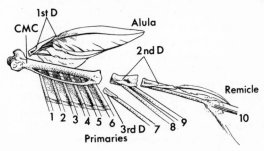

1st D
CMC
Alula
2nd D
Remicle
1 2 3 4 5 6   3rd D   7   8   9   10
Primaries

thus ensuring a smooth feather contour at the junction of wing and body.

In the 'ratites', it is to be noted that the quills of the primaries are not fixed into grooves on the manus but lie loosely over the bones, their bases projecting beyond the bone margin. In penguins, the feathers have evolved a scale-like structure and there are no true primary feathers.

Alula or Bastard Wing. This, also called ' ala spuria ', consists of a number of small quill feathers attached to the first digit. As mentioned, it is used in swimming by certain ducks ; it is also used in flight, particularly by birds-of-prey (Falconiformes), being of importance in the prevention of stalling (see FLIGHT). It is present in *Rhea*, providing further evidence of the flying ancestry of the ' ratites ', as shown by de Beer (1956).

Claws. Three large digital claws were present in *Archaeopteryx*, and the presence of claws in modern birds must be regarded as primitive remnants, particularly as they are more commonly found in nestlings and are later absorbed. In structure, they are composed of horny epithelium, like other claws. They are found only on the 1st and 2nd digits, and persist in adult life on the 1st digit in the Secretary-bird *Sagittarius serpentarius* and the Black-necked (or Derbian) Screamer *Chauna chavaria* ; mention has already been made of the Hoatzin.

Spurs. These are used in combat. A spur consists of a conical bony core with an external horny sheath. They are invariably situated on the radial side of the carpus or metacarpus. The Spur-winged Goose (above) is an example of a bird with a carpal spur arising from the scaphoid ; the jacanas (Jacanidae) and the Spur-winged Plover have spurs arising from the first metacarpal, and the Black-necked Screamer has one on the 1st and the 2nd metacarpal. A carpal spur is present in sheathbills (Chionididae).

Ornamental Plumes. These are occasionally present on the wing and are erected in display. Thus the Standard-wing *Semioptera wallacii* (Paradisaeidae) has 2 long plumes arising from the minor tectrices, near the distal end of the ulna. The remarkable ' sails ' of the Mandarin Duck *Aix galericulata* are modified humeral feathers and are prominent in display. In some nightjars (Caprimulgidae) the innermost primary is greatly elongated, forming an ornamental train (with the second primary to a lesser extent) in the Pennant-winged Nightjar *Semeiophorus vexillarius* and ending in a racket in the Standard-winged Nightjar *Macrodipteryx longipennis*. In cranes (Gruidae) the innermost secondaries are elongated and incoherent plumes that, when the bird is at rest, droop over the hind

end of the body. (For the wing plumes of male *Argusianus argus* see PHEASANT.)

Proportions. While one can point out certain principles in the shape and relative size of the wing, and correlate these with the mode of life of the bird, there are an enormous number of variations within these generalities.

Birds that spend most of their time in flight have evolved long, narrow wings (which tend to be pointed in sea birds but broader in land birds), with the primaries often separated to expose the ' slots ' through which the air passes, thus reducing vortex formation over the wing tip. The relative lengthening of the wing has been brought about in the albatrosses (Diomedeidae) by the development of a humerus of great length with a short manus, whereas in the swifts (Apodidae) the reverse is true and the primaries are relatively long ; these are used in lateral steering and are, therefore, associated with the aerial insect-catching activities of swifts, whereas albatrosses simply glide in the air and feed off the water.

Slow fliers, and those that hunt in enclosed areas such as woodland, have relatively shorter and more rounded wings ; excellent examples are the rounded wing of the Sparrowhawk *Accipiter nisus* compared with the pointed wings of the falcons (Falconidae), and the same applies respectively to the Jay *Garrulus glandarius* and the Rook *Corvus frugilegus*.

The frequency of the wing-beat increases as the size of the wing decreases, relative to body weight, reaching its maximum in the hummingbirds (Trochilidae) with up to 80 beats per second (see FLIGHT).   J.G.H.

Bellairs, A. d'A. & Jenkin, C. R. 1960. The skeleton of birds. *In* Marshall, A. J. (ed.). Biology and Comparative Physiology of Birds vol. 1. New York and London.
Berger, A. J. 1960. The musculature. *In* Marshall (as above).
de Beer, G. 1956. The evolution of the ratites. Bull. Brit. Mus. (Nat. Hist.), Zool. 4 : 57–70.
Fisher, H. I. 1955. Avian anatomy, 1925–1950, and some suggested problems. *In* Wolfson, A. (ed.). Recent Studies in Avian Biology. Urbana, Ill.
Simpson, G. G. 1946. Fossil Penguins. Bull. Amer. Mus. Nat. Hist. 87 : 1–99.

WING-CLIP: see RINGING

WING FORMULA: a statement of, mainly, the relative lengths of the primary feathers, especially the more distal ones ; in certain taxonomic groups a valuable aid to the identification of closely allied species that are difficult to differentiate in some plumages. The character is species-specific, and the relations (as distinct from absolute measurements) are constant within narrow limits. A supplementary criterion is the presence of ' emargination' on certain of the primaries ; this is a narrowing of the web on one side (usually the outer) of the feather towards the tip, producing a tapering effect. The method can be applied both to birds alive in the hand or to museum skins, but care has to be taken to ensure that critical feathers are completely grown (following moult) and not too badly abraded by wear. It is especially useful in dealing with Old World warblers (Sylviinae) and with some New World groups such as the tyrant-flycatchers (Tyrannidae) and the vireos (Vireoninae)—also, among non-passerines, with the harriers (Circinae).

For example, in the Willow Warbler *Phylloscopus trochilus* the much reduced outermost or 10th (1st in another notation) primary is 3–6 mm. longer than the longest primary covert ; in the Chiffchaff *P. collybita* it is 5–9 mm. longer ; and in the Wood Warbler *P. sibilatrix* it is 2–5 mm. shorter than the covert. In the Willow Warbler the 8th and 7th (3rd and 4th) primaries are the longest and equal to each other, while the others are progressively shorter —by amounts that can be stated in relation to the longest—in the order 6th, 9th, 5th, 4th (5th, 2nd, 6th, 7th, numbered from the outside) ; in the Chiffchaff the 8th, 7th, and 6th (3rd, 4th, and 5th) are longest and equal, while the others usually diminish in the order 5th, 4th, 9th, 3rd (6th, 7th, 2nd, 8th). Further, in the Willow Warbler, the 8th to 6th (3rd to 5th) primaries are emarginated on their outer webs ; and in the Chiffchaff the 8th to 5th (3rd to 6th) are so emarginated.

WINGS, COMPARATIVE ANATOMY OF:
the structure of the wing in birds as compared with that in other flying animals. The power of true flight, as distinct from gliding or passive 'ballooning', has been acquired four separate times in the course of evolution. Each method involves the use of wings that are analogous in being organs used in actively striking the air. The wings of insects, however, are not homologous with the others, being outgrowths from the dorsolateral areas of the two posterior segments of the thorax. In the other three instances, all among animals conforming with the general vertebrate plan (see ANIMAL KINGDOM), the wings are forelimbs adapted to the purpose ; but the several modifications differ widely in detail. The bird's wing is unique in having the surface area composed of feathers, borne on an arm in which the bony elements of the manus are much reduced. In the extinct pterodactyls (Order Pterosauria, Class Reptilia) and in the bats (Order Chiroptera, Class Mammalia) the surface area consists of a membranous fold of skin borne on the arm and hand, the latter extended by elongated digits. In ptero-

dactyls, represented in the geological record from the lower Jurassic to the upper Cretaceous, the extension of the skin was carried on an extremely elongated outermost digit (usually reckoned the 5th). In bats the larger part of the membrane is extended by elongated metacarpals and phalanges of digits 2 to 5 (the pollex being free, and clawed) ; a smaller part is anterior to the anterior margin of the arm, beginning from the side of the neck. In bats the wing is in fact more than a forelimb, as the membrane stretches down the side of the body and has its relatively small posterior part extended by the hind leg and the tail.

WING SOUNDS: see INSTRUMENTAL SOUNDS

WINTER VISITORS: see VISITOR

WIRE-BIRD: alternative name for the St Helena Sand Plover *Charadrius pecuarius sanctaehelenae* (see PLOVER (1)).

WISHBONE: the FURCULA ; and see SKELETON.

WISP: see ASSEMBLY, NOUN OF

WOLFFIAN DUCTS: see REPRODUCTIVE SYSTEM

WOODCHAT: name, alternatively 'Woodchat Shrike', of *Lanius senator* (see SHRIKE).

WOODCOCK: substantive name (commonly unchanged in the plural) of *Scolopax* spp. and *Philohela minor* (see under SANDPIPER).

WOODCREEPER: substantive name, alternatively 'woodhewer' (formerly usual), of most species of Dendrocolaptidae (Passeriformes, suborder Tyranni) ; in the plural, general term for the family. In size, plumage, and habits this Neotropical family of nearly 50 species is rather uniform. The majority are between 8 and 15 inches in total length, the genera *Glyphorynchus* (wedgebills) and *Sittasomus* being exceptions and averaging about 5–6 inches. Characteristically the plumage is olive, with rufous wings and tail, light or buff striations on the head, and similarly striated or barred under parts. A few, such as the Narrow-billed Woodcreeper *Lepidocolaptes angustirostris*, by an excess of striations become almost white below ; others, such as *Sittasomus* and *Dendrocincla* spp., lack striations, but although the latter retain the standard plumage colours of olive and rufous the former are pure dark grey or yellowish below. The wing is normally developed. The shafts of the rectrices are characteristically stiffened and the whole tail developed as in woodpeckers (Picidae) for a support in climbing trees. The bill is mostly stout and

$\frac{1}{2}$

Ruddy Woodcreeper *Dendrocincla homochroa*, of tropical Middle America and Venezuela. *C.E.T.K.*

well developed, often rather compressed, long or moderately so, and more or less decurved. The extreme development is in the Scythebill (or Sickle-bill) *Campylorhamphus falcularius*, which has a long ($2\frac{1}{2}$–3 inch), scimitar-shaped bill, representing about a third or a quarter of the total length of the bird. On the other hand, the wedgebills have short, straight bills with an upturned lower mandible ; and other genera such as *Deconychura*, *Dendrocincla*, and *Dendrexetastes* have stout, rather short, straight bills. The legs are short, with powerful feet and long sharp claws.

Thus the family is well adapted for an arboreal existence and the birds generally behave much like treecreepers (Certhiidae) or woodpeckers, searching for their food by climbing spirally up tree-trunks and hammering at the bark, then flying in an undulating manner to another tree and repeating the performance. Yet some species, such as the Great Rufous Woodcreeper *Xiphocolaptes major* of northern Argentina, are adapted to feeding on the ground, and the Ocreous-billed Woodcreeper *Dendrocincla meruloides* in Trinidad follows columns of marching ants. No doubt the food always consists of insects.

The voice seems to vary considerably, being recorded as loud, musical, and melancholy for the Narrow-billed Woodcreeper ; a loud ' whee-whee-whee ' as well as challenging notes for Bridge's Wood-hewer *Drymornis bridgesii* ; and a long-drawn-out trill for the Streak-headed Woodcreeper *Lepidocolaptes souleyetii*. They tend to be solitary birds, naturally inhabiting forested or wooded areas, but the mode of life of most species is poorly known.

The nests and eggs of very few species have ever been described, but so far as is known all build nests of leaves and vegetable materials in old wood-pecker holes, hollow stumps, and trees, between the leaves of epiphytes or palm trees, and in other such enclosed places. The eggs are always white and more or less glossy, and the clutch size is usually 2 and rarely 3. The incubation period has been observed only in the Streak-headed Woodcreeper, as 15 days ; and the nestling period in that species and in the Spot-crowned Woodcreeper *Lepidocolaptes affinis* as 19 days.

The family comprises 13 genera and 48 species, and ranges from Mexico (Sonora Province, in the north-west) to northern Argentina, east and central Bolivia, and Peru ; it also reaches Trinidad and Tobago, but is not found in the Antilles. Thus, the range is closely similar to that of the antbirds (Formicariidae) and is essentially Neotropical. The Narrow-billed Woodcreeper is said to be a summer visitor to the area of Buenos Aires, but no doubt the family is otherwise essentially non-migratory.

S.M.

Peters, J. L. 1951. Check-list of Birds of the World vol. 7. Cambridge, Mass.
Skutch, A. F. 1945. Life history of the Allied Wood-hewer. Condor 47 : 85–94.

WOODHAUNTER: *Hyloctistes subulatus* (for family see OVENBIRD (1)).

WOODHEN: alternative name for the wekas *Gallirallus* spp. (see RAIL).

WOODHEWER: see WOODCREEPER

WOOD-HOOPOE: substantive name of species of Phoeniculidae (Coraciiformes, suborder Coracii) ; in the plural, general term for the family. The species of the genus *Rhinopomastus* are called ' scimitar-bills '.

This small group, restricted to Africa, is treated by some authors as a subfamily of the Upupidae (see HOOPOE), but the wood-hoopoes—also called ' tree-hoopoes '—are very unlike the true hoopoes in general appearance. Much slimmer in build than the well-known and widely distributed *Upupa epops*, they lack the ornamental crest and strikingly patterned plumage. The most notable feature is the long graduated tail of 10 feathers, without stiff shafts ; the wings are short and rounded, with in some species (e.g. the Senegal Wood-hoopoe *Phoeniculus senegalensis*) a broad white band very conspicuous when the bird flies up from the ground. The tarsus is feathered for half its length ; and the 3rd and 4th toes are fused at the base. Very sharp, abruptly curved nails befit species which creep about the tree-trunks. The bill, which is red, black, orange, or yellow, is fairly long and gently curved in *Phoeniculus*, shorter and straighter in *Scoptelus*, fine and sickle-shaped in *Rhinopomastus*—these are the only 3 genera, and about a dozen species have been described (now usually reduced to 6).

Plumage is mainly blue and green with metallic gloss, the tails are often ornamented with sub-apical white spots ; one species has the head buffish or nearly white, another chestnut, another pale brown. Their habitat is the tree-covered country ranging from the semi-arid bush to at least the edge of the tropical rain-forest, where the Buff-headed Wood-hoopoe *P. bollei* and the Forest Wood-hoopoe *S. brunneiceps* both occur. On the whole, wood-hoopoes are much more typical of the savanna and thorn country, and most species do not occur within the heavy forest except in clearings.

Wood-hoopoes are insect-eaters, and in quest of their prey they climb about the boughs and tree-trunks showing remarkable acrobatic skill ; some keep much to the tree-tops and are seldom seen. Berries are occasionally eaten, and the seeds of fruits have been found in the stomach.

Eggs are laid, and the young reared, in the cavities of trees, little nest being made ; a strong unpleasant smell is characteristic. The eggs are uniform pale blue or dark french grey, in some species spotted with brown ; the clutch usually numbers 3. Incubating females of the Green Wood-hoopoe (or Kakelaar) *P. purpureus* are said to be extremely loth to abandon their eggs, a significant fact because of the relationship of hoopoes and hornbills (Bucerotidae).

See Plate 30 (colour).   D.A.B.

Peters, J. L. 1945. Check-list of Birds of the World vol. 5. Cambridge, Mass.

WOOD-IBIS: substantive name of *Mycteria americana* and *Ibis* spp. ; in the plural, general term for the subfamily Mycteriinae of the Ciconiidae (see STORK).

WOODLARK: *Lullula arborea* (see LARK).

WOODNYMPH: substantive name of *Thalurania* spp. and *Cyanophaia bicolor* (for family see HUMMINGBIRD).

WOODPECKER: substantive name of most species of Picidae (Piciformes, suborder Pici) ; in the plural, general term for the family. The name is derived from the habit of climbing on trees and drilling into the bark for insect prey, a feeding method which attains its greatest development in this family. A few have special names, such as 'flicker' and 'sapsucker' ; and the family includes the small woodpeckers known as 'piculets', and also the wrynecks.

Most species are small to medium-sized ($3\frac{1}{4}$–$13\frac{1}{4}$ inches in length), but a few are large (up to $22\frac{1}{2}$ inches). Plumage colour may be black, white, yellow, red, brown, or green, and is usually a combination of several with one or two predominating ; the sexes are almost identical, the major difference being (usually) the presence of red or yellow on the head of the male. Many are barred, spotted, or streaked, especially below. Some are crested. The tail is wedge-shaped (rarely rounded) with 12 rectrices, but 8 in *Verreauxia* while the outer pair are rudimentary or missing in *Sasia* and *Phloeoceastes pollens*. The stiff tail of the true woodpeckers serves as a support when the bird is climbing ; in the other subfamilies it is soft. The central pair of rectrices are shed in the moult after the others have regrown, an adaptation to preserve the supporting function of the tail. The rounded wing has 10 primaries, the outer one reduced ; the inner two are much smaller in the juvenile plumage. A complete juvenile moult occurs in the woodpeckers although not in other piciform birds.

The distinctive climbing and feeding habits of the woodpeckers are reflected in their specialised morphology. The tongue is extraordinarily long, worm-like, and mobile ; it is capable of an extreme degree of protrusion owing to the great length of the supporting bones ('horns'). The hyoids usually curve round the back of the skull, and end near the base of the bill ; the tips may enter the right cavity of the upper mandible (*Jynx*, the left) through the corresponding nostril, or even curve around the right orbit (*Dendrocopos villosus*, *Hemicircus*). Sometimes the 'horns' loop downwards along the side of the neck (*Picus viridis*, *Jynx*). The hard tip of the tongue is more or less bordered with bristles or barbs. When coated with mucus from the well-developed glands at its base, the tongue can be used as a 'lime-twig' for catching ants, as a brush for licking the sap of trees, or as a lance to spear larger insects. The long tracheo-hyoid muscles retract the tongue ; these are often interlaced in a most complicated manner before inserting on the trachea. In the true woodpeckers, the bill is strong, straight, and chisel-like ; in the Jynginae and Picumninae

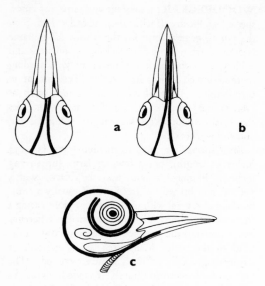

FIG 1. Progressively different dispositions of the hyoid bones ('horns') in Picidae :

(a) the horns end at the base of the bill, as in *Chryso-colaptes validus, C. guttacristatus, Liopicus mahratthensis, Dendrocopos* spp., *Veniliornis olivinus, Picumnus* spp., etc.

(b) the horns end in the right cavity of the upper mandible, as in *Dinopium javanense, Chrysoptilus melanochloros, Picus puniceus, Colaptes agricola,* etc.

(c) the horns end below, behind, or upon the right orbit, as in *Dendrocopos villosus, Hemicircus concretus,* and *H. canente.*   *J. Steinbacher.*

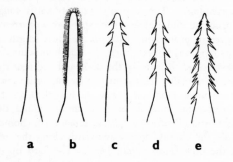

FIG 2. Different forms of tongue-tips in Picidae :

(a) smooth, without any bristles (*Jynx*).

(b) brush-like (*Sphyrapicus varius, Leuconerpes candidus, Melanerpes formicivorus*).

(c) with 2–3 barbs (*Chrysoptilus melanochloros*).

(d) with 4–6 barbs (*Celeus flavescens, Veniliornis olivinus, Ceophloeus lineatus*).

(e) with groups of barbs of different sizes (*Campephilus melanoleucos, Melanerpes aurifrons, Scapaneus trachelopyrus*).   *J. Steinbacher.*

weak and more rounded. The nostrils are covered by bristle-like feathers that protect the nostrils from wood dust. The palate is a true schizognathous type, the vomer being present as a minute medial bone. The head of most woodpeckers is large, the neck slender but with exceedingly powerful muscles.

The legs are short, the feet strong and with large curved claws. When the bird is climbing, the 2nd and 3rd toes are directed forward and the 4th laterally, the 1st being vestigial (lost in *Picoides, Dinopium,* and *Sasia*) or held laterally (*Campephilus*) ; however, in hopping on the ground or perching, the toes are held in a typical zygodactyl fashion. The oil gland is bipartite, usually tufted and well developed (missing in some *Campethera* spp. ; naked in *Dinopium* and *Gecinulus*).

Most woodpeckers are solitary and usually resident or (in the northern parts of their range) vagrant, only *Jynx, Colaptes,* and *Sphyrapicus* being migratory in high degree. The flight is strong but not sustained, undulating except in the largest species. The food consists of insects, fruits, nuts, and the sap of trees— sometimes this diet changes seasonally or the food is partly stored. Almost all woodpeckers have a loud and harsh voice, some have 'laughing' or ringing cries. Many species produce an instrumental 'drumming' sound by very rapid blows with the bill on dead branches (or sometimes on metal objects). Typical forms are arboreal, but some species feed and even breed on the ground. The 'pecking woodpeckers' mainly climb on trees, but rarely perch ; they bore into the bark and wood for hidden larvae of beetles and carve out cavities for their nests. The 'ground woodpeckers' prefer stumps or rotten branches where many insects (especially ants) have their favourite haunts. In treeless regions of South America and South Africa, some species always live on the ground (*Colaptes, Geocolaptes olivaceus*) ; they make their nest holes in the banks of earth (*Colaptes rupicola* colonially) or in the concrete-like constructions of ground-termites.

The nests of woodpeckers are without lining. The 2–8 glossy white eggs are incubated by male and female (by night, the male). The incubation period is very short, 11–17 days. The young at hatching are blind and naked (*Melanerpes aurifrons* with sparse down) and are cared for by both parents. Although nidicolous, the young are able to leave the nest and climb about before they are capable of flight.

The range of the family is world-wide except in extreme latitudes, but excluding Madagascar, Australia, and most islands east of the Philippines, Celebes, and Alor. The woodpeckers are divided into 3 subfamilies—the wrynecks (Jynginae) with 2 species, the soft-tailed woodpeckers or piculets (Picumninae) with 29, and the true woodpeckers (Picinae) with 179—210 altogether.

Jynginae. The wrynecks are believed to represent the ancestral type of the family. They perch and rarely cling to the branches of trees ; their plumage is soft and brown, grey, and black in a mottled cryptic pattern. Twisting motions of the neck when the bird is frightened are responsible for the name. The Wryneck *Jynx torquilla* is the migratory species (5 subspp.) in the Palaearctic Region ; the range of *J. ruficollis* is in tropical Africa.

Picumninae. The tiny piculets are grey or olive green above, with under parts white, spotted or barred with black. The genus *Picumnus* (5 spp.) is distributed in tropical South America and southeast Asia, *Nesoctites* (1 sp.) on the island of Haiti, *Verreauxia* (1 sp.) in West Africa and central Africa, and *Sasia* (1 sp.) in south-east Asia. They can climb and perch on trees and branches. The short bill is not strong enough to drill into trees but is used on rotten wood to obtain insects or their larvae and to excavate nest holes.

Picinae. The true woodpeckers are especially well represented in the Americas and in the Indo-Malayan area. In North America are the common Yellow-shafted Flicker *Colaptes auratus*, the large Pileated Woodpecker *Dryocopus pileatus*, and the perhaps extinct Ivory-billed Woodpecker *Campephilus principalis* (like *D. pileatus*, black and white with a red crest), the Sapsucker *Sphyrapicus varius*, the Golden-fronted Woodpecker *Melanerpes aurifrons*, the Red-headed Woodpecker *M. erythrocephalus*, and some species of the genus *Dendrocopos* (also represented in other parts of the world). Typical forms in South America are the many species of the genera *Chrysoptilus*, *Piculus*, *Phloeoceastes*, *Celeus*, and *Veniliornis*.

In Europe are the 3 species of spotted woodpeckers, *Dendrocopos major*, *D. medius*, and *D. minor*, which can be found in most arboreal areas, as well as the more terrestrial Green Woodpecker *Picus viridis* and Grey Woodpecker *P. canus*. The Black Woodpecker *Dryocopus martius* prefers pine forests to deciduous woods ; and the Three-toed Woodpecker *Picoides tridactylus* is confined to higher mountains and to the northern parts of Europe and Asia—and also of North America. Most of the European species are also represented in the Palaearctic parts of Asia.

The genera *Campethera*, *Mesopicos*, *Thripias*, *Geocolaptes*, *Dendropicos*, and *Polipicus*, together with some species of *Dendrocopos*, are widely distributed in Africa south of the Sahara. In south-east Asia and in the Indo-Malayan area, the most typical genera are *Meiglyptes*, *Mulleripicus*, *Micropternus*, *Blythipicus*, *Dinopium*, *Chrysocolaptes*, and *Hemicircus* ; here also are some species of the genera *Picus*, *Dryocopus*, and *Dendrocopos*.

See Plate 13a (phot.). J.S.

Beeker, W. J. 1953. Feeding adaptations and systematics in the avian order Piciformes. J. Washington Acad. Sci. 43 : 293–299.

Bent, A. C. 1939. Life histories of North American woodpeckers. Order Piciformes. Bull. U.S. Natl. Mus. 174.

Bock, W. J. & Miller, W. D. 1959. The scansorial foot of the woodpeckers, with comments on the evolution of perching and climbing feet in birds. Amer. Mus. Novit. no. 1931 : 1–45.

Burt, W. H. 1930. Adaptive modifications in the woodpeckers. Univ. Calif. Publ., Zool. 3 : 455–524.

Leiber, A. 1907. Vergleichende Anatomie der Spechtzunge. Zoologica (Stuttgart) 20 (Heft 51) : 1–79.

Peters, J. L. 1948. Check-list of Birds of the World vol. 6. Cambridge, Mass.

Scharnke, H. 1931. Beiträge zur Morphologie und Entwicklungeschichte der Zunge der Trochilidae, Meliphagidae und Picidae. J. Orn. 79 : 425–491.

Skutch, A. F. 1948. Life history of the Olivaceous Piculet and related forms. Ibis 90 : 433–449.

Steinbacher, J. 1934. Untersuchungen über den Zungenapparat indischer Spechte. J. Orn. 8 : 399–408.

Steinbacher, J. 1935. Ueber den Zungenapparat sudafrikanischer Spechte. Orn. Mber. 43 : 85–89.

Steinbacher, J. 1941. Weitere Untersuchungen über den Zungenapparat afrikanischer Spechte. Orn. Mber. 49 : 16–137.

Steinbacher, J. 1955. Zur Morphologie und Anatomie des Zungenapparates brasilianischer Spechte. Senckenbergiana Biol. 36 : 1–8.

Steinbacher, J. 1957. Über den Zungenapparat einiger neotropischer Spechte. Senckenbergiana Biol. 38 : 259–270.

Vaurie, C. 1959. Systematic notes on Palearctic birds. nos. 34, 35, 36. Picidae. Amer. Mus. Novit. nos. 1945 : 1–21 ; 1946 : 1–29 ; 1951 : 1–21.

Voous, K. H. 1947. The history of the distribution of the genus *Dendrocopos*. Limosa 20 : 1–142.

WOOD-QUAIL : substantive name of *Odontophorus* spp. found in Neotropical woodlands (for family see PHEASANT).

WOOD-RAIL : in the plural, general term for certain genera of Rallidae (see RAIL).

WOOD-SHRIKE : name sometimes applied to species of Campephagidae or, in the plural, used generally for the family (see CUCKOO-SHRIKE) ; also, sometimes, similarly in respect of the Prionopinae (see SHRIKE).

WOODSTAR : substantive name of *Chaetocercus jourdanii*, *Myrmia micrura*, *Myrtis fanny*, and *Philodice* spp. (for family see HUMMINGBIRD).

WOOD-SWALLOW : substantive name, alternatively ' swallow-shrike ', of the species of Artamidae (Passeriformes, suborder Oscines) ; in the plural, in either form, general term for the family. These birds constitute a peculiar group that seems to have originated in Australia ; their nearest relatives are unknown, and they are certainly neither swallows (Hirundinidae) nor shrikes (Laniidae).

General Characteristics. The wood-swallows are stoutly built birds of from $5\frac{1}{4}$ to 8 inches in length. The bill is stout, moderately long, slightly decurved, and pointed ; it has a wide gape. The legs are short, the feet strong. The tail is blunt and rather short. The wings are long and pointed, reaching almost to the tip of the tail. The plumage colour of all species, except a partly chestnut Australian one, is a mixture of black, grey, and white. The sexes are alike, or nearly so. Alone among passerines, the wood-swallows possess powder-down feathers ; the tips of these break up into a kind of dusting powder, used by the birds in dressing the plumage.

Habits. Despite the name, wood-swallows are not birds of high forest but of open country and scrub in the lowlands. They usually sit quietly on an exposed dead branch of a tree, from which they pursue insects after the manner of flycatchers (Muscicapinae). They are partial to telegraph wires where these exist. The tail is often waggled from side to side. Their flight is exceedingly graceful ; it is often interrupted by long periods of gliding, for which the wings are well adapted. The larger species are able to soar on thermal up-currents.

Wood-swallows may be identified from a long distance by their habit of huddling close together, four or five birds on a bare branch. In some of the species, the birds sleep in compact knots, one standing on another. They are very pugnacious, and will violently attack passing birds as large as crows (Corvidae) and harriers (Circinae). The voice is described as consisting of twittering notes and harsh cries.

Breeding. Whistler's description of the breeding of the species found in India is generally applicable. The nest is usually placed on the top of a projecting stump or branch, occasionally in a hole ; a favourite site is a palm tree, on the bases of the leaves, or on the rough projections whence the leaves have fallen. The site is usually 30–40 feet from the ground. Some Australian species, however, nest in shrubs or bushes within 10 feet of the ground. The Little Wood-swallow *Artamus minor* haunts cliffs and broken country, where it nests in crevices among the rocks or on ledges in caverns.

The nest itself is a shallow, loose cup of fine grasses, roots, fibres, feathers, and similar materials, as a rule with no definite lining. The 2–4 eggs somewhat resemble those of shrikes, being spotted and blotched on a white to cream base. The nidicolous young are hatched with some down on the upper parts. Parental duties are shared by both sexes. Nestlings of the Papuan Wood-swallow *A. maximus* have been observed being fed by four or five adults.

Distribution. The family is centred on Australia and the south-west Pacific. One species extends westwards to Malaysia, but without reaching the mainland of Asia ; another is widespread in south-east Asia from eastern India and Ceylon, through Burma and Siam, to western China.

In South Australia, West Australia, and New South Wales, some species are migratory. Thus, the Masked Wood-swallow *A. personatus*, described as invading the southern portion of West Australia on a large scale in some seasons, in South Australia arrives regularly in September in flocks, with the White-browed Wood-swallow *A. superciliosus*, and departs in January. Local movements of this type have been noticed also in northern Burma.

Examples. The family includes only the genus *Artamus*. As there is no recent monograph of the group, the exact number of species can be given only as from 10 (Mayr 1962) to 15, of which 6 are wholly or partly Australian.

One of the best-known members of the family is the species found in south-east Asia, the Ashy Swallow-shrike *A. fuscus*. Whistler describes it thus : ' The Swallow-shrike is a gregarious bird, breeding in colonies and spending its time in large flocks which feed and rest together. It is specialised for the purpose of feeding on the wing, and in the air looks like a large grey swallow, though easily distinguished by the constantly uttered harsh cry and by the slow-sailing flight. The flocks settle in rows on some lofty bough or the top of a tall bamboo and thence sally into the air in pursuit of passing insects ; they fly round in a wide circle, though seldom for more than a minute or two at a time, and then return to the perch where they huddle closely together.' In spite of the wide range, no subspecies have been recognised.

The White-breasted Swallow-shrike *A. leucorhynchus* ranges from the Philippines and Borneo to Fiji and Australia, in a number of different subspecies. In Borneo, although it is common in open country from the coast to the interior, it is perhaps typically a bird of the casuarina trees fringing the sea-shore. According to Cayley this is a most useful species in Australia, destroying immense numbers of injurious insects and their larvae.

Three of the Australian species have already been mentioned ; of these, the White-browed Wood-swallow is the largest member of the family and has chestnut under parts and white above the eyes.

See Plate 47a (phot.).   B.E.S.

Cayley, N. W. 1951. What Bird is That ? Sydney.
Mayr, E. 1945. Birds of the South-west Pacific. New York.
Mayr, E. 1962. Family Artamidae. *In* Mayr, E. & Greenway, J. C., Jr. (eds.). Check-list of Birds of the World vol. 15. Cambridge, Mass.
Serventy, D. A. & Whittell, H. M. 1962. Birds of Western Australia. 3rd ed. Perth, W.A.
Smythies, B. E. 1953. The Birds of Burma. Edinburgh.
Smythies, B. E. 1960. The Birds of Borneo. Edinburgh.
Whistler, H. 1949. Popular Handbook of Indian Birds. 4th ed. London.
Short accounts and illustrations of one or more species are given in the above recent works.

WOOD-WARBLER: alternative general term for the American warblers or Parulidae (see WARBLER (2)) ; also, in Britain, the name of *Phylloscopus sibilatrix* in the subfamily Sylviinae of the Muscicapidae (see WARBLER (1)).

WORMS, PARASITIC: see ENDOPARASITE

WRECK: an occasional disaster affecting pelagic species of birds, e.g. storm-petrels (Hydrobatidae) and Little Auk *Plautus alle*, when these are swept ashore or inland in large numbers by persistent gales (see OCEANIC BIRDS).

WREN (1): substantive name of the species of Troglodytidae (Passeriformes, suborder Oscines) ; in the plural, general term for the family. Traditionally, ' Wren ' without qualification is the name of the Holarctic species *Troglodytes troglodytes*, known as ' Winter Wren ' in North America to distinguish it from other members of the family found there. The name is also applied, or misapplied, to various unrelated birds of small size—see succeeding entries.

The family Troglodytidae consists of 12–14 genera, according to views held, and about 60 species. Many subspecies of species such as *T. troglodytes* are recognised, but much of this variation is clinal, although some of the insular forms of the Wren are well differentiated. The family is restricted to the New World except for *T. troglodytes*, which has invaded and established itself in much of temperate Eurasia and in North Africa, particularly in mountainous areas. The greatest concentration of genera and species is in tropical America.

Wrens are small or medium-sized birds ($3\frac{3}{4}$–$8\frac{3}{4}$ inches long), in the main clothed in various tints of brown with lighter under parts and dark barring on the remiges and rectrices. Some have stumpy

Long-billed Marsh Wren, *Cistothorus palustris*, of N. America. *C.E.T.K.*

tails, and a number bear conspicuous black and white, or near-white, stripes or other markings. The sexes are alike in plumage.

In general, wrens are active and mainly insectivorous birds with slender curved bills, strong feet, and relatively short, rounded wings. They tend to frequent dense, fairly low, vegetation where their presence is apprehended more readily by ear than by eye, although the large cactus wrens *Campylorhynchus* spp. make themselves more conspicuous visually than most other wrens. Species have occupied habitats varying from rain-forest and marsh to desert scrub, moors, and cliffs. Some species show interesting adaptability in foraging : the Northern Cactus Wren *Campylorhynchus brunneicapillus* will overturn stones and mud-pats like a Turnstone *Arenaria interpres*, Song Wrens *Cyphorhinus phaeocephala* push up fallen leaves in search of prey, and Wrens *T. troglodytes* occasionally snatch small fish from pools. Some species will enter enclosed spaces more readily than most birds. Southern House Wrens *Troglodytes aedon* subsp. rain-bathe ; Banded-back Wrens *Campylorhynchus zonatus* and Wrens *T. troglodytes* dew-bathe. A number of species bathe in standing water and dust-bathe, but anting has not been recorded. Few, if any, definite instances of injury simulation have been observed, although the agitated fluttering of birds disturbed at the nest has been reported as distraction display.

Song is highly developed, and the family includes some of the world's finest singers, such as the Quadrille Wren *Cyphorhinus aradus*. Numerous species hold territory and sing during most months of the year. The Wren *T. troglodytes* uses song in territorial defence, courtship, nest-invitation, signalling between male and female, attracting other individuals to a roost, and in other ways. Many other wrens also have a rich repertoire of song signals. Duetting is characteristic of a number of tropical species.

Few wrens are migratory. Those inhabiting tropical forest are monogamous and remain paired from year to year, but some species in more northerly latitudes, such as the Northern House Wren *Troglodytes aedon* subsp., Long-billed Marsh Wren *Cistothorus palustris*, Short-billed Marsh Wren (Sedge Wren) *Cistothorus platensis*, and the Wren *T. troglodytes* are known or believed to be polygamous to a greater or lesser extent. In the latter species polygamy is more accentuated in well vegetated areas than in bleak areas and is probably correlated with the availability of food. Polygamy is also associated with a number of integrated adaptations including multiple nest building, breeding in covered nests or cavities, persistent song, and reduction in the aid given by the male in tending the young. The potentiality for one or the other integrated pattern of behaviour may be manifested only when birds breed in the appropriate environment.

Most species build roofed nests, although some, including the House Wren, Rufous-browed Wren *T. rufociliatus*, and Ochraceous Wren *T. ochraceus*, make cupped structures in cavities. In the majority of species male and female collaborate in building; but the males of polygamous species may usually do most of the work, leaving it to the female to titivate and line the structure already prepared. A covered nest can be favourable to polygamy because of the protection it affords to nestlings tended mainly or entirely by the female (see POLYGAMY). Some species build roosting nests that differ in design from the breeding nest (see ROOSTING). The Rock Wren *Salpinctes obsoletus* paves the entrance to the nest with pebbles, and several species incorporate fragments of snake-skin in the nest.

In all species the hen alone incubates. The ground colour of the eggs is usually white or nearly so. Blotching or speckling in shades of brown or lilac may be sparse or dense. Conforming to the general rule, wrens nesting in the tropics tend to have smaller clutches (2–5 eggs) than species in northern latitudes (see POPULATION DYNAMICS). The Carolina Wren *Thryothorus ludovicianus* and some tropical species have relatively slow incubation rhythms and may sit for an hour or more. Connubial feeding is performed by the males of some species. The period from egg-laying to the independence of the young tends to be longer than in many other small passerines. Most Central American

wrens remain in the nest for 16–18 days. Overlapping broods may occur in some species. Birds other than the parents have been known to help with feeding young ; two such auxiliaries were observed at a nest of the Banded-back Wren, and young Southern House Wrens may occasionally assist with feeding the nestlings of a later brood.

Most wrens roost in cavities or empty nests. Among those which sleep in pairs, or in family groups consisting of parents and independent young, are the Highland Wood Wren *Henicorhina leucophrys*, Banded-back Wren, Rufous-naped Wren *Campylorhynchus rufinucha* and Song Wren *Cyphorhinus aradus phaeocephalus*. Communal roosting in winter is characteristic of *Troglodytes t. troglodytes*, *T. t. indigenus*, and *T. t. hiemalis*, but as yet there are no records of such behaviour by the northern insular races. The young of the Wren *T. troglodytes*, Bewick Wren *Thryomanes bewickii*, Northern Cactus Wren, Southern House Wren, Banded-back Wren, Lowland Wood Wren *Henicorhina leucosticta*, Highland Wood Wren, and Ochraceous Wren are led to a dormitory by the parents. Multiple nest building among wrens apparently evolved in the tropics, primarily as a procedure enabling the birds to find shelter from predators ; but it has become for the Holarctic species an adaptation facilitating polygamy and survival during inclement weather.

E.A.A.

Anderson, A. H. & Anderson, A. 1957–61. Life history of the Cactus Wren. Condor 59 : 274–296 ; 61 : 186–205 ; 62 : 351–369 ; 63 : 87–94.

Armstrong, E. A. 1955. The Wren. London.

Bent, A. C. 1948. Life histories of North American nuthatches, wrens, thrashers and their allies. Bull. U.S. Natl. Mus. 195 : 113–295.

Kendeigh, S. C. 1941. Territorial and mating behaviour of the House Wren. Illinois Biol. Monogr. 22 : 1–356.

Paynter, R. A. & Vaurie, C. 1960. Family Troglodytidae. *In* Mayr, E. & Greenway, J. C., Jr. (eds.). Check-list of Birds of the World vol. 9. Cambridge, Mass.

Skutch, A. F. 1960. Life Histories of Central American Birds. Pt. II. (Pacific Coast Avifauna no. 34.) Los Angeles.

WREN (2): substantive name of many species of the subfamily Malurinae of the Muscicapidae (Passeriformes, suborder Oscines) ; in the form ' Australian wrens ', sometimes ' Australian warblers ' or ' wren-warblers ', general term for the subfamily. The members are warbler-like birds, found in Australia, New Guinea, and New Zealand, that have in the past been arranged in several families, with many of them being retained in the Sylviinae (see WARBLER (1)). Mayr & Amadon have, however, proposed that they all be referred to a subfamily, Malurinae, as part of the Old World primitive insect-eaters (Muscicapidae) and standing near to the Sylviinae. There are some 80 species of these birds and they fall into several subgroups.

The most distinctive is the series of species associated with the nominate genus *Malurus*. These are brilliantly plumaged, long-tailed birds, variously known in common speech as 'superb warblers', 'blue wrens', or 'fairy wrens'. *Malurus*, with 10 species, is the most diversified genus, and the colour pattern includes combinations of brilliant metallic blues and purples, jet black, rufous, red, and satin-white. One species of *Malurus* extends into New Guinea, where the two species of *Todopsis* and one of *Chenorhamphus* have similar colourings. *Clytomyias*, from the same island, has no blue in the plumage. The Australian emu-wrens *Stipiturus* spp. are mainly brown coloured and are remarkable for the reduction in the number of the tail feathers to 6 and the modification of these to long, loosely-barbed appendages remarkably like the feathers of emus (Dromaiidae) in appearance.

The other large group of related genera are the thornbills or thornbill-warblers, *Gerygone*, *Acanthiza*, and *Sericornis* (scrub-wrens), each with a large number of similar species. They are small tree and thicket dwellers, of quieter colourings than the *Malurus* assemblage but with rather similar habits in many respects, including a prolonged continuance of family ties in many cases, with the young of the first clutch assisting with the care of the later broods. Associated genera are *Pyrrholaemus* (Redthroat, near *Sericornis*), *Smicrornis* (weebills), *Hylacola* (heath-wrens), *Calamanthus* (field-wrens), and *Aphelocephala* (whitefaces).

Other genera now placed in the subfamily, and formerly ranked with the Sylviinae, include *Chthonicola*, *Origma*, *Pycnoptilus* (Pilot-bird), *Amytornis* (grass-wrens), and *Dasyornis* (bristle-birds).

The nests of the birds of this subfamily are neatly woven domed or globular structures, with a side entrance, and either pensile in the foliage, or else placed among forked twigs in trees, or in a crevice, or near the ground. The eggs are 2–4 in number. These domed nests are regularly parasitised by a number of Australian cuckoos (Cuculidae), often much larger than their hosts.

Mayr & Amadon also include in the assemblage some genera that do not appear to be very closely related. These are all builders of open cup-shaped nests. They include *Eremiornis* (Spinifex-bird), perhaps better retained in its old place with the Sylviinae; *Epthianura*, with chat-like habits; and *Cincloramphus* (songlarks), large strong-flying birds, ground-nesters of behaviour resembling that of

larks (Alaudidae) or pipits *Anthus* spp., and with regular migratory habits unknown otherwise in the Malurinae (see also under RAIL-BABBLER).

See Plate 7 (colour).   D.L.S.

Mayr, E. & Amadon, D. 1951. A classification of recent birds. Amer. Mus. Novit. no. 1496 : 1–42.

WREN (3): substantive name of 3 out of the 4 species of Xenicidae (Passeriformes, suborder Tyranni) ; in the form 'New Zealand wrens', general term for the family (also called ' Acanthisittidae '). This distinctive group is peculiar to New Zealand and is believed to represent one of the most ancient avian colonisations of that country during the Tertiary Period (Fleming). They have been rather vaguely placed near the pittas (Pittidae), the only mesomyodian group in the neighbouring area ; but although this is supported by some structural evidence, the birds do not resemble the pittas in ecology or habits. Their affinities with the pittas are probably no closer than with the New World mesomyodian groups.

The 4 known species, 1 now extinct, are placed in either 2 or 3 genera. It seems likely that, through adaptive radiation, 2 of the species developed at least partly ground-living habits, but the other 2 are strongly arboreal.

The Rifleman *Acanthisitta chloris* and the Bush Wren *Xenicus longipes* originally occurred widely in both North and South Islands, the former species being evidently much the more abundant. The modification brought about by settlement has obscured the original ecological relationships of these species, for early reports suggest that they were widespread from high altitudes to sea level. The Bush Wren is now excessively rare, or possibly extinct, in the North Island, and rare in the South Island. The Rifleman, however, is abundant in the beech forest which still clothes much of the mountain chains of both islands, the wet region of Fiordland, and the comparatively dry eastern slopes of the South Island. It occurs less abundantly in mixed forest, but the extent of this type of forest is now limited. Apparently the Bush Wrens succumbed in most places to one or more of the factors incidental to human settlement. The Rifleman persisted, and may be adaptable under modified conditions, tending to enter partly modified or settled habitats, although only in certain areas so far.

In both Rifleman and Bush Wren a North Island and a South Island subspecies have been described, differing only slightly ; but a third and more distinctive subspecies of the Bush Wren developed on Stewart Island (formerly) and its neighbouring islets. The status of the ' Alpine Rifleman ' recorded from

South Island wet mountain areas (' *A. c. citrina* ') will be clarified only when the necessary field investigation and taxonomic study have been carried out.

The third surviving species, the Rock Wren *Xenicus gilviventris*, is restricted in range to the South Island.

NS

Rifleman *Acanthisitta chloris*, of the family of New Zealand wrens. *C.E.T.K.*

The Stephen Island Wren *Xenicus* (' *Traversia* ') *lyalli*, discovered in 1894, attracted much attention because it was supposed to be flightless ; had this been true it would have been the only flightless passerine. However, the species became extinct almost as soon as it was discovered, the population on the island at that time being destroyed by a cat. Although weak flight is suggested by the short, rounded wings and soft plumage, there is no clear evidence of flightlessness ; and apparently the anatomy of the specimens received little attention. The only observations were those of the lighthouse keeper on the island, Lyall, who saw the birds but twice, on both occasions in the evening ; they ran like mice and ' did not fly at all ' (Rothschild). The species has generally been regarded as highly distinct and has therefore sometimes been placed in a third genus, ' Traversia '. On this basis it could be considered as a remnant of an earlier colonisation of New Zealand, rather than as a long-isolated *Xenicus*. On geographical grounds alone, it is unlikely to be merely an insular representative of either Bush Wren or Rock Wren, the island being only two miles from the nearest point on the South Island coast.

So far as is known, members of the family are entirely insectivorous. Breeding habits are uniform (unknown for the Stephen Island Wren) ; the nest consists of abundant material, loosely woven, with an entrance at the side, and is concealed in a hollow trunk or under bark. The Rifleman and the Bush Wren rarely nest at ground level (except the Stewart Island Bush Wren on islets with only low coastal forest) ; the Rock Wren nests in rock crevices in comparable sites to those of the arboreal species. Eggs are white in all species. The sexes are unlike in the Rifleman, but alike (but female duller) in *Xenicus* spp.

The Rifleman feeds by actively searching at all levels, although rarely on the forest floor ; it obtains much food from bark crevices and epiphytic mosses and lichens but explores all portions of the tree as far as the twigs, both in second storey and canopy. The main note is a high-pitched ' zee '. The nest is most commonly some distance inside a decaying trunk or branch. After the breeding season, August–January, family parties persist for some weeks. The Bush Wren, of which comparatively little has ever been recorded, apparently has less creeper-like habits than the Rifleman. It feeds less on trunks and more amongst foliage, and it is stated sometimes to feed on the ground. The Rock Wren obtains its food on the rock surfaces of open screes and moraines. To some extent it enters subalpine scrub to feed, and in larger measure for shelter.

Both the Bush Wren and the Rock Wren have the habit of bobbing the whole body, a vigorous action repeated frequently on alighting. This action, in the Rock Wren, varies in different portions of the range—a much slower and less frequent bobbing being noted in a population examined in a portion of Fiordland. This, together with morphological characters, led to the separation of a subspecies, *X. g. rineyi*, but according to more recent investigation this is of doubtful status.   E.G.T.

WREN (4): an alternative substantive name, popularly misapplied to certain birds of small size other than those mentioned above, e.g. the ' Willow Wren ' (Willow Warbler) *Phylloscopus trochilus*, ' Wood Wren ' (Wood Warbler) *P. sibilatrix*, and ' Golden-crested Wren ' (Goldcrest) *Regulus regulus* (for all of which see WARBLER (1)), and babblers in the genera *Microura*, *Spelaeornis*, and *Sphenocichla* (see BABBLER) ; also forms part of various compound substantive names as shown below.

WREN, ANT-: see ANTWREN ; and ANTBIRD

WREN-BABBLER: see under BABBLER

WREN, BUSH-: see WREN (3)

WREN, GNAT-: see GNATWREN

WREN-THRUSH: *Zelodonia coronata* (see THRUSH).

WREN-TIT: *Chamaea fasciata* of western North America, a bird of much-debated affinities treated in this work as belonging to the subfamily Timaliinae of the Muscicapidae (see BABBLER).

WREN-WARBLER: substantive name of *Prinia* spp. (see WARBLER (1)) ; also, in the plural, alternative term for the Malurinae (see WREN (2)).

WRIST: see under MUSCULATURE ; SKELETON ; WING

WRYBILL: or Wrybilled Plover, *Anarhynchus frontalis* (see PLOVER (1)) ; see Plate 15 (phot.).

WRYNECK: substantive name of *Jynx* spp. (see under WOODPECKER).

X Y Z

XANTHOCHROISM: see PLUMAGE, ABNORMAL AND ABERRANT

XENICIDAE: see under PASSERIFORMES ; and WREN (3)

XEROPHILOUS: adapted to living in a dry climate.

XENOPS: generic name used as substantive name of *Xenops* spp., sometimes called 'recurved-bills' (see OVENBIRD (1) ; and RECURVED-BILL).

YARAK: term used in FALCONRY.

YELLOWBILL: *Ceuthmochares aereus* (see CUCKOO) ; also used for another African species, *Anas undulata* (for family see DUCK).

YELLOWHAMMER: name, alternatively 'Yellow Bunting' (compare German 'Ammer'= bunting), of *Emberiza citrinella* (see BUNTING) ; colloquially applied in North America to the Flicker *Colaptes auratus* (see WOODPECKER).

YELLOWHEAD: *Mohoua ochrocephala* of New Zealand (for subfamily see FLYCATCHER (1)).

YELLOWLEGS: substantive name of two American species of *Tringa* ; in British usage sometimes unnecessarily altered to 'yellowshank' on the analogy of 'redshank' and 'greenshank' (see SANDPIPER).

YELLOWSHANK: see above

YELLOWTHROAT: substantive name of species of *Geothlypis* ; used without qualification, in North America, for *G. trichas* (see WARBLER (2)).

YOLK: see EGG

YOLK-SAC: see DEVELOPMENT, EMBRYONIC

YOUNG BIRD: a rather vague term applicable to a bird from the time of hatching (when it ceases to be an embryo) until the attainment of sexual maturity ; the use of a more exact term is generally preferable. The bird is technically a 'pullus' ('pull.') until it is full-grown and flying ; the ability to fly is the usual criterion, except in flightless species, but does not suffice alone in birds that have precocious flight. During the same period a bird may, in ordinary speech, be called a 'chick', especially in species where the pulli are active ; or a 'nestling' while remaining in the nest. After the pullus stage a bird is described as 'juvenile' while wearing its first plumage of true feathers. Thereafter a bird may still be 'immature' (the beginning point is vague) until it attains sexual maturity, the usual criterion of which is the assumption of full 'adult' plumage (but see MATURITY) ; in some species this immature stage lasts for a few years, and the successive plumages may be distinguishable one from another (see also under MOULT).

Colloquially, there are special terms for the young of certain species (see CYGNET ; DUCKLING ; EYASS ; GOSLING ; OWLET).

Certain terms describe the condition of pulli in different kinds of birds. The young of some species are 'precocial', i.e. capable of locomotion more or less immediately after hatching ; others are 'altricial', i.e. incapable of locomotion. The young may be 'ptilopaedic', i.e. covered with down, usually dense, when hatched ; or they may be 'psilopaedic', i.e. naked or with only sparse dorsal down (and usually blind) when hatched. Young that leave the nest immediately or soon after hatching are termed 'nidifugous' ; those that remain in the nest are termed 'nidicolous'. Nidifugous young are necessarily both precocial and ptilopaedic, but nidicolous young are not in all the species psilopaedic or even wholly altricial.

Nice, in an important recent monograph on the development of behaviour in young birds, has classified the state of maturity of 'hatchlings' as follows :

FIG 1. Newly hatched Lapwing *Vanellus vanellus*—precocial, nidifugous, ptilopaedic, and open-eyed. *K.S.*

FIG 2. Newly hatched Blackbird *Turdus merula*—altricial, nidicolous, psilopaedic, and blind. *K.S.*

Precocials—eyes open, down covered, leave nest first day or two
1. Independent of parents (e.g. Megapodiidae)
2. Follow parents but find own food (e.g. Anatidae, Charadriidae)
3. Follow parents and shown food by them (e.g. Phasianidae in part)
4. Follow parents and are fed by them (e.g. Podicipitidae, Rallidae).

Semi-precocials—eyes open, down covered, stay at nest until able to walk, fed by parents (e.g. Laridae).

Semi-altricials—down-covered, unable to leave nest, fed by parents
1. Eyes open (e.g. Ardeidae, Falconiformes)
2. Eyes closed (e.g. Strigiformes).

Altricials—eyes closed, little or no down, unable to leave nest, fed by parents (e.g. Passeriformes).

As the author points out, precocial and semi-precocial birds are actually or potentially mobile, while semi-altricial and altricial young are sedentary. The semi-precocial birds are physically well developed, but because of the feeding habits of the adults must stay on or near the nest until fledged. Semi-altricial and altricial young are physically unable to leave the nest, but the former are well provided with down from the start and some are hatched with their eyes open. Only in the first three kinds of precocials are the young not fed by the parents, and only in the first two are they not even shown food. Thus (she says) 'we have a progression from chicks so developed in every respect that they need no parental care to chicks so helpless that they demand prolonged and specialised care'.

The newly hatched chick of the domestic fowl has only about 3 per cent of the weight of an adult; yet growth to full size is achieved in a remarkably short time. In some small passerines the period is as short as ten days. On the other hand, young King Penguins *Aptenodytes patagonica* hatched late in the season have a period of arrested growth during the winter and may lose half their autumn weight during that time (see PENGUIN; WEIGHT).

For characters and behaviour particularly associated with the pullus stage see especially BEHAVIOUR, DEVELOPMENT OF; DEVELOPMENT, POSTEMBRYONIC; EGG-TOOTH; FEEDING OF YOUNG; FLIGHT, PRECOCIOUS; GROWTH; HATCHING; PARASITISM; PARENTAL CARE.

See Plates 18 (colour), and 34ab, 37a, 38b, 39ab, 40ab, 45ab, 46ab, 47ab, 48a (phot.).

Nice, M. M. 1962. Development of behaviour in precocial birds. Trans. Linn. Soc. N.Y. 8 : 1-211.

ZELEDONIIDAE: a monotypic family recognised by some authors, but here merged in the subfamily Turdinae of the Muscicapidae (see THRUSH).

ZONATION, DISTRIBUTIONAL: see DISTRIBUTION, GEOGRAPHICAL

ZONE: see LIFE ZONES

ZOOGEOGRAPHY: see DISTRIBUTION, GEOGRAPHICAL (with further cross-references); ECOLOGY; IRRUPTION; MIGRATION; RANGE EXPANSION

ZOOLOGICAL RECORD: an annual publication of the Zoological Society of London, the 'Aves' and other sections being obtainable separately. This is an essential tool for keeping abreast of the current literature, or searching the past literature, in any branch of zoology. As complete a list as possible of books and papers published during the year is given alphabetically under authors' names ; and there are elaborate indices to this under subject, geographical, and taxonomic heads. The series goes back to 1864 ; Alfred Newton was the first recorder of the ornithological literature. See also BIBLIOGRAPHY.

ZOOLOGY: the scientific study of animals (see ANIMAL KINGDOM) ; as such, one of the main divisions of BIOLOGY. Zoology may be subdivided according to the particular classes of animals under study ; thus the study of birds (Class Aves) is a branch of it (see ORNITHOLOGY).

Alternatively, zoology may be subdivided according to the disciplines brought to bear upon the material ; thus, for example, physiology is a subject cutting across the boundaries of Class. If the two sets of dividing lines be regarded as forming a grid, it isolates a large number of specialised subjects of the type of, e.g., avian physiology ; but for the most part such restriction of scope is undesirable. The ethologist, for instance, has much to gain from the comparative study of the behaviour of different kinds of animals. Again, there is the question of interrelations between animals at all levels of evolution ; the ecologist, especially, must take a wide view and consider not only animals of all kinds, but plants as well.

There are, of course, many purposes for which the segregation of a Class, such as birds, is a practical necessity. This applies notably to systematic studies ; and it is obviously true of the present work. At the same time, the aim should be to integrate ornithology as far as possible with zoology as a whole.

There are obviously many basic principles and theoretical concepts of zoology—indeed often of biology—that are valid for ornithology in common with other branches. There are also various zoological techniques that are applicable to the study of birds as well as of other classes of animals. A body of conventions relating to the naming of animals is accepted by all zoologists, and the code formulating these is binding on ornithologists equally with other specialists (see NOMENCLATURE).

The great museums of zoology (or of natural history, more broadly) are the most important institutions of their kind for ornithologists (see MUSEUM). The same is true of libraries, maintained by zoological or more general scientific societies.

Much original work relating to birds is published in zoological journals, general or specialised, other than those devoted particularly to ornithology. The chief bibliographical guide to current ornithological literature is an annual publication of the Zoological Society of London (see preceding entry).

ZOÖME: see under BIOME

ZOONOSIS: general term (plural 'zoonoses') for any disease naturally transmitted, directly or indirectly, between other vertebrate animals and man. Birds are in some cases the other vertebrate animals concerned ; psittacosis (ornithosis) is an example of a zoonosis transmitted directly from birds to man, and some types of virus encephalitis are transmissible from birds to man by an insect or other arthropod vector (see DISEASE ; PSITTACOSIS ; VECTOR).

Williams, M. C. 1957. Birds in relation to the anthropod-borne virus zoonoses. Ibis 99 : 303–306.

ZOSTEROPIDAE: a family of the Passeriformes, suborder Oscines (see WHITE-EYE (1)).

ZOSTEROPS: generic name often used as common name (see WHITE-EYE (1)).

ZUGUNRUHE: German term, sometimes used in English writings, for pre-migratory restlessness (see MIGRATION).

ZWISCHENZUG: German term, difficult to translate, for nomadic movements performed by birds of some species between the breeding season and true migration. 'Between migration' not being a possible expression in the English language, either in grammar or sense, the nearest literal equivalent is probably 'interim movements'. They are sometimes, when performed by adults, referred to as 'post-nuptial' (see MIGRATION).

ZYGAPOPHYSIS: one of the articulating processes of a vertebra (see SKELETON).

ZYGODACTYL: having two toes directed forwards and two back (see LEG). When toes I and II instead of I and IV are directed backwards, the condition may be called 'heterodactyl'.

ZYGOMATIC ARCH: the bony arch of the cheek (see SKELETON).

' Shall we not then salute the halcyon, and so go back to the city by the sands, for it is time ? '
                                                          Plato, *trans*. Ruskin

Index of Generic Names

The Dictionary, being alphabetically arranged and abundantly provided with cross-references, serves as its own index for most purposes. It is, however, based mainly on English names and terms, although there are entries under the scientific names of taxa of family-group level and above. An index of generic names that are mentioned in the text accordingly seems to be a desirable adjunct. A few of these names, because they are used also as English words, do in fact appear as entry headings.

The index is selective, in that references are restricted to (a) the group article dealing with the appropriate family or subfamily, if the genus is mentioned therein ; (b) entries under recognised English names for members of the genus ; (c) any entry containing the sole mention of a genus ; (d) items containing relevant illustrations ; and, occasionally, (e) a general subject article that gives substantial information about a genus. As regards this last, mention of a genus as an example supporting some general statement, or merely for comparison, has not usually been regarded as sufficient reason for including a reference.

An asterisk (*) denotes the appropriate group article. Where an entry includes a relevant text-figure, that is indicated. Certain familiar but here (or generally) discarded generic names are mentioned in the text within quotation marks and are given cross-references below to the names actually used in this work.

Psophia	*TRUMPETER; Plate 32
Psophodes	*RAIL-BABBLER; WHIPBIRD
Pteridophora	*BIRD-OF-PARADISE
Pternistis	
(see also *Francolinus*)	FRANCOLIN; SPURFOWL
Pterocles	*SANDGROUSE (Fig.)
Pterocnemia	*RHEA
Pterodroma	CAHOW; *PETREL
Pteroglossus	ARAÇARI; *TOUCAN
Pterophanes	*HUMMINGBIRD; SAPPHIRE-WING
Pteropodocys	*CUCKOO-SHRIKE
Pteroptochos	*TAPACULO; TURCO
Pteruthius	*BABBLER; SHRIKE-BABBLER
Ptilinopus	*PIGEON; Plates 6, 17
Ptilocichla	*BABBLER
Ptilogonys	PTILOGONYS; *SILKY FLYCATCHER
Ptilonorhynchus	*BOWERBIRD
Ptilopachus	*PHEASANT
Ptiloris	*BIRD-OF-PARADISE; RIFLE-BIRD
Ptilostomus	*CROW (1); PIAPIAC
Ptochoptera	EMERALD
Ptychoramphus	*AUK; AUKLET
Ptyonoprogne	*SWALLOW
Ptyrticus	*BABBLER
Pucrasia	KOKLAS; *PHEASANT
Puffinus	*PETREL; SHEARWATER; Plate 16
Pycnonotus	*BULBUL (Fig.)
Pycnoptilus	PILOT-BIRD; *WREN (2)
Pygarrhichas	*OVENBIRD (1); TREERUNNER
Pygoscelis	ANTARCTIC; EXCRETION, EXTRARENAL (Fig.); *PENGUIN (Fig.); Plates 10, 25
Pyriglena	*ANTBIRD; FIRE-EYE
Pyrocephalus	*FLYCATCHER (2)
Pyroderus	FRUITCROW
Pyrrhocorax	CHOUGH (1); *CROW (1)
Pyrrholaemus	REDTHROAT; *WREN (2)
Pyrrhula	BULLFINCH; *FINCH; Plate 6
Pyrrhuloxia	CARDINAL; *CARDINAL-GROSBEAK (Fig.); PYRRHULOXIA
Pytilia	*WEAVER-FINCH
Quelea	DIOCH; QUELEA CONTROL; *WEAVER
Querula	FRUITCROW
Quiscalus	GRACKLE; *ORIOLE (2)

Rallicula	*RAIL
Rallina	*RAIL
Rallus	*RAIL
Ramphastos	*TOUCAN
Ramphocaenus	*GNATCATCHER
Ramphocelus	*TANAGER
Ramphocinclus	*MOCKINGBIRD; TREMBLER
Ramphocoris	*LARK
Ramphodon	SAWBILL
Ramphomicron	THORNBILL
Ramsayornis	*HONEYEATER
Raphus	*DODO
Recurvirostra	*AVOCET (Fig.); BILL (Fig.); LEG (Fig.); Plate 27
Regulus	FIRECREST; GOLDCREST; KINGLET; *WARBLER (1)
Remiornis	DIATRYMIFORMES
Remiz	*TIT
Rhabdornis	*NUTHATCH
Rhagologus	*THICKHEAD
Rhamphocharis	*FLOWERPECKER
Rhea	*RHEA (Fig.)
Rhegminornis	CHARADRIIFORMES
Rheinartia	ARGUS; *PHEASANT
Rhinocorax, see *Corvus*	
Rhinocrypta	GALLITO; *TAPACULO; Plate 32
Rhinomyias	MUSCICAPIDAE
Rhinoplax	*HORNBILL; IVORY, HORNBILL
Rhinopomastus	SCIMITAR-BILL; *WOOD-HOOPOE
Rhinoptilus	*COURSER; Plate 43 (egg)
Rhipidura	FANTAIL; *FLYCATCHER (1); Plate 35
Rhizothera	*PHEASANT
Rhodinocichla	QUEO; *TANAGER; THRUSH-TANAGER
Rhodonessa	*DUCK
Rhodopechys	*FINCH
Rhodophoneus	*SHRIKE
Rhodostethia, see *Larus*	
Rhodothraupis	*CARDINAL-GROSBEAK
Rhopocichla	*BABBLER
Rhopodytes	*CUCKOO; MALAKOHA
Rhopornis	*ANTBIRD; ANTCATCHER
Rhynchocyclus	FLATBILL; *FLYCATCHER (2)
Rhynchopsitta	IRRUPTION
Rhynchortyx	*PHEASANT
Rhynochetos	*KAGU (Fig.)
Rhyticeros, see *Aceros*	
Rhytipterna	MOURNER

Measurement Conversion Tables
British and Metric Systems

Linear 12 inches (ins.)=1 foot; 3 feet=1 yard; 1760 yds.=1 mile.
DEPTH : 6 ft.=1 fathom.
MARINE DISTANCE : 6080 ft.=1 nautical mile.
10 millimetres (mm.)=1 centimetre; 100 cm.=1 metre; 1000 m.=1 kilometre.
MICROSCOPIC : 0·001 mm.=1 micron (μ)

Conversion factors

Inches to millimetres	25·40	Millimetres to inches	0·03937
Feet to metres	0·3048	Metres to feet	3·281
Miles to kilometres	1·609	Kilometres to miles	0·6214

Surface 144 square inches=1 sq. foot; 9 sq. ft.=1 sq. yard; 4840 sq. yds.=1 acre;
640 acres=1 sq. mile.
10 000 cm^2=1 m^2; 10 000 m^2=1 hectare; 100 hectares=1 km^2

Conversion factors

Sq. ins to cm^2	6·4516	cm^2 to sq. ins.	0·155
Sq. ft. to m^2	0·0929	m^2 to sq. ft.	10·7639
Acres to hectares	0·4047	hectares to acres	2·47105
Sq. miles to km^2	2·590	Km^2 to sq. miles	0·3861

Weight 16 ounces (oz.)=1 pound (lb.); 1000 grams (gm.)=1 kilogram (kg.)

Conversion factors

Ounces to grams	28·35	Grams to ounces	0·03527
Pounds to kilograms	0·4536	Kilograms to pounds	2·205

Temperature 32° Fahrenheit=0° Celsius (Centigrade) : 212° F=100° C. (Nine degrees F=five degrees C)

Conversion formulae (points on scale)
F° to C°   subtract 32 and multiply by $\frac{5}{9}$ C° to F°   multiply by $\frac{9}{5}$ and add 32